Figures that are part of the mandatory provisions of the *Code* appear in the *Code* text, as do Annex A figures. These figures are printed in black and are numbered in accordance with the paragraphs in which they are referenced.

Helpful commentary exhibits and tables are provided to aid the user in understanding the *Code* provisions in even greater detail. Color is used to distinguish these items from both the mandatory *Code* provisions and the nonmandatory Annex A material.

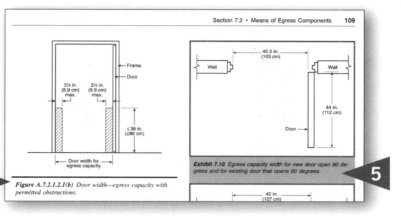

Figure A.7.2.1.2.1(b) *Door width—egress capacity with permitted obstructions.*

Exhibit 7.10 *Egress capacity width for new door open 90 degrees and for existing door that opens 90 degrees.*

4

5

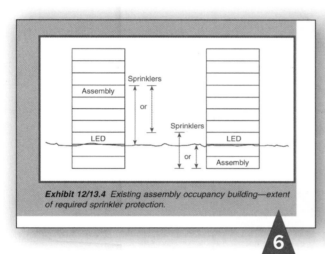

Exhibit 12/13.4 *Existing assembly occupancy building—extent of required sprinkler protection.*

6

Exhibit 12/13.5 *Library reading rooms for which Code specifies an occupant load factor of 50 net ft² (4.6 net m²).*

Commentary exhibits, including both drawings and photographs, provide detailed views of *Code* concepts. These helpful exhibits are enclosed in green boxes and numbered sequentially throughout each handbook chapter. Green shading over the caption also makes these exhibits easily discernible.

7

Tables that visually organize complex information for easy access are featured throughout the mandatory *Code* provisions, the commentary text, and the Annex A explanatory material. The use of color and the numbering system make it easy to determine at a glance whether a table is part of the mandatory provisions of the *Code* or a listing of nonmandatory data.

Table 20/21.2 *Comparison of Applicable Requirements for Occupancy*

Building Feature	Kidney Dialysis Center (new ambulatory health care occupancy)	Lawyers' Office (existing business occupancy)
Occupancy separation	Regulated by 20.1.2.1; corridor wall and partition between space A and tenant C must be 1-hour fire resistance–rated.	No regulation.
Egress door locking	Addressed by 20.1.2.4 and 20.1.1.1.5; doors permitted to be locked if for clinical needs of the patients, but staff must be present to release such locks.	Doors not permitted to be locked while space is occupied in accordance with 7.2.1.5.1.
Minimum construction	Regulated by 20.1.6, but because building is single story, any NFPA 220 construction type is acceptable.	No regulation.
Delayed-egress and access-controlled doors	Limited to exterior doors by 20.2.2.2; must meet 7.2.1.6.	No limitation other than having to meet 7.2.1.6; given that building is not sprinklered, it is doubtful that delayed-egress doors will qualify for use.
Automatic door closing	In addition to release via methods of 7.2.1.8 (smoke detection, power failure, manual action), initiation of the required fire alarm must release the hold-open devices in accordance with 20.2.2.3.	Release hold-open devices via methods of 7.2.1.8 (smoke detection, power failure, manual action).
Door width	Minimum 32-in. (81-cm) clear width in accordance	Minimum 28 in. (71 cm) door leaf width in accordance

Life Safety Code Handbook®

Life Safety Code Handbook

EIGHTH EDITION

EDITED BY

Ron Coté, P.E.

With the complete text of the 2000 edition of NFPA *101®*, *Life Safety Code®*

National Fire Protection Association, Quincy, Massachusetts

Product Manager: Pam Powell
Project Editor: Joyce Grandy
Copy Editor: Pamela Nolan
Text Processing: Kathy Barber
Composition: Modern Graphics

Art Coordinator: Nancy Maria
Illustrations: Todd Bowman and George Nichols
Cover Design: Greenwood Associates
Manufacturing: Ellen Glisker
Printer: Quebecor World—Taunton

Notice Concerning Liability: Publication of this handbook is for the purpose of circulating information and opinion among those concerned for fire and electrical safety and related subjects. While every effort has been made to achieve a work of high quality, neither the NFPA nor the contributors to this handbook guarantee the accuracy or completeness of or assume any liability in connection with the information and opinions contained in this handbook. The NFPA and the contributors shall in no event be liable for any personal injury, property, or other damages of any nature whatsoever, whether special, indirect, consequential, or compensatory, directly or indirectly resulting from the publication, use of, or reliance upon this handbook.

This handbook is published with the understanding that the NFPA and the contributors to this handbook are supplying information and opinion but are not attempting to render engineering or other professional services. If such services are required, the assistance of an appropriate professional should be sought.

Notice Concerning Code Interpretations: This eighth edition of the *Life Safety Code Handbook* is based on the 2000 edition of NFPA *101®*, *Life Safety Code®*. All NFPA codes, standards, recommended practices, and guides are developed in accordance with the published procedures of the NFPA by technical committees comprised of volunteers drawn from a broad array of relevant interests. The handbook contains the complete text of NFPA *101*, accompanied by explanatory commentary and other supplementary materials.

The commentary and supplementary materials in this handbook are not a part of the *Code* and do not constitute Formal Interpretations of the NFPA (which can be obtained only through requests processed by the responsible technical committees in accordance with the published procedures of the NFPA). The commentary and supplementary materials, therefore, solely reflect the personal opinions of the editor or other contributors and do not necessarily represent the official position of the NFPA or its technical committees.

®Registered Trademark National Fire Protection Association, Inc.

NFPA No.: 101HB00
ISBN: 0-87765-448-4
Library of Congress Card Catalog No.: 00132115

Printed in the United States of America
07 08   09   10   7   6   5

Contents

Preface

For 80 years, the National Fire Protection Association has been the developer and publisher of the *Life Safety Code*. Formerly known as the *Building Exits Code*, the *Code* is prepared by the NFPA Committees on Safety to Life — fourteen of the more than 200 technical committees operating within the framework of NFPA's consensus standards-development system. The members of the Committees on Safety to Life are highly qualified individuals who have demonstrated knowledge and competence in the design and construction of buildings and structures, in the manufacture and testing of building components and accessories, and in the enforcement of regulations pertaining to life safety from fire and other related hazards encountered in buildings and structures.

The *Life Safety Code* is a unique document; its contents address specific requirements that have a direct influence on safety to life in both new construction *and* existing buildings — not new construction alone. Moreover, although the *Code*'s paramount concern is life safety and not protection of property per se, there are also — by observance of the *Code*'s requirements — ancillary benefits to property protection.

The impact that application of the *Code* can have on saving lives is difficult to measure; however, it is reasonable to assume that its influence is extremely significant. For example, of the many fatal public building fires investigated by NFPA, invariably one or more of the building features contributing to loss of life from fire were in violation of the requirements of the *Code*.

NFPA recognizes that a code suitable for enforcement must — by the nature of its purpose — be concise and without explanatory text. In addition, a code cannot be written to cover every situation that will be encountered; thus, it must be applied with judgment and used with good sense and with an awareness of the rationale for the requirements to be enforced. A little help and counsel along the way can make the job a lot easier; hence, NFPA has also developed this *Life Safety Code Handbook*.

This handbook gives users of the *Life Safety Code* back-ground information on the reasons for certain *Code* provisions. It also provides some suggestions, through its text and illustrations, on how some *Code* requirements can be implemented effectively. This kind of information is intended to provide users of the *Code* with a better understanding of, and appreciation for, the requirements contained in the *Code*. The net result should be buildings and structures that are increasingly more fire safe. The reader is cautioned, however, to look upon the commentary that appears in the handbook as the views of the editor and — where commentary reads relatively the same as in earlier editions — the contributors to earlier editions of the handbook. The commentary does not necessarily reflect the official position of NFPA.

This edition of the handbook reflects the two major changes made for the 2000 edition of the *Code*, that is, the reformatting that expanded the *Code* from 33 chapters to 42 chapters, and the addition of a new Chapter 5 offering a performance-based option for life safety. The cross-reference table of 1997 versus 2000 edition paragraph numbers, located at the end of the handbook, should be of particular help to readers who are familiar with the previous edition of the *Code* and want to locate corresponding text in the 2000 edition. For this edition, James Lake revised the commentary for Chapters 9, 24, 26, 28/29, 30/31, and 32/33.

Handbook commentary has been added to accompany the new Chapter 5 performance-based option, to explain its intent, and to lead the reader through implementation examples for some of its varied pieces. The Chapter 5 commentary was prepared by Doug Beller, Brian Gagnon, John Hall, and Jennifer Sapochetti.

Where a pair of occupancy chapters address a given occupancy (for example, Chapter 12 for new assembly occupancies and Chapter 13 for existing assembly occupancies), the *Code* text for both chapters is presented in side-by-side columns to permit easy comparison. Further, the accompanying commentary points out differences between the provisions applicable to new construction and to existing buildings.

Ron Coté, P.E., Editor
Principal Life Safety Engineer
National Fire Protection Association

PART ONE

Life Safety Code and Commentary

Part One of this handbook includes the complete text of the 2000 *Life Safety Code*, which is made up of mandatory chapters (1 through 42) and nonmandatory annex material. The mandatory *Code* provisions found in Chapters 1 through 42 were prepared by the fourteen Committees on Safety to Life within the framework of NFPA's consensus standards-development system. Because these provisions are designed to be suitable for adoption into law, or for reference by other codes and standards, the text is concise, without extended explanation.

The material found in Annex A of the *Code* was also developed by the Committees on Safety to Life within NFPA's standards system. The annex material is designed to assist users in interpreting the mandatory *Code* provisions. It is not considered to be part of the requirements of the *Code*; it is advisory or informational. An asterisk (*) following a *Code* paragraph number indicates that nonmandatory material pertaining to that paragraph appears in Annex A. For readers' convenience, in this handbook, Annex A material has been interspersed among the mandatory *Code* text to appear immediately following its base paragraph in the body of the *Code* text.

The explanatory commentary accompanying the *Code* was prepared by the handbook editor. The commentary follows the *Code* text it discusses and is easily identified by green shading. Designed to help users understand and apply *Code* provisions, it gives detailed explanations of the reasoning behind *Code* requirements, examples of calculations, applications of requirements, and tables of useful information. More than 400 drawings and photographs show practical applications of specific *Code* provisions. Used together with the *Code*, the commentary provides a rich resource for assessing the level of life safety from fires in buildings.

CHAPTER 1

Administration

The basic philosophy and core requirements of the *Life Safety Code* are presented in the first eleven chapters of the *Code*. The scope, purpose, and application of the *Code* are positioned in Chapter 1 to allow the building blocks or fundamentals of the *Code* to be described, understood, and correctly applied.

While any part of this handbook might be relevant and directly applicable to a specific type of structure or occupancy, the user is encouraged to develop a sound understanding of the rudimentary concepts of occupant life safety. Such understanding includes recognizing where the *Code* applies and the extent to which the designer, authority having jurisdiction, or both, should apply the *Code* requirements for new versus existing buildings. See, for example, Section 1.4 and its associated annex material.

The long-standing recognition of "equivalency" (see Section 1.5) is also an important concept not only in NFPA *101* but also in the NFPA codes and standards used in combination with the *Life Safety Code*. The equivalency concept allows for innovative approaches to life safety and fire safety. While the *Code* is a comprehensive document, it is conceivable that situations that the *Code* does not contemplate might arise. Equivalency considerations allow for the situation to be evaluated and for a mutually agreeable solution to be developed.

cited as such, and shall be referred to herein as "this *Code*" or "the *Code*."

As discussed in the preface to this handbook, the title of the *Code* was changed from the *Building Exits Code* to the *Life Safety Code* in 1966. The change in title expanded the scope of the *Code* from a specification-based code for stairs, doors, and fire escapes to a performance- and specification-based code that addresses the myriad factors that affect life safety in the event of fire.

In some cases, the *Code* addresses non-fire, day-to-day, building occupant issues. For example, in 12.2.5.4.3 and 13.2.5.4.3, which apply to assembly occupancies, access and egress routes are required to be maintained so that crowd management, security, and emergency medical personnel are able to move without undue hindrance to any individual at any time.

Section 1.2* Scope

A.1.2 The following is a suggested procedure for determining the *Code* requirements for a building or structure:

(1) Determine the occupancy classification by referring to the occupancy definitions in Chapter 6 and the occupancy Chapters 12 through 42 *(see 6.1.14 for buildings with more than one use).*

(2) Determine if the building or structure is new or existing *(see the definitions in Chapter 3).*

(3) Determine the occupant load *(see 7.3.1).*

(4) Determine the hazard of contents *(see Section 6.2).*

Section 1.1 Title

1.1.1 Code Title.

NFPA *101®*, *Code for Safety to Life from Fire in Buildings and Structures*, shall be known as the *Life Safety Code®*, is

(5) Refer to the applicable occupancy chapter of the *Code* (Chapters 12 through 42) (see Chapters 1 through 4 and 6 through 11, as needed, for general information (such as definitions) or as directed by the occupancy chapter).

(6) Determine the occupancy subclassification or special use condition, if any, by referring to Chapters 18 and 19, health care occupancies; Chapters 22 and 23, detention and correctional occupancies; Chapters 28 and 29, hotels and dormitories; Chapters 32 and 33, residential board and care occupancies; and Chapters 36 and 37, mercantile occupancies, which contain subclassifications or special use definitions.

(7) Proceed through the applicable occupancy chapter to verify compliance with each referenced section, subsection, paragraph, subparagraph, and referenced codes, standards, and other documents.

(8) Where two or more requirements apply, the occupancy chapter generally takes precedence over the base Chapters 1 through 4 and 6 through 11.

(9) Where two or more occupancy chapters apply, such as in a mixed occupancy (see 6.1.14), the most restrictive requirements apply.

The steps outlined in A.1.2 were developed to help the user determine which *Code* requirements might apply to a given building if the more prevalent, prescriptive, specification-based life safety systems option is used. If the new performance-based option is used, see 4.4.3.

Because specific occupancy requirements are detailed in separate chapters, the *Code* user should first identify the proper occupancy classification for a building. This will direct the *Code* user to the appropriate chapter(s) for that occupancy.

For example, a jewelry retail sales operation (that is, a jewelry store) occupying all of the twelfth floor of a multi-tenant building uses 5000 ft² (465 m²), or 95 percent, of the floor area for sales purposes. Using the occupancy classification criteria and definitions found in Chapter 6, the jewelry store should be classified as a mercantile occupancy. In determining that the floor is a mercantile occupancy, the *Code* user narrows the range of choice of applicable occupancy chapters from Chapters 12 through 42 to the two that specifically address mercantile occupancies—Chapter 36 or Chapter 37.

Using the definition of *existing building* found in 3.3.60, the user can determine whether the building is subject to the requirements for new construction or for existing buildings. If the jewelry store used in the example was occupied subsequent to the adoption of the *Code* currently being enforced, the user determines that the life safety features required are those that apply to new construction. Thus, the user could narrow the applicable occupancy requirements to those for new mercantile occupancies as detailed in Chapter 36.

The *Code* user next identifies the subclassification of the mercantile occupancy as Class A, Class B, or Class C based on the 5000-ft² (465-m²) floor area used for sales purposes. Because the jewelry store occupies more than 3000 ft² (280 m²) but less than 30,000 ft² (2800 m²), it is classified as a Class B mercantile occupancy. The user then locates the requirements of Chapter 36 that specifically apply to Class B mercantile occupancies. The user notes that Chapter 36 does not repeat the requirements found in Chapters 1 through 4 and Chapters 6 through 10 because the *Code* mandatorily references the use of these chapters. Because the jewelry store is located in the highrise portion of the building, 36.4.2 requires compliance with a portion of the high-rise building requirements of Chapter 11—specifically, the automatic sprinkler system provisions of 11.8.2.1.

In this example, the *Code* user recognizes that the requirements of Chapters 1 through 4, Chapters 6 through 10, a portion of Chapter 11, and Chapter 36 apply and are required to be met. This selection process is outlined in Exhibit 1.1.

1.2.1* Danger to Life from Fire.

The *Code* addresses those construction, protection, and occupancy features necessary to minimize danger to life from fire, including smoke, fumes, or panic.

A.1.2.1 The *Code* recognizes that panic in a burning building might be uncontrollable but deals with the potential panic hazard through measures designed to prevent the development of panic. Experience indicates that panic seldom develops, even in the presence of potential danger, as long as occupants of buildings are moving toward exits that they can see within a reasonable distance without obstructions or undue congestion in the path of travel. However, any uncertainty as to the location or adequacy of means of egress, the presence of smoke, or the stoppage of egress travel, such as might occur when one person stumbles and falls on the stairs, is potentially conducive to panic. The danger of panic is greatest when there are large numbers of people in a confined area.

Panic is *not* a typical reaction of occupants in a burning building. Studies of building fires indicate that occupants typically exhibit altruistic behavior toward others. Human response to a threatening situation

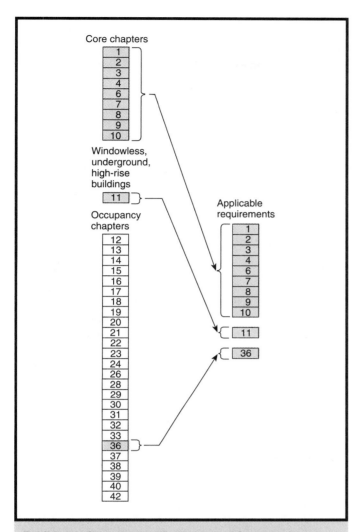

Exhibit 1.1 *Selecting specification-based Code requirements that apply to a given occupancy.*

might follow one of a variety of behaviors. Individuals might choose to investigate, sound an alarm, assist with rescue, seek help, or flee. Such actions constitute normal behavior, even when taken collectively. Most people avoid direct contact with a fire while under-taking another action.

Crowd behavior in large assembly occupancy venues is more difficult to predict and manage. The life safety evaluation, required of large assembly oc-cupancies by the provisions of Chapters 12 and 13, deals not only with fire but also with fire, storm, collapse, crowd behavior, and other related factors for which a checklist is provided in A.12.4.1.3 and A.13.4.1.3.

1.2.2 Egress Facilities.

The *Code* establishes minimum criteria for the design of egress facilities so as to permit prompt escape of occupants from buildings or, where desirable, into safe areas within buildings.

Relocating building occupants to safe areas within a building might include moving them, as specified in (1) through (3), to one of the following locations:

(1) Into an area of refuge
(2) Through doors in a horizontal exit into another fire compartment
(3) Through doors in a smoke barrier into another smoke compartment

In some cases, an egress system that relies on total evacuation to the exterior is not practical. For example, in a health care occupancy, building evacua-tion might expose patients to conditions more dan-gerous than those encountered in relocating the patients from a fire compartment to a safe smoke compartment on the same floor. For most occupan-cies, the *Code* provisions permit the designer to choose whether the egress system relies on full evacu-ation. For occupancies such as health care, a protect-in-place strategy is used that requires the subdivision of floors into two or more smoke compartments, re-gardless of the presence of fire exit stairs.

1.2.3 Other Considerations.

The *Code* addresses other considerations that are essential to life safety in recognition of the fact that life safety is more than a matter of egress. The *Code* also addresses protective features and systems, building services, operating features, maintenance activities, and other provisions in recognition of the fact that achieving an acceptable degree of life safety depends on additional safeguards to provide adequate egress time or protection for people exposed to fire.

Numerous elements impact the overall level of life safety. The *Code* addresses many of these factors, in-cluding combustibility of interior finishes and the evacuation preparedness of occupants. However, other areas are not addressed, such as the influence of public education on fire safety.

1.2.4 Areas Not Addressed.

The *Code* does not address the following:

(1)* General fire prevention or building construction fea-tures that are normally a function of fire prevention codes and building codes

A.1.2.4(1) This *Code* is intended to be adopted and used as part of a comprehensive program of building regulations that include building, mechanical, plumbing, electrical, fuel gas, fire prevention, and land use regulations.

(2) Prevention of personal injuries incurred by an individual's own negligence

(3) Preservation of property from loss by fire

The *Code* is not intended to be either a building code or a fire prevention code. However, in the interest of public safety, the *Code* does contain provisions typically associated with a fire prevention code or building code. For example, although construction requirements are typically considered the domain of a building code, Chapters 18 and 19 provide minimum, fire-rated construction requirements for buildings housing health care occupancies. The construction requirements are provided to ensure the structural integrity of the building for the period of time required for staff to evacuate those occupants incapable of self-preservation.

Similarly, the provisions of Chapters 12 and 13— for assembly occupancies—require fire-rated building construction, depending on the number of occupants and the levels of the building occupied as assembly occupancies. The requirement recognizes the lengthy time periods necessary to evacuate large numbers of persons, especially from floors above the level of exit discharge. Thus, fire-rated building construction is intended to ensure the structural integrity of the building for the period of time required for occupants to evacuate.

Although preventative measures are typically associated with a fire prevention code, the operating features sections located at the end of most of the occupancy chapters contain requirements that do the following:

(1) Limit the flammability of contents introduced into certain occupancies

(2) Regulate smoking

(3) Require the training of facility employees

These operational items, when combined with egress and other specific occupancy chapter requirements, provide an appropriate life safety package.

The *Code* intentionally excludes traditional building code topics such as wind loads, seismic considerations, and exterior exposure protection.

Although the *Code* requirements were developed to provide life safety from fire, adherence to its requirements might assist in property conservation and prevention of personal injuries. For example, the au-

tomatic sprinkler systems required for life safety purposes provide substantial property protection benefits as well.

Section 1.3* Purpose

A.1.3 The *Code* endeavors to avoid requirements that might involve unreasonable hardships or unnecessary inconvenience or interference with the normal use and occupancy of a building but provides for fire safety consistent with the public interest.

Buildings are normally designed to accommodate a specific functional need. The *Code* considers the normal occupancy of a building and attempts not to interfere with its regular use or to set requirements that cause unreasonable hardship or unnecessary inconvenience to its normal functioning. For example, although self-closing devices on doors help to ensure continuous fire- and smoke-compartmentation, the health care occupancy provisions of this *Code* do not require self-closing devices on patient room doors because of the day-to-day functional need for staff to monitor conditions while doors remain open. The health care occupancy chapters achieve the intended minimum level of life safety, without unduly interfering with normal operation of the facility, by combining other features and protection schemes. For example, 18.7.2.1 and 19.7.2.1, which apply to new and existing health care occupancies, require that staff establish procedures to be followed in case of fire, including closing doors to isolate the fire area and confine the effects of the fire.

1.3.1* Code Purpose.

The purpose of this *Code* is to provide minimum requirements, with due regard to function, for the design, operation, and maintenance of buildings and structures for safety to life from fire. Its provisions will also aid life safety in similar emergencies.

This *Code* specifies the **minimum** requirements that collectively help to ensure safety to occupants from fires and similar emergencies to the degree specified by the objective stated in Section 4.2. However, it is not the *Code*'s intent to prevent the user from exceeding the specified minimum requirements. See also 4.6.8.

In addressing life safety from fire and similar emergencies, the *Code* focuses on the movement of people in an emergency. However, many of the building features that assist with the safe movement of people in an emergency also provide increased safety during normal building use. For example, new stairs—in other than dwelling units—are not permitted to have a riser height that exceeds 7 in. (17.8 cm) and are required to provide a tread depth of at least 11 in. (27.9 cm) to reduce the potential to trip under emergency egress use. This safe stair geometry also reduces the potential of tripping whenever the stair is used.

A.1.3.1 Protection of occupants is achieved by the combination of prevention, protection, egress, and other features with due regard to the capabilities and reliability of the features involved. The level of life safety from fire is defined through requirements directed at the following:

(1) Prevention of ignition
(2) Detection of fire
(3) Control of fire development
(4) Confinement of the effects of fire
(5) Extinguishment of fire
(6) Provision of refuge and/or evacuation facilities
(7) Staff reaction
(8) Provision of fire safety information to occupants

The occupancy chapters make varying use of any or all of the protection features in A.1.3.1(1) through (8). A business occupancy located in a single-story building uses fewer of the protection features to accomplish the intended minimum level of life safety than does a health care occupancy. A health care occupancy accomplishes its minimum level of life safety by extensively applying the features of A.1.3.1(1) through (7) using a defend-in-place strategy. This strategy recognizes that the occupants of a health care occupancy are both incapable of self-preservation and difficult to move, particularly to other floors or to the exterior of the building.

Section 1.4* Application

A.1.4 It is the intent of Section 1.4 that a building, addition, or alteration designed to meet the requirements of a prior edition of the *Code* be required to meet those requirements for the life of the building. It is intended that the initial assessment of the building, when new, should be based on new occupancy requirements for the edition of the *Code* in effect on the date of plan approval. Subsequent assessments of the building should be based on new occupancy requirements of that same edition of the *Code* for the life of the building. Requirements for existing buildings in this edition of the *Code* apply if those requirements are more restrictive.

There are some cases where the requirements for new construction are less restrictive, and it might be justified to permit an existing building to use the less restrictive requirements. However, extreme care needs to be exercised when granting such permission, because the less restrictive provision might be the result of a new requirement elsewhere in the *Code*. For example, in editions of the *Code* prior to 1991, corridors in new health care occupancies were required to have a 1-hour fire resistance rating. Since 1991, these corridors have been required only to resist the passage of smoke. However, this provision is based on the new requirement that all new health care facilities be protected throughout by automatic sprinklers.

1.4.1* New and Existing Buildings and Structures.

The *Code* shall apply to both new construction and existing buildings and existing structures.

A.1.4.1 In various chapters, there are specific provisions for existing buildings and structures that might differ from those for new construction.

In order to provide a minimum level of life safety to all occupancies in all structures, the *Code* applies to both new construction and existing buildings. Provisions exist throughout the *Code* that apply specifically to existing buildings. Also, the *Code* contains requirements for new construction that have been modified to apply to existing buildings. The modifications were made to limit the resulting disruption and financial impact on existing buildings to those modifications necessary to provide the minimum level of life safety. The requirements applicable to new construction are often more stringent than those for existing buildings, because providing appropriate life safety requirements is considered less disruptive and more cost-effective during construction. If no modification for existing buildings appears within a *Code* requirement, the same provision applies for new construction and existing buildings.

See also 4.6.3, 4.6.4, 4.6.7, 4.6.9, and the definitions of *existing* and *existing building* in 3.3.59 and 3.3.60, respectively.

1.4.2 Vehicles and Vessels.

The *Code* shall apply to vehicles, vessels, or other similar conveyances, as defined in Section 11.6; in which case such vehicles and vessels shall be treated as buildings.

Section 1.5 Equivalency

Section 1.5, Equivalency, presents a powerful design alternative that permits individual and multiple specification-based requirements to be satisfied by components and systems that the authority having jurisdiction is convinced meet the goals, objectives, and intended level of life safety. Where all life safety systems, rather than individual and multiple specification-based systems, are engineered to meet the goals and objectives, true performance-based design is permitted in accordance with Chapter 5. In other words, equivalency deals with discrete, manageable pieces of the overall life safety system; performance-based design treats the system as a whole. See Section 4.4.

1.5.1* Nothing in this *Code* is intended to prevent the use of systems, methods, or devices of equivalent or superior quality, strength, fire resistance, effectiveness, durability, and safety over those prescribed by this *Code*. Technical documentation shall be submitted to the authority having jurisdiction to demonstrate equivalency. The system, method, or device shall be approved for the intended purpose by the authority having jurisdiction.

A.1.5.1 Before a particular mathematical fire model or evaluation system is used, its purpose and limitations need to be known. The technical documentation should clearly identify any assumptions included in the evaluation. Also, it is the intent of the Committee on Safety to Life to recognize that future editions of this *Code* are a further refinement of this edition and earlier editions. The changes in future editions will reflect the continuing input of the fire protection/life safety community in its attempt to meet the purpose stated in this *Code*.

With each new edition, the *Code* continues its evolution from a specification code to a performance-oriented code. For this 2000 edition of the *Code*, a complete performance-based design approach in accordance with Chapter 5 is permitted by Section 4.4. However, the traditional, widely accepted, specification-based approach is maintained as an option.

Subsection 1.5.1 recognizes that, although the majority of the *Code* uses specification language as the basis for enforcement, it should not inhibit the use of alternate or equivalent systems or design approaches to comply with *Code*-specified performance criteria. It is stipulated, however, that equivalency must be demonstrated by appropriate technical documentation. The evaluation and approval of equivalencies is the responsibility of the authority having jurisdiction.

The *Code* contemplates several forms of equivalency:

(a) *Code-Specified Alternative.* The *Code* presents a written requirement and then provides an alternate method of obtaining the desired level of protection, usually via an exception. For example, for new educational occupancies, 14.3.6 requires that interior corridors be constructed of 1-hour fire resistance–rated assemblies. However, Exception No. 2 to 14.3.6 allows the 1-hour rating requirement to be reduced to that of a nonrated smoke partition if the building is protected throughout by an approved, supervised automatic sprinkler system. Thus, the *Code* specifies that the combination of smoke partitions and sprinkler protection is the equivalent of 1-hour fire resistance–rated corridor walls for new educational occupancies.

(b) *NFPA 101A Equivalency Methodologies.* NFPA 101A, *Guide on Alternative Approaches to Life Safety*,[1] provides a set of equivalency methodologies that can used to assess equivalency for health care occupancies, detention and correctional occupancies, board and care occupancies, and business occupancies. Each system awards positive point values for providing a building with strong life safety and fire protection features and assesses negative point values for unsafe conditions. Factors are weighted with respect to their impact on life safety principles. Positive point values are permitted to offset negative point values. The completed evaluations are presented to the authority having jurisdiction for review and approval.

In addition to the fire safety evaluation systems, NFPA 101A contains a procedure for determining the evacuation capability for board and care occupancies. Use of this method is also subject to the review and approval of the authority having jurisdiction.

(c) *More Recent Edition of the Code.* As explained in A.1.5.1, future editions of the *Code* are considered refinements of earlier editions because they clarify intent with respect to the revised topics. Use of a newer edition in its entirety should be considered as equivalent to use of an earlier edition.

Caution must be exercised when applying this concept. It is important to recognize that specific provisions are part of a carefully crafted set of requirements that result in a desired level of life safety. A revision to one portion of the *Code* might be a part of, or the result of, changes to other parts of the *Code*.

Therefore, it would be inappropriate to refer only to a specific section of a more recent edition of the *Code* that reflects a less stringent requirement than previous editions, without taking into account any associated provisions that may have become more stringent to compensate for the more relaxed subject provision. See also A.1.4 for an example illustrating this point.

It is not the intent of the *Code* to limit the user to the three specified methods of judging equivalency. It is the intent to allow emerging technology to be used to satisfy the prescribed performance requirements. Fire modeling has developed to the stage that authorities having jurisdiction are routinely approving equivalency on such results. Additionally, results of fire tests and other documented forms of engineering analysis have received the approval of authorities having jurisdiction.

1.5.2* Equivalent Compliance.

Alternative systems, methods, or devices approved as equivalent by the authority having jurisdiction shall be recognized as being in compliance with this *Code*.

Subsection 1.5.2 emphasizes that there is more than one way to achieve *Code* compliance. A building either follows the specification criteria, achieves equivalency, or meets the requirements that apply to a full performance-based design. Where the equivalency option is used as an alternative approach to life safety, and the alternative is judged by the authority having jurisdiction as providing equivalency to the *Code* requirements, a building is considered to be *Code* compliant. Compliance through equivalency does not differ from compliance through strict adherence to the specification-based requirements; however, compliance through equivalency differs from a waiver that permits continued use of a noncomplying building.

A.1.5.2 An equivalent method of protection provides an equal or greater level of safety. It is not a waiver or deletion of a *Code* requirement.

The prescriptive provisions of this *Code* provide specific requirements for broad classifications of buildings and structures. These requirements are stated in terms of fixed values, such as maximum travel distance, minimum fire resistance ratings, and minimum features of required systems, such as, detection, alarm, suppression, and ventilation, and not in terms of overall building or system performance.

However, the equivalency clause in 1.5.2 permits the use of alternative systems, methods, or devices to meet the intent of the prescribed code provisions where approved as being equivalent. Equivalency provides an opportunity for a performance-based design approach. Through the rigor of a performance-based design, it can be demonstrated whether or not a building design is satisfactory and complies with the implicit or explicit intent of the applicable code requirement.

When employing the equivalency clause, it is important to clearly identify the prescriptive-based code provision being addressed (scope), to provide an interpretation of the intent of the provision (goals and objectives), to provide an alternative approach (proposed design), and to provide appropriate support for the suggested alternative (evaluation of proposed designs).

Performance resulting from proposed designs can be compared to the performance of the design features required by this *Code*. Using prescribed features as a baseline for comparison, it can then be demonstrated in the evaluation whether a proposed design offers the intended level of performance. A comparison of safety provided can be used as the basis for establishing equivalency.

Section 1.6 Units and Formulas

1.6.1 SI Units.

Metric units of measurement in this *Code* are in accordance with the modernized metric system known as the International System of Units (SI).

1.6.2 Primary and Equivalent Values.

If a value for a measurement as given in this *Code* is followed by an equivalent value in other units, the first stated value shall be regarded as the requirement. A given equivalent value might be approximate.

The metric values that appear within parentheses immediately following the U.S. Customary Units values might be mistaken as intentionally precise values that represent the requirement rather than an approximation. For example, 7.2.1.2.3 requires that door openings in means of egress provide clear width of at least 32 in. (81 cm). Because the value 81 cm is not a nice round value, such as 80 or 90, it appears to be precise and can be easily mistaken for the requirement. However, 81 cm is an approximation derived by multiplying 32 in. by the conversion factor of 2.54 cm per inch and rounding the resultant value of 81.28 to 81. As explained in 1.6.2, the first stated value, in U.S. Customary Units, is the requirement and the equivalent value, in metric units, is the approximation.

1.6.3 Conversion Procedure.

SI units have been converted by multiplying the quantity by the conversion factor and then rounding the result to the appropriate number of significant digits.

Section 1.7 Enforcement

1.7.1 Administration and Enforcement.

This *Code* shall be administered and enforced by the authority having jurisdiction designated by the governing authority.

Reference Cited in Commentary

1. NFPA 101A, *Guide on Alternative Approaches to Life Safety*, 1998 edition, National Fire Protection Association, Quincy, MA. (Note: The 1998 edition of NFPA 101A is calibrated to measure equivalency against the requirements of the 1997 edition of the *Code*. The 2001 edition of NFPA 101A will measure equivalency against the requirements of the 2000 edition of the *Code*. NFPA 101A is published one year after its companion edition of the *Code*, since it is necessary to have the *Code* revisions finalized before calibrating the NFPA 101A fire safety evaluation systems.)

CHAPTER 2

Mandatory References

This chapter contains the mandatory referenced publications. Annex B contains nonmandatory referenced publications. In previous editions of the *Code*, the chapter used to list the mandatory referenced publications was located after the occupancy chapters but before the appendices (currently the annexes). NFPA style and format policies now dictate that the mandatory referenced publications appear in Chapter 2. By positioning the information immediately after Chapter 1, Administration, the *Code* user is presented with the complete list of publications needed for effective use of the *Code.* In the same way, for example, that the provisions of Chapter 7, Means of Egress, are mandated, the provisions of the publications that are mandated by the *Code* are also requirements. Regardless of whether an actual requirement resides within the *Code* or is mandatorily referenced and appears only in the referenced publication, it is a requirement that must be met in order to achieve compliance with the *Code*.

The *Life Safety Code* achieves its intended level of occupant safety by mandating the installation of various building features and systems. Where specific equipment and systems are required, their proper installation and maintenance is important. Rather than develop its own installation criteria, the *Code* relies on expert documents by mandating their use. The referenced document becomes a legally enforceable part of NFPA *101*.

The level of reference to a particular document varies in some cases. For example, although NFPA 72, *National Fire Alarm Code®,*[1] allows numerous occupant-notification measures, NFPA *101* might limit the options that can be used for an occupancy. In 14.3.4.3.1.1, positive alarm sequence notification is permitted for new educational occupancies. Rather than specifying the role of positive alarm sequence,

14-3.4.3.1.1 refers to 9.6.3. Within this subsection of the *Code*, 9.6.3.4 points the user to NFPA 72 for the detailed criteria applicable to positive alarm sequence, provided that the occupancy chapter has given permission for its use. Chapter 14 allows positive alarm sequence for new educational occupancies in accordance with NFPA 72, which, in turn, results in the reference to NFPA 72 in Chapter 2.

Another occupant notification method, the presignal system as described in NFPA 72, is addressed by the *Code*. Once again, though, an occupancy chapter must permit the presignal system. A presignal system is not permitted for use in educational occupancies. Therefore, even though it is recognized in NFPA 72, this occupant notification method is not permitted for schools. Thus, not all of the options offered by a referenced document can be used. The user of the *Code* must be aware of the reference and of any limitations or caveats on use of the referenced documents.

NFPA *101*, like other NFPA codes and standards, can mandate the use of a referenced document only if that document is an ANSI consensus code or standard. NFPA policy does not permit mandating the use of a referenced document that has not been developed under consensus procedures, nor does it permit reference to those documents developed by committees whose membership is not balanced with respect to user interests. A code or standard written by a committee dominated by an interest group has too great a potential for bias.

NOTE: (See Annex B for other referenced publications that are advisory and thus do not constitute part of the requirements of this *Code*.)

2.1 The following documents or portions thereof are referenced within this *Code* as mandatory requirements and shall be considered part of the requirements of this *Code.* The edition indicated for each referenced mandatory document is the current edition as of the date of the NFPA issuance of this *Code.* Some of these mandatory documents might also be referenced in this *Code* for specific informational purposes and, therefore, are also listed in Annex B.

The numbers in parentheses represent the paragraph numbers from chapters of this *Code* that reference the given publication in a mandatory way.

The Committee on Safety to Life recognizes that it is sometimes impractical to continually upgrade existing buildings or installations to comply with all the requirements of the following referenced publications. Existing buildings or installations that do not comply with the provisions of the following referenced publications shall be permitted to be continued in service, provided the lack of conformity with these standards does not present a serious hazard to the occupants as determined by the authority having jurisdiction.

> The listed documents are mandatory only to the extent called for in the *Code.* For example, although NFPA 13, *Standard for the Installation of Sprinkler Systems,*[2] is listed here, this does not mean that all buildings must be sprinklered. Rather, where the *Code* requires them to be sprinklered, NFPA 13 is to be used for sprinkler installation. See 9.7.1.1 as an example of *Code* language that mandatorily references the use of another NFPA document, that is, NFPA 13. The *Code* recognizes that existing installations need not be continuously upgraded as new editions of the referenced standards are adopted.

2.1.1 NFPA Publications.

National Fire Protection Association, 1 Batterymarch Park, P.O. Box 9101, Quincy, MA 02269-9101.

NFPA 10, *Standard for Portable Fire Extinguishers,* 1998 edition. (9.7.4.1)

NFPA 13, *Standard for the Installation of Sprinkler Systems,* 1999 edition. [8.2.5.12 Exc. No. 1, 9.7.1.1, 9.7.4.2, 12.4.5.7, 12.4.5.12, 12.7.4.3.7 Exc. No. 1, 13.4.5.12, 13.7.4.3.7 Exc. No. 1, 18.3.5.5, 19.3.5.5, 26.3.5.1 Exc. No. 1, 28.1.5, 28.3.5.1 Exc., 29.1.5, 29.3.5.1 Exc. No. 1, 30.3.5.1 Exc. No. 1, 30.3.5.1 Exc. No. 2, 31.2.2.1.3, 31.3.5.1 Exc. No. 2, 32.2.3.5.2 Exc. No. 3, 33.2.3.5.2 Exc. No. 3, 36.4.4.2.5(2), 36.4.5.3.1(1), 36.4.5.5(1), 37.4.4.2.5(2), 37.4.5.3.1(1), 37.4.5.5(1), 38.1.5.2, 39.1.5.2]

NFPA 13D, *Standard for the Installation of Sprinkler Systems in One- and Two-Family Dwellings and Manufactured Homes,* 1999 edition. [9.7.1.1 Exc. No. 2, 24.3.5, 26.3.5.1, 32.2.3.5.2 Exc. No. 1, 32.2.3.5.2 Exc. No. 2, 33.2.3.5.2 Exc. No. 1, 33.2.3.5.2 Exc. No. 2]

NFPA 13R, *Standard for the Installation of Sprinkler Systems in Residential Occupancies up to and Including Four Stories in Height,* 1999 edition. [9.7.1.1 Exc. No. 1, 24.3.5, 26.3.5.1, 28.3.5.1, 29.3.5.1, 30.3.5.1, 31.3.5.1, 32.2.3.5.2 Exc. No. 4, 32.2.3.5.2 Exc. No. 5, 32.3.3.5.1 Exc. No. 1, 33.2.3.5.2 Exc. No. 4, 33.2.3.5.2 Exc. No. 5, 33.3.3.5.1 Exc. No. 1]

NFPA 14, *Standard for the Installation of Standpipe, Private Hydrants, and Hose Systems,* 2000 edition. (9.7.4.2, 12.4.5.12, 13.4.5.12)

NFPA 25, *Standard for the Inspection, Testing, and Maintenance of Water-Based Fire Protection Systems,* 1998 edition. (9.7.5, 9.7.6.2)

NFPA 30, *Flammable and Combustible Liquids Code,* 1996 edition. [8.4.3.1, 36.4.5.3.1(2), 36.4.5.5(2), 37.4.5.3.1(2), 37.4.5.5(2), 42.2.6.3 Exc. No. 2]

NFPA 30B, *Code for the Manufacture and Storage of Aerosol Products,* 1998 edition. [36.4.5.3.1(3), 36.4.5.5(3), 37.4.5.3.1(3), 37.4.5.5(3)]

NFPA 31, *Standard for the Installation of Oil-Burning Equipment,* 1997 edition. (9.2.2)

NFPA 40, *Standard for the Storage and Handling of Cellulose Nitrate Motion Picture Film,* 1997 edition. (12.4.6.1, 12.4.6.3, 13.4.6.1, 13.4.6.3)

NFPA 45, *Standard on Fire Protection for Laboratories Using Chemicals,* 1996 edition. (8.4.4, 9.2.4)

NFPA 54, *National Fuel Gas Code,* 1999 edition. (8.4.3.1, 9.1.1, 9.2.2, 14.5.2.2, 15.5.2.2, 16.5.2.2, 17.5.2.2, 26.5.2.2, 28.5.2.2 Exc., 29.5.2.2 Exc., 30.5.2.2, 31.5.2.2 Exc.)

NFPA 58, *Liquefied Petroleum Gas Code,* 1999 edition. [8.4.3.1, 9.1.1, 11.9.5.1.3, 11.10.7.1.3, 11.11.6.1.3, 12.7.1.4(5), 13.7.1.4(5)]

NFPA 70, *National Electrical Code®,* 1999 edition. (7.9.2.4, 8.2.5.13, 9.1.2, 9.2.2, 9.6.1.4, 9.6.1.7, 10.2.4.5, 11.8.4.2, 11.8.4.2, 12.4.3.4, 22.5.1.2, 23.5.1.2, 23.5.1.2 Exc.)

NFPA 72, *National Fire Alarm Code,* 1999 edition. [7.2.1.8.2(3), 7.2.1.9.2(4), 8.2.4.4.3, 8.3.5.2, 8.3.5.2 Exc. No. 2, 8.3.5.3, 9.6.1.4, 9.6.1.7, 9.6.2.8, 9.6.2.9, 9.6.2.10.1, 9.6.2.10.2, 9.6.3.4, 9.6.3.5, 9.6.3.6, 9.6.3.7 Exc. No. 2, 9.6.3.10, 9.6.4, 9.6.5.4, 9.7.2.1, 11.8.3.2, 14.3.4.2.3(1), 15.3.4.2.3(1), 22.3.4.1.2, 22.3.7.9, 23.3.4.1.2, 23.3.7.9, 32.3.3.4.8]

NFPA 80, *Standard for Fire Doors and Fire Windows,* 1999 edition. [7.2.1.14(5), 8.2.3.2.1(a), 8.2.3.2.2, 8.2.4.3.4, 18.3.6.3.1, 18.3.6.3.6, 19.3.6.3.1, 19.3.6.3.6]

NFPA 82, *Standard on Incinerators and Waste and Linen Handling Systems and Equipment,* 1999 edition. (9.5.2)

NFPA 88A, *Standard for Parking Structures,* 1998 edition. (28.3.5.4, 30.3.5.4)

NFPA 90A, *Standard for the Installation of Air-Conditioning and Ventilating Systems,* 1999 edition. (8.2.7.1 Exc. No. 2, 9.2.1)

NFPA 90B, *Standard for the Installation of Warm Air Heating and Air-Conditioning Systems,* 1999 edition. (9.2.1)

NFPA 91, *Standard for Exhaust Systems for Air Conveying of Vapors, Gases, Mists, and Noncombustible Particulate Solids,* 1999 edition. (9.2.2)

NFPA 96, *Standard for Ventilation Control and Fire Protection of Commercial Cooking Operations,* 1998 edition. (9.2.3)

NFPA 99, *Standard for Health Care Facilities,* 1999 edition. (8.4.4 Exc., 8.4.5, 9.2.4, 18.2.9.2, 18.2.10.2, Table 18.3.2.1, 18.3.2.2, 18.3.2.3, 18.3.2.4, 18.5.1.2, 18.5.1.3, 19.3.2.2, 19.3.2.3, 19.3.2.4, 20.2.9.2, 20.3.2.1, 20.3.2.2, 21.2.9.2, 21.3.2.1, 21.3.2.2)

NFPA 101A, *Guide on Alternative Approaches to Life Safety,* 1998 edition. (33.2.1.3.2 Exc. No. 5, 33.2.3.6.1 Exc. No. 4)

NFPA 110, *Standard for Emergency and Standby Power Systems,* 1999 edition. (7.9.2.3, 9.1.3, 11.8.4.2)

NFPA 111, *Standard on Stored Electrical Energy Emergency and Standby Power Systems,* 1996 edition. (7.9.2.3, 9.1.4)

NFPA 160, *Standard for Flame Effects Before an Audience,* 1998 edition. (12.7.2 Exc. No. 2, 13.7.2 Exc. No. 2)

NFPA 211, *Standard for Chimneys, Fireplaces, Vents, and Solid Fuel-Burning Appliances,* 2000 edition. (9.2.2)

NFPA 220, *Standard on Types of Building Construction,* 1999 edition. (8.2.1, 10.2.3.1 Exc. No. 1, 20.1.6.2, 21.1.6.2)

NFPA 221, *Standard for Fire Walls and Fire Barrier Walls,* 1997 edition. [8.2.1(1), 8.2.2.2]

NFPA 230, *Standard for the Fire Protection of Storage,* 1999 edition [36.4.5.3.1(4), 36.4.5.5(4), 37.4.5.3.1(4), 37.4.5.5(4)]

NFPA 231D, *Standard for Storage of Rubber Tires,* 1998 edition. [36.4.5.3.1(5), 36.4.5.5(5), 37.4.5.3.1(5), 37.4.5.5(5)]

NFPA 241, *Standard for Safeguarding Construction, Alteration, and Demolition Operations,* 1996 edition. (18.7.9.2, 19.7.9.2, 20.7.9.2, 21.7.9.2)

NFPA 251, *Standard Methods of Tests of Fire Endurance of Building Construction and Materials,* 1999 edition. [3.3.21, 3.3.160, 8.2.3.1.1, 8.2.3.1.1 Exc. No. 2, 12.4.5.7(e)]

NFPA 252, *Standard Methods of Fire Tests of Door Assemblies,* 1999 edition. [3.3.159, 8.2.3.2.1(a), 8.2.3.2.3.1 Exc. No. 1 to (2), 8.2.3.2.3.1 Exc. to (3), 8.3.4.2(1)]

NFPA 253, *Standard Method of Test for Critical Radiant Flux of Floor Covering Systems Using a Radiant Heat Energy Source,* 2000 edition. (10.2.7.1)

NFPA 255, *Standard Method of Test of Surface Burning Characteristics of Building Materials,* 2000 edition. [10.2.3.1, 10.2.3.1 Exc. No. 1, 10.2.3.1 Exc. No. 2, 10.2.3.2, 12.4.5.7(f)]

NFPA 256, *Standard Methods of Fire Tests of Roof Coverings,* 1998 edition. [11.9.1.5, 11.10.1.4, 18.1.6.2 Exc.

(a), 19.1.6.2 Exc. (a), 23.1.6.3 Exc. No. 1(a), 32.3.1.3.3 Exc.(a), 33.3.1.3.3 Exc.(a)]

NFPA 257, *Standard on Fire Test for Window and Glass Block Assemblies,* 2000 edition. [3.3.159, 8.2.3.2.2(1)]

NFPA 259, *Standard Test Method for Potential Heat of Building Materials,* 1998 edition (3.3.118)

NFPA 260, *Standard Methods of Tests and Classification System for Cigarette Ignition Resistance of Components of Upholstered Furniture,* 1998 edition. [10.3.2(1)]

NFPA 261, *Standard Method of Test for Determining Resistance of Mock-Up Upholstered Furniture Material Assemblies to Ignition by Smoldering Cigarettes,* 1998 edition. [10.3.2(2)]

NFPA 265, *Standard Methods of Fire Tests for Evaluating Room Fire Growth Contribution of Textile Wall Coverings,* 1998 edition. [10.2.3.5, 10.2.3.5.1, 10.2.3.5.2, 10.2.4.1.5, 10.2.4.2(5)]

NFPA 266, *Standard Method of Test for Fire Characteristics of Upholstered Furniture Exposed to Flaming Ignition Source,* 1998 edition. (10.3.3)

NFPA 267, *Standard Method of Test for Fire Characteristics of Mattresses and Bedding Assemblies Exposed to Flaming Ignition Source,* 1998 edition. (10.3.4)

NFPA 286, *Standard Methods of Fire Tests for Evaluating Contribution of Wall and Ceiling Interior Finish to Room Fire Growth,* 2000 edition. [10.2.3.1 Exc. No. 1, 10.2.3.5, 10.2.3.5.3, 10.2.4.2(6)]

NFPA 418, *Standard for Heliports,* 1995 edition. (18.3.2.7)

NFPA 430, *Code for the Storage of Liquid and Solid Oxidizers,* 2000 edition. [36.4.5.3.1(6), 37.4.5.3.1(6)]

NFPA 432, *Code for the Storage of Organic Peroxide Formulations,* 1997 edition. [36.4.5.3.1(7), 37.4.5.3.1(7)]

NFPA 434, *Code for the Storage of Pesticides,* 1998 edition. [36.4.5.3.1(8), 37.4.5.3.1(8)]

NFPA 701, *Standard Methods of Fire Tests for Flame Propagation of Textiles and Films,* 1999 edition. [10.3.1, 12.4.5.11, 12.7.4.3.4(3), 13.4.5.11, 13.7.4.3.4(3)]

NFPA 703, *Standard for Fire Retardant Impregnated Wood and Fire Retardant Coatings for Building Materials,* 1995 edition. [10.2.6.1, 12.7.4.3.4(2), 13.7.4.3.4(2)]

NFPA 1126, *Standard for the Use of Pyrotechnics before a Proximate Audience,* 1996 edition. (12.7.2 Exc. No. 1, 13.7.2 Exc. No. 1)

2.1.2 Other Publications.

ANSI A14.3-1984, *Safety Code for Fixed Ladders,* American National Standards Institute, 11 West 42nd Street, New York, NY 10036. (7.2.9.2.1)

CABO/ANSI A117.1-1992, *American National Standard for Accessible and Usable Buildings and Facilities,* American National Standards Institute, 11 West 42nd Street, New York, NY 10036. (3.3.14.1, 7.2.12.3.5, 7.10.1.3, 9.6.3.6)

ANSI A1264.1-1989, *Safety Requirements for Workplace Floor and Wall Openings, Stairs and Railing Systems,* American National Standards Institute, 11 West 42nd Street, New York, NY 10036. (7.2.9.2.1 Exc. No. 2, 40.2.2.10)

ANSI/UL 2079, *Test of Fire Resistance of Building Joint Systems,* Underwriters Laboratories Inc., 333 Pfingsten Rd., Northbrook, IL 60062. (8.2.5.2 Exc. No. 3)

ASME/ANSI A17.1-1993, *Safety Code for Elevators and Escalators,* including Addenda A17.1a-1994 and A17.1b-1995, American Society of Mechanical Engineers, Three Park Avenue, New York, NY 10016-5990. (7.2.12.2.4, 7.2.13.9, 7.2.13.11, 9.4.2, 9.4.4, 9.4.8)

ASME/ANSI A17.3-1993, *Safety Code for Existing Elevators and Escalators,* including Addenda A17.3a-1994 and A17.3b-1995, American Society of Mechanical Engineers, Three Park Avenue, New York, NY 10016-5990. (9.4.3, 9.4.5)

ASTM D 2898, *Test Method for Accelarated Weathering of Fire-Retardant-Treated Wood for Fire Testing,* American Society for Testing and Materials, 100 Barr Harbor Drive, West Conshohocken, PA 19428-2959. (12.4.8.3.2, 12.4.8.3.3 Exc., 13.4.8.3.2 Exc., 13.4.8.3.3 Exc.)

ASTM E 136-1982, *Standard Test Method for Behavior of Materials in a Vertical Tube Furnace at 750°C,* American Society for Testing and Materials, 100 Barr Harbor Drive, West Conshohocken, PA 19428-2959. (3.3.131)

ASTM E 1537, *Standard Method for Fire Testing of Real Scale Upholstered Furniture Items,* American Society for Testing and Materials, 100 Barr Harbor Drive, West Conshohocken, PA 19428-2959. (10.3.3)

ASTM E 1590-1994, *Standard Method for Fire Testing of Real Scale Mattresses,* American Society for Testing and Materials, 100 Barr Harbor Drive, West Conshohocken, PA. 19428-2959. (10.3.4)

ASTM E 1591-1994, *Standard Guide for Data for Fire Models,* American Society for Testing and Materials, 100 Barr Harbor Drive, West Conshohocken, PA 19428-2959. (5.6.3.1)

ASTM F 851-1983, *Standard Test Method for Self-Rising Seat Mechanisms,* American Society for Testing and Materials, 100 Barr Harbor Drive, West Conshohocken, PA. 19428-2959. (12.2.5.5.1, 13.2.5.5.1)

ASTM G 26, *Practice for Operating Light/Exposure Apparatus (Zenon-Arc Type) With and Without Water for Exposure of Non-Metallic Materials,* American Society for

Testing and Materials, 100 Barr Harbor Drive, West Conshocken, PA 19428-2959. (3.3.211)

BHMA/ANSI A-156.19-1997, *American National Standard for Power Assist and Low Energy Power Operated Doors,* Builders Hardware Manufacturers Association, 355 Lexington Avenue – 17th Floor, New York, NY 10017-6603. [7.2.1.9.2(6)]

Code of Federal Regulations 16, Part 1632. [10.3.2(3)]

UL 924, *Standard for Safety Emergency Lighting and Power Equipment,* Underwriters Laboratories Inc., 333 Pfingsten Rd., Northbrook, IL 60062. (7.10.7.1)

UL 1975, *Standard for Fire Tests for Foamed Plastics Used for Decorative Purposes,* Underwriters Laboratories Inc., 333 Pfingsten Rd., Northbrook, IL 60062. [10.3.7, 12.4.5.11, 12.7.3.3, 12.7.4.3.4(6), 12.7.4.3.4(7), 12.7.4.3.6, 13.7.3.3, 13.7.4.3.4(6), 13.7.4.3.4(7), 13.7.4.3.6]

Webster's Third New International Dictionary of the English Language, Unabridged.

This chapter contains mandatory references to other documents. As noted in the commentary to 2.1, the extent to which these documents are mandatory is specified within the *Code.* After each mandatory reference in Chapter 2, a paragraph or series of paragraph numbers appears within parentheses. These references indicate the location of the document as referenced within NFPA *101.*

The reasons for locating all mandatory references in a single chapter are, first, to simplify use of the *Code* and, second, to make it easier for adopting jurisdictions to update the references in only one location rather than throughout the *Code.* The editions of the referenced publications listed in Chapter 2 are legally referenced editions unless the jurisdiction, when adopting the *Code,* has updated the list of codes and standards.

References Cited in Commentary

1. NFPA 72, *National Fire Alarm Code®,* 1999 edition, National Fire Protection Association, Quincy, MA.
2. NFPA 13, *Standard for the Installation of Sprinkler Systems,* 1999 edition, National Fire Protection Association, Quincy, MA.

CHAPTER 3

Definitions

Anyone who has ever participated in a code-development process—whether it be NFPA's or that of another organization—knows of the many hours spent deliberating whether the language is clear and easily understood and whether it expresses the committee's intent. Establishing the requirements for a code is not an easy task. During committee meetings, the question is usually asked whether everyone will understand the limits or application of a particular rule. Invariably, the same questions are asked about select words or terms.

When terms or words used in the *Code* fall outside of generally accepted meanings or dictionary definitions—or otherwise require a clarification—they are defined in Chapter 3. When a word is not defined, the *Code* intends for the user to employ the dictionary definition—in this case, *Webster's Third New International Dictionary of the English Language, Unabridged.*[1] (See 3.1.3.)

As an example, the word *exit* has numerous meanings in the dictionary. Included is the definition "used as stage direction for a specified actor to leave the stage." Another definition includes the following three versions: (1) "the act of going away or out," (2) "death," and (3) "a passage or a way out." To the layperson, the phrase "passage or a way out" is probably what is understood when one hears the term *exit* used or sees an exit sign. The NFPA *101* definition, however, is somewhat more detailed and is used to fix the limits on what actually constitutes an exit. The NFPA *101* definition is:

> **Exit.** That portion of a means of egress that is separated from all other spaces of a building or structure by construction or equipment as required to provide a protected way of travel to the exit discharge.

This is but one of several terms defined in Chapter 3 of the *Code*. The definitions of the occupancy classifications (for example, assembly occupancy, mercantile occupancy, industrial occupancy) appear in Chapter 3 and are repeated in their entirety in Chapter 6 to assist the user of the *Code* in properly classifying the occupancy.

The final point about defined terms in NFPA documents is that the definitions should not contain any requirements. To the extent possible, defined terms merely provide the meaning of a term within the context of the *Code*.

Section 3.1 General

3.1.1 The following terms, for the purposes of this *Code*, shall have the meanings given in this chapter, if not otherwise modified for a specific occupancy.

3.1.2 Words used in the present tense shall include the future; words used in the masculine gender shall include the feminine and neuter; the singular number shall include the plural, and the plural number shall include the singular.

3.1.3 Where terms are not defined in this chapter or within an occupancy chapter, they shall be defined using their ordinarily accepted meanings within the context in which they are used. *Webster's Third New International Dictionary of the English Language, Unabridged,* shall be a source for ordinarily accepted meaning.

In previous editions of the *Code*, definitions appeared in Chapter 3 if the defined term was general in nature, was used in more than one chapter, or was applicable to more than one occupancy. Terms applicable only to one occupancy were typically defined within the chapters addressing that occupancy. Cross-references were maintained so that a user looking for an occupancy-specific definition in Chapter 3—and finding only the term without its definition—would be directed to the occupancy chapter for the full definition.

In this edition of the *Code*, all defined terms and their definitions appear in Chapter 3. Where the term has particular applicability to a specific chapter or occupancy, the term—without definition—appears in the definitions subsection of that chapter and a cross-reference sends the user to Chapter 3 for the full definition.

The one exception to the rule—that full definitions appear only in Chapter 3—occurs in Chapter 6, *Classification of Occupancy and Hazard of Contents*. The definitions of each of the occupancies (for example, assembly, educational, health care, residential) appear in their entirety in Chapter 3 and are repeated in their entirety in Chapter 6. The repetition is desirable so that a user attempting to classify an occupancy has access to all the definitions for purposes of comparison. If the user had to rely solely on the definitions of Chapter 3 when considering occupancy classification, the task would be more difficult.

Section 3.2 Official NFPA Definitions

3.2.1* Approved. Acceptable to the authority having jurisdiction.

A.3.2.1 Approved. The National Fire Protection Association does not approve, inspect, or certify any installations, procedures, equipment, or materials; nor does it approve or evaluate testing laboratories. In determining the acceptability of installations, procedures, equipment, or materials, the authority having jurisdiction may base acceptance on compliance with NFPA or other appropriate standards. In the absence of such standards, said authority may require evidence of proper installation, procedure, or use. The authority having jurisdiction may also refer to the listings or labeling practices of an organization that is concerned with product evaluations and is thus in a position to determine compliance with appropriate standards for the current production of listed items.

3.2.2* Authority Having Jurisdiction. The organization, office, or individual responsible for approving equipment, materials, an installation, or a procedure.

A.3.2.2 Authority Having Jurisdiction. The phrase "authority having jurisdiction" is used in NFPA documents in a broad manner, since jurisdictions and approval agencies vary, as do their responsibilities. Where public safety is primary, the authority having jurisdiction may be a federal, state, local, or other regional department or individual such as a fire chief; fire marshal; chief of a fire prevention bureau, labor department, or health department; building official; electrical inspector; or others having statutory authority. For insurance purposes, an insurance inspection department, rating bureau, or other insurance company representative may be the authority having jurisdiction. In many circumstances, the property owner or his or her designated agent assumes the role of the authority having jurisdiction; at government installations, the commanding officer or departmental official may be the authority having jurisdiction.

3.2.3* Code. A standard that is an extensive compilation of provisions covering broad subject matter or that is suitable for adoption into law independently of other codes and standards.

A.3.2.3 Code. The decision to designate a standard as a "code" is based on such factors as the size and scope of the document, its intended use and form of adoption, and whether it contains substantial enforcement and administrative provisions.

3.2.4 Labeled. Equipment or materials to which has been attached a label, symbol, or other identifying mark of an organization that is acceptable to the authority having jurisdiction and concerned with product evaluation, that maintains periodic inspection of production of labeled equipment or materials, and by whose labeling the manufacturer indicates compliance with appropriate standards or performance in a specified manner.

3.2.5* Listed. Equipment, materials, or services included in a list published by an organization that is acceptable to the authority having jurisdiction and concerned with evaluation of products or services, that maintains periodic inspection of production of listed equipment or materials or periodic evaluation of services, and whose listing states that either the equipment, material, or service meets appropriate designated standards or has been tested and found suitable for a specified purpose.

A.3.2.5 Listed. The means for identifying listed equipment may vary for each organization concerned with product evaluation; some organizations do not recognize equipment as listed unless it is also labeled. The authority having jurisdiction should utilize the system employed by the listing organization to identify a listed product.

3.2.6 Shall. Indicates a mandatory requirement.

3.2.7 Should. Indicates a recommendation or that which is advised but not required.

Section 3.3 General Definitions

3.3.1 Accessible Area of Refuge. See 3.3.14.1, *Area of Refuge, Accessible.*

3.3.2 Accessible Means of Egress. See 3.3.121.1, *Means of Egress, Accessible.*

3.3.3 Addition. An extension or increase in the floor area or height of a building or structure.

3.3.4 Air-Inflated Structure. See 3.3.197.1, *Structure, Air-Inflated.*

3.3.5 Air-Supported Structure. See 3.3.197.2, *Structure, Air-Supported.*

3.3.6* Aisle Accessway. The initial portion of an exit access that leads to an aisle.

A.3.3.6 Aisle Accessway. Aisle accessway is the term used for the previously unnamed means of egress component leading to an aisle or other means of egress. For example, circulation space between parallel rows of seats having a width of 1 ft to 2 ft (0.3 m to 0.6 m) and a length not exceeding 100 ft (30 m) is an aisle accessway. Some of the circulation space between tables or seats in restaurants might be considered aisle accessway.

Depending on the width of aisle accessway, which is influenced by its length and expected utilization, the movement of a person through the aisle accessway might require others to change their individual speed of movement, alter their postures, move their chairs out of the way, or proceed ahead of the person.

3.3.7 Alternative Calculation Procedure. A calculation procedure that differs from the procedure originally employed by the design team but that provides predictions for the same variables of interest.

3.3.8 Ambulatory Health Care Occupancy. See 3.3.134.1, *Occupancy, Ambulatory Health Care.*

3.3.9 Analysis, Sensitivity. An analysis performed to determine the degree to which a predicted output will vary given a specified change in an input parameter, usually in relation to models.

3.3.10 Analysis, Uncertainty. An analysis performed to determine the degree to which a predicted value will vary.

3.3.11 Anchor Store. A department store or major merchandising center that has direct access to the covered mall but in which all required means of egress is independent of the covered mall.

3.3.12 Apartment Building. See 3.3.25.1, *Building, Apartment.*

3.3.13 Area. See 3.3.81, *Floor Area, Gross* and 3.3.82, *Floor Area, Net.*

3.3.13.1 Area, Gross Leasable. The total floor area designated for tenant occupancy and exclusive use, expressed in square feet (square meters), measured from the centerlines of adjoining partitions and exteriors of outside walls.

3.3.13.2 Area, Hazardous. An area of a structure or building that poses a degree of hazard greater than that normal to the general occupancy of the building or structure, such as areas used for the storage or use of combustibles or flammables; toxic, noxious, or corrosive materials; or heat-producing appliances.

3.3.13.3 Area, Living. Any normally occupiable space in a residential occupancy, other than sleeping rooms or rooms that are intended for combination sleeping/living, bathrooms, toilet compartments, kitchens, closets, halls, storage or utility spaces, and similar areas.

3.3.14* Area of Refuge. An area that is either (1) a story in a building where the building is protected throughout by an approved, supervised automatic sprinkler system and has not less than two accessible rooms or spaces separated from each other by smoke-resisting partitions; or (2) a space located in a path of travel leading to a public way that is protected from the effects of fire, either by means of separation from other spaces in the same building or by virtue of location, thereby permitting a delay in egress travel from any level.

A.3.3.14 Area of Refuge. An area of refuge has a temporary use during egress. It generally serves as a staging area that provides relative safety to its occupants while potential emergencies are assessed, decisions are made, and mitigating activities are begun. Taking refuge within such an area is, thus, a stage of the total egress process; a stage between egress from the immediately threatened area and egress to a public way.

An area of refuge might be another building connected by a bridge or balcony, a compartment of a subdivided story, an elevator lobby, or an enlarged story-level exit stair landing. An area of refuge is accessible by means of horizontal travel or, as a minimum, via an accessible route meeting the requirements of CABO/ANSI A117.1, *American National Standard for Accessible and Usable Buildings and Facilities.*

This *Code* recognizes any floor in a building protected throughout by an approved, supervised automatic sprinkler system as an area of refuge. This recognition acknowledges the ability of a properly designed and functioning automatic sprinkler system to control a fire at its point of origin and to limit the production of toxic products to a level that is not life threatening.

The requirement for separated rooms or spaces can be met on an otherwise undivided floor by enclosing the elevator lobby with ordinary glass or other simple enclosing partitions that are smoke resisting.

For some occupancies, one accessible room or space is permitted.

3.3.14.1 Area of Refuge, Accessible. An area of refuge that complies with the accessible route requirements of CABO/ANSI A117.1, *American National Standard for Accessible and Usable Buildings and Facilities.*

3.3.15 Assembly Occupancy. See 3.3.134.2, *Occupancy, Assembly.*

3.3.16 Atmosphere, Common. The atmosphere that exists between rooms, spaces, or areas within a building that are not separated by an approved smoke barrier.

3.3.17 Atmosphere, Separate. The atmosphere that exists between rooms, spaces, or areas that are separated by an approved smoke barrier.

3.3.18* Atrium. A large-volume space created by a floor opening or series of floor openings connecting two or more stories that is covered at the top of the series of openings and is used for purposes other than an enclosed stairway; elevator hoistway; escalator opening; or utility shaft used for plumbing, electrical, air-conditioning, or communications facilities.

A.3.3.18 Atrium. As defined in NFPA 92B, *Guide for Smoke Management Systems in Malls, Atria, and Large Areas,* a large-volume space is an uncompartmented space, generally two or more stories in height, within which smoke from a fire either in the space or in a communicating space can move and accumulate without restriction. Atria and covered malls are examples of large-volume spaces.

3.3.19 Automatic. That which provides a function without the necessity of human intervention.

3.3.20* Barrier, Smoke. A continuous membrane, or a membrane with discontinuities created by protected openings, where such membrane is designed and constructed to restrict the movement of smoke.

A.3.3.20 Barrier, Smoke. A smoke barrier might be vertically- or horizontally-aligned, such as a wall, floor, or ceiling assembly. A smoke barrier might or might not have a fire resistance rating. Application of smoke barrier criteria where required elsewhere in the *Code* should be in accordance with Section 8.3.

3.3.21* Barrier, Thermal. A material that limits the average temperature rise of an unexposed surface to not more than 250°F (139°C) for a specified fire exposure complying with the standard time-temperature curve of NFPA 251, *Standard Methods of Tests of Fire Endurance of Building Construction and Materials.*

A.3.3.21 Barrier, Thermal. Finish ratings, as published in the UL *Fire Resistance Directory,* are one way of determining thermal barrier.

3.3.22* Birth Center. A facility in which low-risk births are expected following normal, uncomplicated pregnancies, and in which professional midwifery care is provided to women during pregnancy, birth, and postpartum.

A.3.3.22 Birth Center. A birth center is a low-volume service for healthy, childbearing women, and their families, who are capable of ambulation in the event of fire or fire-threatening events. Birth center mothers and babies have minimal analgesia, no general or regional anesthesia, and are capable of ambulation, even in second-stage labor.

3.3.23 Bleachers. A grandstand in which the seats are not provided with backrests.

3.3.24 Board and Care. See 3.3.163, *Residential Board and Care Occupancy.*

3.3.25* Building. Any structure used or intended for supporting or sheltering any use or occupancy.

A.3.3.25 Building. The term *building* is to be understood as if followed by the words *or portions thereof. (See also Structure, A.3.3.197.)*

3.3.25.1* Building, Apartment. A building containing three or more dwelling units with independent cooking and bathroom facilities.

A.3.3.25.1 Building, Apartment. The *Code* specifies, that wherever there are three or more living units in a building, the building is considered an apartment building and is required to comply with either Chapter 30 or 31, as appropriate. Townhouse units are considered to be apartment buildings if there are three or more units in the building. The type of wall required between units in order to consider them to be separate buildings is normally established by the authority having jurisdiction. If the units are separated by a wall of sufficient fire resistance and structural integrity to be considered as separate buildings, then the provisions of Chapter 24 apply to each townhouse. Condominium status is a form of ownership, not occupancy; for example, there are condominium warehouses, condominium apartments, and condominium offices.

3.3.25.2 Building, Bulk Merchandising Retail. A building in which the sales area includes the storage of combustible materials on pallets, in solid piles, or in racks in excess of 12 ft (3.7 m) in storage height.

3.3.25.3* Building, Covered Mall. A building, including the covered mall, enclosing a number of tenants and occupancies wherein two or more tenants have a main entrance into the covered mall.

A.3.3.25.3 Building, Covered Mall. Covered mall buildings are occupied primarily by mercantile occupancies. However, they can include other occupancies such as drinking and dining establishments, entertainment and amusement facilities, offices, and similar uses that are incidental to the primary use of the building.

3.3.25.4* Building, Existing. A building erected or officially authorized prior to the effective date of the adoption of this edition of the *Code* by the agency or jurisdiction.

A.3.3.25.4 Building, Existing. With respect to judging whether a building should be considered existing, the deciding factor is not when the building was designed or when construction started but, rather, the date plans were approved for construction by the appropriate authority having jurisdiction.

3.3.25.5* Building, Flexible Plan and Open Plan Educational or Day-Care. A building or portion of a building designed for multiple teaching stations.

A.3.3.25.5 Building, Flexible Plan and Open Plan Educational or Day-Care. Flexible plan buildings have movable corridor walls and movable partitions of full-height construction with doors leading from rooms to corridors. Open plan buildings have rooms and corridors delineated by tables, chairs, desks, bookcases, counters, low-height partitions, or similar furnishings. It is the intent that low-height partitions not exceed 5 ft (1.5 m).

3.3.25.6* Building, High-Rise. A building greater than 75 ft (23 m) in height where the building height is measured from the lowest level of fire department vehicle access to the floor of the highest occupiable story.

A.3.3.25.6 Building, High-Rise. It is the intent of this definition that, in determining the level from which the highest occupiable floor is to be measured, the enforcing agency should exercise reasonable judgment, including consideration of overall accessibility to the building by fire department personnel and vehicular equipment. Where a building is situated on a sloping terrain and there is building access on more than one level, the enforcing agency might select the level that provides the most logical and adequate fire department access.

3.3.25.7* Building, Historic. A structure and its associated additions and site deemed to have historical, architectural, or cultural significance by a local, regional, or national jurisdiction.

A.3.3.25.7 Building, Historic. Designation for a historic building might be in an official national, regional, or local historic register, listing, or inventory.

3.3.25.8* Building, Special Amusement. A building that is temporary, permanent, or mobile that contains a device or system that conveys passengers or provides a walkway along, around, or over a course in any direction as a form of amusement arranged so that the egress path is not readily apparent due to visual or audio distractions or an intentionally confounded egress path, or is not readily available due to the mode of conveyance through the building or structure.

A.3.3.25.8 Building, Special Amusement. Such structures include amusements such as a haunted house, a roller coaster-type ride within a building, a multilevel play structure within a building, a submarine ride, and similar amusements where the occupants are not in the open air.

3.3.26 Bulk Merchandising Retail Building. See 3.3.25.2, *Building, Bulk Merchandising Retail.*

3.3.27 Business Occupancy. See 3.3.134.3, *Occupancy, Business.*

3.3.28 Cellular or Foamed Plastic. See 3.3.148, *Plastic, Cellular or Foamed.*

3.3.29 Combustible. A material that, in the form in which it is used and under the conditions anticipated, will ignite and burn; a material that does not meet the definition of noncombustible or limited-combustible.

3.3.30 Combustion. A chemical process that involves oxidation sufficient to produce light or heat.

3.3.31 Common Atmosphere. See 3.3.16, *Atmosphere, Common.*

3.3.32* Common Path of Travel. The portion of exit access that must be traversed before two separate and distinct paths of travel to two exits are available.

A.3.3.32 Common Path of Travel. Common path of travel is measured in the same manner as travel distance but terminates at that point where two separate and distinct routes become available. Paths that merge are common paths of travel.

3.3.33 Contents and Furnishings. Objects, goods, or products placed inside a structure for functional, operational, or decorative reasons, excluding parts of the building structure, building service equipment, and items meeting the definition of interior finish.

3.3.34 Court. An open, uncovered, unoccupied space, unobstructed to the sky, bounded on three or more sides by exterior building walls.

3.3.34.1 Court, Enclosed. A court bounded on all sides by the exterior walls of a building or by the exterior walls and lot lines on which walls are permitted.

3.3.35 Covered Mall. A covered or roofed interior area used as a pedestrian way and connected to a building(s) or portions of a building housing single or multiple tenants.

3.3.36 Covered Mall Building. See 3.3.25.3, *Building, Covered Mall.*

3.3.37* Critical Radiant Flux. The level of incident radiant heat energy on a floor-covering system at the most distant flameout point.

A.3.3.37 Critical Radiant Flux. Critical radiant flux is the property determined by the test procedure of NFPA 253, *Standard Method of Test for Critical Radiant Flux of Floor Covering Systems Using a Radiant Heat Energy Source.* The unit of measurement of critical radiant flux is watts per square centimeter (W/cm²).

3.3.38 Data Conversion. The process of developing the input data set for the assessment method of choice.

3.3.39* Day-Care Home. A building or portion of a building in which more than three but not more than 12 clients receive care, maintenance, and supervision, by other than their relative(s) or legal guardians(s), for less than 24 hours per day.

A.3.3.39 Day-Care Home. A day-care home is generally located within a dwelling unit.

3.3.40 Day-Care Occupancy. See 3.3.134.4, *Occupancy Day-Care.*

3.3.41 Design Fire Scenario. See 3.3.76.1, *Fire Scenario, Design.*

3.3.42* Design Specifications. Building characteristics and other conditions that are under the control of the design team.

A.3.3.42 Design Specifications. Design specifications include both hardware and human factors, such as the conditions produced by maintenance and training. For purposes of performance-based design, the design specifications of interest are those that affect the ability of the building to meet the stated goals and objectives.

3.3.43 Design Team. A group of stakeholders including, but not limited to, representatives of the architect, client, and any pertinent engineers and other designers.

3.3.44 Detention and Correctional Occupancy. See 3.3.134.5, *Occupancy, Detention and Correctional.*

3.3.45 Detention and Correctional Residential Housing Area. See 3.3.165, *Residential Housing Area, Detention and Correctional.*

3.3.46* Dormitory. A building or a space in a building in which group sleeping accommodations are provided for more than 16 persons who are not members of the same family in one room or a series of closely associated rooms under joint occupancy and single management, with or without meals, but without individual cooking facilities.

A.3.3.46 Dormitory. Rooms within dormitories intended for the use of individuals for combined living and sleeping purposes are guest rooms or guest suites. Examples of dormitories are college dormitories, fraternity and sorority houses, and military barracks.

3.3.47 Draft Stop. A continuous membrane used to subdivide a concealed space to restrict the passage of smoke, heat, and flames.

3.3.48 Dwelling Unit. A single unit, providing complete, independent living facilities for one or more persons, including permanent provisions for living, sleeping, eating, cooking, and sanitation.

3.3.49 Educational Occupancy. See 3.3.134.6, *Occupancy, Educational.*

3.3.50* Electroluminescent. Refers to a light-emitting capacitor in which alternating current excites phosphor atoms placed between electrically conductive surfaces and produces light.

A.3.3.50 Electroluminescent. This light source is typically contained inside the device.

3.3.51 Elevator Evacuation System. A system, including a vertical series of elevator lobbies and associated elevator lobby doors, an elevator shaft(s), and a machine room(s), that provides protection from fire effects for elevator passengers, people waiting to use elevators, and elevator equipment so that elevators can be used safely for egress.

3.3.52 Elevator Lobby. A space from which people directly enter an elevator car(s) and to which people directly leave an elevator car(s).

3.3.53 Elevator Lobby Door. A door between an elevator lobby and another building space other than the elevator shaft.

3.3.54 Emergency Access Opening. A window, panel, or similar opening in which (1) the opening has dimensions of not less than 22 in. (55.9 cm) in width and 24 in. (61 cm) in height and is unobstructed to allow for ventilation and rescue operations from the exterior, (2) the bottom of the opening is not more than 44 in. (112 cm) above the floor,

(3) the opening is readily identifiable from both the exterior and interior, and (4) the opening is readily openable from both the exterior and interior.

3.3.55 Enclosed Court. See 3.3.34.1, *Court, Enclosed.*

3.3.56* Evacuation Capability. The ability of occupants, residents, and staff as a group either to evacuate a building or to relocate from the point of occupancy to a point of safety.

A.3.3.56 Evacuation Capability. The evacuation capability of the residents and staff is a function of both the ability of the residents to evacuate and the assistance provided by the staff. It is intended that the evacuation capability be determined by the procedure acceptable to the authority having jurisdiction. It is also intended that the timing of drills, the rating of residents, and similar actions related to determining the evacuation capability be performed by persons approved by or acceptable to the authority having jurisdiction. The evacuation capability can be determined by the use of the definitions in 3.3.54, 3.3.140, 3.3.203, 3.3.205, 3.3.210, and 3.3.212, the application of NFPA 101A, *Guide on Alternative Approaches to Life Safety,* Chapter 5, or a program of drills (timed).

Where drills are used in determining evacuation capability, it is suggested that the facility conduct and record fire drills six times per year on a bimonthly basis, with a minimum of two drills conducted during the night when residents are sleeping, and that the facility conduct the drills in consultation with the authority having jurisdiction. Records should indicate the time taken to reach a point of safety, date and time of day, location of simulated fire origin, escape paths used, and comments relating to residents who resisted or failed to participate in the drills.

Translation of drill times to evacuation capability is determined as follows:

(1) 3 minutes or less—prompt
(2) Over 3 minutes, but not in excess of 13 minutes—slow
(3) More than 13 minutes—impractical

Evacuation capability, in all cases, is based on the time of day or night when evacuation of the facility would be most difficult, such as, when residents are sleeping or fewer staff are present.

Evacuation capability determination is considered slow if the following conditions are met:

(1) All residents are able to travel to centralized dining facilities without continuous staff assistance.
(2) There is continuous staffing whenever there are residents in the facility.

3.3.56.1 Evacuation Capability, Impractical. The inability of a group to reliably move to a point of safety in a timely manner.

3.3.56.2 Evacuation Capability, Prompt. The ability of a group to move reliably to a point of safety in a timely manner that is equivalent to the capacity of a household in the general population.

3.3.56.3 Evacuation Capability, Slow. The ability of a group to move reliably to a point of safety in a timely manner, but not as rapidly as members of a household in the general population.

3.3.57 Exhibit. A space or portable structure used for the display of products or services.

3.3.58 Exhibitor. An individual or entity engaged in the display of the products or services offered.

3.3.59* Existing. That which is already in existence on the date this edition of the Code goes into effect.

A.3.3.59 Existing. See *Building, Existing,* A.3.3.25.4.

3.3.60 Existing Building. See 3.3.25.4, *Building, Existing.*

3.3.61* Exit. That portion of a means of egress that is separated from all other spaces of a building or structure by construction or equipment as required to provide a protected way of travel to the exit discharge.

A.3.3.61 Exit. Exits include exterior exit doors, exit passageways, horizontal exits, exit stairs, and exit ramps. In the case of a stairway, the exit incudes the stair enclosure, the door to the stair enclosure, stairs and landings inside the enclosure, the door from the stair enclosure to the outside or to the level of exit discharge, and any exit passageway and its associated doors if such are provided so as to discharge the stair directly to the outside. In the case of a door leading directly from the street floor to the street or open air, the exit comprises only the door.

Doors of small individual rooms, as in hotels, while constituting exit access from the room, are not referred to as exits except where they lead directly to the outside of the building from the street floor.

3.3.61.1* Exit, Horizontal. A way of passage from one building to an area of refuge in another building on approximately the same level, or a way of passage through or around a fire barrier to an area of refuge on approximately the same level in the same building that affords safety from fire and smoke originating from the area of incidence and areas communicating therewith.

A.3.3.61.1 Exit, Horizontal. Horizontal exits should not be confused with egress through doors in smoke barriers. Doors in smoke barriers are designed only for temporary protection against smoke, whereas horizontal exits provide protection against serious fire for a relatively long period of time in addition to providing immediate protection from smoke. *(See 7.2.4.)*

3.3.62 Exit Access. That portion of a means of egress that leads to an exit.

3.3.63 Exit Discharge. That portion of a means of egress between the termination of an exit and a public way.

3.3.63.1 Exit Discharge, Level of. (1) The lowest story from which not less than 50 percent of the required number of exits and not less than 50 percent of the required egress capacity from such a story discharge directly outside at grade; (2) the story with the smallest elevation change needed to reach grade where no story has 50 percent or more of the required number of exits and 50 percent or more of the required egress capacity from such a story discharge directly outside at grade.

3.3.64 Exposition. An event in which the display of products or services is organized to bring together the provider and user of the products or services.

3.3.65 Exposition Facility. A convention center, hotel, or other building at which exposition events are held.

3.3.66* Exposure Fire. A fire that starts at a location that is remote from the area being protected and grows to expose that which is being protected.

A.3.3.66 Exposure Fire. An exposure fire usually refers to a fire that starts outside a building, such as a wildlands fire or vehicle fire, and that consequently exposes the building to a fire.

3.3.67 Externally Illuminated. See 3.3.106, *Illuminated, Externally.*

3.3.68 Festival Seating. See 3.3.171, *Seating, Festival.*

3.3.69* Fire Barrier. A continuous membrane or a membrane with discontinuities created by protected openings with a specified fire protection rating, where such membrane is designed and constructed with a specified fire resistance rating to limit the spread of fire and that also restricts the movement of smoke.

A.3.3.69 Fire Barrier. A fire barrier might be vertically- or horizontally-aligned, such as a wall or floor assembly.

3.3.70 Fire Barrier Wall. See 3.3.208, *Wall, Fire Barrier.*

3.3.71* Fire Compartment. A space within a building that is enclosed by fire barriers on all sides, including the top and bottom.

A.3.3.71 Fire Compartment. Additional fire compartment information is contained in 8.2.2.

In the provisions for fire compartments utilizing the outside walls of a building, it is not intended that the outside wall be specifically fire resistance–rated unless required by other standards. Likewise, it is not intended for outside windows or doors to be protected, unless specifically required for exposure protection by another section of this *Code* or by other standards.

3.3.72 Fire Exit Hardware. A door-latching assembly incorporating a device that releases the latch upon the application of a force in the direction of egress travel and provides fire protection where used as part of a fire door assembly.

3.3.73* Fire Model. A structured approach to predicting one or more effects of a fire.

A.3.3.73 Fire Model. Due to the complex nature of the principles involved, models are often packaged as computer software. Any relevant input data, assumptions, and limitations needed to properly implement the model will be attached to the fire models.

3.3.74 Fire Protection Rating. See 3.3.159, *Rating, Fire Protection.*

3.3.75 Fire Resistance Rating. See 3.3.160, *Rating, Fire Resistance.*

3.3.76* Fire Scenario. A set of conditions that defines the development of fire, the spread of combustion products throughout a building or portion of a building, the reactions of people to fire, and the effects of combustion products.

A.3.3.76 Fire Scenario. A fire scenario defines the conditions under which a proposed design is expected to meet the fire safety goals. Factors typically include fuel characteristics, ignition sources, ventilation, building characteristics, and occupant locations and characteristics. The term fire scenario includes more than the characteristics of the fire itself but excludes design specifications and excludes any characteristics that do not vary from one fire to another; the latter are called assumptions. The term fire scenario is used here to mean only those specifications required to calculate the fire's development and effects but, in other contexts, the term might be used to mean both the initial specifications and the subsequent development and effects (that is, a complete description of fire from conditions prior to ignition to conditions following extinguishment).

3.3.76.1 Fire Scenario, Design. A fire scenario used for evaluation of a proposed design.

3.3.77* Fire Watch. A person or persons assigned to an area for the purpose of protecting the occupants from fire or similar emergencies.

A.3.3.77 Fire Watch. Duties of the fire watch might include notifying the fire department and building occupants of an emergency, preventing a fire from occurring, or extinguishing small fires.

3.3.78* Flame Spread. The propagation of flame over a surface.

A.3.3.78 Flame Spread. See Section 10.2.

3.3.79* Flashover. A stage in the development of a contained fire in which all exposed surfaces reach ignition temperatures more or less simultaneously and fire spreads rapidly throughout the space.

A.3.3.79 Flashover. Flashover occurs when the surface temperatures of combustible contents rise, producing pyrolysis gases, and the room heat flux becomes sufficient to heat all such gases to their ignition temperatures.

3.3.80 Flexible Plan and Open Plan Educational or Day-Care Building. See 3.3.25.5, *Building, Flexible Plan and Open Plan Educational or Day-Care.*

3.3.81* Floor Area, Gross. The floor area within the inside perimeter of the outside walls of the building under consideration with no deduction for hallways, stairs, closets, thickness of interior walls, columns, or other features.

A.3.3.81 Floor Area, Gross. Where the term *floor area* is used, it should be understood to be gross floor area unless otherwise specified.

3.3.82 Floor Area, Net. The floor area that is the actual occupied area, not including accessory unoccupied areas or thickness of walls.

3.3.83 Flow Time. A component of total evacuation time that is the time during which there is crowd flow past a point in the means of egress system.

3.3.84 Fly Gallery. A raised floor area above a stage from which the movement of scenery and operation of other stage effects are controlled.

3.3.85 Folding and Telescopic Seating. See 3.3.172, *Seating, Folding and Telescopic.*

3.3.86* Fuel Load. The total quantity of combustible contents of a building, space, or fire area.

A.3.3.86 Fuel Load. Fuel load includes interior finish and trim.

3.3.87 General Industrial Occupancy. See 3.3.134.8.1, *Occupancy, Industrial, General.*

3.3.88 Goal. A nonspecific overall outcome to be achieved that is measured on a qualitative basis.

3.3.89* Grandstand. A structure that provides tiered or stepped seating.

A.3.3.89 Grandstand. Where the term grandstand is preceded by an adjective denoting a material, it means a grandstand the essential members of which, exclusive of seating, are of the material designated.

3.3.90 Gridiron. The structural framing over a stage supporting equipment for hanging or flying scenery and other stage effects.

3.3.91 Gross Floor Area. See 3.3.81, *Floor Area, Gross.*

3.3.92 Gross Leasable Area. See 3.3.13.1, *Area, Gross Leasable.*

3.3.93 Guard. A vertical protective barrier erected along exposed edges of stairways, balconies, and similar areas.

3.3.94 Guest Room. An accommodation combining living, sleeping, sanitary, and storage facilities within a compartment.

3.3.95 Guest Suite. An accommodation with two or more contiguous rooms comprising a compartment, with or without doors between such rooms, that provides living, sleeping, sanitary, and storage facilities.

3.3.96 Handrail. A bar, pipe, or similar member designed to furnish persons with a handhold.

3.3.97 Hazardous Area. See 3.3.13.2, *Area, Hazardous.*

3.3.98 Health Care Occupancy. See 3.3.134.7, *Occupancy, Health Care.*

3.3.99* Heat Release Rate (HRR). The rate at which heat energy is generated by burning.

A.3.3.99 Heat Release Rate (HRR). The heat release rate of a fuel is related to its chemistry, physical form, and availability of oxidant and is ordinarily expressed as British thermal units per second (Btu/s) or kilowatts (kW).

Chapter 40 and Chapter 42 include detailed provisions on high hazard occupancy.

3.3.100 High Hazard Industrial Occupancy. See 3.3.134.8.2, *Occupancy, Industrial, High Hazard.*

3.3.101 High-Rise Building. See 3.3.25.6, *Building, High-Rise.*

3.3.102 Historic Building. See 3.3.25.7, *Building, Historic.*

3.3.103 Horizontal Exit. See 3.3.61.1, *Exit, Horizontal.*

3.3.104 Hospital. A building or portion thereof used on a 24-hour basis for the medical, psychiatric, obstetrical, or surgical care of four or more inpatients.

3.3.105* Hotel. A building or groups of buildings under the same management in which there are sleeping accommodations for more than 16 persons and primarily used by transients for lodging with or without meals.

A.3.3.105 Hotel. So-called apartment hotels should be classified as hotels because they are potentially subject to the same transient occupancy as hotels. Transients are those who occupy accommodations for less than 30 days.

3.3.106* Illuminated, Externally. Refers to an illumination source that is contained outside of the device or sign legend area that is to be illuminated.

A.3.3.106 Illuminated, Externally. The light source is typically a dedicated incandescent or fluorescent source.

3.3.107* Illuminated, Internally. Refers to an illumination source that is contained inside the device or legend that is illuminated.

A.3.3.107 Illuminated, Internally. The light source is typically incandescent, fluorescent, electroluminescent, photoluminescent, light-emitting diodes, or self-luminous.

3.3.108 Impractical Evacuation Capability. See 3.3.56.1, *Evacuation Capability, Impractical.*

3.3.109 Incapacitation. A condition under which humans do not function adequately and become unable to escape untenable conditions.

3.3.110 Industrial Occupancy. See 3.3.134.8, *Occupancy, Industrial.*

3.3.111 Input Data Specification. Information required by the verification method.

3.3.112* Interior Finish. The exposed surfaces of walls, ceilings, and floors within buildings.

A.3.3.112 Interior Finish. Interior finish is not intended to apply to surfaces within spaces such as those that are concealed or inaccessible. Furnishings that, in some cases, might be secured in place for functional reasons should not be considered as interior finish.

3.3.112.1 Interior Ceiling Finish. The interior finish of ceilings.

3.3.112.2* Interior Floor Finish. The interior finish of floors, ramps, stair treads and risers, and other walking surfaces.

A.3.3.112.2 Interior Floor Finish. Interior floor finish includes coverings applied over a normal finished floor or stair treads and risers.

3.3.112.3 Interior Wall Finish. The interior finish of columns, fixed or movable walls, and fixed or movable partitions.

3.3.113 Internally Illuminated. See 3.3.107, *Illuminated, Internally.*

3.3.114 Legitimate Stage. See 3.3.191.1, *Stage, Legitimate.*

3.3.115 Level of Exit Discharge. See 3.3.63.1, *Exit Discharge, Level of.*

3.3.116 Life Safety Evaluation. A written review dealing with the adequacy of life safety features relative to fire, storm, collapse, crowd behavior, and other related safety considerations.

3.3.117* Limited Care Facility. A building or portion of a building used on a 24-hour basis for the housing of four or more persons who are incapable of self-preservation because of age; physical limitations due to accident or illness; or limitations such as mental retardation/developmental disability, mental illness, or chemical dependency.

A.3.3.117 Limited Care Facility. Limited care facilities and residential board and care occupancies both provide care to people with physical and mental limitations. However, the goals and programs of the two types of occupancies differ greatly. The requirements in this *Code* for limited care facilities are based on the assumption that these are medical facilities, that they provide medical care and treatment, and that the patients are not trained to respond to the fire alarm; that is, the patients do not participate in fire drills but, rather, they await rescue. *(See Section 18.7.)*

The requirements for residential board and care occupancies are based on the assumption that the residents are provided with personal care and activities that foster continued independence, that the residents are encouraged and taught to overcome their limitations, and that most residents, including all residents in prompt and slow homes, are trained to respond to fire drills, to the extent they are able. Residents are required to participate in fire drills. *(See Section 32.7.)*

3.3.118* Limited-Combustible. Refers to a building construction material not complying with the definition of noncombustible (see 3.3.131) that, in the form in which it is used, has a potential heat value not exceeding 3500 Btu/lb (8141 kJ/kg), where tested in accordance with NFPA 259, *Standard Test Method for Potential Heat of Building Materials,* and includes (1) materials having a structural base of noncombustible material, with a surfacing not exceeding a thickness of ⅛ in. (3.2 mm) that has a flame spread index not greater than 50; and (2) materials, in the form and thickness used, other than as described in (1), having neither a flame spread index greater than 25 nor evidence of continued progressive combustion, and of such composition that surfaces that would be exposed by cutting through the material on any plane would have neither a flame spread index greater than 25 nor evidence of continued progressive combustion.

A.3.3.118 Limited-Combustible. Materials subject to increase in combustibility or flame spread index beyond the limits herein established through the effects of age, moisture, or other atmospheric condition are considered combustible. See NFPA 259, *Standard Test Method for Potential Heat of Building Materials,* and NFPA 220, *Standard on Types of Building Construction.*

3.3.119 Living Area. See 3.3.13.3, *Area, Living.*

3.3.120 Lodging or Rooming House. A building or portion thereof that does not qualify as a one- or two-family dwelling, that provides sleeping accommodations for a total of 16 or fewer people on a transient or permanent basis, without personal care services, with or without meals, but without separate cooking facilities for individual occupants.

3.3.121* Means of Egress. A continuous and unobstructed way of travel from any point in a building or structure to a public way consisting of three separate and distinct parts: (1) the exit access, (2) the exit, and (3) the exit discharge.

A.3.3.121 Means of Egress. A means of egress comprises the vertical and horizontal travel and incudes intervening room spaces, doorways, hallways, corridors, passageways, balconies, ramps, stairs, elevators, enclosures, lobbies, escalators, horizontal exits, courts, and yards.

3.3.121.1 Means of Egress, Accessible. A path of travel, usable by a person with a severe mobility impairment, that leads to a public way or an area of refuge.

3.3.122 Means of Escape. A way out of a building or structure that does not conform to the strict definition of means of egress but does provide an alternate way out.

3.3.123 Membrane. A thin, flexible, water-impervious material capable of being supported by an air pressure of 1.5 in. (38.1 mm) water column.

3.3.124 Membrane Structure. See 3.3.197.3, *Structure, Membrane.*

3.3.125 Mercantile Occupancy. See 3.3.134.9, *Occupancy, Mercantile.*

3.3.126 Mezzanine. An intermediate level between the floor and the ceiling of any room or space.

3.3.127 Mixed Occupancy. See 3.3.134.10, *Occupancy, Mixed.*

3.3.128 Multilevel Play Structure. See 3.3.197.4, *Structure, Multilevel Play.*

3.3.129 Multipurpose Assembly Occupancy. See 3.3.134.11, *Occupancy, Multipurpose Assembly.*

3.3.130 Net Floor Area. See 3.3.82, *Floor Area, Net.*

3.3.131 Noncombustible. Refers to a material that, in the form in which it is used and under the conditions anticipated, does not ignite, burn, support combustion, or release flammable vapors, when subjected to fire or heat. Materials that are reported as passing ASTM E 136, *Standard Test Method for Behavior of Materials in a Vertical Tube Furnace at 750 Degrees C,* are considered noncombustible materials.

3.3.132 Nursing Home. A building or portion of a building used on a 24-hour basis for the housing and nursing care of four or more persons who, because of mental or physical incapacity, might be unable to provide for their own needs and safety without the assistance of another person.

3.3.133* Objective. A requirement that needs to be met to achieve a goal.

A.3.3.133 Objective. Objectives define a series of actions necessary to make the achievement of a goal more likely. Objectives are stated in more specific terms than goals and are measured on a more quantitative, rather than qualitative, basis.

3.3.134 Occupancy. The purpose for which a building or portion thereof is used or intended to be used.

3.3.134.1 Occupancy, Ambulatory Health Care. A building or portion thereof used to provide services or treatment simultaneously to four or more patients that (1) provides, on an outpatient basis, treatment for patients that renders the patients incapable of taking action for self-preservation under emergency conditions without the assistance of others; or (2) provides, on an outpatient basis, anesthesia that renders the patients incapable of taking action for self-preservation under emergency conditions without the assistance of others.

3.3.134.2* Occupancy, Assembly. An occupancy (1) used for a gathering of 50 or more persons for deliberation, worship, entertainment, eating, drinking, amusement, awaiting transportation, or similar uses; or (2) used as a special amusement building, regardless of occupant load.

A.3.3.134.2 Occupancy, Assembly. Assembly occupancies might include the following:

(1) Armories
(2) Assembly halls
(3) Auditoriums
(4) Bowling lanes
(5) Club rooms
(6) College and university classrooms, 50 persons and over
(7) Conference rooms
(8) Courtrooms
(9) Dance halls
(10) Drinking establishments

(11) Exhibition halls
(12) Gymnasiums
(13) Libraries
(14) Mortuary chapels
(15) Motion picture theaters
(16) Museums
(17) Passenger stations and terminals of air, surface, underground, and marine public transportation facilities
(18) Places of religious worship
(19) Pool rooms
(20) Recreation piers
(21) Restaurants
(22) Skating rinks
(23) Special amusement buildings regardless of occupant load
(24) Theaters

Assembly occupancies are characterized by the presence or potential presence of crowds with attendant panic hazard in case of fire or other emergency. They are generally open or occasionally open to the public, and the occupants, who are present voluntarily, are not ordinarily subject to discipline or control. Such buildings are ordinarily occupied by able-bodied persons and are not used for sleeping purposes. Special conference rooms, snack areas, and other areas incidental to, and under the control of, the management of other occupancies, such as offices, fall under the 50-person limitation.

Restaurants and drinking establishments with an occupant load of fewer than 50 persons should be classified as mercantile occupancies.

For special amusement buildings, see 12.4.7 and 13.4.7.

3.3.134.3* Occupancy, Business. An occupancy used for account and record keeping or the transaction of business other than mercantile.

A.3.3.134.3 Occupancy, Business. Business occupancies include the following:

(1) Air traffic control towers (ATCTs)
(2) City halls
(3) College and university instructional buildings, classrooms under 50 persons, and instructional laboratories
(4) Courthouses
(5) Dentists' offices
(6) Doctors' offices
(7) General offices
(8) Outpatient clinics, ambulatory
(9) Town halls

Doctors' and dentists' offices are included, unless of such character as to be classified as ambulatory health care occupancies. (See 3.3.8.)

Birth centers occupied by fewer than four patients, not including infants, at any one time; not providing sleeping

facilities for four or more occupants; and not providing treatment procedures that render four or more patients, not including infants, incapable of self-preservation at any one time should be classified as business occupancies. For birth centers occupied by patients not meeting these parameters, see Chapter 18 or Chapter 19, as appropriate.

Service facilities common to city office buildings such as newsstands, lunch counters serving fewer than 50 persons, barber shops, and beauty parlors are included in the business occupancy group.

City halls, town halls, and court houses are included in this occupancy group insofar as their principal function is the transaction of public business and the keeping of books and records. Insofar as they are used for assembly purposes, they are classified as assembly occupancies.

3.3.134.4* Occupancy, Day-Care. An occupancy in which four or more clients receive care, maintenance, and supervision, by other than their relatives or legal guardians, for less than 24 hours per day.

A.3.3.134.4 Occupancy, Day-Care. Day-care occupancies include the following:

(1) Adult day-care occupancies, except where part of a health care occupancy
(2) Child day-care occupancies
(3) Day-care homes
(4) Kindergarten classes that are incidental to a child day-care occupancy
(5) Nursery schools

In areas where public schools offer only half-day kindergarten programs, many child day-care occupancies offer state-approved kindergarten classes for children who need full-day care. As these classes are normally incidental to the day-care occupancy, the requirements of the day-care occupancy should be followed.

3.3.134.5* Occupancy, Detention and Correctional. An occupancy used to house four or more persons under varied degrees of restraint or security where such occupants are mostly incapable of self-preservation because of security measures not under the occupants' control.

A.3.3.134.5 Occupancy, Detention and Correctional. Detention and correctional occupancies include the following:

(1) Adult and juvenile substance abuse centers
(2) Adult and juvenile work camps
(3) Adult community residential centers
(4) Adult correctional institutions
(5) Adult local detention facilities
(6) Juvenile community residential centers
(7) Juvenile detention facilities
(8) Juvenile training schools

3.3.134.6* Occupancy, Educational. An occupancy used for educational purposes through the twelfth grade by six or more persons for four or more hours per day or more than 12 hours per week.

A.3.3.134.6 Occupancy, Educational. Educational occupancies include the following:

(1) Academies
(2) Kindergartens
(3) Schools

An educational occupancy is distinguished from an assembly occupancy in that the same occupants are regularly present.

3.3.134.7* Occupancy, Health Care. An occupancy used for purposes of medical or other treatment or care of four or more persons where such occupants are mostly incapable of self-preservation due to age, physical or mental disability, or because of security measures not under the occupants' control.

A.3.3.134.7 Occupancy, Health Care. Health care occupancies include the following:

(1) Ambulatory health care facilities
(2) Hospitals
(3) Limited care facilities
(4) Nursing homes

Occupants of health care occupancies typically have physical or mental illness, disease, or infirmity. They also include infants, convalescents, or infirm aged persons.

3.3.134.8* Occupancy, Industrial. An occupancy in which products are manufactured or in which processing, assembling, mixing, packaging, finishing, decorating, or repair operations are conducted.

A.3.3.134.8 Occupancy, Industrial. Industrial occupancies include the following:

(1) Dry cleaning plants
(2) Factories of all kinds
(3) Food processing plants
(4) Gas plants
(5) Hangars (for servicing/maintenance)
(6) Laundries
(7) Power plants
(8) Pumping stations
(9) Refineries
(10) Sawmills
(11) Telephone exchanges

In evaluating the appropriate classification of laboratories, the authority having jurisdiction should treat each case individually based on the extent and nature of the associated hazards. Some laboratories are classified as occupancies

other than industrial; for example, a physical therapy laboratory or a computer laboratory.

3.3.134.8.1* Occupancy, Industrial, General. An industrial occupancy in which ordinary and low hazard industrial operations are conducted in buildings of conventional design suitable for various types of industrial processes.

A.3.3.134.8.1 Occupancy, Industrial, General. General industrial occupancies include multistory buildings where floors are occupied by different tenants or buildings suitable for such occupancy and, therefore, are subject to possible use for types of industrial processes with a high density of employee population.

3.3.134.8.2* Occupancy, Industrial, High Hazard. An industrial occupancy in which industrial operations that include high hazard materials, processes, or contents are conducted.

A.3.3.134.8.2 Occupancy, Industrial, High Hazard. A high hazard occupancy includes occupancies where gasoline and other flammable liquids are handled, used, or stored under such conditions that involve possible release of flammable vapors; where grain dust, wood flour or plastic dusts, aluminum or magnesium dust, or other explosive dusts are produced; where hazardous chemicals or explosives are manufactured, stored, or handled; where cotton or other combustible fibers are processed or handled under conditions that might produce flammable flyings; and where other situations of similar hazard exist. Chapter 40 and Chapter 42 include detailed provisions on high hazard occupancy.

3.3.134.8.3 Occupancy, Industrial, Special Purpose. An industrial occupancy in which ordinary and low hazard industrial operations are conducted in buildings designed for and suitable only for particular types of operations, characterized by a relatively low density of employee population, with much of the area occupied by machinery or equipment.

3.3.134.9* Occupancy, Mercantile. An occupancy used for the display and sale of merchandise.

A.3.3.134.9 Occupancy, Mercantile. Mercantile occupancies include the following:

(1) Auction rooms
(2) Department stores
(3) Drugstores
(4) Restaurants with fewer than 50 persons
(5) Shopping centers
(6) Supermarkets

Office, storage, and service facilities incidental to the sale of merchandise and located in the same building should be considered part of the mercantile occupancy classification.

3.3.134.10* Occupancy, Mixed. An occupancy in which two or more classes of occupancy exist in the same building or structure and where such classes are intermingled so that separate safeguards are impracticable.

A.3.3.134.10 Occupancy, Mixed. With only a few exceptions, the *Code* sets no specific occupancy separation requirements. The authority having jurisdiction determines the separation needed, if any, based on 6.1.14 and subsection __.1.2 of each occupancy chapter. The local building code or the model building codes might be consulted by the authority having jurisdiction in making this determination, keeping life safety rather than property protection in mind.

3.3.134.11 Occupancy, Multipurpose Assembly. An assembly room designed to accommodate temporarily any of several possible assembly uses.

3.3.134.12* Occupancy, Residential. An occupancy that provides sleeping accommodations for purposes other than health care or detention and correctional.

A.3.3.134.12 Occupancy, Residential. Residential occupancies are treated as separate occupancies in this *Code* as follows:

(1) One- and two-family dwellings (Chapter 24)
(2) Lodging or rooming houses (Chapter 26)
(3) Hotels, motels, and dormitories (Chapters 28 and 29)
(4) Apartment buildings (Chapters 30 and 31)

3.3.134.13* Occupancy, Residential Board and Care. A building or portion thereof that is used for lodging and boarding of four or more residents, not related by blood or marriage to the owners or operators, for the purpose of providing personal care services.

A.3.3.134.13 Occupancy, Residential Board and Care. The following are examples of facilities that are classified as residential board and care occupancies:

(1) A group housing arrangement for physically or mentally handicapped persons who normally attend school in the community, attend worship in the community, or otherwise use community facilities
(2) A group housing arrangement for physically or mentally handicapped persons who are undergoing training in preparation for independent living, for paid employment, or for other normal community activities
(3) A group housing arrangement for the elderly that provides personal care services but that does not provide nursing care
(4) Facilities for social rehabilitation, alcoholism, drug abuse, or mental health problems that contain a group housing arrangement and that provide personal care services but do not provide acute care
(5) Assisted living facilities

(6) Other group housing arrangements that provide personal care services but not nursing care

3.3.134.14* Occupancy, Storage. An occupancy used primarily for the storage or sheltering of goods, merchandise, products, vehicles, or animals.

A.3.3.134.14 Occupancy, Storage. Storage occupancies include the following:

(1) Barns
(2) Bulk oil storage
(3) Cold storage
(4) Freight terminals
(5) Grain elevators
(6) Hangars (for storage only)
(7) Parking structures
(8) Stables
(9) Truck and marine terminals
(10) Warehouses

Storage occupancies are characterized by the presence of relatively small numbers of persons in proportion to the area.

3.3.135 Occupant Characteristics. The abilities or behaviors of people before and during a fire.

3.3.136 Occupant Load. The total number of persons that might occupy a building or portion thereof at any one time.

3.3.137 Occupiable Story. See 3.3.194.1, *Story, Occupiable.*

3.3.138 Open-Air Mercantile Operation. An operation conducted outside of all structures, with the operations area devoid of all walls and roofs except for small, individual, weather canopies.

3.3.139 Open-Air Parking Structure. See 3.3.197.6, *Structure, Open-Air Parking.*

3.3.140 Open Structure. See 3.3.197.5, *Structure, Open.*

3.3.141* Outside Stair. A stair with not less than one side open to the outer air.

A.3.3.141 Outside Stair. See 7.2.2.

3.3.142 Panic Hardware. A door-latching assembly incorporating a device that releases the latch upon the application of a force in the direction of egress travel.

3.3.143* Performance Criteria. Threshold values on measurement scales that are based on quantified performance objectives.

A.3.3.143 Performance Criteria. Performance criteria are stated in engineering terms. Engineering terms include temperatures, radiant heat flux, and levels of exposure to fire products. Performance criteria provide threshold values used to evaluate a proposed design.

3.3.144 Permanent Structure. See 3.3.197.7, *Structure, Permanent.*

3.3.145* Personal Care. The care of residents who do not require chronic or convalescent medical or nursing care.

A.3.3.145 Personal Care. Personal care involves responsibility for the safety of the resident while inside the building. Personal care might include daily awareness by the management of the resident's functioning and whereabouts, making and reminding a resident of appointments, the ability and readiness for intervention in the event of a resident experiencing a crisis, supervision in the areas of nutrition and medication, and actual provision of transient medical care.

3.3.146* Photoluminescent. Having the property of emitting light that continues for a length of time after excitation by visible or invisible light has been removed.

A.3.3.146 Photoluminescent. The light source is considered internally illuminated.

3.3.147 Pinrail. A rail on or above a stage through which belaying pins are inserted and to which lines are fastened.

3.3.148* Plastic, Cellular or Foamed. A heterogeneous system comprised of not less than two phases, one of which is a continuous polymeric organic material, and the second of which is deliberately introduced for the purpose of distributing gas in voids throughout the material.

A.3.3.148 Plastic, Cellular or Foamed. Cellular or foamed plastic might contain foamed and unfoamed polymeric or monomeric precursors (prepolymer, if used), plasticizers, fillers, extenders, catalysts, blowing agents, colorants, stabilizers, lubricants, surfactants, pigments, reaction control agents, processing aids, and flame retardants.

3.3.149* Platform. The raised area within a building used for the presentation of music, plays, or other entertainment.

A.3.3.149 Platform. Platforms also include the head tables for special guests; the raised area for lecturers and speakers; boxing and wrestling rings; theater-in-the-round; and for similar purposes wherein there are no overhead drops, pieces of scenery, or stage effects other than lighting and a screening valance. A platform is not intended to be prohibited from using a curtain as a valance to screen or hide the electric conduit, lighting track, or similar fixtures, nor is a platform prohibited from using curtains that are used to obscure the back wall of the stage; a curtain between the auditorium and the stage (grand or house curtain), a maximum of four leg drops; or a valance to screen light panels, plumbing, and similar equipment from view.

3.3.149.1 Platform, Temporary. A platform erected within an area for not more than 30 days.

3.3.150 Plenum. A compartment or chamber to which one or more air ducts are connected and that forms part of the air distribution system.

3.3.151 Point of Safety. A location that (a) is exterior to and away from a building; or (b) is within a building of any type construction protected throughout by an approved automatic sprinkler system and that is either (1) within an exit enclosure meeting the requirements of this *Code,* or (2) within another portion of the building that is separated by smoke barriers in accordance with Section 8.3, with not less than a ½-hour fire resistance rating, and that portion of the building has access to a means of escape or exit that conforms to the requirements of this *Code* and does not necessitate return to the area of fire involvement; or (c) is within a building of Type I, Type II(222), Type II(111), Type III(211), Type IV, or Type V(111) construction (see 8.2.1) and is either (1) within an exit enclosure meeting the requirements of this *Code,* or (2) within another portion of the building that is separated by smoke barriers in accordance with Section 8.3, with not less than a ½-hour fire resistance rating, and that portion of the building has access to a means of escape or exit that conforms to the requirements of this *Code* and does not necessitate return to the area of fire involvement.

3.3.152 Private Party Tent. See 3.3.201.1, *Tent, Private Party.*

3.3.153 Professional Engineer. An engineer who is registered or licensed to practice engineering.

3.3.154 Prompt Evacuation Capability. See 3.3.56.2, *Evacuation Capability, Prompt.*

3.3.155* Proposed Design. A design developed by a design team and submitted to the authority having jurisdiction for approval.

A.3.3.155 Proposed Design. The design team might develop a number of trial designs that will be evaluated to determine if they meet the performance criteria. One of the trial designs will be selected from those that meet the performance criteria for submission to the authority having jurisdiction as the proposed design.

The proposed design is not necessarily limited to fire protection systems and building features. It also includes any component of the proposed design that is installed, established, or maintained for the purpose of life safety, without which the proposed design could fail to achieve specified performance criteria. Therefore, the proposed design often includes emergency procedures and organizational structures that are needed to meet the performance criteria specified for the proposed design.

3.3.156 Proscenium Wall. See 3.3.209, *Wall, Proscenium.*

3.3.157 Public Way. A street, alley, or other similar parcel of land essentially open to the outside air deeded, dedicated, or otherwise permanently appropriated to the public for public use and having a clear width and height of not less than 10 ft (3 m).

3.3.158* Ramp. A walking surface that has a slope steeper than 1 in 20.

A.3.3.158 Ramp. See 7.2.5.

3.3.159 Rating, Fire Protection. The designation indicating the duration of the fire test exposure to which a fire door assembly or fire window assembly was exposed and for which it met all the acceptance criteria as determined in accordance with NFPA 252, *Standard Methods of Fire Tests of Door Assemblies,* or NFPA 257, *Standard on Fire Test for Window and Glass Block Assemblies,* respectively.

3.3.160 Rating, Fire Resistance. The time, in minutes or hours, that materials or assemblies have withstood a fire exposure as established in accordance with the test procedures of NFPA 251, *Standard Methods of Tests of Fire Endurance of Building Construction and Materials.*

3.3.161 Regular Stage. See 3.3.191.2, *Stage, Regular.*

3.3.162 Resident, Residential Board and Care. A person who receives personal care and resides in a residential board and care facility.

3.3.163 Residential Board and Care Occupancy. See 3.3.134.13, *Occupancy, Residential Board and Care.*

3.3.164 Residential Board and Care Resident. See 3.3.162, *Resident, Residential Board and Care.*

3.3.165 Residential Housing Area, Detention and Correctional. Sleeping areas and any contiguous day room, group activity space, or other common space for customary access of residents.

3.3.166 Residential Occupancy. See 3.3.134.12, *Occupancy, Residential.*

3.3.167 Safe Location. A location remote or separated from the effects of a fire so that such effects no longer pose a threat.

3.3.168 Safety Factor. A factor applied to a predicted value to ensure that a sufficient safety margin is maintained.

3.3.169 Safety Margin. The difference between a predicted value and the actual value where a fault condition is expected.

3.3.170 Sally Port (Security Vestibule). A compartment provided with two or more doors where the intended purpose is to prevent continuous and unobstructed passage by allowing the release of only one door at a time.

3.3.171* Seating, Festival. A form of audience/spectator accommodation in which no seating, other than a floor or ground surface, is provided for the audience/ spectators gathered to observe a performance.

A.3.3.171 Seating, Festival. Festival seating describes situations in assembly occupancies where live entertainment events are held that are expected to result in overcrowding and high audience density that can compromise public safety. It is not the intent to apply the term festival seating to exhibitions; sports events; dances; conventions; and bona fide political, religious, and educational events. Assembly occupancies with 15 ft² (1.4 m²) or more per person should not be considered festival seating.

3.3.172 Seating, Folding and Telescopic. A structure that is used for tiered seating of persons and whose overall shape and size can be reduced, without being dismantled, for purposes of moving or storing.

3.3.173 Seating, Smoke-Protected Assembly. Seating served by means of egress that is not subject to smoke accumulation within or under the structure.

3.3.174 Self-Closing. Equipped with an approved device that ensures closing after opening.

3.3.175* Self-Luminous. Illuminated by a self-contained power source and operated independently of external power sources.

A.3.3.175 Self-Luminous. An example of a self-contained power source is tritium gas. Batteries do not qualify as a self-contained power source. The light source is typically contained inside the device.

3.3.176* Self-Preservation (Day-Care Occupancy). The ability of a client to evacuate a day-care occupancy without direct intervention by a staff member.

A.3.3.176 Self-Preservation (Day-Care Occupancy). Examples of clients who are incapable of self-preservation include infants, clients who are unable to use stairs because of confinement to a wheelchair or other physical disability, and clients who cannot follow directions or a group to the outside of a facility due to mental or behavioral disorders. It is the intent of this *Code* to classify children under the age of 24 months as incapable of self-preservation. Examples of direct intervention by staff members include carrying a client, pushing a client outside in a wheelchair, and guiding a client by direct hand-holding or continued bodily contact. If clients cannot exit the building by themselves with minimal intervention from staff members, such as verbal orders, classification as incapable of self-preservation should be considered.

3.3.177 Sensitivity Analysis. See 3.3.9, *Analysis, Sensitivity.*

3.3.178 Separate Atmosphere. See 3.3.17, *Atmosphere, Separate.*

3.3.179 Severe Mobility Impairment. The ability to move to stairs but without the ability to use the stairs.

3.3.180 Slow Evacuation Capability. See 3.3.56.3, *Evacuation Capability, Slow.*

3.3.181 Smoke Alarm. A single- or multiple-station alarm that responds to smoke.

3.3.182 Smoke Barrier. See 3.3.20, *Barrier, Smoke.*

3.3.183* Smoke Compartment. A space within a building enclosed by smoke barriers on all sides, including the top and bottom.

A.3.3.183 Smoke Compartment. In the provision of smoke compartments using the outside walls or the roof of a building, it is not intended that outside walls or roofs or any openings therein be capable of resisting the passage of smoke. Application of smoke compartment criteria where required elsewhere in the Code should be in accordance with Section 8.3.

3.3.184 Smoke Detector. A device that detects visible or invisible particles of combustion.

3.3.185* Smoke Partition. A continuous membrane that is designed to form a barrier to limit the transfer of smoke.

A.3.3.185 Smoke Partition. A smoke partition is not required to have a fire resistance rating.

3.3.186* Smokeproof Enclosure. A stair enclosure designed to limit the movement of products of combustion produced by a fire.

A.3.3.186 Smokeproof Enclosure. For further guidance, see the following publications:

(1) *ASHRAE Handbook and Product Directory— Fundamentals*
(2) *Design of Smoke Management Systems,* by Klote and Milke
(3) NFPA 105, *Recommended Practice for the Installation of Smoke-Control Door Assemblies*

3.3.187 Smoke-Protected Assembly Seating. See 3.3.173, *Seating, Smoke-Protected Assembly.*

3.3.188 Special Amusement Building. See 3.3.25.8, *Building, Special Amusement.*

3.3.189 Special Purpose Industrial Occupancy. See 3.3.134.8.3, *Occupancy, Industrial, Special Purpose.*

3.3.190 Staff (Residential Board and Care). Persons who provide personal care services, supervision, or assistance.

3.3.191 Stage. A space within a building used for entertainment and utilizing drops or scenery or other stage effects.

3.3.191.1 Stage, Legitimate. A stage with a height greater than 50 ft (15 m) measured from the lowest point on the stage floor to the highest point of the roof or floor deck above.

3.3.191.2 Stage, Regular. A stage with a height of 50 ft (15 m) or less measured from the lowest point on the deck above.

3.3.192 Stakeholder. An individual, or representative of same, having an interest in the successful completion of a project.

3.3.193 Storage Occupancy. See 3.3.134.14, *Occupancy, Storage.*

3.3.194 Story. The portion of a building located between the upper surface of a floor and the upper surface of the floor or roof next above.

3.3.194.1* Story, Occupiable. A story occupied by people on a regular basis.

A.3.3.194.1 Story, Occupiable. Stories used exclusively for mechanical equipment rooms, elevator penthouses, and similar spaces are not occupiable stories.

3.3.195 Street. A public thoroughfare that has been dedicated for vehicular use by the public and can be used for access by fire department vehicles.

3.3.196* Street Floor. A story or floor level accessible from the street or from outside a building at ground level, with the floor level at the main entrance located not more than three risers above or below ground level and arranged and utilized to qualify as the main floor.

A.3.3.196 Street Floor. Where, due to differences in street levels, there are two or more stories accessible from the street, each is a street floor. Where there is no floor level within the specified limits for a street floor above or below ground level, the building has no street floor.

3.3.197* Structure. That which is built or constructed.

A.3.3.197 Structure. The term structure is to be understood as if followed by the words or portion thereof. *(See also Building, A.3.3.25.)*

3.3.197.1 Structure, Air-Inflated. A structure whose shape is maintained by air pressure in cells or tubes forming all or part of the enclosure of the usable area and in which the occupants are not within the pressurized area used to support the structure.

3.3.197.2* Structure, Air-Supported. A structure whose shape is maintained by air pressure and in which occupants are within the elevated pressure area.

A.3.3.197.2 Structure, Air-Supported. A cable-restrained air-supported structure is one in which the uplift is resisted by cables or webbing that is anchored by various methods to the membrane or that might be an integral part of the membrane. It is not a tensioned-membrane structure.

3.3.197.3 Structure, Membrane. A building or portion of a building incorporating an air-inflated, air-supported, tensioned-membrane structure; a membrane roof; or a membrane-covered rigid frame to protect habitable or usable space.

3.3.197.4 Structure, Multilevel Play. A structure that consists of tubes, slides, crawling areas, and jumping areas that is located within a building and is used for climbing and entertainment, generally by children.

3.3.197.5* Structure, Open. A structure that supports equipment and operations not enclosed within building walls.

A.3.3.197.5 Structure, Open. Open structures are often found in oil refining, chemical processing, or power plants. Roofs or canopies without enclosing walls are not considered an enclosure.

3.3.197.6 Structure, Open-Air Parking. A structure used for the parking or storage of motor vehicles that have (1) uniformly distributed openings in exterior walls on not less than two sides totaling not less than 40 percent of the building perimeter, (2) aggregate areas of such openings in exterior walls in each level not less than 20 percent of the total perimeter wall area of each level, and (3) interior wall lines and columns not less than 20 percent open with openings distributed to allow ventilation.

3.3.197.7 Structure, Permanent. A building or structure that is intended to remain in place for a period of more than 180 consecutive days.

3.3.197.8 Structure, Temporary. A building or structure not meeting the definition of permanent structure. *(See 3.3.197.7.)*

3.3.197.9 Structure, Tensioned-Membrane. A membrane structure incorporating a membrane and a structural support system such as arches, columns and cables, or beams wherein the stresses developed in the tensioned membrane interact with those in the structural support so that the entire assembly acts together to resist the applied loads.

3.3.197.10* Structure, Underground. A structure or portions of a structure in which the floor level is below the level of exit discharge.

A.3.3.197.10 Structure, Underground. In determining openings in exterior walls, doors or access panels are permitted to be included. Windows are also permitted to be included if they are openable or provide a breakable glazed area.

3.3.197.11 Structure, Water-Surrounded. A structure fully surrounded by water.

3.3.197.12 Structure, Windowless. A structure or portions of a structure lacking access openings.

3.3.198 Temporary Platform. See 3.3.149.1, *Platform, Temporary.*

3.3.199 Temporary Structure. See 3.3.197.8, *Structure, Temporary.*

3.3.200 Tensioned-Membrane Structure.

See 3.3.197.9, *Structure, Tensioned-Membrane.*

3.3.201* Tent. A temporary structure, the covering of which is made of pliable material that achieves its support by mechanical means such as beams, columns, poles, or arches, or by rope or cables, or both.

A.3.3.201 Tent. A tent might also include a temporary tensioned-membrane structure.

3.3.201.1 Tent, Private Party. A tent erected in the yard of a private residence for entertainment, recreation, dining, a reception, or similar function.

3.3.202 Thermal Barrier. See 3.3.21, *Barrier, Thermal.*

3.3.203 Tower. An enclosed independent structure or portion of a building with elevated levels for support of equipment or occupied for observation, control, operation, signaling, or similar limited use where (1) the elevated levels are provided to allow adequate observation or line-of-sight for personnel or equipment, and (2) the levels within the tower below the observation level and equipment room for that level are not occupied.

3.3.204 Uncertainty Analysis. See 3.3.10, *Analysis, Uncertainty.*

3.3.205 Underground Structure. See 3.3.197.10, *Structure, Underground.*

3.3.206 Verification Method. A procedure or process used to demonstrate or confirm that the proposed design meets the specified criteria.

3.3.207 Vertical Opening. An opening through a floor or roof.

3.3.208 Wall, Fire Barrier. A wall, other than a fire wall, that has a fire resistance rating.

3.3.209 Wall, Proscenium. The wall that separates the stage from the auditorium or house.

3.3.210 Water-Surrounded Structure. See 3.3.197.11, *Structure, Water-Surrounded.*

3.3.211 Weathered-Membrane Material. Membrane material that has been subjected to not less than 3000 hours in a weatherometer in accordance with ASTM G 26, *Practice for Operating Light/Exposure Apparatus (Zenon-Arc Type) With and Without Water for Exposure of Non-Metallic Materials, or approved equivalent.*

3.3.212 Windowless Structure. See 3.3.197.12, *Structure, Windowless.*

3.3.213 Yard. An open, unoccupied space other than a court, unobstructed from the ground to the sky on the lot on which a building is situated.

Reference Cited in Commentary

1. *Webster's Third New International Dictionary of the English Language, Unabridged.*

CHAPTER 4

General

The subjects addressed in Chapter 4 of this edition of the *Code* were part of Chapter 1, General, in earlier editions. NFPA style and format policies now dictate that Chapter 1, Administration, include only title, scope, purpose, application, equivalency, and units and formulas sections. All other general provisions are contained in a Chapter 4, General, which follows Chapter 2, Mandatory References, and Chapter 3, Definitions.

The 2000 edition the *Code* includes one relatively major change—that being the addition of a new Chapter 5, Performance-Based Option. As a part of the effort to codify a performance-based option, a recasting of some front portions of the *Code* occurred. This included specifying the goals, objectives, and assumptions. (See Sections 4.1, 4.2, and 4.3.) All three of these topics have been addressed in the *Code* since 1991 as part of previous versions of Chapter 1.

New to this edition of the *Code* is Section 4.4. The user is offered a performance-based option that is much more than the equivalency option that has appeared for many editions. Building designers and owners have the prerogative of following the prescriptive requirements of the *Code*, or they can develop an acceptable performance-based design in careful consultation with the authority having jurisdiction.

Section 4.5 incorporates the fundamental requirements from Chapter 2 of recent editions of the *Code*.

Section 4.6 presents the philosophy associated with enforcement of the *Code*—namely, who enforces it and when it applies to special conditions. Paragraph 4.6.9.2 mandates a warrant of fitness for buildings that have utilized the performance-based option. The

warrant of fitness is basically a verification method of assuring the authority having jurisdiction that the terms and conditions that were part of the performance-based design have not been modified to the point that the building is unsafe.

Section 4.7 rounds out the chapter by presenting the operational details associated with emergency egress and relocation drills.

Section 4.1* Goals

A.4.1 The goals in Section 4.1 reflect the scope of this *Code* *(see Section 1.2)*. Other fire safety goals that are outside the scope of this *Code* might also need to be considered, such as property protection and continuity of operations. Compliance with this *Code* can assist in meeting goals outside of the *Code*'s scope.

The goals in Section 4.1 apply regardless of whether the prescriptive-based option of 4.4.1(1) and 4.4.2 or the performance-based option of 4.4.1(2) and 4.4.3 is used. For prescriptive-based life safety systems, compliance with the specifications of Chapter 4 and Chapters 6 through 42 provides a level of life safety that meets the goals of Section 4.1. For performance-based life safety systems, compliance with the goals needs to be demonstrated in the required documentation package with consideration to not only the goals but also the objectives (see Section 4.2) and performance criteria (see Section 5.2) associated with specific design fire scenarios (see Section 5.5).

4.1.1* Fire and Similar Emergency.

The goal of this *Code* is to provide an environment for the occupants that is reasonably safe from fire and similar emergencies by the following means:

A.4.1.1 Reasonable safety risk is further defined by subsequent language in this *Code*.

(1)* Protection of occupants not intimate with the initial fire development

A.4.1.1(1) The phrase "intimate with the initial fire development" refers to the person(s) at the ignition source or first materials burning and not to all persons within the same room or area.

(2) Improvement of the survivability of occupants intimate with the initial fire development

4.1.2* Crowd Movement.

An additional goal is to provide for reasonably safe emergency crowd movement and, where required, reasonably safe nonemergency crowd movement.

A.4.1.2 An assembly occupancy is an example of an occupancy where the goal of providing for reasonably safe emergency and nonemergency crowd movement has applicability. A detention or correctional occupancy is an example of an occupancy where emergency and nonemergency crowd movement is better addressed by detention and correctional facilities specialists than by this *Code*.

An example of a requirement for nonemergency crowd movement appears in 12.2.5.4.3 and 13.2.5.4.3, which apply to assembly occupancies, where access and egress routes are required to be maintained so that crowd management, security, and emergency medical personnel are able to move without undue hindrance to any individual at any time. However, almost all other occupancy chapters remain silent on the subject of nonemergency crowd movement—some by choice and some because the subject has not been discussed at technical committee meetings. The detention and correctional occupancies chapters deliberately remain silent on the subject because movement of residents is a very specialized art that is best addressed by professionals in the daily operation of such facilities where security concerns are paramount. It is important to note that, per the purpose statement in 1.3.1, the minimum requirements of this *Code* were developed with due regard for function. The *Code* endeavors to avoid requirements that might interfere with the normal use and occupancy of a building.

Section 4.2 Objectives

As in the case of application of the goals of Section 4.1, the objectives of Section 4.2 apply regardless of whether the prescriptive-based option of 4.4.2 or the performance-based option of 4.4.3 is used. For prescriptive-based life safety systems, compliance with the specifications of Chapter 4 and Chapters 6 through 42 provides a level of life safety that meets the objectives of Section 4.2. For performance-based life safety systems, compliance with the objectives needs to be demonstrated in the required documentation with consideration to not only the objectives but also the goals (see Section 4.1), and performance criteria (see Section 5.2) associated with specific design fire scenarios (see Section 5.5).

The objectives present requirements that must be satisfied in order to achieve the goals of Section 4.1. Objectives are stated in more specific terms than goals and tend to be more quantitative than qualitative. The goals of Section 4.1 are general enough to apply to numerous NFPA documents. The objectives are more specific to the *Life Safety Code* itself. Goals and objectives, taken together, form the initial targets at which a performance-based life safety system can take aim. The goals and objectives alone do not provide sufficient detail to develop and measure the performance of a design. Rather, the performance criteria and other elements of Chapter 5, Performance-Based Option, are needed to flesh out the subject in sufficient detail.

4.2.1 Occupant Protection.

A structure shall be designed, constructed, and maintained to protect occupants who are not intimate with the initial fire development for the time needed to evacuate, relocate, or defend in place.

4.2.2 Structural Integrity.

Structural integrity shall be maintained for the time needed to evacuate, relocate, or defend in place occupants who are not intimate with the initial fire development.

4.2.3 Systems Effectiveness.

Systems utilized to achieve the goals of Section 4.1 shall be effective in mitigating the hazard or condition for which they are being used, shall be reliable, shall be maintained to the level at which they were designed to operate, and shall remain operational.

Section 4.3 Assumption

4.3.1* Single Fire Source.

The protection methods of this *Code* assume a single fire source.

A.4.3.1 Additional assumptions that need to be identified for a performance-based design are addressed in Chapter 5.

For the user of the traditional, prescriptive, specification-based requirements, the single fire source assumption is a piece of explanatory material and not a requirement. The assumption explains that the *Code* authors developed the requirements with the challenge of a single fire source in mind. Thus, most occupancy chapters require a minimum of two means of egress; if one is blocked by the single fire, then the other should be available for egress. Had the *Code* been written to protect against fires that begin in two locations, then it probably would be common to find occupancy chapter requirements for a minimum of three means of egress. Historically, the *Code's* approach to protecting against a single source fire has proved to meet society's expectations.

Section 4.4 Life Safety Compliance Options

4.4.1 Options.

Life safety meeting the goals and objectives of Sections 4.1 and 4.2 shall be provided in accordance with either of the following:

(1) The prescriptive-based provisions per 4.4.2
(2) The performance-based provisions per 4.4.3

Prior editions of the *Code* required compliance with the prescriptive, specification-based requirements and offered some additional design flexibility via the equivalency concept contained in Section 1.5. The current edition offers the new option of designing the life safety systems, *in toto*, using a performance-based approach. Both the prescriptive-based and performance-based options are tied to the goals and objectives of Sections 4.1 and 4.2, respectively.

Both the prescriptive-based and performance-based options are offered as equivalent, with neither option designated as the preferred method. Given that performance-based design is new to most *Code* users and that it is complicated to use, most traditional buildings will probably continue to be designed and built to comply with the prescriptive requirements. The performance-based approach will be reserved for use on large, complicated structures where the additional costs associated with such a design can be offset by savings on prescriptive features that can be omitted from the design. The performance-based option also is to be used for innovative designs that are likely to be prohibited by the prescriptive requirements. For example, many years ago before atria were specifically addressed in the *Code*, a designer proposing to build an atrium building would likely have been challenged by the authority having jurisdiction who might view the atrium as a hole in the building's floors through which smoke and other products of combustion would be spread. In subsequent editions of the *Code*, the inclusion of provisions for atria showed that, with full building sprinkler and smoke control systems, the atrium could be turned into a fire and life safety asset—one that serves as a smoke dispersion and accumulation chamber early in the fire so as to permit exit access through the atrium. The performance-based approach offers a host of new tools that are used to prove the efficacy of unique designs and unusual, functionally dictated use spaces.

4.4.2 Prescriptive-Based Option.

4.4.2.1 A prescriptive-based life safety design shall be in accordance with Chapters 1 through 4, Chapters 6 through 11, and the applicable occupancy Chapters 12 through 42 of this *Code*.

A prescriptive-based life safety design is the traditional norm. Each applicable requirement is met individually and the resultant level of life safety is deemed to meet the goals and objectives of Sections 4.1 and 4.2, respectively. The requirements are chosen, depending on occupancy classification, from a wide host of possible *Code* chapters, namely, any and all chapters except Chapter 5, Performance-Based Option.

4.4.2.2 Where specific requirements contained in Chapters 11 through 42 differ from general requirements contained in Chapters 1 through 4, and Chapters 6 through 10, the requirements of Chapters 11 through 42 shall govern.

The *Life Safety Code* is formatted such that Chapters 1 through 4 and 6 through 10 contain administrative provisions and fundamental requirements establishing minimum acceptable criteria for all types of occupancies. Chapters 12 through 42 of the *Code* establish criteria for life safety based upon the characteristic needs of specific occupancies. Chapter 11 further modifies those provisions if unusual situations exist or the building is windowless, underground, or high rise. Where requirements differ between the general provisions of Chapters 1 through 4 and 6 through 10 and the more specific provisions of Chapters 11 through 42, the requirements contained in Chapters 11 through 42 take precedence.

To avoid conflicts, if an occupancy chapter exempts itself from a requirement of a core chapter, the core chapter will usually contain an exception allowing the deviation from the requirement. For example, although 7.2.2.3.3 requires treads of stairs and landing floors to be solid, Exception No. 1 to 7.2.2.3.3 permits noncombustible, grated stair treads and landings in various specified occupancies including industrial occupancies as provided in Chapter 40. Exception No. 1 to 40.2.2.3.1 confirms the exemption for noncombustible, grated stair treads and landings in industrial occupancies.

4.4.3 Performance-Based Option.

A performance-based life safety design shall be in accordance with Chapters 1, 2, and 3, Sections 4.1 through 4.4, 4.6.9.2, and Chapter 5 of this *Code*.

A performance-based life safety design is exempt from the myriad prescriptive, specification-based requirements but must meet the administrative and general requirements of Chapters 1 and 4. The design must also adhere to the definitions of Chapter 3 so that the authority having jurisdiction that judges the performance of the design can communicate with the designer in terminology that is common to all *Code* users. More importantly, the performance-based design must meet the provisions contained in Chapter 5, Performance-Based Option. Chapter 5 contains a limited number of prescriptive provisions that have been retained from Chapter 7, Means of Egress, for applicability to the performance-based design. See Section 5.3.

Section 4.5 Fundamental Requirements

Section 4.5 outlines the fundamental concepts that are addressed in detail by the requirements contained in the other chapters of the *Code*. The same fundamental concepts, as briefly detailed in this section, apply both to prescriptive-based and performance-based life safety designs. Achieving the life safety fundamentals helps to ensure a reasonable level of life safety in building design and arrangement. The following are the fundamentals:

(1) Provide for adequate safety without dependence on any single safeguard
(2) Provide an appropriate degree of life safety considering the size, shape, and nature of the occupancy
(3) Provide for backup or redundant egress arrangements
(4) Ensure that the egress paths are clear, unobstructed, and unlocked
(5) Ensure that the exits and egress routes are clearly marked to avoid confusion and provide the cues needed for their effective use
(6) Provide adequate lighting
(7) Ensure prompt occupant response by providing early warning of fire
(8) Ensure the suitable enclosure of vertical openings
(9) Ensure compliance with applicable installation standards
(10) Maintain all required features in proper working order

4.5.1 Multiple Safeguards.

The design of every building or structure intended for human occupancy shall be such that reliance for safety to life does not depend solely on any single safeguard. An additional safeguard(s) shall be provided for life safety in case any single safeguard is ineffective due to inappropriate human actions or system failure.

4.5.2 Appropriateness of Safeguards.

Every building or structure shall be provided with means of egress and other safeguards of the kinds, numbers, locations, and capacities appropriate to the individual building or structure, with due regard to the following:

(1) Character of the occupancy
(2) Capabilities of the occupants
(3) Number of persons exposed

(4) Fire protection available

(5) Height and type of construction of the building or structure

(6) Other factors necessary to provide occupants with a reasonable degree of safety

4.5.3 Means of Egress.

4.5.3.1 Number of Means of Egress. Two means of egress, as a minimum, shall be provided in every building or structure, section, and area where size, occupancy, and arrangement endanger occupants attempting to use a single means of egress that is blocked by fire or smoke. The two means of egress shall be arranged to minimize the possibility that both might be rendered impassable by the same emergency condition.

4.5.3.2 Unobstructed Egress. In every occupied building or structure, means of egress from all parts of the building shall be maintained free and unobstructed. No lock or fastening shall be permitted that prevents free escape from the inside of any building other than in health care occupancies and detention and correctional occupancies where staff are continually on duty and effective provisions are made to remove occupants in case of fire or other emergency. Means of egress shall be accessible to the extent necessary to ensure reasonable safety for occupants having impaired mobility.

4.5.3.3 Awareness of Egress System. Every exit shall be clearly visible, or the route to reach every exit shall be conspicuously indicated. Each means of egress, in its entirety, shall be arranged or marked so that the way to a place of safety is indicated in a clear manner.

4.5.3.4 Lighting. Where artificial illumination is needed in a building or structure, egress facilities shall be included in the lighting design.

4.5.4* Occupant Notification.

In every building or structure of such size, arrangement, or occupancy that a fire itself might not provide adequate occupant warning, fire alarm facilities shall be provided where necessary to warn occupants of the existence of fire.

A.4.5.4 Fire alarms alert occupants to initiate emergency procedures, facilitate orderly conduct of fire drills, and initiate response by emergency services.

4.5.5 Vertical Openings.

Every vertical opening between the floors of a building shall be suitably enclosed or protected, as necessary, to afford reasonable safety to occupants while using the means of egress and to prevent spread of fire, smoke, or fumes through vertical openings from floor to floor before occupants have entered exits.

4.5.6 System Design/Installation.

Any fire protection system, building service equipment, feature of protection, or safeguard provided for life safety shall be designed, installed, and approved in accordance with applicable NFPA standards.

4.5.7 Maintenance.

Whenever or wherever any device, equipment, system, condition, arrangement, level of protection, or any other feature is required for compliance with the provisions of this *Code*, such device, equipment, system, condition, arrangement, level of protection, or other feature shall thereafter be maintained unless the *Code* exempts such maintenance.

Section 4.6 General Requirements

4.6.1 Authority Having Jurisdiction.

The authority having jurisdiction (AHJ) is the person or office enforcing the *Code*. In cases where the *Code* is to be legally enforced, the AHJ is usually a fire marshal or building official. The AHJ can also be a safety office, insurance engineering department, accreditation service, other agency, or specified personnel within those groups, especially where the *Code* is to be enforced at other than a governmental level. It is common for multiple authorities having jurisdiction to review the same project while enforcing this *Code* and/or other codes. For example, under the *Code* several agencies, such as state and local fire marshals; federal, state, and local health care licensing agencies; Joint Commission on Accreditation of Healthcare Organizations (JCAHO) accreditation personnel; insurance inspectors; and building inspectors, perform inspections in health care facilities.

4.6.1.1 The authority having jurisdiction shall determine whether the provisions of this *Code* are met.

4.6.1.2 Any requirements that are essential for the safety of building occupants and that are not specifically provided for by this *Code* shall be determined by the authority having jurisdiction.

The provisions of Section 4.6 give the authority having jurisdiction the final determination of whether adequate life safety is provided in a building. When the authority having jurisdiction determines that the *Code* has not specifically addressed a particular life safety situation, the authority can supplement the requirements in the *Code* to address the specific situation. The power to supplement requirements is an important responsibility, because the *Code* cannot anticipate every type of building and occupancy configuration.

4.6.1.3 Where it is evident that a reasonable degree of safety is provided, any requirement shall be permitted to be modified if its application would be hazardous under normal occupancy conditions in the judgment of the authority having jurisdiction.

The provision of 4.6.1.3 gives the authority having jurisdiction latitude in permitting a requirement to be modified if the strict enforcement of the provision would otherwise create more of a hazard and, thus, less overall life safety than is achieved by modification. For example, the *Code* requires an exit sign at an exit and, via the provisions of 7.10.1.2, requires that the sign be readily visible from any direction of exit access. If the exit door in question is installed in the plane of a corridor wall, the exit sign would need to be positioned perpendicular to the corridor wall. If there is limited headroom at the door, perhaps due to a ceiling projection such as a beam running across the corridor at that point, the exit sign might create the potential for occupants to bump their heads. This provision permits the authority having jurisdiction to allow the exit sign to be mounted flush against the corridor wall based on judgment that a reasonable degree of safety is provided.

4.6.2* Historic Buildings.

The provisions of this *Code* shall be permitted to be modified by the authority having jurisdiction for buildings or structures identified and classified as historic buildings or structures where it is evident that a reasonable degree of safety is provided.

Rather than providing historic buildings with a blanket exemption from *Code* requirements, the provision of 4.6.2 reinforces the concept that existing buildings, as well as new construction, need to meet minimum life safety criteria. This provision permits the authority having jurisdiction to offer some leniency by not enforcing every requirement to its fullest. Rather, as

long as the authority having jurisdiction judges that a reasonable degree of safety is provided, compliance with the modified requirement is adequate.

Historic buildings might have numerous design defects, such as open stair shafts or highly combustible interior finishes. Rather than waiving requirements, the authority having jurisdiction might require that the facility attain a level of safety equivalent or nearly equivalent to that mandated by the *Code*. The authority having jurisdiction might require the use of sprinkler systems, smoke detection systems, voice alarm systems for staged evacuation, smoke control systems, or other appropriate features to overcome the existing life safety defects. The use of such features are in lieu of rebuilding the structure to the *Code*'s specification requirements, which might totally destroy the historical character of the structure. The alternatives used in such an instance might actually raise the building's life safety to levels many times greater than that which previously existed.

A.4.6.2 See A.4.6.3.

4.6.3* Modification of Requirements for Existing Buildings.

Where it is evident that a reasonable degree of safety is provided, the requirements for existing buildings shall be permitted to be modified if their application would be impractical in the judgment of the authority having jurisdiction.

A.4.6.3 In existing buildings, it is not always practical to strictly apply the provisions of this *Code*. Physical limitations can cause the need for disproportionate effort or expense with little increase in life safety. In such cases, the authority having jurisdiction should be satisfied that reasonable life safety is ensured.

In existing buildings, it is intended that any condition that represents a serious threat to life be mitigated by the application of appropriate safeguards. It is not intended to require modifications for conditions that do not represent a significant threat to life, even though such conditions are not literally in compliance with the *Code*.

The provisions of 4.6.3 give the authority having jurisdiction some leeway in applying the *Code* to existing buildings. The *Code* recognizes there might be situations where applying the requirements to existing situations is not practical, so this provision gives the authority having jurisdiction the authority to modify those requirements. However, the *Code* reemphasizes that a reasonable degree of safety must be provided.

4.6.4 Time Allowed for Compliance.

A limited but reasonable time, commensurate with the magnitude of expenditure, disruption of services, and degree of hazard, shall be allowed for compliance with any part of this *Code* for existing buildings.

In some cases, appreciable costs—in terms of actual monetary expenditures and disruption of daily activities—might be involved in immediately bringing an existing building into *Code* compliance. Where this is true, it is appropriate for the operator or owner of the facility to formulate a schedule, approved by the authority having jurisdiction, that allows suitable periods of time for correcting various deficiencies. However, the degree of hazard is an important consideration in this instance and, if the degree of hazard is serious enough, it might be necessary to close the building to occupancy while renovations are made to bring the building features associated with the serious hazard into compliance. Once the building is reoccupied, the authority having jurisdiction might allow some reasonable, additional time for bringing the remaining deficient features into code compliance with the requirements that apply specifically to existing buildings.

4.6.5 Referenced Publications.

Existing buildings or installations that do not comply with the provisions of the referenced standards contained in this document *(see Chapter 2)* shall be permitted to be continued in service, provided that the lack of conformity with these standards does not present a serious hazard to the occupants as determined by the authority having jurisdiction.

The *Code* mandates that the fire and life safety systems used for compliance are to be installed in accordance with the requirements of more than 50 NFPA codes and standards and more than a dozen documents developed by other organizations. Mandatorily referenced documents are listed in Chapter 2 and cite a specific edition.

In recognition that it is impractical to expect systems to be continually upgraded to meet the newest edition of an installation standard, the authority having jurisdiction is permitted to continue in use systems whose lack of conformity with the referenced standards does not present a serious hazard.

4.6.6 Additions.

Additions shall conform to the provisions for new construction.

Although an addition must conform to the requirements for new construction, the existing portion of the building is generally permitted to conform to the requirements for existing buildings. The exceptions to this rule involve assembly and mercantile occupancies. For example, mercantile occupancies further subclassify the occupancy into a Class A, Class B, or Class C occupancy, based on the floor area used for sales purposes. If consideration of the combined space created by the addition and the existing portion of the building results in a reclassification from Class C to Class B or from Class B to Class A, the existing portion of the building must also meet the requirements applicable to new construction. See 36.1.1.3 and 37.1.1.3.

For assembly occupancies, the same concept exists, but its application criteria are specified differently, given that assembly occupancies no longer use the subclassification scheme (i.e., Class A, Class B, and Class C). The existing portion of the assembly occupancy building is required to meet the provisions that apply to new construction under either of the following conditions (see 13.1.1.3):

(1) The occupant load of the combined space created by the addition and the existing assembly area increases from less than 500 to more than 500 so as to require a third exit.
(2) The occupant load of the combined space created by the addition and the existing assembly area increases from less than 1000 to more than 1000 so as to require a fourth exit.

4.6.7* Modernization or Renovation.

Any alteration or any installation of new equipment shall meet, as nearly as practicable, the requirements for new construction. Only the altered, renovated, or modernized portion of an existing building, system, or individual component shall be required to meet the provisions of this *Code* that are applicable to new construction. If the alteration, renovation, or modernization adversely impacts required life safety features, additional upgrading shall be required. Existing life safety features that do not meet the requirements for new buildings, but that exceed the requirements for existing buildings, shall not be further diminished. In no case shall the resulting life safety features be less than those required for existing buildings.

A.4.6.7 The following is an example of what is intended by 4.6.7. In a hospital that has 6-ft (1.8-m) wide corridors, such corridors cannot be reduced in width, even though the provisions for existing hospitals do not require 6-ft (1.8-m) wide corridors. However, if a hospital has 10-ft (3-m) wide corridors, they are permitted to be reduced to 8 ft (2.4 m) in width, which is the requirement for new construction. If the hospital corridor is 3 ft (0.9 m) wide, it would have to be increased to 4 ft (1.2 m). If alterations require replacement of a portion of a hospital corridor wall, such portion of the corridor would not be required to be increased to 8 ft (2.4 m) in width, unless it was practical to do so.

Only those existing building features, systems, or components undergoing change or alteration must conform with the *Code* provisions applicable to new construction. For example, in an occupancy that requires 1-hour fire resistance–rated corridors for new construction but that permits existing $1/2$-hour fire resistance–rated corridors to remain in use, a renovation project is undertaken to replace existing doors in the corridor walls. There is no requirement that the renovation project be expanded in scope to include replacing the existing, code-complying, $1/2$-hour fire resistance–rated corridor walls with walls having the minimum 1-hour fire resistance rating required for new construction.

Conformance with the provisions applicable to new construction might not be practical if the existing structure involved cannot reasonably accommodate the feature required for new construction. For example, a hospital might have an existing corridor 6 ft (1.8 m) wide that, if replaced, is normally required to be 8 ft (2.4 m) wide as specified for new construction. However, if the building's column spacing is 7 ft × 7 ft (2.1 m × 2.1 m), there is no easy and effective way to achieve an 8-ft (2.4-m) corridor width. The authority having jurisdiction judges whether a 6-ft (1.8-m) wide or even a 7-ft (2.1-m) wide corridor is adequate or whether additional provisions are required to permit a corridor less than 8 ft (2.4 m) in width to be rebuilt.

Where renovations or alterations are made, they must comply with the requirements for new construction to the extent practicable. For example, it is practicable to install carpeting meeting the requirements for new interior floor finish. Similarly, where a corridor wall is to be rebuilt, it might not be practicable to widen the corridor to meet the minimum width requirements for new corridors, but most likely it will be practicable to rebuild the corridor to meet the required fire resistance rating for new construction.

Another example is the installation of a new smoke barrier in an existing hospital. A smoke barrier can be made to meet nearly all the requirements for a new smoke barrier. However, if the corridor across which the smoke barrier extends is not sufficiently wide to install two 41.5-in. (105-cm) clear width doors,

the requirement for two 41.5-in. (105-cm) clear width doors would have to be modified. The authority having jurisdiction judges such a modification and might permit a set of doors or possibly a single door of a width that the corridor could accommodate. The requirement to perform renovations as nearly as practicable with the requirements for new construction might seem arbitrary, but it is necessary to allow evaluation on a case-by-case basis.

The last sentence of 4.6.7 captures an important, but elusive, concept. In applying the requirements for new construction to a renovated component or system, it is important to compare the requirements for new construction to those for existing buildings. This comparison ensures that the level of safety afforded by compliance with the requirement for new construction is not less than that provided by complying with the corresponding requirement applicable to existing buildings. For example, Chapter 28, which applies to new hotels/dormitories, includes no requirement for smoke barriers because all new hotels/ dormitories must either be protected by automatic sprinklers or provide direct exterior exit access from all guest rooms. During renovation of a floor in an existing, nonsprinklered hotel that utilizes inside corridors for exit access from guest rooms, the absence of a requirement for smoke barriers in Chapter 28 (see 28.3.7) must not be applied to the existing building. Rather, the requirements of 29.3.7 for cross-corridor smoke barriers applies. See also A.1.4 for another example of the same concept.

4.6.8 Provisions in Excess of Code Requirements.

Nothing in this *Code* shall be construed to prohibit a better type of building construction, an additional means of egress, or an otherwise safer condition than that specified by the minimum requirements of this *Code*.

Although the *Life Safety Code* is a minimum-requirement code, it does not prohibit the use of a design that exceeds the provisions of the *Code*. In practice, however, economic considerations usually discourage the use of a design that exceeds minimum requirements.

However, there have been instances where money was saved or additional money generated when *Code* provisions were exceeded. For example, a hotel was constructed with full automatic sprinkler protection, although such protection was not required by the code in effect at the time. By sprinklering the building, a third stairway was permitted to be eliminated because of the increased travel distance allowed in a sprinklered building. The construction cost of the stair was saved, and additional revenue-producing guest rooms were built in the space that the stair otherwise would have occupied.

4.6.9 Conditions for Occupancy.

4.6.9.1 No new construction or existing building shall be occupied in whole or in part in violation of the provisions of this *Code* unless the following conditions exist:

(1) A plan of correction has been approved.
(2) The occupancy classification remains the same.
(3) No serious life safety hazard exists as judged by the authority having jurisdiction.

From an enforcement standpoint, this paragraph is probably one of the most important in the *Code*, because it states that a building, whether new or existing, cannot be occupied if it is in violation of the provisions of the *Code*.

Because the *Code* applies retroactively, 4.6.9.1 prohibits the use of existing, nonconforming facilities. However, 4.6.9.1 does permit the building to continue to be used, provided that the occupancy classification remains the same and there is no serious life safety hazard, as judged by the authority having jurisdiction, that would constitute an imminent threat. Such permission does not exempt the building from compliance with the *Code* but permits it to continue to be used. A limited but reasonable time (see 4.6.4), for bringing the building into compliance with the *Code* to the extent deemed necessary by the authority having jurisdiction under 4.6.3 must be established and fulfilled.

4.6.9.2 Where compliance with this *Code* is effected by means of a performance-based design, the owner shall annually certify compliance with the conditions and limitations of the design by submitting a warrant of fitness acceptable to the authority having jurisdiction. The warrant of fitness shall attest that the building features, systems, and use have been inspected and confirmed to remain consistent with design specifications outlined in the documentation required by Section 5.8 and that they continue to satisfy the goals and objectives specified in Sections 4.1 and 4.2. *(See Chapter 5.)*

Traditional, specification-based life safety systems rely on the combined effect of all required features, systems and arrangements to provide the intended level of life safety. This overlap of protection schemes and the resulting redundancy in protection methods, which are mandated by the prescriptive requirements, have historically provided flexibility for the building to undergo changes in how the space is configured and used. For example, a business occupancy floor arranged to provide executives with private offices could be renovated by removing the office walls, installing modular furniture and cubicles, and creating an open-office floor plan for use by telemarketers. The occupancy would remain as a business occupancy and the prescriptive requirements applicable to business occupancies would require little, if anything, extra to be provided to retain the level of life safety that existed prior to the renovation.

However, had the original executive office floor been designed using the performance-based option, the removal of office walls would need to be analyzed with respect to its effect on the life safety systems. The performance-based design might have been based on a scenario in which a fire would not propagate beyond one of the private offices due to fire-rated compartmentation. By removing the office walls and creating an open floor plan, the compartmentation premise would be lost. Further analysis would be needed to determine whether the life safety systems installed as part of the performance-based design meet the goals and objectives after the renovation.

Although the example cited in this commentary centers on a substantial renovation that involves removal of office walls, subtle changes that "creep" into a building over time might also adversely affect a life safety system designed using the performance-based option. For this reason, 4.6.9.2 requires annual certification via a warrant of fitness.

The provisions of 4.6.9.2 are positioned here in Chapter 4 in the hope that the requirement will be noticed and enforced. Had the requirement appeared in Chapter 5, Performance-Based Option, it might have gone unnoticed after the performance-based design is completed and the certificate of occupancy issued.

4.6.10 Construction, Repair, and Improvement Operations.

4.6.10.1* Buildings or portions of buildings shall be permitted to be occupied during construction, repair, alterations, or additions only where required means of egress and required fire protection features are in place and continuously maintained for the portion occupied or where alternative life safety measures acceptable to the authority having jurisdiction are in place.

A.4.6.10.1 Fatal fires have occurred when, for example, a required stair has been closed for repairs or removed for rebuilding, or when a required automatic sprinkler system has been shut off to change piping.

> The provisions of 4.6.10.1 help to control a relatively common practice—the occupation of completed portions of a partially completed structure. To permit such occupation, the *Code* requires that egress features for the portion occupied be complete and maintained to be usable. In many cases the egress facilities, although completed, are not usable because they are blocked with stored building materials and equipment needed for the ongoing construction, or doors are locked to limit access to parts of the building still under construction. In such cases occupancy should be prohibited.
>
> To permit occupation of completed portions of a partially completed structure, the *Code* also requires fire protection features to be in place and to be continuously maintained. The incidence of fire is more frequent, and therefore more likely, during construction, repairs, and alterations. Extra caution and concern need to be exercised to ensure adequate egress capacity and arrangement during periods of construction in any occupied building.
>
> The exception recognizes that in lieu of strict adherence to the egress and fire protection features, alternative life safety measures might make the building safe enough to be occupied. As usual, it is the authority having jurisdiction who is charged with judging whether the alternative measures provide an acceptable remedy. This paragraph is conceptually similar to 4.6.9.1.

4.6.10.2* In buildings under construction, adequate escape facilities shall be maintained at all times for the use of construction workers. Escape facilities shall consist of doors, walkways, stairs, ramps, fire escapes, ladders, or other approved means or devices arranged in accordance with the general principles of the *Code* insofar as they can reasonably be applied to buildings under construction.

A.4.6.10.2 See also NFPA 241, *Standard for Safeguarding Construction, Alteration, and Demolition Operations.*

4.6.10.3 Flammable or explosive substances or equipment for repairs or alterations shall be permitted in a building

while the building is occupied if the condition of use and safeguards provided do not create any additional danger or impediment to egress beyond the normally permissible conditions in the building.

4.6.11* Changes of Occupancy.

In any building or structure, whether or not a physical alteration is needed, a change from one occupancy classification to another shall be permitted only where such a structure, building, or portion thereof conforms with the requirements of this *Code* that apply to new construction for the proposed new use or, where specifically permitted elsewhere in the *Code*, existing construction features shall be permitted to be continued in use in conversions.

A.4.6.11 Examples of changes from one occupancy subclassification to another subclassification of the same occupancy could include a change from a Class B to a Class A mercantile occupancy. Hospitals and nursing homes are both health care occupancies and are defined separately, but they are not established as separate suboccupancies; thus, a change from one to the other does not constitute a change of occupancy subclassification.

For example, a building was used as a hospital but has been closed for four years. It is again to be used as a hospital. As long as the building was not used as another occupancy during the time it was closed, it would be considered an existing hospital.

Hotels and apartments, although both residential occupancies, are treated separately, and a change from one to the other constitutes a change of occupancy.

> In addition to requiring that the provisions for new construction be applied to an existing building upon change of occupancy, former editions of the *Code* required that the provisions for new construction be applied upon change from one occupancy subclassification to another subclassification of the same occupancy. Although the provision is no longer contained in 4.6.11, the concept has not been lost and has been included in the individual occupancy chapters for application as appropriate for the occupancy. For example, 18.1.1.4.4 and 19.1.1.4.4 mandate that a change from one health care occupancy subclassification to another requires compliance with the requirements for new construction. Three exceptions then allow that any of the following changes do not constitute a change of occupancy or occupancy subclassification:
>
> (1) From a hospital to a nursing home
> (2) From a nursing home to a hospital
> (3) From a hospital or nursing home to a limited care facility

(4) From a hospital or nursing home to an ambulatory health care facility.

Similarly, in 36.1.1.4 and 37.1.1.4, which apply to mercantile occupancies, a change from Class C to Class A or Class B or from Class B to Class A must meet the provisions applicable to new construction; but a change from Class A to Class B or Class C or from Class B to Class C is permitted to comply with the requirements applicable to existing mercantile occupancies.

Although 4.6.11 requires that the provisions for new construction be applied to an existing building upon change of occupancy, Chapter 32, New Residential Board and Care Occupancies, applies special rules to conversions. For example, if an existing hotel is converted to a large board and care facility, existing corridor walls are exempted from the $^1/_2$-hour fire resistance rating requirement of 32.3.3.6.3 (see exception to 32.3.3.6.3 and the explanation of *conversion* in 32/33.1.1.3). This is another example of an occupancy-specific requirement, taking precedence over a general core chapter requirement, as explained in the commentary following 4.4.2.2.

4.6.12 Maintenance and Testing.

4.6.12.1 Whenever or wherever any device, equipment, system, condition, arrangement, level of protection, or any other feature is required for compliance with the provisions of this *Code*, such device, equipment, system, condition, arrangement, level of protection, or other feature shall thereafter be continuously maintained in accordance with applicable NFPA requirements or as directed by the authority having jurisdiction.

Paragraph 4.6.12.1 emphasizes the importance of maintaining items required by the *Code*. It is useless to have an egress door that will not open, a self-closing device that does not close the door, or a sprinkler system with no water.

4.6.12.2* Existing life safety features obvious to the public, if not required by the *Code*, shall be either maintained or removed.

A.4.6.12.2 Examples of such features include automatic sprinklers, fire alarm systems, standpipes, and portable fire extinguishers. The presence of a life safety feature, such as sprinklers or fire alarm devices, creates a reasonable expectation by the public that these safety features are functional. When systems are inoperable or taken out of service

but the devices remain, they present a false sense of safety. Also, before taking any life safety features out of service, extreme care needs to be exercised to ensure that the feature is not required, was not originally provided as an alternative or equivalency, or is no longer required due to other new requirements in the current *Code*. It is not intended that the entire system or protection feature be removed. Instead, components such as sprinklers, initiating devices, notification appliances, standpipe hose, and exit systems should be removed to reduce the likelihood of relying on inoperable systems or features.

The *Code* directs that nonrequired life safety features that are obvious to the public are to be either maintained or removed to prevent false expectations or a false sense of security by building occupants. For example, if the water supply to a nonrequired wet standpipe system were permanently shut off because the system piping leaked but the hose and nozzle for occupant use were left attached to the standpipe, an occupant could be endangered while attempting to use the system. If the nonrequired standpipe system were turned off and abandoned, it would be necessary, as a minimum, to remove all hoses and nozzles and to place prominent signage at each outlet station advising that the system is out of service. The standpipe system piping, however, would not have to be removed.

4.6.12.3 Equipment requiring periodic testing or operation to ensure its maintenance shall be tested or operated as specified elsewhere in this *Code* or as directed by the authority having jurisdiction.

4.6.12.4 Maintenance and testing shall be under the supervision of a responsible person who shall ensure that testing and maintenance are made at specified intervals in accordance with applicable NFPA standards or as directed by the authority having jurisdiction.

Section 4.7* Fire Drills

A.4.7 The purpose of emergency egress and relocation drills is to educate the participants in the fire safety features of the building, the egress facilities available, and the procedures to be followed. Speed in emptying buildings or relocating occupants, while desirable, is not the only objective. Prior to an evaluation of the performance of an emergency egress and relocation drill, an opportunity for instruction and practice should be provided. This educational opportunity should be presented in a nonthreatening manner, with consideration to the prior knowledge, age, and ability of audience.

The usefulness of an emergency egress and relocation drill and the extent to which it can be performed depends on the character of the occupancy.

In buildings where the occupant load is of a changing character, such as hotels or department stores, no regularly organized emergency egress and relocation drill is possible. In such cases, the emergency egress and relocation drills are to be limited to the regular employees, who can, however, be thoroughly schooled in the proper procedure and can be trained to properly direct other occupants of the building in case of emergency evacuation or relocation. In occupancies such as hospitals, regular employees can be rehearsed in the proper procedure in case of fire; such training always is advisable in all occupancies whether or not regular emergency egress and relocation drills can be held.

> Subsections 4.7.1 through 4.7.6 and the associated material from Annex A serve as a primer on how to conduct an emergency egress and relocation drill. Section __.7, Operating Features, of some of the occupancy chapters provides emergency egress and relocation drill details that directly correlate a drill with the characteristics of the occupancy. An understanding of how the drill details have been matched to the needs of the occupants can be gained by comparing 14.7.1 (new educational occupancies) with 18.7.1 (new health care occupancies).

4.7.1 Where Required.

Emergency egress and relocation drills conforming to the provisions of this *Code* shall be conducted as specified by the provisions of Chapters 11 through 42, or by appropriate action of the authority having jurisdiction. Drills shall be designed in cooperation with the local authorities.

4.7.2* Drill Frequency.

Emergency egress and relocation drills, where required by Chapters 11 through 42 or the authority having jurisdiction, shall be held with sufficient frequency to familiarize occupants with the drill procedure and to establish conduct of

the drill as a matter of routine. Drills shall include suitable procedures to ensure that all persons subject to the drill participate.

A.4.7.2 If an emergency egress and relocation drill is considered merely as a routine exercise from which some persons are allowed to be excused, there is a grave danger that, in an actual emergency, the evacuation and relocation will not be successful. However, there might be circumstances under which all occupants do not participate in an emergency egress and relocation drill; for example, infirm or bedridden patients in a health care occupancy.

4.7.3 Competency.

Responsibility for the planning and conduct of drills shall be assigned only to competent persons qualified to exercise leadership.

4.7.4 Orderly Evacuation.

In the conduct of drills, emphasis shall be placed on orderly evacuation rather than on speed.

4.7.5* Simulated Conditions.

Drills shall be held at expected and unexpected times and under varying conditions to simulate the unusual conditions that can occur in an actual emergency.

A.4.7.5 Fire is always unexpected. If the drill is always held in the same way at the same time, it loses much of its value. When, for some reason during an actual fire, it is not possible to follow the usual routine of the emergency egress and relocation drill to which occupants have become accustomed, confusion and panic might ensue. Drills should be carefully planned to simulate actual fire conditions. Not only should drills be held at varying times, but different means of exit or relocation areas should be used, based on an assumption that fire or smoke might prevent the use of normal egress and relocation avenues.

4.7.6 Relocation Area.

Drill participants shall relocate to a predetermined location and remain at such location until a recall or dismissal signal is given.

CHAPTER 5

Performance-Based Option

Chapter 5 of this *Code* provides a performance-based alternative to the prescriptive provisions. This chapter is not intended to replace the prescriptive *Code*; however, it can be used instead of the prescriptive requirements if desired by the designer. This performance-based option outlines a process that can be used to determine whether the building design satisfies the fire safety goals and objectives specified in the *Code*. The performanced-based option provides the engineer with design flexibility.

Examples of performance-based design include the development of fire safety designs for unique architectural problems not anticipated by the current *Code*. The performance option requires the designer and the authority having jurisdiction (AHJ) to agree on the interpretation of the *Code* in terms of goals, objectives, desired levels of safety, appropriate fire scenarios, assumptions, and safety factors. The performance-based option in this chapter addresses these issues explicitly while also presenting information regarding the selection of appropriate calculation methods and input values. Additionally, this chapter outlines a documentation procedure that improves the transmission of information from the designer to the AHJ, thereby aiding in the approval of safe, cost-effective designs.

Many of the concepts incorporated in this chapter have never been included in an earlier code or standard. For this reason, simple examples are included to give the user a better idea of the concepts being discussed. The examples are provided for illustrative purposes and are generally based on specific building occupancies, but the concepts and ideas presented should be applicable across a range of occupancies.

Section 5.1 General Requirements

5.1.1* Application.

The requirements of this chapter shall apply to life safety systems designed to the performance-based option permitted by 4.4.3.

A.5.1.1 Chapter 5 of this *Code* provides requirements for the evaluation of a performance-based life safety design. The evaluation process is summarized in Figure A.5.1.1.

Code Criteria. On the left hand side of Figure A.5.1.1 is input from the *Code*. The life safety goals have been stated in Section 4.1. The objectives necessary to achieve these goals are stated in Section 4.2. Section 5.2 specifies the measures that are to be used to determine whether the objectives have been met.

Input. At the top of Figure A.5.1.1 is the input necessary to evaluate a life safety design.

The design specifications are to include certain retained prescriptive requirements as specified in Section 5.3. All assumptions about the life safety design and the response of the building and its occupants to a fire are to be clearly stated as indicated in Section 5.4. Scenarios are used to assess the adequacy of the design. Eight sets of initiating events are specified for which the ensuing outcomes are to be satisfactory.

Performance Assessment. Appropriate methods for assessing performance are to be used per Section 5.6. Safety factors are to be applied to account for uncertainties in the assessment as stated in Section 5.7. If the resulting predicted outcome of the scenarios is bounded by the performance criteria, then the objectives have been met and the life safety design is considered to be in compliance with this *Code*. Although not part of this *Code*, a design that fails to comply can be changed and reassessed as indicated on the right hand side of Figure A.5.1.1.

Documentation. The approval and acceptance of a life safety design are dependent on the quality of the documentation of the process. Section 5.8 specifies a minimum set of documentation that is to accompany a submission.

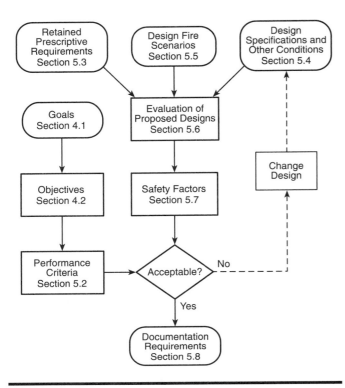

Figure A.5.1.1 Performance-based Life Safety Code compliance process.

The performance option of this *Code* establishes acceptable levels of risk to occupants of buildings and structures as addressed in Section 1.2. While the performance option of this *Code* does contain goals, objectives and performance criteria necessary to provide an acceptable level of risk to occupants, it does not describe how to meet the goals, objectives, and performance criteria. Design and engineering are needed to develop solutions that meet the provisions of Chapter 5. The *SFPE Engineering Guide to Performance-Based Fire Protection Analysis and Design of Buildings* provides a framework for these assessments. Other useful references include the *Australian Fire Engineering Guidelines and the British Standard Firesafety Engineering in Buildings.*

Exhibit 5.1 provides a design tool for guidance through a performance-based design. This guide follows the same pattern as Figure A.5.1.1, with the *Code*-specified goals, objectives, and criteria on the left side

of the chart, but it goes into more detail on how the general and specific requirements included in this *Code* are used to formulate the various aspects of the design input. Several aspects of the design input are covered in various sections of this chapter, while others are developed or determined by the design team based on the proposed building design. Once completed, the design input is then used with the chosen verification methods to obtain design output, to which a safety factor is applied. After applying the safety factor, the output can be compared to the fire safety criteria to determine whether the design passes or fails, after which the building design either is submitted for approval or is reevaluated after modifications are made to satisfy the criteria.

5.1.2 Goals and Objectives.

The performance-based design shall meet the goals and objectives of this *Code* in accordance with Sections 4.1 and 4.2.

5.1.3* Approved Qualifications.

The performance-based design shall be prepared by a person with qualifications acceptable to the authority having jurisdiction. *(See also 5.8.12.)*

A.5.1.3 Qualifications should include experience, education, and credentials that demonstrate knowledgeable and responsible use of applicable models and methods.

The qualifications needed by designers who develop performance-based designs are undefined. Currently no certification or credential exists that formally identifies an individual as being capable of adequately developing performance-based designs. Instead, more general credentials are available that indicate proficiency in fields such as architecture or fire protection engineering. Other criteria that have been used to demonstrate knowledge and responsible use of the methods include full membership in a professional society such as the Society of Fire Protection Engineers. When previous experience is identified as a qualification, it is necessary that this experience be in developing performance-based designs. Other relevant experience includes the use of models and data in the reconstruction of fires as part of fire investigations. Some models and test methods have courses built around them, at which certificates of participation are issued.

5.1.4* Independent Review.

The authority having jurisdiction shall be permitted to require an approved, independent third party to review the

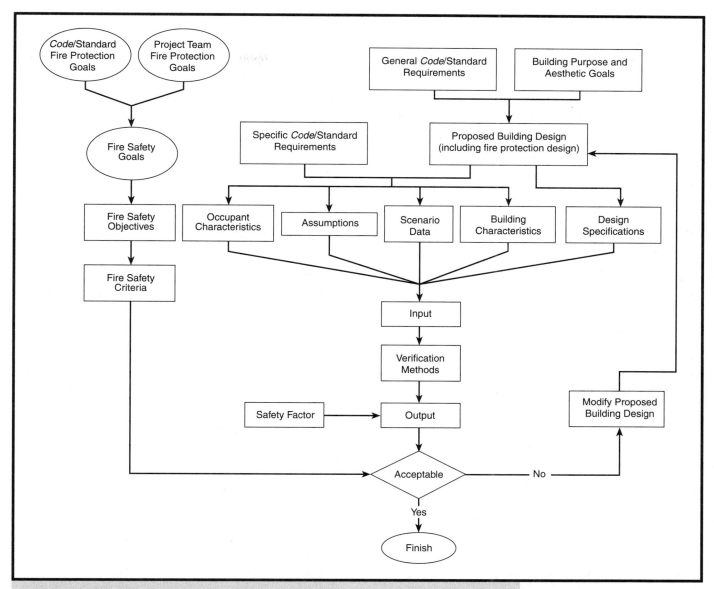

Exhibit 5.1 *Performance-based design process.*

proposed design and provide an evaluation of the design to the authority having jurisdiction.

A.5.1.4 A third-party reviewer is a person or group of persons chosen by the authority having jurisdiction to review proposed performance-based designs.

> The owner or developer may include a fee for third-party review in the budget for the performance-based project. This fee does not indicate that the third-party reviewer is responsible or beholden to the owner. The owner provides the funds for the authority having

> jurisdiction to hire a third-party reviewer. The third-party reviewer then provides all findings to the authority having jurisdiction.

5.1.5 Sources of Data.

Data sources shall be identified and documented for each input data requirement that must be met using a source other than a design fire scenario, an assumption, or a building design specification. The degree of conservatism reflected in such data shall be specified, and a justification for the source shall be provided.

5.1.6 Final Determination.

The authority having jurisdiction shall make the final determination as to whether the performance objectives have been met.

5.1.7* Maintenance of Design Features.

The design features required for the building to continue to meet the performance goals and objectives of this *Code* shall be maintained for the life of the building. Such performance goals and objectives shall include complying with all documented assumptions and design specifications. Any variations shall require the approval of the authority having jurisdiction prior to the actual change. *(See also 4.6.9.2.)*

A.5.1.7 Continued compliance with the goals and objectives of the *Code* involves many factors. The building construction—including openings, interior finish, and fire- and smoke-resistive construction—and the building and fire protection systems need to retain at least the same level of performance as is provided for the original design parameters. The use and occupancy should not change to the degree that assumptions made about the occupant characteristics, combustibility of furnishings, and existence of trained personnel are no longer valid. In addition, actions provided by other personnel, such as emergency responders, should not be diminished below the documented assumed levels. Also, actions needed to maintain reliability of systems at the anticipated level need to meet the initial design criteria.

The long-term maintenance of a performance-based design is an issue that has been identified as noteworthy, but for which a general solution has not been identified due to the limited experience with performance-based designs to date. Long-term maintenance is essentially a management-of-change issue. On approval of the performance-based (building) design, it becomes a *de facto* building-specific code. As such, the provisions of the design must be maintained for the lifetime of the building. New Zealand has dealt with this issue by using independent qualified persons (IQP) who certify annually that a building remains compliant after a certificate of occupancy has been issued.

Example: Maintenance of Design Features

In 5.1.7, the *Code* requires that the design features of the building be maintained for the life of the building. The design features that might be modified include the following:

(1) Occupancy and use of the structure
(2) Design specifications
(3) Assumptions made by the design team regarding the building conditions, emergency response personnel, or staff assistance
(4) Characteristics of the building and occupants

The following example shows how great an impact a minor change can have on the design input of a performance-based design. The example does not involve a change in the occupancy of the building, but simply a change in building use. The building in question is an educational facility, originally designed and used as a high school but being modified for use as a grammar school.

This type of change in building use does not require major modifications to the building structure; however, the shops and labs in the high school would have to be converted into spaces that normally are used in an elementary school, such as classrooms, offices, or storage space. Outside of these modified spaces, the design specifications remain the same. Additionally, many of the assumptions remain unchanged, such as the worst case time for ignition, the ambient temperature, or the status of the ventilation system. However, changes are required in the characteristics used as design input.

The designer overseeing the change in building use needs to re-evaluate occupant characteristics, based on the fact that the building was designed with the typical occupant falling into the 14- to 18-year-old category. Now the typical new occupant age will range from about 4 to 8 years of age. This change may lead to differences in movement speed, reaction time, and type of reaction. Additionally, the designer might have to make modifications in the location and number of occupants considered in the evaluation, based on the new use. Additional changes would have to be made regarding the need for, and level of, staff assistance.

Modifications might also be required in building characteristics, such as the fuel load. The change in building use could lead to differences in the amount and type of fuel. More items geared toward young children might or might not mean more, faster-burning materials. The building might no longer contain shop or lab areas, which act as a fire hazard, but it might have additional storage space, which can add significantly to the fuel load. The designer should investigate the impact of the different fuel loads in the two building uses.

Based on the specific building, there may be additional factors that have to be modified in the design input before the building is re-evaluated. No matter how small the modification might be, the building stakeholders should ensure that the building performance remains at a level that meets the performance goals and objectives. This investigation might simply entail verifying that the new value for part of the design input is still within the allowable range, or it might entail a complete re-evaluation of the structure. In either case, the authority having jurisdiction needs to be consulted before any changes are made.

5.1.8 Special Definitions.

A list of special terms used in this chapter follows:

Alternative Calculation Procedure. See 3.3.7.

Data Conversion. See 3.3.38.

Design Fire Scenario. See 3.3.41.

Design Specifications. See 3.3.42.

Design Team. See 3.3.43.

Exposure Fire. See 3.3.66.

Fire Model. See 3.3.73.

Fire Scenario. See 3.3.76.

Fuel Load. See 3.3.86.

Incapacitation. See 3.3.109.

Input Data Specification. See 3.3.111.

Occupant Characteristics. See 3.3.135.

Performance Criteria. See 3.3.143.

Proposed Design. See 3.3.155.

Safe Location. See 3.3.167.

Safety Factor. See 3.3.168.

Safety Margin. See 3.3.169.

Sensitivity Analysis. See 3.3.177.

Stakeholder. See 3.3.192.

Uncertainty Analysis. See 3.3.204.

Verification Method. See 3.3.206.

Section 5.2 Performance Criteria

5.2.1 General.

A design shall meet the objectives specified in Section 4.2 if, for each design fire scenario, assumption, and design specification, the performance criterion in 5.2.2 is met.

5.2.2* Performance Criterion.

No occupant who is not intimate with ignition shall be exposed to instantaneous or cumulative untenable conditions.

A.5.2.2 One of the following methods can be used to avoid exposing occupants to untenable conditions.

(a) The design team can set detailed performance criteria that ensures that occupants are not incapacitated by fire effects. The *SFPE Engineering Guide to Performance-Based Fire Protection Analysis and Design of Buildings* describes a process of establishing tenability limits.

The guide references D. A. Purser, "Toxicity Assessment of Combustion Products," Chapter 2–8, *SFPE Handbook of Fire Protection Engineering,* National Fire Protection Association, Quincy, MA, 1995, which describes a fractional effective dose (FED) calculation approach also contained in the 1996 edition of NFPA 269, *Standard Test Method for Developing Toxic Potency Data for Use in Fire Hazard Modeling.* FED addresses carbon monoxide, hydrogen cyanide, carbon dioxide, hydrogen chloride, hydrogen bromide, and anoxia effects. It is possible to use the test data, combined with laboratory experience, to estimate the FED value that leads to the survival of virtually all people. This value is about 0.8.

There is a relationship between exposures leading to death and those leading to incapacitation. Kaplan (Kaplan et al., *Journal of Fire Science* 2, 286–305 (1984)) found that rodent susceptibility is similar to that of humans and that for the narcotic gases, CO and HCN, incapacitation occurs at one-third to one-half of the lethal exposure. Gann (Gann et al., *Fire and Materials* 18, 193 (1994)) found that carbon monoxide dominates the lethality of fire smoke, since most fire deaths occur remote from the fire room, in fires that have proceeded past flashover. Thus, if an FED value of 0.8 were used for a nonlethal exposure, an FED of 0.3 would be reasonable for a nonincapacitating exposure.

If the authority having jurisdiction or the design professional is concerned with potential toxic fire effects other than those addressed by the FED procedure as documented, then the calculation procedure can be expanded by adding additional terms to the FED equation, with each term expressed as a ratio. The numerator of the ratio is the cumulative exposure to that fire effect, measured as an integral of the product of instantaneous exposure (concentration for toxic products) and time. The denominator of the ratio is the quantity of cumulative exposure for which FED equals the chosen threshold value (that is, 0.8 or 0.3) based on that fire effect alone.

ASTM is actively considering standards that would extend the list of toxic fire effects with standard values.

If the authority having jurisdiction or the design professional is concerned with potential fire effects other than toxicity, then the calculation procedure can be modified to include other fire effects, such as thermal effects.

For buildings where an unusually large fraction of the occupants are especially vulnerable, the calculation procedure should be modified to use FED values lower than 0.8 or 0.3.

(b) For each design fire scenario and the design specifications, conditions, and assumptions, the design team can demonstrate that each room or area will be fully evacuated before the smoke and toxic gas layer in that room descends to a level lower than 6 ft (1.8 m) above the floor. The timing of such an evacuation means that no occupant is exposed to fire effects. Such an evacuation requires calculation of the locations, movement, and behavior of occupants, because fire effects and occupants are kept separate by moving the occupants. A level of 5 ft (1.5 m) is often used in calculations, but at that level, a large fraction of the population would not be able to stand, walk, or run normally and still avoid inhalation of toxic gases. They would have to bend over or otherwise move their heads closer to the floor level.

(c) For each design fire scenario and the design specifications and assumptions, the design team can demonstrate that the smoke and toxic gas layer will not descend to a level lower than 6 ft (1.8 m) above the floor in any occupied room. The advantage of this procedure is that it conservatively requires that no occupant need be exposed to fire effects, regardless of where occupants are or where they move. This removes the need to make any calculations regarding occupants, including their behavior, movement locations, pre-fire characteristics, and reactions to fire effects. This procedure is even more conservative and simpler than the procedure in item (b), because it does not allow fire effects in occupied rooms to develop to a point where people could be affected at any time during the fire.

(d) For each design fire scenario and the design specifications and assumptions, the design team can demonstrate that no fire effects will reach any occupied room. The advantage of this procedure is that it removes the need to make any calculations regarding occupants, including their behavior, movement, locations, pre-fire characteristics, and reactions to fire effects. A further advantage is that it also removes the need for some of the modeling of fire effects, because it is not necessary to model the filling of rooms, only the spread of fire effects to those rooms. This procedure is even more conservative and simpler than the procedures in items (b) and (c), because it does not allow any fire effects in occupied rooms.

The methods described in A.5.2.2 provide an indication of the variety of ways of demonstrating that a proposed design meets the performance criteria and, therefore, the objectives. The methods also illustrate how different approaches can result in different margins of safety. Specifically, the second, third and fourth methods are all similar in their approach—they deal with smoke filling of a room. The second method concentrates on evacuating people before the smoke level reaches 6 ft (1.8 m) above the floor. This

method presumes that the smoke will eventually reach a lower level and could, therefore, expose people crawling under the smoke layer. This method results in a relatively small margin of safety. The third method has a presumably more proactive design in that it intends to prevent the smoke layer from descending any lower than 6 ft (1.8 m) above the floor. This method intends to prevent exposure to occupants without their leaving the room, unless they are taller than 6 ft (1.8 m) and unwilling or unable to bend over. This method produces a greater margin of safety than that of the second method. The margin of safety for the fourth method is the greatest—excluding the room of fire origin—because it requires the proposed design to prevent smoke from reaching any occupied room.

Three additional points are relevant to these methods. The first is that the final performance criteria might be the result of an agreement with the authority having jurisdiction, who might require or accept a different threshold other than the 6-ft (1.8-m) threshold cited. In both methods using 6 ft (1.8 m) as the point above the floor below which smoke should not descend, a value of 7 ft, 6.5 ft, or 5 ft (2.1 m, 2 m, 1.5 m) could have been justified instead, based on the use of different fractions of the population requiring protection—given that some people are taller than 6 ft (1.8 m)—or different safety margins on the uncertainty calculation of the smoke layer height. The threshold for smoke layer height, and many others, needs to be a subject of discussion before the performance-based design is begun.

The second point is that the fourth method presumes that the room of fire is unoccupied. Depending on the facility and the scenario, this might not be a reasonable assumption. If it is not, the criteria for safety for the room of fire origin needs to be set separately.

The final point, outlined in the following discussion, is provided to demonstrate the differences among the second, third, and fourth methods described in this commentary with respect to the level of analysis required, not with regard to their use as a specification for performing an analysis or determining whether the design meets the performance criterion for the method. Depending on the method selected for use in the evaluation, the designer needs to perform different types and levels of analysis. If it is decided to use the second method, which states that the smoke and toxic gas will not descend to a level lower than 6 ft (1.8 m) before the area is fully evacuated, then the designer needs to model both the fire and smoke spread in the building to determine the time each space becomes untenable. Additionally, the designer needs to model each occupant's egress from the building, determining the times at which each space is occupied or fully evacuated. The models and the levels of fire and smoke spread and occupant egress can then be compared to determine if the toxic gas level and smoke descend beyond the specified level before the area is fully evacuated. This analysis path requires detailed modeling of both the toxic gas spread and the evacuation of the occupants. Care must be taken to ensure that the modeling is completed conservatively and accurately, as the second method does not provide a large margin for error inherent in the design.

If the third method, which states that the smoke and toxic gas layer will not descend below 6 feet (1.8 m) in any occupied room, is selected, then the analysis becomes both less complicated and more conservative. After determining each occupied space in the building, including spaces that will be occupied during occupant egress, the analysis will consist of a determination of when and whether the smoke and toxic gas layer will descend below the specified level in these areas. While the design still needs a detailed analysis of the fire and the spread of the products of combustion to determine the level of filling in each occupied area, such an analysis need not consider the building occupants or any actions they might take before or during the emergency.

If the stakeholders wish to design the building to satisfy the fourth method, which states that no fire effects will reach any occupied area, then the analysis becomes even less complicated and more conservative than that of the third method. The designer should evaluate the building for each fire scenario to determine only if the smoke and toxic products of combustion will spread beyond the room of origin to occupied areas. This process often requires less complicated design tools and verification methods, as the rate and degree of smoke movement in the building is irrelevant as long as the designer can determine whether the smoke or toxic gas will travel into occupied areas.

Section 5.3 Retained Prescriptive Requirements

5.3.1* Systems and Features.

All fire protection systems and features of the building shall comply with applicable NFPA standards for those systems and features.

A.5.3.1 This requirement applies both to systems and features required by the *Code* that reference applicable standards and to any additional systems or features included in the design at the discretion of the design team. The referenced standards are hereby expected to state maintenance, testing, and other requirements needed to provide positive assurance of an acceptable level of reliability. The referenced standards themselves might be prescriptive- or performance-based.

5.3.2 Means of Egress.

The design shall comply with the following requirements in addition to the performance criteria of Section 5.2 and the methods of Sections 5.4 through 5.8:

(1) Changes in Level in Means of Egress—7.1.7
(2) Guards—7.1.8
(3) Doors—7.2.1
(4) Stairs—7.2.2

Exception: The provisions of 7.2.2.5.1, 7.2.2.5.2, 7.2.2.6.2, 7.2.2.6.3, and 7.2.2.6.4 shall be exempted.

(5) Ramps—7.2.5

Exception: The provisions of 7.2.5.3.1, 7.2.5.5, and 7.2.5.6.1 shall be exempted.

(6) Fire Escape Ladders—7.2.9
(7) Alternating Tread Devices—7.2.11
(8) Capacity of Means of Egress—7.3

Exception: The provisions of 7.3.3 and 7.3.4 shall be exempted.

(9) Impediments to Egress—7.5.2
(10) Illumination of Means of Egress—7.8
(11) Emergency Lighting—7.9
(12) Marking of Means of Egress—7.10

The prescriptive provisions listed in 5.3.2 for the means of egress do not readily lend themselves to performance-based calculation. However, these aspects cannot be excluded from the design. Therefore, these prescriptive provisions are retained for performance-based designs. For example, prescriptive exit sign requirements help to assure the effectiveness of the means of egress; emergency lighting along the egress path provides prescriptive reliability for the illumination needed for effective exiting. A rationale for retaining these prescriptive requirements is that existing models of evacuation behavior are not sophisticated enough to quantify the effect of signs or lighting on the speed and effectiveness of exiting behavior.

5.3.3 Equivalency.

Equivalent designs for the features covered in the retained prescriptive requirements mandated by 5.3.2 shall be addressed in accordance with the equivalency provisions of Section 1.5.

Section 5.4 Design Specifications and Other Conditions

5.4.1* Clear Statement.

Design specifications and other conditions used in the performance-based design shall be clearly stated and shown to be realistic and sustainable.

A.5.4.1 The design specifications and other conditions will form the input to evaluation of proposed designs *(see Section 5.6)*. Where a specification or condition is not known, a reasonable estimation is permitted. However, the design team will need to take steps to ensure that the estimation is valid during the life of the building. Any estimations need to be documented. *(See Section 5.8.)*

An example of an estimation could be a material property value needed as input by a computer fire model. Typically, computer fire models allow a single value to be input for material properties. However, if the material property varies with temperature, there is a question as to which single value adequately characterizes the material. The single value used to estimate the behavior of the material over the entire temperature range that might be experienced during the course of a fire needs to be conservatively selected and documented.

5.4.2 Assumptions and Design Specifications Data.

5.4.2.1 Each assumption and design specification used in the design shall be accurately translated into input data specifications, as appropriate for the calculation method or model.

The documentation of the performance-based analysis is to clearly indicate the process for converting assumptions and design specifications into input data specifications. In some cases the conversion process is straightforward. For example, room dimensions are explicitly stated in the design specification and can be used as input data without modification. However, if the designer assumes that a certain material will be the fuel consumed by the fire, then the process of

converting that assumption into a heat release rate curve, a mass loss curve, toxic potency values, flame spread rate, or other data for modeling needs to be described.

Example: Design Specifications

The source of much of the input data for the verification methods is the design specifications for the building. The design specifications are to include all the information from the building design that affects the ability of the building to meet the stated goals and objectives. In addition to the building plans and drawings, the design specification information is to be presented for use by the designer and the authority having jurisdiction. Both parties then review the information and implement it as input data specifications. To give an impression of the type of information that should be included with the design specifications, a simple example—based upon a hypothetical, four-story business occupancy building—is presented. This example building plan is shown in Exhibit 5.2, which is not drawn to scale. The fire protection and egress features for the building are not designed to meet the prescriptive *Code* requirements, with the exception of those items listed in 5.3.2. Additionally, the building has not been analyzed using the methods in Chapter 5. To conserve time and space, the systems, features, and construction details specified in this example are not explained in full detail, since this information is available from a variety of other sources. However, when completing an actual performance-based design, detailed information on each system and construction feature, such as an automatic sprinkler system or a fire barrier wall, needs to be compiled and presented for use by the designer and the authority having jurisdiction.

Building Layout. A description of the layout and dimensions of the building is to be developed. This description is to include a breakdown of each area to be considered in the performance-based design, as well as a description of the building as a whole.

Building footprint—100 ft × 250 ft (30.5 m × 76.2 m)

Building height—50 ft (15.2 m)

Story height (top of floor slab to bottom of slab on next floor)—12 ft (4.2 m)

Floor height (below false ceiling)—10 ft (3 m)

Steel frame construction (interior columns)—W8 × 28 steel columns protected by two layers of gypsum wallboard—total 1 in. (2.5 cm) thick; in-

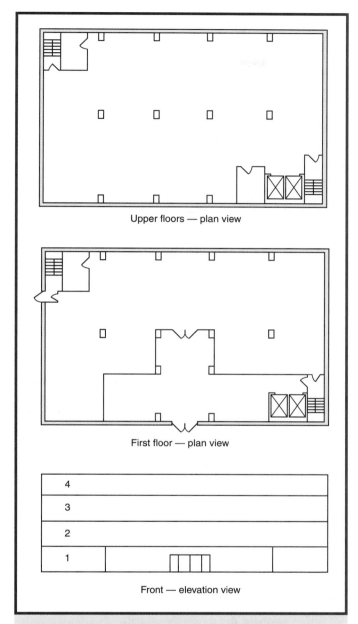

Upper floors — plan view

First floor — plan view

Front — elevation view

Exhibit 5.2 *Four-story business occupancy building.*

clude design and construction details for column protection

Poured on deck concrete slab—6 in. (15.2 cm) thick, supported by prefabricated joists

Interior finish material—gypsum wallboard

Ceiling construction—include design and fabrication details for ceiling construction and materials

Automatic sprinkler system—installed throughout per NFPA 13, *Standard for the Installation of Sprinkler Systems*[1]; include all specifications for the sprinkler system normally included in a prescriptive system design (for example, information relative to design density, RTI, spacing)

Alarm system—initiation by means of waterflow alarm incorporated into sprinkler system that operates when flow of water is equal to or greater than that from single sprinkler; waterflow alarm activates evacuation signal designed per NFPA 72, *National Fire Alarm Code*[2]; include all specification and design information for alarm system normally provided for a prescriptive design

HVAC system—designed and installed per NFPA 90A, *Standard for the Installation of Air Conditioning and Ventilating Systems*,[3] and applicable, regional plumbing and mechanical code.

Stairs

Two exit stair enclosures located in opposite corners of building

Stair enclosures—10 ft × 25 ft (3 m × 7.6 m)

Stair riser height—6 in. (15.2 cm)

Stair tread depth—12 in. (38.1 cm)

Stair clear width—48 in. (122 cm)

Stairs enclosed with 2-hour fire resistance–rated barrier walls (provide design and construction details)

1 ½-hour fire protection–rated, self-closing, 32-in. (81.3-cm) clear width doors

Elevators

Two 12 ft × 12 ft (3.7 m × 3.7 m) elevators separated from rest of building by 2-hour fire resistance–rated barrier walls (provide design and construction details)

Elevator installation per ASME/ANSI A17.1, *Safety Code for Elevators and Escalators*[4]

Storage room

Located on upper floors next to elevator lobby

Dimensions—20 ft × 25 ft (6.1 m × 7.6 m)

Nonbearing walls constructed of gypsum wallboard mounted on metal studs

32-in. (81.3-cm) clear width self-closing door

Rest room

Located adjacent to second stair enclosure

Dimensions—15 ft × 25 ft (4.6 m × 7.6 m)

Nonbearing walls constructed of gypsum wall-board mounted on metal studs

32-in. (81.3-cm) clear width self-closing door

Entranceway (ground floor)

Separated from remainder of first floor by 2-hour fire resistance–rated barrier walls (provide design and construction details)

Two main doors for entry into office space on ground floor—1 ½-hour fire protection–rated, self-closing, 40-in. (102-cm) clear width

Two exterior exit doors off lobby—self-closing, 40-in. (102-cm) clear width

Dimensions indicated on drawing

Emergency lighting and marking of the means of egress—specify details and design per *Code*'s prescriptive requirements.

Example: Assumptions

In addition to compiling building specifications, a variety of assumptions need to be made by the designer in developing a performance-based design. These assumptions are to remain constant and consistent throughout the analysis of the building. This example is included to provide information relating to the type of assumptions that might be made on a 15-story hypothetical hotel occupancy building. Similar to the design specifications, this information is provided in a list format. Certain assumptions made by the design team can be included with different sections of the design input, such as assumptions regarding the location of the occupants, which would be included with the occupant characteristics. Additionally, any assumptions that do not remain constant across the various scenarios cannot be classified as assumptions, and instead become scenario-related data. The breakdown of information should be agreed on with the AHJ before a design is submitted.

Status of Ventilation System. Information relating to the ventilation system and its status at the time of ignition should be included among the assumptions. While the design and construction information pertaining to the ventilation system would be included in the design specifications, the assumptions relating to this system would relate purely to its status at the time of the fire—mainly whether it was on or off.

Additionally, information relating to whether the ventilation system would remain on throughout the fire scenarios—or whether an automatic device will shut down the system—could be included in this data. This example assumes that the ventilation system is on and operating normally at time of ignition.

Ambient Temperature. Ambient temperature is based on the anticipated condition of the building at the time of ignition. For most modern buildings, ambient temperature is dependent on the occupancy classification, since many buildings now incorporate heating/ventilation systems that maintain a constant temperature. This example has an ambient temperature of 70°F (21°C).

Ignition Time. Assume worst-case time of day for the various fire scenarios. In the case of a hotel, the worst-case time is in the evening or very early morning hours, when the occupants are expected to be sleeping.

Egress Paths. Assumptions regarding the condition of the egress ways, and whether they are clear of debris are to be made. These assumptions are generally dependent on the anticipated use of the building, as certain building types are more likely than others to have objects stored or placed in the egress paths. In this example, the assumption that each stairway is clear of clutter and debris is based on daily verification by a hotel employee. However, the lobby area—which might be used as a primary means of egress—is often cluttered with items such as luggage or chairs, and the designer needs to estimate a usable egress width.

Mobility Impairment. Assume one mobility impaired occupant per floor of the structure. The mobility impairments affect the occupant characteristics of these individuals. The actual number of mobility impaired individuals using the building might be based on one of the following:

(1) The severity of the impairments
(2) Local jurisdictional requirements
(3) Selection by the design team based on the location of the structure and the anticipated clientele
(4) The number of rooms properly equipped to house mobility impaired individuals

Occupant Age Distribution. Assumptions regarding the age distribution of occupants are to be made. Tests have shown that groups of occupants separated by age have different movement speeds, and the design team needs to conservatively estimate the number of middle-aged adults, elderly, and children who will be located within the structure.

System Performance. Assume that all systems perform as designed unless the scenario specifically mandates a system failure.

Egress Path Selection. Assume that all occupants attempt to egress via the exit with which they are the most familiar or that they will attempt to use the path followed when entering the building. Since most occupants will probably have used the elevator, assume occupants will use the first exit stair encountered in moving toward the elevators.

Fire Fighter Staging. Depending on the time passed to fire fighter arrival, assume that the speed of occupant movement on stairs will be reduced by half for the stairs that the fire department uses as a staging area.

5.4.2.2 Any assumption and design specifications that the design analyses do not explicitly address or incorporate and that are, therefore, omitted from input data specifications shall be identified, and a sensitivity analysis of the consequences of that omission shall be performed.

The term *design analyses* as used in 5.4.2.2 means the baseline analyses of the proposed design. The design analyses are compiled into a report and submitted to the AHJ for approval. An example of design specifications and assumptions would not be included in the baseline analyses if, for example, the designer originally considered either incorporating an automatic suppression system into the building design or designing the building to rely on manual suppression if a fire occurs. The designer would perform an analyses on each of these options and include the option that best satisfies the performance criteria at the lowest cost into the proposed design. The rejected option would be included as an appendix in the submittal to the AHJ. The material included in this appendix would indicate why the rejected option was not included in the analyses, as well as how the building performance would change if the rejected option were to be incorporated into the design.

5.4.2.3 Any assumption and design specifications modified in input data specifications, because of limitations in test methods or other data generation procedures, shall be identified, and a sensitivity analysis of the consequences of the modification shall be performed.

For example, new and innovative designs for detection systems, suppression systems, or overall building layout and egress system might be incorporated into a performance-based design. Unfortunately, while the design team may feel that these systems and modifications provide a marked improvement in the performance of the building, they might not be quantifiable in the models used to analyze the structure. If the new and innovative design specifications and assumptions are such that they cannot be directly implemented into a model, the design team needs to provide justification for selection of input values to be used for the specifications and assumptions. This justification needs to include the following:

(1) A detailed description of the new or innovative system
(2) Rationale behind its selection for incorporation into the building design
(3) Reason for not incorporating specifications and assumptions directly into the model input
(4) Anticipated level of performance
(5) Improvements expected from the system
(6) Means of specifying input values in the input data specifications

Due to the level of uncertainty involved in this type of input data specification development, the design team needs to perform a sensitivity analysis on any of the input values formulated using this procedure. An example of a type of system whose design specification cannot be directly incorporated into the input data specifications is a new detection and alarm system that has not been fully tested in the arrangement and layout of the proposed building. If the design team can provide justification that the system's performance cannot be accurately predicted by the model, then modifications should be made to the input data specification to account for the differences in the results of the analysis and the performance of the system.

5.4.3 Building Characteristics.

Characteristics of the building or its contents, equipment, or operations that are not inherent in the design specifications, but that affect occupant behavior or the rate of hazard development, shall be explicitly identified.

Building characteristics that are not classified as design specifications tend to be limited to particular spaces within the building, are often occupancy or purpose driven, or tend to be long-term or transitory adjustments by occupants to problems in the functionality of the basic design. The building characteristics depend largely on the materials used to decorate and furnish the building and on the anticipated layout of such materials. The identification of building characteristics needs to take into account the intended use of the building and potential aging effects on those used. The identification of building characteristics of concern requires considerable experience with the hazard-related consequences of both typical and problematic operations in occupancies of the type proposed.

Examples of building characteristics include the anticipated layout, fuel load, and burning characteristics of a work area comprised of cubicles in a business occupancy. In addition to the flammability characteristics of the interior lining materials of a structure, an additional modification could be included with the building characteristics to account for the potential buildup of combustible dust or hydrocarbon residue on the material in an industrial complex. Buildings in which there is a high rate of occupant turnover and movement, such as educational facilities or dormitories, might include doors—and more importantly fire doors—that are routinely blocked open allowing the uninhibited passage of smoke and other fire products of combustion. Designers of a mercantile occupancy might deliberately or inadvertently create a maze-like effect, which not only affects evacuation times, but might also lead to anxiety and confusion in the occupants during an emergency.

Example: Building Characteristics

The description of the building characteristics is to include all of the information related to the building and its various contents and features that is not included with the design specifications. Various examples of building characteristics are provided in this commentary. However, this example includes a more detailed example of the type of items that should be included with the building characteristics when developing a performance-based design. Additionally, this example presents differences in, and modifications that would be required for, the building characteristics if the intended use is changed from a business occupancy to a mercantile occupancy. The different occupancy types can lead to large differences in the smoke production and spread throughout the structure, as well as differences in evacuation time. The designer needs to carefully select and document the characteristics of the specific building. The designer also needs to use conservative estimates of the various building characteristics, particularly if

there is a possibility that the owner might change the building type or occupancy.

The building in question is a three-story office building that is being converted into a three-level department store. The following provides a description of the building characteristics that might be used in the original performance-based design for the business occupancy.

Office Space. The space is divided throughout by work cubicles. A base case office setup for cubicle arrangement is to be specified. Arrangements are to be analyzed using sensitivity analysis to determine allowable level of variance in office setup.

Fuel Load. The fuel load is dependent on office setup. A fixed fuel load is to be used as limited types of materials are available for consumption. The fuel load will consist of materials such as office furniture, computers, cubicle finishing materials, and paper. Tests that measure the burning rate of office cubicles and different office setups are to be consulted to determine the total combined fuel load. The flammability of each potential fuel item in the area of ignition is to be estimated. Other potential sources of fuel in a business occupancy include the interior finish materials and paper or office equipment in storage areas.

The flammability information for the fuel sources, such as the heat release rate, rate of flame spread, and mass loss rate, can be determined from several sources. The flammability data for the fuels in question might be available in typical fire protection texts, such as the *NFPA Fire Protection Handbook*,[5] the *SFPE Handbook of Fire Protection Engineering*,[6] and Drysdale's *An Introduction to Fire Dynamics*.[7] This information can also be estimated using the results from small-scale tests, such as those from a cone calorimeter or a LIFT apparatus. A more accurate determination of the flammability characteristics can be produced in large-scale testing of the fuels in question. This is not to suggest that the designer conduct large-scale testing of the anticipated fuel sources for each design; however, a review of large-scale tests completed on items similar to those in question at fire testing labs such as the National Institute of Standards and Technology (NIST), Building and Fire Research Laboratory might provide accurate estimates of the required material properties. NIST has compiled this research in reports available for downloading on their web site or at their research library, such as *A Survey of Fuel Loads in Contemporary Office Buildings*[8] by Caro and Milke. The flammability of the specific items in question should be documented as accurately as possible.

Egress Paths. Despite the variability of the office setup, business occupancies typically will have clear, fixed paths of egress. The egress paths will generally consist of a perimeter loop around the office core, along with multiple aisleways leading from the interior offices to the perimeter loop. Based on the type of business occupying the structure, the designer should determine whether the egress paths are likely to remain clear of clutter and debris. This facet of the building characteristics could also be included with the design assumptions.

Fire Doors. The condition of the fire doors in the structure is to be specified with the building characteristics. Business occupancies generally keep fire doors in the structure closed due to the limited need to block the doors open, since, generally, occupant turnover is not large, and movement of furniture is periodic.

The preceding characteristics are assumptions relating to the building's function. These business occupancy characteristics can be compared to those identified for the department store in order to determine which characteristics can be replaced with new values for the new occupancy. Generally, some differences exist, and if the new characteristics vary significantly, the designer might have to re-evaluate the performance of the structure completely. The following presents the types of information that are to be included with the building characteristics for the renovated mercantile occupancy spaces.

Mercantile Space. As in the case of the business occupancy, a base case setup of the mercantile space is to be specified. However, a mercantile occupancy generally modifies the arrangement and setup of the building contents more frequently than a business occupancy, based on the type of store involved. The design is to be sufficiently robust so that most every typical arrangement of the mercantile occupancy is allowed, with the exception of extreme cases utilizing highly volatile or flammable substances.

Fuel Load. The fuel load for a mercantile occupancy is based primarily on the intended merchandise. The fuel load can vary greatly depending on the type of store and even the time of year. The design is to be based on the worst-case fuel load that the designer feels might be in the building at any time of the year. Due to the nature of many mercantile occupancies, the fuel load could consist of various items, ranging from electronics, plastics, food products, wood materials, upholstered furniture, and seasonal decorations. When determining the fuel load, the designer needs to take into consideration the type of store that is to occupy the space.

Egress Paths. Many mercantile establishments either inadvertently or deliberately create maze-like paths that run through the store. While such paths might keep the shopper in the store for longer periods, causing them to view more of the merchandise, it will also cause longer evacuation times and can lead to anxiety during emergencies. Additionally, due to restocking operations and the moving of merchandise, the egress paths and aisleways in a mercantile occupancy might be partially or fully blocked.

Fire Doors. Mercantile occupancies are frequently moving items and storing contents and may have large occupant loads moving between different spaces. These effects might result in the fire doors within the structure being blocked open, which allows smoke and other products of combustion to spread uninhibited throughout the structure. The evaluation should consider this issue, or the designer should take steps to ensure that the fire doors remain closed.

5.4.4* Operational Status and Effectiveness of Building Features and Systems.

The performance of fire protection systems and building features shall reflect the documented performance of the components of those systems or features unless design specifications are incorporated to modify the expected performance.

A.5.4.4 Systems addressed by this requirement include automatic fire suppression systems and fire alarm systems. Performance issues that need to be documented might include response time indexes, discharge densities and distribution patterns. Calculations should not include an unlimited supply of extinguishing agent if only a limited supply will be provided in the actual structure or building.

Subsection 5.4.4 and its annex language are meant to help ensure that the performance-based design analysis is realistic and reflects the anticipated operation of the systems. In other words, the systems installed in buildings are limited—not like Hollywood guns that never run out of bullets. Designers need to make sure that the analysis deals with the systems in a practical manner and are characteristic of how they will be installed in the building.

Some of the issues of concern are reliability issues, which are separately addressed in 5.5.3.8 through mandatory analysis of scenarios with systems and features rendered unavailable. Subsection 5.4.4 addresses inherent performance limitations rather than reliability concerns. For example, there are different modes of fire detection (such as ionization smoke detectors, photoelectric smoke detectors, fixed-temperature heat detectors, rate-of-rise heat detectors) that provide different speeds of response to different fire scenarios. Also, automatic fire sprinklers use varying design densities of different agents, resulting in different speeds and degrees of effectiveness, depending on fire scenario. Fire doors are rated for different duration and are expected to withstand different levels of heat impact before failing. Additionally, fire barrier walls are expected to exhibit various performance levels, particularly if one extends from the floor to the roof while another extends to a level below the roof.

5.4.5 Occupant Characteristics.

5.4.5.1* General. The selection of occupant characteristics to be used in the design calculations shall be approved by the authority having jurisdiction and shall provide an accurate reflection of the expected population of building users. Occupant characteristics shall represent the normal occupant profile, unless design specifications are used to modify the expected occupant features. Occupant characteristics shall not vary across fire scenarios except as authorized by the authority having jurisdiction.

A.5.4.5.1 Examples of design features that might be incorporated to modify expected occupant characteristics include training, use of staff to assist with notification and movement, or type of notification appliance used.

5.4.5.2* Response Characteristics. The basic response characteristics of sensibility, reactivity, mobility, and susceptibility shall be evaluated. Such estimates shall reflect the expected distribution of characteristics of a population appropriate to the use of the building. The source of data for these characteristics shall be documented.

A.5.4.5.2 The four basic characteristics—sensibility, reactivity, mobility, and susceptibility—comprise a minimum, exhaustive set of mutually exclusive performance characteristics of people in buildings that can affect a fire safety system's ability to meet life safety objectives. The characteristics are briefly described as follows.

(a) Sensibility—to physical cues. Ability to sense the sounding of an alarm; can also include discernment and discrimination of visual and olfactory cues in addition to auditory emanations from the fire itself.

(b) Reactivity—ability to interpret correctly cues and take appropriate action. Can be function of cognitive capacity, speed of instinctive reaction, or group dynamics; might

need to consider reliability or likelihood of a wrong decision, as in situations where familiarity with the premises influences wayfinding.

(c) Mobility—speed of movement. Determined by individual capabilities as well as crowding phenomena such as arching at doorways.

(d) Susceptibility—to products of combustion. Metabolism, lung capacity, pulmonary disease, allergies, or other physical limitations that affect survivability in a fire environment.

In application, as with the use of computer evacuation models, assumptions can address a larger number of factors that are components of these basic performance characteristics. Examples follow.

Alertness	Awake/asleep, can depend on time of day
Responsiveness	Ability to sense cues and react
Commitment	Degree to which occupant is committed to an activity underway before the alarm
Focal point	Point at which an occupant's attention is focused, for example, to front of classroom, stage, or server in business environment
Physical and mental capabilities	Can affect ability to sense, respond, and react to cues; might be related to age or disability
Role	Can determine whether occupant will lead or follow others
Familiarity	Can depend on time spent in building or participation in emergency training
Social affiliation	Extent to which an occupant will act/react as an individual or as a member of a group
Condition	Over the course of the fire, the effects — both physiological and psychological — of the fire and its combustion products on each occupant

5.4.5.3 Location. It shall be assumed that in every normally occupied room or area at least one person shall be located at the most remote point from the exits.

All occupant locations at the beginning of the fire must be specified. This information is critical for egress analysis, since travel distances to the exits must be known. Depending on the scenarios of interest, conditions within selected egress paths must be analyzed. However, the conditions in the room of fire origin always need to be determined.

5.4.5.4* Number of Occupants. The design shall be based on the maximum number of people that every occupied room or area is expected to contain. Where the success or failure of the design is contingent on the number of occupants not exceeding a certain maximum, operational controls shall be used to ensure that a greater number of people could not occupy a room.

A.5.4.5.4 The number of people expected to be contained in a room or area should be based on the occupant load factor specified in Table 7.3.1.2 or other approved sources.

Other approved sources for occupant loads might be zoning regulations, or the authority having jurisdiction might specify a higher occupant load than that of Table 7.3.1.2 to provide an additional safety margin.

Example: Response Characteristics, Location, and Number of Occupants

The occupant characteristics specified for a performance-based design need to provide an accurate representation of the abilities and behaviors of the building occupants before and during the fire. This information is critical to a performance-based design if the design is to be based on and compared with the second method of A.5.2.2. This criterion selection requires that each room or area be fully evacuated before the smoke layer in that room descends below 6 ft (1.8 m) above the floor. To show that each space is clear before the smoke layer reaches this level, the designer must document the spread of fire, its products of combustion, and the movement of people throughout the building during the emergency as accurately as possible using current verification methods. To model the evacuation of the building, characteristics of the occupants of that building must be formulated. The overall function of occupant characteristics is the estimation of the time required to evacuate the building. Therefore, the designer also needs to formulate response characteristics, which dictate how the occupants perceive the fire threat, the time required to respond to this threat, and the time to evacuate the building once the decision has been made to leave. Additionally, the designer is to determine the number and location of people occupying the structure at the time of the fire initiation. Staff assistance and emergency response are other

functions that impact evacuation time and are presented in separate examples in this chapter.

This example presents a sample of occupant characteristics that could be used as the basis for an egress analysis. It is critical that the designer account for pre-movement activities when completing an egress analysis, as occupants will often spend as much time, if not far more, deciding and preparing to leave than actually moving through the building.[9] The list of occupant characteristics is based on a hypothetical, three-story apartment building as shown in Exhibit 5.3. This building has two enclosed exit stairs located in the opposite corners of the structure. The stair on the bottom right-hand side of Exhibit 5.3 is assumed to be the main, front stairway for the structure, and consequently the egress path with which most of the people in the building are most familiar. The building is laid out such that there are 16 one-bedroom apartments and six three-bedroom apartments.

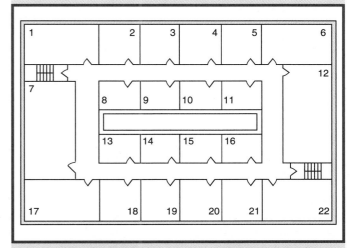

Exhibit 5.3 *Three-story apartment building—typical floor, plan view.*

16 small apartments

    Single bedroom

    Two people per apartment

    Two mobility-impaired people (walking disabled) per floor. Base case locations, apartments 3 and 14—subject to sensitivity analysis.

Large apartments

    Three bedrooms

    Three apartments with two adults and two children; three apartments with two adults and three children; base case locations, five-person apartments 7, 12, and 17. Distribution of four- and five-person apartments subject to sensitivity mana-lysis.

Notification Time. Notification time is the time from ignition until the sounding of the alarm. Notification time is dependent on the fire scene and design specification of the detection and alarm.

Reaction Time. Assume everyone in the building is sleeping at the time of alarm. This state of sensibility presents a delay in the reaction time of the occupants. Additionally, average reaction time is highly influenced by the performance of the detection and alarm system. Tests have shown that the performance of an alarm system, and the occupants' attitude to the sounding of the alarm, has a dramatic effect on the average delay time.[10] The average reaction time of adult occupants is to be determined based on the condition of occupants at the time of alarm (sleeping), design features and audibility of the alarm system, and any local regulation relating to delay times to be used in egress analysis. This example assumes that children will not react and prepare to evacuate without prompting from adults; therefore, only an estimate for adults is to be provided. The predicted range of reaction time is to be provided.

Pre-evacuation Time. An additional factor that needs to be considered when performing egress analyses is pre-evacuation activities that occupants engage in before leaving the building. These activities range from getting dressed, packing up valuable belongings, gathering children or pets, and finding a jacket. The location of the building might factor into the delay time, as occupants are more reluctant to go outside in particularly cold weather, and—before they do—more time will be spent finding and donning jackets and other clothing. In the case of mobility-impaired individuals who require mobility aids, delay time will also include the time required to find, gather, and begin using these devices. An average time for the pre-evacuation activities is to be specified for each of the apartment groups. For this example, the apartments housing two adults and no children have pre-evacuation times based on the time required to get dressed, gather items such as a jacket, keys, shoes, and wallet, and then begin to egress the building. An additional amount of time should be added for those apartments housing mobility-impaired individuals. For those apartments housing children, an additional time factor should be added for the time required to get the children together, dressed, and ready to move out of the building. Information on the reaction time and pre-evacuation activ-

ities and time is critical for the completion of an accurate egress analysis. This information can be found in the NFPA *Fire Protection Handbook*, the *SFPE Handbook of Fire Protection Engineering*, or tests such as those cited in the Proulx and Fahy paper.

The following evacuation times are also to be included in the egress analysis:

(1) Adult apartments pre-evacuation time—provide predicted range based on specific occupant characteristics and available literature and test data
(2) Adult apartments for mobility-impaired individuals pre-evacuation time—provide predicted range
(3) Apartments with children pre-evacuation time—provide predicted range

Travel Time. The final component of an egress analysis is the calculation of the time required for occupants to leave the structure once they begin to evacuate. This travel time is primarily based on the location of the occupants and the speed at which they can navigate through the building. Depending on the structure in question, the occupants' ability to move might be affected by crowding phenomena and unfamiliarity with the structure. Other factors that influence travel time are as follows:

(1) Families remain in a group throughout evacuation and move at the speed of the slowest member.
(2) Everyone in the building is familiar with the structure.
(3) Occupants egress via the most familiar path, unless fire or products of combustion block that path. Assume occupants from apartments 1, 2, 3, 7, 8, 9, and 17 attempt to use the stairway in the upper left-hand corner of the building, while the rest of the occupants use the stairway in the bottom right-hand corner of the building. Occupant movement speeds are available from several sources, including the NFPA *Fire Protection Handbook*, *SFPE Handbook of Fire Protection Engineering*, and Fruin's *Pedestrian Planning Design*,[11] or from tests on different samples of the population.

Movement speeds for the following are to be included in the egress analysis:

(1) Adults on floor—provide predicted range based upon available literature and test data
(2) Adults on stairs—provide predicted range
(3) Families with children on floor—provide predicted range

(4) Families with children on stairs—provide predicted range
(5) Mobility-impaired adults on floor—provide predicted range
(6) Mobility-impaired adults on stairs—provide predicted range

$$\text{Egress time} = t_n + t_r + t_p + t_t$$

where:

t_n = notification time
t_r = reaction time
t_p = pre-evacuation time
t_t = travel time

5.4.5.5* Staff Assistance. The ability of trained employees to be included as part of the fire safety system shall be identified and documented.

A.5.4.5.5 For example, in hospitals, staff characteristic such as number, location, quality, and frequency of training should be considered.

Example: Staff Assistance

Certain occupancies or building types might require the incorporation of staff assistance into the evacuation procedure in order for the occupants to evacuate the building safely. The incorporation of trained staff assistance in public places such as department stores, shopping malls, theaters, arenas, or similar buildings can help occupants unfamiliar with the building find emergency exits, accelerating their departure and reducing the overall evacuation time. However, it is important that staff members who are accounted for in a design be properly trained and drilled so that they are familiar with their role in the evacuation of the building.

Other examples of where staff assistance might be required are nursing homes, hospitals, and residential board and care facilities. In facilities housing the elderly or mentally- or physically-impaired individuals, occupants might be slow to react to warning or alarm systems and might be slow in moving. Depending on the severity of the impairment of the occupants, evacuation time might approach infinity without the incorporation of staff assistance. One example of the type of building that might necessitate staff assistance to be incorporated into the performance-based design is a nursing home that houses nonambulatory occupants incapable of self-preserva-

tion. Impairments of the occupants might range from inability to hear an alarm, inability to comprehend the significance of an alarm, the inability to walk unassisted, or the inability to move without the use of a wheelchair. Due to the varied nature of the occupants' conditions, the designer will most likely be unable to predict the types of impairments that the occupants of that building will have at any specific time.

The hypothetical building in question for this example is a two-story nursing home, with six occupant rooms, an entrance/waiting room, a desk/office area, and a cafeteria/lounge on the first floor; and 12 occupant rooms on the second floor. Exhibit 5.4 shows a plan view for each floor.

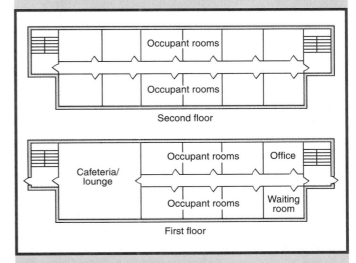

Exhibit 5.4 *Two-story nursing home.*

There are a total of eighteen rooms, each housing two occupants. This equates to a total permanent occupancy by thirty-six patients. These people might suffer from a variety of impairments, which will greatly affect their ability to egress the building in a timely manner in the event of an emergency. This example assumes that any occupant confined to a wheelchair is housed on the ground floor. The occupant characteristics for this building are not discussed in detail for this example, as they were presented in the commentary to A.5.4.5.4. However, this example briefly presents the impact of staff assistance on the various time components that can be used to determine the total egress time.

It is assumed that the occupants of the building are sleeping. Because there is a fairly high likelihood that some of the occupants of this building are hearing impaired or might be unable to comprehend and react to an alarm, the reaction time for this component of the population could be infinite. Additionally, elderly occupants might take more time getting dressed and preparing to leave, further lengthening the pre-evacuation time. There is a high likelihood that some of the occupants of this structure suffer from mobility or mental impairments, which also affect their travel time. Some of the occupants might be unable to move without assistance, so their travel time will be infinite, while others might simply move at a very slow pace.

Due to the effects of various impairments on egress time, staff assistance can be factored into a design to negate some of these effects. For this example, it is assumed that the building is staffed full time with three nurses, seven aides, and a desk clerk. Two of the nurses and four of the aides are located on the second floor. The actual level of staff required in a structure of this type might be restricted by local jurisdictions and individual company specifications. The designer should work with the building owner and stakeholders to develop a written facility fire safety plan that outlines each person's responsibility in the event of a fire. For this example, it is assumed that upon alarm and confirmation of a fire, the desk clerk is to notify and interact with the fire department, while the nurses and aides help the occupants to evacuate the building.

The designer must make certain assumptions regarding the staff of the facility in question and the degree to which they will affect the occupant response characteristics and evacuation. There must be a basis for each assumption made by the designer regarding staff assistance, and each should be documented. Sample assumptions might include the following:

(1) All patients are under 24-hour supervision and their location is always known.
(2) Wheelchair-bound patients are located on the first floor only, and the occupants either are seated in, or located near, their wheelchairs.
(3) The facility has an emergency evacuation plan that is practiced twice a year.
(4) Each nurse and aide is assigned a patient or group of patients who they must ensure escape safely from the building.
(5) Upon hearing an alarm, the staff verifies that there is a fire, then notifies each of the occupants and proceeds to take the following actions:

a. The staff closes the door to each room upon leaving to prevent smoke from entering that room.
b. After notifying each occupant, the staff begins helping those in need of assistance in moving through the building.

The effects of staff assistance on the time to evacuation can be stated with each component of the egress analysis time, based on the assumptions made. The first component of the egress time calculation is the time to notification. This component is generally based on the sounding of the alarm, but one of the assumptions for this example is that the staff verifies a fire before helping to notify the occupants. This action introduces a time delay in the notification time. The second and third components of the egress time calculation are the reaction and pre-evacuation times. As previously discussed, these times might be dramatically affected by hearing, mental, or physical impairments. When the staff is notifying the occupants of the fire, they need to ensure that each occupant capable of evacuating without assistance begins to react, or staff is to help them to begin evacuating the structure. This might include getting each occupant dressed and prepared to leave, as well as placing the occupants into wheelchairs if necessary.

The delay estimate for staff assistance must include consideration of the fact that each member of the staff might be responsible for more than one person and that there might be delays associated with each person. For the example presented here, the average staff member is assigned three or four people, and an average delay developed depends on the anticipated level of impairment associated with each person. These actions introduce further delays in the reaction and pre-evacuation activities.

Finally, the staff aids the occupants in moving through the building. This might include wheeling them out of the building, walking next to them throughout the egress process, or simply directing them out of the building. Initially, estimates are to be made for each of these delays, and these estimates are to be confirmed by the evacuation drills.

5.4.6 Emergency Response Personnel.

Design characteristics or other conditions related to the availability, speed of response, effectiveness, roles, and other characteristics of emergency response personnel shall be specified, estimated, or characterized sufficiently for evaluation of the design.

Depending on the design in question, it might be desirable to omit the operations of emergency response personnel. If this is the case, this assumption is to be documented as part of the final design.

Example: Emergency Response Personnel

Depending on the type of occupancy and the use of the building, the designer might wish to incorporate the actions of emergency personnel into the evaluation of the structure. The design team needs to make many assumptions regarding the time to arrival and overall capabilities of the response personnel, and these assumptions must be incorporated into the design documentation. The designer cannot simply assume that the fire department will arrive 30 seconds after the initial fire alarm and suppress the fire immediately upon arrival. This example is provided to present the type of questions that should be addressed regarding emergency response personnel, as well as some of the assumptions that might be made.

The facility in this example is located in the outskirts of a suburban town. This industrial occupancy manufactures plastic products and runs two shifts per day. There are two buildings on the campus, one housing the administrative personnel and design team offices as well as a cafeteria and lounge. In the other building all of the manufacturing takes place. The town has two full-time fire stations, both with the same resources. One is located 5 miles from the facility and the other 10 miles from the facility. The processes used in manufacturing the product are hazardous and involve the use of toxic and flammable chemicals.

As the designer, when determining what types of assumptions can be made about the emergency response personnel, it might be useful to develop a list of questions to ask the owner and AHJ or fire department representative on the design team. The answers to questions like the following can help the user assess what level of dependence the design should have on the arrival of the fire department:

(1) Is there a fire brigade on site?
(2) What is this brigade's level of training?
(3) What is the estimated response time of the local fire department?
(4) How many response personnel will respond with the first arriving company? Second arrival?
(5) Is the local fire department trained and familiar with the facility?

(6) When an alarm is sounded does the signal go straight to the local fire department or a security station on site, who will assess the situation before calling the local fire department?
(7) What types of hazards exist on site? Where are they located?
(8) Do these hazards pose health threats to the surrounding community? To the employees? To the fire fighters?
(9) Does the local fire department have the equipment to respond to the types of fire incidents that could develop?
(10) Does the municipality or the plant supply this equipment?
(11) If supplied by the company, is this equipment stored on site?
(12) What type of access does the fire department have to the site?
(13) How long will it take the fire fighters to set up for suppression efforts at a range of locations on the campus?

All assumptions based on the fire department's response time need to be verified as feasible by the fire department. The overall intention of these questions regarding the fire department and its capabilities is to determine the time to arrival, the time to agent application, and the time to suppression. This information can then be incorporated into the building evaluation. These various times should take into consideration not just the fire department, but also the building, as the designer should be aware that certain building designs present more challenging situations than others do. When emergency response personnel are to be an important part of the fire safety design, the designer needs to try to make the building as friendly to the fire department as possible. To facilitate this process, the designer should consult with the fire department early in and throughout the process to ensure that the design is optimized for firefighting operations and that any assumptions made regarding the fire department are accurate.

5.4.7* Post-construction Conditions.

Design characteristics or other conditions related to activities during the life of building that affect the ability of the building to meet the stated goals and objectives shall be specified, estimated, or characterized sufficiently for evaluation of the design.

A.5.4.7 Design proposals need to state explicitly any design specifications or estimations regarding building fire safety plans, inspection programs, or other ongoing programs whose performance is necessary for the building, when occupied and operational, to meet the stated goals and objectives.

Programs of interest include any maintenance, training, labeling, or certification programs required to ensure operational status or reliability in building systems or features.

> This paragraph relates to the management-of-change issues discussed in 5.1.7. One design characteristic that typically changes post-construction is the fuel load. The design basis fuel load must anticipate such changes, no matter what their size. Increased quantities of fuel load that involve materials that are easier to ignite and that involve higher and faster growing heat release rates, with higher smoke generation rates, could have a significant impact on the performance-based design. Neither the designer nor the authority having jurisdiction will want to re-analyze the design's acceptability fully whenever post-construction conditions change slightly. To avoid that need while retaining safety, the designer must use assumptions that are more conservative than the conditions actually anticipated, and also identify those conditions of greatest sensitivity that must be maintained or re-analyzed.

5.4.8 Off-Site Conditions.

Design characteristics or other conditions related to resources or conditions outside the property being designed that affect the ability of the building to meet the stated goals and objectives shall be specified, estimated, or characterized sufficiently for evaluation of the design.

> Off-site conditions are considered to be outside the property line and out of the control of the owner/operator. One example of an off-site condition is the status of the public water main. If the fire protection design relies on a sprinkler system fed by the public water main, then the analysis should consider the possibility that the public water main won't deliver the required amount of water.

5.4.9* Consistency of Assumptions.

The design shall not include mutually inconsistent assumptions, specifications, or statements of conditions.

A.5.4.9 This includes assumptions about the interrelations between the performance of building elements and systems, occupant behavior, or emergency response actions that conflict with each other. For each fire scenario, care needs to

be taken to ensure that conflicts in actions do not occur. Typical conflicts could include (1) assuming a fire door will remain closed during the fire to contain smoke, while this same door is used by occupants during egress from the area, (2) assuming fire apparatus will arrive immediately from a distant location to provide water to fire department connections and similar situations.

For example, an assumption that compartmentation blocking the passage of fire and smoke will be maintained at the door to a stairwell cannot be paired with an assumption that evacuation through that door will extend over many minutes.

5.4.10* Special Provisions.

Additional provisions not covered by the design specifications, conditions, estimations, and assumptions provided in Section 5.4 but that are required for the design to comply with the performance objectives shall be documented.

A.5.4.10 This includes provisions that are in excess of basic requirements covered by referenced codes and standards, typical design requirements, and operating procedures. It includes provisions such as more frequent periodic testing and maintenance to increase the reliability of fire protection systems, redundant systems to increase reliability, on-site guard service to enhance detection of fires and aid in fire response procedures, staff training, availability and performance of emergency response personnel, and other factors.

Section 5.5* Design Fire Scenarios

A.5.5 Design fire scenarios define the challenge a building is expected to withstand. Design fire scenarios capture and limit value judgments on the type and severity of the fire challenge to which a proposed fire safety system needs to respond. The system includes any and all aspects of the proposed design that are intended to mitigate the effects of a fire, such as egress system, automatic detection and suppression, barriers, staff training, and placement of manual extinguishers.

Design fire scenarios come from two sources: those that are specified in paragraphs 5.5.3.1 through 5.5.3.8, and those that are developed by the design team based on the unique characteristics of the building as required by 5.5.2. In most, if not all, cases, more than one design fire scenario will be developed to meet the requirements of 5.5.2.

Once the set of design fire scenarios is established, both those specified by 5.5.3.1 through 5.5.3.8 and those that are developed as required by 5.5.2, they need to be quantified into a format that can be used for the evaluation of proposed designs. The *SFPE Engineering Guide to Performance-Based Fire Protection Analysis and Design of Buildings* outlines a process and identifies tools and references that can be used at each step of this process.

5.5.1 Design Fire Scenarios.

The authority having jurisdiction shall approve the parameters involved in design fire scenarios. The proposed design shall be considered to meet the goals and objectives if it achieves the performance criteria for each required design fire scenario. *(See 5.5.3.)*

5.5.2* Evaluation.

Design fire scenarios shall be evaluated using a method acceptable to the authority having jurisdiction and appropriate for the conditions. Each design fire scenario shall be challenging, but realistic, with respect to at least one of the following scenario specifications:

(1) Initial fire location
(2) Early rate of growth in fire severity
(3) Smoke generation

The scenario specifications shall be as challenging as any that could realistically occur in the building.

A.5.5.2 The protection systems and features used to meet the challenge of the design fire scenario should be typical of, and consistent with, those used for other similar areas of the building. They should not be designed to be more effective in the building area addressed than in similar areas not included and that are, therefore, not explicitly evaluated.

Annex entry A.5.5 indicates that 5.5.2 will typically force one or more scenarios to be considered in addition to those specified in 5.5.3.1 through 5.5.3.8. The eight scenarios specified in 5.5.3 are to be considered for all performance-based designs but they do not necessarily represent a comprehensive set of scenarios. There may be additional scenarios truly unique to the proposed facility that need to be analyzed. The intent of including nonspecific scenarios (as opposed to the specific scenarios of 5.5.3) is to capture those scenarios where (see 5.5.2) initial fire location, early rate of growth in fire severity or smoke generation, poses a greater problem than those conditions captured by the scenarios in 5.5.3. However, there are also other conditions that may require development of scenarios—overcrowding of a specific space being just one example. Additional scenarios might also be specified by the authority having jurisdiction to account for an historical, local fire that the authority having jurisdiction is determined not to have happen again.

The following suggests how suitable scenarios may be developed.

Introduction. To provide a comprehensive design (that is, to demonstrate how the fire safety system will respond to a variety of fires), more than one scenario should be considered. It is suggested that, at a minimum, the following three types of scenarios be considered:

(1) High frequency, low consequence (typical)
(2) Low frequency, high consequence (high challenge)
(3) Special problems

Scenario (1) is used to demonstrate that the fire safety system can manage fires that start as relatively small fires but are frequent (for example, waste basket fire). Scenario (2) should present a greater challenge to the fire safety system (for example, fire in an egress path). The intent is to consider a larger fire but not one that is so unrealistically large that it ensures the proposed design (or any other) will not perform adequately. The first two scenario types tacitly assume that the fire safety system will function as designed. However, scenario (3) is included to account for those situations in which some aspect of the fire safety system might be compromised (for example, improperly closed valve on a sprinkler system, detection/alarm system temporarily out of service, multiple ignitions as characteristic of an arson fire, degradation of egress system after an earthquake or other natural disaster). Scenario (3) can also be used to consider the reliability of the fire safety system design.

Exhibit 5.5 provides general scenarios—those that may be experienced by most, if not all, occupancies. Exhibit 5.5 presents examples of typical and high-challenge fires, based on slow, moderate, and fast developing fires that expose people in the room of origin who are not intimate with ignition and when they are not in the room of origin. Exhibit 5.5 also presents examples of special problem fires for these same individuals.

The leftmost column of Exhibit 5.5 indicates a general fire type, characterized by the rate at which a potential fire hazard might develop. Fire development is defined by a heat release rate curve. An additional factor in defining the type of fire is the peak heat release rate, which must be severe enough to challenge the fire safety system but not so severe that no design can effectively reduce the hazards of the postulated fires. The peak heat release rate is a function of the amount of fuel of the first item ignited, if the fire doesn't spread beyond it, or the maximum

| Fire Type | Scenario | |
	Occupant in Room of Fire Origin but Not Intimate	Room of Fire Origin Normally Unoccupied
Slow developing fire	• Cigarette ignition of upholstered furniture • Electrical ignition of small appliance or lighting, or overloaded outlet	• Overloaded or failed wiring igniting switch gear, electrical devices, or insulation, followed by ignition of wooden structural members
Moderate developing fire	• Kitchen/cooking fire • Trash can fire • Open flame ignition of upholstered furniture	• Wildland or exposure fire (e.g., from a neighboring building or parked car) • Lightning-induced ignition of building roof • Laundry room fire
Fast developing fire	• Flammable liquids	• Flammable liquid storage
Shielded from systems, or other problems present	• Fire with impaired "first line of defense" • Shielded flaming fires; limited fuel and larger	• External trash collection or trash chute fire • Flammable liquid storage • Room of fire origin door open • Fire in egress path

Exhibit 5.5 General scenarios.

amount of fuel within the room of origin (that is, room goes to flashover).

Scenario Components. At a minimum a fire scenario consists of the following:

(1) Ignition factors (source, location, and material; other items ignited if applicable)
(2) At least one heat release rate curve (HRRC)
(3) Occupant locations (see 5.4.5.3)
(4) Occupant characteristics (see 5.4.5.2)
(5) Special factors (shielded, systems unreliable, open door)

Ignition Factors. Ignition factors include the source of ignition; the material that is first ignited and, if it is a solid, where it is ignited; and whether other items are also ignited. Ignition factors to consider when constructing these aspects of the scenario are shown in Exhibit 5.6.

Ignition Sources. Ignition sources are of primary interest when considering the frequency of design fires. Possible sources of ignition include the following:

Ignition Source	First Item Ignited	Second Item Ignited
Cigarette	Electrical equipment[1]	Structural assembly[2]
Electrical lighting	Wiring	Library book stack
Incendiary	Seating	Merchandise display
Spontaneous combustion	Sets and decorations	Carpets
Stove/hot plate	Exhibit displays	Curtains
Process inherent[3]	Upholstered furniture	
	Electrical appliance	
	Trash	
	Ordinary combustibles[4]	
	Gas leaks	
	Flammable liquids	
	Mattress	
	Medical equipment	
	Process inherent[3]	

[1]Includes, but is not limited to, dust collectors, uninterruptable power supplies, generators, HVAC equipment, dryers, and freezers.

[2]Consists of exterior/interior wall or ceiling finish, wall studs, ceiling joists, and insulation.

[3]Applies primarily to industrial settings.

[4]Includes mixtures of paper, common plastics, and other materials.

Exhibit 5.6 Ignition factors.

(1) Smoking
(2) Open flame
(3) Electrical source
(4) Incendiary
(5) Hot surface
(6) Spontaneous combustion
(7) Radiant source

Various electrical ignition scenarios are possible and historical data should be consulted to determine which is most appropriate for the scenario and occupancy being considered. In addition to smoking related ignitions and open flames, another example of incendiary ignition might be a "runaway" industrial reaction. Hot surfaces are most often associated with either cooking (stoves, hot plates) or industrial processes (engines, furnaces). Spontaneous combustion is essentially an uncontrolled exothermic chemical reaction, due to either a buildup of flammable vapors (for example, due to improper storage or decomposition) or accidental mixing of reactive chemicals (for example, some cleaning fluids). A common radiant source is a portable heater.

First Item Ignited. The first item ignited is somewhat dependent on the ignition source. For example, an overheated electrical wire is most likely to ignite its own insulation; cooking fires usually ignite items close to the flames, not structural assemblies (for example, wall or ceiling finish materials). The first item ignited is of interest for two reasons. The first is that it may pose either a thermal or a nonthermal hazard by itself (an example is an occupied mattress or the toxic products resulting from its combustion). The second reason is that the first item might ignite a second item that poses an additional or greater hazard. Examples of second items include merchandise, structural assemblies, and carpets capable of releasing toxic combustion products. The second item column of Exhibit 5.6 may not be necessary if the first item ignited presents enough of a hazard by itself. Certain types of upholstered furniture fall into this category because of the toxic combustion products released and a relatively high heat release rate.

Second Item Ignited. Ignition of a second item is important in scenarios involving flashover or where structural stability is an issue. Ignition of a second item should be reflected in the heat release rate curve for the room of origin. Ignition of a second item can have two effects on the room heat release rate curve:

(1) The peak heat release rate might be increased.
(2) The growth phase of the fire might be accelerated.

The possibility of both phenomena occurring might be applicable to certain scenarios (for example, if the second item involves flammable liquids or gases).

Heat Release Rate Curves. Heat release rate curves can be constructed by referring to the *SFPE Handbook of Fire Protection Engineering* and Drysdale's *An Introduction to Fire Dynamics*.

Special Factors. There are several factors not discussed that might be critical to the development of scenarios.

(a) *Ignition Location.* The location of the point of ignition can affect the eventual course and spread of a fire. In some cases, specifying a location also implies additional items in the scenario. For example, a kitchen fire could actually be a cooking fire that involves a burner igniting loose clothing or a grease fire igniting "ordinary" combustibles nearby.

(b) *Fire Spread.* With regard to fire spread, the point of ignition is significant because it might, in part, determine the severity of the fire. An aspect of this issue is the availability of oxygen. If the first item ignited is an upholstered chair, two different scenarios result depending on whether the ignition location is on the outside (for example, by a waste basket fire) or on the inside (for example, a cigarette between a seat cushion and arm of the chair). In the former case a flaming fire is likely to occur, while in the latter, a smoldering fire with copious amounts of products of combustion results. Additionally, the point of origin might be conducive to localized flashover. Localized flashover has been observed in experiments involving bunk beds and desks with enclosed leg wells (modesty panels). These geometries tend to concentrate heat energy such that an intense fire is created in a relatively small area.

(c) *Relative Location.* Relative location is somewhat related to the localized flashover. These fires are characterized by the ignition point being shielded from the fire protection systems. The problem is that the initial fire development is not sensed by the fire detection system and thus the detection response is delayed. This results in a larger fire at the time of detection and a commensurate decrease in the time to evacuate. A common scenario involving shielded fires is a fire in warehouse rack storage.

(d) *Interference with Evacuation.* The loss or degradation of any one egress path can place a significant burden on the fire safety system of a facility. One way that this can occur is to have a fire originate in some aspect of the egress system. There are varying degrees of severity. If more than two exits are available, the loss of one will have a lesser impact than if only one or two exits are available. If a fire originates in a location shared by more than one egress path (for example, where two egress paths merge into a single corridor or a dead-end corridor), the impact is greater than if the fire originates in one of several parallel egress routes.

(e) *Compartmentation Barriers.* This situation involves the fire breaching a barrier or originating in a concealed space or on an exterior surface. When the fire breaches a barrier, the potential for a severe fire increases. The problem with fire originating in a concealed space or an exterior surface is similar to that addressed in item (c), "relative location" (fire shielded from detection or suppression systems).

General Design Scenarios. The general scenarios shown in Exhibit 5.7 are recommended as a starting point since they encompass the issues addressed in earlier commentary. For those instances where Exhibit 5.7 does not apply, a process is provided for customizing the selection of scenario components for site-specific scenarios that address the concepts of these general scenarios.

Development of Scenarios. The following are steps for use in specifying fire scenarios.

(a) Common scenarios can be specified partly through routine statistical analysis of fire experience in similar buildings. An advantage of common or typical scenarios is that they provide a good picture of what the building's performance will usually be if fire occurs. Such scenarios also tend to fit easily within the scope of available fire models and calculation methods. This means the authority having jurisdiction can review the results for these scenarios to obtain a basic sense of the building's level of safety and the appropriateness of the calculations.

(b) High-challenge scenarios are any scenarios that pose unusual fire challenges to the building design. High-challenge scenarios can be developed by refining common scenarios (for example, changing the area of fire origin) to create a greater challenge. Also, high-challenge scenarios can be developed by reducing the challenge in scenarios previously identified as beyond the design expectations (that is, too severe to use as the basis for evaluation).

The following are illustrative techniques for developing high-challenge scenarios from common scenarios.

(a) Change the area of fire origin. Consider an area (for example, bedrooms) where occupants are likely to be particularly vulnerable. Consider an area (for example, concealed spaces, external surfaces) where fire can develop outside the effective range of key fire protection features (for example, detectors, sprinklers). Consider an area (for example, egress corridors) that is critical to occupant movement to safety.

(b) Increase the initial size or speed of the development of the fire. This might be done by adjusting the parameters in a fire growth model (for example, increasing the alpha value in a t-squared modeled fire; reflecting a fast or ultra-fast fire; increasing the peak heat release rate value for the fire) or by increas-

Typical Scenario	High-Challenge Scenario	Special Problem Scenario
Fast growth in room contents	Flammable liquids in means of egress	Ordinary fire in typical unoccupied room with sprinklers or detectors out of commission
Ordinary fire in attic or "challenging" concealed space	Largest room fire, fastest growth consistent with use; worst occupant characteristics	
Ordinary fire in typical occupied room with people not intimate with ignition	Worst flame spread fire, if area critical to egress; or flammable room linings or decorations	
Slow developing fire in typical occupied room with worst case occupant characteristics		

Exhibit 5.7 General design scenarios.

ing the assumed room fuel load or decreasing the space between major combustible items.

(c) Assume common degradations in design assumptions. For example, assume the doors are blocked open, allowing the passage of fire effects to secondary spaces; or assume an unlimited oxygen supply for fire growth that could result from open doors, broken windows, or other circumstances.

(d) Increase the toxicity or yields of products of combustion.

Developing high-challenge scenarios from scenarios beyond design expectations involves less challenging quantitative assumptions. For example, if the bomb used in the New York City World Trade Center incident of 1993 is deemed too severe for a high-rise office building, how small a bomb would constitute an appropriate high-challenge test? Or, if the *Code* cannot assure protection of occupants who are intimate with initial fire development, how close can occupants be and not be considered intimate?

5.5.3* Required Design Fire Scenarios.

Scenarios selected as design fire scenarios shall include, but shall not be limited to, those specified in 5.5.3.1 through 5.5.3.8.

Exception: Design fire scenarios demonstrated by the design team to the satisfaction of the authority having jurisdiction as inappropriate for the building use and conditions shall not be required to be evaluated fully.

Example: Exception to Required Design Fire Scenarios

One or more of the required scenarios might not be applicable. For instance, if the designer is analyzing a building that serves primarily as a warehouse but also has limited office space, and that building does not have any concealed wall or ceiling spaces, then design fire scenario 4 might not be applicable.

Another example of a situation in which one of the required scenarios might not apply to a particular design is a building isolated from any possible exposure to outside fire sources, which eliminates the need to evaluate the building using design fire scenario 7. The possible ignition or fuel sources for an exposure fire might include trees or vegetation, cars, delivery trucks, or dumpsters. If the designer can show the authority having jurisdiction that the build-

ing is designed such that there would be no vegetation around the perimeter, no personnel or delivery vehicles could park next to or even within a certain distance of the building, and no man-made flammable objects would be placed around the perimeter of the building, then this scenario might not be applicable.

Each of the theoretical examples would be very rare, and justifying the inappropriateness of any of the scenarios can be very difficult for the designer. The majority of buildings to which one or more of the required scenarios do not apply will generally be a very specialized case, such as an aircraft hangar with no concealed spaces or a research lab with no external fuel sources that could lead to an exposure fire. If the designer believes that one or more of the scenarios do not apply to the building in question, the designer should consult the authority having jurisdiction early in the evaluation process and provide written justification on why these do not apply.

A.5.5.3 It is desirable to consider a wide variety of different fire scenarios to evaluate the complete life safety capabilities of the building or structure. Fire scenarios should not be limited to a single or a couple of worst case fire scenarios.

The descriptive terms used to indicate the rate of fire growth for the scenarios are intended to be generic. Use of t-squared fires is not required for any scenario.

5.5.3.1* Design Fire Scenario 1. Design fire scenario 1 is an occupancy-specific design fire scenario representative of a typical fire for the occupancy. This design fire scenario shall explicitly account for the following:

(1) Occupant activities
(2) Number and location
(3) Room size
(4) Furnishings and contents
(5) Fuel properties and ignition sources
(6) Ventilation conditions

The first item ignited and its location shall be explicitly defined.

A.5.5.3.1 Scenario 1. An example of such a scenario for a health care occupancy would involve a patient room with two occupied beds with a fire initially involving one bed and the room door open. This is a cursory example in that much of the explicitly required information indicated in 5.5.3.1 can be determined from the information provided in the example. Note that it is usually necessary to consider more than one scenario to capture the features and conditions typical of an occupancy.

The idea behind design fire scenario 1 is to ensure that the fires that a given occupancy type is likely to encounter most often are considered in the design analysis. These fire scenarios can also be considered to be the statistically most significant scenarios—those that happen most often in the type of facility being designed. These scenarios have a great degree of variety, from the small fires experienced weekly at aluminum rolling mills to the kitchen fires in high-rise apartment buildings (i.e., residences).

5.5.3.2* Design Fire Scenario 2. Design fire scenario 2 is an ultrafast-developing fire, in the primary means of egress, with interior doors open at the start of the fire. This design fire scenario shall address the concern regarding a reduction in the number of available means of egress.

A.5.5.3.2 Scenario 2. Examples of such scenarios are a fire involving ignition of gasoline as an accelerant in a means of egress, clothing racks in corridors, renovation materials, or other fuel configurations that can cause an ultrafast fire. The means of egress chosen is the doorway with the largest egress capacity among doorways normally used in the ordinary operation of the building. The baseline occupant characteristics for the property are assumed. At ignition, doors are assumed to be open throughout the building.

Design fire scenario 2 is intended to provide information on the maximum potential spread of fire effects, mostly smoke and toxic products. It answers the question, "What is the maximum extent of smoke that may be experienced if an egress path is blocked?"

5.5.3.3* Design Fire Scenario 3. Design fire scenario 3 is a fire that starts in a normally unoccupied room that can potentially endanger a large number of occupants in a large room or other area. This design fire scenario shall address the concern regarding a fire starting in a normally unoccupied room and migrating into the space that can, potentially, hold the greatest number of occupants in the building.

A.5.5.3.3 Scenario 3. An example of such a scenario is a fire in a storage room adjacent to the largest occupiable room in the building. The contents of the room of fire origin are specified to provide the largest fuel load and the most rapid growth in fire severity consistent with the normal use of the room. The adjacent occupiable room is assumed to be filled to capacity with occupants. Occupants are assumed to be somewhat impaired in whatever form is most consistent with the intended use of the building. At ignition, doors from both rooms are assumed to be open. Depending on the

design, doorways connect the two rooms or they connect via a common hallway or corridor.

For purposes of this scenario, an occupiable room is a room that might contain people, that is, a location within a building where people are typically found.

5.5.3.4* Design Fire Scenario 4. Design fire scenario 4 is a fire that originates in a concealed wall- or ceiling-space adjacent to a large occupied room. This design fire scenario shall address the concern regarding a fire originating in a concealed space that does not have either a detection system or suppression system and then spreading into the room within the building that can, potentially, hold the greatest number of occupants.

A.5.5.3.4 Scenario 4. An example of such a scenario is a fire originating in a concealed wall- or ceiling-space adjacent to a large, occupied function room. Ignition involves concealed combustibles, including wire or cable insulation and thermal or acoustical insulation. The adjacent function room is assumed to be occupied to capacity. The baseline occupant characteristics for the property are assumed. At ignition, doors are assumed to be open throughout the building.

5.5.3.5* Design Fire Scenario 5. Design fire scenario 5 is a slowly developing fire, shielded from fire protection systems, in close proximity to a high occupancy area. This design fire scenario shall address the concern regarding a relatively small ignition source causing a significant fire.

A.5.5.3.5 Scenario 5. An example of such a scenario is a cigarette fire in a trash can. The trash can is close enough to room contents to ignite more substantial fuel sources but is not close enough to any occupant to create an intimate-with-ignition situation. If the intended use of the property involves the potential for some occupants to be incapable of movement at any time, then the room of origin is chosen as the type of room likely to have such occupants, filled to capacity with occupants in that condition. If the intended use of the property does not involve the potential for some occupants to be incapable of movement, then the room of origin is chosen to be an assembly or function area characteristic of the use of the property, and the trash can is placed so that it is shielded by furniture from suppression systems. At ignition, doors are assumed to be open throughout the building.

5.5.3.6* Design Fire Scenario 6. Design fire scenario 6 is the most severe fire resulting from the largest possible fuel load characteristic of the normal operation of the building. This design fire scenario shall address the concern regarding a rapidly developing fire with occupants present.

A.5.5.3.6 Scenario 6. An example of such a scenario is a fire originating in the largest fuel load of combustibles possible in normal operation in a function or assembly room, or in a process/manufacturing area, characteristic of the normal operation of the property. The configuration, type, and geometry of the combustibles are chosen so as to produce the most rapid and severe fire growth or smoke generation consistent with the normal operation of the property. The baseline occupant characteristics for the property are assumed. At ignition, doors are assumed to be closed throughout the building.

This scenario includes everything from a big couch fire in a small dwelling to a rack fire in combustible liquids stock in a big box retail store.

> The Dupont Plaza Hotel fire of 1986 in San Juan, Puerto Rico, is an example of a design fire scenario 6. The storage of chairs was part of the normal operating procedures of the hotel. Their location and potential heat release of the chairs were evidently considered a small threat due to the lack of an ignition source. Unfortunately, a source was supplied with tragic results.

5.5.3.7* Design Fire Scenario 7. Design fire scenario 7 is an outside exposure fire. This design fire scenario shall address the concern regarding a fire starting at a location remote from the area of concern and either spreading into the area, blocking escape from the area, or developing untenable conditions within the area.

A.5.5.3.7 Scenario 7. An example of such a scenario is an exposure fire. The initiating fire is the closest and most severe fire possible consistent with the placement and type of adjacent properties and the placement of plants and combustible adornments on the property. The baseline occupant characteristics for the property are assumed.

This category includes wildlands/urban interface fires and exterior wood shingle problems, where applicable.

5.5.3.8* Design Fire Scenario 8. Design fire scenario 8 is a fire originating in ordinary combustibles in a room or area with each passive or active fire protection system independently rendered ineffective. This set of design fire scenarios shall address concern regarding each fire protection system or fire protection feature, considered individually, being unreliable or becoming unavailable.

A.5.5.3.8 Scenario 8. This scenario addresses a set of conditions with a typical fire originating in the building with any one passive or active fire protection system or feature being ineffective. Examples include unprotected openings between floors or between fire walls or fire barrier walls, rated fire doors fail to close automatically or are blocked open, sprinkler system water supply shut off, fire alarm system nonoperative, smoke management system not opera-

tional, or automatic smoke dampers blocked open. This scenario should represent a reasonable challenge to the other building features provided by the design and presumed to be available.

The concept of a fire originating in ordinary combustibles is intentionally selected for this scenario. This fire, although presenting a realistic challenge to the building and the associated building systems, does not represent the worst case scenario or the most challenging fire for the building. Examples include the following:

(a) A fire originating in ordinary combustibles in the corridor of a patient wing of a hospital. Staff is assumed not to close any patient room doors upon detection of fire. The baseline occupant characteristics for the property are assumed, and the patient rooms off the corridor are assumed to be filled to capacity. At ignition, doors to patient rooms are not equipped with self-closing devices and are assumed to be open throughout the smoke compartment.

(b) A fire originating in ordinary combustibles in a large assembly room or area in the interior of the building. The automatic suppression systems are assumed to be out of operation. The baseline occupant characteristics for the property are assumed, and the room of origin is assumed to be filled to capacity. At ignition, doors are assumed to be closed throughout the building.

(c) A fire originating in ordinary combustibles in an unoccupied small function room adjacent to a large assembly room or area in the interior of the building. The automatic detection systems are assumed to be out of operation. The baseline occupant characteristics for the property are assumed, the room of origin is assumed to be unoccupied, and the assembly room is assumed to be filled to capacity. At ignition, doors are assumed to be closed throughout the building.

Exception*: This scenario shall not be required to be applied to fire protection systems for which both the level of reliability and the design performance in the absence of the system are acceptable to the authority having jurisdiction.

A.5.5.3.8 Exception The exception is applied to each active or passive fire protection system individually and requires two different types of information to be developed by analysis and approved by the authority having jurisdiction. System reliability is to be analyzed and accepted. Design performance in the absence of the system is also to be analyzed and accepted, but acceptable performance does not require fully meeting the stated goals and objectives. It might not be possible to meet fully the goals and objectives if a key system is unavailable, and yet no system is totally reliable. The authority having jurisdiction will determine which level of performance, possibly short of the stated goals and objectives, is acceptable, given the very low probability (that is, the system's unreliability probability) that the system will not be available.

The design fire scenario 8 provides information to the authority having jurisdiction by answering a series of "What if?" questions. For example, what if the hotel sprinkler system is out of service when a fire occurs? What might be the extent of the fire and smoke and their subsequent effects on the egress system? Similar questions can be posed for other fire protection system components and subsystems.

5.5.4 Design Fire Scenarios Data.

5.5.4.1 Each design fire scenario used in the performance-based design proposal shall be translated into input data specifications, as appropriate for the calculation method or model.

5.5.4.2 Any design fire scenario specifications that the design analyses do not explicitly address or incorporate and that are, therefore, omitted from input data specifications shall be identified, and a sensitivity analysis of the consequences of that omission shall be performed.

Paragraph 5.5.4.2 is included to remind the designer that even if every design fire specification cannot be incorporated into a specific design tool or verification method, each must be addressed in the analysis in some manner. An example of cases where design fire specifications could not be incorporated into a specific design analysis would result from the use of an evacuation model that does not address crowding or queuing effects. This model does not address the particular delay hazard initiated by design fire scenario 2, which reduces the means of egress from the building. Additionally, many fire effects models do not address barrier breach, which fail to address or incorporate the defining characteristics of design fire scenario 4, a concealed space fire threatening an adjacent, occupied space.

Despite the fact that these models do not incorporate particular aspects of the design fire scenario specifications, these aspects must be addressed in the design, either through conservative assumptions supported by accepted technical resources or test data or by comparative techniques that will conservatively account for these effects. A sensitivity analysis should be performed on the omission of these aspects, as well as the techniques used to account for these omissions.

5.5.4.3 Any design fire scenario specifications modified in input data specifications, because of limitations in test methods or other data generation procedures, shall be identified, and a sensitivity analysis of the consequences of the modification shall be performed.

Paragraph 5.5.4.3 essentially expresses the same concern as in 5.5.4.2; however, the concern arises more from a limitation in available data than from a limitation of the model. Typically, both types of limitations will be present. When analyzing design fire scenario 2, there may not be a model available that accounts for crowding or queuing, or there may be only a model that assumes uniform speeds and sizes of occupants due to lack of data on expected ranges of occupant characteristics. These effects will tend to produce results for an estimated speed of evacuation, in the absence of turbulence, that are unrealistically fast. Additionally, in design fire scenario 4 there may be no model to determine time to barrier breach, and insufficient data on burn-through or failure behavior of the materials and assemblies proposed in the design.

Section 5.6* Evaluation of Proposed Designs

A.5.6 The *SFPE Engineering Guide to Performance-Based Fire Protection Analysis and Design of Buildings* outlines a process for evaluating whether trial designs meet the performance criteria during the design fire scenarios.

The procedures described in Sections 5.2 and 5.4 identify required design fire scenarios among the design fire scenarios within which a proposed fire safety design is required to perform and the associated untenable conditions that are to be avoided in order to maintain life safety. Section 5.6 discusses methods that form the link from the scenarios and criteria to the goals and objectives.

Assessment methods are used to demonstrate that the proposed design will achieve the stated goals/objectives, by providing information indicating that the performance criteria of Section 5.2 can be adequately met. Assessment methods are permitted to be either tests or modeling.

Tests. Test results can be directly used to assess a fire safety design when they accurately represent the scenarios developed by using Section 5.4 and provide output data matching the performance criteria in Section 5.2. Since the performance criteria for this *Code* are stated in terms of human exposure to lethal fire effects, no test will suffice. However, tests will be needed to produce data for use in models and other calculation methods.

Standardized Tests. Standardized tests are conducted on various systems and components to determine whether they meet some predetermined, typically prescriptive criteria. Results are given on a pass/fail basis: the test specimen either does or does not meet the pre-established criteria. The actual performance of the test specimen is not usually recorded.

Scale. Tests can be either small, intermediate, or full scale. Small-scale tests are used to test activation of detection and suppression devices and the flammability and toxicity of materials. Usually, the item to be tested is placed within the testing device or apparatus. Intermediate-scale tests can be used to determine the adequacy of system components, for example, doors and windows, as opposed to entire systems. The difference between small- and intermediate-scale tests is usually one of definition provided by those conducting the test. Full-scale tests are typically used to test building and structural components or entire systems. The difference between intermediate- and large-scale tests is also subject to the definition of those performing the test. Full-scale tests are intended to most closely depict performance of the test subject as installed in the field, that is, most closely represent real world performance.

Full-scale building evacuations can provide information on how the evacuation of a structure is likely to occur for an existing building with a given population without subjecting occupants to the real physical or psychological effects of a fire.

Data Uses. The data obtained from standardized tests have three uses for verification purposes. The test results can be used instead of a model. This use is typically the role of full-scale test results. The test results can be used as a basis for validating the model. The model predictions match well with the test results. Therefore, the model can be used in situations similar to the test scenario. The test results can be used as input to models. This is typically the use of small-scale tests, specifically flammability tests.

Start-Up Test. Start-up test results can be used to demonstrate that the fire safety system performs as designed. The system design might be based on modeling. If the start-up test indicates a deficiency, then the system needs to be adjusted and retested until it can be demonstrated that the design can meet the performance criteria. Typically, start-up tests apply only to the installation to which they are designed.

Experimental Data. Experimental data from nonstandardized tests can be used when the specified scenario and the experimental setup are similar. Typically, experimental data are applicable to a greater variety of scenarios than are standardized test results.

Human and Organizational Performance Tests. Certain tests determine whether inputs used to determine human performance criteria remain valid during the occupancy of a building. Tests of human and organizational performance might include any of the following:

(1) Evacuation times measured during fire drills
(2) Querying emergency response team members to determine whether they know required procedures
(3) Field tests to ensure that emergency response team members can execute tasks within predetermined times and accuracy limits.

Design proposals should include descriptions of any tests that are needed to determine whether stated goals, objectives and performance criteria are being met.

Modeling. Models can be used to predict the performance criteria for a given scenario. Because of the limitations on use of tests alone for this purpose, models are expected to be used in most, if not all, performance-based design assessments.

Fire models do not model fires, they model the effects of a (user) specified fire, that is, a heat release rate curve is input. For ease, the term fire model will be used instead of the more accurate fire effects model.

The effect of fire and its toxic products on the occupants can be modeled, as can the movement and behavior of occupants during the fire. The term evacuation model will be used to describe models that predict the location and movements of occupants, and the term tenability model will be used to describe models that predict the effects on occupants of specified levels of exposure to fire effects.

Types of Fire Models. Fire models will be used to predict fire-related performance criteria. Fire models can be either probabilistic or deterministic. Several types of deterministic models are available: computational fluid dynamics (CFD or field) models, zone models, purpose-built models, and hand calculations. Probabilistic fire models are also available, but are less likely to be used for this purpose.

Probabilistic fire models use the probabilities as well as the severity of various events as the basis of evaluation. Some probabilistic models incorporate deterministic models, but this is not a requirement. Probabilistic models attempt to predict the likelihood or probability that events or severity associated with an unwanted fire will occur or the "expected" loss, which can be thought of as the probability-weighted average severity across all possible scenarios. Probabilistic models can be manifested as fault or event trees or other system models that use frequency or probability data as input. These models tend to be manifested as computer software, but this is not a requirement. Furthermore, the discussion that follows under "Sources of Models" can also be applied to probabilistic models, although it concentrates on deterministic models.

CFD models provide the most accurate predictions of all the deterministic models, because they divide a given space into thousands of smaller volumes. However, since they are still models, they are not absolute in their depiction of reality. In addition, they are much more expensive to use because they are computationally intensive. Because of their expense, complexity, and intensive computational needs, CFD models require much greater scrutiny than do zone models. It is much more difficult to provide multiple runs of CFD models to check sensitivity to a variety of factors such as design fire cell resolution and ventilation.

Zone models are more widely used than CFD models because they provide reasonably accurate predictions in much less time. It is much easier to assess the sensitivity of different parameters with zone models because they generally run much faster and the output is much easier to interpret. Prediction of fire growth and spread has a large number of variables associated with it. Consequently, the zone models with their crudeness and speed have advantages over the more complex CFD models.

Purpose-built models (also known as stand-alone models) are similar to zone models in their ease of use. However, purpose-built models do not provide a comprehensive model. Instead, they predict the value of one variable of interest. For example, such a model can predict the conditions of a ceiling jet at a specified location under a ceiling, but a zone model would "transport" those conditions throughout the enclosure.

Purpose-built models might or might not be manifested as computer software. Models that are not are referred to as hand calculations. These purpose-built models are, therefore, simple enough that the data management capabilities of a computer are not necessary. Many of these calculations are found in the *SFPE Handbook of Fire Protection Engineering*.

Types of Evacuation Models. There are three categories of evacuation models that can be considered: single-parameter estimation methods, movement models, and behavioral simulation models.

Single-parameter estimations are generally used for simple estimates of movement time. They are usually based on equations derived from observations of movement in nonemergency situations. They can be hand calculations or simple computer models. Examples include calculation methods for flow times based on widths of exit paths and travel times based on travel distances. Sources for these methods include the *SFPE Handbook of Fire Protection Engineering* and the NFPA *Fire Protection Handbook*.

Movement models generally handle large numbers of people in a network flow similar to water in pipes or ball bearings in chutes. They tend to optimize occupant behavior, resulting in predicted evacuation times that can be unrealistic and far from conservative. However, they can be useful in an overall assessment of a design, especially in early evaluation stages where an unacceptable result with this sort of model indicates that the design has failed to achieve the life safety objectives.

Behavioral simulation models take into consideration more of the variables related to occupant movement and behavior. Occupants are treated as individuals and can have

characteristics assigned to them uniquely, allowing a more realistic simulation of the design under consideration. However, given the limited availability of data for the development of these models, for their verification by their authors, or for input when using them, their predictive reliability is questionable.

Tenability Models. In general, tenability models will be needed only to automate calculations for the time-of-exposure effect equations referenced in A.5.2.2.

Other Models. Models can be used to describe combustion (as noted, most fire models only characterize fire effects), automatic system performance, and other elements of the calculation. There are few models in common use for these purposes, so they are not described further here.

Sources of Models. Compendia of computer fire models are found in Friedman's *Survey of Computer Models for Fire and Smoke* and the *SFPE Computer Software Directory*. Within these references are models that were developed by the Building Fire Research Laboratory of National Institute of Standards and Technology, which can be downloaded from the Internet at http://www.bfrl.nist.gov/864/fmabs.html. Evacuation models in all three categories are discussed in the *SFPE Handbook of Fire Protection Engineering* and the NFPA *Fire Protection Handbook*.

Validation. Models undergo limited validation. Most can be considered demonstrated only for the experimental results they were based on or the limited set of scenarios to which the model developers compared the model's output, or a combination of both.

The Society of Fire Protection Engineers has a task group that independently evaluates computer models. As of January 1998, they are preparing to finish their first evaluation and have chosen a second model to evaluate. Until more models can be independently evaluated, the model user has to rely on the available documentation and previous experience for guidance regarding the appropriate use of a given model.

The design professional should present and the authority having jurisdiction, when deciding whether to approve a proposal, should consider the strength of the evidence presented for the validity, accuracy, relevance, and precision of the proposed methods. An element in establishing the strength of scientific evidence is the extent of external review and acceptance of the evidence by peers of the authors of that evidence.

Models have limitations. Most are not user-friendly. For that reason, experienced users will be able to construct more reasonable models and better interpret output than novices. It is for these reasons that the third-party review and equivalency sections are provided. This is not meant to discourage the use of models, only to indicate that they should be used with caution by those well-versed in their nuances.

Input Data. The first step in using a model is to develop the input data. The heat release rate curve specified by the user is the driving force of a fire effects model. If this curve is incorrectly defined, the subsequent results are not usable. In addition to the smoldering and growth phases that will be specified as part of the scenario definition, two additional phases are needed to complete the input heat release rate curve—steady burning and burnout.

Steady burning is characterized by its duration, which is a function of the total amount of fuel available to be burned. In determining the duration of this phase, the designer needs to consider how much fuel has been assumed to be consumed in the smoldering and growth phases and how much is assumed to be consumed in the burnout phase that follows. A common assumption is that the burnout phase is the mirror image of the preceding phases, with a reversed heat release rate curve and the same amount of fuel consumed in the burnout phase as in the growth phase. Depending on the assumptions made regarding the amount of fuel consumed during burnout, the time at which this phase starts is likely to be easy to determine.

The above discussion assumes that the burning objects are solid (for example, tables and chairs). If liquid or gaseous fuels are involved, then the shape of the curve will be different. For example, smoldering is not relevant for burning liquids or gases, and the growth period is very short, typically measured in seconds. Peak heat release rate can depend primarily on the rate of release, on the leak rate (gases and liquid sprays), or on the extent of spill (pooled liquids). The steady burning phase is once again dependent upon the amount of fuel available to burn. Like the growth phase, the burnout phase is typically short (for example, closing a valve), although it is conceivable that longer times might be appropriate, depending on the extinguishment scenario.

Material properties are usually needed for all fuel items, both initial and secondary, and the enclosure surfaces of involved rooms or spaces.

For all fires of consequence, it is reasonable to assume that the fire receives adequate ventilation. If there is insufficient oxygen, the fire will not be sustained. An overabundance of oxygen is only a concern in special cases (for example, hermetically sealed spaces) when a fire might not occur due to dilution of the fuel (that is, a flammable mixture is not produced). Therefore, given that the scenarios of interest will occur in nonhermetically sealed enclosures, it is reasonable to assume that adequate ventilation is available and that, if a fire starts, it will continue to burn until it either runs out of fuel or is extinguished by other means. The only variable that might need to be assumed is the total vent width.

Maximum fire extent is affected by two geometric aspects: burning object proximity to walls and overall enclosure dimensions.

Conservatively, when a fire is "against a wall" or "in a corner," the effective heat release of the fire can be doubled and quadrupled, respectively. In order for the burning object

to be considered against the wall or in the corner, it needs to be either touching the enclosure surface or within 2 in. (about 5 cm) of the surface. The reasoning behind this convention is that a wall effectively cuts the fire plume in half, while a corner results in one quarter of the plume if the burning object is closer to the center of the room. Conceptually, the same amount of combustible vapors are produced, regardless of the burning object's position, but the presence of walls/corners results in a smaller volume in which to burn them. In other words, walls and corners effectively concentrate the flammable vapors resulting from pyrolysis of the fuel.

The room dimensions affect the time required for a room to flashover. For a given amount and type of fuel, under the same ventilation conditions, a small room will flashover before a large room. In a large room with a small amount of fuel, a fire will behave as if it is burning outside, that is, adequate oxygen for burning and no concentration of heat exist. If the fuel package is unchanged but the dimensions of the room are decreased, then the room will begin to have an affect on the fire, assuming adequate ventilation. The presence of the relatively smaller enclosure results in the buildup of a hot layer of smoke and other products of combustion under the ceiling. This buildup, in turn, feeds more heat back to the seat of the fire, which results in an increase in the pyrolysis rate of the fuel and thus increases the amount of heat energy released by the fire. The room enclosure surfaces themselves also contribute to this radiation feedback effect.

Probabilistic data is expressed as either a frequency (units of inverse time) or a probability (unitless but applicable to a stated period of time). An example of the former is the expected number of failures per year and the range of the latter is between zero and one, inclusive. Probabilities can be either objective or subjective. Subjective probabilities express a degree of belief that an event will occur. Objective probabilities are based on historical data and can be expressed as a reliability of an item such as a component or a system.

5.6.1 General.

A proposed design's performance shall be assessed relative to each performance objective in Section 4.2 and each applicable scenario in 5.5.3, with the assessment conducted through the use of appropriate calculation methods. The authority having jurisdiction shall approve the choice of assessment methods.

The verification process starts with the submittal of a proposed design to the AHJ. If the AHJ does not consider itself qualified to perform an adequate review of the performance-based design, the AHJ might specify a qualified third party reviewer. The expense associated with the third-party review process is typically incurred by the owner.

The first step of the process is to identify the goals, and the objectives relating to those goals. Attention must be paid to objectives that apply to the facility as a whole and those that apply to only limited aspects of the facility. The authority having jurisdiction's purpose in this review is to determine whether the designer/owner's objectives are commensurate with society's objectives. Next, the AHJ reviews the performance criteria that relate to each of the objectives, for consistency and reasonableness—do they form a comprehensive package and are they realistic? The next step involves the characteristics of whatever is being protected—people, property, and so on. Once again, a comprehensive, cohesive set of assumptions is sought.

Essentially, this means that the logic flow and justification for the choices made are sound. Check the links between each of the components to ensure that the design process flows—objectives are to be met by demonstrating that criteria have been achieved through the judicious use of verification methods. Assumptions need to be reasonable, consistent, comprehensive, cohesive, and supported by adequate references.

Since the designer has submitted a design proposal, it seems safe to assume that the designer's proposal "ensures" that all criteria are met for all scenarios. Ultimately, the authority having jurisdiction is interested in determining whether a credible job was done by the designer so that the predicted results provide a sufficient margin of safety to permit the design to be approved. Because of the complexity of this issue, many discussions can be anticipated between the authority having jurisdiction, the designer, and, if used, the third-party reviewer.

5.6.2 Use.

The design professional shall use the assessment methods to demonstrate that the proposed design will achieve the goals and objectives, as measured by the performance criteria in light of the safety margins and uncertainty analysis, for each scenario, given the assumptions.

The choice of which model to select depends on the objectives, the performance criteria to be predicted, and the scenarios to be considered. The model selected should use most, if not all, of the input data specifications and must produce design output that

can be directly compared to the performance criteria selected as a baseline for the analysis. Two criteria are usually of the most interest: upper layer temperature and the height of the smoke layer interface. If the objective is to reduce property damage in a telephone vault, then a purpose-built model that predicts smoke filling is adequate. If the objective is the life safety of those not intimate with the fire—both within the room of origin and adjacent egress paths—in a rectilinear room, then a zone model is adequate. If life safety is the objective and the fire occurs in a more geometrically challenging configuration (for example, amusement park fun house or enclosed amusement ride), then a field model is appropriate. If the effects on occupants are to be estimated, an evacuation or toxicity model needs to be used.

5.6.3 Input Data.

5.6.3.1 Data. Input data for computer fire models shall be obtained in accordance with ASTM E 1591, *Standard Guide for Data for Fire Models.* Data for use in analytical models that are not computer-based fire models shall be obtained using appropriate measurement, recording, and storage techniques to ensure the applicability of the data to the analytical method being used.

5.6.3.2 Data Requirements. A complete listing of input data requirements for all models, engineering methods, and other calculation or verification methods required or proposed as part of the performance-based design shall be provided.

Documentation of the assumptions made by the model user while developing the input data is critical. If the model user does not explicitly state the values used and the references from which they are taken, the credibility of the analysis is decreased.

5.6.3.3* Uncertainty and Conservatism of Data. Uncertainty in input data shall be analyzed and, as determined appropriate by the authority having jurisdiction, addressed through the use of conservative values.

A.5.6.3.3 Procedures used to develop required input data need to preserve the intended conservatism of all scenarios and assumptions. Conservatism is only one means to address the uncertainty inherent in calculations and does not remove the need to consider safety factors, sensitivity analysis, and other methods of dealing with uncertainty. The *SFPE Engineering Guide to Performance-Based Fire Protection Analysis and Design of Buildings* outlines a process for identifying and treating uncertainty.

5.6.4* Output Data.

The assessment methods used shall accurately and appropriately produce the required output data from input data based on the design specifications, assumptions, and scenarios.

A.5.6.4 An assessment method translates input data, which might include test specifications, parameters or variables for modeling, or other data, into output data, which are measured against the performance criteria. Computer fire models should be evaluated for their predictive capability in accordance with ASTM E 1355, *Standard Guide for Evaluating the Predictive Capability of Fire Models.*

The design team is to select verification methods that produce output data that can be directly compared to the performance criteria. Any additional output data needs to be included with the analysis results and submitted to the authority having jurisdiction for review.

5.6.5 Validity.

Evidence shall be provided to confirm that the assessment methods are valid and appropriate for the proposed building, use, and conditions.

If the chosen assessment method is a computer model, then the validity of the model, with regard to the scenario being modeled, might be in question. By choosing a particular model, the designer is tacitly assuming that the model is valid for the particular scenario. Two situations are possible: Either the assumption is correct (and there's nothing to worry about) or the assumption is not correct. If the assumption is not correct, this does not immediately invalidate the entire analysis. Part of the argument for using a particular model is that it is the only tool available (that is, constrained by available resources) that can be used. If a sensitivity analysis is also performed, this will go a long way in demonstrating that a range of conditions have been considered and the "real" answer has been adequately bounded by the results of the sensitivity analysis.

Section 5.7 Safety Factors

5.7.1* General.

Approved safety factors shall be included in the design methods and calculations to reflect uncertainty in the assumptions,

data, and other factors associated with the performance-based design.

A.5.7.1 The assessment of precision required in 5.8.2 will require a sensitivity and uncertainty analysis, which can be translated into safety factors.

Sensitivity Analysis. The first run a model user makes should be labeled as the base case, using the nominal values of the various input parameters. However, the model user should not rely on a single run as the basis for any performance-based fire safety system design. Ideally, each variable or parameter that the model user made to develop the nominal input data should have multiple runs associated with it, as should combinations of key variables and parameters. Thus, a sensitivity analysis should be conducted that provides the model user with data that indicates how the effects of a real fire might vary and how the response of the proposed fire safety design might also vary.

The interpretation of a model's predictions can be a difficult exercise if the model user does not have knowledge of fire dynamics or human behavior.

In addition to justification of the base case input data specification values, the design team should include an allowable range of values determined using a sensitivity analysis. The design team should investigate the effects of varying key components and variables independently—and in combination—and should document the effects of this variation.

Reasonableness Check. The model user should first try to determine whether the predictions actually make sense, that is, they don't upset intuition or preconceived expectations. Most likely, if the results don't pass this test, an input error has been committed.

Sometimes the predictions appear to be reasonable but are, in fact, incorrect. For example, a model can predict higher temperatures farther from the fire than close to it. The values themselves might be reasonable, for example, they are not hotter than the fire, but they don't "flow" down the energy as expected.

A margin of safety can be developed using the results of the sensitivity analysis in conjunction with the performance criteria to provide the possible range of time during which a condition is estimated to occur.

Safety factors and margin of safety are two concepts used to quantify the amount of uncertainty in engineering analyses. Safety factors are used to provide a margin of safety and represent, or address, the gap in knowledge between the theoretically perfect model, that is, reality and the engineering models that can only partially represent reality.

Safety factors can be applied to either the predicted level of a physical condition or to the time at which the condition is predicted to occur. Thus, a physical or a temporal safety factor, or both, can be applied to any predicted condition. A predicted condition (that is, a parameter's value) and the time at which it occurs are best represented as distributions. Ideally, a computer fire model predicts the expected or nominal value of the distribution. Safety factors are intended to represent the spread of these distributions.

Given the uncertainty associated with data acquisition and reduction, and the limitations of computer modeling, any condition predicted by a computer model can be thought of as an expected or nominal value within a broader range. For example, an upper layer temperature of 600°C is predicted at a given time. If the modeled scenario is then tested (that is, full-scale experiment based on the computer model's input data), the actual temperature at that given time could be 640°C or 585°C. Therefore, the temperature should be reported as 600°C +40°C, −15°C or a range of 585°C to 640°C.

Ideally, predictions are reported as a nominal value, a percentage, or an absolute value. As an example, an upper layer temperature prediction could be reported as "600°C, 30°C" or "600°C, 5 percent." In this case, the physical safety factor is 0.05 (that is, the amount by which the nominal value should be degraded and enhanced). Given the state-of-the-art of computer fire modeling, this is a very low safety factor. Physical safety factors tend to be on the order of tens of percent. A safety factor of 50 percent is not unheard of.

Part of the problem in establishing safety factors is that it is difficult to state the percentage or range that is appropriate. These values can be obtained when the computer model predictions are compared to test data. However, using computer fire models in a design mode does not facilitate this since (1) the room being analyzed has not been built yet and (2) test scenarios do not necessarily depict the intended design.

A sensitivity analysis should be performed based on the assumptions that affect the condition of interest. A base case that uses all nominal values for input parameters should be developed. The input parameters should be varied over reasonable ranges and the variation in predicted output should be noted. This output variation can then become the basis for physical safety factors.

The temporal safety factor addresses the issue of when a condition is predicted and is a function of the rate at which processes are expected to occur. If a condition is predicted to occur 2 minutes after the start of the fire, then this can be used as a nominal value. A process similar to that described above for physical safety factors can also be employed to develop temporal safety factors. In this case, however, the rates (for example, of heat release and toxic product generation) will be varied instead of absolute values (for example, material properties).

The margin of safety can be thought of as a reflection of societal values and can be imposed by the authority having

jurisdiction for that purpose. Since the time for which a condition is predicted will most likely be the focus of the authority having jurisdiction (for example, the model predicts occupants will have 5 minutes to safely evacuate), the margin of safety will be characterized by temporal aspects and tacitly applied to the physical margin of safety.

Escaping the harmful effects of fire (or mitigating them) is, effectively, a race against time. When assessing fire safety system designs based on computer model predictions, the choice of an acceptable time is important. When an authority having jurisdiction is faced with the predicted time of untenability, a decision needs to be made regarding whether sufficient time is available to ensure the safety of building occupants. The authority having jurisdiction is assessing the margin of safety. Is there sufficient time to get everyone out safely? If the authority having jurisdiction feels that the predicted egress time is too close to the time of untenability, then the authority having jurisdiction can impose an additional time that the designer will have to incorporate into the system design. In other words, the authority having jurisdiction can impose a greater margin of safety than that originally proposed by the designer.

Section 5.8 Documentation Requirements

5.8.1* General.

All aspects of the design, including those described in 5.8.2 through 5.8.14, shall be documented. The format and content of the documentation shall be acceptable to the authority having jurisdiction.

A.5.8.1 The *SFPE Engineering Guide to Performance-Based Fire Protection Analysis and Design of Buildings* describes the documentation that should be provided for a performance-based design.

Proper documentation of a performance design is critical to the design acceptance and construction. Proper documentation will also ensure that all parties involved understand what is necessary for the design implementation, maintenance, and continuity of the fire protection design. If attention to details is maintained in the documentation, then there should be little dispute during approval, construction, start-up, and use.

Poor documentation could result in rejection of an otherwise good design, poor implementation of the design, inadequate system maintenance and reliability, and an incomplete record for future changes or for testing the design forensically.

5.8.2* Technical References and Resources.

The authority having jurisdiction shall be provided with sufficient documentation to support the validity, accuracy, relevance, and precision of the proposed methods. The engineering standards, calculation methods, and other forms of scientific information provided shall be appropriate for the particular application and methodologies used.

A.5.8.2 The sources, methodologies, and data used in performance-based designs should be based on technical references that are widely accepted and used by the appropriate professions and professional groups. This acceptance is often based on documents that are developed, reviewed, and validated under one of the following processes:

(1) Standards developed under an open consensus process conducted by recognized professional societies, codes or standards organizations, or governmental bodies

(2) Technical references that are subject to a peer review process and published in widely recognized peer-reviewed journals, conference reports, or other publications

(3) Resource publications such as the *SFPE Handbook of Fire Protection Engineering,* which are widely recognized technical sources of information

The following factors are helpful in determining the acceptability of the individual method or source:

(a) Extent of general acceptance in the relevant professional community. Indications of this acceptance include peer-reviewed publication, widespread citation in the technical literature, and adoption by or within a consensus document.

(b) Extent of documentation of the method, including the analytical method itself, assumptions, scope, limitations, data sources, and data reduction methods.

(c) Extent of validation and analysis of uncertainties. This includes comparison of the overall method with experimental data to estimate error rates as well as analysis of the uncertainties of input data, uncertainties and limitations in the analytical method, and uncertainties in the associated performance criteria.

(d) Extent to which the method is based on sound scientific principles.

(e) Extent to which the proposed application is within the stated scope and limitations of the supporting information, including the range of applicability for which there is documented validation. Factors such as spatial dimensions, occupant characteristics, and ambient conditions, can limit valid applications.

In many cases, a method will be built from, and will include, numerous component analyses. These component analyses should be evaluated using the same factors that are applied to the overall method as outlined in items (a) through (e).

A method to address a specific fire safety issue, within documented limitations or validation regimes, might not exist. In such a case, sources and calculation methods can be used outside of their limitations, provided that the design team recognizes the limitations and addresses the resulting implications.

The technical references and methodologies to be used in a performance-based design should be closely evaluated by the design team and the authority having jurisdiction, and possibly by a third-party reviewer. The strength of the technical justification should be judged using criteria in items (a) through (e). This justification can be strengthened by the presence of data obtained from fire testing.

5.8.3 Building Design Specifications.

All details of the proposed building design that affect the ability of the building to meet the stated goals and objectives shall be documented.

5.8.4 Performance Criteria.

Performance criteria, with sources, shall be documented.

5.8.5 Occupant Characteristics.

Assumptions about occupant characteristics shall be documented.

5.8.6 Design Fire Scenarios.

Descriptions of design fire scenarios shall be documented.

5.8.7 Input Data.

Input data to models and assessment methods, including sensitivity analyses, shall be documented.

5.8.8 Output Data.

Output data from models and assessment methods, including sensitivity analyses, shall be documented.

5.8.9 Safety Factors.

The safety factors utilized shall be documented.

5.8.10 Prescriptive Requirements.

Retained prescriptive requirements shall be documented.

5.8.11* Modeling Features.

A.5.8.11 Documentation for modeling should conform to ASTM 1472, *Standard Guide for Documenting Computer Software,* although most, if not all, models were originally developed before this standard was promulgated.

5.8.11.1 Assumptions made by the model user, and descriptions of models and methods used, including known limitations, shall be documented.

5.8.11.2 Documentation shall be provided to verify that the assessment methods have been used validly and appropriately to address the design specifications, assumptions, and scenarios.

5.8.12 Evidence of Modeler Capability.

The design team's relevant experience with the models, test methods, data bases, and other assessment methods used in the performance-based design proposal shall be documented.

5.8.13 Performance Evaluation.

The performance evaluation summary shall be documented.

5.8.14 Use of Performance-Based Design Option.

Design proposals shall include documentation that provides anyone involved in the ownership or management of the building with notification of the following:

(1) The building was approved as a performance-based design with certain specified design criteria and assumptions.

(2) Any remodeling, modification, renovation, change in use, or change in the established assumptions will require a re-evaluation and reapproval.

References Cited in Commentary

1. NFPA 13, *Standard for the Installation of Sprinkler Systems*, 1999 edition, National Fire Protection Association, Quincy, MA.
2. NFPA 72, *National Fire Alarm Code®*, 1999 edition, National Fire Protection Association, Quincy, MA.
3. NFPA 90A, *Standard for the Installation of Air-Conditioning and Ventilating Systems*, 1999 edition, National Fire Protection Association, Quincy, MA.
4. ASME/ANSI A17.1 *Safety Code for Elevators and Escalators*, American Society of Mechanical Engineers, Three Park Avenue, New York, NY 10016-5990.
5. NFPA, *Fire Protection Handbook*, 18th ed., National Fire Protection Association, Quincy, MA, 1997.
6. *SFPE Handbook of Fire Protection Engineering*, 2nd ed., National Fire Protection Association, Quincy, MA, 1995.
7. Drysdale, D., *An Introduction to Fire Dynamics*, 2d ed., John Wiley & Sons, Chichester, UK, 1999.
8. Caro, T. and Milke, J., NIST-GCR-96-697, "A Survey of Fuel Loads in Contemporary Office Buildings," Gaithersburg, MD: National Institute of Standards and Technology, September 1996.
9. Proulx, G., "Evacuation Time and Movement in Apartment Buildings," *Fire Safety Journal*, 24, No. 3 (1995) 229–246.
10. Proulx, G. and Fahy, R., "The Time Delay to Start Evacuation: Review of Five Case Studies," *Proceedings of the Fifth International Symposium on Fire Safety Science*, International Association for Fire Safety Science, 1997.
11. Fruin, J. J., *Pedestrian Planning and Design*, ed. George R. Strakosch, Metropolitan Association of Urban Designers and Environmental Planners, Inc., New York, 1987.

CHAPTER 6

Classification of Occupancy and Hazard of Contents

This chapter addresses the following two important considerations in establishing necessary life safety levels:

(1) Proper classification of an occupancy
(2) Categorization of the relative hazard presented by the occupancy, building, or use within the building

Proper classification of the occupancy is crucial to ensure that the correct chapters and sections of the *Code* are used. It is important to note that the occupancy classification of a building often encompasses more than one category. It is common for a mixture of occupancy types to coexist within a single building. For example, a hotel often consists of a mixed occupancy that includes hotel, assembly, mercantile, and business occupancies.

The occupancy classification scheme uses general descriptions of each occupancy (for example, assembly, educational, day care, or health care). Since the *Code* is not a "one size fits all" document, the selection of the proper occupancy is of paramount importance. The annex text that accompanies each of the occupancy classifications provides lists of the most common building uses for each classification.

Hazard of contents, as addressed in Section 6.2, describes the relative hazard associated with the contents and operational aspects of the building. Hazard of contents is a relative term that is used to describe the potential threat to occupants from a fire that occurs in a given occupancy type.

Section 6.1 Classification of Occupancy

Each of the occupancy groupings addressed by Chapter 6 was developed to reflect the design features,

usage patterns, and unique life safety needs of occupants who are characteristic of a given occupancy. This approach was used to assess the degree to which the features contained in the core chapters need to be combined to achieve the minimum level of life safety necessary for an occupancy. It is extremely important that the correct occupancy classification be made, because the *Code* requirements differ for each occupancy. Improper classification might result in an inadequate level of life safety or overspending on nonrequired items. The occupancy groupings are as follows:

(a) *Assembly.* Assembly occupancies generally contain large numbers of people who are unfamiliar with the space and are therefore subject to indecision regarding the best means of egress in an emergency.

(b) *Educational.* Educational occupancies primarily include the large numbers of young people found in school buildings.

(c) *Day-Care.* Day-care occupancies, as in the case of educational occupancies, contain both young and adult occupants who are under the supervision of adults other than their relatives or legal guardians. In cases where day-care occupancies cater to preschool age children, the occupants might need to be carried out of the facility during evacuation.

(d) *Health Care and Ambulatory Health Care.* Health care and ambulatory health care occupancies are characterized by occupants who are incapable of self-preservation. In a health care occupancy, the occupants are not necessarily able to use exits, regardless of the number of exits provided. Occupants might be immobile, wired to monitoring equipment, debilitated, or recovering from surgery; or they might be disabled in some other way. The *Code*, in this instance, calls for a defend-in-place design strategy that uses horizontal movement and compartmentation. It recognizes that the occupants are to be provided enough protection to enable them to survive the fire by remaining in the structure, at least temporarily.

(e) *Detention and Correctional.* Detention and correctional occupancies, as in the case of health care occupancies, house occupants who are incapable of self-preservation. In detention and correctional occupancy, however, the incapability for self-preservation is due to the security imposed on the occupants. Because doors are not unlocked to allow free egress to the public way, the defend-in-place design strategy is used.

(f) *Residential.* Residential occupancies are characterized by occupants who are asleep for a portion of the time they occupy the building. Thus, they might be unaware of an incipient fire and might be trapped before egress can occur. This occupancy group is further divided into one- and two-family dwellings, lodging and rooming houses, hotels and dormitories, apartment buildings, and board and care facilities. Each occupancy in the group has characteristic needs that differ from the others. For this reason, separate chapters address each of these subgroups.

(g) *Mercantile.* Mercantile occupancies, as in the case of assembly occupancies, are characterized by large numbers of people who gather in a space that is relatively unfamiliar to them. In addition, mercantile occupancies often contain sizable quantities of combustible contents and use circuitous egress paths that are deliberately arranged to force occupants to travel around displays of materials that are available for sale.

(h) *Business.* Business occupancies generally have a lower occupant density than mercantile occupancies, and the occupants are usually more familiar with their surroundings. However, confusing and indirect egress paths are often developed due to office layouts and the arrangement of tenant spaces. The *Code* requirements address the needs of visitors unfamiliar with the building.

(i) *Industrial.* Industrial occupancies expose occupants to a wide range of processes and materials of varying hazard. Special purpose industrial occupancies, which are characterized by large installations of equipment that dominate the space, are addressed separately from general purpose industrial facilities, which have higher densities of human occupancy.

(j) *Storage.* Storage occupancies are characterized by relatively low densities of human occupancy and

by varied hazards associated with the materials stored.

6.1.1 General.

6.1.1.1 Occupancy Classification. The occupancy of a building or structure, or portion of a building or structure, shall be classified in accordance with 6.1.2 through 6.1.13. Occupancy classification shall be subject to the ruling of the authority having jurisdiction where there is a question of proper classification in any individual case.

Because the appropriate occupancy classification is not always easily determined, the *Code* assigns the authority having jurisdiction the responsibility for determining whether the designer, owner's representative, or other applicable person has correctly classified the occupancy.

6.1.1.2 Special Structures. Occupancies in special structures shall conform to the requirements of the specific occupancy Chapters 12 through 42, except as modified by Chapter 11.

The provision of 6.1.1.2 clarifies that placing an occupancy in a special structure—such as a windowless, underground, water-surrounded, or high-rise building—does not create a unique occupancy. Rather, the occupancy is classified as one of those addressed by Chapters 12 through 42. Chapter 11 is then consulted to find any permitted modifications that apply to the unusual structure.

6.1.2 Assembly.

For requirements, see Chapters 12 and 13.

6.1.2.1* Definition—Assembly Occupancy. An occupancy (1) used for a gathering of 50 or more persons for deliberation, worship, entertainment, eating, drinking, amusement, awaiting transportation, or similar uses; or (2) used as a special amusement building, regardless of occupant load.

A.6.1.2.1 Assembly Occupancy. Assembly occupancies might include the following:

(1) Armories
(2) Assembly halls
(3) Auditoriums
(4) Bowling lanes

(5) Club rooms
(6) College and university classrooms, 50 persons and over
(7) Conference rooms
(8) Courtrooms
(9) Dance halls
(10) Drinking establishments
(11) Exhibition halls
(12) Gymnasiums
(13) Libraries
(14) Mortuary chapels
(15) Motion picture theaters
(16) Museums
(17) Passenger stations and terminals of air, surface, underground, and marine public transportation facilities
(18) Places of religious worship
(19) Pool rooms
(20) Recreation piers
(21) Restaurants
(22) Skating rinks
(23) Special amusement buildings regardless of occupant load
(24) Theaters

Assembly occupancies are characterized by the presence or potential presence of crowds with attendant panic hazard in case of fire or other emergency. They are generally or occasionally open to the public, and the occupants, who are present voluntarily, are not ordinarily subject to discipline or control. Such buildings are ordinarily occupied by able-bodied persons and are not used for sleeping purposes. Special conference rooms, snack areas, and other areas incidental to, and under the control of, the management of other occupancies, such as offices, fall under the 50-person limitation.

Restaurants and drinking establishments with an occupant load of fewer than 50 persons should be classified as mercantile occupancies.

For special amusement buildings, see 12.4.7 and 13.4.7.

> The annex subpart (2) of 6.1.2.1 clarifies that a special amusement building is an assembly occupancy, even if the occupant load is fewer than 50 persons. As an assembly occupancy, a special amusement building is subject to the provisions of Chapters 12 or 13, especially 12.4.7 or 13.4.7. If an assembly occupancy were not subject to these provisions, the house of horror amusement building at a carnival, for example, might be treated as a business occupancy, because it does not have the minimum 50-person occupant load typically associated with an assembly occupancy. If it were treated as a business occupancy, the necessary level of life safety would probably not be provided.

> Because special amusement buildings purposely confound the egress path and further confuse the occupants with sound and lighting effects, they need to meet the special requirements of 12.4.7 or 13.4.7. For other than special amusement buildings, the threshold at which an assembly use becomes an assembly occupancy is the 50-person occupant load.

6.1.2.2 Small Assembly Uses. Occupancy of any room or space for assembly purposes by fewer than 50 persons in an other occupancy and incidental to such other occupancy shall be classified as part of the other occupancy and shall be subject to the provisions applicable thereto.

6.1.3 Educational.

For requirements, see Chapters 14 and 15.

6.1.3.1* Definition—Educational Occupancy. An occupancy used for educational purposes through the twelfth grade by six or more persons for four or more hours per day or more than 12 hours per week.

A.6.1.3.1 Educational Occupancy. Educational occupancies include the following:

(1) Academies
(2) Kindergartens
(3) Schools

An educational occupancy is distinguished from an assembly occupancy in that the same occupants are regularly present.

> Educational occupancies are limited to facilities used for educational purposes through the twelfth grade. College classroom buildings do not meet this criterion and are classified as business occupancies. Where the occupant load of a classroom is 50 or more, the appropriate occupancy classification is assembly, regardless of educational grade level.

6.1.3.2 Other Occupancies. Other occupancies associated with educational institutions shall be in accordance with the appropriate parts of this *Code*.

6.1.3.3 Incidental Instruction. In cases where instruction is incidental to some other occupancy, the section of this *Code* governing such other occupancy shall apply.

6.1.4 Day-Care.

For requirements, see Chapters 16 and 17.

6.1.4.1* Definition—Day-Care Occupancy. An occupancy in which four or more clients receive care, maintenance, and supervision, by other than their relatives or legal guardians, for less than 24 hours per day.

A.6.1.4.1 Day-Care Occupancy. Day-care occupancies include the following:

(1) Adult day-care occupancies, except where part of a health care occupancy
(2) Child day-care occupancies
(3) Day-care homes
(4) Kindergarten classes that are incidental to a child day-care occupancy
(5) Nursery schools

In areas where public schools offer only half-day kindergarten programs, many child day-care occupancies offer state-approved kindergarten classes for children who need full-day care. As these classes are normally incidental to the day-care occupancy, the requirements of the day-care occupancy should be followed.

Day-care occupancies are similar to educational occupancies. In this edition of the *Code*, the day-care occupancies chapters have been located to immediately follow those that apply to educational occupancies.

6.1.5 Health Care.

For requirements, see Chapters 18 and 19.

6.1.5.1* Definition—Health Care Occupancy. An occupancy used for purposes of medical or other treatment or care of four or more persons where such occupants are mostly incapable of self-preservation due to age, physical or mental disability, or because of security measures not under the occupants' control.

A.6.1.5.1 Health Care Occupancy. Health care occupancies include the following:

(1) Hospitals
(2) Limited care facilities
(3) Nursing homes

Occupants of health care occupancies typically have physical or mental illness, disease, or infirmity. They also include infants, convalescents, or infirm aged persons.

Chapters 18 through 21 address hospitals, nursing homes, limited care facilities, and ambulatory health care occupancies. Each of these subclassifications of health care occupancies is defined in 3.3.104, 3.3.132, 3.3.117, and 3.3.8, respectively. The definitions specify that each type of facility accommodates four or more persons. Because Chapter 24 permits a living unit

housing a family and up to three outsiders to be classified as a one-family dwelling, a home with three or fewer persons incapable of self-preservation does not constitute a health care occupancy.

A definition of *birth center* appears in 3.3.22. Also, guidance for when a birth center is to be classified as a business occupancy, and when it should be classified as a health care occupancy, is provided in the annex material associated with business occupancy classification. See A.3.3.22, *birth center,* and the third paragraph of A.6.1.11.1.

6.1.6 Ambulatory Health Care.

For requirements, see Chapters 20 and 21.

6.1.6.1 Definition—Ambulatory Health Care Occupancy. A building or portion thereof used to provide services or treatment simultaneously to four or more patients that (1) provides, on an outpatient basis, treatment for patients that renders the patients incapable of taking action for self-preservation under emergency conditions without the assistance of others, or (2) provides, on an outpatient basis, anesthesia that renders the patients incapable of taking action for self-preservation under emergency conditions without the assistance of others.

Chapters 22 and 23 are intended to apply only to those areas of detention and correctional facilities used for occupant housing, such as sleeping and day activity areas. Other occupied spaces within the facility are to receive an occupancy classification representative of the use and are to be regulated by the applicable provisions of Chapters 12 through 21 and Chapters 24 through 42. The occupancy requirements of Chapters 12 through 21 and Chapters 24 through 42 are usually modified due to special security needs. For example, cafeterias are regulated using the assembly occupancy chapters, and metal shops follow the requirements of the industrial occupancy chapter.

6.1.7 Detention and Correctional.

For requirements, see Chapters 22 and 23.

6.1.7.1* Definition—Detention and Correctional Occupancy. An occupancy used to house four or more persons under varied degrees of restraint or security where such occupants are mostly incapable of self-preservation because of security measures not under the occupants' control.

A.6.1.7.1 Detention and Correctional Occupancy. Detention and correctional occupancies include the following:

(1) Adult and juvenile substance abuse centers
(2) Adult and juvenile work camps
(3) Adult community residential centers
(4) Adult correctional institutions
(5) Adult local detention facilities
(6) Juvenile community residential centers
(7) Juvenile detention facilities
(8) Juvenile training schools

> The residential occupancy subclassifications of one-and two-family dwellings, lodging or rooming houses, hotels, dormitories, apartment buildings, and board and care facilities are defined in 3.3.48, 3.3.120, 3.3.105, 3.3.46, 3.3.12, and 3.3.24, respectively.
>
> Although occupants sleep in health care occupancies and detention and correctional occupancies, they occupy such facilities for other than normal residential purposes. Because the occupants of these facilities are incapable of self-preservation—in one case due to illness or infirmity and, in the other, as a result of security imposed outside the control of the occupants—the provisions that apply to normal residential occupancies might not provide the necessary level of life safety. The user is referred to Chapters 18 and 19 for health care occupancies and Chapters 22 and 23 for detention and correctional occupancies. See also 6.1.5 and 6.1.6.

6.1.7.2* Nonresidential Uses. Within detention and correctional facilities, uses other than residential housing shall be in accordance with the appropriate chapter of the *Code*. *(See 22.1.2.1 and 23.1.2.1.)*

A.6.1.7.2 Chapters 22 and 23 address the residential housing areas of the detention and correctional occupancy as defined in 3.3.45. Examples of uses other than residential housing include gymnasiums or industries.

6.1.8 Residential.

For requirements, see Chapters 24 through 31.

6.1.8.1* Definition—Residential Occupancy. An occupancy that provides sleeping accommodations for purposes other than health care or detention and correctional.

A.6.1.8.1 Residential Occupancy. Residential occupancies are treated as separate occupancies in this *Code* as follows:

(1) One- and two-family dwellings (Chapter 24)
(2) Lodging or rooming houses (Chapter 26)
(3) Hotels, motels, and dormitories (Chapters 28 and 29)
(4) Apartment buildings (Chapters 30 and 31)

6.1.9 Residential Board and Care.

For requirements, see Chapters 32 and 33.

6.1.9.1* Definition—Residential Board and Care Occupancy. A building or portion thereof that is used for lodging and boarding of four or more residents, not related by blood or marriage to the owners or operators, for the purpose of providing personal care services.

A.6.1.9.1 Residential Board and Care Occupancy. The following are examples of facilities that are classified as residential board and care occupancies:

(1) A group housing arrangement for physically or mentally handicapped persons who normally attend school in the community, attend worship in the community, or otherwise use community facilities
(2) A group housing arrangement for physically or mentally handicapped persons who are undergoing training in preparation for independent living, for paid employment, or for other normal community activities
(3) A group housing arrangement for the elderly that provides personal care services but that does not provide nursing care
(4) Facilities for social rehabilitation, alcoholism, drug abuse, or mental health problems that contain a group housing arrangement and that provide personal care services but do not provide acute care
(5) Assisted living facilities
(6) Other group housing arrangements that provide personal care services but not nursing care

6.1.10 Mercantile.

For requirements, see Chapters 36 and 37.

6.1.10.1* Definition—Mercantile Occupancy. An occupancy used for the display and sale of merchandise.

A.6.1.10.1 Mercantile Occupancy. Mercantile occupancies include the following:

(1) Auction rooms
(2) Department stores
(3) Drugstores
(4) Restaurants with fewer than 50 persons
(5) Shopping centers
(6) Supermarkets

Office, storage, and service facilities incidental to the sale of merchandise and located in the same building should be considered part of the mercantile occupancy classification.

> Bulk merchandising retail buildings, which characteristically consist of a warehouse-type building occu-

pied for sales purposes, are a subclass of mercantile occupancy with a greater potential for hazards than more traditional mercantile operations. (See also 36.4.5 and 37.4.5.)

6.1.11 Business.

For requirements, see Chapters 38 and 39.

6.1.11.1* Definition—Business Occupancy. An occupancy used for account and record keeping or the transaction of business other than mercantile.

A.6.1.11.1 Business Occupancy. Business occupancies include the following:

(1) Air traffic control towers (ATCTs)
(2) City halls
(3) College and university instructional buildings, classrooms under 50 persons, and instructional laboratories
(4) Courthouses
(5) Dentists' offices
(6) Doctors' offices
(7) General offices
(8) Outpatient clinics, ambulatory
(9) Town halls

Doctors' and dentists' offices are included, unless of such character as to be classified as ambulatory health care occupancies as defined in 3.3.8.

Birth centers occupied by fewer than four patients, not including infants, at any one time; not providing sleeping facilities for four or more occupants; and not providing treatment procedures that render four or more patients, not including infants, incapable of self-preservation at any one time should be classified as business occupancies. For birth centers occupied by patients not meeting these parameters, see Chapter 18 or Chapter 19, as appropriate.

Service facilities common to city office buildings such as newsstands, lunch counters serving fewer than 50 persons, barber shops, and beauty parlors are included in the business occupancy group.

City halls, town halls, and court houses are included in this occupancy group insofar as their principal function is the transaction of public business and the keeping of books and records. Insofar as they are used for assembly purposes, they are classified as assembly occupancies.

Depending on the characteristics of a laboratory, it may be classified as a business occupancy, industrial occupancy, or other occupancy (see also A.6.1.2.1).

The third paragraph of A.6.1.11.1 provides guidance for when a birth center is to be classified as a business occupancy and when it is to be classified as a health care occupancy. A definition of *birth center* appears in 3.3.22. (Also, see A.3.3.22, *birth center*.)

6.1.12 Industrial.

For requirements, see Chapter 40.

6.1.12.1* Definition—Industrial Occupancy. An occupancy in which products are manufactured or in which processing, assembling, mixing, packaging, finishing, decorating, or repair operations are conducted.

A.6.1.12.1 Industrial Occupancy. Industrial occupancies include the following:

(1) Dry cleaning plants
(2) Factories of all kinds
(3) Food processing plants
(4) Gas plants
(5) Hangars (for servicing/maintenance)
(6) Laundries
(7) Power plants
(8) Pumping stations
(9) Refineries
(10) Sawmills
(11) Telephone exchanges

In evaluating the appropriate classification of laboratories, the authority having jurisdiction should treat each case individually based on the extent and nature of the associated hazards. Some laboratories are classified as occupancies other than industrial; for example, a physical therapy laboratory or a computer laboratory.

6.1.13 Storage.

For requirements, see Chapter 42.

6.1.13.1* Definition—Storage Occupancy. An occupancy used primarily for the storage or sheltering of goods, merchandise, products, vehicles, or animals.

A.6.1.13.1 Storage Occupancy. Storage occupancies include the following:

(1) Barns
(2) Bulk oil storage
(3) Cold storage
(4) Freight terminals
(5) Grain elevators
(6) Hangars (for storage only)
(7) Parking structures
(8) Stables
(9) Truck and marine terminals
(10) Warehouses

Storage occupancies are characterized by the presence of relatively small numbers of persons in proportion to the area.

> Bulk merchandising retail buildings, which characteristically consist of a warehouse-type building occupied for sales purposes, are a subclass of mercantile occupancy rather than a storage occupancy. (See also 36.4.5 and 37.4.5.)

6.1.14 Mixed Occupancies.

6.1.14.1* Definition—Mixed Occupancy. An occupancy in which two or more classes of occupancy exist in the same building or structure and where such classes are intermingled so that separate safeguards are impracticable.

A.6.1.14.1 Mixed Occupancy. With only a few exceptions, the *Code* sets no specific occupancy separation requirements. The authority having jurisdiction determines the separation needed, if any, based on 6.1.14 and subsection __.1.2 of each occupancy chapter. The local building code or the model building codes might be consulted by the authority having jurisdiction in making this determination, keeping life safety rather than property protection in mind.

6.1.14.2 Applicable Requirements. Where a mixed occupancy classification occurs, the means of egress facilities, construction, protection, and other safeguards shall comply with the most restrictive life safety requirements of the occupancies involved.

Exception: * *Where incidental to another occupancy, buildings used as follows shall be permitted to be considered part of the predominant occupancy and subject to the provisions of the Code that apply to the predominant occupancy:*

(a) *Mercantile, business, industrial, or storage use*
(b) *Nonresidential use with an occupant load fewer than that established by Section 6.1 for the occupancy threshold*

A.6.1.14.2 Exception. Examples of uses that might be incidental to another occupancy include the following:

(1) A newsstand (mercantile) in an office building
(2) A giftshop (mercantile) in a hotel
(3) A small storage area (storage) in any occupancy
(4) Minor office space (business) in any occupancy
(5) A maintenance area (industrial) in any occupancy

Examples of uses that have occupant loads below the occupancy classification threshold levels include the following:

(1) An assembly use with fewer than 50 persons within a business occupancy

(2) An educational use with fewer than 6 persons within an apartment building

The exception to 6.1.14.2 clarifies that some, but not all, incidental uses can be considered part of the predominant occupancy. Incidental residential uses, regardless of the number of persons for whom sleeping accommodations are provided, are to be treated as residential occupancies. For example, if there are sleeping facilities for five fire fighters in a fire station, the *Code* does not permit the building to be classified simply as a storage occupancy. Rather, the proper classification is a mixed occupancy that is part storage occupancy and part residential occupancy (that is, lodging/rooming house). The requirements that apply to both occupancies need to be compared, and the more stringent provisions apply.

In addition, a day-care use is not exempted by either criterion of the exception to 6.1.14.2. For example, a small day-care center located in a high-rise office building is not permitted to be considered part of the predominant business occupancy. The more stringent of the requirements that apply to day-care occupancies and business occupancies need to be implemented.

Classifying a building as a mixed occupancy is an incomplete classification. Rather, a classification of mixed occupancy is to include mention of the occupancy types involved. For example, a building with spaces used for storage intermingled with spaces used for sales is to be classified as a mixed occupancy that is part storage occupancy and part mercantile occupancy.

The *Code* does not typically require that one occupancy be separated from an abutting occupancy by fire resistance–rated barriers, as is often required by building codes. Some of the occupancy chapters do require a specific fire resistance–rated separation between dissimilar occupancies if each is to be considered individually. However, the determination of whether a fire resistance–rated separation is needed and its required hourly rating is left to the authority having jurisdiction (AHJ) on a case-by-case basis.

In a mixed occupancy, where the occupancies are so intermingled that separate safeguards cannot be provided, the entire facility is to meet the most restrictive life safety requirements for all the occupancies involved. In many cases, an occupancy requires a type of protection to be provided throughout the structure, regardless of fire separation, unless the structure was built as separate buildings. If the AHJ accepts an arrangement as the equivalent of separate buildings, even though it is contained within a single structure, the requirement in question might be permitted to be applied to only the building area on the applicable side of the separating fire barrier.

A simple example of a building with multiple uses not constituting a mixed occupancy is illustrated in Exhibit 6.1. Because each individual-use space is arranged to meet its egress requirements independent of its neighbors, each space can be adequately protected by meeting only the occupancy requirements that apply to that space.

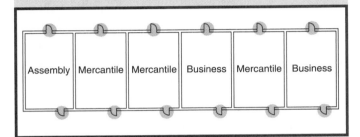

| Assembly | Mercantile | Mercantile | Business | Mercantile | Business |

Exhibit 6.1 A building that contains more than one occupancy but is not a mixed occupancy.

An example of a common mixed occupancy arrangement is illustrated in Exhibit 6.2. Because the assembly occupancy (that is, the auditorium) shares the internal corridor egress system with the educa-

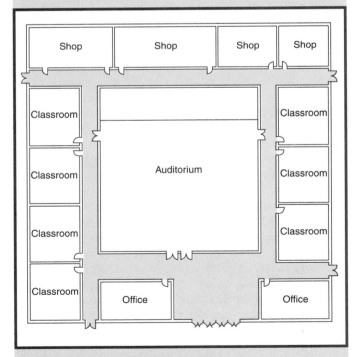

Exhibit 6.2 Mixed occupancy building.

tional occupancy classrooms and shops, it is determined that providing separate safeguards is impractical. Therefore, the uses and arrangement create a mixed occupancy that is part assembly occupancy and part educational occupancy.

If the building in Exhibit 6.2 is existing, the requirements of Chapter 13 are compared with those of Chapter 15 for each of the subjects addressed by the *Code*. In each case, the more stringent requirement applies to the entire building. For example, the interior corridor requirements of 15.3.6 for existing educational occupancies are stricter than those that apply to existing assembly occupancies and, thus, apply throughout the building. The panic hardware requirements of 13.2.2.2.3 for existing assembly occupancies are slightly more stringent than those that apply to existing educational occupancies and, thus, apply throughout the mixed occupancy. With regard to travel distance, both Chapter 13 and Chapter 15 limit travel distance to the nearest exit to a maximum of 150 ft (45 m) in a nonsprinklered building, so this requirement applies throughout the building.

Section 6.2 Hazard of Contents

6.2.1 General.

6.2.1.1 For the purpose of this *Code,* the hazard of contents shall be the relative danger of the start and spread of fire, the danger of smoke or gases generated, and the danger of explosion or other occurrence potentially endangering the lives and safety of the occupants of the building or structure.

The classification of hazard of contents is based on the potential threat to life presented by the contents. A fuel load that might be considered as a *light hazard* in terms of its ease of extinguishment by a sprinkler system might, in fact, produce enough smoke and other products of combustion to threaten the lives of the occupants. In this case, the *Code* requires the material to be classified as *ordinary hazard* contents.

The *Code*'s method of classifying hazard of contents is based on life safety. For this reason, the *Code*'s provisions are not readily incorporated into the design criteria of other codes where hazard classification is based on property preservation. Many *light hazard* materials, in terms of extinguishment characteristics, are required to be treated as *ordinary hazards* under the *Code*. For example, a business occupancy might be classified as *light hazard* contents by NFPA

13, *Standard for the Installation of Sprinkler Systems,*[1] for purposes of sprinkler system design but be considered *ordinary hazard* contents for purposes of applying *Life Safety Code* requirements.

The *Life Safety Code* classifies contents based on the threat of fire, explosions, and other similar events. It does not specifically consider the danger posed by toxic chemical, etiologic contamination, or similar hazards.

6.2.1.2 Hazard of contents shall be determined by the authority having jurisdiction on the basis of the character of the contents and the processes or operations conducted in the building or structure.

6.2.1.3* For the purpose of this *Code,* where different degrees of hazard of contents exist in different parts of a building or structure, the most hazardous shall govern the classification, unless hazardous areas are separated or protected as specified in Section 8.4 and the applicable sections of Chapters 11 through 42.

A.6.2.1.3 Under this provision, any violation of the requirements of Chapter 11 through Chapter 42 for separation or protection of hazardous operation or storage would inherently involve violation of the other sections of the *Code,* unless additional egress facilities appropriate to high hazard contents were provided.

The presence of a high hazard contents area on a floor does not have to result in classification of the entire floor as a high hazard contents area if separation or protection is provided in accordance with the requirements of Section 8.4. Once the potential hazard has been mitigated either by automatic sprinkler protection or via isolation from the remainder of the floor by fire resistance–rated construction, the floor is permitted to be treated as an ordinary hazard contents area. For example, in a new hospital the high hazard contents area created by a soiled-linen storage room is required to be protected by a combination of sprinkler protection and 1-hour fire resistance–rated storage room walls with 45-minute fire protection–rated doors. Having thus protected the high hazard contents soiled-linen storage room, other life safety features are permitted to be provided using the requirements that apply to ordinary hazard contents—not the stricter provisions that apply to occupancies having high hazard contents. For details on the limitations—such as maximum 75-ft (23-m) travel distance—imposed on occupancies having high hazard contents, see Section 7.11.

6.2.2 Classification of Hazard of Contents.

6.2.2.1* The hazard of contents of any building or structure shall be classified as low, ordinary, or high in accordance with 6.2.2.2, 6.2.2.3, and 6.2.2.4.

A.6.2.2.1 These classifications do not apply to the application of sprinkler protection classifications. (See NFPA 13, *Standard for the Installation of Sprinkler Systems.*)

6.2.2.2* Low Hazard. Low hazard contents shall be classified as those of such low combustibility that no self-propagating fire therein can occur.

A.6.2.2.2 Chapter 42 recognizes storage of noncombustible materials as low hazard. In other occupancies it is assumed that, even where the actual contents hazard is normally low, there is sufficient likelihood that some combustible materials or hazardous operations will be introduced in connection with building repair or maintenance, or some psychological factor might create conditions conducive to panic, so that the egress facilities cannot safely be reduced below those specified for ordinary hazard contents.

Very few occupancies qualify as having low hazard contents. When pressed for an example of low hazard contents, the cautious offer "pig iron ingots stored underwater." A more realistic and useful example of low hazard contents might be metal parts stored in metal containers on metal—not wood—pallets supported by metal shelving. If the same metal parts stored in metal containers were placed on wood pallets, the pallets would be capable of sustaining a self-propagating fire; and the hazard of contents classification would be ordinary.

6.2.2.3* Ordinary Hazard. Ordinary hazard contents shall be classified as those that are likely to burn with moderate rapidity or to give off a considerable volume of smoke.

A.6.2.2.3 Ordinary hazard classification represents the conditions found in most buildings and is the basis for the general requirements of this *Code.*

The fear of poisonous fumes or explosions is necessarily a relative matter to be determined on a judgment basis. All smoke contains some toxic fire gases but, under conditions of ordinary hazard, there should be no unduly dangerous exposure during the period necessary to escape from the fire area, assuming there are proper exits.

6.2.2.4* High Hazard. High hazard contents shall be classified as those that are likely to burn with extreme rapidity or from which explosions are likely. *(For means of egress requirements, see Section 7.11.)*

A.6.2.2.4 High hazard contents include occupancies where flammable liquids are handled or used or are stored under conditions involving possible release of flammable vapors; where grain dust, wood flour or plastic dust, aluminum or magnesium dust, or other explosive dusts are produced; where hazardous chemicals or explosives are manufactured, stored, or handled; where cotton or other combustible fibers are processed or handled under conditions producing flammable flyings; and other situations of similar hazard.

Chapter 40 and Chapter 42 include detailed provisions on high hazard contents.

Occupancies containing low hazard or high hazard contents are rare. In deciding which hazard classification applies, users need to ask the following questions:

(1) Do the contents qualify for a low hazard classification?
(2) Do the contents qualify for a high hazard classification?

If the answer to each of these questions is no, then the hazard of contents classification is ordinary.

Once an ordinary hazard of contents classification is made, the application of *Code* requirements becomes simple, because the vast majority of the provisions are written to apply to ordinary hazard contents without mentioning ordinary hazard specifically. Generally, specialized requirements apply to high hazard contents, such as those in Section 7.11, and the few exceptions for which application is limited to low hazard contents, such as the unlimited travel distance permitted in low hazard storage occupancies by 42.2.6.1.

Reference Cited in Commentary

1. NFPA 13, *Standard for the Installation of Sprinkler Systems*, 1999 edition, National Fire Protection Association, Quincy, MA.

CHAPTER 7

Means of Egress

The earliest editions of the *Life Safety Code* were titled the *Building Exits Code*. This title made it evident that one of the main themes addressed in the *Code* is that sufficient exits are needed to allow the building occupants to leave the building safely during a fire.

The term *means of egress* is defined in 3.3.121 as "a continuous and unobstructed way of travel from any point in a building or structure to a public way consisting of three separate and distinct parts: (1) the exit access, (2) the exit, and (3) the exit discharge." The concept of the three-part means of egress was codified in the *Code* in 1956. Since that time, this concept has been well understood and its philosophy has been implemented by code officials and building designers.

Since multiple components make up the means of egress, this chapter is segmented to describe the key elements that are typical of egress features.

Separation of the means of egress from other use areas is important to ensure a route of safe passage for the occupants. Subsection 7.1.3 establishes a set of basic principles concerning the separation and segregation of exits to achieve this objective.

Section 7.2 establishes criteria applicable to a variety of components that might constitute a part of the means of egress. These components include everything from doors and stairs—components that are permitted by all occupancy chapters—to specialized components such as alternating tread devices—a component that is not permitted by all occupancy chapters.

The method used to determine the number of occupants who can safely move through any of these individual components is addressed in Section 7.3, which deals with the capacity of the means of egress. Part of this approach also involves establishing how many people can reasonably be expected to occupy a given area; Section 7.3 also presents the occupant load factors.

Sections 7.4 through 7.7 relate to the number, arrangement, measurement, and discharge of the means of egress. These four sections address not only the proper number of exits and exit access points, they also control the distance to the exits and the placement of the exits with respect to one another.

The illumination of the means of egress, emergency lighting, and the marking of the means of egress with appropriate signage are related topics. The portions of this chapter that address these subjects were written in recognition that simply having enough exits that are properly arranged does not guarantee that the exits are readily apparent in a variety of circumstances. Normal illumination for the means of egress is governed by Section 7.8, while emergency lighting provisions are addressed in Section 7.9. Section 7.10 establishes the requirements for proper marking of the means of egress with various types of exit signs.

Sections 7.11 and 7.12 of this chapter provide general rules for egress arrangement for high hazard areas and for mechanical equipment rooms.

Section 7.1 General

The purpose of this chapter is to establish minimum requirements for the means of egress for application to all occupancy classifications. In agreement with the 1.4.1 application statement, Chapter 7 presents requirements that apply to both new construction and existing buildings. Where the requirements of this chapter are unsuitable for a specific occupancy or impose an unreasonable burden on an existing facility, exemptions are provided as part of the text.

Sometimes the exemptions take the form of a concise exception that refers the user to the specific occupancy chapter. Only by consulting the complete text in the specific occupancy chapter does the user learn the details of the exemption from the Chapter 7 requirements. For example, where 7.2.1.5.1 requires that egress doors remain unlocked, Exception No. 1 cues the user to the fact that, for health care occupancies and detention and correctional occupancies, locked doors are permitted under certain conditions. Exception No. 1 uses the phrase "where otherwise provided in Chapters 18 through 23" to refer the user to the referenced chapter in which the details around which the exception is made conditional are found. For example, Exception No. 2 to 18.2.2.2.2 permits locked doors in health care occupancies where the clinical needs of the patients require specialized security measures for their safety, with the provision that keys are carried by staff at all times.

In addition to specifying means of egress features that are required to be provided in all occupancies, Chapter 7 presents other features that, although not required, are permitted to be part of the means of egress if specified conditions are met. Recognizing that some provisions detailed in this chapter might not be suitable to a particular occupancy, the *Code* often introduces such features using the language "where permitted in Chapters 12 through 42." For example, doors in means of egress might be equipped with the access-controlled entrance and egress locking system addressed in 7.2.1.6.2 only where specifically permitted by an occupancy chapter. New business occupancies are permitted to use such a system via 38.2.2.2.5 wording that reads "access-controlled egress doors complying with 7.2.1.6.2 shall be permitted." If an occupancy chapter is silent on the use of access-controlled egress doors, such doors are prohibited within the required means of egress serving that occupancy.

Chapter 7 also presents features that are mandatory only when another part of the *Code* specifically requires the use of that component, system, or arrangement. Recognizing that some of the features detailed in this way in Chapter 7 might not be necessary for a particular occupancy, the *Code* often introduces such features using the language "where required in Chapters 11 through 42." For example, Section 7.10 provides details for exit signs but does not require such signs. Section 7.10 is written to include all the criteria necessary for providing exit signs

if another part of the *Code*—typically an occupancy chapter—requires exit signs in accordance with Section 7.10. New assembly occupancies require exit signs via the wording of 12.2.10 that reads "means of egress shall have signs in accordance with Section 7.10."

Thus, some of the provisions of Chapter 7 are absolute requirements that apply to all occupancies unless specific exemptions are presented via exceptions; some provisions are permitted to be used only if another part of the *Code*—typically an occupancy chapter—specifically includes language permitting such use; and some provisions apply only where another part of the *Code*—typically an occupancy chapter—specifically includes language requiring the use of that feature.

7.1.1* Application.

Means of egress for both new and existing buildings shall comply with this chapter. *(See also 4.5.3.)*

Means of egress are to comply with the requirements of this chapter and those detailed in the appropriate occupancy chapter. To avoid creating conflicting requirements, the occupancy chapters, Chapters 12 through 42, are permitted to establish provisions or requirements less stringent than those in Chapter 7 only if a corresponding exception is added to the Chapter 7 requirement from which the exemption applies. However, if an occupancy chapter is written to be more stringent than Chapter 7, it only needs to include the stricter requirement. In accordance with 4.4.2.2, where the specific requirements of the occupancy chapters differ from the general requirements contained in Chapters 1 through 4 and Chapters 6 through 10, the more specific occupancy chapter requirements govern. See also the commentary following 4.4.2.2.

A.7.1.1 Portable ladders, rope fire escapes, and similar emergency escape devices can have a useful function in facilitating escape from burning buildings lacking adequate exits of the stair or other standard type, but they are not the equivalent of standard exits, and their use is not in any way recognized by this *Code* as satisfying the requirements for means of egress. Furthermore, many such devices are of types unsuitable for use by aged or infirm persons or by small children. Therefore, such devices can provide a false sense of security and should not be used as an excuse for not providing standard exit facilities.

The *Code* relies on standard components such as doors, stairs, and ramps to create a reliable means of egress system usable by persons of all ages. Emergency escape devices such as portable ladders and rope fire escapes, for the reasons explained in A.7.1.1, receive no credit toward satisfying *Code* requirements.

7.1.2 Definitions.

The occupant of a building must be protected from obstacles to safe egress. To achieve this goal, the protection of each component in the egress system is to be considered. Clear and concise definitions of the terms in 7.1.2 appear in Chapter 3. These definitions help explain the special features of each component. The term *means of egress* has been used for many years, but it was not until the late 1950s that its definition was expanded to comprise three separate and distinct parts: (1) the exit access, (2) the exit, and (3) the exit discharge. Until the late 1950s, the term *exit* was used more often than the term *means of egress*, a fact evidenced by the *Code*'s original title, the *Building Exits Code*.

Accessible Area of Refuge. See 3.3.1.

For an area of refuge to be considered an accessible area of refuge, it must be capable of being reached by a person in a wheelchair without traveling over stairs or other obstacles. ICC/ANSI A117.1, *American National Standard for Accessible and Usable Buildings and Facilities*, provides additional details on accessible routes.[1] This edition of the *Life Safety Code* references the 1998 edition of ICC/ANSI A117.1, which was processed in an effort to achieve harmony with the Americans with Disabilities Act Accessibility Guidelines (ADAAG). Parallel changes to the ADAAG are being processed via government rule-making procedures.

Accessible Means of Egress. See 3.3.2.

A means of egress is considered an accessible means of egress if it meets one of the following criteria:

(1) A wheelchair-bound person is able to travel unassisted through the exit access, exit, and exit discharge to a public way (that is, ramp-type travel and not stair-type travel if elevation differences are involved), or

(2) A wheelchair-bound person is able to travel unassisted through that portion of the exit access necessary to reach an area of refuge.

The area of refuge specified in item (2) serves as a temporary haven from the effects of the fire. The person with the severe mobility impairment must have the ability to travel from the area of refuge to the public way, although such travel might depend on the assistance of others. If elevation differences are involved, an elevator might be used or the person might be carried on an extra-wide stair. See also 7.5.4.

Area of Refuge. See 3.3.14.

Common Path of Travel. See 3.3.32.

Electroluminescent. See 3.3.50.

Elevator Evacuation System. See 3.3.51.

Elevator Lobby. See 3.3.52.

Elevator Lobby Door. See 3.3.53.

The terms *elevator evacuation system, elevator lobby,* and *elevator lobby door* are defined for purposes of applying 7.2.13. Although elevators are addressed in 7.2.13 as a component of a means of egress system, the restrictions imposed recognize the elevator only as a second means of egress from a tower provided with limited occupant load, sprinkler protection throughout the tower building, and other detailed features. See also 11.3.2.2.2.

Exit. See 3.3.61.

The *exit* is that portion of the means of egress that is separated from other building spaces by enclosing it within construction having the minimum degree of fire resistance specified by 7.1.3.2, with limited openings through the enclosing construction and protection of such openings. The exit might include doors, stairs, ramps, smokeproof enclosures, exit passageways, and outside balconies. In each case, the exit components are required to conform to the *Code* specifications for fire protection and the dimensional and arrangement criteria. In its simplest form, an exit is a doorway or a door opening directly to the exterior at grade. An exit, other than a door opening directly to the outside, provides a protected path of travel.

In the case of a stairway, the exit includes the stair enclosure, the door into the stairway enclosure, the stairs and landings inside the enclosure, and the door from the enclosure to the street or exit discharge.

The entrance to an exit is part of the exit and usually consists of a fire protection–rated door assembly that provides a protected entrance into a protected area. A fire door, however, does not always signal an entrance to an exit. A door or fire door between a hotel room and a corridor or a fire door across a corridor or lobby is not part of an exit, unless the corridor or lobby and all other openings into the corridor or lobby are separated and protected as required for an exit in accordance with 7.1.3.2.

Various building features—where properly arranged and constructed—might constitute an exit. Examples include an exterior exit door, an exit passageway, a horizontal exit, an exit stair, or an exit ramp.

Several types of exits, as they might actually occur in some buildings, are shown in Exhibit 7.1 as shaded areas. On the second floor, exits include the following:

(1) Two exit stairs enclosed by fire-rated barriers including a rated self-closing door
(2) A horizontal exit consisting of a fire-rated barrier, including rated self-closing doors, completely dividing the floor into two fire compartments

On the first floor, exits include the following:

(1) Two doors from the corridor directly to the outside at grade level
(2) A horizontal exit that is a vertical extension of and therefore similar to the horizontal exit on the second floor

(3) An exit passageway that connects one of the second floor exit stairs directly with the outside and is separated from the remainder of the floor by fire-rated barriers, including rated self-closing doors

For detailed requirements for a horizontal exit, see 7.2.4. For detailed requirements for an exit passageway, see 7.2.6.

Exit Access. See 3.3.62.

The exit access includes the rooms and building spaces people occupy and the doors, aisles, corridors, unenclosed stairs, and unenclosed ramps that are traversed to reach an exit. Spaces constituting exit access are shown in Exhibit 7.2 as shaded areas. All spaces occupied and traversed in reaching an exit are considered the exit access portion of the means of egress. The shading shown in the figures indicates that exit access comprises more floor area than either of the other components of means of egress—the exit and exit discharge.

Exit Discharge. See 3.3.63.

Because some exits do not discharge directly into a public way, the exit discharge is defined as providing

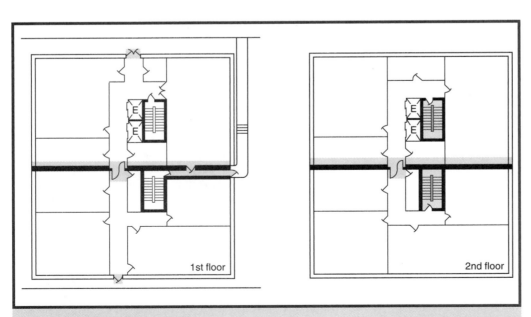

Exhibit 7.1 *Various forms of exits.*

1st floor

2nd floor

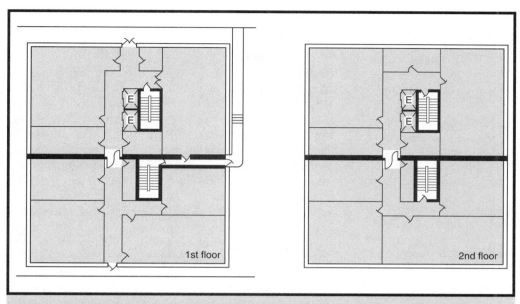

Exhibit 7.2 *Spaces constituting exit access.*

building occupants with a path of travel from the termination of an exit to a public way. This path of travel might be inside the building, as permitted by 7.7.2, or outside. Where an exit opens onto an alley, court, or yard, a safe path of travel is to be provided to a public way or some equivalent safe area. This portion of the means of egress is the exit discharge. See also 7.7.1.

Forms of exit discharge are shown in Exhibit 7.3 as shaded areas. Because occupants leave the build-

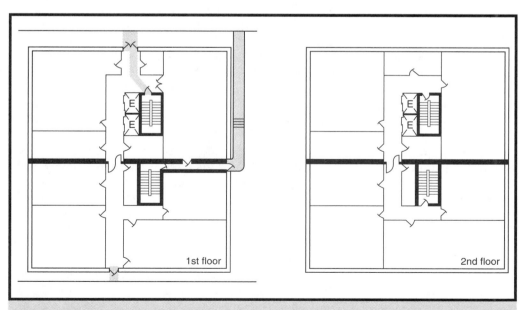

Exhibit 7.3 *Spaces constituting exit discharge.*

ing at the first floor only, no exit discharge occurs on the second floor. The first floor exit discharge includes the following:

(1) The exterior space beginning at the exit doors from the corridor and continuing to the public way (street)
(2) The exterior walkway along the side of the building beginning at the door from the exit passageway and continuing to the public way
(3) The interior path of travel from the second floor exit stair discharging through a portion of the first floor corridor.

For an occupant of the second floor who needs to travel across a portion of the first floor, the area traveled is considered exit discharge, yet an occupant of the first floor who travels across the same space is considered to be within exit access. See also 7.7.2.

Externally Illuminated. See 3.3.67.
Horizontal Exit. See 3.3.103.

A horizontal exit is a fire barrier with fire doors that provide passage from one fire compartment of a building to another fire compartment in the same building or in an adjoining building on approximately the same level. Substantial fire separations are required, because the area to which egress is made serves as a temporary safe haven. The horizontal exit might be a combination of a 2-hour fire resistance–rated barrier separating a building into two areas with $1^{1}/_{2}$-hour fire protection–rated door assemblies that allow travel from one side of the barrier to the other; or the horizontal exit might be a bridge or balcony that allows travel to an adjoining building. An example of a horizontal exit is depicted in Exhibit 7.1 by the barrier running across the center of the building and providing a continuous separation from outside wall to opposite outside wall.

Horizontal exits are particularly useful in health care occupancies and in detention and correctional occupancies where they are important components of an effective defend-in-place strategy. Horizontal exits make it possible to move nonambulatory patients horizontally to a temporary safe area rather than vertically down stairs. They also provide added safety to residents of detention and correctional occupancies by allowing relocation within a building rather than relying on staff to unlock doors to allow residents to evacuate to the outside. For details on horizontal exits, see 7.2.4.

Internally Illuminated. See 3.3.113.
Means of Egress. See 3.3.121.

A means of egress, by definition, provides a path of egress travel to a public way. In effect, the *Code* emphasizes the need to move building occupants to a safe place. In means of egress arrangements on university campuses, military bases, resorts, and other large complexes, there are numerous areas a building occupant could reach before reaching a public way that affords the intended level of safety from a building fire. It is the *Code*'s intent that occupants be able to move to a safe place from which they can continue to move away from the burning building as necessary. At that safe point, *Code* requirements cease to apply. This concept provides the basis for A.7.8.1.1, which is applicable to illumination of means of egress. The annex text states that the extent to which illumination needs to be provided outside the building—that is, within the exit discharge portion of the means of egress—should be to either a public way or a distance away from the building that is considered safe, whichever is closest to the building being evacuated.

From every location in a building, a means of egress or path of travel is required over which a person can move to gain access to the outside or to a place of safety. Any persons who gain entrance to a building usually have available to them that ingress route by which to egress. However, one important consideration makes egressing more than just reversing one's route of entry, especially if emergency conditions exist. This reverse route might consist of features that, though they were not obstacles upon entrance, prove to be such upon egress. For example, a door hinged to swing in the direction of entry can become an obstacle when one attempts to leave the building in the opposite direction. The door swings against the flow of traffic—a flow that, during emergency egress, is greatly increased as compared with the leisurely flow of people entering a building.

A basic principle of the *Code* requires that every component of a means of egress be operable by and under the control of the occupants attempting egress. Where the *Code* makes exceptions to this basic concept—for example, in health care occupancies where locked doors are permitted if it is necessary for the clinical needs of the patients—it does so by substituting requirements adequate to achieve the same level of life safety as would be provided if the means of egress system were fully under the control of the building occupants.

Photoluminescent. See 3.3.146.

Ramp. See 3.3.158.

Requirements for ramps used in a means of egress are found in 7.2.5.

Self-Luminous. See 3.3.175.

Severe Mobility Impairment. See 3.3.179.

See the definition of *accessible means of egress* in 3.3.121.1, which uses the term *severe mobility impairment*. See also 7.5.4.1, which requires areas accessible to persons with severe mobility impairment to be provided with accessible means of egress.

Smokeproof Enclosure. See 3.3.186.

7.1.3 Separation of Means of Egress.

(See also Section 8.2.)

7.1.3.1 Exit Access Corridors. Corridors used as exit access and serving an area having an occupant load exceeding 30 shall be separated from other parts of the building by walls having not less than a 1-hour fire resistance rating in accordance with 8.2.3.

Exception No. 1: This requirement shall not apply to existing buildings, provided the occupancy classification does not change.

Exception No. 2: This requirement shall not apply where otherwise provided in Chapters 12 through 42.

Paragraph 7.1.3.1 requires protection via fire-rated corridor walls of exit access corridors serving more than 30 occupants. Note that the requirement for the corridor walls to be fire resistance–rated, which is not a requirement for the floor/ceiling or roof/ceiling assemblies forming the top and bottom of the corridor compartment, provides separation only between the corridor and other spaces on the same floor. To provide the necessary degree of separation between the corridor and spaces on floors above or below, one then has to rely on the provisions of 8.2.5.1, for example, to ensure that the floor is smoke resisting—or rely on the requirements of subsection __.1.6 of an occupancy chapter, for example, to require fire resistance–rated floor construction.

Exception No. 1 to 7.1.3.1 exempts existing corridors, provided that the occupancy classification does not change. Therefore, if the occupancy classification of an existing building changes, the 1-hour corridor wall requirement applies, unless the specific occupancy involved has different requirements. Most of the occupancy chapters establish exit access corridor wall requirements that supersede the requirements of 7.1.3.1. Also, some of the occupancy chapters establish corridor wall requirements for existing buildings. These special corridor wall provisions usually appear in subsection __.3.6 of an occupancy chapter. For example, 14.3.6 and 40.3.6 address special requirements for corridor walls in new educational occupancies and industrial occupancies, respectively. If no special requirements appear in subsection __.3.6, the provisions of 7.1.3.1 prevail.

Paragraph 7.1.3.1 does not require corridors but does require that, where corridors do exist and where they serve an area having an occupant load of more than 30 persons, they must be separated from other (that is, noncorridor) spaces on that floor by corridor walls. The construction of the barrier forming the corridor walls and the opening protection are regulated by 8.2.3. Wall segments that serve both as a corridor wall and as part of an exit enclosure must meet the more stringent provisions required for the enclosure of exits. Similarly, wall segments that serve both as a corridor wall and enclosure protection of hazardous contents areas must meet the more stringent provisions required for protection from the hazardous contents area.

Exhibit 7.4 is an example of the protection of exit access corridors required by 7.1.3.1. Note the difference in the required protection for the corridor wall segments serving also as enclosure protection from the hazardous contents area (see Section 8.4) and as part of the enclosure of an exit (see 7.1.3.2).

7.1.3.2 Exits.

7.1.3.2.1 Where this *Code* requires an exit to be separated from other parts of the building, the separating construction shall meet the requirements of Section 8.2 and the following.

(a)* The separation shall have not less than a 1-hour fire resistance rating where the exit connects three stories or less.

(b)* The separation shall have not less than a 2-hour fire resistance rating where the exit connects four or more stories. The separation shall be constructed of an assembly of noncombustible or limited-combustible materials and shall be supported by construction having not less than a 2-hour fire resistance rating.

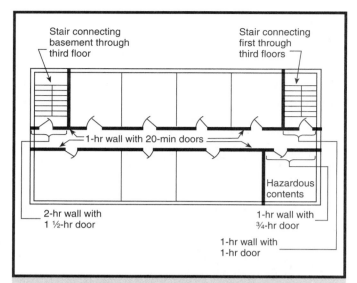

Stair connecting basement through third floor

Stair connecting first through third floors

1-hr wall with 20-min doors

Hazardous contents

2-hr wall with 1 ½-hr door

1-hr wall with ¾-hr door

1-hr wall with 1-hr door

Exhibit 7.4 *Protection of exit access corridors.*

A.7.1.3.2.1(a) and (b) In existing buildings, existing walls in good repair consisting of lath and plaster, gypsum wallboard, or masonry units can usually provide satisfactory protection for the purposes of this requirement where a 1-hour fire resistance rating is required. Further evaluation might be needed where a 2-hour fire resistance rating is required. Additional guidelines can be found in Appendix D of NFPA 914, *Recommended Practice for Fire Protection in Historic Structures,* and in the *SFPE Handbook of Fire Protection Engineering.*

Exception No. 1: In existing non-high-rise buildings, existing exit stair enclosures shall have not less than a 1-hour fire resistance rating.

Exception No. 2: In existing buildings protected throughout by an approved, supervised automatic sprinkler system in accordance with Section 9.7, existing exit stair enclosures shall have not less than a 1-hour fire resistance rating.

Exception No. 3: One-hour enclosures in accordance with 28.2.2.1.2, 29.2.2.1.2, 30.2.2.1.2, and 31.2.2.1.2 shall be permitted as an alternative.

(c) Openings in the separation shall be protected by fire door assemblies equipped with door closers complying with 7.2.1.8.

(d) Openings in exit enclosures shall be limited to those necessary for access to the enclosure from normally occupied spaces and corridors and for egress from the enclosure.

Exception No. 1: Openings in exit passageways in covered mall buildings as provided in Chapters 36 and 37 shall be permitted.

Exception No. 2: In buildings of Type I or Type II construction, existing fire-protection rated doors shall be permitted to interstitial spaces provided that such space meets the following criteria:

(a) The space is used solely for distribution of pipes, ducts, and conduits.

(b) The space contains no storage.

(c) The space is separated from the exit enclosure in accordance with 8.2.3.

(e) Penetrations into and openings through an exit enclosure assembly shall be prohibited except for the following:

(1) Electrical conduit serving the stairway
(2) Required exit doors
(3) Ductwork and equipment necessary for independent stair pressurization
(4) Water or steam piping necessary for the heating or cooling of the exit enclosure
(5) Sprinkler piping
(6) Standpipes

Exception No. 1: Existing penetrations protected in accordance with 8.2.3.2.4 shall be permitted.

Exception No. 2: Penetrations for fire alarm circuits shall be permitted within enclosures where fire alarm circuits are installed in metal conduit and penetrations are protected in accordance with 8.2.3.2.4.

(f) Penetrations or communicating openings shall be prohibited between adjacent exit enclosures.

Exits must provide protection from fire originating inside or outside the exit. Protection from fire originating within the enclosure is accomplished by prohibiting use of the enclosure for any purpose that could possibly interfere with the exit functioning as a protected path of travel (see 7.1.3.2.3) and by limiting the combustibility of wall and ceiling interior finish materials within exit enclosures (see 7.1.4). Details on interior wall and ceiling finish are contained in Section 10.2 and subsection ___.3.3 of occupancy Chapters 12 through 42. Protection from fire originating outside the exit enclosure is accomplished by separating construction having a specified degree of fire resistance and by careful control of openings into the exit enclosure itself. The only openings permitted in the fire barriers between the exit and the building spaces are those needed to enter the exit from any normally occupied space and those needed to leave the exit to reach the exit discharge. In other words, only openings necessary for an occupant to enter and leave the exit enclosure are permitted.

The degree of fire resistance required depends on the number of stories or floor levels the exit connects, not the height of the building. It is possible to have stairs in a high-rise building connecting only three or fewer stories. In such a case, the enclosing construction is not required to be more than 1-hour fire resistance rated. See Exhibit 7.5. Where connecting four stories or more, exit stairs must be separated from other spaces within the building by 2-hour fire resistance–rated noncombustible or limited-combustible construction. Where connecting three or fewer stories, the separation is permitted to be reduced to a minimum 1-hour rating. Via Exception No. 1 and Exception No. 2 to 7.1.3.2.1(b), existing exit stair enclosures in existing non-high-rise buildings or in existing sprinklered buildings—regardless of height—are permitted a 1-hour fire resistance rating. As indicated by Exception No. 3 to 7.1.3.2.1(b), some occupancy chapters reduce the 2-hour fire resistance–rated construction requirement to 1 hour— even for new construction—if the building is protected throughout by an approved, supervised automatic sprinkler system. An example can be found in 28.2.2.1.2.

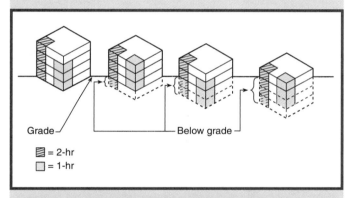

Exhibit 7.5 *Required separating construction for exit stairs.*

The doors in walls of exit enclosures are to be 1-hour fire protection–rated door assemblies where used in 1-hour fire resistance–rated enclosures, and 1¹/₂-hour fire protection–rated door assemblies where used in 2-hour fire resistance–rated enclosures. See 8.2.3.2.3.

If a pair of fire doors opening in the same direction without a center mullion post between the door panels is to be used in an opening in an exit enclosure, it would be prudent to choose a pair of doors listed for use without an overlapping astragal plate. Pairs of doors with an astragal must be arranged to close

in a particular sequence to ensure full closure. A coordinator is required to accomplish the sequential closing, and the record of coordinators functioning properly is poor. However, a pair of doors without an astragal could pass considerable smoke through any gap between the meeting edges of the doors and into the exit; therefore, the use of pairs of fire doors opening in the same direction into an exit enclosure should be discouraged.

The <u>only openings permitted</u> in the exit enclosure <u>are for doors providing access into the enclosure from normally occupied space</u>s and for doors providing egress from the enclosure into the exit discharge. These doors are required to be self-closing fire doors as described in 7.2.1.8. No opening through the exit enclosure walls—including a door—is permitted from storage rooms, closets, boiler rooms, equipment spaces, utility rooms, electrical vaults, or similar spaces that are not normally occupied. Panels providing access to building spaces cannot be installed in the walls or ceilings of exit enclosures, regardless of whether the panels have a fire resistance rating.

Exception No. 1 to 7.1.3.2.1(d) permits openings from normally unoccupied spaces within the exit enclosures created by exit passageways in covered mall buildings as detailed in Chapters 36 and 37. By consulting the provisions of 36.4.4.2.5 and 37.4.4.2.5, one finds that rooms housing building service equipment, service elevators, and janitor closets—spaces not normally occupied—are permitted to open directly onto exit passageways. For an explanation of this deviation from the requirement of 7.1.3.2.1(d), see the commentary following 36.4.4.2.5 and 37.4.4.2.5.

Exception No. 2 to 7.1.3.2.1(d) recognizes that, in some existing buildings, it is safe to permit unoccupied rooms to open directly onto an exit stair enclosure. For example, in some existing hospitals, it is common to have interstitial spaces above the ceiling of each floor for purposes of running pipes, ducts, and conduits. The interstitial spaces appear much like separate floors. For example, in an elevation view of a four-story hospital, it would appear that there are eight stories. Every other floor would be occupied by patients, and the alternating "floors" created by the interstitial spaces would house the service pipes, ducts, and conduits. This arrangement is depicted in Exhibit 7.6. Access to the patient floors and to the interstitial space "floors" would be by means of fire–protection rated doors from the stair enclosure. See Exception No. 2 to 7.1.3.2.1(d) for the other criteria necessary to permit the existing situation to be continued in use.

Exit enclosure penetrations generally are

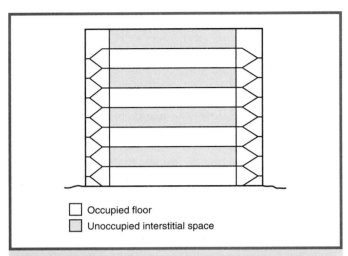

Exhibit 7.6 *Unoccupied interstitial spaces with openings to exit stair enclosure.*

prohibited for new construction. Penetrations for ductwork for pressurization of smokeproof enclosures might be permitted (see 7.2.3), but penetration by other ductwork is prohibited. Similarly, penetrations are permitted for the following:

(1) Water and steam piping necessary for the heating and cooling of the exit enclosure
(2) Electrical conduit serving the exit enclosure
(3) Fire alarm system circuit wiring installed in metallic conduit and serving the building
(4) Standpipe and sprinkler piping serving the building

Openings to the exterior of the building are not regulated, provided that there is no potential fire exposure from an adjacent source. Such openings need not be protected with fire protection–rated assemblies, because they are not separating the exit from other parts of the building. See 7.2.2.5.2.

7.1.3.2.2 An exit enclosure shall provide a continuous protected path of travel to an exit discharge.

Subparagraph 7.1.3.2.2 emphasizes that exit enclosures, and the protection they afford the occupants, must be continuous. It is a fundamental premise that, once an occupant has been provided the level of protection afforded by an exit, that level of protection must be maintained to the exit discharge.

This subparagraph prohibits an exit stair or exit ramp arrangement that requires a person to leave

the exit enclosure, become exposed to conditions on a floor, and then re-enter the exit enclosure to continue moving to the exit discharge. Exhibit 7.7 shows an unacceptable arrangement. The discontinuity of leaving the stair enclosure, becoming exposed to potential fire conditions on a floor, and then re-entering the exit enclosure to continue moving to the level of exit discharge creates too great a potential for endangering occupants.

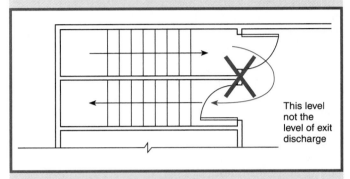

Exhibit 7.7 *Unacceptable arrangement for enclosing a stair serving as a required exit.*

7.1.3.2.3* An exit enclosure shall not be used for any purpose that has the potential to interfere with its use as an exit and, if so designated, as an area of refuge. *(See also 7.2.2.5.3.)*

A.7.1.3.2.3 This provision prohibits the use of exit enclosures for storage or for installation of equipment not necessary for safety. Occupancy is prohibited other than for egress, refuge, and access. The intent is that the exit enclosure essentially be "sterile" with respect to fire safety hazards.

Subparagraph 7.1.3.2.3 prohibits the use of an exit enclosure for any purpose that could potentially interfere with its use as an exit or as an area of refuge. For example, use of an exit enclosure to house vending machines, copying machines, or storage, or to run electrical distribution wires and cables to areas of the building, is prohibited. Standpipes and emergency lighting that are part of the life safety features are permitted only if their arrangement does not interfere with the passage of people. This limitation covers more than mechanical obstruction of the egress path; it includes any use that could interfere with the use of the exit. See also 7.1.10.1 and 7.2.2.5.3.

The preceding prohibitions also apply to exit passageways because they too are exit enclosures.

7.1.4 Interior Finish in Exits.

The flame spread of interior finish on walls and ceilings shall be limited to Class A or Class B in exit enclosures in accordance with Section 10.2. *(See Chapters 12 through 42 for further limitations.)*

Subsection 7.1.4 regulates interior wall and ceiling finish within exit enclosures, such as enclosed exit stairs. The intent is to minimize the possibility of fire spreading into and within the exit enclosure. Except as modified by occupancy Chapters 12 through 42, the interior wall and ceiling finish in exit enclosures is required to be either Class A or Class B as detailed in Section 10.2. Because 7.1.4 does not prohibit the use of the provisions of 10.2.8.1, Class C interior wall and ceiling finish would be permitted within an exit enclosure if the enclosure and adjacent areas of the building were protected by automatic sprinklers.

As explained in the commentary following 4.4.2.2, the occupancy chapters can modify the requirements of Chapters 1 through 4 and Chapters 6 through 11. In some cases, the modification results in a more stringent requirement. In others, the result is a relaxation of a base chapter requirement. Interior finish is addressed in detail in Section 10.2, with each occupancy setting specific limitations in subsection ___.3.3 of an occupancy chapter. For both new and existing health care occupancies, the interior finish requirements of 18.3.3 and 19.3.3 result in more stringent criteria for wall and ceiling finish within exit enclosures than are required by 7.1.4. For example, where new interior wall finish is applied within the exit enclosure of an existing nonsprinklered health care occupancy, the requirement is for Class A—not Class B—materials. If the enclosure and adjacent smoke compartments of the building are sprinklered, the requirement is for Class B—not Class C—materials. In this case, the occupancy chapter, considering the needs of its typical occupant group (that is, persons incapable of self-preservation for whom a defend-in-place strategy is employed), tailors its provisions to help achieve the intended minimum level of life safety.

7.1.5* Headroom.

Means of egress shall be designed and maintained to provide headroom as provided in other sections of this *Code* and shall be not less than 7 ft 6 in. (2.3 m) with projections from the ceiling not less than 6 ft 8 in. (2 m) nominal height above the finished floor. The minimum ceiling height shall be maintained for not less than two-thirds of the ceiling

area of any room or space, provided the ceilin remaining ceiling area is not less than 6 ft 8 Headroom on stairs shall be not less than 6 ft 8 in. (2 m) and shall be measured vertically above a plane parallel to and tangent with the most forward projection of the stair tread.

Exception No. 1: In existing buildings, the ceiling height shall not be less than 7 ft (2.1 m) from the floor with no projection below a 6-ft 8-in. (2-m) nominal height from the floor.

Exception No. 2: Headroom in industrial equipment access areas provided in Chapter 40 shall be permitted.

The minimum 6-ft 8-in. (203-cm) clearance that is to be maintained below any projections descending from the minimum ceiling height is intended to be measured as a nominal dimension. Thus, it is the intent of 7.1.5 to recognize the clearance provided in passing through the door frame associated with a standard 6-ft 8-in. (203-cm) door. Subsection 7.1.5 and the dimensional criteria of 7.2.2.2.1 also allow the 6-ft 8-in. (203-cm) minimum headroom height on stairways. Subsection 7.1.5 explains how to measure the headroom on stairs. Headroom measurement is illustrated in Exhibit 7.8. The nominal dimension, 6 ft 8 in. (203 cm), is permitted for projections descending from the ceiling and for stairs.

[handwritten margin note: NOT CLEAR HEIGHT AS IN CLEAR WIDTH]

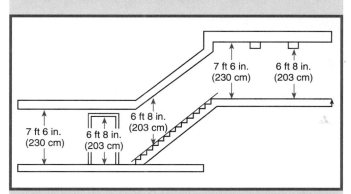

Exhibit 7.8 *Headroom measurement.*

Prior editions of the *Code* left unanswered the question of how many 6-ft 8-in. (203-cm) projections are too many, so as to leave too little area with at least 7 ft 6 in. (230 cm) of headroom height. This edition of the *Code* requires the 7-ft 6-in. minimum headroom to be maintained for at least two-thirds of the ceiling area of any room or space.

For industrial occupancies, 40.2.5.6 extends the use of the minimum 6-ft 8-in. (203-cm) headroom allowance to industrial equipment access walkways, platforms, ramps, and stairs that serve as a component of the means of egress for not more than 20 people.

A.7.1.5 For the purpose of this requirement, projections include devices such as lighting equipment, emergency signaling equipment, environmental controls and equipment, security devices, signs, and decorations that are typically limited in area.

7.1.6 Walking Surfaces in the Means of Egress.

7.1.6.1 General. Walking surfaces in the means of egress shall comply with 7.1.6.2 through 7.1.6.4.

Exception: Existing walking surfaces shall be permitted where approved by the authority having jurisdiction.

The vast majority of a building occupant's egress travel time is spent on walking surfaces rather than passing through doors and some of the other egress components detailed in Section 7.2. Yet, prior editions of the *Code* remained silent on the needed characteristics of walking surfaces.

The current provisions applicable to walking surfaces are minimal. They address elevation changes that might cause tripping hazards, maximum slope, and slip resistance that relates to safe use. It is expected that the provisions of 7.1.6 will be further expanded for future editions of the *Code*. For example, by addressing slip resistance (see 7.1.6.4), in the generalized subsection applicable to walking surfaces, it is no longer necessary to repeat similar provisions for the applicable components of means of egress, such as ramps, stair treads, and landing surfaces.

7.1.6.2 Changes in Elevation. Abrupt changes in elevation of walking surfaces shall not exceed ¼ in. (0.6 cm). Changes in elevation exceeding ¼ in. (0.6 cm), but not exceeding ½ in. (1.3 cm), shall be beveled 1 to 2. Changes in elevation exceeding ½ in. (1.3 cm) shall be considered a change in level and shall be subject to the requirements of 7.1.7.

7.1.6.3 Level. Walking surfaces shall be nominally level. The slope of a walking surface in the direction of travel shall not exceed 1 in 20 unless the ramp requirements of 7.2.5 are met. The slope perpendicular to the direction of travel shall not exceed 1 in 48.

7.1.6.4* Slip Resistance. Walking surfaces shall be slip resistant under foreseeable conditions. The walking surface of each element in the means of egress shall be uniformly slip resistant along the natural path of travel.

A.7.1.6.4 The foreseeable conditions are the conditions that are likely to be present at the location of the walking surface during the use of the building or area. A foreseeable condition of a swimming pool deck is that it is likely to be wet.

Regarding the slip resistance of treads, it should be recognized that, when walking up or down stairs, a person's foot exerts a smaller horizontal force against treads than is exerted when walking on level floors. Therefore, materials used for floors that are acceptable as slip resistant (as described by ASTM F 1637, *Standard Practice for Safe Walking Surfaces*) provide adequate slip resistance where used for stair treads. Such slip resistance includes the important leading edges of treads, the part of the tread that the foot first contacts during descent, which is the most critical direction of travel. If stair treads are wet, there is an increased danger of slipping, just as there is an increased danger of slipping on wet floors of similar materials. A small wash or drainage slope on exterior stair treads is, therefore, recommended to shed water. (See Templer, J. A., *The Staircase: Studies of Hazards, Falls, and Safer Design*, Cambridge, MA: MIT Press, 1992.)

7.1.7 Changes in Level in Means of Egress.

7.1.7.1 Changes in level in means of egress shall be achieved either by a ramp or a stair where the elevation difference exceeds 21 in. (53.3 cm).

7.1.7.2* Changes in level in means of egress not in excess of 21 in. (53.3 cm) shall be achieved either by a ramp or by a stair complying with the requirements of 7.2.2. The presence and location of ramped portions of walkways shall be readily apparent. The tread depth of such stair shall be not less than 13 in. (33 cm), and the presence and location of each step shall be readily apparent.

Exception: Tread depth in industrial equipment access areas as provided in Chapter 40 shall be permitted.

Prior to 1988, the *Code* prohibited stairs where changes of elevation were less than 21 in. (53.3 cm), because steps spanning such small elevation differences go unnoticed and create conditions conducive to missteps. The minimum 13-in. (33-cm) tread depth and the requirement to make the presence and location of each step readily apparent were established to help reduce missteps. The annex text for 7.1.7.2 provides additional details on stair arrangement to help reduce the problem. Exhibit 7.9 illustrates an arrangement intended to meet the requirements of 7.1.7.2. In the figure, tread depth has been increased over the usual minimum 11 in. (27.9 cm) to a minimum of 13 in. (33 cm). The leading edge of each tread has been marked to make its presence and location readily apparent.

Small elevation differences connected by ramps might also go unnoticed and create conditions conducive to missteps. The second sentence of 7.1.7.2 was added to cover the hazards of trips and other missteps on ramps whose presence is not clear to persons walking in an area where a small change of elevation is otherwise not evident. Although the consequences of a misstep are usually not as severe on ramps as they are on stairs, hazard mitigation is needed.

Single risers and other combinations of a few risers are considered stairs and must meet all the requirements for stairs. Because such risers are considered stairs, handrails are needed along the natural path of egress travel.

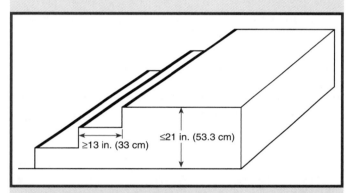

Exhibit 7.9 *Special features for stairs involving changes in elevation of 21 in. (53.3 cm) or less.*

A.7.1.7.2 Aside from the problems created for persons who are mobility impaired, small changes of elevations in floors are best avoided because of the increased occurrence of missteps where the presence of single steps, a series of steps, or a ramp is not readily apparent. While small changes of elevation pose significant fall risks in the case of individual movement, they are even more undesirable where crowds traverse the area.

A contrasting marking stripe on each stepping surface can be helpful at the nosing or leading edge so that the location of each step is readily apparent, especially when viewed in descent. Such stripes should be not less than 1 in. (2.5 cm) but should not exceed 2 in. (5.0 cm) in width. Other methods could include a relatively higher level of lighting, contrasting colors, contrasting textures, highly prominent handrails, warning signs, a combination thereof, or other similar means. The construction or application of marking stripes should be such that slip resistance is consis-

tent over the walking surface and no tripping hazard is created *(see also A.7.2.2.3.3)*. Depending on the distractions of the surroundings, the familiarity of users with a particular small change of level, and especially the number of people that might be in a group traversing the change of level (thereby reducing visibility of the level changes), a strong argument can be made for the elimination of steps and ramps that might pose a risk of missteps.

7.1.8 Guards.

Guards in accordance with 7.2.2.4 shall be provided at the open sides of means of egress that exceed 30 in. (76 cm) above the floor or grade below.

7.1.9 Impediments to Egress.

Any device or alarm installed to restrict the improper use of a means of egress shall be designed and installed so that it cannot, even in case of failure, impede or prevent emergency use of such means of egress unless otherwise provided in 7.2.1.6 and Chapters 18, 19, 22, and 23.

7.1.10 Means of Egress Reliability.

7.1.10.1* Means of egress shall be continuously maintained free of all obstructions or impediments to full instant use in the case of fire or other emergency.

For a given occupancy, the combination of requirements contained in Chapters 7 and 8 and in the corresponding occupancy chapter provide for an adequately sized and protected means of egress system. This provision emphasizes the importance of maintaining the egress system usable at all times. In the case of a Class A mercantile occupancy, the minimum 5-ft (1.5-m) aisle width required by 36.2.5.6 and 37.2.5.6 must not, subsequent to receipt of the store's occupancy permit, be filled with mid-aisle displays that reduce the exit access aisle width to less than 5 ft (1.5 m). Similarly, in a business occupancy with an exit stair of the minimum 44-in. (112-cm) width required by 7.2.2.2.1, the stair width must not be reduced by the introduction of a mechanized chair lift that is installed, for example, to comply with legislation mandating accessibility for persons with mobility impairments. In an apartment building complex, the required width of the outside exit discharge sidewalk that runs along the side of the building must not be reduced by the presence of a trash dumpster on either a temporary or permanent basis.

Paragraph 7.1.10.1 does not designate responsibility for keeping the means of egress (that is, exit accesses, exits, and exit discharges) free and clear of obstructions. The individuals responsible for each facility—whether managers, owners, or operators—must make certain that the required egress components are maintained in usable condition. The authority having jurisdiction has the power to enforce this requirement.

A.7.1.10.1 A proper means of egress allows unobstructed travel at all times. Any type of barrier including, but not limited to, the accumulations of snow and ice in those climates subject to such accumulations is an impediment to free movement in the means of egress.

7.1.10.2 Furnishings and Decorations in Means of Egress.

Paragraphs 7.1.10.2.1 through 7.1.10.2.3 provide guidance for the interior decoration and maintenance of buildings that serve, for example, as restaurants and theaters where the mirrored wall surfaces and excessive decoration that are used to establish a style or theme often camouflage and, in some cases, obstruct exits. For such occupancies, care must be taken to ensure that the required, standard, well-marked exit access that leads to an unobstructed exit is not obscured in the pursuit of period or style authenticity. For example, a restaurant that is heavily decorated with red wall coverings might use green exit signs to help meet the requirements of these paragraphs, despite the fact that Chapter 7 does not specify exit sign color.

7.1.10.2.1 No furnishings, decorations, or other objects shall obstruct exits, access thereto, egress therefrom, or visibility thereof.

7.1.10.2.2 There shall be no obstructions by railings, barriers, or gates that divide the open space into sections appurtenant to individual rooms, apartments, or other occupied spaces. Where the authority having jurisdiction finds the required path of travel to be obstructed by furniture or other movable objects, the authority shall be permitted to require that such objects be secured out of the way or shall be permitted to require that railings or other permanent barriers be installed to protect the path of travel against encroachment.

Paragraph 7.1.10.2.2 relates to the arrangement of furniture, as well as to the arrangement of railings, gates, or barriers found in lobbies, foyers, waiting spaces, or staging areas of businesses, hospitals, health care

clinics, hotels, and apartments. Because these large spaces are often subdivided by furniture (for example, chairs, tables, and plants) or by railings and gates, furnishings must be prevented from blocking access to exits. This paragraph recommends fastening furnishings so that they are clear of access to exits or placing railings around furnishings to ensure that they are held within a fixed area and cannot be easily moved or rearranged. This prevents obstruction of the access to exits. The *Code* recognizes the problem created by storage that is placed within the exit access aisles of storage rooms in mercantile occupancies, which is a violation of *Code* requirements. Both Chapters 36 and 37, in accordance with the provisions of 36.2.5.10(4) and 37.2.5.10(4), require fixed barriers to emphasize that such exit access is a specific condition that must be met to permit egress to pass through storerooms.

7.1.10.2.3 Mirrors shall not be placed on exit doors. Mirrors shall not be placed in or adjacent to any exit in such a manner as to confuse the direction of egress.

Section 7.2 Means of Egress Components

Many different components of a building or structure are encountered while traversing a means of egress. These components comprise the means of egress and include such items as doors, including necessary hardware; stairs and ramps, including handrails and guards; horizontal exits; exit passageways; and areas of refuge. The composition, properties, use, limits, and function of such components have an effect on the usability of the means of egress system.

Portable ladders, rope ladders, and similar devices are not recognized by the *Code* as providing any portion of the required capacity of a means of egress. In addition, they should not be considered in any way as an upgrade of an inadequate existing means of egress. Although such devices might have been used to provide additional safety under emergency conditions, they are unreliable and can lead to a false sense of security. They are often unusable by small children, older people, persons with disabilities, or those who simply have not been trained in the use of these devices. See also A.7.1.1.

The components of a means of egress are required to meet certain standards, be built in a prescribed manner, and perform at a level specified by the *Code*. Depending on whether the component is part of the access to an exit, is itself the exit, or is the exit discharge, the applicable requirements might differ. In most instances, the requirements applicable to a given component are the same regardless of where it is used within the means of egress system. For example, for new stair construction, the riser height must not exceed 7 in. (17.8 cm); the tread depth must be at least 11 in. (27.9 cm); and the handrails must be installed at both sides. These requirements apply regardless of where the stairs are placed within the means of egress (for example, unenclosed exit access stairs, enclosed exit stairs, or outside exit discharge stairs).

7.2.1 Doors.

7.2.1.1 General.

Doors serve multiple purposes that relate to the comfort and safety of building occupants and provide protection from the following:

(1) Weather, drafts, noise, and disturbance from adjoining areas
(2) Trespass by unauthorized persons
(3) Fire and smoke, with which this *Code* is concerned

The three broad categories of doors, each providing varying degrees of protection from fire and smoke, are as follows:

(a) *Non-Fire–Rated Door.* A non-fire–rated door is a door such as is used in one- and two-family dwelling construction. While not fire–rated, such doors do provide a limited degree of protection, especially from smoke, if closed.

(b) *Fire-Rated Assembly.* A fire–rated assembly is referred to as a fire door. It has passed the standard fire test for doors, NFPA 252, *Standard Methods of Fire Tests of Door Assemblies.*[2] A fire door withstands a severe fire and hose stream exposure for the period specified by a *Code* requirement. The fire protection rating specified by the *Code* varies, depending on the uses and occupancy type involved.

(c) *Smoke-Stop Door.* A smoke-stop door is usually of lighter construction than a fire door. Its function is to provide a temporary barrier against the passage of heat, smoke, and gases.

None of these doors will perform satisfactorily if left open during a fire, thus allowing the entry of fire and combustion products into what should be a safer area than the fire area. The history of fires is full of tragic examples of those who died because of an open door. There are also many examples of people saved because a door was closed. Less frequent, but nonetheless tragic, are those situations in which doors needed for escape were blocked or locked, resulting in dire consequences. Numerous *Code* requirements, particularly those contained in 7.2.1, address these concerns.

Some types of doors that are designed to prevent the spread of fire through wall openings for property protection purposes might be unsuitable for use in means of egress. Certain doors pose the potential for entrapment if they cannot be operated or personal injury if they are used. This category includes various rolling-shutter and sliding doors. However, under limited conditions, certain horizontal sliding doors are permitted to be within the exit access path. For example, Exception No. 6 to 7.2.1.4.1 is used by 39.2.2.2.7, 40.2.2.2.4, and 42.2.2.2.4 to permit existing sliding doors to be positioned within the exit access path of existing business, industrial, and storage occupancies if additional criteria are met. The provisions help to ensure that the door will be open when conditions in the door's vicinity are tenable for people movement, and closed once it is no longer safe for persons to seek egress via that exit access path.

See also 7.2.1.14 for a specialized form of sliding door that has desirable life safety features.

7.2.1.1.1 A door assembly in a means of egress shall conform to the general requirements of Section 7.1 and to the special requirements of 7.2.1. Such an assembly shall be designated as a door.

Subparagraph 7.2.1.1.1 advises that the *Code* uses the term *door* to mean door assembly. Thus, wherever the *Code* refers to a rated door or fire door, it is referring to the entire door assembly. If any single component is not properly provided, installed, and functioning, the assembly is not a fire protection–rated assembly. For example, if a listed fire door leaf and frame are installed with positive latch and hinges but the required self-closing device is omitted, the assembly cannot be considered a fire door and is not considered to have any particular fire protection rating.

7.2.1.1.2 Every door and every principal entrance that is required to serve as an exit shall be designed and constructed so that the path of egress travel is obvious and direct. Windows that, because of their physical configuration or design and the materials used in their construction, have the potential to be mistaken for doors shall be made inaccessible to the occupants by barriers or railings.

The purpose of the barrier rails required by 7.2.1.1.2 is to prevent one from walking through a window. Such barriers are not required to comply with the requirements of 7.2.2.4 applicable to guards. For example, intermediate rails or balusters spaced to meet the 4-in. (10.1-cm) diameter sphere requirement of 7.2.2.4.6(3) are not needed. A simple barrier rail, without ornamental grille-like fill or closely spaced balusters, will adequately warn occupants to avoid walking into a glass wall or large window pane.

7.2.1.1.3* For the purposes of Section 7.2, a building shall be considered to be occupied at any time it is open for general occupancy, any time it is open to the public, or at any other time it is occupied by more than 10 persons.

A.7.2.1.1.3 Although 7.2.1.1.3 and 7.2.1.5.1 permit locking of means of egress doors where a building is not considered occupied, the *Code* does not intend to permit occupants to be locked beyond their control in buildings or building spaces, except for detention and correctional occupancies and health care occupancies.

Many industrial, storage, and business occupancy buildings are never open to or accessible to the public; the only occupants are employees and authorized visitors. Therefore, the term *occupied* in 7.2.1.1.3 also includes the condition of being *open for general occupancy*. That is, the facility is *operating* or *functioning*.

The intent of permitting a building with 10 or fewer occupants to be considered unoccupied—if it is not open for general occupancy and not open to the public—is to allow small security details or small cleaning crews inside a building without applying all the *Code* requirements. This will allow doors to be locked and lights to be turned off without violating the *Code*. The limited number of occupants will use lights as they need them and then turn them off. In the case of security personnel, they will carry their own lights and keys. For example, see the criteria of Exception No. 2(d) to 7.2.1.5 for making a key available to occupants, which is applicable to a special type of key-operated dead bolt lock.

The wording of A.7.2.1.1.3 reiterates that it is not the intent to allow people, no matter how few the number, to be locked in a building without a ready means of egress. Even in detention and correctional facilities, where locked doors are permitted, 24-hour staffing must be provided in sufficient numbers to start the release of locks necessary for emergency evacuation or rescue and initiate other necessary emergency actions within 2 minutes of alarm. See 22.7.1.1 and 23.7.1.1.

7.2.1.2 Width.

Door width measurements might be used in calculating egress capacity or in determining if a minimum door width requirement is met. Depending on the purpose for which the door width measurement is used, the allowable encroachments on width vary. See commentary to A.7.2.1.2.1 and A.7.2.1.2.2.

7.2.1.2.1* **Egress Capacity Width.** In determining the egress width for swinging doors for purposes of calculating capacity, only the clear width of the doorway when the door is open 90 degrees shall be measured. In determining the egress width for other types of doors for purposes of calculating capacity, only the clear width of the doorway when the door is in the full open position shall be measured. Clear width of doorways shall be measured between the face of the door and the stop in accordance with 7.3.2.

Exception: In determining the width of any existing door installation for purposes of calculating capacity, only the clear width of the doorway when the door is in the full open position shall be measured. Clear width shall be determined in accordance with 7.3.2.

A.7.2.1.2.1 Figures A.7.2.1.2.1(a) and A.7.2.1.2.1(b) illustrate the method of measuring door width for purposes of calculating egress capacity.

The method of measuring clear width required by 7.2.1.2.1 is for purposes of determining the egress capacity of the door, not for meeting minimum door size requirements specified elsewhere in the *Code*. The egress capacity width will be less than the door leaf width, because deductions in width are made for the stops built into the door frame and for the

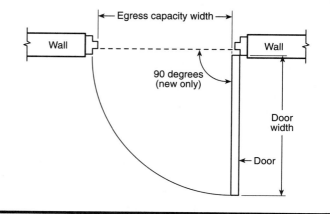

Figure A.7.2.1.2.1(a) Door width—egress capacity.

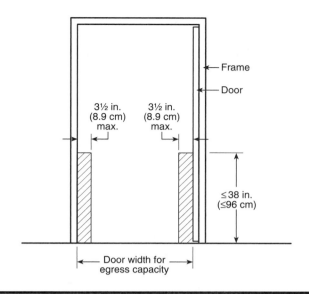

Figure A.7.2.1.2.1(b) *Door width—egress capacity with permitted obstructions.*

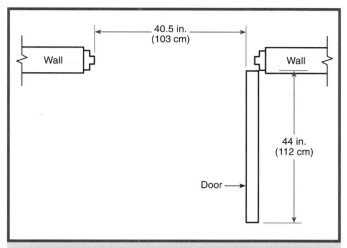

Exhibit 7.10 *Egress capacity width for new door open 90 degrees and for existing door that opens 90 degrees.*

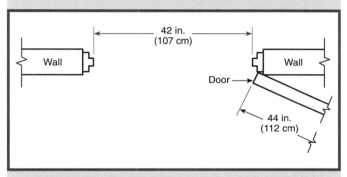

Exhibit 7.11 *Egress capacity width for existing door that opens more than 90 degrees.*

encroachment created by the thickness of the door where its stile edge extends into the door opening.

The width measurement for new doors is to be made with the door open 90 degrees if the door can be opened at least 90 degrees. Doors that open more than 90 degrees—permitting the stile edge of the door to move out of the door opening—receive no additional width credit based on the inability of most people to push the door, especially a door with a self-closing device, open more than 90 degrees prior to moving through the door opening. The exception to 7.2.1.2.1 exempts existing doors from the 90-degree criterion. Rather, the egress capacity width measurement for existing doors is made with the door in the fully open position—regardless of whether that position is less than or more than 90 degrees.

Exhibit 7.10 depicts a new door. It also might apply to an existing door that opens exactly 90 degrees. The 44-in (112-cm) width door leaf provides approximately 40.5 in. (103 cm) of egress capacity width, measured in accordance with 7.2.1.2.1. Note the reduction in egress width, as compared to the door leaf width, caused by the stop in the door frame at the left of the figure and the stile edge of the door at the right of the figure.

Exhibit 7.11 depicts an existing door that can be opened more than 90 degrees so that the stile edge of the door moves out of the framed door opening. The 44-in (112-cm) width door leaf provides approximately 42 in. (107 cm) of egress capacity width, mea-

sured in accordance with 7.2.1.2.1. Note the reduction in egress width, as compared to the door leaf width, caused by the stops at each side of the door frame.

Exhibit 7.12 depicts an existing door that can be opened less than 90 degrees due to a pipe column that prevents the door from opening any further. The 44-in (112-cm) width door leaf provides approximately 38 in. (96.5 cm) of egress capacity width, measured in accordance with 7.2.1.2.1. Note the reduction in egress width, as compared to the door leaf width, caused by the stop at the left of the figure and the door leaf itself at the right of the figure. The 38-in. (96.5-cm) dimension is measured to the face of the door at a point where the intersection with the door creates a right angle, thus ensuring that the minimum width is measured.

The wording of 7.2.1.2.1 permits the clear width to be measured in accordance with 7.3.2. Thus, projections of not more than 3 ½ in. (8.9 cm) are permitted at each side of the door, provided that such projec-

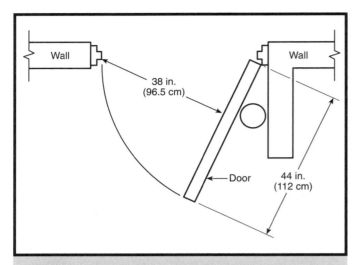

Exhibit 7.12 *Egress capacity width for existing door that opens less than 90 degrees.*

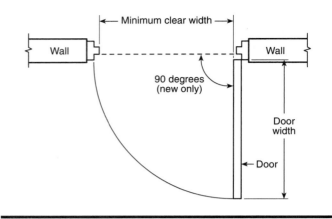

Figure A.7.2.1.2.2(a) *Minimum clear width.*

tions do not extend above 38 in. (96 cm) in height. For example, for a 40-in. (102-cm) width door opening, although there might be only 33 in. (84 cm) of *true* clear width between the projections near floor level, capacity calculations are permitted that assume an available clear width of 40 in. (102 cm).

These concepts are illustrated in Figures A.7.2.1.2.1(a) and A.7.2.1.2.1(b).

7.2.1.2.2* Minimum Width Measurement. For purposes of determining minimum door width, the door leaf width shall be used unless clear width is specified. Where clear width is specified, there shall be no projections into the required clear door opening width, measured in accordance with 7.2.1.2.1, lower than 34 in. (86 cm) above the floor or ground. Projections into the required clear door opening width that are not less than 34 in. (86 cm) but that do not exceed 80 in. (203 cm) above the floor or ground shall be limited to the hinge side of each door opening and shall not exceed 4 in. (10.1 cm).

Projections exceeding 80 in. (203 cm) above the floor or ground shall not be limited.

A.7.2.1.2.2 Figures A.7.2.1.2.2(a) and A.7.2.1.2.2(b) illustrate the method of measuring clear width for doors.

In cases where a chapter requires a door width, for example, of not less than 36 in. (91 cm), this requirement can be met by a door leaf of the minimum specified width if the term clear width does not appear as part of the minimum width requirement. A pair of cross-corridor doors subject to such a requirement would be judged under the following criteria:

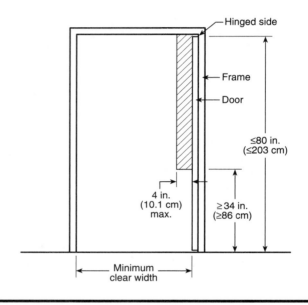

Figure A.7.2.1.2.2(b) *Minimum clear width with permitted obstructions.*

(1) Each door leaf is required to be not less than 36 in. (91 cm) in width.
(2) The pair of doors is required to provide sufficient, clear, unobstructed width (which will be less than the door leaf width measurement) to handle its assigned occupant load, based on a calculation using the appropriate egress capacity factor in Table 7.3.3.1.

Where swinging doors do not open at least 90 degrees, the clear width of the doorway should be measured between the face of the door and the stop.

It is not the intent to regulate projections above the 80-in. (203-cm) height.

Subparagraph 7.2.1.2.2 details two methods for measuring door width for application of minimum door width provisions. The two methods are provided to recognize that some provisions in the *Code* allow for the door leaf width to be used to satisfy a minimum door width requirement, while other provisions require a door's clear width measurement to be used. For door width measurements used in egress capacity calculations see 7.2.1.2.1.

Where clear width is to be used to judge whether a *Code* provision for minimum door width is met, no projections into the clear width within 34 in. (86 cm) of the floor are permitted. Thus, where 7.2.1.2.3 requires door openings to be at least 32 in. (81 cm) in clear width, that full clear width must be available near the floor to accommodate, for example, the width of a wheelchair and the wheelchair user's arms and hands.

At heights above 34 in. (86 cm), encroachment on clear width is permitted only on the hinge side of the door opening and, then, only if the projection into the clear width does not exceed 4 in. (10.1 cm). The allowance for the projection is intended to permit panic hardware or fire exit hardware—installed at least 4 in. (10.2 cm) above the minimum 30-in. (76-cm) mounting height—to encroach on clear width. The 4-in. (10.1-cm) encroachment allowance is likely to be insufficient to exempt the projections created by most hydraulic door closers. Note, however, that projections above the floor of more than 80 in. (203 cm) are permitted. Thus, for many doors that exceed the minimum, nominal height of 80 in. (203 cm), the projection created by a door closer is not an issue.

These concepts are illustrated in Figures A.7.2.1.2.2(a) and A.7.2.1.2.2(b).

7.2.1.2.3 Minimum Width. Door openings in means of egress shall be not less than 32 in. (81 cm) in clear width. Where a pair of doors is provided, not less than one of the doors shall provide not less than a 32-in. (81-cm) clear width opening.

Exception No. 1:   Exit access doors serving a room not exceeding 70 ft² (6.5 m²) and not required to be accessible to persons with severe mobility impairments shall be not less than 24 in. (61 cm) in door leaf width.

Exception No. 2:   Doors serving a building or portion thereof not required to be accessible to persons with severe mobility impairments shall be permitted to be 28 in. (71 cm) in door leaf width.

Exception No. 3:   In existing buildings, the existing door leaf width shall be not less than 28 in. (71 cm).

Exception No. 4:   This requirement shall not apply as otherwise provided in Chapters 22 and 23.

Exception No. 5:   This requirement shall not apply to interior doors as provided in Chapter 24.

Exception No. 6:   A power-operated door leaf located within a two-leaf opening shall be exempt from the minimum 32-in. (81-cm) single-leaf requirement in accordance with Exception No. 2 to 7.2.1.9.

Exception No. 7:   This requirement shall not apply to revolving doors as provided in 7.2.1.10.

Generally, various doors are encountered as one travels the means of egress route. Each door opening must provide sufficient clear width to accommodate the number of people expected to pass through that doorway during emergency egress and must meet any absolute minimum widths specified by other provisions of the *Code*. The door width necessary to accommodate a specified number of persons is calculated from the occupant load served and the capacity factors applicable to level egress components as provided in Table 7.3.3.1. Regardless of the occupant load served and the corresponding calculated minimum usable width required, new door openings generally are not permitted to be less than 32 in. (81 cm) in clear width. This width permits the passage of wheelchairs. However, this minimum width might not be adequate for the normal use of the doorway for purposes other than emergency egress. Thus, door widths in excess of those required by the *Code* are often provided voluntarily for purposes of day-to-day function.

If a door in a new business occupancy is to serve 120 occupants, for example, the minimum clear door width calculated from the perspective of occupant load served would be 24 in. (61 cm). However, a door providing only 24 in. (61 cm) of clear width would not satisfy 7.2.1.2.3, which requires that, as a minimum, the door must provide 32 in. (81 cm) of clear width. Because more than one requirement affects door width, a comparison must be made between the calculated minimum width and the more arbitrary minimum width requirement of 7.2.1.2.3. Having performed the comparison, the number that results in the greater width—in this case, the 32 in. (81 cm)—must be used.

Where another *Code* section specifies a width

greater than 32 in. (81 cm), the greater width must be provided. Generally, the greater width is specified in terms of clear width. For example, in new health care occupancies the minimum width for patient room doors and cross-corridor doors is 41.5 in. (105 cm) in clear width [see 18.2.3.5(1)]. The 41.5-in. (105-cm) minimum clear width requirement unintentionally connotes a precision and accuracy that one might expect resulted from a detailed research program. In reality, the 41.5-in. (105-cm) requirement represents an attempt to quantify the clear width realized when a typical 44-in. (112-cm) wide door leaf is swung to its fully open position. For many editions of the *Code*, new health care occupancies specified the required minimum as 44 in. (112 cm) of door leaf width, not of clear opening. If a minimum 44-in (112-cm) door leaf had its swing restricted to not more than 90 degrees, it often would provide a clear width opening of less than the 41.5 in. (105 cm) currently required.

The exceptions to 7.2.1.2.3 modify the minimum 32-in. (81-cm) clear width requirement so as to recognize smaller door widths for the specific situations they address.

Exception No. 1 to 7.2.1.2.3 permits a small room, likely occupied by only a couple of people and not required to be accessible to people with severe mobility impairments, to use a 24-in. (61-cm) width door. This exception does not specify clear width, so a minimum 24-in. (61-cm) wide door leaf would be sufficient.

Exception No. 2 to 7.2.1.2.3 also addresses doors serving spaces not required to be accessible to people with severe mobility impairments. In lieu of a room size, the exception can be applied regardless of occupant load, but the door leaf width must be at least 28 in. (71 cm).

Earlier editions of the *Code* specified that no single door in a doorway is permitted to be less than 28 in. (71 cm) wide. To keep from automatically creating a situation of noncompliance where there had previously been compliance, Exception No. 3 to 7.2.1.2.3 exempts existing buildings from the minimum 32-in. (81-cm) clear width requirement if the door width, that is, the leaf width, is at least 28 in. (71 cm).

For security and operations purposes, Exception No. 4 to 7.2.1.2.3 permits detention and correctional facilities to have doors of smaller width. See Chapters 22 and 23.

Chapter 24 establishes that doors within dwelling units are within the *means of escape* and not the *means of egress*. It permits such doors, whether new or existing, to be a minimum of 28 in. (71 cm)

in leaf width. Exception No. 5 to 7.2.1.2.3 recognizes this allowance.

It is the intent of the *Code* that a doorway not create a bottleneck in the means of egress. At times, another component of the means of egress might be larger than required, creating the illusion of a bottleneck at an appropriately sized doorway. However, a door opening with a width that is adequate for the occupant load served and with at least a 32-in. (81-cm) clear width is sufficient. A door serving a hallway often is not as wide as the hallway. This is illustrated in Exhibit 7.13. Because operational features of the occupancy, in addition to the occupant load, are considered in determining required corridor width, the corridor might be wider than the exit door serving the corridor. In this example of a new school, the corridor is required by 14.2.3.2 to be 6 ft (1.8 m) wide, as a minimum, and wider only if it serves more than 360 persons. The exit door is required by 7.2.1.2.3 to be 32 in. (81 cm) wide, as a minimum, and wider only if it serves more than 160 persons.

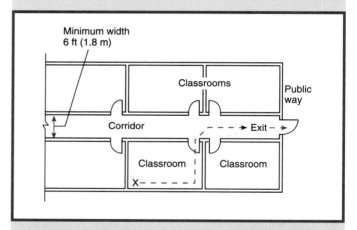

Exhibit 7.13 *Exit door width and corridor width relationship.*

In a health care facility, the corridor and doorway widths are usually much wider than the occupant load dictates. In this instance, the sizes of the corridor and door openings are governed by the necessity to move patients on gurneys. Patients are often connected to equipment and must be moved horizontally along the means of egress route.

Note that, since the 1997 edition, the *Code* no longer restricts door leaf width to a maximum of 48 in. (122 cm). Provided that the door and its hardware

are maintained in good working order, there is insufficient reason to limit the maximum width of a door.

7.2.1.3 Floor Level. The elevation of the floor surfaces on both sides of a door shall not vary by more than ½ in. (1.3 cm). The elevation shall be maintained on both sides of the doorway for a distance not less than the width of the widest leaf. Thresholds at doorways shall not exceed ½ in. (1.3 cm) in height. Raised thresholds and floor level changes in excess of ¼ in. (0.64 cm) at doorways shall be bevelled with a slope not steeper than 1 in 2.

Exception No. 1:   In one- and two-family dwellings and in existing buildings where the door discharges to the outside or to an exterior balcony or exterior exit access, the floor level outside the door shall be permitted to be one step lower than the inside, but shall not be in excess of 8 in. (20.3 cm) lower.

Exception No. 2:   In one- and two-family dwellings and existing buildings, a door at the top of a stair shall be permitted to open directly at a stair, provided that the door does not swing over the stair and the door serves an area with an occupant load of fewer than 50 persons.

The detailed dimensional tolerances specified for thresholds at door openings are intended to permit persons in wheelchairs to move easily through door openings. Given that arrangements meeting the criteria are useful to persons with disabilities, the same arrangement provides for the safe use of doors by other occupants.

In earlier editions, the *Code* permitted the floor level outside exterior doors to be one step lower, but not more than 8 in. (20.3 cm) lower, than the floor level inside the door. This was permitted to avoid blocking the outward swing of the door by a buildup of snow or ice. The requirements of 7.2.1.3 are practical for new construction because of the importance of avoiding tripping hazards and because other provisions of the *Code* require that the means of egress be maintained free of obstructions and protected from the weather, thus providing for the removal of snow or ice accumulations. One- and two-family dwellings and existing buildings continue to be permitted to use one exterior step.

Exception No. 2 to 7.2.1.3 recognizes an existing situation in which a door at the top of a stair opens directly at the stair without providing a level landing on the stair side of the door opening. In this case, however, the door swings away from the stair, rather than swinging over the stair. This is permitted in one- and two-family dwellings and existing buildings where the area served by the door has an occupant load of fewer than 50 persons. Exception No. 2 to 7.2.1.3 permits this situation as an exemption to the requirement that there be a level landing on each side of the door that is at least as deep in the direction of stair run as the door is wide. See Exhibit 7.14. The wording of Exception No. 2 to 7.2.1.3 is repeated as Exception No. 2 to 7.2.2.3.2 for consistency. Otherwise, the requirement that stairs have landings at door openings would apply without exception.

The exception does not permit the dangerous practice of swinging the door out over the stair, because it would force a person climbing the stairs to reach for the door knob and back away by descending to a tread located a riser or two lower in order to pull the door open while attempting to maintain stability on the stair. Neither does the exception permit another dangerous practice of opening a door directly at the bottom of a stair without providing a level landing on the stair side of the door opening. Such an action would force a person descending the stair to lean forward and downward to reach the latch release and then push the door open while standing on a tread located one or more risers above the base of the door while attempting to maintain stability on the stair.

Exhibit 7.14 *Door opening directly at the top of a stair, but not swinging over the stair.*

7.2.1.4 Swing and Force to Open.

The provisions regulating the direction of door swing appear in Chapter 7 in 7.2.1.4.2, 7.2.1.4.3, and

7.2.4.3.6(1). Subparagraph 7.2.1.4.2 requires a door serving a room or area with an occupant load of 50 or more persons to swing in the direction of egress travel. Subparagraph 7.2.1.4.3 requires a door used in an exit enclosure or serving a high hazard contents area to swing in the direction of egress travel. Subparagraph 7.2.4.3.6(1) requires a swinging fire door used in a horizontal exit to swing in the direction of egress travel. If none of these three requirements applies, a door is permitted to swing against the direction of egress travel. See commentary following 7.2.1.4.2.

7.2.1.4.1* Any door in a means of egress shall be of the side-hinged or pivoted-swinging type. The door shall be designed and installed so that it is capable of swinging from any position to the full required width of the opening in which it is installed.

Subparagraph 7.2.1.4.1 requires that doors within the means of egress be side-hinged or pivoted-swinging. These types of doors are most familiar to the general public, and their operation is readily understood.

Furthermore, 7.2.1.4.1 requires that the door be capable of swinging to the full required width of the opening. The required width is determined by two width considerations. The first consideration involves the width required for egress capacity purposes. For example, if a door in a business occupancy needs to accommodate 180 persons, the applicable capacity factor from Table 7.3.3.1 dictates that a 36-in. (91.4-cm) opening is to be provided. The second consideration involves the minimum clear width required regardless of occupant load served. For the business occupancy in question, the minimum clear width is specified in 7.2.1.2.3 as 32 in. (81 cm). In this example, the required width is the larger of the two widths—the 36 in. (91.4 cm) calculated from the egress capacity consideration.

Exception No. 1: Sliding doors as provided in Chapters 22 and 23, and doors as provided in Chapters 24, 32, and 33.

Some occupancy chapters provide exceptions to the requirement that doors be of the side-hinged or pivoted-swinging type. As referenced in Exception No. 1 to 7.2.1.4.1, detention and correctional occupancies allow certain sliding doors because swinging doors can become readily accessible weapons for use by

residents against staff. Also, Exception No. 1 to 7.2.1.4.1 advises that Chapters 24, 32, and 33, which apply to one- and two-family dwellings and residential board and care occupancies, do not require that doors be swinging. This exception recognizes the smaller numbers of persons using doors within dwellings and the familiarity those occupants have with the operation of other door types, such as sliding doors.

Exception No. 2: Where permitted in Chapters 12 through 42, horizontal sliding or vertical rolling security grilles or doors that are part of the required means of egress shall be permitted, provided that they meet the following criteria:

(a) Such grilles or doors shall remain secured in the full open position during the period of occupancy by the general public.

(b) On or adjacent to the grille or door, there shall be a readily visible, durable sign in letters not less than 1 in. (2.5 cm) high on a contrasting background that reads as follows:

> *THIS DOOR TO REMAIN OPEN*
> *WHEN THE BUILDING IS OCCUPIED*

(c) Doors or grilles shall not be brought to the closed position when the space is occupied.

(d) Doors or grilles shall be operable from within the space without the use of any special knowledge or effort.

(e) Where two or more means of egress are required, not more than half of the means of egress shall be equipped with horizontal sliding or vertical rolling grilles or doors.

Exception No. 2 to 7.2.1.4.1 allows for horizontal sliding or vertical rolling security grilles or doors to be used in lieu of side-hinged or pivoted-swinging type doors, provided that the exception is specifically allowed by the applicable occupancy chapter. This exception permits the type of security doors and grilles normally found in covered shopping mall buildings. Note that there is a difference between Exception No. 2(a) and Exception No. 2(c) to 7.2.1.4.1. Exception No. 2(a) requires that the door be fully open when the space is occupied by the public, while Exception No. 2(c) states that the door cannot be closed when the space is occupied. This allows the common practice of leaving the door partially closed at closing time and other times when restricting entry to the general public is desired. See the explanation of the term *occupied* in 7.2.1.1.3 and its commentary.

The following occupancies allow the use of the

horizontal sliding or vertical rolling doors complying with Exception No. 2 to 7.2.1.4.1. See referenced paragraphs for additional restrictions, if any, imposed by the occupancy chapter:

(1) Assembly occupancies (see 12.2.2.2.2, 13.2.2.2.2)
(2) Mercantile occupancies (see 36.2.2.2.6, 37.2.2.2.6)
(3) Business occupancies (see 38.2.2.2.6, 39.2.2.2.6)

Exception No. 3: Horizontal sliding doors complying with 7.2.1.14 shall be permitted.

Exception No. 3 to 7.2.1.4.1 recognizes the use of a special form of horizontal sliding door under detailed conditions. One of the characteristic features of this door is the operability in the direction of door travel when a specified force is applied in the direction of occupant travel. See also 7.2.1.14.

Exception No. 4: Doors to private garages, business areas, industrial areas, and storage areas with an occupant load not exceeding 10, where such private garages, business areas, industrial areas, and storage areas contain low or ordinary hazard contents, shall be exempt from this requirement.

Exception No. 4 to 7.2.1.4.1 recognizes that many private garages, small businesses, and industrial and storage buildings typically have only an overhead rolling or horizontal sliding door and no side-hinged door. Provided the maximum 10-person occupant load is not exceeded and there are no high-hazard contents, such doors are allowed to substitute for side-hinged or pivoted-swinging doors.

Exception No. 5: Revolving doors complying with 7.2.1.10 shall be permitted.

Exception No. 5 to 7.2.1.4.1 cross-references the provisions of 7.2.1.10, which apply to revolving doors. If this exception did not exist, it might be assumed, incorrectly, that revolving doors violate the requirement for doors to be side-hinged or pivoted-swinging.

Exception No. 6: Existing fusible link–operated horizontal sliding or vertical rolling fire doors shall be permitted to be used as provided in Chapters 12 through 42.

Exception No. 6 to 7.2.1.4.1 legitimizes provisions of Chapters 39, 40, and 42 that recognize existing fusible link–operated horizontal sliding or vertical rolling fire doors within the means of egress if additional conditions are met. Exception No. 6 to 7.2.1.4.1 is used by 39.2.2.2.7, 40.2.2.2.4, and 42.2.2.2.4 to permit existing sliding doors to be positioned within the exit access of existing business, industrial, and storage occupancies if additional criteria are met. These provisions help to ensure that the door is open when conditions in the door's vicinity are tenable for people movement and that it is closed once it is no longer safe for persons to seek egress via that exit access path.

A.7.2.1.4.1 Where doors are subject to two-way traffic, or where their opening can interfere with pedestrian traffic, an appropriately located vision panel can reduce the chance of accidents.

Swinging doors in horizontal or vertical rolling partitions complying with the following should be permitted in a means of egress where the following criteria are met:

(1) The door or doors comply with 7.2.1.4.
(2) The partition in which the doors are mounted complies with the applicable fire protection rating and closes upon smoke detection or power failure at a speed not exceeding 9 in./s (23 cm/s) and not less than 6 in./s (15 cm/s).
(3) The doors mounted in the partition are self-closing or automatic-closing in accordance with 7.2.1.8.

7.2.1.4.2 Doors required to be of the side-hinged or pivoted-swinging type shall swing in the direction of egress travel where serving a room or area with an occupant load of 50 or more.

Ideally, all doors in a means of egress would swing in the direction of egress travel. However, because of operational concerns there are cases where door swing in the direction of egress travel is not desirable. For example, a classroom door that swings into a corridor serving as an exit access for several classrooms might open against another door or against the flow of people and possibly restrict the width available as corridor exit access. The *Code* recognizes this danger and permits the classroom/corridor door from a room with an occupant load of fewer than 50 persons to swing against the direction of egress travel. This provision limits the number of people using a door that swings against egress travel to that which is safe. The *Code* also recognizes similar constraints with regard to an exterior exit door; although such a door is considered an exit, the *Code* does not require that it swing in the direction of egress travel unless it serves 50 or more occupants.

Exhibit 7.15 illustrates considerations involved in evaluating door swing direction as addressed in 7.2.1.4.2 and 7.2.1.4.3. Door C is permitted to swing back into the room if the room has an occupant load of fewer than 50 persons and does not have high hazard contents (see 7.2.1.4.3). Door D must swing in the direction of egress travel if the room has an occupant load of 50 or more. Door E, although it is an exit door, is not used in an exit enclosure, so it is permitted to swing back into the room if the occupant load is less than 50 and the room does not have high hazard contents. Doors A and B are related to the provisions of 7.2.1.4.4. They open into the corridor directly opposite each other. Although this does not violate any *Code* provision, it is preferable that doors not be arranged to swing in a direction that blocks the use of the corridor when both are open.

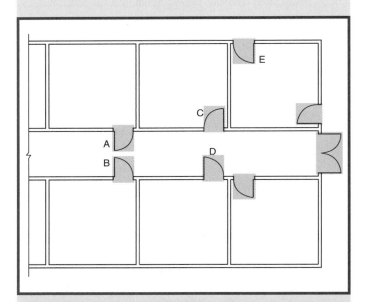

Exhibit 7.15 *Door swing considerations.*

Exception No. 1:   Doors in horizontal exits shall not be required to swing in the direction of egress travel where exempted in 7.2.4.3.6.

Exception No. 1 to 7.2.1.4.2 recognizes that the provisions of 7.2.4.3.6 exempt doors in horizontal exits from having to swing in the direction of egress travel in accordance with specific allowances and conditions for existing health care occupancies and existing de-

tention and correctional occupancies. For these occupancies, staff is expected to be able to control occupant movement at horizontal exit doors to prevent a crowd from pushing against a door that is arranged to open only by swinging back toward the occupants. See Exception No. 1 to 7.2.4.3.6(3).

Exception No. 2:   Smoke barrier doors shall not be required to swing in the direction of egress travel as provided in Chapter 19.

Exception No. 2 to 7.2.1.4.2 exempts smoke barrier doors from having to swing in the direction of egress travel in existing health care facilities. Such doors usually span the width of a corridor. Because existing health care occupancies are permitted to have corridors as narrow as 48 in. (122 cm), it might be impractical to install a pair of doors swinging in opposite directions. The single door recognized by the exception swings in the correct direction for occupants on one side and swings against the direction of egress travel for occupants on the other side. Because staff directs the egress movement necessary during an emergency, the direction of door swing problem is alleviated.

7.2.1.4.3 A door shall swing in the direction of egress travel where used in an exit enclosure or where serving a high hazard contents area, unless it is a door from an individual living unit that opens directly into an exit enclosure.

Subparagraph 7.2.1.4.3 addresses the common design in apartment buildings in which doors from the exit enclosure into apartment units normally swing into the apartment units. This design is common in a three-story, single-exit, garden-apartment. The swing of the door in this arrangement is not a significant concern. The exception also addresses another situation common to hotels where guest room doors frequently open directly into an exit enclosure created to enclose a formerly open stair. Because it is often necessary to use part of the corridor to create a stair landing for the newly enclosed exit stair, the exception offers some relief without compromising safety.

A conflict sometimes arises between the requirement of the *Life Safety Code* — that doors to hazardous contents areas swing in the direction of egress travel—and the desire of those who are responsible for explosion control—that doors to areas subject to explosion be required to swing inward to impede spreading the effects of a blast to adjacent rooms and spaces. In new construction, this conflict can usually be resolved if the hazardous contents area can be located on an outside wall of the main building; the required egress doors then open directly to the outside. This arrangement is not only desirable for life safety considerations but also easily allows the doors to swing outward; this design is also favorable for explosion relief. Subsequently, convenience doors that are not required for egress and that are positioned in partitions separating the hazardous area from the remainder of the building can be permitted to swing toward the hazardous area to help contain the explosion if so desired. In existing situations, or where the hazardous area must be located internal to a building and away from exterior walls, the conflict is not easily resolved. The authority having jurisdiction needs to work with the building owner, insurer, and other involved parties to determine how best to reduce the exposure hazard while adequately providing needed life safety to those who work in the hazardous area. See also Section 7.11.

7.2.1.4.4* During its swing, any door in a means of egress shall leave not less than one-half of the required width of an aisle, corridor, passageway, or landing unobstructed and shall not project more than 7 in. (17.8 cm) into the required width of an aisle, corridor, passageway, or landing, when fully open. Doors shall not open directly onto a stair without a landing. The landing shall have a width not less than the width of the door. *(See 7.2.1.3.)*

Exception: In existing buildings, a door providing access to a stair shall not be required to maintain any minimum unobstructed width during its swing, provided that it meets the requirement that limits projection to not more than 7 in. (17.8 cm) into the required width of a stair or landing when the door is fully open.

A.7.2.1.4.4 The requirement of 7.2.1.4.4 is not intended to apply to the swing of cross-corridor doors such as smoke barrier doors and horizontal exits.

Doors capable of swinging a full 180 degrees, so that they rest flat against the wall in which the door opening is installed, have a greater utility than doors capable of swinging only 90 degrees. The 180-degree swinging door can be fully opened into a corridor without significant intrusion on corridor width. The 90-degree swinging door, however, might either have to open into an unusually wide corridor or be set into an alcove, or otherwise be recessed so as not to exceed the maximum encroachment allowed by 7.2.1.4.4.

Note that 7.2.1.4.4 requires that, during its swing, a door must leave unobstructed at least one-half of the required width of a corridor. This requirement differs from requiring that, during its swing, a door must not obstruct more than one-half of the width of a corridor. For example, in a corridor that is required to be 44 in. (123 cm) wide but that is voluntarily constructed to be 56 in. (142 cm) wide, a 34-in. (86-cm) wide door—one that provides the minimum 32-in. (81-cm) clear width required by 7.2.1.2.3— would swing to encroach on 34 in. (86 cm) of the corridor width. Although this encroachment is more than one-half of the *actual* corridor width, it does leave one-half of the *required* corridor width [22 in. (56 cm)] unobstructed. Such an arrangement meets the requirement of 7.2.1.4.4.

Doors that swing within a recessed pocket of the corridor so as not to protrude into the required corridor width provide the best arrangement for clear passage through an exit access corridor. Doors that swing 180 degrees so that they come to rest against a wall and do not extend into more than 7 in. (17.8 cm) of required corridor width provide an acceptable arrangement. A door that swings 90 degrees so that it comes to rest in the path of travel is considered not to encroach excessively on the exit access corridor width if not more than 7 in. (17.8 cm) of the required width of the corridor remains obstructed. Any door swinging into the corridor must leave at least one-half of the required corridor width unobstructed during its entire swing. See Exhibit 7.16.

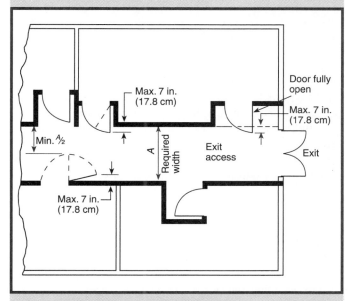

Exhibit 7.16 *Door swing into a corridor.*

Doors serving as an entrance into an enclosed stair should not unduly block the stair landing or the stairs. Ideally, the door would not reduce the required width either during its swing or while at rest. However, the *Code* does allow encroachment on the stair landing as shown in Exhibit 7.17. Where the total occupant load of all floors served by the stair is fewer than 50 persons, 7.2.2.2.1 permits a 36-in. (91-cm) wide stair; in this case, the $B \geq A/2$ rule shown in Exhibit 7.17 would require that the clearance between the leading edge of the opening door and stair newel post be at least 18 in. (45.7 cm). However, for most stairs, 7.2.2.2.1 requires a 44-in. (112-cm) clear width. In cases such as these, the $B \geq A/2$ rule would require that the clearance between the leading edge of the opening door and stair newel post be at least 22 in. (56 cm).

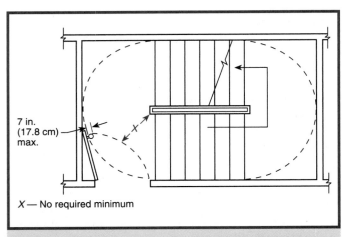

7 in. (17.8 cm) max.

X — No required minimum

Exhibit 7.18 *Encroachment during door swing not limited in existing buildings.*

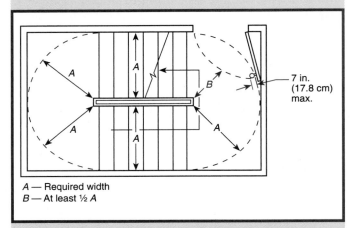

A — Required width
B — At least ½ *A*

Exhibit 7.17 *Minimum required unobstructed clearance with door encroaching on landing in new buildings.*

An acceptable arrangement for a door opening onto a stair landing in an existing building is shown in Exhibit 7.18. In lieu of a $B \geq A/2$ rule, existing stairs are not required to maintain given clearance between the leading edge of the opening door and stair newel post. However, the maximum 7-in. (17.8-cm) encroachment when the door is fully open still applies.

7.2.1.4.5 The forces required to fully open any door manually in a means of egress shall not exceed 15 lbf (67 N) to release the latch, 30 lbf (133 N) to set the door in motion, and 15 lbf (67 N) to open the door to the minimum required width. Opening forces for interior side-hinged or pivoted-swinging doors without closers shall not exceed 5 lbf (22 N). These forces shall be applied at the latch stile.

Exception No. 1:   The opening force for existing doors in existing buildings shall not exceed 50 lbf (222 N) applied to the latch stile.

Exception No. 2:   The opening forces for horizontal sliding doors shall be as provided in Chapters 22 and 23.

Exception No. 3:   The opening forces for power-operated doors shall be as provided in 7.2.1.9.

The *Code* recognizes that several movements are necessary to operate a door from its closed to its fully open position. Subparagraph 7.2.1.4.5 identifies each of the movements and limits the force needed to accomplish each. As a result, the force required to unlatch the door is limited to 15 lbf (67 N); the force necessary to start the door in motion, or to overcome its inertia, is limited to not more than 30 lbf (133 N); and the force necessary to move the door to its fully open position is limited to not more than 15 lbf (67 N).

Care must be taken to ensure that the 30 lbf (133 N) needed to overcome the inertia of a door in a means of egress is not exceeded for doors opening into pressurized stairs. The pressure necessary to protect the stair often might be such that 30 lbf (133 N) is insufficient to open the door. The use of barometric relief dampers or other pressure-regulating methods might be required. See NFPA 92A, *Recommended Practice for Smoke-Control Systems*, Chapter 2.[3]

A person with a severe mobility impairment, such as someone who uses a wheelchair, might find it difficult or impossible to exert even the 15 lbf (67 N) specified by 7.2.1.4.5. Specification of a lower operating force for self-closing doors might adversely affect the door closer's ability to perform its intended function of returning an open door to the fully closed and latched position. For interior side-hinged or pivoted-swinging doors without closers, no conflict exists between the needs of a closer and those of a person with physical disabilities. Therefore, the *Code* specifies that such doors be operable when no more than 5 lbf (22 N) is applied at the latch stile.

Circumstances such as wet floors, smooth-soled shoes, and light body weight can render many people incapable of exerting 50 lbf (222 N) horizontally. Therefore, the maximum 50-lbf (222-N) operating requirement of earlier editions of the *Code* remains applicable only to existing doors via the provisions of Exception No. 1 to 7.2.1.4.5.

Exception No. 2 and Exception No. 3 address special situations where the operating force requirements of 7.2.1.4.5 cannot be applied. For horizontal sliding doors in detention and correctional occupancies, see 22.2.11.4 and 23.2.11.4. For requirements specific to power-operated doors, see 7.2.1.9.

7.2.1.4.6 Screen doors and storm doors used in a means of egress shall be subject to the requirements for direction of swing that are applicable to other doors used in a means of egress.

Various functional arrangements of screen or storm doors can be provided without allowing a door to swing against the direction of egress travel. A screen or storm door might be permitted to be used in proximity to a doorway with an ordinary door by providing a vestibule of sufficient size to allow the inner door to swing outward without interfering with the operation of the door at the outer end of the vestibule. See Exhibit 7.19.

7.2.1.5 Locks, Latches, and Alarm Devices.

An increase in theft, muggings, and similar crimes has led to the practice of providing extra security on exit doors and the exit access doors to which they lead. Such a practice, particularly where doors to exit stairs and exit discharges are involved, is an open invitation to tragedy in the event of fire or other emergency. The provisions of 7.2.1.5 are aimed at preventing locked doors in means of egress or any other unnecessary interference with the orderly movement of people through doors in the event of fire. The *Code* has attempted to accomplish this objective while

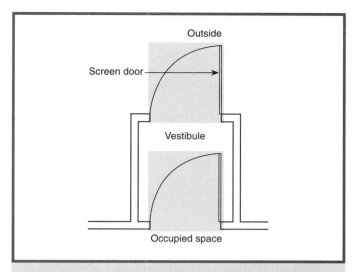

Exhibit 7.19 *Arrangement of vestibule leading to screen door complying with 7.2.1.4.6.*

maintaining features that are essential to security within the building.

A study of structural fires that occurred between 1981 and 1985 and that was reported to U.S. fire departments found that 117 fire deaths a year involved locks or gates that prevented escape.[4] Most of these deaths occurred in fires in residential occupancies. This report also described a number of incidents, including those that follow.

In a Texas dwelling fire, seven people died when a space heater ignited a sofa. Two of the adults who died were overcome while they struggled to unlock the dead bolt lock on the front door and the security bars.

In another Texas dwelling fire, three people died when a bedridden woman accidentally ignited her bedding with a cigarette. The other two victims died while trying to escape past burglar bars, double-cylinder dead bolt locks, and a security bar on a sliding glass door.

The report also found that makeshift security arrangements, such as windows that had been nailed shut, were factors in more multiple-fatality fires than in cases where more expensive security devices such as security bars and gates were used. The conflict between some security provisions and sound fire safety practices takes many forms. Also see Supplements 1 and 7.

The requirement that doors be easily openable from the egress side is consistent with the concept that all components in the means of egress must be under the control of the occupants. This requirement prohibits the use of key locks or hard-to-use devices, such as door handles or latches covered with glass that has to be broken. Where panic hardware or fire exit hardware is used, no device that might interfere with its operation can be used; however, this does not prevent the use of alarm connections that indicate that the door is in use.

Requirements for doors leading to exits also apply to doors that open to roofs where exit stairs terminate at a recognized roof exit and to exit discharge doors leading to the street or other public way.

7.2.1.5.1 Doors shall be arranged to be opened readily from the egress side whenever the building is occupied. Locks, if provided, shall not require the use of a key, a tool, or special knowledge or effort for operation from the egress side.

Subparagraph 7.2.1.5.1 establishes the principle that doors must be able to be opened easily from the side from which egress is to be made. It prohibits the installation of locks that require the use of a key to open the door from the inside. Subparagraph 7.2.1.1.3 defines *occupied* for the purpose of this requirement. The *Code* prohibits the installation and use of such a lock where the building is occupied.

Exception No. 1: *This requirement shall not apply where otherwise provided in Chapters 18 through 23.*

Exception No. 1 to 7.2.1.5.1 cross-references the provisions applicable to health care occupancies and detention and correctional occupancies where doors locked against egress by building occupants are permitted under specific conditions. For examples, see 18.1.1.1.5, the exceptions to 18.2.2.2.2, Exception No. 1 to 18.2.2.2.4, 18.2.2.2.5, and similar provisions in Chapter 19. Also see 22.2.11.2 and 22.2.11.5 through 22.2.11.10, and similar provisions in Chapter 23.

Exception No. 2: *Exterior doors shall be permitted to have key-operated locks from the egress side, provided that the following criteria are met:*

(a) Permission to use this exception is provided in Chapters 12 through 42 for the specific occupancy.

(b) On or adjacent to the door, there is a readily visible, durable sign in letters not less than 1 in. (2.5 cm) high on a contrasting background that reads as follows:

*THIS DOOR TO REMAIN UNLOCKED
WHEN THE BUILDING IS OCCUPIED*

(c) The locking device is of a type that is readily distinguishable as locked.

(d) A key is immediately available to any occupant inside the building when it is locked.

Exception No. 2 shall be permitted to be revoked by the authority having jurisdiction for cause.

Exception No. 2 to 7.2.1.5.1 is provided for key-operated locks under four conditions—one of which is that the appropriate occupancy chapter must specifically allow use of the exception. Compliance with Exception No. 2(c), which requires that the locking device be of a type readily distinguishable as locked, is to be judged by the authority having jurisdiction. Locks specifically designed to meet this requirement often have an indicating window mechanism that displays the word *open* when the device is in the unlocked position and displays the word *locked* when the device is in the locked position.

In permitting up to 10 persons in a locked building, the *Code* does not dismiss them as unimportant. The *Code* is recognizing that there are instances where a building must be occupied by security personnel or by janitorial crews when it is locked. Such persons are generally familiar with the premises, and the *Code* requires that they have keys available for egress when necessary. Also see commentary following A.7.2.1.1.3.

The following occupancies allow the use of the key-operated lock addressed by Exception No. 2. Additional restrictions that might be imposed by the occupancy chapter are contained in the paragraphs referenced within parentheses. For example, in new assembly occupancies, use of a key-operated lock is restricted to the main exit of a building with an occupant load of not more than 500 persons. In addition, the main exit of the building is required to consist of a single door or single pair of doors, and any latch on this door(s) is required to be released by panic hardware.

The occupancies are as follows:

(1) Assembly occupancies (see Exception No. 1 to 12.2.2.2.3, Exception No. 1 to 13.2.2.2.3)
(2) Mercantile occupancies (see 27.2.2.2.2, 37.2.2.2.2)
(3) Business occupancies (see 38.2.2.2.2, 39.2.2.2.2)

Exception No. 3: *Where permitted in Chapters 12 through 42, key operation shall be permitted, provided that the key cannot be removed when the door is locked from the side from which egress is to be made.*

Exception No. 3 to 7.2.1.5.1 permits the "captive key" hardware, as is permitted in lodging and rooming houses via the provisions of 26.2.8. The captive key lock has the potential for misuse and must be used carefully. The design of the lock is such that an occupant could unlock the door from the inside, thus freeing the key; move through the door, taking the key to the outside; lock the door from the outside; and leave the property—potentially leaving others locked in the building until another key is located and inserted into the lock. Thus, this lock is permitted limited use within the occupancy chapters.

7.2.1.5.2* Every door in a stair enclosure serving more than four stories shall allow re-entry from the stair enclosure to the interior of the building, or an automatic release shall be provided to unlock all stair enclosure doors to allow re-entry. Such automatic release shall be actuated with the initiation of the building fire alarm system.

Every door in a stair enclosure serving more than four stories in a new building [see Exception No. 2(a) to 7.2.1.5.2] must be arranged to permit re-entry into the building. However, the *Code* recognizes the need for varying degrees of security and does specify some equivalent alternatives. Stairway doors are permitted to be locked from the stairwell side if arranged to unlock automatically upon initiation of the fire alarm system.

Exception No. 1:   Doors on stair enclosures shall be permitted to be equipped with hardware that prevents re-entry into the interior of the building, provided that the following criteria are met:

(a)   There shall be not less than two levels where it is possible to leave the stair enclosure.

(b)   There shall be not more than four stories intervening between stories where it is possible to leave the stair enclosure.

(c)   Re-entry shall be possible on the top or next to top story that allows access to another exit.

(d)   Doors allowing re-entry shall be identified as such on the stair side of the door.

(e)   Doors not allowing re-entry shall be provided with a sign on the stair side indicating the location of the nearest door, in each direction of travel, that allows re-entry or exit.

Exception No. 1 to 7.2.1.5.2 permits some stair enclosure doors, regardless of occupancy, to be locked to prevent re-entry on selected floors. In such instances,

there must be at least two levels with unlocked doors providing a way out of the stairway, one of which must be the top floor or the next to top floor; the other is usually the door at the level of exit discharge. For stair enclosures serving more than six or seven stories, more than two unlocked re-entry points are required, because the *Code* prohibits more than four floors between floors that provide a way out of the stairway. This arrangement provides flexibility, especially in office buildings that, for security reasons, might need to prevent re-entry on certain floors. At the same time, the provision ensures that one can re-enter the building without having to travel up or down too many flights of stairs. Any door providing a way out of the stair enclosure must be identified as such on the stairwell side. See Exhibit 7.20.

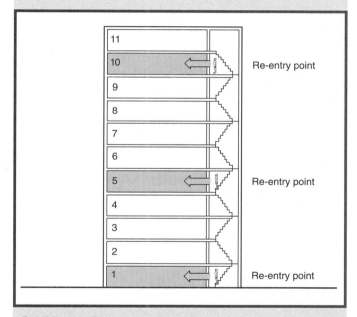

Exhibit 7.20 *Stairway re-entry option.*

Exception No. 2:   This requirement shall not apply to the following:

(a)   Existing installations as permitted in Chapters 12 through 42

(b)   Stair enclosures serving a building permitted to have a single exit in accordance with Chapters 11 through 42

(c)   Stair enclosures where otherwise provided in Chapters 18 and 22

Exception No. 2(b) to 7.2.1.5.2 recognizes that re-entry in buildings permitted to have a single exit is not necessary. In most single-exit buildings, the doors from the stairway open directly into the occupant space. Most of the single-exit buildings recognized by the occupancy chapters are no more than four stories in height and are exempt from the stairwell re-entry provisions via the base paragraph of 7.2.1.5.2.

A.7.2.1.5.2 It is intended that the re-entry provisions apply only to enclosed exit stairs, not to outside stairs. This arrangement makes it possible to leave the stairway at such floor if the fire renders the lower part of the stair unusable during egress or if the occupants seek refuge on another floor.

7.2.1.5.3 If a stair enclosure allows access to the roof of the building, the door to the roof either shall be kept locked or shall allow re-entry from the roof.

Subparagraph 7.2.1.5.3 was written to prevent building occupants from being trapped on a roof by a locked door that does not permit re-entry into the building. If security concerns, for example, dictate that rooftop doors are to be locked from the outside, then the doors also need to be locked from the inside to prevent unauthorized persons from going to the roof and becoming trapped. Note that there is no requirement that stair enclosure doors provide rooftop access. Heroic helicopter rescues from rooftops of burning buildings are Hollywood movie illusions that seldom happen in real life.

7.2.1.5.4* A latch or other fastening device on a door shall be provided with a releasing device having an obvious method of operation and that is readily operated under all lighting conditions. The releasing mechanism for any latch shall be located not less than 34 in. (86 cm), and not more than 48 in. (122 cm), above the finished floor. Doors shall be operable with not more than one releasing operation.

Subparagraph 7.2.1.5.4 requires that, where a latch or other similar device is provided, the method of operation of its releasing device must be obvious, even in the dark. The intention of this requirement is that the method of release be one that is familiar to the average person. Generally, a two-step release, such as a knob and an independent slide bolt, is not acceptable. In most occupancies, it is important that a single action unlatch the door. Furthermore, the *Code* specifies that the latch release mechanism be located at least 34 in. (86 cm) and not more than 48 in. (122 cm) above the floor, so that the latch release is located in a position that is neither too low nor too

high to be reached by persons in wheelchairs. Note that the minimum mounting height is a new *Code* requirement; via Exception No. 2 to 7.2.1.5.4, it is not retroactively applicable to existing installations. The maximum mounting height for the latch release also helps to ensure that children can reach the latch.

A.7.2.1.5.4 Examples of devices that might be arranged to release latches include knobs, levers, and panic bars. This requirement is permitted to be satisfied by the use of conventional types of hardware, whereby the door is released by turning a lever, knob, or handle or by pushing against a panic bar, but not by unfamiliar methods of operation such as a blow to break glass. The operating devices should be capable of being operated with one hand and should not require tight grasping, tight pinching, or twisting of the wrist to operate.

Exception No. 1:* Egress doors from individual living units and guest rooms of residential occupancies shall be permitted to be provided with devices that require not more than one additional releasing operation, provided that such device is operable from the inside without the use of a key or tool and is mounted at a height not exceeding 48 in. (122 cm) above the finished floor. Existing security devices shall be permitted to have two additional releasing operations. Existing security devices other than automatic latching devices shall not be located more than 60 in. (152 cm) above the finished floor. Automatic latching devices shall not be located more than 48 in. (122 cm) above the finished floor.

A.7.2.1.5.4 Exception No. 1 Examples of devices that, when used with a latch, can be arranged to require not more than one additional releasing operation include night latches, dead bolts, and security chains.

Exception No. 1 to A.7.2.1.5.4 recognizes the use, in residential living units and hotel guest rooms, of one additional device requiring release in new construction and two additional devices requiring release in existing installations. This exception allows an existing condition to continue where a hotel room door, for example, has hardware arranged such that one operation releases the security chain or bar (that is, night latch), another operation releases the dead bolt, usually via a thumb turn–type knob, and a third operation releases the door latch, usually by turning the door knob or operating the door lever. However, in new installations, if a night latch or security device is installed, then one operation would release the security device, and a second operation, such as turning the door knob or operating the door lever, would have to release both the dead bolt and normal door latch.

Also, the *Code* prohibits supplemental automatic latching security devices from being located more than 48 in. (122 cm) above the floor, even in existing buildings. This prohibition is intended to prevent children and wheelchair users from being trapped in a space when an automatic latching device that is located above reach range engages, locking the door. Existing security devices that must be physically engaged are permitted in locations not more than 60 in. (152 cm) above the floor, based on the assumption that the person engaging such a device is present to disengage it when needed.

Exception No. 2: The minimum mounting height for the releasing mechanism shall not be applicable to existing installations.

7.2.1.5.5 Where pairs of doors are required in a means of egress, each leaf of the pair shall be provided with its own releasing device. Devices that depend on the release of one door before the other shall not be used.

This requirement of 7.2.1.5.5 for independent releasing hardware applies only to pairs of doors in a common door opening where both door leaves are required for means of egress. If a second leaf is provided for a reason other than required egress, that leaf can have a releasing mechanism that requires the egress leaf to be released first. However, in such a case, the leaf not used for egress must be arranged so as not to be mistaken for the egress door.

Exception: Where exit doors are used in pairs and approved automatic flush bolts are used, the door leaf equipped with the automatic flush bolts shall have no doorknob or surface-mounted hardware. The unlatching of any leaf shall not require more than one operation.

The exception to 7.2.1.5.5 allows a pair of doors—both a part of the required means of egress—to be placed within a common frame, whereby one leaf has no visible releasing hardware but has approved automatic flush bolts that release that leaf when the other leaf, which has visible hardware, is released. Therefore, the user is directed to the leaf with releasing hardware and disengages the latch on that leaf, and the other leaf automatically unlatches to allow its use if pushed in the direction of door travel.

7.2.1.5.6* Devices shall not be installed in connection with any door on which panic hardware or fire exit hardware is required where such device prevents or is intended to prevent the free use of the door for purposes of egress.

Exception: This requirement shall not apply where otherwise provided in 7.2.1.6.

A.7.2.1.5.6 Examples of devices prohibited by this requirement include locks, padlocks, hasps, bars, chains, or combinations thereof.

It is not the intent of 7.2.1.5.6 to require panic hardware or fire exit hardware. That requirement is made by the various occupancy chapters. It is the intent, however, that where panic hardware or fire exit hardware is installed, no device or arrangement is to interfere with its intended function. The intended function is the release of the latch when pressure—such as that exerted by persons crushing up against the door—is applied to the bar or pad extending across the majority of the door width.

7.2.1.6 Special Locking Arrangements.

The special locking arrangements described in 7.2.1.6 include delayed-egress locks and access-controlled egress doors. See 7.2.1.6.1 and 7.2.1.6.2.

7.2.1.6.1 Delayed-Egress Locks. Approved, listed, delayed-egress locks shall be permitted to be installed on doors serving low and ordinary hazard contents in buildings protected throughout by an approved, supervised automatic fire detection system in accordance with Section 9.6, or an approved, supervised automatic sprinkler system in accordance with Section 9.7, and where permitted in Chapters 12 through 42, provided that the following criteria are met.

(a) The doors shall unlock upon actuation of an approved, supervised automatic sprinkler system in accordance with Section 9.7 or upon the actuation of any heat detector or activation of not more than two smoke detectors of an approved, supervised automatic fire detection system in accordance with Section 9.6.

(b) The doors shall unlock upon loss of power controlling the lock or locking mechanism.

(c) An irreversible process shall release the lock within 15 seconds upon application of a force to the release device required in 7.2.1.5.4 that shall not be required to exceed 15 lbf (67 N) nor be required to be continuously applied for more than 3 seconds. The initiation of the release process shall activate an audible signal in the vicinity of the door.

Once the door lock has been released by the application of force to the releasing device, relocking shall be by manual means only.

Exception: Where approved by the authority having jurisdiction, a delay not exceeding 30 seconds shall be permitted.

(d)* On the door adjacent to the release device, there shall be a readily visible, durable sign in letters not less than 1 in. (2.5 cm) high and not less than ⅛ in. (0.3 cm) in stroke width on a contrasting background that reads as follows:

PUSH UNTIL ALARM SOUNDS
DOOR CAN BE OPENED IN 15 SECONDS

A.7.2.1.6.1(d) In the event that the authority having jurisdiction has permitted increased operation time, the sign should reflect the appropriate time.

Delayed-egress locks prevent a door from being opened for 15 or 30 seconds under either nonemergency conditions or those encountered very early in a fire or similar emergency. Delayed-egress locks are to be used only where specifically permitted by the appropriate occupancy chapter. Use is further limited to buildings protected throughout by either an approved, supervised automatic fire detection system or an approved, supervised automatic sprinkler system. In addition, 7.2.1.6.1(a) requires that the locking devices unlock upon activation of that corresponding detection or sprinkler system. The required detection system provides early warning, or the alternately required sprinkler system provides early control of the fire, each to the degree necessary to make tolerable the delay experienced in waiting for the door to be unlocked.

Subparagraph 7.2.1.6.1(b) provides a fail-safe feature where, upon loss of the electrical power that controls the lock, immediate unlocking occurs.

Subparagraph 7.2.1.6.1(c) requires that, once the release device is manually activated, the door must unlock within 15 seconds [or 30 seconds with specific permission of the authority having jurisdiction via Exception to 7.2.1.6.1(c)]. This action must be irreversible and cannot require the user to maintain pressure on the release device for more than 3 seconds. To provide occupants attempting egress with cues to indicate that the system is functioning, a signal is sounded in the vicinity of the door. Additionally, the signage required by 7.2.1.6.1(d) provides useful, reassuring information.

After the door is physically opened (that is, swung on its hinges away from the door frame), it is permitted to be relocked by manual means only. Relocking generally involves returning the door to its closed and latched position and then resetting the system to engage the lock.

Note that the unlocking required by 7.2.1.6.1(a), (b), and (c) need not automatically open the door. Rather, the door is permitted to remain latched. The unlocking permits the user to open the door immediately by operating the releasing mechanism on the door. Security is not sacrificed. Of course, any exterior exit door is permitted to be locked against building entry at any time.

The following occupancies allow the use of delayed-egress locks in accordance with 7.2.1.6.1. Additional restrictions that might be imposed by the occupancy chapter are contained in the paragraphs referenced within parentheses. For example, health care occupancies, hotels and dormitories, and apartment buildings permit delayed-egress locks if all the conditions of 7.2.1.6.1 are met and only one such lock is encountered along any natural path of egress travel. Ambulatory health care facilities permit delayed-egress locks if all the conditions of 7.2.1.6.1 are met and the door is an exterior door.

The occupancies are as follows:

(1) Assembly occupancies (see 12.2.2.2.4, 13.2.2.2.4)
(2) Educational occupancies (see 14.2.2.2.3, 15.2.2.2.3)
(3) Day-care centers (see 16.2.2.2.3, 17.2.2.2.3)
(4) Health care occupancies (see Exception No. 2 to 18.2.2.2.4, Exception No. 2 to 19.2.2.2.4)
(5) Ambulatory health care centers (see 20.2.2.2, 21.2.2.2)
(6) Lodging and rooming houses (see exception to 26.2.7)
(7) Hotels (see Exception No. 1 to 28.2.2.2.2, Exception No. 1 to 29.2.2.2.2)
(8) Apartment buildings (see Exception No. 1 to 30.2.2.2.2, Exception No. 1 to 31.2.2.2.2)
(9) Board and care facilities [see Exception No. 1 to 32.3.2.2.2(3), Exception No. 1 to 33.3.2.2.2(3)]
(10) Mercantile occupancies (see 36.2.2.2.4, 37.2.2.2.4)
(11) Business occupancies (see 38.2.2.2.4, 39.2.2.2.4)
(12) Industrial occupancies (see 40.2.2.2.2)
(13) Storage occupancies (see 42.2.2.2.2, 42.8.2.2.2)

7.2.1.6.2 Access-Controlled Egress Doors. Where permitted in Chapters 11 through 42, doors in the means of egress shall be permitted to be equipped with an approved entrance and egress access control system, provided that the following criteria are met.

(a) A sensor shall be provided on the egress side and arranged to detect an occupant approaching the doors, and the doors shall be arranged to unlock in the direction of egress upon detection of an approaching occupant or loss of power to the sensor.

(b) Loss of power to the part of the access control system that locks the doors shall automatically unlock the doors in the direction of egress.

(c) The doors shall be arranged to unlock in the direction of egress from a manual release device located 40 in. to 48 in. (102 cm to 122 cm) vertically above the floor and within 5 ft (1.5 m) of the secured doors. The manual release device shall be readily accessible and clearly identified by a sign that reads as follows:

PUSH TO EXIT

When operated, the manual release device shall result in direct interruption of power to the lock—independent of the access control system electronics—and the doors shall remain unlocked for not less than 30 seconds.

(d) Activation of the building fire-protective signaling system, if provided, shall automatically unlock the doors in the direction of egress, and the doors shall remain unlocked until the fire-protective signaling system has been manually reset.

(e) Activation of the building automatic sprinkler or fire detection system, if provided, shall automatically unlock the doors in the direction of egress and the doors shall remain unlocked until the fire-protective signaling system has been manually reset.

The access-controlled egress doors addressed by 7.2.1.6.2 are intended to be locked from the outside of the building and require a magnetic card or similar instrument for authorized entry. However, such doors are to be arranged to be usable for egress purposes whenever the building is occupied. The reason the *Code* addresses these doors under the subject of special locking arrangements is that such doors generally do not have the door-mounted manual latch/lock release typically installed on a door. The absence of the door-mounted manual latch/lock release is to prevent a person on the outside from inserting a wire hanger or other tool between the gaps at the door edges to reach the release. Use of access-controlled egress doors requires specific occupancy chapter permission.

The following occupancies allow the use of access-controlled egress doors in accordance with 7.2.1.6.2. Additional restrictions that might be imposed by the occupancy chapter are contained in the paragraphs referenced within parentheses. For example, the provisions of 36.2.2.2.5 and 37.2.2.2.5, which apply to mercantile occupancies, permit access-controlled egress doors if all conditions of

7.2.1.6.2 are met and the building is protected throughout by an approved, supervised fire detection system or an approved automatic sprinkler system. The occupancies are as follows:

(1) Assembly occupancies (see 12.2.2.2.5, 13.2.2.2.5)
(2) Educational occupancies (see 14.2.2.2.3, 15.2.2.2.3)
(3) Day-care centers (see 16.2.2.2.3, 17.2.2.2.3)
(4) Health care occupancies (see Exception No. 3 to 18.2.2.2.4, Exception No. 3 to 19.2.2.2.4)
(5) Ambulatory health care centers (see 20.2.2.2, 21.2.2.2)
(6) Hotels (see Exception No. 2 to 28.2.2.2.2, Exception No. 2 to 29.2.2.2.2)
(7) Apartment buildings (see Exception No. 2 to 30.2.2.2.2, Exception No. 2 to 31.2.2.2.2)
(8) Board and care facilities [see Exception No. 2 to 32.3.2.2.2(3), Exception No. 2 to 33.3.2.2.2(3)]
(9) Mercantile occupancies (see 36.2.2.2.5, 37.2.2.2.5)
(10) Business occupancies (see 38.2.2.2.5, 39.2.2.2.5)
(11) Industrial occupancies (see 40.2.2.2.3)
(12) Storage occupancies (see 42.2.2.2.3, 42.8.2.2.2.2)

Subparagraph 7.2.1.6.2(a) provides for the door to unlock when a sensor detects an occupant approaching the door. This method is the normal primary means of releasing the lock to permit occupants to leave the building. If the sensor and the release system fail, the requirements of 7.2.1.6.2(c) provide a backup system consisting of a manual lock-release mounted at a usable height in the immediate vicinity of the door opening. The *Code* permits the manual release to be installed as much as 5 ft (1.5 m) from the secured door, recognizing that the glass side lights featured on many of these doors are an impractical place to install a manual release device.

Additionally, 7.2.1.6.2(b) requires a fail-safe feature to unlock the door immediately upon loss of the electrical power that controls the lock.

Subparagraphs 7.2.1.6.2(a), (b), and (c) work together to help ensure that the door is usable at all times, before and during a fire emergency. Subparagraphs 7.2.1.6.2(d) and (e) provide added assurance that the door is usable under fire emergency conditions. If the building has a fire alarm system, initiation of that system must unlock the door. If the building has either a fire detection system or a sprinkler system, activation of such system must unlock the door.

7.2.1.7 Panic Hardware and Fire Exit Hardware.

The difference between panic hardware and fire exit hardware is that fire exit hardware is tested and listed for use on fire-rated doors; panic hardware is not (see 7.2.1.7.2). As the terms imply, *panic hardware* and *fire exit hardware* are designed for ease of use and functional reliability under conditions that range from an orderly evacuation to that of hurried egress that might accompany a fast-spreading fire.

The provisions of 7.2.1.7 do not require panic hardware but set the requirements for such hardware if it is required by the applicable occupancy chapter.

The following occupancies require the use of panic hardware or fire exit hardware. Additional restrictions that might be imposed by the occupancy chapter are contained in the paragraphs referenced within parentheses.

The occupancies are as follows:

(1) Assembly occupancies (see 12.2.2.2.3, 13.2.2.2.3)
(2) Educational occupancies (see 14.2.2.2.2, 15.2.2.2.2)
(3) Day-care centers (see 16.2.2.2.2, 17.2.2.2.2)

Additionally, 7.11.5, which applies to high hazard contents areas, requires doors from spaces with occupant loads of more than five persons to be provided with a latch or lock only if panic hardware or fire exit hardware is installed to release the latch or lock.

Although not required by the other occupancy chapters, panic hardware or fire exit hardware is often used in other occupancies, either because an assembly occupancy is located within the occupancy or because it is used as a means of complying with 7.2.1.5.4.

7.2.1.7.1 Where a door is required to be equipped with panic or fire exit hardware, such hardware shall meet the following criteria:

(1) It shall consist of cross bars or push pads, the actuating portion of which extends across not less than one-half of the width of the door leaf and not less than 34 in. (86 cm), nor not more than 48 in. (122 cm), above the floor.

Exception: Existing installations shall be permitted to be minimum 30 in. (76 cm) above the floor.

(2) It shall be constructed so that a horizontal force not to exceed 15 lbf (66 N) actuates the cross bar or push pad and latches.

Panic hardware and fire exit hardware are required to be instantly and easily released. Panic hardware and fire exit hardware are to be located 30 in. to 44 in. (76 cm to 112 cm) above the floor, and the actuating portion is to extend at least one-half the width of the door leaf. Such hardware, where mounted to a door

surface, might reduce the usable, clear width of a doorway. Provided that the hardware is installed at least 4 in. (10.2 cm) above the minimum 30-in. (76-cm) mounting height, the provisions of 7.2.1.2.2 permit a 4-in. (10.2-cm) encroachment on clear width without forcing a reduction in reported clear width. At heights below 34 in. (86 cm), the panic hardware or fire exit hardware might create a reduction in clear width sufficient to obstruct wheelchair passage through the opening associated with a 34-in. (86-cm) width door leaf.

The maximum force that the device can require for operation is 15 lbf (67 N). This is the force needed to release the latching device only. The force needed to open the door itself is governed by 7.2.1.4.5.

7.2.1.7.2 Only approved panic hardware shall be used on doors that are not fire doors. Only approved fire exit hardware shall be used on fire doors.

It is not the intent of 7.2.1.7.2 to require the use of panic hardware or fire exit hardware. The two requirements of this paragraph are as follows:

(1) Only approved hardware is to be used.
(2) Where such devices are used on fire-rated doors, they must have been tested for use on fire-rated doors.

Fire exit hardware is tested for use on fire-rated doors; panic hardware is not.

7.2.1.7.3 Required panic hardware and fire exit hardware shall not be equipped with any locking device, set screw, or other arrangement that prevents the release of the latch when pressure is applied to the releasing device. Devices that hold the latch in the retracted position shall be prohibited on fire exit hardware unless listed and approved for that purpose.

Exception: This requirement shall not apply where otherwise provided in Chapters 22 and 23.

It is the intent of the *Code* to allow the use of the delayed-egress lock described by 7.2.1.6.1 where panic hardware is required if the applicable occupancy chapter specifically permits its use. In these cases, the bar, which 7.2.1.7.1(1) requires to extend across at least half the door width, serves as the device that initiates the irreversible process that results in the door unlocking within the 15 or 30 seconds specified.

Panic hardware, which is prohibited from being

used on fire-rated doors, often features the ability to "dog" the bar in the down position so as to hold the door latch in the retracted position. This latch-retracting feature is generally not available on fire exit hardware, because it would violate the listing of the rated fire door assembly. Rated doors must self-latch upon being brought to the closed position by the required closing device. A latch helps to keep the door closed under the pressures generated by a fire.

7.2.1.8 Self-Closing Devices.

7.2.1.8.1* A door normally required to be kept closed shall not be secured in the open position at any time and shall be self-closing or automatic-closing in accordance with 7.2.1.8.2.

A.7.2.1.8.1 Examples of doors designed to normally be kept closed include those to a stair enclosure or horizontal exit.

7.2.1.8.2 In any building of low or ordinary hazard contents, as defined in 6.2.2.2 and 6.2.2.3, or where approved by the authority having jurisdiction, doors shall be permitted to be automatic-closing, provided that the following criteria are met:

(1) Upon release of the hold-open mechanism, the door becomes self-closing.
(2) The release device is designed so that the door instantly releases manually and upon release becomes self-closing, or the door can be readily closed.
(3) The automatic releasing mechanism or medium is activated by the operation of approved smoke detectors installed in accordance with the requirements for smoke detectors for door release service in NFPA 72, *National Fire Alarm Code*®.
(4) Upon loss of power to the hold-open device, the hold-open mechanism is released and the door becomes self-closing.
(5) The release by means of smoke detection of one door in a stair enclosure results in closing all doors serving that stair.

Fire doors in a means of egress route should be kept in the closed position, particularly those serving as entrances to a stair enclosure or positioned in a horizontal exit; however, it is in the latter two locations that doors so often are held open by some type of door-stopping chock. The requirement that these doors be self-closing is not sufficient, because this feature works only when the door can move freely. Often a door is held open to aid in the free flow of normal traffic. This practice establishes conditions

conducive to the rapid spread of fire, smoke, and heat to other sections of the building—the very situation that the stringent compartmentation requirements for the exit enclosure intend to prevent.

Recognizing that tampering with the self-closing feature might occur—and in an effort to encourage the use of effective positive measures rather than ineffective prohibitions that often go ignored—the *Code* presents criteria for holding doors in the open position. It permits doors to be held open in buildings that house low or ordinary hazard contents or where the authority having jurisdiction gives approval.

Specific requirements found elsewhere in the *Code* mandate the use of automatic-closing devices rather than making their use an option. For example, 7.2.4.3.8 requires that horizontal exit doors that span a corridor be automatic-closing in accordance with 7.2.1.8. The requirement of 7.2.4.3.8 recognizes that cross-corridor doors without an automatic release feature are often wedged open to facilitate normal pedestrian movement. Such wedges compromise the safety intended to be provided by the horizontal exit door.

The provisions of 7.2.1.8.2 allow for doors to be held open by an automatic-releasing device. The triggering of the automatic release is done through the operation of smoke detectors installed in accordance with the requirements for *smoke detectors for door release service* as specified in NFPA 72, *National Fire Alarm Code*®.[5] Fusible links are not an acceptable trigger in this system, because untenable smoke conditions could easily render an exit enclosure or adjoining fire compartment unusable long before the temperature in the vicinity of the door opening has risen enough to operate the fusible link.

Additionally, loss of power to the device providing the hold-open feature must cause immediate automatic release. A manual method of release is also required. The manual method might involve tugging on the door to cause its release. Therefore, magnetic devices with significant holding forces that are not easily overcome by a deliberate tug on the door cannot be used. Once the hold-open device is released, the self-closing device installed on the door swings the door to its closed position. On a fire protection–rated door, the required door latch then engages.

The doors held open in accordance with the provisions of 7.2.1.8.2 can be arranged to close simultaneously throughout the building or only in the affected zones. Zoning is generally better, because it permits doors in areas unaffected by the emergency to remain open to accommodate normal use. If protecting a room, that room might be considered a zone. If protecting a stair enclosure, the entire stair enclosure is considered a zone, and the signal to close one door in the enclosing walls must close all doors in that stair enclosure.

With the exception of certain hazardous areas where flash fires or explosions could occur, the use of automatic closers in accordance with these provisions is permitted. Use of automatic-closing equipment should be encouraged to prevent doors from being secured open by other means. Wedges, for example, need to be removed before the self-closer installed on the door can move the door to its closed position.

7.2.1.9* Powered Doors.

A.7.2.1.9 Powered doors are divided into two categories—power assisted and power operated. Power-assisted doors that conform to ANSI/BHMA A156.19, *American National Standard for Power Assist & Low Energy Power Operated Doors,* use limited power to operate the door. They require fewer safeguards as compared to full power–operated doors. These door operators are for swinging doors only. Power-operated doors that conform to ANSI/BHMA A156.10, *American National Standard for Power Operated Pedestrian Doors,* require more power to operate the door and require additional safeguards to provide protection against personal injury. Power-operated doors can be swinging, sliding, or folding doors.

7.2.1.9.1* General. Where means of egress doors are operated by power upon the approach of a person or doors with power-assisted manual operation, the design shall be such that, in the event of power failure, the door opens manually to allow egress travel or closes where necessary to safeguard the means of egress. The forces required to open such doors manually shall not exceed those required in 7.2.1.4.5, except that the force required to set the door in motion shall not exceed 50 lbf (222 N). The door shall be designed and installed so that when a force is applied to the door on the side from which egress is made, it shall be capable of swinging from any position to the full use of the required width of the opening in which it is installed (see 7.2.1.4). On the egress side of each door, there shall be a readily visible, durable sign that reads as follows:

IN EMERGENCY, PUSH TO OPEN

The sign shall be in letters not less than 1 in. (2.5 cm) high on a contrasting background.

A.7.2.1.9.1 An example of the type of door addressed by 7.2.1.9.1 is one actuated by a motion-sensing device upon the approach of a person.

Power-operated sliding doors activated by some automatic mechanism are permitted, provided that their movement can be manually overpowered and the door can be made to swing in the direction of egress travel while still providing the required egress capacity. The feature for manual operation must work at all times, even when other features of the door's mechanism (such as the treadle, the electric eye, or the sliding rail) have failed. Such a door must be arranged so it can be made to swing manually from any position, whether fully or partially closed. Care must be taken to ensure that the enclosing construction of any door pocket does not defeat its ability to swing. Note that the breakaway feature cannot require a force in excess of 50 lbf (222 N).

The sign advising that the door can be pushed open in an emergency provides the user with information that might not be intuitively obvious. Typically, the user sees the door operate under power; often such normal operation involves the use of power to slide the door to the side of the opening. The emergency manual mode of operation often relies on a breakaway feature that permits the door to become side-hinged and swinging when pushed in the direction of egress travel.

Exception No. 1: Sliding, power-operated doors in exit access serving an occupant load of fewer than 50 that manually open in the direction of door travel with forces not exceeding those required in 7.2.1.4.5 shall not be required to have a swing-out feature. The required sign shall read as follows:

IN EMERGENCY, SLIDE TO OPEN

Exception No. 1 to 7.2.1.9.1 was developed to recognize that swinging doors, other than those in exit enclosures, serving an occupant load of fewer than 50 persons are permitted to swing against the direction of egress travel. The exception considers a sliding door that can be manually opened with forces not exceeding those required of swinging doors to be equivalent to a door that swings against the direction of egress travel. Again, because the door is power-operated during normal use, a sign must be provided advising the user that force can be used to slide the door to its open position in an emergency mode—that is, on loss of power or equipment malfunction.

Exception No. 2:* In the emergency breakout mode, a door leaf located within a two-leaf opening shall be exempt from the minimum 32-in. (81-cm) single-leaf requirement of

7.2.1.2.3, provided that the clear width of the single leaf is not less than 30 in. (76 cm).

A.7.2.1.9.1 Exception No. 2 Although a single power-operated door leaf located within a two-leaf opening might alone not provide more than 30 in. (76 cm) of clear width in the emergency breakout mode, where both leaves are broken out to become side-hinged, the required egress width is permitted to be provided by the width of the entire opening.

Exception No. 3:   For a biparting sliding door in the emergency breakout mode, a door leaf located within a multiple-leaf opening shall be exempt from the minimum 32-in. (81-cm) single-leaf requirement of 7.2.1.2.3 if a clear opening of not less than 32 in. (81 cm) is provided by all leafs broken out.

Exception No. 2 and Exception No. 3 to 7.2.1.9.1 were developed to recognize a design limitation of power-operated doors currently manufactured and widely in use. Power-operated doors that are capable of providing the minimum 32-in. (81-cm) clear width for a single leaf as required by 7.2.1.2.3 generally are not capable of providing the same minimum 32-in. (81-cm) clear width in the emergency breakout mode. As long as there are multiple leaves within a single opening and each is provided with the breakout feature, the 32-in. (81-cm) single leaf requirement is relaxed, because the minimum required width can be provided by the entire opening with multiple door leafs broken out.

Exception No. 4:   Doors complying with 7.2.1.14 shall be permitted to be used.

Exception No. 5:   This requirement shall not apply where otherwise   provided in Chapters 22 and 23.

7.2.1.9.2 Doors Required to Be Self-Closing. Where doors are required to be self-closing and (1) are operated by power upon the approach of a person or (2) are provided with power-assisted manual operation, they shall be permitted in the means of egress under the following conditions:

(1) Doors can be opened manually in accordance with 7.2.1.9.1 to allow egress travel in the event of power failure.
(2) New doors remain in the closed position unless actuated or opened manually.
(3) When actuated, new doors remain open for not more than 30 seconds.
(4) Doors held open for any period of time close—and the power-assist mechanism ceases to function—upon operation of approved smoke detectors installed in such

a way as to detect smoke on either side of the door opening in accordance with the provisions of NFPA 72, *National Fire Alarm Code.*
(5) Doors required to be self-latching are either self-latching or become self-latching upon operation of approved smoke detectors per 7.2.1.9.2(4).
(6) New power-assisted swinging doors comply with BHMA/ANSI A156.19, *American National Standard for Power Assist and Low Energy Power Operated Doors.*

If a door that is required to be self-closing by a provision of the *Code* is a powered door, the possibility of competing functions creating conflict exists. The intent of the self-closing requirement is to keep the door in its closed position except when someone is moving through the door opening; the intent of a powered door is either to make the door open automatically upon approach of a person or to open via power assist when a limited force is applied against the door. Under fire conditions, boxes falling from shelving, for example, might cause either the approach-actuated powered door or force-actuated power-assist door to open. The provisions of 7.2.1.9.2(4) require that, upon detection of smoke, the door closes and the power-assist mechanism ceases to function. This requirement emphasizes that the need for the door to be in its closed position is paramount compared to the need to use the door easily under fire conditions.

7.2.1.10 Revolving Doors.

Note that 7.2.1.10.1 applies to all revolving doors, not only those in the means of egress. Also, 7.2.1.10.3 applies specifically to doors not within the required means of egress.

7.2.1.10.1 Revolving doors shall comply with the following.

(a) Revolving doors shall be capable of being collapsed into a book-fold position, unless they are existing revolving doors approved by the authority having jurisdiction.

(b) When revolving doors are collapsed into the book-fold position, the parallel egress paths formed shall provide an aggregate width of 36 in. (91 cm), unless they are existing revolving doors approved by the authority having jurisdiction.

(c) Revolving doors shall not be used within 10 ft (3 m) of the foot or the top of stairs or escalators. Under all conditions, there shall be a dispersal area acceptable to the authority having jurisdiction between the stairs or escalators and the revolving door.

(d) The revolutions per minute (rpm) of revolving doors shall not exceed the values in Table 7.2.1.10.1.

(e) Each revolving door shall have a conforming side-hinged swinging door in the same wall as the revolving door and within 10 ft (3 m) of the revolving door.

Table 7.2.1.10.1 Revolving Door Maximum Speed

Inside Diameter	Power-Driven Speed Control (rpm)	Manual Speed Control (rpm)
6 ft 6 in. (2.4 m)	11	12
7 ft 0 in. (2.1 m)	10	11
7 ft 6 in. (2.3 m)	9	11
8 ft 0 in. (2.4 m)	9	10
8 ft 6 in. (2.6 m)	8	9
9 ft 0 in (2.7 m)	8	9
9 ft 6 in (2.9 m)	7	8
10 ft 0 in. (3.0 m)	7	8

Exception No. 1: Revolving doors shall be permitted without adjacent swinging doors, required by 7.2.1.10.1(e), for street floor elevator lobbies, provided that no stairways or doors from other parts of the building discharge through the lobby and the lobby has no occupancy other than as a means of travel between the elevators and street.

Exception No. 2: The requirement of 7.2.1.10.1(e) shall not apply to existing revolving doors where the number of revolving doors does not exceed the number of swinging doors within 20 ft (6.1 m).

The provisions of 7.2.1.10.1, which apply to revolving doors, address collapsibility, width of egress path, location, speed of rotation, and supplementary swinging doors. Subparagraphs 7.2.1.10.1(a) and (b) require collapsibility to provide egress paths, albeit narrow paths, to each side of the center column with attached book-fold position doors. Subparagraph 7.2.1.10.1(c), which requires that revolving doors not be used within 10 ft (3 m) of the foot of or top of stairs or escalators, is meant to prevent the crushing accumulation of occupants if egress travel is slowed at the door. Subparagraph 7.2.1.10.1(e) provides redundant egress via a nearby side-hinged swinging door if the revolving door prevents egress upon failure of its emergency features. Exception No. 1 to 7.2.1.10.1(e) specifies a safe arrangement under which the additional swinging door is not needed.

7.2.1.10.2 Where permitted in Chapters 12 through 42, revolving doors shall be permitted as a component in a means of egress, provided that the following criteria are met:

(1) Revolving doors shall not be given credit for more than 50 percent of the required egress capacity.
(2) Each revolving door shall not be credited with not more than 50 persons capacity or, if of not less than a 9-ft (2.7-m) diameter, revolving doors shall be permitted egress capacity based on the clear opening width provided when collapsed into a book-fold position.
(3) Revolving doors shall be capable of being collapsed into a book-fold position when a force not exceeding 130 lbf (578 N) is applied to the wings within 3 in. (7.6 cm) of the outer edge.

The following occupancies allow the use of a revolving door in a means of egress. Additional restrictions that might be imposed by the occupancy chapter are contained in the paragraphs referenced in parentheses.

The occupancies are as follows:

(1) Assembly occupancies (see 12.2.2.2.6, 13.2.2.2.6)
(2) Hotels (see 28.2.2.2.3, 29.2.2.2.3)
(3) Apartments (see 30.2.2.2.3, 31.2.2.2.3)
(4) Board and care facilities [see 32.3.2.2.2(4) and 33.3.2.2.2(4)]
(5) Mercantile occupancies (see 36.2.2.2.8, 37.2.2.2.8)
(6) Business occupancies (see 38.2.2.2.6, 39.2.2.2.8)

Revolving doors present the potential for problems when too many people try to use them in too short a period of time. The congestion created is one reason why their use is prohibited at the foot or top of stairs. Because of the potential danger that such doors present, they are not permitted to provide more than 50 percent of the required egress capacity. Where revolving doors are used, they each receive credit for a maximum of 50 persons, regardless of the width of the revolving panel.

7.2.1.10.3 Revolving doors not used as a component of a means of egress shall have a collapsing force not exceeding 180 lbf (800 N).

Exception: This requirement shall not apply to revolving doors, provided that the collapsing force is reduced to a force not to exceed 130 lbf (578 N) under the following conditions:

(a) If a power failure occurs, or if power is removed to the device holding the wings in position

(b) If an actuation of the automatic sprinkler system occurs where such a system is provided

(c) If an actuation of a smoke detection system that is installed to provide coverage in all areas within the building that are within 75 ft (23 m) of the revolving doors occurs

(d) If an actuation of a clearly identified manual control switch in an approved location that reduces the holding force to a force not to exceed 130 lbf (578 N) occurs

Note that the provisions of 7.2.1.10.3 apply even if the door is not within the required means of egress. The criteria contained in the Exception to 7.2.1.10.3 need to be satisfied only if the collapsing force is in excess of 180 lbf (800 N).

7.2.1.11 Turnstiles.

The intent of 7.2.1.11 is to provide guidance on how best to place turnstiles in a building, to describe the circumstances under which they are permitted, and to reduce the chances of their improper use during an emergency.

7.2.1.11.1 Turnstiles or similar devices that restrict travel to one direction or are used to collect fares or admission charges shall not be placed so as to obstruct any required means of egress.

Exception No. 1: Approved turnstiles not exceeding 39 in. (99 cm) in height that turn freely in the direction of egress travel shall be permitted where revolving doors are permitted in Chapters 12 through 42.

Exception No. 2: Where turnstiles are approved by the authority having jurisdiction and permitted in Chapters 12 through 42, each turnstile shall be credited for 50 persons capacity, provided that such turnstiles meet the following criteria:

(a) They freewheel in the egress direction when primary power is lost, and freewheel in the direction of egress travel upon manual release by an employee assigned in the area.

(b) They are not given credit for more than 50 percent of the required egress width.

(c) They are not in excess of 39 in. (99 cm) in height and have a clear width of not less than 16 ½ in. (41.9 cm).

7.2.1.11.2 Turnstiles exceeding 39 in. (99 cm) in height shall meet the requirements for revolving doors in 7.2.1.10.

7.2.1.11.3 Turnstiles located in or furnishing access to required exits shall provide not less than 16 ½ in. (41.9 cm) clear width at and below a height of 39 in. (99 cm) and at least 22 in. (55.9 cm) clear width at heights above 39 in. (99 cm).

Generally, turnstiles are installed to prevent or control entry. As such, they are not always suitable for installation in a means of egress. Turnstiles are permitted in locations where revolving doors are permitted; see the commentary on 7.2.1.10.2 for a list of occupancies that permit revolving doors. The coexistence of turnstiles and revolving doors is not meant to imply that there is a relationship between them with respect to their purpose. The revolving door is not meant to restrict traffic in either direction, while the turnstile is often used to do just that, with the restriction or obstruction to traffic movement usually in the direction of building entry. Yet, if a turnstile does not restrict egress, it might be assumed to be the equivalent of a revolving door. At heights not exceeding 39 in. (99 cm), a freewheeling turnstile is not required to provide the collapsibility features required of a revolving door; turnstiles with heights exceeding 39 in. (99 cm) must be provided with all the features applicable to revolving doors.

Some turnstiles do not turn in the direction of entry until coin operated. Others require no coin for operation and are used simply to count numbers of people. Perhaps the most dangerous are those that do not bar entry but specifically bar egress. This might occur in large mercantile occupancies where turnstiles turn freely on entering but do not turn in the direction of egress, thereby causing patrons to reroute their egress through checkout stands. It is possible that the patrons of places using one-way turnstiles are quite aware of this limitation and know the correct path to take for emergency egress; however, this cannot be relied on, especially if the turnstiles are placed near the exit doors. In emergencies, occupants might head for what appears to be the shortest route to the outside, only to find it blocked by a turnstile preventing movement in that direction.

Some occupancy chapters permit turnstiles to provide a portion of the required egress capacity. Where recognized, they are permitted to be installed, provided that they are in strict compliance with the dimensional criteria and performance requirements of Exception No. 2 to 7.2.1.11.1. Turnstiles are not permitted to provide more than 50 percent of the required egress capacity, and no single turnstile can be given egress capacity for more than 50 persons.

7.2.1.12 Doors in Folding Partitions. Where permanently mounted folding or movable partitions divide a room into smaller spaces, a swinging door or open doorway shall be provided as an exit access from each such space.

Exception No. 1:   A door or opening in the folding partition shall not be required, provided that the following criteria are met:

(a) The subdivided space is not used by more than 20 persons at any time.

(b) The use of the space is under adult supervision.

(c) The partitions are arranged so that they do not extend across any aisle or corridor used as an exit access to the required exits from the story.

(d) The partitions conform to the interior finish and other requirements of this Code.

(e) The partitions are of an approved type, have a simple method of release, and are capable of being opened quickly and easily by experienced persons in case of emergency.

Exception No. 2:   Where a subdivided space is provided with not less than two means of egress, the swinging door in the folding partition shall not be required, and one such means of egress shall be permitted to be equipped with a horizontal sliding door complying with 7.2.1.14.

Although Exception No. 1(c) to 7.2.1.12 might appear to contradict the exception's intent, it refers to exit access for the rest of the floor, not exit access for the small space created by closing the partition.

7.2.1.13 Balanced Doors. If panic hardware is installed on balanced doors, the panic hardware shall be of the push-pad type, and the pad shall not extend more than approximately one-half the width of the door, measured from the latch side. *(See 7.2.1.7.1(1).)*

Balanced doors do not have side hinges but have a pivot point that is set in a small distance. This arrangement helps reduce the force needed to open the door. With balanced doors, where the hinge or pivot point is set in from the edge of the door leaf, care must be taken to position the panic hardware device on the latch side of the pivot point; otherwise, pushing on the bar might actually help to hold the door closed. This arrangement might be effectively accomplished using pushpad panic hardware, which more readily instructs the user where to push. Exhibit 7.21 depicts a balanced door; Exhibit 7.22 illustrates the difference between traditional panic hardware and pushpad panic hardware.

7.2.1.14 Horizontal Sliding Doors. Horizontal sliding doors shall be permitted in means of egress, provided that the following criteria are met:

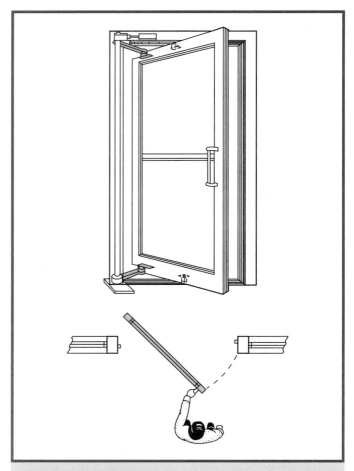

Exhibit 7.21 Balanced door.

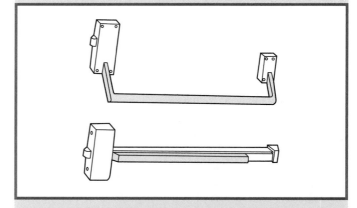

Exhibit 7.22 Traditional panic hardware (top) and pushpad panic hardware (bottom).

(1) The door is readily operable from either side without special knowledge or effort.
(2) The force that, when applied to the operating device in the direction of egress, is required to operate the door is not more than 15 lbf (67 N).

(3) The force required to operate the door in the direction of door travel is not more than 30 lbf (133 N) to set the door in motion and is not more than 15 lbf (67 N) to close the door or open it to the minimum required width.

(4) The door is operable with a force not more than 50 lbf (222 N) when a force of 250 lbf (1110 N) is applied perpendicularly to the door adjacent to the operating device, unless the door is an existing horizontal sliding exit access door serving an area with an occupant load of fewer than 50.

(5) The door assembly complies with the fire protection rating and, where rated, is self-closing or automatic-closing by means of smoke detection in accordance with 7.2.1.8, and is installed in accordance with NFPA 80, *Standard for Fire Doors and Fire Windows.*

The special type of horizontal sliding door addressed by 7.2.1.14 is different from a traditional horizontal sliding door. When force is applied in the direction of egress travel to the door actuator, the door must slide to the side to allow passage. This concept is illustrated in Exhibit 7.23.

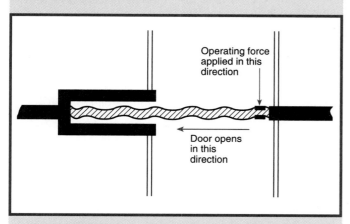

Exhibit 7.23 *Horizontal sliding door operation.*

Although the provisions of 7.2.1.14 do not require specific occupancy chapter permission for use of horizontal sliding doors, some occupancy chapters impose additional restrictions. For example, 28.2.2.2.4 prohibits these doors from being installed across a corridor in a new hotel or dormitory.

The requirements for the installation of horizontal sliding doors include the following:

(1) Simple method of operation from either side without special knowledge or effort

(2) Force necessary to operate the door

(3) Fire protection rating applicable to door location and purpose

(4) Automatic-closing means by smoke detection or means for self-closing

The force requirements of 7.2.1.14(3) and (4) help to assure that the door can be operated if the usual method of operation required by 7.2.1.14(2) fails.

Traditional sliding doors cannot comply with these requirements. It is important that sliding doors be evaluated for compliance with all the requirements of 7.2.1.14.

An example of the type of door discussed in 7.2.1.14 is shown in Exhibit 7.24.

Exhibit 7.24 *Horizontal sliding door addressed by 7.2.1.14. (Photo courtesy of Won-Door Corp.)*

7.2.2 Stairs.

Stairs, whether interior or exterior to a building, serve multiple functions. Functions include normal occupant movement among the floors of a building, emergency egress in case of fire, and rescue and fire-control operations conducted by fire fighters.

Stairs are used within any of the three components of a means of egress system, that is, the exit access, the exit, and the exit discharge. Stairs are one of the most commonly used building elements on a day-to-day, nonemergency basis. Because of their frequent use, stairs are one of the most common scenes of accidents. The *Code* focuses much attention on stairs to help ensure their effective use during emergency egress. These requirements for emergency egress help to ensure that stairs are safe to use on a regular basis.

7.2.2.1 General. Stairs used as a component in the means of egress shall conform to the general requirements of Section 7.1 and to the special requirements of this subsection.

Exception No. 1: This requirement shall not apply to aisle stairs as provided in Chapters 12 and 13.

Aisle stairs (that is, stepped aisles) are detailed in 12.2.5.6 and 13.2.5.6.

Exception No. 2: This requirement shall not apply to existing noncomplying stairs where approved by the authority having jurisdiction.

Although stairs can serve within any of the three components of the means of egress, they are most often located within an exit. To be considered an exit, interior stairs must be separated from the other spaces on the floor in accordance with 7.1.3.2. Unenclosed interior stairs normally serve as exit access rather than as exits. Where an interior stair connects two or more stories, it creates a vertical opening and must meet the requirements applicable to such, regardless of whether it is an exit. See the vertical opening protection provisions of 8.2.5.

It is sometimes more difficult to determine whether outside stairs are part of the exit access, the exit, or the exit discharge. To be considered an exit, outside stairs need to be separated from the interior of the building by fire-rated construction in accordance with 7.2.2.6.3. Outside stairs adjacent to the building that are unprotected would normally be considered part of the exit access where serving occupants of upper stories, with the user reaching the exit and exit discharge simultaneously at the base of the last stair flight. Where stairs occur in a sidewalk that connects an exit door to a public way, the stairs are part of the exit discharge.

7.2.2.2 Dimensional Criteria.

7.2.2.2.1 Standard Stairs. Stairs shall be in accordance with the following:

(a) New stairs shall be in accordance with Table 7.2.2.2.1(a).

Exception: This requirement shall not apply to industrial equipment access areas as otherwise provided in Chapter 40.

(b)* Existing stairs shall be permitted to remain in use, provided that they meet the requirements for existing stairs shown in Table 7.2.2.2.1(b). Where approved by the author-

Table 7.2.2.2.1(a) New Stairs

Minimum width clear of all obstructions, except projections not more than 3½ in. (8.9 cm) at or below handrail height on each side	44 in. (112 cm); 36 in. (91 cm) where total occupant load of all stories served by stairways is fewer than 50
Maximum height of risers	7 in. (17.8 cm)
Minimum height of risers	4 in. (10.2 cm)
Minimum tread depth	11 in. (27.9 cm)
Minimum headroom	6 ft 8 in. (203 cm)
Maximum height between landings	12 ft (3.7 m)
Landing	*(See 7.2.1.3 and 7.2.1.4.4.)*

Table 7.2.2.2.1(b) Existing Stairs

Feature	Class A	Class B
Minimum width clear of all obstructions, except projections not more than 3½ in. (8.9 cm) at or below handrail height on each side	44 in. (112 cm)	44 in. (112 cm)
	36 in. (91 cm) where total occupant load of all stories served by stairways is fewer than 50	
Maximum height of risers	7½ in. (19.1 cm)	8 in. (20.3 cm)
Minimum tread depth	10 in. (25.4 cm)	9 in. (22.9 cm)
Minimum headroom	6 ft 8 in. (203 cm)	6 ft 8 in. (203 cm)
Maximum height between landings	12 ft (3.7 m)	12 ft (3.7 m)
Landing	*(See 7.2.1.3 and 7.2.1.4.4.)*	

ity having jurisdiction, existing stairs shall be permitted to be rebuilt in accordance with the dimensional criteria of Table 7.2.2.2.1(b) and in accordance with other *Code* requirements in 7.2.2 for stairs.

Exception: This requirement shall not apply to industrial equipment access areas as otherwise provided in Chapter 40.

A.7.2.2.2.1(b) It is the intent of 7.2.2.2.1(b) to permit the use of Table 7.2.2.2.1(b) in existing buildings, even where there is a change in occupancy per 4.6.11. Safety improvements should be made that are reasonable and feasible at minimal cost. Improvements include removal, repair, or replacement of step coverings as described in A.7.2.2.3.5, particularly Figure A.7.2.2.3.5(e), and addition of functional handrails and guardrails in place of or in conjunction with other rails as described in 7.2.2.4.

Tables 7.2.2.2.1(a) and (b) present the required stair geometry for both new and existing stairs.

Editions of the *Code* prior to 1981 required that "the height of every riser and the width of every tread be so proportioned that the sum of two risers and a tread, exclusive of its nosing or projection, is not less than 24 in. (61 cm) nor more than 25 in. (64 cm)." This requirement was deleted because it was based on a 300-year-old French formula in which the inch was a slightly larger unit of measure than it is today. Moreover, people's feet and stride length—the basis for the formula—were somewhat smaller at that time. Also, the requirement was originally intended only for stairs of moderate steepness or pitch. These reasons, as well as information gathered by researchers on people movement, explain why the requirement was replaced by requirements that ensure good step geometry.

Because of the hardship and impracticality of rebuilding all existing stairs to the newer requirements, the *Code* permits existing stairs in existing buildings to comply with previous requirements. It also allows existing stairs to be rebuilt to the previous dimensional criteria, because a new stair might not fit in an existing stair enclosure. However, the rebuilt stair utilizing the older geometry must meet all other requirements of 7.2.2, including handrail criteria. The wording of A.7.2.2.2.1(b) provides guidance for judging the improvements that are reasonable.

Existing stairs are classified as Class A and Class B. There is little difference between the two classes. As shown in Exhibit 7.25, the difference lies in the tread depth and riser height. Riser height, tread depth, and stair width requirements are illustrated for both new and existing stairs. Note that new stairs must have a lower riser height and a greater tread depth than existing stairs.

If the total occupant load of all floors served by the stair is fewer than 50, the minimum width can be reduced from 44 in. (112 cm) to 36 in. (91 cm). The occupancy chapters applicable to existing buildings specify the class of existing stair that is permitted to be used. For example, 15.2.2.3.2 requires Class A stairs for existing educational occupancies but permits Class B stairs where not used for student access. Also,

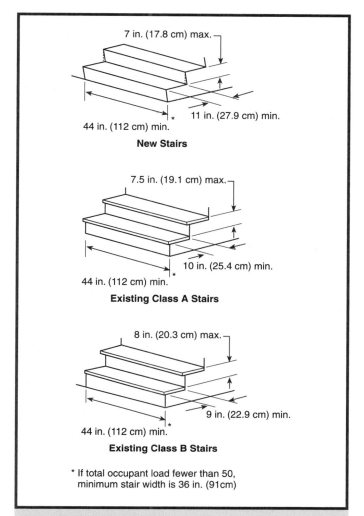

Exhibit 7.25 Stair specifications.

17.2.2.3.2 permits existing Class A stairs for existing day-care occupancies, and 17.2.2.3.3 permits existing Class B stairs where not used for client access. If an occupancy chapter applicable to existing buildings does not specify the class of existing stair that is permitted to be used, Class A or Class B is permitted. A change of occupancy does not require that stairs be rebuilt to meet the requirements applicable to new construction.

See 7.1.7.2 for special requirements where stairs provide a total elevation change of not more than 21 in. (53.3 cm).

7.2.2.2.2 Curved Stairs. Curved stairs shall be permitted as a component in a means of egress, provided that the depth of tread is not less than 11 in. (27.9 cm) at a point 12 in.

(30.5 cm) from the narrower end of the tread and the smallest radius is not less than twice the stair width.

Exception: Existing curved stairs shall be permitted, provided that the depth of tread is not less than 10 in. (25.4 cm) and the smallest radius is not less than twice the stair width.

Subparagraph 7.2.2.2.2 relates the degree of curvature to the width of the curved stair, as shown in Exhibit 7.26. Dimension *B* must be at least twice dimension *A*. Dimension *C*, which is measured at the so-called "inner walking line," must be at least 11 in. (27.9 cm). This relationship of smallest radius to stair width should be based on the actual width of the stair, rather than on the required width only. Otherwise, unsafe conditions toward the outside of wide-curved stairs could be created. The 11-in. (27.9-cm) tread depth is measured at the inner walking line where feet land when walking on the inner part of the stair.

The measurement method for curved stairs that is specified by the *Code* is more closely related to how such stairs are used, with reference to a minimum 11-in. (27.9-cm) tread depth at the inner walking line. This concept has been used in the *Code*'s requirement for winders for some time (see 7.2.2.2.4). With the minimum tread depth stated as a dimension similar to that applicable to other stairs permitted in the

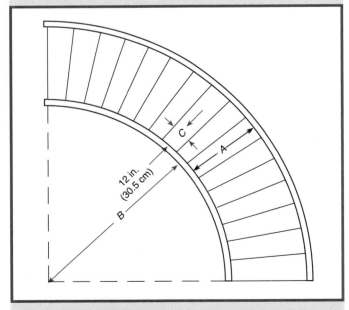

Exhibit 7.26 *Curved stairs.*

required means of egress, it is more evident that curved stairs are an acceptable egress component for any occupancy.

7.2.2.2.3 Spiral Stairs.

7.2.2.2.3.1 Where specifically permitted for individual occupancies by Chapters 12 through 42, spiral stairs shall be permitted as a component in a means of egress in accordance with 7.2.2.2.3.2 through 7.2.2.2.3.4.

7.2.2.2.3.2 Spiral stairs shall be permitted provided the following criteria are met:

(1) Riser heights shall not exceed 7 in. (17.8 cm).
(2) The stairway shall have a tread depth of not less than 11 in. (27.9 cm) for a portion of the stairway width sufficient to provide egress capacity for the occupant load served in accordance with 7.3.3.1.
(3) At the outer side of the stairway, an additional 10 ½ in. (26.7 cm) of width shall be provided clear to the other handrail, and this width shall not be included as part of the required egress capacity.
(4) Handrails complying with 7.2.2.4 shall be provided on both sides of the spiral stairway.
(5) The inner handrail shall be located within 24 in. (61.0 cm), measured horizontally, of the point where a tread depth not less than 11 in. (27.9 cm) is provided.
(6) The turn of the stairway shall be such that descending users have the outer handrail at their right side.

7.2.2.2.3.3 Where the occupant load served does not exceed three, spiral stairs shall be permitted, provided that the following criteria are met:

(1) The clear width of the stairs shall be not less than 26 in. (66 cm).
(2) The height of risers shall not exceed 9 ½ in. (24.1 cm).
(3) The headroom shall be not less than 6 ft 6 in. (198 cm).
(4) Treads shall have a depth not less than 7 ½ in. (19.1 cm) at a point 12 in. (30.5 cm) from the narrower edge.
(5) All treads shall be identical.
(6) Handrails shall be provided on both sides of the stairway.

7.2.2.2.3.4 Within dwelling units, guest rooms and guest suites, and existing buildings, where the occupant load served does not exceed five, spiral stairs shall be permitted, provided that the following criteria are met:

(1) The clear width of the stairs shall be not less than 26 in. (66 cm).
(2) The height of risers shall not exceed 9 ½ in. (24.1 cm).
(3) The headroom shall be not less than 6 ft 6 in. (198 cm).
(4) Treads shall have a depth not less than 7 ½ in. (19.1 cm) at a point 12 in. (30.5 cm) from the narrower edge.
(5) All treads shall be identical.

Spiral stairs can be used only where expressly allowed by the appropriate occupancy chapter. The following occupancies allow the use of spiral stairs. Some occupancy chapters establish additional limitations. For example, in assembly occupancies, spiral stairs are permitted only from lighting and access catwalks, galleries, and gridirons. In apartment buildings, spiral stairs are permitted only within a dwelling unit, not within the common spaces and egress paths serving multiple dwelling units.

The occupancies are as follows:

(1) Assembly occupancies (see 12.2.2.3.2.2, 13.2.2.3.2.2)
(2) Detention and correctional occupancies (see 22.2.2.3.2, 23.2.2.3.2)
(3) One- and two-family dwellings (see 24.2.5.3)
(4) Apartments (see 30.2.2.3.3, 31.2.2.3.3)
(5) Mercantile occupancies (see 36.2.2.3.2, 37.2.2.3.2)
(6) Business occupancies (see 38.2.2.3.2, 39.2.2.3.2)
(7) Industrial occupancies (see 40.2.2.3.2)
(8) Storage occupancies (see 42.2.2.3.2)

The requirement of 7.2.2.2.3.2 is new to this edition of the *Code*. It is significant in that it includes a spiral stair geometry that can be used without a prespecified maximum occupant limit. The number of occupants permitted to use a spiral stair depends on how much egress width is provided. The term *egress width* has a specific meaning in this instance. It excludes the narrow part of the tapered tread that has less than 11 in. (27.9 cm) of tread depth. It also excludes the outer 10 ½ in. (26.7 cm) of tread width. Note that handrails are required at both sides. Also, the turn of the stairway must be such that the outer handrail is available to descending users at their right side. These criteria are depicted in Exhibit 7.27. An

additional criterion is that the riser height not exceed 7 in. (17.8 cm), as is required for traditional stairs in accordance with Table 7.2.2.2.1(a).

The requirement of 7.2.2.2.3.3 retains the dimensional criteria for spiral stairs from earlier editions of the *Code* but changes the maximum number of occupants served by the stair from five to three and requires that handrails be provided at both sides of the stair.

The requirement of 7.2.2.2.3.4 applies to existing spiral stairs as well as to those in new dwelling units, guest rooms, and guest suites. The traditional five-person limit and the requirement that a handrail be at the open side have been retained.

7.2.2.2.4* Winders. Where specified in Chapters 12 through 42, winders shall be permitted in stairs. Winders shall have a tread depth not less than 6 in. (15.2 cm) and a tread depth not less than 11 in. (27.9 cm) at a point 12 in. (30.5 cm) from the narrowest edge.

Exception: Existing winders shall be permitted to be continued in use, provided that they have a tread depth not less than 6 in. (15.2 cm) and a tread depth not less than 9 in. (22.9 cm) at a point 12 in. (30.5 cm) from the narrowest edge.

A.7.2.2.2.4 If properly designed and constructed, stairs with winders are not necessarily more dangerous than other stairs. Attention to the following factors helps to make winders generally more effective for egress and safety. Handrails should be continuous, without breaks at newel posts, from story to story. Handrails located at a greater than normal distance from the inner turn of winders can improve safety by constraining stair users to walk on the portion of the treads providing deeper treads, which should have not less than 11 in. (27.9 cm) of depth. Combinations of straight flights and winders are best arranged with winders located only below the straight flight. This arrangement is best because the winders provide larger tread dimensions over much of their width than do typical treads on straight flights. A descending person will, thus, be unlikely to experience a reduction of tread depth during descent, a condition of nonuniformity that is best avoided.

A winder is a tapered tread used to change the direction the stair runs. Because winders introduce a variation in the stair geometry and their effective tread depths are less than 11 in. (27.9 cm), they are suited to limited applications. At one time, the *Code* prohibited winders. Chapter 7 now sets applicable criteria for winders if the appropriate occupancy chapter

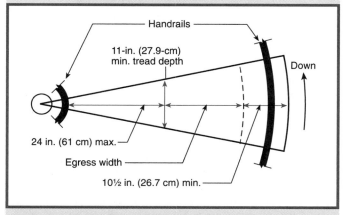

Exhibit 7.27 *Spiral stair tread dimensional criteria reflecting the requirements of 7.2.2.2.3.2.*

specifically permits their use. Other than within dwelling units, the *Code* limits winders to existing installations. Exhibit 7.28 illustrates the dimensional criteria required.

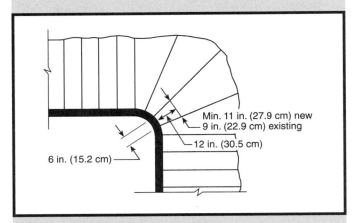

Exhibit 7.28 *Acceptable winders.*

The following occupancies allow the use of winders. Some occupancy chapters establish additional limitations. For example, in apartment buildings, winders are permitted to serve only within a living unit and not within the common spaces such as corridors and lobbies.

The occupancies are as follows:

(1) One- and two-family dwellings (see 24.2.5.3)
(2) Lodging and rooming houses (see 26.2.6)
(3) Apartments (see 30.2.2.3.4, 31.2.2.3.4)
(4) Board and care facilities (see 32.2.2.6.2, 33.2.2.6.2)
(5) Existing mercantile occupancies (see 37.2.2.3.3)
(6) Existing business occupancies (see 39.2.2.3.3)
(7) Existing industrial occupancies (see 40.2.2.3.3)
(8) Existing storage occupancies (see 42.2.2.3.3, 42.8.2.2.3.2)

7.2.2.3 Stair Details.

7.2.2.3.1 Construction.

7.2.2.3.1.1 All stairs serving as required means of egress shall be of permanent fixed construction, unless they are stairs serving seating that is designed to be repositioned in accordance with Chapters 12 and 13.

The requirement of 7.2.2.3.1.1 recognizes the functional requirement in theaters, for example, where seating sections are added, removed, or repositioned depending on the specific theatrical production. It

is impractical for stairs associated with such seating sections to be of fixed, permanent construction.

7.2.2.3.1.2 Each stair, platform, and landing, not including handrails and existing stairs, in buildings required in this *Code* to be of Type I or Type II construction shall be of noncombustible material throughout.

The requirement of 7.2.2.3.1.2 covers the combustibility of materials used to construct new stairs. Stairs are permitted to be of combustible construction if the building is permitted to be of Type III, Type IV, or Type V construction as defined in NFPA 220, *Standard on Types of Building Construction.*[6] If the building is required to be of Type I or Type II construction, which limits building materials to those that are noncombustible, the materials used for new stair construction must also be noncombustible.

7.2.2.3.2 Landings. Stairs shall have landings at door openings. Stairs and intermediate landings shall continue with no decrease in width along the direction of egress travel. In new buildings, every landing shall have a dimension measured in the direction of travel that is not less than the width of the stair.

Exception No. 1:   Landings shall not be required to exceed 4 ft (122 cm) in the direction of travel, provided that the stair has a straight run.

Exception No. 2:   In one- and two-family dwellings and existing buildings, a door at the top of the stair shall be permitted to open directly at a stair, provided that the door does not swing over the stair and the door serves an area with an occupant load of fewer than 50 persons.

Stairs must have landings at door openings. It is unsafe to move through a door opening and immediately begin vertical travel on a stair. Exception No. 2 to 7.2.2.3.2 does provide an exception to this requirement for dwellings and existing buildings. The wording of Exception No. 2 is repeated as Exception No. 2 to 7.2.1.3 for consistency. Otherwise, the requirement for a level landing that is at least as deep in the direction of stair run as the door is wide, on each side of the door, would apply without exception.

Intermediate stair landings of the minimum depth specified by 7.2.2.3.2 serve as effective breaks in runs of stairs, which allows persons who slip or trip to halt their fall. Exhibit 7.29 illustrates the minimum landing depth required by 7.2.2.3.2.

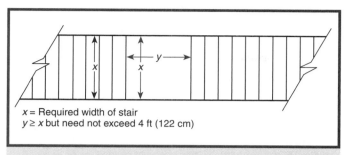

x = Required width of stair
y ≥ x but need not exceed 4 ft (122 cm)

Exhibit 7.29 *Uniform width of stairs and intermediate landings.*

7.2.2.3.3* Tread and Landing Surfaces. Stair treads and landings shall be solid, without perforations, and free of projections or lips that could trip stair users. If not vertical, risers shall be permitted to slope under the tread at an angle not to exceed 30 degrees from vertical; however, the permitted projection of the nosing shall not exceed 1 ½ in. (3.8 cm).

Exception No. 1: This requirement shall not apply to noncombustible grated stair treads and landings as provided in Chapters 12, 13, 22, 23, and 40.

Exception No. 2: The requirement for the maximum projection of the nosing shall not apply to existing stairs.

Solid treads and solid landing floors provide a visual barrier that shields the user's view of the vertical drop beneath the stair. Persons with a fear of high places are more comfortable using such stairs. Grated and expanded metal treads and landings might catch a user's heel and present a tripping hazard. Noncombustible grated stair treads are permitted in areas not accessed by the general public, such as catwalks and gridirons in theaters, resident housing areas in prisons, and factories and other industrial occupancies.

The *Code* does not directly mandate solid risers on stairs. Rather, the requirement that treads be free of projections or lips that could trip stair users is a performance-based provision that indirectly mandates solid risers on egress stairs used in the upward direction. Given that a riser is provided, the maximum slope—established as 30 degrees from the vertical with not more than a 1 ½ in. (3.8 cm) nosing projection—is intended to keep an ascending user's toes from becoming caught under the tread if the user has a disability that prevents pulling the foot backwards to clear the lip created by the stair tread. This relatively new provision is not retroactively applicable to existing stairs.

A.7.2.2.3.3 The tripping hazard referred to in 7.2.2.3.3 occurs especially during descent, where the tread walking surface has projections such as strips of high-friction materials or lips from metal pan stairs that are not completely filled with concrete or other material. Tread nosings that project over adjacent treads can also be a tripping hazard. CABO/ANSI A117.1, *American National Standard for Accessible and Usable Buildings and Facilities,* illustrates projecting nosing configurations that minimize the hazard.

Where environmental conditions (such as illumination levels and directionality or a complex visual field that draws a person's attention away from stair treads) lead to a hazardous reduction in one's ability to perceive stair treads, they should be made of a material that allows ready discrimination of the number and position of treads. In all cases, the leading edges of all treads should be readily visible during both ascent and descent. A major factor in injury-producing stair accidents and in the ability to use stairs efficiently in conditions such as egress is the clarity of the stair treads as separate stepping surfaces.

7.2.2.3.4* Tread Slope. Tread slope shall not exceed ¼ in./ft (2 cm/m) (a slope of 1 in 48).

A.7.2.2.3.4 A small drainage slope for stair treads subject to wetting can improve tread slip resistance *(see also A.7.2.2.3.3).* A consistent slope to a side of the stair, where drainage is possible, might be preferable to a front-to-back slope of the treads. Providing a pitch of ⅛ in. to ¼ in./ft (1 cm to 2 cm/m) aids the shedding of water from a nominally horizontal surface.

Sloping treads are intentionally used to avoid water accumulation on stairs. They might also be unintentionally created where treads erode unevenly through usage or where differential settlement occurs. The limitation in slope is intended to reduce the dimensional nonuniformity of the effective riser heights and to reduce the chance of slipping on sloping treads.

7.2.2.3.5* Riser Height and Tread Depth. Riser height shall be measured as the vertical distance between tread nosings. Tread depth shall be measured horizontally between the vertical planes of the foremost projection of adjacent treads and at a right angle to the tread's leading edge but shall not include bevelled or rounded tread surfaces that slope more than 20 degrees (a slope of 1 in 2.75). At tread nosings, such bevelling or rounding shall not exceed ½ in. (1.3 cm) in horizontal dimension.

A.7.2.2.3.5 Figures A.7.2.2.3.5(a), (b), (c), and (d) illustrate the method for measuring riser height and tread depth. Stairs that are covered with resilient floor coverings might need additional tread depth beyond the minimum specified in the *Code.* Any horizontal projection of resilient covering materials beyond the tread nosing and riser, such as carpet and underlayment, can interfere with users' feet and thereby reduce usable tread depth. At the tread nosing, such resilient covering materials might not be capable of providing stable support for users' feet. Generally, effective tread depth is reduced by the uncompressed thickness of such resilient coverings and might be further reduced over time if coverings are not well secured and consequently move forward at the nosings. *(See Figure A.7.2.2.3.5(e).)*

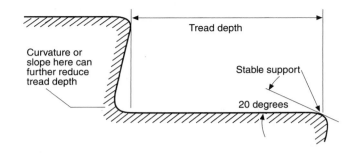

Figure A.7.2.2.3.5(d) Tread measurement with stable support at leading edge.

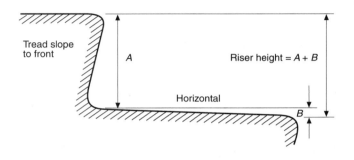

Figure A.7.2.2.3.5(a) Riser measurement with tread slope to front.

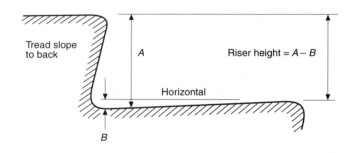

Figure A.7.2.2.3.5(b) Riser measurement with tread slope to back.

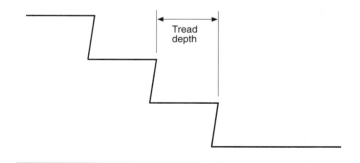

Figure A.7.2.2.3.5(c) Tread depth.

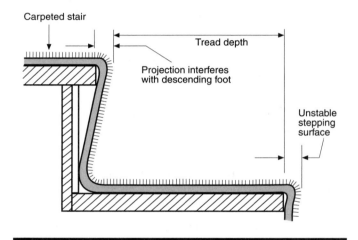

Figure A.7.2.2.3.5(e) Tread measurement with unstable stepping surface at leading edge.

Measurement of riser and tread dimensions needs to represent the actual heights and depths experienced by those using the stairs. Therefore, the tread dimension is not to include any part of the tread that is not functional for normal foot placement, especially where the tread slopes mores than 20 degrees from the horizontal. Normal placement of the foot onto the step nosings results in an initial contact angle of less than 20 degrees. Therefore, any part of the nosing sloping more than an angle of 20 degrees is ineffective and might create a tripping hazard. The limitation of a $^1/_2$-in. (1.3-cm) horizontal dimension for beveling or rounding of the step nosings is also related to tripping hazards. This beveling or rounding also reduces the chance of a slip occurring when the foot initially contacts the nosing during descent of the stair. By following this rule, the designer also achieves acceptable step dimensions while keeping the space used for the stair to a minimum.

Stair designers should keep in mind the possibility that a stair that originally was designed without a resilient covering might someday be carpeted, thereby possibly reducing significantly the effective tread depth of the steps. Designing such stairs to provide slightly more than the minimum required tread depths is especially prudent in these cases. In addition, those responsible for maintaining stairs should keep in mind that the addition of resilient coverings might reduce steps tread dimensions to below the standard, and the dimensions will be further reduced if the coverings are not installed and maintained tight against the underlying steps.

The stair provisions of Chapter 24, which apply to one- and two-family dwellings, permit a new stair within a living unit (including an apartment living unit or a hotel/dormitory guest room/suite) to have a minimum 10-in. (25.4-cm) tread depth in lieu of the minimum 11 in. (27.9 cm) required by Table 7.2.2.2.1(a). Although the designer is allowed to specify a minimum 10-in. (25.4-cm) tread depth, such specification is seldom prudent. A prudent individual should be able to predict easily that the stair will be carpeted at some time during the life of the building. The issue of whether Chapter 24 should permit a 10-in. (25.4-cm) tread depth for stairs in living units, given the difficulty of continually enforcing the requirement in a location that the authority having jurisdiction seldom visits following issuance of a certificate of occupancy, is one that is debated during each code-revision cycle.

7.2.2.3.6 Dimensional Uniformity. There shall be no variation in excess of ³/₁₀ in. (0.5 cm) in the depth of adjacent treads or in the height of adjacent risers, and the tolerance between the largest and smallest riser or between the largest and smallest tread shall not exceed ⅜ in. (1 cm) in any flight.

Exception: Where the bottom riser adjoins a sloping public way, walk, or driveway having an established grade and serving as a landing, a variation in height of the bottom riser not to exceed 3 in. in every 3 ft (7.6 cm in every 91 cm) of stairway width shall be permitted.

Many accidents have resulted from irregularities in stair geometry from one step to an adjacent step or over an entire run of stairs. There should be no design irregularities. Variations due to construction are permitted, provided that the variation between adjacent

treads or adjacent risers does not exceed ³/₁₆ in. (0.5 cm) and that the difference between the largest and smallest riser, as well as the difference between the largest and smallest tread, in any flight of stairs does not exceed ³/₈ in. (1.0 cm). See Exhibit 7.30.

Exhibit 7.30 illustrates a stair that has various nonuniformities or irregularities. Note that the treads are not all uniformly horizontal and the risers are not all vertical. This situation, which illustrates construction errors, is sometimes encountered with cast-in-place concrete stairs. Exhibit 7.30 shows unacceptable nonuniformities of the dimensions measured in accordance with 7.2.2.3.6. The nonuniformities measured at the backs of the treads and along the risers might be greater or smaller depending on how the treads and risers slope.

Where the riser at the base of a stair abuts sloping public property, such as a public sidewalk, the building owner usually has no right to alter the grade of the public property. Therefore, the exception to 7.2.2.3.6 accepts a certain minimum across-the-stair slope not in excess of 1 in 12. Exhibit 7.31 illustrates this exception.

7.2.2.4 Guards and Handrails.

7.2.2.4.1* Guards. Means of egress that are more than 30 in. (76 cm) above the floor or grade below shall be provided with guards to prevent falls over the open side.

A.7.2.2.4.1 Means of egress components that might require protection with guards include stairs, landings, balconies, corridors, passageways, floor or roof openings, ramps, aisles, porches, and mezzanines.

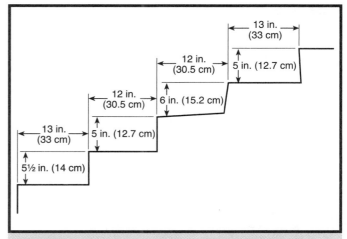

Exhibit 7.30 *Variations in tread and riser dimensions.*

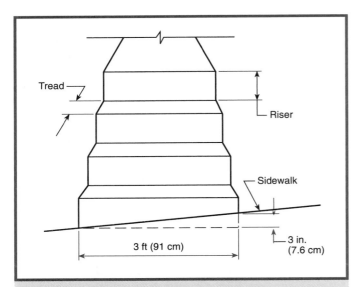

Exhibit 7.31 *Permissible across-the-stair slope.*

Subparagraph 7.2.2.4.1 requires guards along means of egress paths where there is a vertical drop of at least 30 in. (76 cm). This requirement has a particular impact on stairs that historically have required only handrails. Guards must be provided on open sides of the stair—including those that "switch back" between adjacent stair flights, regardless of the horizontal distance between those flights. The minimum 42-in. (107-cm) high guard, used in place of the minimum 34-in. (86-cm) handrail, is needed to prevent the 95 percentile male from falling over the rail upon striking the side of a stair. On switch-back flights of stairs, the required guard is intended to keep a person from falling to the adjacent stair flight. See 7.2.2.4.6 for guard details—especially Exception No. 3 to 7.2.2.4.6(2), which permits existing guards on existing stairs to be a minimum of 30 in. (76 cm) high.

Where the *Code* specifically permits guards to be omitted, such language is provided. For example, in 12.2.11.1.6, which applies to assembly occupancies, guards are exempted on the audience side of stages; raised platforms; and other raised floor areas, such as runways, ramps, and side stages used for entertainment or presentations. Similarly, permanent guards are not required at vertical openings in the performance area of stages. Nor are guards required in assembly occupancies where the side of an elevated walking surface is required to be open for the normal functioning of special lighting or for the access and use of other special equipment.

NFPA staff are often asked whether guards can

be omitted at the open edge of loading docks. Given that the *Code* provides no specific exception for loading docks, it is the intent that the general provisions of 7.2.2.4.1 apply. However, Chapter 4 gives the authority having jurisdiction great latitude in making judgment calls where protection equivalent to that required by the *Code* is provided. Examples of judgment calls made by the authority having jurisdiction are presented in the three scenarios that follow.

(a) *Scenario 1.* A loading dock is 30 ft (9.1 m) deep [that is, the building wall is set back 30 ft (9.1 m) from the open edge of the dock]. At the open edge of the dock, there is more than 30 in. (76 cm) of vertical drop to the ground below. The egress system relies on passage along the width of the loading dock as part of the exit discharge leading to the public way. A 44-in. (112-cm) wide aisle has been stenciled on the floor running parallel to and adjacent to the building wall. Building management strictly enforces a policy that keeps the aisle clear at all times. The authority having jurisdiction judges that, in traveling along the designated path, the building occupants never come close to the open edge of the dock and, thus, guards are not required.

(b) *Scenario 2.* The same physical arrangement exists as in scenario 1, but the authority having jurisdiction inspects the facility and finds stacked materials in the designated aisle and across the depth of the loading dock. During emergency egress, the building occupants would need to travel close to the open edge of the dock to get around the stacked materials. The authority having jurisdiction judges that, in this case, the guard provisions of 7.2.2.4.1 need to be followed.

(c) *Scenario 3.* The loading dock is only 10 ft (3 m) deep. Materials are placed in a haphazard fashion on the dock. There is no designated egress path and, thus, building occupants can be expected to have to travel near the open edge of the dock. The authority having jurisdiction judges that guards are needed.

7.2.2.4.2* Handrails. Stairs and ramps shall have handrails on both sides. In addition, handrails shall be provided within 30 in. (76 cm) of all portions of the required egress width of stairs. The required egress width shall be provided along the natural path of travel. *(See also 7.2.2.4.5.)*

Exception No. 1: On existing stairs, handrails shall be provided within 44 in. (112 cm) of all portions of the required egress width of stairs.

Exception No. 2: If a single step or a ramp is part of a curb that separates a sidewalk from a vehicular way, it shall not be required to have a handrail.

Exception No. 3: Existing stairs, existing ramps, stairs within dwelling units and within guest rooms, and ramps within dwelling units and guest rooms shall be permitted to have a handrail on one side only.

A.7.2.2.4.2 The intent of this provision is to place handrails for the required egress width only, regardless of the actual width. The required egress width is provided along the natural path of travel to and from the building. Examples of this requirement are shown in Figure A.7.2.2.4.2. The reduced intermediate handrail spacing of 60 in. (152 cm) along with a handrail height within the permissible height limits allows users to reach and grasp one handrail. Except as noted in 7.2.2.4.3 and 7.2.2.4.5, handrails are not required on stair landings.

Handrails are required on each side of new stairs and ramps, but they are not required on landings, except as noted in 7.2.2.4.3 and 7.2.2.4.5. Handrails are also required on at least one side of existing stairs. The handrails provide support for people using stairs and can serve as a guide if smoke enters the stairway in a quantity sufficient to obscure vision or if the stair lighting system fails.

For handrails to be effective, they must be within reach of each file of people using the stair. In new construction, handrails need to be provided within 30 in. (76 cm) of all portions of the required egress width and, for existing stairs, within 44 in. (112 cm). The maximum 30-in. (76-cm) distance from a point on a new stair to the nearer handrail is based on the facts that people can only reach about 24 in. (60 cm) to the side to grasp a handrail and that a person's body has width. Exhibit 7.32 depicts people movement on a stair, seen in overhead plan view. The staggered filling of the stair surfaces is typical of that observed during building evacuation where movement, speed, density, and flow are near optimum for safe, comfortable crowd movement.

Because Tables 7.2.2.2.1(a) and (b) and the Exception to 7.3.2 permit handrails to project as much as $3^1/_2$ in. (8.9 cm) into the stair clear width at each side of the stair, center handrails are needed on new stairs more than, approximately, 67 in. (170 cm) wide, or $3^1/_2$ in. + 30 in. + 30 in. + $3^1/_2$ in. (9 cm + 76 cm + 76 cm + 9 cm), as illustrated in Exhibit 7.33. Similarly, center handrails are needed on existing stairs more than, approximately, 95 in. (242 cm) wide, or $3^1/_2$ in. + 44 in. + 44 in. + $3^1/_2$ in. (9 cm + 112 cm + 112 cm + 9 cm).

On monumental stairs, which are characterized by their extreme widths, the required handrails should be located along the normal path of travel to

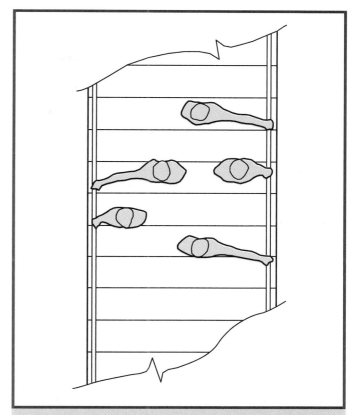

Exhibit 7.32 Overhead plan view of stair with handrails within maximum 30-in. (76-cm) reach.

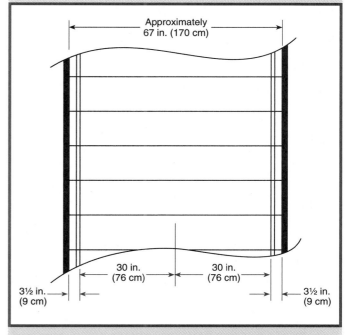

Exhibit 7.33 Maximum required width permitted without center handrail on new stair.

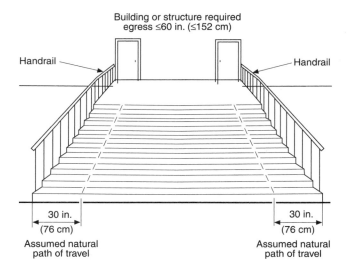

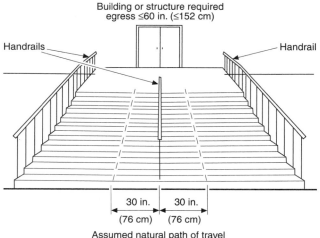

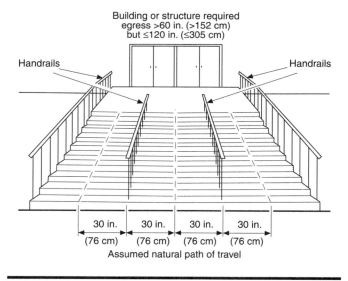

Figure A.7.2.2.4.2 *Assumed natural paths of travel on monumental stairs with various handrail locations.*

and from the building. Figure A.7.2.2.4.2 illustrates the placement of handrails required on wide, monumental stairs. Handrails are provided along the natural paths of travel from the associated doors.

7.2.2.4.3 Continuity. Required guards and handrails shall continue for the full length of each flight of stairs. At turns of new stairs, inside handrails shall be continuous between flights at landings.

It is not the intent of this *Code* to require handrails on stair landings. However, new interior handrails on stairs that change direction at a landing must be continuous. See the turn detailed in the plan view of Figure A.7.2.2.4.5.

The commentary following 7.2.2.4.1 explains the need for guards on open sides of stairs where there is at least a 30-in. (76-cm) vertical distance to fall. The 30-in. (76-cm) criterion—considered alone—would seem to exempt the guard from running past the last couple of risers at the base of each stair flight; however, this criterion must be considered in conjunction with 7.2.2.4.3, which mandates that the required guard is to continue for the full length of each flight of stairs.

7.2.2.4.4 Projections. The design of guards and handrails and the hardware for attaching handrails to guards, balusters, or walls shall be such that there are no projections that might engage loose clothing. Openings in guards shall be designed to prevent loose clothing from becoming wedged in such openings.

7.2.2.4.5* Handrail Details.

(1) Handrails on stairs shall be not less than 34 in. (86 cm) and not more than 38 in. (96 cm) above the surface of the tread, measured vertically to the top of the rail from the leading edge of the tread.

A.7.2.2.4.5 Figure A.7.2.2.4.5 illustrates some of the requirements of 7.2.2.4.5.

See 12.2.5.6.7 and 13.2.5.6.7 for requirements for handrails on aisle stairs in assembly occupancies.

Exception No. 1: The height of required handrails that form part of a guard shall be permitted to exceed 38 in. (96 cm) but shall not exceed 42 in. (107 cm), measured vertically to the top of the rail from the leading edge of the tread.

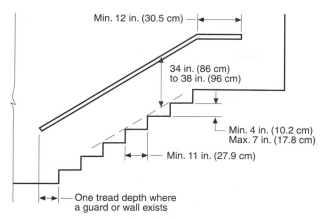

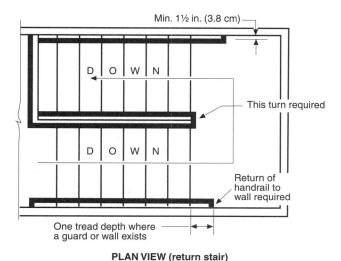

Figure A.7.2.2.4.5 Handrail details.

Exception No. 2:   Existing required handrails shall be permitted to be not less than 30 in. (76 cm) and not more than 38 in. (96 cm) above the upper surface of the tread, measured vertically to the top of the rail from the leading edge of the tread.

Exception No. 3:*   Additional handrails that are lower or higher than the main handrail shall be permitted.

Handrail height was the subject of extensive research by the National Research Council of Canada.

Very high handrails have been tested in field and laboratory conditions. Heights up to about 42 in. (107 cm) are very effective in helping people stabilize themselves to arrest a fall. Therefore, a guard-

height railing that also meets the graspability criteria for handrails [see 7.2.2.4.5(3)] serves well as a handrail also. This dual function is the reason Exception No. 1 to 7.2.2.4.5(1) permits the rail at the top of a 42-in. (107-cm) high guard to serve as a handrail if it meets the graspability criteria. Three different types of studies of handrail height for stairs all led to the conclusion that the handrail heights previously required by the *Code* were inadequate. The studies included anthropometric analyses such as illustrated in Exhibit 7.34, field studies of the use of various handrails, and laboratory studies where the functional capability of users to grasp a handrail—as if arresting a fall—could be accurately measured and compared for a range of handrail conditions.

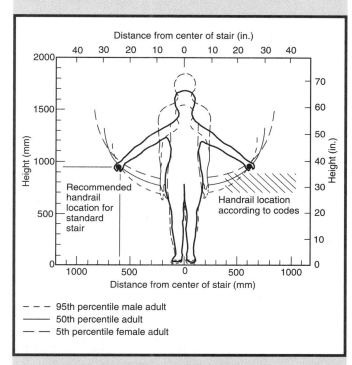

Exhibit 7.34 Anthropometric analysis of reach.

See Exhibit 7.34. One of the studies leading to the requirement for higher handrails and closer lateral spacing included this anthropometric analysis of user capability to reach a handrail positioned to the side. The left side of the figure shows the recommended height and spacing of handrails; on the right is the location of handrails permitted by pre-1988 editions of the *Code*. People in the middle of a wide stair will be unable to reach the lower, more distant handrails; therefore, this condition is not desirable when a stair is crowded, as during emergency egress.

The studies included a wide range of ages and sizes of people, from young children to those in their seventies. Most functional heights—even for elderly persons tested—were in the range of 36 in. to 38 in. (91 cm to 97 cm), and the average height most preferred by elderly persons tested was about 37 in. (94 cm). These studies were reported in "Review of Stair-Safety Research with an Emphasis on Canadian Studies" by Jake Pauls.[7] The recommendation for lower handrails for young children is particularly important for family dwellings and for child day-care facilities.

Exhibit 7.35 is a frame from the documentary film, *The Stair Event*. It shows field testing of an adjustable-height handrail in an aisle stair in Canada's Edmonton Commonwealth Stadium. Evidence from such field testing, from anthropometric analyses, and from laboratory testing with a range of younger and older adults led to the higher handrail heights first introduced in the 1988 edition of the *Code*. The upper handrail is located 37 in. (94 cm) above tread nosings, which, in the laboratory testing, was the average preferred height for elderly people and an especially effective height for arresting a fall that occurs while descending a stair. The lower railing, provided for children, is approximately 24 in. (60 cm) above the tread nosings. Note that even in this case of ascent, one of the children has chosen to use the higher railing, located at about his shoulder height, in preference to the lower one. A moment after this frame was taken, the smaller of the two boys also chose to use the upper handrail, which was located at about the height of his head. This behavior has been ob-

Exhibit 7.35 *Field testing of handrail height. (Photo courtesy of Jake Pauls.)*

served in other studies of children, that is, when given a choice of handrail heights, they often select one between shoulder and head height.

A.7.2.2.4.5 Exception No. 3 Additional handrails, beyond those required by the Code, are permitted at heights other than those stipulated. For example, where children under the age of 5 are major users of a facility, an additional handrail at a height in the range of 28 in. to 32 in. (71 cm to 81 cm) might be useful. Generally, children prefer to use, and can effectively use, handrails that are located at shoulder to head height due to their developmental characteristics and their less developed balance and walking abilities. At age 3, head height ranges from 35 in. to 40 in. (89 cm to 102 cm); shoulder height averages 29 in. (74 cm). At age 5, head height ranges from 39 in. to 46 in. (99 cm to 117 cm); shoulder height ranges from 31 in. to 37 in. (79 cm to 94 cm).

(2)* New handrails shall provide a clearance of not less than 1 ½ in. (3.8 cm) between the handrail and the wall to which it is fastened.

A.7.2.2.4.5(2) This 1½-in. (3.8-cm) clearance assumes that the wall and other surfaces adjacent to the handrail are smooth. Where rough surfaces are used, greater clearances are recommended. Ergonomic studies suggest that not less than 2¼ in. (5.7 cm) is a more appropriate clearance, even to smooth surfaces. It is important to note that the 3½-in. (8.9-cm) projection allowance of Tables 7.2.2.2.1(a) and (b) and 7.3.2 does not prohibit such larger clearances; the 3½ in. (8.9 cm) refers to stair width required for egress capacity, for example, not the actual width.

(3)* Handrails shall have a circular cross section with an outside diameter of not less than 1 ¼ in. (3.2 cm) and not more than 2 in. (5 cm).

A.7.2.2.4.5(3) Handrails should be designed so they can be grasped firmly with a comfortable grip and so the hand can be slid along the rail without encountering obstructions. The profile of the rail should comfortably match the hand grips. For example, a round profile such as is provided by the simplest round tubing or pipe having an outside diameter of 1½ in. to 2 in. (3.8 cm to 5 cm) provides good graspability for adults. Factors such as the use of a handrail by small children and the wall-fixing details should be taken into account in assessing handrail graspability. The most functional as well as the most preferred handrail shape and size is circular with a 1½-in. (3.8-cm) outside diameter (according to research conducted using adults). Handrails used predominantly by children should be designed at the lower end of the permitted dimensional range.

Handrails are one of the most important components of a stair; therefore, design excesses such as oversized wood handrail sections should be avoided unless there is a readily perceived and easily grasped handhold provided. In handrail design, it is useful to remember at all times the effectiveness of a simple round profile that allows some locking action by fingers as they curl around the handrail.

Perimeter dimension, referred to in the exception to 7.2.2.4.5(3), is the length of the shortest loop that wraps completely around the railing.

Subparagraph 7.2.2.4.5(3) introduces a subtle but important requirement for handrails—graspability. People are incapable of exerting sufficient finger pressure to grasp a handrail adequately where using only a *pinch grip*; a *power grip*, where fingers curl around and under a properly shaped and sized railing, is much more effective. Exhibit 7.36 shows examples of acceptable and unacceptable handrails. Example 1 shows a handrail with a shape and an offset from the wall that provides graspability. Example 2 shows a handrail of a size and shape that are unacceptable from a graspability standpoint.

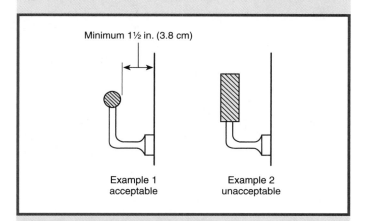

Exhibit 7.36 *Handrail graspability features.*

Exhibit 7.37 illustrates acceptable, unacceptable, and marginal handrail shapes and sizes based on a Canadian study that used younger and older adults and tested functional capability as well as user preference. The traditional residential handrail section, shown at the bottom center, did not perform well in the functional testing; it was not a comfortable shape to grasp in comparison with other section shapes. A key difference between the acceptable and unacceptable handrail sections is the ability to wrap the fingers around the handrail completely to achieve a power grip. Unacceptable sections permit only a pinch grip, which is ineffective in arresting a fall, even for people with ordinary hand dexterity and strength.

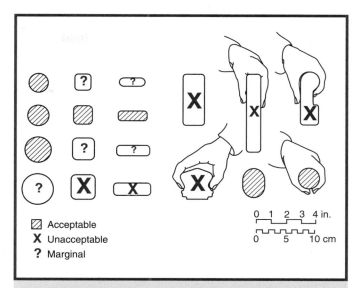

Exhibit 7.37 *Acceptable, unacceptable, and marginal handrail sections.*

Exception: Any other shape with a perimeter dimension of not less than 4 in. (10.2 cm), but not more than 6¼ in. (15.9 cm), and with the largest cross-sectional dimension not more than 2 ¼ in. (5.7 cm) shall be permitted, provided that edges are rounded so as to provide a radius of not less than ⅛ in. (0.3 cm).

(4) New handrails shall be continuously graspable along their entire length.

Exception: Handrail brackets or balusters attached to the bottom surface of the handrail shall not be considered to be obstructions to graspability, provided that the following criteria are met:

(a) They do not project horizontally beyond the sides of the handrail within 1 ½ in. (3.75 cm) of the bottom of the handrail and provided that, for each ½ in. (1.3 cm) of additional handrail perimeter dimension above 4 in. (10 cm), the vertical clearance dimension of 1 ½ in. (3.75 cm) can be reduced by ⅛ in. (0.3 cm).

(b) They have edges with a radius of not less than ⅛ in. (0.3 cm).

(c) They obstruct not in excess of 20 percent of the handrail length.

The exception to 7.2.2.4.5(4) recognizes that handrail brackets and other forms of support are necessary but need to be designed to permit the hand to slide along the handrail without encountering obstructions that would force the release of one's grip. Exhibit 7.38

shows a handrail that has been positioned above the horizontal extension of the supporting bracket by the required minimum 1½ in. (3.75 cm). Note how the fingers of the hand have sufficient space to point downward in a natural grasping position without encountering the handrail bracket.

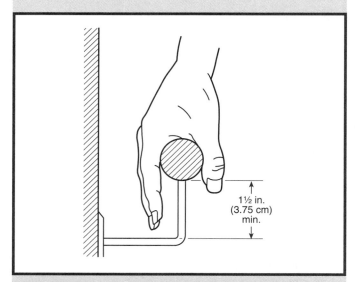

Exhibit 7.38 Minimum clearance to handrail brackets.

(5) New handrail ends shall be returned to the wall or floor or shall terminate at newel posts.
(6) New handrails that are not continuous between flights shall extend horizontally, at the required height, not less than 12 in. (30.5 cm) beyond the top riser and continue to slope for a depth of one tread beyond the bottom riser.

Exception: Within dwelling units the handrail shall be permitted to extend, at the required height, to points directly above the top and bottom risers.

7.2.2.4.6 Guard Details.

(1) The height of guards required in 7.2.2.4.1 shall be measured vertically to the top of the guard from the surface adjacent thereto.
(2) Guards shall be not less than 42 in. (107 cm) high.

Exception No. 1: Existing guards within dwelling units shall be permitted to be not less than 36 in. (91 cm) high.

Exception No. 2: The requirement of 7.2.2.4.6(2) shall not apply where otherwise provided in Chapters 12 and 13.

Exception No. 3: *Existing guards on existing stairs shall be permitted to be not less than 30 in. (76 cm) high.*

A.7.2.2.4.6 Exception No. 3 This reduction in required height applies only to the stair, not to the landings.

(3)* Open guards, other than approved, existing open guards, shall have intermediate rails or an ornamental pattern such that a sphere 4 in. (10.1 cm) in diameter shall not pass through any opening up to a height of 34 in. (86 cm).

A.7.2.2.4.6(3) Vertical intermediate rails are preferred to reduce climbability.

The criterion for a 6-in. (15.2-cm) diameter sphere was changed to a 4-in. (10.1-cm) diameter sphere for the 1991 edition of the *Code*. This change was made based on the submission of a proposal that received the backing of the American Academy of Pediatrics. Approximately 950 out of 1000 children under age 10 can pass through a 6-in. (15.2-cm) wide opening. To prevent small children from falling through guards and to prevent them from being caught in openings, the configuration and construction of a guard must meet certain minimum requirements. Rather than requiring detailed specifications to be met for intermediate rails, the *Code* sets a performance criterion that allows alternative solutions.

Note that the 4-in. (10.1-cm) diameter sphere criterion applies to the portion of the guard that extends from the walking surface to a height of 34 in. (86 cm). Although the top rail of the guard must extend to a minimum height of 42 in. (107 cm), the space in the guard above 34 in. (86 cm) is not required to prevent the passage of a 4-in. (10.1-cm) diameter sphere. This provision is illustrated in Exhibit 7.39.

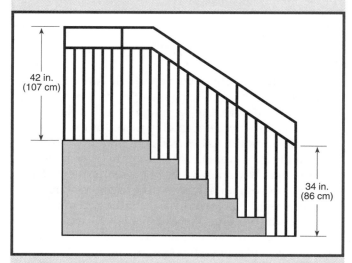

Exhibit 7.39 Height extension for application of 4-in. (10.1-cm) diameter sphere criterion for guards.

Exception No. 1: The triangular openings formed by the riser, tread, and bottom element of a guardrail at the open side of a stair shall be of such size that a sphere 6 in. (15.2 cm) in diameter shall not pass through the triangular opening.

Exception No. 2: In detention and correctional occupancies, in industrial occupancies, and in storage occupancies, the clear distance between intermediate rails, measured at right angles to the rails, shall not exceed 21 in. (53.3 cm).

7.2.2.5 Enclosure and Protection of Stairs.

7.2.2.5.1 Enclosures. All inside stairs serving as an exit or exit component shall be enclosed in accordance with 7.1.3.2. All other inside stairs shall be protected in accordance with 8.2.5.

Subparagraph 7.2.2.5.1 emphasizes that enclosure protection for stairs depends on whether they serve within an exit or involve a vertical opening between floors. Stairs that are not used as exits but that involve vertical openings are not subject to the requirements of 7.1.3.2 but must be protected in accordance with 8.2.5. Many interior stairs serve as exits and are vertical openings. Therefore, they must meet the requirements of 7.1.3.2 for exits, and, as an element that creates vertical openings, they also must comply with 8.2.5. Compliance with 8.2.5 does not ensure compliance with 7.1.3.2. Stairs that are neither within an exit nor part of vertical openings, such as stairs to a platform or stage, or those running between two different floor levels on the same story, would not have to comply with either 7.1.3.2 or 8.2.5.

Exception: In existing buildings, where a two-story exit enclosure connects the story of exit discharge with an adjacent story, the exit shall be permitted to be enclosed only on the story of exit discharge, provided that not less than 50 percent of the number and capacity of exits on the story of exit discharge are independent of such enclosures.

The provisions of the exception to 7.2.2.5.1 recognize existing two-story stairs that, rather than being fully enclosed at both the top and bottom, are separated only from the level of exit discharge. Because such a stair is open to another floor, it might compromise the use of the stair enclosure for egress purposes by occupants of the level of exit discharge. The *Code* requires that at least half of the egress for the level of exit discharge be independent of the stair enclosure. This requirement limits the effect of occupants who are forced to travel into an enclosure that is smoke-filled due to a fire on another floor that is

open to the stair. See Exhibit 7.40. The existing stair connecting the first and second floors, although separated from the first floor, is open to the second floor. This arrangement is permitted because a minimum of 50 percent of the first floor egress can be satisfied independently from use of the stair enclosure via the door that opens directly to the outside at grade level at the right of the figure.

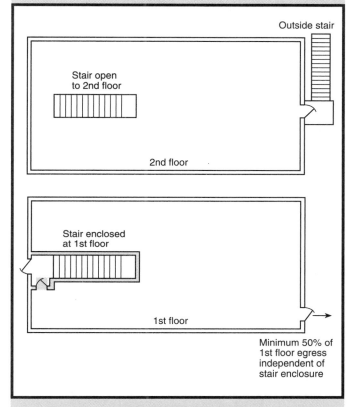

Exhibit 7.40 *Partial enclosure of existing stair.*

7.2.2.5.2* Exposures. Where nonrated walls or unprotected openings enclose the exterior of a stairway, other than an existing stairway, and the walls or openings are exposed by other parts of the building at an angle of less than 180 degrees, the building enclosure walls within 10 ft (3 m) horizontally of the nonrated wall or unprotected opening shall be constructed as required for stairway enclosures, including opening protectives. Construction shall extend vertically from the ground to a point 10 ft (3 m) above the topmost landing of the stairs or to the roofline, whichever is lower.

Exception: The fire resistance rating of the separation extending 10 ft (3 m) from the stairs shall not be required to exceed 1 hour where openings have not less than a ¾-hour fire protection rating.

Subparagraph 7.2.2.5.2 only applies where the stair is required to be enclosed either to create an exit or to protect a vertical opening.

A.7.2.2.5.2 The purpose of this provision is to protect the exterior wall of a stairway from fires in other portions of the building. If the exterior wall of the stair is flush with the building exterior wall, the fire would need to travel around 180 degrees in order to impact the stair. This has not been a problem in existing buildings, so no protection is required. However, if the angle of exposure is less than 180 degrees, protection of either the stair wall or building wall is required.

Figures A.7.2.2.5.2 (a), (b), and (c) illustrate the requirement, assuming nonrated glass on the exterior wall of the stair is used.

7.2.2.5.3* Usable Space. There shall be no enclosed, usable space within an exit enclosure, including under stairs,

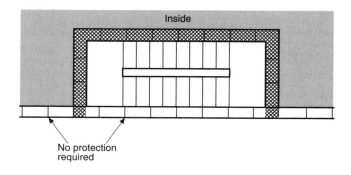

Figure A.7.2.2.5.2(a) *Stairway with nonrated exterior wall in same plane as building exterior wall.*

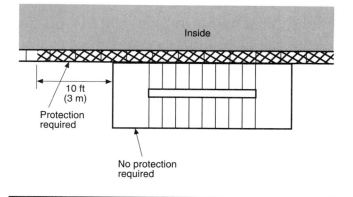

Figure A.7.2.2.5.2(b) *Stairway with unprotected exterior perimeter protruding past building exterior wall.*

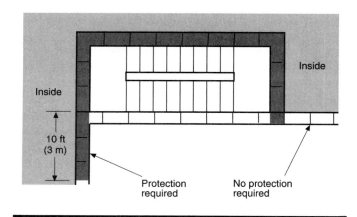

Figure A.7.2.2.5.2(c) *Stairway with nonrated exterior wall exposed by adjacent exterior wall of building.*

nor shall any open space within the enclosure be used for any purpose that has the potential to interfere with egress.

Exception: Enclosed, usable space shall be permitted under stairs, provided that the space is separated from the stair enclosure by the same fire resistance as the exit enclosure. Entrance to such enclosed usable space shall not be from within the stair enclosure. (See also 7.1.3.2.3.)

Subparagraph 7.2.2.5.3 states that, within an exit enclosure, no enclosed, usable space is permitted, nor is any open space permitted to be used for any purpose that could interfere with the use of the exit enclosure. An enclosed, usable space under a stair is permitted to be considered outside the exit enclosure if the walls and soffits of the enclosed space meet the same protection requirements as the stair enclosure, thereby separating the space from the exit enclosure. The door to the space is not permitted to open into the exit enclosure, per 7.1.3.2.1(d). See Exhibit 7.41.

A.7.2.2.5.3 An example of a use with the potential to interfere with egress is storage.

7.2.2.5.4* Stair Identification Signs. Stairs serving five or more stories shall be provided with signage within the enclosure at each floor landing. The signage shall indicate the story, the terminus of the top and bottom of the stair enclosure, and the identification of the stair enclosure. The signage also shall state the story of, and the direction to, exit discharge. The signage shall be inside the enclosure located approximately 5 ft (1.5 m) above the floor landing in a position that is readily visible when the door is in the open or closed position.

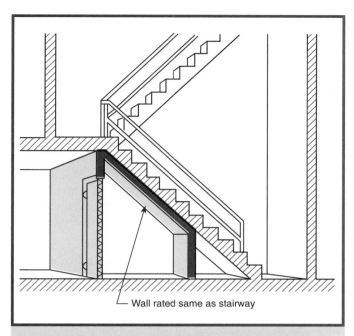

Wall rated same as stairway

Exhibit 7.41 Enclosed, usable space under flight of stairs.

NORTH STAIR

FLOOR

5

SUBBASEMENT TO 24TH FLOOR
NO ROOF ACCESS
↓ DOWN TO FIRST FLOOR
FOR EXIT DISCHARGE

Exhibit 7.42 Stair sign details.

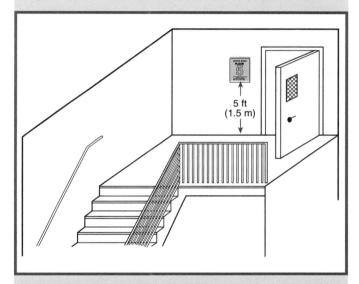

5 ft
(1.5 m)

Exhibit 7.43 Stair sign placement.

A.7.2.2.5.4 The intent of this provision is to provide vital egress information to the occupants of a building and to fire fighters. To reduce information overload to occupants during emergency egress, a sign indicating the floor level of and the direction to the exit discharge is permitted to be placed as a separate sign with another sign indicating the floor level, the terminus of the top and bottom of the stair enclosure, and the identification of the stair.

The provisions of 7.2.2.5.4 require the posting of important information at each floor landing in each stairwell if the stair serves five or more stories. The term *signage* is used to signify that the required information might appear on multiple signs mounted adjacent to each other. The information is for firefighting personnel and building occupants in an emergency. The information most helpful to fire fighters can be put on one sign, and the information most useful to occupants on another. See A.7.2.2.5.4.

The signage must identify the stair, indicate the floor level of the landing and where the stairwell terminates at the top and bottom, and identify and show the direction to the exit discharge. Exhibit 7.42 is an example of a single sign providing all the required information. Exhibit 7.43 illustrates the placement required to ensure that the sign is readily visible whether the door is in the open or closed position.

The indication of the direction to the level of exit discharge can be extremely useful to occupants of a building, especially if they are located below the level of exit discharge. The natural tendency of occupants is to attempt egress by traveling downward in a stair; this is counterproductive where the exit discharge is located on an upper level. Also, many buildings have multiple levels of entrance, which creates confusion with respect to travel direction in a given stair.

The requirements of 7.2.2.5.4 are not exempted for existing buildings, because it is feasible and cost effective to install signs providing the requested information. Because stair enclosures are usually not as aesthetically well finished as occupied portions of a building, the requirement for signage is often met by stenciling the information directly onto the walls.

7.2.2.5.5 Egress Direction Signs. Wherever an enclosed stair requires travel in an upward direction to reach the level of exit discharge, signs with directional indicators indicating the direction to the level of exit discharge shall be provided at each floor level landing from which upward direction of travel is required. Such signage shall be readily visible when the door is in the open or closed position.

Exception No. 1: This requirement shall not apply where signs required by 7.2.2.5.4 are provided.

Exception No. 2: Stairs extending not more than one story below the level of exit discharge where the exit discharge is clearly obvious shall not be subject to this requirement.

7.2.2.6 Special Provisions for Outside Stairs.

7.2.2.6.1 Access. Where approved by the authority having jurisdiction, outside stairs shall be permitted to lead to roofs of other sections of a building or an adjoining building where the construction is fire resistive and there is a continuous and safe means of egress from the roof. *(See also 7.7.6.)*

7.2.2.6.2* Visual Protection. Outside stairs shall be arranged to avoid any impediments to the use of the stairs by persons having a fear of high places. For stairs more than three stories in height, any arrangement intended to meet this requirement shall be not less than 4 ft (1.2 m) in height.

A.7.2.2.6.2 The guards that are required by 7.2.2.4 will usually meet this requirement where the stair is not more than three stories high. Special architectural treatment, including application of such devices as metal or masonry screens and grilles, will usually be necessary to comply with the intent of this requirement for stairs over three stories in height.

Outside stairs frequently have an open side. Required rails and guards help to prevent falls but do nothing to shield the user's view of the vertical drop. For outside stairs on high buildings, the fear of height might interfere with the use of such stairs; therefore, 7.2.2.6.2 requires a 4-ft (122-cm) high visual barrier to be provided.

7.2.2.6.3 Separation and Protection of Outside Stairs. Outside stairs shall be separated from the interior of the building by walls with the fire resistance rating required for enclosed stairs with fixed or self-closing opening protectives. This construction shall extend vertically from the ground to a point 10 ft (3 m) above the topmost landing of the stairs or to the roofline, whichever is lower, and to a point not less than 10 ft (3 m) horizontally.

Subparagraph 7.2.2.6.3 applies only where the outside stair serves as an exit. See commentary following Exception No. 2 to 7.2.2.1.

An important consideration is the proximity of outside stairs to openings in the building wall through which fire emerging from the building could render the stairs useless as a means of egress. Protection against such an occurrence is achieved as follows:

(1) Protection from openings by separation distances
(2) Protection of openings by fire-rated doors and fire-rated windows, which must be done if the openings are positioned in a wall so that the separation distances are less than are required.

The old fire escape arrangement where a window access is positioned immediately below a fire escape landing creates the potential for fire exposure of the fire escape. This is a situation to avoid. The separation and protection provisions in 7.2.2.6.3 for outside stairs are illustrated in Exhibits 7.44 through 7.46.

In Exhibit 7.44, if openings are within 10 ft (3 m) of the outside stairs, they must be protected (see 7.2.2.6.3). However, the fire resistance ratings in

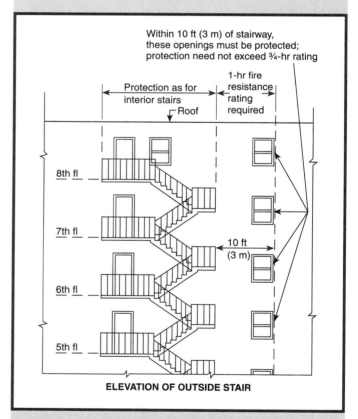

Exhibit 7.44 *Protection of openings for outside stairs— Example 1.*

the 10-ft (3-m) extension need not exceed 1 hour, and fire protection rating for the opening need not exceed ³/₄ hour.

In Exhibit 7.45, the fire resistance rating for the walls of the 10-ft (3-m) extension is a minimum of 1 hour. The fire resistance rating for the walls within the short dashed lines is based on the number of stories served by the outside stair, the same as for interior stairs.

In Exhibit 7.46, Exception No. 1 to 7.2.2.6.3 is illustrated in the top figure (a). Exception No. 2 to 7.2.2.6.3, which is restricted to stairways serving no more that two adjacent stories, is illustrated in the bottom figure (b). This same figure illustrates Exception No. 3 to 7.2.2.6.3, but this exception permits stairways to serve up to three adjacent stories and is restricted to use in existing buildings.

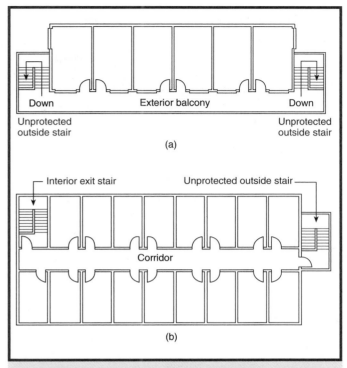

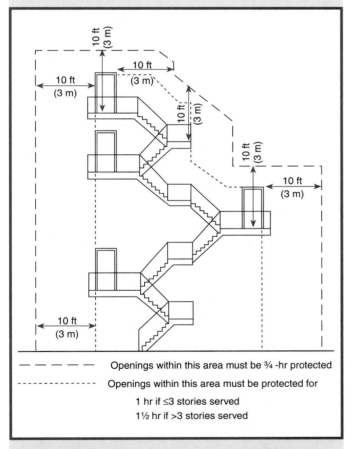

Exhibit 7.45 *Protection of openings for outside stairs— Example 2.*

Exception No. 1: Outside stairs serving an exterior exit access balcony that has two remote outside stairways or ramps shall be permitted to be unprotected.

Exhibit 7.46 *Protection of openings for outside stairs— Examples 3 and 4.*

Exception No. 2: Outside stairs serving not in excess of two adjacent stories, including the story of exit discharge, shall be permitted to be unprotected where there is a remotely located second exit.

Exception No. 3: In existing buildings, existing outside stairs serving not in excess of three adjacent stories, including the story of exit discharge, shall be permitted to be unprotected where there is a remotely located second exit.

Exception No. 4: The fire resistance rating of the separation extending 10 ft (3 m) from the stairs shall not be required to exceed 1 hour where openings have not less than a ³/₄-hour fire protection rating.

7.2.2.6.4 Protection of Openings. All openings below an outside stair shall be protected with an assembly having not less than a ³/₄-hour fire protection rating as follows:

(1) Where located in a court, the smallest dimension of which does not exceed one-third its height
(2) Where located in an alcove having a width that does not exceed one-third its height and a depth that does not exceed one-fourth its height

Exhibit 7.47 illustrates the provisions of 7.2.2.6.4. The bases for the required protection of openings below open, outside stairs discharging to a courtyard are as follows:

(1) If D or W is less than one-third of H, all openings within the courtyard below the open, outside stairs must be protected.
(2) If D is greater than one-fourth of H, and W is less than one-third of H, protection is required at openings.

Example 1

    $H = 60$ ft (18.3 m)
    D or $W < 20$ ft (6.1 m)

Therefore, special protection is required.

Example 2

    $H = 60$ ft (18.3 m)
    $D > 15$ ft (4.6 m)
    $W < 20$ ft (6.1 m)

Therefore, special protection is required.

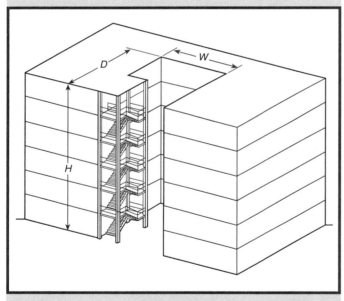

Exhibit 7.47 *Bases for required protection of openings below open, outside stairs discharging to courtyard.*

7.2.2.6.5* Water Accumulation. Outside stairs and landings, other than existing outside stairs and landings, shall be designed to minimize water accumulation on their surfaces.

A.7.2.2.6.5 See A.7.2.2.3.4.

7.2.2.6.6 Openness. Outside stairs, other than existing outside stairs, shall be not less than 50 percent open on one side. Outside stairs shall be arranged to restrict the accumulation of smoke.

7.2.3 Smokeproof Enclosures.

7.2.3.1 General. Where smokeproof enclosures are required in other sections of this *Code*, they shall comply with 7.2.3, unless they are existing smokeproof enclosures approved by the authority having jurisdiction.

A smokeproof enclosure is a stair enclosure designed to limit the infiltration of heat, smoke, and fire gases from a fire in any part of a building. A smokeproof enclosure improves protection against the products of combustion entering the actual stairway enclosure. The *Code* requires the use of smokeproof enclosures in 31.2.11 for existing nonsprinklered high-rise apartment buildings.

7.2.3.2 Performance Design. An appropriate design method shall be used to provide a system that meets the definition of smokeproof enclosure. The smokeproof enclosure shall be permitted to be created by using natural ventilation, by using mechanical ventilation incorporating a vestibule, or by pressurizing the stair enclosure.

Paragraph 7.2.3.2 requires that smokeproof enclosures meet the performance criterion contained in the definition of smokeproof enclosure in 3.3.186. Paragraph 7.2.3.2 also specifies three different means of creating smokeproof enclosures as follows:

(1) By use of natural ventilation as detailed in 7.2.3.7
(2) By mechanical ventilation in accordance with 7.2.3.8
(3) By pressurizing the stair enclosure as outlined in 7.2.3.9

However, the *Code* does not restrict the design to one of the three methods detailed if the design meets the performance requirements and is acceptable to the authority having jurisdiction. This alternative is especially important for existing smokeproof enclosures, because they often do not meet all the specifications that follow.

Exhibit 7.48 illustrates four variations of smokeproof enclosures that meet the specific *Code* criteria contained in 7.2.3.4 through 7.2.3.8. Plan A utilizes an open air vestibule. Plan B shows entrance to the smokeproof enclosure by way of an outside balcony. Plan C provides a stair enclosure entrance common to two buildings or two building areas. In Plan D, smoke and gases entering the vestibule are exhausted

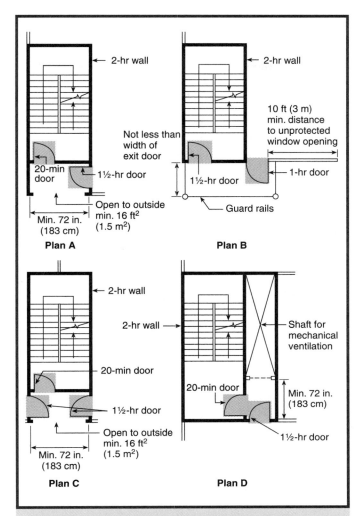

Exhibit 7.48 Four variations of smokeproof enclosures.

by mechanical ventilation. In each case, a double entrance to the stair enclosure with at least one side open or vented is characteristic of the type of construction. Pressurization of the stair enclosure in the event of fire provides an attractive alternative and is a means of eliminating the entrance vestibule.

7.2.3.3 Enclosure. A smokeproof enclosure shall be enclosed from the highest point to the lowest point by barriers having 2-hour fire resistance ratings. Where a vestibule is used, it shall be within the 2-hour-rated enclosure and shall be considered part of the smokeproof enclosure.

Paragraph 7.2.3.3 requires that the smokeproof enclosure and all of its components be within the required 2-hour fire resistance–rated enclosure, with openings therein protected by a door having a 1¹/₂-hour fire

protection rating. Such an arrangement protects the smokeproof enclosure from the direct attack of fire. However, the door from the vestibule (within the 2-hour rated enclosure) into the actual stairway requires only a 20-minute fire protection rating, because the purpose of this door is to minimize air or smoke leakage.

7.2.3.4 Vestibule. Where a vestibule is provided, the doorway into the vestibule shall be protected with an approved fire door assembly having a 1 ½-hour fire protection rating, and the fire door assembly from the vestibule to the smokeproof enclosure shall have not less than a 20-minute fire protection rating. Doors shall be designed to minimize air leakage and shall be self-closing or shall be automatic-closing by actuation of a smoke detector within 10 ft (3 m) of the vestibule door.

7.2.3.5 Discharge. Every smokeproof enclosure shall discharge into a public way, into a yard or court having direct access to a public way, or into an exit passageway. Such exit passageways shall be without openings other than the entrance from the smokeproof enclosure and the door to the outside yard, court, or public way. The exit passageway shall be separated from the remainder of the building by a 2-hour fire resistance rating.

Note that 7.2.3.5 prohibits smokeproof enclosures from discharging through the level of exit discharge. It emphasizes the need for continuity to a public way, the exit discharge that leads to a public way, or an exit passageway that leads to an exit discharge that leads to a public way. Because an exit passageway is an exit, it is permitted to have only those openings necessary for building occupant egress.

7.2.3.6 Access. Access to the smokeproof enclosure stair shall be by way of a vestibule or by way of an exterior balcony.

Exception: This requirement shall not apply to smokeproof enclosures consisting of a pressurized stair enclosure complying with 7.2.3.9.

7.2.3.7 Natural Ventilation. Smokeproof enclosures using natural ventilation shall comply with 7.2.3.3 and the following.

(a) Where access to the stair is by means of an open exterior balcony, the door assembly to the stair shall have a 1 ½-hour fire protection rating and shall be self-closing or shall be automatic-closing by actuation of a smoke detector. Openings adjacent to such exterior balconies shall be protected in accordance with 7.2.2.6.5.

(b) Every vestibule shall have a net area of not less than 16 ft² (1.5 m²) of opening in an exterior wall facing an exterior court, yard, or public space not less than 20 ft (6.1 m) in width.

(c) Every vestibule shall have a minimum dimension of not less than the required width of the corridor leading to it and a dimension of not less than 72 in. (183 cm) in the direction of travel.

7.2.3.8 Mechanical Ventilation. Smokeproof enclosures using mechanical ventilation shall comply with 7.2.3.3 and the following.

(a) Vestibules shall have a dimension of not less than 44 in. (112 cm) in width and not less than 72 in. (183 cm) in direction of travel.

(b) The vestibule shall be provided with not less than one air change per minute, and the exhaust shall be 150 percent of the supply. Supply air shall enter and exhaust air shall discharge from the vestibule through separate tightly constructed ducts used only for those purposes. Supply air shall enter the vestibule within 6 in. (15.2 cm) of the floor level. The top of the exhaust register shall be located not more than 6 in. (15.2 cm) below the top of the trap and shall be entirely within the smoke trap area. Doors, when in the open position, shall not obstruct duct openings. Controlling dampers shall be permitted in duct openings if needed to meet the design requirements.

(c) To serve as a smoke and heat trap and to provide an upward-moving air column, the vestibule ceiling shall be not less than 20 in. (50.8 cm) higher than the door opening into the vestibule. The height shall be permitted to be decreased where justified by engineering design and field testing.

(d) The stair shall be provided with a dampered relief opening at the top and supplied mechanically with sufficient air to discharge at least 2500 ft³/min (70.8 m³/min) through the relief opening while maintaining a positive pressure of not less than 0.10 in. water column (25 Pa) in the stair relative to the vestibule with all doors closed.

> Exhibit 7.49 illustrates an elevation view of a smoke-proof enclosure vestibule that uses mechanical ventilation.

7.2.3.9 Stair Pressurization.

7.2.3.9.1* Smokeproof enclosures using stair pressurization shall use an approved engineered system with a design pressure difference across the barrier of not less than 0.05 in. water column (12.5 Pa) in sprinklered buildings, or 0.10 in.

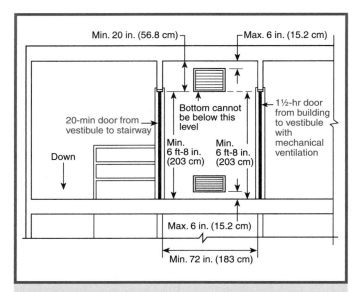

Exhibit 7.49 *Mechanical ventilation form of smokeproof enclosure.*

water column (25 Pa) in nonsprinklered buildings, and shall be capable of maintaining these pressure differences under likely conditions of stack effect or wind. The pressure difference across doors shall exceed that which allows the door to begin to be opened by a force of 30 lbf (133 N) in accordance with 7.2.1.4.5.

A.7.2.3.9.1 The design pressure differences required by 7.2.3.9.1 are based on specific gas temperatures and ceiling heights. The system is required to be approved because anticipated conditions might be different from those on which the design pressure differences were calculated and, thus, different design pressure differences might be needed. For additional information on necessary minimum design pressure differences, including calculational techniques, or maximum pressure differences across doors to ensure reasonable operating forces, see NFPA 92A, *Recommended Practice for Smoke-Control Systems.*

> Pressurized stairs are permitted to be used as smoke-proof enclosures in either nonsprinklered or sprinklered buildings. However, the design pressure difference across the barrier in a nonsprinklered building is required to be twice that required in a sprinklered building.

7.2.3.9.2 Equipment and ductwork for stair pressurization shall be located as specified by one of the following:

(1) Exterior to the building and directly connected to the stairway by ductwork enclosed in noncombustible construction
(2) Within the stair enclosure with intake and exhaust air directly to the outside or through ductwork enclosed by a 2-hour fire-resistive rating
(3) Within the building if separated from the remainder of the building, including other mechanical equipment, by a 2-hour fire-resistive rating

Exception: Where the building, including the stairway enclosure, is protected throughout by an approved, supervised automatic sprinkler system installed in accordance with Section 9.7, the fire resistance rating shall be permitted to be not less than 1 hour.

In all cases specified by 7.2.3.9.2(1) through (3), openings into the required fire resistance rating shall be limited to those needed for maintenance and operation and shall be protected by self-closing fire protection–rated devices in accordance with 8.2.3.2.3.

Exhibits 7.50(a), 7.50(b), and 7.50(c) illustrate some potential arrangements that comply with 7.2.3.9.2.

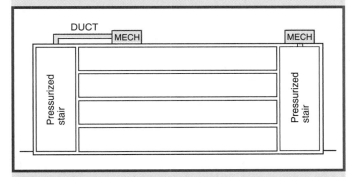

Exhibit 7.50(a) Mechanical equipment and ductwork complying with 7.2.3.9.2(1).

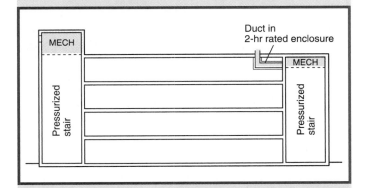

Exhibit 7.50(b) Mechanical equipment and ductwork complying with 7.2.3.9.2(2).

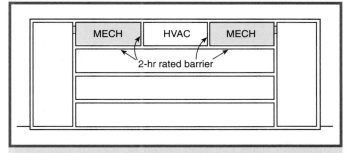

Exhibit 7.50(c) Mechanical equipment and ductwork complying with 7.2.3.9.2(3).

7.2.3.10 Activation of Mechanical Ventilation and Pressurized Stair Systems.

7.2.3.10.1 For both mechanical ventilation and pressurized stair enclosure systems, the activation of the systems shall be initiated by a smoke detector installed in an approved location within 10 ft (3 m) of the entrance to the smokeproof enclosure.

7.2.3.10.2 The required mechanical systems shall operate upon the activation of the smoke detectors specified in 7.2.3.10.1 and by manual controls accessible to the fire department. The required system also shall be initiated by the following, if provided:

(1) Waterflow signal from a complete automatic sprinkler system
(2) General evacuation alarm signal *(See 9.6.3.7.)*

7.2.3.11 Door Closers. The activation of an automatic-closing device on any door in the smokeproof enclosure shall activate all other automatic-closing devices on doors in the smokeproof enclosure.

7.2.3.12 Standby Power. Standby power for mechanical ventilation equipment shall be provided by an approved, self-contained generator that is set to operate whenever there is a loss of power in the normal house current. The generator shall be located in a room having a minimum 1-hour fire resistance–rated separation from the remainder of the building. The generator shall have a fuel supply not less than that which is adequate to operate the equipment for 2 hours.

7.2.3.13 Testing. Before the mechanical equipment is accepted by the authority having jurisdiction, it shall be tested to confirm that the mechanical equipment is operating in compliance with the requirements of 7.2.3. All operating parts of the system shall be tested semiannually by approved personnel, and a log shall be kept of the results.

7.2.4 Horizontal Exits.

7.2.4.1 General.

7.2.4.1.1 Where horizontal exits are used in the means of egress, they shall conform to the general requirements of Section 7.1 and the requirements of 7.2.4.

7.2.4.1.2* Horizontal exits shall be permitted to be substituted for other exits where the total egress capacity of the other exits (stairs, ramps, doors leading outside the building) is not less than half that required for the entire area of the building or connected buildings and provided that none of the other exits is a horizontal exit.

Exception: This requirement shall not apply where otherwise provided in Chapters 18, 19, 22, and 23.

A horizontal exit is a combination of fire-rated walls with fire-rated doors providing passage from one building area into another building area; each area is a fire compartment independent of the other compartment. A horizontal exit, however, need not be confined to one building. It can be used as a bridge from one building to another. Just as with other types of exits, the horizontal exit has components consisting of doors and enclosure walls. Structural features, such as bridges and balconies, are often used in the passage from one area to the other. Horizontal exits typically do not include stairs or ramps, because they are usually located on the same level as the area from which escape is desired.

Horizontal exits are internal exits that might be located some distance from a door leading to the outside at grade level, so the *Code* permits them to provide not more than one-half the required number of exits or egress capacity of the building or buildings that they connect. However, in health care occupancies and detention and correctional occupancies, special exceptions apply.

Before any space can be used as an occupant accumulation area on either side of a horizontal exit, it must satisfy certain criteria. Such a space, although separated with 2-hour fire barriers (see 7.2.4.3 for details on the fire barrier), cannot be used as a horizontal exit unless there is at least one standard type of exit, not an additional horizontal exit, leading from the space. Additionally, the compartment must be large enough to provide occupant accumulation space for the occupants of both the fire compartment containing the fire and the non-fire compartment, allowing 3 ft² (0.28 m²) of floor space per person. The required accumulation space per person is increased in health care occupancies, because occupants might

be on beds and stretchers, and is also increased in detention and correctional occupancies where the residents are normally held in the non-fire compartment for a considerable time rather than being released to the outside. The nature of a horizontal exit is such that it provides psychological comfort. Being held in an area or building that is away from the fire reassures occupants and prevents disorderly movement.

Exhibit 7.51 illustrates how to apply the requirement when substituting horizontal exits for other exits. Note that the doors in the horizontal exits (circled) substitute for exit stair enclosures for the occupants on either side of the 2-hour fire resistance–rated barrier that creates the horizontal exit. The doors permit the elimination of the three stair enclosures closest to the horizontal exits, stair enclosures that would otherwise be required if the entire floor area were left undivided.

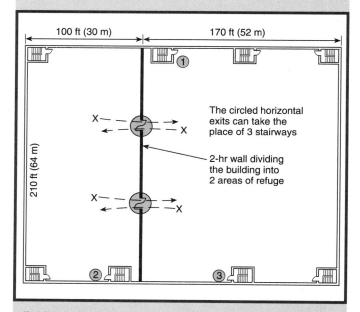

Exhibit 7.51 *Example of substituting horizontal exits for other exits.*

A.7.2.4.1.2 Example. One way to provide the required egress capacity from the upper floor of a department store building 350 ft × 200 ft (107 m × 60 m), with an occupant load of 1166 per floor, would be to furnish eight 44-in. (112-cm) stairs. *(See Figure A.7.2.4.1.2(a).)*

Assume that this building is divided into two sections by a fire barrier meeting the requirements for a horizontal exit, one 130 ft × 200 ft (40 m × 60 m) and the other 220 ft × 200 ft (67 m × 60 m), with two pairs of 46-in. (117-cm) double egress doors, with each door providing 44 in.

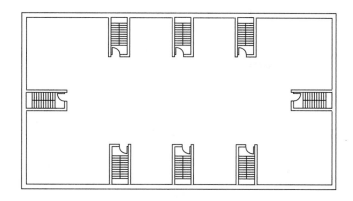

Figure A.7.2.4.1.2(a) *Eight exits, none via horizontal exit, required to provide the necessary egress capacity.*

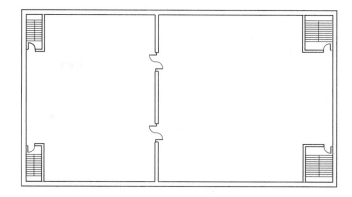

Figure A.7.2.4.1.2(c) *Number of stairs further reduced by widening stairs in larger compartment, but not to less than one-half the required number and capacity of exits from that compartment.*

(112 cm) of clear egress width *(see Figure A.7.2.4.1.2(b)).* The smaller section, considered separately, will require the equivalent of three 44-in. (112-cm) exit stairs and the larger section will require five such exits. The horizontal exits will serve as one of the three exits required for the smaller section and two of the five exits required for the larger section. Therefore, only two 44-in. (112-cm) exit stairs from the smaller section and three 44-in. (112-cm) exit stairs from the larger section will be required, if the exits can be arranged to meet the requirements for the 150-ft (45-m) travel distance permitted from any point in a nonsprinklered building. Thus, the total number of exit stairs required for the building will be five, as compared with eight if no horizontal exit had been provided.

Another option would be the use of two 56-in. (142-cm) exit stairs from the larger section, which would reduce the total number of stairways required from the floor to four *(see Figure A.7.2.4.1.2(c)).* However, if the building were

further subdivided by a second fire wall meeting the requirements for a horizontal exit, no further reduction in stairways would be permitted in order to comply with the requirement that horizontal exits provide a maximum of one-half of egress capacity.

7.2.4.2 Fire Compartments.

7.2.4.2.1 Every fire compartment for which credit is allowed in connection with a horizontal exit shall have, in addition to the horizontal exit or exits, at least one exit, but not less than 50 percent of the required number and capacity of exits, that is not a horizontal exit. Any fire compartment not having an exit leading outside shall be considered as part of an adjoining compartment with an exit leading to the outside.

Exception: This requirement shall not apply where otherwise provided in Chapters 18, 19, 22, and 23.

7.2.4.2.2 Every horizontal exit for which credit is given shall be arranged so that there are continuously available paths of travel leading from each side of the exit to stairways or other means of egress leading to outside the building.

7.2.4.2.3 Wherever either side of the horizontal exit is occupied, the doors used in connection with the horizontal exit shall be unlocked from the egress side.

Exception: This requirement shall not apply where otherwise provided in Chapters 18, 19, 22, and 23.

7.2.4.2.4 The floor area on either side of a horizontal exit shall be sufficient to hold the occupants of both floor areas, providing at least 3 ft² (0.28 m²) clear floor area per person.

Exception: Special floor area requirements shall be permitted where provided in Chapters 18, 19, 22, and 23.

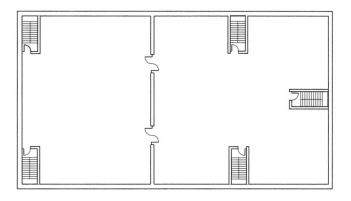

Figure A.7.2.4.1.2(b) *Number of stairs reduced by three through use of two horizontal exits; egress capacity not reduced.*

The design of a horizontal exit or the incorporation of a horizontal exit into a building is not complicated. For proper arrangement of the total means of egress system, it is simply a matter of designing each separated portion, or compartment, as if it were a completely separate building. The point of passage through the horizontal exit is treated as if it were, in fact, an exterior exit door. In determining the required egress capacities from each separated portion or compartment, the occupant loads of multiple compartments are not to be combined.

Although each compartment must contain sufficient available floor area [at least 3 ft² (0.28 m²) per person for the total occupant load of both compartments], occupants will not remain in the safe compartment indefinitely. Egress from the safe compartment continues through its other exits, such as enclosed exit stairs or doors to the outside. The 2-hour fire resistance–rated barrier separating the safe compartment from the compartment of fire origin provides the additional time needed for all occupants to egress the building. Egress through other exits might be relatively slow, because such exits are typically sized for occupants of that safe compartment alone, not the combined loads of both compartments.

7.2.4.3 Fire Barriers.

7.2.4.3.1 Fire barriers separating building areas between which there are horizontal exits shall have a 2-hour fire resistance rating and shall provide a separation that is continuous to ground. *(See also 8.2.3.)*

Exception: Where a fire barrier provides a horizontal exit in any story of a building, such fire barrier shall not be required on other stories, provided that the following criteria are met:

(a) The stories on which the fire barrier is omitted are separated from the story with the horizontal exit by construction having a fire resistance rating at least equal to that of the horizontal exit fire barrier.

(b) Vertical openings between the story with the horizontal exit and the open fire area story are enclosed with construction having a fire resistance rating at least equal to that of the horizontal exit fire barrier.

(c) All required exits, other than horizontal exits, discharge directly to the outside.

Exhibit 7.52 illustrates how the exception to 7.2.4.3.1 can be used to avoid extending the 2-hour fire resistance–rated barrier through all floors. Horizontal

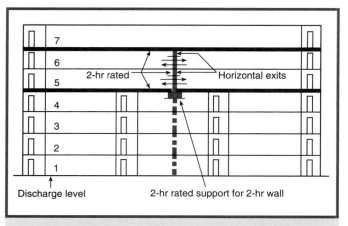

Exhibit 7.52 Building with horizontal exits on certain floors only.

exits occur on floors 5 and 6 only. Fire-rated floor construction and associated supporting construction provide the needed separation between the floors with and without horizontal exits.

7.2.4.3.2 Where fire barriers serving horizontal exits, other than existing horizontal exits, terminate at outside walls, and the outside walls are at an angle of less than 180 degrees for a distance of 10 ft (3 m) on each side of the horizontal exit, the outside walls shall have not less than a 1-hour fire resistance rating with not less than ¾-hour fire protection rating opening protectives for a distance of 10 ft (3 m) on each side of the horizontal exit.

Subparagraph 7.2.4.3.2 requires additional protection where the horizontal exit wall joins the building's exterior wall if there is potential at that location for fire to spread to the adjoining fire compartment. Such potential is judged to exist where the building walls on each side of the horizontal exit expose each other at an angle of less than 180 degrees. The intent is the same as in 7.2.2.6.3 for the protection of exterior walls associated with interior stairs.

The required 10-ft (3-m) extensions to each side of the 2-hour fire resistance–rated horizontal exit only need to have a 1-hour fire resistance rating. One-hour fire-resistance–rated walls are permitted ³/₄-hour fire protection–rated opening protectives; therefore, the rated extensions are permitted to use fire windows.

The concept of the 180-degree rule is illustrated in Exhibit 7.53. Where the building walls on each side of the horizontal exit expose each other at an angle of less than 180 degrees, additional 10-ft (3-m), 1-hour fire protection–rated extensions to each side of the horizontal exit are required. At the right of

Exhibit 7.53, additional protection is not required where the building walls at each side of the horizontal exit expose each other at a full 180 degrees.

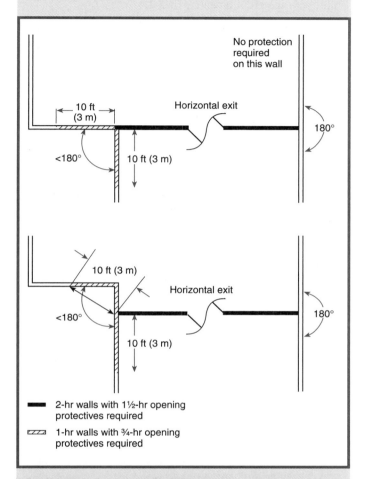

Exhibit 7.53 *Protection of building exterior walls abutting a horizontal exit.*

7.2.4.3.3 Fire barriers forming horizontal exits shall not be penetrated by ducts, unless such ducts are existing penetrations protected by approved and listed fire dampers.

Exception No. 1: This requirement shall not apply to buildings protected throughout by an approved, supervised automatic sprinkler system in accordance with Section 9.7.

Exception No. 2: This requirement shall not apply to duct penetrations permitted in Chapters 22 and 23 and protected by combination fire dampers/smoke leakage–rated dampers that meet the smoke damper actuation requirements of 8.3.5.

Subparagraph 7.2.4.3.3 addresses horizontal exit barrier penetrations other than those provided for doors used for accessing the adjacent fire compartments.

Because horizontal exit barriers usually subdivide floor spaces, any prohibition on penetrations by ductwork complicates the design and installation of the heating, ventilating, and air conditioning system. Exception No. 1 to 7.2.4.3.3 provides for an acceptable level of safety and permits duct penetrations. Such penetrations are allowed if the building is protected throughout by sprinklers. The penetrating duct also requires an approved fire damper, because the horizontal exit is a 2-hour fire-rated barrier.

Subparagraph 7.2.4.3.3 recognizes existing ductwork penetrations only if the penetrations are protected by listed fire dampers that are also approved by the authority having jurisdiction.

Exception No. 2 to 7.2.4.3.3 recognizes that local policy prohibits some detention and correctional occupancies from having automatic sprinkler protection. Nonsprinklered buildings are not permitted to use Exception No. 1, yet horizontal exits are desirable means of egress features in this defend-in-place occupancy. Duct penetrations, therefore, are permitted if protected by combination fire/smoke leakage-rated dampers that meet the smoke damper actuation requirements of 8.3.5.

7.2.4.3.4 Any opening in such fire barriers shall be protected as provided in 8.2.3.2.3.

7.2.4.3.5 Doors in horizontal exits shall comply with 7.2.1.4, unless they are sliding doors as otherwise provided in Chapters 40 and 42.

An exception for industrial occupancies in Chapter 40 and an exception for storage occupancies in Chapter 42 permit a fire-rated sliding door in addition to a swinging door in a door opening in a horizontal exit. Such a door might be installed for property protection, insurance-related reasons, or building code compliance. See 40.2.2.5.2 and 42.2.2.5.2.

7.2.4.3.6 Swinging fire doors shall be permitted in horizontal exits, provided that the criteria of both 7.2.4.3.6(1) and (2), or the criteria of 7.2.4.3.6(1) and (3), are met as follows:

(1) The doors shall swing in the direction of egress travel.
(2) Where a horizontal exit serves areas on both sides of a fire barrier, there shall be adjacent openings with swinging doors that open in opposite directions, with signs on each side of the fire barrier identifying the door that swings with the travel from that side.

Exception: Sleeping room areas in detention and correctional occupancies shall be exempt from the sign requirement.

(3) The doors shall be of any other approved arrangement, provided that the doors always swing with any possible egress travel.

Exception No. 1: The requirements of 7.2.4.3.6 shall not apply to horizontal exit door swing as provided in Chapters 19 and 23.

Exception No. 2: The requirements of 7.2.4.3.6 shall not apply to horizontal exit doors in corridors no greater than 6 ft (1.8 m) wide in existing buildings.

> Exception No. 2 to 7.2.4.3.6 recognizes the impracticality and hardship of installing a pair of doors that meets the minimum width requirements of 7.2.1.2.3 in an opening across an existing corridor that is 6 ft (1.8 m) or less in width.

7.2.4.3.7* Doors in horizontal exits shall be designed and installed to minimize air leakage.

A.7.2.4.3.7 For further information, see NFPA 105, *Recommended Practice for the Installation of Smoke-Control Door Assemblies.*

7.2.4.3.8* All fire doors in horizontal exits shall be self-closing or automatic-closing in accordance with 7.2.1.8. Horizontal exit doors located across a corridor shall be automatic-closing in accordance with 7.2.1.8.

Exception: Where approved by the authority having jurisdiction, existing cross-corridor doors in horizontal exits shall be permitted to be self-closing.

A.7.2.4.3.8 Fusible link–actuated automatic-closing doors do not qualify for use in horizontal exits under these provisions, as smoke might pass through the opening before there is sufficient heat to release the hold-open device.

Such doors are also objectionable because, once closed, they are difficult to open and would inhibit orderly egress.

> Because cross-corridor doors are so commonly wedged open in violation of *Code* requirements, 7.2.4.3.8 does not offer the option of using self-closing doors but mandates the use of automatic-closing doors in these horizontal exit, cross-corridor locations. Because the authority having jurisdiction can observe if the wedging open of doors has been a problem in existing installations, the exception gives the enforcer the authority to permit existing self-closing doors to continue to be used.

7.2.4.4 Bridges and Balconies.

7.2.4.4.1 Each bridge or balcony used in conjunction with horizontal exits shall have guards and handrails in conformity with the requirements of 7.2.2.4.

7.2.4.4.2 Every bridge or balcony shall be not less than the width of the door to which it leads and shall be not less than 44 in. (112 cm) wide for new construction.

7.2.4.4.3 Where the bridge or balcony serves as a horizontal exit in one direction, the door shall be required to swing only in the direction of egress travel.

Exception: This requirement shall not apply to horizontal exit door swing as provided in Chapters 19 and 23.

7.2.4.4.4 Where the bridge or balcony serves as a horizontal exit in both directions, doors shall be provided in pairs that swing in opposite directions. Only the door swinging in the direction of egress travel shall be included in the determination of egress capacity.

Exception No. 1: This requirement shall not apply if the bridge or balcony has sufficient floor area to accommodate the occupant load of either connected building or fire area on the basis of 3 ft² (0.28 m²) per person.

Exception No. 2: In existing buildings, doors on both ends of the bridge or balcony shall be permitted to swing out from the building where approved by the authority having jurisdiction.

Exception No. 3: This requirement shall not apply to horizontal exit door swing as provided in Chapters 19 and 23.

7.2.4.4.5 In climates subject to the accumulation of snow and ice, the bridge or balcony floor shall be protected to prevent the accumulation of snow and ice.

Exception: In existing buildings, one step, not to exceed 8 in. (20.3 cm), shall be permitted below the level of the inside floor.

7.2.4.4.6 In both of the connected buildings or fire areas, all wall openings, any part of which is within 10 ft (3 m) of any bridge or balcony, as measured horizontally or below, shall be protected with fire doors or fixed fire window assemblies having a ¾-hour fire protection rating.

Exception: This requirement shall not apply to existing bridges and balconies where approved by the authority having jurisdiction.

7.2.5 Ramps.

> Ramps are permitted as a part of a means of egress and are preferred over stairs under some circumstances. To quote from a 1974 publication:

One can consider ramps and steps simply as prosthetic devices for assisting the human organism in climbing from floor to floor . . . When one must consider the energy cost of both horizontal and vertical movement, one finds that a ramp with a gradient of less than about eight degrees is more economical than any stairway that is likely to be encountered in normal activity.[8]

The National Bureau of Standards (now the National Institute of Standards and Technology – NIST) study states in part:

For certain occupancies, such as schools and institutions, they [ramps] are believed to be more satisfactory and their use in these buildings is recommended . . . Ramps have a rate of discharge between that of stairways and level passageways.[9]

7.2.5.1 General. Every ramp used as a component in a means of egress shall conform to the general requirements of Section 7.1 and to the special requirements of this subsection.

7.2.5.2 Dimensional Criteria. Ramps shall be in accordance with the following:

(1) New ramps shall be in accordance with Table 7.2.5.2(a).

Exception No. 1: The maximum slope requirement shall not apply to ramps as otherwise provided in Chapter 12.

Exception No. 2: The requirement of 7.2.5.2(1) shall not apply to industrial equipment access areas as otherwise provided in Chapter 40.

Exception No. 3: Ramps providing access to vehicles, vessels, mobile structures, and aircraft shall not be required to comply with the maximum slope or maximum rise for a single ramp run.

(2) Existing ramps shall be permitted to remain in use or be rebuilt, provided that they meet the requirements shown in Table 7.2.5.2(b).

Table 7.2.5.2(a) New Ramps

Minimum width clear of all obstructions, except projections not more than 3½ in. (8.9 cm) at or below handrail height on each side	44 in. (112 cm)
Maximum slope	1 in 12
Maximum cross slope	1 in 48
Maximum rise for a single ramp run	30 in. (76 cm)

Table 7.2.5.2(b) Existing Ramps

Feature	Class A	Class B
Minimum width	44 in. (122 cm)	30 in. (76 cm)
Maximum slope	1 in 10	1 in 8
Maximum height between landings	12 ft (3.7 m)	12 ft (3.7 m)

Exception No. 1: Existing Class B ramps with slopes not steeper than 1 in 6 shall be permitted to remain in use where approved by the authority having jurisdiction.

Exception No. 2: Existing ramps with slopes not steeper than 1 in 10 shall not be required to be provided with landings.

Exception No. 3: The requirement of 7.2.5.2(2) shall not apply to industrial equipment access areas as otherwise provided in Chapter 40.

Exception No. 4: Ramps providing access to vehicles, vessels, mobile structures, and aircraft shall not be required to comply with the maximum slope or maximum rise for a single ramp run.

The dimensional criteria and other details applicable to ramps were extensively rewritten for the 1994 edition of the *Code*. In the 1994 and 1997 editions, the maximum allowed slope of a new ramp varied with the total vertical rise provided by the ramp. For the 2000 edition, the slope of new ramps is limited to a maximum of 1 in 12. Such ramps are particularly useful for persons with severe mobility impairment. See ICC/ANSI A117.1, *American National Standard for Accessible and Usable Buildings and Facilities.*

Paragraph 7.2.5.2(2) continues to recognize existing ramps and the rebuilding of existing ramps to the former criteria that classified ramps as Class A and Class B.

Exception No. 3 to 7.2.5.2(1) and Exception No. 4 to 7.2.5.2(2) recognize that ramps providing access to vehicles, vessels, mobile structures, and aircraft must be able to accommodate the variety of conditions encountered. For example, not all ships have entrances mounted at the same height, and, due to tidal influences, the water level rises and falls with respect to a stationary pier. Because ships are regulated under special rules, have their own exiting programs, and usually provide staff assistance during the disembarkation process, the maximum ramp slope requirements of Table 7.2.5.2(a) and Table 7.2.5.2(b) are exempted.

7.2.5.3 Ramp Details.

7.2.5.3.1 Construction. Ramp construction shall be as follows.

(a) All ramps serving as required means of egress shall be of permanent fixed construction.

(b) Each ramp in buildings required by this *Code* to be of Type I or Type II construction shall be noncombustible or limited-combustible throughout. The ramp floor and landings shall be solid and without perforations.

7.2.5.3.2 Landings. Ramp landings shall be as follows.

(a) Ramps shall have landings located at the top, at the bottom, and at doors opening onto the ramp. The slope of the landing shall not be steeper than 1 in 48. Every landing shall have a width not less than the width of the ramp. Every landing shall be not less than 60 in. (152 cm) long in the direction of travel.

Exception: The minimum 60-in. (152-cm) length requirement shall not apply to existing approved landings.

(b) Any changes in travel direction shall be made only at landings. Ramps and intermediate landings shall continue with no decrease in width along the direction of egress travel.

Exception: Existing ramps shall be permitted to change direction without a landing.

Landings are required to be nearly horizontal to provide transition areas to and from ramps that are usable to persons with severe mobility impairments. Landings at doors allow for movement through the door without the burden of dealing with a sloping floor section. The requirement for intermediate landings on ramps is similar to that part of 7.2.2.3.2 applicable to landings on stairs.

The minimum 60-in. (152-cm) landing depth, measured in the direction of travel, is intended to accommodate a person in a wheelchair.

The effect of the first sentence of 7.2.5.3.2(b) is to outlaw curved ramps. With a curved ramp, the travel direction changes continually. The change in direction is accomplished by introducing a cross slope that might make use of the ramp by persons with severe mobility impairments overly burdensome. Thus, the *Code* requires that any changes in travel direction occur only at level landings.

7.2.5.3.3 Drop-Offs. Ramps and landings with drop-offs shall have curbs, walls, railings, or projecting surfaces that prevent people from traveling off the edge of the ramp. Curbs or barriers shall be not less than 4 in. (10.1 cm) in height.

7.2.5.4 Guards and Handrails. Guards complying with 7.2.2.4 shall be provided for ramps. Handrails complying with 7.2.2.4 shall be provided along both sides of a ramp run with a rise greater than 6 in. (15.2 cm). The height of handrails and guards shall be measured vertically to the top of the guard or rail from the walking surface adjacent thereto.

Exception: This requirement shall not apply to guards and handrails provided for ramped aisles in accordance with Chapters 12 and 13.

Ramps are subject to the guard and handrail requirements of 7.2.2.4. Note, however, that the handrail requirements apply to ramps only if the ramp run has a rise of more than 6 in. (15.2 cm).

7.2.5.5 Enclosure and Protection of Ramps. Ramps in a required means of egress shall be enclosed or protected as a stair in accordance with 7.2.2.5 and 7.2.2.6. The use of Exception Nos. 2 and 3 to 7.2.2.6.3 shall be prohibited.

7.2.5.6 Special Provisions for Outside Ramps.

Outside ramps are permitted to serve as part of a means of egress subject to the criteria governing exit access, exits, and exit discharge.

7.2.5.6.1* Visual Protection. Outside ramps shall be arranged to avoid any impediments to their use by persons having a fear of high places. For ramps more than three stories in height, any arrangement intended to meet this requirement shall be at least 4 ft (122 cm) in height.

A.7.2.5.6.1 The guards required by 7.2.2.4 for the unenclosed sides of ramps will usually meet this requirement where the ramp is not more than three stories high. Special architectural treatment, including application of such devices as metal or masonry screens and grilles, will usually be necessary to comply with the intent of the requirements for ramps over three stories in height.

7.2.5.6.2* Water Accumulation. Outside ramps and landings shall be designed to minimize water accumulation on their surfaces.

A.7.2.5.6.2 Providing a pitch of ⅛ in. to ¼ in./ft (1 cm to 2 cm/m) will aid the shedding of water from a nominally horizontal surface.

7.2.6* Exit Passageways.

A.7.2.6 An exit passageway serves as a horizontal means of exit travel that is protected from fire in a manner similar to an enclosed interior exit stair. Where it is desired to offset exit stairs in a multistory building, an exit passageway can be used to preserve the continuity of the protected exit by connecting the bottom of one stair to the top of the stair that continues to the street floor. Probably the most important use of an exit passageway is to satisfy the requirement that at least 50 percent of the exit stairs discharge directly outside from multistory buildings (see 7.7.2). Thus, if it is impractical to locate the stair on an exterior wall, an exit passageway can be connected to the bottom of the stair to convey the occupants safely to an outside exit door. In buildings of extremely large area, such as shopping malls and some factories, the exit passageway can be used to advantage where the travel distance to reach an exit would otherwise be excessive.

The word *exit* used in the term *exit passageway* helps to distinguish the difference between an exit passageway and an ordinary passageway or corridor. An exit passageway is an exit; it provides a path of travel offering the same level of protection and safety that is required of an enclosed exit stair. An exit passageway is a versatile feature, because it can be used to extend an exit, or, as is done in many cases, it can be used to bring an exit closer to where the occupants are located.

In Exhibit 7.54(a), an exit passageway is used to continue the exit to the outside from one of the two enclosed interior exit stairs. This arrangement might be used to help comply with the requirements of 7.7.2, which mandate that at least one-half of the egress capacity and number of exits must discharge directly to the outside at the level of exit discharge.

Extending the exit stair's required enclosure to include a portion of the corridor creates an exit passageway that brings the exit closer to the occupants, as is demonstrated by Exhibit 7.54(b). Travel distance measurement ends at entrance E1 to the exit passageway. The distance from X to E2 exceeds the allowed travel distance. The distance from X to E1 is within the allowed travel distance. Extension of an enclosure is often used where travel distance to the exit enclosure would otherwise be in excess of *Code* allowance. Because it is an exit, an exit passageway qualifies as the point at which travel distance measurement ends.

In Exhibit 7.54(c), the two exit passageways marked A bring exits within allowable travel distances for the occupants in the covered mall. This arrangement is an example of the design adaptation previously described in the commentary on Exhibit

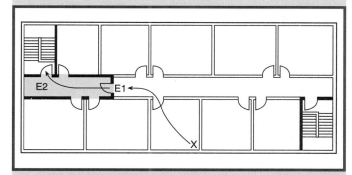

Exhibit 7.54(b) *Exit passageway used to keep travel distance from becoming excessive.*

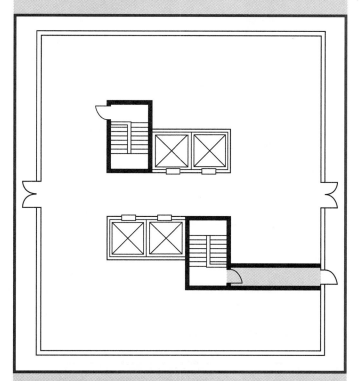

Exhibit 7.54(a) *Exit passageway used to connect exit stair with exterior of building.*

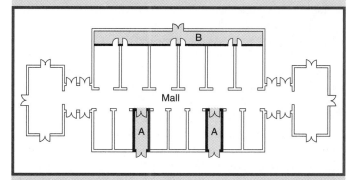

Exhibit 7.54(c) *Exit passageways used for multiple purposes in covered mall building.*

7.54(b). The exit passageway marked B allows occupants of multiple stores in the covered mall to enter the exit directly from the rear of each store. This arrangement is often used to limit the number of doors that open directly to the outside for security purposes.

7.2.6.1* General. Exit passageways used as exit components shall conform to the general requirements of Section 7.1 and to the requirements of 7.2.6.

A.7.2.6.1 Examples of building elements that might be arranged as exit passageways include hallways, corridors, passages, tunnels, underfloor passageways, or overhead passageways.

7.2.6.2 Enclosure. An exit passageway shall be separated from other parts of the building as specified in 7.1.3.2.

Exception No. 1: Fire windows in accordance with 8.2.3.2.2 shall be permitted to be installed in such a separation in a building protected throughout by an approved, supervised automatic sprinkler system in accordance with Section 9.7.

Exception No. 2: Existing fixed wired glass panels in steel sash shall be permitted to be continued in use in such a separation in buildings protected throughout by an approved, supervised automatic sprinkler system in accordance with Section 9.7.

7.2.6.3 Stair Discharge. An exit passageway that serves as a discharge from a stair enclosure shall have not less than the same fire resistance rating and opening protective fire protection rating as those required for the stair enclosure.

Paragraph 7.2.6.2 requires exit passageways to have walls with the hourly fire resistance ratings and doors with the fire protection ratings required of exit stair enclosures, as detailed in 7.1.3.2.1(a) or 7.1.3.2.1(b). The requirement also limits door openings into and penetrations through the exit enclosure created by the exit passageway, as detailed in 7.1.3.2.1(d) and 7.1.3.2.1(e). In Exhibit 7.55, exit passageway A on the first floor—the level of exit discharge—opens at one end to a five-story exit stair enclosure and at the other end to a door to the outside. This exit passageway also serves as a horizontal continuation of, and discharge for, the stair enclosure. In serving as a discharge for the exit stair, the exit passageway must provide the same degree of protection required of the stair enclosure. Given that the exit stair must be enclosed by 2-hour fire resistance–rated construction

because it serves four or more stories, the exit passageway must also be enclosed by 2-hour fire resistance–rated construction. This protection is addressed in 7.2.6.3.

In Exhibit 7.55, exit passageway B, on the fourth floor, is used to provide the safety of an exit to occupants traveling to the exit stair enclosure. This exit passageway might have been built to meet the travel distance limitation. If a rated wall and door separate exit passageway B from the 2-hour exit stair enclosure, the required rating of exit passageway B is only 1 hour, because the exit passageway serves only the occupants of the fourth floor. A similar 1-hour fire resistance–rated enclosure requirement applies, for example, to a horizontal exit serving a single-story of a shopping mall building. Contrast this configuration with exit passageway A on the first floor, which potentially serves occupants of the second through fifth floors and must provide a continuation of the 2-hour separation required of the stair enclosure.

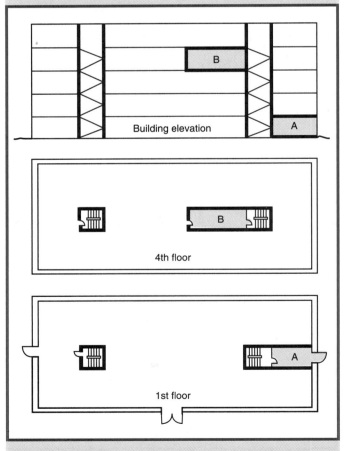

Exhibit 7.55 *Exit passageways with fire resistance–rated enclosures and fire protection–rated doors.*

For the same reasons that the stair enclosure cannot have doors opening directly onto it from normally unoccupied spaces, a storage room, for example, is prohibited from opening directly onto exit passageways A and B and the exit stair enclosures. Penetrations through the enclosing walls are limited to those necessary for the functioning of life safety systems, such as lighting powered by electrical cables that enter the exit enclosure via properly sealed conduit penetrations. Ductwork for climate control is prohibited from penetrating enclosing walls. Thus, the exit passageways and the exit stair enclosures must receive their heating and cooling by systems independent of those serving the remainder of the building. Ductwork serving other parts of the floor must be routed around, not through, the outside of the enclosures.

7.2.6.4 Width. The width of an exit passageway shall be adequate to accommodate the aggregate required capacity of all exits that discharge through it.

*Exception No. 1:** Where an exit passageway serves occupants of the level of exit discharge as well as other stories, the capacity shall not be required to be aggregated.*

A.7.2.6.4 Exception No. 1 Where an exit passageway serves occupants on the level of exit discharge as well as other floors, it should not be required that the occupant loads be added, thus increasing the width of the exit passageway. The situation is the same as that in which occupants from the level of exit discharge join occupants from upper floors for a few feet of horizontal travel through a stair enclosure.

Exception No. 2:   As provided in Chapters 36 and 37, an exit passageway in a covered mall building shall be permitted to accommodate occupant loads independently from the covered mall and the tenant spaces. (See the exception to 36.2.2.7 and the exception to 37.2.2.7.)

The annex text in A.7.2.6.4, Exception No. 1, explains the exemption to aggregate the sizing of exit passageways where accommodating occupant loads from various floors. See the annex text and commentary associated with the exception to 36.2.2.7 for a detailed explanation of the situation permitted in covered mall buildings by Exception No. 2 to 7.2.6.4.

7.2.6.5 Floor. The floor shall be solid and without perforations.

7.2.7 Escalators and Moving Walks.

Escalators and moving walks shall not constitute a part of the required means of egress, unless they are previously approved escalators and moving walks in existing buildings.

Older editions of the *Code* allowed some egress capacity credit for escalators. Because riser/tread sections of escalators and standing surfaces of moving walks are removed for maintenance, it cannot be ensured that occupants will be able to walk on these devices when emergency egress is needed. Therefore, new escalators and moving walks receive no credit within the required means of egress. Existing, previously approved escalators and moving walks are permitted to continue to be used as part of the means of egress if permitted by the occupancy chapter. Although not permitted as part of the required means of egress in new construction, escalators and moving walks, where installed, must comply with ASME/ANSI A17.1, *Safety Code for Elevators and Escalators.*[10]

Escalators are acceptable as an egress component in existing buildings only in the following occupancies:

(1) Existing assembly occupancies (see 13.2.2.8)
(2) Existing hotels (see 29.2.2.8)
(3) Existing apartment buildings (see 31.2.2.8)
(4) Existing mercantile occupancies (see 37.2.2.8)
(5) Existing business occupancies (see 39.2.2.8)
(6) Existing industrial occupancies (see 40.2.2.8)

When evaluating escalators in existing buildings, the following factors should be considered.

(a) The escalator should comply with the applicable requirements for stairs in 7.2.2. It is assumed that, where escalators serve as required means of egress, they will continue to operate in case of fire. However, if they stop due to electric current failure or other cause, they can be used as ordinary stairs.

(b) Escalators constituting a means of egress should operate only in the direction of egress. Usually escalators are provided in pairs, with one separate stairway moving up and another moving down; however, if the electric power fails and both stop, two stairs would be available for downward movement. In this situation, one might propose that both stairways be accepted as constituting a means of egress, since the power could be turned off intentionally. The problem is that, in an emergency, the power might not be turned off, and one stairway would continue to move against traffic. For this reason, only those escalators moving in the direction of egress should be allowed to be part of a means of egress.

(c) Escalators should be of the horizontal-tread type and, with the exception of step tread surfaces, handrails, and step wheels, should be of noncombustible construction throughout.

(d) A single escalator that is 32 in. (81 cm) wide should be given credit for 75 people. An escalator that is 48 in. (122 cm) wide should be given credit for 150 people. Even though a person does not have to exert any energy or do any moving while on an operating escalator, there are many people who are frightened by escalators and many who are extremely cautious in approaching them. These are factors that could contribute to a bottleneck. Thus, it is recognized that an escalator would have to be wider than a stair to accommodate the same number of people.

(e) There should be unobstructed spaces of at least 4 in. (10.2 cm) outside the handrail and above the handrail for the full length of the escalator.

(f) No single escalator should travel uninterrupted in a vertical direction for more than one story.

The guidelines of (a) through (f) in this commentary were taken from older editions of the *Code* and were required in those years when escalators were given credit in new construction and are offered here as guidance for existing escalator installations.

Even in an existing building, an escalator cannot be counted as an exit unless it is enclosed as an exit in accordance with 7.1.3.2. Such an arrangement is rare. Typically, an existing escalator might serve as exit access or exit discharge.

Most of the same principles that apply to the design and operation of escalators also apply when evaluating existing moving walkways. The major difference is that a moving walkway that moves in the direction of egress travel can be evaluated in terms of the usual egress width and associated capacity rather than the larger dimensions specified for escalators in item (d) of this commentary.

7.2.8 Fire Escape Stairs.

Fire escape stairs and ladders have fallen into disfavor for a variety of reasons, including the following:

(1) Unsightly appearance
(2) Possible icing in winter weather
(3) Expense of maintenance (that is, the metal is subject to corrosion)

(4) Possibility of users being trapped by a fire below
(5) Fear of height and, therefore, an objection to using fire escape stairs and ladders

On the other hand, well-maintained fire escape stairs can and have saved many lives when smoke-filled stairs have become impassable. A classic example is the June 5, 1946, fire in the 22-story LaSalle Hotel in Chicago. Hundreds of people made their escape from the building on outside fire escape stairs.[11]

In the past, fire fighters have found outside fire escape stairs advantageous. However, instances can be cited where corroded fire escapes have collapsed, or where people have been fatally burned because fire broke out of windows or doors at a lower level as they were descending on a fire escape. The *Code* requires proper means of egress using interior or outside stairs and the gradual phasing out of fire escape stairs as new buildings replace old ones.

Fire escape stairs can, however, help correct serious means of egress deficiencies in existing buildings and are helpful to fire department rescue and fire-fighting efforts. If fire escape stairs are part of an existing building, or must be included on a building (perhaps due to insufficient space for an outside stair in accordance with 7.2.2), they must adhere to the provisions of the *Code* to provide an acceptable level of life safety.

7.2.8.1 General.

7.2.8.1.1 Fire escape stairs shall comply with the provisions of 7.2.8, unless they are existing fire escape stairs approved by the authority having jurisdiction.

Fire escape stairs as specified in 7.2.8 of the *Code* should not be confused with the outside stairs covered in 7.2.2. Neither should the fire escape stairs specified by 7.2.8.1.1 of the *Code* be confused with the inferior fire escapes that are commonly found on old buildings. Such steep, inadequate, and flimsy fire escapes, unshielded against fire in the structure to which they are attached, might give an occupant a false sense of security. Such escape stairs are not recognized by this *Code*.

Even the fire escape stairs constructed in accordance with this *Code* have limitations that might prevent their effective use during a fire. Even where window protection is provided, conditions might be such that fire, or the smoke from fire, on lower floors might render the stairs impassable before the occupants of the upper floors have had time to use them.

Fire escape stairs might be blocked by snow or ice when they are most needed. People are likely to be timid about descending fire escape stairs from a considerable height, so their downward travel is much slower than for inside stairs. Slower travel is a factor even where *Code*-specified solid-tread stairs without perforations are used in place of ordinary slatted-tread construction. Fire escape stairs are not the usual means of egress. Occupants of buildings will not use them as readily in case of fire as they will an inside stair, which is the more common egress component. Because fire escape stairs are an emergency device and are not ordinarily used, their proper upkeep is often neglected.

7.2.8.1.2 Fire escape stairs shall not constitute any of the required means of egress.

Exception No. 1: Fire escape stairs shall be permitted on existing buildings as provided in Chapters 11 through 42 but shall not constitute more than 50 percent of the required means of egress.

Exception No. 2: New fire escape stairs shall be permitted to be erected on existing buildings only where the authority having jurisdiction has determined that outside stairs are impractical (see 7.2.2). New fire escape stairs shall not incorporate ladders or access windows, regardless of occupancy classification or occupant load served.

No recognition of any kind is given by the *Code* to the use of fire escape stairs in new buildings for any of the three parts of a means of egress. A token recognition of 50 percent of egress capacity is given for their use in existing buildings, simply because the fire escape stairs have already been installed or because such stairs might be the only feasible way in which to upgrade a means of egress in an existing building.

In most cases, outside stairs complying with 7.2.2 must be used rather than fire escape stairs. However, the *Code* recognizes, that in the case of some existing buildings, there are situations in which modifying stairs to comply with 7.2.2 would be impractical. For example, the space between the building and the property line might be too narrow to accommodate a *Code*-conforming stair, or it might be necessary to have the stair located over a sidewalk, alley, or similar space that cannot be permanently blocked by stair construction.

Fire escape stairs are regarded as an expedient remedy for deficiencies in means of egress of existing

buildings where it might not be feasible to provide outside stairs or properly enclosed, additional inside stairways required by the *Code*.

Authorities having jurisdiction might wish to impose additional requirements because of climate. Effective use of fire escape stairs might be seriously impaired by conditions such as snow and ice. In such a case, egress capacity credit for the fire escape stairs might be reduced.

7.2.8.1.3 Fire escape stairs of the return-platform type with superimposed runs or of the straight-run type with a platform that continues in the same direction shall be permitted. Either type shall be permitted to be parallel to or at right angles to buildings. Either type shall be permitted to be attached to buildings or erected independently of buildings and connected by walkways.

7.2.8.2 Protection of Openings. Fire escape stairs shall be exposed to the smallest possible number of window and door openings. Each opening shall be protected with approved fire door or fire window assemblies where the opening or any portion of the opening is located as follows.

(a) *Horizontally.* Within 15 ft (4.5 m) of any balcony, platform, or stairway constituting a component of the fire escape stair.

(b) *Below.* Within three stories or 35 ft (10 m) of any balcony, platform, walkway, or stairway constituting a component of the fire escape stair, or within two stories or 20 ft (6 m) of a platform or walkway leading from any story to the fire escape stair.

(c) *Above.* Within 10 ft (3 m) of any balcony, platform, or walkway, as measured vertically, or within 10 ft (3 m) of any stair tread surface, as measured vertically.

(d) *Top Story.* Where stairs do not lead to the roof, no wall opening protection required.

(e) *Court.* Facing a court served by a fire escape stair where the least dimension of the court does not exceed one-third of the height to the uppermost platform of the fire escape stair, measured from the ground.

(f) *Alcove.* Facing an alcove served by a fire escape stair where the width of the alcove does not exceed one-third, or the depth does not exceed one-fourth, of the height to the uppermost platform of the fire escape stair, measured from the ground.

Exception No. 1: The provisions of 7.2.8.2 shall be permitted to be modified by the authority having jurisdiction in consideration of automatic sprinkler protection, low hazard occupancy, or other special conditions.

Exception No. 2: The provisions of 7.2.8.2 that require the protection of window openings shall not be required where such window opening is necessary for access to existing fire escape stairs.

7.2.8.3 Access.

7.2.8.3.1 Access to fire escape stairs shall be in accordance with 7.2.8.4 and 7.5.1.2.

Exhibit 7.56 illustrates the minimum opening dimensions for windows that open onto fire escape stairs serving more than 10 occupants. The figure also depicts the maximum interior measurements from the floor to the windowsill. See Table 7.2.8.4.1(a) and Table 7.2.8.4.1(b).

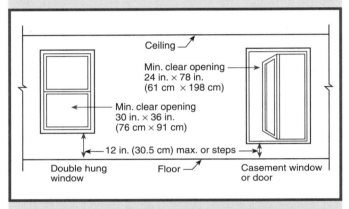

Ceiling

Min. clear opening
24 in. × 78 in.
(61 cm × 198 cm)

Min. clear opening
30 in. × 36 in.
(76 cm × 91 cm)

12 in. (30.5 cm) max. or steps

Double hung window   Floor   Casement window or door

Exhibit 7.56 *Window openings for access to fire escape stairs.*

7.2.8.3.2 Where access is permitted by way of windows, the windows shall be arranged and maintained so as to be easily opened. Screening or storm windows that restrict free access to the fire escape stair shall be prohibited.

7.2.8.3.3 Fire escape stairs shall extend to the roof in all cases where the roof is subject to occupancy or provides an area of safe refuge.

Exception: If the roof has a pitch that does not exceed 1 to 6, fire escape ladders in accordance with 7.2.9 or alternating tread devices in accordance with 7.2.11 shall be provided for access to the roof.

7.2.8.3.4 Access to a fire escape stair shall be directly to a balcony, landing, or platform and shall not exceed the floor or windowsill level and shall not be more than 8 in. (20.3 cm) below the floor level or 18 in. (45.7 cm) below the windowsill.

The height requirements of 7.2.8.3.4 establish the maximum distance, on the outside of the building, down to the balcony, landing, or platform of the fire escape stair, measured from the windowsill level or from the floor level.

7.2.8.4 Stair Details.

Generally, the requirements for fire escape stairs are similar to those specified for outside stairs. The major difference between the two types of stairs is the dimensions in Table 7.1. Table 7.1 also details the differ-

Table 7.1 Differences Between Outside Stairs and Fire Escape Stairs

| Design Factor | New Outside Stair | Existing Outside Stair | | Fire Escape Stair | |
		Class A	Class B	Normal	Small Buildings
Accepted as exit	Yes	Yes	Yes	Existing buildings	Existing buildings
Width	44 in.†	44 in.†	44 in.†	22 in.	18 in.
Maximum rise	7 in.	7½ in.	8 in.	9 in.	12 in.
Minimum tread	11 in.	10 in.	9 in.	9 in.	6 in.
Tread construction	Solid	Solid	Solid	Solid	Metal bars
Access by windows	No	No	No	Yes	Yes
Swinging stair accepted	No	No	No	Yes	Yes
Ladder accepted	No	No	No	No	Yes

Notes:
1. For SI units, 1 in. = 2.54 cm.
2. The capacity of normal fire escape stairs is 45 persons if accessed by doors and 20 if accessed by windows where it is necessary to climb over a sill. On small buildings, the capacity is 10 persons; 5 if winders or a ladder from bottom landing; or 1 if both winders and a ladder from bottom landing.
†36 in. where serving occupant load of fewer than 50.

ences between the generally accepted fire escape stair of existing buildings and the lighter fire escape stair considered acceptable for "very small" existing buildings serving 10 or fewer occupants.

The existing fire escape stair with a minimum width of 22 in. (55.9 cm) is a type that is permitted for buildings of small or moderate size, depending on the specific features of an installation.

The existing fire escape stair with a minimum width of 18 in. (45.7 cm) represents the absolute minimum that is permitted. Because of access over windowsills, steep pitch, and a narrow width, travel down such stairs will be necessarily slow and possibly dangerous. Even worse are stairs with spiral stair treads or stairs that terminate at a balcony above ground level with a fixed or movable ladder extending downward from the balcony. These stairs are suitable only in situations where a very small number of occupants is involved.

7.2.8.4.1 General. Fire escape stairs shall comply with the requirements of Table 7.2.8.4.1(a). Replacement of fire escape stairs shall comply with the requirements of Table 7.2.8.4.1(b).

7.2.8.4.2 Slip Resistance. Stair treads and landings of new or replacement fire escape stairs shall have slip-resistant surfaces.

7.2.8.5 Guards, Handrails, and Visual Enclosures.

7.2.8.5.1 All fire escape stairs shall have walls or guards and handrails on both sides in accordance with 7.2.2.4.

7.2.8.5.2 Replacement fire escape stairs in occupancies serving more than 10 occupants shall have visual enclosures to avoid any impediments to stair use by persons having a fear of high places. For stairs more than three stories in height, any arrangement intended to meet this requirement shall be at least 42 in. (107 cm) in height.

7.2.8.6 Materials and Strength.

7.2.8.6.1 Noncombustible materials shall be used for the construction of all components of fire escape stairs.

7.2.8.6.2 The authority having jurisdiction shall be permitted to approve any existing fire escape stair that has been shown by load test or other satisfactory evidence to have adequate strength.

7.2.8.7* Swinging Stairs.

In cases where the use of a fire escape stair would block a sidewalk or other public way or provide ready access for intruders, the following solution is offered. The discharge might be counterweighted and the unlocked swinging stair designed so that a 150-lb (68-kg) weight applied at one quarter of the length of the stair from the pivot point causes the stair to drop into the usable position. See 7.2.8.7.7.

A.7.2.8.7 Swinging stairs, although superior to fire escape ladders, are generally unsatisfactory, even for emergency use. Although such stairs are permitted by this *Code*, they should not be used where it is reasonably possible to terminate the fire escape stair at the ground.

7.2.8.7.1 A single swinging stair section shall be permitted to terminate fire escape stairs over sidewalks, alleys, or driveways where it is impractical to make the termination with fire escape stairs.

7.2.8.7.2 Swinging stair sections shall not be located over doors, over the path of travel from any other exit, or in any locations where there are likely to be obstructions.

7.2.8.7.3 The width of swinging stair sections shall be at least that of the fire escape stairs above.

7.2.8.7.4 The pitch of swinging stair sections shall not exceed the pitch of the fire escape stairs above.

7.2.8.7.5 Guards and handrails shall be provided in accordance with 7.2.2.4 and shall be similar in height and construction to those used with the fire escape stairs above. Guards and handrails shall be designed to prevent any possibility of injury to persons where stairs swing downward. The clearance between moving sections and any other portion of the stair system where hands have the potential to be caught shall be not less than 4 in. (10.2 cm).

7.2.8.7.6 If the distance from the lowest platform to ground is not less than 12 ft (3.7 m), an intermediate balcony not more than 12 ft (3.7 m) from the ground and not less than 7 ft (2.1 m) in the clear underneath shall be provided, with width not less than that of the stairs and length not less than 4 ft (1.2 m).

7.2.8.7.7 Swinging stairs shall be counterbalanced about a pivot, and cables shall not be used. A weight of 150 lb (68 kg) located one step from the pivot shall not cause the stairs to swing downward, and a weight of 150 lb (68 kg) located one quarter of the length of the swinging stairs from the pivot shall cause the stairs to swing down.

7.2.8.7.8 The pivot for swinging stairs shall be of a corrosion-resistant assembly or shall have clearances to prevent sticking due to corrosion.

Table 7.2.8.4.1(a) Fire Escape Stairs

Feature	Serving More than 10 Occupants	Serving 10 or Fewer Occupants
Minimum widths	22 in. (55.9 cm) clear between rails	18 in. (45.7 cm) clear between rails
Minimum horizontal dimension of any landing or platform	22 in. (55.9 cm) clear	18 in. (45.7 cm) clear
Maximum riser height	9 in. (22.9 cm)	12 in. (30.5 cm)
Minimum tread, exclusive of nosing	9 in. (22.9 cm)	6 in. (15.3 cm)
Minimum nosing or projection	1 in. (2.5 cm)	No requirement
Tread construction	Solid ½-in. (1.3-cm) diameter perforations permitted	Flat metal bars on edge or square bars secured against turning, spaced 1¼ in. (3.2 cm) maximum on centers
Winders	None	Permitted subject to capacity penalty
Risers	None	No requirement
Spiral	None	Permitted subject to capacity penalty
Maximum height between landings	12 ft (3.7 m)	No requirement
Headroom, minimum	6 ft 8 in. (203 cm)	Same
Access to escape	Door or casement windows, 24 in. 6 ft 6 in. (61 cm × 198 cm); or double-hung windows, 30 in. × 36 in. (76 cm × 91 cm) clear opening	Windows providing a clear opening of at least 20 in. (50.8 cm) in width, 24 in. (61 cm) in height, and 5.7 ft² (0.53 m²) in area
Level of access opening	Not over 12 in. (30.5 cm) above floor; steps if higher	Same
Discharge to ground	Swinging stair section permitted if approved by authority having jurisdiction	Swinging stair, or ladder if approved by authority having jurisdiction
Capacity, number of persons	0.5 in. (1.3 cm) per person, if access by door; 1.0 in. (2.5 cm) per person, if access by climbing over window sill	10; if winders or ladder from bottom balcony, 5; if both, 1

7.2.8.7.9* Devices shall not be installed to lock a swinging stair section in the up position.

A.7.2.8.7.9 A latch is desirable for holding swinging stairs down after they have swung to the ground.

7.2.8.8 Intervening Spaces.

7.2.8.8.1 Where approved by the authority having jurisdiction, fire escape stairs shall be permitted to lead to an adjoining roof that is crossed before continuing downward travel. The direction of travel shall be clearly marked, and walkways with guards and handrails complying with 7.2.2.4 shall be provided.

7.2.8.8.2 Where approved by the authority having jurisdiction, fire escape stairs shall be permitted to be used in combination with inside or outside stairs complying with 7.2.2, provided that a continuous safe path of travel is maintained.

7.2.9 Fire Escape Ladders.

7.2.9.1 General. Fire escape ladders complying with 7.2.9.2 and 7.2.9.3 shall be permitted in the means of egress only where providing one of the following:

(1) Access to unoccupied roof spaces as permitted in 7.2.8.3.3
(2) A second means of egress from storage elevators as permitted in Chapter 42
(3) A means of egress from towers and elevated platforms around machinery or similar spaces subject to occupancy not to exceed three persons who are all capable of using the ladder
(4) A secondary means of egress from boiler rooms or similar spaces subject to occupancy not to exceed three persons who are all capable of using the ladder
(5) Access to the ground from the lowest balcony or landing of a fire escape stair for small buildings as permitted in

Table 7.2.8.4.1(b) Replacement Fire Escape Stairs

Feature	Serving More than 10 Occupants	Serving 10 or Fewer Occupants
Minimum widths	22 in. (55.9 cm) clear between rails	Same
Minimum horizontal dimension of any landing or platform	22 in. (55.9 cm)	Same
Maximum riser height	9 in. (22.9 cm)	Same
Minimum tread, exclusive of nosing	10 in. (25.4 cm)	Same
Tread construction	Solid, ½-in. (1.3-cm) diameter perforations permitted	Same
Winders	None	Permitted subject to 7.2.2.2.4
Spiral	None	Permitted subject to 7.2.2.2.3
Risers	None	None
Maximum height between landings	12 ft (3.7 m)	Same
Headroom, minimum	6 ft 8 in. (203 cm)	Same
Access to escape	Door or casement windows, 24 in. 6 ft 6 in. (61 cm × 198 cm); or double-hung windows, 30 in. × 36 in. (7 cm × 91 cm) clear opening	Windows providing a clear opening of at least 20 in. (50.8 cm) in width, 24 in. (61 cm) in height, and 5.7 ft² (0.53 m²) in area
Level of access opening	Not over 12 in. (30.5 cm) above floor; steps if higher	Same
Discharge to ground	Swinging stair section permitted if approved by authority having jurisdiction	Same
Capacity, number of persons	0.5 in. (1.3 cm) per person, if access by door; 1.0 in. (2.5 cm) per person, if access by climbing over window sill	10

7.2.8.4 where approved by the authority having jurisdiction

The intent of the *Code* is not to encourage the use of ladders but to provide access to an exit from any regularly occupied area. The *Code* contains provisions for fire escape ladders only because these ladders are sometimes one of the only practical means of moving from one space to another along what might be a path of escape from spaces not normally occupied. The provisions of 7.2.9.1 constitute the minimal recognition given fire escape ladders by this *Code*. The *Code* does specify requirements for ladder construction and installation to ensure structural integrity and ease of use if ladders must be used. Subsection 7.2.11 also addresses alternating tread devices for use under conditions similar to those specified for fire escape ladders.

7.2.9.2 Construction and Installation.

7.2.9.2.1 Fire escape ladders shall comply with ANSI A14.3, *Safety Code for Fixed Ladders*.

Exception No. 1: Existing ladders complying with the edition of this Code that was in effect when the ladders were installed shall be permitted where approved by the authority having jurisdiction.

Exception No. 2: Exception No. 2 Industrial stairs complying with the minimum requirements for fixed stairs of ANSI A1264.1, Safety Requirements for Workplace Floor and Wall Openings, Stairs and Railing Systems, shall be permitted where fire escape ladders are permitted in accordance with Chapter 40.

Fixed industrial stairs can have dimensional criteria that are comparable to ladders or that are nearly comparable to existing means of egress stairs in accordance with 7.2.2. Exception No. 2 to 7.2.9.2.1 recognizes that some industrial stairs are safer to use than ladders and allows such stairs to be used at locations where fire escape ladders are permitted in industrial occupancies.

7.2.9.2.2 Ladders shall be installed with a pitch that exceeds 75 degrees.

7.2.9.3 Access. The lowest rung of any ladder shall not be more than 12 in. (30.5 cm) above the level of the surface beneath it.

7.2.10 Slide Escapes.

7.2.10.1 General.

7.2.10.1.1 A slide escape shall be permitted as a component in a means of egress where permitted in Chapters 12 through 42.

Slide escapes are permitted in specified locations as a component in a means of egress and can even be considered as exits. Ordinarily, an occupant enters a slide escape through a window or special opening in an exterior wall. From that point on, the slide escape functions as an exit discharge. If the slide escape is entered from within the building, it is considered an exit and must be protected by enclosure as required by 7.1.3.2.

Where provided, slide escapes should be used regularly in practice drills or for normal egress so that occupants are familiar with their use.

A slide pole of the type found in fire stations is not considered a slide escape.

Slide escapes are permitted in means of egress only in high hazard industrial occupancies and existing storage occupancies. See 40.2.2.11 and 42.2.2.10.

7.2.10.1.2 Each slide escape shall be of an approved type.

7.2.10.2 Capacity.

7.2.10.2.1 Slide escapes, where permitted as required means of egress, shall be rated at a capacity of 60 persons.

7.2.10.2.2 Slide escapes shall not constitute more than 25 percent of the required egress capacity from any building or structure or any individual story thereof.

Exception: This requirement shall not apply where otherwise provided in Chapter 40.

The 25 percent limitation on slide escapes as required means of egress emphasizes that other, more common egress components must comprise the majority of the egress capacity.

7.2.11* Alternating Tread Devices.

A.7.2.11 Special consideration should be given prior to the application of such devices where children, the elderly, or physically disabled persons use such devices. These devices present obstacles in ascent and descent that differ from those for stairs and ladders.

As used in the *Code*, an *alternating tread device* is an intermediate form of climbing implement that is between a ladder and a stair. It consists of a steep succession of treads that alternate from the left side to the right side at intervals of one riser height. A person using the device is forced to place the correct foot on each tread. This alternating tread design, now generally manufactured as a series of treads supported by a central spine, permits stairlike half-treads to be used with ladderlike slopes. The use of such devices, which might be awkward due to unfamiliarity or infrequent use, might be acceptable for some occupancies and locations where the alternative means of changing levels are ladders or ships' ladders, devices that generally have pitches of 50 degrees to 75 degrees. Such pitches are approximately twice those permitted for stairs by the *Code*.

An advantage of alternating tread devices is that one can descend with one's back to the device—unlike a ladder where one can only descend safely while facing the ladder because of the more limited surface area and depth of ladder rungs. A further benefit of the device is that objects can be carried more easily while ascending or descending, because the handrails provide support under the arms, which are left free. The *Code* limits the use of alternating tread devices to those situations where a ladder is acceptable. Exhibit 7.57 illustrates an alternating tread device.

7.2.11.1 Alternating tread devices complying with 7.2.11.2 shall be permitted in the means of egress only where providing one of the following:

(1) Access to unoccupied roof spaces as permitted in 7.2.8.3.3
(2) A second means of egress from storage elevators as permitted in Chapter 42
(3) A means of egress from towers and elevated platforms around machinery or similar spaces subject to occupancy not to exceed three persons who are all capable of using the alternating tread device
(4) A secondary means of egress from boiler rooms or similar spaces subject to occupancy not to exceed three persons who are all capable of using the alternating tread device

7.2.11.2 Alternating tread devices shall comply with the following:

Exhibit 7.57 *Alternating tread device.*

(1) Handrails shall be provided on both sides of alternating tread devices in accordance with 7.2.2.4.5.
(2) The clear width between handrails shall be not less than 17 in. (43.2 cm) and not more than 24 in. (61 cm).
(3) Headroom shall be not less than 6 ft 8 in. (2 m).
(4) The angle of the device shall be between 50 degrees and 68 degrees to horizontal.
(5) The height of the riser shall not exceed 9.5 in. (24.1 cm).

(6) Treads shall have a projected tread depth of not less than 5.8 in. (14.7 cm), measured in accordance with 7.2.2, with each tread providing 9.5 in. (24.1 cm) of depth, including tread overlap.
(7) A distance of not less than 6 in. (15.2 cm) shall be provided between the stair handrail and any other object.
(8) The initial tread of the stair shall begin at the same elevation as the platform, landing, or floor surface.
(9) The alternating treads shall not be laterally separated by a distance of more than 2 in. (5.0 cm).
(10) The occupant load served shall not exceed three.

7.2.12 Areas of Refuge.

Subsection 7.2.12 presents the detailed criteria applicable to an area of refuge. The term *area of refuge* (see 3.3.14) and the related terms *accessible area of refuge* (see 3.3.1) and *accessible means of egress* (see 3.3.2) are defined in Chapter 3.

Subsection 7.5.4 requires accessible means of egress in all new construction, regardless of occupancy classification, in areas accessible to persons with severe mobility impairment. Because an accessible means of egress must be usable by a person with severe mobility impairment, the components most commonly used in such means of egress will be ramps and areas of refuge. Areas of refuge will be extensively used from the upper stories of multistory buildings where it might not be feasible to install ramp systems.

The criteria of 7.2.12 were written to bring the *Code* into substantial agreement with the Americans with Disabilities Act Accessibility Guidelines for Buildings and Facilities (ADAAG)[12] and ICC/ANSI A117.1, *American National Standard for Accessible and Usable Buildings and Facilities.*

7.2.12.1 General. An area of refuge used as part of a required accessible means of egress in accordance with 7.5.4, or used as a part of any required means of egress, shall conform to the following:

(1) The general requirements of Section 7.1
(2) The requirements of 7.2.12.2 and 7.2.12.3

Exception: The requirement of 7.2.12.1(2) shall not apply to areas of refuge consisting of stories of buildings protected throughout by an approved, supervised automatic sprinkler system in accordance with Section 9.7.

The provisions of the exception to 7.2.12.1(2) and the definition of *area of refuge* in 3.3.14 are interrelated.

Their combined effect is to permit three forms of area of refuge to serve as part of an accessible means of egress as follows.

(a) On a floor of a building not protected throughout by an approved, supervised automatic sprinkler system, the area of refuge must meet the special requirements of 7.2.12.2 and 7.2.12.3, as well as the general requirements of Section 7.1.

(b) On a floor of a building protected throughout by an approved, supervised automatic sprinkler system—and involving an occupancy that does not exempt itself from the minimum two accessible rooms provision of the definition of *area of refuge*—the area of refuge is exempt from the special requirements of 7.2.12.2 and 7.2.12.3. However, the area of refuge must meet the general requirements of Section 7.1 and consist of at least two accessible rooms or spaces separated from each other by smoke-resisting partitions. The following occupancies do not exempt themselves from the minimum two accessible rooms provision of the definition of *area of refuge*:

(1) Assembly
(2) Educational
(3) Health care
(4) Detention and correctional
(5) Board and care
(6) Industrial
(7) Storage

(c) On a floor of a building protected throughout by an approved, supervised automatic sprinkler system—and involving an occupancy that exempts itself from the minimum two accessible rooms provision of the definition of *area of refuge*—the area of refuge is exempt from the special requirements of 7.2.12.2 and 7.2.12.3 and is also exempt from having to provide the two accessible rooms or spaces separated from each other by smoke-resisting partitions. However, the area of refuge must meet the general requirements of Section 7.1. The following occupancies exempt themselves from the minimum two accessible rooms provision of the definition of *area of refuge*:

(1) Hotels and dormitories
(2) Apartment buildings
(3) Mercantile
(4) Business

7.2.12.2 Accessibility.

7.2.12.2.1 Required portions of an area of refuge shall be accessible from the space they serve by an accessible means of egress.

To help ensure that the area of refuge can be accessed by persons with mobility impairments, 7.2.12.2.1 requires such accessibility via an accessible means of egress. Thus, a person attempting to reach the area of refuge must be provided with either level floor travel or ramp travel, not stairs. Similarly, the door to the area of refuge must provide sufficient clear width, typically the 32-in. (81-cm) minimum specified by 7.2.1.2.3, to permit a person in a wheelchair to move through the door opening. See the definition of *accessible means of egress* in 3.3.2.

7.2.12.2.2 Required portions of an area of refuge shall have access to a public way, without requiring return to the building spaces through which travel to the area of refuge occurred, via an exit or an elevator.

An area of refuge is intended to provide only a temporary point of safety to permit delayed egress travel from any level. Therefore, an area of refuge cannot be a room or space whose only access to the building spaces is through the room or space through which the user arrived. Such an arrangement might trap a person within the area of refuge, since no egress other than that which requires travel back through the space where the fire is located has been provided. Rather, the area of refuge must provide access to a public way via either an elevator or an exit such as an enclosed exit stair.

7.2.12.2.3* Where the exit providing egress from an area of refuge to a public way that is in accordance with 7.2.12.2.2 includes stairs, the clear width of landings and stair flights, measured between handrails and at all points below handrail height, shall not be less than 48 in. (122 cm).

The *Code* requires 48 in. (122 cm) of clear width between handrails on exit stairs that provide the required access from the area of refuge to the exit discharge. The 48-in. (122-cm) clear width requirement is wider than the minimum 44 in. (112 cm) required by Tables 7.2.2.2.1(a) and (b) for stairs, which typically provides only 37 in. (94 cm) of clear width between handrails. The extra width is required to facilitate the carrying of persons in wheelchairs as explained in A.7.2.12.2.3. The minimum 48-in. (122-cm) stair width is a clear width dimension measured between handrails. The allowance of 7.2.2.2.1 that permits handrails to encroach as much as 3$^1/_2$ in. (8.9 cm) on each side of a stair without considering the reduced clear width does not apply. For a stair with normal handrails to provide the required 48-in (122-cm) clear width, the stair needs to be approximately 55 in. (140 cm) wide.

Exception No. 1:   The minimum 48-in. (122-cm) clear width shall not be required where the area of refuge is separated from the remainder of the story by a horizontal exit meeting the requirements of 7.2.4. (See also 7.2.12.3.4.).

Exception No. 1 to 7.2.12.2.3 exempts areas of refuge created by horizontal exits from the extra-wide stair requirement. Horizontal exits in accordance with 7.2.4 consist of barriers with a minimum 2-hour fire resistance rating. The 2-hour rating increases the time for which the area of refuge can maintain tenable conditions. It is believed that this increase in time allows a slower evacuation on a narrower, typical stair to be effectively accomplished.

Exception No. 2:   For stairs where egress is in the descending direction, a clear width of not less than 37 in. (94 cm), measured at and below handrail height, shall be permitted if approved alternative measures are provided that do not necessitate carrying occupied wheelchairs on the stairs.

Exception No. 2 to 7.2.12.2.3 recognizes a 44-in. (112-cm) stair with handrails encroaching up to $3^1/_2$ in. (8.9 cm) so as to provide a minimum 37-in. (94-cm) clear width. However, egress must be in the descending direction, which is easier than climbing stairs and lifting persons with disabilities. Also, egress must not involve carrying occupied wheelchairs on the stairs. Special controlled-descent boards, chairs, and other devices, which are operable by one able-bodied person, are available. Such devices can be effectively used with the 37-in. (94-cm) clear width afforded by the typical 44-in (112-cm) width stair.

Exception No. 3:   Existing stairs and landings that provide a clear width of not less than 37 in. (94 cm), measured at and below handrail height, shall be permitted.

Exception No. 3 to 7.2.12.2.3 recognizes that areas of refuge might be created in existing buildings with existing 44-in (112-cm) stairs that provide only 37-in. (94-cm) clear width because of handrail encroachment. To require the stairs in such buildings to be widened retroactively would create a severe hardship.

A.7.2.12.2.3 The clear width of not less than 48 in. (122 cm) is needed for a three-person carry of an occupied wheelchair up or down a stair. This procedure, as well as the more difficult two-person wheelchair carry or roll, requires training and experience. Safer, alternative stair descent measures for transporting a person who normally requires a wheelchair include evacuation chairs and self-braking stair descent devices. In addition to having such devices available where needed, and having persons trained and experienced in their use, it is important to have people trained and experienced in wheelchair transfer techniques.

In view of the logistical difficulties as well as the dangers inherent in carrying occupied wheelchairs or otherwise transporting their occupants on stairs, the preferred means of egress from an area of refuge consists of facilities normally employed for ingress and egress by people using wheelchairs. Foremost among these options are elevators meeting the fire-fighter service requirements of ASME/ANSI A17.1, *Safety Code for Elevators and Escalators.*

7.2.12.2.4* Where an elevator provides access from an area of refuge to a public way that is in accordance with 7.2.12.2.2, the elevator shall be approved for fire fighter service as provided in Section 211 of ASME/ANSI A17.1, *Safety Code for Elevators and Escalators.* The power supply shall be protected against interruption from fire occurring within the building but outside the area of refuge. The elevator shall be located in a shaft system meeting the requirements for smokeproof enclosures in accordance with 7.2.3.

An elevator used to provide the required access from the area of refuge to the exit discharge must be safe to operate in a building with a fire. The *Code* requires such an elevator to have the fire fighter service features required by ASME/ANSI A17.1, *Safety Code for Elevators and Escalators.* One of these features is elevator recall, whereby the elevator is taken out of service if smoke is detected in the elevator machine room of any elevator lobby it serves. Fire service personnel or other trained persons can put the elevator back into service for manual operation.

Also, the power supply for the elevator must be protected against interruption caused by fire occurring within the building but outside the area of refuge. The electrical wiring would require enclosure within protecting construction if it runs through other floors or other areas on the same floor as the area of refuge. The *Code*'s intent is to ensure that, if it is safe to operate an elevator within a portion of the building, a fire in some other area must not adversely affect the power to the elevator. If the fire is in the same area as the elevator, it will not be safe to operate.

Therefore, the electrical wiring in the same area as the elevator is not required to be protected.

In order for an elevator to pass a fire floor safely, its shaft must be kept free of smoke. The elevator must be located in a shaft system meeting the requirements of 7.2.3 for smokeproof enclosures. To achieve such compliance, the elevator lobbies on each floor need to be separated from the remainder of the floor. In effect, elevator vestibules are required. See 7.2.3 for additional details on smokeproof enclosures.

Exception No. 1:   The smokeproof enclosure shall not be required for areas of refuge that are more than 1000 ft² (93 m²) and that are created by a horizontal exit meeting the requirements of 7.2.4.

Exception No. 1 to 7.2.12.2.4 exempts the smokeproof enclosure for areas of refuge that use an elevator, are more than 1000 ft² (93 m²) in area, and are created by horizontal exits. Horizontal exits in accordance with 7.2.4 consist of barriers with a minimum 2-hour fire resistance rating. The 2-hour rating increases the time for which the area of refuge can maintain tenable conditions.

Exception No. 2:   The smokeproof enclosure shall not be required for elevators complying with 7.2.13.

A.7.2.12.2.4 The use of elevators for egress, especially during an emergency such as a fire, is not an approach to be taken without considerable planning, ongoing effort, and a high degree of understanding by everyone involved with the evacuation of persons with mobility impairments. Due in part to the limited capacity of elevators, as well as to the conflicting demands for elevator use for fire-fighting activities, even elevators in accordance with 7.2.12.2.4 cannot be considered as satisfying any of the *Code*'s requirements for egress capacity, number of means of egress, or travel distance to an exit.

7.2.12.2.5 The area of refuge shall be provided with a two-way communication system for communication between the area of refuge and a central control point. The door to the stair enclosure or the elevator door and the associated portion of the area of refuge that the stair enclosure door or elevator door serves shall be identified by signage. *(See 7.2.12.3.5.)*

7.2.12.2.6* Instructions for summoning assistance, via the two-way communication system, and written identification of the area of refuge location shall be posted adjacent to the two-way communication system.

A.7.2.12.2.6 The instructions should include the following:

(1) Directions to find other means of egress
(2) Advice that persons able to use exit stairs do so as soon as possible, unless they are assisting others
(3) Information on planned availability of assistance in the use of stairs or supervised operation of elevators and how to summon such assistance
(4) Directions for use of the emergency communication system

To facilitate an adequate degree of understanding of the use of areas of refuge and of the associated assisted egress procedures, information should be provided to those using the facilities. The exact content of the information, its organization (for example, as a set of instructions), and its format (for example, either posted instructions in the area of refuge or information otherwise transmitted to facility users) should be determined on a case-by-case basis. The information should be tailored to the specific facility, its emergency plan, the intended audience, and the intended presentation format. The following provides suggested information content addressing two situations.

(a) *Refuge with Elevator Use.* An area of refuge provided in the elevator lobby serves as a staging area for persons unable to use stairs and needing assistance for their evacuation during an emergency. The elevator(s) will be taken out of automatic service and operated by emergency service personnel. Persons unable to evacuate down the exit stairs without assistance and needing transportation by elevator should make certain the elevator lobby doors are closed while they wait in the elevator lobby for assistance. The two-way communication system should be used if there is a delay of more than several minutes in the arrival of an elevator that will provide transportation to the ground floor. Alternatively, another refuge area, and assistance with evacuation, is available in the designated exit stair.

(b) *Refuge with Stair Use.* An area of refuge within the designated exit stair serves as a staging area for persons needing assistance for their evacuation during an emergency. Persons unable to use the stairs unassisted, or who wish to move down the stairs at a slower pace, should wait on the stair landing. The two-way communication system should be used if assistance is needed.

In a nonsprinklered building, either an elevator or a stair will be provided as access from the area of refuge to a public way, and it cannot be ensured that persons with mobility impairments will be able to use the elevator or stair without assistance. For example, an elevator might have been called out of service because smoke was detected in one of the elevator lobbies serving that elevator. Therefore, the *Code* requires a two-way communication system between the area of refuge and a central control point; the communication system will be used to summon assistance. Additionally, signage and instructions are required to help complete the package of features for use by persons with disabilities.

These requirements for communication capability, signage, and instructions are not required for areas of refuge in buildings protected throughout by approved, supervised automatic sprinkler systems.

7.2.12.3 Details.

7.2.12.3.1* Each area of refuge shall be sized to accommodate one wheelchair space of 30 in. × 48 in. (76 cm × 122 cm) for each 200 occupants, or portion thereof, based on the occupant load served by the area of refuge. Such wheelchair spaces shall maintain the width of a means of egress to not less than that required for the occupant load served and to not less than 36 in. (91 cm).

A.7.2.12.3.1 Figure A.7.2.12.3.1 illustrates the application of the minimum space requirement to an area of refuge located within an exit stair enclosure. Note that each of the two required spaces is sufficient to allow the parking of a standard wheelchair. Preferably, such spaces should be provided adjacent to each other in a location where the presence of people taking temporary shelter in an area of refuge will be immediately apparent to rescue personnel and other evacuees.

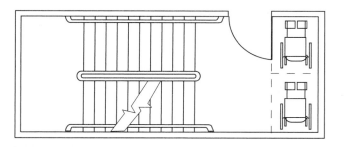

Figure A.7.2.12.3.1 *Exit stair used as an area of refuge.*

7.2.12.3.2* For any area of refuge that does not exceed 1000 ft² (93 m²), it shall be demonstrated by calculation or test that tenable conditions are maintained within the area of refuge for a period of 15 minutes when the exposing space on the other side of the separation creating the area of refuge is subjected to the maximum expected fire conditions.

Areas of refuge of less than 1000 ft² (93 m) might be more easily affected than larger areas by the products of combustion from a fire in the area on the other side of the separating barrier. Thus, tenability must be demonstrated by calculation or test. An area of refuge within an exit stair enclosure, as shown in Figure A.7.2.12.3.1, would be required to demonstrate tenability. However, an area of refuge consisting of half a 2200-ft² (205-m²) floor would not be required to do so.

A.7.2.12.3.2 The method of meeting the tenability performance criteria required of an area of refuge of less than 1000 ft² (93 m²) can involve controlling the exposing fire (for example, via automatic sprinkler protection), installing smoke-resisting doors in the smoke-resisting barriers *(see NFPA 105, Recommended Practice for the Installation of Smoke-Control Door Assemblies),* providing smoke control to prevent or limit smoke migration through cracks or other leakage paths *(see NFPA 92A, Recommended Practice for Smoke-Control Systems),* or providing other means or a combination of these means.

Calculations, if used, need to be based on established engineering relationships and equations. Such calculational procedures are described in NFPA 92A, *Recommended Practice for Smoke-Control Systems, Design of Smoke Management Systems,* and the *SFPE Handbook of Fire Protection Engineering.* Tenable conditions are those that maintain the temperature of any smoke in the area of refuge at less than 200°F (93°C) if the smoke is more than 5 ft (1.5 m) above the floor, and at less than 120°F (49°C) if the smoke descends below the 5-ft (1.5-m) level in the area of refuge. Also, if the smoke descends below the 5-ft (1.5-m) level, tenable conditions require not less than 16 percent oxygen and not more than 30,000 ppm/min exposure to carbon monoxide. The exposing conditions used in the calculations should be in accordance with the following:

(1) The exposing space is sprinkler protected: the temperature of the exposing smoke is 200°F (93°C), the smoke layer extends to the floor, the oxygen content is 16 percent, and the carbon monoxide concentration is 2000 ppm (0.2 percent).
(2) The exposing space is a nonsprinklered corridor finished with Class A interior wall and ceiling finish: the temperature of the exposing smoke is 600°F (315°C), the smoke layer extends to a level 2 ft (0.6 m) above the floor, the oxygen content is 3 percent, and the carbon monoxide concentration is 50,000 ppm (5 percent).
(3) The exposing space is either not a corridor or, if a corridor, the corridor is not finished with a Class A interior wall and ceiling finish: the temperature of the

exposing smoke is 1500°F (815°C), the smoke layer extends to a level 2 ft (0.6 m) above the floor, the oxygen content is 3 percent, and the carbon monoxide concentration is 50,000 ppm (5 percent).

7.2.12.3.3 Access to any designated wheelchair space in an area of refuge shall not be through more than one adjoining wheelchair space.

7.2.12.3.4* Each area of refuge shall be separated from the remainder of the story by a barrier with not less than a 1-hour fire resistance rating, unless a greater rating is required in other provisions of this *Code*. Such barriers, and any openings in them, shall minimize air leakage and retard the passage of smoke. Doors in such barriers shall have not less than a 20-minute fire protection rating, unless a greater rating is required in other provisions of this *Code*, and shall be either self-closing or automatic-closing in accordance with 7.2.1.8.2. Ducts shall be permitted to penetrate such barriers, unless prohibited in other provisions of this *Code*, and shall be provided with smoke-actuated dampers or other approved means to resist the transfer of smoke into the area of refuge.

Exception: Existing barriers with a minimum 30-minute fire resistance rating shall be permitted.

A.7.2.12.3.4 Requirements for fire resistance ratings in excess of 1 hour, fire protection ratings in excess of 20 minutes, and prohibitions on duct penetrations appear in other *Code* sections. For example, if the barrier creating the area of refuge is also part of an exit stair enclosure that connects more than three stories or is a horizontal exit, a fire resistance rating of the barrier of not less than 2 hours and a fire protection rating for opening protectives such as doors of not less than 1½ hours would be required for most occupancies.

For further information on door openings in smoke-resisting barriers, see NFPA 105, *Recommended Practice for the Installation of Smoke-Control Door Assemblies.*

Generally, by providing one barrier that subdivides a floor area, two areas of refuge can be created. This subdivision method and the possibility of creating areas of refuge within compartmented elevator lobbies or on enlarged stair landings of exit stair enclosures make less onerous any requirement for a story to have more than one accessible means of egress.

As explained in the commentary following the exception to 7.2.12.1(2), these requirements for fire resistance–rated separating barriers and fire protection–rated separating doors are not required for areas of refuge in buildings protected throughout by approved, supervised automatic sprinkler systems.

Exhibits 7.58(a) through 7.58(e) illustrate several arrangements of areas of refuge.

Exhibit 7.58(a) depicts an area of refuge in a new sprinklered business occupancy. The exception to 38.2.2.12 exempts the floor that serves as an area of refuge from having to provide two rooms or spaces separated from each other by smoke-resistant partitions if the building is protected throughout by an approved, supervised automatic sprinkler system. The open floor area depicted meets the requirements for an area of refuge.

Exhibit 7.58(b) depicts an area of refuge in a new sprinklered industrial occupancy. Industrial occupancies are not exempt from the area of refuge provision for two rooms or spaces separated from each other by smoke-resistant partitions. Thus, in this building, which is protected throughout by an approved, supervised automatic sprinkler system, a second room on this floor is provided. Although the separating barriers and door are not required to be

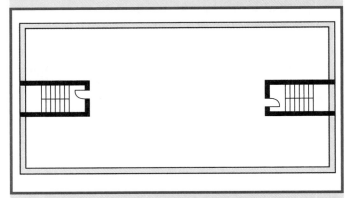

Exhibit 7.58(a) *Area of refuge in new sprinklered business occupancy.*

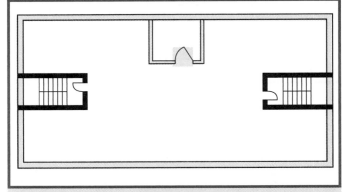

Exhibit 7.58(b) *Area of refuge in new sprinklered industrial occupancy.*

fire rated, they must be smoke resistant. With this arrangement, the floor meets the requirements for an area of refuge.

Exhibit 7.58(c) depicts areas of refuge in non-sprinklered new construction. The barrier dividing the floor into two areas of refuge has a 1-hour fire resistance rating; the door has a 20-minute fire protection rating. Each area is more than 1000 ft² (93 m²), and no tenability calculations are required. In the area of refuge at the left, the elevator is provided with fire fighter service features and serves as access to the public way; the stair in that compartment is permitted to have the usual 44-in. (112-cm) width. In the area of refuge at the right, the stair serves as access to the public way and must be approximately 55 in. (140 cm) wide to provide the required 48-in. (122-cm) clear width between handrails. Two-way communication capability, signage, and posted instructions are required in each area of refuge.

Exhibit 7.58(d) depicts areas of refuge created by a horizontal exit in new construction. The barrier dividing the floor into two areas of refuge is a horizontal exit with a 2-hour fire resistance rating; the doors have a 1¹/₂-hour fire protection rating. Each area is more than 1000 ft² (93 m²), and no tenability calculations are required. Because the separating barrier is a horizontal exit, the stairs are permitted to be typical 44-in. (112-cm) width stairs. Two-way communication capability, signage, and posted instructions are required in each area of refuge.

Exhibit 7.58(e) depicts an area of refuge that uses space within the exit stair enclosure in nonsprinklered new construction. The exit stair enclosure walls at the right of the figure provide the barrier that creates two areas of refuge on the floor. The area of refuge within that exit stair enclosure is less than

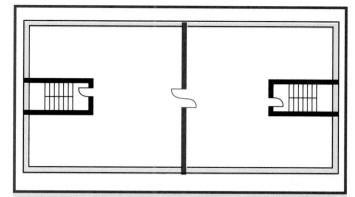

Exhibit 7.58(d) Areas of refuge created by horizontal exit in new construction.

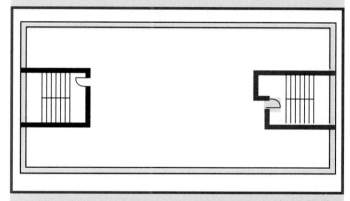

Exhibit 7.58(e) Area of refuge using space within exit stair enclosure in nonsprinklered new construction.

1000 ft² (93 m²), and tenability must be demonstrated. The remainder of the floor serves as the second area of refuge; it is larger than 1000 ft² (93 m²), and no tenability calculation is required. Access from each area of refuge to a public way is provided by stairs. The stairs must be approximately 55 in. (140 cm) wide to provide the required 48-in. (122-cm) clear width between handrails. Two-way communication capability, signage, and posted instructions are required in each area of refuge.

7.2.12.3.5 Each area of refuge shall be identified by a sign stating the following:

AREA OF REFUGE

The sign shall conform to the requirements of CABO/ANSI A117.1, *American National Standard for Accessible and Usable Buildings and Facilities*, for such signage and shall display the international symbol of accessibility. Signs also shall be located as follows:

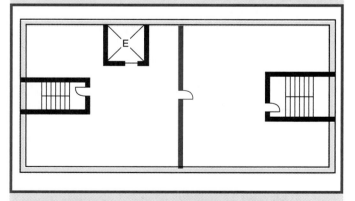

Exhibit 7.58(c) Areas of refuge in nonsprinklered new construction.

(1) At each door providing access to the area of refuge
(2) At all exits not providing an accessible means of egress, as defined in 3.3.2
(3) Where necessary to indicate clearly the direction to an area of refuge

Signs shall be illuminated as required for exit signs where exit sign illumination is required.

7.2.12.3.6 Tactile signage complying with CABO/ANSI A117.1, *American National Standard for Accessible and Usable Buildings and Facilities*, shall be located at each door to an area of refuge.

7.2.13 Elevators.

Prior to the 1997 edition, the *Code* treated elevators as a means of moving persons with mobility impairment from an area of refuge to the exit discharge (see 7.2.12). The earlier editions also addressed the situation of taking an elevator out of service and making it available to fire fighters to prevent its misuse by building occupants during a fire (see Section 9.4). However, elevators were not recognized as a component of typical means of egress. The concept of elevators as a component of the means of egress, which is addressed in 7.2.13, was new to the 1997 edition of the *Code*.

7.2.13.1* General. An elevator complying with the requirements of Section 9.4 and 7.2.13 shall be permitted to be used as a second means of egress from towers, as defined in 3.3.203, provided that the following criteria are met:

(1) The tower and any attached structure shall be protected throughout by an approved, supervised automatic sprinkler system in accordance with Section 9.7.
(2) The tower shall be subject to occupancy not to exceed 90 persons.
(3) Primary egress discharges shall be directly to the outside.
(4) No high hazard content areas shall exist in the tower or attached structure.
(5) One hundred percent of the egress capacity shall be provided independent of the elevators.
(6) An evacuation plan shall be implemented, specifically including the elevator, and staff personnel shall be trained in operations and procedures for elevator emergency use in normal operating mode prior to fire fighter recall.
(7) The tower shall not be used by the general public.

A.7.2.13.1 It is the intent of 7.2.13 that elevators serving as a means of egress serve only independent towers or the tower portion of any integral structure. For elevators that are used as a component in the means of egress, the elevator

lobbies, elevator shaft, and machine room need to be protected from the effects of fire.

Subsections 7.2.1 through 7.2.12 are formatted to describe one of 12 potential components of means of egress, such as doors (7.2.1), stairs (7.2.2), ramps (7.2.5), or slide escapes (7.2.10). The occupancy chapters specify whether each of these components is permitted to be used within the required means of egress. The recognition of these components by the occupancy chapters ranges from "permitted by all" for doors to "very limited use" for slide escapes in high hazard industrial and existing storage occupancies. However, in each case, it is the occupancy chapter that determines the applicability of any of the 12 egress components. Subsection 7.2.13 is formatted differently. It limits the use of elevators within means of egress to serving only as a secondary, not primary, means of egress from towers.

The recognition of elevators for emergency egress is limited to towers not used by the general public. The occupants will generally be employees, who are familiar with the structure because of repeated occupancy. Although the public has been taught not to use elevators during fire or similar emergency, the tower's employees can be trained to use elevators effectively for egress.

Note that 7.2.13.1(1) requires the tower to be sprinklered to keep conditions tenable while the elevator is being used. Subparagraph 7.2.13.1(2) limits occupancy in the tower to a maximum of 90 persons. Subparagraph 7.2.13.1(5) requires that 100 percent of the egress capacity be provided without considering the capacity provided by the elevator. Thus, the elevator helps to satisfy the requirement for a redundant, second egress route, but the primary route (typically a stair) must be sized to accommodate the entire occupant load.

The restrictions imposed on the use of elevator evacuation systems resulted from the consensus process by which the *Code* is revised. One faction favored recognition of elevator evacuation systems for any occupancy. The other faction did not want elevators to be recognized at all. As tangible experience is gained in the design and use of elevator evacuation systems, additional recognition of the emergency egress use of elevators will be included in future editions of the *Code*.

7.2.13.2 Elevator Evacuation System Capacity.

7.2.13.2.1 The elevator car shall have a capacity of not less than eight persons.

7.2.13.2.2 The elevator lobby shall have a capacity of not less than 50 percent of the occupant load of the area served by the lobby. The capacity shall be calculated by using 3 ft² (0.28 m²) per person and shall also include one wheelchair space of 30 in. × 48 in. (76 cm × 122 cm) for each 50 persons, or fraction thereof, of the total occupant load served by that lobby.

7.2.13.3 Elevator Lobby. On every floor served by the elevator, there shall be an elevator lobby. Barriers forming the elevator lobby shall have a fire resistance rating of not less than 1 hour and shall be arranged as a smoke barrier in accordance with Section 8.3.

7.2.13.4 Elevator Lobby Doors. Elevator lobby doors shall have a fire protection rating of at least 1 hour. The transmitted temperature end point shall not exceed 450°F (250°C) above ambient at the end of 30 minutes of the fire exposure specified in the test method referenced in 8.2.3.2.1(a). Elevator lobby doors shall be self-closing or automatic-closing in accordance with 7.2.1.8.

7.2.13.5 Door Activation. The elevator lobby doors shall close in response to a signal from a smoke detector located directly outside the elevator lobby adjacent to or on each door opening. Closing of lobby doors in response to a signal from the building fire alarm system shall be permitted. Closing of one elevator lobby door by means of smoke detector or a signal from the building fire alarm system shall result in closing of all elevator lobby doors serving that elevator evacuation system.

7.2.13.6* Water Protection. Building elements shall be used to restrict water exposure of elevator equipment.

A.7.2.13.6 One or more of the following approaches can be used to restrict exposure of elevator equipment to water:

(1) A combination of sealed elevator lobby doors, sloped floors, floor drains, and sealed elevator shaft walls is used.

(2) The elevator is mounted on the building exterior that normally operates in the elements, and seals are used on the elevator lobby doors.

(3) The elevator shaft is separated from the building at each floor by an exterior elevator lobby designed to prevent water entry into the elevator shaft.

Information gained from ongoing research concerning waterflow and elevators could lead to the development of water-resistive or water-protected elevator equipment specifically for fire applications. Such equipment should be used only with the building elements (for example, sealed elevator lobby doors, sloped floors, floor drains) for which it is developed. Further information is available from the NIST publication, *Feasibility of Fire Evacuation by Elevators at FAA Control Towers.*

7.2.13.7* Power and Control Wiring. Elevator equipment, elevator communications, elevator machine room cooling, and elevator controller cooling shall be supplied by both normal and standby power. Wiring for power and control shall be located and properly protected to ensure at least 1 hour of operation in the event of a fire.

A.7.2.13.7 Cooling equipment dedicated to the elevator machine room can be used to minimize requirements for standby power.

7.2.13.8* Communications. Two-way communication systems shall be provided between elevator lobbies and a central control point and between elevator cars and a central control point. Communications wiring shall be protected to ensure at least 1 hour of operation in the event of fire.

A.7.2.13.8 Communication between elevator lobbies and a central control point can be by telephone or intercom. Auditory alarms should be designed so that they do not interfere with people talking on communications systems.

7.2.13.9* Elevator Operation. Elevators shall be provided with fire fighter service in accordance with ASME/ANSI A17.1, *Safety Code for Elevators and Escalators.*

A.7.2.13.9 Smoke detection in the elevator lobby will result in a Phase I recall of the elevators. The elevators will then be automatically taken out of normal service and will be available to be operated by emergency service personnel.

7.2.13.10 Maintenance. Where an elevator lobby is served by only one elevator car, the elevator evacuation system shall have a program of scheduled maintenance during times of building shutdown or low building activity. Repairs shall be performed within 24 hours of breakdown.

7.2.13.11 Earthquake Protection. Elevators shall have the capability of orderly shutdowns during earthquakes at locations where such shutdowns are an option of ASME/ANSI A17.1, *Safety Code for Elevators and Escalators.*

7.2.13.12 Signage. Signage shall comply with 7.10.8.2.

Section 7.3 Capacity of Means of Egress

7.3.1 Occupant Load.

7.3.1.1 The total capacity of the means of egress for any story, balcony, tier, or other occupied space shall be sufficient for the occupant load thereof.

It is a basic concept of the *Code* that the means of egress system be sized to accommodate all people occupying a building.

The geometry of a building, its occupancy and related occupant load, and the travel distance to exits dictate, in large measure, the location of exits, the number of exits, and the capacity of exits and access thereto. As a consequence, the exits themselves influence the plan and layout of the entire system of means of egress. The number of people that the means of egress system can accommodate is determined not solely by the capacity of the exits but also by the number of persons each component within the means of egress can accommodate. Very wide corridors that lead to very wide exit-stair enclosure doors that then lead to much narrower stairs provide a system comparable to average width corridors that lead to average width exit-stair enclosure doors that then lead to average width stairs. A system is only as good as its most constricting component.

The number of people or occupant load for which the means of egress system must provide egress capacity is calculated or determined. The occupant load is to reflect the maximum number of people anticipated to occupy the building rooms or spaces at any given time and under all probable situations. The occupant load must not be based only on normal occupancy.

Occupant load distribution in buildings might vary, with greater concentrations of people in some areas. However, good egress system design should ensure that egress capacity distribution among the exits is basically balanced. Multiple means of egress are required to provide alternate routes in case one of the means of egress becomes obstructed by the fire and becomes unavailable. Although the exit with the greatest share of the total required egress capacity might be the exit closest to the majority of the occupants, it might also be the exit that is lost in a fire. Consequently, a disproportionate amount of the total egress capacity might be lost.

7.3.1.2* The occupant load in any building or portion thereof shall be not less than the number of persons determined by dividing the floor area assigned to that use by the occupant load factor for that use as specified in Table 7.3.1.2. Where both gross and net area figures are given for the same occupancy, calculations shall be made by applying the gross area figure to the gross area of the portion of the building devoted to the use for which the gross area figure is specified and by applying the net area figure to the net area of the use for which the net area figure is specified.

Occupant load is determined by the nature of the use of a building or space and the amount of space

Table 7.3.1.2 Occupant Load Factor

Use	ft²† (per person)	m²† (per person)
Assembly Use		
Concentrated use, without fixed seating	7 net	0.65 net
Less concentrated use, without fixed seating	15 net	1.4 net
Bench-type seating	1 person/18 linear in.	1 person/45.7 linear cm
Fixed seating	Number of fixed seats	Number of fixed seats
Waiting spaces	*See 12.1.7.2 and 13.1.7.2.*	*See 12.1.7.2 and 13.1.7.2.*
Kitchens	100	9.3
Library stack areas	100	9.3
Library reading rooms	50 net	4.6 net
Swimming pools	50—of water surface	4.6—of water surface
Swimming pool decks	30	2.8
Exercise rooms with equipment	50	4.6
Exercise rooms without equipment	15	1.4
Stages	15 net	1.4 net
Lighting and access catwalks, galleries, gridirons	100 net	9.3 net
Casinos and similar gaming areas	11	1
Skating rinks	50	4.6
Educational Use		
Classrooms	20 net	1.9 net
Shops, laboratories, vocational rooms	50 net	4.6 net
Day-Care Use	35 net	3.3 net
Health Care Use		
Inpatient treatment departments	240	22.3
Sleeping departments	120	11.1
Detention and Correctional Use	120	11.1
Residential Use		
Hotels and dormitories	200	18.6
Apartment buildings	200	18.6
Board and care, large	200	18.6

Table 7.3.1.2 Continued

Use	ft²† (per person)	m²† (per person)
Industrial Use		
General and high hazard industrial	100	9.3
Special purpose industrial	NA‡	NA‡
Business Use	100	9.3
Storage Use (other than mercantile storerooms)	NA‡	NA‡
Mercantile Use		
Sales area on street floor§ ◇	30	2.8
Sales area on two or more street floors ◇	40	3.7
Sales area on floor below street floor ◇	30	2.8
Sales area on floors above street floor ◇	60	5.6
Floors or portions of floors used only for offices	*See business use.*	*See business use.*
Floors or portions of floors used only for storage, receiving, and shipping, and not open to general public	300	27.9
Covered mall buildings	Per factors applicable to use of space#	Per factors applicable to use of space#

†All factors expressed in gross area unless marked "net".

‡Not applicable. The occupant load shall be not less than the maximum probable number of occupants present at any time.

§For the purpose of determining occupant load in mercantile occupancies where, due to differences in grade of streets on different sides, two or more floors directly accessible from streets (not including alleys or similar back streets) exist, each such floor shall be considered a street floor. The occupant load factor shall be one person for each 40 ft² (3.7 m²) of gross floor area of sales space.

◇ In mercantile occupancies with no street floor, as defined in 3.3.196, but with access directly from the street by stairs or escalators, the principal floor at the point of entrance to the mercantile occupancy shall be considered the street floor.

#The portions of the covered mall, where considered a pedestrian way and not used as gross leasable area, shall not be assessed an occupant load based on Table 7.3.1.2. However, means of egress from a covered mall pedestrian way shall be provided for an occupant load determined by dividing the gross leasable area of the covered mall building (not including anchor stores) by the appropriate lowest whole number occupant load factor from Figure 7.3.1.2.

Each individual tenant space shall have means of egress to the outside or to the covered mall based on occupant loads figured by using the appropriate occupant load factor from Table 7.3.1.2.

Each individual anchor store shall have means of egress independent of the covered mall.

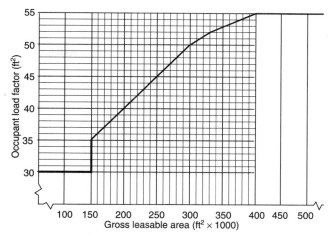

Note: For SI units, 1ft² = 0.093 m².

Figure 7.3.1.2 *Covered mall buildings occupant load factors.*

available for that use. Since different generic uses will be characterized by different occupant densities, Table 7.3.1.2 has established occupant load factors for each use. The first column of the table is deliberately headed *use* rather than *occupancy* because the use of an area might differ from its occupancy classification. For example, a meeting room for fewer than 50 people in an office building is not an assembly occupancy; it is a business occupancy, but its occupant load is based on an assembly use. The same concept applies to a classroom in a university, which, although classified as a business occupancy, would have its occupant load based on educational use (for traditional classroom style) or assembly use (for lecture style).

The occupant load factor, as a density factor, assumes the presence of at least one person for each specified unit of area. Note that some values are for net area, while others are based on gross area. The gross area figure applies to the building as a whole (the area within the confining perimeter walls of the building); the net area figure applies to actual occupied spaces, such as classroom spaces, and does not include the corridors, the area occupied by walls, or other unoccupied areas.

Cases of mixed use might exist where, for example, an assembly use space having an occupant load based on net floor area might be located in a building that is primarily a business occupancy, a classification for which the occupant load is based on gross area. In such instances, the net area calculations should be performed for those specific areas that use occupant load factors based on net area; the remaining floor area can then be used to calculate the occupant load for the uses employing gross floor area. This is illustrated Exhibit 7.59.

In Exhibit 7.59, the majority of the 4800-ft² (446-m²) gross floor area is used for business purposes and is occupied by desks, chairs, file cabinets, office machines, and associated office personnel. Rooms A and B are conference rooms with tables and chairs used on a regular basis primarily by company personnel from other floors in the building. These rooms can be expected to be occupied simultaneously with the remainder of the floor. Each conference room provides 320 ft² (30 m²) of net usable area. Because neither conference room can accommodate 50 or more persons, an assembly occupancy is not created. Rather, the floor is a business occupancy with some assembly use.

Because occupant load is calculated based on *use* of the space (not occupancy classification), the occupant load of the floor shown in Exhibit 7.59 is calculated using occupant load factors for both an assembly use, which is based on net area, and a business use, which is based on gross area. The occupant load of the assembly use spaces (conference rooms A and B) is calculated first. Using Table 7.3.1.2, a net area factor of 15 ft² (1.4 m²) per person for assembly, *less concentrated use*, is chosen. The two conference rooms must be assumed to have an occupant load of at least 43 persons based on the following calculation:

640 ft²/15 ft² per person = 43 persons
(60 m²/1.4 m² per person = 43 persons)

Next, the occupant load of the remainder of the floor must be calculated. The use is business, so a gross area factor of 100 ft² (9.3 m²) per person is chosen using Table 7.3.1.2. Because the net area usable as conference rooms has already been assigned an occu-

pant load, that area can be subtracted from the gross floor area, and the remaining business use area is then assigned an occupant load as follows:

$$\left(\begin{array}{c}4800 \text{ ft}^2 \\ \text{gross area}\end{array}\right) - \left(\begin{array}{c}640 \text{ ft}^2 \text{ net} \\ \text{assembly} \\ \text{use area}\end{array}\right) = 4160 \text{ ft}^2$$

$$\left[\left(\begin{array}{c}446 \text{ m}^2 \\ \text{gross area}\end{array}\right) - \left(\begin{array}{c}60 \text{ m}^2 \text{ net} \\ \text{assembly} \\ \text{use area}\end{array}\right) = 386 \text{ m}^2\right]$$

$$\frac{4160 \text{ ft}^2 \text{ gross business use area}}{100 \text{ ft}^2 \text{ per person}} = 42 \text{ persons}$$

$$\left[\frac{386 \text{ m}^2 \text{ gross business use area}}{9.3 \text{ m}^2 \text{ per person}} = 42 \text{ persons}\right]$$

Adding together the assembly use and business use occupant loads results in 43 + 42 = 85 persons, which is the occupant load for the floor.

Egress capacity must be provided for at least the number of persons determined by dividing each area of the space by the appropriate occupant load factor. This calculation must be performed regardless of whether the building operator claims that the occupant load will never reach the occupant load determined by calculation. However, if the building operator plans to have more occupants present than the number determined by calculation using occupant load factors, the means of egress system must be sized to accommodate that larger number. In return for providing the larger egress system, the building operator is permitted to claim the larger number of persons as the occupant load. This concept is further explained in the commentary following 7.3.1.3.1.

A.7.3.1.2 The normal occupant load is not necessarily a suitable criterion, as the greatest hazard can occur when an unusually large crowd is present, which is a condition often difficult for authorities having jurisdiction to control by regulatory measures. The principle of this *Code* is to provide means of egress for the maximum probable number of occupants rather than to attempt to limit occupants to a number commensurate with available means of egress. However, limits of occupancy are specified in certain special cases for other reasons.

Suggested occupant load factors for components of large airport terminal buildings are given in Table A.7.3.1.2. However, the authority having jurisdiction might elect to use different occupant load factors, provided that egress requirements are satisfied.

Covered Mall Buildings. The figure used in determining the occupancy load for covered mall shopping centers of

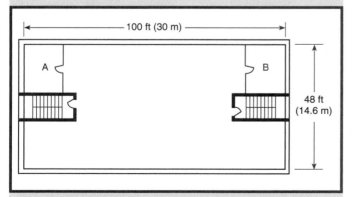

Exhibit 7.59 Floor area for occupant load considerations.

Table A.7.3.1.2 Airport Terminal Occupant Load Factors

Airport Terminal Area	ft² (gross)	m² (gross)
Concourse	100	9.3
Waiting areas	15	1.4
Baggage claim	20	1.9
Baggage handling	300	27.9

varying sizes was arrived at empirically by surveying over 270 covered mall shopping centers, by studying mercantile occupancy parking requirements, and by observing the number of occupants per vehicle during peak seasons.

These studies show that, with an increase in shopping center size, there is a decrease in the number of occupants per square foot of gross leasable area.

This phenomenon is explained when one considers that above a certain shopping center gross leasable area (approximately 600,000 ft² (56,000 m²)), there exists a multiplicity of the same types of stores. The purpose of duplicate types of stores is to increase the choices available to a customer for any given type of merchandise. Therefore, when shopping center size increases, the occupant load increases as well, but at a declining rate. In using Table 7.3.1.2, the occupant load factor is applied only to the gross leasable area that uses the covered mall as a means of egress.

7.3.1.3 Occupant Load Increases.

7.3.1.3.1 The occupant load in any building or portion thereof shall be permitted to be increased from the occupant load established for the given use in accordance with 7.3.1.2 where all other requirements of this *Code* are also met, based on such increased occupant load.

The *Code*'s intent for other than assembly occupancies is not to restrict the occupant load of a building based on the floor area of the building. Nor is the *Code* specifying the minimum area needed by each occupant for efficient use of the space. An occupant load is established for use in sizing the means of egress system and in determining thresholds at which additional provisions, such as mandatory sprinklers, become applicable. If *Code* provisions can be met for a larger number of persons than the calculation determines, the larger number of occupants is permitted to be present, provided that the authority having jurisdiction is satisfied that all corridors, aisles, stairs, and other means of egress components can accommodate the larger occupant load.

For example, an office area of 20,000 ft² (1860 m²) would be assigned an occupant load of 200 persons

if the typical 100-ft² (9.3-m²) occupant load factor were used. However, the occupant load would be permitted to be increased if all *Code* provisions dependent on numbers of persons were met for the increased load.

Assembly occupancies have special but similar provisions for increasing occupant load. Densities greater than one person for each 5 ft² (0.46 m²) are prohibited, because movement speeds are reduced to a crawl where the density exceeds one person for each 3-ft² (0.28-m²) density. This density is approaching the jam point at which movement stops. See commentary on 12.1.7.2.

7.3.1.3.2 The authority having jurisdiction shall be permitted to require an approved aisle, seating, or fixed equipment diagram to substantiate any increase in occupant load and shall be permitted to require that such a diagram be posted in an approved location.

7.3.1.4 Where exits serve more than one story, only the occupant load of each story considered individually shall be used in computing the required capacity of the exits at that story, provided that the required egress capacity of the exit is not decreased in the direction of egress travel.

Paragraph 7.3.1.4 provides that, once a maximum required egress capacity is determined, such required capacity must be maintained—in the direction of egress travel—for the remainder of the egress system.

Required stair width is determined by the required egress capacity of each floor the stair serves. It is not necessary to accumulate occupant loads from floor to floor to determine stair width. Each story or floor level is considered separately when calculating the occupant load to be served by the means of egress from that floor. The size or width of the stair need only accommodate the portion of the floor's occupant load assigned to that stair. However, in a multistory building, the floor requiring the greatest egress capacity dictates the minimum width of egress components, such as stairs, from that floor in the direction of egress travel. It is not permissible to reduce such stair width on the floors below, that is, stairs included in the direction of egress travel. Exits serving floors above the floor of greatest egress capacity are permitted to use components with widths that are less than or equal to those of that floor.

Exhibit 7.60 illustrates the intent of 7.3.1.4. It is not necessary to accumulate required egress capacity from floor to floor; no decrease in egress capacity is permitted in the direction of egress travel.

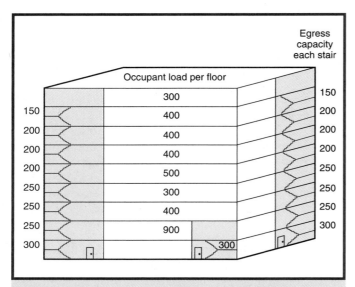

Exhibit 7.60 *Capacity of exit stairs serving multiple floors.*

7.3.1.5 Where means of egress from a story above and a story below converge at an intermediate story, the capacity of the means of egress from the point of convergence shall be not less than the sum of the capacity of the two means of egress.

Exhibit 7.61 illustrates the intent of 7.3.1.5. Convergence from floors above and below requires the accumulation of required egress capacity. Note that occupants of the second floor have moved down the stairs and converged with occupants of the basement, who have moved up the stairs. The occupants (X) of

the first floor experience level travel through the stair enclosure; they are not considered to have merged from above or below; they do not have their egress capacity added to that of the second floor and basement.

7.3.1.6 Where any required egress capacity from a balcony or mezzanine passes through the room below, that required capacity shall be added to the required egress capacity of the room in which it is located.

Mezzanines and balconies are considered as part of the room in which they are located. Occupants of mezzanines and balconies experience the effects of a fire in the room to which such spaces are open as readily as the occupants of those spaces. Thus, mezzanines and balconies must have their occupant load added to that of the room or space in which they are located if their egress passes through that room or space.

An example is depicted in Exhibit 7.62. There is no direct access to the enclosed exit stair from the mezzanine; therefore, egress from the mezzanine is through the main floor. Thus, the street floor egress capacity must accommodate the occupant load of the street floor and that of the mezzanine. If the main floor has an occupant load of 200 persons and the mezzanine has an occupant load of 50 persons, the egress capacity for the room must accommodate at least 200 + 50, or 250 persons.

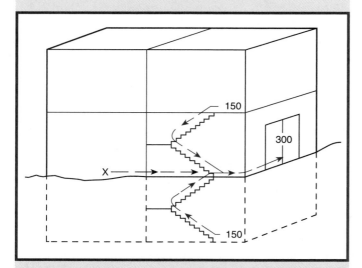

Exhibit 7.61 *Capacity of exit stairs where occupants from floors above and below converge.*

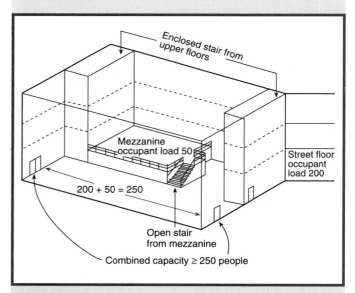

Exhibit 7.62 *Capacity of main floor with mezzanine egress through that floor.*

7.3.2* Measurement of Means of Egress.

The width of means of egress shall be measured in the clear at the narrowest point of the exit component under consideration.

Exception: Projections not more than 3 ½ in. (8.9 cm) on each side shall be permitted at 38 in. (96 cm) and below.

A.7.3.2 For further information on stair capacity, see Chapter 2 of the 1998 edition of NFPA 101A, *Guide on Alternative Approaches to Life Safety.*

The exception to 7.3.2 permits maximum 3¹/₂-in. (8.9-cm) projections at each side of an egress component, provided that such projections occur at or below 38 in. (96 cm), which is the maximum mounting height for handrails. Note that such encroachments are not limited to items such as handrails that are required by the *Code*. The encroachment might be the result of wainscoting applied to the lower portion of a wall, or it might be caused by the metal stringers to which metal pan stair treads and risers are welded. Figure A.7.2.1.2.1(b) depicts the allowable encroachment at each side of a door. The same encroachment is permitted along stairs, corridors, passageways, and other components of the means of egress.

Projections at or below 38 in. (96 cm) (that is, handrail height) and not exceeding 3¹/₂ in. (8.9 cm) do not adversely restrict the effective width of stairs or corridors, because the human body is normally widest at shoulder level. Also, the body sway associated with walking, particularly on stairs, is greater at shoulder height than at waist height. Other projections, however, might constitute obstructions and cause impediments to the free flow of pedestrian travel. The *Code*, therefore, bases the measurements of widths of means of egress used for egress capacity calculation purposes on the clear, net, usable, unobstructed width. Only those projections specified are permitted to encroach on the required widths. Note that the minimum clear width of 48-in. (122-cm) wide stairs serving areas of refuge as required by 7.2.12.2.3 does not allow for handrail and other encroachments located below handrail height. This prohibition is based on providing sufficient clear width to carry a person in a wheelchair on the stair. Also see 7.2.1.2.1.

7.3.3 Egress Capacity.

7.3.3.1 Egress capacity for approved components of means of egress shall be based on the capacity factors shown in Table 7.3.3.1.

Table 7.3.3.1 Capacity Factors

Area	Stairways (width per person) in.	cm	Level Components and Ramps (width per person) in.	cm
Board and care	0.4	1.0	0.2	0.5
Health care, sprinklered	0.3	0.8	0.2	0.5
Health care, nonsprinklered	0.6	1.5	0.5	1.3
High hazard contents	0.7	1.8	0.4	1.0
All others	0.3	0.8	0.2	0.5

A significant change in egress capacity calculations was introduced in the 1988 edition of the *Code*. The unit of exit width formerly used as a measure of egress capacity was replaced by a system of smaller increments of egress width and capacity. For egress widths that were close to, and no smaller than, the previously used units [22 in. (55.9 cm)] and half units [12 in. (30.5 cm)], there is little difference in the egress capacities calculated by the two methods. For other widths, such as for doors and nonstandard stairs, the new method of using smaller increments (approximating a linear formula) provides increased egress capacity. This concept is demonstrated in the following examples.

Example 1

The common combination of a 34-in. (86-cm) clear width door that provides access to a stair 44 in. (112 cm) wide with a 34-in (86-cm) clear width discharge door has a capacity based on the capacity of its least efficient element. The individual capacities of the elements are calculated by dividing the widths by the appropriate capacity factor from Table 7.3.3.1. The doors have a capacity of 34 in. (86 cm) divided by 0.2 in. (0.5 cm) per person, or 170 persons. The stair has a capacity of 44 in. (112 cm) divided by 0.3 in. (0.8 cm) per person, or 147 persons. The capacity of the exit is 147, the smaller of the two capacities. Under the pre-1988 use of the unit of exit width method, the capacities were 150 for the 1¹/₂-unit doors [those 34 in. (86 cm) or more in width] and 150 for the 2-unit stair.

Example 2

If the entry doorway provides 32 in. (81 cm) in clear width, the stair is 54 in. (137 cm) wide, and the discharge doorway provides 36 in. (91 cm) in clear width, the individual capacities are, respectively, as follows:

(1) 32 in. (81 cm) divided by 0.2 in. (0.5 cm) per person, or 160 persons, for the entry door
(2) 54 in. (137 cm) divided by 0.3 in. (0.8 cm) per person, or 180 persons, for the stair
(3) 36 in. (91 cm) divided by 0.2 in. (0.5 cm) per person, or 180 persons, for the discharge door

Therefore, the capacity of the overall combination is the smallest of the three capacities—160 persons as provided by the entry door. Under the previous unit of exit width method, the capacities would have been, respectively, as follows:

(1) 1 unit for the entry door times 100 persons per unit, or 100 persons
(2) 2 units for the stair times 75 persons per unit, or 150 persons
(3) 1.5 units for the discharge door times 100 persons per unit, or 150 persons

Therefore, the capacity for the combination as previously calculated using the unit of exit width would have been only 100 persons based on the entry door.

The width per person figures specified in Table 7.3.3.1 are based on previously used values credited for full units. The chief difference is that small increments are now considered to add to the capacity. Although Canadian research studies of egress movement in tall office buildings and in larger assembly occupancy buildings have demonstrated the validity of the small increment approach, there was evidence for this approach even in some significant early studies of egress and exit design. Two early, influential reports are of interest. One dates from 1935 in the United States.[13] The other was published in 1952 in Great Britain.[14] Both reports are provided in a discussion of the issue of exit unit size that was published in 1984 in *Fire Technology*.[15] These excerpts clearly show that the small increment approach was an unsettled issue even in those reports that were thought to support only the unit width method. More recent evidence has related egress facility width and crowd flow capacity. Clear documentation shows that crowds do not move in regular files or lanes, especially on stairs where side-to-side body sway almost prevents people from walking shoulder to shoulder. The combination of the recent evidence and docu-

mentation has led to the change to the more linear, small increment method.

The capacity figures found in Table 7.3.3.1 are simply derived from previously used combinations of egress component width and capacity, such as 75 persons per 22-in. (55.8-cm) unit of exit width for stairs (22 divided by 75 is 0.293, which, when rounded to the closest single digit, is 0.3). Similarly, for level and ramped components, the derivation is simply 22 divided by 100, which is rounded to 0.2.

The differences in the width figures specified in Table 7.3.3.1 arise from the following factors. Stairs entail a totally different type of movement, by both individuals and crowds, than do level and ramped components. There are differences in biomechanics as well as in the difficulty of seeing (or otherwise detecting) the next stepping surface in order to avoid misstepping and suffering a fall and resulting injury. The approximate ratio of 3 to 2, relating the required widths vertical travel on stairs and level travel on floors, is based on previous ratios and on empirical observations.

The greater range of width requirements for different occupancies reflects the following two factors:

(1) The need for a much more rapid egress time in the case of high hazard occupancies
(2) The slower movement and greater need for assistance from others during evacuations in health care and related institutional and semi-institutional occupancies

In summary, given the designer's knowledge of the occupancy, the occupant load of the floor level, and the type of egress component, the required minimum width for each component can be determined by simple multiplication (that is, multiply the occupant load by the appropriate width-per-person factor found in Table 7.3.3.1 to obtain the minimum width of the component under consideration). If the width of the component under consideration is known, divide that width by the appropriate width-per-person factor to obtain the number of persons the component can accommodate over the entire evacuation. These calculated minimum widths are then considered along with other *Code* requirements, including minimum widths based on other factors, in order to design a system in which performance will be closely matched from one part of the system to another.

7.3.3.2   The required capacity of a corridor shall be the occupant load that utilizes the corridor for exit access divided by the required number of exits to which the corridor connects, but the corridor capacity shall be not less than the required capacity of the exit to which the corridor leads.

For example, in Exhibit 7.63, a corridor system serves a floor with a 660-person occupant load and the floor has three means of egress. The corridor must be wide enough to accommodate the portion of the floor's occupant load that it serves. Typical design practice is to divide the floor occupant load by the number of means of egress provided. In this three-exit example, no portion of the corridor needs capacity for more than one-third of the floor's occupant load, which by calculation is 660 ÷ 3 = 220 persons. The corridor width would be required to be 220 persons times 0.2 in. (0.5 cm) per person, or 44 in. (112 cm) wide. Some occupancies, such as health care occupancies, require wider minimum corridor widths than the 44-in. (112-cm) width calculated.

If the required capacity of the corridor for some unusual arrangement ends up being smaller than the required capacity of the exit to which it leads, the *Code* states that the corridor required capacity cannot be less than the required capacity of the exit to which it leads. In other words, the corridor cannot create a bottleneck that is too narrow and impedes the flow of occupants to the exit door.

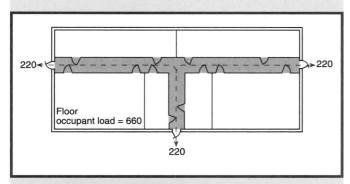

Exhibit 7.63 *Corridor capacity.*

7.3.4 Minimum Width.

7.3.4.1 The width of any means of egress shall be not less than that required for a given egress component in Chapter 7 or Chapters 12 through 42, and shall be not less than 36 in. (91 cm).

Exception No. 1:* The width of exit access formed by furniture and movable partitions, serving not more than six people and having a length not exceeding 50 ft (15 m), shall be not less than 18 in. (45.7 cm) at and below a height of 38 in. (96 cm), or 28 in. (71 cm) above a height of 38 in. (96 cm), provided that widths not less than 36 in. (91 cm)

for new exit access and 28 in. (71 cm) for existing exit access are provided without moving permanent walls.

A.7.3.4.1 Exception No. 1 This exception provides for minimum widths for small spaces such as individual offices. The intent is that this exception applies to spaces formed by furniture and movable walls so that accommodations can easily be made for mobility-impaired individuals. One side of a path could be a fixed wall, provided that the other side is movable. This does not exempt the door widths or widths of fixed-wall corridors, regardless of the number of people or length.

Figure A.7.3.4.1 presents selected anthropometric data for adults. The male and female figures depicted in the figure are average, 50th percentile, in size. Some dimensions apply to very large, 97.5 percentile, adults (noted as 97.5 P).

Exception No. 1 to 7.3.4.1 and the associated annex explain the intent behind permitting spaces, such as individual offices or work stations, an exemption from the 36-in. (91-cm) minimum width requirement of 7.3.4.1 for new construction. If any one path (for example, a miniaisle) requires a maximum of 6 people to travel no more than 50 ft (15 m) to reach a minimum 36-in. (91-cm) wide egress path (for example, a major aisle), the miniaisle is permitted to be as narrow as 28 in. (71 cm). The width of the miniaisle is permitted to be reduced further to 18 in. (45.7 cm) near the floor but not at points more than 38 in. (96 cm) above the floor, as might be characteristic of a small bookcase.

Other miniaisles within the same room are permitted the same reduction in required width, provided that each individually meets the 6-person and 50-ft (15-m) criteria for travel to a minimum 36-in. (91-cm) wide egress path. This is illustrated in Exhibit 7.64. The minimum 28-in. (71-cm) width (shown as dimension *x*) allowed by Exception No. 1 to 7.3.4.1 is a relaxation of the 36-in. (91-cm) minimum required by 7.3.4.1. This width can be further reduced to 18 in. (45.7 cm) (shown as dimension *y*) at floor level up to a height of 38 in. (96 cm) above the floor. Both width reduction options are conditional on a maximum of 6 people traveling no more than 50 ft (15 m) along a resultant miniaisle to reach a minimum 36-in. (91-cm) wide exit access component such as an aisle.

Use of Exception No. 1 is not limited to business occupancies. The same provisions could be applied to factory work stations in an industrial occupancy or to library study carrels in an assembly occupancy.

Exception No. 2: This requirement shall not apply to doors as otherwise provided for in 7.2.1.2.

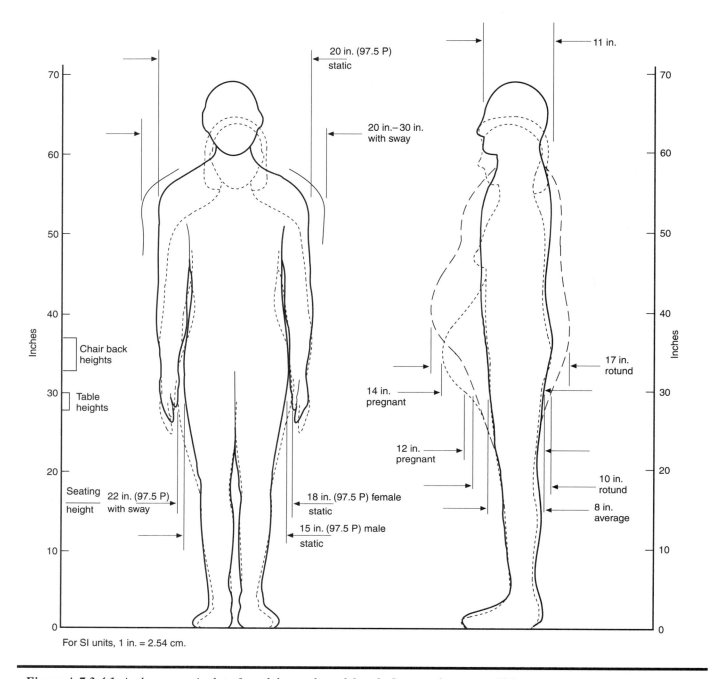

For SI units, 1 in. = 2.54 cm.

Figure A.7.3.4.1 *Anthropometric data for adults; male and female figures of average, 50th*
percentile, size, some dimensions apply to very large, 97.5 percentile (97.5 P), adults.

Exception No. 3:   In existing buildings, the width shall be
permitted to be not less than 28 in. (71 cm).

Exception No. 4:   This requirement shall not apply to aisles
and aisle accessways as otherwise provided in Chapters 12
and 13.

Exception No. 5:   This requirement shall not apply to indus-
trial equipment access as otherwise provided in Chapter 40.

The minimum width required in any egress path is
dependent on the occupancy and is thus specified in
Chapters 12 through 42 for individual occupancies.
The widths are based on experience and on observations of the manner in which people move along the
paths used for egress purposes. The minimum width
permitted for any egress component other than a

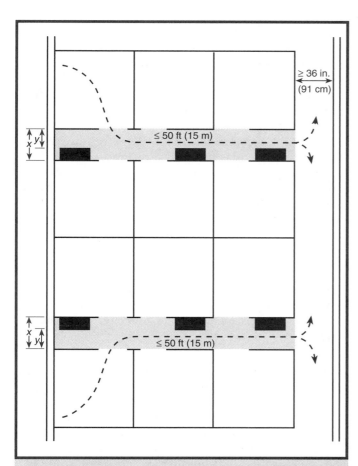

Exhibit 7.64 *Minimum exit access width created by movable furniture and partitions.*

door is 36 in. (91 cm), but most occupancies require additional width. Educational occupancies require a corridor width of not less than 6 ft (1.8 m). Health care occupancies require a corridor width of not less than 8 ft (2.4 m), which reflects the need to move bedridden patients and multiple lines of people along the path to an exit. Hotels, apartment buildings, and business occupancies generally require 44-in. (112-cm) minimum width corridors. Other occupancies rely wholly on the provisions of 7.3.4.1.

7.3.4.2   Where a single exit access leads to an exit, its capacity in terms of width shall be not less than the required capacity of the exit to which it leads. Where more than one exit access leads to an exit, each shall have a width adequate for the number of persons it accommodates.

The intent of 7.3.4.2 is to balance the flow of persons from the exit access to the exit to avoid a bottleneck

and to ensure that the occupants being served by the exit can, in fact, reach it.

Section 7.4 Number of Means of Egress

7.4.1 General.

7.4.1.1   The number of means of egress from any balcony, mezzanine, story, or portion thereof shall be not less than two.

Exception No. 1:   This requirement shall not apply where a single means of egress is permitted in Chapters 11 through 42.

Exception No. 2:   A mezzanine or balcony shall be permitted to have a single means of egress, provided that the common path of travel limitations of Chapters 12 through 42 are met.

Most of the occupancy chapters provide redundancy with respect to the number of means of egress by requiring at least two means of egress. Some occupancies identify specific arrangements under which only a single means of egress is needed. Where large numbers of occupants are to be present, more than two means of egress must be provided as required by 7.4.1.2.

Mezzanines are required to have the same number of means of egress as any story of the building, unless an occupant can reach either the single exit or the bottom of a single open stair within the allowable common path of travel permitted for the applicable occupancy.

Exhibit 7.65 illustrates the mezzanine provisions of 7.4.1.1 and Exception No. 2 to 7.4.1.1, which are not intended to override the provisions for openness of mezzanines imposed by 8.2.6.3. In Exhibit 7.65, the top figure (a) illustrates the requirement for a minimum of two means of egress in 7.4.1.1. One means of egress is an open stair to the floor below, and the other is an enclosed exit stair. Both could be open stairs to the floor below unless the openness requirements of 8.2.6.3 are not met. If the mezzanine were enclosed, such that more than 10 persons were in the enclosed area, 8.2.6.3 would require a second means of egress [similar to the enclosed exit stair in figure (a)] that provides direct access from the enclosed area to an exit at the mezzanine level. In the bottom figure (b), a single means of egress is permitted, in accordance with Exception No. 2 to 7.4.1.1, because the

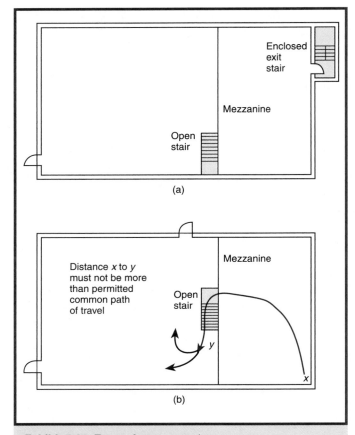

Exhibit 7.65 *Egress from mezzanines.*

common path of travel is within the limits specified for the occupancy involved.

See also Section 7.5 with respect to remoteness of exits and common paths of travel; 7.6.2 with respect to measuring travel distance in the plane of the tread nosings on open stairs; and 8.2.6 on mezzanines.

7.4.1.2 The number of means of egress from any story or portion thereof, other than for existing buildings as permitted in Chapters 12 through 42, shall be as follows:

(1) Occupant load more than 500 but not more than 1000—not less than 3
(2) Occupant load more than 1000—not less than 4

Chapter 7 requires a minimum number of means of egress unless otherwise specified by the occupancy chapters. Several occupancies establish not only the minimum number of means of egress but also the minimum number of actual exits that must be provided on each floor. For example, for business occupancies, 38.2.4 requires access to two exits and further

requires that both of the exits be provided on the floor. In contrast, for industrial occupancies, 40.2.4.1 requires access to two exits and further requires that at least one of the exits is to be located on the floor. Access to the other exit can involve traveling to another floor via an egress component such as an open stair.

In most occupancies, meeting the requirements for egress capacities and travel distances means the required minimum number of means of egress will automatically be met. However, in occupancies characterized by high occupant loads, such as assembly and mercantile occupancies, compliance with requirements for more than two exits might require specific attention.

7.4.1.3 Accessible means of egress in accordance with 7.5.4, not utilizing elevators, shall be permitted to serve as any or all of the required minimum number of means of egress.

Because an accessible means of egress can effectively serve the needs of persons with mobility impairments, the same accessible means of egress should effectively serve the needs of persons without disabilities. Therefore, the *Code* permits accessible means of egress to fulfill any requirements for means of egress. However, this permission does not apply to elevators because of the small number of occupants accommodated during each run of the elevator and concerns that the elevator might be automatically called out of service upon the detection of smoke in an elevator lobby on any floor served by the elevator.

7.4.1.4 The occupant load of each story considered individually shall be required to be used in computing the number of means of egress at each story, provided that the required number of means of egress is not decreased in the direction of egress travel.

Similar to the procedures for determining required egress capacity (see 7.3.1.4), the number of required means of egress is based on a floor-by-floor consideration, rather than the accumulation of the occupant loads of all floors. For example, see Exhibit 7.66 where the fourth floor of the building has an occupant load of 600 persons and would require three means of egress. The third floor of the same building has an occupant load of 400 persons and would require two means of egress; regardless of the fact that the two floors together have an occupant load in excess of

1000 persons, four means of egress are not required. However, the number of means of egress cannot decrease as an occupant proceeds along the egress path. The three exits required from the fourth floor in this example cannot be merged into two exits on the third floor, even though the third floor requires only two exits. On any floor requiring only two exits, one of the three exits could be left inaccessible (blind) on that floor as shown at exit 3 in Exhibit 7.66 on the third and fifth floors. The second floor, with an occupant load of 1500 persons, requires a fourth means of egress.

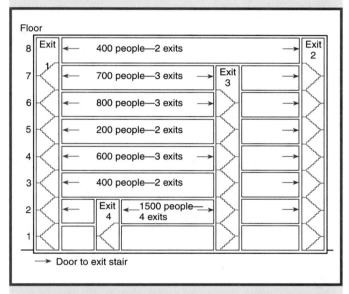

Exhibit 7.66 *Minimum number of required means of egress.*

7.4.1.5 Doors, other than the hoistway door; the elevator car door; and doors that are readily openable from the car side without a key, tool, special knowledge, or special effort, shall be prohibited at the point of access to an elevator car.

Paragraph 7.4.1.5 prohibits the installation of a door at the entrance to an elevator unless that door is readily operable by those in the elevator. This prohibition prevents entrapment between the elevator and the door. The primary concern is the potential for an occupant to enter this small space and become trapped during a fire.

7.4.1.6 Elevator lobbies shall have access to at least one exit. Such exit access shall not require the use of a key, tool, special knowledge, or special effort.

The purpose of 7.4.1.6 is to ensure that an occupant who has gained access to an elevator lobby can get out of the lobby without the use of a tool or key. It is not uncommon, especially in office buildings where a tenant occupies an entire floor, for the elevator lobby to be locked after normal business hours to prevent entry into the tenant space. This problem is illustrated in Exhibit 7.67. Because the doors between the elevator lobby and the tenant spaces can be locked, access to an exit is not assured to a person who arrives at the floor via elevator. At least one exit must be accessible from the elevator lobby. The situation can be corrected by repositioning one of the exit stair enclosures so that it is in the elevator lobby.

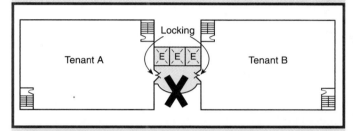

Exhibit 7.67 *Exit access from an elevator lobby.*

Section 7.5 Arrangement of Means of Egress

7.5.1 General.

7.5.1.1 Exits shall be located and exit access shall be arranged so that exits are readily accessible at all times.

7.5.1.2* Where exits are not immediately accessible from an open floor area, continuous passageways, aisles, or corridors leading directly to every exit shall be maintained and shall be arranged to provide access for each occupant to not less than two exits by separate ways of travel. Exit access corridors shall provide access to not less than two approved exits without passing through any intervening rooms other than corridors, lobbies, and other spaces permitted to be open to the corridor.

Paragraph 7.5.1.2 reinforces the desirability of always being able to move in different directions from any location so as to permit different paths of travel to different exits. However, typical floor layouts and furnishing arrangements often create spaces where travel in a single direction is necessary for a limited distance before it becomes possible to travel in different directions.

Exception No. 1: This requirement shall not apply where a single exit is permitted in Chapters 12 through 42.

Exception No. 1 to 7.5.1.2 recognizes that a single exit creates a condition under which travel is possible in only one direction. The conditions under which an occupancy chapter permits a single exit usually produce a situation that is as safe as, or safer than, a building that is provided with two exits but includes substantial common path of travel before access to both exits is possible.

Exception No. 2: Where common paths of travel are permitted for an occupancy in Chapters 12 through 42, such common paths of travel shall be permitted but shall not exceed the limit specified.

Exception No. 2 to 7.5.1.2 recognizes common paths of travel within the limits set by the individual occupancy chapters. For additional information on common paths of travel, see A.7.5.1.6.

Exception No. 3: Existing corridors that require passage through a room to access an exit shall be permitted to continue to be used, provided that the following criteria are met:

(a) Such arrangement is approved by the authority having jurisdiction.

(b) The path of travel is marked in accordance with Section 7.10.

(c) Doors to such rooms comply with 7.2.1.

(d) Such arrangement is not prohibited by the occupancy chapter.

The requirement of 7.5.1.2 that corridors provide access to at least two exits without passing through intervening rooms (other than corridors) was new to the 1997 edition of the *Code*. A similar requirement had been in effect for health care occupancies for many years.

The exit access arrangement illustrated in Exhibit 7.68 is deficient. Occupants reaching the corridor have access only to exit B without leaving the protection afforded by the corridor. Paragraph 7.5.1.2 re-

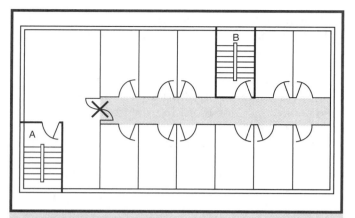

Exhibit 7.68 *Corridor exit access.*

quires access to both exit A and exit B without leaving the corridor and traveling within another use area. One possible solution to this problem would be to extend the corridor wall to the far left of the floor so as to connect directly with exit stair enclosure A.

Exception No. 3 to 7.5.1.2 recognizes the continued use of existing corridors that force occupants to travel through a room to access an exit. If the exemption were not permitted, existing arrangements that were in compliance with earlier editions of the *Code* might suddenly be considered as noncompliant.

Exception No. 4: Corridors that are not required to be fire resistance rated shall be permitted to discharge into open floor plan areas.

A.7.5.1.2 See A.7.5.1.6.

7.5.1.3 Where more than one exit is required from a building or portion thereof, such exits shall be remotely located from each other and shall be arranged and constructed to minimize the possibility that more than one has the potential to be blocked by any one fire or other emergency condition.

It is a precept of life safety in buildings, repeated many times in the *Code*, that if multiple exits are required, they should be not only separate but also remote from one another. While the objective of this requirement is clear (if one exit is blocked by smoke or fire, the other needs to be maintained available), the term *remote* cannot always be sharply defined.

Where exits are located at each end of a long corridor or at each end or side of a building, they qualify as remotely located exits. However, core-type buildings with elevators, service shafts, and stairs in one central or side core introduce some challenging problems with respect to exit remoteness. Exhibit 7.69 shows two core-type buildings that illustrate this problem.

Exhibit 7.69 (top view) shows the plan of the Rault Center Building in New Orleans where five women were trapped by fire on the 15th floor. Travel to both

exit stairs was blocked by fire, and the women finally jumped to the roof of an adjacent eight-story building. Four of the five died.[16]

Exhibit 7.69 (bottom view) shows the plan of the twentieth floor of a New York City office building. An incendiary device was set off somewhere near the lobby reception area. One of 15 people on the floor at the time made it to the stair exit, but the other 14 were trapped and rescued by fire fighters. One of the 14 died.[17]

With more attention given to life safety during the design stage, a much better solution might have been devised for these buildings. In the upper plan view of Exhibit 7.70, the exit stairs are not as remote from each other as practicable. They are both located on the same end of the core, a detriment when tenants, current and future, lay out their own partition arrangements to suit their needs. By removing the elevator lobby from the core, as shown in the lower plan of Exhibit 7.70, and adding a corridor around

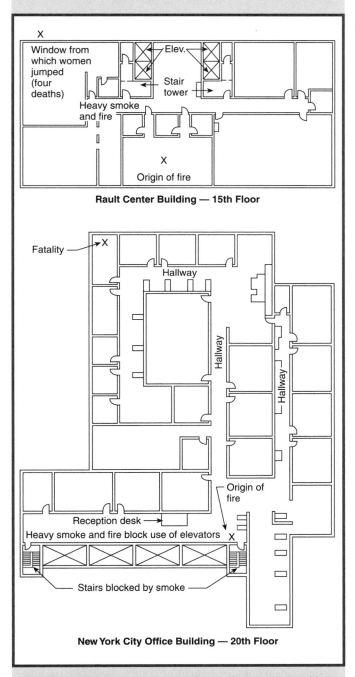

Exhibit 7.69 *Plan views of upper floors of two core-type high-rise buildings where fires occurred.*

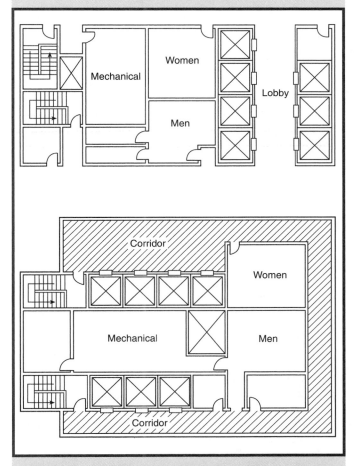

Exhibit 7.70 *Access to exits in core-type multitenant buildings.*

three sides of the core, the designer can ensure that tenants will have access to two remote exits. This solution also assists in providing two ways out of each tenant space. The figures illustrate how, with thought and imagination and little, if any, added expense, a poor design can be greatly improved.

Also see the commentary following 7.5.1.4.

7.5.1.4* Where two exits or exit access doors are required, they shall be placed at a distance from one another not less than one-half the length of the maximum overall diagonal dimension of the building or area to be served, measured in a straight line between the nearest edge of the exit doors or exit access doors. Where exit enclosures are provided as the required exits and are interconnected by not less than a 1-hour fire resistance–rated corridor, exit separation shall be permitted to be measured along the line of travel within the corridor.

Where more than two exits or exit access doors are required, at least two of the required exits or exit access doors shall be arranged to comply with the minimum separation distance requirement. The other exits or exit access doors shall be located so that if one becomes blocked, the others shall be available.

Exception No. 1: In buildings protected throughout by an approved, supervised automatic sprinkler system in accordance with Section 9.7, the minimum separation distance between two exits or exit access doors measured in accordance with 7.5.1.4 shall be not less than one-third the length of the maximum overall diagonal dimension of the building or area to be served.

Exception No. 2: In existing buildings, where more than one exit or exit access door is required, such exits or exit access doors shall be permitted to be remotely located in accordance with 7.5.1.3.

Since 1988, the *Code* has contained a remoteness formula referred to as the *one-half diagonal rule*. This rule is stated in full in the first paragraph of 7.5.1.4. Figures A.7.5.1.4(a) through A.7.5.1.4(e) detail the application of the rule. The *Code* uses the one-half diagonal rule to quantify remoteness and to make certain that exits are sufficiently remote to ensure, with reasonable certainty, that multiple exits will not be obstructed by the same fire. The exit separation is permitted to be reduced to one-third of the maximum overall diagonal measurement in fully sprinklered buildings, because the sprinkler system is expected to control the fire so that the use of multiple exits will not be lost.

Although existing buildings are exempt from the diagonal rule, they still must meet remoteness via the performance requirement of 7.5.1.3.

Exhibit 7.71 illustrates the provision of 7.5.1.4, which permits the distance between exit enclosures to be measured along a minimum 1-hour fire resistance–rated corridor with appropriate fire protection–rated doors. Although the exit enclosures are physically closer to each other than the dimension measured along the corridor, the exits will behave, under fire conditions, as if they were a corridor length apart.

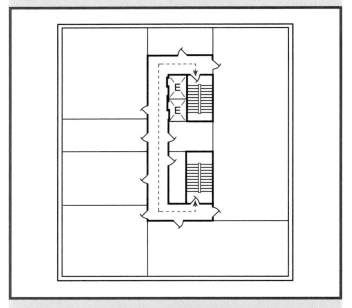

Exhibit 7.71 *Exit remoteness measured along 1-hour rated corridor.*

A.7.5.1.4 Figures A.7.5.1.4(a) through (e) illustrate the method of measurement intended by 7.5.1.4.

7.5.1.5* Interlocking or scissor stairs shall be permitted to be considered separate exits if enclosed in accordance with 7.1.3.2 and separated from each other by 2-hour fire resistance–rated noncombustible construction. There shall be no penetrations or communicating openings, whether protected or not, between the stair enclosures.

A.7.5.1.5 It is difficult in actual practice to construct scissor stairs so that products of combustion that have entered one stairway do not penetrate into the other. Use as separate required exits is discouraged. The term *limited-combustible* is intentionally not included in 7.5.1.5. The user's attention is directed to the definitions of *limited-combustible* and *noncombustible* in 3.3.118 and 3.3.131, respectively.

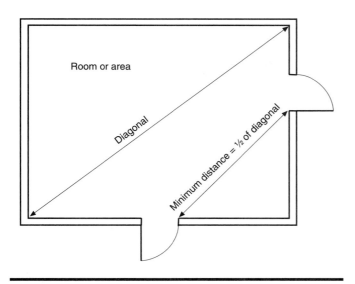

Figure A.7.5.1.4(a) *Diagonal rule for exit remoteness.*

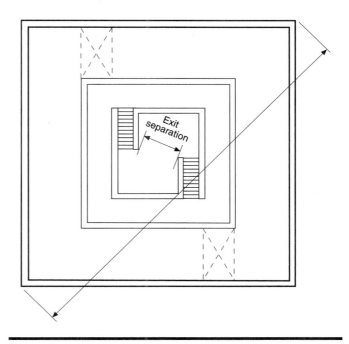

Figure A.7.5.1.4(c) *Exit separation and diagonal measurement of area served.*

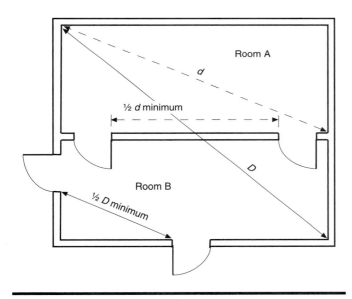

Figure A.7.5.1.4(b) *Diagonal rule for exit and exit access remoteness.*

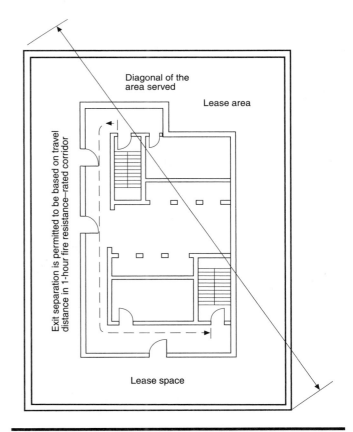

Figure A.7.5.1.4(d) *Exit separation measured along corridor path.*

Scissors stairs (see Exhibit 7.72) are specifically addressed to ensure that they will perform the same as two more widely separated exit stairs under fire conditions. Some design professionals believe they are hazardous and should not be permitted; others believe just the opposite. Generally, the principal objection is that scissors stairs cannot be reliably built

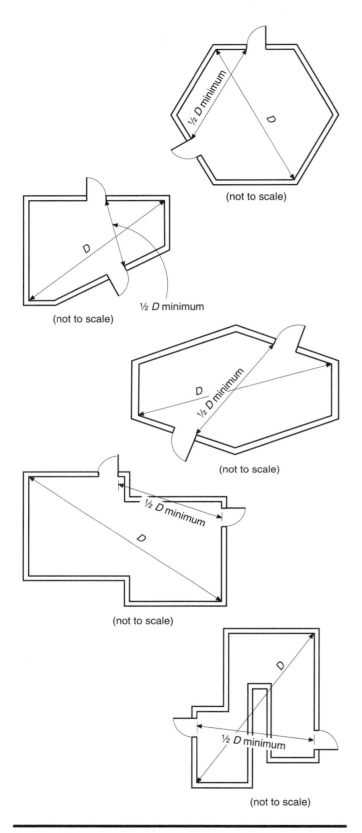

Figure A.7.5.1.4(e) *Diagonal measurement for unusually shaped areas.*

to create an absolute barrier to the passage of smoke and toxic gases between the stairs. Even if such a barrier is created, there is still concern that settling of the building or exposure to fire conditions might result in the cracking of the separating wall, which could permit smoke and gases to pass from one exit stair into the other. On the other hand, those who do not believe that scissors stairs present such problems point to their advantages in reducing construction costs and saving space.

The *Code* requires separating construction to be noncombustible and 2-hour fire resistance–rated. See the definition of *noncombustible* in 3.3.131. Some form of masonry or poured concrete wall is normally used to meet the definition of *noncombustible*. Although scissors stairs can be located with their entrances remote from one another and their discharges also remotely placed, the remoteness requirements are applicable to scissors stairs only if they are to be considered as separate exits. Where not sufficiently separated or not remote from each other, scissors stairs cannot be used as separate exits but can be considered as a single exit, with their combined egress width providing increased capacity over that of a single stair. These points are illustrated in Exhibits 7.72 and 7.73.

In Exhibit 7.72, the two entwined stairways sharing the same enclosing walls are called scissors stairs.

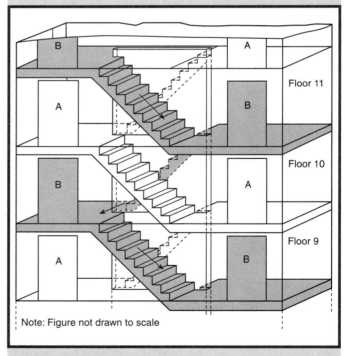

Note: Figure not drawn to scale

Exhibit 7.72 *Scissors stairs.*

To be considered separate exits, the stairs must be completely separated from each other. In effect, each stair's enclosure must consist of a fire resistance–rated tube entwined around the other stair in a form similar to a helix. This arrangement results in space and cost savings by permitting the stairs to share the common enclosing walls that separate them from the remainder of the building. With this arrangement, two independent escape paths are created, similar to those provided by two independent stair enclosures positioned at a distance from each other. The continuity of all walls provides a complete separation at all points. The arrows designate the direction of egress travel in stair B.

Exhibit 7.73 illustrates some of the advantages of scissors stairs versus conventional exit stairs. The two stairs, positioned at the center of the figure and highlighted by placement within the oval, are entwined to create a set of scissors stairs. They provide the same degree of remoteness as the separate and independent stairs shown by the dashed lines at the sides of the figure and encircled. Travel distance to either the scissors stairs or the independent stairs is equal, even if the independent exit stairs were located at the opposite corners (X).

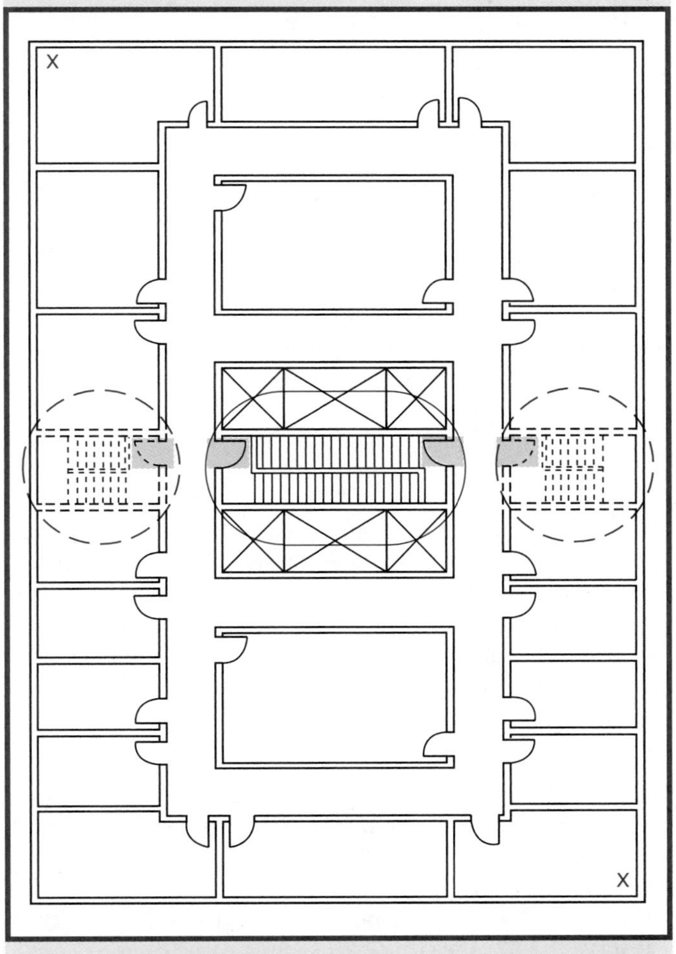

7.5.1.6* Exit access shall be arranged so that there are no dead ends in corridors, unless permitted by and limited to the length specified in Chapters 12 through 42.

A dead end exists in a corridor where the corridor continues past an exit and creates a pocket into which an occupant might travel. The occupant then recognizes there is no exit at that end of the pocket and is forced into retracing the original path to reach the exit. Although relatively short dead-end corridors are permitted for most occupancies by the chapter applicable to that occupancy, it is a better practice to avoid them as much as possible; dead ends increase the danger of people becoming trapped during a fire. Compliance with the limits on dead-end corridors does not necessarily mean that the requirements for remoteness of exits are met. Requirements for remoteness are especially difficult to meet in small buildings or buildings with short public hallways.

Exhibit 7.74 illustrates examples of two common types of dead-end corridors. In moving toward exits, occupants from building spaces other than the rooms served by the dead-end portion of the corridor could mistakenly travel into the dead end. Similarly, any occupant of the floor might mistakenly travel into the dead end created by the elevator lobby. Neither of the dead-end pockets leads to an exit.

For persons occupying the two rooms located at the very end of the dead-end corridor section, the travel from those rooms through this portion of the

Exhibit 7.73 *Scissors stairs contrasted with conventional exit stairs.*

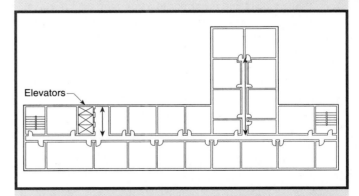

Exhibit 7.74 *Examples of common types of dead-end corridors.*

corridor system involves the concept of common path of travel, not dead-end corridors. Because the concepts of dead-end corridors and common path of travel are often confused, dead ends have been blamed for fire deaths more correctly attributable to common path of travel problems. For example, the report on a 1977 Rhode Island dormitory fire in which 10 people died read:

> Dead-end corridors approximately 61 feet long existed at each end of the dormitory. These dead-ends were allowed by the Rhode Island building code in effect at the time when the building renovations were made in 1972. . . . A factor contributing to four of the . . . deaths and several of the injuries was the long, dead-end corridor. Residents who left their rooms in this dead end were . . . [kept from reaching] their only exit.[18]

For the occupants of the other five rooms with doors opening into the dead-end corridor section in Exhibit 7.74, the concepts of both dead-end corridors and common path of travel are applicable. Although occupants must travel in one direction to reach an exit, they also might mistakenly turn the wrong way when leaving their rooms and travel into the remainder of the dead-end pocket, only to have to retrace their steps to reach an exit.

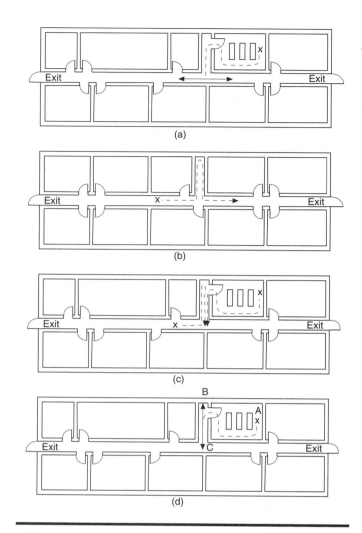

Figure A.7.5.1.6 *Common paths of travel and dead-end corridors.*

A.7.5.1.6 The terms *dead end* and *common path of travel* are commonly used interchangeably. While the concepts of each are similar in practice, they are two different concepts.

A common path of travel exists where a space is arranged so that occupants within that space are able to travel in only one direction to reach any of the exits or to reach the point at which the occupants have the choice of two paths of travel to remote exits. Part (a) of Figure A.7.5.1.6 is an example of a common path of travel.

While a dead end is similar to a common path of travel, a dead end can exist where there is no path of travel from an occupied space but can also exist where an occupant enters a corridor thinking there is an exit at the end and, finding none, is forced to retrace his or her path to reach a choice of exits. Part (b) of Figure A.7.5.1.6 is an example of such a dead-end arrangement.

Combining the two concepts, part (c) of Figure A.7.5.1.6 is an example of a combined dead-end/common path of travel problem.

Common paths of travel and dead-end travel are measured using the same principles used to measure travel distance as described in Section 7.6 of the *Code*. Starting in the room shown in part (d) of Figure A.7.5.1.6, measurement

is made from the most remote point in the room, A, along the natural path of travel, and through the doorway along the centerline of the corridor to point C, located at the centerline of the corridor, which then provides the choice of two different paths to remote exits; this is common path of travel. The space between point B and point C is a dead end. *(See 3.3.32 for the definition of common path of travel.)*

Common paths of travel are explained in A.7.5.1.6. The portion of the exit access travel to which an occupant is steered in one direction only without the option of traveling in another independent direction toward an exit is common path of travel (see definition in 3.3.32). Exhibit 7.75 shows examples of common paths of travel. Common paths of travel are

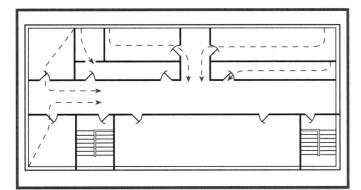

Exhibit 7.75 *Common paths of travel.*

illustrated by the dashed lines. In each case illustrated, an occupant is steered in only one direction before reaching a point at which travel in independent directions becomes possible. Common path of travel might exist only within rooms and occupied spaces or it might exist within the combination of room space and corridors.

Exhibit 7.76 depicts the Rault Center Building shown in the top view of Exhibit 7.69 under the discussion of exit remoteness. In the top view (a), the

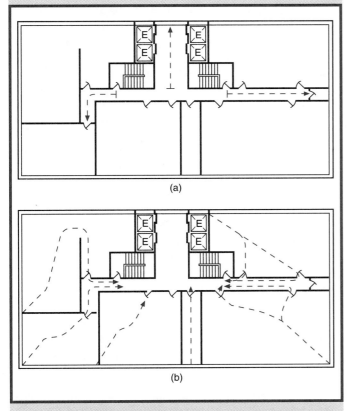

Exhibit 7.76 *Dead-end corridors and common paths of travel.*

dashed lines indicate the extent of the three dead-end pockets in the corridor. In the bottom view (b), the numerous common paths of travel are illustrated by dashed lines.

7.5.1.7 Exit access from rooms or spaces shall be permitted to be through adjoining or intervening rooms or areas, provided that such adjoining rooms are accessory to the area served. Foyers, lobbies, and reception rooms constructed as required for corridors shall not be construed as intervening rooms. Exit access shall be arranged so that it is not necessary to pass through any area identified under Protection from Hazards in Chapters 11 through 42.

Paragraph 7.5.1.7 permits exit access travel through adjoining spaces if such spaces are accessory to the area served and such travel is not through any area identified under protection from hazards (generally subsection ___.3.2 of an occupancy chapter). Exhibit 7.77 illustrates exit access travel through intervening spaces that are under the control of the tenant and are not hazardous. Even though the hazardous contents storage room is under the control of the occupants of tenant space A, the hazard makes passage through the room unsafe. Passage from tenant space A into tenant space B is not permitted, because there is no assurance that the door into tenant space B will be left unlocked, unblocked, and usable to occupants of tenant space A.

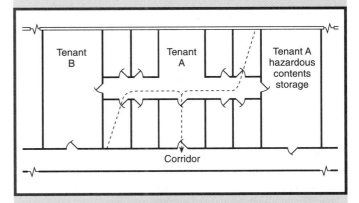

Exhibit 7.77 *Exit access through adjoining rooms.*

7.5.2 Impediments to Egress.

(See also 7.1.9 and 7.2.1.5.)

7.5.2.1 Access to an exit shall not be through kitchens, storerooms other than as provided in Chapters 36 and 37, restrooms, workrooms, closets, bedrooms or similar spaces, or other rooms or spaces subject to locking, unless passage through such rooms or spaces is permitted for the occupancy by Chapters 18, 19, 22, and 23.

Paragraph 7.5.2.1, in combination with 7.5.1.7, prevents exit access from passing through certain rooms due to either increased relative hazard or potential blockage or locking.

7.5.2.2* Exit access and exit doors shall be designed and arranged to be clearly recognizable. Hangings or draperies shall not be placed over exit doors or located to conceal or obscure any exit. Mirrors shall not be placed on exit doors. Mirrors shall not be placed in or adjacent to any exit in such a manner as to confuse the direction of exit.

Exception: Curtains shall be permitted across means of egress openings in tent walls if the following criteria are met:

(a) They are distinctly marked in contrast to the tent wall so as to be recognizable as means of egress.

(b) They are installed across an opening that is at least 6 ft (1.8 m) in width.

(c) They are hung from slide rings or equivalent hardware so as to be readily moved to the side to create an unobstructed opening in the tent wall of the minimum width required for door openings.

A.7.5.2.2 Doors that lead through wall paneling and that harmonize in appearance with the rest of the wall to avoid detracting from some desired aesthetic or decorative effect are not acceptable, as casual occupants might not be aware of such means of egress even though it is visible.

See also 7.1.10.1.

7.5.3 Exterior Ways of Exit Access.

These provisions of 7.5.3 apply to exit access in the typical "motel" arrangement where exit access is provided via an open-air exit access balcony to an open stair. This arrangement is also common in apartment buildings and office buildings in warm climates. An understanding of these provisions is important, because many of the exceptions from the mandatory sprinkler requirements for the various residential occupancies conditionally apply where exterior exit access is provided.

7.5.3.1 Exit access shall be permitted to be by means of any exterior balcony, porch, gallery, or roof that conforms to the requirements of this chapter.

7.5.3.2 The long side of the balcony, porch, gallery, or similar space shall be at least 50 percent open and shall be arranged to restrict the accumulation of smoke.

Exterior ways of exit access need significant openings to the exterior so as not to become smoke-logged and unusable. Paragraph 7.5.3.2 establishes that at least 50 percent of the long side of the balcony, porch, gallery, or similar space is required to be open.

7.5.3.3 Exterior exit access balconies shall be separated from the interior of the building by walls and opening protectives as required for corridors, unless the exterior exit access balcony is served by at least two remote stairs that are accessed without any occupant needing to travel past an unprotected opening to reach one of the stairs, or where dead ends on the exterior exit access do not exceed 20 ft (6.1 m).

Paragraph 7.5.3.3 requires the exterior exit access to be protected by separating construction from the interior of the building via the same rules that are applicable to corridors. However, this requirement does not apply to exit access served by at least two remote stairs as detailed. Such an arrangement is used more often than the rated construction required by 7.5.3.3. To use this arrangement, access must be possible to both of the required remote stairs, and one of those stairs must be reached without traveling past an unprotected opening.

Exhibit 7.78 illustrates three arrangements permitted by 7.5.3.3. In illustrations (a) and (b), it is possible for occupants of all rooms to avoid having to travel past any opening from which fire might issue in order to reach one of the stairs; thus, fire-rated walls and doors are not required. In illustration (c) the occupants of rooms at the ends of the building must travel past other rooms to reach a stair; thus, fire resistance–rated walls and fire protection–rated opening protectives, such as windows and doors, are required in the areas indicated.

Paragraph 7.5.3.3 offers another alternative to rated wall construction and rated opening protectives along an exterior exit access path. Provided that the dead end does not exceed 20 ft (6.1 m), the occupant using the exterior exit access will not be exposed to an excessive number of unprotected openings.

7.5.3.4 Exterior exit access shall be arranged so that there are no dead ends in excess of those permitted for dead-end corridors in Chapters 11 through 42.

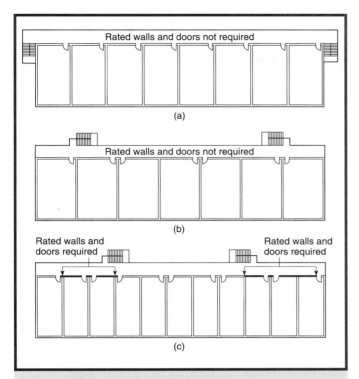

Rated walls and doors not required

(a)

Rated walls and doors not required

(b)

Rated walls and doors required | Rated walls and doors required

(c)

Exhibit 7.78 *Exterior ways of exit access.*

Because 7.5.3.3 permits unrated construction along a maximum 20-ft (6.1-m) dead-end exterior exit access path, it seems logical to recognize longer dead ends, as permitted by some of the occupancy chapters, where the exterior exit access path is protected by rated walls and rated opening protectives.

7.5.4 Accessible Means of Egress.

7.5.4.1* Areas accessible to people with severe mobility impairment, other than in existing buildings, shall have not less than two accessible means of egress. Access shall be provided to not less than one accessible area of refuge or one accessible exit providing an accessible route to an exit discharge and shall remain within the allowable travel distance.

Exception No. 1: Exit access travel along the accessible means of egress shall be permitted to be common for the distances permitted as common paths of travel.

Exception No. 2: A single accessible means of egress shall be permitted from buildings or areas of buildings permitted to have a single exit.

Exception No. 3: This requirement shall not apply to health care occupancies protected throughout by an approved, supervised automatic sprinkler system in accordance with Section 9.7.

Paragraph 7.5.4.1 requires that accessible means of egress be provided for all areas accessible to persons with severe mobility impairment. *Accessible means of egress* is defined in 3.3.2 as a path of travel, usable by a person with a severe mobility impairment, that leads to a public way or an area of refuge. *Severe mobility impairment* is defined in 3.3.179 as the ability to move to stairs without the ability to use the stairs.

For a single-story building with typical exit doors to the exterior at grade level, the requirement for accessible means of egress is normally met without having to provide any additional features. For a multistory building involving vertical travel to grade level, the requirement for accessible means of egress from the upper floors might be met by providing ramps. Because ramp systems use considerable space, the requirement for accessible means of egress from the upper floors will most often be met by providing areas of refuge meeting the requirements of 7.2.12.

Exhibit 7.79 illustrates arrangements providing accessible means of egress. In illustrations (a) and (b), accessible means of egress are provided via ground level doors or ramps from the second story. In illustration (c), areas of refuge with rated barrier and extra-width stairs in accordance with 7.2.12 provide accessible means of egress. In illustration (d), the floor of a fully sprinklered building with a second accessible room on the floor creates an area of refuge via the definition in 3.3.14, thus providing an accessible means of egress

The *Code* does not require areas of refuge; it requires accessible means of egress. The easiest way to meet the requirements for accessible means of egress in multistory buildings is by providing areas of refuge. See 7.2.12.

Paragraph 7.5.4.1 clarifies that the requirement for accessible means of egress is not retrospectively required in existing buildings, unless specifically required by the applicable occupancy chapter.

A.7.5.4.1 An accessible means of egress should comply with the accessible route requirements of CABO/ANSI A117.1, *American National Standard for Accessible and Usable Buildings and Facilities.*

7.5.4.2 If two accessible means of egress are required, the exits serving these paths shall be placed at a distance from one another not less than one-half the length of the maximum overall diagonal dimension of the building or area to be served, measured in a straight line between the nearest edge of the exit doors or exit access doors. Where exit enclosures are provided as the required exits and are interconnected by

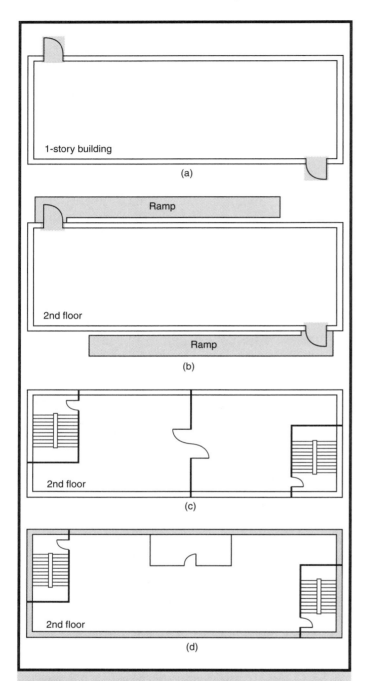

1-story building

(a)

Ramp

2nd floor

Ramp

(b)

2nd floor

(c)

2nd floor

(d)

Exhibit 7.79 Accessible means of egress.

egress paths. It is analogous to 7.5.1.4, which establishes remoteness for means of egress using the half-diagonal rule. See A.7.5.1.4.

Exception No. 1: This requirement shall not apply to buildings protected throughout by an approved, supervised automatic sprinkler system in accordance with Section 9.7.

Exception No. 2: This requirement shall not apply where the physical arrangement of means of egress prevents the possibility that access to both accessible means of egress will be blocked by any one fire or other emergency condition as approved by the authority having jurisdiction.

7.5.4.3   Each required accessible means of egress shall be continuous from each accessible occupied area to a public way or area of refuge in accordance with 7.2.12.2.2.

7.5.4.4   Where an exit stair is used in an accessible means of egress, it shall comply with 7.2.12.2.3 and shall either incorporate an area of refuge within an enlarged story-level landing or shall be accessed from an area of refuge.

7.5.4.5   To be considered part of an accessible means of egress, an elevator shall be in accordance with 7.2.12.2.4.

7.5.4.6   To be considered part of an accessible means of egress, a smoke barrier in accordance with Section 8.3 with not less than a 1-hour fire resistance rating, or a horizontal exit in accordance with 7.2.4, shall discharge to an area of refuge in accordance with 7.2.12.

7.5.4.7   Accessible stories that are four or more stories above or below a story of exit discharge shall have not less than one elevator complying with 7.5.4.5.

Where it might be necessary to carry persons and their wheelchairs on stairs for four or more stories to the ground level, the *Code* requires at least one elevator complying with 7.5.4.5.

Section 7.6 Measurement of Travel Distance to Exits

The *Code* specifies the maximum distance that occupants are permitted to travel from their position in a building to the nearest exit. There is no formula by which this distance can be established.

The factors upon which the maximum allowed travel distances are based include the following:

not less than a 1-hour fire resistance–rated corridor, exit separation shall be permitted to be measured along the line of travel within the corridor.

Paragraph 7.5.4.2 establishes criteria for judging the remoteness of exits serving accessible means of

(1) Number, age, and physical condition of building occupants and the rate at which they can be expected to move
(2) Type and number of obstructions (for example, display cases, seating, heavy machinery) around which occupants must travel
(3) Number of people in any room or space and the distance from the farthest point in that room to the door
(4) Amount and nature of combustibles expected in a particular occupancy
(5) Rapidity with which fire might spread (a function of type of construction, materials used, degree of compartmentation, and presence or absence of automatic fire detection and extinguishing systems)

Allowable travel distances will vary with the type and size of occupancy and the degree of hazard present. As shown in Table A.7.6.1, maximum travel distances in nonsprinklered buildings can vary from 75 ft (23 m) in high hazard storage occupancies to 400 ft (122 m) in sprinklered, special-purpose industrial occupancies meeting additional criteria. For most occupancies, the allowable travel distance is permitted to be increased if the building is protected throughout by automatic sprinkler systems.

Where the occupant has been provided with at least two paths of travel to an exit, it becomes important that the time needed to travel the shorter of the two paths not be so great as to place the occupant in further danger. Many factors have been considered and weighed in establishing the maximum permitted travel distances. Because there are no formulae or exact criteria for determining these distances, they are the result of observing people who are in motion, consensus judgment, and many years of studying the results of fires in which the pre-fire conditions of a building were known.

Excessive travel distances can be a factor in large losses of life in fires because they increase the time required to reach the safety of an exit, whether the exit is a door directly to the outside or into a properly enclosed exit stair on an upper floor of a building. There is evidence that excessive travel distances played a role in a number of the fatalities on the casino floor at the MGM Grand Hotel fire in Las Vegas in 1980.[19] Of the 85 fatalities, 18 victims were located on the casino level, and some apparently were overrun by the flame front.

7.6.1* The travel distance in any occupied space to not less than one exit, measured in accordance with 7.6.2 through

7.6.5, shall not exceed the limits specified in this *Code. (See 7.6.4.)*

The maximum permitted travel distance is that length of travel path that must not be exceeded to reach the nearest exit. Although more than one exit might be required, the distance to those exits, other than the nearest, is not regulated.

A.7.6.1 Table A.7.6.1 is a compilation of the requirements of the individual occupancy chapters (Chapters 12 through 41) for permissible length of common path of travel, dead-end corridors, and travel distance to not less than one of the required exits.

A dead end exists where an occupant enters a corridor thinking there is an exit at the end and, finding none, is forced to retrace the path traveled to reach a choice of egress travel paths. Although relatively short dead ends are permitted by this *Code,* it is better practice to eliminate them wherever possible, as they increase the danger of persons being trapped in case of fire. Compliance with the dead-end limits does not necessarily mean that the requirements for remoteness of exits have been met. Such lack of compliance is particularly true in small buildings or buildings with short public hallways. Adequate remoteness can be obtained in such cases by further reducing the length of dead ends. *(See also A.7.5.1.6.)*

7.6.2* The travel distance to an exit shall be measured on the floor or other walking surface along the centerline of the natural path of travel, starting from the most remote point subject to occupancy, curving around any corners or obstructions with a 1-ft (0.3-m) clearance therefrom, and ending at the center of the doorway or other point at which the exit begins. Where measurement includes stairs, the measurement shall be taken in the plane of the tread nosing.

Exception: Travel distance measurement shall be permitted to terminate at a smoke barrier as provided in Chapter 23.

A.7.6.2 The natural exit access (path of travel) will be influenced by the contents and occupancy of the building. Furniture, fixtures, machinery, or storage can serve to increase the length of travel. It is good practice in building design to recognize the influence of contents and occupancy by spacing exits for a completely open floor area at closer intervals than is required, thus reducing the hazard of excessive travel distances due to the introduction of furniture, fixtures, machinery, or storage and minimizing the possibility of violating the travel distance requirements of this *Code.*

Table A.7.6.1 Common Path, Dead-End, and Travel Distance Limits (by occupancy)

Type of Occupancy	Common Path Limit Unsprinklered ft (m)	Common Path Limit Sprinklered ft (m)	Dead-End Limit Unsprinklered ft (m)	Dead-End Limit Sprinklered ft (m)	Travel Distance Limit Unsprinklered ft (m)	Travel Distance Limit Sprinklered ft (m)
Assembly						
New	20/75 (6.1/23)[a,b]	20/75 (6.1/23)[a,b]	0/20 (0/6.1)[b]	0/20 (0/6.1)[b]	150 (45)[c]	200 (60)[c]
Existing	20/75 (6.1/23)[a,b]	20/75 (6.1/23)[a,b]	0/20 (0/6.1)[b]	0/20 (0/6.1)[b]	150 (45)[c]	200 (60)[c]
Educational						
New	75 (23)	100 (30)	20 (6.1)	50 (15)	150 (45)	200 (60)
Existing	75 (23)	100 (30)	20 (6.1)	50 (15)	150 (45)	200 (60)
Day-Care						
New day-care center	75 (23)	100 (30)	20 (6.1)	50 (15)	150 (45)[d]	200 (60)[d]
Existing day-care center	75 (23)	100 (30)	20 (6.1)	50 (15)	150 (45)[d]	200 (60)[d]
Health Care						
New	NR	NR	30 (9.1)	30 (9.1)	NA	200 (60)[d]
Existing	NR	NR	NR	NR	150 (45)[d]	200 (60)[d]
Ambulatory Health Care						
New	75 (23)[e]	100 (30)[e]	20 (6.1)	50 (15)	150 (45)[d]	200 (60)[d]
Existing	75 (23)[e]	100 (30)[e]	50 (15)	50 (15)	150 (45)[d]	200 (60)[d]
Detention and Correctional						
New—Use conditions II, III, IV	50 (15)	100 (30)	50 (15)	50 (15)	150 (45)[d]	200 (60)[d]
New—Use condition V	50 (15)	100 (30)	20 (6.1)	20 (6.1)	150 (45)[d]	200 (60)[d]
Existing—Use conditions II, III, IV, V	50 (15)[f]	100 (30)[f]	NR	NR	150 (45)[d]	200 (60)[d]
Residential						
One- and two-family dwellings	NR	NR	NR	NR	NR	NR
Lodging or rooming houses	NR	NR	NR	NR	NR	NR
Hotels and Dormitories						
New	35 (10.7)[g,i]	50 (15)[g,i]	35 (10.7)	50 (15)	175 (53)[d,h]	325 (99)[d,h]
Existing	35 (10.7)[g]	50 (15)[g]	50 (15)	50 (15)	175 (53)[d,h]	325 (99)[d,h]
Apartments						
New	35 (10.7)[g]	50 (15)[g]	35 (10.7)	50 (15)	175 (53)[d,h]	325 (99)[d,h]
Existing	35 (10.7)[g]	50 (15)[g]	50 (15)	50 (15)	175 (53)[d,h]	325 (99)[d,h]
Board and Care						
Small, new and existing	NR	NR	NR	NR	NR	NR
Large, new	NA	125 (38)[i]	NA	50 (15)	NA	325 (99)[d,h]
Large, existing	110 (33)	160 (49)	50 (15)	50 (15)	175 (53)[d,h]	325 (99)[d,h]
Mercantile						
Class A, B, C						
New	75 (23)	100 (30)	20 (6.1)	50 (15)	100 (30)	200 (60)
Existing	75 (23)	100 (30)	50 (15)	50 (15)	150 (45)	200 (60)

Table A.7.6.1 Continued

Type of Occupancy	Common Path Limit		Dead-End Limit		Travel Distance Limit	
	Unsprinklered ft (m)	Sprinklered ft (m)	Unsprinklered ft (m)	Sprinklered ft (m)	Unsprinklered ft (m)	Sprinklered ft (m)
Open air	NR	NR	0 (0)	0 (0)	NR	NR
Covered Mall						
New	75 (23)	100 (30)	20 (6.1)	50 (15)	100 (30)	400 (120)^j
Existing	75 (23)	100 (30)	50 (15)	50 (15)	150 (45)	400 (120)^j
Business						
New	75 (23)^k	100 (30)^k	20 (6.1)	50 (15)	200 (60)	300 (91)
Existing	75 (23)^k	100 (30)^k	50 (15)	50 (15)	200 (60)	300 (91)
Industrial						
General	50 (15)	100 (30)	50 (15)	50 (15)	200 (60)^n	250 (75)^l
Special purpose	50 (15)	100 (30)	50 (15)	50 (15)	300 (91)	400 (122)
High hazard	0 (0)	0 (0)	0 (0)	0 (0)	75 (23)	75 (23)
Aircraft servicing hangars, ground floor	50 (15)^m	50 (15)^m	50 (15)^m	50 (15)^m	note n	note n
Aircraft servicing hangars, mezzanine floor	50 (15)^m	50 (15)^m	50 (15)^m	50 (15)^m	75 (23)	75 (23)
Storage						
Low hazard	NR	NR	NR	NR	NR	NR
Ordinary hazard	50 (15)	100 (30)	50 (15)	100 (30)	200 (60)	400 (122)
High hazard	0 (0)	0 (0)	0 (0)	0 (0)	75 (23)	100 (30)
Parking garages, open	50 (15)	50 (15)	50 (15)	50 (15)	300 (91)	400 (122)
Parking garages, enclosed	50 (15)	50 (15)	50 (15)	50 (15)	150 (45)	200 (60)
Aircraft storage hangars, ground floor	50 (15)^m	100 (30)^m	50 (15)^m	50 (15)^m	note n	note n
Aircraft servicing hangars, mezzanine floor	50 (15)^m	75 (23)^m	50 (15)^m	50 (15)^m	75 (23)	75 (23)
Underground spaces in grain elevators	50 (15)^m	100 (30)^m	50 (15)^m	100 (30)^m	200 (60)	400 (122)

NA: Not applicable.

NR: No requirement.

[a]20 ft (6.1 m) for common path serving >50 persons; 75 ft (23 m) for common path serving ≤50 persons.

[b]Dead-end corridors not permitted; 20 ft (6.1 m) dead-end aisles permitted.

[c]See chapters 12 and 13 for special considerations for smoke-protected assembly seating in arenas and stadia.

[d]This dimension is for the total travel distance, assuming incremental portions have fully utilized their permitted maximums. For travel distance within the room, and from the room exit access door to the exit, see the appropriate occupancy chapter.

[e]See business occupancies Chapters 38 and 39.

[f]See Chapter 23 for special considerations for existing common paths.

[g]This dimension is from the room/corridor or suite/corridor exit access door to the exit; thus, it applies to corridor common path.

[h]See appropriate occupancy chapter for special travel distance considerations for exterior ways of exit access.

[i]See appropriate occupancy chapter for requirement for second exit access based on room area.

[j]See Sections 36.4 and 37.4 for special travel distance considerations in covered malls considered pedestrian ways.

[k]See Chapters 38 and 39 for special common path considerations for single tenant spaces.

[l]See Chapter 40 for industrial occupancy special travel distance considerations.

[m]See Chapters 40 and 42 for special requirements if high hazard.

[n]See Chapters 40 and 42 for special requirements on spacing of doors in aircraft hangars.

Exhibit 7.80 illustrates the path along which travel distance to an exit is measured. In illustration (a), the stair is not appropriately enclosed to qualify as an exit; second floor travel distance measurement continues to the first floor at the exit door to the outside. In illustration (b), the stair is properly enclosed and constitutes an exit; travel distance measurement ends on the second floor at the entrance door to the stair enclosure. The travel paths, marked as 1 through 6 in Exhibit 7.80 show that travel distance is measured as follows:

(1) Starting at the most remote point subject to occupancy
(2) On the floor or other walking surface
(3) Along the centerline of the natural path of travel
(4) Around corners and obstructions with a clearance of 1 ft (0.3 m)
(5) Over open exit access ramps and open exit access stairs in the plane of tread nosings
(6) Ending where the exit begins

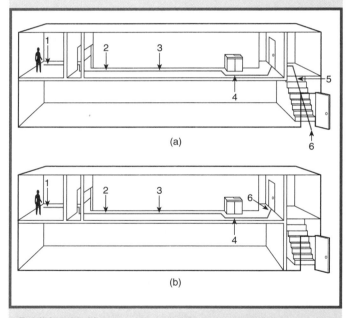

Exhibit 7.80 *Measuring travel distance to an exit.*

Travel distance is that length of travel to an exterior exit door [as shown in Exhibit 7.80, illustration (a)], an enclosed exit stair [as shown in Exhibit 7.80, illustration (b)], an exit passageway, or a horizontal exit. It includes all travel within the occupied space until an occupant reaches that level of protection afforded by an exit. Therefore, where stairs form part of an exit access rather than an exit, the travel over such stairs is included in the travel distance measurement [as shown in Exhibit 7.80, illustration (a)].

The measurement of travel distance along stairs is to be made in the plane of the tread nosings, not along each riser and tread. This measurement is illustrated in Exhibit 7.81.

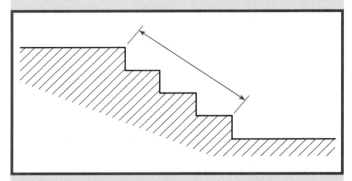

Exhibit 7.81 *Measuring travel distance on stairs.*

In reviewing plans for compliance with the travel distance limitations established for any occupancy, it is important to know the natural path of travel and the obstacles that are present. In Exhibit 7.82, illustrations (a) and (b) depict the same building. In illustration (a), points X and Y are located at the same physical distance from the exit door. Without further information related to the layout of furniture and partitions, it isn't clear whether the occupant will be able to travel in a straight line as shown from point Y to the exit door, or if the occupant will need to follow a longer travel path that zig zags around obstacles as shown from point X to the exit door. A prudent designer, with lack of knowledge about the actual placement of furniture and partitions, will not assume that travel distance is a straight line measurement. Rather, the prudent designer would estimate the travel distance to be at least the distance calculated by adding travel path segments L1 and L2.

In Exhibit 7.82, illustration (b), the placement of partitions appears on the plan. An occupant is unable to travel in a straight "bee line" path to the exit door from either point X or point Y; the partitions preclude this. Further, the occupant at point Y must first move in a direction opposite from that of the building's exit door to reach the room door before turning and traveling in a direction toward the exit door. In this case, the travel distance is calculated by adding together travel path segments L3, L4, and L5.

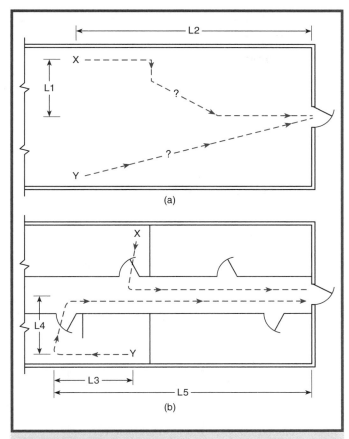

Exhibit 7.82 *Measuring travel distance along the natural path of travel.*

7.6.3* Where open stairways or ramps are permitted as a path of travel to required exits, the distance shall include the travel on the stairway or ramp and the travel from the end of the stairway or ramp to an outside door or other exit in addition to the distance traveled to reach the stairway or ramp.

A.7.6.3 Examples of locations where open stairways might exist include between mezzanines or balconies and the floor below.

7.6.4 Travel distance limitations shall be as provided in Chapters 11 through 42 and, for high hazard areas, shall be in accordance with Section 7.11.

Although Section 7.6 establishes the method for measuring travel distance, it does not set the maximum travel distance permitted for a specific occupancy.

Travel distance limitations are contained in subsection __.2.6 of Chapters 12 through 42. The travel distance limitations for all occupancies are summarized in Table A.7.6.1.

In the 1988 edition of the *Code*, the maximum permitted travel distances were increased in most occupancies to maintain the status quo, because an exception was deleted that permitted the travel within small rooms or spaces to be excluded from the overall measurement of travel distance. This former provision exempted rooms that contained six or fewer people, and that had a travel distance within them of less than 50 ft (15 m), from being included in the overall travel distance measurement.

7.6.5 Where any part of an exterior exit is within 10 ft (3 m) of horizontal distance of any unprotected building opening, as permitted by an exception to 7.2.2.6.3 for outside stairs, the travel distance to the exit shall include the length of travel to ground level.

The intent of 7.6.5 is to clarify that, if the exterior stair is exposed by unprotected building openings, it is not considered an exit but is considered exit access, and the travel distance includes the measurement along the stair.

Section 7.7 Discharge from Exits

7.7.1* <u>Exits shall terminate directly at a public way or at an exterior exit discharge.</u> Yards, courts, open spaces, or other portions of the exit discharge shall be of required width and size to provide all occupants with a safe access to a public way.

Exception No. 1: This requirement shall not apply to interior exit discharge as otherwise provided in 7.7.2.

Exception No. 2: This requirement shall not apply to rooftop exit discharge as otherwise provided in 7.7.6.

Exception No. 3: Means of egress shall be permitted to terminate in an exterior area of refuge as provided in Chapters 22 and 23.

The principle addressed in 7.7.1 is that, once a building occupant reaches an exit (the protected portion of the means of egress), the level of protection afforded by that exit cannot be reduced or eliminated.

Therefore, except as noted, all exits must be continuous to a public way or other safe place, or to an exit discharge that must, in turn, be continuous to the public way.

It is not sufficient to permit the egress system to terminate at the outside of a building, because there might not be enough space to provide safe movement away from the building. Also, the terminus of the egress system cannot be located at the outside in a closed court from which travel back through the building might be necessary to get away from the building. In such a case, an exit passageway at least as wide as the exit itself and constructed as specified for exits is required to provide travel from the courtyard to the safe place.

A.7.7.1 An exit from the upper stories, in which the direction of egress travel is generally downward, should not be arranged so that it is necessary to change to travel in an upward direction at any point before discharging to the outside. A similar prohibition of reversal of the vertical component of travel should be applied to exits from stories below the floor of exit discharge. However, an exception is permitted in the case of stairs used in connection with overhead or underfloor exit passageways that serve the street floor only.

It is important that ample roadways be available from buildings in which there are large numbers of occupants so that exits will not be blocked by persons already outside. Two or more avenues of departure should be available for all but very small places. Location of a larger theater, for example, on a narrow dead-end street, might be prohibited by the authority having jurisdiction under this rule, unless some alternate way of travel to another street is available.

Exterior walking surfaces within the exit discharge are not required to be paved and often are provided by grass or similar surfaces. Where discharging exits into yards, across lawns, or onto similar surfaces, in addition to providing the required width to allow all occupants safe access to a public way, such access also is required to meet the following:

(1) The provisions of 7.1.7 with respect to changes in elevation
(2) The provisions of 7.2.2 for stairs, as applicable
(3) The provisions of 7.2.5 for ramps, as applicable
(4) The provisions of 7.1.10 with respect to maintaining the means of egress free of obstructions that would prevent its use, such as snow and the need for its removal in some climates

7.7.2 Not more than 50 percent of the required number of exits, and not more than 50 percent of the required egress

capacity, shall be permitted to discharge through areas on the level of exit discharge, provided that the criteria of 7.7.2(1) through (3) are met:

(1) Such discharge shall lead to a free and unobstructed way to the exterior of the building, and such way is readily visible and identifiable from the point of discharge from the exit.
(2) The level of discharge shall be protected throughout by an approved, automatic sprinkler system in accordance with Section 9.7, or the portion of the level of discharge used for this purpose shall be protected by an approved, automatic sprinkler system in accordance with Section 9.7 and shall be separated from the nonsprinklered portion of the floor by a fire resistance rating meeting the requirements for the enclosure of exits *(see 7.1.3.2.1)*.

Exception: The requirement of 7.7.2(2) shall not apply where the discharge area is a vestibule or foyer meeting all of the following:

(a) The depth from the exterior of the building shall not be more than 10 ft (3 m) and the length shall not be more than 30 ft (9.1 m).

(b) The foyer shall be separated from the remainder of the level of discharge by construction providing protection not less than the equivalent of wired glass in steel frames.

(c) The foyer shall serve only as means of egress and shall include an exit directly to the outside.

(3) The entire area on the level of discharge shall be separated from areas below by construction having a fire resistance rating not less than that required for the exit enclosure.

Exception No. 1: Levels below the level of discharge shall be permitted to be open to the level of discharge in an atrium in accordance with 8.2.5.6.

Exception No. 2: One hundred percent of the exits shall be permitted to discharge through areas on the level of exit discharge as provided in Chapters 22 and 23.

Exception No. 3: In existing buildings, the 50 percent limit on egress capacity shall not apply if the 50 percent limit on the required number of exits is met.

The intent of 7.7.2 is to provide an exit stair enclosure that discharges through the level of exit discharge with approximately the same level of protection offered to exits that discharge directly to the outside. Probably the most often-asked questions concern the requirements of 7.7.2(2). The intent of 7.7.2(2) is to require that the entire level of exit discharge and any area connected to the level of discharge with access to the discharge area be protected by automatic sprinklers. As an alternative, if sprinkler protection is installed only in the portion of the level of exit discharge used for travel from the exit stair enclosure door to the door to the outside, the sprinklered area must be separated from the rest of the level of discharge by construction as required for exits (see 7.1.3.2). An exception to the sprinkler requirement is the 10 ft × 30 ft (3 m × 9.1 m) maximum wired-glass foyer, which can be used only for egress and, thus, has no occupancy of its own.

Use of the 50 percent rule for discharge through the level of exit discharge is not dependent on occupancy permission; thus, it can be used in all occupancies. However, detention and correctional occupancies (see 22.2.7.2 and 23.2.7.2) permit 100 percent of the exits and 100 percent of the egress capacity to discharge through the level of exit discharge. Hotels and mercantile occupancies (see 28.2.7.3, 29.2.7.3, 36.2.7.2, and 37.2.7.2) establish additional requirements limiting the distance occupants are permitted to travel within their exit discharge through the ground level to the door to the outside.

Exhibit 7.83 illustrates exit discharge arrangements meeting the requirements of 7.7.2. The stairs provide four required exits from the upper floors.

Exit stair A discharges directly outside. Exit stair B is also considered to discharge directly outside, because its attached exit passageway affords protected passage to the door to the outside. The other two exit stairs, C and D, are permitted to discharge across the first floor, because they do not constitute more than 50 percent of the number of exits from an upper floor or more than 50 percent of the egress capacity of any upper floor. Exit stair C discharges into an area on the discharge level that is sprinklered and separated from the remainder of the floor and the basement, which are not sprinklered. The hourly fire resistance rating of the floor slab and the separating fire barrier are the same as required for the enclosure of exit stair C. Exit stair D discharges into a wired-glass foyer in the nonsprinklered portion of the floor in accordance with the exception to 7.7.2(2).

7.7.3 The exit discharge shall be arranged and marked to make clear the direction of egress to a public way. Stairs shall be arranged so as to make clear the direction of egress to a public way. Stairs that continue more than one-half story beyond the level of exit discharge shall be interrupted at the level of exit discharge by partitions, doors, or other effective means.

Exhibit 7.84 illustrates a stair design intended to minimize the possibility of occupants traveling on stairs and inadvertently continuing past the exit discharge

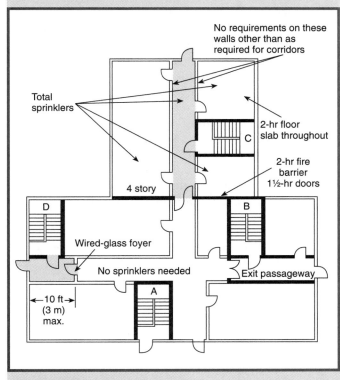

Exhibit 7.83 *Exit discharge.*

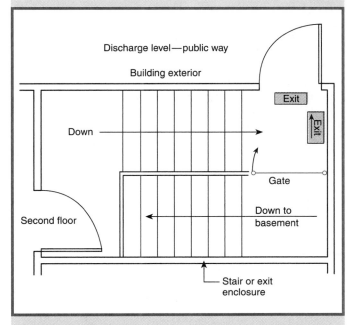

Exhibit 7.84 *Interruption of exit stair at level of exit discharge.*

level, stopping at the basement level where the stair ends but where there is no discharge, and then retracing their steps to the level of exit discharge. The barrier needed to cue the occupant that the level of discharge has been reached can be a partition, railings, a gate, or another physical barrier that effectively interrupts the flow of travel, forcing a person to perform a deliberate act to get past the barrier.

7.7.4 Doors, stairs, ramps, corridors, exit passageways, bridges, balconies, escalators, moving walks, and other components of an exit discharge shall comply with the detailed requirements of this chapter for such components.

7.7.5 Signs.

(See 7.2.2.5.4 and 7.2.2.5.5.)

7.7.6 Where approved by the authority having jurisdiction, exits shall be permitted to discharge to roofs or other sections of the building or an adjoining building where the following criteria are met:

(1) The roof construction has a fire resistance rating not less than that required for the exit enclosure.
(2) There is a continuous and safe means of egress from the roof.

An exit discharge to a roof is not acceptable, unless there is another continuous and safe means of egress from the roof and unless the roof construction affords protection against fire that is at least equivalent to that of the stair enclosure. Helicopter rescue from roofs is not dependable enough to be given credit as an exit; many factors in such a rescue are too unpredictable for this to be a consideration.

Outside stairs leading to the roofs of other sections of the building or onto the roofs of adjoining buildings are acceptable as part of the means of egress, but only with the approval of the authority having jurisdiction. The conditions and settings of such paths of travel are likely to be so varied that it is virtually impossible to cover them by written provisions. Each situation is best judged individually by the authority having jurisdiction.

Section 7.8 Illumination of Means of Egress

When fire occurs in a building, the degree of visibility in corridors, stairs, and passageways might mean the difference between orderly evacuation and chaos and

possibly the difference between life and death. A brief glance at the history of fires reveals several noteworthy fires in which the failure of normal or emergency lighting was a major factor in the casualties incurred. A list of some of these fires follows:

Iroquois Theater, Chicago, 1903	602 deaths[20]
Cocoanut Grove Night Club, Boston, 1942	492 deaths[21]
Baltimore Oyster Roast, 1956	11 deaths[22]
Apartment house, Boston, 1971	8 deaths[23]
Summerland, Isle of Man, 1973	50 deaths[24]
Mental hospital, Mississippi, 1978	15 deaths[25]

The report on the 1971 Massachusetts apartment fire where eight people died stated: "Among the conditions contributing to the . . . loss of life were . . . the lack of emergency lighting and the lack of illuminated exit signs."

The report on the 1973 fire in the amusement complex on the Isle of Man in Great Britain, where 50 people died, stated, "The problems with the evacuation are . . . (5) an insufficient number of exit signs and directional signs . . . (7) The emergency lighting did not come on when the main power was shut off by a staff member in an act of misguided zeal."

The report on the 1978 mental hospital fire in Mississippi, where 15 people died, stated:

Heat and flame . . . impinged directly on the emergency lighting conduit, causing . . . a short circuit to occur. The short tripped the circuit breaker . . . leaving the north end of the building without emergency lighting. However, in this fire, the emergency lighting circuits on the first floor were not used. The dual-function lighting circuits were switched in the "off" position in both wards. The attendant entering Ward 1 to evacuate the residents did not turn the lights on. In Ward 2, the switch could not be reached by the attendants, and the circuit shorted out soon after the discovery of the fire. The darkness contributed to the difficulty in evacuating both wards.[26]

A lack of illuminated exit signs in several key places was also noted in the report.

7.8.1 General.

7.8.1.1* Illumination of means of egress shall be provided in accordance with Section 7.8 for every building and structure where required in Chapters 11 through 42. For the purposes of this requirement, exit access shall include only designated stairs, aisles, corridors, ramps, escalators, and passageways leading to an exit. For the purposes of this requirement, exit discharge shall include only designated stairs, aisles, corridors, ramps, escalators, walkways, and exit passageways leading to a public way.

A.7.8.1.1 Illumination provided outside the building should be to either a public way or a distance away from the building that is considered safe, whichever is closest to the building being evacuated.

Illumination of means of egress is not required unless specifically called for in the appropriate occupancy chapter. However, all occupancy chapters do require illumination, but there are a few exemptions. For example, in new assembly occupancies, 12.2.8 exempts private-party tents not larger than 1200 ft² (111.5 m²) from the illumination requirement. Subsection __.2.8 (for example, 36.2.8 for new mercantile occupancies) of each occupancy chapter provides illumination requirements.

7.8.1.2 Illumination of means of egress shall be continuous during the time that the conditions of occupancy require that the means of egress be available for use. Artificial lighting shall be employed at such locations and for such periods of time as required to maintain the illumination to the minimum criteria values herein specified. *NIGHT LIGHTING, UNSWITCHED*

Exception: Automatic, motion sensor–type lighting switches shall be permitted within the means of egress, provided that the switch controllers are equipped for fail-safe operation, the illumination timers are set for a minimum 15-minute duration, and the motion sensor is activated by any occupant movement in the area served by the lighting units.

7.8.1.3* The floors and other walking surfaces within an exit and within the portions of the exit access and exit discharge designated in 7.8.1.1 shall be illuminated to values of at least 1 ft-candle (10 lux) measured at the floor.

A.7.8.1.3 A desirable form of means of egress lighting is by lights recessed in walls about 1 ft (30 cm) above the floor. Such lights are not likely to be obscured by smoke.

Exception No. 1: In assembly occupancies, the illumination of the floors of exit access shall be at least 0.2 ft-candle (2 lux) during periods of performances or projections involving directed light.

Exception No. 2: * *This requirement shall not apply where operations or processes require low lighting levels.*

A.7.8.1.3 Exception No. 2 Some processes, such as manufacturing or handling of photosensitive materials, cannot be performed in areas provided with the minimum specified lighting levels. The use of spaces with lighting levels below 1 ft-candle (10 lux) might necessitate additional safety measures, such as written emergency plans, training of new employees in emergency evacuation procedures, and periodic fire drills.

The *Code* requires that there be at least 1 ft-candle (10 lux) of illumination at floor level in all three elements of a means of egress, that is, the exit access, the exit, and the exit discharge. For the purposes of Section 7.8, the *Code* limits exit access to designated stairs, aisles, corridors, ramps, escalators, and passageways leading to an exit. Such components should include those portions of the exit access serving occupied spaces. It is not necessary to keep the lights on in all rooms if the rooms are not occupied. For the purposes of Section 7.8, the *Code* limits exit discharge to designated stairs, aisles, corridors, ramps, escalators, walkways, and passageways leading to a public way. *Designated* is meant to be designation by the authority having jurisdiction. While motion pictures, slides, and the like are being shown in theaters, auditoriums, and other assembly occupancies, Exception No. 1 to 7.8.1.3 permits the level of illumination can be reduced to 0.2 ft-candle (2 lux).

7.8.1.4* Required illumination shall be arranged so that the failure of any single lighting unit does not result in an illumination level of less than 0.2 ft-candle (2 lux) in any designated area.

All lights, circuits, or auxiliary power must be arranged to ensure continuity of egress lighting. This arrangement can be accomplished by means such as use of duplicate light bulbs in fixtures, overlapping light patterns, or overlapping dual circuits.

A.7.8.1.4 An example of the failure of any single lighting unit is the burning out of an electric bulb.

7.8.1.5 The equipment or units installed to meet the requirements of Section 7.10 also shall be permitted to serve the function of illumination of means of egress, provided that all requirements of Section 7.8 for such illumination are met.

7.8.2 Sources of Illumination.

7.8.2.1* Illumination of means of egress shall be from a source considered reliable by the authority having jurisdiction.

A.7.8.2.1 An example of a power source with reasonably ensured reliability is a public utility electric service.

7.8.2.2 Battery-operated electric lights and other types of portable lamps or lanterns shall not be used for primary illumination of means of egress. Battery-operated electric lights shall be permitted to be used as an emergency source to the extent permitted under Section 7.9.

Section 7.9 Emergency Lighting

Emergency lighting is not required unless specifically called for in the appropriate occupancy chapter. Most occupancy chapters require emergency lighting in medium-to-large buildings. Subsection __.2.9 (for example, 12.2.9 or 36.2.9 for new assembly and new mercantile occupancies) of each occupancy chapter provides emergency lighting requirements.

7.9.1 General.

7.9.1.1* Emergency lighting facilities for means of egress shall be provided in accordance with Section 7.9 for the following:

(1) Buildings or structures where required in Chapters 11 through 42
(2) Underground and windowless structures as addressed in Section 11.7
(3) High-rise buildings as required by other sections of this *Code*
(4) Doors equipped with delayed egress locks
(5) The stair shaft and vestibule of smokeproof enclosures, which shall be permitted to include a standby generator that is installed for the smokeproof enclosure mechanical ventilation equipment and used for the stair shaft and vestibule emergency lighting power supply

For the purposes of this requirement, exit access shall include only designated stairs, aisles, corridors, ramps, escalators, and passageways leading to an exit. For the purposes of this requirement, exit discharge shall include only designated stairs, ramps, aisles, walkways, and escalators leading to a public way.

A.7.9.1.1 Emergency lighting provided outside the building should be to either a public way or a distance away from the building that is considered safe, whichever is closest to the building being evacuated.

7.9.1.2 Where maintenance of illumination depends on changing from one energy source to another, a delay of not more than 10 seconds shall be permitted.

An on-site generator driven by a prime mover must be automatically started and capable of picking up the emergency lighting load within 10 seconds. Where the generator set is not able to supply power within this time frame, an auxiliary power source must be provided.

Some turbine-driven emergency generators take longer than 10 seconds to reach operating speed. A backup battery pack, such as an uninterruptible power supply (UPS), capable of delivering emergency power for a few minutes must be used in conjunction with any on-site generator that cannot meet the 10-second requirement.

Section 700-5 of NFPA 70, *National Electrical Code®*,[27] allows use of an emergency generator for load shedding and peak load shaving, provided that these loads can be disconnected when normal power to the emergency lighting system is lost.

Although not required by NFPA 70, the use of bypass-isolation transfer switches should be considered. These devices allow maintenance and repair of the transfer switch mechanism without interruption of power to the emergency loads. Bypass switches are interlocked to prevent simultaneous interconnection of the two power sources, and isolation of the transfer switch is usually accomplished by operation of a drawout handle. This type of construction should be used where continuity of electrical service to the emergency system is essential. See Exhibit 7.85.

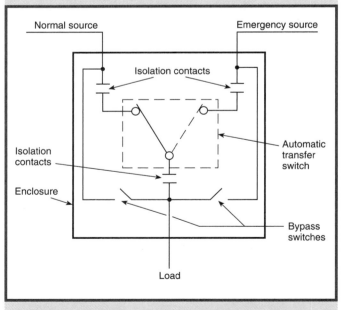

Exhibit 7.85 Schematic of bypass-isolation transfer switch.

7.9.2 Performance of System.

7.9.2.1*   Emergency illumination shall be provided for not less than 1 ½ hours in the event of failure of normal lighting. Emergency lighting facilities shall be arranged to provide initial illumination that is not less than an average of 1 ft-candle (10 lux) and, at any point, not less than 0.1 ft-candle (1 lux), measured along the path of egress at floor level. Illumination levels shall be permitted to decline to not less than an average of 0.6 ft-candle (6 lux) and, at any point, not less than 0.06 ft-candle (0.6 lux) at the end of the 1½ hours. A maximum-to-minimum illumination uniformity ratio of 40 to 1 shall not be exceeded.

A.7.9.2.1   The illumination uniformity ratio is determined by the following formula:

$$\frac{\text{Maximum illumination at any point}}{\text{Minimum illumination at any point}}$$

The *Code* requires a 1-ft-candle (10-lux) average and establishes a 0.1-ft-candle (1-lux) minimum, with a uniformity ratio maximum of 40 to 1 to prevent excessively bright and dark spots.

7.9.2.2*   The emergency lighting system shall be arranged to provide the required illumination automatically in the event of any of the following:

(1)   Interruption of normal lighting such as any failure of a public utility or other outside electrical power supply
(2)   Opening of a circuit breaker or fuse
(3)   Manual act(s), including accidental opening of a switch controlling normal lighting facilities

A.7.9.2.2   Where approved by the authority having jurisdiction, this requirement is permitted to be met by means such as the following.

(a)   Two separate electric lighting systems with independent wiring, each adequate alone to provide the specified lighting. One such system is permitted to be supplied from an outside source such as a public utility service and the other from an electric generator on the premises driven by an independent source of power. Both sources of illumination should be in regular simultaneous operation whenever the building is occupied during periods of darkness.

(b)   An electric circuit or circuits used only for means of egress illumination, with two independent electric sources arranged so that, on the failure of one, the other will automatically and immediately operate. One such source is permitted to be a connection from a public utility or similar outside power source and the other an approved storage battery with suitable provision to keep it automatically charged. Such a battery should be provided with automatic controls that, after operation of the battery due to failure of the primary power source or to turn-off the primary electric source for the lights, the battery will be shut off after its specified period of operation and will be automatically recharged and ready for further service when the primary current source is turned on again.

(c)   Electric battery–operated emergency lighting systems complying with the provisions of 7.9.2.2 and operating on a separate circuit and at a voltage different from that of the primary light can be used where permitted. *(See NFPA 70, National Electrical Code®.)*

These requirements are not intended to prohibit the connection of a feeder serving exit lighting and similar emergency functions ahead of the service disconnecting means, but such provision does not constitute an acceptable alternate source of power. Such a connection furnishes only supplementary protection for emergency electrical functions, particularly where intended to allow the fire department to open the main disconnect without hampering exit activities. Provision should be made to alert the fire department that certain power and lighting is fed by an emergency generator and will continue operation after the service disconnect is opened.

Where emergency lighting is provided by automatic transfer between normal power service and an emergency generator, it is the intent to prohibit the installation, for any reason, of a single switch that can interrupt both energy sources.

Six methods of providing emergency power are recognized in NFPA 70, *National Electrical Code*; however, some of these sources do not meet the requirements for emergency lighting under the *Life Safety Code*.

Storage batteries are an acceptable emergency source and are permitted to be used to supply continuous, required emergency lighting. For this arrangement, two separate lighting systems with independent wiring are employed. One system is permitted to be supplied from a public utility and the other from storage batteries. Either supply source must have sufficient capacity, and emergency lighting must be designed so that adequate light is available for a specified time if one system fails.

Instead of installing two separate wiring systems, a single emergency system connected to an automatic transfer switch is often used. The two sources of power, normal and emergency, are connected to the transfer switch, which automatically switches the emergency lighting load from the normal source to the emergency source upon loss of normal power. When normal power is restored, the emergency load is transferred to the normal source.

Batteries that are used for the emergency source must be suitable for the application. Automotive-type batteries are not acceptable.

Where an on-site generator is the emergency power source, it is generally controlled by a transfer switch. Upon loss of normal emergency power, a signal is sent to start the generator. When the generator is running at rated speed and its output voltage is correct, the emergency load is connected to this source by operation of the automatic transfer switch. This transfer must take place in 10 seconds or less. See Exhibit 7.86.

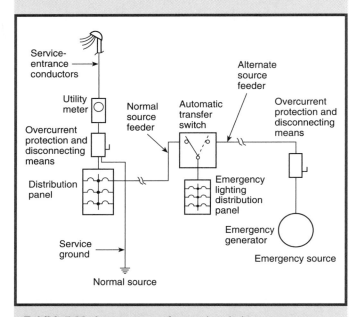

Exhibit 7.86 *Arrangement of normal and alternate sources where emergency power is supplied from on-site generator.*

Exhibit 7.87 shows two methods of obtaining an emergency power supply by connection ahead of the service disconnecting means. Although not prohibited by NFPA 70, this method does not comply with the requirements for emergency lighting of the *Life Safety Code* and might not be acceptable to the authority having jurisdiction. Before considering this method to supply emergency power for other than emergency lighting, the reliability of the utility system in the area must be evaluated, and the risk to building occupants must be carefully thought out. This arrangement only provides protection from electrical failures in the occupancy, such as blown fuses,

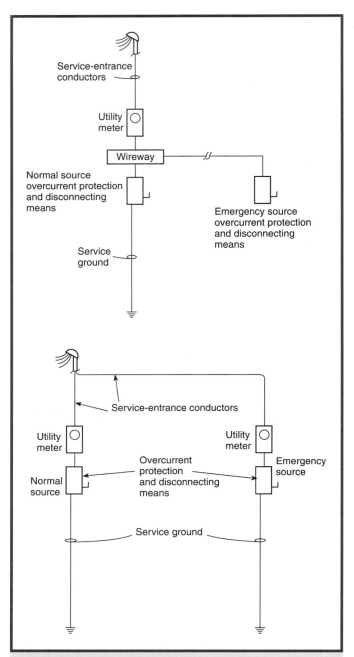

Exhibit 7.87 *Two methods (not Life Safety Code compliant) of obtaining an emergency source by connection ahead of service disconnecting means.*

tripped circuit breakers, or a localized fire at such locations as the electrical service or distribution panels. In such instances, the availability of the emergency source is dependent on the reliability of the public utility.

The advantage of connecting the emergency lighting circuit to the main power line on the live side of the main disconnect is service continuity if the main switch is thrown by employees or fire fighters as a precautionary measure. The *Code* does not prohibit this practice; however, it should be noted that this method does not meet the requirements for emergency lighting.

Two separate services, one for normal power and the other for emergency power, are also recognized by NFPA 70, subject to approval by the authority having jurisdiction but, again, not acceptable by the *Life Safety Code* for emergency lighting. Usually this method provides a higher degree of reliability than the connection ahead of the service disconnecting means but does not satisfy the requirements of 7.9.2.2. However, underground loop systems in downtown areas of large cities are quite reliable. Many public utilities have not experienced an outage on their loop systems for many years, but there is no protection from any electrical failures that might occur outside of the occupancy. One way to reduce the possibility of simultaneous loss of both power sources is to use different voltages for the normal and emergency systems, taking power for each system from separate manholes or employing other schemes that provide both electrical and physical separation between the normal and emergency sources. See Exhibit 7.88.

Individual battery-operated lights can also be used for emergency lighting. Specific rules in NFPA 70 govern installation. These products are referred to in NFPA 70 as *unit equipment*.

To qualify for emergency lighting, each unit equipment must have a rechargeable battery, a battery-charging means, provisions for one or more lamps, and a relay to energize the lamps automatically upon failure of the normal supply. Unit equipment must be connected to the same branch circuit that supplies normal lighting to the area in which the unit equipment is located. Connection to this branch circuit must be ahead of, or on the line side of, any switches controlling the normal lighting. An exception in NFPA 70 allows connection of unit equipment directly to a branch circuit from a panelboard that also supplies a minimum of three normal lighting circuits to the area in which the unit equipment is installed. The overcurrent device protecting this unit equipment circuit must be provided with a lock-on feature that will prevent accidental disconnection.

7.9.2.3   Emergency generators providing power to emergency lighting systems shall be installed, tested, and maintained in accordance with NFPA 110, *Standard for Emergency and Standby Power Systems*. Stored electrical energy systems, where required in this *Code*, shall be in-

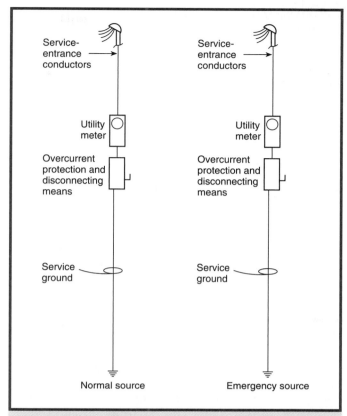

Exhibit 7.88 *Two separate services to the same building permitted by NFPA 70, National Electrical Code, but not recognized by Life Safety Code for emergency lighting.*

stalled and tested in accordance with NFPA 111, *Standard on Stored Electrical Energy Emergency and Standby Power Systems*.

7.9.2.4*   Battery-operated emergency lights shall use only reliable types of rechargeable batteries provided with suitable facilities for maintaining them in properly charged condition. Batteries used in such lights or units shall be approved for their intended use and shall comply with NFPA 70, *National Electrical Code®*.

A.7.9.2.4 Automobile-type lead storage batteries are not suitable by reason of their relatively short life when not subject to frequent discharge and recharge as occurs in automobile operation.

For proper selection and maintenance of appropriate batteries, see NFPA 70, *National Electrical Code.*

7.9.2.5   The emergency lighting system shall be either continuously in operation or shall be capable of repeated automatic operation without manual intervention.

7.9.3 Periodic Testing of Emergency Lighting Equipment.

A functional test shall be conducted on every required emergency lighting system at 30-day intervals for not less than 30 seconds. An annual test shall be conducted on every required battery-powered emergency lighting system for not less than 1 ½ hours. Equipment shall be fully operational for the duration of the test. Written records of visual inspections and tests shall be kept by the owner for inspection by the authority having jurisdiction.

Exception: Self-testing/self-diagnostic, battery-operated emergency lighting equipment that automatically performs a test for not less than 30 seconds and diagnostic routine not less than once every 30 days and indicates failures by a status indicator shall be exempt from the 30-day functional test, provided that a visual inspection is performed at 30-day intervals.

Section 7.10 Marking of Means of Egress

In the fatal Westchase Hilton Hotel fire, which occurred in Houston, Texas, March 1982, "several people were confused by the exit markings or the similarity of exit doors and adjacent storage room doors. The directional exit signs within the exit foyers at the ends of the hotel corridors indicated that the exit path from this point would be perpendicular to the exit access corridor. Some of the occupants moved toward the locked storage room doors and away from the exits."[28] See also commentary on Sections 7.8 and 7.9.

7.10.1 General.

7.10.1.1 Where Required. Means of egress shall be marked in accordance with Section 7.10 where required in Chapters 11 through 42.

Marking of means of egress is not required unless specifically called for by the applicable occupancy chapter. Subsection ___.2.10 (for example, 12.2.10 for new assembly occupancies) of each occupancy chapter details where exit signs and directional exit signs are required.

7.10.1.2* Exits. Exits, other than main exterior exit doors that obviously and clearly are identifiable as exits, shall be marked by an approved sign readily visible from any direction of exit access.

A.7.10.1.2 Where a main entrance serves also as an exit, it will usually be sufficiently obvious to occupants so that no exit sign is needed.

The character of the occupancy has a practical effect on the need for signs. In any assembly occupancy, hotel, department store, or other building subject to transient occupancy, the need for signs will be greater than in a building subject to permanent or semipermanent occupancy by the same people, such as an apartment house where the residents are presumed to be familiar with exit facilities by reason of regular use thereof. Even in a permanent residence-type building, however, there is need for signs to identify exit facilities such as outside stairs that are not subject to regular use during the normal occupancy of the building.

There are many types of situations where the actual need for signs is debatable. In cases of doubt, however, it is desirable to be on the safe side by providing signs, particularly as posting signs does not ordinarily involve any material expense or inconvenience.

The requirement for the locations of exit signs visible from any direction of exit access is illustrated in Figure A.7.10.1.2.

7.10.1.3 Exit Stair Door Tactile Signage. Tactile signage shall be located at each door into an exit stair enclosure, and such signage shall read as follows:

EXIT

Signage shall comply with CABO/ANSI A117.1, *American National Standard for Accessible and Usable Buildings and Facilities*, and shall be installed adjacent to the latch side of the door 60 in. (152 cm) above the finished floor to the centerline of the sign.

Exception: This requirement shall not apply to existing buildings, provided that the occupancy classification does not change.

The standardized location of required tactile signage permits persons with vision impairment to locate the sign easily. For the same reasons that the requirements of 7.5.4 on accessible means of egress are not required for existing buildings, tactile signage is not required in existing buildings unless the occupancy classification changes. Under 4.6.11, the requirements applicable to new construction must be followed if the occupancy classification of an existing building changes.

7.10.1.4* Exit Access. Access to exits shall be marked by approved, readily visible signs in all cases where the exit or way to reach the exit is not readily apparent to the occu-

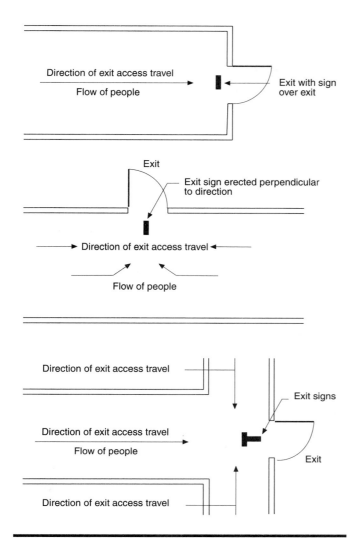

Figure A.7.10.1.2 *Location of exit signs.*

pants. Sign placement shall be such that no point in an exit access corridor is in excess of 100 ft (30 m) from the nearest externally illuminated sign and is not in excess of the marked rating for internally illuminated signs.

The placement distance requirement in 7.10.1.4 applies only within new exit access corridors. Internally illuminated signs are required by 7.10.7.1 to be listed in accordance with UL 924, *Standard for Safety Emergency Lighting and Power Equipment.*[29] The testing procedures of UL 924 determine a distance rating for the listed sign. Externally illuminated signs are not required to be listed and have no distance rating assigned to them. Thus, the *Code* establishes a maximum 100-ft (30-m) distance between an externally

illuminated sign and any point in an exit access corridor.

The allowance by 7.10.1.4 to position internally illuminated signs based on their listed distance rating is another step toward promoting performance-based design in lieu of the traditional prescription-based approach [that is, use of the maximum 100-ft (30-m) distance]. Yet, the lighting industry needs to make information such as distance ratings readily available. This commentary was written in August 1999. At NFPA headquarters in Quincy, Massachusetts, three factory-sealed boxes were opened that contained listed exit signs that the building engineer had kept in inventory for replacement purposes. The signs were identical light-emitting diode models with punchouts for the chevron-shaped directional indicator required by 7.10.6.2. In other words, these signs represented 1999 state-of-the-art design. Each had the required label indicating an Underwriters Laboratories listing. The signs and the accompanying installation literature made no reference to a distance rating. This situation is disconcerting because signs with unique distance ratings are those that must be positioned at distances of less than the traditional 100-ft (30-m) criterion. Thus, the authority having jurisdiction—when judging an installation of internally illuminated directional exit signs for which the distance rating is not easily discerned—cannot simply fall back on the 100-ft (30-m) criterion; the 100-ft (30-m) criterion does not ensure effective sign placement.

Exception: Signs in exit access corridors in existing buildings shall not be required to meet the placement distance requirements.

A.7.10.1.4 Based on 6-in. (15.2-cm) high letters, it is recognized that exit signs are legible at a distance of 100 ft (30 m). However, placing signs every 100 ft (30 m) in other than exit access corridors might create operating difficulties or encourage placement of a sign above the line of sight. To resolve the viewing distance versus placement issue, consideration should be given to increasing the size of the exit legend to the viewing distance proportionally if signs are placed at greater distances.

7.10.1.5* Floor Proximity Exit Signs. Where floor proximity exit signs are required in Chapters 11 through 42, signs shall be placed near the floor level in addition to those signs required for doors or corridors. These signs shall be illuminated in accordance with 7.10.5. Externally illuminated signs shall be sized in accordance with 7.10.6.1. The bottom of the sign shall be not less than 6 in. (15.2 cm) but not more than 8 in. (20.3 cm) above the floor. For exit doors, the sign shall be mounted on the door or adjacent to the door with the nearest edge of the sign within 4 in. (10.2 cm) of the door frame.

A.7.10.1.5 See A.7.10.3.

Because locations near the ceiling might be the first to become obstructed by smoke, the provision of 7.10.1.5 makes it possible for the occupancy chapters to specify floor proximity signs to supplement the regular exit signs that are usually placed above the exit doors or near the ceiling in corridors. They are not intended to replace standard exit signs but are designed as an extra asset to a building occupant seeking egress in a smoke-filled environment. Because the signs are positioned near the floor, they will be among the last signs to become obscured by the descending smoke layer.

The provisions of 7.10.1.5 can be used as guidance on the placement and installation of floor proximity signs, even though they might not be required.

The only occupancies currently mandating floor proximity exit signs are assembly occupancies, where they are required in special amusement buildings in accordance with the provisions of 12.4.7 and 13.4.7.

7.10.1.6* Floor Proximity Egress Path Marking. Where floor proximity egress path marking is required in Chapters 11 through 42, a listed and approved floor proximity egress path marking system that is internally illuminated shall be installed within 8 in. (20.3 cm) of the floor. The system shall provide a visible delineation of the path of travel along the designated exit access and shall be essentially continuous, except as interrupted by doorways, hallways, corridors, or other such architectural features. The system shall operate continuously or at any time the building fire alarm system is activated. The activation, duration, and continuity of operation of the system shall be in accordance with 7.9.2.

A.7.10.1.6 See 3.3.113 for definition of *internally illuminated.*

Paragraph 7.10.1.6 provides a standard for floor proximity egress path marking for mandatory use by the occupancy chapters or for voluntary use by any party. This type of marking has been mandatory on aircraft for several years. It is not mandatory for any occupancy under the *Code.* However, it could be used as part of the egress marking system required for special amusement buildings by the provisions of 12.4.7 and 13.4.7.

7.10.1.7* Visibility. Every sign required in Section 7.10 shall be located and of such size, distinctive color, and design that it is readily visible and shall provide contrast with decorations, interior finish, or other signs. No decorations, furnishings, or equipment that impairs visibility of a sign shall be permitted. No brightly illuminated sign (for other than exit purposes), display, or object in or near the line of vision of the required exit sign that could detract attention from the exit sign shall be permitted.

In some locations, an otherwise adequate exit sign or directional exit sign might be rendered inconspicuous by a high-intensity illuminated advertising sign in the immediate vicinity. For this reason, such signs are not allowed in the line of vision of any required sign addressed by Section 7.10.

The location of exit signs and directional exit signs is not specified. Usually they are placed above exit doors and near the ceiling. There are those who argue, with reason, that smoke builds up more rapidly at higher levels, and signs positioned near the floor would be visible for a much longer time during a fire. However, when several people are moving toward an exit, those in the rear might not be able to see signs located near the floor because of the obstruction created by others. Also, in the absence of careful housekeeping, such signs might be damaged or blocked. Thus, the *Code* simply states that exit signs and directional exit signs are to be located to be readily visible and to provide contrast with their surroundings. See also 7.10.1.5 and commentary.

A.7.10.1.7 In stores, for example, an otherwise adequate exit sign could be rendered inconspicuous by a high-intensity illuminated advertising sign located in the immediate vicinity.

Red is the traditional color for exit signs and is required by law in many places. However, at an early stage in the development of the *Code,* a provision made green the color for exit signs, following the concept of traffic lights in which green indicates safety and red is the signal to stop. During the period when green signs were specified by the *Code,* many such signs were installed, but the traditional red signs also remained. In 1949, the Fire Marshals Association of North America voted to request that red be restored as the required exit sign color, as it was found that the provision for green involved difficulties in law enactment that were out of proportion to the importance of safety. Accordingly, the 10th edition of the *Code* specified red where not otherwise required by law. The present text avoids any specific requirement for color on the assumption that either red or green will be used in most cases and that there are some situations in which a color other than red or green could actually provide better visibility.

As indicated in A.7.10.1.7, the issue of sign color has been the subject of considerable debate. The *Building Exits Code* required, from its first edition in 1927 through 1947, that exit signs use white letters on a green field, unless such color was contrary to local law. The annex text in A.7.10.1.7 describes the development of events since 1949. Currently, color is not specified.

7.10.2* Directional Signs.

A sign complying with 7.10.3 with a directional indicator showing the direction of travel shall be placed in every location where the direction of travel to reach the nearest exit is not apparent.

A.7.10.2 A sign complying with 7.10.2 indicating the direction of the nearest approved exit should be placed at the point of entrance to any escalator or moving walk. *(See A.7.10.3.)*

Subsection 7.10.2 mandates that a directional sign is to be placed where the direction of travel to reach the nearest exit is not apparent. The directional sign uses an exit sign to which one or two directional indicators are added. For externally illuminated signs, which are not required to be laboratory listed, the detailed criteria for the directional indicator appear in 7.10.6.2. Internally illuminated signs, which are required be tested and listed in accordance with UL 924, *Standard for Safety Emergency Lighting and Power Equipment,* have their directional indicators evaluated by the performance criteria of the UL 924 test procedure; they are exempt from the specification-based criteria of 7.10.6.2.

The requirement of 7.10.2 is somewhat performance-based in that it adds another directional exit sign wherever the direction of travel to reach the *nearest* exit is not apparent. The enforcement of this provision will typically be somewhat subjective, because a judgment call must be made as to whether the direction of travel to reach the nearest exit is apparent. A strict reading and application of the requirement, especially with respect to the word *nearest,* could conceivably lead to the installation of many more signs than are practically needed.

See Exhibit 7.89(a), which depicts a warehouse with storage racks and aisles. The racks are of suffi-

cient height and construction to prevent an occupant from seeing either of the exit doors from the building. The designer is charged with specifying exit sign and directional sign placement that meets the provisions of Section 7.10. An occupant standing at point X within an aisle has a choice of many possible paths for travel to the two exit doors; there are no dead-end aisles in which to become trapped. The criterion test for exit sign placement is 7.10.2, which requires that a directional sign be placed in every location where the direction of travel to reach the *nearest* exit, is not apparent. Exit door 1 is the nearest exit, but exit door 1 and exit door 2 cannot be seen from within the aisle or from within any of the three cross-aisles. A strict interpretation of 7.10.2, coupled with the requirement of 7.10.1.2 that the exit doors themselves be provided with exit signs, might lead to the installation of 20 signs as shown in Exhibit 7.89(b). A reasonable person would argue that it is neither unreasonable nor unsafe to reduce the number of signs so as to require the occupant to travel to either of the two nearest cross-aisles in order to see a directional sign that leads to an exit. A check for reasonableness could lead to the placement of eight signs as shown in Exhibit 7.89(c).

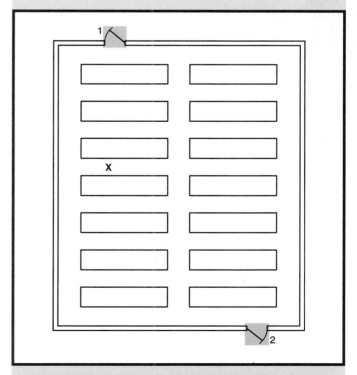

Exhibit 7.89(a) *Warehouse exit sign and directional sign placement to be determined.*

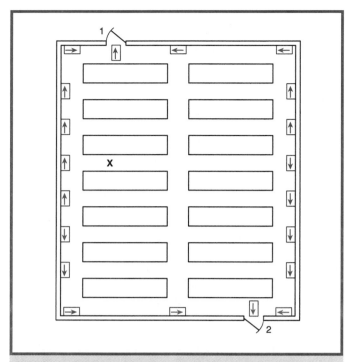

Exhibit 7.89(b) *Excessive placement of directional signs.*

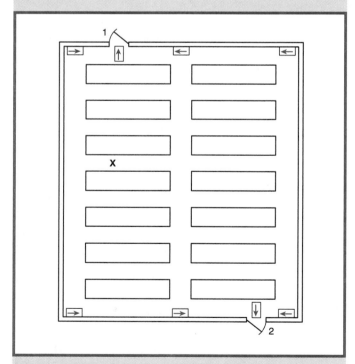

Exhibit 7.89(c) *Reasonable placement of directional signs.*

7.10.3* Sign Legend.

Signs required by 7.10.1 and 7.10.2 shall have the word EXIT or other appropriate wording in plainly legible letters.

A.7.10.3 Where graphics are used, the symbols provided in NFPA 170, *Standard for Fire Safety Symbols,* should be used. Such signs need to provide equal visibility and illumination and are to comply with the other requirements of Section 7.10.

Subsection 7.10.3 is written to permit a word other than EXIT where the alternative wording is appropriate. In countries where Spanish is the predominant language, one might find the word SALIDA. In Canada, where signage appears in both French and English, exit signs have been increased in size to accommodate the words EXIT and SORTIE.

Although 7.10.3 refers to "wording in plainly legible letters," it is evident from the language of A.7.10.3 that it is not the intent to prohibit graphics in lieu of words. NFPA 170, *Standard for Fire Safety Symbols,* is referenced.[30] Graphics have the advantage of being nonspecific to a written language.

NFPA 170 provides a symbol for an emergency exit that should be considered the equivalent of the *Life Safety Code*'s exit sign. NFPA 170 also provides two symbols that—when used together—designate an emergency exit route. This diptych uses the emergency exit symbol and an arrow symbol and should be considered the equivalent of the *Code*'s directional exit sign. See Exhibit 7.90(a) and Exhibit 7.90(b).

Exhibit 7.90(a) *NFPA 170 symbol for emergency exit.*

Exhibit 7.90(b) *NFPA 170 symbols for emergency exit route.*

7.10.4* Power Source.

Where emergency lighting facilities are required by the applicable provisions of Chapters 11 through 42 for individual occupancies, the signs, other than approved self-luminous signs, shall be illuminated by the emergency lighting facilities. The level of illumination of the signs shall be in accordance with 7.10.6.3 or 7.10.7 for the required emergency lighting duration as specified in 7.9.2.1. However, the level of illumination shall be permitted to decline to 60 percent at the end of the emergency lighting duration.

A.7.10.4 It is not the intent of this paragraph to require emergency lighting but only to have the sign illuminated by emergency lighting if emergency lighting is required and provided.

It is not the intent to require that the entire stroke width and entire stroke height of all letters comprising the word EXIT be visible per the requirements of 7.10.6.3 under normal or emergency lighting operation, provided that the sign is visible and legible at a 100-ft (30-m) distance under all room illumination conditions.

The text of A.7.10.4 explains that it is not the intent of 7.10.4 to require an emergency power source for the illumination of exit signs. Rather, it is the intent that the required exit signs be provided with emergency power if the occupancy is required to have emergency lighting. For example, there are business occupancies that are small enough to be exempt from the emergency lighting requirement of 38.2.9.1 and 39.2.9.1. Yet, business occupancies are required to have exit signs in accordance with Section 7.10. Such exit signs are required to be illuminated per 7.10.5.1. In the small business occupancy that is exempt from emergency lighting, if a power failure occurs, the exit signs are permitted to go dark. The business occupancy example can be contrasted with an assembly occupancy. Assembly occupancies are required to have emergency lighting and exit signs. The exit signs must be illuminated in accordance with 7.10.5.1 when the building's normal power is available; the illumination must also be maintained in accordance with 7.10.4 upon failure of the normal power service.

7.10.5 Illumination of Signs.

7.10.5.1* General. Every sign required by 7.10.1.2 or 7.10.1.4, other than where operations or processes require low lighting levels, shall be suitably illuminated by a reliable light source. Externally and internally illuminated signs shall be legible in both the normal and emergency lighting mode.

A.7.10.5.1 See A.7.8.1.3, Exception No. 2.

Internally illuminated signs are particularly useful in occupancies where reduction of normal illumination is permitted, such as in motion picture theaters. However, the intent of 7.10.5.1 is to treat externally illuminated and internally illuminated signs equally with no preference shown to one or the other. Subsequent subsections then treat each type of sign via a specialized package of requirements, such as 7.10.6 for externally illuminated signs and 7.10.7 for internally illuminated signs. This format is provided because externally illuminated signs are not required to be tested and listed by a laboratory. Due to the lack of testing, it is necessary for the *Code* to specify detailed criteria such as the letter height and stroke width addressed in 7.10.6.1 and illumination levels as addressed in 7.10.6.3. Because internally illuminated signs must be laboratory tested and listed, the *Code* can rely on the listing to ensure that necessary criteria are met.

7.10.5.2* Continuous Illumination. Every sign required to be illuminated by 7.10.6.3 and 7.10.7 shall be continuously illuminated as required under the provisions of Section 7.8.

A.7.10.5.2 It is the intent to prohibit a freely accessible light switch to control the illumination of either an internally or externally illuminated exit sign.

Exception:* Illumination for signs shall be permitted to flash on and off upon activation of the fire alarm system.

A.7.10.5.2 Exception The flashing repetition rate should be approximately one cycle per second, and the duration of the off-time should not exceed¼ second per cycle. During on-time, the illumination levels need to be provided in accordance with 7.10.6.3. Flashing signs, when activated with the fire alarm system, might be of assistance.

7.10.6 Externally Illuminated Signs.

7.10.6.1* Size of Signs. Externally illuminated signs required by 7.10.1 and 7.10.2, other than approved existing signs, shall have the word EXIT or other appropriate wording in plainly legible letters not less than 6 in. (15.2 cm) high with the principal strokes of letters not less than ¾ in. (1.9 cm) wide. The word EXIT shall have letters of a width not less than 2 in. (5 cm), except the letter I, and the minimum spacing between letters shall be not less than ⅜ in. (1 cm). Signs larger than the minimum established in this paragraph shall have letter widths, strokes, and spacing in proportion to their height.

Exception No. 1: This requirement shall not apply to existing signs having the required wording in plainly legible letters not less than 4 in. (10.2 cm) high.

Exception No. 2: This requirement shall not apply to marking required by 7.10.1.3 and 7.10.1.5.

Traditionally, the letters in an exit sign have been required to be 6 in. (15.2 cm) in height with the principal strokes not less than ³/₄ in. (1.9 cm) wide. In an effort to increase visibility, the *Code* requires that the letters, other than *I*, be at least 2 in. (5 cm) wide and have a minimum spacing between letters of ³/₈ in. (1.0 cm). These dimensional criteria have been maintained, but they apply only to externally illuminated signs. Internally illuminated signs are exempt from these criteria because they must be tested and listed in accordance with UL 924, *Standard for Safety Emergency Lighting and Power Equipment.* The UL 924 test procedures include assessing the readability of a sign's letters.

A.7.10.6.1 Experience has shown that the word EXIT or other appropriate wording is plainly legible at 100 ft (30 m) if the letters are as large as specified in 7.10.6.1.

7.10.6.2* Size and Location of Directional Indicator. The directional indicator shall be located outside of the EXIT legend, not less than ³/₈ in. (1 cm) from any letter. The directional indicator shall be of a chevron type, as shown in Figure 7.10.6.2. The directional indicator shall be identifiable as a directional indicator at a distance of 40 ft (12.2 m). A directional indicator larger than the minimum established in this paragraph shall be proportionately increased in height, width and stroke. The directional indicator shall be located at the end of the sign for the direction indicated.

Figure 7.10.6.2 Chevron-type indicator.

To improve the effectiveness of directional indicators on directional exit signs, the requirements have been changed over the last several years. The directional

indicator cannot be positioned between the letters in the word EXIT. The directional indicator, which formerly was an arrow, must be a chevron. Research showed that a chevron indicator was more effective than an arrow. Performance criteria are specified to ensure that the chevron is of adequate size, contrast, and illumination. A specific size is not required, because size depends on factors such as color, contrast, and illumination. However, the directional indicator must be identifiable as a directional indicator at a minimum distance of 40 ft (12.2 m), which is another performance-based requirement.

Exception: This requirement shall not apply to approved existing signs.

A.7.10.6.2 Figure A.7.10.6.2 shows examples of acceptable locations of directional indicators with regard to left and right orientation. Directional indicators are permitted to be placed under the horizontal stroke of the letter T, provided that the spacing of not less than ⅜ in. (1 cm) is maintained from the horizontal and vertical strokes of the letter T.

Figure A.7.10.6.2 Directional indicators.

7.10.6.3* Level of Illumination. Externally illuminated signs shall be illuminated by not less than 5 ft-candles (54 lux) at the illuminated surface and shall have a contrast ratio of not less than 0.5.

A.7.10.6.3 Colors providing a good contrast are red or green letters on matte white background. Glossy background and glossy letter colors should be avoided.

The average luminance of the letters and background is measured in footlamberts or candela per square meter. The contrast ratio is computed from these measurements by the following formula:

$$\text{Contrast} = \frac{Lg - Le}{Lg}$$

Where *Lg* is the greater luminance and *Le* is the lesser luminance, either the variable *Lg* or *Le* is permitted to represent the letters, and the remaining variable will represent the background. The average luminance of the letters and background can be computed by measuring the luminance at the positions indicated in Figure A.7.10.6.3 by numbered spots.

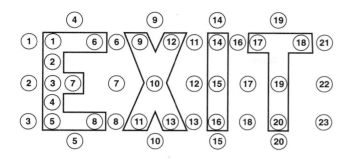

Figure A.7.10.6.3 Measurement of exit sign luminance.

7.10.7 Internally Illuminated Signs.

7.10.7.1 Listing. Internally illuminated signs, other than approved existing signs, or existing signs having the required wording in legible letters not less than 4 in. (10.2 cm) high, shall be listed in accordance with UL 924, *Standard for Safety Emergency Lighting and Power Equipment.*

Exception: This requirement shall not apply to signs that are in accordance with 7.10.1.3 and 7.10.1.5.

Internally illuminated signs must be laboratory tested and listed in accordance with UL 924, *Standard for Safety Emergency Lighting and Power Equipment.* Reliance is placed on the laboratory having conducted a comprehensive examination. By relying on the laboratory listing, the *Code* does not need to address the detailed criteria that it requires of externally illuminated signs, which are not required to be listed.

7.10.7.2* Photoluminescent Signs. The face of a photoluminescent sign shall be continually illuminated while the building is occupied. The illumination levels on the face of the photoluminescent sign shall be in accordance with its listing. The charging illumination shall be a reliable light source as determined by the authority having jurisdiction. The charging light source shall be of a type specified in the product markings.

A.7.10.7.2 Photoluminescent signs need a specific minimum level of light on the face of the sign to ensure that the sign is charged for emergency operation and legibility in both the normal and emergency modes. Additionally, the type of light source (for example, incandescent, fluorescent, halogen, metal halide) is important. Each light source produces different types of visible and invisible light (for example, UV) that might affect the ability of some photoluminescent signs to charge and might also affect the amount of light output available during emergency mode. This type of sign would not be suitable where the illumination levels are permitted to decline. The charging light source should not be connected to automatic timers, because the continuous illumination of the sign is needed; otherwise, the sign illumination would not be available because it would be discharged.

A photoluminescent sign absorbs light from an activation light source in order to emit light (that is, luminesce). The sign continues to emit light for a time after the activation light source has been removed. The requirements of 7.10.7.2 for photoluminescent signs are new to the 2000 edition of the *Code.* Note that these requirements are contained as a subset of the internally illuminated sign requirements of 7.10.7. A photoluminescent sign is an internally illuminated sign. As such, even prior to the publication of this edition of the *Code,* photoluminescent exit signs were permitted, provided that they were listed in accordance with UL 924, *Standard for Safety Emergency Lighting and Power Equipment.*

This commentary was written in the fall of 1999. At that time, Underwriters Laboratories had not modified UL 924 to assess performance criteria unique to photoluminescent exit signs. For example, the test standard had no provision addressing the activation light source, intensity, and time for conducting the visibility test. The standard did not have product marking requirements related to minimum activation light level, viewing distance, and replacement dates that will be needed by authorities having jurisdiction in determining the suitability of a photoluminescent exit sign in a given application. Underwriters Laboratories personnel advised the NFPA Technical Committee on Means of Egress that the current edition of UL 924 would not fully assess the performance of a photoluminescent exit sign to ensure performance for life safety.

Laboratories in addition to Underwriters Laboratories perform testing and list products to UL standards. In the event that one of the laboratories were to list a photoluminescent sign in accordance with the edition of UL 924 that was current in the fall of 1999, the requirements of the 1997 edition of the *Code* would be met. The Technical Committee on Means of Egress added the requirements contained in 7.10.7.2 to the 2000 edition of the *Code* to highlight some of the special considerations that are needed to use photoluminescent exit signs effectively for life safety.

7.10.8 Special Signs.

7.10.8.1* No Exit. Any door, passage, or stairway that is neither an exit nor a way of exit access and that is located or arranged so that it is likely to be mistaken for an exit shall be identified by a sign that reads as follows:

NO
EXIT

Such sign shall have the word NO in letters 2 in. (5 cm) high with a stroke width of ⅜ in. (1 cm) and the word EXIT in letters 1 in. (2.5 cm) high, with the word EXIT below the word NO.

Exception: This requirement shall not apply to approved existing signs.

A.7.10.8.1 The likelihood of occupants mistaking passageways or stairways that lead to dead-end spaces for exit doors and becoming trapped governs the need for exit signs. Thus, such areas should be marked with a sign that reads as follows:

NO EXIT

Supplementary identification indicating the character of the area, such as TO BASEMENT, STOREROOM, LINEN CLOSET, or the like, is permitted to be provided. *(See A.7.10.2.)*

7.10.8.2 Elevator Signs. Elevators that are a part of a means of egress *(see 7.2.13.1)* shall have the following signs, with minimum letter height of ⅝ in. (1.6 cm), in every elevator lobby:

(1)* Signs that indicate that the elevator can be used for egress, including any restrictions on use

A.7.10.8.2(1) These signs are to be used in place of signs that indicate that elevators are not to be used during fires. Examples of these signs include the following:

In the event of fire, this elevator will be used by the fire department for evacuation of people.

PROTECTED ELEVATOR—USABLE IN EMERGENCIES

(2)* Signs that indicate the operational status of elevators

A.7.10.8.2(2) The wording of these signs should reflect human behavior in fires and the control specifics of the elevator system. Subparagraph 7.10.8.2 addresses signs, but provisions for notification of the vision impaired need to be considered. For information about human behavior with respect to elevator evacuation see Groner and Levin, "Human Factors Considerations in the Potential for Using Elevators in Building Emergency Evacuation Plans"; Levin and Groner, "Human Behavior Aspects of Staging Areas for Fire Safety in GSA Buildings"; and Levin and Groner, "Human Factors Considerations for the Potential Use of Elevators for Fire Evacuation of FAA Air Traffic Control Towers." Some examples of messages on signs that could be displayed are shown in Table A.7.10.8.2(2).

Table A.7.10.8.2(2) Elevator Status Messages

Elevator Status	Message
Normal use	Elevator in Service
Elevators recalled and waiting for fire service	Please Wait for Fire Department or Use Stairs
Elevator out of service	Elevator Out of Service

> The requirements for elevator signs apply only where the elevator is part of the means of egress. The only current application is for elevators used as the second means of egress from a tower. See 7.2.13.1.

7.10.9 Testing and Maintenance.

7.10.9.1 Inspection. Exit signs shall be visually inspected for operation of the illumination sources at intervals not to exceed 30 days.

7.10.9.2 Testing. Exit signs connected to or provided with a battery-operated emergency illumination source, where required in 7.10.4, shall be tested and maintained in accordance with 7.9.3.

Section 7.11 Special Provisions for Occupancies with High Hazard Contents

(See Section 6.2.)

> The wording associated with the classification of *high hazard contents* from 6.2.2.4 states that "high hazard contents shall be classified as those that are likely to burn with extreme rapidity or from which explosions are likely."

7.11.1* Where the contents are classified as high hazard, exits shall be provided and arranged to permit all occupants to escape from the building or structure or from the hazardous area thereof to the outside or to a place of safety with a travel distance of not more than 75 ft (23 m), measured as required in 7.6.2.

Exception: This requirement shall not apply to storage occupancies as otherwise provided in Chapter 42.

A.7.11.1 Seventy-five feet (23 m) can be traversed in approximately 10 seconds to 15 seconds, even when allowing for a momentary delay to decide which way to go, during which it can be assumed that the average individual can hold his or her breath.

Subsection 7.11.1 does not limit occupants to a 75-ft (23-m) travel distance, but requires escape from the hazardous area itself with no more than 75 ft (23 m) of travel. The place of safety outside the hazardous area is permitted to be within the building's exit access; additional travel might be necessary to reach an exit.

7.11.2 Egress capacity for high hazard contents areas shall be based on 0.7 in./person (1.8 cm/person) for stairs or 0.4 in./person (1.0 cm/person) for level components and ramps in accordance with 7.3.3.1.

7.11.3 Not less than two means of egress shall be provided from each building or hazardous area thereof, unless rooms or spaces do not exceed 200 ft² (18.6 m²), have an occupant load not exceeding three persons, and have a travel distance to the room door not exceeding 25 ft (7.6 m).

Subsection 7.11.3 recognizes that it is not always necessary or feasible to provide two ways out of very small high hazard contents spaces. Provided that all three conditional features—limited room area, occupant load, and travel distance—can be met, a single means of egress is permitted.

7.11.4 Means of egress, for other than rooms or spaces that do not exceed 200 ft² (18.6 m²), have an occupant load not exceeding three persons, and have a travel distance to the room door not exceeding 25 ft (7.6 m), shall be arranged so that there are no dead ends in corridors.

7.11.5 Doors serving high hazard contents areas with occupant loads in excess of five shall be permitted to be provided with a latch or lock only if the latch or lock is panic hardware or fire exit hardware complying with 7.2.1.7.

It is not the intent of the *Code* to apply the provisions of Section 7.11 to the hazardous areas addressed by subsection __.3.2 of each occupancy chapter. Those hazardous areas are generally rooms or spaces with

contents that make them somewhat more hazardous than the rooms or spaces normally associated with a given occupancy. For example, soiled linen storage rooms in a health care occupancy create contents that are more hazardous than those within a patient room, but they don't create a hazard that warrants protection by Section 7.11. The decision as to when an area is sufficiently hazardous to warrant protection by the requirements of Section 7.11 is left to the authority having jurisdiction.

Section 7.12 Mechanical Equipment Rooms, Boiler Rooms, and Furnace Rooms

Section 7.12 applies to mechanical equipment rooms, boiler rooms, and furnace rooms in all buildings, regardless of occupancy. The number of exits and common path of travel limitations in these spaces are addressed independent of the occupancy in which they are located. The presence of these rooms does not result in a facility being designated a mixed occupancy.

7.12.1 Mechanical equipment rooms, boiler rooms, furnace rooms, and similar spaces shall be arranged to limit common path of travel to a distance not exceeding 50 ft (15 m).

Exception No. 1: A common path of travel not exceeding 100 ft (30 m) shall be permitted in the following locations:

(a) In buildings protected throughout by an approved, supervised automatic sprinkler system in accordance with Section 9.7

(b) In mechanical equipment rooms with no fuel-fired equipment

(c) In existing buildings

Exception No. 2: In an existing building, a common path of travel not exceeding 150 ft (45 m) shall be permitted if all of the following criteria are met:

(a) The building is protected throughout by an approved, supervised automatic sprinkler system installed in accordance with Section 9.7.

(b) No fuel-fired equipment is within the space.

(c) The egress path is readily identifiable.

Exception No. 3: This requirement shall not apply to rooms or spaces in existing health care occupancies complying with the arrangement of means of egress provisions of 19.2.5 and the travel distance limits of 19.2.6.

7.12.2 Stories used exclusively for mechanical equipment, furnaces, or boilers shall be permitted to have a single means of egress where the travel distance to an exit on that story is not in excess of the common path of travel limitations of 7.12.1.

Subparagraph 7.12.2 is especially useful in equipment penthouses and for basement furnace and boiler rooms. As long as the common path of travel specified by 7.12.1 is not exceeded, a story used exclusively for mechanical equipment, boilers, or furnaces is permitted to be served by a single exit.

References Cited in Commentary

1. ICC/ANSI A117.1, 1998 edition, *American National Standard for Accessible and Usable Buildings and Facilities*, American National Standards Institute, 11 West 42nd Street, 13th floor, New York, NY 10036.
2. NFPA 252, *Standard Methods of Fire Tests of Door Assemblies*, 1999 edition, National Fire Protection Association, Quincy, MA.
3. NFPA 92A, *Recommended Practice for Smoke-Control Systems*, 1996 edition, National Fire Protection Association, Quincy, MA.
4. Alison Norton, "When Security Provisions Threaten Fire Safety," *Fire Journal* 82, no. 6 (November/December 1988): 40, 42, 45, 76–77.
5. NFPA 72, *National Fire Alarm Code*, 1999 edition, National Fire Protection Association, Quincy, MA.
6. NFPA 220, *Standard on Types of Building Construction*, 1999 edition, National Fire Protection Association, Quincy, MA.
7. Jake Pauls, "Review of Stair-Safety Research with an Emphasis on Canadian Studies," *Ergonomics* 28, no. 7 (1985): 999–1010.
8. Fitch, Templar, Corcoran, "The Dimensions of Stairs," *Scientific American* (October 1974).
9. *Design and Construction of Building Exits*, Miscellaneous Publication M 51, October 10, 1935, National Bureau of Standards, Washington, DC (out of print).
10. ASME/ANSI A17.1, *Safety Code for Elevators and Escalators*, 1996 edition including addenda A17.1a-1997 and A17.1b-1998, American Society of Mechanical Engineers, 345 East 47th Street, New York, NY 10017.
11. Paul Robert Lyons, *Fire in America*, NFPA SPP-33, National Fire Protection Association, Quincy, MA, 1976, p. 190.
12. *Americans with Disabilities Act Accessibility Guidelines for Buildings and Facilities* (ADAAG), U.S. Architectural and Transportation Barriers Compliance Board, Washington, DC, 1992.
13. *Design and Construction of Building Exits*, Miscellaneous Publication M51.
14. Research Report No. 95, August 1958, "Second Report of the Operational Research Team on the Capacity of Footways," London: London Transit Board Research.
15. Jake Pauls, "Development of Knowledge about Means of Egress," *Fire Technology* 20, no. 2 (May 1984): 28–40.
16. Laurence D. Watrous, "High-Rise Fire in New Orleans," *Fire Journal* 67, no. 3 (May 1973), 6–9.
17. Robert F. Mendes, *Fighting High-Rise Building Fires—Tactics and Logistics*, NFPA FSP-44, National Fire Protection Association, Quincy, MA, 1975.
18. David P. Demers, "Ten Students Die in Providence College Dormitory Fire," *Fire Journal* 72, no. 4 (July 1978): 59–63, 103.
19. NFPA LS-4, 1982, "Investigation Report on the MGM Grand Hotel Fire, Las Vegas, NV, Nov. 21, 1980."
20. R. S. Moulton, "Emergency Lighting for Fire Safety," *NFPA Quarterly* 50, no. 2 (October 1956): 93–96.
21. See note 20.
22. See note 20.
23. A. Elwood Willey, "Unsafe Existing Conditions! Apartment House Fire, Boston, Massachusetts," *Fire Journal* 65, no. 4 (July 1971): 16–23.
24. James K. Lathrop, "The Summerland Fire: 50 Die on Isle of Man," *Fire Journal* 69, no. 2 (March 1975): 5–12.
25. James Bell, "Fifteen Residents Die in Mental Hospital Fire," *Fire Journal* 73, no. 4 (July 1979): 68–76.
26. See note 25.
27. NFPA 70, *National Electrical Code*, 1999 edition, National Fire Protection Association, Quincy, MA.
28. NFPA Investigation Report, "Westchase Hilton Hotel Fire, Houston, Texas, March 6, 1982, 12 Fatalities."
29. UL 924, *Standard for Safety Emergency Lighting and Power Equipment*, Underwriters Laboratories, Northbrook, IL.
30. NFPA 170, *Standard for Fire Safety Symbols*, 1999 edition, National Fire Protection Association, Quincy, MA.

CHAPTER 8

Features of Fire Protection

Chapter 8 establishes basic requirements for features of fire protection, which include the following:

(1) Construction
(2) Compartmentation through use of fire barriers
(3) Protection of vertical openings
(4) Protection of concealed spaces
(5) Subdivision of building space through use of smoke barriers
(6) Protection from hazards

This chapter specifies a menu of protection options that are mandated to varying degrees by specific occupancy chapters. However, some of the provisions of this chapter apply as requirements to all occupancies.

While the title suggests that the chapter encompasses any and all subject matter dealing with fire protection and fire safety, Chapter 8 focuses on a number of building features that contribute to minimizing the impact of a fire on the building occupants. The bulk of this protection scheme is associated with a series of methods and techniques that are used to control the construction and compartmentation features of a building.

Managing the spread of a fire from the room of origin, or between floors in a building, is an important consideration. Section 8.2 addresses the need to separate and compartmentalize egress components such as stairs and corridors. Means of egress components such as the exit stair are designed to be a safe haven once an occupant reaches the stair. This chapter provides the level of detail needed to keep heat, fire, and smoke out of such stairs.

Recognizing that there are acceptable, safe methods for permitting building spaces to be open to each other, Chapter 8 addresses openings between floors, such as an atrium opening that communicates among the multiple floors of a building.

The *Code* mandates that openings through or into separated areas be protected with appropriately rated doors, windows, or other devices that will prevent or minimize the movement of the products of combustion into or through these areas.

Section 8.1 General

8.1.1 Application.

The features of fire protection set forth in this chapter apply to both new construction and existing buildings.

Lack of compartmentation and rapid fire development have been primary factors in numerous multiple-fatality fires, especially in residential occupancies. Smoke spread throughout a floor where the floor was not subdivided by smoke barriers has been identified as a factor contributing to loss of life in fires reported in health care occupancies. Unprotected vertical openings have repeatedly provided the route for fire spread in fires in various occupancies. The ongoing role played by these factors in fires demonstrates the need to apply Chapter 8 requirements to both new construction and existing buildings.

Section 8.2 Construction and Compartmentation

The general requirements in Section 8.2 limit smoke and fire penetration and protect exit access corridors, exits, and other areas of the building from fire in adjoining areas and on other floors. Construction and compartmentation requirements vary by occupancy and are specified in Chapters 12 through 42 of the *Code*.

To preserve the integrity of the compartment, or safe area, all openings for doors, ducts, and building services (for example, electric power, telephone, water supply, and waste lines) must also be effectively closed or fitted with automatic closures. Equally important, and sometimes overlooked, are concealed spaces, particularly those above suspended ceilings, that frequently have been the means of spreading fire into otherwise protected areas.[1] In some instances, these interstitial spaces might be 8 ft (2.4 m) or more in height; in others, they might serve as supply- or return-air plenum chambers for air conditioning systems. Proper protection of concealed spaces can include firestopping, draftstopping, automatic extinguishment, area limitations, and other limitations on the combustibility of contents, interior linings, and construction materials. For specific protection details, see 8.2.7.

In Section 8.2, and throughout the *Code*, a distinction is made between smoke partitions, smoke barriers, and fire barriers. The function of a smoke partition and a smoke barrier is to restrict the passage of smoke, including fire gases. The fire barrier needs to be reasonably airtight under increased air pressure on the fire side from heated air expansion. The fire barrier must prevent the passage of heat and flame for a designated time. The fire barrier must be capable of withstanding direct impingement by the fire as determined by large-scale tests conducted in accordance with the following:

(1) NFPA 251, *Standard Methods of Tests of Fire Endurance of Building Construction and Materials*[2]
(2) NFPA 252, *Standard Methods of Fire Tests of Door Assemblies*[3]

8.2.1* Construction.

Buildings or structures occupied or used in accordance with the individual occupancy chapters (Chapters 12 through 42) shall meet the minimum construction requirements of those chapters. NFPA 220, *Standard on Types of Building Construction*, shall be used to determine the requirements for the construction classification. Where the building or facility includes additions or connected structures of different construction types, the rating and classification of the structure shall be based on either of the following:

(1) Separate buildings if a 2-hour or greater vertically-aligned fire barrier wall in accordance with NFPA 221,

Standard for Fire Walls and Fire Barrier Walls, exists between the portions of the building

Exception: The requirement of 8.2.1(1) shall not apply to previously approved separations between buildings.

(2) The least fire-resistive type of construction of the connected portions, if no such separation is provided

A.8.2.1   Table A.8.2.1 is Table 3-1 from NFPA 220, *Standard on Types of Building Construction*, and is reproduced in this annex for the convenience of users of this *Code*.

The *Code* is not a building code. However, in certain occupancies, minimum construction requirements are established to help maintain structural integrity for the time needed for evacuation. In the case of health care occupancies, an even longer time is needed to ensure the safety of sick occupants; a safe fire and smoke compartment needs to be established within the building but away from the zone of fire origin.

Paragraph 8.2.1 does not set minimum construction requirements but references the detailed classification criteria of NFPA 220, *Standard on Types of Building Construction*.[4] Therefore, construction types specified in other sections of the *Code* (particularly in the occupancy Chapters 12 through 42) can use a shorthand notation, such as *Type I(332)*, without additional, expansive detail. The user then refers to NFPA 220 for the necessary details.

Some buildings are comprised of sections and wings of differing construction types. For example, the portion of the building first constructed might be of Type III(200) construction; the next addition of Type II(111) construction, and the most current section of the building of Type V(000) construction (see Exhibit 8.1). In prior editions of the *Code* it was left to the user and the authority having jurisdiction to determine the construction type classification assigned to a building with multiple construction types. In the 2000 edition of the *Code*, 8.2.1 specifies the minimum fire resistance rating required of a vertically-aligned fire barrier to create the equivalent of separate buildings, each of one construction type.

In Exhibit 8.1, illustration (a), the minimum 2-hour fire resistance–rated, vertically-aligned fire barrier (that is, a wall and not a floor) is provided between the three portions of the building with differing construction types. For purposes of applying the minimum construction requirements, each section is permitted to be treated as a separate building; one building is of Type III(200) construction, a second

Table A.8.2.1 Fire Resistance Ratings (in hours) for Type I through Type V Construction

	Type I		Type II			Type III		Type IV	Type V	
	443	**332**	**222**	**111**	**000**	**211**	**200**	**2HH**	**111**	**000**
Exterior Bearing Walls –										
Supporting more than one floor, columns, or other bearing walls......	4	3	2	1	0*	2	2	2	1	0*
Supporting one floor only.....................	4	3	2	1	0*	2	2	2	1	0*
Supporting a roof only.........................	4	3	1	1	0*	2	2	2	1	0*
Interior Bearing Walls –										
Supporting more than one floor, columns, or other bearing walls......	4	3	2	1	0	1	0	2	1	0
Supporting one floor only.....................	3	2	2	1	0	1	0	1	1	0
Supporting a roof only.........................	3	2	1	1	0	1	0	1	1	0
Columns –										
Supporting more than one floor, columns, or other bearing walls......	4	3	2	1	0	1	0	H	1	0
Supporting one floor only.....................	3	2	2	1	0	1	0	H	1	0
Supporting a roof only.........................	3	2	1	1	0	1	0	H	1	0
Beams, Girders, Trusses, and Arches –										
Supporting more than one floor, columns, or other bearing walls......	4	3	2	1	0	1	0	H	1	0
Supporting one floor only.....................	3	2	2	1	0	1	0	H	1	0
Supporting a roof only.........................	3	2	1	1	0	1	0	H	1	0
Floor Construction	3	2	2	1	0	1	0	H	1	0
Roof Construction	2	1½	1	1	0	1	0	H	1	0
Exterior Nonbearing Walls	0*	0*	0*	0*	0*	0*	0*	0*	0*	0*

▨ Represents those members that are permittd to be of approved combustible material.
H: Heavy timber members (see NFPA 220, *Standard on Types of Building Construction,* for requirements).
*Requirements for fire resistance of exterior walls, the provision of spandrel wall sections, and the limitation or protection of wall openings are not related to construction type. Such requirements need to be specified in other standards and codes, where appropriate, and might be required in addition to the requirements of NFPA 220, *Standard on Types of Building Construction,* for the construction type.

building is of Type II(111) construction, and a third is of Type V(000) construction. In Exhibit 8.1, illustration (b), the non-rated partitions separating the portions of the building of varying construction types do not provide a minimum 2-hour fire resistance rating, so the building is classified as one building having the least fire resistance offered by any of the three construction types. Thus, the building construction is classified as Type V(000).

Table A.8.2.1 provides the *Code* user with a reprint of the key table from NFPA 220. The table summarizes the text of the document. Note that the shorthand notation, such as *Type I(332)*, provides the minimum hourly fire resistance ratings required to meet the definition of that construction type for only three components of the building — exterior bearing walls, structural frame/columns/girders, and floor construction. To meet the definition fully, other building components, such as roof construction and interior

bearing walls, need to have certain, minimum fire resistance ratings. Thus, the shorthand notation alone does not provide all the needed information. NFPA 220 should be consulted as necessary.

The minimum construction requirements of other sections of the *Code* might establish criteria, in addition to those of NFPA 220, for use in judging compliance with the definition of a specific building construction type, such as in Chapter 18, applicable to new health care occupancies. In this case, an overall life safety package is necessary for a population that is incapable of self-preservation and thus difficult to protect; therefore, 18.1.6.3 requires that, for a building to be classified as either Type I or Type II construction, it must meet the requirements of NFPA 220 and have noncombustible or limited-combustible interior nonbearing walls. Interior nonbearing walls are not addressed by NFPA 220.

Table 8.1 matches the various NFPA 220 construc-

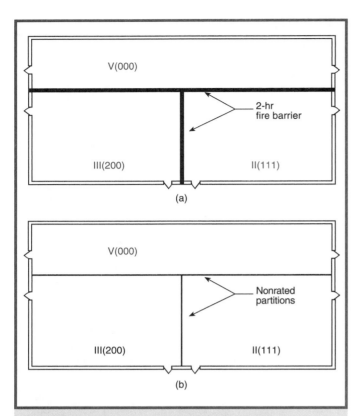

Exhibit 8.1 Building comprised of sections with varying construction types.

tion types with their approximate equivalent construction types, as contained in the following three model building codes published by U.S. regional building code officials organizations:

(1) *Uniform Building Code* (UBC)[5]
(2) *BOCA National Building Code* (BNBC)[6]
(3) *Standard Building Code* (SBC)[7]

For example, a building that NFPA 220 classifies as Type I(332), the UBC classifies as Type I FR, the BNBC classifies as Type 1B, and the SBC classifies as Type II. When using the *Life Safety Code* in conjunction with one of these building codes, the authority having jurisdiction might wish to use Table 8.1 to consider

(per Section 1.5) the corresponding construction classification.

8.2.2 Compartmentation.

8.2.2.1 Where required by Chapters 12 through 42, every building shall be divided into compartments to limit the spread of fire and restrict the movement of smoke.

8.2.2.2* Fire compartments shall be formed with fire barriers that are continuous from outside wall to outside wall, from one fire barrier to another, or a combination thereof, including continuity through all concealed spaces, such as those found above a ceiling, including interstitial spaces. Walls used as fire barriers shall comply with Chapter 3 of NFPA 221, *Standard for Fire Walls and Fire Barrier Walls*. The NFPA 221 limitation on percentage width of openings shall not apply.

Exception: A fire barrier required for an occupied space below an interstitial space shall not be required to extend through the interstitial space, provided that the construction assembly forming the bottom of the interstitial space has a fire resistance rating not less than that of the fire barrier.

The mandatory reference to NFPA 221, *Standard for Fire Walls and Fire Barrier Walls*,[8] has the effect of applying only one requirement not already covered elsewhere in Chapter 8 of the *Code*. The additional requirement is that fire barrier walls and their supports must withstand a minimum uniform load of 5 psf (0.24 kPa) from either direction applied perpendicular to the face of the wall. This requirement is intended to help ensure structural integrity during fires, even if building contents fall against the fire barrier.

A.8.2.2.2 To ensure that a fire barrier is continuous, it is necessary to seal completely all openings where the fire barrier abuts other fire barriers, the exterior walls, the floor below, and the floor or ceiling above. In the exception to 8.2.2.2, the fire resistance rating of the bottom of the interstitial space is provided by that membrane alone. Ceilings of

Table 8.1 Cross-Reference of Building Construction Types

NFPA 220	I(443)	I(332)	II(222)	II(111)	II(000)	III(211)	III(200)	IV(2HH)	V(111)	V(000)
UBC	—	I FR	II FR	II 1-hr	II N	III 1-hr	III N	IV HT	V 1-hr	V-N
B/NBC	1A	1B	2A	2B	2C	3A	3B	4	5A	5B
SBC	I	II	—	IV 1-hr	IV unp	V 1-hr	V unp	III	VI 1-hr	VI unp

unp—Unprotected

rated floor/ceiling and roof/ceiling assemblies do not necessarily provide the required fire resistance.

In Exhibit 8.2, the bold, solid lines designate a variety of fire barriers that meet the requirement of horizontal continuity to prevent a fire from spreading around the end of the barrier into the adjoining fire compartment.

Fire barrier A divides the building into two distinct fire compartments by running continuously from an outside wall to an outside wall. This barrier could, but does not, have door openings that would be protected by fire protection–rated door assemblies meeting the requirements of 8.2.3.2. Fire barrier B further subdivides the building into a third fire compartment and achieves its required continuity by running from an outside wall to a fire barrier (barrier A). The door opening is allowed if protected by an appropriately rated fire door assembly.

The fire barriers surrounding room C meet the continuity requirement by running from one fire barrier, to another fire barrier, to another; they envelop the room. This arrangement is commonly used to isolate the room and, thus, meet the protection requirements associated with protecting a hazardous area such as a hazardous contents storage room.

Fire barriers are often used to meet the protection and isolation requirements associated with corridors. Corridor D is protected by fire barriers that run from an outside wall to a fire barrier, to another fire barrier, to an outside wall. It isolates the corridor from other spaces on the floor and meets the horizontal continuity requirements.

In addition to horizontal continuity, fire barriers are required to be vertically continuous through all interstitial spaces.

In some cases, above-ceiling and between-floors interstitial spaces contain a considerable fuel load and are readily accessible by people. The possibility that an interstitial space will be used for storage should not be overlooked. These factors must be considered to determine whether an interstitial space is, in fact, another floor. See Exhibit 7.6, which illustrates an exit enclosure and egress provision of Chapter 7 but also shows interstitial spaces that constitute the equivalent of separate floors.

Normally, ceilings are not tested alone but are tested as part of a floor/ceiling or roof/ceiling assembly. The test does not indicate the performance of the ceiling but the performance of the total assembly. For example, the ceiling of a 1-hour floor/ceiling assembly might experience failure in a fire in less than 20 minutes, but the overall assembly might pass the 1-hour test. Often a designer or contractor will refer to a 1-hour or 2-hour ceiling and request permission to terminate a fire barrier at the ceiling, but, in reality, the ceiling is part of a 1-hour or 2-hour floor/ceiling or roof/ceiling assembly. Because the ceiling itself does not provide the appropriately rated fire barrier against which the wall assembly can be terminated, the fire barrier must run through and above the ceiling; it must extend from slab to slab.

Tests reported by the Gypsum Association in the *Fire Resistance Design Manual* indicate that two layers of ⅝-in. (1.6-cm), fire-rated, Type X gypsum wallboard, applied at right angles to the underside of nominal 2 in. × 10 in. (nominal 5 cm × 25 cm) wood joists and spaced 24 in. (61 cm) on centers, with the face layer of the gypsum board offset by 24 in. (61 cm) from the base layer joints, will provide 1-hour fire resistance protection for the wood framing.[9] Using this information, the authority having jurisdiction could judge that such a ceiling meets the intent of the exception to 8.2.2.2, and could allow for a 1-hour fire resistance–rated wall assembly to terminate tightly against the underside of such ceiling.

Illustration (a) of Exhibit 8.3 shows a 1-hour fire resistance–rated wall assembly continuing up through the ceiling and void space of a 1-hour fire resistance–rated floor/ceiling assembly so as to terminate tightly against the underside of the floor slab to achieve the required vertical continuity. In Exhibit 8.3, illustration (b), the exception to 8.2.2.2 is used to allow for the 1-hour rated wall assembly to terminate

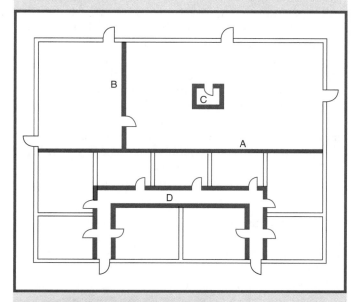

Exhibit 8.2 *Typical fire barriers.*

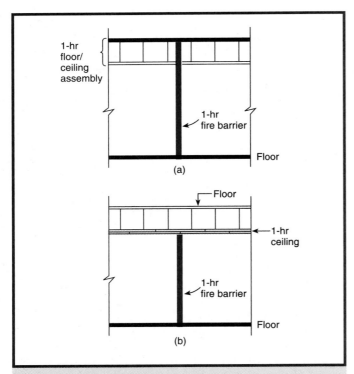

Exhibit 8.3 *Fire barrier vertical continuity.*

at a ceiling that provides the required 1-hour of fire resistance rating by itself.

Some occupancies do allow the fire barrier to terminate at the underside (that is, ceiling) of a fire protection–rated floor/ceiling assembly. However, caution must be exercised, because ceilings of these assemblies are often improperly installed or, once installed, have their integrity violated during routine building maintenance.

8.2.3 Fire Barriers.

8.2.3.1 Fire Resistance–Rated Assemblies.

8.2.3.1.1 Floor-ceiling assemblies and walls used as fire barriers, including supporting construction, shall be of a design that has been tested to meet the conditions of acceptance of NFPA 251, *Standard Methods of Tests of Fire Endurance of Building Construction and Materials*. Fire barriers shall be continuous in accordance with 8.2.2.2.

The fire resistance of a fire barrier is determined by the test method described in NFPA 251, *Standard Methods of Tests of Fire Endurance of Building Construction and Materials*. The test is also commonly known by its ASTM designation, ASTM E 119, *Standard Test Methods for Fire Tests of Building Construction and Mate-*

rials.[10] The NFPA 251/ASTM E 119 test standard provides for the construction of the particular assembly to be rated and the actual testing of the assembly in the test furnace. The test is conducted under very rigid conditions, so that test results on the same assembly are reproducible and tests of different assemblies are comparable. Temperatures in the furnace are generated in strict accordance with the standard time-temperature curve and reach levels of 1000°F, 1300°F, 1550°F, 1700°F, and 1850°F (538°C, 704°C, 843°C, 927°C, and 1010°C) at intervals 5, 10, 30, 60, and 120 minutes into the test. Temperatures both in the furnace and on the unexposed side of the assembly being tested are monitored and recorded at specified intervals and locations. During the course of the test, cotton waste is placed against the unexposed surface and observed for flaming. During the test, the assembly being tested is also loaded the same way that it would be expected to be loaded when installed in a building.

The following are acceptance criteria for a successfully completed fire test on an assembly for a specified time period:

(1) Cotton waste on unexposed side does not ignite.
(2) Temperature rise on the unexposed side does not exceed 325°F (180°C) at any point or an average of 250°F (139°C).
(3) Assembly must continue to support design loads.

The criteria in (1) through (3) apply to floor, roof, wall, and partition assemblies. In addition, wall and partition assemblies that are to be rated at 1 hour or more are subjected to the hose stream test. A duplicate specimen of the assembly to be rated is tested in the furnace for one-half the time specified as the fire resistance rating in the fire endurance test. This specimen is then removed from the furnace and immediately subjected to the hose stream test. If there is any projection of water beyond the unexposed surface, the assembly is considered to have failed.

NFPA 251 testing is commonly done by testing laboratories, which normally issue a report of the test and then list the assembly. Listings of tested fire resistance–rated assemblies are found in publications of laboratories that conduct fire testing, such as the following:

(1) Underwriters Laboratories Fire Resistance Directory[11]
(2) Factory Mutual Specification Tested Products Guide[12]
(3) Omega Point Laboratories Directory of Listed Building Products, Materials & Assemblies[13]

It is important that the assembly that is constructed is the same as that listed. For example, if a floor/ceiling assembly calls for clips on the ceiling tiles, the clips must be installed and maintained. Another example is the special treatment often required for lights or air ducts in suspended ceilings. A common problem in walls is the installation of an untested material between the wallboard and the studs or the installation of recessed wall fixtures, which requires the removal of wallboard.

Exception No. 1: Structural elements shall be required to have only the fire resistance rating required for the construction classification of the building where such elements support nonbearing wall or partition assemblies having a required fire resistance rating of 1 hour or less and where such elements do not serve as exit enclosures or protection for vertical openings.

If Exception No. 1 to 8.2.3.1.1 was not included in the *Code*, a two-story building, for example, used for an occupancy that (1) allows Type II(000) construction to be occupied and (2) requires the presence of 1-hour fire resistance–rated corridor walls would be required to upgrade all construction supporting the nonbearing second floor corridor walls (that is, the columns, beams, and girders supporting the second floor) to a 1-hour fire resistance rating. Because the purpose of 1-hour rated corridor walls is not to provide structural integrity but to provide barriers that create fire compartments on the floor on which they are installed, the exception allows the unprotected, noncombustible Type II(000) building to be occupied in accordance with subsection __.1.6 of the applicable occupancy chapter.

Exhibit 8.4 further illustrates the use of Exception No. 1 to 8.2.3.1.1. The floor shown in figure (a) is the second of a two-story building that, based on the occupancy, is allowed to be placed in a building of Type II(000) construction as defined by NFPA 220, *Standard on Types of Building Construction* (see A.8.2.1 and its associated commentary). In addition, the occupancy in question requires (1) corridor walls with a 1-hour fire resistance rating, and (2) enclosure of hazardous area rooms, interior exit stairs, and vertical openings, such as elevator and ventilating (HVAC) shafts, by 1-hour fire resistance–rated barriers. As shown in illustration (b) of Exhibit 8.4, the exception allows for the building construction that supports the second floor corridor walls and the walls enclosing the hazardous storage room to remain unprotected, but such construction is to be noncombustible as

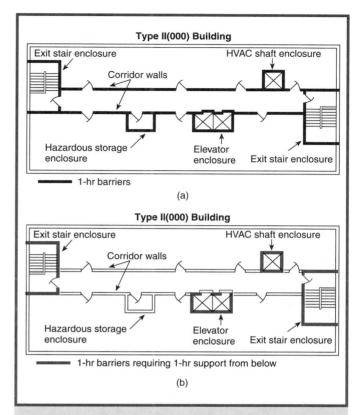

Exhibit 8.4 Fire barriers and rated structural supports.

specified by building construction Type II(000). However, the second floor 1-hour rated fire barriers enclosing the exit stairs, and the elevator shaft and the HVAC shaft, must be supported by 1-hour fire resistance–rated construction. In illustration (b), only those fire barriers depicted by bold, solid lines are required to be supported by 1-hour rated construction from below.

Exception No. 2:* This requirement shall not apply to assemblies calculated to have equivalent fire resistance, provided that the calculations are based on the conditions of acceptance and the fire exposure specified in NFPA 251, Standard Methods of Tests of Fire Endurance of Building Construction and Materials.

A.8.2.3.1.1 Exception No. 2 Methods for calculating the fire endurance of assemblies of the following materials are found in the publications referenced:

(1) Concrete and masonry
  a. ACI 2/6R, *Guide for Determining the Fire Endurance of Concrete Elements*
  b. Concrete and Masonry Industry Firesafety Committee, *Analytical Methods of Determining Fire Endur-*

ance of Concrete and Masonry Members—Model Code Approved Procedures
  c. CRSI, *Reinforced Concrete Fire Resistance*
  d. PCI, *Design for Fire Resistance of Precast Prestressed Concrete*
(2) Steel
  a. AISI, *Designing Fire Protection for Steel Columns*
  b. AISI, *Designing Fire Protection for Steel Beams*
  c. AISI, *Designing Fire Protection for Steel Trusses*
(3) Wood
  a. American Forest & Paper Association, *Design of Fire-Resistive Exposed Wood Members*
  b. UBC, *Methods for Calculating Fire Resistance of Wood-Framed Walls, Floors and Roofs*

Exception No. 3:   This requirement shall not apply to structural elements supporting floor assemblies in accordance with the exception to 18.1.6.2.

The following illustrates the use of calculating fire resistance as allowed by Exception No. 2 to 8.2.3.1.1.

A designer who wants to provide a 2-hour fire resistance rating for a W14 × 233 steel column by boxing the column with gypsum wallboard cannot find such an assembly in the *Underwriters Laboratories Fire Resistance Directory.* Design No. X520 and design No. X521 come very close to providing the needed information but deal with W14 × 228 steel columns; they show that, with one layer of ½-in. (1.3-cm) thick gypsum wallboard, the assembly will provide a 2-hour fire resistance rating. The *UL Directory* further explains that most structural steel producers began rolling a new series of structural shapes in accordance with ASTM A 6, *Standard Specification for General Requirements for Rolled Steel Plates, Shapes, Sheet Piling, and Bars for Structural Use,* in 1978 and that some of the column sizes specified for individual designs might have been discontinued.[14] The designer chooses not to make a judgment call as to whether the W14 × 233 column will provide the same rating as the discontinued W14 × 228 shape by comparing flange and web thickness. Instead, the designer chooses to calculate the fire resistance rating of a W14 × 233 steel column with a single layer of ½-in. (1.3-cm) gypsum wallboard built around the column in a box profile using criteria from the AISI *Designing Fire Protection for Steel Columns.*[15]

Based on results from accumulated fire test data, the AISI manual presents the following formula for calculating the fire endurance of steel columns protected by gypsum wallboard:

$$R = 130 \left[\frac{h(W'/D)}{2} \right]^{0.75}$$

where:
  R = fire resistance (minutes)
  h = thickness of gypsum wallboard (in.)
  W' = weight of steel column and gypsum wallboard protection (lb/ft)
  D = heated perimeter of steel column (in.) [for box profile, inside perimeter of gypsum wallboard material, calculated as $D = 2(a + b)$ per Exhibit 8.5.]

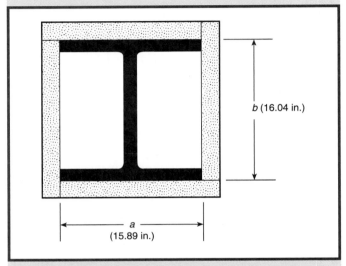

Exhibit 8.5 *Box profile of gypsum wallboard around steel column for which fire resistance rating of assembly can be calculated.*

The total weight (W') of both the column and its gypsum wallboard protection is calculated using the following formula:

$$W' = W + \frac{50(h)(D)}{144}$$

where W = weight of steel column (lb/ft).
  Performing the calculations yields the following:

$$D = 2(a + b)$$
$$= 2(15.89 + 16.04)$$
$$= 63.86 \text{ in.}$$

$$W' = W + \frac{50(h)(D)}{144}$$
$$= 233 + \frac{50(0.5)(63.86)}{144}$$
$$= 244.09 \text{ lb/ft}$$

$$W'/D = \frac{244.09}{63.86} = 3.82$$

$$R = 130\left[\frac{h(W'/D)}{2}\right]^{0.75}$$

$$= 130\left[\frac{(0.50)(3.82)}{2}\right]^{0.75}$$

$$= 125.6 \text{ min (approximately 2 hours)}$$

Based on the calculation for fire endurance, the designer specifies, with a degree of comfort, that the 2-hour fire resistance rating for the assembly consisting of the W14 × 233 steel column and gypsum-wallboard box profile enclosure be achieved using a single layer of ½-in. (1.3-cm) gypsum wallboard.

8.2.3.1.2 Fire barriers used to provide enclosure, subdivision, or protection under this *Code* shall be classified in accordance with one of the following fire resistance ratings:

(1) 2-hour fire resistance rating
(2) 1-hour fire resistance rating
(3)* ½-hour fire resistance rating

Fire resistance testing of building construction per NFPA 251/ASTM E 119 allows for assemblies to be assigned fire resistance ratings up through the category of *8 hours and over*. Ratings of more than 2 hours are used primarily in protecting property. The *Code* requires no more than a 2-hour fire resistance rating for building construction, even in the health care and detention and correctional occupancy chapters. These chapters promote a defend-in-place strategy, because it emphasizes life safety over property protection. Thus, in subsections __.1.6 in the health care and detention and correctional occupancy chapters, construction Types I(443), I(332), and II(222) are grouped to be treated as equivalent. A design professional can specify that material assemblies with 3-hour or 4-hour fire resistance ratings are to be used. However, no reduction in requirements, other than those allowed for construction with a 2-hour fire resistance rating, are permitted.

A.8.2.3.1.2(3) Walls in good condition with lath and plaster, or gypsum board of not less than ½-in. (1.3 cm), on each side can be considered as providing at least a ½-hour fire resistance rating. Additional information on archaic material assemblies can be found in Appendix D of NFPA 914, *Recommended Practice for Fire Protection in Historic Structures*.

Prior to 1997, the *Code* included ¾-hour and ⅓-hour fire resistance rating classifications in addition to the current ½-hour classification. The range of fractional-hour ratings mistakenly implied a degree of accuracy and preciseness. The range has been revised so that the only fire resistance rating of less than 1 hour is the ½-hour classification. Because some occupancies, such as existing health care occupancies, previously permitted a fire resistance rating of ⅓-hour fire but now require ½-hour, A.8.2.3.1.2(3) provides guidance on evaluating existing fire barriers. The change from the ⅓-hour to the ½-hour classification was not intended to create a condition of noncompliance where existing fire barriers had previously complied with *Code* requirements. A previously approved ⅓-hour fire resistance–rated barrier should be considered as complying with the requirement for a ½-hour fire barrier.

8.2.3.2 Fire Protection–Rated Opening Protectives.

8.2.3.2.1 Door assemblies in fire barriers shall be of an approved type with the appropriate fire protection rating for the location in which they are installed and shall comply with the following.

(a)* Fire doors shall be installed in accordance with NFPA 80, *Standard for Fire Doors and Fire Windows*. Fire doors shall be of a design that has been tested to meet the conditions of acceptance of NFPA 252, *Standard Methods of Fire Tests of Door Assemblies*.

A.8.2.3.2.1(a) Some doors have been tested to meet the conditions of acceptance of NFPA 251, *Standard Methods of Tests of Fire Endurance of Building Construction and Materials*. Where such assemblies are used, the provisions of 8.2.3.1 should be applied instead of those of 8.2.3.2.

Exception: The requirement of 8.2.3.2.1(a) shall not apply where otherwise specified by 8.2.3.2.3.1.

(b) Fire doors shall be self-closing or automatic-closing in accordance with 7.2.1.8 and, where used within the means of egress, shall comply with the provisions of 7.2.1.

Fire protection–rated door assemblies are tested in accordance with NFPA 252, *Standard Methods of Fire Tests of Door Assemblies*. NFPA 252 is also commonly known as ASTM E 152, *Standard Methods of Fire Tests of Door Assemblies*.[16] Such assemblies must be installed in accordance with the requirements of NFPA 80, *Standard for Fire Doors and Fire Windows*.[17] Where the *Code* uses the term *door*, it includes not only the door leaf or slab but also the doorway, frame, and necessary hardware, including hinges. Where describing a fire door, the applicable standards similarly define a fire protection–rated assembly as including all these components as well as a listed door closer and positive latching.

If they are to be effective, fire doors must not only be closed but also be held closed. Building fires are capable of generating pressures sufficient to force fire doors open if they are not held closed with positive latching, thereby rendering the doors incapable of protecting the opening in which they are installed.

The acceptance criteria for fire protection–rated assemblies, such as fire doors, differ from those for fire resistance–rated construction, such as a wall or floor/ceiling assembly. The limitation of temperature rise through the fire door is not normally a measure of acceptance, although it is for a fire resistance–rated assembly such as a wall. In addition, during the course of the fire test, fire doors will expand on the exposed side and, as a result, will warp — sometimes expanding through the door opening at the top of the door. This expansion and warping result in some flaming through the top of the door openings. The test standard recognizes this phenomenon, and a certain amount of such flaming is permitted under the acceptance criteria. This does not adversely affect safety, given that fire protection–rated assemblies are intended to protect relatively small openings in larger fire resistance–rated barriers. Also, to maintain the door as usable, combustible materials are not to be piled in front of the door opening. See also commentary following 8.2.3.1.1 and 8.2.3.2.3.1.

8.2.3.2.2 Fire window assemblies shall be permitted in fire barriers having a required fire resistance rating of 1 hour or less and shall be of an approved type with the appropriate fire protection rating for the location in which they are installed. Fire windows shall be installed in accordance with NFPA 80, *Standard for Fire Doors and Fire Windows*, and shall comply with the following:

(1)* Fire windows used in fire barriers, other than existing fire window installations of wired glass and other fire-rated glazing material in approved metal frames, shall be of a design that has been tested to meet the conditions of acceptance of NFPA 257, *Standard on Fire Test for Window and Glass Block Assemblies*.

A.8.2.3.2.2(1) Some window assemblies have been tested to meet the conditions of acceptance of NFPA 251, *Standard Methods of Tests of Fire Endurance of Building Construction and Materials*. Where such assemblies are used, the provisions of 8.2.3.1 should be applied instead of those of 8.2.3.2.

(2) Fire windows used in fire barriers, other than existing fire window installations of wired glass and other fire-

rated glazing material in approved metal frames, shall not exceed 25 percent of the area of the fire barrier in which they are used.

Exception: Fire-rated glazing material shall be permitted to be installed in approved existing frames.

The provisions of 8.2.3.2.2 provide guidelines for fire window assemblies that parallel those covered by 8.2.3.2.1 for fire door assemblies. In this subparagraph, and consistently throughout the *Code*, new glazing for use in fire barriers and fire doors is regulated by performance-oriented criteria, which refer to fire-rated glazing, in lieu of the more traditional but prescriptive requirements previously applicable to wired glass. The requirements limit the installation of fire windows used in fire barriers to not more than 25 percent of the area of the fire barrier in which they are used; however, exceptions were adopted to continue to recognize the current practice of using greater percentages of wired glass for existing fire windows and vision panels in fire doors.

8.2.3.2.3* **Opening Protectives.**

A.8.2.3.2.3 Longer ratings might be required where doors are provided for property protection as well as life safety.

NFPA 80, *Standard for Fire Doors and Fire Windows*, should be consulted for standard practice in the selection and installation of fire doors.

8.2.3.2.3.1 Every opening in a fire barrier shall be protected to limit the spread of fire and restrict the movement of smoke from one side of the fire barrier to the other. The fire protection rating for opening protectives shall be as follows:

(1) 2-hour fire barrier—1½-hour fire protection rating
(2) 1-hour fire barrier—1-hour fire protection rating where used for vertical openings or exit enclosures, or ¾-hour fire protection rating where used for other than vertical openings or exit enclosures, unless a lesser fire protection rating is specified by Chapter 7 or Chapters 11 through 42

Exception No. 1: Where the fire barrier specified in 8.2.3.2.3.1(2) is provided as a result of a requirement that corridor walls or smoke barriers be of 1-hour fire resistance–rated construction, the opening protectives shall be permitted to have not less than a 20-minute fire protection rating when tested in accordance with NFPA 252, Standard Methods of Fire Tests of Door Assemblies, without the hose stream test.

Exception No. 2: The requirement of 8.2.3.2.3.1(2) shall not apply where special requirements for doors in 1-hour fire resistance–rated corridor walls and 1-hour fire resistance–rated smoke barriers are specified in Chapters 18 through 21.

Exception No. 3:   Existing doors having a ¾-hour fire protection rating shall be permitted to continue to be used in vertical openings and in exit enclosures in lieu of the 1-hour rating required by 8.2.3.2.3.1(2).

(3) ½-hour fire barrier—20-minute fire protection rating

Exception: Twenty-minute fire protection–rated doors shall be exempt from the hose stream test of NFPA 252, Standard Methods of Fire Tests of Door Assemblies.

Whereas 8.2.3.1.2 addressed the fire resistance rating of fire barriers, 8.2.3.2.3.1 addresses the fire protection rating of opening protectives installed in fire barriers. Fire barriers have fire resistance ratings; opening protectives, such as fire doors, have fire protection ratings. For a better understanding of the difference in test methods used for rating fire barriers and fire doors, compare the commentaries following 8.2.3.1.1 and 8.2.3.2.1.

In general, 1-hour fire barriers for the protection of vertical openings (for example, the shafts enclosing maximum three-story exit stairs) require doors with a 1-hour fire protection rating. One-hour fire barriers for other than vertical opening protection, such as those used to isolate a hazardous contents room, require doors with a ¾-hour fire protection rating.

The provisions of 8.2.3.2.3.1(2) allow Chapter 7 and the occupancy chapters to alter this general rule. However, for the most part, such attention is usually done only with regard to the requirement that corridor walls be of a 1-hour fire resistance rating. Exception No. 1 allows for a 1-hour fire resistance–rated corridor wall or smoke barrier to have a door with a 20-minute fire protection rating.

Exception No. 2 recognizes the special requirements contained in Chapters 18 through 21 for health care and ambulatory health care occupancies, which, for example, allow the omission of the self-closing device on patient room doors installed in corridor walls. In this case, the special requirements recognize the functional needs for open doors in these facilities, and a true fire protection–rated patient room door assembly is not required.

In some cases, the fire protection ratings of the opening protectives are allowed to be of a lower rating than the fire resistance rating of the fire barrier openings to be protected. For example, a 2-hour fire resistance–rated fire barrier is allowed to have its openings protected by 1½-hour fire protection–rated

door assemblies. The perceived mismatch of ratings actually accomplishes a reasonable, practical match — as explained in the following paragraphs.

The test procedures on which the ratings are based, that is, NFPA 251/ASTM E 119 for fire barriers, and NFPA 252/ASTM E 152 (see commentary following 8.2.3.2.1) for fire doors, are different.

Although combustibles placed against a fire resistance–rated wall expose the wall to a considerable fire challenge, usually a fire protection–rated door assembly will not have similar combustibles placed against it because the opening must be clear to use the door. Such a scenario suggests that, if a door is not to be used and combustible storage is to be placed at the door opening, the door should be removed and the opening filled with material to restore the wall to its required fire resistance rating.

8.2.3.2.3.2 Where a 20-minute fire protection–rated door is required in existing buildings, an existing 1¾-in. (4.4-cm) solid, bonded wood-core door, or an existing steel-clad (tin-clad) wood door, or an existing solid-core steel door with positive latch and closer shall be permitted.

Exception: This requirement shall not apply where otherwise specified by Chapters 11 through 42.

8.2.3.2.4 Penetrations and Miscellaneous Openings in Fire Barriers.

8.2.3.2.4.1* Openings in fire barriers for air-handling ductwork or air movement shall be protected in accordance with 9.2.1.

A.8.2.3.2.4.1 In engineered smoke management systems, the designer should consider the use of high-temperature links on fire dampers where air-handling ducts penetrate fire barriers.

In referencing 9.2.1 for the protection of openings in fire barriers for air-handling ductwork or air movement, the *Code* mandates that the requirements of NFPA 90A, *Standard for the Installation of Air-Conditioning and Ventilating Systems,*[18] and not the usual *Life Safety Code* requirements for opening protectives (8.2.3.2.3.1), apply to heating, ventilating, and air conditioning system (HVAC) penetrations of fire barriers. NFPA 90A requires that approved fire dampers be provided in all air transfer openings in partitions that are required to have a fire resistance rating. It also requires that approved fire dampers be provided where ducts or air grilles penetrate partitions that are required to have a fire resistance rating of 2 hours or more. Thus, although any air transfer opening would have to be fire dampered in a required fire barrier of any rating, penetrations by ducts or air grilles would not have to be fire dampered if the required rating of the fire barrier were less than 2 hours. These requirements are depicted in Exhibit 8.6.

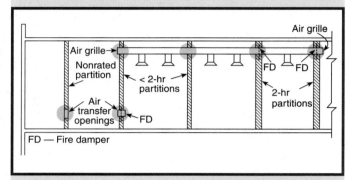

Exhibit 8.6 *Fire damper requirements of NFPA 90A for HVAC penetrations of partitions.*

8.2.3.2.4.2* Pipes, conduits, bus ducts, cables, wires, air ducts, pneumatic tubes and ducts, and similar building service equipment that pass through fire barriers shall be protected as follows:

A.8.2.3.2.4.2 Penetrations through fire barriers by cables, wires, pipes, tubes, conduits, vents, and other penetrating items, as well as insulation and coverings on penetrating items, should meet one of the following criteria:

(1) They should be tested in accordance with NFPA 251, *Standard Methods of Tests of Fire Endurance of Building Construction and Materials,* as part of a rated assembly.
(2) They should be protected by an approved through-penetration system that has been tested in accordance with ASTM E 814, *Methods for Fire Tests of Through-Penetration Fire Stops.*

In lieu of A.8.2.3.2.4.2(1) or (2), the annular space around the penetrating item is permitted to be protected where the penetrating item is a cable or wire without a combustible jacket or where it is a noncombustible cable, wire, pipe, tube, conduit, or vent. The material used to fill the annular space, that is, spaces between a sleeve and a penetrating item and between a sleeve and a fire barrier, should prevent the passage of flame and hot gases that are sufficient to ignite cotton waste when subjected to the time-temperature fire conditions of NFPA 251, *Standard Methods of Tests of Fire Endurance of Building Construction and Materials.* The test should be performed under a positive pressure differential of not less than 0.01 in. water column (2.5 Pa) at the location of the penetration for a time equivalent to the required fire resistance rating of the assembly

penetrated. Where sleeves are used, the sleeves should be noncombustible and should be securely fastened to the fire barrier.

Concrete, mortar, or grout is permitted to be used to fill the annular spaces around iron, steel, or copper pipe, around tube or conduit, or around wires and cables with steel jackets that penetrate concrete or masonry fire barriers. The nominal diameter of the penetrating item should not exceed 6 in. (15.2 cm), and the opening size should not exceed 144 in.^{2} (929 cm^2). The thickness of concrete, mortar, or grout should be the full thickness of the barrier or the thickness necessary to provide a fire resistance rating not less than the required fire resistance rating of the barrier penetrated.

Openings for steel electrical outlet boxes not exceeding 16 in.^{2} (103 cm^2) that are not listed for use in fire resistance–rated assemblies should be permitted, provided that the area of such openings does not exceed 100 in.^{2} (645 cm^2) for any 100 ft^2 (9.3 m^2) of enclosure wall area. Outlet boxes on opposite sides of the enclosure should be separated by a horizontal distance of not less than 24 in. (61 cm). Membrane penetrations for electrical outlet boxes of any material should be permitted, provided that such boxes are tested for use in fire-rated assemblies and installed in accordance with the tested assembly.

(1) The space between the penetrating item and the fire barrier shall meet one of the following conditions:
    a. It shall be filled with a material that is capable of maintaining the fire resistance of the fire barrier.
    b. It shall be protected by an approved device that is designed for the specific purpose.
(2) Where the penetrating item uses a sleeve to penetrate the fire barrier, the sleeve shall be solidly set in the fire barrier, and the space between the item and the sleeve shall meet one of the following conditions:
    a. It shall be filled with a material that is capable of maintaining the fire resistance of the fire barrier.
    b. It shall be protected by an approved device that is designed for the specific purpose.
(3)* Insulation and coverings for pipes and ducts shall not pass through the fire barrier unless one of the following conditions is met:
    a. The material shall be capable of maintaining the fire resistance of the fire barrier.
    b. The material shall be protected by an approved device that is designed for the specific purpose.

A.8.2.3.2.4.2(3) See NFPA 90A, *Standard for the Installation of Air-Conditioning and Ventilating Systems,* for additional information on air-handling ducts passing through fire barriers.

(4) Where designs take transmission of vibration into consideration, any vibration isolation shall meet one of the following conditions:

a. It shall be made on either side of the fire barrier.

b. It shall be made by an approved device that is designed for the specific purpose.

One source of information on tested materials, devices, and systems for protecting through-penetrations of fire resistance–rated barriers is "Through-Penetration Firestop Systems" (Volume II) of the *Fire Resistance Directory*, published by Underwriters Laboratories.[19] Such devices and systems are designed to resist the spread of fire through openings in fire resistance–rated floor or wall barriers that accommodate penetrating items, such as electrical cables, cable trays, conduits, and pipes. Such devices and systems are classified by UL with respect to installation in a wall only, installation in a floor only, or installation in a wall or floor. The basic standard used by Underwriters Laboratories to investigate products in this category is UL 1479, *Fire Tests of Through-Penetration Firestops.*[20] UL 1479 is similar to ASTM E 814, *Standard Test Method for Fire Tests of Through-Penetration Fire Stops* (see A.8.2.3.2.4.2).[21] A sampling of the currently classified devices includes the use of the following:

(1) Ceramic fibers
(2) Foamed silicones
(3) Mineral wool batts
(4) Intumescent sheets
(5) Sealing blankets and plugs
(6) Fittings and couplings
(7) Various caulks, putties and mastics
(8) Spring-loaded guillotine blades

Over the life of a building, it is important to maintain the integrity of barriers to protect against fire penetration. Renovations or any changes to building utilities will tend to violate the compartmentation provided when a building is first occupied.

Exhibit 8.7 illustrates some of the typical fire barrier penetrations, which are covered in 8.2.3.2.4.

8.2.4 Smoke Partitions.

Subsection 8.2.4 is new for the 2000 edition of the *Code.* It is intended to serve as another menu-like item that can be referenced by other parts of the *Code,* especially the occupancy chapters, instead of repeating detailed, slightly-varying criteria in many chapters. In future editions of the *Code,* more occupancy chapters will reference 8.2.4 on smoke partitions where exceptions from the typical 1-hour fire resistance–rated corridor wall requirement are provided for sprinklered buildings. For an example of a

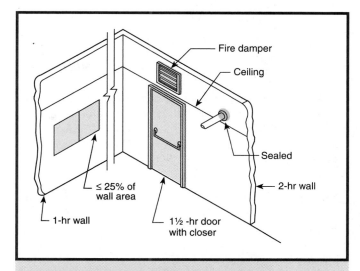

Exhibit 8.7 *Typical penetrations of a fire barrier.*

mandate for the use of the smoke partitions provisions of 8.2.4 in large residential board and care occupancies, see 32.3.3.6.5 and 33.3.3.6.5.

The new smoke partition requirements provide other sections of the *Code* with another tool that can be referenced. The smoke partition provisions were written to offer options not previously available under the provisions for fire barriers and smoke barriers. For example, a smoke partition is not required to have a fire resistance rating, but a fire barrier must have a rating. Also, a smoke partition is not required to have a smoke leakage–rated damper where ductwork runs through the partition, but a duct penetration of a smoke barrier typically must be provided with a damper.

8.2.4.1 Where required elsewhere in this *Code*, smoke partitions shall be provided to limit the transfer of smoke.

Chapter 8 does not require the installation of smoke partitions but provides detailed criteria for smoke partitions required by other sections of the *Code.* A smoke partition is a continuous membrane designed to form a barrier to limit the transfer of smoke. See the definition of the term *smoke partition* in 3.3.185.

8.2.4.2 Smoke partitions shall extend from the floor to the underside of the floor or roof deck above, through any concealed spaces, such as those above suspended ceilings, and through interstitial structural and mechanical spaces.

*Exception:** Smoke partitions shall be permitted to terminate at the underside of a monolithic or suspended ceiling system where the following conditions are met:*

(a) The ceiling system forms a continuous membrane.

(b) A smoketight joint is provided between the top of the smoke partition and the bottom of the suspended ceiling.

(c) The space above the ceiling is not used as a plenum.

A.8.2.4.2 Exception An architectural, exposed, suspended-grid acoustical tile ceiling with penetrations for sprinklers, ducted HVAC supply and return air diffusers, speakers, and recessed light fixtures is capable of limiting the transfer of smoke.

The concept of limiting the transfer of smoke from one side of a smoke partition to the other is different from the concept of preventing any and all smoke from transferring to the other side of a partition. A smoke partition should be thought of as a barrier that reasonably limits, but doesn't prevent, smoke transfer. As such, there are suspended ceiling systems and monolithic surfaced ceilings that provide resistance to smoke transfer that is approximately equal to the traditional, nonrated corridor wall or partition. The exception to 8.2.4.2 permits smoke partitions to terminate tightly against the underside of such ceilings. The annex text further describes the concept. The list of acceptable penetrating items (for example, speakers, recessed light fixtures, and ducted HVAC air diffusers) makes it clear that a smoke partition doesn't prevent all smoke transfer; rather, it limits the transfer of smoke to an acceptable life safety level.

8.2.4.3 Doors.

8.2.4.3.1 Doors in smoke partitions shall comply with 8.2.4.3.2 through 8.2.4.3.5.

8.2.4.3.2 Doors shall comply with the provisions of 7.2.1.

8.2.4.3.3 Doors shall not include louvers.

8.2.4.3.4* Door clearances shall be in accordance with NFPA 80, *Standard for Fire Doors and Fire Windows.*

A.8.2.4.3.4 Gasketing of doors should not be necessary, as the clearances in NFPA 80, *Standard for Fire Doors and Fire Windows,* effectively achieve resistance to the passage of smoke if the door is relatively tight-fitting.

NFPA 80, *Standard for Fire Doors and Fire Windows,* permits clearances of 1/8 in. (3.2 mm) between the door frame and the top and sides of the door. For swinging doors with builder's hardware, NFPA 80 permits the following clearances:

(1) 3/8 in. (9.5 mm) between the bottom of the door and a raised noncombustible sill
(2) 3/4 in. (19.1 mm) between the bottom of the door and the floor where no sill exists
(3) 5/8 in. (15.9 mm) between the bottom of the door and rigid floor tile
(4) 1/2 in. (12.7 mm) between the bottom of the door and floor coverings such as carpet

With the allowed clearances, some smoke will pass to the opposite side of a closed door. It is important to remember that the intent of the smoke partition is not to prevent all smoke transfer but, rather, to limit the transfer of smoke to an acceptable life safety level.

8.2.4.3.5 Doors shall be self-closing or automatic-closing in accordance with 7.2.1.8.

The five sets of provisions applicable to doors in smoke partitions are individually numbered as 8.2.4.3.1 through 8.2.4.3.5 to permit each to be singled out in the references made by other sections of the *Code* that require smoke partitions. For example, the self-closing requirement of 8.2.4.3.5 is exempted in large residential board and care occupancies under specified conditions, but the other door provisions are retained. See 32.3.3.6.5 and 33.3.3.6.5.

8.2.4.4 Penetrations and Miscellaneous Openings in Smoke Partitions.

8.2.4.4.1 Pipes, conduits, bus ducts, cables, wires, air ducts, pneumatic tubes and ducts, and similar building service equipment that pass through smoke partitions shall be protected as follows:

(1) The space between the penetrating item and the smoke partition shall meet one of the following conditions:
   a. It shall be filled with a material that is capable of limiting the transfer of smoke.
   b. It shall be protected by an approved device that is designed for the specific purpose.
(2) Where the penetrating item uses a sleeve to penetrate the smoke partition, the sleeve shall be solidly set in the smoke partition, and the space between the item and the sleeve shall meet one of the following conditions:
   a. It shall be filled with a material that is capable of limiting the transfer of smoke.
   b. It shall be protected by an approved device that is designed for the specific purpose.
(3) Where designs take transmission of vibrations into consideration, any vibration isolation shall meet one of the following conditions:

a. It shall be made on either side of the smoke partitions.
b. It shall be made by an approved device that is designed for the specific purpose.

8.2.4.4.2 Openings located at points where smoke partitions meet the outside walls, other smoke partitions, smoke barriers, or fire barriers of a building shall meet one of the following conditions:

(1) They shall be filled with a material that is capable of limiting the transfer of smoke.
(2) They shall be made by an approved device that is designed for the specific purpose.

8.2.4.4.3* Air transfer openings in smoke partitions shall be provided with approved dampers designed to limit the transfer of smoke. Dampers in air transfer openings shall close upon detection of smoke by approved smoke detectors installed in accordance with NFPA 72, *National Fire Alarm Code*.

If ductwork runs to a smoke partition, pierces the partition, and continues its run on the other side of the partition, no transfer opening exists. Given that no transfer opening is present, there is no requirement for a smoke leakage–rated damper. If such ducted HVAC systems without dampers are to spread smoke, spread will occur via migration, because the provisions of NFPA 90A, *Standard for the Installation of Air-Conditioning and Ventilating Systems*, require the automatic shutdown of most of the fans that would otherwise push and pull smoke through the ductwork.

A.8.2.4.4.3 An air transfer opening as defined in NFPA 90A, *Standard for the Installation of Air-Conditioning and Ventilating Systems*, is an opening designed to allow the movement of environmental air between two contiguous spaces.

8.2.5 Vertical Openings.

Unprotected or improperly protected vertical openings have consistently been major contributing factors in multiple-death fires. This is particularly well illustrated by the two deadliest hotel fires in recent decades in the U.S. and its possessions.[22]

The unprotected vertical opening between the ballroom level, where fire originated in the 1986 DuPont Plaza Hotel in which 97 people died in San Juan, Puerto Rico, and the casino level, where nearly all the deaths occurred, would not be allowed by the *Code*, given the lack of other fire protection design features of that area.[23]

In the 1980 MGM Grand Hotel fire in Las Vegas, Nevada, where 85 people died, smoke spread occurred via unprotected vertical openings (concealed spaces, elevator shafts) and insufficiently protected exit stair enclosures.[24] Many factors contributed to the vertical smoke spread, including the following:

(1) Unprotected seismic joint shafts and elevator hoistways
(2) Insufficiently fire resistance–rated construction used in interior stair enclosures
(3) Exposure of exit stair and exit passageway spaces to casino level plenum air
(4) Heating, ventilating, and air conditioning systems with fire dampers that did not operate

Most of the hotel and motel fires of recent decades that have resulted in 10 or more fatalities have involved unprotected vertical openings, typically unenclosed interior stairs.

8.2.5.1 Every floor that separates stories in a building shall be constructed as a smoke barrier to provide a basic degree of compartmentation. *(See 3.3.182 for definition of Smoke Barrier.)*

Exception: This requirement shall not apply where otherwise specified by 8.2.5.5, 8.2.5.6, or Chapters 11 through 42.

Although the *Code* requires that every floor be constructed as a smoke barrier, the intent of the requirement is tempered to emphasize that a basic degree of compartmentation be provided. The reference to the definition of *smoke barrier* in 3.3.182 provides the user with the information that such barriers might have protected openings. Thus, it is not the *Code*'s intent that every floor must restrict the passage of smoke to the same degree as that of a required smoke barrier in accordance with the provisions of Section 8.3. Even required smoke barriers, which must comply with Section 8.3, are afforded the use of Exception No. 4 to 8.3.5.1, which allows smoke dampers to be omitted where ducts penetrate floors that serve as smoke barriers. See commentary on Exception No. 4 to 8.3.5.1.

8.2.5.2* Openings through floors, such as stairways, hoistways for elevators, dumbwaiters, and inclined and vertical conveyors; shaftways used for light, ventilation, or building services; or expansion joints and seismic joints used to allow structural movements shall be enclosed with fire barrier walls. Such enclosures shall be continuous from floor to floor or floor to roof. Openings shall be protected as appropriate for the fire resistance rating of the barrier.

Exception No. 1: This requirement shall not apply where otherwise specified by 8.2.5.5, 8.2.5.6, 8.2.5.7, or Chapters 11 through 42.

Exception No. 2: This requirement shall not apply to escalators and moving walks protected in accordance with 8.2.5.11.

Exception No. 3: * *This requirement shall not apply to expansion or seismic joints designed to prevent the penetration of fire and shown to have a fire resistance rating of not less than the required fire resistance rating of the floor when tested in accordance with ANSI/UL 2079, Test of Fire Resistance of Building Joint Systems.*

A.8.2.5.2 Exception No. 3 One method of determining the fire resistance rating of expansion and seismic joints is by testing in accordance with UL 2079, *Test for Fire Resistance of Building Joint Systems.*

It is important to note that 8.2.5.1 and 8.2.5.2 apply to all occupancies, unless the specific occupancy provides an exception. Protection of vertical openings is normally covered in subsection __.3.1 (for example, 12.3.1 for new assembly occupancies or 18.3.1 for new health care occupancies) of each occupancy chapter.

Protection of vertical openings is of extreme importance if fire casualties are to be reduced. In report after report of fires involving fatalities, unprotected vertical openings were a major factor contributing to loss of life.

Vertical fire spread is a major factor contributing to the extensive property damage characteristic of large-loss building fires; thus a correlation frequently exists between loss of life from fire and monetary loss from fire. Vertical fire spread relates directly to the lack of protection for vertical openings, because the principal structural weakness responsible for the vertical spread of fire is the absence of the fire cutoffs at openings between floors.

Exhibit 8.8 illustrates some typical floor openings in buildings. If the exit stairs at each end of the building are not properly enclosed per the requirements of 7.1.3.2, they do not qualify as an exit. If the exit stairs do not comply with the requirements of 8.2.5 and subsection __.3.1 of the appropriate occupancy chapter, they create unprotected vertical openings. The other floor openings illustrated in Exhibit 8.8 are not affected by the requirements applicable to exits, but if these openings are not properly enclosed, they create unprotected vertical openings.

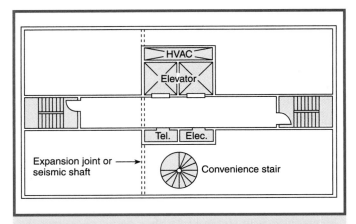

Exhibit 8.8 *Typical floor openings that, if not properly enclosed, might spread the effects of a fire from floor to floor.*

Based on lessons learned from the Las Vegas MGM Grand Hotel fire, the 1988 edition of the *Code* expanded the list of floor openings to include expansion joints and seismic joints that allow structural movements. In lieu of full enclosure from floor to floor, Exception No. 3 to 8.2.5.2 specifically recognizes the use of fire protection–rated expansion or seismic joints, with a minimum rating of not less than the required fire resistance rating of the floor. Without appropriately rated joints, the enclosure requirements might be satisfied by an arrangement of walls and doors as shown in Exhibit 8.9. The enclosure of the seismic joint running horizontally across the building and vertically through all floors is accomplished by back-to-back fire resistance–rated barriers and cross-corridor fire protection–rated door assemblies.

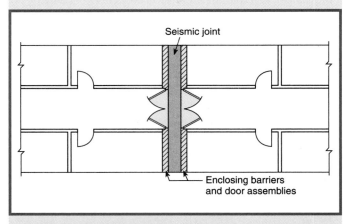

Exhibit 8.9 *Enclosure of seismic joint.*

Exception No. 4:   Enclosure shall not be required for pneumatic tube conveyors protected in accordance with 8.2.3.2.4.2.

Exception No. 5:   This requirement shall not apply to existing mail chutes where one of the following conditions is met:

(a) The cross-sectional area does not exceed 16 in.^{2} (103 cm^2).

(b) The building is protected throughout by an approved automatic sprinkler system in accordance with Section 9.7.

A.8.2.5.2 Penetrations through floor/ceiling and roof/ceiling assemblies should be protected using the methods specified in Tables A.8.2.5.2(a) and (b).

Protection methods for penetrations are as follows:

(a) *Method A.* 2-hour fire resistance–rated shaft enclosure

(b) *Method B.* 1-hour fire resistance–rated shaft enclosure

(c) *Method C.* Protection of the annular space around the penetrating item

C1 = Protection at the ceiling line
C2 = Protection at the floor line

(d) *Method D.* Installation of an approved fire damper in a duct penetration in accordance with its listing

D1 = Ceiling damper at the ceiling line
D2 = Fire damper at the floor line

(e) *Method E.* Use of an approved, through-penetration protection system tested in accordance with ASTM E 814, *Methods for Fire Tests of Through-Penetration Fire Stops,* at a positive pressure differential between the exposed and unexposed surfaces of the test assembly of not less than 0.01 in. water column (2.5 Pa)

Systems should have an F rating of not less than 1 hour but not less than the required fire resistance rating of the assembly being penetrated. Systems protecting floor penetrations should have a T rating of not less than 1 hour but not less than the required fire resistance rating of the floor being penetrated. Floor penetrations contained within the cavity of a wall at the location of the floor penetration do not require a T rating.

(f) *Method F.* No requirements
(g) *Method G.* Penetrations permitted only when tested

Table A.8.2.5.2(a) Nonrated Floor and Roof Assemblies

Penetration Location	Conduits, Pipes, and Tubes† NC	C	Ducts NC	C	Factory-Built Appliance Vents and Chimneys NC	C	Cables and Wires NC and C
Penetration through three floors or more (connecting four stories or more)	A, C2, or E	A or E	A				A or E
Penetration through two floors, maximum (connecting three stories, maximum)	A, B, C2, or E	A, B, or E	A or B	A or B	A, B, or C2	A or B	A, B, or E
Penetration through one floor, maximum (connecting two stories maximum)	A, B, C2, or E		A, B, C2, or D2		A, B, or C2		A, B, C2, or E
Penetration through roof/ceiling assembly Penetration through roof membrane only	F						

C: Combustible.
NC: Noncombustible.
†Pipes and tubes carrying hazardous materials might require additional protection.

Table A.8.2.5.2(b) Rated Floor and Roof Assemblies

Penetration Location			Penetrating Material Classification						
			Conduits, Pipes, and Tubes[†]		**Ducts**		**Factory-Built Appliance Vents and Chimneys**		**Cables and Wires**
			NC	C	NC	C	NC	C	NC and C
Penetration through three floors or more (connecting four stories or more)			A, E, or G	A or E	A				A or E
Penetration through two floors, maximum (connecting three stories, maximum)			A, B, C2, E, or G	A, B, E, or G	A or B		A or B		A, B, E, or G
Penetration through one floor, maximum (connecting two stories, maximum)	Monolithic fire-rated assembly		A, B, C2, E, or G	A, B, E, or G	A, B, or D2[‡]		A, B, or C2	A or B	A, B, C2, E, or G
	Fire-rated assembly with membrane protection	Ceiling membrane penetrated	A, B, C1[§], E, or G		A, B, D1[§], or G		A, B, or C1[§]		A, B, C1[§], E, or G
		Floor membrane penetrated	A, B, C2, E, or G		A, B, or D2[‡]		A, B, or C2		A, B, C2, E, or G
Penetration through roof/ceiling assembly	Ceiling membrane		A, B, C1[§], E, or G		A, B, D1[§], or G		A, B, or C1[§]		A, B, C1[§], E, or G
	Roof membrane								
Penetration through roof membrane only			F						

C: Combustible.

NC: Noncombustible.

[†]Pipes and tubes carrying hazardous materials might require additional protection.

[‡]Duct is required to be part of fully ducted system (transfer grilles not permitted).

[§]Aggregate area of openings not to exceed 100 in.² (0.065 m²)/100 ft² (9.3 m²).

in accordance with NFPA 251, *Standard Methods of Tests of Fire Endurance of Building Construction and Materials,* as a part of the rated assembly

Penetrations of nonrated assemblies should be protected as required by Table A.8.2.5.2(a). Penetrations of rated assemblies should be protected as required by Table A.8.2.5.2(b).

Expansion joints are usually found only in large buildings (that is, not less than 200 ft (60 m) in either length or width, or both) of steel or concrete construction. They are provided to allow the separate portions of the structural frame to expand and contract with temperature and moisture changes without adversely affecting the building's structural integrity or serviceability. Expansion joints can usually be identified by the following characteristics:

(1) A double row of columns
(2) A width of 1 in. to 3 in. (2.5 cm to 7.6 cm)
(3) A steel plate cover that is attached to the floor on one side of the joint and is free to slide on the other side

Expansion joints should not be confused with control or construction joints.

Control joints are normally found in concrete or masonry walls and concrete slabs-on-grade. They are provided for the following purposes:

(1) To prevent cracking of the wall or slab due to excessive tensile forces in the concrete or masonry caused by shrinkage upon drying
(2) To induce cracking due to excessive tensile forces caused by drying or shrinkage expected to occur at a predetermined location; hence, the term *control joint*

Construction joints are used as stopping and starting points for two successive concrete placements (pours) in walls, floors, and beams. Since a construction joint is required to be designed to transfer load across the joints, separation due to thermal- or moisture-induced movements is not anticipated.

Seismic joints might be found in buildings other than

those that are rectangular in plan (for example, L- and T-shaped buildings) in areas where the risk of an earthquake is moderate to high. Such joints in multistory buildings can be as much as 12 in. (30.5 cm) in width. They are provided to allow the separated portions of the building to act independently of each other to undergo differential lateral displacements when an earthquake occurs.

With expansion or seismic joints, consideration should be given to the ability of the protecting system to remain in place and perform its intended function after repeated movements of the joint, and with the width of the joint varying from its maximum to minimum width. In the case of seismic joints, the protection system can be damaged during an earthquake that otherwise is not strong enough to cause major structural damage to the building. Therefore, it is necessary to conduct an inspection of such buildings after an earthquake.

8.2.5.3 Vertical openings (shafts) that do not extend to the bottom or the top of the building or structure shall be enclosed at the lowest or highest level of the shaft, respectively, with construction in accordance with 8.2.5.4.

Exception: Shafts shall be permitted to terminate in a room or space having a use related to the purpose of the shaft, provided that the room or space is separated from the remainder of the building by construction having a fire resistance rating and opening protectives in accordance with 8.2.5.4 and 8.2.3.2.3.

Some shafts commonly found in buildings do not extend through the entire height of the building. For example, in a high-rise building, a percentage of the overall number of elevator shafts will service only the lower-rise portion of the building. Such shafts might run from the street level through the twentieth floor of a 40-story building. In a typical hotel that devotes the first couple of stories to assembly occupancy uses and locates guest rooms above in the hotel occupancy tower, the shafts associated with guest room bathroom exhaust might begin at the third floor and continue to the roof. In such cases, although the shaft walls are constructed of fire resistance–rated assemblies, an unprotected shaft ceiling/top or unprotected shaft floor/bottom would allow fire and other products of combustion to travel vertically to some other part of the building. Because of this concern, 8.2.5.3 requires that those shaft ceilings or floors be protected by construction as required for the shaft walls.

Exhibit 8.10 illustrates various shaft arrangements. Shafts that do not run the full height of a building must be capped by floors or ceilings of fire

resistance–rated construction at least equal to the required rating of the shaft-enclosing walls. Shaft A runs vertically for the full height of the building and requires only vertical fire barriers to separate the shaft from the remainder of the interior of the building. Because neither shaft B nor shaft C extends the full height of the building, horizontal fire barriers must be provided to complete the shaft envelope with a floor for shaft B and a ceiling for shaft C. Shaft D, which is used for heating, ventilating, and air conditioning (HVAC), extends vertically from the second floor to the roof; the exception to 8.2.5.3, makes it unnecessary to install a rated floor barrier between shaft D and the mechanical equipment room, E. In this case, the ceiling and walls of the mechanical equipment room, used for purposes related to the use of the HVAC shaft, must be constructed of material of at least the same hourly rating as required for shaft D. The room enclosure thus becomes an extension of the shaft. Access to room E from within the building would be gained through appropriately rated fire door assemblies.

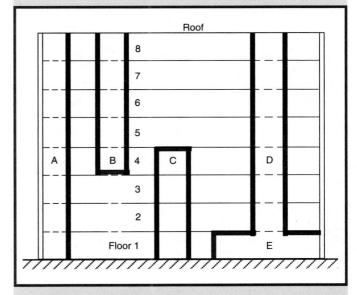

Exhibit 8.10 *Shaft enclosures.*

8.2.5.4* The fire resistance rating for the enclosure of floor openings shall be not less than as follows *(see 7.1.3.2.1 for enclosure of exits):*

(1) Enclosures connecting four stories or more in new construction—2-hour fire barriers
(2) Other enclosures in new construction—1-hour fire barriers

(3) Existing enclosures in existing buildings—½-hour fire barriers

(4) As specified in Chapter 26 for lodging and rooming houses, in Chapter 28 for new hotels, and in Chapter 30 for new apartment buildings

A.8.2.5.4 The application of the 2-hour rule in buildings not divided into stories is permitted to be based on the number of levels of platforms or walkways served by the stairs.

The key to understanding 8.2.5.4 is that the *Code's* concern is with the number of stories connected via the vertical opening, not the height of the building. For example, if there is a vertical opening between the second, third, and fourth stories of an eight-story building, the opening connects fewer than four floors and the enclosure must be of 1-hour rather than 2-hour fire resistance–rated construction.

Where addressing vertical openings, the *Code* does not use the height of buildings or a designated number of floors above ground as the basis for its rated enclosure requirements. Rather, such requirements are based on the total number of floors connected by the vertical opening. Where a vertical opening in new construction connects four stories or more, the enclosure protection afforded must have at least a 2-hour fire resistance rating. This requirement applies to stories that are all above the exit discharge level, or all below the exit discharge level, or to any combination thereof. Where three or fewer stories are connected by a vertical opening in new construction, the enclosure rating must be at least 1 hour. Existing vertical openings, regardless of the number of stories they connect, require protection by ½-hour fire resistance–rated enclosures.

See Exhibit 8.11 for illustrations of the vertical opening protection requirements for new construc-

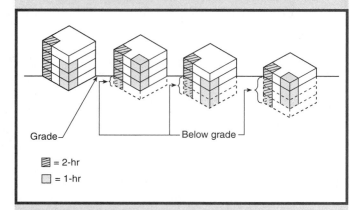

Exhibit 8.11 *Vertical opening protection.*

tion. Although Exhibit 8.11 depicts vertical openings that resemble exit stair enclosures, the same requirements apply to any type of vertical opening, including exit access stairs and elevator, electrical, HVAC, and seismic shafts.

Experience shows that, under some circumstances, each of the 1-hour and 2-hour rating levels provides a comfortable period of time for the occupants of a building to evacuate. On the other hand, there are times when the integrity of the construction will be taxed to its limit; for example, during a fire that has gone undetected for a long period. This type of fire can generate heavy smoke and toxic gases that complicate evacuation by blocking the exit access.

An interior exit stair (see definition of *exit* in 3.3.61) must be enclosed to be separated from other building spaces and to provide a protected way of travel to the exit discharge. If not properly enclosed, the exit not only fails to meet the definition of an exit but also creates an unprotected vertical opening. Thus, an exit stair must meet the requirements for enclosure of an exit (see 7.1.3.2), as well as those for protection of vertical openings in accordance with 8.2.5.4, as modified by the applicable occupancy chapter. Because the requirements for enclosure of exits are more stringent than the requirements for protection of vertical openings, once the more stringent requirements have been met, the other requirements are usually met automatically.

Paragraph 8.2.5.4(4) references the hotel, apartment, and lodging and rooming house occupancy chapters, which allow exceptions to the requirements of 8.2.5.4, under certain conditions. Some of the exceptions permit 1-hour rated enclosures, regardless of the number of stories connected, if the building is protected throughout by automatic sprinklers. Although these occupancy chapters use exceptions to temper the basic Chapter 8 requirements with respect to the enclosure of vertical openings, it is possible for a specific occupancy chapter to be more stringent. For example, see 19.3.1.1, which requires 1-hour enclosures in existing health care occupancies rather than the ½-hour enclosures that would otherwise be permitted by 8.2.5.4(3).

8.2.5.5 Unless prohibited by Chapters 12 through 42, unenclosed floor openings forming a communicating space between floor levels shall be permitted, provided that the following conditions are met:

(1) The communicating space does not connect more than three contiguous stories.

(2) The lowest or next to lowest story within the communicating space is a street floor.

(3) The entire floor area of the communicating space is open and unobstructed such that a fire in any part of the space will be readily obvious to the occupants of the space prior to the time it becomes an occupant hazard.

(4) The communicating space is separated from the remainder of the building by fire barriers with not less than a 1-hour fire resistance rating.

Exception No. 1: In buildings protected throughout by an approved automatic sprinkler system in accordance with Section 9.7, a smoke barrier in accordance with Section 8.3 shall be permitted to serve as the separation required by 8.2.5.5(4).

Exception No. 2: The requirement of 8.2.5.5(4) shall not apply to fully sprinklered residential housing units of detention and correctional occupancies in accordance with Exception No. 2 to 22.3.1.1 and Exception No. 2 to 23.3.1.1.

(5) The communicating space has ordinary hazard contents protected throughout by an approved automatic sprinkler system in accordance with Section 9.7 or has only low hazard contents. *(See 6.2.2.)*

(6) Egress capacity is sufficient to provide for all the occupants of all levels within the communicating space to simultaneously egress the communicating space by considering it as single floor area in determining the required egress capacity.

(7)* Each occupant within the communicating space has access to not less than one exit without having to traverse another story within the communicating space.

A.8.2.5.5(7) Given that a mezzanine meeting the maximum one-third area criterion of 8.2.6.2.1 is not considered a story, it is permitted, therefore, to have 100 percent of its exit access within the communicating area run back through the story below.

(8) Each occupant not in the communicating space has access to not less than one exit without having to enter the communicating space.

Paragraph 8.2.5.5 recognizes a vertical opening that is exempt from the normal enclosure requirements of 8.2.4.4 under the following two conditions:

(1) Use of the provision is not specifically prohibited by the pertinent occupancy chapter for the occupancy type in question.

(2) All the alternative protection provisions of 8.2.5.5(1) through (8) are met.

The following paragraphs explain and illustrate the provisions of 8.2.5.5(1) through (8).

(a) The vertical space cannot connect or communicate among more than three stories, and all connected stories are required to be contiguous to each other. The building itself, which houses the vertical opening in question, is permitted to be more than three stories in height. For example, the vertical opening might communicate among floors one through three of a six-story building. See Exhibit 8.12.

The provisions of 8.2.5.5 are often referred to as the "mini-atrium" requirements. The requirements, because they are limited to a maximum three-story vertical opening, are not as stringent as those of 8.2.5.6, which is applicable to atria that can involve vertical openings that communicate among 50 or 100 stories or more. A two- or three-story atrium can be adequately protected by the requirements of 8.2.5.5 without having to resort to the requirements of 8.2.5.6. The fact that a two- or three-story space is labeled as an atrium on building plans does not necessarily mean that it must be protected by the requirements of 8.2.5.6. A two- or three-story vertical opening, regardless of whether or not it is called an atrium, should be allowed to be protected per the requirements of 8.2.5.5, provided that the occupancy chapter(s) involved doesn't prohibit the use of 8.2.5.5, and the requirements of 8.2.5.5(1) through (8) are met.

(b) The lowest of the maximum three communicating floor levels is at, or not more than one level below, the street level. In other words, the vertical opening can communicate among only the first, second, and third floors or among the basement, first, and second floors. See space A in Exhibit 8.12. As previously mentioned, additional building floor levels might be present either above or below the floors

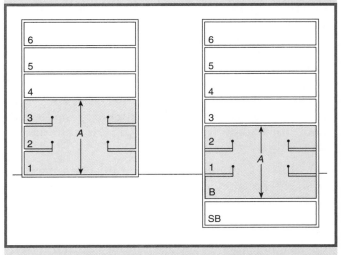

Exhibit 8.12 *Permitted location of three-story vertical opening.*

involving the vertical opening, but these additional floors cannot be left open to the vertical opening. The more stringent set of provisions for atriums per 8.2.5.6 should be considered where it is necessary or desirable either to have more than three levels open or to locate the communicating levels such that the lowest level does not meet the placement requirement with respect to street level.

(c) The communicating space includes all of the areas within the vertical opening itself and all of the adjoining areas left open to the vertical opening, as well as those areas not separated by minimum 1-hour fire resistance–rated barriers. The communicating space must be open and unobstructed so that occupants of the space will be aware of fire and smoke conditions emanating from any part of the communicating space prior to the time that such conditions become a hazard.

The provisions of 8.2.5.5 were originally written as an exception to the enclosure requirements for vertical openings in 8.2.5.1 to recognize typical mercantile occupancy construction practices, which left partial, mezzanine-like floors open to the main street-level shopping floor below. These arrangements were sufficiently open so that, where coupled with the other provisions of the exception, they allowed sufficient time for the necessary awareness of emergency conditions and for occupants to use the egress system. These provisions were not intended to be used for an unenclosed stair. The size of the small opening created by an unenclosed stair is insufficient to provide occupants on all levels connected by the stair with the needed degree of awareness.

Between the two extremes of vast amounts of openness (as in the case of the mezzanine-like floors described in the previous paragraph) and little or no openness (as depicted by the unenclosed stair), judging sufficient openness becomes difficult. Through the use of the equivalency concept addressed in Section 1.5 of the *Code*, some authorities having jurisdiction have allowed complete automatic smoke detection systems with proper occupant notification features to be substituted for the openness and unobstructedness required by 8.2.5.5(3) for awareness and early warning purposes.

(d) The communicating space must be separated from the remainder of the building by fire barriers with a minimum 1-hour fire resistance rating. Once the boundaries of the communicating space are established, based on determining how much area is open enough [per the requirement of 8.2.5.5(3) above] to permit awareness and early warning, then areas outside these boundaries must be separated from the communicating space associated with the vertical opening by barriers with a minimum 1-hour fire resistance rating. If the building is fully sprinklered, the barriers are permitted to be nonrated but must resist the passage of smoke and meet the other smoke barrier requirements of Section 8.3. It is thought that the sprinkler system will control the fire and make fire resistance–rated barriers unnecessary. The smoke barriers will control the limited smoke, under sprinklered conditions, and help maintain a tenable means of egress route.

For example, consider a hotel building with fingerlike guest room wings fanning out from the vertical opening. It can be assumed that the guest room wing corridors will need separation from the vertical opening, because occupants in the corridor on the second or third floor will not be readily aware of a fire on the first floor before it becomes a hazard to their safety. The required 1-hour separation can be provided, while maintaining the perception of openness, by isolating the guest room wings from the vertical opening through the use of pairs of cross-corridor doors held open with automatic release devices. See Exhibit 8.13.

(e) If the communicating space [the vertical opening itself and all adjoining areas open to it as described in item (c)] has *ordinary hazard* contents (as explained in Section 6.2 of this *Code*, as opposed to the NFPA 13, *Standard for the Installation of Sprinkler Systems*, definition of *ordinary hazard occupancies*), all areas within the confines of the communicating space must be sprinklered.[25] If the contents are *low hazard* (again as explained in Section 6.2 of this *Code*, not *light hazard occupancies* as defined in NFPA 13), no sprinklering is required by 8.2.5.5. However, as intended by Section 6.2, most occupancies are classified as ordinary hazard. Because only low hazard and ordinary hazard contents are addressed in 8.2.5.5(5), high hazard contents are prohibited from any vertical openings recognized by 8.2.5.5.

Although sprinklering is required with ordinary hazard contents, only the communicating space (as previously defined) needs to be sprinklered, according to the provisions of 8.2.5.5. The sprinkler system should cover all areas within the boundaries established by the 1-hour fire barriers that are required by item (d). See Exhibit 8.13.

In Exhibit 8.13, the cross-corridor fire doors are held open by automatic release devices so that the corridor appears to be open to the communicating area of the vertical opening. Yet, because there are doors and a barrier at that location, it demarcates the

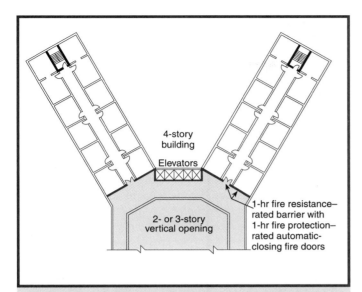

Exhibit 8.13 *Separation of two- or three-story communicating space from remainder of building.*

boundary between the communicating space and the floor area outside the communicating space. Sprinkler protection must be provided for the vertical opening and the shaded adjoining areas up to the 1-hour barriers.

(f) Because all occupants within the communicating area might be exposed within a short time to the effects of a fire within the area, simultaneous evacuation capability needs to be provided. Thus, the combined occupant load for all spaces, on all levels, within the boundaries of the communicating area needs to be included when sizing the means of egress for the communicating area. This requirement is more stringent than the guidelines of 7.3.1.4, which exempt the accumulation of occupant loads from various floors.

(g) Per the requirements of 8.2.5.5(3) and (4), the communicating space is that space that is sufficiently open to the vertical opening to allow ready awareness of fire conditions on that and other levels within the communicating space. Areas that are remote enough from the vertical opening to lose the requisite awareness are then located on the other side of 1-hour fire resistance–rated fire barriers and are considered to be outside the communicating space. Thus, in a typical office building making use of the provisions of 8.2.5.5, for example, some occupants work and are normally stationed within the communicating space, while others work and are stationed outside the communicating space. This arrangement is shown in Exhibit 8.14.

Paragraph 8.2.5.5(7) requires that occupants located within the communicating space have access to at least one exit without having to traverse another story within the communicating space. The communicating space shown in Exhibit 8.14 would meet this requirement by having occupants travel horizontally across the communicating space, pass through the fire doors in the fire-rated barrier into one of the building wings designated as "floor area outside the communicating space," and continue to that wing's enclosed exit stair. In other words, the occupants of the communicating space are not permitted to use the open stairs exclusively to travel to another level of the communicating space to reach the required exits.

In the example illustrated in Exhibit 8.14, assume that some occupants of the communicating space are farther from either of the enclosed exit stairs, which are located at each end of the building, than the travel distance allowed by other *Code* requirements. Further, assume that those same occupants of the communicating space can travel down the open stair and across the bottom floor of the vertical opening to an exterior exit door within the allowable travel distance limitation. The open stair, although it is not an exit, could be considered as exit access, and the door to the outside at the lowest level of the vertical opening could then be regarded as the nearest *Code*-complying exit for those occupants. Either of the enclosed exit stairs at the end of the building could then serve as the second exit for those occupants of the communicating space. The enclosed exit stairs would then serve the following three purposes, none of which would be as the primary exit for those occupants of the communicating space:

(1) The stairs would satisfy the business occupancy chapters' requirements that the minimum two required exits occur on the floor.

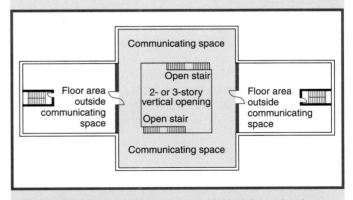

Exhibit 8.14 *Exit access arrangement for building using the two- or three-story vertical opening provision.*

(2) Either stair would satisfy the requirement of 8.2.5.5(7) that the occupants of the communicating space have access to at least one exit without having to traverse another story within the communicating space.

(3) Each stair would satisfy the requirement of 8.2.5.5(8), discussed in the commentary that follows, which mandates that each occupant not located within the communicating space is to have access to at least one exit without entering the communicating space.

(h) Although all occupants must have access to two separate exits, the occupants who are located on any of the maximum of three floors that are permitted to communicate with the vertical opening, but who are not within the communicating space (as illustrated in Exhibit 8.14 by the wings located at each end of the building), must be able to reach one of the two required exits without entering the communicating space. This requirement is satisfied by locating an enclosed exit stair within each of the floor areas outside the communicating space.

The provisions of 8.2.5.5 are permitted unless prohibited by an occupancy chapter. For an example of an occupancy that prohibits the two- or three-story vertical opening, see Exception No. 4 to 18.3.1.1 and Exception No. 4 to 19.3.1.1, which apply to health care occupancies. For an example of an occupancy that provides requirements in addition to those of 8.2.5.5(1) through (8), see 14.3.1 and 15.3.1, which apply to educational occupancies. Chapters 14 and 15 require that the entire building, rather than only the communicating space, be protected by a supervised automatic sprinkler system.

8.2.5.6* Unless prohibited by Chapters 12 through 42, an atrium shall be permitted, provided that the following conditions are met:

A.8.2.5.6 Where atriums are used, there is an added degree of safety to occupants because of the large volume of space into which smoke can be dissipated. However, there is a need to ensure that dangerous concentrations of smoke are promptly removed from the atrium, and the exhaust system needs careful design. For information about systems that can be used to provide smoke protection in these spaces, see the following:

(1) NFPA 92B, *Guide for Smoke Management Systems in Malls, Atria, and Large Areas*

(2) *Design of Smoke Management Systems*

(1) In other than existing, previously approved atria, atriums are separated from the adjacent spaces by fire barriers

with not less than a 1-hour fire resistance rating with opening protectives for corridor walls. *(See 8.2.3.2.3.1(2), Exception No. 1.)*

Exception No. 1: Any number of levels of the building shall be permitted to open directly to the atrium without enclosure based on the results of the engineering analysis required in 8.2.5.6(5).

Exception No. 2:* Glass walls and inoperable windows shall be permitted in lieu of the fire barriers where automatic sprinklers are spaced along both sides of the glass wall and the inoperable window at intervals not to exceed 6 ft (1.8 m). The automatic sprinklers shall be located at a distance from the glass not to exceed 1 ft (0.3 m) and shall be arranged so that the entire surface of the glass is wet upon operation of the sprinklers. The glass shall be tempered, wired, or laminated glass held in place by a gasket system that allows the glass framing system to deflect without breaking (loading) the glass before the sprinklers operate. Automatic sprinklers shall not be required on the atrium side of the glass wall and the inoperable windows where there is no walkway or other floor area on the atrium side above the main floor level. Doors in such walls shall be glass or other material that resists the passage of smoke. Doors shall be self-closing or automatic-closing upon detection of smoke.

A.8.2.5.6(1) Exception No. 2 The intent of the requirement for closely spaced sprinklers to wet the atrium glass wall is to ensure that the surface of the glass is wet upon operation of the sprinklers, with a maximum spacing of sprinklers of 6 ft (1.8 m) on centers. Provided that it can be shown that the glass can be wet by the sprinklers using a given discharge rate and that the 8-ft (1.8-m) spacing is not exceeded, the intent of the requirement is met.

(2) Access to exits is permitted to be within the atrium, and exit discharge in accordance with 7.7.2 is permitted to be within the atrium.

(3) The occupancy within the space meets the specifications for classification as low or ordinary hazard contents. *(See 6.2.2.)*

(4) The entire building is protected throughout by an approved, supervised automatic sprinkler system in accordance with Section 9.7.

(5)* For other than existing, previously approved atria, an engineering analysis is performed that demonstrates that the building is designed to keep the smoke layer interface above the highest unprotected opening to adjoining spaces, or 6 ft (1.85 m) above the highest floor level of exit access open to the atrium for a period equal to 1.5 times the calculated egress time or 20 minutes, whichever is greater.

A.8.2.5.6(5) See NFPA 92B, *Guide for Smoke Management Systems in Malls, Atria, and Large Areas.*

The engineering analysis should include the following elements:

(1) Fire dynamics, including fire size and location, materials likely to be burning, fire plume geometry, fire plume or smoke layer impact on means of egress, and tenability conditions during the period of occupant egress

(2) Response and performance of building systems, including passive barriers, automatic detection and extinguishing, and smoke control

(3) Response time required for building occupants to reach building exits, including any time required to exit through the atrium as permitted by 8.2.5.6(2)

(6)* In other than existing, previously approved atria, where an engineered smoke control system is installed to meet the requirements of 8.2.5.6(5), the system is independently activated by each of the following:
a. The required automatic sprinkler system
b. Manual controls that are readily accessible to the fire department

A.8.2.5.6(6) Activation of the ventilation system by manual fire alarms, extinguishing systems, and detection systems can cause unwanted operation of the system, and it is suggested that consideration be given to zoning of the activation functions so the ventilation system operates only when actually needed.

Atria are permitted in accordance with the provisions of 8.2.5.6 unless prohibited by an occupancy chapter. Although no occupancy chapter prohibits atria, some require additional criteria. For example, health care occupancies prohibit the open floors addressed by Exception No. 1 to 8.2.5.6(1) from involving patient sleeping and treatment rooms. Thus, there would need to be, at a minimum, a smoke-resisting membrane, such as a glass window, between the patient room and the atrium space.

Exhibits 8.15(a) and 8.15(b) illustrate a typical atrium.

Paragraph 8.2.5.6 addresses a vertical opening that communicates among more than the three floors addressed by the "mini-atrium" provision of 8.2.5.5. Although the atrium provisions are not prohibited from being used for two- or three-story, atrium-like vertical openings, the design professional should be allowed to protect such areas in accordance with the less stringent provisions of 8.2.5.5, provided that the occupancy chapter in question doesn't prohibit the use of 8.2.5.5. Use of the provisions of 8.2.5.5 should adequately protect a two- or three-story atrium. The __.3.1 subsections of health care occupancy chapters 18 and 19, which address the protection of vertical openings, prohibit the use of the mini-atrium provi-

sions of 8.2.5.5. Thus, in health care occupancies, a two- or three-story atrium-like vertical opening is allowed only if it meets all criteria of 8.2.5.6 applicable to large atria. For certain designs, 8.2.5.5 is not desirable due to its restriction on exit access within the vertical opening. For example, a three-story hotel would prefer to use the more stringent provisions of 8.2.5.6 because they would permit the guests rooms to have exit access through the atrium, whereas 8.2.5.5 would not allow exit access to be solely through the mini-atrium.

The protection provisions of 8.2.5.6(1) through (6) are explained and illustrated in the paragraphs that follow.

(a) In accordance with the requirements of 8.2.5.4(1), a vertical opening of four or more stories in new construction generally must be separated from the rest of the building by an enclosure of 2-hour fire resistance–rated construction. However, the atrium provisions work together as an overall package in allowing the construction that separates other areas of the building from the atrium to be reduced to a 1-hour fire resistance rating. Further,

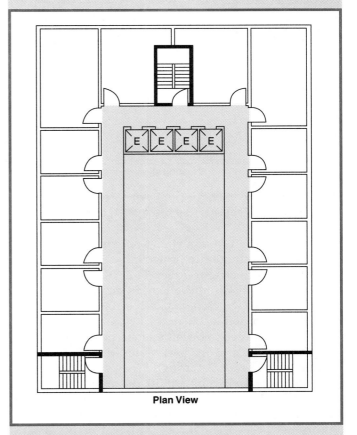

Plan View

Exhibit 8.15(a) *Plan view of a typical atrium.*

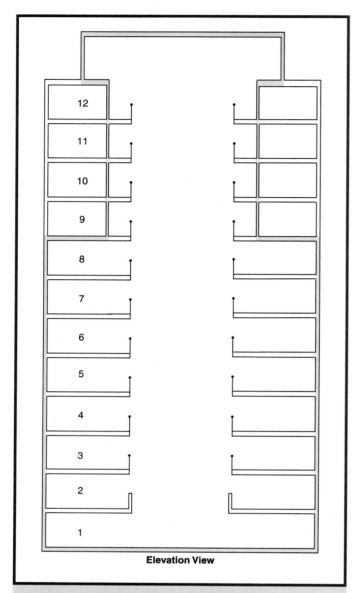

Exhibit 8.15(b) *Elevation view of a typical atrium.*

needed. For example, for health care occupancies, Chapters 18 and 19 limit the location of the open levels allowed by Exception No. 1 to 8.2.5.6(1) so that patient treatment and sleeping rooms are not left open to the atrium.

To allow visual contact between the atrium and floors that have not been proven by engineering analysis to warrant openness, Exception No. 2 to 8.2.5.6(1) exempts the 1-hour rated separation if a smoke-resisting separation is provided. Exception No. 2 to 8.2.5.6(1) recognizes the use of glass walls, vision panels, and windows in lieu of actual 1-hour fire resistance–rated construction. Paragraph A.8.2.5.6(1), Exception No. 2, explains the intent of the requirement for directing closely spaced sprinklers at the glass walls.

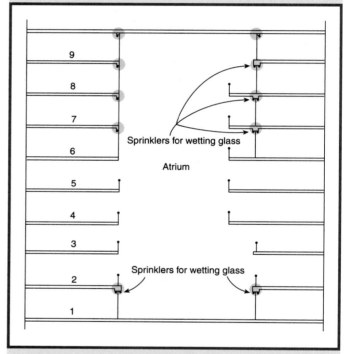

Exhibit 8.16 *Floor levels open to atrium.*

the doors in the 1-hour atrium fire barrier are permitted to be 20-minute fire protection–rated assemblies as allowed for corridor doors. Thus, the intent of the 1-hour separation requirement is mainly to provide a carefully constructed smoke-resistant barrier.

Per Exception No. 1 to 8.2.5.6(1), any number of levels is permitted to be left open to the atrium based on the engineering analysis required in 8.2.5.6(5). In Exhibit 8.16, levels 2 through 5 have been left open to the atrium. In Exhibit 8.15(b), the open levels occur on floors 1 through 8. Some occupancy chapters modify the atrium requirements as needed to afford the users of those occupancies the level of life safety

The concept of wetting the glass that is exposed to a fire, without specifying a water application rate, is similar to boiling water in a Pyrex® container over an open flame. As long as there is some water present to absorb the heat, the glass itself does not reach excessive temperatures that would cause failure. To ensure that water will reach the surface of the glass, window blinds and draperies must not be placed between the line of closely spaced sprinklers and the glass. Careful design will allow for the sprinklers to be placed close enough to the glass so that blinds and draperies can be installed using normal installation practice.

The allowance to omit lines of closely spaced sprinklers on the atrium side of glass walls, which are to be used in lieu of 1-hour fire resistance–rated barriers, is intended to apply to the floor levels above the atrium main floor level. In other words, if glass walls are used on the main floor level in lieu of a 1-hour enclosure, sprinklers must be installed on both sides of the glass at that level, because combustibles might be placed on the floor on the atrium side of the glass. See Exhibit 8.16.

(b) The exit stairs must be enclosed in accordance with the exit enclosure requirements of 7.1.3.2, although they are allowed to be within the communicating space and located so as to require building occupants to walk through the communicating space of the atrium in order to gain access to the stairs. Exhibit 8.15(a) shows three such exit stair enclosures located within the communicating space, with all occupants of the floor required to walk within the communicating space across the interior exit access balcony of that floor in order to gain access to the stairs. On the level of exit discharge, up to 50 percent of those three exits is permitted to discharge occupants from upper or lower floors in accordance with the provisions of 7.7.2, thus forcing some occupants to walk across the floor of the atrium to reach a door to the outside. The stringent requirements of 8.2.5.6(1) through (6) ensure an adequate overall life safety package, allowing the exit access and as much as half of the exit discharge to be within the atrium.

(c) The occupancy within the communicating space [the vertical opening and all floor areas left open to the vertical opening, such as balcony-like walking surfaces and the levels allowed to be left completely open via the provisions of Exception No. 1 to 8.2.5.6(1)] is limited to low or ordinary hazard contents as addressed in 6.2.2. High hazard contents are thus prohibited from being placed within the communicating space but could be within hazardous area rooms surrounded by fire resistance–rated walls in accordance with the provisions of Section 8.4. Because the provisions of 8.2.5.6(4) require that the building be completely protected by an approved, supervised automatic sprinkler system, the presence of only low hazard contents within the communicating space does not exempt the space from the sprinkler requirement; whereas, under the mini-atrium provisions of 8.2.5.5, such an exemption is allowed.

(d) The entire building, rather than only the communicating space involving the atrium opening, must be protected by an approved, supervised automatic sprinkler system meeting the requirements of Section 9.7. Assuming that the atrium is located in a hotel building of five or more stories, for example, the provisions of Section 9.7 require the use of NFPA 13, *Standard for the Installation of Sprinkler Systems*.

(e) An engineered smoke control or smoke removal system acceptable to the authority having jurisdiction has been required since the atrium provisions were first introduced into the *Life Safety Code* in the 1981 edition. As advisory but nonmandatory information, the appendix of earlier editions suggested that, depending on atrium height and volume, either four or six air changes per hour could provide the smoke exhaust rate needed to meet the tenability conditions intended by the requirement for atrium smoke control.

The guideline for six air changes per hour came to be considered law by many authorities having jurisdiction and was thus accepted as the norm by many system designers. Authorities having jurisdiction then subjected such systems to acceptance testing using smoke bombs that produce cold smoke, which does not have the heat, buoyancy, and entrainment of air from a real fire. The acceptance criteria were further complicated by those who mistakenly believed that the intent of the smoke control requirement was, for example, that no smoke be visible within the atrium at the end of a 10-minute test. Designers found that, to ensure that the acceptance test could be passed, the system should provide approximately ten to twelve air changes per hour. In effect, atrium smoke control systems were typically designed to pass the acceptance test with no consideration or assurance of effective smoke control under fire conditions. NFPA 92B, *Guide for Smoke Management Systems in Malls, Atria, and Large Areas*, warns that a system designed in accordance with NFPA 92B and capable of providing the intended smoke management might not pass smoke bomb tests.[26] Conversely, it is possible for a system that is incapable of providing the intended smoke management to pass smoke bomb tests. Because of the impracticality of conducting real fire tests within an atrium, the acceptance tests described in NFPA 92B are directed at those aspects of smoke management systems that can be verified.

Using performance-based criteria, 8.2.5.6(5) requires that an engineering analysis be performed to demonstrate that smoke will be managed for the time needed to evacuate the building. To accomplish this, 8.2.5.6(5) requires the analysis to prove that the smoke layer interface will be maintained above the highest unprotected opening to adjoining spaces, or 6 ft (1.85 m) above the highest floor level of exit access open to the atrium for a time equal to 1.5 times the calculated egress time or 20 minutes, whichever is greater. For a protect-in-place occupancy, such as health care, the evacuation time is considered to be infinite, which means that the smoke control performance criteria must be maintained indefinitely.

In Exhibit 8.15(b), floors 1 through 8 are open to the atrium and floors 9 through 12 use the atrium balconies for exit access. The engineering analysis will most likely determine that a high-capacity smoke management system will be needed to meet the performance-based criteria for maintaining the smoke layer interface 6 ft (1.85 m) above the walking surface of the twelfth-floor exit access balcony (the highest floor level with exit access in the atrium). The smoke control system will need to begin removing smoke early in the fire, because there is little accumulation capacity in the space above the twelfth floor and beneath the ceiling of the atrium. Contrast this situation with that shown in Exhibit 8.17 in which floors 10 through 12 do not use the atrium for exit access. Although a smoke control system will be needed to meet the performance-based smoke control criteria, the system might be of a less aggressive design, given that the smoke can bank down from the ceiling of the atrium to below the tenth floor before affecting occupant egress.

NFPA 92B, *Guide for Smoke Management Systems in Malls, Atria, and Large Areas*, quantifies the physics associated with atrium smoke control and presents methodologies for system design in an understandable and useful format. The guidelines of NFPA 92B allow the system designer to design a system and prepare the associated documentation for the authority having jurisdiction to assess for adequacy in meeting the performance criteria of 8.2.5.6(5). For example, the designer and the authority having jurisdiction agree that an acceptable design must provide for the level of smoke-filling to be maintained at least 6 ft (1.85 m) above the highest floor level open to the atrium and the highest floor level used for exit access within the atrium for a minimum of 20 minutes after actuation of the fire alarm system.

The following example, which is illustrated in Exhibit 8.17, makes use of the guidelines of NFPA 92B in designing a smoke management system that meets the smoke-filling criterion agreed to by the designer and the authority having jurisdiction.

The proposed atrium building is to be twelve

stories in height, with the fifth floor as the highest level open to the atrium and the ninth floor as the highest walking level within the atrium. Further, the atrium ceiling is to be 120 ft (36.6 m) above the floor; the atrium opening is to be rectangular with horizontal dimensions of 100 ft × 200 ft (30.4 m × 61 m); and the atrium is to be furnished with upholstered furniture and wood and plastic tables characteristic of the fire loading typically associated with a business occupancy.

Note that the following example and analysis use the formulae from those portions of NFPA 92B that use the conventional U.S. Customary units (for example, feet, square feet, Btu per second, pounds per cubic foot, cubic feet per minute). Although it is standard practice within this handbook to provide metric or SI units, where applicable, as parenthetically enclosed equivalents, SI equivalents are not provided in the calculations that follow. Rather, the reader is referred to Appendix D of NFPA 92B, where SI unit forms of all 25 equations used in the guide are available.

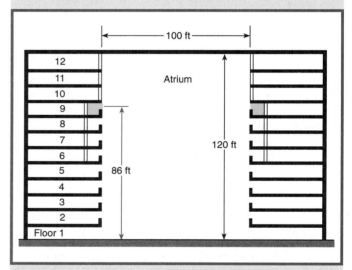

Exhibit 8.17 *Twelve-story atrium for which smoke control is to be provided.*

If the designer prefers to install spot smoke detectors for activation of the smoke control system and initiation of the building fire alarm at the top of the atrium only, the designer would need to determine if smoke will reach the ceiling or stratify at a given distance below the ceiling in the case of the selected design fire. Stratification occurs when the temperature of the rising plume equals the temperature of the surrounding air and the fire has insufficient energy to "push" the smoke layer any higher.

Computational methods, which are beyond the scope of this analysis, are available for determining the potential for stratification below the atrium ceiling. For example, in an atrium that is known to have a discrete ambient temperature change at a given elevation above the floor level (perhaps due to solar loading), the designer can determine the height at which the fire plume centerline temperature equals the ambient temperature. Stratification can be assumed to occur at that height.

To further compound the issue, detection of smoke by spot-type detectors at ceiling heights greater than 30 ft requires its own engineering analysis, which is also beyond the scope of this example. For such analyses, consult Schifiliti and Pucci's "Fire Detection Modeling, State of the Art." [27]

Stratification is not a concern after the smoke management system activates, because the natural buoyancy of the smoke (or lack thereof) will be negligible compared to the pressure differences and air movement created by the system. Stratification can, however, have a significant adverse effect on the time to system initiation from the start of the fire. The designer might wish to design the detection system for activation of the smoke management system in a manner that ensures prompt detection regardless of the ambient conditions in the atrium at the time of the fire. Projected-beam smoke detectors, which are capable of measuring the light obscuration caused by smoke particles, can be arranged to quickly detect either a developing smoke layer or the rising smoke plume. In either case, a series of beam detectors is to be installed at strategic points within the atrium. Projected-beam smoke detectors can be arranged to provide a highly reliable means of detecting a fire within the atrium in its early stages. In all cases, the requirements of NFPA 72, *National Fire Alarm Code*, and the detector manufacturer's installation guidelines should be followed.[28]

For the remainder of this exercise, it is assumed that the atrium is provided with projected-beam smoke detectors arranged to activate the smoke management system and initiate the building fire alarm relatively quickly following the onset of fire, and before the smoke level descends to within 6 ft of the highest level of exit access open to the atrium.

Having equated the furniture arrangement as typical of the combustible loading associated with a business occupancy, the designer feels comfortable assuming a typical heat-release rate per unit floor area of 20 Btu/ft²-sec, which realistically translates to a design fire heat-release rate, Q, from steady fire of 5000 Btu/sec. The convective portion of the heat-

release rate, Q_c, can be estimated as 70 percent of the heat-release rate, Q.

The designer next calculates the volumetric exhaust rate required to keep smoke 86 ft above the atrium floor (that is, 6 ft above the highest walking level in the atrium which, in this case, is the ninth floor balcony whose floor is at the 80-ft elevation). From the guidance offered in NFPA 92B, *Guide for Smoke Management Systems in Malls, Atria, and Large Areas*, the designer locates the design fire in the center of the floor of the atrium so as to keep the fire away from the walls and thus create the worst-case condition. With the fire at the center of the atrium floor, an axisymmetric fire plume is expected for which air is entrained from all sides and along the entire height of the plume until the plume becomes submerged in the smoke layer. See Exhibit 8.18. This leads the designer to the use of equation 13 of NFPA 92B to determine the flame height:

$$z_1 = 0.533Q_c^{2/5}$$

where:

z_1 = limiting elevation (ft)

Q_c = convective portion of heat-release rate (Btu/sec), established previously as 70 percent of the heat-release rate, Q

In this case,

Q_c = 0.7(5000 Btu/sec)
    = 3500 Btu/sec

Substituting gives

z_1 = 0.533(3500)^{2/5}
    = 13.9 ft

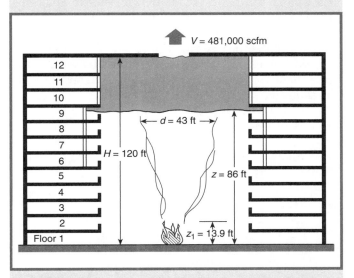

Exhibit 8.18 *Axisymmetric fire plume and associated smoke interface.*

With the design interface of the smoke layer at 86 ft above the floor level, the flame height is less than the design smoke layer height. Thus, equation 14 in 3-7.1.2 of NFPA 92B, which follows, can be used to determine the smoke production rate at the height of the smoke layer interface:

$$m = 0.022Q_c^{1/3} z^{5/3} + 0.0042Q_c \quad \text{(for } z > z_1)$$

where:

m = smoke production rate at height of smoke layer interface (lb/sec)

Q_c = convective portion of heat-release rate (Btu/sec)

z = height above the fuel (ft)

In this case,

Q_c = 3500 Btu/sec, as developed in previous calculations

z = 86 ft (that is, 6 ft above the 80-ft walking surface)

Substituting gives

$$m = 0.022(3500)^{1/3}(86)^{5/3} + 0.0042(3500)$$
$$= 574 \text{ lb/sec}$$

If the smoke exhaust rate is equal to the smoke production rate, the smoke layer depth will be stabilized at the design height (that is, the 86-ft elevation) and, thus, all balconies and areas open to the atrium will remain tenable as the fire continues to burn.

Before converting the smoke production rate to a volumetric flow rate, it is necessary to determine the temperature rise above ambient of the smoke at time of venting in order to establish the density of the smoke during the vented stage. As explained by the last note in Table 3-5 of NFPA 92B, the maximum temperature rise will occur if the total heat loss factor is equal to zero. Use the vented stage temperature rise formula from Table 3-5, simplified by setting the total heat loss factor equal to zero, to determine ΔT as follows:

$$\Delta T = 60 \frac{Q_c}{(\rho c V)}$$

which, through use of equation 16 of 3-7.1.5 of NFPA 92B, can be reduced to

$$\Delta T = \frac{Q_c}{mc}$$

where:

ΔT = temperature rise above ambient of smoke at time of venting (°F)

Q_c = 3500 Btu/sec, as developed in previous calculations

m = 574 lb/sec, as developed in previous calculations

c = 0.24 Btu/lb–°F specific heat of smoke, assuming smoke equals air

Substituting gives

$$\Delta T = \frac{3500}{574(0.24)}$$
$$= 25°F$$

Assuming ambient temperature of 68°F, the temperature of smoke is $T_s = 25 + 68 = 93°F$.

Using an alternate form of the equation shown in A-3-7.1.5 of NFPA 92B, the density of smoke at 93°F can be calculated as follows:

$$\rho = \rho_o \frac{T_o}{T_s}$$

where:

ρ = density of heated smoke

ρ_o = 0.075 (see A-3-7.1.5 of NFPA 92B)

T_o = 68 + 460

T_s = 93 + 460

Substituting gives

$$\rho = 0.075\left(\frac{68 + 460}{93 + 460}\right)$$
$$= 0.0716 \text{ lb/ft}^3$$

The smoke production rate can be converted to a volumetric flow rate using equation 16 from 3-7.1.5 of NFPA 92B as follows:

$$V = 60 \, m/\rho$$

where:

m = smoke production rate, 574 lb/sec as calculated

ρ = density of heated smoke, 0.0716 lb/ft³ as calculated

Substituting gives

$$V = 60(574 / 0.0716)$$
$$= 481,000 \text{ scfm}$$

The preceding calculations assume that the smoke plume has not widened to contact the walls of the atrium prior to reaching the design interface height of 86 ft above the atrium floor in this example. As a plume rises, it also widens. If the plume were to contact all of the walls of the atrium prior to reaching the ceiling, the smoke interface would be considered as occurring at the height of contact with all of the surrounding walls. No additional smoke generation can be assumed to occur above that height, because additional air entrainment into the plume is considered to be negligible above the point of contact. To check if the widening plume has contacted the walls of the atrium, equation 23 from Section 3-8 of NFPA 92B can be used to predict the total plume diameter, d, at the interface height, z, as follows:

$$d = 0.5z$$
$$= 0.5(86)$$
$$= 43 \text{ ft}$$

Thus, in this 100 ft $\times$ 200 ft atrium area, the smoke does not contact the walls prior to reaching the design interface height of 86 ft. Mechanical systems capable of extracting approximately 480,000 scfm are then designed. The substantiation package is submitted to the authority having jurisdiction for approval.

Acceptance testing of the system then involves verifying the function of the system components in the intended sequence for varying initiation scenarios. In addition, the system should be evaluated by measuring the following:

(1) Total volumetric flow rate
(2) Airflow velocities
(3) Airflow direction
(4) Door-opening forces (forces permitted by the *Code* should not be exceeded when smoke management system is operating)
(5) Pressure differentials
(6) Ambient temperature

If the measurements are within the previously agreed-upon system design specifications, the system should be deemed as passing. Note again that no reference is made to the use of subjective test criteria such as cold smoke bombs. The measurements are obtained objectively and can be performed by professional mechanical, HVAC, or fire protection engineers. NFPA 92A, *Recommended Practice for Smoke-Control Systems*,[29] and NFPA 92B, *Guide for Smoke Management Systems in Malls, Atria, and Large Areas*, offer detailed guidance on the equipment needed and procedures for conducting acceptance tests on engineered smoke management systems.

(f) The provisions of 8.2.5.6(6) address the activation of mechanical systems that might be designed to meet the performance-based smoke management requirements of 8.2.5.6(5). In some buildings that have large atrium openings, but no upper floors open to the atrium, and no exit access on those upper floors through the atrium, and that are used by ambulatory occupants, it might be possible to meet smoke control criteria without any mechanical systems by allowing the large atrium to accumulate smoke above the heads of all atrium occupants. The purpose of the engineering analysis required by 8.2.5.6(5) is to determine what, if any, mechanical smoke control is needed. Alternatively, tenability of the means of egress might be able to be maintained through passive ventilation of the atrium. The required engineering analysis should evaluate several protection scenarios.

As addressed by A.8.2.5.6(6), automatic activation of the atrium smoke management system, especially upon initiation of the building alarm system via operation of a manual fire alarm box, could result in the activation of the smoke management system in the incorrect mode. For example, a building occupant walking along the sixth floor exit access balcony within the atrium might see flames and smoke on the third floor, which is open to the atrium. The occupant might walk to the exit stair enclosure on the sixth floor and operate the manual fire alarm box. The building fire alarm system might incorrectly assume that the fire is on the sixth level. The third floor, which is the actual fire floor, might incorrectly be identified as a non-fire floor. The smoke management system might positively pressurize the third floor and move large volumes of air across the third-floor opening into the atrium in an effort to keep smoke from entering the third-floor communicating space. In reality, the smoke management system would accomplish exactly the opposite of what it was designed to do; it would spread the smoke and other products of combustion from the third floor fire into the atrium. The sixth floor would mistakenly be negatively pressurized (exhausted) and would pull in the smoke and gases from the third floor fire via the atrium. For this reason, NFPA 92A and NFPA 92B recommend arranging smoke management systems to activate only via automatic initiating devices, such as smoke detectors and automatic sprinklers. However, controls for manual operation of the system by the fire department are required by 8.2.5.6(6)b. Smoke management systems should not be arranged to activate via manual fire alarm boxes that are accessible to building occupants.

The manual controls required by 8.2.5.6(6)b must be readily accessible to the responding fire department personnel so that the smoke management system's mode of operation can be overridden and tailored to the specific needs of the emergency. These and other concepts on effective smoke management are covered in NFPA 92A, *Recommended Practice for Smoke-Control Systems*, and NFPA 92B, *Guide for Smoke Management Systems in Malls, Atria, and Large Areas*.

8.2.5.7 A vertical opening serving as other than an exit enclosure, connecting only two adjacent stories, and piercing only one floor shall be permitted to be open to one of the two stories.

Paragraph 8.2.5.7 recognizes a maximum two-story exit access stair that is separated from one of the two floors but not both. The separating barrier will keep the effects of a fire on one of the two levels from spreading to the other floor. Because the exit access stair is not an exit, this arrangement does not violate the requirements of 7.1.3.2. Exhibit 8.19 illustrates this allowance. As an alternative, the stair could be separated from floor 3 and open to floor 2.

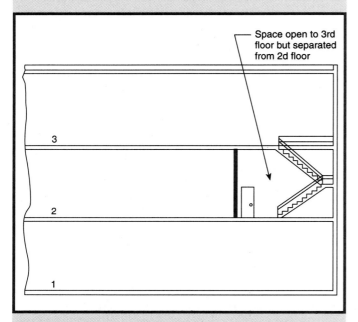

Space open to 3rd floor but separated from 2d floor

3

2

1

Exhibit 8.19 Vertical opening protection by fire barrier at one floor level only.

8.2.5.8 Where permitted by Chapters 12 through 42, unenclosed vertical openings not concealed within the building construction shall be permitted as follows:

(1) Such openings shall connect not more than two adjacent stories (one floor pierced only).
(2) Such openings shall be separated from unprotected vertical openings serving other floors by a barrier complying with 8.2.5.4.
(3) Such openings shall be separated from corridors.
(4)* Such openings shall not serve as a required means of egress.

A.8.2.5.8(4) This requirement prohibits means of egress down or up the convenience opening. It does not prohibit

means of escape from running down or up the convenience opening within residential dwelling units.

The provisions of 8.2.5.8 address a convenience opening, often taking the form of a nonrequired stair, which many of the occupancy chapters have recognized for many years. In editions of the *Code* prior to 1997, occupancy chapters specified the detailed criteria contained in 8.2.5.8(1) through (4). The provisions appear in 8.2.5.8 with the conditional statement "where permitted by Chapters 12 through 42." Therefore, any occupancy chapter can reference the provisions of 8.2.5.8 without having to repeat the detailed criteria. For example, in 38.3.1.1, which is applicable to new business occupancies, the detailed criteria have been dropped and Exception No. 1 to 38.3.1.1 permits "unenclosed vertical openings in accordance with 8.2.5.8." This permits, for example, a two-level office or reference library in an office building to have an unenclosed convenience stair.

Paragraph 8.2.5.8(1) restricts the application of Exception No. 1 to 38.3.1.1 to two adjacent levels only. Paragraph 8.2.5.8(2) requires the opening to be separated from other vertical openings serving other floors; this requirement prevents the linking of individual openings that would otherwise create a means for spreading the effects of fire among multiple floors. Paragraph 8.2.5.8(3) requires that the areas connected by the opening be separated from corridors. Paragraph 8.2.5.8(4) requires that the stairs cannot be part of the means of egress. The space would be required to have access to exits on both levels so occupants would not have to rely on the open stair as part of the required means of egress. One possible application of these provisions is shown in Exhibit 8.20.

8.2.5.9 Where there are three or fewer elevator cars in a building, they shall be permitted to be located within the same hoistway enclosure. Where there are four elevator cars, they shall be divided in such a manner that not less than two separate hoistway enclosures are provided. Where there are more than four elevator cars, the number of elevator cars located within a single hoistway enclosure shall not exceed four.

Exception: This requirement shall not apply to existing hoistways in existing buildings.

The requirements addressed by 8.2.5.9 help to ensure that smoke and fire in an elevator hoistway will not prevent the use of all elevators in any building that

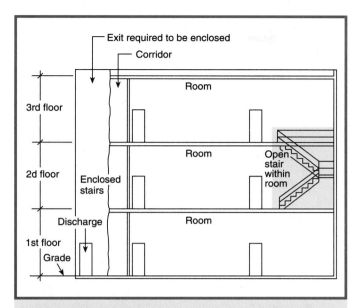

Exhibit 8.20 Elevation view of unenclosed two-story stair serving as a convenience opening.

has four or more elevators. If a building has four elevators, a maximum of three elevators are allowed within the same elevator hoistway or shaft. If the building has more than four elevators, no more than four elevators can be in one shaft. If smoke and fire prevent the use of the elevators within one hoistway, an elevator in another hoistway might be usable. Because of the maximum limit of four elevators per hoistway, a building with nine to twelve elevators must have a minimum of three hoistways.

The requirements of 8.2.5.9 mesh well with the high-rise building requirements of 11.8.4.2, which are applicable to standby power. The required standby power system must be connected to at least one elevator serving all floors of the building. Additionally, elevator standby power must be transferable to any elevator. If the hoistway containing the elevator initially powered by the standby power system becomes untenable, the switching requirement will allow for an elevator in a different hoistway to be placed back into service.

8.2.5.10 Service openings for conveyors, elevators, and dumbwaiters, where required to be open on more than one story at the same time for purposes of operation, shall be provided with closing devices in accordance with 7.2.1.8.

8.2.5.11 Any escalators or moving walks serving as a required exit in existing buildings shall be enclosed in the same manner as exit stairways. *(See 7.2.7.)*

Where used as an exit, an escalator must be completely enclosed with fire-rated construction, including entrance and discharge doors. It is rare to find an escalator enclosed in such a manner. Escalators located within the required means of egress in existing buildings that maintain compliance with the *Code* usually make use of one of the exceptions to 8.2.5.12 to avoid creating an unprotected vertical opening. By doing so they are classified as exit access. Note that 7.2.7 prohibits escalators from constituting any part of the required means of egress in new buildings. Thus, in new construction, an escalator can be installed but is not recognized as satisfying the requirements for exit access, exit, or exit discharge.

8.2.5.12 Moving walks not constituting an exit and escalators, other than escalators in large open areas such as atriums and enclosed shopping malls, shall have their floor openings enclosed or protected as required for other vertical openings.

Exception No. 1:* In buildings protected throughout by an approved automatic sprinkler system in accordance with Section 9.7, escalators or moving walk openings shall be permitted to be protected in accordance with the method detailed in NFPA 13, Standard for the Installation of Sprinkler Systems, or in accordance with a method approved by the authority having jurisdiction.

A.8.2.5.12 Exception No. 1 The intent of the exception is to place a limitation on the size of the opening to which the protection applies. The total floor opening should not exceed twice the projected area of the escalator or moving walk at the floor. Also, the arrangement of the opening is not intended to circumvent the requirements of 8.2.5.6.

As with any opening through a floor, the openings around the outer perimeter of the escalators should be considered as vertical openings. The sprinkler draftstop installation is intended to provide adequate protection for these openings, provided that the criteria of NFPA 13, *Standard for the Installation of Sprinkler Systems,* as well as the area criteria described in the preceding paragraph, are met.

Exception No. 2: Escalators shall be permitted to be protected in accordance with 8.2.5.13.

Exception No. 2 to 8.2.5.12 provides that new escalators (which cannot be part of the means of egress) and existing escalators not serving as exits (see 8.2.5.11) need not be enclosed if certain provisions are met.

The sprinkler-draft curtain method is detailed in NFPA 13, *Standard for the Installation of Sprinkler*

Systems. It consists of surrounding the escalator opening, in an otherwise fully sprinklered building, with an 18-in. (45.7-cm) deep draft stop located on the underside of the floor to which the escalator ascends. This draft stop serves to delay the heat, smoke, and combustion gases developed in the early stages of a fire on that floor from entering into the escalator well. A row of closely spaced automatic sprinklers located outside of the draft stop also surrounds the escalator well. As sprinklers along this surrounding row are individually activated by heat, their water discharge patterns combine to create a water curtain. A typical installation is shown in Exhibit 8.21. In combination with the sprinkler system in the building, this system should delay fire spread effectively and allow time for evacuation.

Prior editions of the *Code* detailed several methods that permitted the use of unenclosed escalators in completely sprinklered buildings where the escalators were not used as exits. In addition to the sprinkler-draft curtain or rolling shutter methods, the authority having jurisdiction might consider one of the following when evaluating existing buildings:

(1) Sprinkler-vent method
(2) Spray nozzle method
(3) Partial enclosure method

The following discussion details these three methods.

(a) *Sprinkler-Vent Method.* Under the conditions specified, escalator or moving walk openings are permitted to be protected by the sprinkler-vent method, which consists of a combination of an automatic fire or smoke detection system, an automatic exhaust system, and an automatic water curtain. This combination of fire protection and system design is required to meet the following criteria and be approved by the authority having jurisdiction.

(1) The exhaust system should be capable of creating a downdraft through the escalator or moving walk floor opening. The downdraft should have an average velocity of not less than 300 ft/min (1.5 m/s) under normal conditions for a period of not less than 30 minutes. This requirement can be met by providing an air intake from the outside

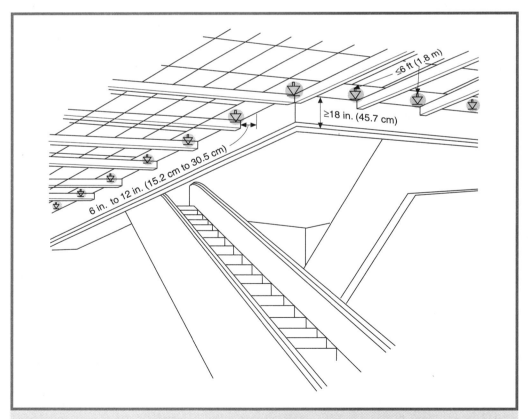

Exhibit 8.21 *Sprinklers around an escalator opening.*

of the building above the floor opening. The test of the system under "normal" conditions requires that the velocity of the downdraft be developed when windows or doors on the several stories normally used for ventilation are open. The size of the exhaust fan and exhaust ducts must be sufficient to meet such ventilation conditions. Experience indicates that fan capacity should be based on a rating of not less than 500 ft³/min/ft² (8.3 m³/s/m²) of moving stairway opening to obtain the 300-ft/min (1.5-m/s) velocity required. If the building is provided with an air conditioning system arranged to be automatically shut down in the event of fire, the test condition should be met with the air conditioning system shut down. The 300-ft/min (1.5-m/s) downdraft through the opening provides for the testing of the exhaust system without requiring the expansion of air that would be present under actual fire conditions.

(2) Operation of the exhaust system for any floor opening should be initiated by an approved device on the involved story and should use one of the following means, in addition to a manual means, for operating and testing the system:

   a. Thermostats (fixed-temperature, rate-of-rise, or a combination of both)

   b. Waterflow in the sprinkler system

   c. Approved, supervised smoke detection located so that the presence of smoke is detected before it enters the stairway

(3) Electric power supply to all parts of the exhaust system and its control devices should be designed and installed for maximum reliability. The electric power supply provision of NFPA 20, *Standard for the Installation of Stationary Pumps for Fire Protection*, can be used as a guide to design and installation features that help to ensure maximum reliability.[30]

(4) Any fan or duct used in connection with an automatic exhaust system should be of the approved type and should be installed in accordance with the applicable standards in Chapter 2 and Annex B.

(5) Periodic tests should be made of the automatic exhaust system, at least quarterly, to maintain the system and the control devices in good working condition.

(6) The water curtain should be formed by open sprinklers or by spray nozzles located and spaced to form a complete and continuous barrier along all exposed sides of the floor opening and to reach from the ceiling to the floor. Water discharge for the water curtain should be not less than approximately 3 gal/min/lineal ft (0.6 L/sec/lineal m) of water curtain, measured horizontally around the opening.

(7) The water curtain should operate automatically from thermal-responsive elements of a fixed-temperature type. These elements should be located with respect to the ceiling/floor opening so that the water curtain actuates upon the advance of heat toward the escalator or moving walk opening.

(8) Every automatic exhaust system (including all motors, controls, and automatic water curtain system) should be supervised in an approved manner that is similar to that specified for automatic sprinkler system supervision.

(b) *Spray Nozzle Method.* Under the conditions specified, escalator openings are permitted to be protected by the spray nozzle method, which consists of a combination of an automatic fire or smoke detection system and a system of high-velocity water spray nozzles. This combination of fire protection and system design is required to meet the following criteria and be approved by the authority having jurisdiction.

(1) Spray nozzles should be of the open type and should have a solid conical spray pattern with discharge angles between 45 and 90 degrees. The number of nozzles, their discharge angles, and their location should be such that the escalator or moving walk opening between the top of the wellway housing and the treadway will be completely filled with dense spray on operation of the system.

(2) The number and size of nozzles and water supply should be sufficient to deliver a discharge of 2 gal of water/ft²/min (1.4 L of water/m²/sec) through the wellway, with the area to be figured perpendicularly to the treadway. See Exhibit 8.22.

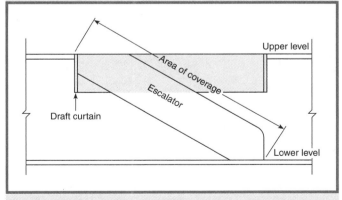

Exhibit 8.22 *Area of coverage for spray nozzle method of protecting escalator openings.*

(3) Spray nozzles should be located to take full advantage of the cooling and counterdraft effect. They should be positioned so that the centerline of spray discharge is as closely in line as possible with the slope of the escalator or moving walk, not more than an angle of 30 degrees with the top slope of the wellway housing. Nozzles should also be positioned so that the centerline of discharge is at an angle of not more than 30 degrees from the vertical sides of the wellway housing.

(4) Spray nozzles should discharge at a minimum pressure of 25 lb/in.² (172 kPa). Water supply piping is permitted to be taken from the sprinkler system, provided that an adequate supply of water is available for the spray nozzles and that the water pressure at the sprinkler farthest from the supply riser is not reduced beyond the required minimum. Water supply taken from the sprinkler system is designed to provide protection from life hazards to the wellway opening during the exit period but is not to be relied on to provide an effective floor cutoff.

(5) Control valves should be readily accessible to minimize water damage.

(6) A noncombustible or limited-combustible draft curtain should be provided that extends at least 20 in. (50.8 cm) below and around the opening, and a solid noncombustible wellway housing at least 5 ft (152 cm) long, measured parallel to the handrail and extending from the top of the handrail enclosure to the soffit of the stairway or ceiling above, should also be provided at each escalator floor opening. Where necessary, spray nozzles should be protected against mechanical damage or tampering that might interfere with proper discharge. See Exhibit 8.23.

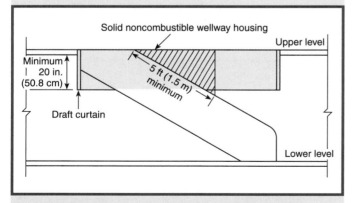

Exhibit 8.23 *The draft curtain and wellway housing method of protecting vertical openings.*

(7) The spray nozzle system should operate automatically from thermal-response elements of the fixed-temperature type and be located with respect to the ceiling/floor opening so that the spray nozzle system actuates upon the advance of heat towards the escalator opening. Supervised smoke detection located in or near the escalator opening is permitted to be used to sound an alarm. The spray nozzle system should also be provided with manual means of operation. It is not desirable to have smoke detection devices activate the spray nozzles; safeguards against accidental discharge must be provided to prevent both panic and property damage.

(8) Control valves for the spray nozzle system and approved smoke detection or thermostatic devices should be supervised in accordance with the applicable provisions of Section 9.6.

(c) *Partial Enclosure Method.* Under the conditions specified, escalator or moving walk openings are permitted to be protected by a partial enclosure, or so-called kiosk, designed to provide an effective barrier to the spread of smoke from floor to floor. This method of fire protection is required to meet the following criteria and be approved by the authority having jurisdiction.

(1) Partial enclosure construction should provide fire resistance equivalent to that specified for stairway enclosures in the same building, with openings therein protected by approved self-closing fire doors. The openings also are permitted to be of approved wired-glass and metal frame construction with wired-glass panel doors.

(2) Fire doors are permitted to be equipped with an electric opening mechanism, which opens the door automatically upon the approach of a person. The mechanism should return the door to its closed position upon any interruption of electric current supply, and it should be adjusted so that the pressures generated by a fire will not cause the door to open.

8.2.5.13 In buildings protected throughout by an approved automatic sprinkler system in accordance with Section 9.7, escalators or moving walk openings shall be permitted to be protected by rolling steel shutters appropriate for the fire resistance rating of the vertical opening protected. The shutters shall close automatically and independently of each other upon smoke detection and sprinkler operation. There shall be a manual means of operating and testing the operation of the shutter. The shutters shall be operated not less than once a week to ensure that they remain in proper operating condition. The shutters shall operate at a speed not to exceed 30 ft/min (0.15 m/s) and shall be equipped with a sensitive leading edge. The leading edge shall arrest the progress of a moving shutter and cause it to retract a distance of approximately 6 in. (15.2 cm) upon the application of a force not exceeding 20 lbf (90 N) applied to the surface of the leading edge. The shutter, following this retraction, shall continue to close. The operating mechanism for the rolling shutter shall be provided with standby power complying with the provisions of NFPA 70, *National Electrical Code.*

8.2.6 Mezzanines.

8.2.6.1 General. A mezzanine shall not be included as a story for the purpose of determining the allowable number of stories in a building.

Exception: Multilevel residential housing areas in detention and correctional occupancies in accordance with Chapters 22 and 23 shall be exempt from the provisions of 8.2.6.2 and 8.2.6.3.

8.2.6.2 Area Limitations.

8.2.6.2.1 The aggregate area of mezzanines within a room, other than those located in special purpose industrial occupancies, shall not exceed one-third the open area of the room in which the mezzanines are located. Enclosed space shall not be included in a determination of the size of the room in which the mezzanine is located.

8.2.6.2.2 There shall be no limit on the number of mezzanines in a room.

8.2.6.2.3 For purposes of determining the allowable mezzanine area, the area of the mezzanines shall not be included in the area of the room.

8.2.6.3 Openness. All portions of a mezzanine, other than walls not more than 42 in. (107 cm) high, columns, and posts, shall be open to and unobstructed from the room in which the mezzanine is located, unless the occupant load of the aggregate area of the enclosed space does not exceed 10.

Exception: A mezzanine having two or more means of egress shall not be required to open into the room in which it is located if not less than one of the means of egress provides direct access from the enclosed area to an exit at the mezzanine level.

The mezzanine provisions of 8.2.6 were new in the 1991 edition of the *Code.* They are based on a report prepared by the Board for the Coordination of the Model Codes (BCMC) in an attempt to standardize

the treatment of mezzanines among three United States regional building code officials' organizations (see the commentary that follows A.8.2.1) and NFPA.

The aggregate area of a mezzanine within a room must not exceed one-third the open area (the unenclosed space) of the room in which the mezzanine is located. The area of the mezzanine is not considered to be part of the total open area of the room for the purposes of this calculation. For other purposes, the area of the mezzanine is considered part of the area of the room. Because a mezzanine is limited to such size, it is exempted from being counted as a building story — thus affecting the applicability of *Code* requirements based on the number of building stories or floors.

Exhibit 8.24 illustrates the use of the one-third area rule for determining whether a level is a mezzanine. A 1000-ft² (93-m²) partial level is positioned above a 3000-ft² (279-m²) main room. This is depicted in the plan view at the top of the figure. Because the one-third area rule compares the area of the upper level to the *open* area of the room in which the partial floor level is located, only the unenclosed space of the room is used in the calculation. In elevation A in

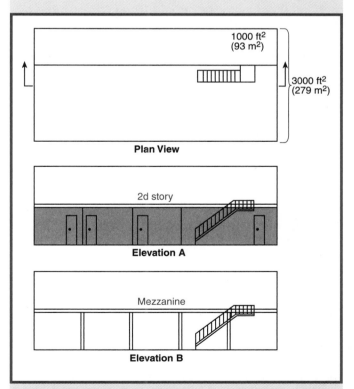

Exhibit 8.24 *Determining whether partial upper level meets one-third area rule to qualify as a mezzanine.*

Exhibit 8.24, the space below the partial floor level is enclosed. The enclosed area beneath the partial upper level is not counted in the area of the main floor. In this case, the area of the upper level is approximately half the area of the open space on the main room below. The size of this area exceeds the one-third allowance, which means that the partial upper level is a floor and not a mezzanine. Contrast this arrangement with the arrangement shown in elevation B at the bottom of Exhibit 8.24. In this case, the space below the partial floor level is open to the main room. The 1000-ft² (93-m²) area of the partial floor level is compared to the full 3000-ft² (279-m²) area of the room below. The one-third area rule is met and the upper level is considered a mezzanine, provided that the other provisions of 8.2.6 are met.

The openness requirements of 8.2.6.3 are intended to provide the mezzanine occupants with a degree of awareness of fire conditions on the floor below that is equivalent to the awareness of the occupants of the fire floor. Because the mezzanine sits above the floor of which it is considered a part, untenable smoke concentrations and the associated loss of visibility due to smoke obscuration might affect the mezzanine level before similarly affecting the floor below. In the same way that openness and awareness are required via the mini-atrium provisions of 8.2.5.5(3), the occupants of the mezzanine should be alerted to a fire in any part of the two-level space before the fire becomes a hazard to their safety.

In recognition of such openness, the *Code* treats the mezzanine no differently than an area or room on the level below the mezzanine. If the mezzanine depicted in Exhibit 8.25(a) were located in a business occupancy, for example, it would be required to follow the same exit access arrangement rules of any other room on the floor below. Thus, if all occupants could travel across the mezzanine, down the open stair to the room below, and as far across the floor of that room as necessary to reach a point where they had access to two different egress paths, and if that total distance did not exceed the allowable common path of travel [that is, 75 ft (23 m), or 100 ft (30 m) if sprinklered per 38.2.5.3, for the new business occupancy in this example], a single exit access from the mezzanine to the floor below would be allowed. If the allowable common path of travel were exceeded, the mezzanine would require a second, remote exit access.

Paragraph 8.2.6.3 recognizes that walls not more than 42 in. (107 cm) high can serve as guards to prevent falls over the open side of a mezzanine but are

low enough to achieve the openness requirement. See 7.2.2.4 for guardrail requirements.

Paragraph 8.2.6.3 also permits a limited amount of enclosed space on the mezzanine to allow for toilet rooms, limited storage, small offices, and similar areas normally separated from the open area of the mezzanine. In Exhibit 8.25(a), the mezzanine is partially enclosed so that the total occupant load of all enclosed rooms does not exceed 10 persons. This permits a partially enclosed mezzanine to use all the benefits available to a fully open mezzanine.

The exception to 8.2.6.3 exempts a mezzanine from being open to the room in which it is located if the occupants of the mezzanine are provided with at least two means of egress and if one of those means of egress provides direct access to an exit at the mezzanine level. This exception permits the mezzanine in Exhibit 8.25(b) to be enclosed, because one of its two means of egress provides access from the mezzanine directly into an exit stair enclosure that discharges to the outside. Occupants of the mezzanine

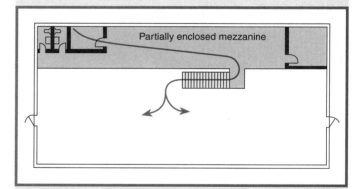

Exhibit 8.25(a) *Open mezzanine.*

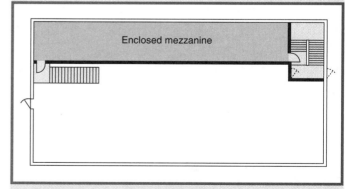

Exhibit 8.25(b) *Enclosed mezzanine.*

are then judged as being adequately safe from a fire on the level below because, even if they learn about that fire later than they would have if the mezzanine were open, one of their means of egress does not require them to return through the room below.

8.2.7 Concealed Spaces.

8.2.7.1* In new Type III, Type IV, or Type V construction, any concealed space in which materials having a flame spread rating greater than Class A (as defined in Section 10.2) are exposed shall be effectively firestopped or draftstopped as follows:

(1) Every exterior and interior wall and partition shall be fire-stopped at each floor level, at the top story ceiling level, and at the level of support for roofs.
(2) Every unoccupied attic space shall be subdivided by draftstops into areas not to exceed 3000 ft² (280 m²).
(3) Any concealed space between the ceiling and the floor or roof above shall be draftstopped for the full depth of the space along the line of support for the floor or roof structural members and, if necessary, at other locations to form areas not to exceed 1000 ft² (93 m²) for any space between the ceiling and floor and 3000 ft² (280 m²) for any space between the ceiling and roof.

Exception No. 1:   This requirement shall not apply where the space is protected throughout by an approved automatic sprinkler system in accordance with Section 9.7.

Exception No. 2:   This requirement shall not apply to concealed spaces serving as plenums. (See NFPA 90A, Standard for the Installation of Air-Conditioning and Ventilating Systems.)

A.8.2.7.1 The area limitations are based on life safety considerations and are not intended to suggest that changes should be made in local building codes having similar or more restrictive requirements that are based on other reasons. Building codes generally contain detailed information on the proper selection and installation of draftstopping and firestopping materials.

The vertical spread of fire through shafts, chases, and hollow wall construction, and the horizontal spread of fire through plenums and open attics are phenomena common to many serious fires. Where such spaces are protected with automatic sprinklers, the risk of unseen fires is minimized. Certain additional precautions are required where this protection is not installed in new buildings of other than Type I or Type II construction as defined by NFPA 220, *Standard on*

Types of Building Construction, as provided in the commentary following 8.2.1, and where the materials used have a flame spread rating of more than 25 (that is, not Class A interior finish).

Draftstopping of attic spaces is particularly important in shopping centers comprised of one story and an attic and in two-story apartment buildings or row houses. Experience has shown that fires starting in one of these occupancy units frequently breaks into the attic space, spreads through the attic, and travels down into adjoining units.

Numerous fires in garden-type apartments have demonstrated two common weaknesses that relate to the lack of adequate firestopping and draftstopping. The following two areas are frequently not firestopped:

(1) Between the underside of the roof deck and the top of fire barriers that do not extend through the roofline
(2) Inside the pipe chase that contains the plumbing vent stack

The vent stack is of particular concern, because it frequently is located between two mirror-image apartment units and interconnects all the floors of the apartment building. A fire that travels into this concealed space can spread to the attic and soon involve the entire structure.

Chapter 3 defines a draft stop as: "a continuous membrane used to subdivide a concealed space to restrict the passage of smoke, heat, and flames."

8.2.7.2   In every existing building, firestopping and draftstopping shall be provided as required by the provisions of Chapters 12 through 42.

An example of an occupancy chapter requirement for firestopping is 19.1.6.4 for existing health care occupancies, which requires firestopping between the basement and first floor.

Section 8.3 Smoke Barriers

8.3.1* General.

Where required by Chapters 12 through 42, smoke barriers shall be provided to subdivide building spaces for the purpose of restricting the movement of smoke.

A.8.3.1 Wherever smoke barriers and doors therein require a degree of fire resistance as specified by requirements in the various occupancy chapters (Chapter 12 through Chapter 42), the construction should be a fire barrier that has been specified to limit the spread of fire and restrict the movement of smoke. *(See 8.2.3.2.)*

It is imprecise to refer to a "1-hour smoke barrier." It is more accurate to refer to a "smoke barrier that additionally has a 1-hour fire resistance rating." A barrier with only a fire resistance rating does not necessarily make an effective smoke barrier. For example, a fire barrier, if rated at less than 2 hours, would not be required to have either a fire damper or smoke damper where ductwork penetrates the barrier. A smoke barrier, in accordance with Section 8.3, would have ducted penetrations protected by smoke dampers per 8.3.5.1. For additional information on fire barrier testing, rating, and installation, see the commentary following 8.2.3.1.1 and 8.2.3.2.4.1.

8.3.2* Continuity.

Smoke barriers required by this *Code* shall be continuous from an outside wall to an outside wall, from a floor to a floor, or from a smoke barrier to a smoke barrier or a combination thereof. Such barriers shall be continuous through all concealed spaces, such as those found above a ceiling, including interstitial spaces.

SEE EX. 8.3

Exception: A smoke barrier required for an occupied space below an interstitial space shall not be required to extend through the interstitial space, provided that the construction assembly forming the bottom of the interstitial space provides resistance to the passage of smoke equal to that provided by the smoke barrier.

A.8.3.2 To ensure that a smoke barrier is continuous, it is necessary to seal completely all openings where the smoke barrier abuts other smoke barriers, fire barriers, exterior walls, the floor below, and the floor or ceiling above.

It is not the intent to prohibit a smoke barrier from stopping at a fire barrier if the fire barrier meets the requirements of a smoke barrier (that is, the fire barrier is a combination smoke barrier/fire barrier).

In occupancies where evacuation is a last resort or is expected to be otherwise delayed, smoke barriers and doors therein will require a degree of fire resistance as specified by the requirements found in the *Code's* occupancy chapters (Chapters 12 through 42).

Other openings in smoke and fire barriers must

be protected as well. Heating, air conditioning, and ventilation ducts provide a ready path for smoke and fire to travel from one area to another unless carefully protected. Penetrations in walls and ceiling construction for utility lines and other building services must be firestopped to prevent fire spread. The hidden spaces behind suspended ceilings and attic spaces are out of sight and easily overlooked.

The exception to 8.3.2 must be used with care. Several chapters require the smoke barrier to be fire resistance rated and, therefore, the smoke barrier would be permitted to terminate at the ceiling only if the ceiling were of the same rating (see commentary on 8.2.2.2). Also, even if no fire resistance rating were required, it is difficult to ensure that a ceiling is smoketight unless it is of monolithic construction without air-handling penetrations. However, this kind of construction is often found in apartment buildings, hotels, and dormitories; consequently, the exception can be useful.

8.3.3 Fire Barrier Used as Smoke Barrier.

A fire barrier shall be permitted to be used as a smoke barrier, provided that it meets the requirements of 8.3.4 through 8.3.6.

8.3.4 Doors.

8.3.4.1* Doors in smoke barriers shall close the opening leaving only the minimum clearance necessary for proper operation and shall be without undercuts, louvers, or grilles.

A.8.3.4.1 The clearance for proper operation of smoke doors is defined as $\frac{1}{8}$ in. (0.3 cm). For additional information on the installation of smoke-control door assemblies, see NFPA 105, *Recommended Practice for the Installation of Smoke-Control Door Assemblies.*

NFPA 105, *Recommended Practice for the Installation of Smoke-Control Door Assemblies*, acknowledges that a nationally recognized test for the measurement of smoke leakage does not exist.[31] However, NFPA 105 recommends that Underwriters Laboratories, UL 1784, *Air Leakage Tests of Door Assemblies*, can be used to measure ambient and warm air leakage rates of door assemblies.[32]

UL 1784 should determine satisfactory performance if recognized design features are also taken into account, such as close-fitting assemblies, limited deflections, and the use of gasketing and sealing materials. The document then provides performance criteria for determining maximum air leakage rates expressed in air volume per time per area of door opening.

8.3.4.2* Where a fire resistance rating for smoke barriers is specified elsewhere in the *Code*, openings shall be protected as follows:

(1) Door opening protectives shall have a fire protection rating of not less than 20 minutes where tested in accordance with NFPA 252, *Standard Methods of Fire Tests of Door Assemblies*, without the hose stream test, unless otherwise specified by Chapters 12 through 42.
(2) Fire windows shall comply with 8.2.3.2.2.

Exception: Latching hardware shall not be required on doors in smoke barriers where so indicated by Chapters 12 through 42.

A.8.3.4.2 In existing installations only, a 1¾-in. (4.4-cm) thick, solid-bonded wood core door has been considered a satisfactory substitute for a door with a 20-minute fire protection rating.

Doors in smoke barriers are not required to have a fire protection rating unless the occupancy chapter requires the smoke barrier to have a fire resistance rating. Therefore, any door that resists the passage of smoke, even a hollow-core wood door or glass door, would be acceptable, provided it is tight-fitting. Stops at the head and sides of the door help resist the passage of smoke. Where a pair of doors is used, it is recommended (but required for cross-corridor door assemblies in new health care occupancies) that they open in opposite directions from each other so that rabbets, bevels, or astragals can be provided at the meeting edges without the use of coordinators. See also 18.3.7.8.

Doors in smoke barriers, while not the equivalent of fire doors and not completely smoketight, are effective in restricting the spread of smoke and reducing drafts, which might otherwise spread fire rapidly. Where the smoke barrier is required by an occupancy chapter to have a fire resistance rating, a 20-minute fire protection–rated door assembly in a smoke partition should be accepted as a reasonable barrier. It has been shown through tests that the commonly used 1¾-in. (4.4-cm) thick solid-wood core door assembly can be expected in fire tests to fail in 22 minutes to 24 minutes, but it has performed well in actual fires when closed.[33] The use of the 20-minute designation replaces a specification standard with a performance standard. The same reference empha-

sizes that even rated fire doors will not keep out smoke because of the clearances necessary for proper door function. Gasketing will help, but a tight-fitting door should keep out enough smoke so that orderly egressing can proceed.

8.3.4.3* Doors in smoke barriers shall be self-closing or automatic-closing in accordance with 7.2.1.8 and shall comply with the provisions of 7.2.1.

A.8.3.4.3 Where, because of operational necessity, it is desired to have smoke barrier doors that are usually open, such doors should be provided with hold-open devices that are activated to close the doors by means of the operation of smoke detectors and other alarm functions.

Doors in a fire separation, horizontal exit, or smoke barrier should be closed at all times to impede the travel of smoke and fire gases. Functionally, however, this decreases efficiency. In a health care occupancy, for example, closed doors limit patient observation by the professional staff. To accommodate such situations, it is practical to presume that the door will be kept open, even with the use of wood chocks and other makeshift devices. Where operational necessity dictates that smoke barrier doors normally are to be kept open, such doors should be provided with hold-open devices that are activated by the operation of smoke detectors to close the doors. See 7.2.1.8 for details on hold-open devices with automatic release. For additional information on the use of smoke detectors for releasing service, see the commentary to 9.6.3.2, Exception No. 2 and Exception No. 3 to 9.6.3.2.

8.3.5 Smoke Dampers.

8.3.5.1 An approved damper designed to resist the passage of smoke shall be provided for each air transfer opening or duct penetration of a required smoke barrier, unless otherwise specifically exempted by Chapters 12 through 42.

Exception No. 1: This requirement shall not apply to ducts or air transfer openings that are part of an engineered smoke control system in accordance with Section 9.3.

Exception No. 2: This requirement shall not apply to ducts where the air continues to move and the air-handling system installed is arranged to prevent recirculation of exhaust or return air under fire emergency conditions.

Exception No. 1 to 8.3.5.1 addresses the omission of dampers in ducts that must remain open so that the smoke control system can operate. Exception No. 2 to 8.3.5.1 is applicable only in very limited cases. It can be used only on small ventilation systems, because NFPA 90A, *Standard for the Installation of Air-Conditioning and Ventilating Systems*, requires that systems over 15,000 ft³/min (7.1 m³/sec) that are not part of a smoke control system shut down upon detection of smoke (see NFPA 90A). Even without the restriction of NFPA 90A, it is difficult to ensure that the air-handling system will be in continuous operation. Because of increased awareness of energy conservation, many systems are cycled or shut down during parts of the day. The cycling or shutdown feature might be added later without recognizing its potential detriment to building life safety. However, the exception can be useful for ductwork for small ventilation systems, such as for bathrooms or small suites.

Exception No. 3: This requirement shall not apply where the air inlet or outlet openings in ducts are limited to a single smoke compartment.

Exception No. 3 to 8.3.5.1 covers situations where an "express" duct has no openings other than in a single smoke compartment. It can reasonably be extended to situations illustrated in Exhibit 8.26.

Exception No. 4: This requirement shall not apply where ducts penetrate floors that serve as smoke barriers.

Exception No. 4 to 8.3.5.1 (which recognizes that 8.2.5.1 requires every floor that separates stories in a building to be constructed as a smoke barrier to provide a basic degree of compartmentation) differentiates between (1) a true smoke barrier in accordance with Section 8.3, which is provided via vertical barriers, and (2) a smoke-resisting horizontal barrier consisting of a floor not subject to the requirements of Section 8.3.

The occupancy chapters (for example, Chapters 18 and 19 for health care occupancies) that mandate the installation of smoke barriers that comply with the requirements of Section 8.3 do so to divide a floor into two or more smoke compartments. They impose no further subdivision using smoke barriers, because that would separate one floor from another and create different smoke compartments stacked upon each other. Rather, the occupancy chapters rely on the vertical opening protection requirements of Chapter 8 to keep fire from spreading from floor to floor. In

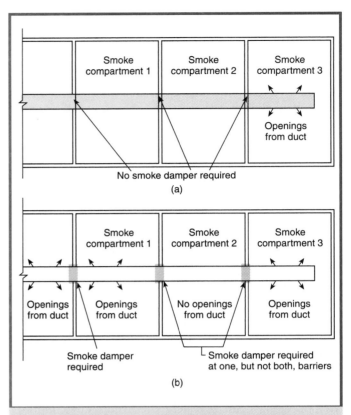

Exhibit 8.26 *Position of smoke dampers in air-handling ductwork.*

combination with 8.2.5.1, the vertical opening protection rules do an adequate job but do not elevate the floor construction to the stringent smoke barrier standards required of vertically positioned barriers that comply with Section 8.3. Ducts penetrating floors are thus exempt from the smoke damper requirements of 8.3.5.1.

Per the requirements of NFPA 90A, *Standard for the Installation of Air-Conditioning and Ventilating Systems*, only a single floor can be penetrated by ductwork not enclosed within a rated shaft system, and such an installation requires a fire damper at the plane of the floor where the penetration is located. Ducts penetrating more than one floor must be enclosed within an appropriately fire-rated shaft. Thus, where a smoke damper is exempted by Exception No. 4 to 8.3.5.1, the resulting openings can potentially act as a minor route for smoke migration from one floor to another before the actuation of a fire damper. The floor, as a whole, serves as an adequate smoke barrier in accordance with the requirements of 8.2.5.1.

8.3.5.2 Required smoke dampers in ducts penetrating smoke barriers shall close upon detection of smoke by approved smoke detectors in accordance with NFPA 72, *National Fire Alarm Code.*

Exception No. 1: Duct detectors shall not be required where ducts penetrate smoke barriers above the smoke barrier doors and the door release detector actuates the damper.

Exception No. 2: Approved smoke detector installations located within the ducts in existing installations shall be exempt from the requirements of NFPA 72, National Fire Alarm Code.

8.3.5.3 Required smoke dampers in air transfer openings shall close upon detection of smoke by approved smoke detectors in accordance with NFPA 72, *National Fire Alarm Code.*

Exception: Where a duct is provided on one side of the smoke barrier, the smoke detectors on the duct side shall be in accordance with 8.3.5.2.

NFPA 72, *National Fire Alarm Code,* provides information on the installation of smoke detectors that close smoke dampers. The damper is permitted to be closed by the same detector that closes the door in a smoke barrier if the dampered duct penetrates the wall above the door. Existing installations of in-duct detectors, which might not be in total compliance with NFPA 72, continue to be recognized.

8.3.6 Penetrations and Miscellaneous Openings in Floors and Smoke Barriers.

8.3.6.1 Pipes, conduits, bus ducts, cables, wires, air ducts, pneumatic tubes and ducts, and similar building service equipment that pass through floors and smoke barriers shall be protected as follows:

(1) The space between the penetrating item and the smoke barrier shall meet one of the following conditions:
   a. It shall be filled with a material that is capable of maintaining the smoke resistance of the smoke barrier.
   b. It shall be protected by an approved device that is designed for the specific purpose.
(2) Where the penetrating item uses a sleeve to penetrate the smoke barrier, the sleeve shall be solidly set in the smoke barrier, and the space between the item and the sleeve shall meet one of the following conditions:
   a. It shall be filled with a material that is capable of maintaining the smoke resistance of the smoke barrier.
   b. It shall be protected by an approved device that is designed for the specific purpose.

(3) Where designs take transmission of vibration into consideration, any vibration isolation shall meet one of the following conditions:
   a. It shall be made on either side of the smoke barrier.
   b. It shall be made by an approved device that is designed for the specific purpose.

8.3.6.2 Openings occurring at points where floors or smoke barriers meet the outside walls, other smoke barriers, or fire barriers of a building shall meet one of the following conditions:

(1) It shall be filled with a material that is capable of maintaining the smoke resistance of the floor or smoke barrier.
(2) It shall be protected by an approved device that is designed for the specific purpose.

As in the case of fire barriers, it is important to maintain the integrity of smoke barriers over the life of a building. Exhibit 8.27 illustrates some of the key items regarding smoke barrier penetrations discussed in 8.3.4 through 8.3.6.

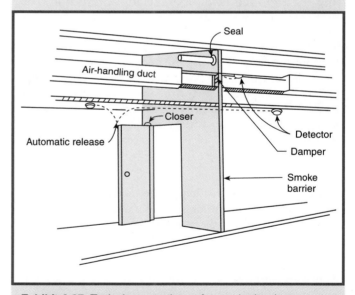

Exhibit 8.27 *Typical penetrations of a smoke barrier.*

Section 8.4 Special Hazard Protection

8.4.1 General.

8.4.1.1* Protection from any area having a degree of hazard greater than that normal to the general occupancy of the building or structure shall be provided by one of the following means:

(1) Enclose the area with a fire barrier without windows that has a 1-hour fire resistance rating in accordance with Section 8.2.
(2) Protect the area with automatic extinguishing systems in accordance with Section 9.7.
(3) Apply both 8.4.1.1(1) and (2) where the hazard is severe or where otherwise specified by Chapters 12 through 42.

A.8.4.1.1 Areas requiring special hazard protection include, but are not limited to, areas such as those used for storage of combustibles or flammables, areas housing heat-producing appliances, or areas used for maintenance purposes.

Paragraph 8.4.1.1 attempts to minimize the effects of fire originating in hazardous areas by isolating those areas that have a high potential for fire or a high fuel load. The occupancy chapters identify the particular hazards against which protection is to be provided and generally address them in subsection __.3.2 of each occupancy chapter. With each new edition of the *Code*, additional occupancy chapters reformat this subsection to include a list of typical hazardous areas and the required level of associated protection. For example, see Table 22.3.2.1 applicable to hazardous areas in new detention and correctional occupancies. This subsection addresses the fundamental fire protection concept of either protecting against known hazards via automatic extinguishment systems or isolating known hazards by means of fire-rated construction. The authority having jurisdiction is responsible for determining the criteria that define a hazardous area.

8.4.1.2 In new construction, where protection is provided with automatic extinguishing systems without fire-resistive separation, the space protected shall be enclosed with smoke partitions in accordance with 8.2.4.

The provisions of 8.4.1.2 require a smoke-resisting enclosure, which includes both surrounding wall barriers and opening protectives such as self-closing doors, where the allowance of 8.4.1.1(2) is used, to protect the hazardous area with automatic sprinkler protection in lieu of a fire-rated enclosure. The smoke-resisting enclosure, although it lacks mandated fire resistance rating, will help to contain the smoke generated prior to sprinkler activation and subsequent to fire control. The concept is illustrated in Exhibit 8.28.

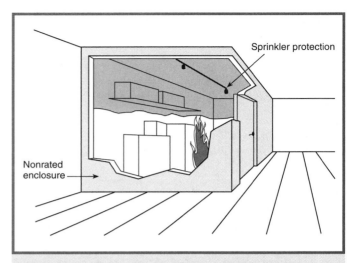

Exhibit 8.28 *Sprinkler-protected hazardous contents area.*

Exception No. 1: This requirement shall not apply to mercantile occupancy general storage areas and stockrooms protected by automatic sprinklers in accordance with Section 9.7.

Exception No. 1 to 8.4.1.2 allows omission of the additional smoke-resisting enclosure or separation for general storage areas in mercantile occupancies that are protected by automatic sprinklers. For example, in a shoe store, a sprinklered shoe storage area could be left open to the sales area. The clerk might go behind a partial-height partition without going through a door opening to get shoes. Another example is a department store, which usually positions its general storage rooms behind floor-to-ceiling wall barriers at the rear of the store along exterior walls. In this case, double-acting doors (that is, those that can swing both into and out of the storage room) that might not adequately resist the passage of smoke as required by 8.4.1.2 could be used if the storage area were sprinklered.

Exception No. 2: This requirement shall not apply to hazardous areas in industrial occupancies protected by automatic extinguishing systems in accordance with 40.3.2.

Exception No. 2 to 8.4.1.2 applies to hazardous areas in industrial occupancies and exempts them from the additional smoke-resisting enclosure requirement if the hazardous area is protected by an automatic extinguishing system. The exception allows the industrial occupancy to function as necessary if each individual hazardous area is provided with automatic extinguishing. The nonhazardous areas might not be sprinklered, but the protected hazardous areas can be left open to the nonhazardous areas.

8.4.1.3 Doors in barriers required to have a fire resistance rating shall have a ¾-hour fire protection rating and shall be self-closing or automatic-closing in accordance with 7.2.1.8.

8.4.2* Explosion Protection.

Where hazardous processes or storage is of such a character as to introduce an explosion potential, an explosion venting system or an explosion suppression system specifically designed for the hazard involved shall be provided.

A.8.4.2 For details, see NFPA 68, *Guide for Venting of Deflagrations*.

If the potential hazard is of an explosive nature, explosion venting or an explosion suppression system is required. NFPA 68, *Guide for Venting of Deflagrations*, contains details of acceptable venting systems[34] and NFPA 69, *Standard on Explosion Prevention Systems*, covers suppression systems.[35] NFPA 654, *Standard for the Prevention of Fire and Dust Explosions from the Manufacturing, Processing, and Handling of Combustible Particulate Solids*, is useful where explosive dusts are encountered.[36]

8.4.3 Flammable Liquids and Gases.

8.4.3.1 The storage and handling of flammable liquids or gases shall be in accordance with the following applicable standards:

(1) NFPA 30, *Flammable and Combustible Liquids Code*
(2) NFPA 54, *National Fuel Gas Code*
(3) NFPA 58, *Liquefied Petroleum Gas Code*

8.4.3.2* No storage or handling of flammable liquids or gases shall be permitted in any location where such storage would jeopardize egress from the structure, unless otherwise permitted by 8.4.3.1.

A.8.4.3.2 NFPA 58, *Liquefied Petroleum Gas Code*, permits portable butane-fueled appliances in restaurants and in attended commercial food catering operations where fueled by not in excess of two 10-oz (0.28-kg) LP-Gas capacity, nonrefillable butane containers having a water capacity not in excess of 1.08 lb (0.4 kg) per container. Containers are

required to be directly connected to the appliance, and manifolding of containers is not permitted. Storage of cylinders is also limited to 24 containers, with an additional 24 permitted where protected by a 2-hour fire resistance–rated barrier.

8.4.4 Laboratories.

Laboratories that use chemicals shall comply with NFPA 45, *Standard on Fire Protection for Laboratories Using Chemicals*, unless otherwise modified by other provisions of this *Code*.

Exception: Laboratories in health care occupancies and medical and dental offices shall comply with NFPA 99, Standard for Health Care Facilities.

8.4.5* Hyperbaric Facilities.

All occupancies containing hyperbaric facilities shall comply with NFPA 99, *Standard for Health Care Facilities*, Chapter 19, unless otherwise modified by other provisions of this *Code*.

A.8.4.5 While the scope of NFPA 99, *Standard for Health Care Facilities*, is limited to health care occupancies, it is the intent that this requirement be applied to hyperbaric facilities used in all occupancies.

Hyperbaric facilities have begun to appear in a variety of occupancies, in addition to health care. For example, hyperbaric chambers have been installed in amusement centers and physical fitness centers and have been promoted as health-enhancing aids. Subsection 8.4.5 extends the use of the provisions of NFPA 99, *Standard for Health Care Facilities*, to hyperbaric facilities regardless of occupancy classification.[37]

References Cited in Commentary

1. *Designing Buildings for Fire Safety*, NFPA SPP-24, National Fire Protection Association, Boston, MA, 1975, pp. 72–74.
2. NFPA 251, *Standard Methods of Tests of Fire Endurance of Building Construction and Materials*, 1999 edition, National Fire Protection Association, Quincy, MA.
3. NFPA 252, *Standard Methods of Fire Tests of Door Assemblies*, 1999 edition, National Fire Protection Association, Quincy, MA.
4. NFPA 220, *Standard on Types of Building Construction*, 1999 edition, National Fire Protection Association, Quincy, MA.
5. *Uniform Building Code*, International Conference of Building Officials, Whittier, CA.

6. BOCA *National Building Code*, Building Officials and Code Administrators International, Inc., Country Club Hills, IL.

7. *Standard Building Code*, Southern Building Code Congress International, Inc., Birmingham, AL.

8. NFPA 221, *Standard for Fire Walls and Fire Barrier Walls*, 1997 edition, National Fire Protection Association, Quincy, MA.

9. *Fire Resistance Design Manual*, Gypsum Association, Washington, DC.

10. ASTM E 119, *Standard Test Methods for Fire Tests of Building Construction and Materials*, American Society for Testing and Materials, West Conshohocken, PA.

11. *Underwriters Laboratories Fire Resistance Directory*, Underwriters Laboratories Inc., Northbrook, IL.

12. *Factory Mutual Specification Tested Products Guide*, Factory Mutual Research Corp., Norwood, MA.

13. *Omega Point Laboratories Directory of Listed Building Products, Materials & Assemblies*, Omega Point Laboratories, Inc., Elmendorf, TX.

14. ASTM A 6, *Standard Specification for General Requirements for Rolled Steel Plates, Shapes, Sheet Piling, and Bars for Structural Use*, American Society for Testing and Materials, West Conshohocken, PA.

15. AISI *Designing Fire Protection for Steel Columns*, American Iron & Steel Institute, Washington, DC.

16. ASTM E 152, *Standard Methods of Fire Tests of Door Assemblies*, American Society for Testing and Materials, West Conshohocken, PA.

17. NFPA 80, *Standard for Fire Doors and Fire Windows*, 1999 edition, National Fire Protection Association, Quincy, MA.

18. NFPA 90A, *Standard for the Installation of Air-Conditioning and Ventilating Systems*, 1999 edition, National Fire Protection Association, Quincy, MA.

19. "Through-Penetration Firestop Systems," Vol. II — *Fire Resistance Directory*, Underwriters Laboratories Inc., Northbrook, IL.

20. UL 1479, *Fire Tests of Through-Penetration Firestops*, Underwriters Laboratories Inc., Northbrook, IL.

21. ASTM E 814, *Standard Test Method for Fire Tests of Through-Penetration Fire Stops*, American Society for Testing and Materials, West Conshohocken, PA.

22. John Hall, Jr., "Report Prepared for the House Subcommittee on Science, Research, and Technology on H.R. 94, The Hotel and Motel Fire Safety Act of 1989," Quincy, MA: NFPA Fire Analysis and Research Division, National Fire Protection Association, Quincy, MA, March 2, 1989.

23. Thomas Klem, "Investigation Report on the DuPont Plaza Hotel Fire," National Fire Protection Association, Quincy, MA, 1987.

24. Richard Best and David Demers, "Investigation Report on the MGM Grand Hotel Fire," National Fire Protection Association, Quincy, MA, 1980.

25. NFPA 13, *Standard for the Installation of Sprinkler Systems*, 1999 edition, National Fire Protection Association, Quincy, MA.

26. NFPA 92B, *Guide for Smoke Management Systems in Malls, Atria, and Large Areas*, 1995 edition, National Fire Protection Association, Quincy, MA.

27. Robert Schifiliti and W. Pucci, "Fire Detection Modeling, State of the Art," Fire Detection Institute, Bloomfield, CT, 1996.

28. NFPA 72, *National Fire Alarm Code®*, 1999 edition, National Fire Protection Association, Quincy, MA.

29. NFPA 92A, *Recommended Practice for Smoke-Control Systems*, 1996 edition, National Fire Protection Association, Quincy, MA.

30. NFPA 20, *Standard for the Installation of Stationary Pumps for Fire Protection*, 1999 edition, National Fire Protection Association, Quincy, MA.

31. NFPA 105, *Recommended Practice for the Installation of Smoke-Control Door Assemblies*, 1999 edition, National Fire Protection Association, Quincy, MA.

32. UL 1784, *Air Leakage Tests of Door Assemblies*, Underwriters Laboratories Inc., Northbrook, IL.

33. J. Degenkolb, "The 20-Minute Door and Other Considerations," *Building Standards*, XLV, no. 1 (January/February 1976).

34. NFPA 68, *Guide for Venting of Deflagrations*, 1998 edition, National Fire Protection Association, Quincy, MA.

35. NFPA 69, *Standard on Explosion Prevention Systems*, 1997 edition, National Fire Protection Association, Quincy, MA.

36. NFPA 654, *Standard for the Prevention of Fire and Dust Explosions from the Manufacturing, Processing, and Handling of Combustible Particulate Solids*, 1997 edition, National Fire Protection Association, Quincy, MA.

37. NFPA 99, *Standard for Health Care Facilities*, 1999 edition, National Fire Protection Association, Quincy, MA.

CHAPTER 9

Building Service and Fire Protection Equipment

As the title indicates, Chapter 9 divides the types of equipment commonly found in buildings into two categories: building service and fire protection. For the most part, the requirements for building service equipment are handled by direct reference to another code or standard with little or no modification or additional requirements in the occupancy chapters. The result is that compliance with the referenced document is required in order for the building to achieve overall compliance with the *Life Safety Code.* Fire protection systems, particularly fire alarm and automatic sprinkler systems, are handled quite differently. For these systems, the *Code* presents a menu of general provisions that are used in conjunction with the installation standards. To apply these provisions, a specific requirement from another section of the *Code* must require their use. For example, 9.6.2.1 addresses alarm system signal initiation and 12.3.4.2 mandates the use of those provisions for alarm systems in new assembly occupancies.

The features that maintain a building safe from fire are varied and work in combination to provide a level of protection for the occupants under a range of potentially adverse conditions. This chapter addresses those systems that help either to maintain a safe environment or to keep the occupants safe from the effects of a fire.

Section 9.6 identifies types of fire alarm initiating and notification systems for life safety. The fire alarm system plays an important role in notifying the building occupants of a fire as well as summoning help from outside sources such as the fire department.

Section 9.7 applies to systems or features used to provide an active method for controlling the effects of a fire. These systems and features include automatic systems—such as sprinkler systems—as well as manual systems—such as standpipes and portable fire extinguishers.

Note that the type of system required, and the conditions under which that system is required, are determined by the requirements in the occupancy chapters.

Section 9.1 Utilities

9.1.1 Gas.

Equipment using gas and related gas piping shall be in accordance with NFPA 54, *National Fuel Gas Code*, or NFPA 58, *Liquefied Petroleum Gas Code*, unless existing installations, which shall be permitted to be continued in service, subject to approval by the authority having jurisdiction.

Although the referenced documents do not specify whether gas piping is allowed to pass through an exit enclosure, such as an enclosed stair, other provisions of the *Life Safety Code* apply. For example, see the provisions of 7.1.3.2.1(d) and 7.1.3.2.1(e) and the commentary following 7.1.3.2.1. These provisions stress that the only openings permitted in the enclosure walls between an exit and other building spaces are those needed to provide access into the exit from any normally occupied space and those needed to provide access out of the exit at the level of exit discharge. In other words, only those openings used by an occupant to enter and leave the exit enclosure are permitted. Gas piping cannot pass through exit enclosure walls. Conversely, the *Code* does not prohibit the installation of gas piping in elevator shafts, dumbwaiters, or chutes. However, these areas are clearly prohibited from containing gas piping by NFPA 54, *National Fuel Gas Code*.[1] Thus, the *Code* and the reference document are used together to address installation safety and life safety.

9.1.2 Electric.

Electrical wiring and equipment shall be in accordance with NFPA 70, *National Electrical Code*, unless existing installations, which shall be permitted to be continued in service, subject to approval by the authority having jurisdiction.

Because electrical wiring might require a complicated system or array involving many specifications and design details, the *Code* does not repeat them; rather, it references NFPA 70, *National Electrical Code*, for design and installation guidance.[2]

The *Life Safety Code* requirements for emergency lighting, addressed by Section 7.9 and, in particular, by 7.9.2.2 with respect to independence of the emergency lighting source and distribution network, exceed the more general guidelines of NFPA 70, *National Electrical Code*. See the commentary throughout Section 7.9.

9.1.3 Emergency Generators.

Emergency generators, where required for compliance with this *Code*, shall be tested and maintained in accordance with NFPA 110, *Standard for Emergency and Standby Power Systems*.

9.1.4 Stored electrical energy systems shall be maintained in accordance with NFPA 111, *Standard on Stored Electrical Energy Emergency and Standby Power Systems*.

Section 9.2 Heating, Ventilating, and Air Conditioning

9.2.1 Air Conditioning, Heating, Ventilating Ductwork, and Related Equipment.

Air conditioning, heating, ventilating ductwork, and related equipment shall be in accordance with NFPA 90A, *Standard for the Installation of Air-Conditioning and Ventilating Systems*, or NFPA 90B, *Standard for the Installation of Warm Air Heating and Air-Conditioning Systems*, as applicable, unless existing installations, which shall be permitted to be continued in service, subject to approval by the authority having jurisdiction.

For the proper installation of HVAC systems, 9.2.1 refers the *Code* user to NFPA 90A, *Standard for the Installation of Air-Conditioning and Ventilating Systems*.[3] For occupancies with small overall volumes such as one- and two-family dwellings, the *Code* refers the user to NFPA 90B, *Standard for the Installation of Warm Air Heating and Air-Conditioning Systems*.[4]

For example, NFPA 90A addresses fire damper requirements for both ductwork and air transfer grilles that penetrate fire resistance–rated barriers. NFPA 90A also prohibits means of egress corridors in health care, detention and correctional, and residential occupancies from being used as a portion of a supply, return, or exhaust air system serving adjoining areas. Exhibit 9.1 identifies some of the

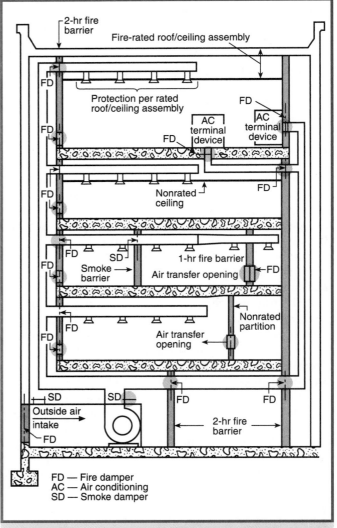

Exhibit 9.1 *Partition and fire barrier penetration protection.*

areas where fire dampers and smoke dampers would be required by NFPA 90A.

9.2.2 Ventilating or Heat-Producing Equipment.

Ventilating or heat-producing equipment shall be in accordance with NFPA 91, *Standard for Exhaust Systems for Air Conveying of Vapors, Gases, Mists, and Noncombustible Particulate Solids;* NFPA 211, *Standard for Chimneys, Fireplaces, Vents, and Solid Fuel-Burning Appliances;* NFPA 31, *Standard for the Installation of Oil-Burning Equipment;* NFPA 54, *National Fuel Gas Code;* or NFPA 70, *National Electrical Code,* as applicable, unless existing installations, which shall be permitted to be continued in service, subject to approval by the authority having jurisdiction.

9.2.3 Commercial Cooking Equipment.

Commercial cooking equipment shall be in accordance with NFPA 96, *Standard for Ventilation Control and Fire Protection of Commercial Cooking Operations,* unless existing installations, which shall be permitted to be continued in service, subject to approval by the authority having jurisdiction.

The occupancy chapters that address the protection of commercial cooking equipment do so in the provisions for the protection of hazards. To understand the intent of the *Code,* close attention must be paid to the manner in which the protection is addressed.

For example, in health care occupancies, the exception to 18.3.2.6, intends that domestic cooking equipment with limited applications is not required to be protected, nor must the space be segregated from the rest of the building. In day-care occupancies, a similar provision appears in 16.3.2.2; however, this provision requires the approval of the authority having jurisdiction to exempt protection and segregation of domestic cooking equipment. In 22.3.2.3, detention and correctional occupancies permit the kitchen to be open to the rest of the building only if protection in accordance with 9.2.3 is provided for the cooking facilities.

In occupancy chapters that do not refer to the protection of cooking facilities, NFPA 96, *Standard on Ventilation Control and Fire Protection of Commercial Cooking Operations,* needs to be consulted to determine the criteria that define commercial cooking equipment and its appropriate required protection.[5]

9.2.4 Ventilating Systems in Laboratories Using Chemicals.

Ventilating systems in laboratories using chemicals shall be in accordance with NFPA 45, *Standard on Fire Protection for Laboratories Using Chemicals,* or NFPA 99, *Standard for Health Care Facilities,* as appropriate.

NFPA 45, *Standard on Fire Protection for Laboratories Using Chemicals,* contains requirements for construction, ventilation, and fire protection in laboratory buildings; and units and work areas in all buildings.[6] For laboratories in health care occupancies, NFPA 99, *Standard for Health Care Facilities,* contains additional requirements.[7] The intent is to apply the requirements from both documents in laboratories in health care facilities.

Section 9.3 Smoke Control

9.3.1* General.

Smoke control systems, where required or permitted by Chapters 11 through 42, shall have an approved maintenance and testing program to ensure operational integrity. The purpose of such smoke control systems shall be to confine smoke to the general area of fire origin and maintain use of the means of egress system.

The provision of 9.3.1 does not itself require smoke control systems but mandates that, if such systems are installed for *Code* compliance, an approved maintenance and testing program must be provided to ensure operational integrity. A smoke control system dedicated to emergency use only will not be subject to the daily use of a combination public address system and emergency occupant notification system. Therefore, maintenance and testing of smoke control systems are necessary.

Some *Code* requirements, such as those applicable to atria, mandate smoke control systems via performance-based language that requires tenable smoke conditions during egress. Annex references are provided to advise users of material that is available to assist in the design of smoke control systems.

A.9.3.1 For guidance on designing, installing, acceptance testing, periodic testing, and maintaining engineered smoke-control systems, see the following *(see A.23.3.1.3 for existing detention and correctional occupancies):*

(1) NFPA 92A, *Recommended Practice for Smoke-Control Systems*

(2) NFPA 92B, *Guide for Smoke Management Systems in Malls, Atria, and Large Areas*
(3) NFPA SPP-53, *Smoke Control in Fire Safety Design*
(4) *Design of Smoke Management Systems*
(5) ASHRAE *Guideline 5: Guideline for Commissioning Smoke Management Systems*

The reference documents that provide design guidance cannot be mandatorily referenced because they themselves do not contain mandatory requirements. NFPA 92A, *Recommended Practice for Smoke-Control Systems*, addresses smoke control management that uses barriers, airflows, and pressure differentials to confine the smoke of a fire to the zone of fire origin and thus maintain a tenable environment in other zones.[8] The guidelines of NFPA 92A can be used to create a smokeproof enclosure using the stair pressurization method described in 7.2.3.9. The document also covers smoke control for elevator hoistways by employing the following methods either singly or in combination:

(1) Fire floor exhaust
(2) Elevator lobby pressurization
(3) Smoketight elevator lobby construction
(4) Elevator hoistway pressurization

NFPA 92A also addresses, in detail, zoned smoke control under which a building can be divided into a number of smoke control zones. Each zone is separated from the others by partitions, floors, and doors that can be closed to inhibit the movement of smoke. A smoke control zone can consist of one or more floors, or a floor can consist of more than one smoke control zone. Some arrangements of smoke control zones are depicted in Exhibit 9.2, illustrations (a) through (e). The smoke zones are indicated by minus signs and pressurized spaces are indicated by plus signs. All nonsmoke zones might be pressurized as in illustrations (a) and (c), or only those nonsmoke zones that are adjacent to the smoke zone might be pressurized as in illustrations (b) and (d). In illustration (e), the smoke zone has been limited to a portion of a floor.

The subject of maintaining tenable conditions within large zones of fire origin (such as atria and shopping malls) is addressed by NFPA 92B, *Guide for Smoke Management Systems in Malls, Atria, and Large Areas*.[9] NFPA 92B provides technical data relevant to the design, installation, testing, operation, and maintenance of smoke management systems in buildings with large-volume spaces. These systems manage smoke within the space where the fire exists or between spaces not separated by smoke barriers. The

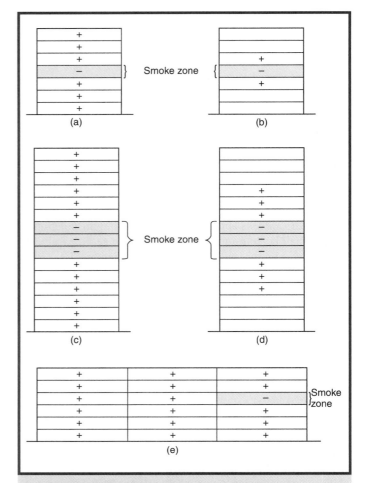

Exhibit 9.2 *Smoke control zone arrangement.*

guidelines of NFPA 92B can be used to implement smoke management systems that help to maintain a tenable environment in the means of egress from large-volume building spaces during the time required for evacuation. The guide also addresses the control and reduction of the smoke migration between the fire area and adjacent spaces. The commentary following 8.2.5.6 on atrium smoke control draws extensively from the theories and applications presented in NFPA 92B. In the example cited in that commentary, a volumetric exhaust rate was calculated following a detailed analysis of the physics associated with fire growth and smoke generation. This analysis concerns a particular atrium building configuration in which the exhaust rate keeps smoke from descending from the ceiling level to a level lower than head height of persons on the highest floor of the building open to the atrium. The summation of the exercise is detailed in Exhibit 8.18 and generalized in Exhibit 9.3.

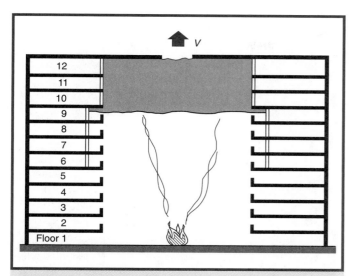

Exhibit 9.3 *Control of smoke layer.*

Although NFPA 92A and NFPA 92B cannot be referenced mandatorily by the *Code*, they should be used in the design, installation, testing, operation, and maintenance of smoke control systems covered by their scope statements.

Section 9.4 Elevators, Escalators, and Conveyors

9.4.1* General.

An elevator, other than an elevator in accordance with 7.2.13, shall not be considered a component in a required means of egress but shall be permitted as a component in an accessible means of egress.

A.9.4.1 Under certain conditions, elevators are recognized as means of egress.

The use of elevators for emergency evacuation purposes where operated by trained emergency service personnel (for example, building personnel, fire personnel) should be utilized in the building evacuation program. Elevators are normally capable of manual, in-car fire fighter operation (Phase II) after elevator recall (Phase I). In addition, there usually are two or more shafts wherever there are more than three elevators, which further enhances the possibilities for elevator use during a fire emergency where operated by trained personnel.

In high-rise buildings, in towers, or in deep underground spaces where travel over considerable vertical distance on stairs can cause persons incapable of such physical effort to collapse before they reach the street exit, stairways are permitted to be used for initial escape from the immediate

area of danger, and elevators are permitted to be used to complete the travel to the street.

It can be reasonably assumed that in all buildings of sufficient height to indicate the need for elevators, elevators will be provided for normal use; for this reason, no requirements for mandatory installation of elevators are included in the Code.

For additional information on elevators, see ASME/ANSI A17.1, *Safety Code for Elevators and Escalators,* and ASME/ANSI A17.3, *Safety Code for Existing Elevators and Escalators.*

In much earlier *Code* editions, the egress capacity of elevators was calculated based on the assumption that three average elevators were roughly equivalent to the formerly used single unit of stairway exit width. Because of this assumption, elevators had been accepted as required egress components under certain limited conditions by prior editions of the *Code.* No such credit has been given since 1956 because of some inherent characteristics that might make elevators unsuitable for emergency exit use. These characteristics are accentuated in modern automatic elevators where no operator is available to exercise judgment in the control of the elevator in case of fire or other emergency. A summary of the reasons elevators are not credited as part of the required means of egress follows.

(a) People seeking to escape from a fire by using an elevator might have to wait at the elevator door for some time; during that time they might be exposed to fire or smoke, or they might become panicky.

(b) Automatic elevators travel to floors by responding to pressed buttons, both in the elevator car and in elevator lobbies. Because this operation cannot be canceled once a button is pressed, it is possible for an elevator descending from floors above a fire to stop automatically at the floor of the fire. The doors will open automatically, thus exposing occupants to fire and smoke.

A further consideration is that an elevator shaft will act as a built-in "chimney" in a high-rise building. Unless positively pressurized with respect to the fire floor, the shaft will carry heat and smoke from a fire and expose passengers to toxic levels of both—even if the elevator does not stop at the floor of the fire and continues to function. An elevator moving within its shaft enclosure might act as a piston within a cylinder and push the smoke and gases of a fire to floors not initially involved.

(c) Modern elevators will not operate until the doors are fully closed. In an emergency, a large number of people might try to crowd into an elevator, preventing the doors from closing and preventing the elevator from operating.

(d) Any power failure, such as the burnout of electric supply cables during a fire, might render the elevators inoperative or might cause people to become trapped in elevators stopped between floors. Under fire conditions, there might not be enough time to rescue the trapped occupants through emergency escape hatches or doors.

Recognizing the viability of elevators to provide people movement the *Code* has, in recent editions, added guidelines addressing the use of elevators in limited circumstances. The following are four circumstances under which an elevator can be part of a building's evacuation plan.

(a) An elevator can be used in a high-rise building for assisting in a staged evacuation. Though it cannot be used as a component of the means of egress, an elevator can be a useful tool in the evacuation of a high-rise building.

(b) An elevator can be used as a means of evacuating people from an area of refuge. Elevators are an effective means of transporting people with severe mobility impairments. Subsection 7.2.12 of the *Code* establishes the criteria for the use of elevators for evacuation from an area of refuge. Exhibit 9.4 is an example of an appropriate elevator placard. Also see the commentary on 7.2.12.

(c) In underground assembly occupancies, the *Code* might require an elevator or escalator for the purposes of assisting in the emergency evacuation in an upward direction. An example of the *Code* requiring an elevator to be used under emergency conditions can be found in 12.4.3.3. Paragraph 12.4.3.3 requires each level of a new assembly occupancy with a floor level more than 30 ft (9.1 m) below the level of exit discharge to be divided into at least two smoke compartments. Each compartment then must be provided with a mechanical means of moving people vertically, such as an elevator or escalator. These requirements are in addition to the provisions for Section 11.7, which addresses underground and windowless structures. In Exhibit 9.5, an escalator is used in smoke zone A and an elevator is used in smoke zone B to provide the mechanical means to move people required by 12.4.3.3.2.

(d) In special types of towers, the *Code* recognizes the use of an elevator as a secondary means of egress. See the commentary on 7.2.13.

Exhibit 9.4 *Elevator placard.*

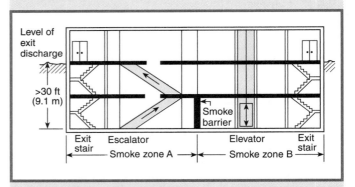

Exhibit 9.5 *Elevator and escalator use in underground assembly occupancy.*

9.4.2 Code Compliance.

For elevator installations, the *Code* requires compliance with either of the following:

(1) ASME/ANSI A17.1, *Safety Code for Elevators and Escalators*[10]

(2) ASME/ANSI A17.3, *Safety Code for Existing Elevators and Escalators*[11]

The *Code* additionally requires that a sprinkler system, if installed, meet the requirements of NFPA 13, *Standard for the Installation of Sprinkler Systems*.[12] ASME/ANSI A17.1 permits sprinklers in elevator hoistways and machine rooms in accordance with NFPA 13 subject to the following provisions:

(1) All risers and returns are to be located outside these spaces.
(2) Branch lines in the hoistway are to supply only the sprinklers on that level.
(3) A means for disconnecting the main line power supply to the affected elevator automatically upon or prior to the application of water from sprinklers located in the machine room or hoistway is to be provided as follows:

    a. The means must be independent of the elevator control and cannot be self-resetting.
    b. The activation of sprinklers outside the hoistway or machine room is not to disconnect the main line power supply.
    c. Smoke detectors are not to be used to activate sprinklers in these spaces or to disconnect the main line power supply.

ASME/ANSI A17.1 and ASME/ANSI A17.3 are also referenced because the *Code* recognizes the use of elevators and escalators under limited conditions and because fire fighters might need to use elevators during fire suppression efforts. Compliance with these documents makes it possible to recall elevators to the ground floor or other pre-designated floor during a fire, thus taking the elevators out of service. The provisions also permit fire fighters to override the controls manually and use the elevators as necessary.

9.4.2.1 Except as modified herein, new elevators, escalators, dumbwaiters, and moving walks shall be in accordance with the requirements of ASME/ANSI A17.1, *Safety Code for Elevators and Escalators*.

9.4.2.2 Except as modified herein, existing elevators, escalators, dumbwaiters, and moving walks shall conform to the requirements of ASME/ANSI A17.3, *Safety Code for Existing Elevators and Escalators*.

9.4.3 Fire Fighters' Service.

9.4.3.1 All new elevators shall conform to the Fire Fighters' Service Requirements of ASME/ANSI A17.1, *Safety Code for Elevators and Escalators*.

9.4.3.2 All existing elevators having a travel distance of 25 ft (7.6 m) or more above or below the level that best serves the needs of emergency personnel for fire fighting or rescue purposes shall conform to the Fire Fighters' Service Requirements of ASME/ANSI A17.3, *Safety Code for Existing Elevators and Escalators*.

Because an elevator stopping at a fire floor (intentionally or unintentionally) is an extreme hazard, the *Code* mandates compliance with the fire fighters' service requirements of ASME/ANSI A17.1 and ASME/ANSI A17.3 in both new and existing buildings. The fire fighters' service requirements establish elevator recall activated by smoke detection in each elevator lobby and in associated elevator machine rooms. A three-position, key-operated switch, normally located in the main lobby at the elevator, controls the recall function. The requirements mandate specific functions for the "on," "off," and "bypass" positions of this switch. The requirements also provide for *emergency in-car operations* or what is often referred to as fire fighters' service. Fire fighters' service requires a three-position, key-operated switch in each elevator car. The functions of the "on," "off," and "hold" positions are specified in the elevator code. For specific details, refer to ASME/ANSI A17.1. Explanatory material on these rules can be found in the ASME *Handbook* A17.1.[13]

Supplement 4 of this *Life Safety Code Handbook* contains extracts from ASME/ANSI A17.1 regarding this issue as well as commentary from the ASME *Handbook* A17.1.

9.4.4 Number of Cars.

The number of elevator cars permitted in a hoistway shall be in accordance with 8.2.5.9.

9.4.5* Elevator Machine Rooms.

Elevator machine rooms that contain solid-state equipment for elevators, other than existing elevators, having a travel distance exceeding 50 ft (15 m) above the level of exit discharge or exceeding 30 ft (9.1 m) below the level of exit discharge shall be provided with independent ventilation or air conditioning systems required to maintain temperature during fire fighters' service operation for elevator operation (see 9.4.4 and 9.4.5). The operating temperature shall be established by the elevator equipment manufacturer's specifications. When standby power is connected to the elevator, the machine room ventilation or air conditioning shall be connected to standby power.

A.9.4.5 Continued operation of solid-state elevator equipment is contingent on maintaining the ambient temperature in the range specified by the elevator manufacturer. If the machine room ventilation/air conditioning is connected to the general building system, and that system is shut down during a fire, the fire department might lose the use of elevators due to excessive heat in the elevator machine room.

Paragraphs 9.4.5 and A.9.4.5 explain the intent of the requirement for a ventilation or air conditioning system to help keep the elevator controls operable. For many typical installations, this can be accomplished by installing an independent through-the-wall air conditioning unit. Regardless of shutdown of the building's HVAC system, the independent unit will continue to run, provided that its power supply is not disabled.

9.4.6 Elevator Testing.

Elevators shall be subject to routine and periodic inspections and tests as specified in ASME/ANSI A17.1, *Safety Code for Elevators and Escalators.* All elevators equipped with fire fighter service in accordance with 9.4.4 and 9.4.5 shall be subject to a monthly operation with a written record of the findings made and kept on the premises as required by ASME/ANSI A17.1, *Safety Code for Elevators and Escalators.*

Because of the new emphasis placed on elevators by the *Code*, it is important to provide an appropriate level of elevator testing to help ensure that the elevator can be used by persons with mobility impairment and trained personnel under fire emergency conditions.

9.4.7 Openings.

Conveyors, elevators, dumbwaiters, and pneumatic conveyors serving various stories of a building shall not open to an exit.

Openings in exit enclosures are strictly limited by the provisions of 7.1.3.2.1(c) and (d) to doors necessary for access to the exit from normally occupied spaces and for leaving the exit enclosure. Elevators and other conveyors are not considered normally occupied areas. Additionally, an elevator with its associated cables, controls, and mechanical equipment would introduce a quantity of combustibles into an exit en-

closure that conflicts with the objective of making the exit enclosure a safe place that is free of combustibles.

Section 9.5 Rubbish Chutes, Incinerators, and Laundry Chutes

9.5.1 Enclosure.

Rubbish chutes and laundry chutes shall be separately enclosed by walls or partitions in accordance with the provisions of Section 8.2. Inlet openings serving chutes shall be protected in accordance with Section 8.2. Doors of such chutes shall open only to a room that is designed and used exclusively for accessing the chute opening. The room shall be separated from other spaces in accordance with Section 8.4.

Exception No. 1: Existing installations having properly enclosed service chutes and properly installed and maintained service openings shall be permitted to have inlets open to a corridor or normally occupied space.

Exception No. 2: Rubbish chutes and laundry chutes shall be permitted to open into rooms not exceeding 400 ft² (37 m²) in area used for storage, provided that the room is protected by automatic sprinklers.

9.5.2 Installation and Maintenance.

Rubbish chutes, laundry chutes, and incinerators shall be installed and maintained in accordance with NFPA 82, *Standard on Incinerators and Waste and Linen Handling Systems and Equipment*, unless existing installations, which shall be permitted to be continued in service, subject to approval by the authority having jurisdiction.

Shafts containing waste and linen chutes must be enclosed according to the requirements for the protection of vertical openings found in Section 8.2. The installation of the chute itself must meet the requirements of NFPA 82, *Standard on Incinerators and Waste and Linen Handling Systems and Equipment.*[14]

Additional concerns regarding chutes opening to other parts of the building need to be addressed. Service openings for loading must be conveniently located. Usually they are located to be accessible from corridors in the upper floors of the building. Location for this purpose is a concern because these corridors serve also as exit access, and a fire in the chute with an open loading door could result in the obstruction of the corridor by smoke and other products of combustion. To address this hazard, the *Code* and NFPA

82 require the construction of service opening rooms to form a buffer between the chute and the building space. Subsection 9.5.1 references the special hazard protection provisions in Section 8.4 for the separation of the service opening. The result is a room that is separated from the rest of the building by construction with a 1-hour fire resistance rating or protected with an automatic extinguishing system. The door to this room is required to have a 3/4-hour fire protection rating. Exhibit 9.6 illustrates the protection arrangement required for waste and linen chutes by NFPA 82.

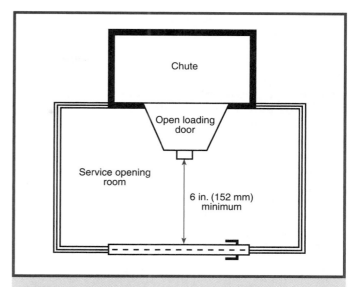

Exhibit 9.7 *Clearance in service opening room.*

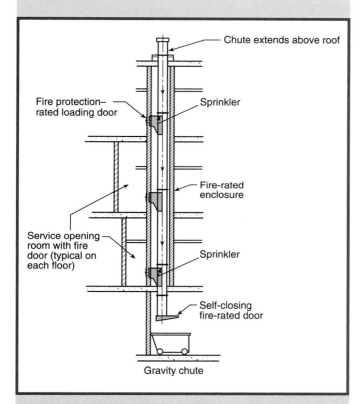

Exhibit 9.6 *Protection of waste and linen chutes.*

Additionally, NFPA 82 requires the service opening room to be sized to maintain a minimum 6-in. (152-mm) clearance between the open chute loading door and the closed room door. Exhibit 9.7 illustrates the measurement of this clearance.

Laundry chutes are often associated with a laundry/storage room. Exception No. 2 to 9.5.1 allows chutes to open into such rooms, provided that the room does not exceed 400 ft² (37 m²) in area. Without this exception, the user might interpret the words *used exclusively* as limiting the use of that room to serving the chute only.

Section 9.6 Fire Detection, Alarm, and Communications Systems

Supplement 2 of this handbook provides additional information regarding fire detection, alarm, and communications systems.

9.6.1 General.

9.6.1.1 The provisions of Section 9.6 shall apply only where specifically required by another section of this *Code*.

Section 9.6 applies only where specifically referenced by another section of the *Code*. Primarily, such references appear in the occupancy chapters. Careful attention to the specific references in the occupancy chapters is necessary, as they might contain additional modifications or exceptions to Section 9.6. For example, 12.3.4.1 for new assembly occupancies contains a general reference to all the requirements of 9.6.1; however, it also contains an exception that exempts voice communication or public address systems from complying with 9.6.1, provided that they meet the requirements of 12.3.4.3.3.

9.6.1.2 Fire detection, alarm, and communications systems installed to make use of an alternative allowed by this *Code* shall be considered required systems and shall meet the provisions of this *Code* applicable to required systems.

The provisions of 9.6.1.2 remind the user that a fire detection, alarm, or associated communications system that is installed to take advantage of a *Code* alternative becomes a required system and is subject to the same requirements, including maintenance. An example of this is a new business occupancy that is not required to have a fire alarm system based on the thresholds established in 38.3.4.1. If, for security reasons, delayed-egress locks are to be installed, they would have to meet the provisions of 7.2.1.6.1. Subparagraph 7.2.1.6.1(a) requires that the locks automatically release upon the activation of an approved, supervised automatic sprinkler system in accordance with Section 9.7 or an approved automatic detection system installed in accordance with Section 9.6. If this alternative is chosen, the fire alarm system becomes a required system and must be installed and maintained in accordance with Section 9.6.

9.6.1.3* The provisions of Section 9.6 cover the basic functions of a complete fire alarm system, including fire detection, alarm, and communications. These systems are primarily intended to provide the indication and warning of abnormal conditions, the summoning of appropriate aid, and the control of occupancy facilities to enhance protection of life.

A.9.6.1.3 Some of the provisions of Section 9.6 originated with NFPA 72, *National Fire Alarm Code®*. For purposes of this *Code*, some provisions of Section 9.6 are more stringent than those of NFPA 72, which should be consulted for additional details.

The provision for early warning of fire accompanied by notification of appropriate authorities is a key element of a fire protection program. Where people are involved, protective signaling carries even greater importance. The intent of 9.6.1.3 is to establish objectives for the performance of the fire alarm system and to allow individual system designs to address occupancy-specific variables.

Certain occupancies might not be required to have a fire alarm system at all. In industrial and storage occupancies, for example, the number of occupants in the facility or the hazard classification of the contents of the building determines whether an

alarm system is required. In educational, mercantile, and business occupancies, there are usually enough people present (at least during a part of the day) to discover an incipient fire. For these occupancies, the *Code* imposes less rigid requirements for protective signaling systems than it would mandate in certain other occupancies. Conversely, for health care occupancies the provisions for the fire alarm system are quite detailed with respect to notification and emergency functions such as smoke door operation.

9.6.1.4 A fire alarm system required for life safety shall be installed, tested, and maintained in accordance with the applicable requirements of NFPA 70, *National Electrical Code*, and NFPA 72, *National Fire Alarm Code*, unless an existing installation, which shall be permitted to be continued in use, subject to the approval of the authority having jurisdiction.

9.6.1.5 All systems and components shall be approved for the purpose for which they are installed.

Approval of both the system as a whole and its individual components is required. Such approval is granted by the authority having jurisdiction. See the definition of *approved* in 3.2.1. Substantiating data could be provided in the form of test reports, listings issued by organizations such as the Factory Mutual System or Underwriters Laboratories Inc., or testing or evaluation by another recognized source.

9.6.1.6 Fire alarm system installation wiring or other transmission paths shall be monitored for integrity in accordance with 9.6.1.4.

A broken or short-circuited wire between a fire alarm system initiating device (for example, a smoke detector) and the central control equipment will render the device inoperative without necessarily providing notification of the malfunction. Monitoring of the system installation wiring will result in an audible trouble signal indicating a circuit break or ground and allow for corrective action to be taken. It is not the intent of 9.6.1.6 to override the provisions for supervision in the codes referenced in 9.6.1.4 but only to highlight those requirements or to mandate them where the referenced codes might provide that such supervision is optional.

9.6.1.7* To ensure operational integrity, the fire alarm system shall have an approved maintenance and testing program complying with the applicable requirements of NFPA 70, *National Electrical Code*, and NFPA 72, *National Fire Alarm Code*.

A.9.6.1.7 Records of conducted maintenance and testing and a copy of the certificate of compliance should be maintained.

The operational integrity of a fire alarm system cannot be ensured without proper maintenance and testing. Thus, the *Code* requires that an approved (that is, acceptable to the authority having jurisdiction) maintenance and testing program be operational on an ongoing basis. As part of the program, it is equally important to retain system acceptance records and subsequent operational test records so comparisons can be made to initial system specifications.

9.6.1.8* Where a required fire alarm system is out of service for more than 4 hours in a 24-hour period, the authority having jurisdiction shall be notified, and the building shall be evacuated or an approved fire watch shall be provided for all parties left unprotected by the shutdown until the fire alarm system has been returned to service.

A.9.6.1.8 A fire watch should at least involve some special action beyond normal staffing, such as assigning an additional security guard(s) to walk the areas affected. These individuals should be specially trained in fire prevention and in occupant and fire department notification techniques, and they should understand the particular fire safety situation for public education purposes. *(Also see NFPA 601, Standard for Security Services in Fire Loss Prevention.)*

A fire alarm system might be shut down for any number of reasons during the life of a building. Some shutdowns are preplanned, controlled, and of short duration, such as during periodic testing and maintenance. Others might be preplanned and of longer duration, such as during times of building or system renovation. Emergency shutdown of the system can be the result of power failure, fire, or other physical damage and might result in a short or lengthy shutdown to repair the system. Advance planning should help ensure that the system, or most of the system, can be restored to service despite the scope of the renovation or the extent of an unexpected impairment. If the alarm system is required by the *Code* or if it was installed to make use of one of the alternatives

offered by the *Code*, it must be in good, operable condition for the building to be considered *Code* compliant.

Instead of designating a building with an inoperative alarm system as noncompliant and prohibiting occupancy under all conditions in accordance with the provisions of 4.6.9.1, 9.6.1.8 differentiates between those alarm system impairments that last less than 4 hours within a 24-hour period and those that last longer. Continued occupancy of a building that has an alarm system impairment of more than 4 hours cumulative within any 24-hour period can be tolerated only if a fire watch acceptable to the authority having jurisdiction is provided. Such lengthy impairments generally indicate a situation that involves a problem more serious in nature than typical system maintenance or testing.

It is the intent of the *Code* that the fire watch result in a heightened awareness of the building's operations and environment. Individuals selected for the fire watch should be able to recognize fire hazards and know the procedures for occupant and fire department notification and occupant evacuation in an emergency.

When developing a plan to address system shutdown, it is important to consider the nature of the shutdown, the location, the increased hazards that are involved, and the necessary actions to mitigate the hazards. The authority having jurisdiction should be involved in the development of these plans.

A parallel requirement in 9.7.6 addresses sprinkler system impairments.

9.6.1.9 For the purposes of this *Code*, a complete fire alarm system shall be used for initiation, notification, and control and shall provide the following.

(a) *Initiation.* The initiation function provides the input signal to the system.

(b) *Notification.* The notification function is the means by which the system advises that human action is required in response to a particular condition.

(c) *Control.* The control function provides outputs to control building equipment to enhance protection of life.

9.6.2 Signal Initiation.

9.6.2.1 Where required by other sections of this *Code*, actuation of the complete fire alarm system shall occur by any or all of the following means of initiation, but shall not be limited to such means:

(1) Manual fire alarm initiation
(2) Automatic detection
(3) Extinguishing system operation

Manual initiation is a requirement common to all occupancies that require fire alarm system installation. Initiation by automatic detection or extinguishing system operation is permitted to serve in lieu of manual initiation for some occupancies. Initiation by automatic detection or extinguishing system operation might be required by an occupancy chapter. For example, new educational occupancies are not required to have an automatic sprinkler system; however, if such a system is installed, 14.3.4.2.2 requires alarm system initiation by operation of the sprinkler system in addition to the manual means. In new health care occupancies, automatic sprinklers are required, and 18.3.4.2 states that initiation of the alarm system is to be by manual means and sprinkler system waterflow alarms. In new Class A mercantile occupancies, a fire alarm system and an automatic sprinkler system are required. However, 36.3.4.2 only requires initiation by manual means. Exception No. 2 to 36.3.4.2 permits alarm initiation by means of sprinkler system activation to serve in lieu of manual initiation but does not require it.

Where both manual and automatic means for alarm system initiation are used, they should be complementary. If one system becomes inoperative—perhaps due to poor maintenance, abuse, or mechanical failure—the second will provide backup support.

9.6.2.2 Manual fire alarm boxes shall be approved for the particular application and shall be used only for fire-protective signaling purposes. Combination fire alarm and guard's tour stations shall be acceptable.

9.6.2.3 A manual fire alarm box shall be provided in the natural exit access path near each required exit from an area, unless modified by another section of this *Code*.

9.6.2.4* Additional manual fire alarm boxes shall be located so that, from any part of the building, no horizontal distance on the same floor exceeding 200 ft (60 m) shall be traversed to reach a manual fire alarm box.

A.9.6.2.4 It is not the intent of 9.6.2.4 to require manual fire alarm boxes to be attached to movable partitions or to equipment, nor is it the intent to require the installation of permanent structures for mounting purposes only.

In a large open area such as a convention hall, it would be impractical to require the installation of manual fire alarm boxes on mounting posts in the middle of the floor. However, it would be reasonable to apply the maximum spacing requirements to boxes located on the perimeter wall of the space.

9.6.2.5 For fire alarm systems using automatic fire detection or waterflow detection devices, not less than one manual fire alarm box shall be provided to initiate a fire alarm signal. This manual fire alarm box shall be located where required by the authority having jurisdiction.

9.6.2.6* Each manual fire alarm box on a system shall be accessible, unobstructed, and visible.

A.9.6.2.6 Manual fire alarm boxes can include those with key-operated locks for detention areas or psychiatric hospitals, manual fire alarm boxes in areas where explosive vapors or dusts might be a hazard, or manual fire alarm boxes in areas with corrosive atmospheres. The appearance of manual fire alarm boxes for special uses often differs from those used in areas of normal occupancy. Manual fire alarm boxes, such as those with locks, that are located in areas where the general public has limited access might need to have signage advising persons to seek assistance from staff in the event a fire is noted.

Paragraphs 9.6.2.3 through 9.6.2.6 establish the criteria for the placement of manual fire alarm boxes. The intent is to provide maximum visibility and easy access in order to increase the probability that building occupants will initiate an alarm as they exit the building. If the alarm box is not located conveniently, or is obstructed from view, it is not likely that an occupant will look for one. Exhibit 9.8 illustrates an appropriate and an inappropriate location for a manual fire alarm box. A typical manual fire alarm box is shown in Exhibit 9.9.

Paragraph 9.6.2.5 is extracted from NFPA 72, *National Fire Alarm Code,* and is restated in the *Life Safety Code* for additional emphasis.[15] This requirement would affect initiation arrangement for occupancies that permit alarm initiation by automatic detection or extinguishing system operation in lieu of manual initiation. For example, a business occupancy using either Exception No. 1 or No. 2 to 38.3.4.2 for alarm initiation still would be required to have one manual fire alarm box in the building in a location approved by the authority having jurisdiction.

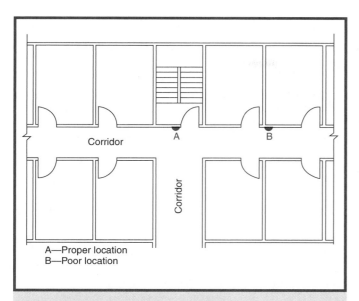

A—Proper location
B—Poor location

Exhibit 9.8 *Manual fire alarm box location.*

Exhibit 9.9 *Typical manual fire alarm box. (Source: Protectowire; photo courtesy of Mammoth Fire Alarms, Inc., Lowell, MA)*

9.6.2.7 Where a sprinkler system provides automatic detection and alarm system initiation, it shall be provided with an approved alarm initiation device that operates when the flow of water is equal to or greater than that from a single automatic sprinkler.

9.6.2.8 Where a complete smoke detection system is required by another section of this *Code*, automatic detection of smoke in accordance with NFPA 72, *National Fire Alarm Code*, shall be provided in all occupiable areas, common areas, and work spaces in those environments suitable for proper smoke detector operation.

9.6.2.9 Where a partial smoke detection system is required by another section of this *Code*, automatic detection of smoke in accordance with NFPA 72, *National Fire Alarm Code*, shall be provided in all common areas and work spaces, such as corridors, lobbies, storage rooms, equipment rooms, and other tenantless spaces in those environments suitable for proper smoke detector operation. Selective smoke detection unique to other sections of this *Code* shall be provided as required by those sections.

Paragraphs 9.6.2.8 and 9.6.2.9 use the terms *complete smoke detection system* and *partial smoke detection system* to provide a standard specification to be used throughout the *Code* wherever these systems are required. The term *selective smoke detection* varies in meaning and relies on another provision of the *Code* to specify the intent. For example, existing, nonsprinklered limited care facilities are required by 19.3.4.5.1 to have a corridor smoke detection system. The system does not meet the specifications of *complete* or *partial* as addressed by 9.6.2.8 or 9.6.2.9, and it is unique to existing limited care facilities.

9.6.2.10 Smoke Alarms.

Smoke alarms need to be positioned correctly. If they are too close to a wall/ceiling intersection, particularly over a door, air currents might cause heat and smoke to bypass the unit completely. Likewise, their location with respect to a dropped beam or other construction can have a similar nullifying effect. Problems can arise where partitions are moved without regard to the location of existing detectors. These problems are illustrated in Exhibit 9.10. NFPA 72, *National Fire Alarm Code*, provides extensive guidance in this area.

9.6.2.10.1 Where required by another section of this *Code*, single-station smoke alarms shall be in accordance with the household fire-warning equipment requirements of NFPA 72, *National Fire Alarm Code*, unless they are system smoke detectors in accordance with NFPA 72, *National Fire Alarm Code,* and are arranged to function in the same manner.

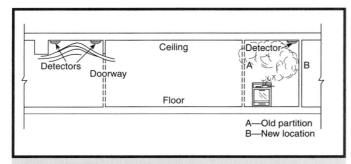

Exhibit 9.10 *Detector location problems to be avoided.*

complies with NFPA 72, *National Fire Alarm Code.* In turn, NFPA 72 requires such systems to indicate a missing battery or low battery power condition at the remotely located alarm system panel.

Compliance with the provisions of NFPA 72 applicable to low-power wireless systems increases the power source reliability to a level comparable to that provided by connection to the building electrical service.

The provisions of 9.6.2.10.1 reference the use of NPFA 72 where single-station smoke alarms that are not part of a fire alarm system are used. See the commentary following 9.6.2.10.2 through 9.6.2.10.4.

The term *single station* is often misunderstood. Single station means that the alarm that senses smoke also sounds an integral sounding device but does not ring a general alarm.

9.6.2.10.2 Smoke alarms, other than battery-operated devices as permitted by other sections of this *Code,* or battery-operated devices complying with 9.6.1.4 and the low-power wireless system requirements of NFPA 72, *National Fire Alarm Code,* shall receive their operating power from the building electrical system.

Single-station smoke alarms, unless exempted by 9.6.2.10.2, must receive their operating power from the electrical system; they must not rely solely on battery power. This provision is based on the experience that battery-operated detectors do not provide the reliability with respect to uninterrupted power supply that building electrical system power provides. Batteries are often removed to avoid nuisance alarms caused by kitchen or bathroom vapors or for use in other devices, such as radios and electronic toys; dead batteries are often not replaced. However, 9.6.2.10.2 permits the occupancy chapters to allow battery-operated, single-station smoke alarms. Such exemptions recognize battery-operated alarms in existing one- and two-family dwellings, in existing lodging and rooming houses, and, under certain conditions, in existing board and care facilities.

Subparagraph 9.6.2.10.2 also clarifies that it is not the *Code's* intent to prohibit low-power wireless technology, in which a battery-operated alarm reports by radio transmission to an alarm panel, if such a device

9.6.2.10.3* In new construction, unless otherwise permitted by another section of this *Code,* where two or more smoke alarms are required within a living unit, suite of rooms, or similar area, they shall be arranged so that operation of any smoke alarm shall cause the alarm in all smoke alarms within the living unit, suite of rooms, or similar area to sound.

Exception: This requirement shall not apply to configurations that provide equivalent distribution of the alarm signal.

Audibility over background noises, such as running water, home appliances, and audio systems, with intervening doors closed between the occupants and the detector sounding device, is of key importance. In multistory or large-area living units, multiple smoke alarms will need to be interconnected so that the sensing of smoke by one sounds the alarms of all devices within that living unit.

A.9.6.2.10.3 A living unit is that structure, area, room, or combination of rooms, including hotel rooms/suites, in which a family or individual lives. A living unit includes living areas only and not common usage areas in multifamily buildings such as corridors, lobbies, and basements.

9.6.2.10.4 The alarms shall sound only within an individual living unit, suite of rooms, or similar area and shall not actuate the building fire alarm system, unless otherwise permitted by the authority having jurisdiction. Remote annunciation shall be permitted.

The intent behind requiring smoke detection within an individual living unit without requiring connection to the overall building alarm system is to provide notification of a smoke condition within a living unit to its occupants. Once the occupants egress their unit to the building's common areas, they can use the manual fire alarm boxes to sound the building alarm to notify occupants of other living units of the emergency.

Interconnection of living unit smoke alarms to the building alarm system often results in numerous nuisance alarms due to the detection of cooking or bathroom shower vapors. Nuisance alarms lead to the deliberate disablement of the system and the resulting lack of early warning. Thus, a complete fire detection (versus smoke detection) system usually includes system smoke detection within building common areas and system heat detection within individual living units. Single-station smoke detectors are then still necessary within each living unit to afford the occupants of each unit early warning of smoke conditions within their unit.

9.6.2.11   Where required by Chapters 11 through 42, an automatic fire detection system shall be provided in hazardous areas for initiation of the signaling system.

9.6.3 Occupant Notification.

9.6.3.1   Occupant notification shall provide signal notification to alert occupants of fire or other emergency as required by other sections of this *Code*.

9.6.3.2   Notification shall be provided by audible and visible signals in accordance with 9.6.3.3 through 9.6.3.12.

Note that 9.6.3.2 and 9.6.3.6 both require that occupant notification be provided by audible and visible signals. Thus, where an occupancy chapter requires an alarm system that provides occupant notification in accordance with Section 9.6, visible signal (as well as the traditional audible signal) must be provided. See also the exceptions to 9.6.3.6.

Exception No. 1:   *Elevator lobby, hoistway, and associated machine room smoke detectors used solely for elevator recall, and heat detectors used solely for elevator power shutdown, shall not be required to activate the building evacuation alarm if the power supply and installation wiring to these detectors are monitored by the building fire alarm system, and the activation of these detectors results in an audible and visible alarm signal at a constantly attended location.*

A.9.6.3.2 Exception No. 1 Elevator lobbies have been considered areas subject to unwanted alarms due to factors such as low ceilings and smoking. In the past several years, new features have become available to reduce this problem. These features are, however, not necessarily included in any specific installation.

Exception No. 2:*   *Smoke detectors used solely for closing dampers or heating, ventilating, and air conditioning system shutdown shall not be required to activate the building evacuation alarm.*

Exception No. 3:*   *Detectors located at doors for the exclusive operation of automatic door release shall not be required to activate the building evacuation alarm.*

A.9.6.3.2 Exception Nos. 2 and 3 The concept addressed by the exceptions is that detectors used for releasing service, such as door or damper closing and fan shutdown, are not required to sound the building alarm.

Exception No. 2 and Exception No. 3 to 9.6.3.2 reaffirm that not all detectors are required to sound the building alarm simply because they are installed on the premises. Detectors used for releasing service, such as for the release of an automatic door hold-open device that allows a door to be self-closing under the presence of smoke, need only perform their intended function. In areas where smoke detection—complete with occupant notification via the building alarm system—is needed to provide the intended level of life safety, the *Code* will specifically require either a complete or partial smoke detection system. Interconnection with the building alarm should not be mandated in the hope of receiving additional detection coverage, because a detector might have been installed for another purpose, such as releasing service.

New health care occupancies, via 18.3.4.3.1, prohibit the use of Exception No. 3 to 9.6.3.2. Thus, if a smoke detector is installed as part of an automatic door release (see 7.2.1.8.2), the activation of the detector must result in occupant notification through the building fire alarm system. See 18.3.4.3.1 and 18.3.4.2.

Exception No. 4:   *Detectors in accordance with the exception to 22.3.4.3.1 and the exception to 23.3.4.3.1 shall not be required to activate the building evacuation alarm.*

9.6.3.3   Where permitted by Chapters 11 through 42, a presignal system shall be permitted where the initial fire alarm signal is automatically transmitted without delay to a municipal fire department, a fire brigade (if provided), and an on-site staff person trained to respond to a fire emergency.

Instead of immediately and automatically sounding a general alarm throughout the building, a presignal system delays the general alarm by sounding alarm devices initially in only an approved and constantly attended area. This area could be, for example, a fire brigade station, guard station, or similar location with trained staff who investigate the signal's origin and subsequently sound a general alarm if necessary. If a presignal system is not intentionally aborted within a predetermined time, an audible general building alarm is sounded.

A delay in sounding the general alarm is inherent in a presignal system, but the delay might do more harm than good in those occupancies with populations that are difficult to evacuate or protect. Therefore, the *Code* requires an occupancy chapter to specifically recognize a presignal system to permit its use. Most occupancies no longer permit presignal systems in new construction but continue to permit them in existing buildings. For example, 40.3.4.3.3 permits an existing presignal system in an industrial occupancy.

A presignal system used in accordance with the provisions of 9.6.3.3 is allowed to delay only the general occupant notification and must, at time of initiation, achieve immediate and automatic notification of emergency forces.

9.6.3.4   Where permitted by Chapters 11 through 42, a positive alarm sequence shall be permitted, provided that it is in accordance with NFPA 72, *National Fire Alarm Code.*

Given that smoke detector sensitivity should result in alarm system initiation sooner than that achieved by either heat detection or manual discovery and use of a pull station, 9.6.3.4 addresses positive alarm sequence, which has detailed requirements in NFPA 72. Positive alarm sequence offers relief from nuisance alarms in buildings equipped with detection technology by allowing a delay in occupant notification. The detector senses smoke, automatically and without delay, sending an alarm signal to a constantly attended location so that trained staff can investigate the origin of the signal. Positive alarm sequence includes all of the following features:

(1) The signal received at the attended location must be acknowledged within 15 seconds, or immediate occupant notification (and emergency forces notification, if required) must occur.
(2) Trained personnel have up to 180 seconds during the alarm investigation phase to evaluate the fire condition and reset the system; if the system is not reset within 180 seconds, immediate occupant notification (and emergency forces notification, if required) must occur.

(3) If a second automatic fire detector is actuated during the investigation phase, immediate occupant notification (and emergency forces notification, if required) must occur.
(4) If any other initiating device, such as a manual pull station, is actuated during the investigation phase, immediate occupant notification (and emergency forces notification, if required) must occur.
(5) The system must provide a means to bypass the positive alarm sequence.

Positive alarm sequence is permitted only if an occupancy chapter specifically allows it by direct reference to 9.6.3.4. The following occupancies permit positive alarm sequence:

(1) Assembly occupancies (12.3.4.3.1, 13.3.4.3.1)
(2) Educational occupancies (exception to 14.3.4.3.1.1, 15.3.4.3.1.1)
(3) Day care occupancies (16.3.4.3.2, 17.3.4.3.2)
(4) Detention and correctional occupancies (22.3.4.3.1, 23.3.4.3.1)
(5) Hotel and dormitory occupancies (exception to 28.3.4.3.1, exception to 29.3.4.3.1)
(6) Apartments (30.3.4.3.1, 31.3.4.3.1)
(7) Mercantile occupancies [exception to 36.3.4.3.1(a), Exception No. 1 to 37.3.4.3.1(a)]
(8) Business occupancies [exception to 38.3.4.3(a), Exception No. 1 to 39.3.4.3(a)]
(9) Industrial occupancies (40.3.4.3.2)
(10) Storage occupancies (42.3.4.3.2, 42.8.3.4.3.2)

9.6.3.5*   Where a standard evacuation signal is required by another section of this *Code*, the evacuation signal shall be the standard fire alarm evacuation signal described in NFPA 72, *National Fire Alarm Code.*

A.9.6.3.5   Effective July 1, 1996, NFPA 72, *National Fire Alarm Code*, requires the use of the standard fire alarm evacuation signal for new alarm system installations in all buildings where the fire plan requires evacuation.

See the commentary following 9.6.3.9.

9.6.3.6   Notification signals for occupants to evacuate shall be by audible and visible signals in accordance with NFPA 72, *National Fire Alarm Code*, and CABO/ANSI A117.1, *American National Standard for Accessible and Usable Buildings and Facilities*, or other means of notification acceptable to the authority having jurisdiction shall be provided.

Exception No. 1:   Areas not subject to occupancy by persons who are hearing impaired shall not be required to comply with the provisions for visible signals.

Visible alarm devices, in addition to the audible alarms, are needed in buildings occupied by persons who are hearing impaired. Exception No. 1 to 9.6.3.6 recognizes that not all buildings are subject to occupancy by those who are hearing impaired. For example, in a special hazard industrial occupancy where, due to employee safety concerns, an adequate hearing level has been judged to be a legitimate condition of employment, there should be no life safety need for visible signals in addition to the normal audible signals. As the provisions of the Americans with Disabilities Act Accessibility Guidelines (ADAAG) discussed in the commentary associated with 7.2.12 receive wider implementation or are expanded in scope, there will be few locations where it is certain that persons with hearing impairments will not be present.

Exception No. 2:   Visible-only signals shall be provided where specifically permitted in health care occupancies in accordance with the provisions of Chapters 18 and 19.

Exception No. 3:   Existing alarm systems shall not be required to comply with the provision for visible signals.

Exception No. 4:   Visible signals shall not be required in lodging or rooming houses in accordance with the provisions of Chapter 26.

9.6.3.7   The general evacuation alarm signal shall operate throughout the entire building.

Exception No. 1:   *Where total evacuation of occupants is impractical due to building configuration, only the occupants in the affected zones shall be initially notified. Provisions shall be made to selectively notify occupants in other zones to afford orderly evacuation of the entire building.*

A.9.6.3.7 Exception No. 1 In order to approve an evacuation plan to selectively notify building occupants, the authority having jurisdiction should consider several building parameters, including building compartmentation, detection and suppression system zones, occupant loads, and the number and arrangement of the means of egress.

In high-rise buildings, it is typical to evacuate the fire floor, the floor(s) above, and the floor immediately below. Other areas are then evacuated as the fire develops.

Exception No. 1 to 9.6.3.7 normally applies to high-rise buildings. It provides for zoned, staged evacuation. This exception anticipates that the portions of the building that do not receive the initial alarm are separated from the areas of immediate emergency by adequate fire resistance–rated construction, such as the 2-hour fire separation that is usually provided between floors of high-rise buildings.

Exception No. 2:   Where occupants are incapable of evacuating themselves because of age, physical or mental disabilities, or physical restraint, the private operating mode as described in NFPA 72, National Fire Alarm Code, shall be permitted to be used. Only the attendants and other personnel required to evacuate occupants from a zone, area, floor, or building shall be required to be notified. This notification shall include means to readily identify the zone, area, floor, or building in need of evacuation.

Exception No. 2 to 9.6.3.7 commonly applies to health care occupancies and detention and correctional occupancies. It is common in these occupancies to use coded messages or a similar method to announce the location of a fire emergency throughout the facility. This allows all members of the emergency response team, regardless of current location within a potentially sprawling facility, to respond to their assigned emergency duties. For example, despite the fact that the facility engineer might be in a building remote from that with the emergency when the coded alarm sounds throughout the facility, the engineer will receive the proper notification to carry out the previously assigned task of checking the fire pump to ensure that it is ready to operate if needed.

Exception No. 3:   Notification within the covered mall per 36.4.4.3.3 and 37.4.4.3.3.

Exception No. 3 to 9.6.3.7 emphasizes that the provisions of Chapters 36 and 37 that apply to covered malls require an alarm system for the covered mall (the covered pedestrian walkway) rather than for the entire covered mall building, which includes both the covered mall and all attached tenant spaces. The individual tenant spaces that are themselves Class A mercantile occupancies must also have an alarm system. Smaller tenant spaces are not required to have alarm systems. The alarm system required in the covered mall must sound throughout the covered mall but need not sound within the tenant spaces. The alarm system required in each Class A mercantile occupancy tenant space must sound within that tenant space but is not required to sound either in the smaller tenant spaces (which are exempt from the alarm system requirement) or in the covered mall.

9.6.3.8 Audible alarm notification appliances shall be of such character and so distributed as to be effectively heard above the average ambient sound level occurring under normal conditions of occupancy.

The authority having jurisdiction needs to review carefully the types and locations of alarm-indicating appliances. Given that audibility above ambient sound level is of primary importance and that each additional sounding device adds cost to a system, a balance should be maintained so that excessive costs are not incurred while the installation of sufficient devices for adequate audibility is ensured. The provision of sufficient devices is extremely important in hotels and apartment buildings. Sounding devices located in corridors might not be audible within living units, especially in new construction, due to increased levels of acoustical insulation.

In new hotels, it has become common to install alarm indicators within each guest room to meet the audibility requirement. With water running in the bathroom, the television operating on high volume, and the air-conditioning system in use, the horn or speaker within the room achieves the required occupant notification that a similar device located in the corridor might not. Additionally, the alarm device often used is a speaker that can produce an alarm tone or deliver a specific voice message. A speaker device is particularly useful in a high-rise building; although it is important to get an initial message to all rooms, different messages will also need to be sent to different parts of the building as part of a zoned evacuation plan.

9.6.3.9 Audible alarm notification appliances shall produce signals that are distinctive from audible signals used for other purposes in the same building.

Where the provisions of Chapters 12 through 42 require an evacuation alarm signal, the standard fire alarm evacuation signal described in NFPA 72, *Na-*

tional Fire Alarm Code, should be used. See 9.6.3.5 and A.9.6.3.5. The standard fire alarm evacuation signal is a three-pulse temporal pattern using any appropriate sound. This signal is illustrated in Exhibit 9.11. The pattern consists of an "on" phase (a) lasting 0.5 second followed by an "off" phase (b) lasting 0.5 second, for three successive "on" periods; these are followed by an "off" phase (c) lasting 1.5 seconds. The signal should be repeated for a period appropriate for the purposes of evacuation of the building but for not less than 180 seconds. A single-stroke bell or chime sounded at "on" intervals lasting 1 second, with a 2-second "off" interval after each third "on" stroke is permitted.

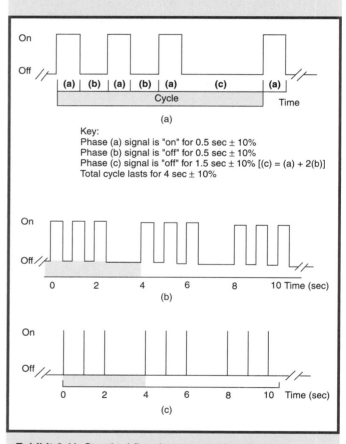

Exhibit 9.11 Standard fire alarm evacuation signal.

The manner of sounding alarms should be standardized to obtain uniformity throughout as large a geographic area as practicable so that people moving from one locality to another will not be misled and confused by differences in the manner of sounding alarms.

Two multiple-fatality fires in hotel occupancies

that occurred in late 1978 and 1979 illustrate the need for standardized fire alarm signals with adequate audibility. In both incidents, which occurred in the middle of the night, many survivors reported not hearing any alarm device or mistaking the alarm for telephones or alarm clocks. An additional multiple-fatality fire in a hotel in 1978 illustrated the special problems with alarm notification where occupants are hearing impaired. In this fire, several elderly occupants removed hearing aids before going to bed, thus challenging the adequacy of the alarm's audibility.

9.6.3.10 Automatically transmitted or live voice evacuation or relocation instructions to occupants shall be permitted and shall be in accordance with NFPA 72, *National Fire Alarm Code.*

Rather than specify additional requirements for recorded or live voice evacuation or relocation instructions, the *Code* mandatorily references NFPA 72, *National Fire Alarm Code,* which contains the necessary requirements.

9.6.3.11 Audible and visible fire alarm notification appliances shall be used only for fire alarm system or other emergency purposes, unless otherwise permitted by another section of this *Code.*

An example of a use permitted by another section of the *Code,* as specified in 9.6.3.11, appears in 14.3.4.3.1.2 for educational occupancies. The fire alarm system in 14.3.4.3.1.2 is permitted to be used to designate class change, provided that the fire alarm signal is distinctively different from the class change signal and overrides all other use.

Exception: Voice communication systems shall be permitted to be used for other purposes, subject to the approval of the authority having jurisdiction, if the fire alarm system takes precedence over all other signals.

The exception to 9.6.3.11 requires the approval of the authority having jurisdiction to permit a voice communication system to be used for some other purpose. The system designer or building operator and the authority having jurisdiction should determine how susceptible the system is to deliberate tampering. For example, in a business occupancy where a

combination emergency voice communication and daily background music system is installed with a speaker located in the ceiling directly over an employee's desk, it should be predicted that the constant, background music might irritate the employee to the point that the speaker will be muffled or otherwise disabled. Therefore, the requirement that the fire alarm system take precedence over all other signals becomes futile; a disabled speaker cannot deliver the required emergency message.

9.6.3.12 Alarm notification signals shall take precedence over all other signals.

9.6.4 Emergency Forces Notification.

Where required by another section of this *Code,* emergency forces notification shall be provided to alert the municipal fire department and fire brigade (if provided) of fire or other emergency.

Where fire department notification is required by another section of this *Code,* the fire alarm system shall be arranged to transmit the alarm automatically via any of the following means acceptable to the authority having jurisdiction and shall be in accordance with NFPA 72, *National Fire Alarm Code:*

(1) Auxiliary alarm system
(2) Central station connection
(3) Proprietary system
(4) Remote station connection

The following is provided to help differentiate among the four alarm transmission methods for fire department notification in 9.6.4.

(a) *Auxiliary Alarm System.* An auxiliary alarm system is a system connected to a municipal fire alarm system for transmitting an alarm of fire to the public fire service communication center. Fire alarms from an auxiliary alarm system are received at the public fire service communication center on the same equipment and by the same methods as alarms transmitted manually from municipal fire alarm boxes located on streets.

(b) *Central Station Fire Alarm System.* A central station fire alarm system is a system or group of systems in which the operations of circuits and devices are signaled automatically to, recorded in, maintained by, and supervised from a listed central station staffed by competent and experienced servers and operators. Upon receipt of a signal, the staff take such action as is required. Such service is controlled and operated by a person or firm whose business is the furnishing, maintaining, and monitoring of supervised fire alarm systems.

(c) *Proprietary Fire Alarm System.* A proprietary fire alarm system is an installation of fire alarm systems that serves contiguous or noncontiguous properties under one ownership from a proprietary supervising station located at the protected property, where trained, competent personnel are in constant attendance. This system includes the proprietary supervising station; power supplies; signal initiating devices; initiating device circuits; signal notification appliances; equipment for the automatic, permanent, visual recording of signals; and equipment for initiating the operation of emergency building control services.

(d) *Remote Station Fire Alarm System.* A remote station fire alarm is a system installed to transmit alarm, supervisory, and trouble signals from one or more protected premises to a remote supervising station location at which appropriate action is taken.

Fire alarm equipment installed for the notification of occupants of a building, in localities under the protection of a regularly organized fire department or private fire brigade, can be arranged to provide the automatic transmission of alarms. These alarms can be transmitted directly or through an approved central station office to the fire department or fire brigade upon operation of an alarm-sending station or system. Where no such connection is provided, a fire alarm box arranged to signal the fire department could be installed at the main entrance to the building, at the telephone switchboard, or somewhere outside the building. The alarm box must be plainly visible during day or night and must be conveniently accessible from the main entrance. While this arrangement is desirable, it is not required by 9.6.4 unless specified by the occupancy chapter.

Exception: For existing installations where none of the means of notification specified in 9.6.4(1) through (4) is available, a plan for notification of the municipal fire department, acceptable to the authority having jurisdiction, shall be permitted.

The extensive availability of reliable communications systems has limited the necessity for this exception (formerly permitted for all occupancies) to existing installations only.

9.6.5 Emergency Control.

9.6.5.1   A fire alarm and control system, where required by another section of this *Code*, shall be arranged to actuate automatically the control functions necessary to make the protected premises safer for building occupants.

9.6.5.2   Where required by another section of this *Code*, the following functions shall be actuated by the complete fire alarm system:

(1) Release of hold-open devices for doors or other opening protectives

Subparagraph 7.2.1.8.2 allows for doors to be automatic-closing if (among other requirements) the detection of smoke automatically releases the device holding the door open, thus allowing the door to become self-closing. Those provisions do not require the building alarm system to release the doors. Subparagraphs 18.2.2.2.6 and 19.2.2.2.6 in the health care chapters are more stringent on the subject and require that the automatic closing of doors is also to occur upon initiation of the building's required fire alarm system. This is an example of an occupancy chapter mandating 9.6.5.2(1) as a requirement that is needed in addition to 7.2.1.8.2—the provision allowing the automatic closing of doors that normally would be required to be self-closing.

(2) Stairwell or elevator shaft pressurization
(3) Smoke management or smoke control systems

Manual fire alarm pull stations generally should not be used to activate smoke control systems other than stair tower pressurization systems due to the likelihood of a person signaling an alarm from a station outside the smoke zone of fire origin. For additional guidance on the subject, see the following:

(1) NFPA 92A, *Recommended Practice for Smoke-Control Systems*
(2) NFPA 92B, *Guide for Smoke Management Systems in Malls, Atria, and Large Areas*

(4) Emergency lighting control

New special amusement buildings are addressed in 12.4.7. Those that operate in reduced lighting levels (for example, a haunted house amusement) must, upon actuation of the required automatic smoke detection system or the required automatic sprinkler system, increase illumination in the means of egress to at least the minimum level required by Section 7.8. The requirements applicable to special amusement buildings augment the concept of using the alarm system to initiate an emergency control function by mandating that conflicting or confusing sounds and visuals stop upon actuation of the required automatic smoke detection system or the required automatic sprinkler system. Thus, in a haunted house amusement, all audible and visual special effects would cease upon alarm so as not to confuse the patrons. A fire alarm horn or strobe might not be recognized if forced to compete with the background special effects common to such an occupancy.

(5) Unlocking of doors

For an example of a *Code* requirement for the activation of the alarm system to unlock a door, see the provisions for delayed-egress door locking addressed by 7.2.1.6.1.

9.6.5.3   The functions specified in 9.6.5.2 shall be permitted to be actuated by any fire alarm and control system where otherwise not required by this *Code*. Additionally, such a fire alarm and control system shall be permitted to recall elevators, as required by Section 9.4, if the activation of the system for this purpose comes only from elevator lobby, hoistway, or associated machine room detectors.

ASME/ANSI A17.1, *Safety Code for Elevators and Escalators*, and ASME/ANSI A17.3, *Safety Code for Existing Elevators and Escalators* (which are referenced mandatorily by Section 9.4), prohibit the recall of elevators by detectors other than those installed in the elevator lobbies, hoistways, and associated elevator machine room. Recall by other detectors leads to numerous nuisance recalls under conditions where it would be safe to operate elevators. To avoid having elevators taken out of service every time any building system detector senses smoke, the recall feature is often deliberately disabled. ASME/ANSI A17.1 and ASME/ANSI A17.3 impose the recall restriction to keep the recall feature operational. Paragraph 9.6.5.3 restates these provisions and permits the elevator lobby and machine room detectors to be part of the building detection, alarm, and communications system.

9.6.5.4*   Installation of emergency control devices shall be in accordance with NFPA 72, *National Fire Alarm Code*. The performance of emergency control functions shall not impair the effective response of all required alarm notification functions.

A.9.6.5.4   Control devices (fire alarm relays) can be located at a motor control center that is located floors away from the device to be activated, such as air-handling units and exhaust fans located on the roof. The requirement for monitoring for integrity only applies to the installation wiring between the fire alarm control unit and the auxiliary fire alarm relay. It does not apply to the wiring between the auxiliary fire alarm relay and the emergency control device (for example, motor stop/start control relay) or between the emergency control device and the equipment to be controlled (for example, air-handling units and exhaust fans). For example, although the auxiliary fire alarm relay is required be located within 3 ft (0.9 m) of the emergency control device, there is no limit specified for the distance between the emergency control device and the equipment to be controlled.

9.6.6 Location of Controls.

Operator controls, alarm indicators, and manual communications capability shall be installed in a control center at a convenient location acceptable to the authority having jurisdiction.

At times it is not practical, either physically or from a security standpoint, to locate control centers adjacent to an entrance. For example, control centers for proprietary protective signaling systems designed in accordance with NFPA 72, *National Fire Alarm Code*, for reasons of security, often need to be located away from public areas. Thus, the *Code* does not require that control centers be located adjacent to an entrance. However, because the controls are intended to be used by the fire department, they need to be located in a position approved by the authority having jurisdiction.

9.6.7 Annunciation.

Subsection 9.6.7 establishes provisions applicable to alarm annunciation to be referenced by another section of the *Code* as part of the overall life safety package needed for a specific occupancy. Alarm annunciation allows trained individuals—such as building engineers, security and safety officers, and responding fire service personnel—to read the indicator lamps or alphanumeric displays of an annunciator unit to identify circuits, associated building locations, and conditions that warrant attention or investigation.

9.6.7.1 Where alarm annunciation is required by another section of this *Code*, it shall comply with 9.6.7.2 through 9.6.7.7.

9.6.7.2 Alarm annunciation at the control center shall be by means of audible and visible indicators.

Paragraph 9.6.7.2 requires alarm annunciation at the control center to be by means of audible as well as visible indication to capture the attention of the trained attendant, who might have numerous job functions within or near the control center that might distract attention from the annunciator unit.

9.6.7.3 For the purposes of alarm annunciation, each floor of the building, other than floors of existing buildings, shall be considered as not less than one zone, unless otherwise permitted by another section of this *Code*.

9.6.7.4 Unless otherwise permitted by another section of this *Code*, if a floor area exceeds 20,000 ft² (1860 m²), additional zoning shall be provided, and the length of any single zone shall not exceed 300 ft (91 m) in any direction.

Exception: Where the building is provided with automatic sprinklers throughout, installed in accordance with Section 9.7, the area of the alarm zone shall be permitted to coincide with the allowable area of the sprinkler zone.

Paragraphs 9.6.7.3 and 9.6.7.4 address the choice of zone locations and zone sizes for meaningful annunciation. In a new multiple-story building required to have alarm annunciation by another section of the *Code*, 9.6.7.3 would not allow two or more floors to be considered as a single zone; an alarm condition would be annunciated as originating in a zone that includes multiple floors and, thus, would not identify the specific area with the emergency. Such a situation would delay the investigation and associated emergency response effort. Paragraph 9.6.7.3 exempts existing alarm annunciation systems so as not to unfairly render existing *Code*-complying installations abruptly noncompliant, thereby avoiding the need for major alterations or a complete replacement of the alarm system.

Paragraph 9.6.7.4 further specifies that no one zone for alarm annunciation purposes, even if it is located entirely on one floor of the building, should be so large that it delays identification of the location from which the alarm was initiated. The maximum zone area and zone dimensional criteria are waived by the exception to 9.6.7.4 for fully sprinklered buildings, allowing the alarm system zoning to coincide with the area of the sprinkler system zone. Depending on the sprinkler system's design, this might result in a zone as large as 52,000 ft² (4831 m²). This requirement helps to achieve consistency in reporting alarms from signaling system devices and from sprinkler system waterflow to the annunciator unit. Although a sprinkler system might be designed and installed by parties different from those who design and install signaling systems, the coordination of these two systems is needed during the design phase in order for systems to complement each other.

9.6.7.5 A system trouble signal shall be annunciated at the control center by means of audible and visible indicators.

9.6.7.6 A system supervisory signal shall be annunciated at the control center by means of audible and visible indicators.

Paragraphs 9.6.7.5 and 9.6.7.6 require that alarm system trouble signals and supervisory signals be annunciated at the control center by both audible and visible indication to help ensure that personnel in attendance will pay attention to the indication and act appropriately. Trouble signals indicate such conditions as a circuit break or ground occurring in the protective signaling system wiring. Supervisory signals indicate a problem with the supervision of sprinkler systems, such as a shut valve. Supervisory signals can also be associated with the supervision of other extinguishing systems and equipment or the maintenance features of other fire protection systems.

9.6.7.7 Where the system serves more than one building, each building shall be considered separately.

Section 9.7 Automatic Sprinklers and Other Extinguishing Equipment

Supplement 3 of this handbook contains additional information on sprinklers and automatic sprinkler systems.

9.7.1 Automatic Sprinklers.

9.7.1.1* Each automatic sprinkler system required by another section of this *Code* shall be in accordance with NFPA 13, *Standard for the Installation of Sprinkler Systems.*

The *Code* requirements for automatic sprinklers are based on the sprinkler experience record, which shows that, where installed properly, a sprinkler system is the most effective device for protecting and safeguarding against loss of life and property. Occupants of a building who are aware of the presence of sprinkler protection can feel secure that any fire will be detected and fought at its origin and that an alarm will be given. The alarm will provide time for occupants to evacuate a burning building before fire can cut off their escape.

Numerous myths exist regarding the operation of automatic sprinklers. Some are reinforced by misrepresentations in the news media or the entertainment industry. The following facts should serve to debunk these myths:

(1) Sprinkler systems do not operate when smoke detectors operate.
(2) All sprinklers in the building do not operate simultaneously unless specifically designed to do so.
(3) Sprinklers do not spray water that has been superheated by the fire, resulting in the scalding of building occupants.
(4) Sprinkler system operation does not cause drowning or electrocution of building occupants.
(5) Sprinkler system operation does not increase the amount of smoke generated by the fire.

Automatic sprinkler systems remain the single most effective means of controlling fire spread for the widest range of buildings and areas. It is for this reason that the *Code* contains numerous exceptions to requirements based on the presence sprinklers.

NFPA 13, *Standard for the Installation of Sprinkler Systems,* covers installation details for standard automatic sprinkler systems. In the interest of both life safety from fire and the protection of property, it will generally be beneficial to provide a complete standard automatic sprinkler installation to protect the entire property. Sprinklers prove beneficial even in situations where the *Code* requires sprinklers only for the isolation and protection of hazardous contents areas.

NFPA 13 is the authoritative source for sprinkler systems with respect to design, installation, and character and adequacy of water supply. Even though there are usually some areas in a building where fires are more likely to start than others, it is impossible to predict where a fire might start and protect only those areas. Thus, where sprinklers are installed, they should be installed throughout a building. The basic requirements of NFPA 13 for spacing, locating, and positioning sprinklers are based on principles that include sprinkler installation throughout the building—including combustible concealed spaces. The *Life Safety Code,* however, in an effort to promote the use of sprinkler systems by reducing the costs, allows sprinklers to be omitted from small closets and bathrooms in various residential occupancies but considers those occupancies to be fully sprinklered. For an example, see Exception No. 2 to 29.3.5.1, which applies to existing hotels.

NFPA 13 provides for the installation of systems of various types that are appropriate for the individual building protected, subject to the approval of the authority having jurisdiction.

NFPA 13D, *Standard for the Installation of Sprinkler Systems in One- and Two-Family Dwellings and Manufactured Homes,* was developed after extensive research that included full-scale fire tests.[16] NFPA 13D introduced the concept of a quick-response residential sprinkler. Unlike its industrial standard spray sprinkler counterpart, which is inherently slow to fuse its relatively massive eutectic solder element, a quick-response, residential sprinkler operates very quickly once its rated temperature is sensed. It begins controlling a fire early in its growth. In addition to being quick to respond, residential sprinklers (as mandated by NFPA 13D) have a specifically designed spray pattern that delivers water to nearly the full height of the walls of small rooms that are characteristic of residential occupancies.

NFPA 13R, *Standard for the Installation of Sprinkler Systems in Residential Occupancies up to and Including Four Stories in Height,* was first published in 1989.[17] NFPA 13R addresses residential sprinklers, which include the quick-response sprinkler technology described in the preceding paragraph in the commentary on NFPA 13D. NFPA 13R thus extends the technological and economic benefits of an NFPA 13D-type system to larger residential buildings while mandating additional requirements that are commensurate with increased building size. The requirements help to ensure improved protection against injury and life loss to building residents, including those within the room of fire origin.

NFPA 25, *Standard for the Inspection, Testing, and Maintenance of Water-Based Fire Protection Systems,* provides information on recommended maintenance procedures.[18]

Exception No. 1: NFPA 13R, Standard for the Installation of Sprinkler Systems in Residential Occupancies up to and Including Four Stories in Height, shall be permitted for use as specifically referenced in Chapters 24 through 33 of this Code.

Exception No. 2: NFPA 13D, Standard for the Installation of Sprinkler Systems in One- and Two-Family Dwellings and Manufactured Homes, shall be permitted for use as provided in Chapters 24, 26, 32, and 33 of this Code.

A.9.7.1.1 For a discussion of the effectiveness of automatic sprinklers as well as a general discussion on automatic sprinklers, see the NFPA *Fire Protection Handbook.* Where partial sprinkler protection is permitted by another section of this *Code*, the limited area systems provisions of NFPA 13, *Standard for the Installation of Sprinkler Systems*, should apply.

9.7.1.2 Sprinkler piping serving not more than six sprinklers for any isolated hazardous area shall be permitted to be connected directly to a domestic water supply system having a capacity sufficient to provide 0.15 gpm/ft^2 (6.1 L/min·m^2) of floor area throughout the entire enclosed area. An indicating shutoff valve shall be installed in an accessible location between the sprinklers and the connection to the domestic water supply.

The general provisions of Section 8.4 for special hazard protection—in combination with the specific requirements of subsection ___.3.2 of each occupancy chapter—make extensive use of sprinklering hazardous contents rooms in otherwise unsprinklered buildings. Paragraph 9.7.1.2 allows for such sprinklers to be supplied by the domestic water supply and its associated distribution piping. The domestic water supply must provide sufficient quantities of water at the appropriate pressures to deliver 0.15 gpm/ft^2 (6.1 L/min/m^2) of floor area within the hazardous contents room. For a 100-ft^2 (9.3-m^2) room, the water supply would have to provide at least 15 gpm (57 L/min) at the pressure appropriate to such a discharge from a specific size and model of sprinkler. Additionally, the provisions of 9.7.1.2 can be used (in lieu of a devoted sprinkler system piping network and water supply) only if any given room requires six or fewer sprinklers for adequate protection, based on the spacing and location rules of the proper installation standards referenced in 9.7.1.1. Another hazardous contents room on the same floor, or in some other part of the building, can obtain its protection by repeating a similar maximum six-sprinkler installation in accordance with 9.7.1.2.

9.7.1.3* In areas protected by automatic sprinklers, automatic heat-detection devices required by other sections of this *Code* shall be permitted to be omitted.

A.9.7.1.3 Properly designed automatic sprinkler systems provide the dual function of both automatic alarms and automatic extinguishment. Dual function is not provided in those cases where early detection of incipient fire and early notification of occupants are needed to initiate actions in behalf of life safety earlier than can be expected from heat-sensitive fire detectors.

Properly designed automatic sprinkler systems provide the dual function of both automatic alarms and automatic extinguishment. Because the operation of an automatic sprinkler system is initiated by a heat-sensing device and works on the same principle as an automatic heat detection and alarm system, the sprinkler system is judged to be capable of serving the same purpose. Even though some sprinkler systems do not sound an alarm on activation, most properly designed systems do. Furthermore, although a particular sprinkler system might not sound an alarm, it does begin immediate extinguishment; this is a feature that is at least as valuable, if not more valuable, than a system that sounds an alarm only.

Detection of smoke, on the other hand, can be accomplished at the incipient stages of a fire and give rise to an earlier warning than that provided by heat detection, so smoke detection is considered in a somewhat different light. One school of thought is that a system that starts suppression of a fire immediately upon detection is better than one that simply detects the fire and sounds an alarm, even though the latter is quicker in the initiation of signal indication. Others believe, however, that an early alarm system is more advantageous. The first group is concerned with the immediate arrest or containment of fire; it might take considerable time for fire fighters to arrive. The second group stresses immediate notification of occupants.

9.7.1.4 Automatic sprinkler systems installed to make use of an alternative permitted by this *Code* shall be considered required systems and shall meet the provisions of this *Code* that apply to required systems.

The provisions of 9.7.1.4 remind the user that an automatic sprinkler system voluntarily installed as a *Code* alternative is considered a required system; therefore, it is subject to the same requirements (including maintenance) that apply to a sprinkler system specifically mandated by the *Code*. For example, if an occupancy that does not require a sprinkler system does allow the use of the delayed-egress door lock addressed by 7.2.1.6.1, and if the designer/building operator meets one of the unlocking provisions of 7.2.1.6.1 via the installation of an approved, supervised automatic sprinkler system, the sprinkler system is considered a required system. Therefore, the system must meet all requirements that apply to a similar system installed to comply with the *Code* in addition to those of the alternative system, such as delayed-egress door locking.

9.7.2 Supervision.

Supervision is not required by 9.7.2. The requirements of 9.7.2 apply where a supervised automatic sprinkler system is specified by the *Code* or where required by the authority having jurisdiction for approval.

9.7.2.1* Supervisory Signals. Where supervised automatic sprinkler systems are required by another section of this *Code*, supervisory attachments shall be installed and monitored for integrity in accordance with NFPA 72, *National Fire Alarm Code*, and a distinctive supervisory signal shall be provided to indicate a condition that would impair the satisfactory operation of the sprinkler system. Monitoring shall include, but shall not be limited to, monitoring of control valves, fire pump power supplies and running conditions, water tank levels and temperatures, tank pressure, and air pressure on dry-pipe valves. Supervisory signals shall sound and shall be displayed either at a location within the protected building that is constantly attended by qualified personnel or at an approved, remotely located receiving facility.

A.9.7.2.1 NFPA 72, *National Fire Alarm Code,* provides details of standard practice in sprinkler supervision. Subject to the approval of the authority having jurisdiction, sprinkler supervision is also permitted to be provided by direct connection to municipal fire departments or, in the case of very large establishments, to a private headquarters providing similar functions. NFPA 72, *National Fire Alarm Code,* covers such matters.

Where municipal fire alarm systems are involved, reference should also be made to NFPA 1221, *Standard for the Installation, Maintenance, and Use of Emergency Services Communications Systems.*

One reason why the automatic sprinkler system has attained a high level of satisfactory performance and response to fire conditions is that, through supervision, it can be kept in operative condition. Of course, keeping the system operative depends on routine maintenance and the owner's willingness to repair the system when there are indications of impairment. Features of the system such as the following can be automatically monitored:

(1) Opening and closing of water control valves
(2) Power supplies for needed pumps
(3) Water tank level

If an undesirable situation develops, a signal is annunciated in the protected building or relayed to a central station.

A supervisory system will also indicate or activate a waterflow alarm. In addition to being transmitted to proprietary or control stations, the waterflow alarm can be transmitted directly to the fire department. The signals for mechanical problems need not burden the fire department unnecessarily, yet those indicating a fire can be received directly.

For additional information on supervisory signal transmission, see the commentary following 9.6.7.6.

9.7.2.2 Alarm Signal Transmission. Where supervision of automatic sprinkler systems is provided in accordance with another provision of this *Code*, waterflow alarms shall be transmitted to an approved, proprietary alarm receiving facility, a remote station, a central station, or the fire department. Such connection shall be in accordance with 9.6.1.4.

9.7.3* Other Automatic Extinguishing Equipment.

A.9.7.3 Automatic extinguishing systems, other than automatic sprinklers, are covered by the following NFPA standards:

(1) NFPA 11, *Standard for Low-Expansion Foam*
(2) NFPA 12, *Standard on Carbon Dioxide Extinguishing Systems*
(3) NFPA 12A, *Standard on Halon 1301 Fire Extinguishing Systems*
(4) NFPA 15, *Standard for Water Spray Fixed Systems for Fire Protection*
(5) NFPA 17, *Standard for Dry Chemical Extinguishing Systems*
(6) NFPA 2001, *Standard on Clean Agent Fire Extinguishing Systems*

Use of special types of extinguishing systems is a matter of engineering judgment on the part of the designer, working in collaboration with the owner and the authorities concerned. Various NFPA standards are available to provide guidance in installation and maintenance procedures.

9.7.3.1 In any occupancy where the character of the potential fuel for fire is such that extinguishment or control of fire is effectively accomplished by a type of automatic extinguishing system other than an automatic sprinkler system, such as water mist, carbon dioxide, dry chemical, foam, Halon 1301, water spray, or a standard extinguishing system of another type, that system shall be permitted to be installed in lieu of an automatic sprinkler system. Such systems shall be installed, inspected, and maintained in accordance with appropriate NFPA standards.

9.7.3.2 If the extinguishing system is installed in lieu of a required, supervised automatic sprinkler system, the activation of the extinguishing system shall activate the building fire alarm system, where provided. The actuation of an extinguishing system that is not installed in lieu of a required, supervised automatic sprinkler system shall be indicated at the building fire alarm system, where provided.

Paragraph 9.7.3.2 requires the activation of a specialized extinguishing system—installed in lieu of a required supervised automatic sprinkler system—to activate the building fire alarm system. This system provides early warning to building occupants so that necessary action, probably evacuation, can occur. If the specialized extinguishing system is not serving as a substitute for the required supervised automatic sprinkler system, its activation need only be indicated at the building fire alarm system. A kitchen cooking hood and duct extinguishing system is an example of specialized extinguishing systems not serving as a substitute for a required supervised automatic sprinkler system. The operation of a kitchen cooking hood and duct extinguishing system would have to be indicated at the building fire alarm system but would not have to result in the generation of audible and visible occupant notification signals.

9.7.4 Manual Extinguishing Equipment.

9.7.4.1* Where required by the provisions of another section of this *Code*, portable fire extinguishers shall be installed, inspected, and maintained in accordance with NFPA 10, *Standard for Portable Fire Extinguishers*.

Portable extinguishers are required throughout health care, ambulatory health care, detention and correctional, mercantile, and business occupancies but only in the hazardous areas of nonsprinklered hotels, nonsprinklered apartment buildings, and large board and care occupancies. Where the *Code* requires portable extinguishers, the number, types, and locations required are beyond the scope of the *Code*. Guidance can be found in NFPA 10, *Standard for Portable Fire Extinguishers*.[19]

A.9.7.4.1 For a description of standard types of extinguishers and their installation, maintenance, and use, see NFPA 10, *Standard for Portable Fire Extinguishers*. The labels of recognized testing laboratories on extinguishers provide evidence of tests indicating the reliability and suitability of the extinguisher for its intended use. Many unlabeled extinguishers are offered for sale that are substandard by reason of insufficient extinguishing capacity, questionable reliability, or ineffective extinguishing agents for fires in ordinary combustible materials or because they pose a personal hazard to the user.

9.7.4.2 Where required by the provisions of another section of this *Code*, standpipe and hose systems shall be provided in accordance with NFPA 14, *Standard for the Installation of Standpipe, Private Hydrants, and Hose Systems*. Where standpipe and hose systems are installed in combination with automatic sprinkler systems, installation shall be in accordance with the appropriate provisions established by NFPA 13, *Standard for the Installation of Sprinkler Systems*, and NFPA 14, *Standard for the Installation of Standpipe, Private Hydrants, and Hose Systems*.

The *Code* has requirements for standpipes or extinguishers only in some of the individual occupancy chapters. For example, standpipes are required on stages of assembly occupancies and in detention and correctional occupancies. Standpipe provisions also appear as part of the Section 11.8 menu of the provisions applicable to high-rise buildings. The following occupancy chapters mandatorily reference all of Section 11.8 and thus specify standpipe requirements for new high-rise buildings:

(1) New assembly occupancies
(2) New educational occupancies
(3) New day-care centers
(4) New health care occupancies
(5) New detention and correctional occupancies
(6) New hotels and dormitories
(7) New apartment buildings
(8) New business occupancies

9.7.5 Maintenance and Testing.

All automatic sprinkler and standpipe systems required by this *Code* shall be inspected, tested, and maintained in accordance with NFPA 25, *Standard for the Inspection, Testing, and Maintenance of Water-Based Fire Protection Systems.*

9.7.6* Sprinkler System Shutdown.

A sprinkler system might be shut down for any number of reasons during the life of a building. Some shutdowns are preplanned, controlled, and of short duration, such as shutdowns during periodic testing and maintenance. Others might be preplanned and of longer duration such as shutdowns during times of building or system renovation. Emergency shutdown of the system can be the result of fire or other physical damage and might result in a short or lengthy shutdown to repair the system. Advance planning should help ensure that the system, or most of the system, can be restored to service despite the scope of the renovation or the extent of an unexpected impairment. If the sprinkler system is required by the *Code*, or if it was installed to make use of one of the alternatives offered by the *Code*, it must be in good, operable condition for the building to be considered *Code* compliant.

Instead of designating a building with an inoperative sprinkler system as noncompliant and prohibiting occupancy under all conditions in accordance with the provisions of 4.6.9.1, 9.7.6 differentiates between those alarm system impairments that last less than 4 hours within a 24-hour period and those that last longer. Continued occupancy of a building that has a sprinkler system impairment of more than 4 hours cumulative within any 24-hour period can be tolerated only if a fire watch acceptable to the authority having jurisdiction is provided. Such lengthy impairments generally indicate a situation that involves a problem more serious in nature than typical system maintenance or testing.

It is the intent of the *Code* that the fire watch result in a heightened awareness of the building's operations and environment. Individuals selected for the fire watch should be able to recognize fire hazards and know the procedures for occupant and fire department notification and occupant evacuation in an emergency.

When developing a plan to address system shutdown, it is important to consider the nature of the shutdown, the location, the increased hazards that are involved, and the necessary actions to mitigate the hazards. The authority having jurisdiction should be involved in the development of these plans.

A parallel requirement in 9.6.1.8 addresses fire alarm system impairments.

A.9.7.6 A fire watch should at least involve some special action beyond normal staffing, such as assigning an additional security guard(s) to walk the areas affected. These individuals should be specially trained in fire prevention and in the use of fire extinguishers and occupant hose lines, in notifying the fire department, in sounding the building fire alarm, and in understanding the particular fire safety situation for public education purposes. Some authorities having jurisdiction require fire fighters to be assigned to the area, with direct radio communication to the local fire department. *(Also see NFPA 601, Standard for Security Services in Fire Loss Prevention.)*

9.7.6.1 Where a required automatic sprinkler system is out of service for more than 4 hours in a 24-hour period, the authority having jurisdiction shall be notified, and the building shall be evacuated or an approved fire watch shall be provided for all parties left unprotected by the shutdown until the sprinkler system has been returned to service.

9.7.6.2 Sprinkler impairment procedures shall comply with NFPA 25, *Standard for the Inspection, Testing, and Maintenance of Water-Based Fire Protection Systems.*

References Cited in Commentary

1. NFPA 54, *National Fuel Gas Code,* 1999 edition, National Fire Protection Association, Quincy, MA.
2. NFPA 70, *National Electrical Code®,* 1999 edition, National Fire Protection Association, Quincy, MA.
3. NFPA 90A, *Standard for the Installation of Air-Conditioning and Ventilating Systems,* 1999 edition, National Fire Protection Association, Quincy, MA.
4. NFPA 90B, *Standard for the Installation of Warm Air Heating and Air-Conditioning Systems,* 1999 edition, National Fire Protection Association, Quincy, MA.
5. NFPA 96, *Standard on Ventilation Control and Fire Protection of Commercial Cooking Operations,* 1998 edition, National Fire Protection Association, Quincy, MA.
6. NFPA 45, *Standard on Fire Protection for Laboratories Using Chemicals,* 1996 edition, National Fire Protection Association, Quincy, MA.
7. NFPA 99, *Standard for Health Care Facilities,* 1999 edition, National Fire Protection Association, Quincy, MA.

8. NFPA 92A, *Recommended Practice for Smoke-Control Systems,* 1996 edition, National Fire Protection Association, Quincy, MA.

9. NFPA 92B, *Guide for Smoke Management Systems in Malls, Atria, and Large Areas,* 1995 edition, National Fire Protection Association, Quincy, MA.

10. ASME/ANSI A17.1, *Safety Code for Elevators and Escalators,* American Society of Mechanical Engineers, New York.

11. ASME/ANSI A17.3, *Safety Code for Existing Elevators and Escalators,* American Society of Mechanical Engineers, New York.

12. NFPA 13, *Standard for the Installation of Sprinkler Systems,* 1999 edition, National Fire Protection Association, Quincy, MA.

13. ASME *Handbook* A17.1, American Society of Mechanical Engineers, New York.

14. NFPA 82, *Standard on Incinerators and Waste and Linen Handling Systems and Equipment,* 1999 edition, National Fire Protection Association, Quincy, MA.

15. NFPA 72, *National Fire Alarm Code®,* 1999 edition, National Fire Protection Association, Quincy, MA.

16. NFPA 13D, *Standard for the Installation of Sprinkler Systems in One- and Two-Family Dwellings and Manufactured Homes,* 1999 edition, National Fire Protection Association, Quincy, MA.

17. NFPA 13R, *Standard for the Installation of Sprinkler Systems in Residential Occupancies up to and Including Four Stories in Height,* 1999 edition, National Fire Protection Association, Quincy, MA.

18. NFPA 25, *Standard for the Inspection, Testing, and Maintenance of Water-Based Fire Protection Systems,* 1998 edition, National Fire Protection Association, Quincy, MA.

19. NFPA 10, *Standard for Portable Fire Extinguishers,* 1998 edition, National Fire Protection Association, Quincy, MA.

CHAPTER 10

Interior Finish, Contents, and Furnishings

Historically, many fire fatalities have been attributed to the quick spread of fire. Often the fire spread occurs along the expanses of exposed wall and ceiling coverings and via the contents of the building. Chapter 10 regulates some of these features.

Chapter 10 establishes basic requirements for interior wall, ceiling, and floor finish and for furnishings and contents. This chapter specifies a menu of protection options, which are mandated to varying degrees by specific occupancy chapters. However, some of the requirements of this chapter apply to all occupancies.

Section 10.2 provides requirements for interior finish, which includes wall, ceiling, and floor finishes. The concept behind the requirements is to slow the flame spread across these finish surfaces to allow additional time for occupants to relocate within, or evacuate from, a building. The fire characteristics of interior finish can play a dramatic role in life safety when a fire occurs.

Section 10.3 addresses the contents and furnishings in a building. Very few occupancy chapters mandate the use of the provisions of this section of the *Code*. The occupancies for which the regulation of furnishings and contents is part of the overall life safety scheme involve occupants who are nonambulatory, who are otherwise restrained or detained, or who are asleep. Contrast this application with the provisions for interior finish that are mandated by all of the occupancy chapters.

Section 10.1 General

Interior finish has been a significant factor in rapid flame spread in many of the deadliest U.S. fires of recent decades. The following are a few examples of such fires.

In June 1989, five people died on the floor of origin of an "intense, rapidly developing fire on the sixth floor of an office building" in Atlanta, Georgia.[1] In this fire, ". . . the fire spread was so fast that the blaze in the corridor had burned itself out by the time fire fighters entered the sixth floor about seven minutes after the initial alarm . . . This is not the first time that multiple layers of wall coverings have been identified as a contributing factor in a fire . . . It is evident that this condition existed in the Atlanta building, that the materials in those layers contributed to the total load in the corridor, and that it is likely they contributed to the rate of fire spread."

Regarding the 1986 DuPont Plaza Hotel fire (see Exhibit 10.1) where 96 people died: "Under the NFPA *Life Safety Code*, interior finish in all ballrooms, including the room of origin, should have been Class A or Class B. The wall finish of the room of origin contributed to the rapid fire growth."[2]

In the 1981 Las Vegas Hilton Hotel fire, combustible carpeting on the walls and ceilings of elevator lobbies contributed to horizontal fire spread on the floor of origin and vertical spread involving 22 floors. Eight people died in this fire.[3]

In a 1978 Holiday Inn fire that killed 10 people, "lightweight plywood paneling in stairway did not meet *Life Safety Code*, was involved early in fire, and produced rapid growth and spread." In a 1979 Holiday Inn fire that also killed 10 people, "carpeting and some wall covering in corridors had excessively high flame-spread properties."[4]

In a 1972 Springfield, Illinois, convalescent nursing home fire that killed 10 of the 41 patients, "the wood-panel finish accelerated fire spread . . . Combustible interior finish — especially interior finish

Exhibit 10.1 *DuPont Plaza Hotel fire, in which rapid fire growth was, in part, due to wall finish in room of origin.*

such as the wood paneling in this facility — should not be allowed where infirm people are housed . . . The paneling on the stairway had completely burned away, permitting fire spread into the first floor through holes in the plaster."[5]

Regarding the 1970 Pioneer International Hotel fire where 28 died:

Under the NFPA *Life Safety Code,* interior finish in all ballrooms, including the room of origin, corridors and stairs were carpeted (100 percent acrylic), with two layers of padding under carpet in corridors and carpeting extending 22 inches up the walls. Above the carpeted areas of the wall were sections of wood, wallpaper, and plastic-laminated plywood. Interior finish contributed to fire.[6]

10.1.1 Application.

The interior finish, contents, and furnishings provisions set forth in this chapter shall apply to new construction and existing buildings.

Highly combustible interior wall and ceiling finishes, and easily ignited contents and furnishings, are repeatedly reported as factors in fire spread in various occupancies. The repeated contribution of these factors to fire spread demonstrates the need to apply Chapter 10 requirements to both new construction and existing buildings.

10.1.2 Special Definitions.

Contents and Furnishings. See 3.3.33.

Flashover. See 3.3.79.

Interior Finish. See 3.3.112.

The faster a fire develops, the greater the threat it represents to the occupants of a building and the more difficult it will be to control. Wall and ceiling surfaces of a building have a major influence on how fast a fire develops. In establishing restrictions for the use of interior finish materials, the *Code's* intention is to prevent entirely or, as a minimum, to limit the spread of fire across the interior surfaces of a building.

Any large fire within a building represents a threat to occupants. A successful fire protection strategy attempts to limit the size of fires. Any interior finish that acts as a "fuse" to spread flame and involve objects remote from the point of origin, or that contributes fuel to the early growth of a fire and causes a large fire, is undesirable. The restrictions found in the *Code* for wall and ceiling finishes vary, depending on the occupancy characteristics. Where occupants are immobile or where security measures restrict freedom of movement (as in health care facilities or detention and correctional facilities), conservative interior finish limits are set. In contrast, more relaxed limits are allowed in industrial or storage occupancies where occupants are assumed to be alert and mobile.

Interior finishes are the interior surfaces of a building that are generally secured in place. Thus, wall, ceiling, and column coverings are considered interior wall and ceiling finishes. The surfaces of movable walls or folding partitions would also be treated as interior wall and ceiling finishes. However, the *Code* allows the authority having jurisdiction to exercise judgment in determining the criteria that constitute interior finish. For example, a tapestry would not normally be considered as interior finish. However, a large tapestry that is secured to and covers a major portion of a wall could promote the rapid growth of fire and might warrant regulation. See the definition of *interior finish* in 3.3.112.

Furnishings (including high-backed, plastic-upholstered restaurant booths) are not normally considered as interior finish, even in cases where the furnishings are fixed in place. See the definition of *contents and furnishings* in 3.3.33.

Interior Ceiling Finish. See 3.3.112.1.

Interior floor finish includes both exposed surfaces of structural floor systems and decorative floor treatments, such as wood flooring, carpet, or other resilient flooring materials. Coverings on stair risers and treads are regulated as interior floor finish, even though risers involve vertical applications. This regulation recognizes that floor coverings on stair risers and treads will perform similarly to other floor surfaces during a fire. See the definition of *interior floor finish* in 3.3.112.2.

Interior Floor Finish. See 3.3.112.2.
Interior Wall Finish. See 3.3.112.3.

Section 10.2* Interior Finish

A.10.2 The requirements pertaining to interior finish are intended to restrict the spread of fire over the continuous surface forming the interior portions of a building.

10.2.1 General.

Classification of interior finish materials shall be in accordance with tests made under conditions simulating actual installations, provided that the authority having jurisdiction shall be permitted to establish the classification of any material on which a rating by standard test is not available.

Exception: Materials applied, in total thickness of less than 1/28 in. (0.09 cm), directly to the surface of walls and ceilings shall be exempt from tests simulating actual installation if they meet the requirements of Class A interior wall or ceiling finish when tested in accordance with 10.2.3.1 using inorganic reinforced cement board as the substrate material.

The exception to 10.2.1 addresses the issue of thin coverings, which was covered in earlier editions of the *Code* by a simply worded, performance-based criterion that was difficult to use and enforce. The *Code* recognized that thin coverings [those less than 1/28 in. (0.09 cm) in thickness] with surface burning characteristics no greater than that of paper will not significantly affect the fire performance of the basic wall or ceiling material. If assurance was provided that such a thin covering had surface burning characteristics no greater than those of paper, the thin material would not be subject to regulation as an interior finish. Therefore, the material's flame spread rating wasn't needed, which, in turn, meant that no fire testing was required. The problem was that, without running fire tests, it was impossible to determine whether the thin material had surface burning characteristics that were greater than those of paper.

The wording of the exception to 10.2.1 is new to the 2000 edition of the *Code*. It no longer exempts thin materials from testing, but it does exempt thin material from testing with the actual substrate or backing material that will be used in the final installed state. If there were no exception, thin materials such as paint (whose liquid suspension state dries to become a thin layer of material) and wallpaper would be required to be fire tested in combination with numerous backing materials. A complete set of test results, representative of the many forms of substrates in common use, would be prohibitively expensive to collect. The exception to 10.2.1 permits the material to be tested only with inorganic reinforced cement board.

Thermally thin coverings such as paint and wallpaper coverings, where secured to a noncombustible substrate such as inorganic reinforced cement board, will not significantly alter the performance of the substrate during a fire. However, thicker coverings, such as multiple layers of wallpaper, can and have contributed to rapid fire growth in actual fires. For example, multiple layers of wall coverings contributed to rapid fire growth in the multiple-death fire in the Holiday Inn in Cambridge, Ohio, which occurred on July 31, 1979.[7] The exception has the effect of requiring any wall or ceiling covering of more than ⅛ in. (0.09 cm) in thickness to undergo the full test series required of other interior finish materials so as to be representative of actual installations.

For proper evaluation and classification, assemblies of materials must be tested as they will actually be installed. For example, the performance of thermally-thin coverings is altered by the nature of the substrate over which they are installed.[8] Adhesives might also be an important factor in performance. In the case of composites (such as textile wall coverings over gypsum board) the adhesive should be sufficient to maintain a bond between the "finish" and the substrate. However, excess adhesive might result in the adhesive contributing to the fire. Tests of textile wall coverings have shown that changing adhesives, or simply changing the application rate for the same adhesive, might significantly alter product performance.[9] Tests to qualify assemblies should use adhesives and application rates similar to actual installations.

Similarly, a product that undergoes testing in intimate contact with a mineral board should be installed in contact with a mineral board or similar substrate. In cases where products are tested in intimate contact with a substrate, performance might also be altered by installing of the product with air space behind the covering.

10.2.2* Use of Interior Finishes.

A.10.2.2 Table A.10.2.2 provides a compilation of the interior finish requirements of. the occupancy chapters (Chapter 12 through Chapter 42) of this *Code*.

10.2.2.1 Requirements for interior wall and ceiling finish shall apply as follows:

(1) Where specified elsewhere in this *Code* for specific occupancies *(See Chapter 7 and Chapters 11 through 42.)*
(2) As specified in 10.2.4

10.2.2.2* Requirements for interior floor finish shall apply only under either or both of the following conditions:

(1) Where floor finish requirements are specified elsewhere in this *Code* for specific occupancies
(2) Where there is a floor finish of unusual hazard

Table A.10.2.2 Interior Finish Classification Limitations

Occupancy	Exits	Access to Exits	Other Spaces
Assembly—New			
>300 occupant load	A	A or B	A or B
≤300 occupant load	A	A or B	A, B, or C
Assembly—Existing			
>300 occupant load	A	A or B	A or B
≤300 occupant load	A	A or B	A, B, or C
Educational—New	A	A or B	A or B, C on low partitions†
Educational—Existing	A	A or B	A, B, or C
Day-Care Centers—New	A	A	A or B
	I or II	I or II	NR
Day-Care Centers—Existing	A or B	A or B	A or B
Group Day-Care Homes—New	A or B	A or B	A, B, or C
Group Day-Care Homes—Existing	A or B	A, B, or C	A, B, or C
Family Day-Care Homes	A or B	A, B, or C	A, B, or C

Table A.10.2.2 Continued

Occupancy	Exits	Access to Exits	Other Spaces
Health Care—New (sprinklers mandatory)	A or B	A or B C on lower portion of corridor wall	A or B C in small individual rooms[†]
Health Care—Existing	A or B	A or B	A or B
Detention and Correctional—New	A[†] I	A[†] I	A, B, or C
Detention and Correctional—Existing	A or B I or II[†]	A or B I or II[†]	A, B, or C
1- and 2–Family Dwellings, Lodging or Rooming Houses	A, B, or C	A, B, or C	A, B, or C
Hotels and Dormitories—New	A I or II	A or B I or II	A, B, or C
Hotels and Dormitories—Existing	A or B I or II[†]	A or B I or II[†]	A, B, or C
Apartment Buildings—New	A I or II[†]	A or B I or II[†]	A, B, or C
Apartment Buildings—Existing	A or B I or II[†]	A or B I or II[†]	A, B, or C
Residential, Board and Care— *(See Chapters 32 and 33.)*			
Mercantile—New	A or B	A or B	A or B
Mercantile—Existing Class A or Class B	A or B	A or B	Ceilings—A or B, walls— A, B, or C
Mercantile—Existing Class C	A, B, or C	A, B, or C	A, B, or C
Business and Ambulatory Health Care—New	A or B I or II	A or B I or II	A, B, or C
Business and Ambulatory Health Care—Existing	A or B	A or B	A, B, or C
Industrial	A or B	A, B, or C	A, B, or C
Storage	A or B	A, B, or C	A, B, or C

NR: No requirement.

Notes:

1. Class A interior wall and ceiling finish—flame spread 0–25, (new) smoke developed 0–450.

2. Class B interior wall and ceiling finish—flame spread 26–75, (new) smoke developed 0–450.

3. Class C interior wall and ceiling finish—flame spread 76–200, (new) smoke developed 0–450.

4. Class I interior floor finish—critical radiant flux, not less than 0.45 W/cm^2.

5. Class II interior floor finish—critical radiant flux, not less than 0.22 W/cm^2.

6. Automatic sprinklers—where a complete standard system of automatic sprinklers is in stalled, interior wall and ceiling finish with flame spread rating not exceeding Class C is permitted to be used in any location where Class B is required and with rating of Class B in any location where Class A is required; similarly, Class II interior floor finish is permitted to be used in any location where Class I is required, and no critical radiant flux rating is required where Class II is required. These provisions do not apply to new health care facilities.

7. Exposed portions of structural members complying with the requirements for heavy timber construction are permitted.

[†]See corresponding chapters for details.

A.10.2.2.2 This paragraph recognizes that traditional finish floors and floor coverings such as wood flooring and resilient floor coverings have not proved to present an unusual hazard.

Experience has shown that traditional floor coverings, such as wood flooring and resilient tile, do not contribute to the early growth of fire. Paragraph 10.2.2.2 acknowledges the satisfactory performance of traditional floor coverings and exempts such materials from the restrictions that would otherwise be applicable. However, the authority having jurisdiction can require substantiation of the performance of any unfamiliar floor covering. For example, imitation wood floors made of plastic, artificial turf, artificial surfaces of athletic fields, and carpeting are types of products that might merit substantiation. Where the authority having jurisdiction judges that a floor covering warrants testing and substantiation, or where an occupancy chapter imposes restrictions, the floor covering would be treated as interior floor finish and would be regulated based on tests conducted in accordance with the flooring radiant panel test required in 10.2.7. The following are examples of occupancy chapters that impose restrictions:

(1) Chapters 16 and 17 (day-care centers)
(2) Chapter 19 (existing health care occupancies)
(3) Chapters 22 and 23 (detention and correctional occupancies)
(4) Chapters 28, 29, 30, and 31 (residential occupancies)

10.2.3 Interior Wall or Ceiling Finish Testing and Classification.

10.2.3.1* Interior wall or ceiling finish that is required elsewhere in this *Code* to be Class A, Class B, or Class C, shall be classified based on test results from NFPA 255, *Standard Method of Test of Surface Burning Characteristics of Building Materials.*

Flame spread and smoke development are both recorded in the results of a test conducted in accordance with NFPA 255, *Standard Method of Test of Surface Burning Characteristics of Building Materials.*[10] This document is also known as ASTM E 84, *Standard Test Method for Surface Burning Characteristics of Building Materials.*[11] Fuel contribution values have not been recorded as a required part of the test procedure for many years.

Exception No. 1:   Exposed portions of structural members complying with the requirements for Type IV(2HH) construc-

tion in accordance with NFPA 220, Standard on Types of Building Construction, shall be exempt from NFPA 255 testing and classification.

Type IV(2HH) construction has traditionally been called "heavy timber construction." Exposed surfaces of the structural members, such as wood columns, beams, and girders, meet the definition of interior wall and ceiling finish. All heavy timber structural members are required to be of substantial thickness as detailed in NFPA 220, *Standard on Types of Building Construction.*[12] Thus, none are thermally thin, so they do not present the concerns addressed in the commentary that follows 10.2.1. Exception No. 1 to 10.2.3.1 recognizes that exposed surfaces of heavy timber structural members can be safely used where Class A, Class B, or Class C interior finish is required. Such wood members often have flame spread ratings in the range of 76 to 200 and, therefore, are classified as Class C interior finish. The exception is based on the fact that the structural members are located at intervals and do not constitute a continuous surface that allows flame to spread, for example, across a ceiling.

Exception No. 2:   Interior wall and ceiling finish tested in accordance with NFPA 286, Standard Methods of Fire Tests for Evaluating Contribution of Wall and Ceiling Interior Finish to Room Fire Growth, shall be exempt from NFPA 255 testing and classification.

Exception No. 2 to 10.2.3.1 permits testing by NFPA 286, *Standard Methods of Fire Tests for Evaluating Contribution of Wall and Ceiling Interior Finish to Room Fire Growth,* for both interior wall finish and interior ceiling finish.[13] NFPA 286 represents an improvement over testing by NFPA 255, *Standard Method of Test of Surface Burning Characteristics of Building Materials.* It was developed specifically to measure the following:

(1) Whether flashover occurs
(2) Extent of flame spread and burning relative to the realistically mounted sample
(3) Peak rate of heat release
(4) Smoke obscuration throughout the test

Note that Exception No. 2 does not require testing per NFPA 286 but offers this test procedure as an alternative to testing by the more traditional NFPA 255.

A.10.2.3.1 See A.10.2.4.1.5.

10.2.3.2* Products required to be tested in accordance with NFPA 255, *Standard Method of Test of Surface Burning*

Characteristics of Building Materials, shall be grouped in the following classes in accordance with their flame spread and smoke development.

(a) *Class A Interior Wall and Ceiling Finish.* Flame spread 0–25; smoke development 0–450. Includes any material classified at 25 or less on the flame spread test scale and 450 or less on the smoke test scale. Any element thereof, when so tested, shall not continue to propagate fire.

(b) *Class B Interior Wall and Ceiling Finish.* Flame spread 26–75; smoke development 0–450. Includes any material classified at more than 25 but not more than 75 on the flame spread test scale and 450 or less on the smoke test scale.

(c) *Class C Interior Wall and Ceiling Finish.* Flame spread 76–200; smoke development 0–450. Includes any material classified at more than 75 but not more than 200 on the flame spread test scale and 450 or less on the smoke test scale.

Exception: Existing interior finish shall be exempt from the smoke development criteria.

The building codes developed by the three U.S. regional building code officials organizations also group interior wall and ceiling finish into three classes. The Class A, Class B, or Class C designations used by the *Life Safety Code* and the *Standard Building Code*[14] correlate directly with the Class I, Class II, or Class III designations used in the BOCA *National Building Code*[15] and the *Uniform Building Code.*[16]

Interior wall and ceiling finish classifications in accordance with 10.2.3.2 are based mainly on flame spread ratings with an additional requirement that smoke development not exceed a common value of 450, regardless of the class into which the material falls based on flame spread. Flame spread ratings offer a general indication of the speed with which fire might spread across the surface of a material. In assessing the hazard posed by a material on the basis of flame spread, it is assumed that a person might be in close proximity to the fire and would be directly exposed to the energy associated with the actual flames. By contrast, the purpose of smoke development ratings is to address obscuration of the egress path by smoke. Given that the smoke development value is a cumulative measurement over the prescribed test duration, it is based on both quantity and rate of smoke liberation. Thus, an interior wall and ceiling finish material with a low smoke development value should provide better visibility in a given egress route than a material with a high smoke development value.

The *Code* requires the use of specific classes of interior wall and ceiling finish materials, which are differentiated by their allowable flame spread rating, based on consideration of their installed location within the building, the building's egress paths, and the occupancy in question. Different classes of interior finish materials are specified for an office area, for example, as opposed to an exit stair enclosure or exit access corridor. The different classes recognize that, when escaping a building, people must move away from the flames while traveling through the means of egress toward an exit. The classes of interior finishes that are considered acceptable within an open office, therefore, are different from those that are required for exit enclosures. Similarly, occupancies used by those who are mobility impaired have stricter interior finish requirements than occupancies used by fully ambulatory occupants. For example, although both hospitals and hotels provide sleeping accommodations, interior finish requirements for hospitals are more stringent because hospital patients are less capable of self-preservation.

The same smoke development limit is used for all three flame spread classifications. This limit recognizes that smoke generated during a fire might affect visibility both in the vicinity of, and remote from, the fire. Large buildings can be quickly filled with smoke as a result of a fire. An upper limit has been established, therefore, that applies to interior finish materials, regardless of the location of the materials.

Existing buildings are exempted from the smoke development limitation. In existing buildings, interior finish materials are restricted only on the basis of flame spread. *Life Safety Code* editions prior to 1976 did not regulate interior finish materials based on smoke development. As a general rule, the replacement of existing materials only because they were previously approved exclusively on the basis of flame spread is not warranted.

The smoke development limit of 450 was determined on the basis of research conducted by Underwriters Laboratories Inc. A 5000-ft³ (140-m³) room was filled with smoke from the tunnel test chamber. The room was equipped with illuminated exit signs. The time required to reach various stages of exit sign obscuration was recorded and compared to the smoke development rating for the different materials involved. The report states that "materials having smoke developed ratings above 325 showed 'good' to 'marginal' visibility — scale readings of 3 to 4.8 — in a few cases; other materials produced conditions of 'marginal' to obscuration in the six minute period."[17]

Considering both time and smoke levels, the limit of 450 on smoke ratings as used in the *Code* has been judged to be reasonable. In considering flame spread and smoke development, it should be emphasized that there is no direct relationship between the two factors. For example, in the report referenced in the previous paragraph, one material had a flame spread rating of 490 and a smoke development factor of 57, while another had a flame spread rating of 44 and a smoke development factor of 1387.

The smoke development limit of 450 is based solely on the level of obscuration. Although not addressed by the requirements for interior finishes, other important factors used in evaluating materials based on smoke generation are the effects of irritability and toxicity caused by gases. Smoke might also act as an irritant, further reducing visibility, and might, in addition, have a debilitating physiological effect on people attempting to escape from a building. Such effects are not evaluated by the current smoke development limit. Previous editions of the *Code* allowed the authority having jurisdiction to regulate products presenting an "unreasonable life hazard due to the character of the products of decomposition." This provision was deleted in the 1988 edition of the *Code* due to the unenforceable nature of the requirement. The adverse physiological effects on the human body caused by exposure to heat and the effects of inhaling hot gases should also be considered as part of an overall hazard risk assessment and should be considered separately from the interior finish requirements of Section 10.2.

A.10.2.3.2 It has been shown that the method of mounting interior finish materials may affect actual performance. Where materials are tested in intimate contact with a substrate to determine a classification, such materials should be installed in intimate contact with a similar substrate. Such details are especially important for "thermally thin" materials. For further information, see NFPA 255, *Standard Method of Test of Surface Burning Characteristics of Building Materials.*

Some interior wall and ceiling finish materials, such as fabrics not applied to a solid backing, do not lend themselves to a test made in accordance with NFPA 255, *Standard Method of Test of Surface Burning Characteristics of Building Materials.* In these cases, the large-scale test outlined in NFPA 701, *Standard Methods of Fire Tests for Flame Propagation of Textiles and Films,* is permitted to be used.

Prior to 1978, the test report described by NFPA 255, *Standard Method of Test of Surface Burning Characteristics of Building Materials,* included an evaluation of the fuel contribution as well as the flame spread rating and the smoke

development value. However, it is now recognized that the measurement on which the fuel contribution is based does not provide a valid measure. Therefore, although the data are recorded during the test, the information is no longer normally reported. Classification of interior wall and ceiling finish thus relies only on flame spread index and smoke development value.

The 450 smoke development value limit is based solely on obscuration. *(See A.10.2.4.1.5.)*

Samples are tested in accordance with NFPA 255, *Standard Method of Test of Surface Burning Characteristics of Building Materials,* using a noncombustible backing. Specimens are tested with adhesives, joints, and under other conditions that simulate the actual installation of a product in a building. NFPA 255 provides a general indication of product performance only if the product is installed in a fashion similar to that which has been tested. Available data demonstrate that the performance of interior finish materials varies, depending on mounting conditions.[18] For example, a product installed over a combustible substrate tends to propagate fire more readily than would be typical of the same product installed over a noncombustible substrate. Further, a wall covering installed with air space behind the covering tends to spread flame more readily than one installed in contact with a noncombustible substrate. Therefore, mounting techniques must be carefully considered in the evaluation of probable product performance.

For example, where decorative fabric is hung in front of a wall surface and covers a significant portion of that wall, the loosely hanging fabric creates a continuous surface that can spread flame. Thus the fabric should comply with the requirements for interior finish. Testing in accordance with NFPA 255, which reports a flame spread rating and smoke development value that can be used to classify interior finish per 10.2.3.2, would not provide meaningful information for the use described in this example. Thus, testing per NFPA 701, *Standard Methods of Fire Tests for Flame Propagation of Textiles and Films,* might be useful to the authority having jurisdiction in judging the safety of hanging fabrics that constitute interior finish.[19]

NFPA 701 describes procedures for intermediate-scale and large-scale tests. The choice of the applicable test method is determined in part by the weight of the material per unit area. Tests using NFPA 701 involve applying a flame to a vertically positioned sample for a specified time. Upon removal of the flame-producing burner, the sample must self-extinguish and must not have charred beyond a specified distance in order to pass the test. Additionally, with the intermediate-scale test, a specified maximum percent weight loss cannot be exceeded. The test in NFPA 701 should help in evaluating the installation, although a strict Class A, Class B, or Class C determination of interior finish classification, per 10.2.3.2, cannot be made.

Exhibit 10.2 illustrates a room tunnel test.

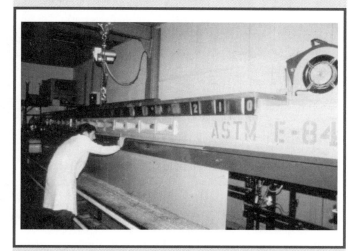

Exhibit 10.2 *Room tunnel test. (Photo courtesy of Hughes Associates, Inc.)*

10.2.3.3 The classification of interior finish specified in 10.2.3.2 shall be that of the basic material used by itself or in combination with other materials.

10.2.3.4 Wherever the use of Class C interior wall and ceiling finish is required, Class A or Class B shall be permitted. Where Class B interior wall and ceiling finish is required, Class A shall be permitted.

Paragraph 10.2.3.4 recognizes that the *Code* sets minimum criteria. An interior finish material that performs better than that specifically prescribed by *Code* is always permitted.

10.2.3.5 Products tested in accordance with NFPA 265, *Standard Methods of Fire Tests for Evaluating Room Fire Growth Contribution of Textile Wall Coverings*, shall comply with the criteria of 10.2.3.5.1 or 10.2.3.5.2. Products tested in accordance with NFPA 286, *Standard Methods of Fire Tests for Evaluating Contribution of Wall and Ceiling Interior Finish to Room Fire Growth*, shall comply with the criteria of 10.2.3.5.3.

10.2.3.5.1* The following criteria shall be met when using method A of the NFPA 265, *Standard Methods of Fire Tests*

for Evaluating Room Fire Growth Contribution of Textile Wall Coverings, test protocol:

(1) Flame shall not spread to the ceiling during the 40-kW exposure.
(2) During the 150-kW exposure, the following criteria shall be met:
   a. Flame shall not spread to the outer extremity of the sample on the 8 ft × 12 ft (2.4 m × 3.7 m) wall.
   b. The specimen shall not burn to the outer extremity of the 2-ft (0.6-m) wide samples mounted vertically in the corner of the room.
   c. Burning droplets that are judged to be capable of igniting the textile wall covering or that persist in burning for 30 seconds or more shall not be formed and dropped to the floor.
   d. Flashover shall not occur.
   e. The maximum instantaneous net peak rate of heat release shall not exceed 300 kW.

A.10.2.3.5.1 The methodology specified in NFPA 265, *Standard Methods of Fire Tests for Evaluating Room Fire Growth Contribution of Textile Wall Coverings*, includes provisions for measuring smoke obscuration. Such measurement is considered desirable but the basis for specific recommended values is not currently available. *(See A.10.2.4.1.5.)*

10.2.3.5.2* The following conditions shall be met when using method B of the NFPA 265, *Standard Methods of Fire Tests for Evaluating Room Fire Growth Contribution of Textile Wall Coverings*, test protocol:

(1) Flame shall not spread to the ceiling during the 40-kW exposure.
(2) During the 150-kW exposure, the following criteria shall be met:
   a. Flame shall not spread to the outer extremities of the sample on the 8 ft × 12 ft (2.4 m × 3.7 m) wall.
   b. Flashover shall not occur.

A.10.2.3.5.2 See A.10.2.3.5.1 and A.10.2.4.1.5.

Exhibit 10.3 illustrates the test equipment required by NFPA 265.

10.2.3.5.3 The following conditions shall be met when using NFPA 286, *Standard Methods of Fire Tests for Evaluating Contribution of Wall and Ceiling Interior Finish to Room Fire Growth*, test protocol:

(1) Flames shall not spread to the ceiling during the 40-kW exposure.
(2) During the 160-kW exposure, the following criteria shall be met:
   a. Flame shall not spread to the outer extremities of the sample on the 8 ft × 12 ft (2.4 m × 3.7 m) wall.
   b. Flashover shall not occur.

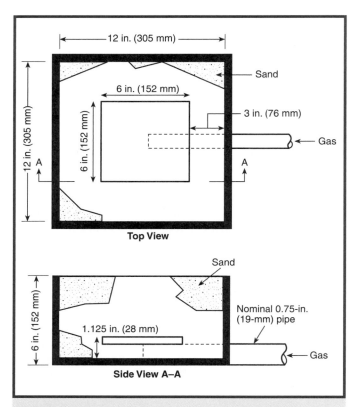

Exhibit 10.3 Schematic of gas burner required by NFPA 265.

Exhibit 10.4 Elevator lobby with carpetlike textile wall and ceiling finish material.

(3) For new installations, the total smoke released throughout the test shall not exceed 1000 m².

10.2.4 Specific Materials.

10.2.4.1 Textile Wall and Textile Ceiling Materials. The use of textile materials on walls or ceilings shall be limited as specified in 10.2.4.1.1 through 10.2.4.1.5.

Prior to the 1988 edition of the *Code*, the danger of carpetlike textile coverings used on walls and ceilings was recognized and regulated by a requirement that only Class A tufted or napped, carpetlike materials be used, even in a sprinklered building. In 1981, eight people died at the nonsprinklered Las Vegas Hilton Hotel when a fire began in an elevator lobby and was fueled by carpetlike, textile wall and ceiling finishes that did not meet the qualifications for Class A interior finish.[20] Other than the textile wall and ceiling finish materials, sheer sunscreen material at the window, and a cushioned seat pad on a metal bench, there was little combustible material to fuel the fire in the elevator lobby. See Exhibit 10.4. Yet, the elevator lobby went to flashover; the fire broke out the win-

dows and climbed to a nearly identical elevator lobby on the floor above; and the events repeated themselves in a leap frog fashion from the eighth floor through the twenty-fourth floor. See Exhibit 10.5.

Research sponsored by the American Textile Manufacturer's Institute (ATMI), conducted by the Fire Research Laboratory of the University of California at Berkeley between March 1985 and January 1986, was described in the report "Room Fire Experiments of Textile Wall Coverings."[21] This research demonstrated that consideration of only the flame spread rating, as measured by NFPA 255, *Standard Method of Test of Surface Burning Characteristics of Building Materials*, might not reliably predict the fire behavior of textile wall and ceiling coverings. Test results indicate

Exhibit 10.5 Resulting fire spread involving elevator lobbies on eighth through twenty-fourth floors.

that some Class A textile wall coverings can produce room flashover when subjected to an ignition source scenario that models a small fuel item (such as a wastebasket) igniting a chair or similar furnishing. However, other Class A textile wall coverings did not produce room flashover when subjected to the same ignition source scenario. Thus, not all Class A textile wall coverings are alike with respect to their potential for producing room flashover. Simply requiring textile wall coverings to be classified as Class A interior wall and ceiling finishes does not ensure the level of life safety intended by the *Code*.

The testing at the University of California was conducted in an 8 ft × 12 ft × 8 ft high (2.4 m × 3.7 m × 2.4 m high) room using a gas diffusion burner as an ignition source. Products undergoing evaluation were applied to the walls of the room. The gas diffusion burner and ignition source were placed in the corner of the room to evaluate various textile wall coverings. Two of the sixteen products tested — one a tufted wall covering, the other a woven wall covering — were known to have flame spread ratings of 25 or less when tested in accordance with NFPA 255. When tested in the room-corner procedure, these two products readily spread flame and caused the fire in the test room to grow quickly to a large size, causing full room involvement — that is, flashover. Concerns about the performance of these low flame spread textile wall coverings led to the requirement for fullscale room-corner testing to qualify products for use in nonsprinklered buildings.

Tests revealed that the method of mounting, including adhesive and application rate, can be critically important. Changing the application rate of the same adhesive or changing the adhesive can cause an assumed safe product to exhibit unsatisfactory performance.

The testing conducted at the University of California included only wall coverings. Caution should be exercised when using combinations of textile wall and ceiling coverings. Experience has shown that combinations of textile wall and ceiling coverings might result in intense burning.[22] Research conducted at the Illinois Institute of Technology Research Institute indicates that flame spread is more likely to occur with combinations of combustible wall and ceiling coverings than in those situations involving only combustible wall coverings or only combustible ceiling coverings.[23] Therefore, full-scale room-corner testing, using an appropriately sized ignition source, is necessary to substantiate the performance of textile wall and ceiling coverings.

With the publication of NFPA 265, *Standard Meth-*

ods of Fire Tests for Evaluating Room Fire Growth Contribution of Textile Wall Coverings,[24] a nationally recognized room-corner fire test to be used specifically for textile wall coverings became available. Its use is addressed in 10.2.3.5, 10.2.4.1.5, and 10.2.4.2. Subparagraphs 10.2.4.1.1 through 10.2.4.1.4 address other conditions under which textile wall coverings are permitted to be used.

For the 2000 edition of the *Code*, NFPA 286, *Standard Methods of Fire Tests for Evaluating Contribution of Wall and Ceiling Interior Finish to Room Fire Growth,* has been recognized as a second test method that is considered adequate for evaluating textile wall coverings. Its use is addressed in Exception No. 2 to 10.2.3.1, 10.2.3.5, A.10.2.4.1.5, and 10.2.4.2.

10.2.4.1.1 Textile materials having a Class A rating *(see 10.2.3.2)* shall be permitted on the walls or ceilings of rooms or areas protected by an approved automatic sprinkler system.

10.2.4.1.2 Textile materials having a Class A rating *(see 10.2.3.2)* shall be permitted on partitions that do not exceed ¾ of the floor-to-ceiling height or do not exceed 8 ft (2.4 m) in height, whichever is less.

10.2.4.1.3 Textile materials having a Class A rating *(see 10.2.3.2)* shall be permitted to extend not more than 4 ft (1.2 m) above the finished floor on ceiling-height walls and ceiling-height partitions.

10.2.4.1.4 Previously approved, existing installations of textile material having a Class A rating *(see 10.2.3.2)* shall be permitted to be continued to be used.

10.2.4.1.5* Textile materials shall be permitted on walls and partitions where tested in accordance with NFPA 265, *Standard Methods of Fire Tests for Evaluating Room Fire Growth Contribution of Textile Wall Coverings. (See 10.2.3.5.)*

A.10.2.4.1.5 Previous editions of the *Code* have regulated textile materials on walls and ceilings using NFPA 255, *Standard Method of Test of Surface Burning Characteristics of Building Materials.* Full-scale room/corner fire test research has shown that flame spread indices produced by NFPA 255 might not reliably predict all aspects of the fire behavior of textile wall and ceiling coverings.

Testing by NFPA 265, *Standard Methods of Fire Tests for Evaluating Room Fire Growth Contribution of Textile Wall Coverings,* uses a reasonably sized ignition source to show that the material will not spread fire to involve objects remote from the area of origin and that the textile product will not generate sufficient energy to cause the room of origin to reach flashover. Acceptance of textile wall covering materials should be contingent on qualification tests in which a specific textile/adhesive pair has been evaluated.

Although NFPA 265, *Standard Methods of Fire Tests for Evaluating Room Fire Growth Contribution of Textile Wall Coverings,* was developed for assessing the performance of textile wall coverings, the method can be, and has been, used to evaluate other types of wall finish. As long as a wall finish is tested using a mounting system, substrate, and adhesive (if appropriate) that are representative of actual use, NFPA 265 provides an evaluation of a product's flammability and smoke obscuration behavior. Moreover, NFPA 286, *Standard Methods of Fire Tests for Evaluating Contribution of Wall and Ceiling Interior Finish to Room Fire Growth,* has now been developed to evaluate other interior finish materials. Manufacturers, installers, and specifiers should be encouraged to use NFPA 265 or NFPA 286, as appropriate,—but not both—because each of these standard fire tests has the ability to characterize actual product behavior, as opposed to data generated by tests using NFPA 255, which only allows comparisons of one product's performance with another. If a manufacturer or installer chooses to test a wall finish in accordance with NFPA 265 or NFPA 286, as appropriate, additional testing in accordance with NFPA 255 is not necessary.

The initial edition of NFPA 265 did not contain smoke obscuration measurements, and previous editions of the Code have not included smoke obscuration requirements based on NFPA 265 tests. The 1998 edition of NFPA 265 does include smoke obscuration measurements.

The test results from NFPA 255, *Standard Method of Test of Surface Burning Characteristics of Building Materials,* are suitable for classification purposes but should not be used as input into fire models, because they are not generated in units suitable for engineering calculations. Actual test results, for heat, smoke, and combustion product release from NFPA 265, *Standard Methods of Fire Tests for Evaluating Room Fire Growth Contribution of Textile Wall Coverings,* might be suitable for use as input into fire models for performance-based design.

10.2.4.2* Expanded Vinyl Wall or Ceiling Coverings. Expanded vinyl wall or ceiling coverings shall comply with one of the following conditions:

(1) Materials having a Class A rating (see 10.2.3.2) shall be permitted on the walls or ceilings of rooms or areas protected by an approved automatic sprinkler system.

(2) Materials having a Class A rating (see 10.2.3.2) shall be permitted on partitions that do not exceed ¾ of the floor-to-ceiling height or do not exceed 8 ft (2.4 m) in height, whichever is less.

(3) Materials having a Class A rating (see 10.2.3.2) shall be permitted up to 4 ft (1.2 m) above the finished floor on ceiling-height walls and ceiling-height partitions.

(4) Existing installations of materials with the appropriate wall finish classification for the occupancy involved, and with classification in accordance with the provisions in 10.2.3.2, shall be permitted to be continued to be used.

(5) Materials shall be permitted on walls and partitions where tested in accordance with NFPA 265, *Standard Methods of Fire Tests for Evaluating Room Fire Growth Contribution of Textile Wall Coverings. (See 10.2.3.5.)*

(6) Materials shall be permitted on walls, partitions, and ceilings where tested in accordance with NFPA 286, *Standard Methods of Fire Tests for Evaluating Contribution of Wall and Ceiling Interior Finish to Room Fire Growth. (See 10.2.3.5.)*

The provisions of 10.2.4.2, which address expanded vinyl wall coverings, are similar to those applicable to textile wall coverings. See 10.2.4.1. For a description of an expanded vinyl wall covering, see A.10.2.4.2.

A.10.2.4.2 Expanded vinyl wall covering consists of a woven textile backing, an expanded vinyl base coat layer, and a nonexpanded vinyl skin coat. The expanded base coat layer is a homogeneous vinyl layer that contains a blowing agent. During processing, the blowing agent decomposes, which causes this layer to expand by forming closed cells. The total thickness of the wall covering is approximately 0.055 in. to 0.070 in. (0.14 cm to 0.18 cm).

10.2.4.3 Cellular or Foamed Plastic. Cellular or foamed plastic materials shall not be used as interior wall and ceiling finish.

The prohibition of 10.2.4.3 on the use of foamed plastics within buildings is based on actual fire experience in which foamed plastics have contributed to very rapid fire development.[25] It is also acknowledged that tunnel testing per NFPA 255 or ASTM E 84 (see 10.2.3.1) might not accurately assess the potential hazard of plastics in general. Therefore, if cellular or foamed plastics are to be used within a building, their use should be substantiated on the basis of full-scale fire tests or fire testing that simulates conditions of actual use.

Exception No. 1: Cellular or foamed plastic material shall be permitted on the basis of fire tests that substantiate their combustibility characteristics for the use intended under actual fire conditions.

Exception No. 2: Cellular or foamed plastic shall be permitted for trim not in excess of 10 percent of the wall or ceiling area, provided that it is not less than 20 lb/ft³ (320 kg/ m³) in density, is limited to ½ in. (1.3 cm) in thickness and 4 in. (10.2 cm) in width, and complies with the requirements for Class A or Class B interior wall and ceiling finish as described in 10.2.3.2; however, the smoke rating shall not be limited.

Exception No. 2 to 10.2.4.3 permits the limited use of plastics as a substitute for traditional wood trim. This exception allows cellular or foamed plastic materials to be used as trim, assuming the performance under fire exposure will be comparable to that of wood. The intent in establishing a minimum density of 20 lb/ft³ (320 kg/m³) is to prohibit the use of lightweight [1 lb/ ft³ to 3 lb/ft³ (16 kg/m³ to 48 kg/m³)] readily available, foamed plastics as trim. To control the mass of the material that can be used, limits have been established on width and thickness.

Limiting plastic trim to Class A or Class B materials, in combination with the 10 percent area limit for walls and ceilings, imposes a greater restriction than that which applies to wood. This limitation ensures that the performance of the plastic trim will be equivalent or superior to that of more traditional materials.

In establishing the 10 percent limit, it is intended that the trim will be used around doors and windows or at the junction of walls and ceilings. Therefore, the trim will be uniformly distributed throughout the room. There would be a significant difference in the probable performance of wall and ceiling finish if the 10 percent limit were concentrated in one area, and Exception No. 2 prohibits such a situation.

10.2.4.4* Light-Transmitting Plastics. Light-transmitting plastics shall be permitted to be used as interior wall and ceiling finish if approved by the authority having jurisdiction.

Light-transmitting plastics are typically regulated by provisions within building codes. Paragraph 10.2.4.4 gives the authority having jurisdiction the ability to regulate light-transmitting plastics; A.10.2.4.4 offers guidance for such regulation.

A.10.2.4.4 Light-transmitting plastics are used for a variety of purposes, including light diffusers, exterior wall panels, skylights, canopies, glazing, and the like. Previous editions of the *Code* have not addressed the use of light-transmitting plastics. Light-transmitting plastics will not normally be used in applications representative of interior finishes. Accordingly, NFPA 255, *Standard Method of Test of Surface Burn-*

ing Characteristics of Building Materials, can produce test results that might or might not apply.

Light-transmitting plastics are regulated by the United States model building codes; see, for example, the *Uniform Building Code,* the *Standard Building Code,* and the *National Building Code.* Model building codes provide adequate regulation for most applications of light-transmitting plastics. Where an authority having jurisdiction determines that a use is contemplated that differs from uses regulated by model building codes, light-transmitting plastics in such applications can be substantiated by fire tests that demonstrate the combustibility characteristics of the light-transmitting plastics for the use intended under actual fire conditions.

10.2.4.5 Surface Nonmetallic Raceways. Where surface nonmetallic raceway products, as permitted by NFPA 70, *National Electrical Code,* are regulated as interior finish, they shall comply with the requirements for Class A interior wall and ceiling finish as described in 10.2.3.2 and tested in the form in which they are used. The smoke rating shall not be limited when the raceway is less than 10 percent of the wall or ceiling area.

Surface-mounted nonmetallic raceways are regulated as interior finish to the same extent as plastic trim. Nonmetallic raceway materials are available that produce a low flame spread rating when tested as interior finish. However, such testing typically records a high smoke development value. Paragraph 10.2.4.5 establishes that smoke is not an important consideration if the nonmetallic raceways are limited to less than 10 percent of the surface area of the wall or ceiling. Paragraph 10.2.4.5 also clarifies that nonmetallic raceway material is to be tested in the form in which it will be used.

10.2.4.6 Decorations and Furnishings. Decorations and furnishings that do not meet the definition of interior finish shall be regulated by the provisions of Section 10.3.

10.2.5 Trim and Incidental Finish.

Interior wall and ceiling finish not in excess of 10 percent of the aggregate wall and ceiling areas of any room or space shall be permitted to be Class C materials in occupancies where interior wall and ceiling finish of Class A or Class B is required.

Subsection 10.2.5 is intended to allow the use of wood trim around doors and windows as a decoration or as functional molding (such as for chair rails). Wood trim (see 10.2.4.3, Exception No. 2, for restrictions applicable to plastic trim) must meet the criteria for Class C materials. Where such trim is used in rooms or spaces requiring the use of Class A or Class B materials, the trim is permitted to constitute not more than 10 percent of the aggregate wall or ceiling area. The intent of the 10 percent area limit is that the trim will be more or less uniformly distributed throughout the room or space. If the trim is concentrated in a single, sizable, continuous pattern (for example, on one wall of a room) the materials could contribute to rapid fire growth, and application of 10.2.5 as substantiation for such a practice would be in error.

10.2.6* Fire-Retardant Coatings.

A.10.2.6 Fire-retardant coatings need to be applied to surfaces properly prepared for the material, and application needs to be consistent with the product listing. Deterioration of coatings applied to interior finishes can occur due to repeated cleaning of the surface or painting over applied coatings.

10.2.6.1 The required flame spread or smoke development classification of existing surfaces of walls, partitions, columns, and ceilings shall be permitted to be secured by applying approved fire-retardant coatings to surfaces having higher flame spread ratings than permitted. Such treatments shall comply with the requirements of NFPA 703, *Standard for Fire Retardant Impregnated Wood and Fire Retardant Coatings for Building Materials.*

10.2.6.2 Fire-retardant coatings shall possess the desired degree of permanency and shall be maintained so as to retain the effectiveness of the treatment under the service conditions encountered in actual use.

Fire-retardant paints, coatings, and penetrants are sometimes used to improve the flame spread ratings of materials or assemblies used as interior finishes within buildings. Fire-retardant treatments are permitted to be used to satisfy the flame spread requirements only for existing interior finish materials within existing buildings.

Fire retardants are generally a surface treatment that — through intumescence or other chemical reaction — will delay the ignition of a material and slow the flame spread. The nature of the material to which the treatment has been applied is not changed. Fire exposures of sufficient duration or intensity can ultimately cause a treated material to burn. Therefore, as a rule, materials with favorable intrinsic performance characteristics are preferred over those that achieve a satisfactory level of performance through the use

of externally applied treatments. However, external treatments, where properly applied and maintained, can be effective in achieving reasonable fire performance.

Fire-retardant paints, coatings, and penetrants must be applied in strict accordance with the manufacturer's instructions and in conformance with the results of fire tests performed on appropriate specimens. Most fire-retardant paints and coatings require an application rate that is three-to-four times greater than that of ordinary paints. Application is usually done by brush, spray, immersion, or pressure treatment. The treatment should be reapplied or renewed at regular intervals. Treatments that might be removed by regular maintenance, washing, or cleaning procedures will require periodic examination and reapplication to maintain the required level of performance.

The use of fire retardants can improve the performance of some materials from Class C to Class B; similarly, Class B materials can, in some cases, be upgraded to Class A. Likewise, materials having flame spread ratings in excess of 200 can sometimes be upgraded to Class C.

In approving fire-retardant treatments, the authority having jurisdiction should consider any increase in smoke generation that is likely to be caused by the treatment; in reducing flame spread, some fire-retardant treatments increase a material's capacity for smoke generation. See the commentary following 10.2.4.5, which addresses surface-mounted nonmetallic raceways.

10.2.7 Interior Floor Finish Testing and Classification.

10.2.7.1* Interior floor finishes shall be classified in accordance with 10.2.7.2 based on test results from NFPA 253, *Standard Method of Test for Critical Radiant Flux of Floor Covering Systems Using a Radiant Heat Energy Source.*

A.10.2.7.1 The flooring radiant panel provides a measure of a floor covering's tendency to spread flames where located in a corridor and exposed to the flame and hot gases from a room fire. The flooring radiant panel test method is to be used as a basis for estimating the fire performance of a floor covering installed in the building corridor. Floor coverings in open building spaces and in rooms within buildings merit no further regulation, provided that it can be shown that the floor covering is at least as resistant to spread of flame as a material that meets the U.S. federal flammability standard 16 *CFR* 1630, *Standard for the Surface Flammability of Carpets and Rugs (FF 1-70).* All carpeting sold in the U.S.

since 1971 is required to meet this standard and, therefore, is not likely to become involved in a fire until a room reaches or approaches flashover. Therefore, no further regulations are necessary for carpet other than carpet in exitways and corridors.

It has not been found necessary or practical to regulate interior floor finishes on the basis of smoke development.

Experience and full-scale fire test data have shown that floor coverings of modest resistance to flame spread are unlikely to become involved in the early growth of a fire. The regulation of flooring materials based on flammability considerations should, therefore, only be undertaken where required by the *Code* or where a need is clearly recognized. The regulation of flooring materials in the general use areas of a building is usually not warranted, except where they are judged to represent an unusual hazard.

Where the judgment is made to regulate floor coverings, the evaluation is to be based on tests conducted in accordance with NFPA 253, *Standard Method of Test for Critical Radiant Flux of Floor Covering Systems Using a Radiant Heat Energy Source.*[26] This document is also known as ASTM E 648, *Standard Test Method for Critical Radiant Flux of Floor-Covering Systems Using a Radiant Heat Energy Source.*[27] The flooring radiant panel test was specifically developed to evaluate the tendency of a floor covering to propagate flame.

Fire tests have been conducted by the National Bureau of Standards (now the National Institute of Standards and Technology).[28] These fire tests demonstrate that carpet that passes the federal flammability standard 16 *CFR* 1630, *Standard for the Surface Flammability of Carpets and Rugs (FF 1-70),* also known as the pill test, is not likely to become involved in a fire until a room reaches or approaches flashover.[29] Since all carpet manufactured for sale in the United States has been required since April 1971 to meet the pill test, no further regulation is necessary for carpet located within rooms.

On the other hand, it has been shown that floor coverings might propagate flame under the influence of a sizable exposure fire. For example, it has been shown that carpet located in a corridor might spread flame when subjected to the energy emanating from the doorway of a room fully developed in fire. The fire discharges flame and hot gases into the corridor causing a radiant heat energy exposure to the floor. It has been shown that the level of energy radiating onto the floor is a significant factor in determining whether progressive flaming will occur. NFPA 253, *Standard Method of Test for Critical Radiant Flux of Floor Covering Systems Using a Radiant Heat Energy Source,*

measures the minimum energy required on the floor covering to sustain flame, measured in W/cm^2. This minimum value is the *critical radiant flux.* The flooring radiant panel test, therefore, measures a floor covering's tendency to spread flames where located in a corridor and exposed to the flame and hot gases from a room fire.

In summary, the flooring radiant panel test is to be used as a basis for estimating the fire performance of a floor covering installed in a building corridor or exit. Floor coverings in open building spaces and in rooms within buildings do not require further regulation, provided that the floor covering is at least as resistant to flame spread as material that meets the federal flammability standard 16 *CFR* 1630, *Standard for the Surface Flammability of Carpets and Rugs (FF 1-70).*

Interior floor finishes should be tested as proposed for use. For example, if a carpet is to be used with a separate underlayment, the carpet should be tested as such. The flooring radiant panel test specifies that a carpet is permitted to be tested using either the standard underlayment specified in NFPA 253, *Standard Method of Test for Critical Radiant Flux of Floor Covering Systems Using a Radiant Heat Energy Source,* or the carpet is permitted to be tested using the actual underlayment proposed for use. Data generated using the standard underlayment is intended to allow the tested carpet to be used over any other underlayment. Where assembly tests are conducted with other than the standard underlayment, the results of such tests are valid only for the specific combination tested.

Floor coverings are not regulated on the basis of smoke generation. Smoke development limits are not believed to be practical or necessary because floor coverings generally will not contribute to a fire until the fire has grown to large proportions. The minimal benefits achieved by imposing smoke development limits do not usually warrant such regulation. In addition, it is not considered practical to regulate on the basis of smoke development, because no regulatory test method that exists has been shown to be capable of producing data that correlates with the performance of products in actual fires.

10.2.7.2　Interior floor finishes shall be grouped in the following classes in accordance with the critical radiant flux ratings.

(a) *Class I Interior Floor Finish.* Critical radiant flux not less than 0.45 W/cm^2 as determined by the test described in 10.2.7.1.

(b) *Class II Interior Floor Finish.* Critical radiant flux not less than 0.22 W/cm² but less than 0.45 W/cm² as determined by the test described in 10.2.7.1.

> Note that, the greater the critical radiant flux value (expressed in W/cm²), the greater the resistance of the floor finish to flame propagation. Thus, a Class I interior floor finish with a critical radiant flux of 0.45 W/cm² or greater should perform better under fire conditions than a Class II interior floor finish material with its lesser critical radiant flux value range of at least 0.22 W/cm² but less than 0.45 W/cm². Contrast this behavior with the classification of interior wall and ceiling interior finish materials in 10.2.3.2, in which higher flame spread ratings generally denote poorer performance under fire conditions.

10.2.7.3 Wherever the use of Class II interior floor finish is required, Class I interior floor finish shall be permitted.

10.2.8 Automatic Sprinklers.

10.2.8.1 Unless specifically prohibited elsewhere in this Code, where an approved automatic sprinkler system is in accordance with Section 9.7, Class C interior wall and ceiling finish materials shall be permitted in any location where Class B is required, and Class B interior wall and ceiling finish materials shall be permitted in any location where Class A is required.

10.2.8.2 Unless specifically prohibited elsewhere in this *Code,* where an approved automatic sprinkler system is in accordance with Section 9.7, Class II interior floor finish shall be permitted in any location where Class I interior floor finish is required, and where Class II is required, no critical radiant flux rating shall be required.

> Fire testing and actual fire experience have shown that automatic sprinklers prevent flame spread across the surface of a wall, ceiling, or floor covering. Flame spread limits (applicable to interior wall and ceiling finishes) and critical radiant flux limits (applicable to interior floor finishes) are reduced in areas protected by an automatic sprinkler system. However, there is a value beyond which the potential for flame spread becomes unacceptably high. For example, in occupancies with the most lenient interior finish requirements, which include fully sprinklered buildings, interior wall and ceiling finishes must meet the criteria for Class C materials.

Section 10.3 Contents and Furnishings

> Section 10.3 provides a detailed menu of provisions that are applicable to contents and furnishings (for example, draperies, upholstered furniture, and mattresses) that can be adopted singly, in various combinations, or in their entirety in accordance with an occupancy's individual operating features requirements. These requirements typically appear in Section __.7 of an occupancy chapter. For example, the provisions for detention and correctional occupancies (22.7.4 and 23.7.4) make extensive, mandatory use of all provisions outlined in the Section 10.3 menu. Provisions for residential board and care occupancies (32.7.5, 33.7.5, A.32.7.5, and A.33.7.5) make partial mandatory and partial advisory use of the menu items contained in Section 10.3.

10.3.1* Where required by the applicable provisions of this *Code*, draperies, curtains, and other similar loosely hanging furnishings and decorations shall be flame resistant as demonstrated by testing in accordance with NFPA 701, *Standard Methods of Fire Tests for Flame Propagation of Textiles and Films.*

A.10.3.1 Testing per NFPA 701, *Standard Methods of Fire Tests for Flame Propagation of Textiles and Films,* applies to textiles and films used in a hanging configuration. If the textiles and films are to be applied to surfaces of buildings or backing materials as interior finishes for use in buildings, they should be treated as interior wall and ceiling finishes in accordance with Section 10.2 of this *Code,* and they should then be tested for flame spread rating and smoke development values in accordance with NFPA 255, *Standard Method of Test of Surface Burning Characteristics of Building Materials,* or for flame spread and flashover in accordance with NFPA 265, *Standard Methods of Fire Tests for Evaluating Room Fire Growth Contribution of Textile Wall Coverings.*

   The test results from NFPA 701 are suitable for classification purposes but should not be used as input into fire models, because they are not generated in units suitable for engineering calculations.

> The testing requirements of NFPA 701, *Standard Methods of Fire Tests for Flame Propagation of Textiles and Films,* measure the level of hazard posed by draperies and other loosely hanging fabrics and films. NFPA 701 describes procedures for an intermediate-scale and large-scale test. The choice of the applicable test

method is determined, in part, by the weight of the material per unit area. Both tests involve applying a flame to a vertically positioned sample for a specified time. Upon removal of the flame-producing burner, the sample must self-extinguish and must not have charred beyond a specified distance in order to pass the test. Additionally, with the intermediate-scale test, a specified maximum percent weight loss cannot be exceeded.

Exhibit 10.6 illustrates a representative test setup from NFPA 701.

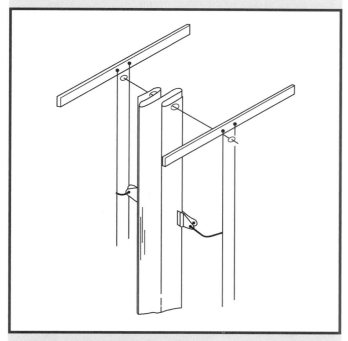

***Exhibit 10.6** Test sample in folds.*

10.3.2* Where required by the applicable provisions of this *Code*, upholstered furniture and mattresses shall be resistant to a cigarette ignition (that is, smoldering) in accordance with the following:

A.10.3.2 The Class I requirement associated with testing per NFPA 260, *Standard Methods of Tests and Classification System for Cigarette Ignition Resistance of Components of Upholstered Furniture;* the char length of not more than 1.5 in. (3.8 cm) required with testing per NFPA 261, *Standard Method of Test for Determining Resistance of Mock-Up Upholstered Furniture Material Assemblies to Ignition by Smoldering Cigarettes;* and the char length of not more than 2 in. (5.1 cm) required in FF4-72, *Standard for the Flammability of Mattresses,* are indicators that the furniture item or

mattress is resistant to a cigarette ignition. Although rooms or spaces protected by an approved automatic sprinkler system are exempt from cigarette ignition resistance testing, a fire that smolders for an excessive period of time without flaming can reduce the tenability within the room or area of fire origin without developing the temperatures necessary to operate automatic sprinklers.

The test results from NFPA 260 and NFPA 261 are suitable for classification purposes but should not be used as input into fire models, because they are not generated in units suitable for engineering calculations.

(1) Where required by the applicable provisions of this *Code,* the components of the upholstered furniture, unless located in rooms or spaces protected by an approved automatic sprinkler system, shall meet the requirements for Class I when tested in accordance with NFPA 260, *Standard Methods of Tests and Classification System for Cigarette Ignition Resistance of Components of Upholstered Furniture.*

(2) Where required by the applicable provisions of this *Code,* mocked-up composites of the upholstered furniture, unless located in rooms or spaces protected by an approved automatic sprinkler system, shall have a char length not exceeding 1.5 in. (3.8 cm) when tested in accordance with NFPA 261, *Standard Method of Test for Determining Resistance of Mock-Up Upholstered Furniture Material Assemblies to Ignition by Smoldering Cigarettes.*

(3)* Where required by the applicable provisions of this *Code,* mattresses, unless located in rooms or spaces protected by an approved automatic sprinkler system, shall have a char length not exceeding 2 in. (5.1 cm) when tested in accordance with Part 1632 of the *Code of Federal Regulations* 16.

A.10.3.2(3) Regardless of sprinkler protection provided, U.S. federal regulations require mattresses in the United States to comply with 16 *CFR* 1632.

The provisions of 10.3.2 address ignition by cigarettes or other smoldering sources in an attempt to reduce the incidence of fires involving upholstered furniture and mattresses. Such ignition sources can smolder for considerable periods before producing flaming ignition.

Two NFPA fire test methods that address the cigarette ignition resistance of upholstered furniture follow:

(1) NFPA 260, *Standard Methods of Tests and Classification System for Cigarette Ignition Resistance of Components of Upholstered Furniture*[30]

(2) NFPA 261, *Standard Method of Test for Determining Resistance of Mock-Up Upholstered Furniture Material Assemblies to Ignition by Smoldering Cigarettes*[31]

One federal test method that is specified for judging the cigarette ignition resistance of mattresses is 16 *CFR* 1632, *Standard for the Flammability of Mattresses and Mattress Pads.*[32]

When purchasing upholstered furniture, consumers should check for flammability labeling.

See Exhibit 10.7 for a representative flammability tag found on upholstered furniture.

NFPA 260 tests individual components of upholstered furniture, such as cover fabric, interior fabric, welt cord, filling/padding, decking materials, and barrier materials. Specimens of the component to be tested are assembled with specimens of standardized materials to create a miniature horizontal base panel and vertical panel tester, a mocked-up arrangement that simulates the junction and surrounding area of a seat cushion and back cushion in a piece of upholstered furniture. Standardizing all the components of the mocked-up tester, except the component being tested, allows the test to measure the ignition resistance of the test component. Components that meet the test criteria are designated as Class I materials. Components that do not meet the test criteria are designated as Class II materials. Upholstered furniture constructed from components that individually received a Class I designation is judged to be resistant to cigarette ignition without testing the actual combination of materials. Cigarette ignition–resistant upholstered furniture can also be constructed using Class II cover fabric materials over conventional polyurethane foam cushions, if a Class I barrier material is used between the Class II fabric and the conventional foam cushion.

NFPA 261 tests a mocked-up assembly consisting of all the actual components that will be used to construct the piece of upholstered furniture, rather than testing the components individually. The test procedure specifies that a char length is to be measured and reported. There are no pass/fail criteria within the document, so 10.3.2(2) specifies that the char length not exceed 1.5 in. (3.8 cm) if the mocked-up assembly is to be considered resistant to cigarette ignition.

NFPA 260 and NFPA 261 address the cigarette ignition resistance of upholstered furniture; 16 *CFR* 1632 addresses the cigarette ignition resistance of mattresses. For this test method, 10.3.2(3) establishes that a char length not exceeding 2 in. (5.1 cm) qualifies the mattress as resistant to cigarette ignition.

10.3.3* Where required by the applicable provisions of this *Code*, upholstered furniture, unless the furniture is located in a room or space protected by an approved automatic sprinkler system, shall have limited rates of heat release when tested in accordance with NFPA 266, *Standard Method of Test for Fire Characteristics of Upholstered Furniture Exposed to Flaming Ignition Source*, or with ASTM E 1537, *Standard Method for Fire Testing of Real Scale Upholstered Furniture Items*, as follows:

(1) The peak rate of heat release for the single upholstered furniture item shall not exceed 250 kW.
(2) The total energy released by the single upholstered furniture item during the first 5 minutes of the test shall not exceed 40 MJ.

A.10.3.3 The intent of the provisions of 10.3.3 is as follows.

(a) The peak heat release rate of not more than 250 kW by a single upholstered furniture item was chosen based on maintaining a tenable environment within the room of fire origin. The sprinkler exception was developed because the sprinkler system helps to maintain tenable conditions even if the single upholstered furniture item were to have a peak rate of heat release in excess of 250 kW.

(b) The total energy release of not more than 40 MJ by the single upholstered furniture item during the first 5 minutes of the test was established as an additional safeguard to protect against the adverse conditions that would be created by an upholstered furniture item that released its heat in other than the usual measured scenario. During the test for measurement of rate of heat release, the instantaneous heat release value usually peaks quickly and then quickly falls off so as to create a triangle-shaped curve. In the atypical case, if the heat release were to peak and remain steady at that elevated level, as opposed to quickly falling off, the 250-kW limit would not ensure safety. Again, only a sprinkler exception is permitted in lieu of the test because of the ability of the sprinkler system to control the fire.

Actual test results for heat, smoke, and combustion product release from NFPA 266, *Standard Method of Test for Fire Characteristics of Upholstered Furniture Exposed to Flaming Ignition Source*, and ASTM E 1537, *Standard Method of Fire Testing of Real Scale Upholstered Furniture Items*, might be suitable for use as input into fire models for performance-based design.

The provisions of 10.3.2 address only one important property of upholstered furniture and mattresses — their resistance to cigarette ignition. The provisions of 10.3.3 and 10.3.4 supplement those provisions by addressing rates of heat release. Different combustible materials vary in their potential to produce heat.

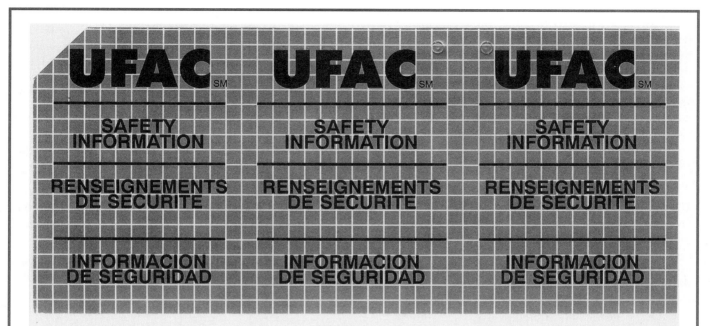

Exhibit 10.7 *Upholstered furniture flammability tag. (Photo courtesy of American Furniture Manufacturers Association and the Upholstered Furniture Action Council.)*

Some plastic materials, for example, have twice as much potential heat per weight of material as wood. However, if the material with twice the potential heat were to burn only half as fast as the material with the lower potential, the two materials would liberate about the same amount of heat during any given period and create approximately equivalent hazards. If one material with a heat potential approximately equal to another material were to burn twice as fast as the other, it would liberate about twice as much heat during any given period and, thus, create a greater hazard than the slower burning material.

Therefore, the property of a material or group of materials expressed by a rate of heat release is important in regulating the combustibility of upholstered furniture and mattresses for use in nonsprinklered areas.

The annex material to 10.3.3 adequately describes the intent of the rates of heat release provisions, which is to prevent any single furniture item from causing room flashover. The material in A.10.3.3 also explains how automatic sprinklers, in certain cases, can serve in lieu of a low rate of heat release.

10.3.4* Where required by the applicable provisions of this *Code*, mattresses, unless the mattress is located in a room or space protected by an approved automatic sprinkler system, shall have limited rates of heat release when tested in accordance with NFPA 267, *Standard Method of Test for Fire Characteristics of Mattresses and Bedding Assemblies Exposed to Flaming Ignition Source*, or ASTM E 1590, *Standard Method for Fire Testing of Real Scale Mattresses*, as follows:

See the commentary following A.10.3.3.

(1) The peak rate of heat release for the mattress shall not exceed 250 kW.
(2) The total energy released by the mattress during the first 5 minutes of the test shall not exceed 40 MJ.

A.10.3.4 The intent of the provisions of 10.3.4 4 is as follows.

(a) The peak heat release rate of not more than 250 kW by a single mattress was chosen based on maintaining a tenable environment within the room of fire origin. The sprinkler exception was developed because the sprinkler system helps to maintain tenable conditions even if the single mattress were to have a peak rate of heat release in excess of 250 kW.

(b) The total energy release of not more than 40 MJ by the single mattress during the first 5 minutes of the test was established as an additional safeguard to protect against the adverse conditions that would be created by a mattress that released its heat in other than the usual measured scenario. During the test for measurement of rate of heat release, the instantaneous heat release value usually peaks quickly and then quickly falls off so as to create a triangle-shaped curve. In the atypical case, if the heat release were to peak and remain steady at that elevated level, as opposed to quickly falling off, the 250-kW limit would not ensure safety. Again, only a sprinkler exception is permitted in lieu of the test because of the ability of the sprinkler system to control the fire.

Actual test results for heat, smoke, and combustion product release from NFPA 267, *Standard Method of Test for Fire Characteristics of Mattresses and Bedding Assemblies Exposed to Flaming Ignition Source*, and ASTM E 1590, *Standard Method for Fire Testing of Real Scale Mattresses*, might be suitable for use as input into fire models for performance-based design.

10.3.5* Furnishings or decorations of an explosive or highly flammable character shall not be used.

A.10.3.5 Christmas trees not effectively flame-retardant treated, ordinary crepe paper decorations, and pyroxylin plastic decorations might be classified as highly flammable.

The *Code* relies on the authority having jurisdiction to exercise judgment in determining the materials that are of an explosive or highly flammable nature.

10.3.6 Fire-retardant coatings shall be maintained to retain the effectiveness of the treatment under service conditions encountered in actual use.

See NFPA 703, *Standard for Fire Retardant Impregnated Wood and Fire Retardant Coatings for Building Materials*.[33]

10.3.7* Where required by the applicable provisions of this *Code*, furnishings and contents made with foamed plastic materials that are unprotected from ignition shall have a heat release rate not exceeding 100 kW when tested in accordance with UL 1975, *Standard for Fire Tests for Foamed Plastics Used for Decorative Purposes*.

A.10.3.7 UL 1975, *Standard for Fire Tests for Foamed Plastics Used for Decorative Purposes*, is not intended for evaluating interior wall and ceiling finish materials.

Actual test results for heat, smoke, and combustion product release from UL 1975 might be suitable for use as input into fire models intended for performance-based design.

References Cited in Commentary

1. Michael Isner, "Five Die in High-Rise Office Building Fire," *Fire Journal* 84, no. 4 (July/August 1990): 50–57, 59.
2. Thomas Klem, "Investigation Report on the Du-Pont Plaza Hotel Fire," National Fire Protection Association, Quincy, MA, 1987.

3. National Fire Protection Association, "Investigation Report on the Las Vegas Hilton Hotel Fire," *Fire Journal* 76, no. 1 (January 1982): 52–63.

4. John Hall, Jr., "Report Prepared for the House Subcommittee on Science, Research, and Technology on H.R. 94, The Hotel and Motel Fire Safety Act of 1989," Quincy, MA: NFPA Fire Analysis and Research Division, National Fire Protection Association, Quincy, MA, March 2, 1989.

5. Laurence Watrous, "Ten Die in Convalescent Home Fire," *Fire Journal* 66, no. 5 (September 1972): 16–20.

6. John Hall, Jr., "Report Prepared for House Subcommittee on Science, Research, and Technology on H.R. 94."

7. David Demers, "Familiar Problems Cause 10 Deaths in Hotel Fire," *Fire Journal* 74, no. 1 (January 1980): 52–56.

8. David Waksman and John B. Ferguson, "Fire Tests of Building Interior Covering Systems," *Fire Technology* 10, no. 3:211–220.

9. Fred Fisher et al., "Room Fire Experiments of Textile Wall Coverings," Fire Research Laboratory, University of California, Berkeley, March 1986.

10. NFPA 255, *Standard Method of Test of Surface Burning Characteristics of Building Materials*, 2000 edition, National Fire Protection Association, Quincy, MA.

11. ASTM E 84, *Standard Test Method for Surface Burning Characteristics of Building Materials*, American Society for Testing and Materials, West Conshohocken, PA.

12. NFPA 220, *Standard on Types of Building Construction*, 1999 edition, National Fire Protection Association, Quincy, MA.

13. NFPA 286, *Standard Methods of Fire Tests for Evaluating Contribution of Wall and Ceiling Interior Finish to Room Fire Growth*, 2000 edition, National Fire Protection Association, Quincy, MA.

14. *Standard Building Code*, Southern Building Code Congress International, Inc., Birmingham, AL.

15. BOCA *National Building Code*, Building Officials and Code Administrators International, Inc., Country Club Hills, IL.

16. *Uniform Building Code*, International Conference of Building Officials, Whittier, CA.

17. Underwriters Laboratories Inc., "Study of Smoke Ratings Developed in Standard Fire Tests in Relation to Visual Observations," Bulletin of Research, No. 56, April 1965.

18. Waksman and Ferguson, "Fire Tests of Building Interior Covering Systems."

19. NFPA 701, *Standard Methods of Fire Tests for Flame Propagation of Textiles and Films*, 1999 edition, National Fire Protection Association, Quincy, MA.

20. NFPA, "Investigation Report on the Las Vegas Hilton Hotel Fire."

21. Fisher et al., "Room Fire Experiments."

22. NFPA, "Investigation Report on the Las Vegas Hilton Hotel Fire."

23. W.J. Christian and T.E. Waterman, "Flame Spread in Corridors: Effects of Location and Area of Wall Finish," *Fire Journal* 65, no. 4 (July 1971): 25–32.

24. NFPA 265, *Standard Methods of Fire Tests for Evaluating Room Fire Growth Contribution of Textile Wall Coverings*, 1998 edition, National Fire Protection Association, Quincy, MA.

25. John Sharry, "Foamed Plastic Fire: Fire Spreads 430 Feet in Eight Minutes," *Fire Journal* 69, no. 1 (January 1975): 5–6, 56.

26. NFPA 253, *Standard Method of Test for Critical Radiant Flux of Floor Covering Systems Using a Radiant Heat Energy Source*, 2000 edition, National Fire Protection Association, Quincy, MA.

27. ASTM E 648, *Standard Test Method for Critical Radiant Flux of Floor-Covering Systems Using a Radiant Heat Energy Source*, American Society for Testing and Materials, West Conshohocken, PA.

28. Tu King-Mon and Sanford Davis, "Flame Spread of Carpet Systems Involved in Room Fires," NBSIR 76-1013, June 1976.

29. Title 16 CFR 1630, *Standard for the Surface Flammability of Carpets and Rugs (FF1-70)*, Code of Federal Regulations, Volume 16, Part 1630, U.S. Government Printing Office, Washington, DC, published annually.

30. NFPA 260, *Standard Methods of Tests and Classification System for Cigarette Ignition Resistance of Components of Upholstered Furniture*, 1998 edition, National Fire Protection Association, Quincy, MA.

31. NFPA 261, *Standard Method of Test for Determining Resistance of Mock-Up Upholstered Furniture Material Assemblies to Ignition by Smoldering Cigarettes*, 1998 edition, National Fire Protection Association, Quincy, MA.

32. Title 16 CFR 1632, *Standard for the Flammability of Mattresses and Mattress Pads*, Code of Federal Regulations, Volume 16, Part 1632, U.S. Government Printing Office, Washington, DC, published annually.

33. NFPA 703, *Standard for Fire Retardant Impregnated Wood and Fire Retardant Coatings for Building Materials*, 1995 edition, National Fire Protection Association, Quincy, MA.

CHAPTER 11

Special Structures and High-Rise Buildings

Section 11.1 General Requirements

Chapter 11 is formatted differently than the other chapters of the *Code*. It is the last of the core chapters that precedes the occupancy chapters. Its scope is potentially applicable to all occupancies. Each subsection is targeted to specific special structures or *unusual* surroundings within which a *usual* occupancy might exist. The facilities to which Chapter 11 provisions might be applied range from a refinery petroleum-cracking plant to an air-traffic control tower. While the life safety and functional use considerations of these properties might, at times, seem to conflict, Chapter 11 provides the necessary guidance to make them safe as well as functional.

A usual occupancy might be housed in unusual surroundings or a special structure. Two examples are a large convention center located on a pier, so that the facility is surrounded by water on three sides, and a moderately sized restaurant located on an upper level of an air-traffic control tower. Exhibit 11.1 is an example of an usual occupancy in an unusual surrounding. An authority having jurisdiction should ensure that any engineered solutions to the special structure's inherent egress deficiencies provide an overall level of life safety equivalent to that specified by the requirements of the occupancy chapter that applies to the structure's use.

Chapter 11 also regulates water-surrounded structures, vehicles and vessels, and windowless and underground structures. These provisions apply regardless of the occupancy classification. For example, a permanently moored ship that is used as restaurant must comply with Chapters 12 or 13 for assembly occupancies, as appropriate, by virtue of the language in 11.6.2.

Section 11.8 presents a series of unique provi-

Exhibit 11.1 *The CN Tower in Toronto.*

sions applicable to high-rise buildings. In each case, the various occupancy chapters might mandate the use of some, all, or none of the high-rise building provisions.

The last three sections of Chapter 11 are new for the 2000 edition of the *Code*. They provide a series of requirements applicable to tents and membrane structures. These requirements are contained in NFPA 102, *Standard for Grandstands, Folding and Telescopic Seating, Tents, and Membrane Structures.*[1] The inclusion of these provisions make this edition of the *Code* more comprehensive.

11.1.1 Application.

The requirements of Sections 11.1 through 11.11 apply to occupancies regulated by Chapters 12 through 42 that are in a special structure. The provisions of the applicable chapter (that is, 12 through 42) shall apply, except as modified by this chapter. Section 11.8 applies to high-rise buildings only where specifically required by Chapters 12 through 42.

Occupancies in special structures pose a special challenge to life safety. Sections 11.1 through 11.6 are intended to supplement the requirements of occupancy Chapters 12 through 42. The provisions of Sections 11.1 through 11.6 might serve as requirements that must be satisfied in addition to those found in the applicable occupancy chapter. For example, 11.5.3 contains additional provisions that apply to a pier used for other than cargo handling or storage, such as an amusement pier. In such a case, the requirements of Chapters 12 or 13 for assembly occupancies and 11.5.3 would apply.

The provisions of Chapter 11 also might take the form of an exception that is permitted to be used in a special structure but that would not be allowed in a usual structure housing the same occupancy. For example, if a business occupancy is housed in a tower, 11.3.2.4.1 permits a single exit from the tower under a strict set of conditions. However, if a similar business occupancy is located on an upper floor of a multistory building and not in a tower, Chapters 38 or 39 would require that two exits be provided on the floor housing the business occupancy. In other words, Chapter 11 might offer an exemption based on the inherent difficulty of providing two remote exits from a tower. Yet, the exemption isn't a waiver that ignores life safety. Rather, the exemption provides criteria and limitations that ensure a safe means of tolerating a single exit.

All occupancies housed in windowless and underground buildings must comply with the provisions of Section 11.7 which include the following:

(1) Complete automatic sprinkler protection
(2) Emergency lighting
(3) Smoke venting
(4) Directional indicator signs for egress paths

These provisions are required in addition to those applicable to the occupancy via its appropriate occupancy chapter (Chapters 12 through 42).

An occupancy in a high-rise building must comply with the requirements of Section 11.8 only to the degree specified by the applicable occupancy chapter. For example, for new hotels, 28.4.1 requires compliance with the full package of high-rise building provisions of Section 11.8; for new health-care occupancies, 18.4.2 requires the sprinkler and standpipe systems detailed in 11.8.2; for new mercantile occupancies, 36.4.2 requires sprinkler systems in accordance with 11.8.2.1; and for most existing buildings, the applicable occupancy chapter does not make mandatory use of any of the provisions of Section 11.8 — although some require existing high-rise buildings to be sprinklered in accordance with Section 9.7 rather than 11.8.1.

Although the *Code* provisions present an essentially complete package of requirements for life safety, the provision of adequate means of egress from many special structures requires unique solutions. In many instances, engineered solutions will supplement the minimum provisions of Chapter 11 and the applicable occupancy chapter. However, the unique character of a structure should not become an excuse for reducing safety to life. The *Code* user is cautioned to exercise judgment when determining the egress requirements for special structures.

11.1.2 Mixed Occupancies.

(See 6.1.14.)

11.1.3 Special Definitions.

(See the defined terms within each special structure section.)

11.1.4 Classification of Occupancy.

Occupancies regulated by Chapters 12 through 42 that are in special structures shall meet the requirements of those chapters, except as modified by this chapter.

11.1.5 Classification of Hazard of Contents.

Classification of hazard of contents shall be in accordance with Section 6.2.

11.1.6 Minimum Construction Requirements.

Minimum construction requirements shall be in accordance with the applicable occupancy chapter.

11.1.7 Occupant Load.

The occupant load of special structures shall be based on the use of the structure as regulated by Chapters 12 through 42.

Section 11.2 Open Structures

11.2.1 Application.

11.2.1.1   The provisions of Section 11.1 shall apply.

11.2.1.2 Definition—Open Structure. See 3.3.140.

11.2.2* Means of Egress.

A.11.2.2 Escape chutes, controlled descent devices, and elevators permitted to provide escape routes in special structures; however, they should not be substituted for the provisions of this *Code*.

11.2.2.1 General. The means of egress provisions of the applicable occupancy chapter (Chapters 12 through 42) shall apply, except as modified by 11.2.2.2 through 11.2.2.10.

11.2.2.2 Means of Egress Components.

11.2.2.2.1 Fire Escape Ladders. Open structures that are designed for occupancy by not more than three persons shall be permitted to be served by fire escape ladders complying with 7.2.9.

11.2.2.3 Capacity of Means of Egress. Open structures shall be exempt from the requirements for capacity of means of egress.

Paragraph 11.2.2.3 recognizes the multiple means of egress available in open structures, such as those found in petrochemical and process industries. An open structure is actually an access platform to the equipment that it surrounds or supports. Normal occupancy is very limited in number and occasional in frequency. If a fire blocks one means of egress, a number of alternate means of egress remain available. An escape route is provided by the fixed means of egress, and rescue is possible from any portion of the structure by use of the emergency procedures of fire-fighting personnel. The potential for exposure of portions of the structure not involved in a fire is minimal, because, in open platforms, flames, heat, and smoke are safely dispersed directly into the atmosphere and not into the uninvolved portions of the structure.

11.2.2.4 Number of Means of Egress.

11.2.2.4.1 The grade level of open structures, which by their very nature contain an infinite number of means of egress, shall be exempt from the requirements for number of means of egress.

11.2.2.4.2 Open structures occupied by not more than three persons, with travel distance not more than 200 ft (60 m), shall be permitted to have a single exit.

11.2.2.5 Arrangement of Means of Egress. (No modifications.)

11.2.2.6 Travel Distance to Exits. Open structures shall be exempt from travel distance limitations.

11.2.2.7 Discharge from Exits. Open structures permitted to have a single exit per 11.2.2.4 shall be permitted to have 100 percent of the exit discharge through areas on the level of exit discharge.

11.2.2.8 Illumination of Means of Egress. Open structures shall be exempt from illumination of means of egress requirements.

11.2.2.9 Emergency Lighting. Open structures shall be exempt from emergency lighting requirements.

11.2.2.10 Marking of Means of Egress. Open structures shall be exempt from marking of means of egress requirements.

11.2.3 Protection.

11.2.3.1 Protection of Vertical Openings. Open structures shall be exempt from protection of vertical opening requirements.

11.2.3.2 Protection from Hazards. Every open structure, other than those structures with only occasional occupancy, shall have automatic, manual, or other protection that is appropriate to the particular hazard and that is designed to minimize danger to occupants in case of fire or other emergency before they have time to use the means of egress.

11.2.3.3 Interior Finish. (No modifications.)

11.2.3.4 Detection, Alarm, and Communications Systems. Open structures shall be exempt from requirements for detection, alarm, and communications systems.

11.2.3.5 Extinguishing Requirements. (No modifications.)

Section 11.3 Towers

11.3.1 Application.

11.3.1.1 The provisions of Section 11.1 shall apply.

11.3.1.2 Definition—Tower. See 3.3.203.

11.3.2 Means of Egress.

11.3.2.1 General. The means of egress provisions of the applicable occupancy chapter (Chapters 12 through 42) shall apply, except as modified by 11.3.2.2 through 11.3.2.10.

11.3.2.2 Means of Egress Components.

11.3.2.2.1 Fire Escape Ladders. Towers, such as forest fire observation or railroad signal towers, that are designed for occupancy by not more than three persons shall be permitted to be served by fire escape ladders complying with 7.2.9.

11.3.2.2.2 Elevators. Towers subject to occupancy by not more than 90 persons shall be permitted to use elevators in the means of egress in accordance with 7.2.13.

11.3.2.3 Capacity of Means of Egress.

11.3.2.3.1 Means of egress for towers shall be provided for the number of persons expected to occupy the space.

11.3.2.3.2 Spaces not subject to human occupancy because of machinery or equipment shall be excluded from consideration.

11.3.2.4* Number of Means of Egress.

A.11.3.2.4 The Washington Monument in Washington, DC, is an example of a tower where it would be impracticable to provide a second stairway.

11.3.2.4.1 Towers shall be permitted to have a single exit if the following conditions are met:

(1) The tower is subject to occupancy by fewer than 25 persons.
(2) The tower is not used for living or sleeping purposes.
(3) The tower is of Type I, Type II, or Type IV construction. *(See 8.2.1.)*
(4) The tower interior wall and ceiling finish is Class A or Class B.
(5) The tower has no combustible materials in the structure, under the structure, or in the immediate vicinity of the structure, except necessary furniture.
(6) There are no high hazard occupancies in the tower or in its immediate vicinity.
(7) Where the tower is located above a building, the single exit from the tower shall be provided by one of the following:
   a. An exit enclosure separated from the building with no door openings to or from the building
   b. An exit enclosure leading directly to an exit enclosure serving the building, with walls and door separating these exit enclosures from each other, and another door allowing access to the top floor of the building that provides access to a second exit serving that floor

Paragraph 11.3.2.4.1 permits a single means of egress from a tower if additional criteria are met. Calculation of the total occupancy of a tower should be based on the actual number expected to occupy the facility [see 11.3.2.4.1(1)]. Limitations on the combustibility and interior finish of the structure are established, so that the potential exposure of the tower occupants to fire is minimal. Types I, II, and IV construction [see 11.3.2.4.1(3)] are defined in NFPA 220, *Standard on Types of Building Construction.*[2]

One difficulty associated with the requirements for exits in towers is the accurate determination of the level of exposure of the tower to combustible materials under or in the immediate vicinity of the structure. Judgment should be used by the authority having jurisdiction and other *Code* users to ensure that arbitrary limitations are not established that excessively restrict the use of the tower. For example, a forest fire tower is usually located in a clearing in a large forest. The proximity of trees to the tower could be interpreted as constituting combustible materials in the immediate vicinity of the tower. Reasonable clearances between the tower and forest — such as a clear space of 50 ft to 100 ft (15 m to 30 m) — could be considered adequate separation for the life safety of the tower's occupants. Similar judgment is required where evaluating the clearance between high hazard occupancies and towers.

The provisions of 11.3.2.4.1(7) are illustrated in Exhibit 11.2. Where the tower is located above a building, special precautions must be taken to prevent use of the tower's single means of egress from being compromised by a fire in the building below. In Exhibit 11.2, illustration (a), the single exit stair enclosure for the tower is separated from the building by rated construction in accordance with 7.1.3.2. Additionally, the single exit stair enclosure for the tower has no openings to the floors of the building above which the tower is positioned, thus preventing a fire on the building floors from entering the enclosure.

In Exhibit 11.2, illustration (b), the single exit stair positioned above the building serves the tower. It provides direct access to the exit stair enclosure on the left, which also serves the building floors. If a fire prevents the use of the exit stair enclosure on the left, the tower stair permits tower occupants to traverse the top floor of the building and access a second exit stair enclosure on the right.

11.3.2.4.2 Towers with 360-degree line-of-sight requirements shall be permitted to have a single means of egress for a distance of travel not exceeding 75 ft (23 m), or 100 ft (30 m) if the tower is protected throughout by an approved, supervised automatic sprinkler system in accordance with Section 9.7.

11.3.2.5 Arrangement of Means of Egress. (No modifications.)

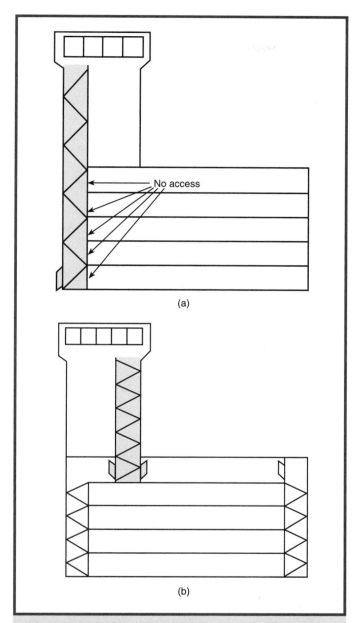

No access

(a)

(b)

Exhibit 11.2 Single exit from a tower.

11.3.2.6 Travel Distance to Exits. Towers where ladders are permitted by 11.3.2.2.1 shall be exempt from travel distance limitations.

11.3.2.7 Discharge from Exits. Towers permitted to have a single exit per 11.3.2.4 shall be permitted to have 100 percent of the exit discharge through areas on the level of exit discharge.

11.3.2.8 Illumination of Means of Egress. Towers where ladders are permitted by 11.3.2.2.1 shall be exempt from illumination of means of egress requirements.

11.3.2.9 Emergency Lighting.

11.3.2.9.1 Towers where ladders are permitted by 11.3.2.2.1 shall be exempt from emergency lighting requirements.

11.3.2.9.2 Locations not routinely inhabited by humans shall be exempt from emergency lighting requirements.

11.3.2.9.3 Structures occupied only during daylight hours, with windows arranged to provide the required level of illumination of all portions of the means of egress during these hours, shall be exempt from emergency lighting requirements where approved by the authority having jurisdiction.

11.3.2.10 Marking of Means of Egress.

11.3.2.10.1 Towers where ladders are permitted by 11.3.2.2.1 shall be exempt from marking of means of egress requirements.

11.3.2.10.2 Locations not routinely inhabited by humans shall be exempt from marking of means of egress requirements.

11.3.3 Protection.

11.3.3.1 Protection of Vertical Openings.

11.3.3.1.1 Towers where ladders are permitted by 11.3.2.2.1 shall be exempt from protection of vertical opening requirements.

11.3.3.1.2 In towers where the support structure is open and there is no occupancy below the top floor level, stairs shall be permitted to be open with no enclosure required, or fire escape stairs shall be permitted.

11.3.3.2 Protection from Hazards. Every tower, other than structures with only occasional occupancy, shall have automatic, manual, or other protection that is appropriate to the particular hazard and that is designed to minimize danger to occupants in case of fire or other emergency before they have time to use the means of egress.

11.3.3.3 Interior Finish. (No modifications.)

11.3.3.4 Detection, Alarm, and Communications Systems. Towers designed for occupancy by not more than three persons shall be exempt from requirements for detection, alarm, and communications systems.

11.3.3.5 Extinguishing Requirements. (No modifications.)

11.3.3.6 Corridors. (No modifications.)

Section 11.4 Water-Surrounded Structures

11.4.1 Application.

11.4.1.1 The provisions of Section 11.1 shall apply.

Exception: Any structure surrounded by water and under the jurisdiction of the U.S. Coast Guard and designed and arranged in accordance with Coast Guard regulations shall be exempt from the requirements of this Code.

11.4.1.2 Definition—Water-Surrounded Structure. See 3.3.210.

11.4.2 Means of Egress.

11.4.2.1 General. The means of egress provisions of the applicable occupancy chapter (Chapters 12 through 42) shall apply, except as modified by 11.4.2.2 through 11.4.2.10.

11.4.2.2 Means of Egress Components. (No modifications.)

11.4.2.3 Capacity of Means of Egress. Spaces in water-surrounded structures that are not subject to human occupancy because of machinery or equipment shall be exempt from the requirements for capacity of means of egress.

11.4.2.4 Number of Means of Egress. (No modifications.)

11.4.2.5 Arrangement of Means of Egress. (No modifications.)

11.4.2.6 Travel Distance to Exits. (No modifications.)

11.4.2.7 Discharge from Exits. Structures permitted to have a single exit per the applicable occupancy chapter shall be permitted to have 100 percent of the exit discharge through areas on the level of exit discharge.

11.4.2.8 Illumination of Means of Egress. (No modifications.)

11.4.2.9 Emergency Lighting.

11.4.2.9.1 Locations not routinely inhabited by humans are exempt from emergency lighting requirements.

11.4.2.9.2 Structures occupied only during daylight hours, with windows arranged to provide the required level of illumination of all portions of the means of egress during these hours, shall be exempt from emergency lighting requirements, where approved by the authority having jurisdiction.

11.4.2.10 Marking of Means of Egress. Locations not routinely inhabited by humans shall be exempt from marking of means of egress requirements.

11.4.3 Protection.

11.4.3.1 Protection of Vertical Openings. (No modifications.)

11.4.3.2 Protection from Hazards. Every water-surrounded structure, other than structures with only occasional occupancy, shall have automatic, manual, or other protection that is appropriate to the particular hazard and that is designed to minimize danger to occupants in case of fire or other emergency before they have time to use the means of egress.

11.4.3.3 Interior Finish. (No modifications.)

11.4.3.4 Detection, Alarm, and Communications Systems. (No modifications.)

11.4.3.5 Extinguishing Requirements. (No modifications.)

11.4.3.6 Corridors. (No modifications.)

Section 11.5* Piers

A.11.5 For further information on pier fire protection, see NFPA 307, *Standard for the Construction and Fire Protection of Marine Terminals, Piers, and Wharves.*

11.5.1 Application.

The provisions of Section 11.1 shall apply.

11.5.2 Number of Means of Egress.

Piers used exclusively to moor cargo vessels and to store material shall be exempt from number of means of egress requirements where provided with proper means of egress from structures thereon to the pier and a single means of access to the mainland, as appropriate with the pier's arrangement.

The intent of 11.5.2 is to recognize the open nature of a pier and to equate a pier with a public way for purposes of egress arrangement. Note that 11.5.2 applies mainly to cargo and storage piers, which are occupied by a limited number of people, the majority of whom are accustomed to the arrangement of piers. The risk to life safety is considered minimal under these conditions, and one exit is acceptable.

11.5.3 Arrangement of Means of Egress.

Piers not meeting the requirements of 11.5.2 and occupied for other than cargo handling and storage shall have means of egress arranged in accordance with Chapters 12 through 42. In addition, one of the following measures shall be provided on piers extending over 150 ft (45 m) from shore to minimize the possibility that fire under or on the pier might block the escape of occupants to shore:

(1) The pier shall be arranged to provide two separate ways to travel to shore, such as by two well-separated walkways or independent structures.
(2) The pier deck shall be open, fire resistive, and set on noncombustible supports.
(3) The pier shall be open, unobstructed, and not less than 50 ft (15 m) in width if less than 500 ft (150 m) long, or its width shall be not less than 10 percent of its length if more than 500 ft (150 m) long.
(4) The pier deck shall be provided with an approved automatic sprinkler system in accordance with Section 9.7 for combustible substructure and all superstructures; and, the sprinkler system shall be supervised if the applicable occupancy chapter requires supervision of sprinkler systems.

> The provisions of 11.5.3 apply to all pier structures, except those structures waived by 11.5.2. Note that these provisions must be applied in addition to those contained in Chapters 12 through 42 for piers that exceed 150 ft (45 m) in length. The provisions of 11.5.3(1) through (4) are not required to be applied in total; in other words, the pier is required to comply with only one of the four subparts.

Section 11.6* Vehicles and Vessels

A.11.6 Fire safety information for manufactured home parks is found in NFPA 501A, *Standard for Fire Safety Criteria for Manufactured Home Installations, Sites, and Communities.*

11.6.1 Vehicles.

Where immobile, attached to a building, or permanently fixed to a foundation, and where subject to human occupancy, the following vehicles shall comply with the requirements of this *Code* that are appropriate to buildings of similar occupancy:

(1) Trailers
(2) Railroad cars
(3) Streetcars
(4) Buses
(5) Conveyances similar to those in 11.6.1(1) through (4)

11.6.2 Vessels.

Any ship, barge, or other vessel permanently fixed to a foundation or mooring, or unable to get underway by means of its own power, and occupied for purposes other than navigation shall be subject to the requirements of this *Code* that apply to buildings of similar occupancy.

Section 11.7 Underground and Windowless Structures

11.7.1 Application.

The provisions of Section 11.1 shall apply.

11.7.2* Special Definitions.

Emergency Access Opening. See 3.3.54.

A.11.7.2 It is not the intent that emergency access openings be readily openable from the exterior by the public but that they can easily be opened with normal fire department equipment.

Underground Structure. See 3.3.205.

> The provision of emergency access openings for ventilation and rescue exempts stories below the level of exit discharge from classification as underground. In Exhibit 11.3, the basement is not considered to be underground if the following conditions apply:
>
> (1) Openings are provided on at least two sides
> (2) Openings are located entirely above the adjoining grade level
> (3) Openings comprise a minimum of 20 ft² (1.9 m²) per 50 lineal ft (15 lineal m) of walls

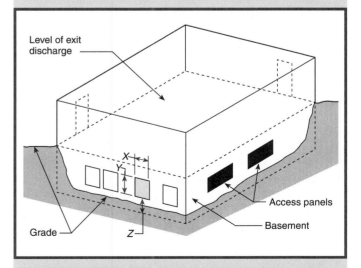

Exhibit 11.3 *Emergency access openings.*

(4) X = minimum width of 22 in. (55.9 cm) of unobstructed opening
Y = minimum height of 24 in. (60 cm) of unobstructed opening
Z = maximum of 44 in. (112 cm) from floor to bottom of opening
(5) Openings are readily identified
(6) Openings are readily openable

The annex text to 11.7.2 explains that access openings need not be readily opened from the exterior by the public. Rather, they need to be opened easily from the interior by building occupants.

Openings are permitted in the form of a window or an access panel.

Windowless Structure. See 3.3.212.

Note that a structure is not considered windowless if certain provisions are made for emergency access openings for ventilation and rescue. The provisions are more stringent for multistory structures than for single-story structures. See the commentary following A.11.7.2, which addresses the term *underground structure*.

11.7.3 Special Provisions for Structures That Are Windowless or Underground.

11.7.3.1   A structure or portion of a structure shall not be considered windowless under the following conditions:

(1) The structure is a one-story structure or portion thereof where the story is provided with grade level doors or emergency access openings on two sides of the building, spaced not more than 125 ft (38 m) apart in the exterior walls.
(2) The structure is a structure or portion thereof more than one story in height where the following criteria are met:
   a. Emergency access openings are provided on the first story as required by 11.7.3.1(1).
   b. Every story above the first floor is provided with emergency access openings on two sides of the building, spaced not more than 30 ft (9.1 m) apart.

11.7.3.2   A structure or portion of a structure shall not be considered an underground structure if the story is provided on not less than two sides with not less than 20 ft² (1.9 m²) of emergency access opening entirely above the adjoining grade level in each 50 lineal ft (15 lineal m) of exterior enclosing wall area.

11.7.3.3   Where windowless or underground structures have an occupant load of more than 50 persons in the win-

dowless or underground portions of the structure, the windowless or underground portions and all areas and floor levels traversed in traveling to the exit discharge shall be protected by an approved, supervised automatic sprinkler system in accordance with Section 9.7.

Exception No. 1:   This requirement shall not apply to existing windowless or underground structures with an occupant load of 100 or fewer persons in the windowless or underground portions of the structure.

Exception No. 2:   This requirement shall not apply to single-story windowless structures that are permitted to have a single exit per Chapters 12 through 42 and with a common path of travel not to exceed 50 ft (15 m).

11.7.3.4   Windowless or underground portions of structures and all areas traversed in traveling to the exit discharge, other than in one- and two-family dwellings, shall be provided with emergency lighting in accordance with Section 7.9.

11.7.4 Additional Provisions for Structures That Are Underground.

11.7.4.1   A structure or portion of a structure shall not be considered an underground structure if the story is provided on not less than two sides with not less than 20 ft² (1.9 m²) of emergency access opening entirely above the adjoining grade level in each 50 lineal ft (15 lineal m) of exterior enclosing wall area.

11.7.4.2   The requirements of 11.7.3 shall apply.

11.7.4.3   Exits from underground structures having an occupant load of more than 100 persons in the underground portions of the structure and having a floor used for human occupancy more than 30 ft (9.1 m) or more than one level below the lowest level of exit discharge shall be as follows:

(1) Exits shall be cut off from the level of exit discharge per 7.1.3.2.
(2) Exits shall be provided with outside smoke-venting facilities or other means to prevent the exits from becoming charged with smoke from any fire in the areas served by the exits.

11.7.4.4   The underground portions of an underground structure, other than an existing underground structure, shall be provided with approved automatic smoke venting in accordance with Section 9.3 where the underground structure has the following:

(1) An occupant load of more than 100 persons in the underground portions of the structure
(2) A floor level used for human occupancy more than 30 ft (9.1 m) or more than one level below the lowest level of exit discharge

(3) Combustible contents, combustible interior finish, or combustible construction

The provisions contained in 11.7.1 through 11.7.4.5 that regulate life safety in underground and windowless buildings are minimal and are considered to be in addition to those contained in Chapters 12 through 42. It is not the intent of these provisions to provide a means of circumventing the life safety provisions contained in other chapters of the *Code*. If the building under consideration is windowless or located underground and — due to its occupancy classification — subject to stricter requirements than those contained in Section 11.7, the stricter provisions of the *Code* must be applied. For example, the provisions of 12.4.3 — which apply to new assembly occupancies located in underground buildings or underground areas of buildings — require that each level located more than 30 ft (9.1 m) below the level of exit discharge be equipped with a mechanical means of moving occupants vertically, such as an elevator or escalator.

Windowless and underground structures pose special risks to life safety, because the buildings cannot be easily vented of products of combustion. In an area from which there is no direct access to the outside and where there are no windows to permit outside fire department rescue operations and ventilation, fire or smoke might tend to produce panic. Therefore, additional corrective measures, such as complete automatic sprinkler protection and automatic smoke-venting systems, must be provided where necessary to ensure an adequate level of life safety.

The provisions of 11.7.4.5 address the need for cues to guide occupants toward the exit and level of exit discharge. Traveling upward in an exit stair might appear illogical, because most egress from buildings involves downward travel within an exit stair enclosure. However, the direction of travel chosen by an occupant can depend on how the occupant entered the building. Paragraph 11.7.4.5 requires that a sign be provided within the exit stair enclosure to direct occupants to the exit discharge. The indicator must be of the same chevron design as required by 7.10.6.2 for directional exit signs.

11.7.4.5 Exit stair enclosures in underground structures having a floor level used for human occupancy more than 30 ft (9.1 m) or more than one level below the lowest level of exit discharge shall be provided with signage in accordance with 7.2.2.5.4 at each floor level landing tra-

versed in traveling to the exit discharge. The signs shall include a chevron-shaped indicator to show direction to the exit discharge.

Section 11.8 High-Rise Buildings

Section 11.8 does not itself require that any special provisions be applied to high-rise buildings. Instead, it provides a menu of options for high-rise buildings that can be wholly or partially mandated by other *Code* sections. For example, Chapters 12, 14, 16, 17, 18, 28, 30, and 38 (which apply to new assembly occupancies, new educational occupancies, new and existing day-care occupancies, new health care occupancies, new hotels and dormitories, new apartment buildings, and new business occupancies, respectively) require high-rise buildings to comply with the entire package of requirements contained in Section 11.8. Chapter 22 (which applies to new detention and correctional occupancies) requires high-rise buildings to comply with the provisions of 11.8.2 that cover extinguishment, which require sprinklers and standpipes. Chapters 15, 36, 40, and 42 (for existing educational occupancies, new mercantile occupancies, new industrial occupancies, and new storage occupancies, respectively) require that new high-rise buildings be sprinklered in accordance with 11.8.2.1.

Exhibit 11.4 illustrates the criteria under which a

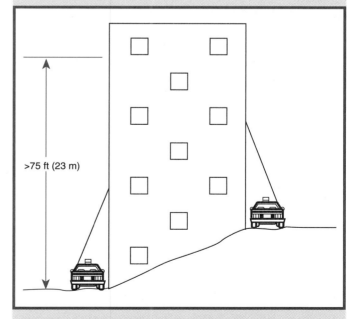

Exhibit 11.4 *Determining if building is high-rise in accordance with the 75-ft (23-m) criterion.*

building is classified as high-rise as specified by the definition of *high-rise building* in 3.3.101. Measurement of the 75-ft (23-m) vertical distance criterion begins at ground level on the lowest side of the building that provides fire department vehicle access. The height measurement ends at the floor of the highest occupiable story. If the vertical distance measurement made in this manner exceeds 75 ft (23 m), the building is considered to be high rise.

The 75-ft (23-m) criterion used for defining a high-rise building was first added to the 1988 edition of the *Code*. Prior to that time, individual occupancy chapters set their own criteria. Business and health care occupancies used provisions similar to the 75-ft (23-m) criterion, while residential occupancies used a six-story criterion. The current method establishes consistency for use throughout the *Code*. The current criteria have been accepted fairly well throughout the United States, but some local jurisdictions set a lower height at which high-rise building provisions apply. The definition does not include buildings less than 75 ft (23 m) in height. Buildings less than 75 ft (23 m), however, can experience the same challenges as true high-rise buildings, because they are set back over a larger one-story section out of reach of fire department ladders. Although the definition does not address the subject completely, it provides a generally acceptable method for determining whether a building is a high-rise building.

High-rise buildings pose several problems as follows:

(1) Potential for wide distribution of smoke to all floors due to significant stack effect (that is, natural draft) within stair towers and other tall shafts
(2) Difficulty in evacuation
(3) Difficulty experienced by fire service personnel in reaching the fire

11.8.1 General.

11.8.1.1   Where required by Chapters 12 through 42, the provisions of Section 11.8 shall apply to high-rise buildings as defined in 3.3.101.

11.8.1.2   In addition to the requirements of Section 11.8, compliance with all other applicable provisions of this *Code* shall be required.

11.8.2 Extinguishing Requirements.

11.8.2.1*   High-rise buildings shall be protected throughout by an approved, supervised automatic sprinkler system in accordance with Section 9.7. A sprinkler control valve and a waterflow device shall be provided for each floor.

A.11.8.2.1   Where an occupancy chapter (Chapter 12 through Chapter 42) permits the omission of sprinklers in specific spaces, such as small bathrooms and closets in residential occupancies, the building is still considered to be protected throughout for the purposes of 11.8.2.1.

11.8.2.2   High-rise buildings shall be protected throughout by a Class I standpipe system in accordance with Section 9.7.

The requirements of 11.8.2.2 expand the menu of provisions that can be mandated for high-rise buildings — in accordance with the various occupancy chapters — to include standpipes. Exhibit 11.5 is an example of a typical standpipe.

Exhibit 11.5 *Typical combination sprinkler/standpipe system with a 2½-in. (63.5 mm) fire department valve.*

Although the *Life Safety Code* has traditionally considered standpipes mainly as property protection devices, limited mandatory standpipe requirements for life safety purposes have been included for many editions of the *Code*. Standpipes are required on stages in assembly occupancies and in resident housing areas of detention and correctional occupancies (see 12.4.5.12, 13.4.5.12, 22.3.5.5, and 23.3.5.5). This requirement is based on the following:

(1) Occupants will not be able to leave the fire area immediately either due to the presence of large numbers of people, as is characteristic of an assembly occupancy, or because doors to the outside will not be unlocked, as might be expected in a detention and correctional occupancy.
(2) Trained persons will be present early in the fire development to make effective use of the standpipe and hose.

Standpipes in high-rise buildings can serve to increase life safety, as well as property protection, because of the lengthy evacuation times associated with tall buildings. In many cases, fire emergency plans advise occupants who are not in immediate danger of exposure to fire to remain within the building to allow responding fire service personnel better access to the standpipes within the exit stair enclosures. Use of standpipes at that time supplements the operation of the required automatic sprinkler system.

11.8.3 Detection, Alarm, and Communications Systems.

11.8.3.1* A fire alarm system using an approved, emergency voice/alarm communication system shall be installed in accordance with Section 9.6.

A.11.8.3.1 The need for voice communication can be based on a decision regarding staged or partial evacuation versus total evacuation of all floors. The determination of need is a function of occupancy classification and building height.

11.8.3.2 Two-way telephone communication service shall be provided for fire department use. This system shall be in accordance with NFPA 72, *National Fire Alarm Code*. The communications system shall operate between the central control station and every elevator car, every elevator lobby, and each floor level of exit stairs.

Exception: This requirement shall not apply where the fire department radio system is approved as an equivalent system.

11.8.4 Emergency Lighting and Standby Power.

11.8.4.1 Emergency lighting in accordance with Section 7.9 shall be provided.

11.8.4.2* Class 1, Type 60, standby power in accordance with NFPA 70, *National Electrical Code*, and NFPA 110, *Standard for Emergency and Standby Power Systems*, shall be provided. The standby power system shall have a capacity and rating sufficient to supply all required equipment. Selective load pickup and load shedding shall be permitted in accordance with NFPA 70, *National Electrical Code*. The standby power system shall be connected to the following:

(1) Emergency lighting system
(2) Fire alarm system
(3) Electric fire pump
(4) Central control station equipment and lighting
(5) Not less than one elevator serving all floors, with standby power transferable to any elevator
(6) Mechanical equipment for smokeproof enclosures
(7) Mechanical equipment required to conform with the requirements of Section 9.3

A.11.8.4.2 The Class 1, Type 60, standby power required by 11.8.4.2 is established in accordance with the provisions of Tables 2-2.2 and 2-2.3 of NFPA 110, *Standard for Emergency and Standby Power Systems*. The last class identification in Table 2-2.3 is for those emergency power systems that might have a different minimum running time requirement than those shown in the table. Therefore, it is the intent that the standby power required by 11.8.4.2 have an operation of not less than 1 hour running time before refueling is required.

11.8.5* Central Control Station.

A central control station shall be provided in a location approved by the fire department. The control station shall contain the following:

(1) Voice fire alarm system panels and controls
(2) Fire department two-way telephone communication service panels and controls where required by another section of this Code
(3) Fire detection and fire alarm system annunciation panels
(4) Elevator floor location and operation annunciators
(5) Sprinkler valve and waterflow annunciators
(6) Emergency generator status indicators
(7) Controls for any automatic stairway door unlocking system
(8) Fire pump status indicators
(9) A telephone for fire department use with controlled access to the public telephone system

A.11.8.5 It is not the intent of the paragraph to require any of the equipment in the list, other than the telephone for fire department use, but only to provide the controls, panels, annunciators, and similar equipment at this location if the equipment is provided or required by another section of the Code.

Section 11.9 Permanent Membrane Structures

The material in Section 11.9 was transferred into the *Code* from NFPA 102, *Standard for Grandstands, Folding and Telescopic Seating, Tents, and Membrane Structures,* so that all the provisions for life safety needed for a permanent membrane structure reside in NFPA *101.* Other material from NFPA 102 that is specific to assembly seating was moved to the assembly occupancy chapters — Chapters 12 and 13. The provisions applicable to permanent membrane structures were included in Chapter 11 because they can apply to any occupancy.

11.9.1 General.

11.9.1.1   The provisions of Section 11.1 shall apply.

11.9.1.2   Membrane materials shall not be used where fire resistance ratings are required for walls or roofs.

Exception No. 1:   Where every part of the roof, including the roof membrane, is not less than 20 ft (6.1 m) above any floor, balcony, or gallery, a noncombustible or limited-combustible membrane shall be permitted to be used as the roof in any type of construction.

Exception No. 2:   With approval of the authority having jurisdiction, membrane materials shall be permitted to be used where every part of the roof membrane is sufficiently above every significant fire potential that the imposed temperature cannot exceed the capability of the membrane, including seams, to maintain its structural integrity.

11.9.1.3   Testing of membrane materials for compliance with Section 11.9 use of the categories of noncombustible and limited-combustible materials shall be performed on weathered-membrane material as defined in 3.3.211.

11.9.1.4   Flame spread of all membrane materials exposed within the structure shall be Class A in accordance with Section 10.2.

11.9.1.5   Roof membranes shall have a roof covering classification, as required by the applicable building codes, when tested in accordance with NFPA 256, *Standard Methods of Fire Tests of Roof Coverings.*

11.9.1.6 Flame Resistance.

11.9.1.6.1   All membrane structure fabric shall be flame resistant in accordance with 10.3.1.

11.9.1.6.2   One of the following shall serve as evidence that the fabric materials have the required flame resistance:

(1) The authority having jurisdiction shall require a certificate or other evidence of acceptance by an organization acceptable to the authority having jurisdiction.
(2) The authority having jurisdiction shall require a report of tests made by other inspection authorities or organizations acceptable to the authority having jurisdiction.

11.9.1.6.3   Where required by the authority having jurisdiction, confirmatory field tests shall be conducted using test specimens from the original material, which shall have been affixed at the time of manufacture to the exterior of the structure.

11.9.2 Tensioned-Membrane Structures.

11.9.2.1   The design, materials, and construction of the building shall be based on plans and specifications prepared by a licensed architect or engineer knowledgeable in tensioned-membrane construction.

11.9.2.2   Material loads and strength shall be based on physical properties of the materials verified and certified by an approved testing laboratory.

11.9.2.3   The membrane roof for structures in climates subject to freezing temperatures and ice buildup shall be composed of two layers with an air space between them through which heated air can be moved to guard against ice accumulation. As an alternative to the two layers, other approved methods that protect against ice accumulation shall be permitted.

11.9.2.4   Roof drains shall be equipped with electrical elements to protect against ice buildup that can prevent the drains from functioning. Such heating elements shall be served by on-site standby electrical power in addition to the normal public service. As an alternative to such electrical elements, other approved methods that protect against ice accumulation shall be permitted.

11.9.3 Air-Supported, Air-Inflated Structures.

11.9.3.1 General. In addition to the general provisions of 11.9.1, the requirements of 11.9.3 shall apply to air-supported structures.

11.9.3.2 Pressurization (Inflation) System. The pressurization system shall consist of one or more operating blower units. The system shall include automatic control of auxiliary blower units to maintain the required operating pressure. This equipment shall meet the following requirements:

(1) Blowers shall be powered by continuous-rated motors at the maximum power required.
(2) Blowers shall have personnel protection, such as inlet screens and belt guards.
(3) Blower systems shall be weather protected.
(4) Blower systems shall be equipped with back-draft check dampers.
(5) There shall be not less than two blower units, each of which has capacity to maintain full inflation pressure with normal leakage.
(6) The blowers shall be designed to be incapable of over-pressurization.
(7) The auxiliary blower unit(s) shall operate automatically if there is any loss of internal pressure or if an operating blower unit becomes inoperative.
(8) The design inflation pressure and the capacity of each blower system shall be certified by a professional engineer.

11.9.3.3 Standby Power System.

11.9.3.3.1 A fully automatic standby power system shall be provided. The system shall be either an auxiliary engine generator set capable of running the blower system or a supplementary blower unit that is sized for 1 times the normal operating capacity and is powered by an internal combustion engine.

11.9.3.3.2 The standby power system shall be fully automatic to ensure continuous inflation in the event of any failure of the primary power. This system shall be capable of operating continuously for a minimum of 4 hours.

11.9.3.3.3 The sizing and capacity of the standby power system shall be certified by a professional engineer.

11.9.4 Maintenance and Operation.

11.9.4.1 Instructions in both operation and maintenance shall be transmitted to the owner by the manufacturer of the tensioned-membrane, air-supported, or air-inflated structure.

11.9.4.2 An annual inspection and required maintenance of each structure shall be performed to ensure safety conditions. At least biennially, the inspection shall be performed by a professional engineer, registered architect, or individual certified by the manufacturer.

11.9.5 Services.

11.9.5.1 Fired Heaters.

11.9.5.1.1 Only labeled heating devices shall be used.

11.9.5.1.2 Fuel-fired heaters and their installation shall be approved by the authority having jurisdiction.

11.9.5.1.3 Containers for liquefied petroleum gases shall be installed not less than 5 ft (1.5 m) from any temporary membrane structure and shall be in accordance with the provisions of NFPA 58, *Liquefied Petroleum Gas Code*.

11.9.5.1.4 Tanks shall be secured in the upright position and protected from vehicular traffic.

11.9.5.2 Electric Heaters.

11.9.5.2.1 Only labeled heaters shall be permitted.

11.9.5.2.2 Heaters shall be connected to electricity by electric cable that is suitable for outside use and is of sufficient size to handle the electrical load.

Section 11.10 Temporary Membrane Structures

The material in Section 11.10 was transferred into the *Code* from NFPA 102, *Standard for Grandstands, Folding and Telescopic Seating, Tents, and Membrane Structures*, so that all the provisions for life safety needed for a temporary membrane structure reside in NFPA *101*. Other material from NFPA 102 that is specific to assembly seating was moved to the assembly occupancy chapters — Chapters 12 and 13. The provisions applicable to temprary membrane structures were included in Chapter 11 because they can apply to any occupancy.

11.10.1 General.

11.10.1.1 The provisions of Section 11.1 shall apply.

11.10.1.2 Membrane structures designed to meet all the requirements of Section 11.10 shall be permitted to be used as temporary buildings subject to the approval of the authority having jurisdiction.

11.10.1.3 Temporary tensioned-membrane structures shall be permitted to comply with Section 11.11 instead of Section 11.10.

11.10.1.4   Roof membranes shall have a roof covering classification, as required by the applicable building codes, when tested in accordance with NFPA 256, *Standard Methods of Fire Tests of Roof Coverings.*

11.10.1.5 Flame Resistance.

11.10.1.5.1 All membrane structure fabric shall be flame resistant in accordance with 10.3.1.

11.10.1.5.2 One of the following shall serve as evidence that the fabric materials have the required flame resistance:

(1) The authority having jurisdiction shall require a certificate or other evidence of acceptance by an organization acceptable to the authority having jurisdiction.
(2) The authority having jurisdiction shall require a report of tests made by other inspection authorities or organizations acceptable to the authority having jurisdiction.

11.10.1.5.3 Where required by the authority having jurisdiction, confirmatory field tests shall be conducted using test specimens from the original material, which shall have been affixed at the time of manufacture to the exterior of the structure.

11.10.2 Fire Hazards.

11.10.2.1 The ground enclosed by any temporary membrane structure, and the ground for a reasonable distance but for not less than 10 ft (3 m) outside of such a structure(s), shall be cleared of all flammable or combustible material or vegetation. This work shall be accomplished to the satisfaction of the authority having jurisdiction prior to the erection of such a structure(s). The premises shall be kept free from such flammable or combustible materials during the period for which the premises are used by the public.

Exception: Removal of flammable or combustible material shall not apply to areas used for necessary support equipment.

11.10.2.2 Where prohibited by the authority having jurisdiction, smoking shall not be permitted in any temporary membrane structure.

11.10.3 Fire-Extinguishing Equipment.

Portable fire-extinguishing equipment of approved types shall be furnished and maintained in temporary membrane structures in such quantity and in such locations as directed by the authority having jurisdiction.

11.10.4 Tensioned-Membrane Structures.

11.10.4.1 The design, materials, and construction of the building shall be based on plans and specifications prepared by a licensed architect or engineer knowledgeable in tension-membrane construction.

11.10.4.2 Material loads and strength shall be based on physical properties of the materials verified and certified by an approved testing laboratory.

11.10.4.3 The membrane roof for structures in climates subject to freezing temperatures and ice buildup shall be composed of two layers with an air space between them through which heated air can be moved to guard against ice accumulation. As an alternative to the two layers, other approved methods that protect against ice accumulation shall be permitted.

11.10.4.4 Roof drains shall be equipped with electrical elements to protect against ice buildup that can prevent the drains from functioning. Such heating elements shall be served by on-site standby electrical power in addition to the normal public service. As an alternative to such electrical elements, other approved methods that protect against ice accumulation shall be permitted.

11.10.5 Air-Supported, Air-Inflated Structures.

11.10.5.1 General. In addition to the general provisions of 11.10.1, the requirements of 11.10.5 shall apply to air-supported structures.

11.10.5.2 Pressurization (Inflation) System. The pressurization system shall consist of one or more operating blower units. The system shall include automatic control of auxiliary blower units to maintain the required operating pressure. This equipment shall meet the following requirements:

(1) Blowers shall be powered by continuous-rated motors at the maximum power required.
(2) Blowers shall have personnel protection, such as inlet screens and belt guards.
(3) Blower systems shall be weather protected.
(4) Blower systems shall be equipped with back-draft check dampers.
(5) There shall be not less than two blower units, each of which has capacity to maintain full inflation pressure with normal leakage.
(6) The blowers shall be designed to be incapable of over-pressurization.
(7) The auxiliary blower unit(s) shall operate automatically if there is any loss of internal pressure or if an operating blower unit becomes inoperative.
(8) The design inflation pressure and the capacity of each blower system shall be certified by a professional engineer.

11.10.5.3 Standby Power System.

11.10.5.3.1 A fully automatic standby power system shall be provided. The system shall be either an auxiliary engine generator set capable of running the blower system or a supplementary blower unit that is sized for 1 times the normal operating capacity and is powered by an internal combustion engine.

11.10.5.3.2 The standby power system shall be fully automatic to ensure continuous inflation in the event of any failure of the primary power. This system shall be capable of operating continuously for a minimum of 4 hours.

11.10.5.3.3 The sizing and capacity of the standby power system shall be certified by a professional engineer.

11.10.6 Maintenance and Operation.

11.10.6.1 Instructions in both operation and maintenance shall be transmitted to the owner by the manufacturer of the tensioned-membrane, air-supported, or air-inflated structure.

11.10.6.2 An annual inspection and required maintenance of each structure shall be performed to ensure safety conditions. At least biennially, the inspection shall be performed by a professional engineer, registered architect, or individual certified by the manufacturer.

11.10.7 Services.

11.10.7.1 Fired Heaters.

11.10.7.1.1 Only labeled heating devices shall be used.

11.10.7.1.2 Fuel-fired heaters and their installation shall be approved by the authority having jurisdiction.

11.10.7.1.3 Containers for liquefied petroleum gases shall be installed not less than 5 ft (1.5 m) from any temporary membrane structure and shall be in accordance with the provisions of NFPA 58, *Liquefied Petroleum Gas Code*.

11.10.7.1.4 Tanks shall be secured in the upright position and protected from vehicular traffic.

11.10.7.2 Electric Heaters.

11.10.7.2.1 Only labeled heaters shall be permitted.

11.10.7.2.2 Heaters used inside a temporary membrane structure shall be approved.

11.10.7.2.3 Heaters shall be connected to electricity by electric cable that is suitable for outside use and is of sufficient size to handle the electrical load.

Section 11.11 Tents

The material in Section 11.11 was transferred into the *Code* from NFPA 102, *Standard for Grandstands, Folding and Telescopic Seating, Tents, and Membrane Structures*, so that all the provisions for life safety needed for a tent reside in NFPA *101*. Other material from NFPA 102 that is specific to assembly seating was moved to the assembly occupancy chapters — Chapters 12 and 13. The provisions applicable to tents were included in Chapter 11 because they can apply to any occupancy.

11.11.1 General.

11.11.1.1 The provisions of Section 11.1 shall apply.

11.11.1.2 Tents shall be permitted only on a temporary basis.

11.11.1.3 Tents shall be erected to cover not more than 75 percent of the premises, unless otherwise approved by the authority having jurisdiction.

11.11.2 Flame Resistance.

11.11.2.1 All tent fabric shall be flame resistant in accordance with 10.3.1.

11.11.2.2 One of the following shall serve as evidence that the tent fabric materials have the required flame resistance:

(1) The authority having jurisdiction shall require a certificate or other evidence of acceptance by an organization acceptable to the authority having jurisdiction.
(2) The authority having jurisdiction shall require a report of tests made by other inspection authorities or organizations acceptable to the authority having jurisdiction.

11.11.2.3 Where required by the authority having jurisdiction, confirmatory field tests shall be conducted using test specimens from the original material, which shall have been affixed at the time of manufacture to the exterior of the tent.

11.11.3 Location and Spacing.

11.11.3.1 There shall be a minimum of 10 ft (3 m) between stake lines.

11.11.3.2 Adjacent tents shall be spaced to provide an area to be used as a means of emergency egress. Where 10 ft (3 m) between stake lines does not meet the requirements for means of egress, the distance necessary for means of egress shall govern.

Exception No. 1: Tents not occupied by the public and not used for the storage of combustible material shall be permitted to be erected less than 10 ft (3 m) from other structures where the authority having jurisdiction deems such close spacing safe from hazard to the public.

Exception No. 2: Tents, each not exceeding 1200 ft² (111.5 m²) in ground area and located in fairgrounds or similar open spaces, shall not be required to be separated from each other, provided that safety precautions meet the approval of the authority having jurisdiction.

11.11.3.3 The placement of tents relative to other structures shall be at the discretion of the authority having jurisdiction, with consideration given to occupancy, use, opening, exposure, and other similar factors.

11.11.4 Fire Hazards.

11.11.4.1 The ground enclosed by any tent, and the ground for a reasonable distance but for not less than 10 ft (3 m) outside of such a tent(s), shall be cleared of all flammable or combustible material or vegetation. This work shall be accomplished to the satisfaction of the authority having jurisdiction prior to the erection of such a tent(s). The premises shall be kept free from such flammable or combustible materials during the period for which the premises are used by the public.

Exception: Removal of flammable or combustible material shall not apply to areas used for necessary support equipment.

11.11.4.2 Where prohibited by the authority having jurisdiction, smoking shall not be permitted in any tent.

11.11.5 Fire-Extinguishing Equipment.

Portable fire-extinguishing equipment of approved types shall be furnished and maintained in tents in such quantity and in such locations as directed by the authority having jurisdiction.

11.11.6 Services.

11.11.6.1 Fired Heaters.

11.11.6.1.1 Only labeled heating devices shall be used.

11.11.6.1.2 Fuel-fired heaters and their installation shall be approved by the authority having jurisdiction.

11.11.6.1.3 Containers for liquefied petroleum gases shall be installed not less than 5 ft (1.5 m) from any tent and shall be in accordance with the provisions of NFPA 58, *Liquefied Petroleum Gas Code.*

11.11.6.1.4 Tanks shall be secured in the upright position and protected from vehicular traffic.

11.11.6.2 Electric Heaters.

11.11.6.2.1 Only labeled heaters shall be permitted.

11.11.6.2.2 Heaters used inside a tent shall be approved.

11.11.6.2.3 Heaters shall be connected to electricity by electric cable that is suitable for outside use and is of sufficient size to handle the electrical load.

References Cited in Commentary

1. NFPA 102, *Standard for Grandstands, Folding and Telescopic Seating, Tents, and Membrane Structures,* 1995 edition, National Fire Protection Association, Quincy, MA.
2. NFPA 220, *Standard on Types of Building Construction,* 1999 edition, National Fire Protection Association, Quincy, MA.

New and Existing Assembly Occupancies

Chapters 12 and 13 are the first of the numerous occupancy chapters that address a specific building use. The occupancy chapters of the *Code* work together with the core chapters to implement the basic and fundamental requirements of the core chapters as appropriate to a specific use. The requirements for assembly occupancies are based on protecting concentrations of occupants in a building or area.

The occupant load factors (see Table 7.3.1.2) for assembly uses accurately reflect the large numbers of occupants in a given area that are characteristic of their use. Large numbers of occupants present unique challenges, such as arranging and designing the egress facilities to move the occupants efficiently and quickly. In addition, there are issues that must be balanced, such as sloping the floor to achieve line-of-sight for audience spectators (for example, in theater performances, sporting events, or concerts) without creating aisle stairs that are too steep to use effectively.

The level of life safety mandated by Chapters 12 and 13 addresses many conditions that are often taken for granted by the public. The exit access from occupant seating areas to aisles in a movie theater, for example, is regulated by Chapter 12/13. Even the arrangement of tables and chairs in a restaurant (see 12/13.2.5.7) is regulated in these chapters to provide a reasonable egress path if a fire occurs.

Sections 12/13.4 address special provisions and contain a series of specific and unique rules for assembly occupancies. The concept of smoke-protected assembly seating (see 12/13.4.2) is intended to provided a realistic egress capacity for an assembly occupancy that performs under fire conditions as if it were outdoors. This concept departs somewhat from the prescriptive rules usually imposed on an occupancy. The use of smoke-protected assembly seating, however, requires a life safety evaluation that addresses many aspects associated with the potential threat to the large number of occupants.

Other special subjects that are addressed in Sections 12/13.4 include stages and platforms (12/13.4.5), projection booths (12/13.4.6), and special amusement buildings (12/13.4.7).

Assembly occupancies include, but are not limited to, buildings or portions of buildings used for gatherings of 50 or more people for such purposes as deliberation, worship, entertainment, eating, drinking, amusement, or awaiting transportation. Assembly occupancies also include special amusement buildings (such as a fun house amusement structure) regardless of occupant load (see 12/13.4.7). Examples of assembly occupancies include the following if they have an occupant load of at least 50 persons:

(1) Armories
(2) Assembly halls
(3) Auditoriums
(4) Bowling establishments
(5) Churches
(6) Club rooms
(7) Conference rooms
(8) Courtrooms
(9) Dance halls
(10) Discotheques
(11) Drinking establishments
(12) Exposition halls
(13) Gymnasiums
(14) Libraries
(15) Mortuary chapels
(16) Motion picture theaters
(17) Multilevel play structures (regardless of occupant load)
(18) Museums

CHAPTER 12 • New	CHAPTER 13 • Existing

(19) Nightclubs
(20) Pool rooms
(21) Recreation piers
(22) Restaurants
(23) Skating rinks
(24) Theaters

Passenger stations and terminals of air, surface, underground, and marine public transportation facilities are also considered assembly occupancies. If the jurisdiction enforcing the *Code* has adopted NFPA 130, *Standard for Fixed Guideway Transit and Passenger Rail Systems*, requirements for transit stations might fall under NFPA 130 rather than this *Code*.[1] See NFPA 130 for additional details.

Also note that 14/15.1.1.2 requires university and college classrooms having a capacity of 50 or more persons to comply with the requirements of the assembly occupancy chapters.

Assembly occupancies with an occupant load of fewer than 50 persons (except for special amusement buildings) are considered incidental to the predominate occupancy in which they are located. For example, a small conference room in an office area is considered part of the overall business occupancy. A freestanding small diner with an occupant load of fewer than 50 persons is normally assigned a mercantile occupancy classification. Regardless of occupancy classification, the occupant load for areas of assembly use should be calculated based on the use of the space, not the occupancy classification, using the occupant load factors of Table 7.3.1.2.

Section 12.1 General Requirements

12.1.1 Application.

The requirements of this chapter apply to the following:

(1) New buildings or portions thereof used as an assembly occupancy (see 1.4.1)
(2) Additions made to, or used as, an assembly occupancy (see 4.6.6)
(3) Alterations, modernizations, or renovations of existing assembly occupancies (see 4.6.7)
(4) Existing buildings or portions thereof upon change of occupancy to an assembly occupancy (see 4.6.11)

Section 13.1 General Requirements

13.1.1 Application.

13.1.1.1 The requirements of this chapter apply to existing buildings or portions thereof currently occupied as assembly occupancies. *(See 3.3.15 for definition of assembly occupancy; see also 12.1.1.)*

Exception: An existing building housing an assembly occupancy established prior to the effective date of this Code shall be permitted to be approved for continued use if it conforms to or is made to conform to the provisions of this Code to the extent that, in the opinion of the authority having jurisdiction, reasonable life safety against the hazards of fire, explosion, and panic is provided and maintained.

13.1.1.2 Additions to existing buildings shall conform to the requirements for new construction. Existing portions of the structure shall not be required to be modified, provided that the new construction has not diminished the fire safety features of the facility.

Exception: Existing portions of buildings shall be upgraded if the addition results in an increase in the required minimum number of separate means of egress in accordance with 7.4.1.2.

13.1.1.3 An assembly occupancy in which an occupant load increase results in an increase in the required minimum number of separate means of egress, in accordance with 7.4.1.2, shall meet the requirements for new construction.

CHAPTER 12 • New	CHAPTER 13 • Existing

The provisions for new assembly occupancies are addressed in Chapter 12, and the provisions for existing assembly occupancies are addressed in Chapter 13.

If an existing building of some other occupancy were to have its classification changed to that of an assembly occupancy, that portion of the building housing the assembly occupancy must comply with Chapter 12 for new assembly occupancies, even though it is located in an existing building (see 4.6.11).

The provisions of 13.1.1.2 clarify that the *Code* mandates that additions to existing assembly occupancies meet the requirements for new construction (see 4.6.6). If construction of the addition causes the occupant load to increase to the point that 7.4.1.2 would require an increase in the required minimum number of separate means of egress, the existing por-

tion of the building must be modified to meet the requirements for new construction.

The provisions of 13.1.1.3 are similar to those of 13.1.1.2 in that, if the use of the space causes the occupant load to increase so that an increase in the required minimum number of separate means of egress is mandated by 7.4.1.2, the existing building must be modified to comply with the requirements of Chapter 12 for new assembly occupancies. Such compliance might be necessary because of renovation of an existing building or because a higher occupant load is granted by the authority having jurisdiction under the provisions of 7.3.1.3. For example, large dining tables might be replaced by small cocktail tables, permitting a larger occupant load even though the building size has not been increased.

12.1.2 Mixed Occupancies.

(See also 6.1.14.)

12.1.2.1* Any assembly occupancy and its access to exits in buildings of other occupancy, such as ballrooms in hotels, restaurants in stores, rooftop assembly occupancies, or assembly rooms in schools, shall be located, separated, or protected to avoid any undue danger to the occupants of the assembly occupancy from a fire originating in the other occupancy or smoke therefrom.

A.12.1.2.1 Depending on the character of construction and the hazard of the occupancy, compliance with this requirement will require physical separation by walls of appropriate fire resistance, protection of the other occupancy by automatic sprinklers, or other appropriate measures.

12.1.2.2 Occupancy of any room or space for assembly purposes by fewer than 50 persons in a building of other occupancy and incidental to such other occupancy shall be classified as part of the other occupancy and shall be subject to the provisions applicable thereto.

12.1.2.3 Assembly occupancies in buildings of other occupancy shall be permitted to use exits common to the assembly occupancy and the other occupancy, provided that the assembly area and the other occupancy considered separately each have exits sufficient to meet the requirements of this *Code*.

12.1.2.4* Exits shall be sufficient for simultaneous occupancy of both the assembly occupancy and other parts of the building, except where the authority having jurisdiction determines that the conditions are such that simultaneous occupancy will not occur.

13.1.2 Mixed Occupancies.

(See also 6.1.14.)

13.1.2.1* Any assembly occupancy and its access to exits in buildings of other occupancy, such as ballrooms in hotels, restaurants in stores, rooftop assembly occupancies, or assembly rooms in schools, shall be located, separated, or protected to avoid any undue danger to the occupants of the assembly occupancy from a fire originating in the other occupancy or smoke therefrom.

A.13.1.2.1 Depending on the character of construction and the hazard of the occupancy, compliance with this requirement will require physical separation by walls of appropriate fire resistance, protection of the other occupancy by automatic sprinklers, or other appropriate measures.

13.1.2.2 Occupancy of any room or space for assembly purposes by fewer than 50 persons in a building of other occupancy and incidental to such other occupancy shall be classified as part of the other occupancy and shall be subject to the provisions applicable thereto.

13.1.2.3 Assembly occupancies in buildings of other occupancy shall be permitted to use exits common to the assembly occupancy and the other occupancy, provided that the assembly area and the other occupancy considered separately each have exits sufficient to meet the requirements of this *Code*.

13.1.2.4* Exits shall be sufficient for simultaneous occupancy of both the assembly occupancy and other parts of the building, except where the authority having jurisdiction determines that the conditions are such that simultaneous occupancy will not occur.

A.12.1.2.4 *Example* An assembly room for the inmates of a detention occupancy will not normally be subject to simultaneous occupancy.

12.1.2.5 Assembly and Mercantile Occupancies in Covered Mall Buildings. The provisions of Chapter 12 shall apply to the assembly occupancy tenant space. The provisions of 36.4.4 shall be permitted to be used outside the assembly occupancy tenant space.

A.13.1.2.4 Example An assembly room for the inmates of a detention occupancy will not normally be subject to simultaneous occupancy.

13.1.2.5 Assembly and Mercantile Occupancies in Covered Mall Buildings. The provisions of Chapter 13 shall apply to the assembly occupancy tenant space. The provisions of 37.4.4 shall be permitted to be used outside the assembly occupancy tenant space.

The intent of 12/13.1.2.1 is to protect the occupants of the assembly occupancy from the effects of a fire originating in another occupancy. While this can be achieved by several methods, the following two considerations are to be taken into account, regardless of the method chosen:

(1) Protection of the means of egress of the assembly occupancy
(2) Level of protection from the other occupancy that can be provided to the assembly occupancy itself

Methods that can be used to protect the assembly occupancy and its means of egress include the following:

(1) Construction of fire-rated partitions
(2) Use of independent exits
(3) Installation of automatic sprinklers
(4) Careful analysis of the requirements of each occupancy when applying the provisions of 6.1.14 pertaining to mixed occupancies

Paragraph 12/13.1.2.2 recognizes that the minimum number of people assembled in one space for which the *Code* requires special provisions (such as requiring a door to swing in the direction of egress travel) is 50 (see 7.2.1.4.2). Therefore, the assembly of 50 persons constitutes a level of risk to life safety high enough to require classifying the occupancy as an assembly occupancy and, consequently, to subject the occupancy to the special requirements contained within Chapters 12 and 13.

In using the provisions of 12/13.1.2.3, note that, where an assembly occupancy shares egress systems with another occupancy, the provisions of 6.1.14 pertaining to mixed occupancies must also be considered. Those provisions require that, in mixed occupancies, the more restrictive requirements for any of the occupancies represented are to be applied to all the occupancies.

In 12/13.1.2.3 and 12/13.1.2.4, the *Code* requires

that each occupancy, considered separately, is to have sufficient exits. Also, where it is possible for simultaneous occupancy to occur, the exits must be sufficient for the combined occupant load.

The provision of 12/13.1.2.4 exempting exits from the simultaneous occupancy requirement should be used judiciously. All possible uses should be considered before it is judged that simultaneous occupancy will or will not occur. A school gymnasium might normally be used only by the school occupants; however, the gymnasium might be used by an outside group during school hours several times a year. A common example is the use of school gymnasiums as polling locations on election day. See Exhibit 12/13.1. A means of egress system sized to accommodate simultaneous occupancy provides maximum flexibility in the use of the building.

Paragraph 12/13.1.2.5 is new for the 2000 edition of the *Code*. It is common for covered mall buildings to include assembly occupancies in addition to mercantile and other occupancies. The assembly occupancies are required to comply with the requirements of Chapters 12 and 13 up to the point in the egress system at which the occupants reach the covered mall. The remainder of the egress path—which passes through the covered mall and exit discharge to the public way—is addressed in the mercantile occupancies chapters in the specialized covered mall building provisions of 36/37.4.4. Subsection 36/37.4.4 requires that egress from the covered mall be sufficient for an occupant load based on the gross leasable area of the overall covered mall building, not a calculation directly related to the area of only the covered mall (that is, the covered pedestrian way that connects the various stores and assembly areas). This calculation does not take into consideration the actual number of persons sent into the covered mall from the assembly occupancy. Yet, this method of calculating the occupant load is reliable. The concept is addressed in the commentary associated with 36/37.4.4.

Exhibit 12/13.1 *Use of school building for simultaneous mixed occupancy purposes.*

12.1.3* Special Definitions.

Aisle Accessway. See 3.3.6.

Exhibit. See 3.3.57.

Exhibitor. See 3.3.58.

Exposition. See 3.3.64.

Exposition Facility. See 3.3.65.

Festival Seating. See 3.3.68.

Flow Time. See 3.3.83.

Fly Gallery. See 3.3.84.

Gridiron. See 3.3.90.

Legitimate Stage. See 3.3.114.

Life Safety Evaluation. See 3.3.116.

Multilevel Play Structure. See 3.3.128.

Multipurpose Assembly Occupancy. See 3.3.129.

Pinrail. See 3.3.147.

Platform. See 3.3.149.

Proscenium Wall. See 3.3.156.

Regular Stage. See 3.3.161.

13.1.3* Special Definitions.

Aisle Accessway. See 3.3.6.

Exhibit. See 3.3.57.

Exhibitor. See 3.3.58.

Exposition. See 3.3.64.

Exposition Facility. See 3.3.65.

Festival Seating. See 3.3.68.

Flow Time. See 3.3.83.

Fly Gallery. See 3.3.84.

Gridiron. See 3.3.90.

Legitimate Stage. See 3.3.114.

Life Safety Evaluation. See 3.3.116.

Multilevel Play Structure. See 3.3.128.

Pinrail. See 3.3.147.

Platform. See 3.3.149.

Proscenium Wall. See 3.3.156.

Regular Stage. See 3.3.161.

Smoke-Protected Assembly Seating. See 3.3.187.
Special Amusement Building. See 3.3.188.
Stage. See 3.3.191.
Temporary Platform. See 3.3.198.

Smoke-Protected Assembly Seating. See 3.3.187.
Special Amusement Building. See 3.3.188.
Stage. See 3.3.191.
Temporary Platform. See 3.3.198.

The terms in 12/13.1.3 have special meanings with respect to assembly occupancies. For definitions of these terms, see Chapter 3. The commentary that follows addresses some of the terms.

The term *aisle accessway* is that part of the exit access (typically the row space occupied by one's legs and feet) located between where an occupant sits and an aisle. See 12/13.2.5.4 and 12/13.2.5.5.

The definitions of the terms *exhibit, exhibitor, exposition,* and *exposition facility* relate to the provisions in 12/13.7.4. The terms are consistent with terms used by the exposition industry.

Festival seating is addressed in 12/13.2.5.4.1.

The term *flow time* is used in the technical literature on egress and is important to understand in relation to the *Code*'s requirements for the capacity of means of egress. Flow time is the time taken by a crowd to pass, for example, through a doorway during group egress. In addition to the time taken to respond to an alarm before egress begins, and to travel the length of an egress route, flow time contributes to the total time needed to evacuate an area after an emergency is detected and an alarm is sounded. In the case of large assembly buildings, flow time is often the largest component of total evacuation time. Although none of the requirements of Chapters 12 and 13 of the *Code* specifically requires flow time to be used, the term is provided to help improve understanding of the nominal performance expected in complying with particular egress capacity requirements. See Table 12/13.2.3.2 and Table 12/13.4.2.3.

The term *life safety evaluation* is used in 12/13.1.7.3, Exception No. 2 to 12/13.2.5.4.1, 12/13.4.1, and 12/13.4.2.2. See A.12/13.4.1.3 in particular. A life safety evaluation addresses more than fire safety. A life safety evaluation considers all life safety hazards that could endanger occupants and require rapid egress or other measures to maintain occupant safety. For example, fire might not be the most likely hazard in some large assembly facilities. Injuries and deaths might result from the actions of a large number of people occupying a limited space during normal occupancy conditions, such as when spectators become especially enthusiastic during an event. A sudden change in weather at an outdoor facility or a partial structural collapse might cause occupants to attempt to escape an area. Such situations must be taken into account during a life safety evaluation. In some cases, special expertise will be required to assess, design, or manage social and behavioral factors, in addition to fire and structural safety considerations. In general, the life safety evaluation requires a comprehensive understanding of occupant characteristics, especially if densely crowded conditions exist.

Multilevel play structures have become commonplace. Some are entities unto themselves and draw patrons strictly because of the amusement offered. Others are operated in conjunction with some other business, such as the play structures attached to fast food restaurants. Multilevel play structures are considered special amusement buildings. Special amusement buildings are assembly occupancies, regardless of occupant load. See 6.1.2.1 and 12/13.4.7.

The term *multipurpose assembly occupancy* is synonymous with the term *multipurpose room* and is used in the provisions of Exception No. 2 to 12.3.5. Multipurpose assembly occupancies are often part of a school, office building, fellowship hall, or other occupancy.

The term *special amusement building* has application in the provisions of 12/13.4.7. Its definition addresses the structure and its use. The structure might be a permanent building or a semitrailer truck or other similar enclosure that is semipermanent or mobile. Special amusement buildings are designed to provide a full enclosure for patrons. Structures that are not fully enclosed (for example, a merry-go-round with a roof and no side walls) are not included in the definition. The definition also includes special amusement buildings within a larger structure, such as an amusement building within a shopping mall. Theaters, movie houses, or similar public assembly occupancies used for amusement or entertainment are not defined as special amusement buildings.

The terms *stage* and *platform* are defined so as to differentiate between the two. The definition of stage should be examined in conjunction with the definition of platform. The intent is to include nontheatrical

| CHAPTER 12 • New | CHAPTER 13 • Existing |

stages, such as those in many grade schools, under the definition of platform. The critical features in defining a stage are hanging curtains, leg drops, and scenery. Many school stages are actually regular stages because they use scenery. Hanging curtains commonly used on platforms are normally used to conceal lighting or to provide a more aesthetic appearance. An arrangement without hanging curtains,

leg drops, or scenery is most likely a platform. A potential problem is the arrangement commonly known as theater-in-the-round. For *Code*-application purposes, if a theater-in-the-round uses scenery, leg drops, or curtains suspended on or above it, it is considered a stage; if it uses only lighting with a valance to hide the electrical fixtures, it is a platform.

A.12.1.3 An understanding of the term *accessory room* might be useful to the enforcer of the *Code*, although the term is not used within the *Code*. An accessory room includes a dressing room, the property master's work and storage rooms, the carpenter's room, or similar rooms necessary for legitimate stage operations.

A.13.1.3 An understanding of the term assessory room might be useful to the enforcer of the *Code*, although the term is not used within the *Code*. An accessory room includes a dressing room, the property master's work and storage rooms, the carpenter's room, or similar rooms necessary for legitimate stage operations.

12.1.4* Classification of Occupancy.

(See 6.1.2.)

A.12.1.4 Assembly occupancy requirements should be determined on a room-by-room basis, a floor-by-floor basis, and a total building basis. The requirements for each room should be based on the occupant load of that room and the requirements for each floor should be based on the occupant load of that floor, but the requirements for the assembly building overall should be based on the total occupant load. Therefore, it is quite feasible to have several assembly occupancies with occupant loads of 300 or less grouped together in a single building. Such a building would be an assembly occupancy with an occupant load of over 1000.

13.1.4* Classification of Occupancy.

(See 6.1.2.)

A.13.1.4 Assembly occupancy requirements should be determined on a room-by-room basis, a floor-by-floor basis, and a total building basis. The requirements for each room should be based on the occupant load of that room and the requirements for each floor should be based on the occupant load of that floor, but the requirements for the assembly building overall should be based on the total occupant load. Therefore, it is quite feasible to have several assembly occupancies with occupant loads of 300 or less grouped together in a single building. Such a building would be an assembly occupancy with an occupant load of over 1000.

The 1994 edition of the *Code* was the last to subclassify assembly occupancies as Class A, Class B, or Class C. The subclassification scheme was based on the number of occupants and permitted requirements to be written for application to one or more of the subclasses. Since the 1997 edition of the *Code*, for example, different requirements apply to different

assembly occupancies with different occupant loads. Such requirements explicitly state the occupant load threshold at which the particular requirement becomes applicable. For example, see the minimum construction requirements in Table 12/13.1.6 that apply, for a given construction type and given floor elevation level, to occupant loads of 300 or 1000.

12.1.5 Classification of Hazard of Contents.

Contents of assembly occupancies shall be classified in accordance with the provisions of Section 6.2.

13.1.5 Classification of Hazard of Contents.

Contents of assembly occupancies shall be classified in accordance with the provisions of Section 6.2.

12.1.6 Minimum Construction Requirements.

The location of an assembly occupancy shall be limited as shown in Table 12.1.6. *(See 8.2.1.)*

13.1.6 Minimum Construction Requirements.

The location of an assembly occupancy shall be limited as shown in Table 13.1.6. *(See 8.2.1.)*

Table 12.1.6 Construction Type Limitations

Type of Construction	Below LED	LED	Number of Levels above LED			
			1	2	3	4
I(443)[†‡§] I(332)[†‡§] II(222)[†‡§]	Any assembly◊	Any assembly	Any assembly	Any assembly	Any assembly	Any assembly; If OL > 300◊
II(111)[†‡§]	Any assembly◊ Limited to 1 level below LED	Any assembly	Any assembly	Any assembly; If OL > 1000◊	Assembly with OL ≤ 1000◊	NP
III(211)[‡] IV(2HH) V(111)	Any assembly◊ Limited to 1 level below LED	Any assembly	Any assembly	Any assembly; If OL > 300◊	Assembly with OL ≤ 1000◊	NP
II(000)	Assembly with OL ≤ 1000◊ Limited to 1 level below LED	Any assembly; If OL > 1000◊	Assembly with OL ≤ 300◊	NP	NP	NP
III(200) V(000)	Assembly with OL ≤ 1000◊ Limited to 1 level below LED	Assembly with OL ≤ 1000	Assembly with OL ≤ 300◊	NP	NP	NP

NP: Not permitted.

LED: Level of exit discharge.

OL: Occupant load.

Note: For the purpose of this table, a mezzanine is not counted as a level.

[†]Where every part of the structural framework of roofs in Type I or Type II construction is 20 ft (6.1 m) or more above the floor immediately below, omission of all fire protection of the structural members shall be permitted, including protection of trusses, roof framing, decking, and portions of columns above 20 ft (6.1 m).

[‡]Where seating treads and risers serve as floors, such seating treads and risers shall be permitted to be of 1-hour fire resistance-rated construction. Structural members supporting seating treads and risers shall conform to the requirements of Table 12.1.6. Joints between seating tread and riser units shall be permitted to be unrated provided that such joints do not involve separation from areas containing high hazard contents and the facility is constructed and operated in accordance with 12.4.2.

[§]In open-air fixed seating facilities, including stadia, omission of fire protection of structural members exposed to the outside atmosphere shall be permitted where substantiated by an approved engineering analysis.

◊Permitted if all the following are protected throughout by an approved, supervised automatic sprinkler system in accordance with Section 9.7:
(1) The level of the assembly occupancy
(2) Any level below the level of the assembly occupancy
(3) In the case of an assembly occupancy located below the level of exit discharge, any level intervening between that level and the level of exit discharge, including the level of exit discharge

Exception No. 1:   This requirement shall not apply to outdoor grandstands of Type I or Type II construction.

Exception No. 2:   This requirement shall not apply to outdoor grandstands of Type III, Type IV, or Type V construction and in accordance with 12.4.8.

Exception No. 3:   This requirement shall not apply to grandstands of noncombustible construction supported by

Exception No. 1:   This requirement shall not apply to outdoor grandstands of Type I or Type II construction.

Exception No. 2:   This requirement shall not apply to outdoor grandstands of Type III, Type IV, or Type V construction and in accordance with 13.4.8.

Exception No. 3:   This requirement shall not apply to grandstands of noncombustible construction supported by

Table 13.1.6 Construction Type Limitations

Type of Construction	Below LED	LED	Number of Levels above LED			
			1	2	3	4
I(443)†‡ I(332)†‡ II(222)†‡	Any assembly§	Any assembly	Any assembly	Any assembly	Any assembly	Any assembly; If OL > 1000§
II(111)†‡	Any assembly§ Limited to 1 level below LED	Any assembly	Any assembly	Any assembly; If OL > 1000§	Assembly with OL ≤ 1000§	NP
III(211) IV(2HH) V(111)	Any assembly§ Limited to 1 level below LED	Any assembly	Any assembly	Any assembly; If OL > 300§	Assembly with OL ≤ 1000§	NP
II(000)	Assembly with OL ≤ 1000§ Limited to 1 level below LED	Any assembly; If OL > 1000§	Assembly with OL ≤ 300§	NP	NP	NP
III(200) V(000)	Assembly with OL ≤ 1000§ Limited to 1 level below LED	Any assembly; If OL > 1000§	Assembly with OL ≤ 300§	NP	NP	NP

NP: Not permitted.

LED: Level of exit discharge.

OL: Occupant load.

Note: For the purpose of this table, a mezzanine is not counted as a level.

†Where every part of the structural framework of roofs in Type I or Type II construction is 20 ft (6.1 m) or more above the floor immediately below, omission of all fire protection of the structural members shall be permitted, including protection of trusses, roof framing, decking, and portions of columns above 20 ft (6.1 m).

‡In open-air fixed seating facilities, including stadia, omission of fire protection of structural members exposed to the outside atmosphere shall be permitted where substantiated by an approved engineering analysis.

§Permitted if all the following are protected throughout by an approved, supervised automatic sprinkler system in accordance with Section 9.7:

(1) The level of the assembly occupancy

(2) Any level below the level of the assembly occupancy

(3) The level of the exit discharge if there are any openings between the level of exit discharge and the exits serving the assembly occupancy

the floor in a building meeting the construction requirements of Table 12.1.6.

Exception No. 4: This requirement shall not apply to assembly occupancies within covered mall buildings in accordance with 36.4.4.

Unlike other occupancy chapter construction tables, Tables 12.1.6 and 13.1.6 are based on levels above the level of exit discharge (LED). Thus, in a normal building with the level of exit discharge at grade, the column headed "1" under "Number of Levels above

the floor in a building meeting the construction requirements of Table 13.1.6.

Exception No. 4: This requirement shall not apply to assembly occupancies within covered mall buildings in accordance with 37.4.4.

LED" in Tables 12.1.6 and 13.1.6 refers to the second story of the building.

Based in part on the lessons learned from the Cocoanut Grove Night Club fire in Boston in 1942, the *Code* limits the number of persons in assembly occupancies located in buildings that are not of the highest fire-resistive construction types. The Cocoanut Grove fire illustrated the effect of a combustible structure, combustible interior finish materials, and a multilevel configuration on the severity of a fire and its death count. The Beverly Hills Supper Club fire in 1977 also illustrated these consequences.[2] See Exhibit 12/13.2.

Subsection 12/13.1.6 restricts the location of assembly occupancies. Construction Types I(443), I(332), and II(222) represent the most highly fire-resistive forms of construction. Their inherent structural stability under fire makes these construction types acceptable for any assembly occupancy. As the fire resistance of the structure diminishes from Type II(111) to Type V(000) construction, the location of assembly occupancies within the building and the permitted number of occupants are restricted. The construction types referenced in the table are based on NFPA 220, *Standard on Types of Building Construction*.[3] See 8.2.1 and Table A.8.2.1.

Note that Tables 12.1.6 and 13.1.6 address the location of the assembly occupancy in relation to the level of exit discharge. For example, if the building in question were a 5-story, Type II(111) building with the level of exit discharge at the first floor, an assembly occupancy with an occupant load in excess of 1000 persons would be permitted to be located on floors 1 through 3 but not on floors 4 and 5. Assembly occupancies with occupant loads of 1000 or fewer persons could be located on floors 1 through 4 but not on floor 5. In some cases (where a ◇ symbol in Table 12.1.6 or a § symbol in Table 13.1.6 appears beside an entry), automatic sprinkler protection is required on certain floors of the building. The extent of the required sprinkler protection is illustrated in Exhibit 12/13.3 for new construction and Exhibit 12/13.4 for an existing assembly occupancy building.

Exhibit 12/13.2 *Beverly Hills Supper Club.*

CHAPTER 12 • New   **CHAPTER 13 • Existing**

In Exhibit 12/13.3, in the building on the left, a new assembly occupancy with an occupant load greater than 300 persons is located on the fifth floor of an 8-story, Type II(222) building. Automatic sprinkler protection is required on the fifth story assembly occupancy floor and all floors below, including those below grade level. In the building on the right in Exhibit 12/13.3, the assembly occupancy is located in the subbasement, two levels below the level of exit discharge of an 8-story, Type II(222) building. Automatic sprinkler protection is required on the subbasement assembly occupancy floor, the basement level between the subbasement and the level of exit discharge, and the level of exit discharge.

In Exhibit 12/13.4, in the building on the left, an existing assembly occupancy with an occupant load greater than 1000 persons is located on the fifth floor of an 8-story, Type II(222) building. Automatic sprinkler protection is required on the fifth story assembly occupancy floor and all floors intervening between the fifth story and the level of exit discharge, including the level of exit discharge if any openings exist between the level of exit discharge and the enclosed exit stairs serving the assembly occupancy. In the building on the right in Exhibit 12/13.4, the assembly occupancy is located in the subbasement, two levels below the level of exit discharge of an 8-story, Type II(222) building. Automatic sprinkler protection is required on the subbasement assembly occupancy floor, the basement level between the subbasement and the level of exit discharge, and the level of exit discharge if any openings exist between the level of exit discharge and the enclosed exit stairs serving the assembly occupancy.

The two primary subsections that address automatic sprinkler protection that might be required in assembly occupancies are 12/13.1.6 and 12/13.3.5. Each of these subsections is to be applied independently of the other to determine whether automatic sprinkler protection is required. For example, an ex-

ception to 12.3.5 or 13.3.5.1 might exempt sprinklers, while the provisions of 12/13.1.6 might require sprinklers for an assembly occupancy with a given occupant load based on building construction type and location within the building. If one subsection requires sprinklers while the other does not, sprinklers are required to be provided.

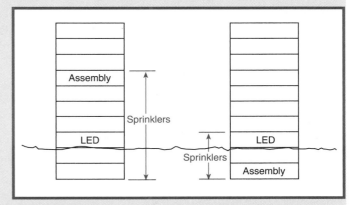

Exhibit 12/13.3 *New assembly occupancy building—extent of required sprinkler protection.*

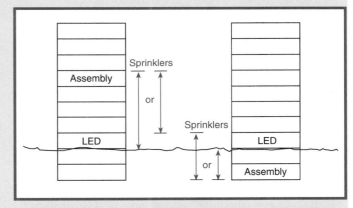

Exhibit 12/13.4 *Existing assembly occupancy building—extent of required sprinkler protection.*

12.1.7 Occupant Load.

12.1.7.1* The occupant load, in number of persons for whom means of egress and other provisions are required, shall be determined on the basis of the occupant load factors of Table 7.3.1.2 that are characteristic of the use of the space or shall be determined as the maximum probable population of the space under consideration, whichever is greater. In areas not in excess of 10,000 ft² (930 m²), the occupant load

13.1.7 Occupant Load.

13.1.7.1* The occupant load, in number of persons for whom means of egress and other provisions are required, shall be determined on the basis of the occupant load factors of Table 7.3.1.2 that are characteristic of the use of the space or shall be determined as the maximum probable population of the space under consideration, whichever is greater. In areas not in excess of 10,000 ft² (930 m²), the occupant load shall not exceed one person in 5 ft² (0.46 m²); in areas in excess of 10,000 ft² (930 m²), the occupant load shall not exceed one person in 7 ft² (0.65 m²).

A.12.1.7.1 The increase in occupant load above that calculated using occupant load factors from Table 7.3.1.2 is permitted if the provisions of 12.1.7.1 are followed. The owner or operator has the right to submit plans and to be permitted an increase in occupant load if the plans comply with the *Code*. The authority having jurisdiction is permitted to reject the plan for increase in occupant load if the plan is unrealistic, inaccurate, or otherwise does not properly reflect compliance with other *Code* requirements. It is not the intent of the provisions of 12.1.7.1 to prohibit an increase in occupant load solely on the basis of exceeding the limits calculated using occupant load factors from Table 7.3.1.2.

To assist in preventing serious overcrowding incidents in sports arenas, stadia, and similar occupancies, spectator standing room should not be permitted between the seating areas and the playing areas, except in horse race and dog track facilities.

Where a capacity or near-capacity audience is anticipated, all seating should be assigned with tickets showing the section, row, and seat number.

Where standing room is permitted, the capacity of the standing area should meet the following criteria:

(1) It should be determined on the basis of 5 ft² (0.46 m²) per person.
(2) It should have its capacity added to the seating capacity in determining egress requirements.
(3) It should be located to the rear of the seating area.
(4) It should be assigned standing-room-only tickets according to the area designated for the purpose.

The number of tickets sold or otherwise distributed should not exceed the aggregate number of seats plus the approved standing room numbers.

12.1.7.2 Waiting Spaces. In theaters and other assembly occupancies where persons are admitted to the building at

shall not exceed one person in 5 ft² (0.46 m²); in areas in excess of 10,000 ft² (930 m²), the occupant load shall not exceed one person in 7 ft² (0.65 m²).

Exception: The authority having jurisdiction shall be permitted to establish the occupant load as the number of persons for which the existing means of egress is adequate, provided that measures are established to prevent occupancy by a greater number of persons.

A.13.1.7.1 The increase in occupant load above that calculated using occupant load factors from Table 7.3.1.2 is permitted, if the provisions of 13.1.7.1 are followed. The owner or operator has the right to submit plans and to be permitted an increase in occupant load if the plans comply with the *Code*. The authority having jurisdiction is permitted to reject the plan for increase in occupant load if the plan is unrealistic, inaccurate, or otherwise does not properly reflect compliance with other *Code* requirements. It is not the intent of the provisions of 13.1.7.1 to prohibit an increase in occupant load solely on the basis of exceeding the limits calculated using occupant load factors from Table 7.3.1.2.

Existing auditorium and arena structures might not be designed for the added occupant load beyond the fixed seating. The authority having jurisdiction should consider exit access and aisles before permitting additional occupant load in areas using seating such as festival seating or movable seating on the auditorium or arena floor area.

To assist in preventing serious overcrowding incidents in sports arenas, stadia, and similar occupancies, spectator standing room should not be permitted between the seating areas and the playing areas, except in horse race and dog track facilities.

Where a capacity or near-capacity audience is anticipated, all seating should be assigned with tickets showing the section, row, and seat number.

Where standing room is permitted, the capacity of the standing area should meet the following criteria:

(1) It should be determined on the basis of 5 ft² (0.46 m²) per person.
(2) It should have its capacity added to the seating capacity in determining egress requirements.
(3) It should be located to the rear of the seating area.
(4) It should be assigned standing-room-only tickets according to the area designated for the purpose.

The number of tickets sold or otherwise distributed should not exceed the aggregate number of seats plus the approved standing room numbers.

13.1.7.2 Waiting Spaces. In theaters and other assembly occupancies where persons are admitted to the building at

CHAPTER 12 • New

CHAPTER 13 • Existing

times when seats are not available, or when the permitted occupant load has been reached based on 12.1.7.1 and persons are allowed to wait in a lobby or similar space until seats or space is available, such use of a lobby or similar space shall not encroach upon the required clear width of exits. The waiting spaces shall be restricted to areas other than the required means of egress. Exits shall be provided for the waiting spaces on the basis of one person for each 3 ft² (0.28 m²) of waiting space area. Such exits shall be in addition to the exits specified for the main auditorium area and shall conform in construction and arrangement to the general rules for exits given in this chapter.

12.1.7.3 Where the occupant load of an assembly occupancy exceeds 6000, a life safety evaluation shall be performed in accordance with 12.4.1.

Exception: Where approved by the authority having jurisdiction, the number of usually seated occupants provided with not less than 15 ft² (1.4 m²) of lawn surface in outdoor facilities shall be permitted to be excluded in determining the need for a life safety evaluation.

times when seats are not available, or when the permitted occupant load has been reached based on 13.1.7.1 and persons are allowed to wait in a lobby or similar space until seats or space is available, such use of a lobby or similar space shall not encroach upon the required clear width of exits. The waiting spaces shall be restricted to areas other than the required means of egress. Exits shall be provided for the waiting spaces on the basis of one person for each 3 ft² (0.28 m²) of waiting space area. Such exits shall be in addition to the exits specified for the main auditorium area and shall conform in construction and arrangement to the general rules for exits given in this chapter.

13.1.7.3 Where the occupant load of an assembly occupancy exceeds 6000, a life safety evaluation shall be performed in accordance with 13.4.1.

Exception: Where approved by the authority having jurisdiction, the number of usually seated occupants provided with not less than 15 ft² (1.4 m²) of lawn surface in outdoor facilities shall be permitted to be excluded in determining the need for a life safety evaluation.

The amount of material presented in 12/13.1.7 has been reduced for the 2000 edition of the *Code*, because all occupant load factors have been moved to Table 7.3.1.2 in the chapter addressing means of egress. Note that occupant load is calculated based on the use of the space, not on the occupancy classification. For example, a small conference room for approximately 30 persons located in a business occupancy doesn't have the requisite 50 persons to constitute an assembly occupancy. The occupancy classification is business, but the occupant load of the conference room is calculated using an occupant load factor from Table 7.3.1.2 for an assembly use, not a business use. Thus, the occupant load factors belong in Chapter 7 so that they can be employed based on the use of the space, regardless of the occupancy classification.

Note that 13.1.7.1 has an exception for existing assembly occupancies for which there is no counterpart in Chapter 12 for new assembly occupancies. The exception to 13.1.7.1 permits the authority having jurisdiction to ignore the calculated occupant load and establish the occupant load of an existing assembly occupancy as the number of persons for which the existing means of egress is adequate. The occupant load is to be posted and staff is to strictly enforce the posted occupant load. For example, the calculated occupant load—derived by dividing the available

floor area by the occupant load factors that represent the uses—might be 1110 persons. Yet, the existing egress system [for example, 3 door openings that are each 64 in. (163 cm) wide] might accommodate only 960 persons. If the authority having jurisdiction believes that the existing assembly occupancy itself can enforce an occupant load of not more than 960, then an occupant load of 960 can be established. Thus, a fourth exit with capacity for at least 150 persons does not have to be added. This is the only provision in the *Code* that permits the established occupant load to be less than the calculated occupant load. The exception was written to recognize that the occupant load factors characteristic of assembly uses are small—such as 7 ft² or 15 ft² (0.65 m² or 1.4 m²) compared to factors such as 100 ft² or 200 ft² (9.3 m² or 18.6 m²), which are characteristic of business and residential uses. These small occupant load factors result in large occupant loads for even modestly sized areas. Rather than forcing an existing assembly occupancy to unneccessarily upgrade its egress system, the existing system is permitted to serve, provided that the maximum number of persons present can be effectively regulated.

Numerous occupant load factors for assembly uses are presented in Table 7.3.1.2. The following commentary explains some of these factors.

One of the assembly use occupant load factors is for concentrated use at 7 net ft² (0.65 net m²) per person. The terminology *one person per 7 net ft² (0.65 net m²)* means that one person is assumed to be present for each 7 ft² (0.65 m²) that is available to be used by occupants after deducting space occupied by such items as permanently fixed counters, partitions, and columns.

The 7-ft² (0.65-m²) occupant load factor is based on open floor space with people standing comfortably. This factor also can be used to estimate occupant load in a multipurpose room where portable chairs are placed in rows for meetings, film viewing, or lectures.

The terminology *one person per 15 net ft² (1.4 net m²)* means that one person is assumed to be present for each 15 ft² (1.4 m²) that is available for use by occupants.

The 15-ft² (1.4-m²) occupant load factor is based on a use where a certain amount of space is occupied by furniture. An example is a space furnished with tables and chairs, as in restaurants or conference rooms.

The occupant load factor for kitchens has particular application to assembly uses, which are often characterized by food service and the resultant kitchen. This factor helps to clarify the method of calculating the total occupant load in restaurants and cafeterias where a portion of the building is used as a kitchen, whether it is a separate room or divided from the dining area by a serving counter. Note that the occupant load of the kitchen is calculated by using gross area. The 100 gross ft² (9.3 gross m²) factor takes into consideration the stoves, sinks, cutting boards, counters, and other culinary machinery necessary to operate a kitchen.

The 100 gross ft² (9.3 gross m²) associated with the occupant load factor for library stack areas takes into consideration the existence of bookshelves and permanent aisles. Reading rooms typically have large magazine racks, chairs, couches, and other furnishings that can require considerable space; an occupant load factor of 50 net ft² (4.6 net m²) is specified. Exhibit 12/13.5 illustrates a typical library reading room.

Swimming pools, pool decks, exercise rooms, skating rinks, and casino or gaming rooms are often parts of assembly occupancies. The occupant load factors are presented in Table 7.3.1.2 to help piece together a realistic occupant load for the entire assembly space.

Exhibit 12/13.5 Library reading rooms for which Code specifies an occupant load factor of 50 net ft² (4.6 net m²).

The occupant load factor for stages is provided because it is necessary to include the occupant load of a stage in the total occupant load. The occupant load factor allows for the occupant load of a stage to be calculated with consistency.

The occupant load factors characteristic of assembly uses reflect the data developed from surveys of typical assembly occupancies.

Consideration needs to be given to the actual use of a room or space. A multi-use room might have several occupant loads, with each load applicable to a specific arrangement and use. This situation is especially common in multipurpose rooms in schools and hotels.

Exhibit 12/13.6(a) illustrates a net 2500-ft² (net 232-m²) room with two 46-in. (117-cm) clear width doors. If the room were to be used as a banquet room with tables and chairs, its occupant load would be based on the 15-ft² (1.4-m²) per person factor. The occupant load calculation would divide the 2500 net ft² (232 net m²) by 15 ft² (1.4 m²) per person for an occupant load of 167 persons. However, if the room were to be used for a stand-up cocktail party with essentially no furniture, the occupant load would be based on the 7-ft² (0.65-m²) per person factor. The occupant load calculation would divide the 2500 net ft² (232 net m²) by 7 ft² (0.65 m²) per person for an occupant load of 357 persons. Thus, based on the two planned forms of assembly use, the room has two occupant loads.

CHAPTER 12 • New   **CHAPTER 13 • Existing**

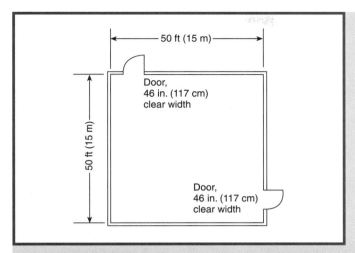

Exhibit 12/13.6(a) *Acceptable scenario where calculated occupant load is less than number of persons means of egress can safely accommodate.*

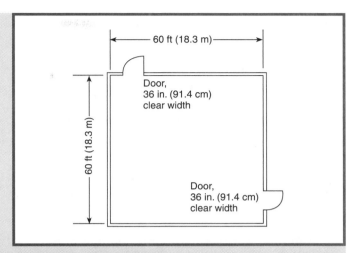

Exhibit 12/13.6(b) *Unacceptable scenario where calculated occupant load is larger than number of persons means of egress can safely accommodate.*

The egress capacity from the room is limited by the width available from the two 46-in. (117-cm) clear width doors. The egress capacity is calculated by dividing the 46-in. (117-cm) clear width by the 0.2 in. (0.5 cm) per person capacity factor for level travel, and multiplying by 2 because of the two identical doors. The calculation shows the room can accommodate 460 occupants. Because each of the occupant loads calculated is less than the egress capacity, the situation is satisfactory.

As noted in the previous two paragraphs, both egress capacity and occupant load must be considered in establishing the permissible occupant load for a room or area. Exhibit 12/13.6(b) illustrates a net 3600-ft² (net 334-m²) room with two 36-in. (91-cm) clear width doors. The egress capacity of the room is calculated by dividing the 36-in. (91-cm) clear width of the doors by the 0.2 in. (0.5 cm) per person capacity factor for level travel, and then multiplying by 2 because of the two identical doors. The calculation shows the room can accommodate 360 occupants. However, an occupant load calculated based on a room size of 3600 net ft² (334 net m²) and 7 ft² (0.65 m²) per person results in an occupant load of 514 persons. Therefore, for new assembly occupancies, the egress capacity must be increased to accommodate at least 514 persons in accordance with Section 7.3, which requires that egress capacity be provided for the

occupant load determined by application of the occupant load factor. For existing assembly occupancies, either of the following is required.

(a) The egress capacity must be increased to accommodate at least 514 persons. The increase is necessary for compliance with Section 7.3, which requires that egress capacity be provided for the occupant load determined by application of the occupant load factor.

(b) The occupant load can be set at 360 occupants—the number of persons for which the existing means of egress is adequate—in accordance with the exception to 13.1.7.1. Use of the exception requires specific approval by the authority having jurisdiction after it has been assured that measures are in place to prevent occupancy by more than 360 persons. This is explained in the introductory commentary on the occupant load provisions of 12/13.1.7.

Often a controversy exists regarding where to use a 7-ft² (0.65-m²) versus a 15-ft² (1.4-m²) occupant load factor. These factors are based on concentrated versus less concentrated use, and choices are based strictly on judgment. Because the occupant load is used in determining the required egress capacity and the construction, alarm, and sprinkler requirements, it is usually safer to provide features for the larger

CHAPTER 12 • New	**CHAPTER 13 • Existing**

occupant load than to try to enforce, usually with great difficulty, a smaller occupant load limit.

Accessibility to the exit access doors of a room is as important as the egress capacity from that room. Therefore, where an increase in occupant load is permitted over that established by 12/13.1.7.1, it must be demonstrated that adequate aisle accessways and aisles leading to the room exit access doors are provided. Where tables abut an aisle, the spacing must allow for chairs and aisles. Consideration should be given to the likelihood that, when occupants leave during an emergency, they might not take time to move chairs out of the aisles. See 12/13.2.5.7.2 and 12/13.2.5.8.3.

Dining and drinking areas make the most frequent use of the provisions of 7.3.1.3 for occupant load increases. There have been large banquet layouts where the occupant load was successfully increased to reflect an occupant load factor of 11 ft² (1 m²) per person instead of the 15 ft² (1.4 m²) per person specified by Table 7.3.1.2. In all cases where an increase in the occupant load is permitted, the authority having jurisdiction should insist on diagrams showing fixture and furniture layouts and should strictly enforce adherence to approved layouts. As noted previously, one room might have several approved occupant loads, depending on the various layouts.

Paragraph 12/13.1.7.1 limits the permitted increase in occupant load. The limits attempt to avoid overcrowding, which affects the movement characteristics of the occupants.

Research by the National Research Council in Canada and by the London Transport Board has shown that, if people are crowded into a space so that each person occupies less than 7 ft² (0.65 m²), movement approaches a shuffle; where each person occupies less than 3 ft² (0.28 m²), "jam point" is approached, and all movement by occupants comes to a virtual stop.

Although 12/13.1.7.1 limits occupant density to one person for each available 5 ft² (0.46 m²), 12/13.1.7.2

allows a density of one person per 3 ft² (0.28 m²) for specially designated waiting spaces. The waiting space cannot be located in, or interfere with, the egress routes from the rest of the assembly occupancy. As shown in Exhibit 12/13.7, such waiting spaces might be associated with a theater where patrons wait for one show to end and for the audience seating chamber to clear of people before those waiting can enter and take seats for the next performance. Similar waiting spaces might be established in an anteroom off the entrance foyer of a restaurant where diners await a table. Space at a bar where patrons gather to place a drink order does not qualify as a waiting space for purposes of the provisions of 12/13.1.7.2.

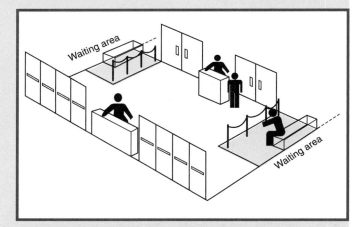

Exhibit 12/13.7 *Designated waiting spaces.*

The life safety evaluation required for large assembly occupancies by 12/13.1.7.3 recognizes that fixed protection and suppression systems alone do not ensure safe egress where large numbers of people are present. Expected crowd behavior is part of such an evaluation. Evaluations also include consideration of techniques to manage any behavioral problems. See 12/13.4.1 and, in particular, A.12/13.4.1.3.

Section 12.2 Means of Egress Requirements

12.2.1 General.

All means of egress shall be in accordance with Chapter 7 and Section 12.2.

Section 13.2 Means of Egress Requirements

13.2.1 General.

All means of egress shall be in accordance with Chapter 7 and Section 13.2.

CHAPTER 12 • New   **CHAPTER 13 • Existing**

12.2.2 Means of Egress Components.

12.2.2.1 Components of means of egress shall be limited to the types described in 12.2.2.2 through 12.2.2.12.

Paragraph 12/13.2.2.1 limits components within the required means of egress to those detailed in 12/13.2.2.2 through 12/13.2.2.12. Note that these paragraphs do not require that the component described must be used. Rather, if the component is used, the provisions of Chapter 7 that apply to the component, as modified by Chapters 12 and 13, must be followed.

The provisions of 12/13.2.2 do not recognize elevators, and, for new assembly occupancies, escalators are not recognized as part of the means of egress. Elevators are not suited for rapid evacuation of the large numbers of people found in these occupancies.

12.2.2.2 Doors.

12.2.2.2.1 Doors complying with 7.2.1 shall be permitted.

12.2.2.2.2 Assembly occupancies with occupant loads of 300 or less in covered malls *(see exception to 36.4.4.1)* shall be permitted to have horizontal or vertical security grilles or doors complying with Exception No. 2 to 7.2.1.4.1 on the main entrance/exits.

12.2.2.2.3 Panic Hardware or Fire Exit Hardware. Any door in a required means of egress from an area having an occupant load of 100 or more persons shall be permitted to be provided with a latch or lock only if the latch or lock is panic hardware or fire exit hardware complying with 7.2.1.7.

Exception No. 1: In assembly occupancies having an occupant load not greater than 500, where the main exit consists of a single door or single pair of doors, locking devices complying with Exception No. 2 to 7.2.1.5.1 shall be permitted to be used on the main exit. Any latching device on such a door(s) shall be released by panic hardware.

Exception No. 2: This requirement shall not apply to delayed-egress locks as permitted in 12.2.2.2.4.

Exception No. 3: This requirement shall not apply to access-controlled egress doors as permitted in 12.2.2.2.5.

12.2.2.2.4 Delayed-egress locks complying with 7.2.1.6.1 shall be permitted on doors other than main entrance/exit doors.

12.2.2.2.5 Doors in the means of egress shall be permitted to be equipped with an approved access control system com-

13.2.2 Means of Egress Components.

13.2.2.1 Components of means of egress shall be limited to the types described in 13.2.2.2 through 13.2.2.12.

Furthermore, elevators introduce other risk factors if used during a fire (see Section 9.4). Chapter 7 does not credit escalators that serve within the required means of egress in new construction. These devices can be installed (and they are often installed in assembly occupancies), but they cannot obstruct or interfere with the required means of egress. However, where a new assembly occupancies is located more than 30 ft (9.1 m) below the level of exit discharge, 12.4.3.3.2 requires a mechanical means of moving people vertically to the level of exit discharge. This requirement can be satisfied via an escalator or an elevator.

13.2.2.2 Doors.

13.2.2.2.1 Doors complying with 7.2.1 shall be permitted.

13.2.2.2.2 Assembly occupancies with occupant loads of 300 or less in covered malls *(see exception to 37.4.4.1)* shall be permitted to have horizontal or vertical security grilles or doors complying with Exception No. 2 to 7.2.1.4.1 on the main entrance/exits.

13.2.2.2.3 Panic Hardware or Fire Exit Hardware. Any door in a required means of egress from an area having an occupant load of 100 or more persons shall be permitted to be provided with a latch or lock only if the latch or lock is panic hardware or fire exit hardware complying with 7.2.1.7.

Exception No. 1: In assembly occupancies having an occupant load not greater than 600, where the main exit consists of a single door or single pair of doors, locking devices complying with Exception No. 2 to 7.2.1.5.1 shall be permitted to be used on the main exit. Any latching device on such a door(s) shall be released by panic hardware.

Exception No. 2: This requirement shall not apply to delayed-egress locks as permitted in 13.2.2.2.4.

Exception No. 3: This requirement shall not apply to access-controlled egress doors as permitted in 13.2.2.2.5.

13.2.2.2.4 Delayed-egress locks complying with 7.2.1.6.1 shall be permitted on doors other than main entrance/exit doors.

13.2.2.2.5 Doors in the means of egress shall be permitted to be equipped with an approved access control system com-

CHAPTER 12 • New	CHAPTER 13 • Existing

plying with 7.2.1.6.2. Doors shall not be locked from the egress side when the assembly occupancy is occupied. *(See 7.2.1.1.3.)*

12.2.2.2.6 Revolving doors complying with the requirements of 7.2.1.10 shall be permitted.

12.2.2.2.7 Turnstiles. No turnstiles or other devices that restrict the movement of persons shall be installed in any assembly occupancy in such a manner as to interfere with required means of egress facilities.

The provision of 12/13.2.2.2.2 allows, for example, small restaurants in covered mall buildings to use the security grilles or doors addressed by Exception No. 2 to 7.2.1.4.1.

Exception No. 1 to 12/13.2.2.2.3 recognizes the particular key-operated deadbolt lock described in Exception No. 2 to 7.2.1.5.1. Using a key-operated deadbolt lock in an assembly occupancy is permitted where all the conditions of Exception No. 2 to 7.2.1.5.1 and Exception No. 1 to 12/13.2.2.2.3 are met. The assembly occupancy is limited to an occupant load of not more than 500 persons (600 for existing assembly occupancies). Use is limited to the main exit based on the assumption that the lock will need to be released for the facility to operate. The main exit is limited to a single door or single pair of doors to ensure that the main exit will be unlocked whenever the building is occupied.

12.2.2.3 Stairs.

12.2.2.3.1 Stairs complying with 7.2.2 shall be permitted.

Exception No. 1:* Stairs serving seating that is designed to be repositioned shall not be required to comply with 7.2.2.3.1.

A.12.2.2.3.1 Exception No. 1 The seating plan and the means of egress should be reviewed each time the seating is substantially rearranged.

Exception No. 2: This requirement shall not apply to stages and platforms as permitted by 12.4.5.

12.2.2.3.2 Catwalk, Gallery, and Gridiron Stairs.

12.2.2.3.2.1 Noncombustible grated stair treads and landing floors shall be permitted in means of egress from lighting and access catwalks, galleries, and gridirons.

---

plying with 7.2.1.6.2. Doors shall not be locked from the egress side when the assembly occupancy is occupied. *(See 7.2.1.1.3.)*

13.2.2.2.6 Revolving doors complying with the requirements of 7.2.1.10 for new construction shall be permitted.

13.2.2.2.7 Turnstiles. No turnstiles or other devices that restrict the movement of persons shall be installed in any assembly occupancy in such a manner as to interfere with required means of egress facilities.

Although delayed-egress locks are addressed by Exception No. 2 to 12/13.2.2.2.3 as an exception to the requirement to provide panic hardware for doors that latch or lock, 12/13.2.2.2.4 further describes the allowance for delayed-egress locks. It allows delayed-egress hardware meeting the requirements of 7.2.1.6.1 to be used on all but the main exit. In addition to other requirements, 7.2.1.6.1 requires that the building be protected throughout by either an approved, supervised automatic sprinkler system or an approved, supervised automatic fire detection system.

Although access-controlled egress doors are permitted by Exception No. 3 to 12/13.2.2.2.3 to omit panic hardware for doors that latch or lock, 12/13.2.2.2.5 further describes the allowance for access-control door locking systems complying with 7.2.1.6.2.

13.2.2.3 Stairs.

13.2.2.3.1 Stairs complying with 7.2.2 shall be permitted.

Exception No. 1:* Stairs serving seating that is designed to be repositioned shall not be required to comply with 7.2.2.3.1.

A.13.2.2.3.1 Exception No. 1 The seating plan and the means of egress should be reviewed each time the seating is substantially rearranged.

Exception No. 2: This requirement shall not apply to stages and platforms as permitted by 13.4.5.

13.2.2.3.2 Catwalk, Gallery, and Gridiron Stairs.

13.2.2.3.2.1 Noncombustible grated stair treads and landing floors shall be permitted in means of egress from lighting and access catwalks, galleries, and gridirons.

| CHAPTER 12 • New | CHAPTER 13 • Existing |

12.2.2.3.2.2 Spiral stairs complying with 7.2.2.2.3 shall be permitted in means of egress from lighting and access catwalks, galleries, and gridirons.

13.2.2.3.2.2 Spiral stairs complying with 7.2.2.2.3 shall be permitted in means of egress from lighting and access catwalks, galleries, and gridirons.

Paragraph 7.2.2.3.1.1 requires that stairs within required means of egress be of permanent fixed construction. Exception No. 1 to 12/13.2.2.3.1 exempts stairs serving seating that is designed to be repositioned from the requirement of 7.2.2.3.1.1. In some

theaters, for example, entire seating sections are moved to accommodate the performance area requirements for a particular presentation. The stairs serving these movable seating sections cannot easily be of fixed permanent construction.

12.2.2.4 Smokeproof Enclosures. Smokeproof enclosures complying with 7.2.3 shall be permitted.

13.2.2.4 Smokeproof Enclosures. Smokeproof enclosures complying with 7.2.3 shall be permitted.

12.2.2.5 Horizontal Exits. Horizontal exits complying with 7.2.4 shall be permitted.

13.2.2.5 Horizontal Exits. Horizontal exits complying with 7.2.4 shall be permitted.

12.2.2.6 Ramps. Ramps complying with 7.2.5 shall be permitted.

13.2.2.6 Ramps. Ramps complying with 7.2.5 shall be permitted.

Exception: Ramps not part of an accessible means of egress and serving only stages or nonpublic areas and ramped aisles shall be permitted to have a slope not steeper than 1 in 8.

12.2.2.7 Exit Passageways. Exit passageways complying with 7.2.6 shall be permitted.

13.2.2.7 Exit Passageways. Exit passageways complying with 7.2.6 shall be permitted.

12.2.2.8   (Reserved.)

13.2.2.8 Escalators and Moving Walks. Escalators and moving walks complying with 7.2.7 shall be permitted.

12.2.2.9   (Reserved.)

13.2.2.9 Fire Escape Stairs. Fire escape stairs complying with 7.2.8 shall be permitted.

12.2.2.10 Fire Escape Ladders. Fire escape ladders complying with 7.2.9 shall be permitted.

13.2.2.10 Fire Escape Ladders. Fire escape ladders complying with 7.2.9 shall be permitted.

12.2.2.11 Alternating Tread Devices. Alternating tread devices complying with 7.2.11 shall be permitted.

13.2.2.11 Alternating Tread Devices. Alternating tread devices complying with 7.2.11 shall be permitted.

12.2.2.12 Areas of Refuge. Areas of refuge complying with 7.2.12 shall be permitted.

13.2.2.12 Areas of Refuge. Areas of refuge complying with 7.2.12 shall be permitted.

12.2.3 Capacity of Means of Egress.

13.2.3 Capacity of Means of Egress.

12.2.3.1   The capacity of means of egress shall be in accordance with Section 7.3 or shall be in accordance with 12.2.3.2 for means of egress serving theater-type seating or similar seating arranged in rows.

13.2.3.1   The capacity of means of egress shall be in accordance with Section 7.3 or shall be in accordance with 13.2.3.2 for means of egress serving theater-type seating or similar seating arranged in rows.

12.2.3.2   Minimum clear widths of aisles and other means of egress serving theater-type seating, or similar seating arranged in rows, shall be in accordance with Table 12.2.3.2.

13.2.3.2   Minimum clear widths of aisles and other means of egress serving theater-type seating, or similar seating arranged in rows, shall be in accordance with Table 13.2.3.2.

| CHAPTER 12 • New | CHAPTER 13 • Existing |

Table 12.2.3.2 Capacity Factors

| Number of Seats | Nominal Flow Time (sec) | Inch of Clear Width per Seat Served | |
		Stairs	Passageways, Ramps, and Doorways
Unlimited	200	0.300*AB*	0.220*C*

Note: For SI units, 1 in. = 2.54 cm.

Table 13.2.3.2 Capacity Factors

| Number of Seats | Nominal Flow Time (sec) | Inch of Clear Width per Seat Served | |
		Stairs	Passageways, Ramps, and Doorways
Unlimited	200	0.300*AB*	0.220*C*

Note: For SI units, 1 in. = 2.54 cm.

The minimum clear widths shown shall be modified in accordance with all of the following:

(1) If risers exceed 7 in. (17.8 cm) in height, multiply the stair width in Table 12.2.3.2 by factor *A,* where

$$A = 1 + \frac{(\text{riser height} - 7 \text{ in.})}{5}$$

(2) Stairs without a handrail located within a 30-in. (76-cm) horizontal distance shall be 25 percent wider than otherwise calculated, that is, multiply by factor *B* = 1.25.

(3) Ramps steeper than 1 in 10 slope where used in ascent shall have their widths increased by 10 percent, that is, multiply by factor *C* = 1.10.

Exception No. 1: This requirement shall not apply to lighting and access catwalks as permitted by 12.4.5.9.

Exception No. 2: This requirement shall not apply to grandstands and folding and telescopic seating as permitted by 12.4.8 and 12.4.9.

The minimum clear widths shown shall be modified in accordance with all of the following:

(1) If risers exceed 7 in. (17.8 cm) in height, multiply the stair width in Table 13.2.3.2 by factor *A,* where

$$A = 1 + \frac{(\text{riser height} - 7 \text{ in.})}{5}$$

(2) Stairs without a handrail located within a 30-in. (76-cm) horizontal distance shall be 25 percent wider than otherwise calculated, that is, multiply by factor *B* = 1.25.

(3) Ramps steeper than 1 in 10 slope where used in ascent shall have their widths increased by 10 percent, that is, multiply by factor *C* = 1.10.

Exception No. 1: This requirement shall not apply to lighting and access catwalks as permitted by 13.4.5.9.

Exception No. 2: This requirement shall not apply to grandstands and folding and telescopic seating as permitted by 13.4.8 and 13.4.9.

Paragraph 12/13.2.3.2 applies only to egress serving theater-type seating or similar seating arranged in rows. See 12/13.2.3.1. Further, Table 12/13.2.3.2 applies to assembly occupancies that are not smoke protected. If the assembly occupancy provides smoke-protected seating, refer to 12/13.4.2 and use the capacity factors of Table 12/13.4.2.3.

In using Table 12/13.2.3.2, the capacity factors might need to be adjusted using factors *A, B,* and *C.* Stair capacity is calculated at 0.3 in. (0.8 cm) per person only if the stair geometry and handrail details comply fully with the requirements of Chapter 7. If the stair riser height exceeds 7 in. (18 cm), the 0.3 in. (0.8 cm) per person factor must be multiplied by factor *A,* which is calculated using the formula in 12/13.2.3.2(1). If the stair does not have a handrail

within a 30-in. (76-cm) horizontal distance, the 0.3 in. (0.8 cm) per person factor must be multiplied by factor *B,* which equals 1.25. If both the riser geometry and handrail deviations occur, the 0.3 in. (0.8 cm) per person factor must be multiplied by both a factor *A* that is greater than 1.0 and a factor *B* of 1.25.

If the stair riser height does not exceed 7 in. (18 cm), factor *A* is still used but is to equal 1.0. Similarly, if the stair does have a handrail within a 30-in. (76-cm) horizontal distance, factor *B* is still used but is to equal 1.0.

For most occupancies, egress capacity involving horizontal travel is calculated at 0.2 in. (0.5 cm) per person. In Table 12/13.2.3.2, egress capacity within the audience seating chamber is penalized by 10 percent to 0.22 in. (0.55 cm) per person. Further, the presence of factor C indicates that additional modification of the capacity factor is necessary if the travel involves ascending a ramp with a slope steeper than 1 in 10. In such cases, the 0.22 in. (0.55 cm) per person capacity factor must be multiplied by a factor C of 1.10.

If the level does not involve ascending a ramp with a slope steeper than 1 in 10, factor C is still used but is to equal 1.0.

Capacity Factor Modification

The following comparative examples demonstrate modification of the capacity factors of 12/13.2.3.2. For simplification, SI (metric) units are not shown, and conversions can be made using 1 in. = 2.54 cm.

Example 1

An auditorium has 5000 seats. It is not smoke protected. One stair is 70 in. wide; riser height is 7 in.; handrails are positioned at each side; an additional handrail runs along the center of the aisle. One ramp is 44 in. wide and rises with a slope of 1 in 12 to the rear exit access door.

The capacity of the stair is determined using the 0.300AB formula from Table 12/13.2.3.2. Because the riser height does not exceed 7 in., factor A = 1.0. Because there is a handrail within a 30-in. horizontal distance, factor B = 1.0. Substituting gives

$$\text{Stair capacity} = \frac{70 \text{ in.}}{(0.300)(1.0)(1.0) \text{ in. per person}}$$
$$= 233 \text{ persons}$$

The capacity of the ramp is determined using the 0.220C formula from Table 12/13.2.3.2. Because the

slope does not exceed 1 in 10, factor C = 1.0. Substituting gives

$$\text{Ramp capacity} = \frac{44 \text{ in.}}{(0.22)(1.0) \text{ in. per person}}$$
$$= 200 \text{ persons}$$

Example 2

An auditorium has 5000 seats. It is not smoke protected. One stair is 70 in. wide; riser height is 7.5 in.; handrails are positioned at each side; there is no handrail along the center of the aisle. One ramp is 44 in. wide and rises with a slope of 1 in 9 to the rear exit access door.

The capacity of the stair is determined using the 0.300AB formula from Table 12/13.2.3.2. Because the riser height exceeds 7 in., factor A must be calculated using the formula in 12/13.2.3.2(1):

$$A = 1 + \frac{(7.5 - 7.0)}{5} = 1.1$$

Because there is not a handrail within a 30-in. horizontal distance, factor B = 1.25. Substituting,

$$\text{Stair capacity} = \frac{70 \text{ in.}}{(0.300)(1.1)(1.25) \text{ in. per person}}$$
$$= 170 \text{ persons}$$

The capacity of the ramp is determined using the 0.220C formula from Table 12/13.2.3.2. Because the ramp is used in ascent for egress and the slope exceeds 1 in 10, factor C = 1.10. Substituting,

$$\text{Ramp capacity} = \frac{44 \text{ in.}}{(0.22)(1.10) \text{ in. per person}}$$
$$= 182 \text{ persons}$$

12.2.3.3 Main Entrance/Exit. Every assembly occupancy shall be provided with a main entrance/exit. The main entrance/exit shall be of sufficient width to accommodate one-half of the total occupant load and shall be at the level of exit discharge or shall connect to a stairway or ramp leading to a street. Each level of an assembly occupancy shall have access to the main entrance/exit, and such access shall have sufficient capacity to accommodate 50 percent of the occupant load of such levels. Where the main entrance/exit from an assembly occupancy is through a lobby or foyer, the aggregate capacity of all exits from the lobby or foyer shall be permitted to provide the required capacity of the main entrance/exit, regardless of whether all such exits serve as entrances to the building.

13.2.3.3 Main Entrance/Exit. Every assembly occupancy shall be provided with a main entrance/exit. The main entrance/exit shall be of sufficient width to accommodate one-half of the total occupant load and shall be at the level of exit discharge or shall connect to a stairway or ramp leading to a street. Where the main entrance/exit from an assembly occupancy is through a lobby or foyer, the aggregate capacity of all exits from the lobby or foyer shall be permitted to provide the required capacity of the main entrance/exit, regardless of whether all such exits serve as entrances to the building.

CHAPTER 12 • New

Exception No. 1: A bowling establishment shall have a main entrance/exit of sufficient capacity to accommodate 50 percent of the total occupant load without regard to the number of aisles that it serves.

Exception No. 2:* In assembly occupancies where there is no well-defined main entrance/exit, exits shall be permitted to be distributed around the perimeter of the building, provided that the total exit width furnishes not less than 100 percent of the width needed to accommodate the permitted occupant load.

A.12.2.3.3 Exception No. 2 The original *Code* wording permitted certain exceptions such as sports arenas and railway stations. If an assembly occupancy is not similar to one of these occupancies, it is frequently rejected. A list of exceptions also raises the question as to why other occupancies are not included and necessitates additions to the list. For example, an exhibit hall of very large size might have several main entrances/exits. A theater extending the width of a block cannot really have a main entrance/exit in one confined location. A restaurant might have a main entrance serving the parking lot and another main entrance for those entering from the street. The authority having jurisdiction needs to determine where such arrangements are acceptable.

12.2.3.4 Other Exits. Each level of an assembly occupancy shall have access to the main entrance/exit and shall be provided with additional exits of sufficient width to accommodate not less than one-half of the total occupant load served by that level. Such exits shall discharge in accordance with 12.2.7. Such exits shall be located as far apart as practicable and as far from the main entrance/exit as practicable. The exits shall be accessible from a cross aisle or a side aisle. *(See 12.2.3.3.)*

Exception: In assembly occupancies where there is no well-defined main entrance/exit, exits shall be permitted to be distributed around the perimeter of the building, provided that the total exit width furnishes not less than 100 percent of the width required to accommodate the permitted occupant load.

12.2.3.5 The width of any exit access corridor serving 50 or more persons shall be not less than 44 in. (112 cm).

CHAPTER 13 • Existing

Exception No. 1: A bowling establishment shall have a main entrance/exit of sufficient capacity to accommodate 50 percent of the total occupant load without regard to the number of aisles that it serves.

Exception No. 2:* In assembly occupancies where there is no well-defined main entrance/exit, exits shall be permitted to be distributed around the perimeter of the building, provided that the total exit width furnishes not less than 100 percent of the width needed to accommodate the permitted occupant load.

A.13.2.3.3 Exception No. 2 The original *Code* wording permitted certain exceptions such as sports arenas and railway stations. If an assembly occupancy is not similar to one of these occupancies, it is frequently rejected. A list of exceptions also raises the question as to why other occupancies are not included and necessitates additions to the list. For example, an exhibit hall of very large size might have several main entrances/exits. A theater extending the width of a block cannot really have a main entrance/exit in one confined location. A restaurant might have a main entrance serving the parking lot and another main entrance for those entering from the street. The authority having jurisdiction needs to determine where such arrangements are acceptable.

13.2.3.4 Other Exits. Each level of an assembly occupancy shall have access to the main entrance/exit and shall be provided with additional exits of sufficient width to accommodate not less than one-half of the total occupant load served by that level. Such exits shall discharge in accordance with 13.2.7. Such exits shall be located as far apart as practicable and as far from the main entrance/exit as practicable. The exits shall be accessible from a cross aisle or a side aisle. *(See 13.2.3.3.)*

Exception: In assembly occupancies where there is no well-defined main entrance/exit, exits shall be permitted to be distributed around the perimeter of the building, provided that the total exit width furnishes not less than 100 percent of the width required to accommodate the permitted occupant load.

The intent of 12/13.2.3.3 is to require that 50 percent of the occupants are able to egress through the same door(s) they used to enter the building. The door through which an occupant enters a building is generally the door most familiar to the occupant. The occupant can be expected to attempt to use that door

for emergency egress. The term *main entrance/exit* clarifies that the *Code* intends the main entrance to a public assembly occupancy to be designated as the main exit.

Where the main entrance is through a lobby, a majority of the occupants can be expected to return to the lobby area during emergency egress. If the lobby has additional doors that are not used as entrance doors (for example, doors A and B in Exhibit 12/13.8), the occupants will be willing to use these doors, because they have reached the lobby with which they are familiar. Thus, the *Code* permits all the lobby doors to serve collectively as the required main exit. See Exhibit 12/13.8.

Exception No. 1 to 12/13.2.3.3, which addresses bowling establishments, is no longer applicable and needs to be deleted when the *Code* is revised. It applied in previous *Code* editions that required the main exit to be at least as wide as the aggregate width of all required aisles leading to the main exit. Bowling

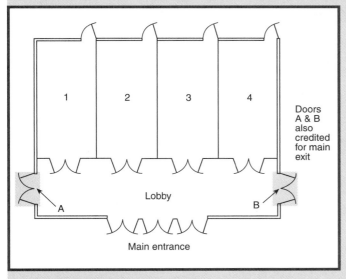

Exhibit 12/13.8 *Main entrance/exit.*

alleys have an unusually large number of aisles for functional purposes. The exception previously modified an excessive main exit width that was required to accommodate the sum of the required aisle widths served by the exit.

Exception No. 2 to 12/13.2.3.3 acknowledges that some assembly occupancy buildings have no well-defined main entrance exit. Occupants enter the building by doors in multiple walls. Under emergency egress, all occupants will not attempt to use the same doors, because some occupants are familiar with certain doors while others are familiar with other doors. In such cases, it is the intent that egress width be distributed among the various exits without any one exit being required to provide 50 percent of the egress capacity. See also 12/13.2.3.4.

A major change to the 1991 edition of the *Code* was the deletion of the requirement that exits other than the main exit must accommodate two-thirds of the occupant load, which resulted in a 16⅔ percent overdesign.

As an example of the requirements of 12/13.2.3.4, if an assembly occupancy has an occupant load of 900 persons, the main exit would have to accommodate 450 persons (50 percent). If, for compliance with 12/13.2.4 and Section 7.4, two additional exits were provided, together they would have to accommodate the remaining 450 persons.

The minimum 44-in. (112-cm) width for exit access corridors serving 50 or more persons—required by 12.2.3.5 in new assembly occupancies only—allows more than one file of persons to travel along the corridor simultaneously. The minimum width also permits persons capable of traveling at normal speed to pass persons who are slower, rather than queuing behind them.

12.2.4* Number of Exits.

A.12.2.4 It is not the intent to require four means of egress from each level of an assembly occupancy building having a total occupant load of more than 1000 where, individually, the floors have occupant loads of less than 1000.

12.2.4.1 The number of exits shall be in accordance with Section 7.4, other than exits for fenced outdoor assembly occupancies in accordance with 12.2.4.2.

13.2.4* Number of Exits.

A.13.2.4 It is not the intent to require four means of egress from each level of an assembly occupancy building having a total occupant load of more than 1000 where, individually, the floors have occupant loads of less than 1000.

13.2.4.1 The number of exits shall be in accordance with Section 7.4, other than fenced outdoor assembly occupancies in accordance with 13.2.4.2.

Exception: Assembly occupancies with occupant loads of 600 or fewer shall have two separate means of egress. As-

CHAPTER 12 • New

CHAPTER 13 • Existing

sembly occupancies with occupant loads greater than 600 but fewer than 1000 shall have three separate means of egress.

12.2.4.2 A fenced outdoor assembly occupancy shall have not less than two widely separated means of egress from the enclosure. If more than 6000 persons are to be served by such means of egress, there shall be not less than three means of egress; if more than 9000 persons are to be served, there shall be not less than four means of egress.

12.2.4.3 Balconies or mezzanines having an occupant load not exceeding 50 shall be permitted to be served by a single means of egress, and such means of egress shall be permitted to lead to the floor below.

12.2.4.4 Balconies or mezzanines having an occupant load exceeding 50 but not exceeding 100 shall have not less than two remote means of egress, but both such means of egress shall be permitted to lead to the floor below.

12.2.4.5 Balconies or mezzanines having an occupant load exceeding 100 shall have means of egress as described in 7.4.1.

12.2.4.6 A second means of egress shall not be required from lighting and access catwalks, galleries, and gridirons where a means of escape to a floor or a roof is provided. Ladders, alternating tread devices, or spiral stairs shall be permitted in such means of escape.

13.2.4.2 A fenced outdoor assembly occupancy shall have not less than two widely separated means of egress from the enclosure. If more than 6000 persons are to be served by such means of egress, there shall be not less than three means of egress; if more than 9000 persons are to be served, there shall be not less than four means of egress.

13.2.4.3 Balconies or mezzanines having an occupant load not exceeding 50 shall be permitted to be served by a single means of egress, and such means of egress shall be permitted to lead to the floor below.

13.2.4.4 Balconies or mezzanines having an occupant load exceeding 50 but not exceeding 100 shall have not less than two remote means of egress, but both such means of egress shall be permitted to lead to the floor below.

13.2.4.5 Balconies or mezzanines having an occupant load exceeding 100 shall have means of egress as described in 7.4.1.

13.2.4.6 A second means of egress shall not be required from lighting and access catwalks, galleries, and gridirons where a means of escape to a floor or a roof is provided. Ladders, alternating tread devices, or spiral stairs shall be permitted in such means of escape.

As the concentration or number of people in an assembly occupancy increases, the need for simultaneous egressing by a sizable group of occupants increases. Therefore, to reduce jamming at doorways (which might lead to panic and disorder), in accordance with the provisions of Section 7.4, more than two exits are needed for large occupant loads.

By permitting a single means of egress from a small balcony, in accordance with 12/13.2.4.3 relief is provided for balconies and mezzanines that do not accommodate more than 50 people, such as choir lofts. See also the exception to 12/13.2.5.1, which increases the permitted common path of travel to 75 ft (23 m) from an area with not more than 50 occupants.

The balconies addressed by 12/13.2.4.4 might typically be found in restaurants or small theaters. The provisions explain that it is important to have two remote means of egress, but, because the total number of occupants does not exceed 100, it is reasonable to allow occupants to egress onto the floor below.

Any balcony or mezzanine that can accommodate more than 100 people, as addressed by 12/13.2.4.5, should be treated as a separate floor with regard to the number of means of egress. Such treatment avoids overloading the means of egress on the floor below and provides mezzanine occupants with independent travel paths in case of fire on the floor below.

12.2.5 Arrangement of Means of Egress.

(See also Section 7.5.)

12.2.5.1 Exits shall be located remotely from each other and shall be arranged to minimize the possibility that they might be blocked by any emergency.

13.2.5 Arrangement of Means of Egress.

(See also Section 7.5.)

13.2.5.1 Exits shall be located remotely from each other and shall be arranged to minimize the possibility that they might be blocked by any emergency.

Exception: A common path of travel shall be permitted for the first 20 ft (6.1 m) from any point where serving any number of occupants and for the first 75 ft (23 m) from any point where serving not more than 50 occupants.

12.2.5.2   Means of egress shall not be permitted through kitchens, storerooms, restrooms, closets, or hazardous areas as described in 12.3.2.

12.2.5.3   Where the floor area of auditoriums and arenas is used for assembly occupancy activities/ events, not less than 50 percent of the occupant load shall have means of egress provided without passing through adjacent fixed seating areas.

Exception: A common path of travel shall be permitted for the first 20 ft (6.1 m) from any point where serving any number of occupants and for the first 75 ft (23 m) from any point where serving not more than 50 occupants.

13.2.5.2   Means of egress shall not be permitted through kitchens, storerooms, restrooms, closets, or hazardous areas as described in 13.3.2.

13.2.5.3   (Reserved.)

Remoteness of exits is an important concept addressed by Chapter 7. Two or more exits that are located too close to each other can quickly become unusable during the same fire. The fundamental principles of the *Code*, as expressed in Section 4.5, require remoteness of exits to the point that a single fire will not simultaneously block the required exits. This same concept of remoteness applies to exit access doors. The remoteness requirements of Section 7.5 and 12/13.2.5.1 must be met.

Revolving rooftop assembly occupancies require special consideration; as the structure revolves, exit signs are often lost from view. To provide an unobstructed panoramic view, the exterior ring-shaped floor area revolves around a small stationary interior core where the exits are often located. In many cases, the two exits are too close to each other to meet remoteness criteria. Usually, at least one stairway from the building core involves a horizontal passage on the floor below to transfer occupants from that stairway to the normal, remotely located exit stairways. This transfer, because it is a continuation of the stairway within the core, must be made via an exit passageway with a fire resistance rating equal to that required for the stair enclosure.

Although exit placement must meet the remoteness criteria of Section 7.5, it is not practical to require immediate access to two exits from every point in a building. Rather, occupants are permitted to be forced to travel in only one direction for a limited

distance before reaching a point where travel in more than one direction becomes possible. This limited travel in one direction is called *common path of travel* (see definition in 3.3.32). See the commentary associated with 7.5.1.6.

The exception to 12/13.2.5.1 establishes two allowable common path of travel limitations as follows:

(1) 20 ft (6.1 m) regardless of occupant load
(2) 75 ft (23 m) where serving not more than 50 persons

Additionally, 12/13.2.5.5.4 permits a 30-ft (9.1-m) common path of travel between a point within an aisle accessway and the aisle serving a seating row. Paragraph 12/13.4.2.6 permits a 50-ft (15-m) common path of travel in seating areas in smoke-protected assembly seating. Thus, the common paths of travel limitations are numerous for assembly occupancies.

The requirement of 12/13.2.5.2 clarifies that exit access travel is not permitted to pass through areas subject to locking or areas presenting a hazard level higher than that normally associated with an assembly occupancy.

The provision of 12.2.5.3 applies only to new assembly occupancies. It is intended to reduce the amount of merging and sharing of means of egress by persons in fixed seating areas and those who are forced to travel from the arena floor up into the seating sections to egress the building.

12.2.5.4 General Requirements for Access and Egress Routes Within Assembly Areas.

12.2.5.4.1 Festival seating shall be prohibited within a building. *(See definition in 3.3.68.)*

13.2.5.4 General Requirements for Access and Egress Routes Within Assembly Areas.

13.2.5.4.1 Festival seating shall be prohibited within a building. *(See definition in 3.3.68.)*

CHAPTER 12 • New

CHAPTER 13 • Existing

Exception No. 1: Festival seating shall be permitted in assembly occupancies having occupant loads of 1000 or less.

Exception No. 2: Festival seating shall be permitted in assembly occupancies where occupant loads exceed 1000 and where an approved life safety evaluation has been performed. (See 12.4.1.)

12.2.5.4.2* Access and egress routes shall be maintained so that any individual is able to move without undue hindrance, on personal initiative and at any time, from an occupied position to the exits.

A.12.2.5.4.2 This requirement and the associated requirement of 12.2.5.4.3 have the effect of prohibiting festival seating unless it truly is a form of seating, such as lawn seating, where generous spaces are commonly maintained between individuals and small groups so that people can circulate freely at any time. Such lawn seating will be characterized by densities of about one person per 15 ft² (1.4 m²). Both requirements prohibit uncontrolled crowd situations, such as in front of stages at rock music concerts where the number and density of people is uncontrolled by architectural or management features.

12.2.5.4.3* Access and egress routes shall be maintained so that crowd management, security, and emergency medical personnel are able to reach any individual at any time, without undue hindrance.

A.12.2.5.4.3 This requirement is intended to facilitate rapid emergency access to individuals who are experiencing a medical emergency, especially in the case of cardiopulmonary difficulties, where there is a need for rapid medical attention from trained personnel. The requirement also addresses the need for security and law enforcement personnel to reach individuals whose behavior is endangering themselves and others.

12.2.5.4.4* The width of aisle accessways and aisles shall provide sufficient egress capacity for the number of persons accommodated by the catchment area served by the aisle accessway or aisle in accordance with 12.2.3.1. Where aisle accessways or aisles converge to form a single path of egress travel, the required egress capacity of that path shall not be less than the combined required capacity of the converging aisle accessways and aisles.

A.12.2.5.4.4 The catchment area served by an aisle accessway or aisle is the portion of the total space that is naturally served by the aisle accessway or aisle. Hence, the requirement for combining the required capacity where paths

Exception No. 1: Festival seating shall be permitted in assembly occupancies having occupant loads of 1000 or less.

Exception No. 2: Festival seating shall be permitted in assembly occupancies where occupant loads exceed 1000 and where an approved life safety evaluation has been performed. (See 13.4.1.)

13.2.5.4.2* Access and egress routes shall be maintained so that any individual is able to move without undue hindrance, on personal initiative and at any time, from an occupied position to the exits.

A.13.2.5.4.2 This requirement and the associated requirement of 13.2.5.4.3 have the effect of prohibiting festival seating unless it truly is a form of seating, such as lawn seating, where generous spaces are commonly maintained between individuals and small groups so that people can circulate freely at any time. Such lawn seating will be characterized by densities of about one person per 15 ft² (1.4 m²). Both requirements prohibit uncontrolled crowd situations, such as in front of stages at rock music concerts where the number and density of people is uncontrolled by architectural or management features.

13.2.5.4.3* Access and egress routes shall be maintained so that crowd management, security, and emergency medical personnel are able to reach any individual at any time, without undue hindrance.

A.13.2.5.4.3 This requirement is intended to facilitate rapid emergency access to individuals who are experiencing a medical emergency, especially in the case of cardiopulmonary difficulties, where there is a need for rapid medical attention from trained personnel. The requirement also addresses the need for security and law enforcement personnel to reach individuals whose behavior is endangering themselves and others.

13.2.5.4.4* The width of aisle accessways and aisles shall provide sufficient egress capacity for the number of persons accommodated by the catchment area served by the aisle accessway or aisle in accordance with 13.2.3.1. Where aisle accessways or aisles converge to form a single path of egress travel, the required egress capacity of that path shall not be less than the combined required capacity of the converging aisle accessways and aisles.

A.13.2.5.4.4 The catchment area served by an aisle accessway or aisle is the portion of the total space that is naturally served by the aisle accessway or aisle. Hence, the requirement for combining the required capacity where paths converge is, in effect, a restatement of the idea of a catchment area. The establishment of catchment areas should be based on a balanced use of all means of egress, with the number of persons in proportion to egress capacity.

12.2.5.4.5 Those portions of aisle accessways and aisles where egress is possible in either of two directions shall be uniform in required width.

Exception: This requirement shall not apply to those portions of aisle accessways where the required width, not including the seat space described by 12.2.5.7.2, does not exceed 12 in. (30.5 cm).

12.2.5.4.6 In the case of side boundaries for aisle accessways or aisles, other than those for nonfixed seating at tables, the clear width shall be measured to boundary elements such as walls, guardrails, handrails, edges of seating, tables, and side edges of treads. The measurement shall be made horizontally to the vertical projection of the elements, resulting in the smallest width measured perpendicularly to the line of travel.

converge is, in effect, a restatement of the idea of a catchment area. The establishment of catchment areas should be based on a balanced use of all means of egress, with the number of persons in proportion to egress capacity.

13.2.5.4.5 Those portions of aisle accessways and aisles where egress is possible in either of two directions shall be uniform in required width.

Exception: This requirement shall not apply to those portions of aisle accessways where the required width, not including the seat space described by 13.2.5.7.2, does not exceed 12 in. (30.5 cm).

13.2.5.4.6 In the case of side boundaries for aisle accessways or aisles, other than those for nonfixed seating at tables, the clear width shall be measured to boundary elements such as walls, guardrails, handrails, edges of seating, tables, and side edges of treads. The measurement shall be made horizontally to the vertical projection of the elements, resulting in the smallest width measured perpendicularly to the line of travel.

Outdoor festival seating, as addressed in 12/13.2.5.4.1, is illustrated in Exhibit 12/13.9. This comfortable, low-density arrangement of people, which provides them with the ability to sit directly on the ground or floor and to move relatively easily through and out of the area, likely evolved from festivals held in open areas. Festival seating has been abused where applied to indoor or outdoor events where the assembled spectators are not controllable in terms of their numbers, location, or behavior. Rock music concerts are examples of events where the festival seating concept might become decidedly unfestive when unmanageable crowds of standing (not seated) people are positioned in front of the stage area and any maintained circulation routes through the assembled crowd are completely lost. Injuries caused by bodies crushing against bodies or portions of the structure are likely when this situation occurs.

A description of a typical crowd crush is found in a report titled "Observations of Crowd Conditions at Rock Concert in Exhibition Stadium, Toronto, 16 July 1980," by J. L. Pauls.[4] Because the number and arrangement of people in this instance were not controlled throughout the event, there were eventually some 30,000 to 40,000 people distributed unevenly in an area of about 125,000 ft² (10,600 m²). The result was an average density of about 1 person per 3.5 ft² (0.33 m²). However, due to localized crowding at the stage

area, several thousand people were at crushing densities of about 1 person per 2 ft² (0.19 m²). Both normal access and emergency access into this congested area were all but impossible, and management efforts to instruct people to move back toward less densely occupied areas proved futile. Incidents such as this led to the requirements of 12/13.2.5.4.1, which prohibits indoor festival seating for more than 1000

Exhibit 12/13.9 *Outdoor festival seating at a rock music concert held in a stadium. (Photograph courtesy of Jake Pauls.)*

persons unless an approved life safety evaluation is utilized.

In performance-oriented language, 12/13.2.5.4.2 prohibits the overcrowding and the blocking of aisles and other portions of the exit access. See the explanation in A.12/A.13.2.5.4.2.

In addition to providing life safety under fire conditions, the requirements of 12/13.2.5.4.3 address the emergency and nonemergency movement of people. Because of the potential for ingress and egress paths to become blocked by the large crowds characteristic of many assembly occupancies, it is important that crowd management, security, and emergency medical personnel are able to move to any individual without undue hindrance at any time. The ability to deal effectively with an emergency while the problem is small often precludes having to deal with a larger emergency later.

The width referenced in 12/13.2.5.4.4 refers to the egress capacity-driven width requirements of 12/13.2.3. The capacity-related width requirements must be considered along with the other minimum width requirements detailed in 12/13.2.5.6.3. The applicable minimum width requirement is the larger of the widths established by the two sets of requirements.

Exhibit 12/13.10 illustrates how catchment areas would be allotted in the case of a theater with four egress doors having approximately equal egress capacity. Note that catchment area apportionment for normal, nonemergency uses often will make use of only some of the available exit access paths and exits, particularly those provided by the main entrance/exit. This arrangement might be quite different from a catchment area apportionment based on a balanced distribution of people in proportion to the egress capacity of individual exits. Facility management procedures must allow for the difficulties of informing people of and directing them to all the available means of egress, especially when normally used, familiar routes become blocked in an emergency.

Note that the term *required egress capacity* is used in 12/13.2.5.4.4 to clarify that the combined required width of the egress routes might be smaller than their combined actual widths, especially where the

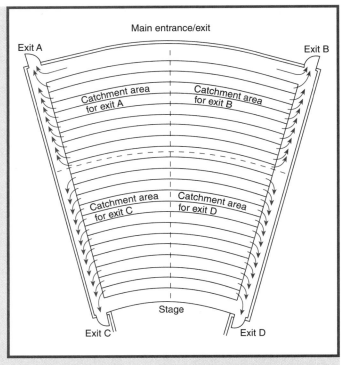

Exhibit 12/13.10 *Catchment areas based on balanced use of all means of egress in proportion to egress capacity.*

individual widths are wider than those applicable to egress capacity required by the *Code*. Widths that exceed *Code* minimums might be provided voluntarily to facilitate day-to-day operations.

The requirement of 12/13.2.5.4.5 prohibits any portion of the aisle or aisle accessway from being narrower than the minimum width required for any portion of the aisle or aisle accessway if egress travel is possible in two directions. Generally, this prohibits aisles and aisle accessways from being hourglass shaped. Where there are two directions of egress travel possible in the aisle or aisle accessway, the width must be at least as wide as the required width of any portion of the aisle or aisle accessway to accommodate efficient egress travel that might have to reverse direction because of blockage at one end of the aisle or aisle accessway.

12.2.5.5* Aisle Accessways Serving Seating Not at Tables.

A.12.2.5.5 For purposes of the means of egress requirements of this *Code*, tablet-arm chair seating is not considered

13.2.5.5* Aisle Accessways Serving Seating Not at Tables.

A.13.2.5.5 For purposes of the means of egress requirements of this *Code*, tablet-arm chair seating is not considered seating at tables. Dinner theater–style configurations are required to comply with the aisle accessway provisions applying to seating at tables and the aisle requirements of 12.2.5.6, if the aisles contain steps or are ramped. Generally, if aisles contain steps or are ramped, all of this *Code*'s requirements for aisles, stairs, and ramps are required to be met. *(Also see 7.1.7 and A.7.1.7.2.)*

12.2.5.5.1* To determine the required clear width of aisle accessways between rows of seating, horizontal measurements shall be made, between vertical planes, from the back of one seat to the front of the most forward projection of the seat immediately behind it. Where the entire row consists of automatic or self-rising seats that comply with ASTM F 851, *Test Method for Self-Rising Seat Mechanisms*, the measurement shall be permitted to be made with the seats in the up position.

A.12.2.5.5.1 Seats having reclining backs are assumed to be in their most upright position when unoccupied.

12.2.5.5.2 The aisle accessway between rows of seating shall have a clear width of not less than 12 in. (30.5 cm), and this minimum shall be increased as a function of row length in accordance with 12.2.5.5.3 and 12.2.5.5.4.

Exception No. 1: If used by not more than four persons, there shall be no minimum clear width requirement for the portion of the aisle accessway having a length not exceeding 6 ft (1.8 m), measured from the center of the seat farthest from the aisle.

Exception No. 2: The number of seats between the farthest seat and an aisle in grandstands, bleachers, and folding and telescopic seating shall not exceed that shown in Table 12.2.5.5.2.

Table 12.2.5.5.2 Maximum Number of Seats Between Farthest Seat and an Aisle

Application	Outdoors	Indoors
Grandstands	*11*	*6*
Bleachers	*20*	*9*
(see 12.2.5.6.1, Exception No. 1)		

seating at tables. Dinner theater–style configurations are required to comply with the aisle accessway provisions applying to seating at tables and the aisle requirements of 13.2.5.6, if the aisles contain steps or are ramped. Generally, if aisles contain steps or are ramped, all of this *Code*'s requirements for aisles, stairs, and ramps are required to be met. *(Also see 7.1.7 and A.7.1.7.2.)*

13.2.5.5.1* To determine the required clear width of aisle accesses between rows of seating, horizontal measurements shall be made, between vertical planes, from the back of one seat to the front of the most forward projection of the seat immediately behind it. Where the entire row consists of automatic or self-rising seats that comply with ASTM F 851, *Test Method for Self-Rising Seat Mechanisms*, the measurement shall be permitted to be made with the seats in the up position.

A.13.2.5.5.1 Seats having reclining backs are assumed to be in their most upright position when unoccupied.

13.2.5.5.2 The aisle accessway between rows of seating shall have a clear width of not less than 12 in. (30.5 cm), and this minimum shall be increased as a function of row length in accordance with 13.2.5.5.3 and 13.2.5.5.4.

Exception No. 1: If used by not more than four persons, there shall be no minimum clear width requirement for the portion of the aisle accessway having a length not exceeding 6 ft (1.8 m), measured from the center of the seat farthest from the aisle.

Exception No. 2: The number of seats between the farthest seat and an aisle in grandstands, bleachers, and folding and telescopic seating shall not exceed that shown in Table 13.2.5.5.2.

Table 13.2.5.5.2 Maximum Number of Seats Between Farthest Seat and an Aisle

Application	Outdoors	Indoors
Grandstands	*11*	*6*
Bleachers	*20*	*9*
(see 13.2.5.6.1, Exception No. 1)		

The method for measuring the width of an aisle accessway formed by rows of chairs is illustrated in Exhibit 12/13.11. In illustration (a) in Exhibit 12/13.11, the seats are not self-rising. In illustration (b), the seats are self-rising.

Aisle accessway is defined in 3.3.6 as the initial portion of an exit access that leads to an aisle. Exhibit 12/13.12 illustrates the aisle accessways formed by rows of chairs. The space between each row of chairs is an aisle accessway. An aisle accessway serves as

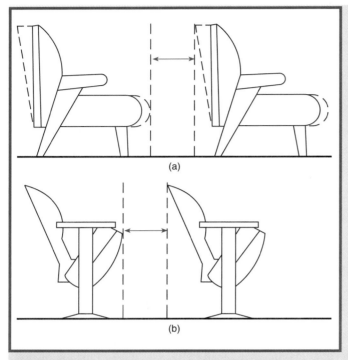

Exhibit 12/13.11 *Measurement of width of aisle accessway formed by rows of chairs.*

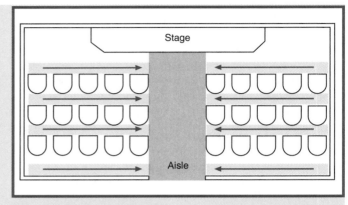

Exhibit 12/13.12 *Aisle accessways.*

the initial portion of the exit access and leads to an aisle as shown by the arrows. Similar aisle accessways might be formed by rows of tables and chairs.

12.2.5.5.3* Rows of seating served by aisles or doorways at both ends shall not exceed 100 seats per row. The 12-in. (30.5-cm) minimum clear width of aisle accessway between such rows shall be increased by 0.3 in. (0.8 cm) for every seat over a total of 14 but shall not be required to exceed 22 in. (55.9 cm).

Exception: This requirement shall not apply to smoke-protected assembly seating as permitted by 12.4.2.4.

A.12.2.5.5.3 The system known as continental seating has one pair of egress doors provided for every five rows that is located close to the ends of the rows. In previous editions of the *Code,* such egress doors were required to provide a clear width of not less than 66 in. (168 cm) discharging into a foyer, into a lobby, or to the exterior of the building. This continental seating arrangement can result in egress flow times (that is, with nominal flow times of approximately 100 seconds, rather than 200 seconds) that are approximately one-half as long as those resulting where side aisles lead to more remote doors. Such superior egress flow time perfor-

13.2.5.5.3* Rows of seating served by aisles or doorways at both ends shall not exceed 100 seats per row. The 12-in. (30.5-cm) minimum clear width of aisle accessway between such rows shall be increased by 0.3 in. (0.8 cm) for every seat over a total of 14 but shall not be required to exceed 22 in. (55.9 cm).

Exception: This requirement shall not apply to smoke-protected assembly seating as permitted by 13.4.2.4.

A.13.2.5.5.3 The system known as continental seating has one pair of egress doors provided for every five rows that is located close to the ends of the rows. In previous editions of the *Code,* such egress doors were required to provide a clear width of not less than 66 in. (168 cm) discharging into a foyer, into a lobby, or to the exterior of the building. This continental seating arrangement can result in egress flow times (that is, with nominal flow times of approximately 100 seconds rather than 200 seconds) that are approximately one-half as long as those resulting where side aisles lead to more remote doors. Such superior egress flow time perfor-

CHAPTER 12 • New   **CHAPTER 13 • Existing**

mance is desirable in some situations; however, special attention should be given either to a comparably good egress capacity for other parts of the egress system or to sufficient space to accommodate queuing outside the seating space.

12.2.5.5.4 Rows of seating served by an aisle or doorway at one end only shall have a path of travel not exceeding 30 ft (9.1 m) in length from any seat to an aisle. The 12-in. (30.5-cm) minimum clear width of aisle accessway between such rows shall be increased by 0.6 in. (1.6 cm) for every seat over a total of seven.

Exception: This requirement shall not apply to smoke-protected assembly seating as permitted by 12.4.2.5 and 12.4.2.6.

12.2.5.5.5 Rows of seating using tablet-arm chairs shall be permitted only if the clear width of aisle accessways complies with the requirements of 12.2.5.6 where the tablet is in the usable position.

Exception: Tablet arms shall be permitted to be measured in the stored position where the tablet arm automatically returns to the stored position when raised manually to a vertical position in one motion and falls to the stored position by force of gravity.

12.2.5.5.6 The depth of seat boards shall not be less than 9 in. (23 cm) where the same level is not used for both seat boards and footboards. Footboards, independent of seats, shall be provided so that there is no horizontal opening that allows the passage of a ½-in. (1.3-cm) diameter sphere.

mance is desirable in some situations; however, special attention should be given either to a comparably good egress capacity for other parts of the egress system or to sufficient space to accommodate queuing outside the seating space.

13.2.5.5.4 Rows of seating served by an aisle or doorway at one end only shall have a path of travel not exceeding 30 ft (9.1 m) in length from any seat to an aisle. The 12-in. (30.5-cm) minimum clear width of aisle accessway between such rows shall be increased by 0.6 in. (1.6 cm) for every seat over a total of seven.

Exception: This requirement shall not apply to smoke-protected assembly seating as permitted by 13.4.2.5 and 13.4.2.6.

13.2.5.5.5 Rows of seating using tablet-arm chairs shall be permitted only if the clear width of aisle accessways complies with the requirements of 13.2.5.6 where the tablet is in the usable position.

Exception: Tablet arms shall be permitted to be measured in the stored position where the tablet arm automatically returns to the stored position when raised manually to a vertical position in one motion and falls to the stored position by force of gravity.

13.2.5.5.6 The depth of seat boards shall not be less than 9 in. (23 cm) where the same level is not used for both seat boards and footboards. Footboards, independent of seats, shall be provided so that there is no horizontal opening that allows the passage of a ½-in. (1.3-cm) diameter sphere.

The annex to 12/13.2.5.5.3 relates the expected egress flow time performance of continental seating, as addressed by the *Code* prior to 1988, to the egress flow time performance of the more flexible, newer requirements for egress width related to capacity (see 12/13.4.2.3). See Exhibit 12/13.13(a) for an example of continental seating. In prior editions of the *Code*, where there were more than 14 seats in a row, this arrangement was required. One hundred seats was the maximum number permitted for one row.

Currently, the *Code* permits design flexibility, based on the continental seating principle of variable minimum spacing for rows of seats and row length, using the provisions of 12/13.2.5.5.3. As reference points for each end of the spacing range, the newer requirement uses the previous 12 in. (30.5 cm) of clearance for rows up to 14 seats in length and 22 in.

(55.9 cm) for rows over 45 seats in length. For example, under the newer requirement, rows with 47 seats require a clearance of 21.9 in. (55.6 cm). This clearance is calculated by subtracting 14 from 47 and multiplying the result, 33, by 0.3 in. (0.8 cm) to obtain 9.9 in. (25.1 cm), which is added to the 12-in. (30.5-cm) minimum aisle accessway width to obtain the total required clear aisle accessway width of 21.9 in. (55.6 cm). Because the aisle accessway width is not required to exceed 22 in. (55.9 cm), seating rows with 48 to 100 seats require 22 in. (55.9 cm) of clear aisle accessway width.

The newer flexibility, which applies to all seating arranged in rows, is based on the assumption that the egress time required for a seating arrangement will be influenced more by the capacity of routes downstream from the rows of seating than by the rows' clear widths. Subsection 12/13.2.3 provides a standardized method for calculating the widths of those routes serving the space containing the seating. The combination of 12/13.2.3 and 12/13.2.5.5 offers designers of theaters, in particular, a great deal of flexibility in laying out blocks of seating while still requiring a standard of egress flow time performance that is based on traditionally accepted egress performance. Traditional performance, nominally about 200 seconds of flow time, is achieved through the application of specific requirements on aisle and cross aisle design. For example, rows longer than 14 seats are permitted, and egress door locations can be more flexibly determined than permitted under the continental seating rules contained in previous *Code* editions.

Exhibit 12/13.13(b) illustrates the seating layout for a theater with 630 seats in one unbroken area, with 21 rows ranging uniformly in length from 20 seats per row at row 1 to 40 seats per row at row 21. The required minimum aisle accessway clear width between the front row (with 20 seats) and the row behind it (with 21 seats) is 14.1 in. (35.8 cm). The required minimum aisle accessway clear width between the back row (with 40 seats) and the row in front of it (with 39 seats) is 19.8 in. (50.3 cm). The designer has the option of making the clear widths of all aisle accessways uniform and at least 19.8 in. (50.3 cm) wide or progressively increasing them from front to back, from at least 14.1 in. (35.8 cm) to at least 19.8 in. (50.3 cm), as the number of seats per row increases.

For the theater shown in Exhibit 12/13.13(b), the option of a traditional layout can be used. The traditional arrangement is a maximum of 14 seats per row for rows served by aisles at both ends and a maximum of 7 seats per row where the row is served by an aisle at only one end and abuts the wall at the other end. This layout would require that more space be devoted to aisles and cross aisles, but this lost space might be partly offset by the minimum 12-in. (30.5-cm) aisle accessway clear width permitted of such rows of seating.

In a seating row served by an aisle at one end only, the occupant of the seat farthest from the aisle must be able to reach the aisle with not more than 30 ft (9.1 m) of aisle accessway travel in accordance with 12/13.2.5.5.4. Exhibit 12/13.14 illustrates a seating row served by an aisle at one end only, where upon reaching the aisle it is not immediately possible to

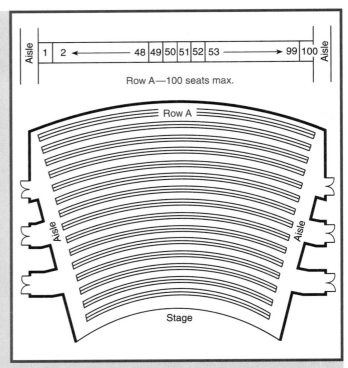

Exhibit 12/13.13(a) *Arrangement of seats and aisles with continental seating.*

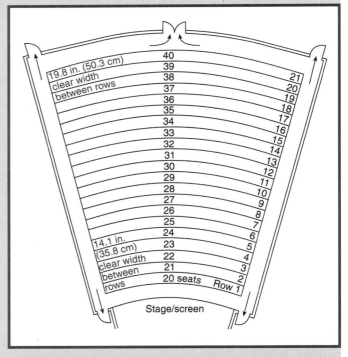

Exhibit 12/13.13(b) *Minimum aisle accessway clear widths.*

CHAPTER 12 • New

CHAPTER 13 • Existing

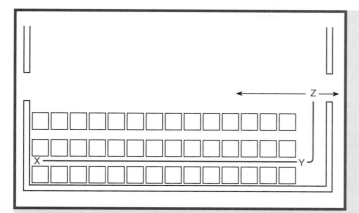

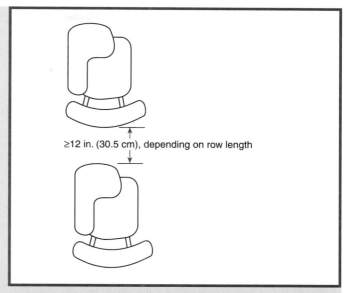

≥12 in. (30.5 cm), depending on row length

Exhibit 12/13.14 Maximum 30-ft (9.1-m) aisle accessway length (point X to point Y) for seating row served by aisle at one end only.

Exhibit 12/13.15 Minimum spacing between rows of seats with fixed tablet arms.

move in either of two egress directions because of the obstruction to egress created by the rear wall of the room. The aisle accessway (point X to point Y) cannot exceed 30 ft (9.1 m). However, upon reaching the aisle, the common path of travel measurement does not end; it continues to point Z, which is the first point at which travel in two independent directions becomes possible. Per the exception to 12/13.2.5.1, the common path of travel (point X to point Z) is permitted to be 75 ft (23 m), because the area served does not exceed 50 persons (in this case, 42 occupants, based on three rows of seats with 14 seats per row).

Tablet-arm chairs with features for storing the tablet arms present little threat to life safety. Where the tablet arm is fixed in the use position, tablet-arm

chairs must be arranged to meet the row spacing requirements of 12/13.2.5.5. Exhibit 12/13.15 illustrates this provision. Measurement is made with the tablet arm in the up (in-use) position. The clear space between the back of a seat and the leading edge of the tablet arm of a chair located behind that seat varies, depending on row length, in accordance with the requirements of 12/13.2.5.5. However, the clear space cannot be less than 12 in. (30.5 cm). The exception to 12/13.2.5.5.5 addresses tablet-arm chairs with self-storing tablet arms.

12.2.5.6 Aisles Serving Seating Not at Tables.

12.2.5.6.1 Aisles shall be provided so that the number of seats served by the nearest aisle is in accordance with 12.2.5.5.2 through 12.2.5.5.4.

Exception No. 1: *Aisles shall not be required in bleachers, provided that all of the following conditions are met.*

(a) Egress from the front row shall not be obstructed by a rail, a guard, or other obstruction.

(b) The row spacing shall be 28 in. (71.1 cm) or less.

(c) The rise per row, including the first row, shall be 6 in. (15.2 cm) or less.

13.2.5.6 Aisles Serving Seating Not at Tables.

13.2.5.6.1 Aisles shall be provided so that the number of seats served by the nearest aisle is in accordance with 13.2.5.5.2 through 13.2.5.5.4.

Exception No. 1: *Aisles shall not be required in bleachers, provided that all of the following conditions are met.*

(a) Egress from the front row shall not be obstructed by a rail, a guard, or other obstruction.

(b) The row spacing shall be 28 in. (71.1 cm) or less.

(c) The rise per row, including the first row, shall be 6 in. (15.2 cm) or less.

CHAPTER 12 • New

CHAPTER 13 • Existing

(d) The number of rows shall not exceed 16.

(e) The seat spaces shall not be physically defined.

(f) Seat boards that are also used as stepping surfaces for descent shall provide a walking surface with a width not less than 12 in. (30.5 cm), and, where there is a depressed footboard, the gap between seat boards of adjacent rows shall not exceed 12 in. (30.5 cm), measured horizontally. Leading edges of such surfaces shall be provided with a contrasting marking stripe so that the location of such leading edge is readily apparent, particularly where viewed in descent. Such stripe shall be not less than 1 in. (2.5 cm) wide and shall not exceed 2 in. (5.1 cm) in width. The marking stripe shall not be required where bleacher surfaces and environmental conditions, under all conditions of use, are such that the location of each leading edge is readily apparent, particularly when viewed in descent.

Exception No. 2: In seating composed entirely of bleachers for which the row-to-row dimension is 28 in. (71 cm) or less, and from which front egress is not limited, aisles shall not be required to exceed 66 in. (168 cm) in width. Such aisles shall not be considered as dead-end aisles.

12.2.5.6.2 Dead-end aisles shall not exceed 20 ft (6.1 m) in length.

Exception No. 1: A longer dead-end aisle shall be permitted where seats served by the dead-end aisle are not more than 24 seats from another aisle, measured along a row of seats having a clear width of not less than 12 in. (30.5 cm) plus 0.6 in. (1.5 cm) for each additional seat over a total of seven in the row.

Exception No. 2: A 16-row, dead-end aisle shall be permitted in folding and telescopic seating and grandstands.

(d) The number of rows shall not exceed 16.

(e) The seat spaces shall not be physically defined.

(f) Seat boards that are also used as stepping surfaces for descent shall provide a walking surface with a width of not less than 12 in. (30.5 cm), and, where there is a depressed footboard, the gap between seat boards of adjacent rows shall not exceed 12 in. (30.5 cm), measured horizontally. Leading edges of such surfaces shall be provided with a contrasting marking stripe so that the location of such leading edge is readily apparent, particularly where viewed in descent. Such stripe shall be not less than 1 in. (2.5 cm) wide and shall not exceed 2 in. (5.1 cm) in width. The marking stripe shall not be required where bleacher surfaces and environmental conditions, under all conditions of use, are such that the location of each leading edge is readily apparent, particularly when viewed in descent.

Exception No. 2: In seating composed entirely of bleachers for which the row-to-row dimension is 28 in. (71 cm) or less, and from which front egress is not limited, aisles shall not be required to exceed 66 in. (168 cm) in width. Such aisles shall not be considered as dead-end aisles.

13.2.5.6.2 Dead-end aisles shall not exceed 20 ft (6.1 m) in length.

Exception No. 1: A longer dead-end aisle shall be permitted where seats served by the dead-end aisle are not more than 24 seats from another aisle, measured along a row of seats having a clear width of not less than 12 in. (30.5 cm) plus 0.6 in. (1.5 cm) for each additional seat over a total of seven in the row.

Exception No. 2: A 16-row, dead-end aisle shall be permitted in folding and telescopic seating and grandstands.

Bleacher seating, as addressed in the exceptions to 12/13.2.5.6.1 does not have seat backs. Provided the row-to-row dimension does not exceed 28 in. (71 cm) and egress is not restricted from the front of the bleacher, occupants can effectively walk on the seating surfaces and not rely on aisles. The maximum 66-in. (168-cm) width aisle should be adequate to serve the needs of persons unable to walk along the seating surfaces.

Exception No. 1 to 12/13.2.5.6.2 formally recognizes the inherent redundancy that exists where a block of seating rows is served by more than one aisle, so that the problem created by the blockage of any one aisle can be mitigated by greater movement along rows to reach a more distant aisle. The excep-

tion recognizes that movement along rows (even with the constricted row widths) provides many routes that permit faster movement to alternative aisles than would be possible with a dedicated cross aisle. Exception No. 1 requires increased aisle accessway clear width to facilitate travel along the seating rows to reach alternative aisles. At the row length limit of 24 seats, the required aisle accessway clear width for use of this exception is 22.2 in. (56.4 cm). The exception is useful in arenas and theaters where it is not easy to provide a cross aisle or a door at the end of an aisle but where it is relatively easy to reach a remote aisle and its associated exit by moving along the aisle accessways created by the seating rows.

CHAPTER 12 • New	CHAPTER 13 • Existing

12.2.5.6.3* The minimum clear width of aisles shall be sufficient to provide egress capacity in accordance with 12.2.3.2 but shall be not less than the following:

(1) 48 in. (122 cm) for stairs having seating on each side, or 36 in. (91 cm) where aisle does not serve more than 50 seats

(2) 36 in. (91 cm) for stairs having seating on only one side

(3) 23 in. (58 cm) between a handrail and seating, or between a guardrail and seating where the aisle is subdivided by a handrail

(4) 42 in. (107 cm) for level or ramped aisles having seating on both sides, or 36 in. (91 cm) where aisle does not serve more than 50 seats

(5) 36 in. (91 cm) for level or ramped aisles having seating on only one side

(6) 23 in. (58 cm) between a handrail or guardrail and seating where the aisle does not serve more than five rows on one side

13.2.5.6.3* The minimum clear width of aisles shall be sufficient to provide egress capacity in accordance with 13.2.3.2 but shall be not less than the following:

(1) 42 in. (107 cm) for stairs having seating on each side

Exception No. 1: The minimum clear width required by 13.2.5.6.3(1) shall be not less than 30 in. (76 cm) for catchment areas having not more than 60 seats.

Exception No. 2: The minimum clear width required by 13.2.5.6.3(1) shall be not less than 36 in. (91 cm) where an aisle does not serve more than 50 seats.

(2) 36 in. (91 cm) for stairs having seating on only one side, or 30 in. (76 cm) for catchment areas having not more than 60 seats

(3) 20 in. (51 cm) between a handrail and seating or between a guardrail and seating where the aisle is subdivided by a handrail

(4) 42 in. (107 cm) for level or ramped aisles having seating on both sides

Exception No. 1: The minimum clear width required by 13.2.3.2(4) shall be not less than 30 in. (76 cm) for catchment areas having not more than 60 seats.

Exception No. 2: The minimum clear width required by 13.2.3.2(4) shall be not less than 36 in. (91 cm) where an aisle does not serve more than 50 seats.

(5) 36 in. (91 cm) for level or ramped aisles having seating on only one side, or 30 in. (76 cm) for catchment areas having not more than 60 seats

(6) 23 in. (58 cm) between a handrail or guardrail and seating where aisle does not serve more than five rows on one side

The minimum aisle widths specified by 12/13.2.5.6.3 will often be wider than the widths calculated for a required egress capacity. Thus, the width specified by 12/13.2.5.6.3 is often the minimum required width. The requirements of 12/13.2.5.6.3 take into account the width needed by individuals moving alone or with others, overtaking others, and moving in counterflow past others on aisles. Differing movement behavior and the need for handrails on different walking surfaces, such as stepped aisles versus level aisles, are considered. Exhibits 12/13.16 and 12/13.17 illustrate how intensively a 48-in. (122-cm) aisle stair subdivided by a center handrail can be used. Exhibit 12/13.18 shows, in an overhead view, a large male walking down one side of a similar aisle stair that is 48 in. (122 cm) wide and subdivided by a handrail. Chair seating is shown adjoining the aisle in these photographs.

Subparagraph 12/13.2.5.6.3(6) is based on the requirement for handrails in aisle stairs. It specifically addresses the allowance for extending such handrails down the center of aisles for as many as five rows, leaving only about 23 in. (58 cm) of nominal width clear to the side of the handrail. This width is readily used by individuals moving in single or staggered file and can be used with tolerable inconvenience where people must pass each other on the same side of the handrail. This provision of the *Code* might be

CHAPTER 12 • New   **CHAPTER 13 • Existing**

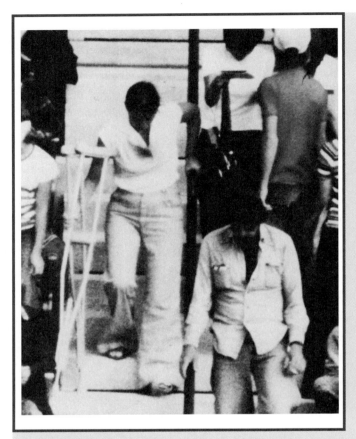

Exhibit 12/13.16 Intensive use of stadium aisle stair, 48 in. (122 cm) wide with central handrail, in a stadium. (Photograph courtesy of Jake Pauls.)

Exhibit 12/13.17 Intensive use of stadium handrail, approximately 34 in. (86.3 cm) high, at center of 48-in. (122-cm) wide aisle stair. (Photograph courtesy of Jake Pauls.)

useful in cases where a short stub aisle is needed to serve rows of seating immediately beside a vomitory.

Generally, the effective width of aisles is often somewhat wider than is necessary for egress stairs or corridors that are bounded on both sides by wall construction. One important exception to this generalization occurs where many people are attempting to sit on undivided benches or bleachers served by

an aisle. The 18-in. (45.7-cm) spacing usually provided for each person is often too small, and there is a natural tendency for people to extend their legs, hips, and shoulders into a significant part of the aisle width. Therefore, it is prudent when designing for crowded, nonchair seating to increase either the width of the seat per person or the minimum aisle widths required by 12/13.2.5.6.3 to facilitate normal circulation in the aisles.

A.12.2.5.6.3 It is the intent to permit handrails to project not more than 3½ in. (8.9 cm) into the clear width of aisles required by 12.2.5.6.3.

12.2.5.6.4* Aisle Stairs and Ramps. Aisles having a gradient steeper than 1 in 20, but not steeper than 1 in 8, shall

A.13.2.5.6.3 It is the intent to permit handrails to project not more than 3½ in. (8.9 cm) into the clear width of aisles required by 13.2.5.6.3.

13.2.5.6.4* Aisle Stairs and Ramps. Aisles having a gradient steeper than 1 in 20, but not steeper than 1 in 8, shall

Exhibit 12/13.18 *Overhead view of 48-in. (122-cm) wide aisle stair, with center handrail, used by a large male. (Photograph courtesy of Jake Pauls.)*

consist of a ramp. Aisles having a gradient steeper than 1 in 8 shall consist of an aisle stair. The exception to 12.2.5.6.8 shall not apply.

Exception No. 1:   Aisles in folding and telescopic seating shall be permitted to be stepped aisles.

Exception No. 2:   The limitation on height between landings in Tables 7.2.2.2.1(a) and (b) shall not apply to aisle stairs.

A.12.2.5.6.4 Technical information about the convenience and safety of ramps and stairs having gradients in the region

consist of a ramp. Aisles having a gradient steeper than 1 in 8 shall consist of an aisle stair. The exception to 13.2.5.6.8 shall not apply.

Exception No. 1:   Aisles in folding and telescopic seating shall be permitted to be stepped aisles.

Exception No. 2:   The limitation on height between landings in Tables 7.2.2.2.1(a) and (b) shall not apply to aisle stairs.

A.13.2.5.6.4 Technical information about the convenience and safety of ramps and stairs having gradients in the region of 1 in 8 clearly suggests that the goal should be slopes for ramps that are less steep and combinations of stair risers and treads that are, for example, superior to 4-in. (10.2-cm) risers and 32-in. (81-cm) treads. This goal should be kept in mind by designers in establishing the gradient of seating areas to be served by aisles.

12.2.5.6.5 Aisle Stair Treads. Aisle stair treads shall meet the following criteria:

(1) There shall be no variation in the depth of adjacent treads that exceeds ³⁄₁₆ in. (0.5 cm).

(2)* Treads shall be not less than 11 in. (27.9 cm).

A.12.2.5.6.5(2) Tread depth is more important to stair safety than is riser height. Therefore, in cases where the seating area gradient is less than 5 in 11, it is recommended that the tread dimension be increased beyond 11 in. (27.9 cm) rather than reducing the riser height. Where the seating area

of 1 in 8 clearly suggests that the goal should be slopes for ramps that are less steep and combinations of stair risers and treads that are, for example, superior to 4-in. (10.2-cm) risers and 32-in. (81-cm) treads. This goal should be kept in mind by designers in establishing the gradient of seating areas to be served by aisles.

13.2.5.6.5 Aisle Stair Treads. Aisle stair treads shall meet the following criteria:

(1) There shall be no variation in the depth of adjacent treads that exceeds ³⁄₁₆ in. (0.5 cm).

Exception No. 1:* In aisle stairs where a single intermediate tread is provided halfway between seating platforms, such intermediate treads shall be permitted to be of a relatively smaller but uniform depth but shall be not less than 13 in. (33 cm).

A.13.2.5.6.5 Exception No. 1 Completely uniform tread dimensions are preferred over aisle stair designs where tread depths alternate between relatively small intermediate treads between seating platforms and relatively large treads at seating platforms. A larger tread that is level with the seating platform is not needed to facilitate easy access to and egress from a row of seating. If this arrangement is used, it is important to provide a tread depth that is better than minimum for the intermediate tread; hence, 13 in. (33.0 cm) is specified. Where nonuniformities exist due to construction tolerance, they should not exceed ³⁄₁₀ in. (0.5 cm) between adjacent treads.

Exception No. 2: In grandstands, bleachers, and folding and telescopic seating, steps shall not be provided in aisles to overcome differences in level unless the gradient exceeds 1 ft in 10 ft (0.3 m in 3 m) of run. Where the rise of seating platform exceeds 11 in. (27.9 cm), an intermediate step shall be provided for the full width of the aisle and shall be proportioned to provide two steps of equal rise per platform. Where the rise of the seating platform exceeds 18 in. (45.7 cm), two intermediate steps for the full width of the aisle shall be provided and proportioned to provide three steps of equal rise per platform. The resulting treads shall be uniform and not less than 9 in. (22.9 cm). The full length of the nose of each step in the aisle shall be conspicuously marked.

(2)* Treads shall be not less than 11 in. (27.9 cm).

A.13.2.5.6.5(2) Tread depth is more important to stair safety than is riser height. Therefore, in cases where the seating area gradient is less than 5 in 11, it is recommended that the tread dimension be increased beyond 11 in. (27.9 cm) rather than reducing the riser height. Where the seating area

CHAPTER 12 • New

CHAPTER 13 • Existing

gradient exceeds 8 in 11, it is recommended that the riser height be increased while maintaining a tread depth of not less than 11 in. (27.9 cm).

(3) All treads shall extend the full width of the aisle.

The requirements of 12/13.2.5.6.4 address the need to design aisle stairs, for example, with all the attention and care required for stairs in general, plus additional care due to the unique design and use conditions encountered with aisles serving seating arranged in rows. Extra attention is especially necessary where large elevation differences exist between the rows of seating. Subparagraph 12/13.2.5.6.4 begins with a general requirement that divides aisles into two categories based on their steepness. Ideally, designing aisles with a gradient of approximately 1 in 8 is to be avoided; however, sightlines might dictate the use of such slopes in some situations. These ramps are relatively steep and problematic for people with walking difficulties. Stairs with a very small rise and long treads also present problems, notably trips and missteps, because the presence of low height risers might not be evident, especially when a crowd is present. Generally, people using aisles are also distracted because of the unusual aisle length, the presence of other people in the aisles, and the presence of those entering the aisles from adjoining seating rows. Therefore, aisles of any slope must be designed with considerable care and attention to human factors.

Allowing unequal-sized treads within aisle stairs, a traditional practice once believed to be useful in facilitating access to seat rows, is not permitted by the *Code* for new assembly occupancies. Even with the increased minimum tread size requirement of older editions of the *Code*, the end result (larger treads at the seat row entry level and smaller intermediate treads between seat row levels) was not as beneficial in terms of stair safety as that provided by consistently sized treads. The desirability of uniformly sized treads holds even for treads as large as 20 in. (50.8 cm) in depth (assuming a relatively low riser height). Handrails (required by 12/13.2.5.6.7) help to compensate for the stretched but consistent stride length that might be needed in such long-tread aisle stairs. It is preferable to keep treads uniform so that the risk of misstepping, particularly the risk of overstepping on relatively smaller treads, is reduced.

For existing aisle stairs, Exception No. 1 to

gradient exceeds 8 in 11, it is recommended that the riser height be increased while maintaining a tread depth of not less than 11 in. (27.9 cm).

(3) All treads shall extend the full width of the aisle.

13.2.5.6.5(1) continues to recognize an intermediate tread between seating platforms but requires that the intermediate treads be uniform in depth and at least 13 in. (33 cm) deep. This exaggerated depth makes the intermediate tread more obvious and provides a deep surface on which to place one's feet.

Special attention must be given to careful design detailing and construction practice in relation to the placement of treads in aisle stairs. Careful site supervision is recommended to avoid serious problems both in cast-in-place concrete construction and in precast concrete construction of aisle stairs. Field research studies of situations where aisle step dimensions are not consistent indicate that the incidence of missteps rises significantly where tolerances of tread uniformity exceed those specified by 12/13.2.5.6.5.

Exhibit 12/13.19 shows a side view of an aisle stair with 11-in. (28-cm) treads used by a person with footwear measuring 12 in. (30.5 cm) in length. This situation is experienced by 5 percent of adults generally, and it might occur more often in those assembly

Exhibit 12/13.19 *Side view of aisle stair with uniform tread depth of 11 in. (17.9 cm). (Photograph courtesy of Jake Pauls.)*

situations attracting a higher proportion of male adults.

With respect to 12/13.2.5.6.5(1), which requires tread depth to be uniform, apparently no difficulty is experienced in entering or leaving the aisles or in entering or leaving the seat row where three 11-in. (17.9-cm) treads at each seat row are provided, as shown in Exhibit 12/13.19.

If treads do not extend the full width of the aisle, a pocket (or drop-off) might occur between the side edge of the tread and the side edge of the seat nearest the aisle. The requirement of 12/13.2.5.6.5(3), that treads extend the full width of the aisle, is intended to help avoid such drop-offs and help prevent missteps and falls.

12.2.5.6.6 Aisle Stair Risers. Aisle stair risers shall meet the following criteria:

(1) Riser heights shall be not less than 4 in. (10.2 cm).

Exception: The riser height of aisle stairs in folding and telescopic seating shall be permitted to be not less than 3½ in. (8.9 cm) and shall not exceed 11 in. (27.9 cm).

(2) Riser heights shall not exceed 8 in. (20.3 cm).

Exception No. 1: Where the gradient of an aisle is steeper than 8 in. (20.3 cm) in rise in 11 in. (27.9 cm) of run to maintain necessary sight lines in the adjoining seating area, the riser height shall be permitted to exceed 8 in. (20.3 cm) but shall not exceed 9 in. (22.9 cm).

Exception No. 2: The riser height of aisle stairs in folding and telescopic seating shall be permitted to be not less than 3½ in. (8.9 cm) and shall not exceed 11 in. (27.9 cm).

(3) Riser heights shall be designed to be uniform in each aisle, and the construction-caused nonuniformities shall not exceed ³⁄₁₆ in. (0.5 cm) between adjacent risers.

Exception: Riser height shall be permitted to be nonuniform only for the purpose of accommodating changes in gradient necessary to maintain sight lines within a seating area and shall be permitted to exceed ³⁄₁₆ in. (0.5 cm) in any flight. Where nonuniformities exceed ³⁄₁₆ in. (0.5 cm) between adjacent risers, the exact location of such nonuniformities shall be indicated by a distinctive marking stripe on each tread at the nosing or leading edge adjacent to the nonuniform risers.

13.2.5.6.6 Aisle Stair Risers. Aisle stair risers shall meet the following criteria:

(1) Riser heights shall be a minimum of 4 in. (10.2 cm).

Exception: The riser height of aisle stairs in folding and telescopic seating shall be permitted to be not less than 3½ in. (8.9 cm) and shall not exceed 11 in. (27.9 cm).

(2) Riser heights shall not exceed 8 in. (20.3 cm).

Exception No. 1: Where the gradient of an aisle is steeper than 8 in. (20.3 cm) in rise in 11 in. (27.9 cm) of run to maintain necessary sight lines in the adjoining seating area, the riser height shall be permitted to exceed 8 in. (20.3 cm) but shall not exceed 11 in. (27.9 cm).

Exception No. 2: The riser height of aisle stairs in folding and telescopic seating shall be permitted to be not less than 3½ in. (8.9 cm) and shall not exceed 11 in. (27.9 cm).

(3) Riser heights shall be designed to be uniform in each aisle, and the construction-caused nonuniformities shall not exceed ³⁄₁₆ in. (0.5 cm) between adjacent risers.

Exception: Riser height shall be permitted to be nonuniform only for the purpose of accommodating changes in gradient necessary to maintain site lines within a seating area and shall be permitted to exceed ³⁄₁₆ in. (0.5 cm) in any flight. Where nonuniformities exceed ³⁄₁₆ in. (0.5 cm) between adjacent risers, the exact location of such nonuniformities shall be indicated by a distinctive marking stripe on each tread at the nosing or leading edge adjacent to the nonuniform risers.

At the minimum slope for which the *Code* requires aisle stairs (that is, slopes steeper than 1 in 8), there is a riser height of 4 in. (10.2 cm) for which the seat platform is 32 in. (81.3 cm) deep. At such low riser heights, which present a tripping hazard if the risers are not detected by people, the tread nosing marking requirement in 12/13.2.5.6.8 is especially significant.

The 1988 edition of the *Code* reduced the maximum riser height permitted for new aisle stairs from 11 in. (27.9 cm) to 9 in. (22.9 cm). In addition to reducing movement safety, the unusually high risers of some aisle stairs reduce the speed and efficiency of movement, especially in the descending direction. This is taken into account in 12/13.2.3.2 where, for

CHAPTER 12 • New	CHAPTER 13 • Existing

each additional inch of riser height above 7 in. (17.9 cm), an additional 20 percent must be added to the required capacity-related width of the aisle to satisfy *Code* requirements and achieve an acceptable egress flow time performance.

A special case is made for severely nonuniform riser heights [those beyond the usual ³/₁₆-in. (0.5-cm) tolerance] only in situations where there is a break in the slope of a seating deck to maintain adequate sightlines. The seating deck slope might change incrementally at each row or, more commonly, a large change might occur at one or more locations. At such

locations, there is often a change in the row-to-row elevation that greatly exceeds the ³/₁₆-in. (0.5-cm) tolerance. Aisle step riser heights will, as a consequence, change radically at this point. It is the duty of the designer and owner to alert people using the aisle of this unusual change in the riser dimensions. Such an alert might constitute more than the usual marking of all step nosings required by 12/13.2.5.6.8. A distinctive color or other standard hazard marking is needed on the step nosings. Additional warning techniques might have to be employed in some cases to help reduce the risk of stumbles and falls.

12.2.5.6.7* Aisle Handrails. Ramped aisles having a gradient exceeding 1 in 12 and aisle stairs shall be provided with handrails at one side or along the centerline and in accordance with 7.2.2.4.5(1), (2), and (3).

Where seating exists on both sides of the aisle, the handrails shall be noncontinuous with gaps or breaks at intervals not exceeding five rows to facilitate access to seating and to allow crossing from one side of the aisle to the other. These gaps or breaks shall have a clear width of not less than 22 in. (55.9 cm) and shall not exceed 36 in. (91 cm), measured horizontally, and the handrail shall have rounded terminations or bends. Where handrails are provided in the middle of aisle stairs, an additional intermediate rail shall be located approximately 12 in. (30 cm) below the main handrail.

Exception No. 1: Handrails shall not be required for ramped aisles having a gradient not steeper than 1 in 8 and having seating on both sides.

Exception No. 2: The requirement for a handrail shall be satisfied by the use of a guard providing a rail that complies with the graspability requirements for handrails and shall be located at a consistent height between 34 in. and 42 in. (86 cm and 107 cm), measured vertically from the top of the rail to the leading edge (nosing) of stair treads or to the adjacent walking surface in the case of a ramp.

A.12.2.5.6.7 Failure to provide a handrail within a 30-in. (76-cm) horizontal distance of all required portions of the aisle stair width means that the egress capacity calculation is required to be modified as specified by 12.2.3.2(2). This modification might lead to an increase in the aisle width. Although this increase will compensate for reduced egress efficiency, it does not help individuals walking on such

13.2.5.6.7* Aisle Handrails. Ramped aisles having a gradient exceeding 1 in 12 and aisle stairs shall be provided with handrails at one side or along the centerline and in accordance with 7.2.2.4.5(1), (2), and (3).

Where seating exists on both sides of the aisle, the handrails shall be noncontinuous with gaps or breaks at intervals not exceeding five rows to facilitate access to seating and to allow crossing from one side of the aisle to the other. These gaps or breaks shall have a clear width of not less than 22 in. (55.9 cm) and shall not exceed 36 in. (91 cm), measured horizontally, and the handrail shall have rounded terminations or bends. Where handrails are provided in the middle of aisle stairs, an additional intermediate rail shall be located approximately 12 in. (30 cm) below the main handrail.

Exception No. 1: Handrails shall not be required for ramped aisles having a gradient not steeper than 1 in 8 and having seating on both sides.

Exception No. 2: The requirement for a handrail shall be satisfied by the use of a guard providing a rail that complies with the graspability requirements for handrails and shall be located at a consistent height between 34 in. and 42 in. (86 cm and 107 cm), measured vertically from the top of the rail to the leading edge (nosing) of stair treads or to the adjacent walking surface in the case of a ramp.

Exception No. 3: Handrails shall not be required where risers do not exceed 7 in. (17.8 cm) in height.

A.13.2.5.6.7 Failure to provide a handrail within a 30-in. (76-cm) horizontal distance of all required portions of the aisle stair width means that the egress capacity calculation is required to be modified as specified by 13.2.3.2(2). This modification might lead to an increase in the aisle width. Although this increase will compensate for reduced egress efficiency, it does not help individuals walking on such portions of stairs to recover from missteps other than by possibly reducing marginally the crowding that might exacerbate the problem of falls. *(See also 7.2.2.4.)*

The *Code* requires handrails on aisle stairs in new construction even where riser heights are less than 7 in. (17.9 cm). This requirement is a result of increased experience with the provision and use of aisle handrails, as well as a general realization that aisles pose unique challenges to users that might go beyond those encountered on other stairs. Exhibits 12/13.16 and 12/13.17 illustrate the variety of use conditions in aisles and the extensive use of handrails. Field research studies show that aisle stair handrails have been used about twice as often as handrails provided to meet *Code* requirements for non-aisle stairs. When one considers the unusual lengths of aisles, the unusual step geometries, and the very complex use conditions—with people entering and leaving the aisle at many rows—this high level of use is not surprising. Aside from their value in increasing the safety and comfort of people using the aisles, handrails also help to improve egress efficiency. This benefit is taken into account in calculation of egress capacity. See 12/13.2.3.2(2).

12.2.5.6.8* Aisle Marking. A contrasting marking stripe shall be provided on each tread at the nosing or leading edge so that the location of such tread is readily apparent, particularly when viewed in descent. Such stripes shall be not less than 1 in. (2.5 cm) wide and shall not exceed 2 in. (5 cm) in width.

Exception: The marking stripe shall not be required where tread surfaces and environmental conditions, under all conditions of use, are such that the location of each tread is readily apparent, particularly when viewed in descent.

A.12.2.5.6.8 Certain tread cover materials such as plush carpets, which are often used in theaters, produce an inherently well-marked tread nosing under most lighting conditions. On the other hand, concrete treads have nosings with a sharp edge and, especially under outdoor lighting conditions, are difficult to discriminate. Therefore, concrete trends require an applied marking stripe. The slip resistance of such marking stripes should be similar to the rest of the treads, and no tripping hazard should be created; luminescent, self-luminous, and electroluminescent tread markings have the advantage of being apparent in reduced light or in the absence of light.

portions of stairs to recover from missteps other than by possibly reducing marginally the crowding that might exacerbate the problem of falls. *(See also 7.2.2.4.)*

The required gaps between sections of center-aisle handrails are illustrated in Exhibit 12/13.18. Spacing such gaps as frequently as every three rows is recommended where there is extensive use of aisles during events. A greater spacing of up to five rows between gaps might be acceptable where there is little use of the aisles during events and little counterflow at any time. Gap size should be kept at the lower end of the permitted range of 22 in. to 36 in. (55.9 cm to 91 cm) where the aisles are unusually steep and handrail use is especially valuable in reducing the risk of falls.

Exception No. 2 to 12/13.2.5.6.7 takes into account the proven utility of handrails that are higher than those permitted, even with the increased handrail height range introduced with the 1988 edition of the *Code*. A guardrail that is 42 in. (107 cm) high (such as at the side of an aisle where there is a vomitory) can be considered a usable handrail if it offers graspability as required for handrails. See 7.2.2.4.5.

13.2.5.6.8* Aisle Marking. A contrasting marking stripe shall be provided on each tread at the nosing or leading edge so that the location of such tread is readily apparent, particularly when viewed in descent. Such stripes shall be not less than 1 in. (2.5 cm) wide and shall not exceed 2 in. (5 cm) in width.

Exception: The marking stripe shall not be required where tread surfaces and environmental conditions, under all conditions of use, are such that the location of each tread is readily apparent, particularly when viewed in descent.

A.13.2.5.6.8 Certain tread cover materials such as plush carpets, which are often used in theaters, produce an inherently well-marked tread nosing under most lighting conditions. On the other hand, concrete treads have nosings with a sharp edge and, especially under outdoor lighting conditions, are difficult to discriminate. Therefore, concrete treads require an applied marking stripe. The slip resistance of such marking stripes should be similar to the rest of the treads, and no tripping hazard should be created; luminescent, self-luminous, and electroluminescent tread markings have the advantage of being apparent in reduced light or in the absence of light.

Exhibit 12/13.20 illustrates some of the step visibility difficulties that are commonly encountered in outdoor facilities with concrete stair treads. Without the helpful shadows from the handrail posts, there would be little indication of the exact location of each tread nosing. This situation requires the applied nosing markings referred to in 12/13.2.5.6.8. The distractions of the playing field and the unusually long aisle further justify making the steps as obvious as possible. Each situation needs to be carefully evaluated, with mock-ups at the design stage and inspection of actual conditions during use, to determine whether any improvements are warranted in marking and lighting such aisles.

Exhibit 12/13.20 *View down stadium aisle stair, provided with center handrail. (Photograph courtesy of Jake Pauls.)*

12.2.5.7* Aisle Accessways Serving Seating at Tables.

A.12.2.5.7 For purposes of the means of egress requirements of this *Code,* seating at counters or at other furnishings is considered to be the same as seating at tables.

12.2.5.7.1 The required clear width of an aisle accessway shall be not less than 12 in. (30.5 cm) where measured in accordance with 12.2.5.7.2 and shall be increased as a function of length in accordance with 12.2.5.7.3.

Exception:* If used by not more than four persons, no minimum clear width shall be required for the portion of aisle accessway having a length not exceeding 6 ft (1.8 m) and located farthest from an aisle.

A.12.2.5.7.1 Exception Effectively, where the aisle accessway is bounded by movable seating, the 12-in. (30.5-cm) minimum width might be increased by about 15 in. to 30 in. (38 cm to 76 cm) as seating is pushed in toward tables. Moreover, it is such movement of chairs during normal and emergency egress situations that makes the zero-clearance exception workable. The exception also applies to booth seating where people sitting closest to the aisle normally move out ahead of people farthest from the aisle.

12.2.5.7.2* Where nonfixed seating is located between a table and an aisle accessway or aisle, the measurement of

13.2.5.7* Aisle Accessways Serving Seating at Tables.

A.13.2.5.7 For purposes of the means of egress requirements of this *Code,* seating at counters or at other furnishings is considered to be the same as seating at tables.

13.2.5.7.1 The required clear width of an aisle accessway shall be not less than 12 in. (30.5 cm) where measured in accordance with 13.2.5.7.2 and shall be increased as a function of length in accordance with 13.2.5.7.3.

Exception:* If used by not more than four persons, no minimum clear width shall be required for the portion of aisle accessway having a length not exceeding 6 ft (1.8 m) and located farthest from an aisle.

A.13.2.5.7.1 Exception Effectively, where the aisle accessway is bounded by movable seating, the 12-in. (30.5-cm) minimum width might be increased by about 15 in. to 30 in. (38 cm to 76 cm) as seating is pushed in toward tables. Moreover, it is such movement of chairs during normal and emergency egress situations that makes the zero-clearance exception workable. The exception also applies to booth seating where people sitting closest to the aisle normally move out ahead of people farthest from the aisle.

13.2.5.7.2* Where nonfixed seating is located between a table and an aisle accessway or aisle, the measurement of

CHAPTER 12 • New	CHAPTER 13 • Existing

required clear width of the aisle accessway or aisle shall be made to a line 19 in. (48.3 cm) away from the edge of the table. The 19-in. (48.3-cm) distance shall be measured perpendicularly to the edge of the table.

A.12.2.5.7.2 See A.12.2.5.8.3.

12.2.5.7.3* The minimum required clear width of an aisle accessway, measured in accordance with 12.2.5.4.6 and 12.2.5.7.2, shall be increased beyond the 12-in. (30.5-cm) requirement of 12.2.5.7.1 by 0.5 in. (1.3 cm) for each additional 12 in. (30.5 cm) or fraction thereof beyond 12 ft (3.7 m) of aisle accessway length, where measured from the center of the seat farthest from an aisle.

A.12.2.5.7.3 The minimum width requirement as a function of accessway length is as follows:

(1) 0 in. (0 cm) for the first 6 ft (1.8 m) of length toward the exit
(2) 12 in. (30.5 cm) for the next 6 ft (1.8 m), that is, up to 12 ft (3.7 m) of length
(3) 12 in. to 24 in. (30.5 cm to 61 cm) for lengths from 12 ft to 36 ft (3.7 m to 10.9 m), the maximum length to the closest aisle or egress doorway permitted by 12.2.5.7.4

Any additional width needed for seating is to be added to these widths, as described in 12.2.5.8.3.

12.2.5.7.4 The path of travel along the aisle accessway shall not exceed 36 ft (10.9 m) from any seat to the closest aisle or egress doorway.

required clear width of the aisle accessway or aisle shall be made to a line 19 in. (48.3 cm) away from the edge of the table. The 19-in. (48.3-cm) distance shall be measured perpendicularly to the edge of the table.

A.13.2.5.7.2 See A.13.2.5.8.3.

13.2.5.7.3* The minimum required clear width of an aisle accessway, measured in accordance with 13.2.5.4.6 and 13.2.5.7.2, shall be increased beyond the 12-in. (30.5-cm) requirement of 13.2.5.7.1 by 0.5 in. (1.3 cm) for each additional 12 in. (30.5 cm) or fraction thereof beyond 12 ft (3.7 m) of aisle accessway length, where measured from the center of the seat farthest from an aisle.

A.13.2.5.7.3 The minimum width requirement as a function of accessway length is as follows:

(1) 0 in. (0 cm) for the first 6 ft (1.8 m) of length toward the exit
(2) 12 in. (30.5 cm) for the next 6 ft (1.8 m), that is, up to 12 ft (3.7 m) of length
(3) 12 in. to 24 in. (30.5 cm to 61 cm) for lengths from 12 ft to 36 ft (3.7 m to 10.9 m), the maximum length to the closest aisle or egress doorway permitted by 13.2.5.7.4

Any additional width needed for seating is to be added to these widths, as described in 13.2.5.8.3.

13.2.5.7.4 The path of travel along the aisle accessway shall not exceed 36 ft (10.9 m) from any seat to the closest aisle or egress doorway.

The exception to 12/13.2.5.7.1 exempts a portion of the aisle accessway from the minimum width requirement under the specific conditions illustrated in Exhibit 12/13.21. The groupings of four chairs within the first 6 ft (1.8 m) of the aisle accessway are unregulated with respect to spacing. From the 6-ft (1.8-m) point away from the wall to the point where the aisle accessway reaches the aisle, the minimum width requirement of 12/13.2.5.7.1 applies.

Figure A.12/13.2.5.8.3 illustrates the provisions of 12/13.2.5.7.2 and 12/13.2.5.8.3. These requirements provide guidance on how aisle accessways and aisles with movable chairs are to be measured.

Exhibit 12/13.22 illustrates the maximum length of aisle accessway at tables permitted with the minimum 12-in. (30.5-cm) clear width. The aisle accessway width is greater than or equal to 12 in. (30.5 cm), with increased spacing of 0.5 in. (1.3 cm) for each additional 12 in. (30.5 cm) of aisle accessway beyond the initial

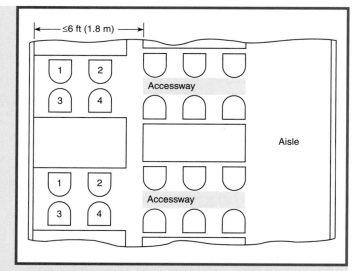

Exhibit 12/13.21 *No minimum aisle accessway width required for first 6 ft (1.8 m) serving four or fewer persons.*

CHAPTER 12 • New   **CHAPTER 13 • Existing**

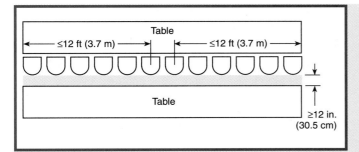

Exhibit 12/13.22 Minimum 12-in. (30.5-cm) aisle accessway at tables.

12 ft (3.7 m) from the center of the seat farthest from an aisle. In accordance with 12/13.2.5.7.2, the presence of chairs at one side of the aisle accessway increases the table-to-table spacing by 19 in. (48.3 cm) above that attributable to the required aisle accessway clear width.

Exhibit 12/13.23 illustrates the maximum length permitted for an aisle accessway serving seating at tables. The total length of the table is slightly more than 72 ft (22 m). Seating at longer tables requires a 36-in. (91-cm) aisle in accordance with the minimum width requirements of 12/13.2.5.8.2 instead of an aisle accessway. For the arrangement shown in Exhibit 12/13.23, the aisle accessway clear width, X, is 12 in.

(30.5 cm) plus 0.5 in. (1.3 cm) for each additional 12 in. (30.5 cm) of aisle accessway beyond the initial 12 ft (3.7 m) from the center seat farthest from an aisle. The aisle accessway clear width is calculated as follows:

$$X = 12 \text{ in.} + [0.5 \text{ in./ft} (36 \text{ ft} - 12 \text{ ft})]$$
$$= 12 \text{ in.} + 12 \text{ in.}$$
$$= 24 \text{ in.}$$

For SI (metric) units,

$$X = 30.5 \text{ cm} + [4.25 \text{ cm/m} (10.9 \text{ m} - 3.7 \text{ m})]$$
$$= 30.5 + 30.5$$
$$= 61 \text{ cm}$$

With the 19-in. (48.3-cm) space required for the chairs, the table-to-table spacing must be ≥43 in. (109 cm).

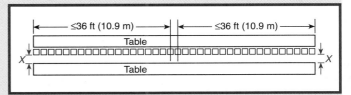

Exhibit 12/13.23 Maximum 36 ft (10.9 m) permitted for an aisle accessway serving seating at tables.

12.2.5.8 Aisles Serving Seating at Tables.

12.2.5.8.1* Aisles that contain steps or that are ramped, such as aisles serving dinner theater–style configurations, shall comply with the requirements of 12.2.5.6.

A.12.2.5.8.1 See 7.1.7 and A.7.1.7.2 for special circulation safety precautions applicable where small elevation differences occur.

12.2.5.8.2* The width of aisles serving seating at tables shall be not less than 44 in. (112 cm) where serving an occupant load exceeding 50, and 36 in. (91 cm) where serving an occupant load of 50 or fewer.

A.12.2.5.8.2 It is important to make facilities accessible to people using wheelchairs. See CABO/ANSI A117.1, *American National Standard for Accessible and Usable Buildings and Facilities,* which provides guidance on appropriate aisle widths.

12.2.5.8.3* Where nonfixed seating is located between a table and an aisle, the measurement of required clear width

13.2.5.8 Aisles Serving Seating at Tables.

13.2.5.8.1* Aisles that contain steps or that are ramped, such as aisles serving dinner theater–style configurations, shall comply with the requirements of 13.2.5.6.

A.13.2.5.8.1 See 7.1.7 and A.7.1.7.2 for special circulation safety precautions applicable where small elevation differences occur.

13.2.5.8.2* The width of aisles serving seating at tables shall be not less than 44 in. (112 cm) where serving an occupant load exceeding 50, and 36 in. (91 cm) where serving an occupant load of 50 or fewer.

A.13.2.5.8.2 It is important to make facilities accessible to people using wheelchairs. See CABO/ANSI A117.1 *American National Standard for Accessible and Usable Buildings and Facilities,* which provides guidance on appropriate aisle widths.

13.2.5.8.3* Where nonfixed seating is located between a table and an aisle, the measurement of required clear width

CHAPTER 12 • New

of the aisle shall be made to a line 19 in. (48.3 cm) away from the edge of the table. The 19-in. (48.3-cm) distance shall be measured perpendicularly to the edge of the table.

A.12.2.5.8.3 Figure A.12.2.5.8.3 shows typical measurements involving seating and tables abutting an aisle. For purposes of the means of egress requirements of this *Code,* seating at counters or other furnishings is considered to be the same as seating at tables.

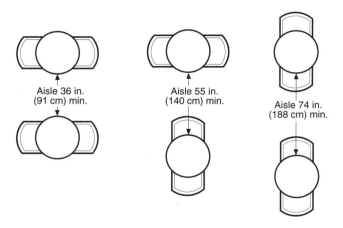

Figure A.12.2.5.8.3 *Seating at tables abutting an aisle.*

12.2.5.9 Approval of Layouts. Where required by the authority having jurisdiction, plans drawn to scale showing the arrangement of furnishings or equipment shall be submitted to the authority by the building owner, manager, or authorized agent to substantiate conformance with the provisions of 12.2.5. Such plans shall constitute the only acceptable arrangement until revised or until additional plans are submitted and approved.

Exception: Temporary deviations from the specifications of the approved plans shall be permitted, provided that the occupant load is not increased and the intent of 12.2.5.9 is maintained.

12.2.6 Travel Distance to Exits.

Exits shall be arranged so that the total length of travel from any point to reach an exit shall not exceed 150 ft (45 m) in any assembly occupancy.

Exception No. 1: The travel distance shall not exceed 200 ft (60 m) in assembly occupancies protected throughout by an approved, supervised automatic sprinkler system in accordance with Section 9.7.

CHAPTER 13 • Existing

of the aisle shall be made to a line 19 in. (48.3 cm) away from the edge of the table. The 19-in. (48.3-cm) distance shall be measured perpendicularly to the edge of the table.

A.13.2.5.8.3 Figure A.13.2.5.8.3 shows typical measurements involving seating and tables abutting an aisle. Note that, for purposes of the means of egress requirements of this *Code,* seating at counters or other furnishings is considered to be the same as seating at tables.

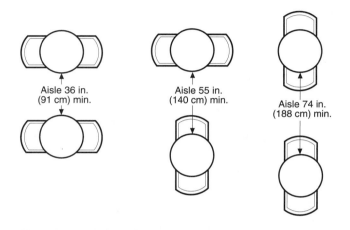

Figure A.13.2.5.8.3 *Seating at tables abutting an aisle.*

13.2.5.9 Approval of Layouts. Where required by the authority having jurisdiction, plans drawn to scale showing the arrangement of furnishings or equipment shall be submitted to the authority by the building owner, manager, or authorized agent to substantiate conformance with the provisions of 13.2.5. Such plans shall constitute the only acceptable arrangement until revised or until additional plans are submitted and approved.

Exception: Temporary deviations from the specifications of the approved plans shall be permitted, provided that the occupant load is not increased and the intent of 13.2.5.9 is maintained.

13.2.6 Travel Distance to Exits.

Exits shall be arranged so that the total length of travel from any point to reach an exit shall not exceed 150 ft (45 m) in any assembly occupancy.

Exception No. 1: The travel distance shall not exceed 200 ft (60 m) in assembly occupancies protected throughout by an approved automatic sprinkler system in accordance with Section 9.7.

Exception No. 2: This requirement shall not apply to smoke-protected assembly seating as permitted by 12.4.2.8 and its exception.

Exception No. 2: This requirement shall not apply to smoke-protected assembly seating as permitted by 13.4.2.8 and its exception.

Travel distance to exits from balconies or galleries that are served by unenclosed stairways must be measured to include the distance on the slope of the stair in the plane of the nosings and the distance from the bottom of the stair to the exit. Travel distance is measured as illustrated in Exhibit 12/13.24 and includes travel along the stair and travel to the exterior exit door at the level of discharge.

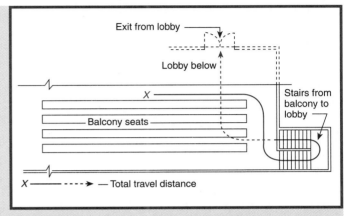

Exhibit 12/13.24 *Measurement of travel distance from balcony with egress by unenclosed stairs.*

12.2.7 Discharge from Exits.

12.2.7.1 Exit discharge shall comply with Section 7.7.

12.2.7.2 The level of exit discharge shall be measured at the point of principal entrance to the building.

12.2.7.3 Where the principal entrance to an assembly occupancy is via a terrace, either raised or depressed, such terrace shall be permitted to be considered to be the level of exit discharge for the purposes of Table 12.1.6 where the following criteria are met:

(1) The terrace is at least as long, measured parallel to the building, as the total width of the exit(s) it serves, but not less than 5 ft (1.5 m) long.
(2) The terrace is at least as wide, measured perpendicularly to the building, as the exit(s) it serves, but not less than 10 ft (3 m) wide.
(3) Required stairs leading from the terrace to grade are protected in accordance with 7.2.2.6.3 or are not less than 10 ft (3 m) from the building.

13.2.7 Discharge from Exits.

13.2.7.1 Exit discharge shall comply with Section 7.7.

13.2.7.2 The level of exit discharge shall be measured at the point of principal entrance to the building.

13.2.7.3 Where the principal entrance to an assembly occupancy is via a terrace, either raised or depressed, such terrace shall be permitted to be considered to be the level of exit discharge for the purposes of Table 13.1.6 where the following criteria are met:

(1) The terrace is at least as long, measured parallel to the building, as the total width of the exit(s) it serves, but not less than 5 ft (1.5 m) long.
(2) The terrace is at least as wide, measured perpendicularly to the building, as the exit(s) it serves, but not less than 5 ft (1.5 m) wide.
(3) Required stairs leading from the terrace to grade are protected in accordance with 7.2.2.6.3 or are not less than 10 ft (3 m) from the building.

The *Code* specifies that 10 ft (3 m) is the minimum terrace depth necessary to allow people to exit the building into a depressed or raised area without causing a jamming effect at the exit. The same result was intended in requiring stairs to be at least 10 ft (3 m)

from the face of the building, unless they are protected as provided in Chapter 7. The requirements of 12/13.2.7.3 are illustrated in Exhibit 12/13.25. Assuming that stair D serves exit B plus one-half of entrance A and that stair E serves exit C plus

CHAPTER 12 • New

CHAPTER 13 • Existing

one-half of entrance A, then X must be equal to or greater than the largest one of the following:

(1) 10 ft (3 m) per 12/13.2.7.3(2)

(2) 5 ft (1.5 m) + ½ of 14 ft (4.2 m) = 12 ft (3.6 m)

(3) 6 ft (1.8 m) + ½ of 14 ft (4.2 m) = 13 ft (3.9 m)

Therefore, $X \geq$ 13 ft (3.9 m).

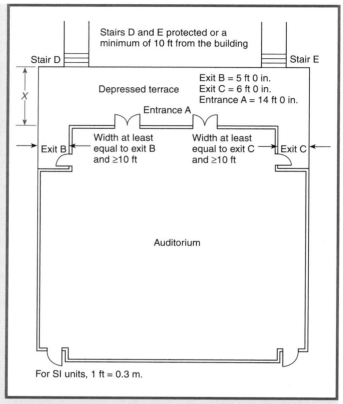

Exhibit 12/13.25 *Assembly occupancy with depressed terrace as principal entrance.*

12.2.8 Illumination of Means of Egress.

Means of egress, other than for private party tents not exceeding 1200 ft² (111.5 m²), shall be illuminated in accordance with Section 7.8.

12.2.9 Emergency Lighting.

Emergency lighting shall be provided in accordance with Section 7.9. Private party tents not exceeding 1200 ft² (111.5 m²) shall not be required to have emergency lighting.

12.2.10 Marking of Means of Egress.

Means of egress shall have signs in accordance with Section 7.10.

Exception: Exit markings shall not be required on the seating side of vomitories from seating areas where exit marking

13.2.8 Illumination of Means of Egress.

Means of egress, other than for private party tents not exceeding 1200 ft² (111.5 m²), shall be illuminated in accordance with Section 7.8.

13.2.9 Emergency Lighting.

Emergency lighting shall be provided in accordance with Section 7.9. Private party tents not exceeding 1200 ft² (111.5 m²) shall not be required to have emergency lighting.

Exception: Assembly occupancies with an occupant load not exceeding 300 and used exclusively for a place of worship shall not be required to have emergency lighting.

13.2.10 Marking of Means of Egress.

Means of egress shall have signs in accordance with Section 7.10.

Exception: Exit markings shall not be required on the seating side of vomitories from seating areas where exit marking is provided in the concourse and where such marking is readily apparent from the vomitories.

12.2.11 Special Means of Egress Features.

12.2.11.1 Guards and Railings.

12.2.11.1.1* Sightline-Constrained Rail Heights. Unless subject to the requirements of 12.2.11.1.2, a fasciae or railing system complying with the guard requirements of 7.2.2.4 and having a height of not less than 26 in. (66 cm) shall be provided where the floor or footboard elevation is more than 30 in. (76 cm) above the floor or grade below and where the fasciae or railing system would otherwise interfere with the sightlines of immediately adjacent seating.

A.12.2.11.1.1 This requirement includes provisions of guards and rails at the front of boxes, galleries, and balconies, and at aisle accessways adjacent to vomitories and orchestra pits.

12.2.11.1.2 At Foot of Aisles. A fasciae or railing system complying with the guard requirements of 7.2.2.4 shall be provided for the full width of the aisle where the foot of the aisle is more than 30 in. (76 cm) above the floor or grade below. The fasciae or railing shall be not less than 36 in. (91 cm) high and shall provide not less than 42 in. (107 cm), measured diagonally, between the top of the rail and the nosing of the nearest tread.

12.2.11.1.3 At Cross Aisles. Guards and railings at cross aisles shall meet the following criteria:

(1) Cross aisles located behind seating rows shall be provided with railings not less than 26 in. (66 cm) above the adjacent floor of the aisle.

Exception: The requirement of 12.2.11.1.3(1) shall not apply where the backs of seats located at the front of the aisle project 24 in. (61 cm) or more above the adjacent floor of the aisle.

(2) Where cross aisles exceed 30 in. (76 cm) above the floor or grade below, guards shall be provided in accordance with 7.2.2.4.

12.2.11.1.4 At Side and Back of Seating Areas. Guards complying with the guard requirements of 7.2.2.4 shall be provided with a height not less than 42 in. (107 cm) above the aisle, aisle accessway, or footboard where the floor elevation exceeds 30 in. (76 cm) above the floor or grade to the side or back of seating.

12.2.11.1.5 Below Seating. Openings between footboards and seat boards shall be provided with intermediate construc-

is provided in the concourse and where such marking is readily apparent from the vomitories.

13.2.11 Special Means of Egress Features.

13.2.11.1 Guards and Railings.

13.2.11.1.1 Boxes, Balconies, and Galleries. Boxes, balconies, and galleries shall meet the following criteria:

(1) The fasciae of boxes, balconies, and galleries shall rise not less than 26 in. (66 cm) above the adjacent floor or shall have substantial railings not less than 26 in. (66 cm) above the adjacent floor.

(2) The height of the rail above footrests on the adjacent floor immediately in front of a row of seats shall be not less than 26 in. (66 cm). Railings at the ends of aisles shall be not less than 36 in. (91 cm) high for the full width of the aisle and shall be not less than 42 in. (107 cm) high for the width of the aisle where steps occur.

Exception: Existing railings 36 in. (91 cm) high at the ends of aisles where steps occur shall be permitted to be continued to be used.

(3) Aisle accessways adjacent to orchestra pits and vomitories, and all cross aisles, shall be provided with railings not less than 26 in. (66 cm) above the adjacent floor.

Exception: The requirement of 13.2.11.1.1(3) shall not apply where the backs of seats located at the front of the aisle project 24 in. (61 cm) or more above the adjacent floor of the aisle.

(4) Guardrails shall not be required on the audience side of stages, raised platforms, and other raised floor areas such as runways, ramps, and side stages used for entertainment or presentations.

(5) Permanent guardrails shall not be required at vertical openings in the performance area of stages.

(6) Guardrails shall not be required where the side of an elevated walking surface is required to be open for the normal functioning of special lighting or for access and use of other special equipment.

tion so that a 4-in. (10.2-cm) diameter sphere cannot pass through the opening.

12.2.11.1.6 Locations Not Requiring Guards. Guards shall not be required in the following locations:

(1) Guards shall not be required on the audience side of stages, of raised platforms, and of other raised floor areas such as runways, ramps, and side stages used for entertainment or presentations.
(2) Permanent guards shall not be required at vertical openings in the performance area of stages.
(3) Guards shall not be required where the side of an elevated walking surface is required to be open for the normal functioning of special lighting or for access and use of other special equipment.

The requirements for guards and handrails for new assembly seating areas were revised for the 1997 edition of the *Code*. The requirements for guards and handrails for existing assembly seating areas remained without revision. The provisions for new construction are, thus, different from those applicable to existing facilities. The following commentary addresses new installations first and existing arrangements second.

Subparagraphs 12.2.11.1.1 and 12.2.11.1.2 clarify that new assembly seating area guards, where the floor is more than 30 in. (76 cm) above the floor or grade below, must comply with the guard requirements of 7.2.2.4. This requirement includes the provision for intermediate rails or balusters to meet the 4-in. (10.1-cm) diameter sphere requirement of 7.2.2.4.6(3), which is illustrated in Exhibit 12/13.26(a).

Subparagraph 12.2.11.1.1 permits a guard height of 26 in. (66 cm) at the front of seating but not at the foot of aisles. Further, the 26-in. (66-cm) height allowance applies only if a 36-in. (91-cm) height rail [as permitted by 12.2.11.1.2 in lieu of the typical 42-in. (107-cm) height guard detailed in 7.2.2.4.6] would otherwise interfere with sightlines of immediately adjacent seating. Note that the heading for paragraph 12.2.11.1.1 is "Sightline-Constrained Rail Heights." The minimum 26-in. (66-cm) height is illustrated in Exhibit 12/13.26(a).

Subparagraph 12.2.11.1.2 requires that a guard be provided at the foot of an aisle if there is more than a 30-in (76-cm) vertical distance to fall. Again, such guards must meet the guard requirements of 7.2.2.4 and must be at least 36 in. (91 cm) in height. See Exhibit 12/13.26(a). Where previous editions of the

Code required a 42-in. (107-cm) guard at the foot of a stepped aisle, the current requirement is for a minimum 36-in. (91-cm) height and a minimum 42 in. (107 cm), measured diagonally between the top of the guardrail and the nosing of the nearest step tread. This requirement is illustrated in Exhibit 12/13.26(b).

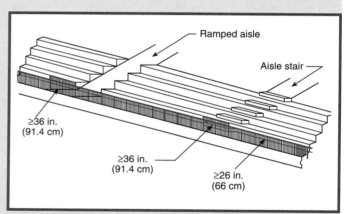

Exhibit 12/13.26(a) New assembly occupancy building with railings installed in accordance with 12.2.11.1.1 and 12.2.11.1.2.

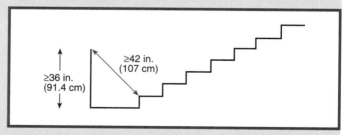

Exhibit 12/13.26(b) New assembly occupancy building with railings installed at foot of stepped aisle in accordance with 12.2.11.1.2.

Where there is a stepped aisle, the requirement of 12.2.11.1.2 to provide a minimum of 42 in. (107 cm), measured diagonally between the top of the guardrail and the nosing of the nearest step tread, will force the guardrail height to be greater than 36 in. (91 cm) if the first riser is positioned too close, horizontally, to the guard. For example, if the first riser is positioned 28 in. (71 cm) horizontally from the guard and an 8-in. (20.3-cm) riser height is used, the minimum 42-in. (107-cm) diagonal distance requirement will force the guardrail height to be a minimum of 39 in. (99 cm). For the same riser height of 8-in. (20.3 cm), in order to have a minimum 36-in. (91-cm) high guardrail at the foot of the stepped aisle, the first step riser will have to be positioned at least 31 in. (79 cm), horizontally from, the guardrail.

Exhibit 12/13.27 illustrates the requirements of 13.2.11.1.1(1) and (2), which apply to guards and rails for existing assembly occupancies. Rail height at the fascia end of a sloping aisle must not be less than 36 in. (91 cm). However, where the aisle is not ramped but has steps, the rail height must be at least 42 in. (107 cm). There is greater danger of people tripping on steps than on a ramped surface with a maximum gradient of 1 ft (0.3 m) of rise to 8 ft (2.4 m) of run.

It is not the intent to reduce the height of guards where sightlines are not a problem, such as with cross aisles at the rear or top of seating areas or where cross aisles are sufficiently below seating that a proper height guard will not interfere with sightlines.

Note that, for existing assembly occupancies, the railings described by 13.2.11.1.1(1) and (2) are, in fact, railings and not the guards required by 7.2.2.4. As depicted in Exhibit 12/13.27, there is no requirement for intermediate rails or balusters—the assembly seating rails are not required to meet the 4-in. (10.1-cm) diameter sphere requirement of 7.2.2.4.6(3). This provision is more lenient than the requirements applicable to new assembly occupancies where 12.2.11.1 requires a railing system to comply with the guard requirements of 7.2.2.4 [see Exhibit 12/13.26(a)].

The *Code* requires a barrier along the downhill side of a cross aisle for both new construction and

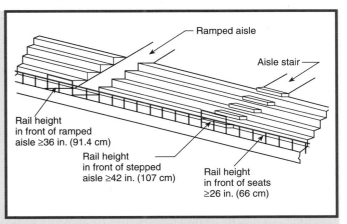

Exhibit 12/13.27 *Existing assembly occupancy building with railings installed in accordance with 13.2.11.1.1(1) and (2).*

existing buildings. The barrier might consist of a rail or the backs of the seats that abut the downhill side of the aisle where the backs project 24 in. (61 cm) or more above the cross aisle. The difference between the 24-in. (61-cm) back height and the required 26-in. (66-cm) railing is not sufficient to require the railing. See Exhibit 12/13.28.

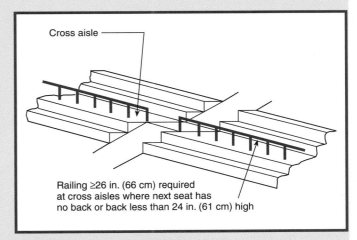

Exhibit 12/13.28 *Barrier for cross aisles.*

Section 12.3 Protection

12.3.1 Protection of Vertical Openings.

Any vertical opening shall be enclosed or protected in accordance with 8.2.5.

Exception No. 1:* Stairs or ramps shall be permitted to be unenclosed between balconies or mezzanines and main assembly areas located below, provided that the balcony or mezzanine is open to the main assembly area.

A.12.3.1 Exception No. 1 The exception presumes the balcony or mezzanine complies with the other provisions of the *Code,* such as travel distance to exits in accordance with 12.2.6 and numbers of exits in accordance with 12.2.4. For the purposes of this exception, a balcony with glazing that provides a visual awareness of the main assembly area is considered open.

Exception No. 2: Exit access stairs from lighting and access catwalks, galleries, and gridirons shall not be required to be enclosed.

Exception No. 3: Assembly occupancies protected by an approved, supervised automatic sprinkler system in accordance with Section 9.7 shall be permitted to have unprotected vertical openings in accordance with 8.2.5.8.

12.3.2 Protection from Hazards.

12.3.2.1 Service Equipment, Hazardous Operations or Processes, and Storage Facilities.

12.3.2.1.1 Rooms containing high-pressure boilers, refrigerating machinery of other than the domestic refrigerator type, large transformers, or other service equipment subject to explosion shall not be located directly under or abutting required exits. All such rooms shall be separated from other

Section 13.3 Protection

13.3.1 Protection of Vertical Openings.

Any vertical opening shall be enclosed or protected in accordance with 8.2.5.

Exception No. 1:* Stairs or ramps shall be permitted to be unenclosed between balconies or mezzanines and main assembly areas located below, provided that the balcony or mezzanine is open to the main assembly area.

A.13.3.1 Exception No. 1 The exception presumes the balcony or mezzanine complies with the other provisions of the *Code,* such as travel distance to exits in accordance with 13.2.6 and numbers of exits in accordance with 13.2.4. For the purposes of this exception, a balcony with glazing that provides a visual awareness of the main assembly area is considered open.

Exception No. 2: Exit access stairs from lighting and access catwalks, galleries, and gridirons shall not be required to be enclosed.

Exception No. 3: Assembly occupancies protected by an approved, supervised automatic sprinkler system in accordance with Section 9.7 shall be permitted to have unprotected vertical openings in accordance with 8.2.5.8.

Exception No. 4: Use of the following alternative materials shall be permitted:

(a) Existing wood lath and plaster

(b) Existing ½-in. (1.3-cm) gypsum wallboard

(c) Existing installations of ¼-in. (0.6-cm) thick wired glass that are, or are rendered, inoperative and fixed in the closed position

(d) Other existing materials having similar fire resistance capabilities

All such assemblies shall be in good repair and free of any condition that would diminish their original fire resistance characteristics.

13.3.2 Protection from Hazards.

13.3.2.1 Service Equipment, Hazardous Operations or Processes, and Storage Facilities.

13.3.2.1.1 Rooms containing high-pressure boilers, refrigerating machinery of other than the domestic refrigerator type, large transformers, or other service equipment subject to explosion shall not be located directly under or abutting required exits. All such rooms shall be separated from other parts of the building by fire barriers in accordance with 8.2.3 that have a fire resistance rating of not less than 1 hour or shall be protected by automatic extinguishing systems in accordance with Section 8.4.

12.3.2.1.2 Vents to the outside air shall be provided in accordance with Section 8.4.

12.3.2.1.3 Rooms or spaces for the storage, processing, or use of materials specified in 12.3.2.1.3(1) through (3) shall be protected in accordance with the following:

(1) Separation from the remainder of the building by fire barriers having a fire resistance rating of not less than 1 hour or protection of such rooms by automatic extinguishing systems as specified in Section 8.4 in the following areas:

   a. Boiler and furnace rooms

Exception: The requirement of 12.3.2.1.3(1)a shall not apply to rooms enclosing furnaces, heating and air-handling equipment, or compressor equipment with a total aggregate input rating less than 200,000 Btu. Such rooms shall not be used for storage unless otherwise protected as required. For installations in attics, the draftstopping requirements of 8.2.7.1(2) shall apply.

   b. Rooms or spaces used for the storage of combustible supplies in quantities deemed hazardous by the authority having jurisdiction
   c. Rooms or spaces used for the storage of hazardous materials or flammable or combustible liquids in quantities deemed hazardous by recognized standards

(2) Separation from the remainder of the building by fire barriers having a fire resistance rating of not less than 1 hour and protection of such rooms by automatic extinguishing systems as specified in Section 8.4 in the following areas:
   a. Laundries
   b. Maintenance shops, including woodworking and painting areas
   c. Rooms or spaces used for processing or use of combustible supplies deemed hazardous by the authority having jurisdiction
   d. Rooms or spaces used for processing or use of hazardous materials or flammable or combustible liquids in quantities deemed hazardous by recognized standards
(3) Where automatic extinguishing is used to meet the requirements of 12.3.2, the protection shall be permitted to be in accordance with 9.7.1.2.

parts of the building by fire barriers in accordance with 8.2.3 that have a fire resistance rating of not less than 1 hour or shall be protected by automatic extinguishing systems in accordance with Section 8.4.

13.3.2.1.2 Vents to the outer air shall be provided in accordance with Section 8.4.

13.3.2.1.3 Rooms or spaces for the storage, processing, or use of materials specified in 13.3.2.1.3(1) through (3) shall be protected in accordance with the following:

(1)* Separation from the remainder of the building by fire barriers having a fire resistance rating of not less than 1 hour or protection of such rooms by automatic extinguishing systems as specified in Section 8.4 in the following areas:

   a. Boiler and furnace rooms

Exception: The requirement of 13.3.2.1.3(1)a shall not apply to rooms enclosing furnaces, heating and air-handling equipment, or compressor equipment with a total aggregate input rating less than 200,000 Btu. Such rooms shall not be used for storage unless otherwise protected as required. For installations in attics, the draftstopping requirements of 8.2.7.1(2) shall apply.

   b. Rooms or spaces used for the storage of combustible supplies in quantities deemed hazardous by the authority having jurisdiction
   c. Rooms or spaces used for the storage of hazardous materials or flammable or combustible liquids in quantities deemed hazardous by recognized standards

A.13.3.2.1.3(1) It is not the intent of this provision to require a smoke barrier that meets the requirements of Section 8.3.

(2) Separation from the remainder of the building by fire barriers having a fire resistance rating of not less than 1 hour and protection of such rooms by automatic extinguishing systems as specified in Section 8.4 in the following areas:
   a. Laundries
   b. Maintenance shops, including woodworking and painting areas
   c. Rooms or spaces used for processing or use of combustible supplies deemed hazardous by the authority having jurisdiction
   d. Rooms or spaces used for processing or use of hazardous materials or flammable or combustible liquids in quantities deemed hazardous by recognized standards
(3) Where automatic extinguishing is used to meet the requirements of 13.3.2, the protection shall be permitted to be in accordance with 9.7.1.2.

The intent of 12/13.3.2.1.3 is to specify the degree of protection necessary for certain hazardous areas. The requirements are separated into two subdivisions—12/13.3.2.1.3(1) and (2)—based on the degree of hazard, and a third—12/13.3.2.1.3(3)—addressing use of the domestic water supply for sprinklers used to protect the hazardous area. The hazards noted in 12/13.3.2.1.3(1) are required to be enclosed in 1-hour construction or protected by sprinklers. If the sprinkler option is chosen, an enclosure is still required; however, the enclosure need not be fire rated but is required only to form a membrane against the passage of smoke.

The hazards noted in 12/13.3.2.1.3(2) must be enclosed in 1-hour construction and be protected by automatic sprinklers.

Exhibits 12/13.29(a) through 12/13.29(c) illustrate the methods of protection specified by 12/13.3.2.1.3. The three different forms of protection of hazardous areas are illustrated in these exhibits. Exhibits 12/13.29(a) and 12/13.29(b) illustrate the two options for complying with 12/13.3.2.1.3(1), that is, separation via fire-rated barriers or protection by automatic sprinklers. Exhibit 12/13.29(c) illustrates the requirement of 12/13.3.2.1.3(2) that both fire resistance–rated separation and automatic sprinkler protection be provided.

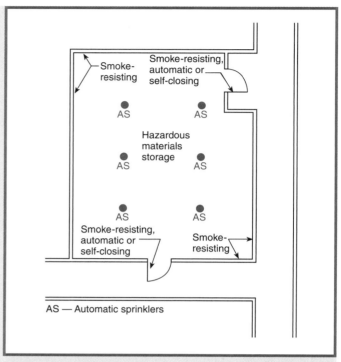

Exhibit 12/13.29(b) *Protection of hazardous areas using automatic sprinklers.*

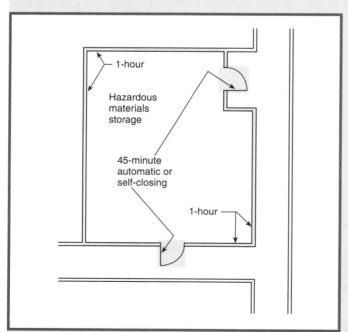

Exhibit 12/13.29(a) *Protection of hazardous areas using fire-rated enclosure.*

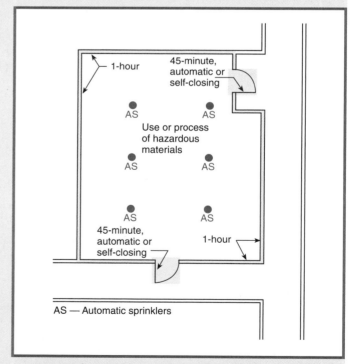

Exhibit 12/13.29(c) *Protection of hazardous areas using both fire-rated enclosure and automatic sprinklers.*

CHAPTER 12 • New	CHAPTER 13 • Existing

12.3.3 Interior Finish.

12.3.3.1 Interior finish shall be in accordance with Section 10.2.

12.3.3.2 Interior wall and ceiling finish materials complying with 10.2.3 shall be Class A or Class B in all corridors and lobbies and shall be Class A in enclosed stairways.

12.3.3.3 Interior wall and ceiling finish materials complying with 10.2.3 shall be Class A or Class B in general assembly areas having occupant loads of more than 300 and shall be Class A, Class B, or Class C in assembly areas having occupant loads of 300 or fewer.

12.3.3.4 Screens on which pictures are projected shall comply with requirements of Class A or Class B interior finish in accordance with 10.2.3.

Evaluation of existing interior finish is sometimes difficult. Where flame spread characteristics cannot be readily determined, the questionable material should be removed or treated with approved flame

12.3.3.5 Interior Floor Finish. (No requirements.)

12.3.4 Detection, Alarm, and Communications Systems.

12.3.4.1 General. Assembly occupancies with occupant loads of more than 300 and all theaters with more than one audience-viewing room shall be provided with an approved fire alarm system in accordance with 9.6.1 and 12.3.4.

Exception No. 1: Assembly occupancies that are a part of a mixed occupancy (see 6.1.14) shall be permitted to be served by a common fire alarm system, provided that the individual requirements of each occupancy are met.

Exception No. 2: Voice communication or public address systems complying with 12.3.4.3.3 shall not be required to comply with 9.6.1.

12.3.4.2 Initiation.

12.3.4.2.1 Initiation of the required fire alarm system shall be by manual means in accordance with 9.6.2.1(1), and the

13.3.3 Interior Finish.

13.3.3.1 Interior finish shall be in accordance with Section 10.2.

13.3.3.2 Interior wall and ceiling finish materials complying with 10.2.3 shall be Class A or Class B in all corridors and lobbies and shall be Class A in enclosed stairways.

13.3.3.3 Interior wall and ceiling finish materials complying with 10.2.3 shall be Class A or Class B in general assembly areas having occupant loads of more than 300, and shall be Class A, Class B, or Class C in assembly areas having occupant loads of 300 or fewer.

13.3.3.4 Screens on which pictures are projected shall comply with requirements of Class A or Class B interior finish in accordance with 10.2.3.

retardants. Where treatment cannot reduce flame spread to the required limits, automatic sprinklers might be provided to help compensate for the deficiency.

13.3.3.5 Interior Floor Finish. (No requirements.)

13.3.4 Detection, Alarm, and Communications Systems.

13.3.4.1 General. Assembly occupancies with occupant loads of more than 300 and all theaters with more than one audience-viewing room shall be provided with an approved fire alarm system in accordance with 9.6.1 and 13.3.4.

Exception No. 1: Assembly occupancies that are a part of a mixed occupancy (see 6.1.14) shall be permitted to be served by a common fire alarm system, provided that the individual requirements of each occupancy are met.

Exception No. 2: Voice communication or public address systems complying with 13.3.4.3.3 shall not be required to comply with 9.6.1.

Exception No. 3: This requirement shall not apply to assembly occupancies where, in the judgment of the authority having jurisdiction, adequate alternative provisions exist or are provided for the discovery of a fire and for alerting the occupants promptly.

13.3.4.2 Initiation.

13.3.4.2.1 Initiation of the required fire alarm system shall be by manual means in accordance with 9.6.2.1(1), and the

CHAPTER 12 • New

CHAPTER 13 • Existing

system shall be provided with an emergency power source. The initiating device shall be capable of transmitting an alarm to a receiving station, located within the building, that is constantly attended when the assembly occupancy is occupied.

Exception No. 1:   This requirement shall not apply to fire alarm systems initiated by means of an approved automatic fire detection system in accordance with 9.6.2.1(2) that provides fire detection throughout the building.

Exception No. 2:   This requirement shall not apply to fire alarm systems initiated by means of an approved automatic sprinkler system in accordance with 9.6.2.1(3) that provides fire detection and protection throughout the building.

12.3.4.2.2* In assembly occupancies with occupant loads of more than 300, automatic detection shall be provided in all hazardous areas that are not normally occupied, unless such areas are protected throughout by an approved, supervised automatic sprinkler system in accordance with Section 9.7.

A.12.3.4.2.2 The intent is to require detectors only in nonsprinklered hazardous areas that are unoccupied. When the building is occupied, the detectors in the unoccupied, unsprinklered hazardous areas will initiate occupant notification. If the building is unoccupied, the fire in the nonsprinklered hazardous area is not a life safety issue, and the detectors, upon activation, are not required to notify anyone. The signal from a detector is permitted to be sent to a control panel in an area that is occupied when the building is occupied, but that is unoccupied when the building is unoccupied, without the need for central station monitoring or the equivalent.

12.3.4.3 Notification.

12.3.4.3.1 The required fire alarm system shall sound an audible alarm in a constantly attended receiving station within the building when occupied for purposes of initiating emergency action. Positive alarm sequence in accordance with 9.6.3.4 shall be permitted.

12.3.4.3.2 Occupant notification shall be by means of visible signals and voice announcements, either live or prerecorded, initiated by the person in the constantly attended location.

12.3.4.3.3 The announcement shall be made via an approved voice communication or public address system, provided with an emergency power source, that is audible above the ambient noise level of the assembly occupancy.

system shall be provided with an emergency power source. The initiating device shall be capable of transmitting an alarm to a receiving station, located within the building, that is constantly attended when the assembly occupancy is occupied.

Exception No. 1:   This requirement shall not apply to fire alarm systems initiated by means of an approved automatic fire detection system in accordance with 9.6.2.1(2) that provides fire detection throughout the building.

Exception No. 2:   This requirement shall not apply to fire alarm systems initiated by means of an approved automatic sprinkler system in accordance with 9.6.2.1(3) that provides fire detection and protection throughout the building.

13.3.4.2.2* In assembly occupancies with occupant loads of more than 300, automatic detection shall be provided in all hazardous areas that are not normally occupied, unless such areas are protected throughout by an approved automatic sprinkler system in accordance with Section 9.7.

A.13.3.4.2.2 The intent is to require detectors only in nonsprinklered hazardous areas that are unoccupied. Where the building is occupied, the detectors in the unoccupied, unsprinklered hazardous areas will initiate occupant notification. If the building is unoccupied, the fire in the nonsprinklered hazardous area is not a life safety issue, and the detectors, upon activation, are not required to notify anyone. The signal from a detector is permitted to be sent to a control panel in an area that is occupied when the building is occupied, but that is unoccupied when the building is unoccupied, without the need for central station monitoring or the equivalent.

13.3.4.3 Notification.

13.3.4.3.1 The required fire alarm system shall sound an audible alarm in a constantly attended receiving station within the building when occupied for purposes of initiating emergency action. A presignal system in accordance with 9.6.3.3 shall be permitted. Positive alarm sequence in accordance with 9.6.3.4 shall be permitted.

13.3.4.3.2 Occupant notification shall be by means of voice announcements, either live or prerecorded, initiated by the person in the constantly attended location.

13.3.4.3.3 The announcement shall be made via an approved voice communication or public address system that is audible above the ambient noise level of the assembly occupancy.

| CHAPTER 12 • New | CHAPTER 13 • Existing |

12.3.4.3.4 Where the authority having jurisdiction determines that a constantly attended location is impractical, a fire alarm system in accordance with Section 9.6 shall be used that meets the following criteria:

(1) It shall be initiated by manual fire alarm boxes in accordance with 9.6.2.1(1) or other approved means.
(2) It shall automatically provide prerecorded evacuation instructions in accordance with 9.6.3.10.

Exception No. 1 to 12/13.3.4.1 clarifies that the alarm system within a building housing occupancies in addition to an assembly occupancy must meet the alarm requirements applicable to each of those occupancies. However, a common alarm system can be shared by all the occupancies within the building. This provision allows an assembly occupancy in a school, hotel, hospital, mall, or other building to be served by the same fire alarm as the predominate occupancy, provided that it also meets the requirements applicable to alarm systems in an assembly occupancy.

Exception No. 2 to 12/13.3.4.1 allows a voice communication system or public address system installed to comply with 12/13.3.4.3.3 to be exempt from the installation requirements of NFPA 72, *National Fire Alarm Code*.[5] The daily use of this system should provide adequate self-supervision.

Exception No. 3 to 13.3.4.1, which applies only to existing assembly occupancies, specifically allows the authority having jurisdiction to permit the continued use of existing alternative means for discovering fire and alerting occupants—even if such means do not meet the myriad requirements of NFPA 72.

The provisions of 12/13.3.4.2.2 recognize that a fire developing in an unoccupied, nonsprinklered, hazardous area while the assembly area is in use could go undiscovered. Although separated by 1-hour fire resistance–rated barriers, these hazardous areas can present a significant hazard to occupants. Be-

13.3.4.3.4 Where the authority having jurisdiction determines that a constantly attended location is impractical, a fire alarm system in accordance with Section 9.6 shall be used that meets the following criteria:

(1) It shall be initiated by manual fire alarm boxes in accordance with 9.6.2.1(1) or other approved means.
(2) It shall automatically provide prerecorded evacuation instructions in accordance with 9.6.3.10.

cause a fire alarm system is already required, the additional requirement for either heat or smoke detection, as appropriate, is not a significant burden. Where sprinkler protection is provided, the fire is expected to be controlled, permitting early detection to be exempted.

The intent of 12/13.3.4 is to provide an alarm system that will not elicit a panic reaction from occupants. The panic reaction is avoided by providing a system that will permit activation by pull stations as required by 9.6.2.1 but that will not sound an audible alarm in the seating or audience areas of the assembly occupancy. In lieu of the audible alarm throughout the assembly occupancy, the system must sound an alarm in a constantly attended location. *Constantly attended*, in this case, means that, during the time the assembly occupancy is in use, the alarm panel must be attended. From that constantly attended location, voice messages that instruct the occupants can be issued via a public address system. This method allows for the orderly evacuation of the occupants and permits the issuance of proper evacuation instructions rather than simply sounding an evacuation alarm that might produce panic. The *Code* permits the use of prerecorded evacuation instructions that will automatically be played upon initiation of the system. With the approval of the authority having jurisdiction, this arrangement is permitted to be used in lieu of the attended station.

12.3.5 Extinguishment Requirements.

Buildings containing assembly occupancies with occupant loads of more than 300 shall be protected by an approved, supervised automatic sprinkler system in accordance with Section 9.7 as follows *(see also 12.1.6, 12.2.6, 12.3.2, and 12.3.6):*

(1) Throughout the story containing the assembly occupancy

13.3.5 Extinguishment Requirements.

(See also 13.1.6, 13.2.6, and 13.3.2.)

13.3.5.1 Fire Suppression Systems. Any assembly occupancy used or capable of being used for exhibition or display purposes shall be protected throughout by an approved automatic sprinkler system in accordance with Section 9.7 where the exhibition or display area exceeds 15,000 ft² (1400 m²).

CHAPTER 12 • New	CHAPTER 13 • Existing

(2) Throughout all stories below the story containing the assembly occupancy

(3) In the case of an assembly occupancy located below the level of exit discharge, throughout all stories intervening between that story and the level of exit discharge, including the level of exit discharge

Exception No. 1:   This requirement shall not apply to assembly occupancies used primarily for worship with fixed seating and not part of a mixed occupancy. (See 6.1.14.)

Exception No. 2:*   This requirement shall not apply to assembly occupancies consisting of a single multipurpose room of less than 12,000 ft² (1100 m²) that are not used for exhibition or display and are not part of a mixed occupancy.

A.12.3.5 Exception No. 2 It is the intent to permit a single multipurpose room of less than 12,000 ft² (1100 m²) to have certain small rooms as part of the single room. These rooms could be a kitchen, office, equipment room, and the like. It is also the intent that an addition could be made to an existing building without requiring that the existing building be sprinklered, where both the new and existing buildings have independent means of egress and a fire-rated separation is provided to isolate one building from the other.

A school gymnasium with egress independent of, and separated from, the school would be included in this exception, as would a function hall attached to a church with a similar egress arrangement.

Exception No. 3:   This requirement shall not apply to gymnasiums, skating rinks, and swimming pools used exclusively for participant sports with no audience facilities for more than 300 persons.

Exception No. 4:   In stadia and arenas, sprinklers shall be permitted to be omitted over the floor area used for contest, performance, or entertainment; over the seating areas; and over open-air concourses where an approved engineering analysis substantiates the ineffectiveness of the sprinkler protection due to building height and combustible loading.

Exception No. 5:   In unenclosed stadia and arenas, sprinklers shall be permitted to be omitted in the following areas:

(a) Press boxes less than 1000 ft² (93 m²)

(b) Storage facilities less than 1000 ft² (93 m²) if enclosed with not less than 1-hour fire resistance–rated construction

(c) Enclosed areas underneath grandstands that comply with 12.4.8.5

Exception No. 1:   In stadia and arenas, sprinklers shall be permitted to be omitted over the floor area used for contest, performance, or entertainment, over the seating areas, and over open-air concourses where an approved engineering analysis substantiates the ineffectiveness of the sprinkler protection due to building height and combustible loading.

Exception No. 2:   In unenclosed stadia and arenas, sprinklers shall be permitted to be omitted in the following areas:

(a) Press boxes less than 1000 ft² (93 m²)

(b) Storage facilities less than 1000 ft² (93 m²) where enclosed with not less than 1-hour fire resistance– rated construction

(c) Enclosed areas underneath grandstands that comply with 13.4.8.5

13.3.5.2 High-Rise Buildings. *(See 13.4.4.)*

Subsection 12/13.3.5 is one of the two primary locations within the chapter where automatic sprinkler protection might be required. The other is 12/13.1.6, which applies to minimum construction requirements. Each of these subsections is to be applied independently to determine whether automatic sprinkler protection is required. For example, if 12/13.1.6 does not require sprinklers for a particular assembly occupancy, based on building construction type and location within the building, 12.3.5 might require automatic sprinklers for that assembly occupancy based on occupant load, or 13.3.5 might require automatic sprinklers based on the floor area that is capable of being used for exhibition purposes. If one subsection requires sprinklers and the other does not, sprinklers must be provided.

The requirement for automatic sprinkler protection for new assembly occupancies with an ocupant load in excess of 300 persons was prompted by the occurrence of fires involving assembly occupancies, most notably the Beverly Hills Supper Club fire in 1977[6] and the MGM Grand Hotel fire in 1980.[7] The exceptions to the general requirement are important in that they limit the areas or buildings requiring sprinkler protection.

The concepts used in the diamond symbol note of Table 12.1.6 and the section symbol note of Table 13.1.6 are also used with regard to which areas must be sprinklered. If a five-story building has an assembly occupancy on the first floor, the floors above the assembly occupancy are not required to be sprinklered by the assembly occupancy provisions; however, sprinklering of those floors might be required by the applicable occupancy chapter. If the assembly occupancy is on the fifth floor, then the fifth floor and all floors below it would be required to be sprinklered.

Exception No. 1 to 12.3.5 exempts new places of worship with fixed seating from the sprinkler requirement of 12.3.5. The life safety record is reasonably good in these occupancies.

Exception No. 2 to 12.3.5 exempts multipurpose assembly occupancies that are contained in one room and have an area of less than 12,000 ft² (1100 m²). If the multipurpose room is used as an exhibition hall or for a display room, the exception does not apply. Exhibit and display halls have been shown to be fire and life safety problems because of the high fuel load and potential for rapid fire spread.

The text of A.12.3.5, Exception No. 2, clarifies that it is not the intent to prohibit the presence of normal ancillary spaces. However, a number of assembly rooms or a mixed occupancy would not be permitted to use this exception.

Exception No. 3 to 12.3.5 exempts gymnasiums, skating rinks (including ice and roller rinks), and swimming pools where there is an audience or spectator gallery with an occupant load of 300 or fewer persons. If the skating rink or swimming pool can be floored over and used for other purposes, then the multipurpose room requirements contained in Exception No. 2 might apply. If the spectator gallery has an occupant load greater than 300, then an automatic sprinkler system is required. In effect, Exception No. 3 exempts the participants on the gym floor, skating rink, or swimming pool from being counted as part of the 300-person threshold at which the provisions of 12.3.5 apply.

Two major questions that arise with regard to 12.3.5 deal with mixed occupancies—especially assembly/educational—and multiple assembly occupancies—especially religious halls with multipurpose rooms.

With regard to mixed occupancies, 6.1.14 states that, if mixed occupancies exist, the more stringent requirements applicable to any of the involved occupancies must be provided for all occupancies. Therefore, schools with assembly occupancies need to be fully sprinklered, unless the assembly occupancy can be treated as a separate occupancy, which would normally require independent egress systems and substantial fire-rated separating construction. If separate occupancies can be established, only the assembly occupancy would need to be sprinklered. Also, many school multipurpose rooms could potentially use Exception No. 2 for exemption from the sprinkler requirement. Exception No. 2 emphasizes that the assembly occupancy is essentially a single room and, thus, cannot be part of a mixed occupancy.

Exception No. 2 to 12.3.5 was originally intended for a typical fellowship hall, such as a VFW, American Legion, or Grange hall. Some ancillary rooms, such as kitchens, restrooms, storage rooms, or minor offices, will exist, and it is not the intent that these ancillary spaces disqualify a facility from using this exception; however, it is the intent that the facility consist essentially of only one major room. Often a church or similar facility would like to apply Exception No. 1 and Exception No. 2. Both exceptions would apply only if each area of the facility were treated separately. In other words, the egress systems of each area would

CHAPTER 12 • New

CHAPTER 13 • Existing

have to be independent of each other, and appropriate fire separation would need to be provided.

The provisions of 13.3.5—which apply to existing assembly occupancies—are not as stringent as those for new assembly occupancies. The requirement ap-

plies to assembly occupancies used or capable of being used for exhibition or display purposes. This requirement would apply to many facilities over 15,000 ft² (1400 m²), unless fixed seating or similar permanent obstruction to exhibition use is provided.

12.3.6 Corridors.

Interior corridors and lobbies shall be constructed in accordance with 7.1.3.1 and 8.2.3.

Exception No. 1: Corridor and lobby protection shall not be required where assembly rooms served by the corridor or lobby have at least 50 percent of their exit capacity discharging directly to the outside, independent of corridors and lobbies.

Exception No. 2: Corridor and lobby protection shall not be required in buildings protected throughout by an approved, supervised automatic sprinkler system in accordance with Section 9.7.

Exception No. 3: Lobbies serving only one assembly area that meet the requirements for intervening rooms (see 7.5.1.7) shall not be required to have a fire resistance rating.

Exception No. 4: Where the corridor ceiling is an assembly having a 1-hour fire resistance rating where tested as a wall, the corridor walls shall be permitted to terminate at the corridor ceiling.

13.3.6 Corridors.

(No requirement.)

The corridor provisions apply only to new assembly occupancies.

Exception No. 1 allows for corridor protection to be eliminated but requires 50 percent of the egress capacity of each assembly room to be direct to the outside, independent of corridors or lobbies. This requirement allows theaters, for example, to use nonrated doors between the audience seating chamber and the lobby. Nonrated doors are not required to latch. Absence of the latch helps to avoid the disruptive noise associated with unlatching the door any time an occupant enters or leaves the room.

Exception No. 2 recognizes the excellent record of automatic sprinkler systems. However, this exception requires the entire building, not only the assembly area, to be sprinklered.

Exception No. 3 recognizes the situation where the lobby serves only one assembly space and where, from a fire perspective, it can be considered part of that assembly space.

Exception No. 4 does not exempt the facility from providing fire-rated corridor walls. It permits the rated fire barrier to terminate tight against a ceiling that is constructed to be equivalent to a 1-hour wall.

Section 12.4 Special Provisions

12.4.1 Life Safety Evaluation.

12.4.1.1* Where a life safety evaluation is required by other provisions of the *Code*, it shall be performed by persons acceptable to the authority having jurisdiction. The life safety evaluation shall include a written assessment of safety measures for conditions listed in 12.4.1.2. The life safety evaluation shall be approved annually by the authority having jurisdiction and shall be updated for special or unusual conditions.

A.12.4.1.1 Life safety evaluations are examples of performance-based approaches to life safety. In this respect, significant guidance in the form and process of life safety evaluations is provided by Chapter 5, keeping in mind the firesafety emphasis in Chapter 5. The general approach to performance criteria, scenarios, evaluation, safety factors, documentation, maintenance, and periodic assessment (including a warrant of fitness) all apply to the broader considerations in a life safety evaluation. A life safety evaluation deals not only with fire but also with fire, storm, collapse, crowd behavior, and other related safety considerations for which a checklist is provided in A.12.4.1.3. Chapter 5 provides guidance, based on fire safety requirements, for establishing a documented case showing that products of combustion in all conceivable fire scenarios will not significantly endanger occupants using means of egress in the facility (for example, because of fire detection, automatic suppression, smoke control, large-volume space, or management procedures). Moreover, means of egress facilities plus facility management capabilities should be adequate to cope with scenarios where certain egress routes are blocked for some reason.

In addition to making realistic assumptions about the capabilities of persons in the facility (for example, an assembled crowd including many disabled persons or persons unfamiliar with the facility), the life safety evaluation should include a factor of safety of not less than 2.0 in all calculations relating to hazard development time and required egress time (the combination of flow time and other time needed to detect and assess an emergency condition, initiate egress, and move along the egress routes). The factor of safety takes into account the possibility that half of the egress routes might not be used (or be usable) in certain situations.

Regarding crowd behavior, the potential hazards created by larger masses of people and greater crowd densities (which can be problematic during ingress, occupancy, and egress) demand that technology be used by designers, managers, and authorities responsible for buildings to compen-

Section 13.4 Special Provisions

13.4.1 Life Safety Evaluation.

13.4.1.1* Where a life safety evaluation is required by other provisions of the *Code*, it shall be performed by persons acceptable to the authority having jurisdiction. The life safety evaluation shall include a written assessment of safety measures for conditions listed in 13.4.1.2. The life safety evaluation shall be approved annually by the authority having jurisdiction and shall be updated for special or unusual conditions.

A.13.4.1.1 Life safety evaluations are examples of performance-based approaches to life safety. In this respect, significant guidance in the form and process of life safety evaluations is provided by Chapter 5, keeping in mind the firesafety emphasis in Chapter 5. The general approach to performance criteria, scenarios, evaluation, safety factors, documentation, maintenance, and periodic assessment (including a warrant of fitness) all apply to the broader considerations in a life safety evaluation. A life safety evaluation deals not only with fire but also with fire, storm, collapse, crowd behavior, and other related safety considerations for which a checklist is provided in A.13.4.1.3. Chapter 5 provides guidance, based on fire safety requirements, for establishing a documented case showing that products of combustion in all conceivable fire scenarios will not significantly endanger occupants using means of egress in the facility (for example, because of fire detection, automatic suppression, smoke control, large-volume space, or management procedures). Moreover, means of egress facilities plus facility management capabilities should be adequate to cope with scenarios where certain egress routes are blocked for some reason.

In addition to making realistic assumptions about the capabilities of persons in the facility (for example, an assembled crowd including many disabled persons or persons unfamiliar with the facility), the life safety evaluation should include a factor of safety of not less than 2.0 in all calculations relating to hazard development time and required egress time (the combination of flow time and other time needed to detect and assess an emergency condition, initiate egress, and move along the egress routes). This factor of safety takes into account the possibility that half of the egress routes might not be used (or usable) in certain situations.

Regarding crowd behavior, the potential hazards created by larger masses of people and greater crowd densities (which can be problematic during ingress, occupancy, and egress) demand that technology be used by designers, managers, and authorities responsible for buildings to compensate for the relaxed egress capacity provisions of Table 12.4.2.3. In very large buildings for assembly use, the hazard of crowd crushes can exceed that of fire or structural failure. Therefore, the building designers, managers, event planners, security personnel, police authorities, and fire authorities, as well as the building construction authorities, should understand the potential problems and solutions, including coordination of their activities. For crowd behavior, this understanding includes factors of space, energy, time, and information, as well as specific crowd management techniques such as metering. Published guidance on these factors and techniques is found in the *SFPE Handbook of Fire Protection Engineering,* Section 3, Chapter 13, pp. 3-263–3-285 (Pauls, J., ''Movement of People''), and the publications referenced therein.

Tables 12.2.3.2 and 12.4.2.3 are based on a linear relationship between number of seats and nominal flow time, with not less than 200 seconds (3.3 minutes) for 2000 seats plus 1 second for every additional 50 seats up to 25,000. Beyond 25,000 total seats, the nominal flow time is limited to 660 seconds (11 minutes). Nominal flow time refers to the flow time for the most able group of patrons; some groups less familiar with the premises or less able groups might take longer to pass a point in the egress system. Although three or more digits are noted in the tables, the resulting calculations should be assumed to provide only two significant figures of precision.

12.4.1.2 Life safety evaluations shall include an assessment of the following conditions and related appropriate safety measures:

(1) Nature of the events and the participants and attendees
(2) Access and egress movement, including crowd density problems
(3) Medical emergencies
(4) Fire hazards
(5) Permanent and temporary structural systems
(6) Severe weather conditions
(7) Earthquakes
(8) Civil or other disturbances
(9) Hazardous materials incidents within and near the facility
(10) Relationships among facility management, event participants, emergency response agencies, and others having a role in the events accommodated in the facility

12.4.1.3* Life safety evaluations shall include assessments of both building systems and management features upon which reliance is placed for the safety of facility occupants. Such assessments shall consider scenarios appropriate to the facility.

sate for the relaxed egress capacity provisions of Table 13.4.2.3. In very large buildings for assembly use, the hazard of crowd crushes can exceed that of fire or structural failure. Therefore, the building designers, managers, event planners, security personnel, police authorities, and fire authorities, as well as the building construction authorities, should understand the potential problems and solutions, including coordination of their activities. For crowd behavior, this understanding includes factors of space, energy, time, and information, as well as specific crowd management techniques such as metering. Published guidance on these factors and techniques is found in the *SFPE Handbook of Fire Protection Engineering,* Section 3, Chapter 13, pp. 3-263–3-285 (Pauls, J., ''Movement of People'') and the publications referenced therein.

Tables 13.2.3.2 and 13.4.2.3 are based on a linear relationship between number of seats and nominal flow time, with not less than 200 seconds (3.3 minutes) for 2000 seats plus 1 second for every additional 50 seats up to 25,000. Beyond 25,000 total seats, the nominal flow time is limited to 660 seconds (11 minutes). Nominal flow time refers to the flow time for the most able group of patrons; some groups less familiar with the premises or less able groups might take longer to pass a point in the egress system. Although three or more digits are noted in the tables, the resulting calculations should be assumed to provide only two significant figures of precision.

13.4.1.2 Life safety evaluations shall include an assessment of the following conditions and the related appropriate safety measures:

(1) Nature of the events and the participants and attendees
(2) Access and egress movement, including crowd density problems
(3) Medical emergencies
(4) Fire hazards
(5) Permanent and temporary structural systems
(6) Severe weather conditions
(7) Earthquakes
(8) Civil or other disturbances
(9) Hazardous materials incidents within and near the facility
(10) Relationships among facility management, event participants, emergency response agencies, and others having a role in the events accommodated in the facility

13.4.1.3* Life safety evaluations shall include assessments of both building systems and management features upon which reliance is placed for the safety of facility occupants. Such assessments shall consider scenarios appropriate to the facility.

A.12.4.1.3 Factors to be considered in a Life Safety Evaluation include the following.

    (a) Nature of the Events Being Accommodated

(1) Ingress, intra-event movement, and egress patterns
(2) Ticketing and seating policies/practices
(3) Event purpose (e.g., sports contest, religious meeting)
(4) Emotional qualities (e.g., competitiveness) of event
(5) Time of day when event held
(6) Time duration of single event
(7) Time duration of attendees' occupancy of the building

    (b) Occupant Characteristics and Behavior

(1) Homogeneity
(2) Cohesiveness
(3) Familiarity with building
(4) Familiarity with similar events
(5) Capability (as influenced by factors such as age, physical abilities)
(6) Socioeconomic factors
(7) Small minority involved with recreational violence
(8) Emotional involvement with the event and other occupants
(9) Use of alcohol or drugs
(10) Food consumption
(11) Washroom utilization

    (c) Management

(1) Clear, contractual arrangements for facility operation/use as follows:

    a. Between facility owner and operator
    b. Between facility operator and event promoter
    c. Between event promoter and performer
    d. Between event promoter and attendee
    e. With police forces
    f. With private security services
    g. With ushering services

(2) Experience with the building
(3) Experience with similar events and attendees
(4) Thorough, up-to-date operations manual
(5) Training of personnel
(6) Supervision of personnel
(7) Communications systems and utilization
(8) Ratios of management and other personnel to attendees
(9) Location/distribution of personnel
(10) Central command location
(11) Rapport between personnel and attendees
(12) Personnel supportive of attendee goals
(13) Attendees respect for personnel due to the following:

A.13.4.1.3 Factors to be considered in a life safety evaluation might include the following.

    (a) Nature of the Events Being Accommodated

(1) Ingress, intra-event movement, and egress patterns
(2) Ticketing and seating policies/practices
(3) Event purpose (e.g., sports contest, religious meeting)
(4) Emotional qualities (e.g., competitiveness) of event
(5) Time of day when event held
(6) Time duration of single event
(7) Time duration of attendees' occupancy of the building

    (b) Occupant Characteristics and Behavior

(1) Homogeneity
(2) Cohesiveness
(3) Familiarity with building
(4) Familiarity with similar events
(5) Capability (as influenced by factors such as age, physical abilities)
(6) Socioeconomic factors
(7) Small minority involved with recreational violence
(8) Emotional involvement with the event and other occupants
(9) Use of alcohol or drugs
(10) Food consumption
(11) Washroom utilization

    (c) Management

(1) Clear, contractual arrangements for facility operation/use as follows:

    a. Between facility owner and operator
    b. Between facility operator and event promoter
    c. Between event promoter and performer
    d. Between event promoter and attendee
    e. With police forces
    f. With private security services
    g. With ushering services

(2) Experience with the building
(3) Experience with similar events and attendees
(4) Thorough, up-to-date operations manual
(5) Training of personnel
(6) Supervision of personnel
(7) Communications systems and utilization
(8) Ratios of management and other personnel to attendees
(9) Location/distribution of personnel
(10) Central command location
(11) Rapport between personnel and attendees
(12) Personnel supportive of attendee goals
(13) Attendees respect for personnel due to the following:

CHAPTER 12 • New	**CHAPTER 13 • Existing**

a. Dress (uniform) standards
b. Age and perceived experience
c. Personnel behavior, including interaction
d. Distinction between crowd management and control
e. Management's concern for facility quality (e.g., cleanliness)
f. Management's concern for entire event experience of attendees (i.e., not just during the occupancy of the building)

(d) Emergency Management Preparedness

(1) Complete range of emergencies addressed in operations manual
(2) Power loss
(3) Fire
(4) Severe weather
(5) Earthquake
(6) Crowd incident
(7) Terrorism
(8) Hazardous materials
(9) Transportation accident (e.g., road, rail, air)
(10) Communications systems available
(11) Personnel and emergency forces ready to respond
(12) Attendees clearly informed of situation and proper behavior

(e) Building Systems

(1) Structural soundness
(2) Normal static loads
(3) Abnormal static loads (e.g., crowds, precipitation)
(4) Dynamic loads (e.g., crowd sway, impact, explosion, wind, earthquake)
(5) Stability of nonstructural components (e.g., lighting)
(6) Stability of movable (e.g., telescoping) structures
(7) Fire protection
(8) Fire prevention (e.g., maintenance, contents, housekeeping)
(9) Compartmentation
(10) Automatic detection and suppression of fire
(11) Smoke control
(12) Alarm and communications systems
(13) Fire department access routes and response capability
(14) Structural integrity
(15) Weather protection
(16) Wind
(17) Precipitation (attendees rush for shelter or hold up egress of others)
(18) Lightning
(19) Circulation systems
(20) Flowline or network analysis
(21) Waywinding and orientation

a. Dress (uniform) standards
b. Age and perceived experience
c. Personnel behavior, including interaction
d. Distinction between crowd management and control
e. Management's concern for facility quality (e.g., cleanliness)
f. Management's concern for entire event experience of attendees (i.e., not just during the occupancy of the building)

(d) Emergency Management Preparedness

(1) Complete range of emergencies addressed in operations manual
(2) Power loss
(3) Fire
(4) Severe weather
(5) Earthquake
(6) Crowd incident
(7) Terrorism
(8) Hazardous materials
(9) Transportation accident (e.g., road, rail, air)
(10) Communications systems available
(11) Personnel and emergency forces ready to respond
(12) Attendees clearly informed of situation and proper behavior

(e) Building Systems

(1) Structural soundness
(2) Normal static loads
(3) Abnormal static loads (e.g., crowds, precipitation)
(4) Dynamic loads (e.g., crowd sway, impact, explosion, wind, earthquake)
(5) Stability of nonstructural components (e.g., lighting)
(6) Stability of movable (e.g., telescoping) structures
(7) Fire protection
(8) Fire prevention (e.g., maintenance, contents, housekeeping)
(9) Compartmentation
(10) Automatic detection and suppression of fire
(11) Smoke control
(12) Alarm and communications systems
(13) Fire department access routes and response capability
(14) Structural integrity
(15) Weather protection
(16) Wind
(17) Precipitation (attendees rush for shelter or hold up egress of others)
(18) Lightning
(19) Circulation systems
(20) Flowline or network analysis
(21) Waywinding and orientation

(22) Merging of paths (e.g., precedence behavior)
(23) Decision/branching points
(24) Route redundancies
(25) Counterflow, crossflow, and queuing situations
(26) Control possibilities, including metering
(27) Flow capacity adequacy
(28) System balance
(29) Movement time performance
(30) Flow times
(31) Travel times
(32) Queuing times
(33) Route quality
(34) Walking surfaces (e.g., traction, discontinuities)
(35) Appropriate widths and boundary conditions
(36) Handrails, guardrails, and other rails
(37) Ramp slopes
(38) Step geometries
(39) Perceptual aspects (e.g., orientation, signage, marking, lighting, glare, distractions)
(40) Route choices, especially for vertical travel
(41) Resting/waiting areas
(42) Levels of service (overall crowd movement quality)
(43) Services
(44) Washroom provision and distribution
(45) Concessions
(46) First aid and EMS facilities
(47) General attendee services

A scenario-based approach to performance-based fire safety is addressed in Chapter 5. In addition to using such scenarios and, more generally, the attention to performance criteria, evaluation, safety factors, documentation, maintenance, and periodic assessment required when the Chapter 5 option is used, life safety evaluations should consider scenarios based on characteristics important in assembly occupancies. These characteristics include the following:

(1) Whether there is a local or mass awareness of an incident, event, or condition that might provoke egress
(2) Whether the incident, event, or condition stays localized or spreads
(3) Whether or not egress is designed by facility occupants
(4) Whether there is a localized start to any egress or mass start to egress
(5) Whether exits are available or not available

Examples of scenarios and sets of characteristics that might occur in a facility include the following.

(a) *Scenario 1.* Characteristics: Mass start, egress desired (by management and attendees), exits not available, local awareness.

Normal egress at the end of an event occurs just as a

(22) Merging of paths (e.g., precedence behavior)
(23) Decision/branching points
(24) Route redundancies
(25) Counterflow, crossflow, and queuing situations
(26) Control possibilities, including metering
(27) Flow capacity adequacy
(28) System balance
(29) Movement time performance
(30) Flow times
(31) Travel times
(32) Queuing times
(33) Route quality
(34) Walking surfaces (e.g., traction, discontinuities)
(35) Appropriate widths and boundary conditions
(36) Handrails, guardrails, and other rails
(37) Ramp slopes
(38) Step geometries
(39) Perceptual aspects (e.g., orientation, signage, marking, lighting, glare, distractions)
(40) Route choices, especially for vertical travel
(41) Resting/waiting areas
(42) Levels of service (overall crowd movement quality)
(43) Services
(44) Washroom provision and distribution
(45) Concessions
(46) First aid and EMS facilities
(47) General attendee services

A scenario-based approach to performance-based fire safety is addressed in Chapter 5. In addition to utilizing such scenarios and, more generally, the attention to performance criteria, evaluation, safety factors, documentation, maintenance, and periodic assessment required when the Chapter 5 option is used, life safety evaluations should consider scenarios based on characteristics important in assembly occupancies. These characteristics include the following:

(1) Whether there is a local or mass awareness of an incident, event, or condition that might provoke egress
(2) Whether the incident, event, or condition stays localized or spreads
(3) Whether or not egress is designed by facility occupants
(4) Whether there is a localized start to any egress or mass start to egress
(5) Whether exits are available or not available

Examples of scenarios and sets of characteristics that might occur in a facility include the following:

(a) *Scenario 1.* Characteristics: Mass start, egress desired (by management and attendees), exits not available, local awareness.

Normal egress at the end of an event occurs just as a

CHAPTER 12 • New

CHAPTER 13 • Existing

severe weather condition induces evacuees at the exterior doors to retard or stop their egress. The backup that occurs in the egress system is not known to most evacuees, who continue to press forward (potentially resulting in a crowd crush).

(b) *Scenario 2.* Characteristics: Mass start, egress not desired (by management), exits possibly not available, mass awareness.

An earthquake occurs during an event. The attendees are relatively safe in the seating area. The means of egress outside the seating areas are relatively unsafe and vulnerable to aftershock damage. Facility management discourages mass egress until the means of egress can be checked and cleared for use.

(c) *Scenario 3.* Characteristics: Local start, incident stays local, egress desired (by attendees and management), exits available, mass awareness.

A localized civil disturbance (for example, firearms violence) provokes localized egress, which is seen by attendees, generally, who then decide to leave also.

(d) *Scenario 4.* Characteristics: Mass start, egress desired, incident spreads, exits not available, mass awareness.

In an open-air facility unprotected from wind, precipitation, and lightning, sudden severe weather prompts egress to shelter but not from the facility. The means of egress congest and block quickly as people in front stop once they are under shelter while people behind them continue to press forward (potentially resulting in a crowd crush).

These scenarios illustrate some of the broader factors to be taken into account when assessing the capability of both building systems and management features on which reliance is placed in a range of situations, not just fire emergencies. Some scenarios also illustrate the conflicting motivations of management and attendees based on differing perceptions of danger and differing knowledge of hazards, countermeasures, and capabilities. Mass egress might not be the most appropriate life safety strategy in some scenarios, such as Scenario 2.

Table A.12.4.1.3 summarizes the characteristics in the scenarios and provides a framework for developing other characteristics and scenarios that might be important for a particular facility, hazard, occupant type, event, or management.

severe weather condition induces evacuees at the exterior doors to retard or stop their egress. The backup that occurs in the egress system is not known to most evacuees, who continue to press forward potentially resulting in a crowd crush.

(b) *Scenario 2.* Characteristics: Mass start, egress not desired (by management), exits possibly not available, mass awareness.

An earthquake occurs during an event. The attendees are relatively safe in the seating area. The means of egress outside the seating areas are relatively unsafe and vulnerable to aftershock damage. Facility management discourages mass egress until the means of egress can be checked and cleared for use.

(c) *Scenario 3.* Characteristics: Local start, incident stays local, egress desired (by attendees and management), exits available, mass awareness.

A localized civil disturbance (for example, firearms violence) provokes localized egress, which is seen by attendees, generally, who then decide to leave also.

(d) *Scenario 4.* Characteristics: Mass start, egress desired, incident spreads, exits not available, mass awareness.

In an open-air facility unprotected from wind, precipitation, and lightning, sudden severe weather prompts egress to shelter but not from the facility. The means of egress congest and block quickly as people in front stop once they are under shelter while people behind them continue to press forward, potentially resulting in a crowd crush.

These scenarios illustrate some of the broader factors to be taken into account when assessing the capability of both building systems and management features on which reliance is placed in a range of situations, not just fire emergencies. Some scenarios also illustrate the conflicting motivations of management and attendees based on differing perceptions of danger and differing knowledge of hazards, countermeasures, and capabilities. Mass egress might not be the most appropriate life safety strategy in some scenarios, such as Scenario 2.

Table A.13.4.1.3 summarizes the characteristics in the scenarios and provides a framework for developing other characteristics and scenarios that might be important for a particular facility, hazard, occupant type, event, or management.

CHAPTER 12 • New   **CHAPTER 13 • Existing**

Table A.12.4.1.3 Life Safety Evaluation Scenario Characteristics Matrix

| | | | | | Management | | Occupants | | | | | | |
| | | | | | | | | | | | | | |
Scenario	Local Awareness	Mass Awareness	Incident Localized	Incident Spreads	Egress Desired	Egress Not Desired	Egress Desired	Egress Not Desired	Local Start	Mass Start	Exits Available	Exits Not Available	Other
1	X				X		X			X		X	
2		X				X				X		X	
3		X	X		X		X		X				
4		X		X			X			X		X	

Table A.13.4.1.3 Life Safety Evaluation Scenario Characteristics Matrix

| | | | | | Management | | Occupants | | | | | | |
| | | | | | | | | | | | | | |
Scenario	Local Awareness	Mass Awareness	Incident Localized	Incident Spreads	Egress Desired	Egress Not Desired	Egress Desired	Egress Not Desired	Local Start	Mass Start	Exits Available	Exits Not Available	Other
1	X				X		X			X		X	
2		X				X				X		X	
3		X	X		X		X		X				
4		X		X			X			X		X	

The preparation of life safety evaluations will become more common as assembly occupancy designers request approval, from authorities having jurisdiction, of designs using the various *Code* provisions that conditionally require the life safety evaluation. For example, to be considered smoke protected and thus be permitted to use the reduced egress capacity criteria of Table 12/13.4.2.3, a building must be sprinklered, be provided with features that prevent smoke-logging, and—most importantly—be assessed using a life safety evaluation conducted in accordance with 12/13.4.1.

The expansive material that is contained in A.12/A.13.4.1.3 helps stress that conducting a life safety evaluation is a complex process that should not be attempted by most *Code* practitioners. The authority having jurisdiction needs to realize that, if an evaluation doesn't cover nearly all of the subjects addressed in A.12/A.13.4.1.3, it should not be approved. A reduced egress capacity system in accordance with 12/13.4.2.3, but for which the life safety evaluation is inadequate, is itself an inadequate egress system. The reduced capacity factors of Table 12/13.4.2.3 are not to be used as a matter of right; rather, their use needs to be earned based on providing a comprehensive life safety evaluation.

12.4.2* Smoke-Protected Assembly Seating.

A.12.4.2 Outdoor facilities are not accepted as inherently smoke-protected but must meet the requirements of smoke-protected assembly seating in order to utilize the special requirements for means of egress.

12.4.2.1 Fire Protection Requirements. To be considered smoke protected, an assembly seating facility shall comply with the following:

(1) All enclosed areas with walls and ceilings in buildings or structures containing smoke-protected assembly seating

13.4.2* Smoke-Protected Assembly Seating.

A.13.4.2 Outdoor facilities are not accepted as inherently smoke-protected but must meet the requirements of smoke-protected assembly seating in order to use the special requirements for means of egress.

13.4.2.1 Fire Protection Requirements. To be considered smoke protected, an assembly seating facility shall comply with the following:

(1) All enclosed areas with walls and ceilings in buildings or structures containing smoke-protected assembly seating

shall be protected with an approved, supervised automatic sprinkler system in accordance with Section 9.7.

Exception No. 1:   The requirement of 12.4.2.1(1) shall not apply to the floor area used for the contest, performance, or entertainment, provided that the roof construction is more than 50 ft (15 m) above the floor level and use is restricted to low fire hazard uses.

Exception No. 2:*   Sprinklers required by 12.4.2.1(1) shall be permitted to be omitted over the floor area used for contest, performance, or entertainment and over the seating areas where an approved engineering analysis substantiates the ineffectiveness of the sprinkler protection due to building height and combustible loading.

A.12.4.2.1 Exception No. 2 The engineering analysis should be part of the life safety evaluation required by 12.4.1.

(2) All means of egress serving a smoke-protected assembly seating area shall be provided with smoke-actuated ventilation facilities or natural ventilation designed to maintain the level of smoke at not less than 6 ft (1.8 m) above the floor of the means of egress.

12.4.2.2 Life Safety Evaluation. To use the provisions of smoke-protected assembly seating, a facility shall be subject to a life safety evaluation in accordance with 12.4.1.

12.4.2.3   Where using Table 12.4.2.3, the number of seats specified shall be within a single assembly space, and interpolation shall be permitted between the specific values

shall be protected with an approved automatic sprinkler system in accordance with Section 9.7.

Exception No. 1:   The requirement of 13.4.2.1(1) shall not apply to the floor area used for the contest, performance, or entertainment, provided that the roof construction is more than 50 ft (15 m) above the floor level and use is restricted to low fire hazard uses.

Exception No. 2:*   Sprinklers required by 13.4.2.1(1) shall be permitted to be omitted over the floor area used for contest, performance, or entertainment and over the seating areas where an approved engineering analysis substantiates the ineffectiveness of the sprinkler protection due to building height and combustible loading.

A.13.4.2.1 Exception No. 2 The engineering analysis should be part of the life safety evaluation required by 13.4.1.

(2) All means of egress serving a smoke-protected assembly seating area shall be provided with smoke-actuated ventilation facilities or natural ventilation designed to maintain the level of smoke at not less than 6 ft (1.8 m) above the floor of the means of egress.

13.4.2.2 Life Safety Evaluation. To use the provisions of smoke-protected assembly seating, a facility shall be subject to a life safety evaluation in accordance with 13.4.1.

13.4.2.3   Where using Table 13.4.2.3, the number of seats specified shall be within a single assembly space, and interpolation shall be permitted between the specific values

Table 12.4.2.3 Capacity Factors

Number of Seats	Nominal Flow Time (sec)	Inch of Clear Width per Seat Served	
		Stairs	Passageways, Ramps, and Doorways
2,000	200	0.300AB	0.200C
5,000	260	0.200AB	0.150C
10,000	360	0.130AB	0.100C
15,000	460	0.096AB	0.070C
20,000	560	0.076AB	0.056C
25,000 or more	600	0.060AB	0.044C

Note: For SI units, 1 in. = 2.54 cm.

Table 13.4.2.3 Capacity Factors

Number of Seats	Nominal Flow Time (sec)	Inch of Clear Width per Seat Served	
		Stairs	Passageways, Ramps, and Doorways
2,000	200	0.300AB	0.200C
5,000	260	0.200AB	0.150C
10,000	360	0.130AB	0.100C
15,000	460	0.096AB	0.070C
20,000	560	0.076AB	0.056C
25,000 or more	600	0.060AB	0.044C

Note: For SI units, 1 in. = 2.54 cm.

CHAPTER 12 • New	CHAPTER 13 • Existing

shown. The minimum clear widths shown shall be modified in accordance with all of the following:

(1) If risers exceed 7 in. (17.8 cm) in height, multiply the stair width in Table 12.4.2.3 by factor A, where

$$A = 1 + \frac{(\text{riser height} - 7 \text{ in.})}{5}$$

(2) Stairs without a handrail located within a 30-in. (76-cm) horizontal distance shall be 25 percent wider than otherwise calculated, that is, multiply by factor $B = 1.25$.

(3) Ramps steeper than 1 in 10 slope where used in ascent shall have their widths increased by 10 percent, that is, multiply by factor $C = 1.10$.

The *Code* requires that extra caution be taken before a facility is permitted to use the less stringent capacity factors. To use the more lenient egress capacity factors contained in Table 12/13.4.2.3 (versus Table 12/13.2.3.2), the authority having jurisdiction must approve an assessment that demonstrates that all life safety hazards have been considered and that control measures have been provided to ensure that occupants evacuating the building will not be endangered by conditions developing faster than the time required to clear the means of egress. This assessment is known as a *life safety evaluation*. A life safety evaluation is a process that should not be undertaken lightly or without special competence in a wide range of life safety issues including, but not limited to, fire safety. See 12/13.4.1.

The nominal flow time values shown in Tables 12/13.2.3.2 and 12/13.4.2.3 are for reference and might be helpful to designers, consultants, managers, and others concerned with the expected performance of an egress system. They are not used for any further purposes (see 3.3.83 for a definition of *flow time*). When conducting the life safety evaluation, the capabilities of the occupants must be taken into account, for example, if the facilities are used by groups of occupants who are unfamiliar with the facility or less able to move quickly and in dense groups than are younger individuals commonly found at athletic events. The need to consider the capabilities of occupants in relation to circulation facility geometry has led to the application of several correction factors for use with the values for clear width in Tables 12/13.2.3.2 and 12/13.4.2.3. Maintaining the best possible geometries should be a priority that is heavily emphasized in new facilities. Therefore, the correc-

shown. The minimum clear widths shown shall be modified in accordance with all of the following:

(1) If risers exceed 7 in. (17.8 cm) in height, multiply the stair width in Table 13.4.2.3 by factor A, where

$$A = 1 + \frac{(\text{riser height} - 7 \text{ in.})}{5}$$

(2) Stairs without a handrail located within a 30-in. (76-cm) horizontal distance shall be 25 percent wider than otherwise calculated, that is, multiply by factor $B = 1.25$.

(3) Ramps steeper than 1 in 10 slope where used in ascent shall have their width increased by 10 percent, that is, multiply by factor $C = 1.10$.

tion factors in the tables, A, B, and C, will usually be 1.0. It might not be possible to achieve this level of safety in existing facilities. However, handrails can be retrofitted on aisles and other means of egress to significantly improve occupant safety and comfort. These factors are taken into account here and in other *Code* requirements for means of egress.

The reduction in required egress capacity factors provided by Table 12/13.4.2.3 must be used with caution. Maintenance of the proper balance among the relative egress capacities of each part of the means of egress system that occupants encounter as they leave the facility is required. Otherwise, the result is queuing or waiting at some points other than the point of origin.

Attention should be given to the occupants' acceptance of the queue or the wait at their seats before proceeding out of the building; however, if a "downstream" component of the means of egress system is relatively underdesigned, even greater attention should be given to the actual and perceived conditions faced by occupants.

Exhibit 12/13.30 shows egress from a large stadium. The egress performance provided is perceived to be acceptable in terms of time and other factors. Occupants' acceptance of the longer egress flow times, permitted by the *Code* for larger assembly facilities, should be taken into account when performing a life safety evaluation for the building. The photograph also shows a collection of people who can be expected to take somewhat longer to clear the building than is the case with football spectators (a reference group for the nominal flow time figures noted in Tables 12/13.2.3.2 and 12/13.4.2.3).

CHAPTER 12 • New	CHAPTER 13 • Existing

Exhibit 12/13.30 *Crowd egress from a large assembly facility that might be eligible for egress capacity factor reductions of Table 12/13.4.2.3. (Photograph courtesy of Jake Pauls.)*

12.4.2.4 Where smoke-protected assembly seating conforms to the requirements of 12.4.2, for rows of seats served by aisles or doorways at both ends, the number of seats per row shall not exceed 100, and the clear width of not less than 12 in. (305 cm) for aisle accessways shall be increased by 0.3 in. (0.8 cm) for every additional seat beyond the number stipulated in Table 12.4.2.4; however, the minimum clear width shall not be required to exceed 22 in. (55.9 cm).

13.4.2.4 Where smoke-protected assembly seating conforms to the requirements of 13.4.2, for rows of seats served by aisles or doorways at both ends, the number of seats per row shall not exceed 100, and the clear width of not less than 12 in. (305 cm) for aisle accessways shall be increased by 0.3 in. (0.8 cm) for every additional seat beyond the number stipulated in Table 13.4.2.4; however, the minimum clear width shall not be required to exceed 22 in. (55.9 cm).

Table 12.4.2.4 Smoke-Protected Assembly Seating

Total Number of Seats in the Space	Number of Seats per Row Permitted to Have a Clear Width Aisle Accessway of Not Less than 12 in. (30.5 cm)	
	Aisle or Doorway at Both Ends of Row	Aisle or Doorway at One End of Row
<4,000	14	7
4,000–6,999	15	7
7,000–9,999	16	8
10,000–12,999	17	8
13,000–15,999	18	9
16,000–18,999	19	9
19,000–21,999	20	10
≥22,000	21	11

Table 13.4.2.4 Smoke-Protected Assembly Seating

Total Number of Seats in the Space	Number of Seats per Row Permitted to Have a Clear Width Aisle Accessway of Not Less than 12 in. (30.5 cm)	
	Aisle or Doorway at Both Ends of Row	Aisle or Doorway at One End of Row
<4,000	14	7
4,000–6,999	15	7
7,000–9,999	16	8
10,000–12,999	17	8
13,000–15,999	18	9
16,000–18,999	19	9
19,000–21,999	20	10
≥22,000	21	11

CHAPTER 12 • New	CHAPTER 13 • Existing

12.4.2.5 Where smoke-protected assembly seating conforms to the requirements of 12.4.2, for rows of seats served by an aisle or doorway at one end only, the aisle accessway clear width of not less than 12 in. (30.5 cm) shall be increased by 0.6 in. (1.6 cm) for every additional seat beyond the number stipulated in Table 12.4.2.4; however, the minimum clear width shall not be required to exceed 22 in. (55.9 cm).

12.4.2.6 Smoke-protected assembly seating conforming with the requirements of 12.4.2 shall be permitted to have a common path of travel of 50 ft (15 m) from any seat to a point where a person has a choice of two directions of egress travel.

12.4.2.7 Aisle Termination. Where smoke-protected assembly seating conforms to the requirements of 12.4.2, the dead ends in aisle stairs shall not exceed a distance of 21 rows.

Exception: A longer dead-end aisle shall be permitted for smoke-protected assembly seating where seats served by the dead-end aisle are not more than 40 seats from another aisle, measured along a row of seats having an aisle accessway with a clear width of not less than 12 in. (30.5 cm) plus 0.3 in. (0.8 cm) for each additional seat above seven in the row.

12.4.2.8 Where smoke-protected assembly seating conforms to the requirements of 12.4.2.1, the travel distance from each seat to the nearest entrance to an egress vomitory portal or egress concourse shall not exceed 400 ft (122 m). The travel distance from the entrance to the vomitory portal or from the egress concourse to an approved egress stair, ramp, or walk at the building exterior shall not exceed 200 ft (60 m).

Exception: In outdoor assembly seating facilities of Type I or Type II construction, where all portions of the means of egress are essentially open to the outside, the travel distance shall not be limited.

12.4.3 Windowless or Underground Buildings.

12.4.3.1 Windowless or underground buildings shall comply with 12.4.3 and Section 11.7.

12.4.3.2 Underground buildings or portions of buildings having a floor level more than 30 ft (9.1 m) below the level of exit discharge shall comply with the requirements of 12.4.3.3 through 12.4.3.5.

Exception No. 1: This requirement shall not apply to areas within buildings used only for service to the building, such as boiler/heater rooms, cable vaults, and dead storage.

13.4.2.5 Where smoke-protected assembly seating conforms with the requirements of 13.4.2, for rows of seats served by an aisle or doorway at one end only, the aisle accessway clear width of not less than 12 in. (30.5 cm) shall be increased by 0.6 in. (1.6 cm) for every additional seat beyond the number stipulated in Table 13.4.2.4; however, the minimum clear width shall not be required to exceed 22 in. (55.9 cm).

13.4.2.6 Smoke-protected assembly seating conforming with the requirements of 13.4.2 shall be permitted to have a common path of travel of 50 ft (15 m) from any seat to a point where a person has a choice of two directions of egress travel.

13.4.2.7 Aisle Termination. Where smoke-protected assembly seating conforms to the requirements of 13.4.2, the dead ends in aisle stairs shall not exceed a distance of 21 rows.

Exception: A longer dead-end aisle shall be permitted for smoke-protected assembly seating where seats served by the dead-end aisle are not more than 40 seats from another aisle, measured along a row of seats having an aisle accessway with a clear width of not less than 12 in. (30.5 cm) plus 0.3 in. (0.8 cm) for each additional seat above seven in the row.

13.4.2.8 Where smoke-protected assembly seating conforms to the requirements of 13.4.2.1, the travel distance from each seat to the nearest entrance to an egress vomitory portal or egress concourse shall not exceed 400 ft (122 m). The travel distance from the entrance to the vomitory portal or from the egress concourse to an approved egress stair, ramp, or walk at the building exterior shall not exceed 200 ft (60 m).

Exception: In outdoor assembly seating facilities of Type I or Type II construction, where all portions of the means of egress are essentially open to the outside, the travel distance shall not be limited.

13.4.3 Windowless or Underground Buildings.

Windowless or underground buildings shall comply with Section 11.7.

Exception No. 2:   This requirement shall not apply to auditoriums without intervening occupiable levels complying with the requirements of this chapter.

12.4.3.3   Each level more than 30 ft (9.1 m) below the level of exit discharge shall be divided into not less than two smoke compartments by a smoke barrier complying with Section 8.3 and shall have a 1-hour fire resistance rating.

12.4.3.3.1   Each smoke compartment shall have access to not less than one exit without passing through the other required compartment. Any doors connecting required compartments shall be tight-fitting, minimum 1-hour rated fire doors designed and installed to minimize smoke leakage and to close and latch automatically upon detection of smoke.

12.4.3.3.2   Each smoke compartment shall be provided with a mechanical means of moving people vertically, such as an elevator or escalator.

12.4.3.3.3   Each smoke compartment shall have an independent air supply and exhaust system capable of smoke control or smoke exhaust functions that provide a smoke exhaust rate of not less than six air changes per hour.

12.4.3.3.4   Each smoke compartment shall be provided with an automatic smoke detection system throughout. The system shall be designed so that the activation of any two detectors causes the smoke control system to operate and the building voice alarm to sound.

12.4.3.4   Any required smoke control or exhaust system shall be provided with a standby power system complying with Article 701 of NFPA 70, *National Electrical Code.*

12.4.3.5   The building shall be provided with an approved, supervised voice alarm system in accordance with Section 9.6. The voice alarm system shall comply with 9.6.3.10. A prerecorded evacuation message shall be provided.

Recognizing the potential hazard that underground buildings pose, the *Code* requires compliance with Section 11.7 and, in addition, for new assembly occupancies requires compliance with the provisions of 12.4.3.3 through 12.4.3.5 if the underground building has an assembly occupancy more than 30 ft (9.1 m) below the level of exit discharge, or if an assembly building has a floor level more than 30 ft (9.1 m) below the level of exit discharge.

Two exceptions to the base requirements of 12.4.3.2 are provided for areas used only for service functions (such as boiler rooms or heater rooms) and for assembly occupancies where there is no occupiable intervening level between the assembly occupancy and the level of exit discharge.

The provisions for underground buildings or portions of assembly buildings with an occupiable floor more than 30 ft (9.1 m) below the level of exit discharge are designed to provide protected areas on the subterranean level. This protection, coupled with a smoke control or smoke exhaust system, will provide sufficient time to egress the building. Elevators or escalators are required in each compartment to help rapidly evacuate the area (see Exhibit 9.4). It is believed that elevators or escalators will not, themselves, create a life safety threat because of the other requirements of 12.4.3, including separate smoke compartments and smoke control or exhaust systems. The elevator or escalator is not being considered the required means of egress; normal exits are still required.

To provide redundancy in the life safety provisions, standby power as defined in Article 701 of NFPA 70, *National Electrical Code*, is required for the smoke control or exhaust system.[8]

To permit orderly evacuation and to reduce the possibility of panic, 12.4.3.5 requires the use of a supervised voice alarm system that will sound a prerecorded evacuation message.

12.4.4 High-Rise Buildings.

High-rise assembly occupancy buildings and high-rise mixed occupancy buildings that house assembly occupancies in the high-rise portions of the building shall comply with Section 11.8.

13.4.4 High-Rise Buildings.

Existing high-rise buildings that house assembly occupancies in high-rise portions of the building shall have the highest level of the assembly occupancy and all levels below protected by an approved, supervised automatic sprinkler system in accordance with Section 9.7. *(See also 13.1.6.)*

A high-rise assembly occupancy has the same inherent life safety dangers that are found in other high-rise buildings. Therefore, the protection provided for high-rise buildings in general should be appropriate and applicable to assembly high-rise occupancies

and portions of high-rise buildings that are used for assembly occupancy. Note that the sprinkler requirement applies even to existing assembly occupancies located in the high-rise portion of a building.

12.4.5 Stages and Platforms.

(See 3.3.166 and 3.3.134.)

12.4.5.1 Materials and Design. Materials used in the construction of platforms and stages shall conform to the applicable requirements of the local building code.

12.4.5.2 Platform Construction. Temporary platforms shall be permitted to be constructed of any materials. The space between the floor and the platform above shall not be used for any purpose other than the electrical wiring to platform equipment.

Permanent platforms shall be of the materials required for the type of building construction in which the permanent platform is located, except that the finish floor shall be permitted to be of wood in all types of construction. Where the space beneath the platform is used for storage or any purpose other than equipment wiring or plumbing, the floor construction shall not be less than 1-hour fire resistive.

12.4.5.3 Stage Construction.

12.4.5.3.1 Regular stages shall be of the materials required for the type of building construction in which they are lo-

13.4.5 Stages and Platforms.

(See 3.3.166 and 3.3.134.)

13.4.5.1 Materials and Design. (Reserved.)

13.4.5.2 Platform Construction. (Reserved.)

13.4.5.3 Stage Construction. (Reserved.)

cated. In all cases, the finish floor shall be permitted to be of wood.

12.4.5.3.2 Legitimate stages shall be constructed of materials required for Type I buildings, except that the area extending from the proscenium opening to the back wall of the stage, and for a distance of 6 ft (183 cm) beyond the proscenium opening on each side, shall be permitted to be constructed of steel or heavy timber covered with a wood floor not less than 1½ in. (3.8 cm) in actual thickness.

12.4.5.3.3 Openings through stage floors (traps) shall be equipped with tight-fitting trap doors of wood having an actual thickness of not less than 1½ in. (3.8 cm) with approved safety locks.

12.4.5.4 Accessory Rooms. Workshops, storerooms, permanent dressing rooms, and other accessory spaces contiguous to stages shall be separated from each other and other building areas by 1-hour fire resistance–rated construction and protected openings.

Exception: A separation shall not be required for stages having a floor area not exceeding 1000 ft² (93 m²).

12.4.5.5 Ventilators. Regular stages in excess of 1000 ft² (93 m²) and legitimate stages shall be provided with emergency ventilation to provide a means of removing smoke and combustion gases directly to the outside in the event of a fire. Ventilation shall be by one, or a combination of, the following methods.

(a) *Smoke Control.* A means complying with Section 9.3 shall be provided to maintain the smoke level at not less than 6 ft (183 cm) above the highest level of assembly seating or above the top of the proscenium opening where a proscenium wall and opening protection are provided. The system shall be activated independently by each of the following:

(1) Activation of the sprinkler system in the stage area
(2) Activation of smoke detectors over the stage area
(3) Activation by manually operated switch at an approved location

The emergency ventilation system shall be supplied by both normal and standby power. The fan(s) power wiring and ducts shall be located and properly protected to ensure not less than 20 minutes of operation in the event of activation.

(b) *Roof Vents.* Two or more vents shall be located near the center of and above the highest part of the stage area. They shall be raised above the roof and shall provide a net-free vent area equal to 5 percent of the stage area. Vents

13.4.5.4 Accessory Rooms. (Reserved.)

13.4.5.5 Ventilators. Regular stages in excess of 1000 ft² (93 m²) and legitimate stages shall be provided with emergency ventilation to provide a means of removing smoke and combustion gases directly to the outside in the event of a fire. Ventilation shall be by one or a combination of the following methods.

(a) *Smoke Control.* A means complying with Section 9.3 shall be provided to maintain the smoke level at not less than 6 ft (183 cm) above the highest level of assembly seating or above the top of the proscenium opening where a proscenium wall and opening protection are provided. The system shall be activated independently by each of the following:

(1) Activation of the sprinkler system in the stage area
(2) Activation of smoke detectors over the stage area
(3) Activation by manually operated switch at an approved location

The emergency ventilation system shall be supplied by both normal and standby power. The fan(s) power wiring and ducts shall be located and properly protected to ensure not less than 20 minutes of operation in the event of activation.

(b) *Roof Vents.* Two or more vents shall be located near the center of and above the highest part of the stage area. They shall be raised above the roof and shall provide a net-free vent area equal to 5 percent of the stage area. Vents shall be constructed to open automatically by approved heat-activated devices. Supplemental means shall be provided for manual operation and periodic testing of the ventilator from the stage floor. Vents shall be labeled.

shall be constructed to open automatically by approved heat-activated devices. Supplemental means shall be provided for manual operation and periodic testing of the ventilator from the stage floor. Vents shall be labeled.

Exception: Existing roof vents that are not labeled shall be permitted to conform to the following requirements.

(a) Vents shall open by spring action or force of gravity sufficient to overcome the effects of neglect, rust, dirt, frost, snow, or expansion by heat or warping of the framework. Glass, if used in vents, shall be protected against falling onto the stage. A wire screen, if used under the glass, shall be placed so that if clogged, it does not reduce the required venting area, interfere with the operating mechanism, or obstruct the distribution of water from an automatic sprinkler. Vents shall be arranged to open automatically by the use of fusible links. The fusible links and operating cable shall hold each door closed against the minimum 30-lb (133-N) counterforce that shall be exerted on each door through its entire arc of travel and for not less than 115 degrees. A manual control shall be provided.

(b) Springs, where employed to actuate vent doors, shall be capable of maintaining full required tension. Springs shall not be stressed more than 50 percent of their rated capacity and shall not be located directly in the airstream nor exposed to the outside.

(c) A fusible link shall be placed in the cable control system on the underside of the vent at or above the roofline, or as approved by the building official, and shall be located so as not to be affected by the operation of an automatic sprinkler system. Remote, manual, or electric controls shall provide for both opening and closing of the vent doors for periodic testing and shall be located at a point on stage designated by the authority having jurisdiction. Where remote control vents are electrical, power failure shall not affect instant operation of the vent in the event of fire. Hand winches shall be permitted to be employed to facilitate operation of manually controlled vents.

(c) *Other Means.* Approved, alternate means of removing smoke and combustion gases shall be permitted.

(c) *Other Means.* Approved, alternate means of removing smoke and combustion gases shall be permitted.

12.4.5.6 Proscenium Walls. Legitimate stages shall be completely separated from the seating area by a proscenium wall of not less than 2-hour fire-resistive, noncombustible construction. The proscenium wall shall extend not less than 4 ft (122 cm) above the roof of the auditorium in combustible construction.

13.4.5.6 Proscenium Walls. (Reserved.)

All openings in the proscenium wall of a legitimate stage shall be protected by a fire assembly having a 1½-hour fire protection rating.

Exception No. 1:   The main proscenium opening used for viewing performances shall be provided with an automatic-closing fire-resistive curtain as described in 12.4.5.7.

Exception No. 2:   Proscenium walls shall not be required in smoke-protected assembly seating facilities constructed and operated in accordance with 12.4.2.

12.4.5.7 Proscenium Opening Protection. Where required by 12.4.5.6, the proscenium opening shall be protected by a fire curtain or an approved water curtain complying with NFPA 13, *Standard for the Installation of Sprinkler Systems.* The fire curtain or water curtain shall be designed to activate upon automatic detection of a fire and upon manual activation.

The fire curtain shall resist the passage of flame and smoke between the stage area and the audience area for 20 minutes.

A fire curtain shall be an opening protective assembly labeled by an approved agency or shall be constructed as follows.

(a) *Asbestos Fabrics.* Where not prohibited by applicable federal, state, or local law, a curtain shall be permitted to be made of one or more thicknesses of not less than a $2\frac{3}{4}$-lb/yd^2 (1.5-kg/m^2) AAA grade wire-inserted asbestos fabric or of another wire-inserted asbestos fabric of fire resistance exceeding $2\frac{3}{4}$-lb/yd^2 (1.5-kg/m^2) AAA grade wire-inserted fabric. Nonasbestos portions of these fabrics, if any, shall be flame-resistant treated so as not to support combustion.

(b) *Other Fabrics.* Curtains not meeting the criteria of 12.4.5.7(a) shall be made of one or more thicknesses of a noncombustible fabric or a fabric with a noncombustible base material. The fabric shall be permitted to be given a coating, provided that the modified fabric meets the criteria detailed in 12.4.5.7. Curtain fabrics shall have a weight of not less than $2\frac{3}{8}$ lb/yd^2 (1.3 kg/m^2).

(c) *Tensile Strength Requirements.* Curtain fabric shall have tensile strength requirements of not less than 400 lbf/in. (540 N/m) in both the warp and fill directions.

(d) *Wire-Insertion Reinforcement Requirements.* The fabric shall be reinforced with noncorrosive wire intertwined with the base fiber at a rate of not less than one wire per yarn. Wire shall not be required, and fabric weight shall be permitted to be less than $2\frac{3}{8}$ lb/yd^2 (1.3 kg/m^2) if it can be substantiated by approved tests that it is equivalent in strength and durability.

(e) *Fire Test.* A sample curtain with not less than two vertical seams shall be subjected to the standard fire test specified in NFPA 251, *Standard Methods of Tests of Fire Endurance of Building Construction and Materials,* as appli-

13.4.5.7 Proscenium Curtain. The proscenium opening of every legitimate stage shall be provided with a curtain constructed and mounted so as to intercept hot gases, flames, and smoke and to prevent flame from a fire on the stage from becoming visible from the auditorium side for a 5-minute period where the curtain is of asbestos. Other materials shall be permitted if they have passed a 30-minute fire test in a small-scale 3-ft × 3-ft (0.9-m × 0.9-m) furnace with the sample mounted in the horizontal plane at the top of the furnace and subjected to the standard time-temperature curve.

The curtain shall be automatic-closing without the use of applied power.

All proscenium curtains shall be in the closed position, except during performances, rehearsals, or similar activities.

Exception No. 1:   In lieu of the protection required herein, all the following shall be provided.

(a) A noncombustible opaque fabric curtain shall be arranged so that it closes automatically.

(b) An automatic, fixed waterspray deluge system shall be located on the auditorium side of the proscenium opening and shall be arranged so that the entire face of the curtain will be wetted. The system shall be activated by combination of rate-of-rise and fixed-temperature detectors located on the ceiling of the stage. Detectors shall be spaced in accordance with their listing. The water supply shall be controlled by a deluge valve and shall be sufficient to keep the curtain completely wet for 30 minutes or until the valve is closed by fire department personnel.

(c) The curtain shall be automatically operated in case of fire by a combination of rate-of-rise and fixed-temperature detectors that also activates the deluge spray system. Stage sprinklers and vents shall be automatically operated by fusible elements in case of fire.

(d) Operation of the stage sprinkler system or spray deluge valve shall automatically activate the emergency ventilating system and close the curtain.

(e) The curtain, vents, and spray deluge system valve shall also be capable of manual operation.

Exception No. 2:   This requirement shall not apply to proscenium fire curtains or water curtains complying with 12.4.5.7.

cable to nonbearing walls and partitions for a period of 30 minutes. The curtain shall overlap the furnace edges by a length that is appropriate to seal the top and sides. It shall have a bottom pocket containing not less than 4 lb/linear ft (5 kg/m) of batten. The unexposed surface of the curtain shall not glow, and neither flame nor smoke shall penetrate the curtain during the test period. Unexposed surface temperature and hose stream test requirements shall not be applicable to this proscenium fire safety curtain test.

(f) *Smoke Test.* Curtain fabrics shall have a smoke density not to exceed 25 where tested in accordance with NFPA 255, *Standard Method of Test of Surface Burning Characteristics of Building Materials.* The curtain fabric shall be tested in the condition in which it is to be used.

(g) *Curtain Operation.* The complete installation of every proscenium curtain shall be subjected to operating tests, and any theater in which a proscenium curtain is placed shall not be open to public performance until after the proscenium curtain has been accepted and approved by the authority having jurisdiction. The curtain shall be automatic-closing without the use of applied power. The curtain also shall be capable of manual operation.

(h) *Curtain Position.* All proscenium curtains shall be in the closed position, except during performances, rehearsals, or similar activities.

12.4.5.8 Gridiron, Fly Galleries, and Pinrails. Structural framing designed only for the attachment of portable or fixed theater equipment, gridirons, galleries, and catwalks shall be constructed of materials consistent with the building type of construction, and a fire resistance rating shall not be required.

Exception: Combustible materials shall be permitted for use as the floors of galleries and catwalks of all types of construction.

12.4.5.9 Catwalks. The clear width of lighting and access catwalks and the means of egress from galleries and gridirons shall be not less than 22 in. (56 cm).

12.4.5.10 Fire Protection. Every stage shall be protected by an approved, supervised automatic sprinkler system in compliance with Section 9.7. The protection shall be provided throughout the stage and in storerooms, workshops, permanent dressing rooms, and other accessory spaces contiguous to such stages.

Exception No. 1: Sprinklers shall not be required for stages 1000 ft² (93 m²) or less in area and 50 ft (15 m) or less in height where curtains, scenery, or other combustible hang-

13.4.5.8 Gridirons, Fly Galleries, and Pinrails. (Reserved.)

13.4.5.9 Catwalks. The clear width of lighting and access catwalks and the means of egress from galleries and gridirons shall be not less than 22 in. (56 cm).

13.4.5.10 Fire Protection. Every stage shall be protected by an approved automatic sprinkler system in compliance with Section 9.7. The protection shall be provided throughout the stage and in storerooms, workshops, permanent dressing rooms, and other accessory spaces contiguous to such stages.

Exception No. 1: Sprinklers shall not be required for stages 1000 ft² (93 m²) or less in area where curtains, scenery, or other combustible hangings are not retractable vertically.

CHAPTER 12 • New	CHAPTER 13 • Existing

ings are not retractable vertically. Combustible hangings shall be limited to a single main curtain, borders, legs, and a single backdrop.

Exception No. 2: Sprinklers shall not be required under stage areas less than 4 ft (1.2 m) in clear height used exclusively for chair or table storage and lined on the inside with ⅝-in. (1.6-cm) Type X gypsum wallboard or the approved equivalent.

12.4.5.11 Flame-Retardant Requirements. Combustible scenery of cloth, film, vegetation (dry), and similar materials shall meet the requirements of NFPA 701, *Standard Methods of Fire Tests for Flame Propagation of Textiles and Films.* Foamed plastics *(see definition of cellular or foamed plastic in 3.3.28)* shall be permitted to be used only by specific approval of the authority having jurisdiction. Scenery and stage properties not separated from the audience by proscenium opening protection shall be of either noncombustible or limited-combustible materials.

In theaters, motion picture theaters, and television stage settings, with or without horizontal projections, and in simulated caves and caverns of foamed plastic, any single fuel package shall have a heat release rate not to exceed 100 kW where tested in accordance with UL 1975, *Standard for Fire Tests for Foamed Plastics Used for Decorative Purposes.*

12.4.5.12* Standpipes. Regular stages over 1000 ft² (93 m²) in area and all legitimate stages shall be equipped with 1½-in. (38-mm) hose lines for first aid fire fighting at each side of the stage. Hose connections shall be in accordance with NFPA 13, *Standard for the Installation of Sprinkler Systems,* unless Class II or Class III standpipes in accordance with NFPA 14, *Standard for the Installation of Standpipe, Private Hydrants, and Hose Systems,* are used.

A.12.4.5.12 Prior editions of the *Code* required stages to be protected by a Class III standpipe system in accordance with NFPA 14, *Standard for the Installation of Standpipe, Private Hydrant, and Hose Systems.* NFPA 14 requires that Class II and Class III standpipes be automatic—not manual—because they are intended to be used by building occupants. Automatic standpipe systems are required to provide not less than 500 gpm (1893 L/min) at 100 psi (6.9 bar). This requirement often can be met only if a fire pump is installed. Installation of a fire pump presents an unreasonable burden for the system supplying the two hose outlets at the side of the stage. The revised wording of 12.4.5.12 offers some relief by permitting the hose outlets to be in accordance with NFPA 13, *Standard for the Installation of Sprinkler Systems.*

Combustible hangings shall be limited to a single main curtain, borders, legs, and a single backdrop.

Exception No. 2: Sprinklers shall not be required under stage areas less than 4 ft (1.2 m) in clear height used exclusively for chair or table storage and lined on the inside with ⅝-in. (1.6-cm) Type X gypsum wallboard or the approved equivalent.

13.4.5.11 Flame-Retardant Requirements. Combustible scenery of cloth, film, vegetation (dry), and similar materials shall meet the requirements of NFPA 701, *Standard Methods of Fire Tests for Flame Propagation of Textiles and Films.* Foamed plastics (see definition of cellular or foamed plastic in 3.3.28) shall be permitted to be used only by specific approval of the authority having jurisdiction. Scenery and stage properties on thrust stages shall be of either noncombustible or limited-combustible materials.

13.4.5.12* Standpipes. Stages over 1000 ft² (93 m²) in area shall be equipped with 1½-in. (38-mm) hose lines for first aid fire fighting at each side of the stage. Hose connections shall be in accordance with NFPA 13, *Standard for the Installation of Sprinkler Systems,* unless Class II or Class III standpipes in accordance with NFPA 14, *Standard for the Installation of Standpipe, Private Hydrants, and Hose Systems,* are used.

A.13.4.5.12 Prior editions of the *Code* required stages to be protected by a Class III standpipe system in accordance with NFPA 14, *Standard for the Installation of Standpipe, Private Hydrant, and Hose Systems.* NFPA 14 requires that Class II and Class III standpipes be automatic—not manual—because they are intended to be used by building occupants. Automatic standpipe systems are required to provide not less than 500 gpm (1893 L/min) at 100 psi (6.9 bar). This requirement often can be met only if a fire pump is installed. Installation of a fire pump presents an unreasonable burden for the system supplying the two hose outlets at the side of the stage. The revised wording of 13.4.5.12 offers some relief by permitting the hose outlets to be in accordance with NFPA 13, *Standard for the Installation of Sprinkler Systems.*

Modern stages pose problems that did not exist in the past. Scenery might be shifted horizontally, vertically, or both ways. The use of thrust stages and arena stages creates other problems.

The classic stage of the past rose high above the proscenium opening to accommodate the rigid asbestos curtain. The high void was a natural place to house combustible scenery for a performance, along with the rigging necessary for handling scene changes. This vertical storage area represented both a high fuel load and a space difficult to reach in case of fire. Many new theaters use a flexible, noncombustible curtain that does not require much height to accommodate it. Scenery on these stages is moved horizontally, thus reducing the distance necessary for storage between the top of the proscenium opening and the stage ceiling. Most combustible scenery is now stored in areas adjacent to the stage. All rigging and lighting is condensed in less vertical space.

Ventilators are addressed in 12/13.4.5.5. Small schools commonly have "stages" that are larger than 500 ft² (46.5 m²) but less than 1000 ft² (93 m²) in area. Small stages such as these do not pose the same fire potential as larger stages. Thus, the venting requirements of 12/13.4.5.5 apply to regular stages larger than 1000 ft² (93 m²) and to all legitimate stages. See the definitions of *stage* in 3.3.191 and *platform* in 3.3.149.

Subpart (a) of 12/13.4.5.5 uses performance-oriented language to specify the intended function of smoke control, if smoke control is the method used to provide the required ventilation. The performance criterion is to maintain the smoke level not less than 6 ft (1.8 m) above the highest level of the assembly seating or above the top of a proscenium opening where a proscenium wall and opening protection are provided. The methods detailed in NFPA 92B, *Guide for Smoke Management Systems in Malls, Atria, and Large Areas*, might be used in designing the smoke control system.[9]

In lieu of a smoke control system, subpart (b) permits roof vents to provide the required ventilation. For existing vents that are not listed, the exception to 13.4.5.5(b) provides prescriptive criteria that help to ensure that the vent will operate as reliably as a vent that is listed.

Subpart (c) to 12/13.4.5.5 allows for other approved means of removing smoke and combustion gases to fulfill the ventilation requirement of 12/13.4.5.5.

Proscenium opening protection is addressed in 12/13.4.5.7. The protection is to be provided by either a fire curtain or an approved water curtain. If a fire curtain is used, it is permitted to be a curtain complying with the criteria of 12.4.5.7(a) through (h), or it can be a labeled opening protective assembly. The option to use a labeled opening protective assembly includes use of a fire door. The horizontal sliding door detailed in 7.2.1.14 might be appropriate for such use.

For existing assembly occupancies, if, instead of the fire-resistant curtain specified in 13.4.5.7, a flexible proscenium curtain is used, the *Code* requires an automatic water spray system with nozzles on the auditorium side of the curtain. This system must be capable of completely wetting the curtain and of maintaining waterflow for at least 30 minutes or until the deluge valve is closed by the fire department.

Exception No. 2 to 13.4.5.7 permits the new fire curtains or water curtains mandated in Chapter 12 to serve in lieu of the curtains detailed in 13.4.5.7.

A proscenium curtain must be subjected to operating tests and be approved before its first use in a public performance. The curtain must be kept in the closed position after each day's performance is completed to help ensure the proper operation of the curtain in an emergency. The 1903 Iroquois Theater fire in Chicago demonstrated that a proscenium curtain might fail to close fully if it is not operated on a regular basis, if it is obstructed temporarily by scenery or props, or if it is obstructed permanently by alterations to the building.

Another benefit of keeping the curtain closed after performances is the prevention of property damage if a fire occurs after hours.

Required standpipes must be located on each side of a stage to provide stagehands and the responding fire department with manual fire-fighting capability in the area of a theater where a fire is most likely to occur. Standpipes are required, regardless of whether the stage has automatic sprinkler protection.

12.4.6 Projection Booths.

12.4.6.1 Film or video projectors or spotlights using light sources that produce particulate matter or toxic gases, or light sources that produce hazardous radiation without protective shielding, shall be located within a projection room complying with 12.3.2.1.3. Where cellulose nitrate film is used, the projection room shall comply with NFPA 40, *Standard for the Storage and Handling of Cellulose Nitrate Motion Picture Film.*

12.4.6.2 Projection Rooms for Safety Film. Projection rooms for safety film shall comply with 12.4.6.2.1 through 12.4.6.2.6.

12.4.6.2.1 Every projection room for safety film shall be of permanent construction consistent with the construction requirements for the type of building in which the projection room is located. Openings shall not be required to be protected. The room shall have a floor area of not less than 80 ft^2 (7.4 m^2) for a single machine and not less than 40 ft^2 (3.7 m^2) for each additional machine. Each motion picture projector, floodlight, spotlight, or similar piece of equipment shall have a clear working space of not less than 30 in. (76 cm) on each side and at its rear, but only one such space shall be required between adjacent projectors.

The projection room and the rooms appurtenant to it shall have a ceiling height of not less than 7 ft 6 in. (2.3 m).

12.4.6.2.2 Each projection room for safety film shall have not less than one out-swinging, self-closing door not less than 30 in. (76 cm) wide and 6 ft 8 in. (2 m) high.

12.4.6.2.3 The aggregate of ports and openings for projection equipment shall not exceed 25 percent of the area of the wall between the projection room and the auditorium. All openings shall be provided with glass or other approved material so as to completely close the opening.

12.4.6.2.4 Projection room ventilation shall be not less than the following.

(a) *Supply Air.* Each projection room shall be provided with adequate air supply inlets arranged to provide well-distributed air throughout the room. Air inlet ducts shall provide an amount of air equivalent to the amount of air being exhausted by projection equipment. Air shall be permitted to be taken from the outside; from adjacent spaces within the building, provided that the volume and infiltration rate is sufficient; or from the building air conditioning system, provided that it is arranged to supply sufficient air whether or not other systems are in operation.

13.4.6 Projection Booths.

13.4.6.1 Film or video projectors or spotlights using light sources that produce particulate matter or toxic gases, or light sources that produce hazardous radiation without protective shielding, shall be located within a projection room complying with 13.3.2.1.3. Where cellulose nitrate film is used, the projection room shall comply with NFPA 40, *Standard for the Storage and Handling of Cellulose Nitrate Motion Picture Film.*

13.4.6.2 Projection Rooms for Safety Film. Projection rooms for safety film shall comply with 13.4.6.2.1 through 13.4.6.2.6.

13.4.6.2.1 Every projection room for safety film shall be of permanent construction consistent with the construction requirements for the type of building in which the projection room is located. Openings shall not be required to be protected. The room shall have a floor area of not less than 80 ft^2 (7.4 m^2) for a single machine and not less than 40 ft^2 (3.7 m^2) for each additional machine. Each motion picture projector, floodlight, spotlight, or similar piece of equipment shall have a clear working space of not less than 30 in. (76 cm) on each side and at its rear, but only one such space shall be required between adjacent projectors.

The projection room and the rooms appurtenant to it shall have a ceiling height of not less than 7 ft 6 in. (2.3 m).

13.4.6.2.2 Each projection room for safety film shall have not less than one out-swinging, self-closing door not less than 30 in. (76 cm) wide and 6 ft 8 in. (2 m) high.

13.4.6.2.3 The aggregate of ports and openings for projection equipment shall not exceed 25 percent of the area of the wall between the projection room and the auditorium. All openings shall be provided with glass or other approved material so as to completely close the opening.

13.4.6.2.4 Projection room ventilation shall be not less than the following.

(a) *Supply Air.* Each projection room shall be provided with adequate air supply inlets arranged to provide well-distributed air throughout the room. Air inlet ducts shall provide an amount of air equivalent to the amount of air being exhausted by projection equipment. Air shall be permitted to be taken from the outside; from adjacent spaces within the building, provided that the volume and infiltration rate is sufficient; or from the building air conditioning system, provided that it is arranged to supply sufficient air whether or not other systems are in operation.

(b) *Exhaust Air.* Projection booths shall be permitted to be exhausted through the lamp exhaust system. The lamp exhaust system shall be positively interconnected with the lamp so that the lamp cannot operate unless there is sufficient airflow required for the lamp. Exhaust air ducts shall terminate at the exterior of the building in such a location that the exhaust air cannot be readily recirculated into any air supply system. The projection room ventilation system shall be permitted also to serve appurtenant rooms, such as the generator room and the rewind room.

12.4.6.2.5 Each projection machine shall be provided with an exhaust duct that draws air from each lamp and exhausts it directly to the outside of the building. The lamp exhaust shall be permitted to exhaust air from the projection room to provide room air circulation. Such ducts shall be of rigid materials, except for a flexible connector approved for the purpose. The projection lamp and projection room exhaust systems shall be permitted to be combined but shall not be interconnected with any other exhaust system or return-air system within the buildings. Specifications for electric arc and xenon projection equipment follow.

(a) *Electric Arc Projection Equipment.* The exhaust capacity shall be 200 ft³/min (0.09 m³/s) for each lamp connected to the lamp exhaust system, or as recommended by the equipment manufacturer. Auxiliary air shall be permitted to be introduced into the system through a screened opening to stabilize the arc.

(b) *Xenon Projection Equipment.* The lamp exhaust system shall exhaust not less than 300 ft³/min (0.14 m³/s) per lamp, or not less than that exhaust volume required or recommended by the equipment manufacturer, whichever is greater.

12.4.6.2.6 Miscellaneous equipment and storage shall be protected as follows:

(1) Each projection room shall be provided with rewind and film storage facilities.
(2) Flammable liquids containers shall be permitted in projection rooms, provided that the following criteria are met:

   a. There are not more than four containers per projection room
   b. No container has capacity exceeding 16 oz (0.5 L)
   c. Containers are of a nonbreakable type

(3) Appurtenant electrical equipment, such as rheostats, transformers, and generators, shall be permitted to be located within the booth or in a separate room of equivalent construction.

(b) *Exhaust Air.* Projection booths shall be permitted to be exhausted through the lamp exhaust system. The lamp exhaust system shall be positively interconnected with the lamp so that the lamp cannot operate unless there is sufficient airflow required for the lamp. Exhaust air ducts shall terminate at the exterior of the building in such a location that the exhaust air cannot be readily recirculated into any air supply system. The projection room ventilation system shall be permitted also to serve appurtenant rooms, such as the generator room and the rewind room.

13.4.6.2.5 Each projection machine shall be provided with an exhaust duct that draws air from each lamp and exhausts it directly to the outside of the building. The lamp exhaust shall be permitted to exhaust air from the projection room to provide room air circulation. Such ducts shall be of rigid materials, except for a flexible connector approved for the purpose. The projection lamp and projection room exhaust systems shall be permitted to be combined but shall not be interconnected with any other exhaust system or return-air system within the buildings. Specifications for electric arc and xenon projection equipment follow.

(a) *Electric Arc Projection Equipment.* The exhaust capacity shall be 200 ft³/min (0.09 m³/s) for each lamp connected to the lamp exhaust system, or as recommended by the equipment manufacturer. Auxiliary air shall be permitted to be introduced into the system through a screened opening to stabilize the arc.

(b) *Xenon Projection Equipment.* The lamp exhaust system shall exhaust not less than 300 ft³/min (0.14 m³/s) per lamp, or not less than that exhaust volume required or recommended by the equipment manufacturer, whichever is greater.

13.4.6.2.6 Miscellaneous equipment and storage shall be protected as follows:

(1) Each projection room shall be provided with rewind and film storage facilities.
(2) Flammable liquids containers shall be permitted in projection rooms, provided that the following criteria are met:

   a. There are not more than four containers per projection room
   b. No container has capacity exceeding 16 oz (0.5 L)
   c. Containers are of a nonbreakable type

(3) Appurtenant electrical equipment, such as rheostats, transformers, and generators, shall be permitted to be located within the booth or in a separate room of equivalent construction.

12.4.6.3 Projection Room Posting. A conspicuous sign with 1-in. (2.5-cm) block letters shall be posted on the outside of each projection room door and within the projection room proper, unless the projection room is constructed in accordance with NFPA 40, *Standard for the Storage and Handling of Cellulose Nitrate Motion Picture Film.* The sign shall state the following:

SAFETY FILM ONLY PERMITTED
IN THIS ROOM

13.4.6.3 Projection Room Posting. A conspicuous sign with 1-in. (2.5-cm) block letters shall be posted on the outside of each projection room door, and within the projection room proper, unless the projection room is constructed in accordance with NFPA 40, *Standard for the Storage and Handling of Cellulose Nitrate Motion Picture Film.* The sign and shall state the following:

SAFETY FILM ONLY PERMITTED
IN THIS ROOM

The requirements for projection booths were developed jointly with those of NFPA 40, *Standard for the Storage and Handling of Cellulose Nitrate Motion Picture Film,* and the motion picture industry when cellulose nitrate film was still being used.[10] Although only safety film is now used (except at film festivals or revivals) and the risk level has been reduced, the primary function of the requirements of 12/13.4.6.1 is to enclose the projection booth, eliminating it as an exposure threat to the theater audience.

The intent of 12/13.4.6.1 is to protect the audience from the dangers associated with light sources, such as electric arc or xenon. Where incandescent light is used, projection booths are not required in assembly occupancies. Note that the booth is required based on the light source, not on the use of film.

The provisions of 12/13.4.6.2 apply only to projection booths for the use of cellulose acetate or other safety film. Although openings in the booth do not need to be protected, they must be provided with glass or other approved material that will completely close the opening and prevent gas, dust, or radiation from contaminating the audience seating area.

New projection equipment in new theaters has a console that draws air in at the floor and up through the projection machine, thus eliminating the need to provide ducts near the floor.

The requirements of 12/13.4.6.2.4 for the ventilation of a projection booth are designed to isolate the booth from the theater so that any products of combustion created by a fire in a projection booth are not circulated into the theater. This isolation is achieved by providing an independent exhaust system for the booth, making certain that the exhaust outlet on the exterior of the building is located at a point where

the air intake for the theater cannot recirculate the exhausted air.

If fresh air for the projection booth's ventilation system is supplied from the general system of the building, it is essential that the combined system be arranged to ensure the required air changes in the booth even when no air is supplied to the general system of the building.

In 12/13.4.6.2.5, the *Code* specifies the minimum capacity for the exhaust system of a projection machine; however, a greater capacity must be provided where recommended by the manufacturer of the projection equipment. The system must be independent of any other ventilation system in the building housing the theater, but it can be combined with projection room ventilation.

The requirement of 12/13.4.6.2.6 for the storage and rewinding of film is intended to prevent these operations from taking place outside the projection booth at some less protected location where, if a fire occurred, the exposure to the theater would be significantly greater. All operations that relate to projection activities must be kept within the protected enclosure afforded by the projection booth.

Paragraph 12/13.4.6.3 requires that, unless the construction of a projection booth complies with NFPA 40, *Standard for the Storage and Handling of Cellulose Nitrate Motion Picture Film,* a conspicuous sign must be posted on the door of the projection booth and also inside the booth. The sign must state:

SAFETY FILM ONLY PERMITTED
IN THIS ROOM

The intent is to ensure that cellulose nitrate film is projected only with adequate safeguards.

12.4.7* Special Amusement Buildings.

A.12.4.7 Where a special amusement building is installed inside another building, such as within an exhibit hall, the special amusement building requirements apply only to the special amusement building. For example, the smoke detectors required by 12.4.7.3 are not required to be connected to the building's system. Where installed in an exhibit hall, such smoke detectors are also required to comply with the provisions applicable to an exhibit.

12.4.7.1 Special amusement buildings, regardless of occupant load, shall meet the requirements for assembly occupancies in addition to the requirements of 12.4.7, unless the multilevel play structures are not more than 10 ft (3 m) in height and have aggregate horizontal projections not exceeding 160 ft² (14.9 m²).

12.4.7.2* Every special amusement building, other than buildings or structures not exceeding 10 ft (3 m) in height and not exceeding 160 ft² (14.9 m²) in horizontal projection, shall be protected throughout by an approved, supervised automatic sprinkler system installed and maintained in accordance with Section 9.7. Where the special amusement building is movable or portable, the sprinkler water supply shall be permitted to be provided by an approved, temporary means.

A.12.4.7.2 It is the intent to provide a suppression system that will act quickly to provide for life safety of the occupants.

12.4.7.3 Where the nature of the special amusement building is such that it operates in reduced lighting levels, the building shall be protected throughout by an approved automatic smoke detection system in accordance with Section 9.6. Actuation of any smoke detection system device shall sound an alarm at a constantly attended location on the premises. Actuation of the automatic sprinkler system, or any other suppression system, or actuation of a smoke detection system having an approved verification or cross-zoning operation capability shall provide the following:

(1) Cause illumination in the means of egress to increase to that required by Section 7.8
(2) Stop any conflicting or confusing sounds and visuals

12.4.7.4 Exit Marking.

12.4.7.4.1 Exit marking shall be in accordance with Section 7.10.

12.4.7.4.2 Floor proximity exit signs shall be provided in accordance with 7.10.1.5.

13.4.7* Special Amusement Buildings.

A.13.4.7 Where a special amusement building is installed inside another building, such as within an exhibit hall, the special amusement building requirements apply only to the special amusement building. For example, the smoke detectors required by 13.4.7.3 are not required to be connected to the building's system. Where installed in an exhibit hall, such smoke detectors are also required to comply with the provisions applicable to an exhibit.

13.4.7.1 Special amusement buildings, regardless of occupant load, shall meet the requirements for assembly occupancies in addition to the requirements of 13.4.7, unless the building is a building in which the multilevel play structures are not more than 10 ft (3 m) in height and have aggregate horizontal projections not exceeding 160 ft² (14.9 m²).

13.4.7.2* Every special amusement building, other than buildings or structures not exceeding 10 ft (3 m) in height and not exceeding 160 ft² (14.9 m²) in horizontal projection, shall be protected throughout by an approved automatic sprinkler system installed and maintained in accordance with Section 9.7. Where the special amusement building is movable or portable, the sprinkler water supply shall be permitted to be provided by an approved, temporary means.

A.13.4.7.2 It is the intent to provide a suppression system that will act quickly to provide for life safety of the occupants.

13.4.7.3 Where the nature of the special amusement building is such that it operates in reduced lighting levels, the building shall be protected throughout by an approved automatic smoke detection system in accordance with Section 9.6. Actuation of any smoke detection system device shall sound an alarm at a constantly attended location on the premises. Actuation of the automatic sprinkler system, or any other suppression system, or actuation of a smoke detection system having an approved verification or cross-zoning operation capability shall provide the following:

(1) Cause illumination in the means of egress to increase to that required by Section 7.8
(2) Stop any conflicting or confusing sounds and visuals

13.4.7.4 Exit Marking.

13.4.7.4.1 Exit marking shall be in accordance with Section 7.10.

13.4.7.4.2 Floor proximity exit signs shall be provided in accordance with 7.10.1.5.

12.4.7.4.3* In special amusement buildings where mazes, mirrors, or other designs are used to confound the egress path, approved directional exit marking that becomes apparent in an emergency shall be provided.

A.12.4.7.4.3 Consideration should be given to the provision of directional exit marking on or adjacent to the floor.

12.4.7.5 Interior Finish. Interior finish shall be Class A throughout in accordance with Section 10.2.

Any special amusement building is considered an assembly occupancy, even if the occupant load is not more than 50 persons. However, special amusement buildings do not include theaters, movie houses, and other similar types of assembly occupancies.

Quick-response automatic sprinklers, as addressed in A.12/A.13.4.7.2, will be appropriate in most cases. However, the design should be reviewed by competent automatic sprinkler designers and the authority having jurisdiction.

It is the intent of 12/13.4.7.3 that the exits and means of egress be well lighted upon the activation

13.4.7.4.3* In special amusement buildings where mazes, mirrors, or other designs are used to confound the egress path, approved directional exit marking that becomes apparent in an emergency shall be provided.

A.13.4.7.4.3 Consideration should be given to the provision of directional exit marking on or adjacent to the floor.

13.4.7.5 Interior Finish. Interior finish shall be Class A throughout in accordance with Section 10.2.

of a smoke detector or suppression system. It is also important that any conflicting or confusing sounds or visuals are to be stopped and that, where a person's relative position to an exit is changed, additional exit signs are to be provided.

In special amusement buildings, the provision of directions to an exit is particularly important. Floor proximity exit signs, as required by 12/13.4.7.4.2, should provide patrons an additional tool to assist them in finding their way out under emergency conditions.

12.4.8 Grandstands.

The *Life Safety Code* means of egress provisions concerning bleacher or grandstand seating and folding or telescopic seating were taken from NFPA 102, *Stand-*

13.4.8 Grandstands.

ard for Grandstands, Folding and Telescopic Seating, Tents, and Membrane Structures.[11]

12.4.8.1 General. Grandstands shall comply with the provisions of this chapter as modified by 12.4.8.

13.4.8.1 General. Grandstands shall comply with the provisions of this chapter as modified by 13.4.8.

Exception: Existing grandstands shall be permitted to be continued to be used subject to the approval of the authority having jurisdiction.

12.4.8.2 Seating.

12.4.8.2.1 Where grandstand seating without backs is used indoors, rows of seats shall be spaced not less than 22 in. (55.9 cm) back-to-back.

12.4.8.2.2 The depth of footboards and seat boards in grandstands shall be not less than 9 in. (22.9 cm). Where the same level is not used for both seat foundations and footrests, footrests independent of seats shall be provided.

12.4.8.2.3 Seats and footrests of grandstands shall be supported securely and fastened in such a manner that they cannot be displaced inadvertently.

13.4.8.2 Seating.

13.4.8.2.1 Where grandstand seating without backs is used indoors, rows of seats shall be spaced not less than 22 in. (55.9 cm) back-to-back.

13.4.8.2.2 The depth of footboards and seat boards in grandstands shall be not less than 9 in. (22.9 cm). Where the same level is not used for both seat foundations and footrests, footrests independent of seats shall be provided.

13.4.8.2.3 Seats and footrests of grandstands shall be supported securely and fastened in such a manner that they cannot be displaced inadvertently.

CHAPTER 12 • New

CHAPTER 13 • Existing

12.4.8.2.4 Individual seats or chairs shall be permitted only if secured in rows in an approved manner, unless seats do not exceed 16 in number and are located on level floors and within railed-in enclosures, such as boxes.

12.4.8.3 Special Requirements—Wood Grandstands.

12.4.8.3.1 An outdoor wood grandstand shall be erected within not less than two-thirds of its height and, in no case, within not less than 10 ft (3 m) of a building.

Exception No. 1: The distance requirement shall not apply for buildings of not less than 1-hour fire resistance–rated construction with openings protected against the fire exposure hazard created by the grandstand.

Exception No. 2: The distance requirement shall not apply where a wall of not less than 1-hour fire resistance–rated construction separates such a grandstand from the building.

12.4.8.3.2 An outdoor wood grandstand unit shall not exceed 10,000 ft² (929 m²) in ground area or 200 ft (61 m) in length. Grandstand units of the maximum size shall be placed not less than 20 ft (6.1 m) apart or shall be separated by walls of 1-hour fire resistance rating. The number of such units erected in any one group shall not exceed three. Each group shall be separated from any other group by a wall of 2-hour fire resistance–rated construction extending 2 ft (0.6 m) above the seat platforms or by an open space of not less than 50 ft (15.2 m).

Exception: Where entirely constructed of labeled fire-retardant-treated wood that has passed the standard rain test, ASTM D 2898, Test Method for Accelerated Weathering of Fire-Retardant-Treated Wood for Fire Testing, or where constructed of members conforming to dimensions for heavy timber construction (Type IV (2HH)), the ground area or length shall be permitted to be doubled.

12.4.8.3.3 The highest level of seat platforms above the ground or the surface at the front of the grandstand for any wood grandstand shall not exceed 20 ft (6.1 m). For portable grandstands within tents or membrane structures, the highest level shall not exceed 12 ft (3.7 m).

Exception: Where entirely constructed of labeled fire-retardant-treated wood that has passed the standard rain test, ASTM D 2898, Test Method for Accelerated Weathering of Fire-Retardant-Treated Wood for Fire Testing, or where constructed of members conforming to dimensions for heavy timber construction (Type IV (2HH)), the height shall be permitted to be doubled.

13.4.8.2.4 Individual seats or chairs shall be permitted only if secured firmly in rows in an approved manner, unless seats do not exceed 16 in number and are located on level floors and within railed-in enclosures, such as boxes.

13.4.8.3 Special Requirements—Wood Grandstands.

13.4.8.3.1 An outdoor wood grandstand shall be erected within not less than two-thirds of its height and, in no case, within not less than 10 ft (3 m) of a building.

Exception No. 1: The distance requirement shall not apply for buildings of not less than 1-hour fire resistance–rated construction with openings protected against the fire exposure hazard created by the grandstand.

Exception No. 2: The distance requirement shall not apply where a wall of not less than 1-hour fire resistance–rated construction separates such a grandstand from the building.

13.4.8.3.2 An outdoor wood grandstand unit shall not exceed 10,000 ft² (929 m²) in ground area or 200 ft (61 m) in length. Grandstand units of the maximum size shall be placed not less than 20 ft (6.1 m) apart or shall be separated by walls of 1-hour fire resistance rating. The number of such units erected in any one group shall not exceed three. Each group shall be separated from any other group by a wall of 2-hour fire resistance–rated construction extending 2 ft (0.6 m) above the seat platforms or by an open space of not less than 50 ft (15.2 m).

Exception: Where entirely constructed of labeled fire-retardant-treated wood that has passed the standard rain test, ASTM D 2898, Test Method for Accelerated Weathering of Fire-Retardant-Treated Wood for Fire Testing, or where constructed of members conforming to dimensions for heavy timber construction (Type IV (2HH)), the ground area or length shall be permitted to be doubled.

13.4.8.3.3 The highest level of seat platforms above the ground or the surface at the front of the grandstand for any wood grandstand shall not exceed 20 ft (6.1 m). For portable grandstands within tents or membrane structures, the highest level shall not exceed 12 ft (3.7 m).

Exception: Where entirely constructed of labeled fire-retardant-treated wood that has passed the standard rain test, ASTM D 2898, Test Method for Accelerated Weathering of Fire-Retardant-Treated Wood for Fire Testing, or where constructed of members conforming to dimensions for heavy timber construction (Type IV (2HH)), the height shall be permitted to be doubled.

CHAPTER 12 • New	**CHAPTER 13 • Existing**

12.4.8.4 Special Requirements—Portable Grandstands.

12.4.8.4.1 Portable grandstands shall conform to the requirements of 12.4.8 for grandstands and the requirements of 12.4.8.4.2 and 12.4.8.4.3.

12.4.8.4.2 Portable grandstands shall be self-contained and shall have within them all necessary parts to withstand and restrain all forces that might be developed during human occupancy. They shall be designed and manufactured so that if any structural members essential to the strength and stability of the structure have been omitted during erection, the presence of unused connection fittings shall make the omissions self-evident. The construction shall be skillfully accomplished to produce the strength required by the design.

12.4.8.4.3 Portable grandstands shall be provided with base plates, sills, floor runners, or sleepers of such area that the permitted bearing capacity of the supporting material is not exceeded. Where portable grandstands rest directly on a base of such character that it is incapable of supporting the load without appreciable settlement, mud sills of suitable material, having sufficient area to prevent undue or dangerous settlement, shall be installed under base plates, runners, or sleepers. All bearing surfaces shall be in contact with each other.

12.4.8.5 Spaces Underneath Grandstands. Spaces underneath a grandstand shall be kept free of flammable or combustible materials, unless protected by an approved, supervised automatic sprinkler system in accordance with Section 9.7.

Exception No. 1: This requirement shall not apply to accessory uses of 300 ft² (28 m²) or less in area where of noncombustible or fire-resistive construction, such as ticket booths, toilet facilities, or concession booths, in otherwise nonsprinklered facilities.

Exception No. 2: This requirement shall not apply to rooms enclosed in not less than 1-hour fire resistance–rated construction that are less than 1000 ft² (93 m²) in area in otherwise nonsprinklered facilities.

12.4.8.6 Guards and Railings.

12.4.8.6.1 Railings or guards not less than 42 in. (107 cm) above the aisle surface or footrest or not less than 36 in. (91 cm) vertically above the center of the seat or seat board surface, whichever is adjacent, shall be provided along those portions of the backs and ends of all grandstands where the seats are more than 4 ft (1.2 m) above the floor or ground.

Exception: This requirement shall not apply where an adjacent wall or fence affords equivalent safeguard.

13.4.8.4 Special Requirements—Portable Grandstands.

13.4.8.4.1 Portable grandstands shall conform to the requirements of 13.4.8 for grandstands and the requirements of 13.4.8.4.2 and 13.4.8.4.3.

13.4.8.4.2 Portable grandstands shall be self-contained and shall have within them all necessary parts to withstand and restrain all forces that might be developed during human occupancy. They shall be designed and manufactured so that if any structural members essential to the strength and stability of the structure have been omitted during erection, the presence of unused connection fittings shall make the omissions self-evident. The construction shall be skillfully accomplished to produce the strength required by the design.

13.4.8.4.3 Portable grandstands shall be provided with base plates, sills, floor runners, or sleepers of such area that the permitted bearing capacity of the supporting material is not exceeded. Where portable grandstands rest directly on a base of such character that it is incapable of supporting the load without appreciable settlement, mud sills of suitable material, having sufficient area to prevent undue or dangerous settlement, shall be installed under base plates, runners, or sleepers. All bearing surfaces shall be in contact with each other.

13.4.8.5 Spaces Underneath Grandstands. Spaces underneath a grandstand shall be kept free of flammable or combustible materials, unless protected by an approved, supervised automatic sprinkler system in accordance with Section 9.7.

Exception No. 1: This requirement shall not apply to accessory uses of 300 ft² (28 m²) or less in area where of noncombustible or fire-resistive construction, such as ticket booths, toilet facilities, or concession booths, in otherwise nonsprinklered facilities.

Exception No. 2: This requirement shall not apply to rooms enclosed in not less than 1-hour fire resistance–rated construction that are less than 1000 ft² (93 m²) in area in otherwise nonsprinklered facilities.

13.4.8.6 Guards and Railings.

13.4.8.6.1 Railings or guards not less than 42 in. (107 cm) above the aisle surface or footrest or not less than 36 in. (91 cm) vertically above the center of the seat or seat board surface, whichever is adjacent, shall be provided along those portions of the backs and ends of all grandstands where the seats are in excess of 4 ft (1.2 m) above the floor or ground.

Exception: This requirement shall not apply where an adjacent wall or fence affords equivalent safeguard.

| CHAPTER 12 • New | CHAPTER 13 • Existing |

12.4.8.6.2 Where the front footrest of any grandstand is more than 2 ft (0.6 m) above the floor, railings or guards not less than 33 in. (84 cm) above such footrests shall be provided.

Exception: In grandstands, or where the front row of seats includes backrests, the rails shall be not less than 26 in. (66 cm) high.

12.4.8.6.3 Cross aisles located within the seating area shall be provided with rails not less than 26 in. (66 cm) high along the front edge of the cross aisle.

Exception: Where the backs of the seats in front of the cross aisle project 24 in. (61 cm) or more above the surface of the cross aisle, the rail shall not be required.

12.4.8.6.4 Vertical openings between guardrails and footboards or seat boards shall be provided with intermediate construction so that a 4-in. (10.2-cm) diameter sphere cannot pass through the opening.

12.4.8.6.5 An opening between the seat board and footboard located more than 30 in. (76 cm) above grade shall be provided with intermediate construction so that a 4-in. (10.2-cm) diameter sphere cannot pass through the opening.

12.4.9 Folding and Telescopic Seating.

12.4.9.1 General. Folding and telescopic seating shall comply with the provisions of this chapter as modified by 12.4.9.

12.4.9.2 Seating.

12.4.9.2.1 The horizontal distance of seats, measured back-to-back, shall be not less than 22 in. (55.9 cm) for seats without backs. There shall be a space of not less than 12 in. (30.5 cm) between the back of each seat and the front of each seat immediately behind it. If seats are of the chair type, the 12-in. (30.5-cm) dimension shall be measured to the front edge of the rear seat in its normal unoccupied position. All measurements shall be taken between plumb lines.

12.4.9.2.2 The depth of footboards (footrests) and seat boards in folding and telescopic seating shall be not less than 9 in. (22.9 cm). Where the same level is not used for both seat foundations and footrests, footrests independent of seats shall be provided.

13.4.8.6.2 Where the front footrest of any grandstand is more than 2 ft (0.6 m) above the floor, railings or guards not less than 33 in. (84 cm) above such footrests shall be provided.

Exception: In grandstands, or where the front row of seats includes backrests, the rails shall be not less than 26 in. (66 cm) high.

13.4.8.6.3 Cross aisles located within the seating area shall be provided with rails not less than 26 in. (66 cm) high along the front edge of the cross aisle.

Exception: Where the backs of the seats in front of the cross aisle project 24 in. (61 cm) or more above the surface of the cross aisle, the rail shall not be required.

13.4.8.6.4 Vertical openings between guardrails and footboards or seat boards shall be provided with intermediate construction so that a 4-in. (10.2-cm) diameter sphere cannot pass through the opening.

13.4.8.6.5 An opening between the seat board and footboard located more than 30 in. (76 cm) above grade shall be provided with intermediate construction so that a 4-in. (10.2-cm) diameter sphere cannot pass through the opening.

13.4.9 Folding and Telescopic Seating.

13.4.9.1 General. Folding and telescopic seating shall comply with the provisions of this chapter as modified by 13.4.9.

Exception: Existing folding and telescopic seating shall be permitted to be continued to be used subject to the approval of the authority having jurisdiction.

13.4.9.2 Seating.

13.4.9.2.1 The horizontal distance of seats, measured back-to-back, shall be not less than 22 in. (55.9 cm) for seats without backs. There shall be a space of not less than 12 in. (30.5 cm) between the back of each seat and the front of each seat immediately behind it. If seats are of the chair type, the 12-in. (30.5-cm) dimension shall be measured to the front edge of the rear seat in its normal unoccupied position. All measurements shall be taken between plumb lines.

13.4.9.2.2 The depth of footboards (footrests) and seat boards in folding and telescopic seating shall be not less than 9 in. (22.9 cm). Where the same level is not used for both seat foundations and footrests, footrests independent of seats shall be provided.

12.4.9.2.3 Individual chair-type seats shall be permitted in folding and telescopic seating only if firmly secured in groups of not less than three.

12.4.9.3 Guards and Railings.

12.4.9.3.1 Railings or guards not less than 42 in. (107 cm) above the aisle surface or footrest or not less than 36 in. (91 cm) vertically above the center of the seat or seat board surface, whichever is adjacent, shall be provided along those portions of the backs and ends of all folding and telescopic seating where the seats are more than 4 ft (1.2 m) above the floor or ground.

Exception: This requirement shall not apply where an adjacent wall or fence affords equivalent safeguard.

12.4.9.3.2 Where the front footrest of folding or telescopic seating is more than 2 ft (0.6 m) above the floor, railings or guards not less than 33 in. (84 cm) above such footrests shall be provided.

Exception: Where the front row of seats includes backrests, the rails shall be not less than 26 in. (66 cm) high.

12.4.9.3.3 Cross aisles located within the seating area shall be provided with rails not less than 26 in. (66 cm) high along the front edge of the cross aisle.

Exception: Where the backs of the seats in front of the cross aisle project 24 in. (61 cm) or more above the surface of the cross aisle, the rail shall not be required.

12.4.9.3.4 Vertical openings between guardrails and footboards or seat boards shall be provided with intermediate construction so that a 4-in. (10.2-cm) diameter sphere cannot pass through the opening.

12.4.9.3.5 An opening between the seat board and footboard located more than 30 in. (76 cm) above grade shall be provided with intermediate construction so that a 4-in. (10.2-cm) diameter sphere cannot pass through the opening.

Section 12.5 Building Services

12.5.1 Utilities.

Utilities shall comply with the provisions of Section 9.1.

12.5.2 Heating, Ventilating, and Air Conditioning Equipment.

Heating, ventilating, and air conditioning equipment shall comply with the provisions of Section 9.2.

13.4.9.2.3 Individual chair-type seats shall be permitted in folding and telescopic seating only if firmly secured in groups of not less than three.

13.4.9.3 Guards and Railings.

13.4.9.3.1 Railings or guards not less than 42 in. (107 cm) above the aisle surface or footrest or not less than 36 in. (91 cm) vertically above the center of the seat or seat board surface, whichever is adjacent, shall be provided along those portions of the backs and ends of all folding and telescopic seating where the seats are more than 4 ft (1.2 m) above the floor or ground.

Exception: This requirement shall not apply where an adjacent wall or fence affords equivalent safeguard.

13.4.9.3.2 Where the front footrest of folding or telescopic seating is more than 2 ft (0.6 m) above the floor, railings or guards not less than 33 in. (84 cm) above such footrests shall be provided.

Exception: Where the front row of seats includes backrests, the rails shall be not less than 26 in. (66 cm) high.

13.4.9.3.3 Cross aisles located within the seating area shall be provided with rails not less than 26 in. (66 cm) high along the front edge of the cross aisle.

Exception: Where the backs of the seats in front of the cross aisle project 24 in. (61 cm) or more above the surface of the cross aisle, the rail shall not be required.

13.4.9.3.4 Vertical openings between guardrails and footboards or seat boards shall be provided with intermediate construction so that a 4-in. (10.2-cm) diameter sphere cannot pass through the opening.

13.4.9.3.5 An opening between the seat board and footboard located more than 30 in. (76 cm) above grade shall be provided with intermediate construction so that a 4-in. (10.2-cm) diameter sphere cannot pass through the opening.

Section 13.5 Building Services

13.5.1 Utilities.

Utilities shall comply with the provisions of Section 9.1.

13.5.2 Heating, Ventilating, and Air Conditioning Equipment.

Heating, ventilating, and air conditioning equipment shall comply with the provisions of Section 9.2.

12.5.3 Elevators, Escalators, and Conveyors.

Elevators, escalators, and conveyors shall comply with the provisions of Section 9.4.

12.5.4 Rubbish Chutes, Incinerators, and Laundry Chutes.

Rubbish chutes, incinerators, and laundry chutes shall comply with the provisions of Section 9.5.

Section 12.6 Reserved

Section 12.7 Operating Features

12.7.1 Special Provisions for Food Service Operations.

12.7.1.1 All devices in connection with the preparation of food shall be installed and operated to avoid hazard to the safety of occupants.

12.7.1.2 All devices in connection with the preparation of food shall be of an approved type and shall be installed in an approved manner.

12.7.1.3 Food preparation facilities shall be protected in accordance with 9.2.3 and shall not be required to have openings protected between food preparation areas and dining areas.

12.7.1.4 Portable Cooking Equipment. Portable cooking equipment that is not flue-connected shall be permitted only as follows:

(1) Equipment fueled by small heat sources that can be readily extinguished by water, such as candles or alcohol-burning equipment, including solid alcohol, shall be permitted to be used, provided that precautions satisfactory to the authority having jurisdiction are taken to prevent ignition of any combustible materials.
(2) Candles shall be permitted to be used on tables used for food service where securely supported on substantial noncombustible bases located to avoid danger of ignition of combustible materials and only where approved by the authority having jurisdiction.
(3) Candle flames shall be protected.
(4) "Flaming sword" or other equipment involving open flames and flamed dishes, such as cherries jubilee or

13.5.3 Elevators, Escalators, and Conveyors.

Elevators, escalators, and conveyors shall comply with the provisions of Section 9.4.

13.5.4 Rubbish Chutes, Incinerators, and Laundry Chutes.

Rubbish chutes, incinerators, and laundry chutes shall comply with the provisions of Section 9.5.

Section 13.6 Reserved

Section 13.7 Operating Features

13.7.1 Special Provisions for Food Service Operations.

13.7.1.1 All devices in connection with the preparation of food shall be installed and operated to avoid hazard to the safety of occupants.

13.7.1.2 All devices in connection with the preparation of food shall be of an approved type and shall be installed in an approved manner.

13.7.1.3 Food preparation facilities shall be protected in accordance with 9.2.3 and shall not be required to have openings protected between food preparation areas and dining areas.

13.7.1.4 Portable Cooking Equipment. Portable cooking equipment that is not flue-connected shall be permitted only as follows:

(1) Equipment fueled by small heat sources that can be readily extinguished by water, such as candles or alcohol-burning equipment, including solid alcohol, shall be permitted to be used, provided that precautions satisfactory to the authority having jurisdiction are taken to prevent ignition of any combustible materials.
(2) Candles shall be permitted to be used on tables used for food service where securely supported on substantial noncombustible bases located to avoid danger of ignition of combustible materials and only where approved by the authority having jurisdiction.
(3)   Candle flames shall be protected.
(4) "Flaming sword" or other equipment involving open flames and flamed dishes, such as cherries jubilee or

crêpe suzette, shall be permitted to be used, provided that precautions subject to the approval of the authority having jurisdiction are taken.

(5)* Listed and approved LP-Gas commercial food service appliances shall be permitted to be used where in accordance with NFPA 58, *Liquefied Petroleum Gas Code.*

A.12.7.1.4(5) NFPA 58, *Liquefied Petroleum Gas Code,* permits portable butane-fueled appliances in restaurants and in attended commercial food catering operations where fueled by not more than two 10-oz (0.28-kg) LP-Gas capacity, nonrefillable butane containers that have a water capacity not exceeding 1.08 lb (0.4 kg) per container. The containers are required to be directly connected to the appliance, and manifolding of containers is not permitted. Storage of cylinders is also limited to 24 containers, with an additional 24 permitted where protected by a 2-hour fire resistance–rated barrier.

An approved type of device, as required by 12/13.7.1.2, means that, with regard to potential fire hazards, the unit is acceptable to the authority having jurisdiction. An "approved manner" of installation means installation acceptable to the authority having jurisdiction.

The *Code* depends on the automatic extinguishing system mandated by 9.2.3 to control any fire on the cooking surfaces and, thus, 12/13.7.1.3 does not require enclosure by rated construction.

12.7.2 Open Flame Devices and Pyrotechnics.

No open flame devices or pyrotechnic device shall be used in any assembly occupancy.

Exception No. 1: Pyrotechnic special effect devices shall be permitted to be used on stages before proximate audiences for ceremonial or religious purposes, as part of a demonstration in exhibits, or as part of a performance, provided that precautions satisfactory to the authority having jurisdiction are taken to prevent ignition of any combustible material and use of the pyrotechnic device complies with NFPA 1126, Standard for the Use of Pyrotechnics before a Proximate Audience.

Exception No. 2: Flame effects before an audience shall be permitted in accordance with NFPA 160, Standard for Flame Effects Before an Audience.

Exception No. 3: Open flame devices shall be permitted to be used in the following situations, provided that precautions satisfactory to the authority having jurisdiction are taken to

crêpe suzette, shall be permitted to be used, provided that precautions subject to the approval of the authority having jurisdiction are taken.

(5)* Listed and approved LP-Gas commercial food service appliances shall be permitted to be used where in accordance with NFPA 58, *Liquefied Petroleum Gas Code.*

A.13.7.1.4(5) NFPA 58, *Liquefied Petroleum Gas Code,* permits portable butane-fueled appliances in restaurants and in attended commercial food catering operations where fueled by not in excess of two 10-oz (0.28-kg) LP-Gas capacity, nonrefillable butane containers that have a water capacity not exceeding 1.08 lb (0.4 kg) per container. The containers are required to be directly connected to the appliance, and manifolding of containers is not permitted. Storage of cylinders is also limited to 24 containers, with and additional 24 permitted where protected by a 2-hour fire resistance–rated barrier.

The list of tragic fires in assembly occupancies caused by "friendly" fire (for example, alcohol or solid alcohol fires in restaurants, flames used for dramatic effects in theaters) is well documented. The requirements of 12/13.7.1.4 and 12/13.7.2 attempt to prevent a fire by tightly controlling the use of open flame devices.

13.7.2 Open Flame Devices and Pyrotechnics.

No open flame devices or pyrotechnic device shall be used in any assembly occupancy.

Exception No. 1: Pyrotechnic special effect devices shall be permitted to be used on stages before proximate audiences for ceremonial or religious purposes, as part of a demonstration in exhibits, or as part of a performance, provided that precautions satisfactory to the authority having jurisdiction are taken to prevent ignition of any combustible material and use of the pyrotechnic device complies with NFPA 1126, Standard for the Use of Pyrotechnics before a Proximate Audience.

Exception No. 2: Flame effects before an audience shall be permitted in accordance with NFPA 160, Standard for Flame Effects Before an Audience.

Exception No. 3: Open flame devices shall be permitted to be used in the following situations, provided that precautions satisfactory to the authority having jurisdiction are taken to prevent ignition of any combustible material or injury to occupants:

(a)* Where necessary for ceremonial or religious purposes

A.12.7.2 Exception No. 3(a) Securely supported altar candles in churches that are well separated from any combustible material are permitted. On the other hand, lighted candles carried by children wearing cotton robes present a hazard too great to be permitted. There are many other situations of intermediate hazard where the authority having jurisdiction will have to exercise judgment.

(b) On stages and platforms as a necessary part of a performance

(c) Where candles on tables are securely supported on substantial noncombustible bases and candle flame is protected.

Exception No. 4: This requirement shall not apply to heat-producing equipment complying with 9.2.2.

Exception No. 5: This requirement shall not apply to food service operations in accordance with 12.7.1.

Exception No. 6: Gas lights shall be permitted to be used, provided that precautions subject to the approval of the authority having jurisdiction are taken to prevent ignition of any combustible materials.

12.7.3 Furnishings, Decorations, and Scenery.

12.7.3.1 Fabrics and films used for decorative purposes, all draperies and curtains, and similar furnishings shall be in accordance with the provisions of 10.3.1.

12.7.3.2 The authority having jurisdiction shall impose controls on the quantity and arrangement of combustible contents in assembly occupancies to provide an adequate level of safety to life from fire.

12.7.3.3* Exposed foamed plastic materials and unprotected materials containing foamed plastic used for decorative purposes or stage scenery shall have a heat release rate not exceeding 100 kW where tested in accordance with UL 1975, *Standard for Fire Tests for Foamed Plastics Used for Decorative Purposes.*

Exception: This requirement shall not apply to individual foamed plastic items or items containing foamed plastic where the foamed plastic does not exceed 1 lb (0.45 kg) in weight.

A.12.7.3.3 The term *unprotected materials containing foamed plastic* is meant to include foamed plastic items

prevent ignition of any combustible material or injury to occupants:

(a)* Where necessary for ceremonial or religious purposes

A.13.7.2 Exception No. 3(a) Securely supported altar candles in churches that are well separated from any combustible material, are permitted. On the other hand, lighted candles carried by children wearing cotton robes present a hazard too great to be permitted. There are many other situations of intermediate hazard where the authority having jurisdiction will have to exercise judgment.

(b) On stages and platforms as a necessary part of a performance

(c) Where candles on tables are securely supported on substantial noncombustible bases and candle flame is protected

Exception No. 4: This requirement shall not apply to heat-producing equipment complying with 9.2.2.

Exception No. 5: This requirement shall not apply to food service operations in accordance with 13.7.1.

Exception No. 6: Gas lights shall be permitted to be used, provided that precautions subject to the approval of authority having jurisdiction are taken to prevent ignition of any combustible materials.

13.7.3 Furnishings, Decorations, and Scenery.

13.7.3.1 Fabrics and films used for decorative purposes, all draperies and curtains, and similar furnishings shall be in accordance with the provisions of 10.3.1.

13.7.3.2 The authority having jurisdiction shall impose controls on the quantity and arrangement of combustible contents in assembly occupancies to provide an adequate level of safety to life from fire.

13.7.3.3* Exposed foamed plastic materials and unprotected materials containing foamed plastic used for decorative purposes or stage scenery shall have a heat release rate not exceeding 100 kW where tested in accordance with UL 1975, *Standard for Fire Tests for Foamed Plastics Used for Decorative Purposes.*

Exception: This requirement shall not apply to individual foamed plastic items or items containing foamed plastic where the foamed plastic does not exceed 1 lb (0.45 kg) in weight.

A.13.7.3.3 The term unprotected materials containing foamed plastic is meant to include foamed plastic items

CHAPTER 12 • New	CHAPTER 13 • Existing

covered by "thermally-thin" combustible fabrics or paint. *(See A.10.2.3.2.)*

12.7.4 Special Provisions for Exposition Facilities.

12.7.4.1 No display or exhibit shall be installed or operated to interfere in any way with access to any required exit or with the visibility of any required exit or required exit sign; nor shall any display block access to fire-fighting equipment.

12.7.4.2 A storage room having an enclosure consisting of a smoke barrier having a fire resistance rating of 1 hour and protected by an automatic extinguishing system shall be provided for combustible materials not on display, including combustible packing crates used to ship exhibitors' supplies and products.

covered by "thermally-thin" combustible fabrics or paint. *(See A.10.2.3.2.)*

13.7.4 Special Provisions for Exposition Facilities.

13.7.4.1 No display or exhibit shall be installed or operated to interfere in any way with access to any required exit or with the visibility of any required exit or required exit sign; nor shall any display block access to fire-fighting equipment.

13.7.4.2 A storage room having an enclosure consisting of a smoke barrier having a fire resistance rating of 1 hour and protected by an automatic extinguishing system shall be provided for combustible materials not on display, including combustible packing crates used to ship exhibitors' supplies and products.

Exposition facilities have problems that differ from those of theaters, restaurants, or other assembly occupancies. They are large, multi-use facilities and have high ceilings appropriate to their size. Combustible materials are frequently displayed, and the containers in which the exhibits are shipped contribute to the fuel load. Due to the size of exhibition halls, most are required by 12/13.3.5.1 and 12/13.1.6 to be protected by automatic sprinklers.

The authority having jurisdiction at the local level is often working with organizations that exhibit on a national basis and that are unaware of the local fire safety regulations. It is the intent that this *Code* provide the more consistent and universal treatment needed in these occupancies and at the same time encourage more uniform enforcement practices.

Prior to the inclusion of 12/13.7.4, the trade show and exposition hall regulations used by many jurisdictions were very similar; however, there was no nationally recognized model code that could be referenced. This lack of a model code presented a hardship as well as confusion between the local authority having jurisdiction and persons responsible for the various functions of the trade show or exposition.

To meet the intent of 12/13.7.4.1, it is advisable to have prepared plans or diagrams to show the arrangement of displays or exhibits, including any that are to be suspended from the ceiling or housed within an overhead structure. Displays or exhibits must not interfere with access to any required exit, and they must not conceal exit signs. See Exhibit 12/13.31. A display should not block access to fire-fighting equip-

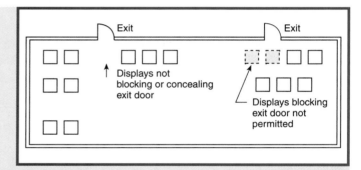

Exhibit 12/13.31 *Arrangement of displays in an exhibition hall.*

ment or interfere with the normal operation of automatic extinguishing equipment or devices for smoke evacuation.

Aisles serving rows of booths are exit accesses; therefore, booths and other temporary construction should be of minimal combustible construction or should be protected to avoid undue hazard of fire that might endanger occupants before they can reach available exits.

Displays or exhibits of combustible material must be limited in quantity in order to reduce the fuel load to an acceptable level. In accordance with 12/13.7.4.2, excess combustible display material and all other combustible materials that are not in use should be kept in a separate storage room until needed. A separation with a fire resistance rating of 1 hour is required between such a storage room and all other parts of the building, and the room must be protected by an automatic sprinkler system.

CHAPTER 12 • New

12.7.4.3 Exhibits.

12.7.4.3.1 Exhibits shall comply with 12.7.4.3.2 through 12.7.4.3.11.

12.7.4.3.2 The travel distance within the exhibit booth or exhibit enclosure to an exit access aisle shall not exceed 50 ft (15 m).

12.7.4.3.3 The upper deck of multilevel exhibits exceeding 300 ft² (27.9 m²) shall have not less than two remote means of egress.

12.7.4.3.4 Exhibit booths shall be constructed of the following:

(1) Noncombustible or limited-combustible materials
(2) Wood exceeding ¼ in. (0.6 cm) nominal thickness or wood not exceeding ¼ in. (0.6 cm) nominal thickness that is pressure-treated, fire-retardant wood meeting the requirements of NFPA 703, *Standard for Fire Retardant Impregnated Wood and Fire Retardant Coatings for Building Materials*
(3)* Flame-retardant materials complying with NFPA 701, *Standard Methods of Fire Tests for Flame Propagation of Textiles and Films*

A.12.7.4.3.4(3) The authority having jurisdiction might use the field flame test contained in NFPA 705, *Recommended Practice for a Field Flame Test for Textiles and Films,* as one method of determining flame retardancy.

(4) Textile wall coverings, such as carpeting and similar products used as wall or ceiling finishes, complying with the provisions of 10.2.2 and 10.2.4
(5) Plastics limited to those that comply with 12.3.3 and Section 10.2
(6) Foamed plastics and materials containing foamed plastics having a heat release rate for any single fuel package that does not exceed 100 kW where tested in accordance with UL 1975, *Standard for Fire Tests for Foamed Plastics Used for Decorative Purposes*
(7) Cardboard, honeycombed paper, and other combustible materials having a heat release rate for any single fuel package that does not exceed 150 kW where tested in accordance with UL 1975, *Standard for Fire Tests for Foamed Plastics Used for Decorative Purposes*

12.7.4.3.5 Curtains, drapes, and decorations shall comply with the applicable portions of 10.3.1.

12.7.4.3.6 Acoustical and decorative material including, but not limited to, cotton, hay, paper, straw, moss, split bamboo, and wood chips shall be flame-retardant treated to the satisfaction of the authority having jurisdiction. Materials that

CHAPTER 13 • Existing

13.7.4.3 Exhibits.

13.7.4.3.1 Exhibits shall comply with 13.7.4.3.2 through 13.7.4.3.11.

13.7.4.3.2 The travel distance within the exhibit booth or exhibit enclosure to an exit access aisle shall not exceed 50 ft (15 m).

13.7.4.3.3 The upper deck of multilevel exhibits greater than 300 ft² (27.9 m²) shall have not less than two remote means of egress.

13.7.4.3.4 Exhibit booths shall be constructed of the following:

(1) Noncombustible or limited-combustible materials
(2) Wood exceeding ¼ in. (0.6 cm) nominal thickness or wood not exceeding ¼ in. (0.6 cm) nominal thickness that is pressure-treated, fire-retardant wood meeting the requirements of NFPA 703, *Standard for Fire Retardant Impregnated Wood and Fire Retardant Coatings for Building Materials*
(3)* Flame-retardant materials complying with NFPA 701, *Standard Methods of Fire Tests for Flame Propagation of Textiles and Films*

A.13.7.4.3.4(3) The authority having jurisdiction might use the field flame test contained in NFPA 705, *Recommended Practice for a Field Flame Test for Textiles and Films,* as one method of determining flame retardancy.

(4) Textile wall coverings, such as carpeting and similar products used as wall or ceiling finishes, complying with the provisions of 10.2.2 and 10.2.4
(5) Plastics limited to those that comply with 12.3.3 and Section 10.2
(6) Foamed plastics and materials containing foamed plastics having a heat release rate for any single fuel package that does not exceed 100 kW where tested in accordance with UL 1975, *Standard for Fire Tests for Foamed Plastics Used for Decorative Purposes*
(7) Cardboard, honeycombed paper, and other combustible materials having a heat release rate for any single fuel package that does not exceed 150 kW where tested in accordance with UL 1975, *Standard for Fire Tests for Foamed Plastics Used for Decorative Purposes*

13.7.4.3.5 Curtains, drapes, and decorations shall comply with the applicable portions of 10.3.1.

13.7.4.3.6 Acoustical and decorative material including, but not limited to, cotton, hay, paper, straw, moss, split bamboo, and wood chips shall be flame-retardant treated to the satisfaction of the authority having jurisdiction. Materials that

| CHAPTER 12 • New | CHAPTER 13 • Existing |

cannot be treated for flame retardancy shall not be used. Foamed plastics and materials containing foamed plastics used as decorative objects such as, but not limited to, mannequins, murals, and signs shall have a heat release rate for any single fuel package that does not exceed 150 kW where tested in accordance with UL 1975, *Standard for Fire Tests for Foamed Plastics Used for Decorative Purposes.*

Exception: Where the aggregate area of such materials is less than 10 percent of the individual floor or wall area, such materials shall be permitted to be used subject to the approval of the authority having jurisdiction.

12.7.4.3.7 The following shall be protected by automatic extinguishing systems:

(1) Single-level exhibit booths exceeding 300 ft² (27.9 m²) and covered with a ceiling
(2) Each level of multilevel exhibit booths, including the uppermost level where the uppermost level is covered with a ceiling

A single exhibit or group of exhibits with ceilings that do not require sprinklers shall be separated by a distance of not less than 10 ft (3 m) where the aggregate ceiling exceeds 300 ft² (27.9 m²).

The water supply and piping for the sprinkler system shall be permitted to be of an approved, temporary means that is provided by a domestic water supply, a standpipe system, or a sprinkler system.

Exception No. 1: Ceilings that are constructed of open grate design or listed dropout ceilings in accordance with NFPA 13, Standard for the Installation of Sprinkler Systems, shall not be considered ceilings within the context of 12.7.4.3.7.

Exception No. 2: Vehicles, boats, and similar exhibited products having over 100 ft² (9.3 m²) of roofed area shall be provided with smoke detectors acceptable to the authority having jurisdiction.

Exception No. 3: *This requirement shall not apply where fire protection of multilevel exhibit booths is consistent with the criteria developed through a life safety evaluation of the exhibition hall in accordance with 12.4.1, subject to approval of the authority having jurisdiction.*

A.12.7.4.3.7 Exception No. 3 See A.12.4.1.1.

The requirement of 12/13.7.4.3.2 applies to a standard exhibit booth arrangement, whether constructed of pipe supports and cloth or paper drapes, or whether

cannot be treated for flame retardancy shall not be used. Foamed plastics and materials containing foamed plastics used as decorative objects such as, but not limited to, mannequins, murals, and signs shall have a heat release rate for any single fuel package that does not exceed 150 kW where tested in accordance with UL 1975, *Standard for Fire Tests for Foamed Plastics Used for Decorative Purposes.*

Exception: Where the aggregate area of such materials is less than 10 percent of the individual floor or wall area, such materials shall be permitted to be used subject to the approval of the authority having jurisdiction.

13.7.4.3.7 The following shall be protected by automatic extinguishing systems:

(1) Single-level exhibit booths exceeding 300 ft² (27.9 m²) and covered with a ceiling
(2) Each level of multilevel exhibit booths, protected throughout, including the uppermost level where the uppermost level is covered with a ceiling

A single exhibit or group of exhibits with ceilings that do not require sprinklers shall be separated by a distance not less than 10 ft (3 m) where the aggregate ceiling exceeds 300 ft² (27.9 m²).

The water supply and piping for the sprinkler system shall be permitted to be of approved, temporary means that is provided by a domestic water supply, a standpipe system, or a sprinkler system.

Exception No. 1: Ceilings that are constructed of open grate design or listed dropout ceilings in accordance with NFPA 13, Standard for the Installation of Sprinkler Systems, shall not be considered ceilings within the context of 13.7.4.3.7.

Exception No. 2: Vehicles, boats, and similar exhibited products having over 100 ft² (9.3 ft²) of roofed area shall be provided with smoke detectors acceptable to the authority having jurisdiction.

Exception No. 3: *This requirement shall not apply where fire protection of multilevel exhibit booths is consistent with the criteria developed through a life safety evaluation of the exhibition hall in accordance with 13.4.1, subject to approval of the authority having jurisdiction.*

A.13.7.4.3.7 Exception No. 3 See A.13.4.1.1.

---

it is a large exhibit enclosure designed and built from other materials, which could include small booths, open displays, large board displays, or other arrangements. This requirement also includes exhibit enclosures that are created by the arrangement of products such as machinery or vehicles. The intent is that travel distance is not to be more than 50 ft (15 m) for occupants that are inside the enclosure, whether they are employees or patrons. Note that this is not travel distance to an exit, but only to an aisle.

The requirement of 12/13.7.4.3.3 ensures that larger exhibits with a second level will provide at least two means of egress to prevent entrapping occupants on the upper level.

Plastics are limited to Class A and Class B for wall and ceiling finishes. The intent of 12/13.7.4.3.4(6) is to prohibit the use of foamed plastics because of their inherent burning characteristics, unless they have been tested for heat-release rate in accordance with UL 1975, *Standard for Fire Tests for Foamed Plastic Used for Decorative Purposes*, and meet the maximum 100-kW threshold. Foamed plastics are used in sign construction and display boards, and, in some cases, the entire booth is constructed of foamed plastics.[12]

Paragraph 12/13.7.4.3.4 is intended to provide direction to manufacturers of exhibit booths as well as decorators, exhibitors, and authorities having jurisdiction. This paragraph focuses on the construction components of the ceilings, walls, and floors of an exhibit booth or display area in addition to the finish treatment. The intent is to regulate the materials used for large signs and display boards; small signs [approximately 2 ft × 3 ft (0.6 m × 0.9 m) or smaller] would not normally be considered part of the wall covering. Paragraph 12/13.7.4.3.4 does not apply to the goods or products that are being displayed.

Large booths and multistory booths pose special life safety problems in exhibit halls. A fire in these booths could grow to proportions large enough to have a significant negative impact on the performance of the building's sprinkler system. The intent of 12/13.7.4.3.7 is to provide sprinkler protection in these booths by means of a temporary tap into the existing sprinkler system. Sprinklers should provide the protection necessary to extinguish a fire in its incipient stage, thus reducing the life hazard to occupants.

Exception No. 1 to 12/13.7.4.3.7 is not really an exception, because the exemption of sprinklers below dropout ceilings is already permitted by the reference document, NFPA 13, *Standard for the Installation of Sprinkler Systems.*[13] The exception was added to emphasize that it is not the intent to prohibit this provision of the sprinkler installation standard from being applied.

Exception No. 2 to 12/13.7.4.3.7 exempts large vehicles (that is, boats, mobile homes, and recreational vehicles) from the sprinkler requirement but requires a smoke detector if the vehicle is larger than 100 ft² (9.3 m²) to provide early warning in the immediate area to allow for orderly evacuation. This provision could most probably be met by single-station, battery-operated smoke alarms.

Exception No. 3 to 12/13.7.4.3.7 allows exposition hall operators to work with the authority having jurisdiction to devise alternate methods of compliance.

12.7.4.3.8 Open flame devices within exhibit booths shall comply with 12.7.2.

12.7.4.3.9 Cooking and food-warming devices in exhibit booths shall comply with 12.7.1 and the following:

(1) Gas-fired devices shall comply with the following:
   a. Natural gas-fired devices shall be in accordance with 9.1.1.

Exception: The requirement of 12.7.4.3.9(1)a shall not apply to compressed natural gas where permitted by the authority having jurisdiction.

   a. The use of LP-Gas cylinders shall be prohibited.

Exception: Nonrefillable LP-Gas cylinders shall be permitted to be used where permitted by the authority having jurisdiction.

13.7.4.3.8 Open flame devices within exhibit booths shall comply with 13.7.2.

13.7.4.3.9 Cooking and food-warming devices in exhibit booths shall comply with 13.7.1 and the following:

(1) Gas-fired devices shall comply with the following:
   a. Natural gas-fired devices shall be in accordance with 9.1.1.

Exception: The requirement of 13.7.4.3.9(1)a shall not apply to compressed natural gas where permitted by the authority having jurisdiction.

   b. The use of LP-Gas cylinders shall be prohibited.

Exception: Nonrefillable LP-Gas cylinders shall be permitted to be used where permitted by the authority having jurisdiction.

(2) The devices shall be isolated from the public by not less than 4 ft (1.2 m) or by a barrier between the devices and the public.

(3) Multi-well cooking equipment using combustible oils or solids shall comply with 9.2.3.

(4) Single-well cooking equipment using combustible oils or solids shall meet the following criteria:

    a. They shall have lids available for immediate use.

    b. They shall be limited to 288 in.^{2} (0.19 m^2) of cooking surface.

    c. They shall be placed on noncombustible surface materials.

    d. They shall be separated from each other by a horizontal distance of not less than 2 ft (0.6 m).

Exception: The requirement of 12.7.4.3.9(4)d shall not apply to multiple single-well cooking equipment where the aggregate cooking surface area does not exceed 288 in.^{2} (0.19 m^2).

    e. They shall be kept at a horizontal distance of not less than 2 ft (0.6 m) from any combustible material.

(5) A 20-B:C fire extinguisher shall be provided within the booth for each device, or an approved automatic extinguishing system shall be provided. *(See 9.7.4.1.)*

12.7.4.3.10 Combustible materials within exhibit booths shall be limited to a one-day supply. Storage of combustible materials behind the booth shall be prohibited. *(See 12.7.3.2 and 12.7.4.2.)*

12.7.4.3.11 Plans for the exposition, in an acceptable form, shall be submitted to the authority having jurisdiction for approval prior to setting up any exhibit. The plan shall show all details of the proposed exposition. No exposition shall occupy any exposition facility without approved plans.

(2) The devices shall be isolated from the public by not less than 4 ft (1.2 m) or by a barrier between the devices and the public.

(3) Multi-well cooking equipment using combustible oils or solids shall comply with 9.2.3.

(4) Single-well cooking equipment using combustible oils or solids shall meet the following criteria:

    a. They shall have lids available for immediate use.

    b. They shall be limited to 288 in.^{2} (0.19 m^2) of cooking surface.

    c. They shall be placed on noncombustible surface materials.

    d. They shall be separated from each other by a horizontal distance of not less than 2 ft (0.6 m).

Exception: The requirement of 13.7.4.3.9(4)d shall not apply to multiple single-well cooking equipment where the aggregate cooking surface area does not exceed 288 in.^{2} (0.19 m^2).

    e. They shall be kept at a horizontal distance of not less than 2 ft (0.6 m) from any combustible material.

(5) A 20-B:C fire extinguisher shall be provided within the booth for each device, or an approved automatic extinguishing system shall be provided. *(See 9.7.4.1.)*

13.7.4.3.10 Combustible materials within exhibit booths shall be limited to a one-day supply. Storage of combustible materials behind the booth shall be prohibited. *(See 13.7.3.2 and 13.7.4.2.)*

13.7.4.3.11 Plans for the exposition, in an acceptable form, shall be submitted to the authority having jurisdiction for approval prior to setting up any exhibit. The plan shall show all details of the proposed exposition. No exposition shall occupy any exposition facility without approved plans.

Open flame devices, as addressed in 12/13.7.4.3.8, should be prohibited, except for religious ceremonies. Where permitted, open flame devices should be restricted to minimize the danger of igniting combustibles. Any use of open flames should be allowed only with the approval by the authority having jurisdiction.

The provisions of 12/13.7.4.3.9(2) require separation distance or a barrier between the public and the device. The purpose is to guard against the dangers of accidental spills of hot greases or foods and to minimize the potential for ignition of combustibles, especially clothing worn by patrons.

Subparts (3) and (4) to 12/13.7.4.3.9 clarify the in-

tent to provide some flexibility. The surface area is large enough to accommodate the average-sized deep-fat fryer. This allows for deep-fat frying and at the same time provides reasonable safeguards.

Part (3) requires that multivat cooking equipment comply with NFPA 96, *Standard for Ventilation Control and Fire Protection of Commercial Cooking Operations.*[14]

The intent of requiring the lid in part (4)(a) is to provide the operator with a ready method of smothering the fire.

Part (4)(c) is required because the bottom surface of many devices could be subject to heating to temperatures that could ignite combustible surfaces.

The minimum separation distances in part (4)(d)

CHAPTER 12 • New　　　　　　　　　　　　**CHAPTER 13 • Existing**

are necessary to minimize the danger of a fire in one device extending into another device; the same principle that applies to 12/13.7.4.3.9(4)(d) applies to (4)(e), except the exposure is combustible decorations or other products as opposed to another cooking device.

Subpart (5) to 12/13.7.4.3.9 requires a 20-B:C extinguisher for each cooking device. The intent is to provide an extinguisher near each cooking device so the operator is able to access the extinguisher readily if a lid does not extinguish the fire or cannot be applied. It is not the intent to permit all extinguishers to be located in one place.

The provisions of 12/13.7.4.3.9 recognize the inherent dangers in cooking and warming devices that are used in an exhibit hall subject to large, transient crowds.

Subparagraph 12/13.7.4.3.10 limits the amount of literature, brochures, boxes, give-aways, and other products that are kept in the exhibit booth. The number of items necessary to constitute a one-day supply

obviously varies. However, the authority having jurisdiction should be able to make a judgment after reviewing the activity anticipated by the exhibitor. Additional supplies and combustible crates (used for shipping) should be kept in a separate storage area having a fire resistance rating of 1 hour and protected by an automatic sprinkler system.

The intent of 12/13.7.4.3.11 is to provide the authority having jurisdiction with a set of plans that shows aisle widths, travel distances, exits, booth locations, display area configurations, types of displays (for example, cooking, machinery, drapery, arts and crafts), location of fire protection equipment (extinguishers, manual fire alarm boxes, hose cabinets), and lobby and registration area usage. This list is not complete, but it provides some guidance in determining the plans that should be submitted. The plan should also be drawn to scale. The scale used is not usually critical provided that it is indicated on the plan.

12.7.4.4 Vehicles. Vehicles on display within an exposition facility shall comply with 12.7.4.4.1 through 12.7.4.4.5.

12.7.4.4.1 All fuel tank openings shall be locked and sealed in an approved manner to prevent the escape of vapors. Fuel tanks shall not contain in excess of one-half their capacity or contain in excess of 10 gal (37.9 L) of fuel, whichever is less.

12.7.4.4.2 At least one battery cable shall be removed from the batteries used to start the vehicle engine. The disconnected battery cable shall then be taped.

12.7.4.4.3 Batteries used to power auxiliary equipment shall be permitted to be kept in service.

12.7.4.4.4 Fueling or defueling of vehicles shall be prohibited.

12.7.4.4.5 Vehicles shall not be moved during exhibit hours.

13.7.4.4 Vehicles. Vehicles on display within an exposition facility shall comply with 13.7.4.4.1 through 13.7.4.4.5.

13.7.4.4.1 All fuel tank openings shall be locked and sealed in an approved manner to prevent the escape of vapors. Fuel tanks shall not contain in excess of one-half their capacity or contain in excess of 10 gal (37.9 L) of fuel, whichever is less.

13.7.4.4.2 At least one battery cable shall be removed from the batteries used to start the vehicle engine. The disconnected battery cable shall then be taped.

13.7.4.4.3 Batteries used to power auxiliary equipment shall be permitted to be kept in service.

13.7.4.4.4 Fueling or defueling of vehicles shall be prohibited.

13.7.4.4.5 Vehicles shall not be moved during exhibit hours.

In accordance with 12/13.7.4.4.1, it is important that fuel tank openings be locked to prevent tampering and accessibility to fuel. It is also important that the tank openings be taped to prevent the escape of flammable vapors. When these *Code* requirements were written, the issue of the quantity of fuel that is allowed in a tank was studied. Some jurisdictions preferred

empty tanks to eliminate fuel while others preferred full tanks to prevent vapors. It was determined that most exhibitors were unaware of the local regulation until they arrived at the exhibit hall. After learning the specific rule (empty or full), exhibitors proceeded to make their adjustment in the adjacent parking area or some other unsuitable area. It is also difficult for

CHAPTER 12 • New

CHAPTER 13 • Existing

the authority having jurisdiction to determine whether a tank is absolutely full or empty. Fueling and defueling by exhibitors outside the hall presented a greater danger than the level of fuel in the tanks, given that the tanks are locked and sealed, and ignition sources are eliminated from the vehicle. However, to avoid excessive quantities of fuel in the exhibition hall, the *Code* does limit the quantity of fuel in tanks.

In accordance with 12/13.7.4.4.2, it is important that at least one of the battery cables be removed from each battery. Many vehicles have more than one battery. The intent is to eliminate the possibility of a spark from the battery that might ignite fuel or surrounding combustibles. Battery cable connectors should be thoroughly taped after they have been removed.

The provision of 12/13.7.4.4.3 allows batteries that cannot be used to start the vehicle to remain in service. These batteries present no more of an ignition hazard than does providing house electrical power to the item on display.

Vehicle movement is addressed in 12/13.7.4.4.5. The movement of vehicles inside the exhibit hall potentially compromises the means of egress by blocking the exit access. Vehicles should be positioned before the hall is opened to the public to avoid adversely affecting the means of egress. There is also a concern regarding the effects of carbon monoxide inside an exhibit hall that is occupied.

Paragraph 12/13.7.4.4 on vehicles is intended to minimize the danger from both fuel and ignition sources.

12.7.4.5 Compressed flammable gases; flammable or combustible liquids; hazardous chemicals or materials; and Class II or greater lasers, blasting agents, and explosives shall be prohibited within exhibit halls.

Exception: The authority having jurisdiction shall be permitted to allow the limited use of any items specified in 12.7.4.5 under special circumstances.

12.7.4.6 Alternatives. *(See Section 1.5.)*

13.7.4.5 Compressed flammable gases; flammable or combustible liquids; hazardous chemicals or materials; and Class II or greater lasers, blasting agents, and explosives shall be prohibited within exhibit halls.

Exception: The authority having jurisdiction shall be permitted to allow the limited use of any items specified in 13.7.4.5 under special circumstances.

13.7.4.6 Alternatives. *(See Section 1.5.)*

Compressed gas containers, as addressed by 12/13.7.4.5, are subject to fire damage that could cause an explosion or create a serious threat to life safety. Flammable and combustible liquids compromise life safety by their inherent capability to contribute to rapid fire spread. Hazardous materials present a variety of hazards to life safety, from their flammability to their toxicity. Class II or greater lasers can cause tissue damage to humans, and blasting agents and explosives can cause a large loss of life or injury if handled improperly.

Many exhibitors wish to display explosives or pesticides or a type of compressed gas container,

among other items. These products can be effectively displayed without bringing the actual product into the hall by using empty containers.

The exception to 12/13.7.4.5 gives the authority having jurisdiction the discretion to permit small amounts of otherwise prohibited materials under special circumstances. For example, an exhibit or trade show for collectors of small arms ammunition or a highly supervised and closed (to the public) vocational trade show using such materials is permitted where special controls and professional supervision are provided.

12.7.5* Crowd Managers.

In assembly occupancies having occupant loads exceeding 1000, there shall be trained crowd managers or crowd manager supervisors at a ratio of 1 crowd manager/supervisor

13.7.5* Crowd Managers.

In assembly occupancies having occupant loads exceeding 1000, there shall be trained crowd managers or crowd manager supervisors at a ratio of 1 crowd manager/supervisor for every 250 occupants. The crowd manager shall receive approved training in crowd management techniques.

Exception No. 1: This requirement shall not apply to assembly occupancies used exclusively for religious worship with an occupant load not exceeding 2000.

Exception No. 2: Where, in the opinion of the authority having jurisdiction, the existence of an approved, supervised automatic sprinkler system and the nature of the event warrant, the ratio of trained crowd managers to occupants shall be permitted to be reduced.

A.12.7.5 The training program in crowd management should develop a clear appreciation of factors of space, energy, time, and information, as well as specific crowd management techniques such as metering. Published guidelines on these factors and techniques are found in the *SFPE Handbook of Fire Protection Engineering*, Section 3, Chapter 13.

The referenced material contained in Section 3, Chapter 13, of the second edition of the *SFPE Handbook of Fire Protection Engineering* makes a distinction between the required crowd management and the more extreme, but nonmandatory, crowd control.[15] Crowd management meshes the design features of a facility, the established operating features of that

12.7.6* Drills.

A.12.7.6 It is important that an adequate number of competent attendants are on duty at all times when the assembly occupancy is occupied.

12.7.6.1 The employees or attendants of assembly occupancies shall be trained and drilled in the duties they are to perform in case of fire, panic, or other emergency to effect orderly exiting.

12.7.6.2 Employees or attendants of assembly occupancies shall be instructed in the proper use of portable fire extinguishers and other manual fire suppression equipment where provided.

12.7.6.3* In theaters, motion picture theaters, auditoriums, and other similar assembly occupancies with occupant loads exceeding 300 where there are noncontinuous programs, an audible announcement shall be made, or a projected image shall be shown, prior to the start of each program to notify occupants of the location of the exits to be used in case of a fire or other emergency.

for every 250 occupants. The crowd manager shall receive approved training in crowd management techniques.

Exception No. 1: This requirement shall not apply to assembly occupancies used exclusively for religious worship with an occupant load not exceeding 2000.

Exception No. 2: Where, in the opinion of the authority having jurisdiction, the existence of an approved, supervised automatic sprinkler system and the nature of the event warrant, the ratio of trained crowd managers to occupants shall be permitted to be reduced.

A.13.7.5 The training program in crowd management should develop a clear appreciation of factors of space, energy, time, and information, as well as specific crowd management techniques such as metering. Published guidelines on these factors and techniques are found in the *SFPE Handbook of Fire Protection Engineering*, Section 3, Chapter 13.

facility, and an understanding of the occupants' expected natural behavior in that facility for a specific type of event. Section 3, Chapter 13, of the *SFPE Handbook of Fire Protection Engineering* cites the Disney amusement complexes as examples of good crowd management. Crowd control, on the other hand, is often necessitated when crowd management fails.

13.7.6* Drills.

A.13.7.6 It is important that an adequate number of competent attendants are on duty at all times when the assembly occupancy is occupied.

13.7.6.1 The employees or attendants of assembly occupancies shall be trained and drilled in the duties they are to perform in case of fire, panic, or other emergency to effect orderly exiting.

13.7.6.2 Employees or attendants of assembly occupancies shall be instructed in the proper use of portable fire extinguishers and other manual fire suppression equipment where provided.

13.7.6.3* In theaters, motion picture theaters, auditoriums, and other similar assembly occupancies with occupant loads exceeding 300 where there are noncontinuous programs, an audible announcement shall be made, or a projected image shall be shown, prior to the start of each program to notify occupants of the location of the exits to be used in case of a fire or other emergency.

Exception: This requirement shall not apply to assembly occupancies in schools where used for nonpublic events.

A.12.7.6.3 It is not the intent of this provision to require an announcement in bowling alleys, cocktail lounges, restaurants, or places of worship.

The provisions of 12/13.7.6.2 do not require fire extinguishers for life safety in an assembly occupancy. However, if fire extinguishers are provided, the staff must be trained in their use to prevent a false sense of security and possible injury. The extent of this training, whether instruction only, or instruction and hands-on use, is determined by the authority having jurisdiction.

The relatively simple requirement of 12/13.7.6.3 for notifying occupants of the location of exits can make a significant difference during an emergency.

12.7.7 Smoking.

12.7.7.1 Smoking in assembly occupancies shall be regulated by the authority having jurisdiction.

12.7.7.2 In rooms or areas where smoking is prohibited, plainly visible signs shall be posted that read as follows:

NO SMOKING

12.7.7.3 No person shall smoke in prohibited areas that are so posted.

Exception: The authority having jurisdiction shall permit smoking on a stage only where it is a necessary and rehearsed part of a performance and only where the smoker is a regular performing member of the cast.

12.7.7.4 Where smoking is permitted, suitable ashtrays or receptacles shall be provided in convenient locations.

12.7.8 Seating.

12.7.8.1 Seats in assembly occupancies accommodating more than 200 persons shall be securely fastened to the floor, except where fastened together in groups of not less than three and not exceeding seven and as permitted by 12.7.8.2. All seats in balconies and galleries shall be securely fastened to the floor, except in places of religious worship.

12.7.8.2 Seats not secured to the floor shall be permitted in restaurants, night clubs, and other occupancies where fastening seats to the floor might be impracticable. Such unsecured seats shall be permitted, provided that, in the area

Exception: This requirement shall not apply to assembly occupancies in schools where used for nonpublic events.

A.13.7.6.3 It is not the intent of this provision to require an announcement in bowling alleys, cocktail lounges, restaurants, or places of worship.

Note that the requirement does not apply to assembly occupancies where the flow of people is constantly changing, such as in a restaurant. Movie theaters commonly meet the provisions of 12/13.7.6.3 through means of sound and screen projection that are presented prior to the main feature, during the same period that notifications of restroom, trash container, and snack bar locations are made and previews are shown. The same complete message is thereby delivered to each audience without the need for human intervention.

13.7.7 Smoking.

13.7.7.1 Smoking in assembly occupancies shall be regulated by the authority having jurisdiction.

13.7.7.2 In rooms or areas where smoking is prohibited, plainly visible signs shall be posted that read as follows:

NO SMOKING

13.7.7.3 No person shall smoke in prohibited areas that are so posted.

Exception: The authority having jurisdiction shall permit smoking on a stage only where it is a necessary and rehearsed part of a performance and only where the smoker is a regular performing member of the cast.

13.7.7.4 Where smoking is permitted, suitable ashtrays or receptacles shall be provided in convenient locations.

13.7.8 Seating.

13.7.8.1 Seats in assembly occupancies accommodating more than 200 persons shall be securely fastened to the floor, except where fastened together in groups of not less than three and not exceeding seven and as permitted by 13.7.8.2. All seats in balconies and galleries shall be securely fastened to the floor, except in places of religious worship.

13.7.8.2 Seats not secured to the floor shall be permitted in restaurants, night clubs, and other occupancies where fastening seats to the floor might be impracticable. Such unsecured seats shall be permitted, provided that, in the area used for seating, excluding such areas as dance floors and stages, there is not more than one seat for each 15 ft² (1.4 m²) of net floor area, and adequate aisles to reach exits are maintained at all times. Seating diagrams shall be submitted for approval by the authority having jurisdiction to permit an increase in occupant load per 7.3.1.3.

12.7.8.3 Every room constituting an assembly occupancy and not having fixed seats shall have the occupant load of the room posted in a conspicuous place near the main exit from the room. Approved signs shall be maintained in a legible manner by the owner or authorized agent. Signs shall be durable and shall indicate the number of occupants permitted for each room use.

The function of 12/13.7.8 is to prevent the movement of seats so that aisles, rows, and access to the exits do not become blocked in an assembly occupancy

12.7.9 Maintenance of Outdoor Grandstands.

The owner shall provide for not less than annual inspection and required maintenance of each outdoor grandstand to ensure safe conditions. At least biennially, the inspection shall be performed by a professional engineer, registered architect, or individual certified by the manufacturer. Where required by the authority having jurisdiction, the owner shall provide certification that such inspection has been performed.

12.7.10 Maintenance and Operation of Folding and Telescopic Seating.

12.7.10.1 Instructions in both maintenance and operation shall be transmitted to the owner by the manufacturer of the seating or his or her representative.

12.7.10.2 Maintenance and operation of folding and telescopic seating shall be the responsibility of the owner or his or her duly authorized representative and shall include the following:

(1) During operation of the folding and telescopic seats, the opening and closing shall be supervised by responsible personnel who shall ensure that the operation is in accordance with the manufacturer's instructions.
(2) Only attachments specifically approved by the manufacturer for the specific installation shall be attached to the seating.
(3) An annual inspection and required maintenance of each grandstand shall be performed to ensure safe conditions.

used for seating, excluding such areas of dance floors and stages, there is not more than one seat for each 15 ft² (1.4 m²) of net floor area, and adequate aisles to reach exits are maintained at all times. Seating diagrams shall be submitted for approval by the authority having jurisdiction to permit an increase in occupant load per 7.3.1.3.

13.7.8.3 Every room constituting an assembly occupancy and not having fixed seats shall have the occupant load of the room posted in a conspicuous place near the main exit from the room. Approved signs shall be maintained in a legible manner by the owner or authorized agent. Signs shall be durable and shall indicate the number of occupants permitted for each room use.

during the jostling that occurs when people flee from a fire.

13.7.9 Maintenance of Outdoor Grandstands.

The owner shall provide for not less than annual inspection and required maintenance of each outdoor grandstand to ensure safe conditions. At least biennially, the inspection shall be performed by a professional engineer, registered architect, or individual certified by the manufacturer. Where required by the authority having jurisdiction, the owner shall provide certification that such inspection has been performed.

13.7.10 Maintenance and Operation of Folding and Telescopic Seating.

13.7.10.1 Instructions in both maintenance and operation shall be transmitted to the owner by the manufacturer of the seating or his or her representative.

13.7.10.2 Maintenance and operation of folding and telescopic seating shall be the responsibility of the owner or his or her duly authorized representative and shall include the following:

(1) During operation of the folding and telescopic seats, the opening and closing shall be supervised by responsible personnel who shall ensure that the operation is in accordance with the manufacturer's instructions.
(2) Only attachments specifically approved by the manufacturer for the specific installation shall be attached to the seating.
(3) An annual inspection and required maintenance of each grandstand shall be performed to ensure safe conditions.

At least biennially, the inspection shall be performed by a professional engineer, registered architect, or individual certified by the manufacturer.

12.7.11 Clothing.

Clothing and personal effects shall not be stored in corridors.

Exception No. 1: This requirement shall not apply to corridors protected by an approved, supervised automatic sprinkler system in accordance with Section 9.7.

Exception No. 2: This requirement shall not apply to corridor areas protected by a smoke detection system in accordance with Section 9.6.

Exception No. 3: This requirement shall not apply to storage in metal lockers, provided that the required egress width is maintained.

Clothing hung on hooks along corridor walls or on racks in lobbies greatly increases the combustible load and will generally allow flame to spread quickly. The provisions of each of the exceptions (control of fire by sprinklers, early warning of incipient stage

At least biennially, the inspection shall be performed by a professional engineer, registered architect, or individual certified by the manufacturer.

13.7.11 Clothing.

Clothing and personal effects shall not be stored in corridors.

Exception No. 1: This requirement shall not apply to corridors protected by an approved automatic sprinkler system in accordance with Section 9.7.

Exception No. 2: This requirement shall not apply to corridor areas protected by a smoke detection system in accordance with Section 9.6.

Exception No. 3: This requirement shall not apply to storage in metal lockers, provided that the required egress width is maintained.

fire via smoke detection, or isolating fuel packages by locating the clothing in metal lockers) helps to mitigate the chance that a clothing fire would render the exit access unusable.

References Cited in Commentary

1. NFPA 130, *Standard for Fixed Guideway Transit and Passenger Rail Systems*, 2000 edition, National Fire Protection Association, Quincy, MA.
2. Richard Best, "Tragedy in Kentucky," *Fire Journal* 72, no. 1 (January 1978) and "Reconstruction of a Tragedy," NFPA LS-72, 1978.
3. NFPA 220, *Standard on Types of Building Construction*, 1999 edition, National Fire Protection Association, Quincy, MA.
4. Jake Pauls, "Observation of Crowd Conditions at Rock Concert in Exhibition Stadium, Toronto, 16 July 1980."
5. NFPA 72, *National Fire Alarm Code®*, 1999 edition, National Fire Protection Association, Quincy, MA.
6. See note 2.
7. Richard Best and David Demers, "Investigation Report on the MGM Grand Hotel Fire," NFPA LS-4, 1980 (rev. 1982).
8. NFPA 70, *National Electrical Code®*, 1999 edition, National Fire Protection Association, Quincy, MA.
9. NFPA 92B, *Guide for Smoke Management in Malls,*

Atria, and Large Areas, 1995 edition, National Fire Protection Association, Quincy, MA.
10. NFPA 40, *Standard for the Storage and Handling of Cellulose Nitrate Motion Picture Film*, 1997 edition, National Fire Protection Association, Quincy, MA.
11. NFPA 102, *Standard for Grandstands, Folding and Telescopic Seating, Tents, and Membrane Structures*, 1995 edition, National Fire Protection Association, Quincy, MA.
12. UL 1975, *Standard for Fire Tests for Foamed Plastic Used for Decorative Purposes*, Underwriters Laboratories Inc., Northbrook, IL.
13. NFPA 13, *Standard for the Installation of Sprinkler Systems*, 1999 edition, National Fire Protection Association, Quincy, MA.
14. NFPA 96, *Standard for Ventilation Control and Fire Protection of Commercial Cooking Operations*, 1998 edition, National Fire Protection Association, Quincy, MA.
15. *SFPE Handbook of Fire Protection Engineering*, National Fire Protection Association, Quincy, MA, 2d edition, 1995.

New and Existing Educational Occupancies

Chapters 14 and 15 work to provide the life safety features necessary to protect students in an educational setting such as a school. These chapters do not apply to college classrooms but do apply to educational settings for students in kindergarten through the twelfth grade. The range of student characteristics and self-preservation abilities found in the educational occupancies regulated by Chapters 14 and 15 requires that student fire safety needs be treated differently from those for adults occupying a college classroom.

Many of the life safety requirements applicable to educational occupancies are the result of lessons learned from fires involving schools in which a large loss of life occurred. Fortunately, such fires are now rare. The protection measures used for this occupancy recognize the structured environment found in a school. For example, class times, time between classes, and activities during class time are rigidly structured. These factors make it possible to train students to respond to a fire by conducting emergency egress and relocation drills.

Smaller children who might be overwhelmed and pushed aside by older students during a fire emergency evacuation or relocation must be housed in classrooms on lower floor levels. Paragraph 14/15.2.1.2 recognizes this problem and establishes criteria to control it. The minimum corridor width requirement (see 14/15.2.3.2) is based on expected student behavior. The wider corridor width accommodates students who are filing out of classrooms and forming parallel lines to proceed down the corridor.

Schools also have one of the more assertive schedules for conducting emergency egress and relocation drills (see 14/15.7.1). The drills not only provide a structured fire escape/relocation plan, they also help to instill fire-safe behavior for long-term use.

Fatal fires have been extremely rare in educational occupancies for many years. Those fires that do occur tend to involve either employees in accidental fires (for example, fires caused by cleaning floors with flammable liquids) or, more often, firesetters trapped by their own fires. Children who died in school fires in recent years have been largely limited to juvenile firesetters, acting as individuals or groups, who are on school grounds after hours without permission.

Section 14.1 General Requirements

14.1.1 Application.

14.1.1.1 The requirements of this chapter apply to the following:

(1) New buildings or portions thereof used as educational occupancies *(see 1.4.1)*
(2) Additions made to, or used as, an educational occupancy *(see 4.6.6)*

Section 15.1 General Requirements

15.1.1 Application.

15.1.1.1 The requirements of this chapter apply to existing buildings or portions thereof currently occupied as educational occupancies. *(See also 14.1.1.)*

(3) Alterations, modernizations, or renovations of existing educational occupancies *(see 4.6.7)*

(4) Existing buildings or portions thereof upon change of occupancy to an educational occupancy *(see 4.6.11)*

14.1.1.2 Educational facilities that do not meet the definition of an educational occupancy shall not be required to comply with this chapter but shall comply with the following requirements:

(1) Instructional building—business occupancy
(2) Classrooms under 50 persons—business occupancy
(3) Classrooms, 50 persons and over—assembly occupancy
(4) Laboratories, instructional—business occupancy
(5) Laboratories, noninstructional—industrial

Paragraph 14.1.1.1 echoes the provision of 4.6.6 that additions must comply with the requirements for new construction. Alterations, modernizations, and renovations must meet the requirements for new construction to the extent practical. A change of occupancy to an educational occupancy requires compliance with the requirements applicable to new construction.

As defined in Chapter 6 and repeated in 14/15.1.4.1, educational occupancies include those buildings, or portions of buildings, used for educating stu-

14.1.2 Mixed Occupancies.

(See also 14.1.4.)

14.1.2.1 Where other types of occupancy exist in the same building as an educational occupancy, the requirements of 6.1.14 of this *Code* shall apply, unless otherwise specified in this chapter.

14.1.2.2 Assembly and Educational. Spaces subject to assembly occupancy shall comply with Chapter 12, including 12.1.2, which provides that where auditorium and gymnasium egress lead through corridors or stairways also serving as egress for other parts of the building, the egress capacity shall be sufficient to allow simultaneous egress from auditorium and classroom sections.

Exception: In the case of an assembly occupancy of a type suitable only for use by the school occupant load and, therefore, not subject to simultaneous occupancy, the same egress capacity shall be permitted to serve both sections.

14.1.2.3 Dormitory and Classrooms. Any building used for both classroom and dormitory purposes shall comply

15.1.1.2 Educational facilities that do not meet the definition of an educational occupancy shall not be required to comply with this chapter but shall comply with the following requirements:

(1) Instructional building—business occupancy
(2) Classrooms under 50 persons—business occupancy
(3) Classrooms, 50 persons and over—assembly occupancy
(4) Laboratories, instructional—business occupancy
(5) Laboratories, noninstructional—industrial

dents through the twelfth grade. The provisions of 14/15.1.1.2 recognize that colleges, universities, and similar educational facilities that do not meet the definition of educational occupancies do not pose the same life safety concerns as elementary and high schools. Because of the maturity of their occupants, college buildings more properly resemble business occupancies. Paragraph 14/15.1.1.2 also identifies other educational uses that are not classified as educational occupancies and specifies how they should be addressed.

15.1.2 Mixed Occupancies.

(See also 15.1.4.)

15.1.2.1 Where other types of occupancy exist in the same building as an educational occupancy, the requirements of 6.1.14 of this *Code* shall apply, unless otherwise specified in this chapter.

15.1.2.2 Assembly and Educational. Spaces subject to assembly occupancy shall comply with Chapter 13, including 13.1.2, which provides that where auditorium and gymnasium egress lead through corridors or stairways also serving as egress for other parts of the building, the egress capacity shall be sufficient to allow simultaneous egress from auditorium and classroom sections.

Exception: In the case of an assembly occupancy of a type suitable only for use by the school occupant load and, therefore, not subject to simultaneous occupancy, the same egress capacity shall be permitted to serve both sections.

15.1.2.3 Dormitory and Classrooms. Any building used for both classroom and dormitory purposes shall comply

| **CHAPTER 14 • New** | **CHAPTER 15 • Existing** |

with the applicable provisions of Chapter 28 in addition to complying with Chapter 14. Where classroom and dormitory sections are not subject to simultaneous occupancy, the same egress capacity shall be permitted to serve both sections.

Paragraph 14/15.1.2.1 refers to 6.1.14 which specifies that, where separate safeguards for each occupancy within the building cannot be maintained, the most stringent requirement applicable to any of the occupancies present is to be applied to all occupancies. For example, one of the occupancies present might have a travel distance limitation stricter than that of the other occupancies present; therefore, the stricter limitation is to be applied throughout the building. An occupancy that differs from the occupancy with the strictest travel distance limit might have the strictest requirements for protection of vertical openings, and these provisions also need to be implemented throughout the building. Similarly, for each subject addressed by the *Code*, a comparison must be made among the requirements applicable to each of the occupancies present and the strictest requirement must be provided throughout the building.

Paragraph 14/15.1.2.2 addresses mixed occupancies that are part assembly and part educational, in recognition of the fact that the occupancy that most typically appears within an educational occupancy building to create a mixed occupancy is an assembly occupancy. Because of the large numbers of occu-

with the applicable provisions of Chapter 29 in addition to complying with Chapter 15. Where classroom and dormitory sections are not subject to simultaneous occupancy, the same egress capacity shall be permitted to serve both sections.

pants characteristic of both assembly and educational occupancies, it is important that their combined occupant loads be used to size the means of egress system if they share common egress components such as corridors and exit stair enclosures. The requirement assumes that the classrooms and assembly areas are likely to be occupied simultaneously. For example, classrooms are often used during the evening for adult or remedial education while a school's gymnasium or auditorium is being used by another group. Where simultaneous occupancy does not occur, the exception to 14/15.1.2.2 permits the shared means of egress to be sized to handle the larger of the uses, either educational or assembly.

Chapters 12 and 13 contain several requirements applicable to assembly occupancies that could have a significant impact on an educational occupancy contained in a mixed use building if the building is not designed so the occupancies can be treated separately. For example, in new construction, if the mixed use creates a mixed occupancy, the building will most likely have to be sprinklered throughout by applying the provisions of 12.3.5.

14.1.3 Special Definitions.

Common Atmosphere. See 3.3.31.

Flexible Plan and Open Plan Educational or Day-Care Building. See 3.3.80.

Separate Atmosphere. See 3.3.178.

14.1.4 Classification of Occupancy.

(See 6.1.3.)

14.1.4.1 Educational occupancies shall include all buildings used for educational purposes through the twelfth grade by six or more persons for four or more hours per day or more than 12 hours per week.

14.1.4.2 Educational occupancies shall include part-day preschools, kindergartens, and other schools whose purpose is primarily educational, even though the children who attend such schools are of preschool age.

15.1.3 Special Definitions.

Common Atmosphere. See 3.3.31.

Flexible Plan and Open Plan Educational or Day-Care Building. See 3.3.80.

Separate Atmosphere. See 3.3.178.

15.1.4 Classification of Occupancy.

(See 6.1.3.)

15.1.4.1 Educational occupancies shall include all buildings used for educational purposes through the twelfth grade by six or more persons for four or more hours per day or more than 12 hours per week.

15.1.4.2 Educational occupancies shall include part-day preschools, kindergartens, and other schools whose purpose is primarily educational, even though the children who attend such schools are of preschool age.

CHAPTER 14 • New

CHAPTER 15 • Existing

14.1.4.3 In cases where instruction is incidental to some other occupancy, the section of this *Code* governing such other occupancy shall apply.

14.1.4.4 Other occupancies associated with educational institutions shall be in accordance with the appropriate parts of this *Code*. (*See Chapters 18, 20, 26, 28, 30, 40, and 42 and 6.1.14.*)

15.1.4.3 In cases where instruction is incidental to some other occupancy, the section of this *Code* governing such other occupancy shall apply.

15.1.4.4 Other occupancies associated with educational institutions shall be in accordance with the appropriate parts of this *Code*. (*See Chapters 19, 21, 26, 29, 31, 40, and 42 and 6.1.14.*)

Paragraph 14/15.1.4.1 has the effect of exempting the following three types of schools from the provisions of Chapters 14 and 15:

(1) Schools with small numbers of students (fewer than six), such as facilities providing private tutoring or individual lessons
(2) Schools with limited operating hours (less than 4 hours per day and not more than 12 hours per week), such as some sports schools or weekend religious instruction schools
(3) Schools that educate people above the high school level, as in the case of universities or military training. Beyond high school, the level of life safety does not have to be as great as that needed for younger students

Paragraph 14/15.1.1.2 provides guidance in determining the classification of facilities that involve educational uses but fail to meet the definition of educational occupancy.

For purposes of determining occupant load, a classroom area—regardless of whether it is part of an educational occupancy—is still considered an educational use, and the occupant load factors provided for educational uses by Table 7.3.1.2 should be used to calculate a realistic occupant load.

Where instruction is incidental to other occupancies, the requirements for the occupancy in which

the instruction takes place are applicable. Church schools used for instruction for a few hours during one or two days of the week are generally classed as part of the assembly occupancy in which instruction takes place.

Paragraph 14/15.1.4.2 classifies part-time day-care facilities as educational occupancies if they primarily provide education in addition to care services. This classification parallels federal guidelines for subsidizing day-care/educational activities at both the federal and state levels. This does not describe a typical day-care facility. Chapters 16 and 17 contain special requirements for typical, noneducational day-care facilities.

The requirement of 14/15.1.4.3 is not as significant as it was when places of higher education were included in 14/15.1.4.1. The following examples describe uses that would, nevertheless, be exempted from the requirements for educational occupancies by 14/15.1.4.1.

In an office building or factory, a few rooms might be used for orientation or instruction in job performance; these rooms are subject to the *Code* requirements for business or industrial occupancies. Barber colleges and beauty schools are frequently located in commercial buildings and should be governed by the requirements applicable to the buildings in which they are located.

14.1.5 Classification of Hazard of Contents.

The contents of educational occupancies shall be classified in accordance with the provisions of Section 6.2.

15.1.5 Classification of Hazard of Contents.

The contents of educational occupancies shall be classified in accordance with the provisions of Section 6.2.

In general, educational occupancies contain ordinary hazard contents. Some laboratories and storage areas might contain high hazard contents. See Section 7.11

for additional egress requirements for areas with high hazard contents.

14.1.6 Minimum Construction Requirements.

(No requirements.)

15.1.6 Minimum Construction Requirements.

(No requirements.)

14.1.7 Occupant Load.

14.1.7.1 The occupant load, in number of persons for whom means of egress and other provisions are required, shall be determined on the basis of the occupant load factors of Table 7.3.1.2 that are characteristic of the use of the space or shall be determined as the maximum probable population of the space under consideration, whichever is greater.

14.1.7.2 The occupant load of an educational occupancy, or a portion thereof, shall be permitted to be modified from that specified in 14.1.7.1 if the necessary aisles and exits are provided. An approved aisle or seating diagram shall be required by the authority having jurisdiction to substantiate such a modification.

The amount of material presented in 14/15.1.7.2 has been reduced for the 2000 edition of the *Code,* because all occupant load factors have been moved to Table 7.3.1.2 in the chapter addressing means of egress. Note that occupant load is calculated based on the use of the space, not on the occupancy classification. The occupant load factors belong in Chapter 7 so that they can be calculated based on the use of the space, regardless of the occupancy classification.

It is not the intent that occupant load factors be applied to require a minimum area per student for functional purposes. Rather, the occupant load factors are used to determine the occupant load for purposes of sizing the means of egress system. The intent is to require adequate egress capacity for those present. Efficient use of classroom space might result in the presence of a greater number of occupants than that determined by calculation using the occupant load factors of Table 7.3.1.2. Paragraph 14/15.1.7.2 permits the occupant load to be established as the maximum probable population if that number exceeds the number determined by calculation using the occupant load factors. However, the means of egress must adequately accommodate all occupants, and all other requirements dependent on the calculated occupant load must be met.

Section 14.2 Means of Egress Requirements

14.2.1 General.

14.2.1.1 Means of egress shall be in accordance with Chapter 7 and Section 14.2.

14.2.1.2 Rooms normally occupied by preschool, kindergarten, or first-grade students shall not be located above or below the level of exit discharge. Rooms normally occupied by second-grade students shall not be located more than one story above the level of exit discharge.

Exception: Rooms or areas located on floor levels other than as specified in 14.2.1.2 shall be permitted to be used where provided with independent means of egress dedicated for use by the preschool, kindergarten, first-grade, or second-grade students.

15.1.7 Occupant Load.

15.1.7.1 The occupant load, in number of persons for whom means of egress and other provisions are required, shall be determined on the basis of the occupant load factors of Table 7.3.1.2 that are characteristic of the use of the space or shall be determined as the maximum probable population of the space under consideration, whichever is greater.

15.1.7.2 The occupant load of an educational occupancy, or a portion thereof, shall be permitted to be modified from that specified in 15.1.7.1 if the necessary aisles and exits are provided. An approved aisle or seating diagram shall be required by the authority having jurisdiction to substantiate such a modification.

Section 15.2 Means of Egress Requirements

15.2.1 General.

15.2.1.1 Means of egress shall be in accordance with Chapter 7 and Section 15.2.

15.2.1.2 Rooms normally occupied by preschool, kindergarten, or first-grade students shall not be located above or below the level of exit discharge. Rooms normally occupied by second-grade students shall not be located more than one story above the level of exit discharge.

Exception: Rooms or areas located on floor levels other than as specified in 15.2.1.2 shall be permitted to be used where provided with independent means of egress dedicated for use by the preschool, kindergarten, first-grade, or second-grade students.

CHAPTER 14 • New **CHAPTER 15 • Existing**

The restrictions on the location of rooms used by preschool, kindergarten, or first- or second-grade pupils were developed to avoid the danger of older—and larger—children overrunning the very young on stairs or ramps during a fire or other incident requiring rapid evacuation. The exception recognizes that the younger students—often with the help of teachers and staff—can use the stairs and ramps effectively if they don't have to compete with the older, larger, and faster students. For a definition of the term *level of exit discharge,* see 3.115.

14.2.2 Means of Egress Components.

14.2.2.1 Components of means of egress shall be limited to the types described in 14.2.2.2 through 14.2.2.10.

14.2.2.2 Doors.

14.2.2.2.1 Doors complying with 7.2.1 shall be permitted.

14.2.2.2.2 Panic Hardware or Fire Exit Hardware. Any door in a required means of egress from an area having an occupant load of 100 or more persons shall be permitted to be provided with a latch or lock only if the latch or lock is panic hardware or fire exit hardware complying with 7.2.1.7.

14.2.2.2.3 Special locking arrangements complying with 7.2.1.6 shall be permitted.

14.2.2.3* Stairs. Stairs complying with 7.2.2 shall be permitted.

A.14.2.2.3 See A.7.2.2.4.5(1), Exception No. 3, regarding additional handrails on stairs that are used extensively by children 5 years of age or less.

14.2.2.4 Smokeproof Enclosures. Smokeproof enclosures complying with 7.2.3 shall be permitted.

14.2.2.5 Horizontal Exits. Horizontal exits complying with 7.2.4 shall be permitted.

14.2.2.6 Ramps. Ramps complying with 7.2.5 shall be permitted.

14.2.2.7 Exit Passageways. Exit passageways complying with 7.2.6 shall be permitted.

14.2.2.8 Fire Escape Ladders. Fire escape ladders complying with 7.2.9 shall be permitted.

15.2.2 Means of Egress Components.

15.2.2.1 Components of means of egress shall be limited to the types described in 15.2.2.2 through 15.2.2.10.

15.2.2.2 Doors.

15.2.2.2.1 Doors complying with 7.2.1 shall be permitted.

15.2.2.2.2 Panic Hardware or Fire Exit Hardware. Any required exit door subject to use by 100 or more persons shall be permitted to be provided with a latch or lock only if the latch or lock is panic hardware or fire exit hardware complying with 7.2.1.7.

15.2.2.2.3 Special locking arrangements complying with 7.2.1.6 shall be permitted.

15.2.2.3* Stairs.

A.15.2.2.3 See A.7.2.2.4.5(1), Exception No. 3, regarding additional handrails on stairs that are used extensively by children 5 years of age or less.

15.2.2.3.1 Stairs complying with 7.2.2 shall be permitted.

15.2.2.3.2 Existing Class A stairs shall be permitted.

15.2.2.3.3 Existing Class B stairs shall be permitted where not used for student access.

15.2.2.4 Smokeproof Enclosures. Smokeproof enclosures complying with 7.2.3 shall be permitted.

15.2.2.5 Horizontal Exits. Horizontal exits complying with 7.2.4 shall be permitted.

15.2.2.6 Ramps. Ramps complying with 7.2.5 shall be permitted.

15.2.2.7 Exit Passageways. Exit passageways complying with 7.2.6 shall be permitted.

15.2.2.8 Fire Escape Ladders. Fire escape ladders complying with 7.2.9 shall be permitted.

| **CHAPTER 14 • New** | **CHAPTER 15 • Existing** |

14.2.2.9 Alternating Tread Devices. Alternating tread devices complying with 7.2.11 shall be permitted.

14.2.2.10 Areas of Refuge. Areas of refuge complying with 7.2.12 shall be permitted.

15.2.2.9 Alternating Tread Devices. Alternating tread devices complying with 7.2.11 shall be permitted.

15.2.2.10 Areas of Refuge. Areas of refuge complying with 7.2.12 shall be permitted.

Subsection 14/15.2.2 lists those components acceptable for use in the means of egress serving an educational occupancy. Some of the components described in Chapter 7 were judged to be unacceptable for educational occupancy egress system use. Note that slide escapes, escalators, fire escape stairs, and revolving doors are not permitted to be credited as providing any of the required means of egress in an educational occupancy.

The panic hardware and fire exit hardware provisions of 14/15.2.2.2.2 include application thresholds expressed in terms of occupant load. For new construction, the occupant load addressed by 14.2.2.2.2 is the total occupant load of the area served and not only the required capacity of the door. For example, if an area of a new educational occupancy has an occupant load of 180 persons and is served by 3 doors, each door is required to have sufficient capacity for 60 persons. However, because the doors serve an overall area with 100 or more persons, any latches on these doors must be arranged to be released by panic hardware or fire exit hardware. The requirement for panic hardware or fire exit hardware in existing educational occupancies is slightly less restrictive than for new educational occupancies. In accordance with 15.2.2.2.2, panic hardware or fire exit hardware is required only on exit doors rather than all egress doors; therefore, the requirement does not apply to exit access doors—such as corridor doors and smoke barrier doors. In addition, 15.2.2.2.2 for existing educational occupancies establishes its criteria on the number of people using the door for egress. For example, if a single-story existing educational occupancy building

with an occupant load of 180 persons has 3 exit doors, each door can be considered as providing egress capacity for 60 persons. Because no individual exit door is required to have a capacity for 100 or more occupants, panic hardware is not required.

Subparagraph 14/15.2.2.2.3 references 7.2.1.6. The provisions of 7.2.1.6 include 7.2.1.6.1, which applies to delayed-egress locks, and 7.2.1.6.2, which applies to access-controlled egress doors. Both sets of features are recognized for use in educational occupancies. To use the provisions for delayed-egress locks, the building must be either fully sprinklered or fully protected by an automatic fire detection system. Although educational occupancies are among the many occupancies that recognize use of the Chapter 7 provisions for delayed-egress locks, the original hardware was developed for educational occupancies. Delayed-egress locking provisions were added to Chapter 7 based on hardware development that addresses security concerns in schools.

Although 14/15.2.2.8 and 14/15.2.2.9 permit fire escape ladders and alternating tread devices as components of the means of egress, the use of such ladders and devices is limited by the provisions of Chapter 7. The provisions of 7.2.9 and 7.2.11 restrict the use of fire escape ladders and alternating tread devices to normally unoccupied areas, such as rooftops or mechanical equipment platforms. Chapter 7 further restricts their use to spaces subject to occupancy by not more than three persons who are all capable of using the ladder or alternating tread device.

14.2.3 Capacity of Means of Egress.

14.2.3.1 Capacity of means of egress shall be in accordance with Section 7.3.

14.2.3.2 Minimum Corridor Width. Exit access corridors shall have not less than 6 ft (1.8 m) of clear width.

15.2.3 Capacity of Means of Egress.

15.2.3.1 Capacity of means of egress shall be in accordance with Section 7.3.

15.2.3.2 Minimum Corridor Width. Exit access corridors shall have not less than 6 ft (1.8 m) of clear width.

CHAPTER 14 • New

CHAPTER 15 • Existing

Note that the minimum corridor width requirement of 14/15.2.3.2 applies regardless of the required capacity of the corridor. Based on egress capacity considerations, larger widths might be necessary for corridors handling large numbers of students; see 14/15.2.3.1 and Section 7.3. Paragraph 14/15.2.3.2 applies to exit access corridors and not to nonrequired service corridors provided for convenience only.

The term *clear width* means a 6-ft (1.8-m) wide clear space with no obstructions other than those permitted by the exception to 7.3.2. Subsection 7.3.2 details the required method for measuring the width of a component of the means of egress. The exception

to 7.3.2 permits projections of not more than 3½ in. (8.9 cm) on each side of the corridor. The projections are permitted to be located at or below a handrail height of 38 in. (96 cm), and the maximum 3½-in. (8.9-cm) width is to be ignored when determining clear width.

The intent of a 6-ft (1.8-m) corridor is to permit two files of students to move simultaneously with sufficient room for teachers or monitors to supervise. Extremely short corridor sections serving only one or two rooms might warrant consideration for some reduction in required width.

14.2.4 Number of Exits.

Not less than two separate exits shall be as follows:

(1) Provided on every story
(2) Accessible from every part of every story and mezzanine

Subsection 14/15.2.4 has been revised for the 2000 edition of the *Code* to clarify intent. Access must be provided to a minimum of two exits, and both required exits must be located on the floor or story in question. A similar provision applies to business occupancies. Contrast this requirement with a related provision for industrial occupancies that requires access to two exits but that mandates that only one of those required exits is to be located on the floor or

15.2.4 Number of Exits.

Not less than two separate exits shall be as follows:

(1) Provided on every story
(2) Accessible from every part of every story and mezzanine

story. Thus, in an educational occupancy, an open exit access stair, if it were allowed without violating the provisions applicable to the protection of vertical openings, is not permitted to serve as access to either of the two required exits. In a multistory educational occupancy building, the requirements of 14/15.2.4 are typically met by providing two properly enclosed exit stairs that can be accessed from all floors above or below the level of exit discharge.

14.2.5 Arrangement of Means of Egress.

(See also Section 7.5.)

14.2.5.1 Means of egress shall be arranged in accordance with Section 7.5.

14.2.5.2 No dead-end corridor shall exceed 20 ft (6.1 m), other than in buildings protected throughout by an approved, supervised automatic sprinkler system in accordance with Section 9.7, in which case dead-end corridors shall not exceed 50 ft (15 m).

14.2.5.3 No common path of travel shall exceed 75 ft (23 m), other than for the first 100 ft (30 m) in a building protected throughout by an approved, supervised automatic sprinkler system in accordance with Section 9.7.

15.2.5 Arrangement of Means of Egress.

(See also Section 7.5.)

15.2.5.1 Means of egress shall be arranged in accordance with Section 7.5.

15.2.5.2 No dead-end corridor shall exceed 20 ft (6.1 m), other than in buildings protected throughout by an approved, supervised automatic sprinkler system in accordance with Section 9.7, in which case dead-end corridors shall not exceed 50 ft (15 m).

15.2.5.3 No common path of travel shall exceed 75 ft (23 m), other than for the first 100 ft (30 m) in a building protected throughout by an approved, supervised automatic sprinkler system in accordance with Section 9.7.

Exception No. 2 to 7.5.1.2 permits individual occupancy chapters to set common path of travel limits if the occupancy chapter chooses to allow any common paths of travel. The 75-ft (23-m) limit established by 14/15.2.5.3 is reasonable enough that small rooms are not required to be provided with a second exit access door. This limit is also strict enough to help ensure that occupants can safely tolerate traveling in only one direction for a limited distance before reaching a point where travel in independent directions becomes possible. Paragraph 14/15.2.5.3 permits the common path of travel to be increased by 25 ft (7.6 m) in recognition of the fire-controlling capabilities of a sprinkler system.

The exception to 7.5.1.6 allows individual occupancy chapters to establish dead-end corridor limits if the occupancy chapter allows any dead-end corridors. Twenty feet (6.1 m) of permitted dead-end corridor, as allowed by 14/15.2.5.2, has been the standard dead-end requirement for educational occupancies in the past—and the limitation still appears reasonable. However, the exception permits the dead end to be increased by 30 ft (9.1 m) in recognition of the fire-controlling capabilities of a sprinkler system.

A floor arrangement with outside doors or stairways at both ends of a central corridor typically creates no dead-end corridors. Small dead-end corridor pockets might be created where stairways are not located at the end of corridors but are located at intermediate points. See Exhibit 14/15.1. Illustration (a) in Exhibit 14/15.1 indicates no dead-end corridors. This arrangement is preferred but is not always practical in terms of building layout and use. In illustration (b), dead-end pockets are shown at each end of the corridor into which occupants might mistakenly travel, only to have to retrace their path to find an exit. However, the length of the dead-end corridor

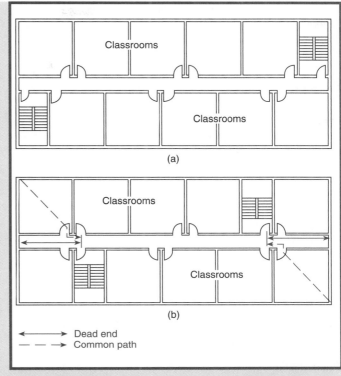

Exhibit 14/15.1 *Dead-end corridors and common path of travel.*

does not exceed the permitted 20 ft (6.1 m). All classrooms have been arranged so that the common path of travel does not exceed the 75-ft (23-m) limitation. This arrangement is acceptable. In an educational occupancy building that is protected throughout by an approved, supervised automatic sprinkler system, the 20-ft (6.1-m) dead-end corridor can be increased to 50 ft (15 m); and the 75-ft (23-m) common path of travel can be increased to 100 ft (30 m).

14.2.5.4 Every room that is normally subject to student occupancy shall have an exit access door leading directly to an exit access corridor or exit.

Exception No. 1: This requirement shall not apply where an exit door opens directly to the outside or to an exterior balcony or corridor as described in 14.2.5.7.

Exception No. 2: One room shall be permitted to intervene between a normally occupied student room and an exit access corridor, provided that all of the following criteria are met:

15.2.5.4 Every room that is normally subject to student occupancy shall have an exit access door leading directly to an exit access corridor or exit.

Exception No. 1: This requirement shall not apply where an exit door opens directly to the outside or to an exterior balcony or corridor as described in 15.2.5.7.

Exception No. 2: One room shall be permitted to intervene between a normally occupied student room and an exit access corridor, provided that all of the following criteria are met:

CHAPTER 14 • New

(a) The travel from a room served by an intervening room to the corridor door or exit shall not exceed 75 ft (23 m).

(b) Clothing, personal effects, or other materials deemed hazardous by the authority having jurisdiction shall be stored in metal lockers, provided that they do not obstruct the exit access, or the intervening room shall be sprinklered in accordance with Section 9.7.

(c) One of the following means of protection shall be provided:

(1) The intervening room shall have approved fire detection that activates the building alarm.
(2) The building shall be protected by an approved, supervised automatic sprinkler system in accordance with Section 9.7.

CHAPTER 15 • Existing

(a) The travel from a room served by an intervening room to the corridor door or exit shall not exceed 75 ft (23 m).

(b) Clothing, personal effects, or other materials deemed hazardous by the authority having jurisdiction shall be stored in metal lockers, provided that they do not obstruct the exit access, or the intervening room shall be sprinklered in accordance with Section 9.7.

(c) One of the following means of protection shall be provided:

(1) The intervening room shall have approved fire detection that activates the building alarm.
(2) The building shall be protected by an approved automatic sprinkler system in accordance with Section 7.7.

Exception No. 3:   Previously approved arrangements shall be permitted to continue to be used with the approval of the authority having jurisdiction.

To ensure ready access to the exit access corridor—which is intended to be a safer portion of the exit access than an occupied room with furnishings—14/15.2.5.4 requires most normally occupied rooms to have a door open directly into an exit access corridor. The use of such a door avoids the need for occupants to pass through intervening rooms that might not be arranged or maintained to permit the orderly evacuation of an occupied space.

Normally occupied rooms that have doors opening directly to the outside at grade or to an exterior exit access balcony are exempted from the base requirement. Also exempted are normally occupied rooms having only one intervening room that meets the following criteria:

(1) Travel distance through the intervening room to the corridor door is limited to 75 ft (23 m).
(2) Personal effects—such as coats and other belongings or other contents deemed hazardous by the authority having jurisdiction—must be kept in metal lockers, or the intervening room must be sprinklered.
(3) Either the intervening room is supplied with fire detectors connected to the building alarm system, or the entire building is protected throughout by an approved automatic sprinkler system.

It is the *Code's* intent that, if metal lockers are chosen as the intervening room fire detection option, smoke detectors rather than heat detectors should be selected to provide for rapid occupant notification. However, heat detectors are allowed to be used if nuisance alarms are anticipated (for example, in automotive or wood shops with attached classrooms).

Exhibits 14/15.2 and 14/15.3 illustrate several possible intervening room configurations that comply with the *Code*. In Exhibit 14/15.2, Room A has no limit on its size other than to satisfy the arrangement and travel distance provisions of 14/15.2.5. Each normally occupied room has a door opening either directly to the corridor or to the exterior (opening at grade or to an exterior exit access balcony) as permitted by Exception No. 1 to 14/15.2.5.4. The arrangement shown in the lower portion of Exhibit 14/15.2 is permitted as long as travel distance from the normally occupied rooms to the corridor (from point X to point C) does not exceed 75 ft (23 m), and clothing and other personal effects in the intervening room are stored in metal lockers along with a fire detection system designed to provide occupant notification (preferably smoke detection for earliest possible notification).

In Exhibit 14/15.3, illustrations (a) and (b) represent acceptable intervening room arrangements. Illustration (a) depicts the limited travel distance from point X to point C along with the intervening room sprinkler system addressed in subpart (b) of Exception No. 2 to 14/15.2.5.4 and the intervening room fire detection system addressed in subpart C(1) of Exception No. 2 to 14/15.2.5.4. Illustration (b) repre-

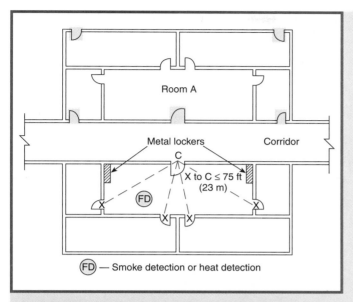

Exhibit 14/15.2 *Room arrangements complying with 14/15.2.5.4, including Exception No. 1 and Exception No. 2.*

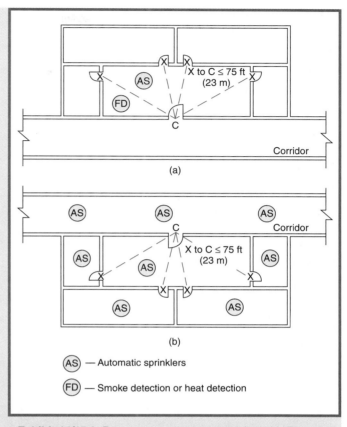

Exhibit 14/15.3 *Room arrangements complying with Exception No. 2 to 14/15.2.5.4.*

sents a building protected throughout by an automatic sprinkler system satisfying both subparts (C)(1) and (2) of Exception No. 2 to 14/15.2.5.4. In effect, even the installation within an intervening room of an automatic sprinkler system that is connected to the building fire alarm system would satisfy the criteria of Exception No. 2 to 14/15.2.5.4, because automatic sprinklers are considered heat detectors. Therefore, this approach would satisfy both parts (b) and (c) to Exception No. 2 to 14/15.2.5.4.

14.2.5.5 Doors that swing into an exit access corridor shall be arranged to prevent interference with corridor travel. *(See also 7.2.1.4.4.)*

14.2.5.6 Aisles. Aisles shall be not less than 30 in. (91 cm) wide. The space between parallel rows of seats shall not be subject to the minimum aisle width, provided that the number of seats that intervene between any seat and an aisle do not exceed six.

14.2.5.7* Exterior Corridors or Balconies. Exterior exit access shall comply with 7.5.3.

A.14.2.5.7 A corridor roofed over and enclosed on its long side and open to the atmosphere at the end is permitted to be considered an exterior corridor if either of the following criteria are met:

15.2.5.5 Doors that swing into an exit access corridor shall be arranged to prevent interference with corridor travel. *(See also 7.2.1.4.4.)*

15.2.5.6 Aisles. Aisles shall be not less than 30 in. (91 cm) wide. The space between parallel rows of seats shall not be subject to the minimum aisle width, provided that the number of seats that intervene between any seat and an aisle do not exceed six.

15.2.5.7* Exterior Corridors or Balconies. Exterior exit access shall comply with 5.5.3.

A.15.2.5.7 A corridor roofed over and enclosed on its long side and open to the atmosphere at the end is permitted to be considered an exterior corridor if either of the following criteria are met:

CHAPTER 14 • New   **CHAPTER 15 • Existing**

(1) Clear story openings for the corridor are provided on both sides of the corridor and above adjacent roofs or buildings, and such clear openings are not less than one-half the height of the corridor walls.

(2) The corridor roof has unobstructed openings to the sky not less than 50 percent of the area of the roof.

The openings are to be equally distributed, and, if louvers are installed, they are to be fixed open with a clear area based on the actual openings between louver vanes.

(1) Clear story openings for the corridor are provided on both sides of the corridor and above adjacent roofs or buildings, and such clear openings are not less than one-half the height of the corridor walls.

(2) The corridor roof has unobstructed openings to the sky not less than 50 percent of the area of the roof.

The openings are to be equally distributed, and, if louvers are installed, they are to be fixed open with a clear area based on the actual openings between louver vanes.

Exhibit 14/15.4 illustrates exterior exit access arranged in accordance with 7.5.3. The stairs have been positioned to comply with the criterion of Exception No. 1 to 7.5.3.3; the arrangement permits an occupant to reach at least one of the stairs without having to travel past an unprotected opening. The distance from any room to nearest stair must not exceed the allowable travel distance.

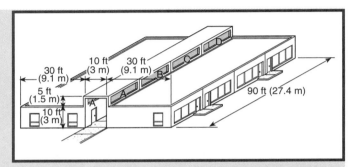

Exhibit 14/15.5(a) *Exterior corridor using clear story openings.*

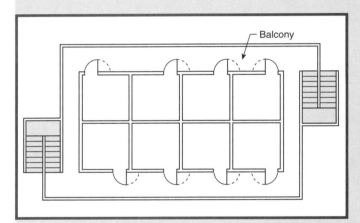

Exhibit 14/15.4 *Exterior exit access via balcony and stairs.*

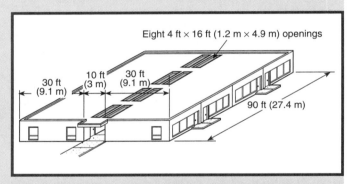

Exhibit 14/15.5(b) *Exterior corridor using roof openings.*

Exhibits 14/15.5(a) and 14/15.5(b) illustrate the use of exterior exit access corridors. In Exhibit 14/15.5(a), the openings labeled A, B, C, and D are clear story openings. The building height is 10 ft (3 m). For a corridor to be considered an outside corridor, the minimum height for the corridor roof is 5 ft (1.5 m). In this figure, the minimum clear story height requirements have been met.

In Exhibit 14/15.5(b), the alternative to the clear

story openings is a roof with unobstructed openings to the sky that are equal to not less than 50 percent of the corridor roof area. The example shown has eight openings. Each opening is 4 ft × 16 ft (1.2 m × 4.9 m), or 64 ft² (5.9 m²). The total corridor roof area is 900 ft² (84 m²). The total unobstructed opening equals 512 ft² (48 m²)—greater than 50 percent of the total roof area. This example is considered an acceptable design.

14.2.6 Travel Distance to Exits.

Travel distance to an exit shall not exceed 150 ft (45 m) from any point in a building. *(See also Section 7.6.)*

15.2.6 Travel Distance to Exits.

Travel distance to an exit shall not exceed 150 ft (45 m) from any point in a building. *(See also Section 7.6.)*

Exception: Travel distance shall not exceed 200 ft (60 m) in educational occupancies protected throughout by an approved, supervised automatic sprinkler system in accordance with Section 9.7.

Exception No. 1: Travel distance shall not exceed 200 ft (60 m) in educational occupancies protected throughout by an approved automatic sprinkler system in accordance with Section 9.7.

Exception No. 2: Previously approved travel distances shall be permitted to continue to be used with the approval of the authority having jurisdiction.

14.2.7 Discharge from Exits.

Discharge from exits shall be arranged in accordance with Section 7.7.

15.2.7 Discharge from Exits.

Discharge from exits shall be arranged in accordance with Section 7.7.

14.2.8 Illumination of Means of Egress.

Means of egress shall be illuminated in accordance with Section 7.8.

15.2.8 Illumination of Means of Egress.

Means of egress shall be illuminated in accordance with Section 7.8.

14.2.9 Emergency Lighting.

Emergency lighting shall be provided in accordance with Section 7.9 in the following areas:

(1) Interior stairs and corridors
(2) Assembly use spaces
(3) Flexible and open plan buildings
(4) Interior or windowless portions of buildings
(5) Shops and laboratories

15.2.9 Emergency Lighting.

Emergency lighting shall be provided in accordance with Section 7.9 in the following areas:

(1) Interior stairs and corridors
(2) Assembly use spaces
(3) Flexible and open plan buildings
(4) Interior or windowless portions of buildings
(5) Shops and laboratories

Normal classrooms, offices, and storage or mechanical spaces do not require emergency lighting. Shops, laboratories, assembly use spaces (such as lecture halls, auditoriums, and dining rooms), and interior and windowless portions of educational occupancies require emergency lighting. Exhibit 14/15.6 illustrates these requirements. Shaded areas indicate where emergency lighting is required. Classroom A and office B are windowless. The lecture hall is an assembly use space. The stairs and corridor are interior to the building. Shops and laboratories are specifically required to be provided with emergency lighting.

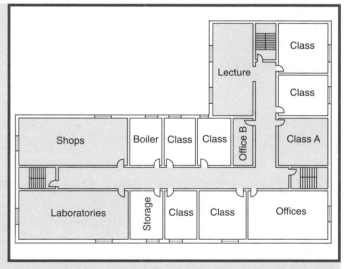

Exhibit 14/15.6 *Areas that require and do not require emergency lighting.*

14.2.10 Marking of Means of Egress.

Means of egress shall have signs in accordance with Section 7.10.

15.2.10 Marking of Means of Egress.

Means of egress shall have signs in accordance with Section 7.10.

14.2.11 Special Means of Egress Features.

14.2.11.1* Windows for Rescue. Every room or space greater than 250 ft² (23.2 m²) used for classroom or other educational purposes or normally subject to student occupancy shall have not less than one outside window for emergency rescue that complies with the following:

(1) Such windows shall be openable from the inside without the use of tools and shall provide a clear opening of not less than 20 in. (51 cm) in width, 24 in. (61 cm) in height, and 5.7 ft² (0.53 m²) in area.
(2) The bottom of the opening shall be not more than 44 in. (112 cm) above the floor, and any latching device shall be capable of being operated from not more than 54 in. (137 cm) above the finished floor.
(3) The clear opening shall allow a rectangular solid, with a width and height that provides not less than the required 5.7-ft² (0.53-m²) opening and a depth of not less than 20 in. (51 cm), to pass fully through the opening.
(4) Such windows shall be accessible by the fire department and shall open into an area having access to a public way.

Exception No. 1: This requirement shall not apply to buildings protected throughout by an approved, supervised automatic sprinkler system in accordance with Section 9.7.

Exception No. 2: This requirement shall not apply where the room or space has a door leading directly to the outside of the building.

Exception No. 3: This requirement shall not apply to rooms located higher than three stories above grade.

15.2.11 Special Means of Egress Features.

15.2.11.1* Windows for Rescue. Every room or space greater than 250 ft² (23.2 m²) used for classroom or other educational purposes or normally subject to student occupancy shall have not less than one outside window for emergency rescue that complies with the following:

(1) Such windows shall be openable from the inside without the use of tools and shall provide a clear opening of not less than 20 in. (51 cm) in width, 24 in. (61 cm) in height, and 5.7 ft² (0.53 m²) in area.
(2) The bottom of the opening shall be not more than 44 in. (112 cm) above the floor, and any latching device shall be capable of being operated from not more than 54 in. (137 cm) above the finished floor.
(3) The clear opening shall allow a rectangular solid, with a width and height that provides not less than the required 5.7-ft² (0.53-m²) opening and a depth of not less than 20 in. (51 cm), to pass fully through the opening.

Exception No. 1: This requirement shall not apply to buildings protected throughout by an approved automatic sprinkler system in accordance with Section 9.7.

Exception No. 2: This requirement shall not apply where the room or space has a door leading directly to the outside of the building.

Exception No. 3: This requirement shall not apply to rooms located higher than three stories above grade.

Exception No. 4: Awning-type or hopper-type windows that are hinged or subdivided to provide a clear opening not less than 600 in.² (3900 cm²) in area, nor any dimension less than 22 in. (55.9 cm), shall be permitted to continue to be used. Screen walls or devices in front of required windows shall not interfere with rescue requirements.

Exception No. 5: This requirement shall not apply where the room or space complies with the following:

(a) Doors shall exist that allow travel between adjacent classrooms. Where such doors are used to travel from classroom to classroom, they shall provide direct access to exits in both directions or direct access to an exit in one direction and to a separate smoke compartment that provides access to another exit in the other direction.

(b) The corridor shall be separated from the classrooms by a wall that resists the passage of smoke, and all doors between the classrooms and the corridor shall be self-closing or automatic-closing in accordance with 7.2.1.8.

(c) The length of travel to exits along such paths shall not exceed 150 ft (45 m).

(d) Each communicating door shall be marked in accordance with Section 7.10.

(e) No locking device shall be permitted on the communicating doors.

A.14.2.11.1 It is highly desirable that all windows be of a type that can be readily opened from inside and to have them large enough and low enough for use by students, teachers, and fire fighters. Windows are permitted to serve as a supplementary means of emergency escape, particularly where ladders can be raised by fire fighters or others.

A.15.2.11.1 It is highly desirable that all windows be of a type that can be readily opened from inside and to have them large enough and low enough for use by students, teachers, and fire fighters. Windows are permitted to serve as a supplementary means of emergency escape, particularly where ladders can be raised by fire fighters or others.

Small rooms of less than 250 ft² (23.2 m²), such as those used for music instruction and student counseling and subject to occupancy by very few students, are exempt from the rescue and ventilation window requirement.

The dimensions specified for windows used for emergency rescue or for ventilation are based on simulations of emergency rescue conducted by the San Diego Fire Department. Windows providing clear openings of identical dimensions are also required for rescue or ventilation in dwellings. Exhibit 14/15.7 illustrates two configurations that provide the required area of 5.7 ft² (0.53 m²) and the minimum opening height and width.

Awning and hopper-type windows might provide the required opening within the plane of the building exterior wall. However, when the window is open, the sash and glazing are outside that plane and might prevent occupants from passing through the opening. Therefore, the criterion for providing an opening through which a minimum size rectangular solid can pass is intended to ensure that occupants can pass through the opening. For existing awning-type windows, Exception No. 4 to 15.2.11.1 offers some relief from the rectangular solid and minimum opening size requirements. Exception No. 4 to 15.2.11.1 is provided in acknowledgment of a feature that was formerly recognized by the *Code*. Although the exception is no longer allowed in new construction, it is still permitted in existing facilities. Exhibit 14/15.8 illustrates the use of Exception No. 4 to 15.2.11.1.

The *Code* intends that the fire department or others are to assist students, especially over ladders. If these emergency rescue windows must be used as a supplementary means of escape, the windows must permit small children in the lower grades to escape unaided. Therefore, storm sashes, screens, or devices in front of the windows must be easy to open or

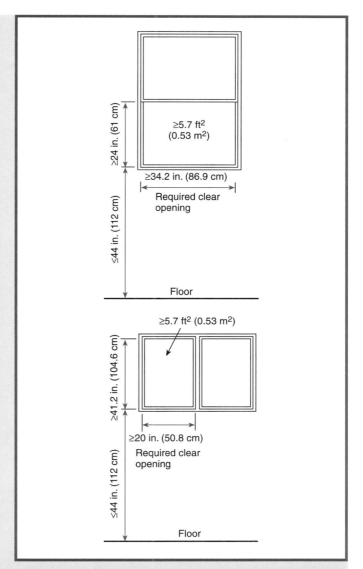

Exhibit 14/15.7 *Windows for rescue or ventilation, minimum required dimensions.*

CHAPTER 14 • New	CHAPTER 15 • Existing

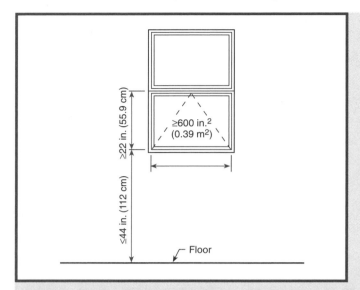

Exhibit 14/15.8 *Existing awning window minimum dimensions permitted by Exception No. 4 to 15.2.11.1.*

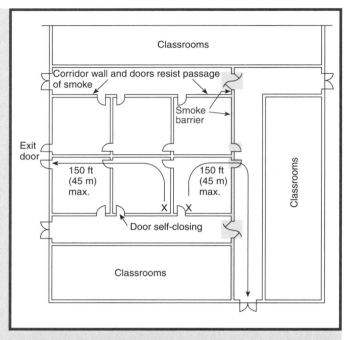

Exhibit 14/15.9 *One method of compensating for windowless classroom in existing buildings as permitted by Exception No. 5 to 15.2.11.1.*

remove, and the sills must be low enough for children to reach.

The *Code* also requires that such windows are to be accessible to the fire department and that occupants, once they escape through the window to the outside, are to have access to a public way.

Emergency rescue windows are not required if a classroom has a door leading directly to the outside or if the building is totally sprinklered. Note that Exception No. 1 requires that the building be protected throughout by an automatic sprinkler system. The purpose of the window is to provide ventilation or means of escape when the interior corridor is blocked by smoke from a fire in another part of the building. Installing sprinklers in only some rooms

does not provide protection from smoke that is emanating from other areas.

It might not be practical to use a window above the third story as an escape window. However, it is reasonable to expect the window to be used for ventilation during a fire. Therefore, Exception No. 3 allows window openings above the third story to be sized for ventilation and not for rescue.

Exception No. 5 to 15.2.11.1 is applicable only in existing buildings. Exhibit 14/15.9 illustrates how the exception can be used.

Section 14.3 Protection

14.3.1 Protection of Vertical Openings.

Any vertical opening, other than unprotected vertical openings in accordance with 8.2.5.8, shall be enclosed or protected in accordance with 8.2.1. Where the provisions of 8.2.5.5 are used, the requirements of 14.3.5.2 shall be met.

Section 15.3 Protection

15.3.1 Protection of Vertical Openings.

Any vertical opening, other than unprotected vertical openings in accordance with 8.2.5.8, shall be enclosed or protected in accordance with 8.2.5. Where the provisions of 8.2.5.5 are used, the requirements of 15.3.5.2 shall be met.

Exception: Stairway enclosures shall not be required under the following conditions:

(a) Where a stairway serves only one adjacent floor, other than a basement

(b) Where a stairway is not connected with stairways serving other floors

(c) Where a stairway is not connected with corridors serving other than the two floors involved

Chapters 14 and 15 require all vertical openings, with the exception of an open and unobstructed "mini-atrium" opening connecting three floors or less (see 8.2.5.5), an atrium (see 8.2.5.6), and a convenience stair (see 8.2.5.8), to be enclosed in accordance with Section 8.2. While not specified by the mini-atrium provisions of 8.2.5.5, 14/15.3.5.2 requires a building to be fully sprinklered to permit the unenclosed vertical opening. The convenience stair might be useful, especially for libraries or offices within schools.

The two-story stair permitted by the exception to 15.3.1 differs from the convenience stair detailed in 8.2.5.8. The exception to 15.3.1 permits an existing two-story school building to have open egress stairs between the first and second floors. Open egress stairs are not permitted in new construction. Basements are excluded from use of the exception to 15.3.1, because basements usually contain hazardous contents areas with high fuel loads, such as storage rooms, boiler rooms, or workshops.

14.3.2 Protection from Hazards.

14.3.2.1 Rooms or spaces for the storage, processing, or use of materials shall be protected in accordance with the following:

(1) Separation from the remainder of the building by fire barriers having a fire resistance rating of not less than 1 hour or protection of such rooms by automatic extinguishing systems as specified in Section 8.4 in the following areas:

a. Boiler and furnace rooms

Exception: Boiler and furnace rooms shall be exempt from the requirement of 14.3.2.1(1)a where they enclose only air-handling equipment.

b. Rooms or spaces used for the storage of combustible supplies in quantities deemed hazardous by the authority having jurisdiction
c. Rooms or spaces used for the storage of hazardous materials or flammable or combustible liquids in quantities deemed hazardous by recognized standards
d. Janitor closets

Exception: Janitor closets protected by automatic sprinklers shall be permitted to have doors with ventilating louvers.

Where janitor closets abut and are entered from a corridor, a louvered door is usually provided for ven-

15.3.2 Protection from Hazards.

15.3.2.1 Rooms or spaces for the storage, processing, or use of materials shall be protected in accordance with the following:

(1) Separation from the remainder of the building by fire barriers having a fire resistance rating of not less than 1 hour or protection of such rooms by automatic extinguishing systems as specified in Section 8.4 in the following areas:

a. Boiler and furnace rooms

Exception: Boiler and furnace rooms shall be exempt from the requirement of 15.3.2.1(1)a where they enclose only air-handling equipment.

b. Rooms or spaces used for the storage of combustible supplies in quantities deemed hazardous by the authority having jurisdiction
c. Rooms or spaces used for the storage of hazardous materials or flammable or combustible liquids in quantities deemed hazardous by recognized standards
d. Janitor closets

Exception: Janitor closets protected by automatic sprinklers shall be permitted to have doors with ventilating louvers.

tilation. It is necessary to provide these spaces with automatic sprinkler protection, because a fire in the

CHAPTER 14 • New

CHAPTER 15 • Existing

janitor closet might directly affect the usability of the corridor for exit access. Paragraph 9.7.1.2 describes an economical method of providing sprinkler protection for such closets by using the normal building water supply. To achieve this protection at reasonable cost, these sprinklers (not more than six for a given room

or space) are permitted to be supplied from the building water supply if the supply is capable of providing the required flow of water. It is advisable to provide a waterflow switch to initiate an alarm when a sprinkler is opened.

(2) Separation from the remainder of the building by fire barriers having a fire resistance rating of not less than 1 hour and protection of such rooms by automatic extinguishing systems as specified in Section 8.4 in the following areas:

a. Laundries
b. Maintenance shops, including woodworking and painting areas
c. Rooms or spaces used for processing or use of combustible supplies deemed hazardous by the authority having jurisdiction
d. Rooms or spaces used for processing or use of hazardous materials or flammable or combustible liquids in quantities deemed hazardous by recognized standards

(3) Where automatic extinguishing is used to meet the requirements of 14.3.2.1(1) or (2), the protection shall be permitted in accordance with 9.7.1.2.

(2) Separation from the remainder of the building by fire barriers having a fire resistance rating of not less than 1 hour and protection of such rooms by automatic extinguishing systems as specified in Section 8.4 in the following areas:

a. Laundries
b. Maintenance shops, including woodworking and painting areas
c. Rooms or spaces used for processing or use of combustible supplies deemed hazardous by the authority having jurisdiction
d. Rooms or spaces used for processing or use of hazardous materials or flammable or combustible liquids in quantities deemed hazardous by recognized standards

(3) Where automatic extinguishing is used to meet the requirements of 15.3.2.1(1) or (2), the protection shall be permitted in accordance with 9.7.1.2.

Exhibits 14/15.10(a) through 14/15.10(c) illustrate the various protection requirements of 14/15.3.2.1.

The intent of 14/15.3.2.1 is to specify the degree of protection necessary for certain hazardous contents areas. The hazards noted in subpart (1) are required to be enclosed in 1-hour construction or are to be protected by automatic sprinklers. If the sprinkler option is chosen for new construction, an enclosure is still required by 8.4.1.2. However, the enclosure is not required to be rated but is only required to form a membrane against the passage of smoke.

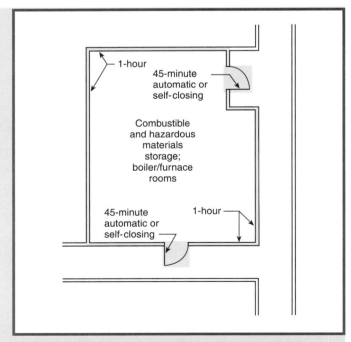

Exhibit 14/15.10(a) *Protection of hazardous contents areas—rated enclosure complying with 14/15.3.2.1(1).*

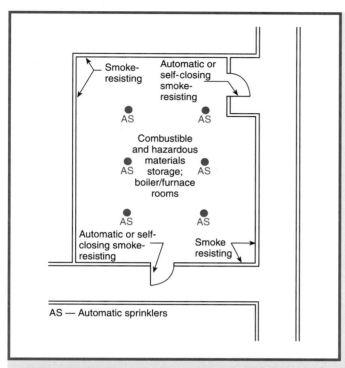

Exhibit 14/15.10(b) Protection of hazardous contents areas— sprinkler protection and smoke-resisting enclosure complying with 14/15.3.2.1(1).

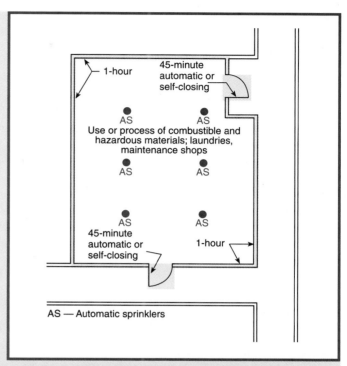

Exhibit 14/15.10(c) Protection of hazardous contents areas— separation by 1-hour rated enclosure and automatic sprinkler protection complying with 14/15.3.2.1(2).

14.3.2.2 Food preparation facilities shall be protected in accordance with 9.2.3 and shall not be required to have openings protected between food preparation areas and dining areas.

15.3.2.2 Food preparation facilities shall be protected in accordance with 9.2.3 and shall not be required to have openings protected between food preparation areas and dining areas.

Openings in the wall between kitchens and dining areas are not restricted and do not need to be protected. The *Code* relies upon the specialized automatic

extinguishing system to control any fire on the cooking surfaces and, thus, does not require openings between the kitchen and dining areas to be protected.

14.3.2.3 Stages shall be protected in accordance with Chapter 12.

15.3.2.3 Stages shall be protected in accordance with Chapter 13.

14.3.3 Interior Finish.

14.3.3.1 Interior finish shall be in accordance with Section 10.2.

14.3.3.2 Interior wall and ceiling finish materials in accordance with 10.2.3 shall be permitted as follows:

(1) Exits—Class A
(2) Other than exits—Class A or Class B

15.3.3 Interior Finish.

15.3.3.1 Interior finish shall be in accordance with Section 10.2.

15.3.3.2 Interior wall and ceiling finish materials in accordance with 10.2.3 shall be permitted as follows:

(1) Exits—Class A
(2) Corridors and lobbies—Class A or Class B

Exception: Low-height partitions not exceeding 5 ft (1.5 m) used in locations other than exits shall be permitted to be Class A, Class B, or Class C.

14.3.3.3 Interior Floor Finish. (No requirements.)

14.3.4 Detection, Alarm, and Communications Systems.

14.3.4.1 General. Educational occupancies shall be provided with a fire alarm system in accordance with Section 9.6.

Exception: This requirement shall not apply to buildings with an area not exceeding 1000 ft² (93 m²) that contains a single classroom and is located not less than 50 ft (15.2 m) from another building.

The limited size, single-classroom building addressed by the exception to 14/15.3.4.1 does not need an alarm system, because the fire will be immediately obvious to the occupants. Emergency egress can begin upon first notice of fire. A fire within a building

14.3.4.2 Initiation.

14.3.4.2.1 Initiation of the required fire alarm system, other than as permitted by 14.3.4.2.3, shall be by manual means in accordance with 9.6.2.1(1).

14.3.4.2.2 In buildings provided with automatic sprinkler protection, the operation of the sprinkler system shall automatically activate the fire alarm system in addition to the initiation means required in 14.3.4.2.1.

14.3.4.2.3 Alternative Protection System. Manual fire alarm boxes shall be permitted to be omitted where all of the following conditions are met:

(1) Interior corridors are protected by smoke detectors using an alarm verification system as described in NFPA 72, *National Fire Alarm Code.*

Exception: Low-height partitions not exceeding 5 ft (1.5 m) used in locations other than exits shall be permitted to be Class A, Class B, or Class C.

(3) All other locations—Class A, Class B, or Class C

15.3.3.3 Interior Floor Finish. (No requirements.)

15.3.4 Detection, Alarm, and Communications Systems.

15.3.4.1 General. Educational occupancies shall be provided with a fire alarm system in accordance with Section 9.6.

Exception: This requirement shall not apply to buildings with an area not exceeding 1000 ft² (93 m²) that contains a single classroom and is located not less than 50 ft (15.2 m) from another building.

located at least 50 ft (15.2 m) from another building should not prove to be detrimental to the occupants of the other building if egress is delayed even though no alarm system is required.

15.3.4.2 Initiation.

15.3.4.2.1 Initiation of the required fire alarm system, other than as permitted by 15.3.4.2.3, shall be by manual means in accordance with 9.6.2.1(1).

Exception: In buildings where all normally occupied spaces are provided with a two-way communication system between such spaces and a constantly attended receiving station from where a general evacuation alarm can be sounded, the manual fire alarm boxes shall not be required, except in locations specifically designated by the authority having jurisdiction.

15.3.4.2.2 In buildings provided with automatic sprinkler protection, the operation of the sprinkler system shall automatically activate the fire alarm system in addition to the initiation means required in 15.3.4.2.1.

15.3.4.2.3 Alternative Protection System. Manual fire alarm boxes shall be permitted to be omitted where all of the following conditions are met:

(1) Interior corridors are protected by smoke detectors using an alarm verification system as described in NFPA 72, *National Fire Alarm Code.*

CHAPTER 14 • New

(2) Spaces such as auditoriums, cafeterias, and gymnasiums are protected by heat or other approved detection devices.

(3) Shops and laboratories involving dusts or vapors are protected by heat or other approved detection devices.

(4) Fire alarm signals are automatically transmitted to the public fire department in accordance with 9.6.4.

(5) Provision is made at a central point to manually activate the evacuation signal or to evacuate only affected areas.

Subparagraph 14/15.3.4.2.3 provides an alternative to the manual fire alarm boxes required by 14/15.3.4.2.1. The alternative is offered as a means to avoid the nuisance alarms initiated through unauthorized use of the building manual fire alarm boxes. By relying on the automatic initiation that is provided by the detection systems addressed in 14/15.3.4.2.3(1) through (3), equivalent protection is provided.

The exception to 15.3.4.2.1—which applies only to existing educational occupancies—recognizes an alternative to a dedicated fire alarm system. Where there is a two-way communication system between classrooms and a constantly attended location where

14.3.4.3 Notification.

14.3.4.3.1 Occupant Notification.

14.3.4.3.1.1 Occupant notification shall be accomplished automatically in accordance with 9.6.3. Positive alarm sequence shall be permitted in accordance with 9.6.3.4.

14.3.4.3.1.2 Where acceptable to the authority having jurisdiction, the fire alarm system shall be permitted to be used for other emergency signaling or for class changes, provided that the fire alarm is distinctive in signal and overrides all other use.

14.3.4.3.1.3 In order to prevent students from being returned to a building that is burning, the recall signal shall be separate and distinct from any other signals. Such signal shall be permitted to be given by use of distinctively colored flags or banners. If the recall signal is electric, the push buttons or other controls shall be kept under lock. The key for such lock shall be in the possession of the principal or another designated person in order to prevent a recall at a time when there is an actual fire. Regardless of the method of recall, the means of giving the signal shall be kept under lock.

14.3.4.3.2 Emergency Forces Notification. Fire department notification shall be accomplished in accordance with 9.6.4.

CHAPTER 15 • Existing

(2) Spaces such as auditoriums, cafeterias, and gymnasiums are protected by heat or other approved detection devices.

(3) Shops and laboratories involving dusts or vapors are protected by heat or other approved detection devices.

(4) Fire alarm signals are automatically transmitted to the public fire department in accordance with 9.6.4.

(5) Provision is made at a central point to manually activate the evacuation signal or to evacuate only affected areas.

a general alarm can be sounded, the requirement for an alarm system—and its requisite manual fire alarm boxes—is exempted. To use this exception, the authority having jurisdiction must designate those manual fire alarm boxes that are allowed to be omitted. For the purposes of this provision, a "constantly attended" location is a location that is attended while the school building is in use as a school. Compliance might involve providing personnel at this location during night classes, when the regular school office staff is not present. The exception to 15.3.4.2.1 is not permitted for new construction due to reliability concerns.

15.3.4.3 Notification.

15.3.4.3.1 Occupant Notification.

15.3.4.3.1.1 Occupant notification shall be accomplished automatically in accordance with 9.6.3. Positive alarm sequence shall be permitted in accordance with 9.6.3.4.

15.3.4.3.1.2 Where acceptable to the authority having jurisdiction, the fire alarm system shall be permitted to be used for other emergency signaling or for class changes, provided that the fire alarm is distinctive in signal and overrides all other use.

15.3.4.3.1.3 In order to prevent students from being returned to a building that is burning, the recall signal shall be separate and distinct from any other signals. Such signal shall be permitted to be given by use of distinctively colored flags or banners. If the recall signal is electric, the push buttons or other controls shall be kept under lock. The key for such lock shall be in the possession of the principal or another designated person in order to prevent a recall at a time when there is an actual fire. Regardless of the method of recall, the means of giving the signal shall be kept under lock.

15.3.4.3.2 Emergency Forces Notification. Wherever any of the school authorities determine that an actual fire exists, they shall immediately call the local fire department using the public fire alarm system or other available facilities.

14.3.5 Extinguishment Requirements.

14.3.5.1 Every portion of educational buildings below the level of exit discharge shall be protected throughout by an approved, supervised automatic sprinkler system in accordance with Section 9.7.

15.3.5 Extinguishment Requirements.

15.3.5.1 Wherever student occupancy exists below the level of exit discharge, every portion of such floor shall be protected throughout by an approved automatic sprinkler system in accordance with Section 9.7. Where student occupancy does not exist on floors below the level of exit discharge, such floors shall be separated from the rest of the building by 1-hour fire resistance–rated construction or shall be protected throughout by an approved automatic sprinkler system in accordance with Section 9.7.

Exception: Where student occupancy exists below the level of exit discharge, automatic sprinkler protection shall not be required, subject to the approval of the authority having jurisdiction, where windows for rescue and ventilation are provided in accordance with 15.2.11.1.

The provisions of 14/15.3.5 address the need for sprinklers based on whether there are levels or floors below the level of exit discharge. For new construction, this provision will normally require basements of schools to be sprinklered; for existing educational occupancies, the basement will need to be sprinklered if it is used for student occupancy. Because the level of exit discharge might sometimes be located between two stories (for example, an occupant one walks up from the first floor and walks down from the second floor to the level of exit discharge), the lower story might need to be sprinklered. See Exhibit 14/15.11. The illustration on the left depicts an arrangement where only the basement is below the level of exit discharge. The illustration on the right depicts a case where the level of exit discharge is between floors 1 and 2; the first floor and basement are below the level of exit discharge.

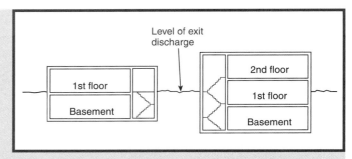

Exhibit 14/15.11 *Automatic sprinkler protection required for levels below level of exit discharge for new construction; and for existing buildings only if levels below level of exit discharge are occupied by students.*

14.3.5.2 Buildings with unprotected openings in accordance with 8.2.5.5 shall be protected throughout by an approved, supervised automatic sprinkler system in accordance with Section 9.7.

15.3.5.2 Buildings with unprotected openings in accordance with 8.2.5.5 shall be protected throughout by an approved, supervised automatic sprinkler system in accordance with Section 9.7.

14.3.6 Corridors.

Corridors shall be separated from other parts of the story by walls having a 1-hour fire resistance rating in accordance with 8.2.3.

Exception No. 1: Corridor protection shall not be required where all spaces normally subject to student occupancy have

15.3.6 Corridors.

Corridors shall be separated from other parts of the story by walls having a ½-hour fire resistance rating in accordance with 8.2.3.

Exception No. 1: Corridor protection shall not be required where all spaces normally subject to student occupancy have not less than one door opening directly to the outside or to an exterior exit access balcony or corridor in accordance with 7.5.3.

Exception No. 2: In buildings protected throughout by an approved, supervised automatic sprinkler system in accordance with Section 9.7, corridor walls shall not be required to be rated, provided that such walls form smoke partitions in accordance with 8.2.4.

Exception No. 3: Where the corridor ceiling is an assembly having a 1-hour fire resistance rating where tested as a wall, the corridor walls shall be permitted to terminate at the corridor ceiling.

Exception No. 4: Lavatories shall not be required to be separated from corridors, provided that they are separated from all other spaces by walls having not less than a 1-hour fire resistance rating in accordance with 8.2.3.

not less than one door opening directly to the outside or to an exterior exit access balcony or corridor in accordance with 7.5.3.

Exception No. 2:* In buildings protected throughout by an approved automatic sprinkler system with valve supervision in accordance with Section 9.7, corridor walls shall not be required to be rated, provided that such walls form smoke partitions in accordance with 8.2.4.

A.15.3.6 Exception No. 2 The exception permits valve supervision in accordance with Section 9.7 rather than requiring that the entire automatic sprinkler system be electrically supervised. It is intended that the valve supervision be performed electrically, not by chaining and locking the valves in the open position.

Exception No. 3: Where the corridor ceiling is an assembly having a ½-hour fire resistance rating where tested as a wall, the corridor wall shall be permitted to terminate at the corridor ceiling.

Exception No. 4: Lavatories shall not be required to be separated from corridors, provided that they are separated from all other spaces by walls having not less than a ½-hour fire resistance rating in accordance with 8.2.3.

Exception No. 5: Existing doors in ½-hour fire resistance–rated corridor walls shall be permitted to be 1 ¾-in. (4.4-cm) thick solid-bonded wood core doors or the equivalent.

Based on the protection provided by an automatic sprinkler system installed throughout the building, Exception No. 2 to 14/15.3.6 allows the corridor wall to terminate at the ceiling, provided that the ceiling resists the passage of smoke (see the exception to 8.2.4.2). Door closures are not required on doors other than doors required to be self-closing for other reasons, such as exit stair enclosure doors. This provision recognizes the teacher/administrator's ability to close doors upon evacuation, thus maintaining the smoke-resisting capability of the corridor wall and doors.

Exception No. 3 to 14/15.3.6 legitimizes the practice of designing a corridor protection system by building a tunnel with walls and ceilings constructed to meet the requirements of a 1-hour rated wall assembly for new construction and a ½-hour rating for existing assemblies.

The walls and doors that typically separate a school lavatory from the corridor often serve to isolate the lavatory, making incidents of violence or illegal drug use difficult to monitor by staff. In recognition of this problem, and given the typically low fuel loads associated with lavatories, Exception No. 4 to 14/15.3.6 exempts the wall separating the lavatory from the corridor from the rated construction requirement, provided that the rated corridor wall continuously separates the lavatory from adjacent rooms. This separation method permits lavatory doors to be omitted from the doorways. Exhibit 14/15.12 illustrates this arrangement.

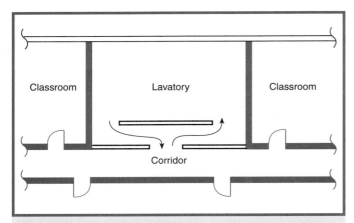

Exhibit 14/15.12 *Lavatory open to corridor but separated from adjacent rooms by continuous, rated corridor wall to building exterior walls.*

14.3.7 Subdivision of Building Spaces.

14.3.7.1 School buildings shall be subdivided into compartments by smoke barriers having a 1-hour fire resistance rating and complying with Section 8.3 where one or both of the following conditions exist:

(1) The maximum area of a compartment, including the aggregate area of all floors having a common atmosphere, exceeds 30,000 ft² (2800 m²).
(2) The length or width of the building exceeds 300 ft (91 m).

Exception No. 1:   This requirement shall not apply where all spaces normally subject to student occupancy have not less than one door opening directly to the outside or to an exterior or exit access balcony or corridor in accordance with 7.5.3.

Exception No. 2:   This requirement shall not apply to buildings that consist of only one story and are protected throughout by an approved, supervised automatic sprinkler system in accordance with Section 9.7.

14.3.7.2 The area of a smoke compartment shall not exceed 30,000 ft² (2800 m²), with no dimension exceeding 300 ft (91 m).

Exception: In buildings protected throughout by an approved, supervised automatic sprinkler system in accordance with Section 9.7, there shall be no limitation on smoke compartment size, provided that the floor is divided into not less than two smoke compartments.

15.3.7 Subdivision of Building Spaces.

15.3.7.1 School buildings shall be subdivided into compartments by smoke barriers complying with Section 8.3 where one or both of the following conditions exist:

(1) The maximum area of a compartment, including the aggregate area of all floors having a common atmosphere, exceeds 30,000 ft² (2800 m²).
(2) The length or width of the building exceeds 300 ft (91 m).

Exception No. 1:   This requirement shall not apply where all classrooms have exterior exit access in accordance with 7.5.3.

Exception No. 2:   This requirement shall not apply to buildings protected throughout by an approved automatic sprinkler system in accordance with Section 9.7.

15.3.7.2 The area of a smoke compartment shall not exceed 30,000 ft² (2800 m²), with no dimension exceeding 300 ft (91 m).

15.3.7.3 Doors in smoke barriers shall be self-latching.

The *Code* requires smoke barriers at maximum intervals of 300 ft (91 m) so that the products of combustion will not affect large numbers of occupants and their exits simultaneously. A primary concern is a situation where a corridor becomes clogged with smoke, resulting in the loss of the exit access. Rooms with exterior exit access provide the occupants a readily available, alternate means of escape in the event that a corridor fills with smoke.

The excellent record of automatic fire sprinklers permits the compartmentation requirements to be reduced.

The provision of 14/15.3.7.2 limits the area of a smoke compartment only if such compartmentation is required by 14/15.3.7.1.

Section 14.4 Special Provisions

14.4.1 Windowless Buildings and Underground Buildings.

Windowless buildings and underground buildings shall comply with Section 11.7.

14.4.2 High-Rise Buildings.

High-rise buildings shall comply with Section 11.8.

An educational occupancy high-rise building poses many of the same problems for occupants and firefighting forces that are posed by other occupancies located in high-rise buildings. Thus, the package of

14.4.3 Flexible Plan and Open Plan Buildings.

14.4.3.1 Flexible plan and open plan buildings shall comply with the requirements of this chapter as modified by 14.4.3.2 through 14.4.3.4.

14.4.3.2 Each room occupied by more than 300 persons shall have two or more means of egress entering into separate atmospheres. Where three or more means of egress are required, the number of means of egress permitted to enter into the same atmosphere shall not exceed two.

14.4.3.3 Flexible plan schools shall be permitted to have walls and partitions rearranged periodically only if revised plans or diagrams have been approved by the authority having jurisdiction.

14.4.3.4 Flexible plan buildings shall be evaluated while all folding walls are extended and in use as well as when they are in the retracted position.

Section 15.4 Special Provisions

15.4.1 Windowless Buildings and Underground Buildings.

Windowless buildings and underground buildings shall comply with Section 11.7.

15.4.2 High-Rise Buildings.

High-rise buildings shall comply with 11.8.2.1.

protection addressed by Section 11.8 is mandatorily referenced for new construction; the sprinkler provisions of 11.8.2.1 are mandatorily referenced for existing educational occupancy high-rise buildings.

15.4.3 Flexible Plan and Open Plan Buildings.

15.4.3.1 Flexible plan and open plan buildings shall comply with the requirements of this chapter as modified by 15.4.3.2 through 15.4.3.4.

15.4.3.2 Each room occupied by more than 300 persons shall have two or more means of egress entering into separate atmospheres. Where three or more means of egress are required, the number of means of egress permitted to enter into the same atmosphere shall not exceed two.

15.4.3.3 Flexible plan schools shall be permitted to have walls and partitions rearranged periodically only if revised plans or diagrams have been approved by the authority having jurisdiction.

15.4.3.4 Flexible plan buildings shall be evaluated while all folding walls are extended and in use as well as when they are in the retracted position.

Flexible plan and open plan buildings are addressed in 14/15.4.3. Rooms occupied by more than 300 persons require special treatment in flexible plan and open plan schools. To ensure the safety of this large number of persons occupying one room, means of egress must be arranged so that each of the egress paths traverses atmospheres that are separate from each other. If more than two separate means of egress paths are required, no more than two are permitted to pass through the same atmosphere. By using this arrangement, one fire should not contaminate or block all exits in an open plan or flexible plan building. See Exhibit 14/15.13.

In accordance with 14/15.4.3.3, approval of revised plans or diagrams is necessary to avoid the possibility of circuitous egress paths or other arrangements that do not comply with the intent of the *Code*. Also, flexible plan buildings are required to meet the requirements for corridor protection as well as those for the subdivision of building spaces using smoke barriers.

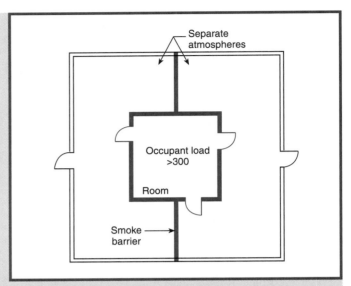

Exhibit 14/15.13 *Example of room in open plan building requiring two or more means of egress into separate atmospheres.*

Section 14.5 Building Services

14.5.1 Utilities.

Utilities shall comply with the provisions of Section 9.1.

14.5.2 Heating, Ventilating, and Air Conditioning Equipment.

14.5.2.1 Heating, ventilating, and air conditioning equipment shall comply with the provisions of Section 9.2.

14.5.2.2 Unvented fuel-fired heating equipment, other than gas space heaters in compliance with NFPA 54, *National Fuel Gas Code*, shall be prohibited.

It is not in the interest of reasonable life safety to allow unvented, fuel-fired equipment in a school building occupied by children. The typical use of unvented equipment might jeopardize the life safety of the students, because improper venting and potential mis-

Section 15.5 Building Services

15.5.1 Utilities.

Utilities shall comply with the provisions of Section 9.1.

15.5.2 Heating, Ventilating, and Air Conditioning Equipment.

15.5.2.1 Heating, ventilating, and air conditioning equipment shall comply with the provisions of Section 9.2.

15.5.2.2 Unvented fuel-fired heating equipment, other than gas space heaters in compliance with NFPA 54, *National Fuel Gas Code*, shall be prohibited.

use by students might result in injury to students, especially younger children. Paragraph 14/15.5.2.2 recognizes a special form of gas space heater that—although not vented in the conventional way—can be used safely.

CHAPTER 14 • New	CHAPTER 15 • Existing

14.5.3 Elevators, Escalators, and Conveyors.

Elevators, escalators, and conveyors shall comply with the provisions of Section 9.4.

14.5.4 Rubbish Chutes, Incinerators, and Laundry Chutes.

Rubbish chutes, incinerators, and laundry chutes shall comply with the provisions of Section 9.5.

Section 14.6 Reserved

Section 14.7 Operating Features

14.7.1 Emergency Egress and Relocation Drills.

14.7.1.1* Emergency egress and relocation drills shall be conducted in accordance with Section 4.7 and the applicable provisions of 14.7.1.2.

A.14.7.1.1 The requirements are, of necessity, general in scope, as it is recognized that they apply to all types of educational occupancies as well as conditions of occupancies, such as truant schools; schools for the mentally handicapped, vision impaired, hearing impaired, and speech impaired; and public schools. It is fully recognized that no one code can meet all the conditions of the various buildings involved, and it will be necessary for site administrators to issue supplements to these requirements, but all supplements should be consistent with these requirements.

14.7.1.2 Emergency egress and relocation drills shall be conducted as follows:

(1) Not less than one emergency egress and relocation drill shall be conducted every month the facility is in session.

Exception: In climates where the weather is severe, the monthly emergency egress and relocation drills shall be permitted to be deferred, provided that the required number of emergency egress and relocation drills is achieved and not less than four are conducted before the drills are deferred.

(2) All occupants of the building shall participate in the drill.
(3) One additional emergency egress and relocation drill, other than for educational occupancies that are open on a year-round basis, shall be required within the first 30 days of operation.

15.5.3 Elevators, Escalators, and Conveyors.

Elevators, escalators, and conveyors shall comply with the provisions of Section 9.4.

15.5.4 Rubbish Chutes, Incinerators, and Laundry Chutes.

Rubbish chutes, incinerators, and laundry chutes shall comply with the provisions of Section 9.5.

Section 15.6 Reserved

Section 15.7 Operating Features

15.7.1 Emergency Egress and Relocation Drills.

15.7.1.1* Emergency egress and relocation drills shall be conducted in accordance with Section 4.7 and the applicable provisions of 15.7.1.2.

A.15.7.1.1 The requirements are, of necessity, general in scope, as it is recognized that they apply to all types of educational occupancies as well as conditions of occupancies, such as truant schools; schools for the mentally handicapped, vision impaired, hearing impaired, and speech impaired; and public schools. It is fully recognized that no one code can meet all the conditions of the various buildings involved, and it will be necessary for site administrators to issue supplements to these requirements, but all supplements should be consistent with these requirements.

15.7.1.2 Emergency egress and relocation drills shall be conducted as follows:

(1) Not less than one emergency egress and relocation drill shall be conducted every month the facility is in session.

Exception: In climates where the weather is severe, the monthly emergency egress and relocation drills shall be permitted to be deferred, provided that the required number of emergency egress and relocation drills is achieved and not less than four are conducted before the drills are deferred.

(2) All occupants of the building shall participate in the drill.
(3) One additional emergency egress and relocation drill, other than for educational occupancies that are open on a year-round basis, shall be required within the first 30 days of operation.

14.7.1.3 All emergency and relocation drill alarms shall be sounded on the fire alarm system.

Emergency egress and relocation drills for educational occupancies, particularly those at the grade school level, are essential to ensure an orderly response during a fire. Unfortunately, the predictability of such drills often leads to their ineffectiveness. When an alarm bell sounds and a fire department monitor appears in a corridor, some teachers ignore the bell, assuming that it is a false alarm. If the bell sounds and a fire department monitor is not seen, teachers opt to either evacuate or remain in the building. This decision is made in the hallway. While the

14.7.2 Inspection.

14.7.2.1* It shall be the duty of principals and teachers to inspect all exit facilities daily to ensure that all stairways, doors, and other exits are in proper condition.

A.14.7.2.1 Particular attention should be given to keeping all doors unlocked; keeping doors that serve to protect the safety of paths of egress closed and under no conditions blocked open, such as doors on stairway enclosures; keeping outside stairs and fire escape stairs free from all obstructions and clear of snow and ice; and allowing no accumulation of snow or ice or materials of any kind outside exit doors that might prevent the opening of the door or interfere with rapid escape from the building.

Any condition likely to interfere with safe egress should be corrected immediately, if possible, or otherwise should be reported at once to the appropriate authorities.

14.7.2.2 Open plan buildings shall require extra surveillance to ensure that exit paths are maintained clear of obstruction and are obvious.

14.7.3 Furnishings and Decorations.

14.7.3.1 Draperies, curtains, and other similar furnishings and decorations in educational occupancies shall be in accordance with the provisions of 10.3.1.

14.7.3.2 Clothing and personal effects shall not be stored in corridors.

Exception No. 1: This requirement shall not apply to corridors protected by an automatic sprinkler system in accordance with Section 9.7.

15.7.1.3 All emergency and relocation drill alarms shall be sounded on the fire alarm system.

bell continues to ring, the students remain in their classrooms. Therefore, when a bell sounds, the primary emphasis should be placed on evacuation or relocation, regardless of who is or is not present in the hallways, or whether or not fire equipment is parked in front of the school. Essentially, the fire department and the school should vary the timing and arrangement of the drills but not the required response, which is orderly evacuation. See also Section 4.7.

15.7.2 Inspection.

15.7.2.1* It shall be the duty of principals and teachers to inspect all exit facilities daily to ensure that all stairways, doors, and other exits are in proper condition.

A.15.7.2.1 Particular attention should be given to keeping all doors unlocked; keeping doors that serve to protect the safety of paths of egress closed and under no conditions blocked open, such as doors on stairway enclosures; keeping outside stairs and fire escape stairs free from all obstructions and clear of snow and ice; and allowing no accumulation of snow or ice or materials of any kind outside exit doors that might prevent the opening of the door or interfere with rapid escape from the building.

Any condition likely to interfere with safe egress should be corrected immediately, if possible, or otherwise should be reported at once to the appropriate authorities.

15.7.2.2 Open plan buildings shall require extra surveillance to ensure that exit paths are maintained clear of obstruction and are obvious.

15.7.3 Furnishings and Decorations.

15.7.3.1 Draperies, curtains, and other similar furnishings and decorations in educational occupancies shall be in accordance with the provisions of 10.3.1.

15.7.3.2 Clothing and personal effects shall not be stored in corridors.

Exception No. 1: This requirement shall not apply to corridors protected by an automatic sprinkler system in accordance with Section 9.7.

CHAPTER 14 • New

CHAPTER 15 • Existing

Exception No. 2: This requirement shall not apply to corridor areas protected by a smoke detection system in accordance with Section 9.6.

Exception No. 3: This requirement shall not apply to storage in metal lockers, provided that the required egress width is maintained.

Clothing hung on hooks along corridor walls or on racks in school lobbies greatly increases the combustible load and will generally allow flame to spread quickly. Because Chapters 14 and 15 regulate the interior wall finish for corridors and lobbies, surfaces covered by combustible clothing that would allow flame to spread more quickly than is permitted by

14.7.3.3 Artwork and teaching materials shall be permitted to be attached directly to the walls and shall not exceed 20 percent of the wall area.

It is advantageous not only to limit the quantity of artwork displayed but also to avoid placing such materials near a room's exit access doors. Because the combustibility of the artwork cannot be effectively

Exception No. 2: This requirement shall not apply to corridor areas protected by a smoke detection system in accordance with Section 9.6.

Exception No. 3: This requirement shall not apply to storage in metal lockers, provided that the required egress width is maintained.

wall surfaces should not be created. The provisions of each of the exceptions to 14/15.7.3.2 (control of fire by sprinklers, early warning of incipient stage fire via smoke detection, or isolating fuel packages by locating the clothing in metal lockers) help to mitigate the potential for a clothing fire to render the exit access unusable.

15.7.3.3 Artwork and teaching materials shall be permitted to be attached directly to the walls and shall not exceed 20 percent of the wall area.

controlled, the quantity, in terms of the percentage of wall area covered, is regulated to avoid creating a continuous combustible surface that will spread flame across the room.

New and Existing Day-Care Occupancies

The 1997 edition of the *Code* separated day-care occupancy requirements from the broad category of educational occupancies. Chapters 16 and 17 address not only traditional child day care, but also the growing field of adult day care. In both cases, these chapters recognize that many of the individuals who occupy these facilities are not totally capable of self-preservation. Very young children will require a certain amount of assistance from the day-care staff to help with relocation or evacuation. Likewise, some adults in adult day care will also require staff assistance during a fire emergency. For these reasons, Chapters 16 and 17 mandate select features that anticipate that these occupants will respond to a fire more slowly than is normal. The requirements address a range of protection features, including the physical location of the day-care facility as it relates to the level of exit discharge (see Table 16.1.6.1 and Table 17.1.6). In reviewing the tables, note that the building construction features become more stringent where the day-care occupancy is located above or below the level of exit discharge. These tables also establish a threshold at which automatic sprinkler protection is required.

The complement of fire alarm systems, sprinkler systems, and other building construction features are addressed in these chapters. Section 16/17.7 specifies the minimum level of staff education, training, and drilling necessary to carry out an effective and efficient fire emergency response plan.

Section 16.1 General Requirements

16.1.1* Application.

A.16.1.1 Day-care occupancies do not provide for the full-time maintenance of a client. Occupancies that provide a primary place of residence are addressed in other occupancy chapters. *(See Chapters 24 through 33.)*

The requirements of Chapter 16 are based on the need to adequately protect the occupants in case of fire. The requirements assume that adequate staffing will be available and are based on staffing similar to that outlined in Table A.16.1.1.

If staff-to-client ratios fall below that suggested by Table A.16.1.1, it is the responsibility of the authority having jurisdiction to determine the additional safeguards beyond the requirements of Chapter 16 that are necessary. Typical additional provisions might include restricting the day-care

Section 17.1 General Requirements

17.1.1* Application.

A.17.1.1 Day-care occupancies do not provide for the full-time maintenance of a client. Occupancies that provide a primary place of residence are addressed in other occupancies. *(See Chapters 24 through 33.)*

The requirements of Chapter 17 are based on the need to adequately protect the occupants in case of fire. The requirements assume that adequate staffing will be available and are based on staffing similar to that outlined in Table A.17.1.1.

If staff-to-client ratios fall below that suggested by Table A.17.1.1, it is the responsibility of the authority having jurisdiction to determine the additional safeguards beyond the requirements of Chapter 17 that are necessary. Typical additional provisions might include restricting the day-care

CHAPTER 16 • New

CHAPTER 17 • Existing

Table A.16.1.1 Staffing

Staff-to-Client Ratio	Age (months)
1:3	0–24
1:4	25–36
1:7	37–60
1:10	61–96
1:12	≥97
1:3	Clients incapable of self-preservation

Table A.17.1.1 Staffing

Staff-to-Client Ratio	Age (months)
1:3	0–24
1:4	25–36
1:7	37–60
1:10	61–96
1:12	≥97
1:3	Clients incapable of self-preservation

occupancy to the level of exit discharge, requiring additional smoke detection, requiring automatic sprinkler protection, requiring better or additional means of egress, and similar types of items, depending on the situation.

16.1.1.1 The requirements of this chapter apply to the following:

(1) New buildings or portions thereof used as day-care occupancies *(see 1.4.1)*
(2) Additions made to, or used as, a day-care occupancy *(see 4.6.6)*
(3) Alterations, modernizations, or renovations of existing day-care occupancies *(see 4.6.7)*
(4) Existing buildings or portions thereof upon change of occupancy to a day-care occupancy *(see 4.6.11)*

16.1.1.2 Sections 16.1 through 16.5 and 16.7 establish life safety requirements for day-care occupancies in which more than 12 clients receive care, maintenance, and supervision by other than their relative(s) or legal guardian(s) for less than 24 hours per day.

16.1.1.3 Sections 16.1 (other than 16.1.6), 16.4, 16.5, 16.6, and 16.7 establish life safety requirements for day-care homes as defined in 16.1.3.

16.1.1.4 Where a facility houses more than one age group or self-preservation capability, the strictest requirements applicable to any group present shall apply throughout the day-care occupancy or building, as appropriate to a given area,

occupancy to the level of exit discharge, requiring additional smoke detection, requiring automatic sprinkler protection, requiring better or additional means of egress, and similar types of items, depending on the situation.

17.1.1.1 The requirements of this chapter apply to existing buildings or portions thereof currently occupied as day-care occupancies. *(See also 16.1.1.1.)*

17.1.1.2 Sections 17.1 through 17.5 and 17.7 establish life safety requirements for existing day-care occupancies in which more than 12 clients receive care, maintenance, and supervision by other than their relative(s) or legal guardian(s) for less than 24 hours per day. An existing day-care occupancy shall be permitted the option of meeting the requirements of Chapter 16 in lieu of Chapter 17. An existing day-care occupancy that meets the requirements of Chapter 16 shall be judged as meeting the requirements of Chapter 17.

17.1.1.3 Sections 17.1 (other than 17.1.6), 17.4, 17.5, 17.6, and 17.7 establish life safety requirements for existing day-care homes as defined in 17.1.3. An existing day-care home shall be permitted the option of meeting the requirements of Chapter 16 in lieu of Chapter 17. An existing day-care home that meets the requirements of Chapter 16 shall be judged as meeting the requirements of Chapter 17.

17.1.1.4 Where a facility houses clients of more than one self-preservation capability, the strictest requirements applicable to any group present shall apply throughout the day-care occupancy or building, as appropriate to a given area,

| **CHAPTER 16 • New** | **CHAPTER 17 • Existing** |

unless the area housing such a group is maintained as a separate fire area.

16.1.1.5 Places of religious worship shall not be required to meet the provisions of this chapter where providing day-care while services are being held in the building.

unless the area housing such a group is maintained as a separate fire area.

17.1.1.5 Places of religious worship shall not be required to meet the provisions of this chapter where providing day-care while services are being held in the building.

The intent of 16/17.1.1.2 is to differentiate between institutions where clients are in residence 24 hours a day (such as orphanages) and day-care facilities where clients who normally reside at another location are provided care. A facility supplying "total care" for each client would provide laundries, dormitories, cafeterias, and other ancillary services not found in a day-care center. The life safety requirements of such a facility would be governed by other occupancy provisions of the *Code*.

Note that, per 17.1.1.2 and 17.1.1.3, an existing day-care center or an existing day-care home meeting the requirements of Chapter 16 is to be judged as meeting the requirements of Chapter 17. Thus, if a day-care center or day-care home is built new in accordance with the requirements of Chapter 16, it later becomes an existing facility. Because the requirements of Chapters 16 and 17 differ, it would be unfair to re-examine the existing facility under the requirements of Chapter 17, because the protection package provided in accordance with Chapter 16 is as good as, if not better than, the package provided by compliance with the requirements of Chapter 17.

The provisions of 16/17.1.1.4 tailor the protection package to the client group with the greatest needs. This concept is similar to that applied by 6.1.14.2 to mixed occupancies. Paragraph 6.1.14.2 requires that

the most stringent *Code* provisions applicable to any of the occupancies present must be applied throughout the facility.

For example, 16.1.6.2 requires smoke barriers in new day-care centers if clients are 2 years old or less. If any client in a facility is 2 years old or less, the floors of the building that they occupy must be provided with smoke barriers. If a portion of the facility is an area that is separate from that occupied by a client 2 years old or less, smoke barriers are not required in that area. A separate fire area is usually constructed with walls that have a fire resistance rating of 2 hours.

Paragraph 16/17.1.1.5 addresses day care within a place of worship while religious services are being held. The parents of the clients of the day-care center would be among those attending a worship service. Parents and others assembled for the worship service would be expected to assist the day-care staff with any necessary evacuation. The requirements of Chapters 16 and 17, therefore, do not apply to such facilities. On the other hand, if day-care operations are conducted in the same building when religious services are not being conducted—such as during the work week—the day-care provisions of Chapters 16 and 17 would be applicable.

16.1.2 Mixed Occupancies.

Mixed occupancies shall meet the following criteria.

(a) *General.* Where day-care occupancies are located in a building containing mixed occupancies, the occupancies, other than day-care occupancies in assembly occupancies used primarily for worship, shall be separated by not less than 1-hour fire resistance–rated barriers constructed in accordance with 8.2.3.

(b) *Day-Care Occupancies in Apartment Buildings.* If the two exit accesses from a day-care occupancy enter the same corridor as an apartment occupancy, the exit accesses shall be separated in the corridor by a smoke barrier having not less than a 1-hour fire resistance rating constructed in

17.1.2 Mixed Occupancies.

Mixed occupancies shall meet the following criteria.

(a) *General.* Where day-care occupancies are located in a building containing mixed occupancies, the occupancies, other than day-care centers in assembly occupancies used primarily for worship, shall be separated by not less than 1-hour fire resistance–rated barriers constructed in accordance with 8.2.3.

(b) *Day-Care Centers in Apartment Buildings.* If the two exit accesses from a day-care occupancy enter the same corridor as an apartment occupancy, the exit accesses shall be separated in the corridor by a smoke barrier having not less than a 1-hour fire resistance rating constructed in accor-

CHAPTER 16 • New

accordance with Section 8.3. The smoke barrier shall be located so that it has an exit on each side.

Where a day-care center is located in a building housing another occupancy, the operators of the center usually have no control over the safety procedures and precautions practiced outside the center. Paragraph 16/17.1.2 requires additional protection to minimize the clients' exposure to potential hazards outside the center.

The reason for requiring corridor subdivision by smoke barriers in accordance with Section 8.3 where

16.1.3 Special Definitions.

Day-Care Home. See 3.3.39.

Flexible Plan and Open Plan Educational or Day-Care Building. See 3.3.80.

Self-Preservation (Day-Care Occupancy). See 3.3.176.

Separate Atmosphere. See 3.3.178.

16.1.4 Classification of Occupancy.

(See 6.1.4.)

16.1.4.1 Occupancies that include part-day preschools, kindergartens, and other schools whose purpose is primarily educational, even though the children who attend such schools are of preschool age, shall comply with the provisions of Chapter 14.

16.1.4.2 Adult day-care occupancies shall include any building or portion thereof used for less than 24 hours per day to house more than three adults requiring care, maintenance, and supervision by other than their relative(s). Clients shall be ambulatory or semiambulatory and shall not be bedridden. Clients shall not exhibit behavior that is harmful to themselves or others.

16.1.4.3* Conversions. A conversion from a day-care home to a day-care occupancy with more than 12 clients shall be permitted only if the day-care occupancy conforms with the requirements of this chapter for new day-care occupancies with more than 12 clients.

CHAPTER 17 • Existing

dance with Section 8.3. The smoke barrier shall be located so that it has an exit on each side.

day-care centers are located in an apartment building is the same as that used in Chapters 18 and 19 for health care facilities. This minimum construction will provide sufficient protection against flame and smoke spread. The 20-minute door, coupled with the 1-hour wall, provides a barrier that will either contain a fire within a space for a limited time after the space has been evacuated, or will prevent a fire from entering an occupied space for a period of time.

17.1.3 Special Definitions.

Day-Care Home. See 3.3.39.

Flexible Plan and Open Plan Educational or Day-Care Building. See 3.3.80.

Self-Preservation (Day-Care Occupancy). See 3.3.176.

Separate Atmosphere. See 3.3.178.

17.1.4 Classification of Occupancy.

(See 6.1.4.)

17.1.4.1 Occupancies that include part-day preschools, kindergartens, and other schools whose purpose is primarily educational, even though the children who attend such schools are of preschool age, shall comply with the provisions of Chapter 15.

17.1.4.2 Adult day-care occupancies shall include any building or portion thereof used for less than 24 hours per day to house more than three adults requiring care, maintenance, and supervision by other than their relative(s). Clients shall be ambulatory or semiambulatory and shall not be bedridden. Clients shall not exhibit behavior that is harmful to themselves or others.

17.1.4.3* Conversions. A conversion from a day-care home to a day-care occupancy with more than 12 clients shall be permitted only if the day-care occupancy conforms with the requirements of Chapter 16 for new day-care occupancies with more than 12 clients.

CHAPTER 16 • New   **CHAPTER 17 • Existing**

The specific reference to an adult day-care occupancy in 16/17.1.4.2 acknowledges that more and more senior citizens are being cared for in day-care centers similar to child day-care centers. The definition of an adult day-care occupancy includes the characteristics of clients who might be cared for in this type of occupancy. Essentially, the capabilities of adult day-care clients clarifies that these occupancies are not nursing homes or old age homes but occupancies used by adults who are capable of self-preservation but who are in need of limited attendance, supervision, or observation.

Earlier editions of the *Code* included several cues for identifying adults who meet the criteria of this description of these clients. However, to avoid the implication that medical training is necessary for assessing such adults, these cues were removed from the *Code*. It might be appropriate, however, to use some of the following guidelines from previous editions to determine the acceptability of a client for adult day-care:

(1) Client does not require medical injections from staff, but might require the administration of oral medication by staff personnel when and as prescribed by a licensed medical examiner.
(2) Client might require limited supervision, attendance, or observation.
(3) Client exhibits acceptable behavior (not harmful to self or others).

Paragraph 16/17.1.4.3 addresses conversions that result in an increase in the number of clients to a number greater than 12. The conversion from a day-care home to a day-care center places a sufficiently greater number of clients at risk so as to justify imposing the requirements for new construction. If the conversion is made in reverse (that is, from an existing day-care center to a day-care home), fewer clients are placed at risk. The existing protection package for the day-care center would be considered adequate to permit treating the post-conversion day-care home as an existing occupancy.

A.16.1.4.3 A conversion from a day-care occupancy with more than 12 clients to a day-care home is not considered a change of occupancy. The resulting day-care home should be permitted to meet the requirements of Chapter 17 for existing day-care homes.

A.17.1.4.3 A conversion from a day-care occupancy with more than 12 clients to a day-care home is not considered a change of occupancy. The resulting day-care home should be permitted to meet the requirements of Chapter 17 for existing day-care homes.

16.1.5 Classification of Hazard of Contents.

The contents of day-care occupancies shall be classified as ordinary hazard in accordance with Section 6.2.

17.1.5 Classification of Hazard of Contents.

The contents of day-care occupancies shall be classified as ordinary hazard in accordance with Section 6.2.

16.1.6 Location and Construction.

16.1.6.1 Day-care occupancies, other than day-care homes, shall be limited to the locations, construction types, and sprinkler protection features specified in Table 16.1.6.1.

17.1.6 Location and Construction.

Day-care occupancies, other than day-care homes, shall be limited to the locations, construction types, and sprinkler protection features specified in Table 17.1.6.

CHAPTER 16 • New **CHAPTER 17 • Existing**

Table 16.1.6.1 Location and Construction Type Limitations

Location of Day-Care Occupancy	Sprinklered Building	Construction Type
1 story below LED	Yes	I(443), I(332), II(222), II(111), II(000), III(211), IV(2HH), or V(111)
Level of exit discharge	No	Any type
1 story above LED	Yes	Any type
	No	I(443), I(332), II(222)
2 or 3 stories above LED	Yes	I(443), I(332), II(222), II(111), II(000), III(211), or V(111)
>3 stories above LED but not high-rise	Yes	I(443), I(332), II(222), or II(111)
High-rise	Yes	I(443), I(332), or II(222)

LED: Level of exit discharge.

16.1.6.2 Where day-care occupancies, other than day-care homes, with clients who are 24 months or less in age or who are incapable of self-preservation are located one or more stories above the level of exit discharge, or where day-care occupancies are located two or more stories above the level of exit discharge, smoke barriers shall be provided to divide such stories into not less than two smoke compartments. The smoke barriers shall be constructed in accordance with Section 8.3 but shall not be required to have a fire resistance rating.

Table 17.1.6 Location and Construction Type Limitations

Location of Day-Care Occupancy	Sprinklered Building	Construction Type
1 story below LED	Yes	I(443), I(332), II(222), II(111), II(000), III(211), IV(2HH), V(111)
	No	I(443), I(332), II(222), II(111), III(211), IV(2HH), V(111)
Level of exit discharge	Yes	Any type
	No	Any type
1 story above LED	Yes	Any type
	No	I(443), I(332), II(222)
	No	II(111)*, III(211)*, V(111)*
2 stories above LED	Yes	I(443), I(332), II(222)
	Yes	II(111)*, III(211)*, V(111)*
	No	I(443), I(332), II(222)
>3 stories above LED but not high-rise	Yes	I(443), I(332), II(222)
	Yes	II(111)*
	No	I(443), I(332), II(222)
High-rise	Yes	I(443), I(332), II(222)
	No	Not permitted

LED: Level of exit discharge.

*Permitted only if clients capable of self-preservation.

Tables 16.1.6.1 and 17.1.6 relate the building construction type, the automatic sprinkler protection, and the floor level permitted to be occupied as a day-care center. For example, a day-care center is permitted to be located on the story of exit discharge in any building, regardless of construction type or automatic sprinkler protection. For a day-care center located one story above the level of exit discharge in a non-sprinklered building, the building must be of Type I(443), Type I(332), or Type II(222) construction. However, if the day-care center is existing and the clients are capable of self-preservation, Type II(111), Type III(211), and Type V(111) construction are also permitted. If the building is of any other construction type, the day-care center is permitted to be located one story above the level of exit discharge only if the building is protected by automatic sprinklers. For other possible combinations of floor levels, building construction type, and building sprinklering see Tables 16.1.6.1 and 17.1.6.

Although Table 16.1.6.1 permits floors above the level of exit discharge to be occupied as new day-care centers if the building is of the required construction type and is sprinklered, the *Code* recognizes that rapid vertical movement to the level of exit discharge might be difficult. Therefore, where clients incapable of self-preservation or 24 months old or less are to be located above the level of exit discharge, the floor must be subdivided into two smoke compartments using smoke barriers. The intent is that at least one

CHAPTER 16 • New   **CHAPTER 17 • Existing**

of the two smoke compartments on the floor is expected to be unaffected by any fire for the time necessary to summon assistance and evacuate, or for the time necessary to control the fire, so that evacuation

is unnecessary. This requirement is relatively new to the *Code* (1994 edition); justification for making the provision retroactive to existing day-care centers was insufficient.

16.1.7 Occupant Load.

16.1.7.1 The occupant load, in number of persons for whom means of egress and other provisions are required, shall be determined on the basis of the occupant load factors of Table 7.3.1.2 that are characteristic of the use of the space or shall be determined as the maximum probable population of the space under consideration, whichever is greater.

16.1.7.2 Where the occupant load is determined as the maximum probable population of the space in accordance with 16.1.7.1, an approved aisle, seating, and exiting diagram shall be required by the authority having jurisdiction to substantiate such a modification.

Many jurisdictions that license day-care centers require the day-care facility to provide a net area of 35 ft^2 (3.3 m^2) per client for functional reasons other than life safety. In Table 7.3.1.2, the *Code* establishes the 35-ft^2 (3.3-m^2) net area occupant load factor solely for the purpose of calculating occupant load and associated egress capacity. The occupant load is required

17.1.7 Occupant Load.

17.1.7.1 The occupant load, in number of persons for whom means of egress and other provisions are required, shall be determined on the basis of the occupant load factors of Table 7.3.1.2 that are characteristic of the use of the space or shall be determined as the maximum probable population of the space under consideration, whichever is greater.

17.1.7.2 Where the occupant load is determined as the maximum probable population of the space in accordance with 17.1.7.1, an approved aisle, seating, and exiting diagram shall be required by the authority having jurisdiction to substantiate such a modification.

to be the maximum number of persons expected to occupy the floor but not less than the number calculated using the occupant load factor.

Where a day-care center occupies a portion of a floor on which another occupancy exists, the occupant load for that floor is the sum of the occupant loads of the two occupancies.

Section 16.2 Means of Egress Requirements

16.2.1 General.

Means of egress shall be in accordance with Chapter 7 and Section 16.2.

16.2.2 Means of Egress Components.

16.2.2.1 Components of means of egress shall be limited to the types described in 16.2.2.2 through 16.2.2.10.

16.2.2.2 Doors.

16.2.2.2.1 General. Doors complying with 7.2.1 shall be permitted.

16.2.2.2.2 Panic Hardware or Fire Exit Hardware. Any door in a required means of egress from an area having an occupant load of 100 or more persons shall be permitted to

Section 17.2 Means of Egress Requirements

17.2.1 General.

Means of egress shall be in accordance with Chapter 7 and Section 17.2.

17.2.2 Means of Egress Components.

17.2.2.1 Components of means of egress shall be limited to the types described in 17.2.2.2 through 17.2.2.10.

17.2.2.2 Doors.

17.2.2.2.1 General. Doors complying with 7.2.1 shall be permitted.

17.2.2.2.2 Panic Hardware or Fire Exit Hardware. Any door in a required means of egress from an area having an occupant load of 100 or more persons shall be permitted to be provided with a latch or lock only if the latch or lock is panic hardware or fire exit hardware complying with 7.2.1.7.

16.2.2.2.3 Special Locking Arrangements. Special locking arrangements complying with 7.2.1.6 shall be permitted.

16.2.2.2.4* Closet Doors. Every closet door latch shall be such that clients can open the door from inside the closet.

A.16.2.2.2.4 The purpose of this requirement is to prevent arrangements where a child can be trapped in a closet. It is intended that this provision be broadly interpreted by the authority having jurisdiction to include equipment such as refrigerators and freezers.

16.2.2.2.5 Bathroom Doors. Every bathroom door lock shall be designed to allow opening of the locked door from the outside in an emergency. The opening device shall be readily accessible to the staff.

The requirement of 16/17.2.2.2.2 for panic hardware or fire exit hardware is based on the total occupant load of the area served and not the required capacity of the door. For example, if an area has an occupant load of 120 persons and is served by 3 doors, each door is required only to have a capacity for 40 persons. However, since each of these doors serves an area with 100 or more persons, any latches on these doors must be arranged to be released by panic hardware or fire exit hardware. The concept employed recognizes

16.2.2.3* Stairs. Stairs complying with 7.2.2 shall be permitted.

A.16.2.2.3 See A.7.2.2.4.5(1), Exception No. 3, regarding additional handrails on stairs that are used extensively by children 5 years of age or less.

16.2.2.4 Smokeproof Enclosures. Smokeproof enclosures complying with 7.2.3 shall be permitted.

16.2.2.5 Horizontal Exits. Horizontal exits complying with 7.2.4 shall be permitted.

be provided with a latch or lock only if the latch or lock is panic hardware or fire exit hardware complying with 7.2.1.7.

17.2.2.2.3 Special Locking Arrangements. Special locking arrangements complying with 7.2.1.6 shall be permitted.

17.2.2.2.4* Closet Doors. Every closet door latch shall be such that clients can open the door from inside the closet.

A.17.2.2.2.4 The purpose of this requirement is to prevent arrangements where a client can be trapped in a closet. It is intended that this provision be broadly interpreted by the authority having jurisdiction to include equipment such as refrigerators and freezers.

17.2.2.2.5 Bathroom Doors. Every bathroom door lock shall be designed to allow opening of the locked door from the outside in an emergency. The opening device shall be readily accessible to the staff.

that it is not possible to predict how many occupants will move to any one of the doors serving the area. The number of persons from the assembled group of 100 or more who travel to any one of the doors might be sufficiently large to cause crowding and shoving. Panic hardware and fire exit hardware are designed to release the door latch when building occupants push up against the actuating mechanism (typically a push pad or bar that must extend across at least one-half the width of the door).

17.2.2.3* Stairs.

A.17.2.2.3 See A.7.2.2.4.5(1), Exception No. 3, regarding additional handrails on stairs that are used extensively by children 5 years of age or less.

17.2.2.3.1 Stairs complying with 7.2.2 shall be permitted.

17.2.2.3.2 Existing Class A stairs shall be permitted.

17.2.2.3.3 Existing Class B stairs shall be permitted where not used by clients.

17.2.2.4 Smokeproof Enclosures. Smokeproof enclosures complying with 7.2.3 shall be permitted.

17.2.2.5 Horizontal Exits.

17.2.2.5.1 Horizontal exits complying with 7.2.4 shall be permitted.

CHAPTER 16 • New	CHAPTER 17 • Existing

17.2.2.5.2 Areas of refuge, other than in buildings provided with smokeproof enclosures or buildings protected throughout by an approved, supervised automatic sprinkler system in accordance with Section 9.7, shall be provided by horizontal exits for occupants of day-care occupancies located above the fifth story.

If an existing day-care center is located in the high-rise portion of a building [that is, on a floor more than 75 ft (23 m) above the lowest level of fire department vehicle access], Table 17.1.6 requires sprinkler protection for the entire building and further requires that the building be of minimum 2-hour fire resistance–rated construction. Table 17.1.6 would permit the continued use of an existing day-care center located above the fifth story of a nonsprinklered building if the building were of minimum 2-hour fire resistance–rated construction. However, such continued use would not be permitted within the high-rise portion of that building. Subparagraph 17.2.2.5.2 does require such an existing, nonsprinklered building to have horizontal exits or smokeproof enclosures to help ensure that clients will survive a fire. The smokeproof enclosures or the areas of refuge created by the horizontal exit provide the occupant protection needed where no sprinklers are provided to control or extinguish the fire. A similar provision does not apply to new day-care centers, because Table 16.1.6.1 requires sprinklers in buildings that house day-care centers on any floors that are two or more stories above the level of exit discharge.

16.2.2.6 Ramps. Ramps complying with 7.2.5 shall be permitted.

16.2.2.7 Exit Passageways. Exit passageways complying with 7.2.6 shall be permitted.

16.2.2.8 Fire Escape Ladders. Fire escape ladders complying with 7.2.9 shall be permitted.

16.2.2.9 Alternating Tread Devices. Alternating tread devices complying with 7.2.11 shall be permitted.

16.2.2.10 Areas of Refuge. Areas of refuge complying with 7.2.12 shall be permitted.

16.2.3 Capacity of Means of Egress.

Capacity of means of egress shall be in accordance with Section 7.3.

16.2.4 Number of Exits.

Each floor occupied by clients shall have not less than two exits in accordance with Chapter 7.

17.2.2.6 Ramps. Ramps complying with 7.2.5 shall be permitted.

17.2.2.7 Exit Passageways. Exit passageways complying with 7.2.6 shall be permitted.

17.2.2.8 Fire Escape Ladders. Fire escape ladders complying with 7.2.9 shall be permitted.

17.2.2.9 Alternating Tread Devices. Alternating tread devices complying with 7.2.11 shall be permitted.

17.2.2.10 Areas of Refuge. Areas of refuge complying with 7.2.12 shall be permitted.

17.2.3 Capacity of Means of Egress.

Capacity of means of egress shall be in accordance with Section 7.3.

17.2.4 Number of Exits.

17.2.4.1 Each floor occupied by clients shall have not less than two exits in accordance with Chapter 7.

17.2.4.2 Where the story below the level of exit discharge is occupied as a day-care occupancy, 17.2.4.2.1 and 17.2.4.2.2 shall apply.

17.2.4.2.1 One means of egress shall be an outside or interior stair in accordance with 7.2.2. An interior stair, if used, shall serve only the story below the level of exit discharge.

CHAPTER 16 • New	CHAPTER 17 • Existing

The interior stair shall be permitted to communicate with the level of exit discharge; however, the exit route from the level of exit discharge shall not pass through the stair enclosure.

17.2.4.2.2 The second means of egress shall be permitted to be via an unenclosed stairway separated from the level of exit discharge in accordance with 8.2.5.4. The path of egress travel on the level of exit discharge shall be protected in accordance with 7.1.3.1.

Exception: The path of egress on the level of exit discharge shall be permitted to be unprotected if the level of exit discharge and the level below the level of exit discharge are protected throughout by a smoke detection system or an approved automatic sprinkler system.

Subsection 17.2.4.2 contains requirements for existing day-care centers located below the level of exit discharge. Similar provisions do not appear in Chapter 16 because Table 16.1.6.1 requires complete sprinklering of the building if a new day-care center is located below the level of exit discharge. This requirement helps to ensure that the occupants of the lower level have a protected egress path that doesn't force them to traverse the street floor. The requirement does help but doesn't guarantee safe egress, because a convenience door is permitted from the street floor into the lower level's stair enclosure. If a fire were to occur on the street floor and if someone were to wedge the door open, smoke and other effects of fire could enter the stair designated for use by the occupants of the lower level. Diligent enforcement is needed to ensure that the self-closing door will not be improperly held open. The intent of 17.2.4.2 is illustrated in Exhibit 16/17.1.

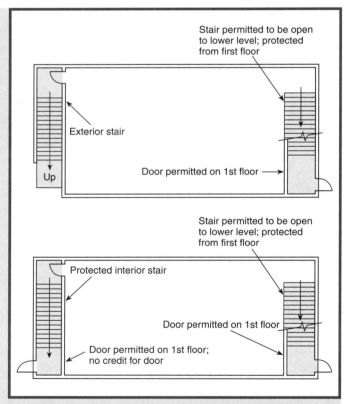

Exhibit 16/17.1 *Egress for levels below level of exit discharge—existing day-care centers.*

16.2.5 Arrangement of Means of Egress.

(See also 16.1.6.2.)

16.2.5.1 Means of egress shall be arranged in accordance with Section 7.5.

17.2.5 Arrangement of Means of Egress.

17.2.5.1 Means of egress shall be arranged in accordance with Section 7.5.

CHAPTER 16 • New

16.2.5.2 No dead-end corridor shall exceed 20 ft (6.1 m), other than in buildings protected throughout by an approved, supervised automatic sprinkler system in accordance with Section 9.7, in which case dead-end corridors shall not exceed 50 ft (15 m).

16.2.5.3 No common path of travel shall exceed 75 ft (23 m), other than for the first 100 ft (30 m) in a building protected throughout by an approved, supervised automatic sprinkler system in accordance with Section 9.7.

The provisions of Chapter 7 give an occupancy chapter the responsibility for permitting or prohibiting dead-end corridors and common path of travel, and for limiting the length of any dead-end corridors and common paths an occupancy chapter does permit.

16.2.6 Travel Distance to Exits.

16.2.6.1 Travel distance shall be measured in accordance with Section 7.6.

16.2.6.2 Travel distance shall meet the following criteria:

(1) The travel distance between any room door intended as an exit access and an exit shall not exceed 100 ft (30 m).
(2) The travel distance between any point in a room and an exit shall not exceed 150 ft (45 m).
(3) The travel distance between any point in a sleeping room and an exit access door in that room shall not exceed 50 ft (15 m).

Exception: The travel distance in 16.2.6.2(1) and (2) shall be permitted to be increased by 50 ft (15 m) in buildings protected throughout by an approved, supervised automatic sprinkler system in accordance with Section 9.7.

As shown in Exhibit 16/17.2, the maximum permitted travel distance from a room door (exit access door to the corridor) to an exit (door to enclosed exit stair) is 100 ft (30 m); if the building is sprinklered, the maximum distance is 150 ft (45 m). The maximum travel distance from a point in a sleeping room to an exit access door from that room is 50 ft (15 m). This within-room travel distance limit is not permitted to be increased, even if the building is sprinklered. The total travel distance from any point (such as the point farthest from the room door) to an exit is 150 ft

CHAPTER 17 • Existing

17.2.5.2 No dead-end corridor shall not exceed 20 ft (6.1 m), other than in buildings protected throughout by an approved, supervised automatic sprinkler system in accordance with Section 9.7, in which case dead-end corridors shall not exceed 50 ft (15 m).

17.2.5.3 Common paths of travel shall not exceed 75 ft (23 m), other than for the first 100 ft (30 m) in a building protected throughout by an approved, supervised automatic sprinkler system in accordance with Section 9.7.

17.2.5.4 The story used below the level of exit discharge shall be in accordance with 17.2.4.2.

The dead-end corridor and common path permitted by 16/17.2.5.2 and 16/17.2.5.3 use limits that other occupancies established years ago. Their applicability to day-care centers seems reasonable.

17.2.6 Travel Distance to Exits.

17.2.6.1 Travel distance shall be measured in accordance with Section 7.6.

17.2.6.2 Travel distance shall meet the following criteria:

(1) The travel distance between any room door intended as an exit access and an exit shall not exceed 100 ft (30 m).
(2) The travel distance between any point in a room and an exit shall not exceed 150 ft (45 m).
(3) The travel distance between any point in a sleeping room and an exit access door in that room shall not exceed 50 ft (15 m).

Exception: The travel distance in 17.2.6.2(1) and (2) shall be permitted to be increased by 50 ft (15 m) in buildings protected throughout by an approved automatic sprinkler system in accordance with Section 9.7.

(45 m), although additional corridor travel is permitted for sprinklered buildings as explained in the exception to 16/17.2.6.2. In a sprinklered building the total permitted travel distance is 200 ft (60 m) only if the full 50 ft (15 m) of within-room exit access and the full 150 ft (45 m) of corridor exit access are used.

Note that, for new construction, the *Code* requires the sprinkler system to be supervised in order to take advantage of the allowance for additional travel distance.

CHAPTER 16 • New	CHAPTER 17 • Existing

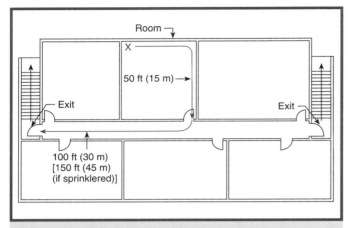

Exhibit 16/17.2 *Maximum travel distance in a day-care center.*

16.2.7 Discharge from Exits.

Discharge from exits shall be arranged in accordance with Section 7.7.

16.2.8 Illumination of Means of Egress.

Means of egress shall be illuminated in accordance with Section 7.8.

16.2.9 Emergency Lighting.

Emergency lighting shall be provided in accordance with Section 7.9 in the following areas:

(1) Interior stairs and corridors
(2) Assembly use spaces
(3) Flexible and open plan buildings
(4) Interior or windowless portions of buildings
(5) Shops and laboratories

16.2.10 Marking of Means of Egress.

Means of egress shall have signs in accordance with Section 7.10.

16.2.11 Special Means of Egress Features.

16.2.11.1 Windows for Rescue. Every room or space normally subject to client occupancy, other than bathrooms, shall have not less than one outside window for emergency rescue that complies with the following:

(1) Such windows shall be openable from the inside without the use of tools and shall provide a clear opening of not less than 20 in. (51 cm) in width, 24 in. (61 cm) in height, and 5.7 ft² (0.53 m²) in area.

17.2.7 Discharge from Exits.

Discharge from exits shall be arranged in accordance with Section 7.7, unless otherwise provided in 17.2.4.2.

17.2.8 Illumination of Means of Egress.

Means of egress shall be illuminated in accordance with Section 7.8.

17.2.9 Emergency Lighting.

Emergency lighting shall be provided in accordance with Section 7.9 in the following areas:

(1) Interior stairs and corridors
(2) Assembly use spaces
(3) Flexible and open plan buildings
(4) Interior or windowless portions of buildings
(5) Shops and laboratories

17.2.10 Marking of Means of Egress.

Means of egress shall have signs in accordance with Section 7.10.

17.2.11 Special Means of Egress Features.

17.2.11.1 Windows for Rescue. Every room or space greater than 250 ft² (23.2 m²) normally subject to client occupancy shall have not less than one outside window for emergency rescue that complies with the following:

(1) Such windows shall be openable from the inside without the use of tools and shall provide a clear opening of not less than 20 in. (51 cm) in width, 24 in. (61 cm) in height, and 5.7 ft² (0.53 m²) in area.

(2) The bottom of the opening shall be not more than 44 in. (112 cm) above the floor.

(3) The clear opening shall allow a rectangular solid, with a width and height that provides not less than the required 5.7-ft² (0.53-m²) opening and a depth of not less than 20 in. (51 cm), to pass fully through the opening.

Exception No. 1: This requirement shall not apply to buildings protected throughout by an approved, supervised automatic sprinkler system in accordance with Section 9.7.

Exception No. 2: This requirement shall not apply where the room or space has a door leading directly to the outside of the building.

The dimensions specified for windows used for emergency rescue are based on simulations of emergency rescue conducted by the San Diego Fire Department. Windows providing clear openings of identical dimensions are also addressed under the provisions for secondary means of escape for dwelling units.

(2) The bottom of the opening shall be not more than 44 in. (112 cm) above the floor.

(3) The clear opening shall allow a rectangular solid, with a width and height that provides not less than the required 5.7 ft² (0.53 m²) opening and a depth of not less than 20 in. (51 cm), to pass fully through the opening.

Exception No. 1: This requirement shall not apply to buildings protected throughout by an approved automatic sprinkler system in accordance with Section 9.7.

Exception No. 2: This requirement shall not apply where the room or space has a door leading directly to the outside of the building.

Exception No. 3: This requirement shall not apply to rooms located higher than three stories above grade.

Exception No. 4: Awning-type or hopper-type windows that are hinged or subdivided to provide a clear opening not less than 600 in.² (3900 cm²) in area, nor any dimension less than 22 in. (55.9 cm), shall be permitted to continue to be used. Screen walls or devices in front of required windows shall not interfere with normal rescue requirements.

Exception No. 5: This requirement shall not apply where the room or space complies with the following:

(a) Doors shall exist that allow travel between adjacent classrooms. Where such doors are used to travel from classroom to classroom, they shall provide direct access to exits in both directions or direct access to an exit in one direction and to a separate smoke compartment that provides access to another exit in the other direction.

(b) The corridor shall be separated from the classrooms by a wall that resists the passage of smoke, and all doors between the classrooms and the corridor shall be self-closing in accordance with 7.2.1.8.

(c) The length of travel to exits along such paths shall not exceed 150 ft (45 m).

(d) Each communicating door shall be marked in accordance with Section 7.10.

(e) No locking device shall be permitted on the communicating doors.

Exhibit 16/17.3 illustrates two configurations that achieve the required area of 5.7 ft² (0.53 m²).

The *Code* intends that the fire department or others are to assist day-care center clients, especially over ladders. If these emergency rescue windows must be used as a supplementary means of escape,

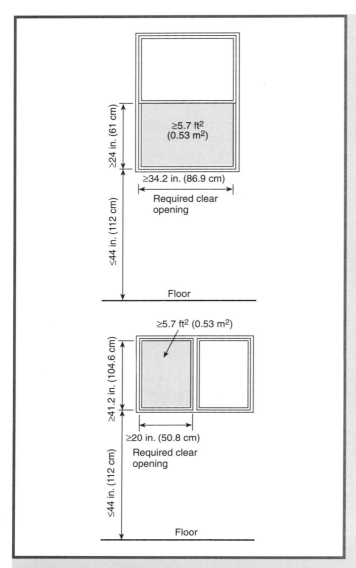

Exhibit 16/17.3 Windows for rescue or ventilation—minimum dimensions.

the windows should permit younger children to escape unaided. Therefore, storm sashes, screens, or devices in front of the windows must be easy to open or remove, and the sills must be low enough for children to reach.

Emergency rescue windows are not required if a room has a door leading directly to the outside or if the building is totally sprinklered in accordance with Exception No. 1 and Exception No. 2 to 16/17.2.11.1.

It might not be practical to use a window above the third story as an escape window. Therefore, Exception No. 3 to 17.2.11.1 exempts the window above the third story in existing day-care centers. This exception will have limited application, because Table 17.1.6 requires most day-care centers located more than three stories above the level of exit discharge to be sprinklered; and per Exception No. 1, sprinklers negate the need for the rescue window. Similarly, the exception is not needed for new construction, because Table 16.1.6.1 requires day-care centers located more than three stories above the level of exit discharge to be sprinklered.

Awning-type and hopper-type windows might provide the required opening within the plane of the building's exterior wall. However, when the window is open, the sash and glazing are located outside that plane and might prevent occupants from passing through the opening. Therefore, the criterion for providing an opening through which a minimum-size, rectangular solid can pass is intended to ensure that occupants can pass through the opening. For existing awning-type windows, Exception No. 4 to 17.2.11.1 offers some relief from the rectangular solid and minimum-size opening requirements. Exhibit 16/17.4 illustrates the use of Exception No. 4 to 17.2.11.1.

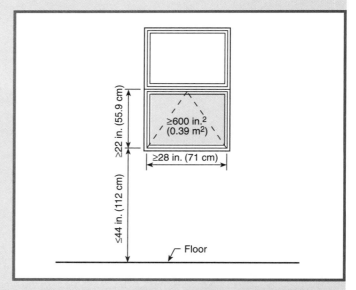

Exhibit 16/17.4 Existing awning window—minimum dimensions.

Section 16.3 Protection

16.3.1 Protection of Vertical Openings.

Any vertical opening, other than unprotected vertical openings in accordance with 8.2.5.8, shall be enclosed or protected in accordance with 8.2.5.

16.3.2 Protection from Hazards.

16.3.2.1 Rooms or spaces for the storage, processing, or use of materials specified in 16.3.2.1(1) through (3) shall be protected in accordance with the following:

(1) Separation from the remainder of the building by fire barriers having a fire resistance rating of not less than 1 hour or protection of such rooms by automatic extinguishing systems as specified in Section 8.4 in the following areas:

    a. Boiler and furnace rooms

Exception: Boiler and furnace rooms shall be exempt from the requirement of 16.3.2.1(1)a where they enclose only air-handling equipment.

    b. Rooms or spaces used for the storage of combustible supplies in quantities deemed hazardous by the authority having jurisdiction
    c. Rooms or spaces used for the storage of hazardous materials or flammable or combustible liquids in quantities deemed hazardous by recognized standards
    d. Janitor closets

Exception: Doors to janitor closets shall be permitted to have ventilating louvers where the space is protected by automatic sprinklers.

(2) Separation from the remainder of the building by fire barriers having a fire resistance rating of not less than 1 hour and protection of such rooms by automatic extinguishing systems as specified in Section 8.4 in the following areas:

    a.* Laundries

A.16.3.2.1(2)a It is not the intent to classify a room with a domestic-type clothes washer and a domestic-type clothes dryer as a laundry.

    b. Maintenance shops, including woodworking and painting areas
    c. Rooms or spaces used for processing or use of combustible supplies deemed hazardous by the authority having jurisdiction

Section 17.3 Protection

17.3.1 Protection of Vertical Openings.

Any vertical opening, other than unprotected vertical openings in accordance with 8.2.5.8, shall be enclosed or protected in accordance with 8.2.5.

17.3.2 Protection from Hazards.

17.3.2.1 Rooms or spaces for the storage, processing, or use of materials specified in 17.3.2.1(1) through (3) shall be protected in accordance with the following:

(1) Separation from the remainder of the building by fire barriers having a fire resistance rating of not less than 1 hour or protection of such rooms by automatic extinguishing systems as specified in Section 8.4 in the following areas:

    a. Boiler and furnace rooms

Exception: Boiler and furnace rooms shall be exempt from the requirement of 17.3.2.1(1)a where they enclose only air-handling equipment.

    b. Rooms or spaces used for the storage of combustible supplies in quantities deemed hazardous by the authority having jurisdiction
    c. Rooms or spaces used for the storage of hazardous materials or flammable or combustible liquids in quantities deemed hazardous by recognized standards
    d. Janitor closets

Exception: Doors to janitor closets shall be permitted to have ventilating louvers where the space is protected by automatic sprinklers.

(2) Separation from the remainder of the building by fire barriers having a fire resistance rating of not less than 1 hour and protection of such rooms by automatic extinguishing systems as specified in Section 8.4 in the following areas:

    a.* Laundries

A.17.3.2.1(2)a It is not the intent to classify a room with a domestic-type clothes washer and a domestic-type clothes dryer as a laundry.

    b. Maintenance shops, including woodworking and painting areas
    c. Rooms or spaces used for processing or use of combustible supplies deemed hazardous by the authority having jurisdiction

CHAPTER 16 • New	CHAPTER 17 • Existing

d. Rooms or spaces used for processing or use of hazardous materials or flammable or combustible liquids in quantities deemed hazardous by recognized standards

(3) Where automatic extinguishing is used to meet the requirements of 16.3.2.1(1) and (2), the protection shall be permitted in accordance with 9.7.1.2.

16.3.2.2 Food preparation facilities protected in accordance with 9.2.3 shall not be required to have openings protected between food preparation areas and dining areas. Where domestic cooking equipment is used for food warming or limited cooking, protection or segregation of food preparation facilities shall not be required if approved by the authority having jurisdiction.

d. Rooms or spaces used for processing or use of hazardous materials or flammable or combustible liquids in quantities deemed hazardous by recognized standards

(3) Where automatic extinguishing is used to meet the requirements of 17.3.2.1(1) and (2), the protection shall be permitted in accordance with 9.7.1.2.

17.3.2.2 Food preparation facilities protected in accordance with 9.2.3 shall not be required to have openings protected between food preparation areas and dining areas. Where domestic cooking equipment is used for food warming or limited cooking, protection or segregation of food preparation facilities shall not be required if approved by the authority having jurisdiction.

The intent of 16/17.3.2.1 is to specify the degree of protection necessary for certain hazardous contents areas. The hazards noted in 16/17.3.2.1(1) are required to be enclosed in 1-hour construction or protected by automatic sprinklers. If the sprinkler option is chosen, 8.4.1.2 still requires an enclosure for new construction. However, the enclosure is not required to be rated but is only required to form a membrane against the passage of smoke.

If sprinklers are provided in new construction, some barrier to control smoke migration is needed. Solid construction materials, such as glass or other non-fire-rated materials, are acceptable if they are installed in a manner that will resist smoke passing from one compartment to another.

Exhibits 16/17.5, 16/17.6, and 16/17.7 illustrate the various protection requirements of 16/17.3.2.1.

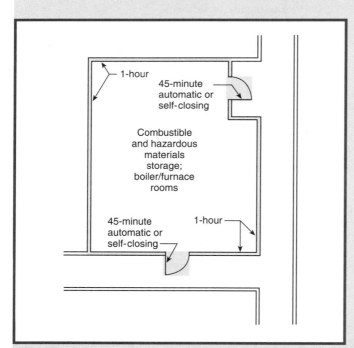

Exhibit 16/17.5 *Protection of hazardous contents areas—rated enclosure complying with 16/17.3.2.1(1).*

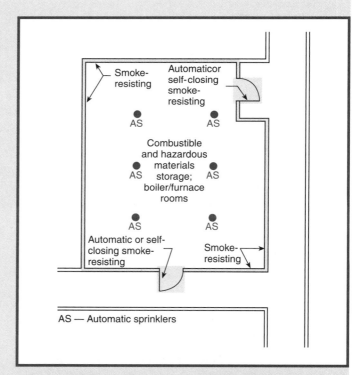

Exhibit 16/17.6 *Protection of hazardous contents areas—sprinkler protection and smoke-resisting enclosure complying with 16/17.3.2.1(1).*

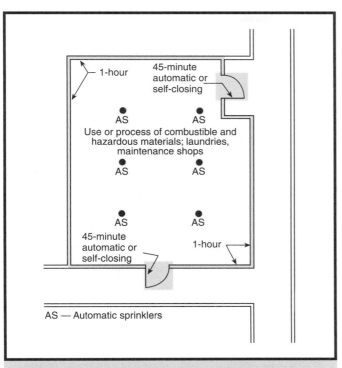

Exhibit 16/17.7 *Protection of hazardous areas—rated enclosure and sprinkler protection complying with 16/17.3.2.1(2).*

16.3.3 Interior Finish.

16.3.3.1 Interior finish shall be in accordance with Section 10.2.

16.3.3.2 Interior Wall and Ceiling Finish. Interior wall and ceiling finish materials in accordance with 10.2.3 shall be Class A in stairways, corridors, and lobbies; in all other occupied areas, interior wall and ceiling finish shall be Class A or Class B.

16.3.3.3 Interior Floor Finish. Interior floor finish materials in accordance with 10.2.7 shall be Class I or Class II within corridors and exits.

16.3.4 Detection, Alarm, and Communications Systems.

16.3.4.1 General. Day-care occupancies, other than day-care occupancies housed in one room, shall be provided with a fire alarm system in accordance with Section 9.6.

16.3.4.2 Initiation. Initiation of the required fire alarm system shall be by manual means and by operation of any required smoke detectors and required sprinkler systems. *(See 16.3.4.5.)*

17.3.3 Interior Finish.

17.3.3.1 Interior finish shall be in accordance with Section 10.2.

17.3.3.2 Interior Wall and Ceiling Finish. Interior wall and ceiling finish materials in accordance with 10.2.3 shall be Class A or Class B throughout.

17.3.3.3 Interior Floor Finish. (No requirements.)

17.3.4 Detection, Alarm, and Communications Systems.

17.3.4.1 General. Day-care occupancies, other than day-care occupancies housed in one room, shall be provided with a fire alarm system in accordance with Section 9.6.

17.3.4.2 Initiation. Initiation of the required fire alarm system shall be by manual means and by operation of any required smoke detectors and required sprinkler systems. *(See 17.3.4.5.)*

CHAPTER 16 • New	CHAPTER 17 • Existing

16.3.4.3 Occupant Notification.

16.3.4.3.1 Occupant notification shall be in accordance with 9.6.3.

16.3.4.3.2 Positive alarm sequence shall be permitted in accordance with 9.6.3.4.

16.3.4.4 Emergency Forces Notification. Fire department notification shall be accomplished in accordance with 9.6.4.

16.3.4.5 Detection. A smoke detection system in accordance with Section 9.6 shall be installed in day-care occupancies, other than those housed in one room. Detectors shall be installed on each story in front of the doors to the stairways and in the corridors of all floors occupied by the day-care occupancy. Detectors also shall be installed in lounges, recreation areas, and sleeping rooms in the day-care occupancy.

17.3.4.3 Occupant Notification.

17.3.4.3.1 Occupant notification shall be in accordance with 9.6.3.

17.3.4.3.2 Positive alarm sequence shall be permitted in accordance with 9.6.3.4.

17.3.4.4 Emergency Forces Notification. Fire department notification, other than for day-care occupancies with not more than 100 clients, shall be accomplished in accordance with 9.6.4.

17.3.4.5 Detection. A smoke detection system in accordance with Section 9.6 shall be installed in day-care occupancies, other than those housed in one room or those housing clients capable of self-preservation if no sleeping facilities are provided. Detectors shall be installed on each story in front of the doors to the stairways and in the corridors of all floors occupied by the day-care occupancy. Detectors also shall be installed in lounges, recreation areas, and sleeping rooms in the day-care occupancy.

Both new and existing day-care centers, other than those housed in a single room, are required to have a fire alarm system. The alarm system is for purposes of occupant notification and fire department notification. Existing day-care centers are exempt from the fire department notification requirement if there are 100 or fewer clients.

Neither new nor existing day-care centers are permitted to use a presignal system. A delay in occupant notification is permitted only if positive alarm sequence in accordance with 9.6.3.4 is provided. Positive alarm sequence includes some fail-safe features not found in presignal systems. If the person staffing the control panel does not acknowledge the signal, general occupant notification occurs automatically.

Also, if a second initiation device reports a fire condition to the control panel, the delay ends and general occupant notification occurs immediately.

Some day-care centers make provisions for clients to nap. Also, parents who work at night might place their children in day-care centers for the purpose of sleeping through the night. Regardless of whether occupants sleep in the center, the smoke detectors required by 16/17.3.4.5 will provide critical extra time to evacuate clients. This requirement does not apply to centers housed in a single room where a fire will be obvious simultaneously to all occupants or to existing day-care centers where the clients are capable of self-preservation and there are no sleeping facilities.

16.3.5 Extinguishment Requirements.

Any required sprinkler systems shall be in accordance with Section 9.7.

16.3.6 Corridors.

Every interior corridor shall be constructed of walls having not less than a 1-hour fire resistance rating in accordance with 8.2.3.

Exception No. 1:   Corridor protection shall not be required where all spaces normally subject to client occupancy have

17.3.5 Extinguishment Requirements.

Any required sprinkler system shall be in accordance with Section 9.7.

17.3.6 Corridors.

Every interior corridor shall be constructed of walls having not less than a ½-hour fire resistance rating in accordance with 8.2.3.

Exception No. 1:   Corridor protection shall not be required where all spaces normally subject to student occupancy have

CHAPTER 16 • New	CHAPTER 17 • Existing

not less than one door opening directly to the outside or to an exterior exit access balcony or corridor in accordance with 7.5.3.

Exception No. 2: In buildings protected throughout by an approved, supervised automatic sprinkler system in accordance with Section 9.7, corridor walls shall not be required to be rated, provided that such walls form smoke partitions in accordance with 8.2.4.

Exception No. 3: Where the corridor ceiling is an assembly having a 1-hour fire resistance rating where tested as a wall, the corridor walls shall be permitted to terminate at the corridor ceiling.

Exception No. 4: Lavatories shall not be required to be separated from corridors, provided that they are separated from all other spaces by walls having not less than a 1-hour fire resistance rating in accordance with 8.2.3.

not less than one door opening directly to the outside or to an exterior exit access balcony or corridor in accordance with 7.5.3.

Exception No. 2: In buildings protected throughout by an approved automatic sprinkler system with valve supervision in accordance with Section 9.7, corridor walls shall not be required to be rated, provided that such walls form smoke partitions in accordance with 8.2.4.

Exception No. 3: Where the corridor ceiling is an assembly having a ½-hour fire resistance rating where tested as a wall, the corridor walls shall be permitted to terminate at the corridor ceiling.

Exception No. 4: Lavatories shall not be required to be separated from corridors, provided that they are separated from all other spaces by walls having not less than a ½-hour fire resistance rating in accordance with 8.2.3.

Exception No. 5: Existing doors in ½-hour fire resistance–rated corridors shall be permitted to be 1 ¾-in. (4.4-cm) thick, solid-bonded wood core doors or the equivalent.

Section 16.4 Special Provisions

16.4.1 Windowless Buildings and Underground Buildings.

Windowless buildings and underground buildings shall comply with Section 11.7.

16.4.2 High-Rise Buildings.

High-rise buildings that house day-care occupancies on floors more than 75 ft (23 m) above the lowest level of fire department vehicle access shall comply with Section 11.8.

As written, 16/17.4.2 requires compliance with Section 11.8 (that is, automatic sprinkler, standpipe, alarm and communications, standby power, and central control station requirements) where a day-care center is located on a floor above the 75-ft (23-m) level.

This requirement will force careful review when considering the placement of a new day-care center

Section 17.4 Special Provisions

17.4.1 Windowless Buildings and Underground Buildings.

Windowless buildings and underground buildings shall comply with Section 11.7.

17.4.2 High-Rise Buildings.

High-rise buildings that house day-care occupancies on floors more than 75 ft (23 m) above the lowest level of fire department vehicle access shall comply with Section 11.8.

above the 75-ft (23-m) level in an existing high-rise building. If the building does not already comply with the requirements of Section 11.8, it will need to be brought into compliance. Note that the high-rise building provisions are equally applicable to an existing day-care center located in the high-rise portion of a building.

16.4.3 Flexible Plan and Open Plan Buildings.

16.4.3.1 Flexible plan and open plan buildings shall comply with the requirements of this chapter as modified by 16.4.3.2 through 16.4.3.4.

16.4.3.2 Flexible plan buildings shall be permitted to have walls and partitions rearranged periodically only if revised plans or diagrams have been approved by the authority having jurisdiction.

16.4.3.3 Flexible plan buildings shall be evaluated while all folding walls are extended and in use as well as when they are in the retracted position.

16.4.3.4 Each room occupied by more than 300 persons shall have two or more means of egress entering into separate atmospheres. Where three or more means of egress are required, the number of means of egress permitted to enter into a common atmosphere shall not exceed two.

17.4.3 Flexible Plan and Open Plan Buildings.

17.4.3.1 Flexible plan and open plan buildings shall comply with the requirements of this chapter as modified by 17.4.3.2 and 17.4.3.3.

17.4.3.2 Flexible plan buildings shall be permitted to have walls and partitions rearranged periodically only if revised plans or diagrams have been approved by the authority having jurisdiction.

17.4.3.3 Flexible plan buildings shall be evaluated while all folding walls are extended and in use as well as when they are in the retracted position.

Section 16.5 Building Services

16.5.1 Utilities.

16.5.1.1 Utilities shall comply with the provisions of Section 9.1.

16.5.1.2 Special protective covers for all electrical receptacles shall be installed in all areas occupied by clients.

16.5.2 Heating, Ventilating, and Air Conditioning Equipment.

16.5.2.1 Heating, ventilating, and air conditioning equipment shall be in accordance with Section 9.2.

16.5.2.2 Unvented fuel-fired room heaters, other than gas space heaters in compliance with NFPA 54, *National Fuel Gas Code,* shall not be permitted.

16.5.2.3 Any heating equipment in spaces occupied by clients shall be provided with partitions, screens, or other means to protect clients from hot surfaces and open flames. If solid partitions are used to provide such protection, provisions shall be made to ensure adequate air for combustion and ventilation for the heating equipment.

16.5.3 Elevators, Escalators, and Conveyors.

Elevators, escalators, and conveyors, other than those in day-care homes, shall comply with the provisions of Section 9.4.

Section 17.5 Building Services

17.5.1 Utilities.

17.5.1.1 Utilities shall comply with the provisions of Section 9.1.

17.5.1.2 Special protective covers for all electrical receptacles shall be installed in all areas occupied by clients.

17.5.2 Heating, Ventilating, and Air Conditioning Equipment.

17.5.2.1 Heating, ventilating, and air conditioning equipment shall be in accordance with Section 9.2.

17.5.2.2 Unvented fuel-fired room heaters, other than gas space heaters in compliance with NFPA 54, *National Fuel Gas Code,* shall not be permitted.

17.5.2.3 Any heating equipment in spaces occupied by clients shall be provided with partitions, screens, or other means to protect clients from hot surfaces and open flames. If solid partitions are used to provide such protection, provisions shall be made to ensure adequate air for combustion and ventilation for the heating equipment.

17.5.3 Elevators, Escalators, and Conveyors.

Elevators, escalators, and conveyors, other than those in day-care homes, shall comply with the provisions of Section 9.4.

16.5.4 Rubbish Chutes, Incinerators, and Laundry Chutes.

Rubbish chutes, incinerators, and laundry chutes, other than those in day-care homes, shall comply with the provisions of Section 9.5.

Clients are subject to serious injury if they insert objects into electrical receptacles. Thus, 16/17.5.1.2 requires protective covers to be provided and maintained to avoid such accidents.

The interest of reasonable life safety is not served by allowing the use of unvented, fuel-fired equipment in buildings occupied by day-care center clients. Thus, 16/17.5.2.2 prohibts such equipment.

17.5.4 Rubbish Chutes, Incinerators, and Laundry Chutes.

Rubbish chutes, incinerators, and laundry chutes, other than those in day-care homes, shall comply with the provisions of Section 9.5.

Paragraph 16/17.5.2.3 recognizes the importance of providing safeguards to protect clients from the hot surfaces of heating equipment. Day-care center clients do not always understand the dangers of hot surfaces. It is important that the heating equipment provide adequate air for combustion. Incomplete or inadequate combustion could cause serious injury or death to occupants.

Section 16.6 Day-Care Homes

16.6.1 General Requirements.

16.6.1.1 Application.

16.6.1.1.1 The requirements of Section 16.6 apply to the following:

(1) New buildings or portions thereof used as day-care homes *(see 1.4.1)*
(2) Additions made to, or used as, a day-care home *(see 4.6.6)*
(3) Alterations, modernizations, or renovations of existing day-care homes *(see 4.6.7)*
(4) Existing buildings or portions thereof upon change of occupancy to a day-care home *(see 4.6.11)*

16.6.1.1.2 Section 16.6 establishes life safety requirements for day-care homes in which more than three, but not more than 12, clients receive care, maintenance, and supervision by other than their relative(s) or legal guardian(s) for less than 24 hours per day, generally within a dwelling unit. *(See also 16.6.1.4.)*

Section 17.6 Day-Care Homes

17.6.1 General Requirements.

17.6.1.1 Application.

17.6.1.1.1 (Reserved.)

17.6.1.1.2* Section 17.6 establishes life safety requirements for existing day-care homes in which more than three, but not more than 12, clients receive care, maintenance, and supervision by other than their relative(s) or legal guardian(s) for less than 24 hours per day, generally within a dwelling unit. An existing day-care home shall be permitted the option of meeting the requirements of Section 16.6 in lieu of Section 17.6. Any existing day-care home that meets the requirements of Chapter 16 shall be judged as meeting the requirements of this chapter. *(See also 17.6.1.4.)*

A.17.6.1.1.2 Day-care homes do not provide for the full-time maintenance of a client. Day-care occupancies that provide a primary place of residence are addressed in other day-care occupancy chapters. *(See Chapters 24 through 33.)*

16.6.1.1.3 Where a facility houses more than one age group or self-preservation capability, the strictest requirements applicable to any group present shall apply throughout the day-care home or building, as appropriate to a given area, unless the area housing such a group is maintained as a separate fire area.

16.6.1.1.4 Facilities that supervise clients on a temporary basis with a parent or guardian in close proximity shall not be required to meet the provisions of Section 16.6.

16.6.1.1.5 Places of religious worship shall not be required to meet the provisions of Section 16.6 where operating a nursery while services are being held in the building.

16.6.1.2 Mixed Occupancies. *(See 16.1.2.)*

16.6.1.3 Special Definitions. *(See 16.1.3.)*

16.6.1.4 Classification of Occupancy.

16.6.1.4.1 Subclassification of Day-Care Homes. Subclassification of day-care homes shall be as follows.

(a) *Family Day-Care Home.* A family day-care home is a day-care home in which more than three, but fewer than seven, clients receive care, maintenance, and supervision by other than their relative(s) or legal guardian(s) for less than 24 hours per day, generally within a dwelling unit. Requirements for family day-care homes are based on a minimum staff-to-client ratio of one staff member for up to six clients, including the caretaker's own children under age six, with the number of clients incapable of self-preservation not to exceed two.

(b) *Group Day-Care Home.* A group day-care home is a day-care home in which not less than seven, but not more than 12, clients receive care, maintenance, and supervision by other than their relative(s) or legal guardian(s) for less than 24 hours per day, generally within a dwelling unit. Requirements for group day-care homes are based on a minimum staff-to-client ratio of two staff members for up to 12 clients, with the number of clients incapable of self-preservation not to exceed three. This staff-to-client ratio shall be permitted to be modified by the authority having jurisdiction where safeguards in addition to those specified by Section 16.6 are provided.

17.6.1.1.3 Where a facility houses clients of more than one self-preservation capability, the strictest requirements applicable to any group present shall apply throughout the day-care home or building, as appropriate to a given area, unless the area housing such a group is maintained as a separate fire area.

17.6.1.1.4 Facilities that supervise clients on a temporary basis with a parent or guardian in close proximity shall not be required to meet the provisions of Section 17.6.

17.6.1.1.5 Places of religious worship shall not be required to meet the provisions of Section 17.6 where operating a day-care home while services are being held in the building.

17.6.1.2 Mixed Occupancies. *(See 17.1.2.)*

17.6.1.3 Special Definitions. *(See 17.1.3.)*

17.6.1.4 Classification of Occupancy.

17.6.1.4.1 Subclassification of Day-Care Homes. Subclassification of day-care homes shall be as follows.

(a) *Family Day-Care Home.* A family day-care home is a day-care home in which more than three, but fewer than seven, clients receive care, maintenance, and supervision by other than their relative(s) or legal guardian(s) for less than 24 hours per day, generally within a dwelling unit. Requirements for family day-care homes are based on a minimum staff-to-client ratio of one staff member for up to six clients, including the caretaker's own children under age six, with the number of clients incapable of self-preservation not to exceed two.

(b) *Group Day-Care Home.* A group day-care home is a day-care home in which not less than seven, but not more than 12, clients receive care, maintenance, and supervision by other than their relative(s) or legal guardian(s) for less than 24 hours per day, generally within a dwelling unit. Requirements for group day-care homes are based on a minimum staff-to-client ratio of two staff members for up to 12 clients, with the number of clients incapable of self-preservation not to exceed three. This staff-to-client ratio shall be permitted to be modified by the authority having jurisdiction where safeguards in addition to those specified by Section 17.6 are provided.

Section 16/17.6 addresses both family day-care homes (4 to 6 clients) and group day-care homes (7 to 12 clients). Where the requirements vary between the two sizes of day-care homes, Section 16/17.6 references the applicable size.

The provisions of Section 16/17.6 recognize that a typical day-care home is usually located in a residential setting. Group day-care homes are often found in buildings comprised primarily of apartment, mercantile, business, or assembly occupancies. Where a center is located in a building housing another occupancy, the operators of the center usually have no control over the safety procedures and precautions practiced outside the center.

16.6.1.4.2* Conversions. A conversion from a day-care home to a day-care occupancy with more than 12 clients shall be permitted only if the day-care occupancy conforms with the requirements of Chapter 16 for new day-care occupancies with more than 12 clients.

A.16.6.1.4.2 A conversion from a day-care occupancy with more than 12 clients to a day-care home is not considered a change of occupancy. The resulting day-care home should be permitted to meet the requirements of Chapter 17 for existing day-care homes.

16.6.1.5 Classification of Hazard of Contents. *(See 16.1.5.)*

16.6.1.6 Location and Construction. No day-care home shall be located more than one story below the level of exit discharge.

16.6.1.7 Occupant Load. (No special requirements.)

16.6.2 Means of Escape Requirements.

16.6.2.1 General. Means of escape shall comply with Section 24.2.

16.6.2.2 (Reserved.)

16.6.2.3 (Reserved.)

16.6.2.4 Number of Means of Escape. The number of means of escape shall comply with Section 24.2 and 16.6.2.4.1 through 16.6.2.4.4.

16.6.2.4.1 In group day-care homes, every story occupied by clients shall have not less than two remotely located means of escape.

16.6.2.4.2 Every room used for sleeping, living, or dining purposes shall have not less than two means of escape, not less than one of which shall be a door or stairway providing a means of unobstructed travel to the outside of the building at street or ground level. The second means of escape shall be permitted to be a window in accordance with 16.2.11.1. No room or space that is accessible only by a ladder or folding stairs or through a trap door shall be occupied for living or sleeping purposes.

16.6.2.4.3 In group day-care homes where spaces on the story above the level of exit discharge are used by clients, not less than one means of escape shall be an exit discharging directly to the outside. The second means of escape shall be permitted to be a window in accordance with 16.2.11.1.

16.6.2.4.4 Where clients occupy a story below the level of exit discharge, not less than one means of escape shall be

17.6.1.4.2* Conversions. A conversion from a day-care home to a day-care occupancy with more than 12 clients shall be permitted only if the day-care occupancy conforms with the requirements of Chapter 16 for new day-care occupancies with more than 12 clients.

A.17.6.1.4.2 A conversion from a day-care occupancy with more than 12 clients to a day-care home is not considered a change of occupancy. The resulting day-care home should be permitted to meet the requirements of Chapter 17 for existing day-care homes.

17.6.1.5 Classification of Hazard of Contents. *(See 17.1.5.)*

17.6.1.6 Location and Construction. No day-care home shall be located more than one story below the ground.

17.6.1.7 Occupant Load. (No special requirements.)

17.6.2 Means of Escape Requirements.

17.6.2.1 General. Means of escape shall comply with Section 24.2.

17.6.2.2 (Reserved.)

17.6.2.3 (Reserved.)

17.6.2.4 Number of Means of Escape. The number of means of escape shall comply with Section 24.2 and 17.6.2.4.1 through 17.6.2.4.4.

17.6.2.4.1 In group day-care homes, every story occupied by clients shall have not less than two remotely located means of escape.

17.6.2.4.2 Every room used for sleeping, living, or dining purposes shall have not less than two means of escape, not less than one of which shall be a door or stairway providing a means of unobstructed travel to the outside of the building at street or ground level. The second means of escape shall be permitted to be a window in accordance with 17.2.11.1. No room or space that is accessible only by a ladder or folding stairs or through a trap door shall be occupied for living or sleeping purposes.

17.6.2.4.3 In group day-care homes where spaces on the story above the level of exit discharge are used by clients, not less than one means of escape shall be an exit discharging directly to the outside. The second means of escape shall be permitted to be a window in accordance with 17.2.11.1.

17.6.2.4.4 Where clients occupy a story below the level of exit discharge, not less than one means of escape shall be an exit discharging directly to the outside, and the vertical travel to ground level shall not exceed 8 ft (2.4 m). The second means of escape shall be permitted to be a window in accordance with 16.2.11.1.

an exit discharging directly to the outside, and the vertical travel to ground level shall not exceed 8 ft (2.4 m). The second means of escape shall be permitted to be a window in accordance with 17.2.11.1.

The concept of means of escape is well developed in Chapter 24 for one- and two-family dwellings. However, 16/17.6.2.4.3 and 16/17.6.2.4.4 require the primary means of escape to discharge directly to the outside if group day-care home clients occupy the second story or basement.

The second floor of a typical single-family dwelling is served by an open stair. The requirement of 16/17.6.2.4.3 mandates that the second floor is to be served by an enclosed exit stair or an exterior stair (not a fire escape) if clients are occupying the second floor. See also 16/17.6.3.1.

The requirement of 16/17.6.2.4.4 is similar to that of 16/17.6.2.4.3 for a second floor and mandates that, where clients are below the level of exit discharge, at least one true exit shall be provided. In addition, per the requirements of 16/17.6.3.1, any stairway to the first floor requires a minimum 20-minute rated door as a separation between the stair and the first floor.

As illustrated in Exhibit 16/17.8, where a group day-care home is located in a basement, an exit is required that opens directly to the outside, with verti-

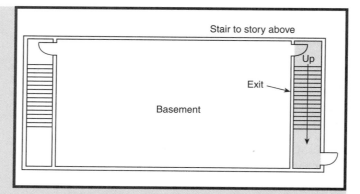

Exhibit 16/17.8 Egress requirements for group day-care home occupying basement.

cal travel to the ground level not exceeding 8 ft (2.4 m). If a stairway to the story above were provided, it would have to be cut off from the basement by a fire barrier containing a door with a fire protection rating of at least 20 minutes. This separation is required at the top or bottom of the stair, but not at both. See also 16/17.6.3.1.

16.6.2.5 Arrangement of Means of Egress.

16.6.2.5.1 A story used above or below the level of exit discharge shall be in accordance with 16.6.2.4.3 and 16.6.2.4.4.

16.6.2.5.2 For group day-care homes, means of egress shall be arranged in accordance with Section 7.5.

16.6.2.5.3 Dead-end corridors shall not exceed 20 ft (6.1 m).

17.6.2.5 Arrangement of Means of Egress.

17.6.2.5.1 A story used above or below the level of exit discharge shall be in accordance with 17.6.2.4.3 or 17.6.2.4.4.

17.6.2.5.2 For group day-care homes, means of egress shall be arranged in accordance with Section 7.5.

17.6.2.5.3 No dead-end corridor shall exceed 20 ft (6.1 m), other than in buildings protected throughout by an approved, supervised automatic sprinkler system in accordance with Section 9.7, in which case dead-end corridors shall not exceed 50 ft (15 m).

16.6.2.6 Travel Distance. Travel distance shall meet the following criteria:

(1) The travel distance between any room door intended as an exit access and an exit shall not exceed 100 ft (30 m).
(2) The travel distance between any point in a room and an exit shall not exceed 150 ft (45 m).

17.6.2.6 Travel Distance. Travel distance shall meet the following criteria:

(1) The travel distance between any room door intended as an exit access and an exit shall not exceed 100 ft (30 m).
(2) The travel distance between any point in a room and an exit shall not exceed 150 ft (45 m).

(3) The travel distance between any point in a sleeping room and an exit access to that room shall not exceed 50 ft (15 m).

Exception: The travel distance in 16.6.2.6(1) and (2) shall be permitted to be increased by 50 ft (15 m) in buildings protected throughout by an approved, supervised automatic sprinkler system in accordance with Section 9.7.

16.6.2.7 Discharge from Exits. *(See 16.6.2.4.)*

16.6.2.8 Illumination of Means of Egress. Means of egress shall be illuminated in accordance with Section 7.8.

16.6.2.9 Emergency Lighting. (No requirements.)

16.6.2.10 Marking of Means of Egress. (No requirements.)

16.6.3 Protection.

16.6.3.1 Protection of Vertical Openings. For group day-care homes, the doorway between the level of exit discharge and any story below shall be equipped with a door assembly having a 20-minute fire protection rating. Where the story above the level of exit discharge is used for sleeping purposes, there shall be a door assembly having a 20-minute fire protection rating at the top or bottom of each stairway.

16.6.3.2 Protection from Hazards. (No requirements.)

16.6.3.3 Interior Finish.

16.6.3.3.1 Interior finish shall be in accordance with Section 10.2.

16.6.3.3.2 In group day-care homes, interior wall and ceiling finish materials in accordance with 8.2.3 shall be Class A or Class B in corridors, stairways, lobbies, and exits. In the exits of family day-care homes, interior wall and ceiling finish materials in accordance with 10.2.3 shall be Class A or Class B.

16.6.3.3.3 Interior wall and ceiling finish materials in accordance with 10.2.3 shall be Class A, Class B, or Class C in occupied spaces.

16.6.3.3.4 Interior Floor Finish. (No requirements.)

16.6.3.4 Detection, Alarm, and Communications Systems.

(3) The travel distance between any point in a sleeping room and an exit access to that room shall not exceed 50 ft (15 m).

Exception: The travel distance in 17.6.2.6(1) and (2) shall be permitted to be increased by 50 ft (15 m) in buildings protected throughout by an approved, supervised automatic sprinkler system in accordance with Section 9.7.

17.6.2.7 Discharge from Exits. *(See 17.6.2.4.)*

17.6.2.8 Illumination of Means of Egress. Means of egress shall be illuminated in accordance with Section 7.8.

17.6.2.9 Emergency Lighting. (No requirements.)

17.6.2.10 Marking of Means of Egress. (No requirements.)

17.6.3 Protection.

17.6.3.1 Protection of Vertical Openings. For group day-care homes, the doorway between the level of exit discharge and any story below shall be equipped with a door assembly having a 20-minute fire protection rating. Where the story above the level of exit discharge is used for sleeping purposes, there shall be a door assembly having a 20-minute fire protection rating at the top or bottom of each stairway.

Exception: Existing self-closing 1 ³/₄-in. (4.4-cm) thick, solid-bonded wood doors without rated frames shall be permitted to be continued to be used by the authority having jurisdiction.

17.6.3.2 Protection from Hazards. (No requirements.)

17.6.3.3 Interior Finish.

17.6.3.3.1 Interior finish shall be in accordance with Section 10.2.

17.6.3.3.2 Interior wall and ceiling finish materials in accordance with 10.2.3 shall be Class A or Class B in exits.

17.6.3.3.3 Interior wall and ceiling finish materials in accordance with 10.2.3 shall be Class A, Class B, or Class C in occupied spaces.

17.6.3.3.4 Interior Floor Finish. (No requirements.)

17.6.3.4 Detection, Alarm, and Communications Systems.

CHAPTER 16 • New	CHAPTER 17 • Existing

16.6.3.4.1 Smoke alarms shall be installed within day-care homes in accordance with 9.6.2.10.

16.6.3.4.2 Where the day-care home is located within a building of another occupancy, such as in an apartment building or office building, any corridors serving the day-care home shall be provided with a smoke detection system in accordance with Section 9.6.

16.6.3.4.3 Single-station smoke alarms in accordance with 9.6.2.10 that are powered by the building electrical system, or system detectors with integral sounding devices in accordance with 9.6.1.4, shall be provided in all rooms used for sleeping.

17.6.3.4.1 Smoke alarms shall be installed within day-care homes in accordance with 9.6.2.10.

17.6.3.4.2 Where the day-care home is located within a building of another occupancy, such as in an apartment building or office building, any corridors serving the day-care home shall be provided with a smoke detection system in accordance with Section 9.6.

17.6.3.4.3 Single-station smoke alarms in accordance with 9.6.2.10 that are powered by the building electrical system, or system detectors with integral sounding devices in accordance with 9.6.1.4, shall be provided in all rooms used for sleeping.

Exception: Existing battery-powered smoke alarms rather than house electrical service–powered smoke alarms shall be permitted where, in the opinion of the authority having jurisdiction, the facility has demonstrated testing, maintenance, and battery replacement programs that ensure reliability of power to the smoke alarms.

The provisions of 16/17.6.3.4 are as follows:

(1) To provide smoke alarms within the day-care home
(2) To provide a smoke detection system in the corri-dor serving the day-care home in a building of mixed occupancy
(3) To require that smoke alarms be installed in each sleeping room

Section 16.7 Operating Features

16.7.1* Fire Emergency Response Plans.

The facility shall have a comprehensive written fire emergency response plan. Copies of the plan shall be made available to all employees. All employees shall be periodically instructed and kept informed with respect to the duties of their position under the plan.

A.16.7.1 The requirements are, of necessity, general in scope, as it is recognized that they apply to all types of day-care occupancies as well as conditions of occupancies, such as truant day-care occupancies; occupancies for the mentally handicapped, vision impaired, hearing impaired, and speech impaired; adult day-care; care of infants; and day-care occupancies. It is fully recognized that no one code can meet all the conditions of the various buildings involved, and it will be necessary for site administrators, through the written fire emergency response plan, to issue supplements to these requirements; however, all supplements should be consistent with these requirements. Additionally, it is recommended

Section 17.7 Operating Features

17.7.1* Fire Emergency Response Plans.

The facility shall have a comprehensive written fire emergency response plan. Copies of the plan shall be made available to all employees. All employees shall be periodically instructed and kept informed with respect to the duties of their position under the plan.

A.17.7.1 The requirements are, of necessity, general in scope, as it is recognized that they apply to all types of day-care occupancies as well as conditions of occupancies, such as truant day-care occupancies; occupancies for the mentally handicapped, vision impaired, hearing impaired, and speech impaired; adult day-care; care of infants; and day-care occupancies. It is fully recognized that no one code can meet all the conditions of the various buildings involved, and it will be necessary for site administrators, through the written fire emergency response plan, to issue supplements to these requirements; however, all supplements should be consistent with these requirements. Additionally, it is recommended that fire safety be a part of the educational programs of the occupancy for clients.

Fire emergency response plans need to be written and made available to all employees, including temporary or substitute staff, so that all employees know what is expected of them during a fire emergency. The elements needed in the written plan should be identified in coordination with the authority having jurisdiction.

The facility fire emergency response plan might be a module of a facility disaster plan that covers other emergencies.

The proper safeguarding of clients during a fire emergency requires prompt and effective response by the facility employees in accordance with the fire emergency response plan. Duties covered under the plan should be assigned by position rather than by employee name. Such assignment ensures that, in the absence of an employee, the duties of the position will be performed by a substitute or temporary employee assigned to the position. Temporary or substitute employees should be instructed in advance regarding their duties under the plan for the position to which they are assigned.

Written fire emergency response plans should include, but should not be limited to, information for employees regarding methods and devices available for alerting occupants of a fire emergency. Employees should know how the fire department is to be alerted. Even where automatic systems are expected to alert the fire department, the written plan should provide for backup alerting procedures by staff. Other responses of employees to a fire emergency should include the following:

(1) Removal of clients in immediate danger to areas of safety, as set forth in the plan
(2) Methods of using building features to confine the fire and its byproducts to the room or area of origin
(3) The control of actions and behaviors of clients during removal or evacuation activities and at predetermined safe assembly areas

The written plan should state clearly the facility policy regarding the actions staff are to take or not take to extinguish a fire.

The written fire emergency response plan should incorporate the emergency egress and relocation drill procedures set forth in 16.7.2.

16.7.2 Emergency Egress and Relocation Drills.

16.7.2.1* Emergency egress and relocation drills shall be conducted in accordance with Section 4.7 and the applicable provisions of 16.7.2.2.

that fire safety be a part of the educational programs of the occupancy for clients.

Fire emergency response plans need to be written and made available to all employees, including temporary or substitute staff, so that all employees know what is expected of them during a fire emergency. The elements needed in the written plan should be identified in coordination with the authority having jurisdiction.

The facility fire emergency response plan might be a module of a facility disaster plan that covers other emergencies.

The proper safeguarding of clients during a fire emergency requires prompt and effective response by the facility employees in accordance with the fire emergency response plan. Duties covered under the plan should be assigned by position rather than by employee name. Such assignment ensures that, in the absence of an employee, the duties of the position will be performed by a substitute or temporary employee assigned to the position. Temporary or substitute employees should be instructed in advance regarding their duties under the plan for the position to which they are assigned.

Written fire emergency response plans should include, but should not be limited to, information for employees about methods and devices available for alerting occupants of a fire emergency. Employees should know how the fire department is to be alerted. Even where automatic systems are expected to alert the fire department, the written plan should provide for backup alerting procedures by staff. Other responses of employees to a fire emergency should include the following:

(1) Removal of clients in immediate danger to areas of safety, as set forth in the plan
(2) Methods of using building features to confine the fire and its byproducts to the room or area of origin
(3) The control of actions and behaviors of clients during removal or evacuation activities and at predetermined safe assembly areas

The written plan should state clearly the facility policy regarding the actions staff are to take or not take to extinguish a fire.

The written fire emergency response plan should incorporate the emergency egress and relocation drill procedures set forth in 17.7.2.

17.7.2 Emergency Egress and Relocation Drills.

17.7.2.1* Emergency egress and relocation drills shall be conducted in accordance with Section 4.7 and the applicable provisions of 17.7.2.2.

A.16.7.2.1 The requirements are, of necessity, general in scope, as it is recognized that they apply to all types of day-care occupancies as well as conditions of occupancies, such as truant day-care occupancies; day-care occupancies for the mentally handicapped, vision impaired, hearing impaired, and speech impaired. It is fully recognized that no one code can meet all the conditions of the various buildings involved, and it will be necessary for site administrators to issue supplements to these requirements, but all supplements should be consistent with these requirements.

16.7.2.2 Emergency egress and relocation drills shall be conducted as follows:

(1) Not less than one emergency egress and relocation drill shall be conducted every month the facility is in session.

Exception: In climates where the weather is severe, the monthly emergency egress and relocation drills shall be permitted to be deferred, provided that the required number of emergency egress and relocation drills is achieved and not less than four are conducted before the drills are deferred.

(2) All occupants of the building shall participate in the drill.
(3) One additional emergency egress and relocation drill, other than for day-care occupancies that are open on a year-round basis, shall be required within the first 30 days of operation.

16.7.3 Inspections.

16.7.3.1 Fire prevention inspections shall be conducted monthly by a trained senior member of the staff. A copy of the latest inspection report shall be posted in a conspicuous place in the day-care facility.

16.7.3.2* It shall be the duty of site administrators and staff members to inspect all exit facilities daily to ensure that all stairways, doors, and other exits are in proper condition.

A.16.7.3.2 Particular attention should be given to keeping all doors unlocked; keeping doors that serve to protect the safety of paths of egress closed and under no conditions blocked open, such as doors on stairway enclosures; keeping outside stairs and fire escape stairs free from all obstructions and clear of snow and ice; and allowing no accumulation of snow or ice or materials of any kind outside exit doors that might prevent the opening of the door or interfere with rapid escape from the building.

16.7.3.3 Open plan buildings shall require extra surveillance to ensure that exit paths are maintained clear of obstruction and are obvious.

A.17.7.2.1 The requirements are, of necessity, general in scope, as it is recognized that they apply to all types of day-care occupancies as well as conditions of occupancies, such as truant day-care occupancies; day-care occupancies for the mentally handicapped, vision impaired, hearing impaired, and speech impaired. It is fully recognized that no one code can meet all the conditions of the various buildings involved, and it will be necessary for site administrators to issue supplements to these requirements, but all supplements should be consistent with these requirements.

17.7.2.2 Emergency egress and relocation drills shall be conducted as follows:

(1) Not less than one emergency egress and relocation drill shall be conducted every month the facility is in session.

Exception: In climates where the weather is severe, the monthly emergency egress and relocation drills shall be permitted to be deferred, provided that the required number of emergency egress and relocation drills is achieved and not less than four are conducted before the drills are deferred.

(2) All occupants of the building shall participate in the drill.
(3) One additional emergency egress and relocation drill, other than for day-care occupancies that are open on a year-round basis, shall be required within the first 30 days of operation.

17.7.3 Inspections.

17.7.3.1 Fire prevention inspections shall be conducted monthly by a trained senior member of the staff. A copy of the latest inspection report shall be posted in a conspicuous place in the day-care facility.

17.7.3.2* It shall be the duty of site administrators and staff members to inspect all exit facilities daily to ensure that all stairways, doors, and other exits are in proper condition.

A.17.7.3.2 Particular attention should be given to keeping all doors unlocked; keeping doors that serve to protect the safety of paths of egress closed and under no conditions blocked open, such as doors on stairway enclosures; keeping outside stairs and fire escape stairs free from all obstructions and clear of snow and ice; and allowing no accumulation of snow or ice or materials of any kind outside exit doors that might prevent the opening of the door or interfere with rapid escape from the building.

17.7.3.3 Open plan buildings shall require extra surveillance to ensure that exit paths are maintained clear of obstruction and are obvious.

16.7.4 Furnishings and Decorations.

16.7.4.1 Draperies, curtains, and other similar furnishings and decorations in day-care occupancies shall be in accordance with the provisions of 10.3.1.

16.7.4.2 Clothing and personal effects shall not be stored in corridors.

Exception No. 1: This requirement shall not apply to corridors protected by an automatic sprinkler system in accordance with Section 9.7.

Exception No. 2: This requirement shall not apply to corridor areas protected by a smoke detection system in accordance with Section 9.6.

Exception No. 3: This requirement shall not apply to storage in metal lockers, provided that the required egress width is maintained.

16.7.4.3 Artwork and teaching materials shall be permitted to be attached directly to the walls and shall not exceed 20 percent of the wall area.

16.7.5* Day-Care Staff.

Adequate adult staff shall be on duty, alert, awake, and in the facility at all times where clients are present.

A.16.7.5 It is the intent that the requirement for adequate adult staff to be awake at all times when clients are present be applied to family day-care and group day-care homes that are operated at night, as well as day-care occupancies.

17.7.4 Furnishings and Decorations.

17.7.4.1 Draperies, curtains, and other similar furnishings and decorations in day-care occupancies shall be in accordance with the provisions of 10.3.1.

17.7.4.2 Clothing and personal effects shall not be stored in corridors.

Exception No. 1: This requirement shall not apply to corridors protected by an automatic sprinkler system in accordance with Section 9.7.

Exception No. 2: This requirement shall not apply to corridor areas protected by a smoke detection system in accordance with Section 9.6.

Exception No. 3: This requirement shall not apply to storage in metal lockers, provided that the required egress width is maintained.

17.7.4.3 Artwork and teaching materials shall be permitted to be attached directly to the walls and shall not exceed 20 percent of the wall area.

17.7.5* Day-Care Staff.

Adequate adult staff shall be on duty, alert, awake, and in the facility at all times where clients are present.

A.17.7.5 It is the intent that the requirement for adequate adult staff to be awake at all times when clients are present be applied to family day-care and group day-care homes that are operated at night, as well as day-care occupancies.

CHAPTERS 18 and 19

New and Existing Health Care Occupancies

Life safety in health care occupancies is so encompassing that it includes nearly the entire gamut of systems, options, and features addressed in the core chapters. Unlike most other buildings and use groups addressed by the *Code*, the least desirable emergency action in a health care occupancy is the wholesale relocation or evacuation of patients. For this reason, a defend-in-place strategy is used.

The *defend-in-place* strategy is implemented using a *total concept* approach. As detailed in 18/19.1.1.3, the total concept approach provides an assortment of features that are deemed necessary to avoid the movement of patients to the outside during a fire. Of course, those patients who might be perilously close to the effects of the fire are given a range of protection features such as being moved to an adjacent smoke compartment on the same floor.

Requirements for allowable building construction types, sprinklers, alarm and detection, and staff training work in harmony to help ensure that a patient can be safely and adequately protected regardless of where a fire starts.

Chapters 18 and 19 also address an allowance for locking doors but only when the clinical needs of the patient demand such measures (see 18/19.1.1.1.5).

Recent history has documented a small number of infant abductions at health care facilities, and some facility operators have inquired about the appropriateness of using 18/19.1.1.1.5 to secure such areas via locked doors. Because infant abduction is a security needs issue, not a patient clinical need, other precautions and approaches need to be considered to address this problem.

Action by staff of a health care facility is an integral part of the life safety features required. The proper response from staff in terms of numbers, actions, and management of the fire can readily influence the outcome of a fire. Whether it be informing patients who are not in jeopardy from the fire or helping to relocate those patients who might be in proximity to the fire, hospital staff have been charged with the responsibility of preserving the safety of their charges.

Staff training, coupled with the traditional built-in systems and features (for example, construction, compartmentation, interior finish, alarm, detection, sprinkler systems, and control of contents and furnishings), provides for one of the safest environments for one of the most vulnerable population groups addressed by the *Code*.

Section 18.1 General Requirements

These chapters cover the requirements for health care occupancies. Prior to the 1976 edition of the *Code*, these occupancies were grouped with penal facilities and were known as "institutional occupancies." De-

Section 19.1 General Requirements

tention and correctional occupancies are addressed by Chapters 22 and 23.

Health care occupancies are those facilities used for the medical care or treatment of four or more

CHAPTER 18 • New

CHAPTER 19 • Existing

persons suffering from physical or mental illness, disease, or infirmity, and for the care of infants, convalescents, or infirm aged persons.

Health care occupancies addressed in this chapter include the following:

(1) Hospitals
(2) Nursing homes
(3) Limited care facilities

18.1.1 Application.

18.1.1.1 General.

18.1.1.1.1 The requirements of this chapter apply to the following:

(1) New buildings or portions thereof used as health care occupancies *(see 1.4.1)*
(2) Additions made to, or used as, a health care occupancy *(see 4.6.6 and 18.1.1.4)*

Exception: The requirement of 18.1.1.1.1 shall not apply to additions classified as occupancies other than health care that are separated from the health care occupancy in accordance with 18.1.2.1(2) and conform to the requirements for the specific occupancy in accordance with Chapters 12 through 17 and Chapters 20 through 42, as appropriate.

(3) Alterations, modernizations, or renovations of existing health care occupancies *(see 4.6.7 and 18.1.1.4)*
(4) Existing buildings or portions thereof upon change of occupancy to a health care occupancy *(see 4.6.11)*

Exception:* Facilities where the authority having jurisdiction has determined equivalent safety has been provided in accordance with Section 1.5.

A.18.1.1.1.1(4) Exception In determining equivalency for conversions, modernizations, renovations, or unusual design concepts of hospitals or nursing homes, the authority having jurisdiction is permitted to accept evaluations based on Chapter 3 of NFPA 101A, *Guide on Alternative Approaches to Life Safety*, utilizing the parameters for new construction.

Renovations, alterations, and modernizations must be performed in accordance with the requirements for new construction—contained in Chapter 18—to the maximum extent possible as required by 4.6.7.

The exception to 18/19.1.1.1.1 emphasizes that Section 1.5 permits alternative designs in lieu of liter-

Hospitals, nursing homes, and limited care facilities provide sleeping facilities for occupants incapable of self-preservation due to age, physical or mental disabilities, or security measures not under their control.

Ambulatory health care facilities differ from other health care occupancies in that they do not provide sleeping facilities and are therefore covered separately in Chapters 20 and 21.

19.1.1 Application.

19.1.1.1 General.

19.1.1.1.1 The requirements of this chapter apply to existing buildings or portions thereof currently occupied as health care occupancies. *(See also 18.1.1.1.1.)*

Exception:* Facilities where the authority having jurisdiction has determined equivalent safety has been provided in accordance with Section 1.5.

A.19.1.1.1.1 Exception In determining equivalency for existing hospitals or nursing homes, the authority having jurisdiction is permitted to accept evaluations based on Chapter 3 of NFPA 101A, *Guide on Alternative Approaches to Life Safety*, utilizing the parameters for existing buildings.

ally implementing *Code* requirements. The alternative design can be judged by the authority having jurisdiction as achieving compliance with *Code* requirements. However, the authority having jurisdiction ultimately determines whether equivalent safety has been provided.

Paragraph 18/19.1.1.1.1 and the accompanying exception are not intended to limit the methods that an authority having jurisdiction might use to determine equivalency. However, as noted in A.18/A.19.1.1.1.1, Exception, Chapter 3 of NFPA 101A, *Guide on Alternative Approaches to Life Safety,*[1] provides an "equivalency system" that uses numerical values to analyze the fire safety effectiveness of a building design and arrangement. This system, known as the fire safety evaluation system (FSES), provides a method for evaluating alternative designs as options to literal *Code* compliance. It is not the intent of the *Code* to limit equivalency evaluations solely to this system. The authority having jurisdiction does retain the power to evaluate and approve alternative designs on the basis of appropriate supporting data. The FSES is permitted to be used to aid in this evaluation. This exception in no way mandates the use of the FSES, nor does it require the authority having jurisdiction to accept the results of an evaluation using the system.

Although the FSES was developed primarily to evaluate alternative designs in existing buildings, it is particularly useful in determining equivalency for conversions, modernizations, renovations, or unusual design concepts, all of which would be considered new construction. However, the FSES is a tool to help determine equivalency, and it should not be used to circumvent *Code* requirements. *Code* requirements must be met, or equivalent safety must be provided by alternative means approved by the authority having jurisdiction.

The 1998 edition of NFPA 101A was calibrated so that its measurement tools would compare alternative designs against the requirements of the 1997 edition of the *Life Safety Code*. It does not measure equivalency against the requirements of the 2000 edition of the *Code*, however, and must not be used in such an attempt. At the time this handbook went to press, the proposed 2001 edition of NFPA 101A was being processed via the NFPA consensus standards-making process. The 2001 edition will have the proper calibration for measuring equivalency against the requirements of the 2000 edition of the *Code*. The revision will be published early in 2001.

18.1.1.1.2 This chapter establishes life safety requirements for the design of all new hospitals, nursing homes, and limited care facilities. The term hospital, wherever used in this *Code,* shall include general hospitals, psychiatric hospitals, and specialty hospitals. The term nursing home, wherever used in this *Code,* shall include nursing and convalescent homes, skilled nursing facilities, intermediate care facilities, and infirmaries in homes for the aged. Where requirements vary, the specific subclass of health care occupancy is named in the paragraph pertaining thereto. Chapter 20 establishes life safety requirements for all new ambulatory health care facilities. Section 18.7 establishes operating features requirements for all health care occupancies.

18.1.1.1.3 Health care facilities regulated by this chapter provide sleeping accommodations for their occupants and are occupied by persons who are mostly incapable of self-preservation because of age, because of physical or mental disability, or because of security measures not under the occupants' control.

18.1.1.1.4 Buildings, or sections of buildings, that primarily house patients who, in the opinion of the governing body of the facility and the governmental agency having jurisdiction, are capable of judgment and appropriate physical action for self-preservation under emergency conditions shall be

19.1.1.1.2 This chapter establishes life safety requirements for all existing hospitals, nursing homes, and limited care facilities. The term hospital, wherever used in this *Code,* shall include general hospitals, psychiatric hospitals, and specialty hospitals. The term nursing home, wherever used in this *Code,* shall include nursing and convalescent homes, skilled nursing facilities, intermediate care facilities, and infirmaries in homes for the aged. Where requirements vary, the specific subclass of health care occupancy is named in the paragraph pertaining thereto. Chapter 21 establishes life safety requirements for all existing ambulatory health care facilities. Section 19.7 establishes operating features requirements for all health care occupancies.

19.1.1.1.3 Health care facilities regulated by this chapter provide sleeping accommodations for their occupants and are occupied by persons who are mostly incapable of self-preservation because of age, because of physical or mental disability, or because of security measures not under the occupants' control.

19.1.1.1.4 Buildings, or sections of buildings, that primarily house patients who, in the opinion of the governing body of the facility and the governmental agency having jurisdiction, are capable of judgment and appropriate physical action for self-preservation under emergency conditions shall be permitted to comply with chapters of this *Code* other than Chapter 18.

18.1.1.1.5 It shall be recognized that, in buildings housing certain types of patients or having detention rooms or a security section, it might be necessary to lock doors and bar windows to confine and protect building inhabitants. In such instances, the authority having jurisdiction shall make appropriate modifications to those sections of this *Code* that would otherwise require means of egress to be kept unlocked.

18.1.1.1.6 Buildings, or sections of buildings, that house older persons and that provide activities that foster continued independence, but that do not include services distinctive to health care occupancies *(see 18.1.3)* as defined in 3.3.98 shall be permitted to comply with the requirements of other chapters of this *Code*, such as Chapter 30 or Chapter 32.

18.1.1.1.7 Facilities that do not provide housing on a 24-hour basis for their occupants shall be classified as other occupancies and shall be covered by other chapters of this *Code*.

18.1.1.1.8* The requirements of this chapter are based on the assumption that staff is available in all patient-occupied areas to perform certain fire safety functions as required in other paragraphs of this chapter.

A.18.1.1.1.8 The *Code* recognizes that certain functions necessary for the life safety of building occupants, such as the closing of corridor doors, the operation of manual fire alarm devices, and the removal of patients from the room of fire origin, require the intervention of facility staff. It is not the intent of 18.1.1.1.8 to specify the levels or locations of staff necessary to meet this requirement.

Paragraphs 18/19.1.1.1.3 through 18/19.1.1.1.8 contain general material applicable to health care occupancies. Occupants in a health care facility might be restrained but are housed primarily for treatment of mental or physical infirmities. Where occupants are restrained for penal or correctional purposes, the building would be classified as a detention and correctional occupancy. Such occupancies are addressed in Chapters 22 and 23.

If a building is used for the treatment or housing of patients, including those with mental disabilities (see 18/19.1.1.1.4) or older persons (see 18/19.1.1.1.6), the building can be classified as an occupancy other than health care under the following conditions:

permitted to comply with chapters of the *Code* other than Chapter 19.

19.1.1.1.5 It shall be recognized that, in buildings housing certain types of patients or having detention rooms or a security section, it might be necessary to lock doors and bar windows to confine and protect building inhabitants. In such instances, the authority having jurisdiction shall make appropriate modifications to those sections of this *Code* that would otherwise require means of egress to be kept unlocked.

19.1.1.1.6 Buildings, or sections of buildings, that house older persons and that provide activities that foster continued independence, but that do not include services distinctive to health care occupancies *(see 19.1.3)* as defined in 3.3.98 shall be permitted to comply with the requirements of other chapters of this *Code*, such as Chapter 31 or Chapter 33.

19.1.1.1.7 Facilities that do not provide housing on a 24-hour basis for their occupants shall be classified as other occupancies and shall be covered by other chapters of this *Code*.

19.1.1.1.8* The requirements of this chapter are based on the assumption that staff is available in all patient-occupied areas to perform certain fire safety functions as required in other paragraphs of this chapter.

A.19.1.1.1.8 The *Code* recognizes that certain functions necessary for the life safety of building occupants, such as the closing of corridor doors, the operation of manual fire alarm devices, and the removal of patients from the room of fire origin, require the intervention of facility staff. It is not the intent of 19.1.1.1.8 to specify the levels or locations of staff necessary to meet this requirement.

(1) Occupants are not restrained by locked doors or other devices.
(2) Patients are ambulatory.
(3) Occupants are capable of perceiving threats and taking appropriate action for self-preservation.

Occupants of health care facilities are considered to be incapable of self-preservation (see 18/19.1.1.1.3) due to age, physical or mental disabilities, or security measures not under their control. A significant number of occupants in health care facilities are assumed to be nonambulatory or bedridden. Other occupants, while capable of self-movement, might have impaired judgment.

Although locking exit doors and barring windows are undesirable in terms of life safety, the *Code* recognizes that, in some cases, it is necessary to restrain people. In these instances, provisions need to be made for the continuous supervision and prompt release of restrained persons (see 18/19.1.1.1.5). Release of occupants should be achieved by a system capable of automatically unlocking doors in the means of egress or by continuously available attendants equipped with keys. In either case, continuous supervision is considered essential. Also see 18/19.2.2.2.4 and 18/19.2.2.2.5.

The *Code* assumes that staff will be in continuous attendance in all health care facilities. In fact, staff are assigned certain critical functions during a fire emergency, such as rescuing patients from the room of origin, closing the door to the room, and activating the fire alarm system. The *Code* does not specify minimum staff/patient ratios, because such provisions are included in licensing criteria and compliance with licensing criteria will normally satisfy the *Code*. Paragraph 18/19.1.1.1.8, in effect, mandates that staff be present. A staff person should be situated to supervise each smoke compartment that is housing patients. A nursing station located to allow visual supervision of two or more smoke compartments is considered adequate. If, because of some unusual arrangement, staff is not available 24 hours a day to provide supervision, alternative means should be provided to ensure an adequate level of fire safety that is in compliance with the *Code*.

18.1.1.2* Goals and Objectives. The goals and objectives of Sections 4.1 and 4.2 shall be met with due consideration for functional requirements. This is accomplished by limiting the development and spread of a fire emergency to the room of fire origin and reducing the need for occupant evacuation, except from the room of fire origin.

A.18.1.1.2 This objective is accomplished in the context of the physical facilities, the type of activities undertaken, the provisions for the capabilities of staff, and the needs of all occupants through requirements directed at the following:

(1) Prevention of ignition
(2) Detection of fire
(3) Control of fire development
(4) Confinement of the effects of fire
(5) Extinguishment of fire
(6) Provision of refuge or evacuation facilities, or both
(7) Staff reaction

18.1.1.3 Total Concept. All health care facilities shall be designed, constructed, maintained, and operated to minimize the possibility of a fire emergency requiring the evacuation of occupants. Because the safety of health care occupants cannot be ensured adequately by dependence on evacuation of the building, their protection from fire shall be provided by appropriate arrangement of facilities, adequate, trained staff, and development of operating and maintenance procedures composed of the following:

(1) Design, construction, and compartmentation
(2) Provision for detection, alarm, and extinguishment
(3) Fire prevention and the planning, training, and drilling programs for the isolation of fire, transfer of occupants to areas of refuge, or evacuation of the building

19.1.1.2* Goals and Objectives. The goals and objectives of Sections 4.1 and 4.2 shall be met with due consideration for functional requirements. This is accomplished by limiting the development and spread of a fire emergency to the room of fire origin and reducing the need for occupant evacuation, except from the room of fire origin.

A.19.1.1.2 This objective is accomplished in the context of the physical facilities, the type of activities undertaken, the provisions for the capabilities of staff, and the needs of all occupants through requirements directed at the following:

(1) Prevention of ignition
(2) Detection of fire
(3) Control of fire development
(4) Confinement of the effects of fire
(5) Extinguishment of fire
(6) Provision of refuge or evacuation facilities, or both
(7) Staff reaction

19.1.1.3 Total Concept. All health care facilities shall be designed, constructed, maintained, and operated to minimize the possibility of a fire emergency requiring the evacuation of occupants. Because the safety of health care occupants cannot be ensured adequately by dependence on evacuation of the building, their protection from fire shall be provided by appropriate arrangement of facilities, adequate staffing, and development of operating and maintenance procedures composed of the following:

(1) Design, construction, and compartmentation
(2) Provision for detection, alarm, and extinguishment
(3) Fire prevention and the planning, training, and drilling programs for the isolation of fire, transfer of occupants to areas of refuge, or evacuation of the building

The well-being of an individual located in the room of fire origin can be reasonably ensured only through complete control of that environment, including construction materials, wall and ceiling finishes, furnishings, decorations, clothing, linens, bedding, and the like. However, no code can prevent injury resulting from a person's careless actions.

Although an effort should be made to protect the individual through fire prevention, the primary objective of the requirements of Chapters 18 and 19 is to limit fire size or to prevent fire from escaping the room of origin and thereby limiting the threat to individuals outside the room of origin. In accordance with the goals of 4.1.1, the same protection scheme should have the benefit of additionally improving the survivability of those occupants who are intimate with the fire development.

Vertical movement of patients within a health care facility is an inefficient, time-consuming process.

One study demonstrated, through the simulated evacuation of patients from a second-story ward to ground level, that more than 30 minutes might be required for evacuation during a fire.

The provisions of Chapters 18 and 19, therefore, are based on a "defend-in-place" strategy, which minimizes the probability of a fire necessitating vertical movement of occupants. Patients in critical care areas might be connected to life-support equipment, making movement difficult and, in some cases, impossible. Barriers are required to provide for the horizontal movement of patients to safe areas on a single-floor level and to maintain a manageable limit on the number of occupants exposed to any single fire. Vertical means of egress (stairs or ramps) should be considered as escape routes for visitors and staff and as a "last line of defense" for the movement of patients.

18.1.1.4 Additions, Conversions, Modernization, Renovation, and Construction Operations.

18.1.1.4.1 Additions. Additions shall be separated from any existing structure not conforming to the provisions within Chapter 19 by a fire barrier having not less than a 2-hour fire resistance rating and constructed of materials as required for the addition. *(See 4.6.11 and 4.6.6.)*

18.1.1.4.2 Communicating openings in dividing fire barriers required by 18.1.1.4.1 shall be permitted only in corridors and shall be protected by approved self-closing fire doors. *(See also Section 8.2.)*

18.1.1.4.3 Doors in barriers required by 18.1.1.4.1 shall normally be kept closed.

Exception: Doors shall be permitted to be held open if they meet the requirements of 18.2.2.2.6.

18.1.1.4.4 Changes of Occupancy. Changes of occupancy shall comply with 4.6.11. A change from one health care occupancy subclassification to another shall require compliance with the requirements for new construction.

Exception No. 1: A change from a hospital to a nursing home or from a nursing home to a hospital shall not be considered a change in occupancy or occupancy subclassification.

Exception No. 2: A change from a hospital or nursing home to a limited care facility shall not be considered a change in occupancy or occupancy subclassification.

19.1.1.4 Additions, Conversions, Modernization, Renovation, and Construction Operations.

19.1.1.4.1 Additions. Additions shall be separated from any existing structure not conforming to the provisions within Chapter 19 by a fire barrier having not less than a 2-hour fire resistance rating and constructed of materials as required for the addition. *(See 4.6.11 and 4.6.6.)*

19.1.1.4.2 Communicating openings in dividing fire barriers required by 19.1.1.4.1 shall be permitted only in corridors and shall be protected by approved self-closing fire doors. *(See also Section 8.2.)*

19.1.1.4.3 Doors in barriers required by 19.1.1.4.1 shall normally be kept closed.

Exception: Doors shall be permitted to be held open if they meet the requirements of 19.2.2.2.6.

19.1.1.4.4 Changes of Occupancy. Changes of occupancy shall comply with 4.6.11. A change from one health care occupancy subclassification to another shall require compliance with the requirements for new construction.

Exception No. 1: A change from a hospital to a nursing home or from a nursing home to a hospital shall not be considered a change in occupancy or occupancy subclassification.

Exception No. 2: A change from a hospital or nursing home to a limited care facility shall not be considered a change in occupancy or occupancy subclassification.

CHAPTER 18 • New

CHAPTER 19 • Existing

Exception No. 3: A change from a hospital or nursing home to an ambulatory health care facility shall not be considered a change in occupancy or occupancy subclassification.

18.1.1.4.5* Renovations, Alterations, and Modernizations. Where major renovations, alterations, or modernizations are made in a nonsprinklered facility, the automatic sprinkler requirements of Chapter 18 shall apply to a smoke compartment undergoing the renovation, alteration, or modernization. However, in cases where the building is not protected throughout by an approved automatic sprinkler system, the requirements of 19.1.6 and 19.2.3.2 shall also apply. Exception No. 2 to 18.3.7.3 shall be permitted only where adjacent smoke compartments are protected throughout by an approved, supervised automatic sprinkler system in accordance with 18.3.5.2. Where minor renovations, alterations, modernizations, or repairs are done in a nonsprinklered facility, the requirements of 18.3.5.1 shall not apply but, in such cases, the renovations, alterations, modernizations, or repairs shall not reduce life safety below the level that previously existed, nor below the level of requirements of Chapter 19 for nonsprinklered buildings. *(See 4.6.7.)*

A.18.1.1.4.5 The *Code* does not attempt to establish specific monetary limits or percentage values to determine whether a project is major or minor, as such a determination requires judgment. It is not the intent of 18.1.1.4.5 to exempt significant renovations and modernization projects for which the *Code* does intend to apply the automatic sprinkler mandate.

For the purpose of this requirement, a floor that is not divided by a smoke barrier is considered one smoke compartment.

18.1.1.4.6 Construction, Repair, and Improvement Operations. *(See 4.6.10.)*

Exception No. 3: A change from a hospital or nursing home to an ambulatory health care facility shall not be considered a change in occupancy or occupancy subclassification.

19.1.1.4.5* Renovations, Alterations, and Modernizations. Where major renovations, alterations, or modernizations are made in a nonsprinklered facility, the automatic sprinkler requirements of Chapter 18 shall apply to a smoke compartment undergoing the renovation, alteration, or modernization. However, in cases where the building is not protected throughout by an approved automatic sprinkler system, the requirements of 19.1.6 and 19.2.3.2 shall also apply. Exception No. 2 to 18.3.7.3 shall be permitted only where adjacent smoke compartments are protected throughout by an approved, supervised automatic sprinkler system in accordance with 18.3.5.2. Where minor renovations, alterations, modernizations, or repairs are done in a nonsprinklered facility, the requirements of 18.3.5.1 shall not apply but, in such cases, the renovations, alterations, modernizations, or repairs shall not reduce life safety below the level that previously existed, nor below the level of the requirements of Chapter 19 for nonsprinklered buildings. *(See 4.6.7.)*

A.19.1.1.4.5 The *Code* does not attempt to establish specific monetary limits or percentage values to determine whether a project is major or minor, as such a determination requires judgment. It is not the intent of 19.1.1.4.5 to exempt significant renovations and modernization projects for which the *Code* does intend to apply the automatic sprinkler mandate.

For the purpose of this requirement, a floor that is not divided by a smoke barrier is considered one smoke compartment.

19.1.1.4.6 Construction, Repair, and Improvement Operations. *(See 4.6.10.)*

Paragraph 18/19.1.1.4.1 establishes separation criteria for additions to existing structures that do not conform to the provisions of Chapter 19. However, if an existing building meets the provisions of Chapter 19, the new addition that complies with Chapter 18 would not be required to be separated from the existing portion of the newly enlarged building.

If additions are required to be separated from existing portions of buildings, barriers must be constructed of assemblies that provide no less than a 2-hour fire resistance rating. If the structural framing of the addition or the existing buildings consists of assemblies that provide less than 2-hour fire resistance, special provision must be made to ensure that

the necessary separation will be maintained for a 2-hour period.

Exhibit 18/19.1 illustrates the provisions of 18/19.1.1.4.1. In illustration (a) the new addition that complies with Chapter 18 must be separated from the existing portion of the building that does not comply with the requirements of Chapter 19 for existing health care occupancies. In illustration (b) the new addition that complies with Chapter 18 is permitted to be open to the existing portion of the building that complies with the requirements of Chapter 19 for existing health care occupancies.

Materials used in the construction of the separation barrier should meet the standards applicable to

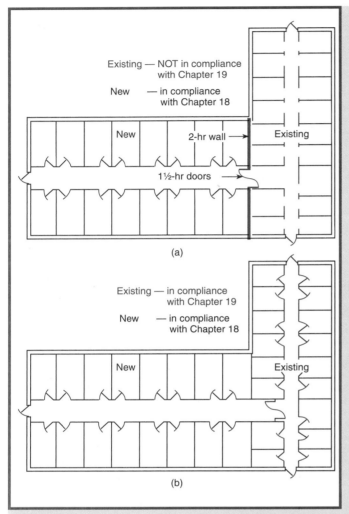

Exhibit 18/19.1 Separation of new construction from existing building.

the addition under construction. That is, if the addition is required to be constructed of noncombustible or limited-combustible materials (construction Types I or II), the materials used in the barrier should be noncombustible or limited-combustible as defined in NFPA 220, *Standard on Types of Building Construction.*[2] Conversely, if the addition is permitted to be constructed of combustible materials, combustible materials are permitted to be used in the fire-rated barrier.

Openings in fire barriers separating additions that comply with Chapter 18 from portions of the building not in compliance with the requirements of Chapter 19 are limited to those that are absolutely

necessary—that is, cross-corridor doors (see 18/19.1.1.4.2). Openings are required to be protected by 1¹/₂-hour fire protection–rated door assemblies. The fire doors are required to be self-closing and to remain closed, or they are permitted to be held open by an automatic release device in accordance with 18/19.2.2.2.6. In illustration (a) of Exhibit 18/19.1 no openings other than the cross-corridor doors would be permitted in the separating barrier. This means there can be no penetrations by ductwork. A convenience door between two rooms on opposite sides of the barrier also would be prohibited. However, as shown in illustration (b) of Exhibit 18/19.1, if the existing section of the building is in compliance with the requirements of Chapter 19, no separation is required. Therefore, unlimited openings are permitted.

Paragraph 18/19.1.1.4.4, via its reference to 4.6.11, requires any building converted to a health care facility from some other type of occupancy—dormitory, for example—to comply with the provisions of Chapter 18 for new health care facilities. Also see 18.1.1.1.1(4). The exceptions to 18/19.1.1.4.4 address changes from one health care occupancy subclassification to another health care occupancy subclassification. Provided the change involves going from a subclassification that is heavily regulated by the *Code* to a subclassification that is either less regulated or at least as regulated, the resulting facility is permitted to be judged by the requirements applicable to an existing facility. However, if the change is in the opposite direction—for example, from an ambulatory health care facility, which the *Code* regulates with a modest package of requirements, to a hospital or nursing home, which the *Code* regulates via an extensive package of requirements—then the resulting facility must be judged against the requirements applicable to a new facility. The three exceptions to 18/19.1.1.4.4 address six of the twelve possible changes among the health care subclassifications. For the following subclassification changes, the resulting facility must meet the requirements applicable to new construction:

(1) A limited care facility conversion to a hospital
(2) A limited care facility conversion to a nursing home
(3) A limited care facility conversion to an ambulatory health care facility
(4) An ambulatory health care facility conversion to a hospital

(5) An ambulatory health care facility conversion to a nursing home

(6) An ambulatory health care facility conversion to a limited care facility

Alterations in health care facilities are regulated by 4.6.7, 18.1.1.1.1(3), and 18/19.1.1.4.5. Alterations must not reduce existing life safety features that do not meet the requirements for new construction but exceed the requirements for existing buildings. For example, a portion of an existing hospital with a 6-ft (1.8-m) wide corridor is to be renovated. Although the hospital is an existing building and existing health care occupancies require no less than 4-ft (1.2-m) wide corridors, the 6-ft (1.8-m) wide corridor must be maintained. Conversely, if a portion of an existing hospital with a 10-ft (3.1-m) wide corridor is to be altered, the corridor is permitted to be reduced to 8 ft (2.4 m) wide, in accordance with the requirement for new construction. As a minimum, in all instances, whether or not renovations or alterations are planned, existing health care occupancies must comply with the requirements of Chapter 19.

Automatic sprinkler protection is required for all new health care facilities (see 18.3.5.1). Existing health care facilities might be nonsprinklered. When major renovations are made in a nonsprinklered existing facility, in addition to performing those planned renovations in accordance with the requirements for new construction, 18/19.1.1.4.5 requires the smoke compartment in which the renovation occurs to be sprinklered. Therefore, although the renovation was not originally planned to include the installation of sprinklers, such installation is required within the smoke compartment being renovated.

Minor renovations—as judged by the authority having jurisdiction—do not trigger the requirement for installing sprinklers. In determining whether renovations are minor or major, the authority having jurisdiction should inquire about other renovations planned over the immediate future. If those individual renovation projects taken as a whole create the equivalent of major renovation, the authority having jurisdiction should require sprinklers as part of the extended project within a given smoke compartment.

Only that smoke compartment undergoing renovation is required to be sprinklered at that time. For example, assume a floor of a hospital is subdivided into three smoke compartments, and only one smoke compartment is undergoing renovation. Only the renovated smoke compartment would require sprinkler installation. Over a few years of multiple renovation projects, the entire building will eventually become fully sprinklered. However, where a building is only partially protected with sprinklers, the construction requirements of 19.1.6 for nonsprinklered buildings must be met, and egress capacity must be based on nonsprinklered criteria. Smoke dampers are permitted to be omitted for ducted penetrations of smoke barriers only where the smoke compartments on both sides of the smoke barrier are fully sprinklered in accordance with 18.3.5.

Although effort should be made to satisfy the criteria for new construction during a building alteration or the installation of new equipment, the *Code* recognizes that such modifications cannot always be achieved. Guidance for achieving equivalency to life safety is provided in Section 1.5. Regardless of circumstances, building alterations or the installation of new service equipment must achieve a level of life safety equivalent to or exceeding the level prescribed for existing buildings.

The introduction of "outside" workers and activities associated with the construction of an addition creates unusual risks of fire in health care occupancies. Special precautions should be taken to guard against the potential exposure created by the introduction of flammable substances or by other hazardous practices that could pose a threat to occupants. See 4.6.10.3.

Temporary fire-resistant barriers should be erected to separate the new construction and associated activity from the functioning areas of the existing buildings. Care should be taken to ensure that these temporary barriers do not block means of egress for the existing building. Special care is also necessary to ensure that all existing equipment for fire protection and all portions of the required means of egress are maintained in full working order. See 4.6.10.1.

Adequate escape facilities should be provided and continuously maintained for the use of construction workers. See 4.6.10.2 and NFPA 241, *Standard for Safeguarding Construction, Alteration, and Demolition Operations*.[3]

18.1.2 Mixed Occupancies.

(See also 6.1.14.)

19.1.2 Mixed Occupancies.

(See also 6.1.14.)

CHAPTER 18 • New	CHAPTER 19 • Existing

18.1.2.1* Sections of health care facilities shall be permitted to be classified as other occupancies, provided that they meet all of the following conditions:

(1) They are not intended to serve health care occupants for purposes of housing, treatment, or customary access by patients incapable of self-preservation.
(2) They are separated from areas of health care occupancies by construction having a fire resistance rating of not less than 2 hours.

A.18.1.2.1 Doctors' offices and treatment and diagnostic facilities intended solely for outpatient care that are physically separated from facilities for the treatment or care of inpatients, but that are otherwise associated with the management of an institution, might be classified as business occupancies rather than health care occupancies.

18.1.2.2* Ambulatory care facilities, medical clinics, and similar facilities that are contiguous to health care occupancies but are primarily intended to provide outpatient services shall be permitted to be classified as business occupancies or ambulatory health care facilities, provided that the facilities are separated from the health care occupancy by not less than 2-hour fire resistance–rated construction and the facility is not intended to provide services simultaneously for four or more health care patients who are litterborne.

A.18.1.2.2 It is the intent that these requirements apply to mobile, transportable, and relocatable structures (in accordance with 1.4.2) where such structures are used to provide shared medical services on an extended or a temporary basis. Where properly separated from the health care occupancy and intended to provide services simultaneously for three or fewer health care patients who are litterborne, the level of protection for such structures should be based on the appropriate occupancy classification of other chapters of this *Code*. Mobile, transportable, or relocatable structures that are not separated from a contiguous health care occupancy or that are intended to provide services simultaneously for four or more health care patients who are litterborne should be classified and designed as health care occupancies.

18.1.2.3 Health care occupancies in buildings housing other occupancies shall be completely separated from them by construction having a fire resistance rating of not less than 2 hours as provided for additions in 18.1.1.4.

18.1.2.4 All means of egress from health care occupancies that traverse non-health care spaces shall conform to the requirements of this *Code* for health care occupancies.

19.1.2.1* Sections of health care facilities shall be permitted to be classified as other occupancies, provided that they meet all of the following conditions:

(1) They are not intended to serve health care occupants for purposes of housing, treatment, or customary access by patients incapable of self-preservation.
(2) They are separated from areas of health care occupancies by construction having a fire resistance rating of not less than 2 hours.

A.19.1.2.1 Doctors' offices and treatment and diagnostic facilities intended solely for outpatient care that are physically separated from facilities for the treatment or care of inpatients, but that are otherwise associated with the management of an institution, might be classified as business occupancies rather than health care occupancies.

19.1.2.2* Ambulatory care facilities, medical clinics, and similar facilities that are contiguous to health care occupancies but are primarily intended to provide outpatient services shall be permitted to be classified as business occupancies or ambulatory health care facilities, provided that the facilities are separated from the health care occupancy by not less than 2-hour fire resistance–rated construction and the facility is not intended to provide services simultaneously for four or more health care patients who are litterborne.

A.19.1.2.2 It is the intent that these requirements apply to mobile, transportable, and relocatable structures (in accordance with 1.4.2) when such structures are used to provide shared medical services on an extended or a temporary basis. When properly separated from the health care occupancy and intended to provide services simultaneously for three or fewer health care patients who are litterborne, the level of protection for such structures should be based on the appropriate occupancy classification of other chapters of this *Code*. Mobile, transportable, or relocatable structures that are not separated from a contiguous health care occupancy or that are intended to provide services simultaneously for four or more health care patients who are litterborne should be classified and designed as health care occupancies.

19.1.2.3 Health care occupancies in buildings housing other occupancies shall be completely separated from them by construction having a fire resistance rating of not less than 2 hours as provided for additions in 19.1.1.4.

19.1.2.4 All means of egress from health care occupancies that traverse non-health care spaces shall conform to the requirements of this *Code* for health care occupancies.

CHAPTER 18 • New

Exception: Exit through a horizontal exit into other contiguous occupancies that do not conform with health care egress provisions, but that do comply with requirements set forth in the appropriate occupancy chapter of this Code, shall be permitted, provided that the occupancy does not contain high hazard contents. The horizontal exit shall comply with the requirements of 18.2.2.5.

18.1.2.5 Egress provisions for areas of health care facilities that correspond to other occupancies shall meet the corresponding requirements of this *Code* for such occupancies. Where the clinical needs of the occupant necessitate the locking of means of egress, staff shall be present for the supervised release of occupants during all times of use.

18.1.2.6 Auditoriums, chapels, staff residential areas, or other occupancies provided in connection with health care facilities shall have means of egress provided in accordance with other applicable sections of this *Code*.

18.1.2.7 Any area with a hazard of contents classified higher than that of the health care occupancy and located in the same building shall be protected as required in 18.3.2.

18.1.2.8 Non-health care–related occupancies classified as containing high hazard contents shall not be permitted in buildings housing health care occupancies.

CHAPTER 19 • Existing

Exception: Exit through a horizontal exit into other contiguous occupancies that do not conform with health care egress provisions, but that do comply with requirements set forth in the appropriate occupancy chapter of this Code, shall be permitted, provided that the occupancy does not contain high hazard contents. The horizontal exit shall comply with the requirements of 19.2.2.5.

19.1.2.5 Egress provisions for areas of health care facilities that correspond to other occupancies shall meet the corresponding requirements of this *Code* for such occupancies. Where the clinical needs of the occupant necessitate the locking of means of egress, staff shall be present for the supervised release of occupants during all times of use.

19.1.2.6 Auditoriums, chapels, staff residential areas, or other occupancies provided in connection with health care facilities shall have means of egress provided in accordance with other applicable sections of this *Code*.

19.1.2.7 Any area with a hazard of contents classified higher than that of the health care occupancy and located in the same building shall be protected as required in 19.3.2.

19.1.2.8 Non-health care–related occupancies classified as containing high hazard contents shall not be permitted in buildings housing health care occupancies.

Paragraphs 18/19.1.2.1 and 18/19.1.2.2 contain criteria for classifying spaces as other occupancies, although these spaces are located in buildings used primarily for health care purposes. For example, 18/19.1.2.1 would allow offices to be classified as business occupancies, cafeterias to be classified as assembly occupancies, or dormitories to be classified as residential occupancies if the requirements of both (1) and (2) of 18/19.1.2.1 are met. Paragraph 18/19.1.2.1(1) notes that customary access by patients incapable of self-preservation is not permitted within the other occupancy. This paragraph is intended to allow an occasional, ambulatory inpatient to visit a doctor's office in an adjacent business occupancy, for example, without requiring classification of the business occupancy as a health care facility. Further, emergency egress from the health care occupancy into the other occupancy would be permitted because emergency egress is not considered customary access (see exception to 18/19.1.2.4).

If the requirements of either (1) or (2) of 18/19.1.2.1 are not met, the area would be considered a mixed occupancy and would require that the more restrictive life safety requirements applicable to the occupancies present be provided. In such cases, one of the occupancies present would be health care, whose occupancy requirements are typically stricter than those of most other occupancies. This requirement would effectively require that health care occupancy requirements be met within this other use area as well as within the health care use portions of the building. See 6.1.14.

Paragraph 18/19.1.2.2 addresses a subject similar to that of 18/19.1.2.1 but specifically covers ambulatory care facilities, medical clinics, and similar areas that primarily provide outpatient services and are associated with or attached to a health care facility. If these facilities are separated by 2-hour fire resistance–rated construction, they are permitted to be classified as ambulatory health care facilities or as business occupancies, whichever applies. If, however, four or more litterborne inpatients are treated simultaneously, the facility must meet the requirements for health care occupancies. Conversely, if three or fewer litterborne inpatients are present in the outpatient facility on a regular basis, the facility would be classified as an occupancy other than health care. The provisions applicable to business occupancies and ambulatory health care facilities are based on the assumption that most people are treated on an outpatient basis.

Note that, subject to certain qualifications, 18/19.1.2.4 allows the means of egress from health care areas using a horizontal exit to traverse non-health care spaces.

Paragraph 18/19.1.2.3 requires that a health care occupancy located in a building of another classification—such as business, storage, mercantile, or industrial—must be separated from the other occupancy by construction having a fire resistance rating of 2 hours, as detailed in 18/19.1.1.4.1. Additionally, the limitation on openings in the separating barrier as addressed by 18/19.1.1.4.2 would apply.

Note that the provisions of 18/19.1.2.3 depend on the occupancy classification, not the fire hazard of contents. Fire hazard of contents is treated in 18/19.1.2.7 and 18/19.1.2.8.

Paragraph 18/19.1.2.4 specifies that the means of egress from health care occupancies that traverse non-health care spaces must conform to the requirements for health care occupancies. However, an exception is allowed where a 2-hour separating barrier is made to meet the requirements for a horizontal exit. Where a 2-hour barrier serves as a horizontal exit, it is acceptable to exit from a health care occupancy into a different occupancy if the other occupancy complies with the *Code* provisions applicable to that other occupancy and does not contain high hazard contents. For example, if a horizontal exit is provided between a hospital and a business occupancy, inpatients are permitted to exit into the business occupancy through a horizontal exit. In this instance, corridor width, corridor partitions, stairway details, and similar features must conform to the provisions of either Chapter 38 or 39, which address business occupancies. However, the horizontal exit must comply with all the requirements of 18/19.2.2.5.

Health care occupancy patients are sometimes moved to nonmedical areas—such as a chapel for religious services or an auditorium for recreation—that typically do not meet the provisions applicable to health care occupancies. Paragraph 18/19.1.2.5 permits such areas to be regulated by the provisions applicable to the corresponding occupancy—which would be an assembly occupancy, in the case of chapels or auditoriums. This paragraph addresses a subject similar to that addressed in 18/19.1.2.6 but adds

the requirement that, where the clinical needs of the occupants necessitate the locking of doors, staff must be present for the supervised unlocking of doors and release of occupants. Without this additional requirement, simply following the provisions applicable to the non-health care occupancy would not assure that procedures were in place for the ready release of occupants.

Auditoriums, chapels, and other areas separated by 2-hour construction and meeting the criteria of 18/19.1.2.1 and 18/19.1.2.2 for other occupancies are required to be designed in accordance with the appropriate occupancy chapter governing their use.

Spaces used for non-health care purposes but located within a health care facility should have means of egress features designed in accordance with the use of the space. For example, if a space located in a health care facility is used as a chapel or auditorium, occupant loads need to be calculated on the basis of an assembly use. Assuming an occupant load is in excess of 50, egress features need to be provided as would be appropriate for an assembly occupancy. In such circumstances, doors in the means of egress need to be side-hinged, need to be arranged to swing in the direction of egress travel (see 7.2.1.4.2), and must not be equipped with a latch or lock unless such a latch or lock is arranged to be released by panic hardware or fire exit hardware (see 12/13.2.2.2.3).

Paragraph 18/19.1.2.7 regulates spaces in a health care facility that, although comprising only a portion of the facility, contain more hazardous materials (in quantity or type) than are usually found in most other spaces. Spaces such as rooms used for the storage of combustible materials, trash collection rooms, gift shops, and paint shops must be protected in accordance with 18/19.3.2.

Paragraph 18/19.1.2.8 prohibits another occupancy, such as storage, that contains highly hazardous contents, such as flammable liquids, from being located in a building housing health care occupancies. This paragraph limits use, based on occupancy classification, with regard to hazard of contents. For example, the paragraph does not intend to exclude laboratory operations from being part of a health care facility. The intent is to prevent a portion of a hospital from being designed and used as an educational or research facility—which would be classified as an educational occupancy, business occupancy, or possibly an industrial occupancy—where laboratories use and store sizable quantities of flammable liquids.

CHAPTER 18 • New | **CHAPTER 19 • Existing**

18.1.3 Special Definitions.

Ambulatory Health Care Occupancy. See 3.3.8.

Hospital. See 3.3.104.

Limited Care Facility. See 3.3.117.

Nursing Home. See 3.3.132.

19.1.3 Special Definitions.

Ambulatory Health Care Occupancy. See 3.3.8.

Hospital. See 3.3.104.

Limited Care Facility. See 3.3.117.

Nursing Home. See 3.3.132.

Section 3.3 defines the terms *hospital, nursing home,* and *limited care facility*. Each must house four or more people incapable of self-preservation on a 24-hour basis to be classified as a health care occupancy.

Occupants of hospitals or nursing homes are assumed to be nonambulatory and incapable of self-preservation. In making this judgment, due consideration should be given to the use of physical restraints and tranquilizing drugs, which can render occupants immobile. Variable staffing criteria and levels of care differentiate hospitals from nursing homes. The difference between nursing homes and limited care facilities is less clear.

Although limited care facilities house four or more occupants incapable of self-preservation due to age or physical or mental limitations, occupants are generally considered to be ambulatory and to require only limited assistance during emergency evacuation. Buildings that house ambulatory occupants who are mentally handicapped or undergoing treatment for alcohol or drug abuse and who can be expected to evacuate a structure with limited assistance meet the criteria for limited care facilities. Day-care facilities that provide care for the aged, children, mentally handicapped, or others would be classified as other than health care if the care or treatment is not provided on a 24-hour basis. See Chapters 16 and 17.

Although age itself is not sufficient justification for developing a separate classification for a health care occupancy, the elderly pose a unique problem in the achievement of fire safety. Experiences in buildings where the elderly are housed demonstrate that the response of the elderly to a fire might not be in the interest of self-preservation. Upon discovering a fire, elderly occupants might ignore it, become transfixed by it, or seek refuge from it in their rooms and fail to notify anyone of the fire. In some cases, the elderly have resisted efforts to remove them from the building and familiar surroundings.

Terms such as *residential, lodging* and *boarding,* and *custodial care* were used in the health care occupancy chapters of earlier editions of the *Code* but have been deleted to avoid confusion with a residential board and care occupancy classification addressed by Chapters 32 and 33. Board and care facilities, personal care homes, halfway houses, or similar facilities house occupants who might require medication and personal care but do not require the close supervision and services typical of the occupants in a health care facility. Therefore, these facilities would be classified as residential occupancies. Occupant capability must be carefully evaluated to determine whether application of health care criteria (Chapters 18 and 19) or application of lesser safeguards associated with residential occupancies (Chapters 32 and 33) is more appropriate.

Prior to the 1981 edition of the *Code,* occupancies that offered medical services on an outpatient basis would have been regulated within the chapter covering business occupancies. The threat to life in an outpatient facility where four or more patients might be subject to medical procedures requiring general anesthesia, treatments such as hemodialysis, or freestanding emergency service is significantly greater than that typical of a business occupancy. Conversely, application of the requirements for health care facilities that contemplate 24-hour care would be unnecessarily restrictive. In establishing the occupancy classification of an ambulatory health care facility, the intent was to develop requirements that fall between the restrictions applicable to business occupancies and health care facilities in terms of the level of life safety provided. See Chapter 20/21.

18.1.4 Classification of Occupancy.

(See 18.1.3.)

19.1.4 Classification of Occupancy.

(See 19.1.3.)

| CHAPTER 18 • New | CHAPTER 19 • Existing |

18.1.5 Classification of Hazard of Contents.

The classification of hazard of contents shall be as defined in Section 6.2.

18.1.6 Minimum Construction Requirements.

18.1.6.1 For the purpose of 18.1.6, the number of stories shall be counted starting with the primary level of exit discharge and ending with the highest occupiable level. For the purposes of 18.1.6, the primary level of exit discharge of a building shall be the lowest story whose floor is level with or above finished grade on the exterior wall line for 50 percent or more of its perimeter. Building levels below the primary level shall not be counted as a story.

18.1.6.2 Health care occupancies shall be limited to the types of building construction shown in Table 18.1.6.2. *(See 8.2.1.)*

Table 18.1.6.2 Construction Type Limitations

| Construction Type | Stories | | | |
	1	2	3	4 or More
I(443)	X	X	X	X
I(332)	X	X	X	X
II(222)	X	X	X	X
II(111)	X	X	X	NP
II(000)	X	NP	NP	NP
III(211)	X	NP	NP	NP
III(200)	NP	NP	NP	NP
IV(2HH)	X	NP	NP	NP
V(111)	X	NP	NP	NP
V(000)	NP	NP	NP	NP

X: Permitted type of construction.
NP: Not permitted.

Exception: Any building of Type I(443), Type I(332), Type II(222), or Type II(111) construction shall be permitted to include roofing systems involving combustible supports, decking, or roofing, provided that the following criteria are met:

(a) The roof covering meets Class A requirements in accordance with NFPA 256, Standard Methods of Fire Tests of Roof Coverings.

(b) The roof is separated from all occupied portions of the building by a noncombustible floor assembly having not less than a 2-hour fire resistance rating that includes not less than 2½ in. (6.4 cm) of concrete or gypsum fill. Structural

19.1.5 Classification of Hazard of Contents.

The classification of hazard of contents shall be as defined in Section 6.2.

19.1.6 Minimum Construction Requirements.

19.1.6.1 For the purpose of 19.1.6, the number of stories shall be counted starting with the primary level of exit discharge and ending with the highest occupiable level. For the purposes of 19.1.6, the primary level of exit discharge of a building shall be the lowest story whose floor is level with or above finished grade on the exterior wall line for 50 percent or more of its perimeter. Building levels below the primary level shall not be counted as a story.

19.1.6.2 Health care occupancies shall be limited to the types of building construction shown in Table 19.1.6.2. *(See 8.2.1.)*

Table 19.1.6.2 Construction Type Limitations

| Construction Type | Stories | | | |
	1	2	3	4 or More
I(443)	X	X	X	X
I(332)	X	X	X	X
II(222)	X	X	X	X
II(111)	X	X*	X*	NP
II(000)	X*	X*	NP	NP
III(211)	X*	X*	NP	NP
III(200)	X*	NP	NP	NP
IV(2HH)	X*	X*	NP	NP
V(111)	X*	X*	NP	NP
V(000)	X*	NP	NP	NP

X: Permitted type of construction.
NP: Not permitted.
*Building requires automatic sprinkler protection *(See 19.3.5.1.)*

Exception: *Any building of Type I(443), Type I(332), Type II(222), or Type II(111) construction shall be permitted to include roofing systems involving combustible supports, decking, or roofing, provided that the following criteria are met:*

(a) The roof covering meets Class C requirements in accordance with NFPA 256, Standard Methods of Fire Tests of Roof Coverings.

(b) The roof is separated from all occupied portions of the building by a noncombustible floor assembly that includes not less than 2½ in. (6.4 cm) of concrete or gypsum fill.

CHAPTER 18 • New   **CHAPTER 19 • Existing**

elements supporting the 2-hour fire resistance–rated floor assembly shall be required to have only the fire resistance rating required of the building.

(c) The attic or other space is either unoccupied or protected throughout by an approved automatic sprinkler system.

A.19.1.6.2 Exception Unoccupied space, for the purposes of this exception, is space not normally occupied by persons, fuel-fired equipment, or hazardous contents.

18.1.6.3 All interior walls and partitions in buildings of Type I or Type II construction shall be of noncombustible or limited-combustible materials.

19.1.6.3 All interior walls and partitions in buildings of Type I or Type II construction shall be of noncombustible or limited-combustible materials.

Exception:* Listed, fire-retardant-treated wood studs shall be permitted within non-load bearing 1-hour fire-rated partitions.

A.19.1.6.3 Exception There is a finish capacity in a 1-hour fire-rated partition that would be expected to prevent the generation of smoke and gases from fire retardant-treated wood studs for an extended time during fire exposure. This *Code* does not intend to permit the use of fire-retardant wood studs and partitions of only 20-minute fire resistance.

18.1.6.4 All buildings with more than one level below the level of exit discharge shall have all such lower levels separated from the level of exit discharge by not less than Type II(111) construction.

19.1.6.4 Each exterior wall of frame construction and all interior stud partitions shall be firestopped to cut off all concealed draft openings, both horizontal and vertical, between any cellar or basement and the first floor. Such firestopping shall consist of wood not less than 2 in. (5 cm) (nominal) thick or shall be of noncombustible material.

Allowable building construction types are determined according to the number of stories in a building. The first story is considered to be the primary level of exit discharge. Only occupiable levels are counted in determining the number of stories. For example, an unoccupied attic would not constitute a story.

Determining the story height of a building located on a sloping grade can be difficult. Paragraph 18/19.1.6.1 notes that a story on a sloping site that is partially below grade should be counted as a story if the floor is level with or above grade along 50 percent or more of the perimeter of the building at the exterior wall. Application of the 50 percent perimeter guideline is illustrated in Exhibit 18/19.2. Because of sloping grade, the primary level of exit discharge is not obvious. The 50 percent perimeter guideline of 18/19.1.6.1 clarifies that, for the arrangement illustrated, the first story is the primary level of exit discharge. Number of stories includes primary level of exit discharge and all occupiable floors located above. This is an example of a three-story building.

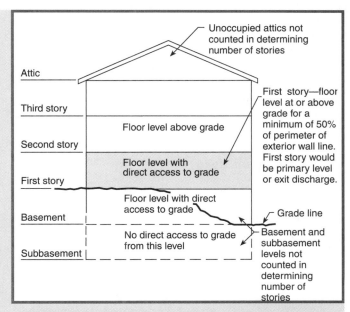

Exhibit 18/19.2 Determining number of stories for application of minimum construction requirements.

Building construction types permitted to be occupied as health care facilities are indicated as a function of number of stories in Table 18/19.1.6.2. See NFPA 220, *Standard on Types of Building Construction*, for definitions of construction types.

New multistory health care facilities and existing, nonsprinklered multistory health care facilities are required to be constructed of noncombustible materials. A minimum 2-hour fire resistance rating is required for building members of structures exceeding three stories. It is recognized that it might not be possible to move patients and that occupants of a health care facility might be required to remain in the structure for the duration of the fire. In specifying 2-hour fire resistance, it is intended that building members be adequately protected against the effects of fire to ensure building stability for the projected fire duration.

Existing two-story buildings that use combustible elements are allowed where completely protected by automatic sprinklers. Type II(111) structures can continue to be occupied with up to three stories where a complete system of electrically supervised automatic sprinklers is provided.

In certain areas, it has been common practice to erect a building with a flat, concrete roof deck. A wood deck on a wood frame peaked roof is then added for weather protection. Paragraph 18/19.1.6.2 contains an exception that permits, under certain conditions, construction of such a combustible roof system on a multistory building without affecting the classification of the building construction. In other words, a Type I or Type II building, which by definition has a roof constructed wholly of noncombustible materials, is permitted to retain its Type I or Type II classification and have a combustible wood "roof" in

accordance with the provisions of the exception to 18/19.1.6.2. The exception to 19.1.6.2 specifies that the existing attic space must be unoccupied or protected with automatic sprinklers. The term *unoccupied* is meant to disallow routine, regular use of the attic, which might increase the likelihood of fire or add a "fuel load" to the nonsprinklered space. Office or combustible storage spaces, for example, would be prohibited. The term *unoccupied* is not intended to prohibit the presence of mechanical equipment requiring periodic maintenance, such as air-handling units. Although 8.2.3.1.1 requires fire-rated assemblies to be supported by fire-rated structural members, the exception to 18.1.6.2 specifically exempts the 2-hour fire resistance–rated floor assembly (that separates the roof from the occupied floors below) from having to be supported on the floors below by 2-hour-rated structural members.

Although NFPA 220, *Standard on Types of Building Construction*, does not set combustibility requirements for nonbearing interior walls and partitions, 18/19.1.6.3 adds requirements that exceed those of NFPA 220. Paragraph 18/19.1.6.3 requires that, in Type I and Type II construction, all interior walls and partitions be constructed of noncombustible or limited-combustible materials. The terms *noncombustible* and *limited-combustible* are defined within NFPA 220 and the definitions are repeated in Chapter 3 of the *Code* for easy reference.

Note that the exception to 19.1.6.3 for existing installations allows listed fire-retardant-treated wood studs within non-load bearing, 1-hour fire resistance–rated partitions. It does not allow them in 30-minute partitions, because the studs would be exposed to fire sooner.

18.1.7 Occupant Load.

The occupant load, in number of persons for whom means of egress and other provisions are required, shall be determined on the basis of the occupant load factors of Table 7.3.1.2 that are characteristic of the use of the space or shall be determined as the maximum probable population of the space under consideration, whichever is greater.

19.1.7 Occupant Load.

The occupant load, in number of persons for whom means of egress and other provisions are required, shall be determined on the basis of the occupant load factors of Table 7.3.1.2 that are characteristic of the use of the space or shall be determined as the maximum probable population of the space under consideration, whichever is greater.

Section 18.2 Means of Egress Requirements

18.2.1 General.

Every aisle, passageway, corridor, exit discharge, exit location, and access shall be in accordance with Chapter 7.

Exception: As modified by 18.2.2 through 18.2.11.

18.2.2* Means of Egress Components.

A.18.2.2 In planning egress, arrangements should be made to transfer patients from one section of a floor to another section of the same floor that is separated by a fire barrier or smoke barrier in such a manner that patients confined to their beds can be transferred in their beds. Where the building design will allow, the section of the corridor containing an entrance or elevator lobby should be separated from corridors leading from it by fire or smoke barriers. Such arrangement, where the lobby is centrally located, will, in effect, produce a smoke lock, placing a double barrier between the area to which patients might be taken and the area from which they need to be evacuated because of threatening smoke and fire.

18.2.2.1 Components of means of egress shall be limited to the types described in 18.2.2.2 through 18.2.2.10.

18.2.2.2 Doors.

18.2.2.2.1 Doors complying with 7.2.1 shall be permitted.

18.2.2.2.2 Locks shall not be permitted on patient sleeping room doors.

Exception No. 1: Key-locking devices that restrict access to the room from the corridor and that are operable only by staff from the corridor side shall be permitted. Such devices shall not restrict egress from the room.

Exception No. 2: Door-locking arrangements shall be permitted in health care occupancies, or portions of health care occupancies, where the clinical needs of the patients require specialized security measures for their safety, provided that keys are carried by staff at all times.

18.2.2.2.3 Doors not located in a required means of egress shall be permitted to be subject to locking.

18.2.2.2.4 Doors within a required means of egress shall not be equipped with a latch or lock that requires the use of a tool or key from the egress side.

Section 19.2 Means of Egress Requirements

19.2.1 General.

Every aisle, passageway, corridor, exit discharge, exit location, and access shall be in accordance with Chapter 7.

Exception: As modified by 19.2.2 through 19.2.11.

19.2.2 Means of Egress Components.

19.2.2.1 Components of means of egress shall be limited to the types described in 19.2.2.2 through 19.2.2.10.

19.2.2.2 Doors.

19.2.2.2.1 Doors complying with 7.2.1 shall be permitted.

19.2.2.2.2 Locks shall not be permitted on patient sleeping room doors.

Exception No. 1: Key-locking devices that restrict access to the room from the corridor and that are operable only by staff from the corridor side shall be permitted. Such devices shall not restrict egress from the room.

Exception No. 2: Door-locking arrangements shall be permitted in health care occupancies, or portions of health care occupancies, where the clinical needs of the patients require specialized security measures for their safety, provided that keys are carried by staff at all times.

19.2.2.2.3 Doors not located in a required means of egress shall be permitted to be subject to locking.

19.2.2.2.4 Doors within a required means of egress shall not be equipped with a latch or lock that requires the use of a tool or key from the egress side.

Exception No. 1: Door-locking arrangements without delayed egress shall be permitted in health care occupancies, or portions of health care occupancies, where the clinical needs of the patients require specialized security measures for their safety, provided that staff can readily unlock such doors at all times. (See 18.1.1.1.5 and 18.2.2.2.5.)

Exception No. 2:* Delayed-egress locks complying with 7.2.1.6.1 shall be permitted, provided that not more than one such device is located in any egress path.

A.18.2.2.2.4 Exception No. 2 The intent of the provision is that a person following the natural path of the means of egress not encounter more than one delayed release device along that path of travel to an exit. Thus, each door from the multiple floors of a building that opens into an enclosed stair is permitted to have its own delayed release device, but an additional delayed release device is not permitted at the level of exit discharge on the door that discharges people from the enclosed stair to the outside.

Exception No. 3: Access-controlled egress doors complying with 7.2.1.6.2 shall be permitted.

18.2.2.2.5 Doors located in the means of egress that are permitted to be locked under other provisions of this chapter shall have adequate provisions made for the rapid removal of occupants by means such as remote control of locks, keying of all locks to keys carried by staff at all times, or other such reliable means available to the staff at all times. Only one such locking device shall be permitted on each door.

Exception: Locks in accordance with Exception Nos. 2 and 3 to 18.2.2.2.4.

18.2.2.2.6* Any door in an exit passageway, stairway enclosure, horizontal exit, smoke barrier, or hazardous area enclosure (except boiler rooms, heater rooms, and mechanical equipment rooms) shall be permitted to be held open only by an automatic release device that complies with 7.2.1.8.2. The automatic sprinkler system and the fire alarm system, and the systems required by 7.2.1.8.2, shall be arranged to initiate the closing action of all such doors throughout the smoke compartment or throughout the entire facility.

A.18.2.2.2.6 It is desirable to keep doors in exit passageways, stair enclosures, horizontal exits, smoke barriers, and required enclosures around hazardous areas closed at all times to impede the travel of smoke and fire gases. Function-

Exception No. 1: Door-locking arrangements without delayed egress shall be permitted in health care occupancies, or portions of health care occupancies, where the clinical needs of the patients require specialized security measures for their safety, provided that staff can readily unlock such doors at all times. (See 19.1.1.1.5 and 19.2.2.2.5.)

Exception No. 2:* Delayed-egress locks complying with 7.2.1.6.1 shall be permitted, provided that not more than one such device is located in any egress path.

A.19.2.2.2.4 Exception No. 2 The intent of the provision is that a person following the natural path of the means of egress not encounter more than one delayed release device along that path of travel to an exit. Thus, each door from the multiple floors of a building that opens into an enclosed stair is permitted to have its own delayed release device, but an additional delayed release device is not permitted at the level of exit discharge on the door that discharges people from the enclosed stair to the outside.

Exception No. 3: Access-controlled egress doors complying with 7.2.1.6.2 shall be permitted.

19.2.2.2.5 Doors located in the means of egress that are permitted to be locked under other provisions of this chapter shall have adequate provisions made for the rapid removal of occupants by means such as remote control of locks, keying of all locks to keys carried by staff at all times, or other such reliable means available to the staff at all times. Only one such locking device shall be permitted on each door.

Exception No. 1: Locks in accordance with Exception Nos. 2 and 3 to 19.2.2.2.4.

Exception No. 2: More than one lock shall be permitted on each door subject to approval of the authority having jurisdiction.

19.2.2.2.6* Any door in an exit passageway, stairway enclosure, horizontal exit, smoke barrier, or hazardous area enclosure shall be permitted to be held open only by an automatic release device that complies with 7.2.1.8.2. The automatic sprinkler system, if provided, and the fire alarm system, and the systems required by 7.2.1.8.2 shall be arranged to initiate the closing action of all such doors throughout the smoke compartment or throughout the entire facility.

A.19.2.2.2.6 It is desirable to keep doors in exit passageways, stair enclosures, horizontal exits, smoke barriers, and required enclosures around hazardous areas closed at all times to impede the travel of smoke and fire gases. Function-

CHAPTER 18 • New

CHAPTER 19 • Existing

ally, however, this involves decreased efficiency and limits patient observation by the staff of an institution. To accommodate such needs, it is practical to presume that such doors will be kept open, even to the extent of employing wood chocks and other makeshift devices. Doors in exit passageways, horizontal exits, and smoke barriers should, therefore, be equipped with automatic hold-open devices activated by the methods described, regardless of whether the original installation of the doors was predicated on a policy of keeping them closed.

18.2.2.2.7 Where doors in a stair enclosure are held open by an automatic release device as permitted in 18.2.2.2.6, initiation of a door-closing action on any level shall cause all doors at all levels in the stair enclosure to close.

18.2.2.2.8 High-rise health care occupancies shall comply with the re-entry provisions of 7.2.1.5.2.

18.2.2.2.9 Horizontal sliding doors, as permitted by 7.2.1.14, that are not automatic-closing shall be limited to a single leaf and shall have a latch or other mechanism that ensures that doors will not rebound into a partially open position if forcefully closed in an emergency.

ally, however, this involves decreased efficiency and limits patient supervision by the staff of a facility. To accommodate such needs, it is practical to presume that such doors will be kept open, even to the extent of employing wood chocks and other makeshift devices. Doors in exit passageways, horizontal exits, and smoke barriers should, therefore, be equipped with automatic hold-open devices actuated by the methods described regardless of whether the original installation of the doors was predicated on a policy of keeping them closed.

19.2.2.2.7 Where doors in a stair enclosure are held open by an automatic release device as permitted in 19.2.2.2.6, initiation of a door-closing action on any level shall cause all doors at all levels in the stair enclosure to close.

19.2.2.2.8* Existing health care occupancies shall be exempt from the re-entry provisions of 7.2.1.5.2.

A.19.2.2.2.8 Doors to the enclosures of interior stair exits should be arranged to open from the stair side at not less than every third floor so that it will be possible to leave the stairway at such floor if fire renders the lower part of the stair unusable during egress or if occupants seek refuge on another floor.

19.2.2.2.9 Horizontal sliding doors, as permitted by 7.2.1.14, that are not automatic-closing shall be limited to a single leaf and shall have a latch or other mechanism that ensures that doors will not rebound into a partially open position if forcefully closed in an emergency.

Paragraphs 18/19.2.2.2.1 through 18/19.2.2.2.9 address the door provisions of 7.2.1 and provide any modifications particular to health care occupancies.

In the 1991 and earlier editions of the *Code*, numerous provisions of Chapter 18/19 specified minimum door width requirements as a leaf width rather than as a clear width. For example, doors from patient rooms to the corridor in new construction were required to be 44 in. (112 cm) wide. The intent was that, after allowing for the stops built into the door frame and the thickness of the protruding hinge stile edge, a 44-in. (112-cm) wide door leaf would provide approximately 41.5 in. (105 cm) of clear, unobstructed width. However, there was no requirement for the door to swing a minimum of 90 degrees from the plane of the door opening, so the intended 41.5 in. (105 cm) of clear, unobstructed width was not assured. Since the 1994 edition, all minimum door width requirements for new health care occupancies are spec-

ified as clear, unobstructed width. For existing doors in health care occupancies, all minimum door width requirements are specified as clear, unobstructed width, but exceptions continue to recognize existing doors with the minimum door leaf widths previously specified.

Exception No. 1 to 18/19.2.2.2.2 allows for access from the corridor to a room to be limited via a locked door that staff can unlock with keys they keep readily available. Limited access would permit, for example, patient isolation rooms to have doors locked from the corridor side only so that other patients could not wander into the room and thus endanger themselves. However, the patient within the isolation room with the door locked from the corridor side needs to be able to open the door from the room side without the use of a key or tool.

Exception No. 2 to 18/19.2.2.2.2 addresses the locking of doors for patient clinical needs. Some health care facilities might need to lock patient room doors against egress for functional purposes involving the clinical needs of patients. For example, if certain patients require confinement because they would otherwise leave their rooms and endanger themselves, locking patient room doors would provide specialized security. If patient room doors are locked against egress, the *Code* requires that staff carry keys at all times so as to be able to unlock doors immediately. Also see 18/19.2.2.2.5, which limits the number of locks per door and specifies that staff must carry keys at all times or that other provisions must be made for the immediate release of patients, using remotely controlled locking devices.

Exception No. 1 to 18/19.2.2.2.4 permits doors encountered along the egress path to the outside the same opportunity for locking that Exception No. 2 to 18/19.2.2.2.2 permits for patient sleeping room doors, provided that staff can readily unlock such doors at all times. Note that 18/19.1.1.1.5 allows the authority having jurisdiction to make appropriate modifications to compensate for locking of egress doors.

Exception No. 2 to 18/19.2.2.2.4 addresses the delayed-egress lock described in 7.2.1.6.1. Paragraph 7.2.1.6.1 specifies detailed requirements for delayed egress locking hardware, including the requirement that the building be protected throughout by automatic sprinklers or automatic fire detection. The exception permits the use of the delayed egress lock on any door in a health care facility. However, only one delayed-egress lock can be encountered along any egress path. For example, in a three-story hospital with an enclosed exit stair at each of the two ends of the building, the doors into the stair enclosures on each of the floors could be equipped with a delayed-egress locking device. However, the door to the outside at the base of each stair enclosure could not be equipped with an additional delayed-egress lock.

In buildings where the locking of doors is necessary, staff must provide continuous supervision in accordance with 18/19.2.2.2.5. Provisions must be made for the prompt release of persons who are restrained either by equipping staff with keys, by providing remote unlocking capabilities for doors, or by other reliable means available to staff at all times. If staff relies on the use of keys, a master key system for facilitating the quick release of occupants should be considered. In existing buildings and with the approval of the authority having jurisdiction, more than one lock on a door is permitted.

Paragraph 18/19.2.2.2.6 modifies the requirements of 7.2.1.8.2 addressing automatic-closing doors. Where health care occupancy doors that are required to be self-closing are held open, an automatic device must close doors upon operation of the building fire alarm system and upon operation of the building sprinkler system. In addition, the doors must be designed to close automatically by actuation of smoke detectors installed to detect smoke on either side of the door. See 7.2.1.8.2 and NFPA 72, *National Fire Alarm Code.*[4] As a further safeguard for stairways, any automatic action that closes a stairway door on one level must close the doors on the other levels of that stairway in accordance with 18/19.2.2.2.7.

Paragraph 18.2.2.2.8 regulates stairway re-entry in new buildings having occupied floor levels more than 75 ft (23 m) above the lowest level of fire department access. In doing so, the *Code* exempts low-rise health care occupancies from the requirements of 7.2.1.5.2. Stair doors in new high-rise health care facilities must allow for re-entry in accordance with Chapter 7. All stair doors must be unlocked, or they must be interlocked with the building fire alarm to unlock automatically in the event of alarm actuation. As for all occupancies, use of Exception No. 1 to 7.2.1.5.2 is permitted. Exception No. 1 allows stair doors to be locked provided that the following requirements are met:

(1) A minimum of two doors are maintained unlocked.
(2) There are no more than four intervening floors between unlocked doors.
(3) Re-entry must be possible at either of the two top floor levels.
(4) Re-entry on either of the two top floor levels must provide access to a different exit.
(5) Unlocked doors must be appropriately marked on the stairwell side.

Existing health care occupancies—even those that are in high-rise buildings—are exempt from the stairwell re-entry provisions.

Paragraph 18/19.2.2.2.9 establishes requirements exceeding those of 7.2.1.14 for horizontal sliding doors. If sliding doors are to be closed manually, they must consist of a single leaf to avoid openings at the meeting edges of the two leafs, and provisions must be made, by use of a latch or other means, to prevent the door from impacting the frame and rebounding to a partially open position when closed forcefully.

The requirements of 7.2.1.14 should be closely reviewed. The sliding door described is highly specialized, and all requirements of 7.2.1.14 must be met. One unique requirement that differentiates this spe-

cial door from a typical horizontal sliding door is that it must slide to the side to allow passage through the door opening when force is applied in the direction of egress travel to the door actuator.

18.2.2.3 Stairs. Stairs complying with 7.2.2 shall be permitted.

18.2.2.4 Smokeproof Enclosures. Smokeproof enclosures complying with 7.2.3 shall be permitted.

18.2.2.5 Horizontal Exits. Horizontal exits complying with 7.2.4 and the modifications of 18.2.2.5.1 through 18.2.2.5.6 shall be permitted.

18.2.2.5.1 Not less than 30 net ft² (2.8 net m²) per patient in a hospital or nursing home, or not less than 15 net ft² (1.4 net m²) per resident in a limited care facility, shall be provided within the aggregated area of corridors, patient rooms, treatment rooms, lounge or dining areas, and other similar areas on each side of the horizontal exit. On stories not housing bed or litterborne patients, not less than 6 net ft² (0.56 net m²) per occupant shall be provided on each side of the horizontal exit for the total number of occupants in adjoining compartments.

18.2.2.5.2 The total egress capacity of the other exits (stairs, ramps, doors leading outside the building) shall not be reduced below one-third of that required for the entire area of the building.

18.2.2.5.3 A single door shall be permitted in a horizontal exit if the exit serves one direction only. Such door shall be a swinging door or a horizontal sliding door complying with 7.2.1.14. The door shall have not less than 41.5 in. (105 cm) in clear width.

18.2.2.5.4 A horizontal exit involving a corridor 8 ft (2.4 m) or more in width serving as a means of egress from both sides of the doorway shall have the opening protected by a pair of swinging doors arranged to swing in opposite directions from each other, with each door having a clear width of not less than 41.5 in. (105 cm), or by a horizontal sliding door complying with 7.2.1.14 that provides a clear width of not less than 83 in. (211 cm).

19.2.2.3 Stairs. Stairs complying with 7.2.2 shall be permitted.

19.2.2.4 Smokeproof Enclosures. Smokeproof enclosures complying with 7.2.3 shall be permitted.

19.2.2.5 Horizontal Exits. Horizontal exits complying with 7.2.4 and the modifications of 19.2.2.5.1 through 19.2.2.5.4 shall be permitted.

19.2.2.5.1 Not less than 30 net ft² (2.8 net m²) per patient in a hospital or nursing home, or not less than 15 net ft² (1.4 net m²) per resident in a limited care facility, shall be provided within the aggregated area of corridors, patient rooms, treatment rooms, lounge or dining areas, and other similar areas on each side of the horizontal exit. On stories not housing bed or litterborne patients, not less than 6 net ft² (0.56 net m²) per occupant shall be provided on each side of the horizontal exit for the total number of occupants in adjoining compartments.

19.2.2.5.2 The total egress capacity of the other exits (stairs, ramps, doors leading outside the building) shall not be reduced below one-third of that required for the entire area of the building.

19.2.2.5.3* A door in a horizontal exit shall not be required to swing with egress travel as specified in 7.2.4.3.6(1).

A.19.2.2.5.3 The waiver of the requirement for doors to swing in the direction of egress travel is based on the assumption that, in this occupancy, there is no possibility of a panic rush that might prevent the opening of doors that swing against egress travel.

A desirable arrangement, which is possible with corridors 8 ft (2.4 m) or more in width, is to have two 42-in. (107-cm) doors, normally closed, each swinging with the egress travel (in opposite directions).

19.2.2.5.4 Door openings in horizontal exits shall be protected by a swinging door providing a clear width of not less than 32 in. (81 cm) or by a horizontal sliding door complying with 7.2.1.14 that provides a clear width of not less than 32 in. (81 cm).

Exception: Existing 34-in. (86-cm) swinging doors.

18.2.2.5.5 A horizontal exit involving a corridor 6 ft (1.8 m) or more in width serving as a means of egress from both sides of the doorway shall have the opening protected by a pair of swinging doors, arranged to swing in opposite directions from each other, with each door having a clear width of not less than 32 in. (81 cm), or by a horizontal sliding door complying with 7.2.1.14 that provides a clear width of not less than 64 in. (163 cm).

18.2.2.5.6 An approved vision panel shall be required in each horizontal exit. Center mullions shall be prohibited.

Special recognition is given to horizontal travel and the use of horizontal exits in health care facilities because of practical difficulties involving vertical egress travel, such as on stairways. Up to two-thirds of the total required egress capacity for a given fire area is permitted to be provided by horizontal exits (see 18/19.2.2.5.2). Every floor and every fire section must have at least one exit consisting of a door leading directly outside the building, an interior stair, an outside stair, a smokeproof enclosure, a ramp, or an exit passageway (see 18/19.2.4.2). No fire area can be served by horizontal exits only. In the event a horizontal exit also serves as a smoke barrier, see commentary associated with 18/19.2.4, and also see 18/19.3.7.

The requirements for horizontal exits in 18/19.2.2.5 are illustrated in Exhibits 18/19.3(a), 18/19.3(b), and 18/19.3(c).

Doors in new horizontal exits are required to swing in the direction of egress travel. In the case of a fire barrier that serves as a new horizontal exit for two adjoining fire areas, a pair of doors arranged with each leaf to swing in a direction opposite from the other, or some equivalent arrangement, must be used. If a fire barrier serves as a horizontal exit from only one fire area, the door opening may be protected by a single door providing 41.5-in. (105-cm) clear width in new hospitals and nursing homes or 32-in. (81-cm) clear width in new limited care facilities. See Exhibit 18/19.3(a).

The *Code* recognizes the use of sliding doors complying with 7.2.1.14 for the protection of openings in horizontal exits. The use of power-operated sliding doors results in an obstruction-free opening for normal traffic while providing adequate fire protection for openings under fire emergency conditions.

Corridors in new limited care facilities and new psychiatric hospitals are required to be 6 ft (183 cm)

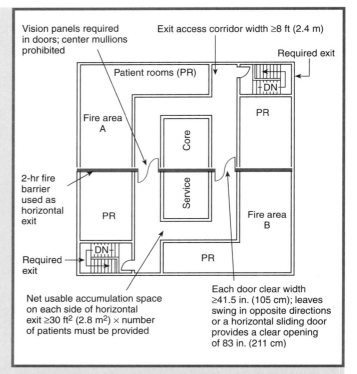

Exhibit 18/19.3(a) *Horizontal exit in a new general hospital or nursing home.*

wide; therefore, it would not be practical to install a pair of 41.5-in. (105-cm) clear width doors to protect corridor openings in a horizontal exit. Recognizing this practical consideration and that no obstructions, such as mullions mounted at the center of a two-door opening, are permitted, doors protecting openings in horizontal exits of such facilities are required to provide a minimum of 32-in. (81-cm) clear width. See Exhibit 18/19.3(b).

CHAPTER 18 • New   **CHAPTER 19 • Existing**

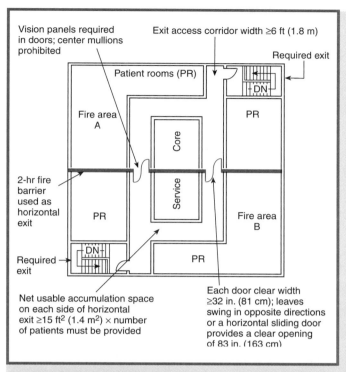

Exhibit 18/19.3(b) Horizontal exit in a new limited care facility or psychiatric hospital.

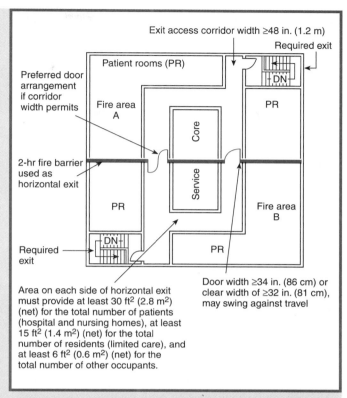

Exhibit 18/19.3(c) Horizontal exit in existing health care occupancy.

Prohibiting center mullions in new construction provides one, large, usable door opening where two doors are positioned within a door frame and eliminates any obstructions that would restrict the movement of patients in beds, in wheelchairs, or on litters.

The *Code* permits corridors in existing health care occupancies to be 4 ft (1.2 m) wide, and it is therefore impractical in many instances to install a pair of cross-corridor doors in a horizontal exit. However, the 4-ft (1.2-m) corridor width will permit the opening of a single door against the flow of travel with minimal difficulty. A power-operated sliding door might be used to reduce problems associated with door swing. The *Code* permits sliding doors complying with 7.2.1.14 for the protection of openings in horizontal exits. The use of power-operated sliding doors results

in an obstruction-free opening for normal traffic, while still providing adequate fire protection for openings.

In the case of an existing fire barrier serving as a horizontal exit for two adjoining fire areas, and where corridor widths will permit, a pair of doors arranged with each leaf to swing in a direction opposite from the other should be used. Each leaf in the pair of doors must either be a minimum of 34 in. (86 cm) wide or provide a clear opening of 32 in. (81 cm). See Exhibit 18/19.3(c).

New horizontal exits in an existing facility are considered to be a renovation and must be installed in accordance with Chapter 18 to the extent feasible (see commentary following 18/19.1.1.4.6 and 4.6.7).

18.2.2.6 Ramps.

18.2.2.6.1 Ramps complying with 7.2.5 shall be permitted.

18.2.2.6.2 Ramps enclosed as exits shall be of sufficient width to provide egress capacity in accordance with 18.2.3.2.

19.2.2.6 Ramps.

19.2.2.6.1 Ramps complying with 7.2.5 shall be permitted.

19.2.2.6.2 Ramps enclosed as exits shall be of sufficient width to provide egress capacity in accordance with 19.2.3.2.

CHAPTER 18 • New	CHAPTER 19 • Existing

Ramps with a slope minimally graduated so as not to be dangerous to use in both normal and emergency traffic require so much space that they would be impracticable in most situations. They are, however, the only practicable method of moving bedridden patients from one story to another, except by elevators, which may not be available during fire conditions. The best plan is to provide for horizontal egress to

another section of the building, minimizing the need for complete evacuation.

Ramps might be the best means for providing egress from doors two or three steps above or below grade level (see 7.1.7) and might compensate for minor differences in floor levels between adjoining sections of buildings. Such ramps must be constructed in accordance with 18/19.2.2.6 and 7.2.5.

18.2.2.7 Exit Passageways. Exit passageways complying with 7.2.6 shall be permitted.

18.2.2.8 Fire Escape Ladders. Fire escape ladders complying with 7.2.9 shall be permitted.

18.2.2.9 Alternating Tread Devices. Alternating tread devices complying with 7.2.11 shall be permitted.

18.2.2.10 Areas of Refuge. Areas of refuge used as part of a required accessible means of egress shall comply with 7.2.12.

18.2.3 Capacity of Means of Egress.

18.2.3.1 The capacity of any required means of egress shall be based on its width, as defined in Section 7.3.

18.2.3.2 The capacity of means of egress providing travel by means of stairs shall be 0.3 in. (0.8 cm) per person, and the capacity of means of egress providing horizontal travel (without stairs) by means such as doors, ramps, or horizontal exits shall be 0.2 in. (0.5 cm) per person.

18.2.3.3* Aisles, corridors, and ramps required for exit access in a hospital or nursing home shall be not less than 8 ft (2.4 m) in clear and unobstructed width. Where ramps are used as exits, see 18.2.2.6.

19.2.2.7 Exit Passageways. Exit passageways complying with 7.2.6 shall be permitted.

19.2.2.8 Fire Escape Ladders. Fire escape ladders complying with 7.2.9 shall be permitted.

19.2.2.9 Alternating Tread Devices. Alternating tread devices complying with 7.2.11 shall be permitted.

19.2.2.10 Areas of Refuge. Areas of refuge used as part of a required accessible means of egress shall comply with 7.2.12.

19.2.3 Capacity of Means of Egress.

19.2.3.1 The capacity of any required means of egress shall be based on its width, as defined in Section 7.3.

19.2.3.2 The capacity of means of egress providing travel by means of stairs shall be 0.6 in. (1.5 cm) per person, and the capacity of means of egress providing horizontal travel (without stairs) by means such as doors, ramps, or horizontal exits shall be 0.5 in. (1.3 cm) per person.

Exception: The capacity of means of egress in health care occupancies protected throughout by an approved, supervised automatic sprinkler system in accordance with 19.3.5.2 shall be 0.3 in. (0.8 cm) per person for travel by means of stairs and 0.2 in. (0.5 cm) per person for horizontal travel without stairs.

19.2.3.3* Any required aisle, corridor, or ramp shall be not less than 4 ft (1.2 m) in clear width where serving as means of egress from patient sleeping rooms. The aisle, corridor, or ramp shall be arranged to avoid any obstructions to the convenient removal of nonambulatory persons carried on stretchers or on mattresses serving as stretchers.

|

A.18.2.3.3 It is not the intent that the required corridor width be maintained clear and unobstructed at all times. Projections into the required width are permitted by the exception to 7.3.2. It is not the intent that 18.2.3.3 supersede 7.3.2. Also, it is recognized that wheeled items in use (such as food service carts, housekeeping carts, gurneys, beds, and similar items) and wheeled crash carts not in use (because they need to be immediately accessible during a clinical emergency) are encountered in health care occupancy corridors. The health care occupancy's fire plan and training program should address the relocation of these items during a fire. Note that "not in use" is not the same as "in storage." Storage is not permitted to be open to the corridor unless it meets one of the exceptions to 18.3.6.1 and is not a hazardous area.

Exception No. 1:* Aisles, corridors, and ramps in adjunct areas not intended for the housing, treatment, or use of inpatients shall be not less than 44 in. (112 cm) in clear and unobstructed width.

A.18.2.3.3 Exception No. 1 Occupant characteristics are an important factor to be evaluated in setting egress criteria. Egress components in nonpatient use areas, such as administrative office spaces, should be evaluated based on actual use. A clear corridor width of not less than 44 in. (112 cm) is specified, assuming occupants in nonpatient areas will be mobile and capable of evacuation without assistance.

Exception No. 2:* Exit access within a room or suite of rooms complying with the requirements of 18.2.5.

A.18.2.3.3 Exception No. 2 Exit access should be arranged to avoid any obstructions to the convenient removal of non-ambulatory persons carried on stretchers or on mattresses serving as stretchers.

18.2.3.4 Aisles, corridors, and ramps required for exit access in a limited care facility or hospital for psychiatric care shall be not less than 6 ft (1.8 m) in clear and unobstructed width. Where ramps are used as exits, see 18.2.2.6.

Exception No. 1:* Aisles, corridors, and ramps in adjunct areas not intended for the housing, treatment, or use of inpatients shall be not less than 44 in. (112 cm) in clear and unobstructed width.

A.18.2.3.4 Exception No. 1 See A.18.2.3.3, Exception No. 1.

Exception No. 2:* Exit access within a room or suite of rooms complying with the requirements of 18.2.5.

A.19.2.3.3 It is not the intent that the required corridor width be maintained clear and unobstructed at all times. Projections into the required width are permitted by the exception to 7.3.2. It is not the intent that 19.2.3.3 supersede 7.3.2. Also, it is recognized that wheeled items in use (such as food service carts, housekeeping carts, gurneys, beds, and similar items) and wheeled crash carts not in use (because they need to be immediately accessible during a clinical emergency) are encountered in health care occupancy corridors. The health care occupancy's fire plan and training program should address the relocation of these items during a fire. Note that "not in use" is not the same as "in storage." Storage is not permitted to be open to the corridor unless it meets one of the exceptions to 19.3.6.1 and is not a hazardous area.

Exception No. 1: Aisles, corridors, and ramps in adjunct areas not intended for the housing, treatment, or use of inpatients shall be not less than 44 in. (112 cm) in clear and unobstructed width.

Exception No. 2: Exit access within a room or suite of rooms complying with the requirements of 19.2.5.

19.2.3.4 (Reserved.)

A.18.2.3.4 Exception No. 2 See A.18.2.3.3, Exception No. 2.

18.2.3.5 The minimum clear width for doors in the means of egress from sleeping rooms; diagnostic and treatment areas, such as x-ray, surgery, or physical therapy; and nursery rooms shall be as follows:

(1) Hospitals and nursing homes—41.5 in. (105 cm)
(2) Psychiatric hospitals and limited care facilities—32 in. (81 cm)

Exception No. 1:   Doors that are located so as not to be subject to use by any health care occupant shall be not less than 32 in. (81 cm) in clear width.

Exception No. 2:   Doors in exit stair enclosures shall be not less than 32 in. (81 cm) in clear width.

Exception No. 3:   Doors serving newborn nurseries shall be not less than 32 in. (81 cm) in clear width.

Exception No. 4:   Where a pair of doors is provided, not less than one of the doors shall provide not less than a 32-in. (81-cm) clear width opening and a rabbet, bevel, or astragal shall be provided at the meeting edge. The inactive leaf shall have an automatic flush bolt to provide positive latching.

19.2.3.5 The minimum clear width for doors in the means of egress from hospitals; nursing homes; limited care facilities; psychiatric hospital sleeping rooms; and diagnostic and treatment areas, such as x-ray, surgery, or physical therapy, shall be not less than 32 in. (81 cm) wide.

Exception No. 1:   Existing 34-in. (86-cm) doors.

Exception No. 2:   Existing 28-in. (71-cm) corridor doors in facilities where the fire plans do not require evacuation by bed, gurney, or wheelchair.

The method used in calculating egress capacity acknowledges that increasing the width of egress systems results in increasing the occupant flow through that system. The provisions of 18/19.2.3.2 compute stair egress capacity in sprinklered health care occupancies on the basis of 0.3 in. (0.8 cm) per person. Therefore, a 44-in. (112-cm) stair provides egress capacity for 146 persons [44 in. (112 cm) / 0.3 in. (0.8 cm) per person = 146 persons]. Similarly, a 50-in. (127-cm) stair provides capacity for 167 persons. In nonsprinklered existing health care occupancies, stair egress capacity is computed on the basis of 0.6 in. (1.5 cm) per person. The capacity of level surfaces and doors in fully sprinklered health care occupancy smoke compartments is computed on the basis of 0.2 in. (0.5 cm) per person, and on 0.5 in. (1.3 cm) per person in nonsprinklered existing health care occupancy smoke compartments. Egress capacity calculations must use clear width as defined in 7.2.1.2.

In earlier editions of the *Code*, egress capacity for health care occupancies was calculated using more conservative egress capacity factors. For example, stair capacity for nonsprinklered health care occupancies was calculated on the basis of 1 in. (2.5 cm) per person rather than the current factor of 0.3 in. (0.8 cm) per person based on the philosophy that extra width was needed to create space that could serve as a refuge area. The capacity of health care egress system components was set conservatively in recognition of the slow rate of travel for patients and the fact that space was needed for patients on litters and in wheelchairs.

Recent editions of the *Code* use a different concept for egress system design in health care occupancies. Life safety from fire in health care facilities relies on a defend-in-place principle. Horizontal exits or smoke barriers are used to subdivide each story to provide an area of refuge on each story without requiring travel by means of stairs. Flow rates for exits (capacity) are established on the assumption that exit stairs will be used principally by able-bodied staff, visitors, and ambulatory patients for emergency evacuation. Nonambulatory patients will remain in the building, and those on the floor of fire origin will be moved horizontally to an area of refuge. The defend-in-place principle is complemented by the requirement that all new health care facilities be fully protected by automatic sprinklers.

Corridor width is addressed in 18/19.2.3.3. Exit access corridors in new general hospitals and nursing homes are required to be 8 ft (2.4 m) in clear width, based on the assumption that, during a fire emergency, some patients might require movement on litters or in wheelchairs. Also, multiple files of persons should be able to use the corridor at one time, with those who move more quickly passing those who move more slowly. Exit access corridors in existing health care occupancies are required to be 4 ft (1.2 m) in clear width. This specified minimum leaves little safety margin. Care is necessary to prevent carts,

furnishings, and other materials from obstructing or interfering with potential occupant movement. Corridors a minimum of 44 in. (112 cm) wide are considered acceptable within areas not subject to use by inpatients in both new and existing occupancy areas such as administrative office spaces, where occupants are assumed to be mobile and capable of evacuation without assistance.

Exhibits 18/19.4(a) and 18/19.4(b) illustrate the minimum clear width requirement of 18/19.2.3.3. For new limited care facilities and psychiatric hospitals, which by definition involve patients who are more ambulatory than those in general hospitals and nursing homes, the required corridor width is 6 ft (1.8 m) instead of 8 ft (2.4 m). Actual corridor width is permitted to be considered as clear width if handrail encroachment does not exceed $3^1/_2$ in. (8.9 cm) on each side of the corridor (see 7.2.1.2.1).

In editions of the *Code* prior to 1994, numerous provisions of Chapter 18/19 specified minimum requirements for door widths as a leaf width rather than as a clear width. For example, new doors from patient rooms to the corridor were required to be 44

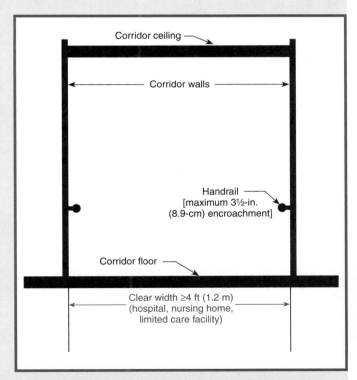

Exhibit 18/19.4(a) *Exit access corridor in new health care facility.*

Exhibit 18/19.4(b) *Exit access corridor in existing health care facility.*

| **CHAPTER 18 • New** | **CHAPTER 19 • Existing** |

in. (112 cm) wide and similarly existing doors were required to be 34 in. (86 cm) wide. The intent was that after allowing for the stops built into the door frame and for the thickness of the protruding hinge stile edge, a 44-in. (112-cm) wide door leaf would provide approximately 41.5 in. (105 cm) of clear, unobstructed width; a 34-in. (86-cm) wide door leaf would provide approximately 32 in. (81 cm) of clear, unobstructed width. However, there was no requirement for the door to swing a minimum of 90 degrees from the plane of the door opening, so the intended clear, unobstructed width was not assured. Since the 1994 edition, minimum door width requirements for health care occupancies have been specified as clear, unobstructed width. Although minimum door width requirements are specified in terms of clear, unobstructed width, exceptions continue to recognize existing doors with the minimum door leaf widths

previously specified. Exhibit 18/19.5 illustrates door leaf measurement, rather than clear opening measurement, as allowed by Exception No. 1 to 19.2.3.5. The exceptions to 19.2.2.5.4 and 19.3.7.7 also permit existing doors to provide the minimum required width via a door leaf measurement.

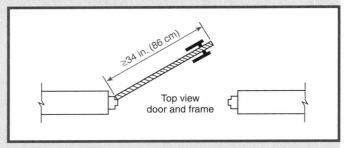

Exhibit 18/19.5 *Minimum door width measurement for existing doors.*

18.2.4 Number of Exits.

18.2.4.1 Not less than two exits of the types described in 18.2.2.2 through 18.2.2.10, remotely located from each other, shall be provided for each floor or fire section of the building.

18.2.4.2 Not less than one exit from each floor or fire section shall be one of the following:

(1) A door leading directly outside the building
(2) A stair
(3) A smokeproof enclosure
(4) A ramp
(5) An exit passageway

Any fire section not meeting these requirements shall be considered part of an adjoining zone. Egress shall not require return through the zone of fire origin.

18.2.4.3* Not less than two exits of the types described in 18.2.2.2 through 18.2.2.10 shall be accessible from each smoke compartment. Egress shall be permitted through an adjacent compartment(s) but shall not require return through the compartment of fire origin.

19.2.4 Number of Exits.

19.2.4.1 Not less than two exits of the types described in 19.2.2.2 through 19.2.2.10, remotely located from each other, shall be provided for each floor or fire section of the building.

19.2.4.2 Not less than one exit from each floor or fire section shall be one of the following:

(1) A door leading directly outside the building
(2) A stair
(3) A smokeproof enclosure
(4) A ramp
(5) An exit passageway

Any fire section not meeting these requirements shall be considered part of an adjoining zone. Egress shall not require return through the zone of fire origin.

19.2.4.3* Not less than two exits of the types described in 19.2.2.2 through 19.2.2.10 shall be accessible from each smoke compartment. Egress shall be permitted through an adjacent compartment(s) but shall not require return through the compartment of fire origin.

Exhibit 18/19.6 can be used to illustrate the application of 18/19.2.4.2. Horizontal exits 1 and 2 form three fire compartments, areas A, B, and C. An enclosed exit stair (that is, an exit other than a horizontal exit)

is provided from areas A and C; area B is provided with two horizontal exits. Paragraph 18/19.2.4.2 requires that area B must be provided with at least one exit other than a horizontal exit. Area B is deficient

CHAPTER 18 • New   **CHAPTER 19 • Existing**

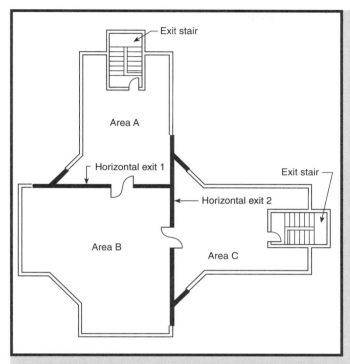

Exhibit 18/19.6 *Arrangement of exits for fire compartments formed by horizontal exit fire barriers.*

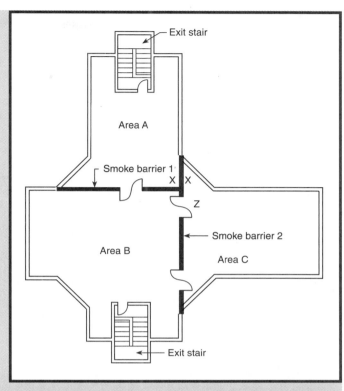

Exhibit 18/19.7 *Arrangement of exits for smoke compartments formed by smoke barriers.*

in that it has no exit other than horizontal exits. Without this additional exit, area B must be consideredpart of one of the adjoining areas—either part of an enlarged area A, in which case horizontal exit 1 would receive no credit for providing egress capacity, or part of an enlarged area C, in which case horizontal exit 2 would receive no credit for providing egress capacity.

Exhibit 18/19.7 can be used to illustrate the application of 18/19.2.4.3. Smoke barriers 1 and 2 form three smoke compartments, areas A, B, and C. Access to two exits is provided from each smoke compartment. For area A, the enclosed exit stair provides access to one exit, and traveling through smoke barrier 1 into area B provides access to the second exit, also an enclosed exit stair. For area B, the enclosed

exit stair provides access to one exit, and traveling through smoke barrier 1 into area A provides access to the second exit, also an enclosed exit stair. For area C, the two remotely located pairs of doors in smoke barrier 2 provide access to the enclosed exit stairs in areas A and B, but passage into area B is required. Area C is deficient in that both of its exit accesses require passage into area B, which might be the smoke compartment of fire origin. To satisfy the provision of 18/19.2.4.3—that egress not require return through the smoke compartment of fire origin—either an enclosed exit stair can be added to area C, or the doors at Z can be relocated to position XX.

A.18.2.4.3 An exit is not necessary for each individual smoke compartment if there is access to an exit through other smoke compartments without passing through the smoke compartment of fire origin.

A.19.2.4.3 An exit is not necessary for each individual smoke compartment if there is access to an exit through other smoke compartments without passing through the smoke compartment of fire origin.

CHAPTER 18 • New	CHAPTER 19 • Existing

18.2.5 Arrangement of Means of Egress.

18.2.5.1 Every habitable room shall have an exit access door leading directly to an exit access corridor.

Exception No. 1: If there is an exit door opening directly to the outside from the room at ground level.

Exception No. 2: Exit access from a patient sleeping room with not more than eight patient beds shall be permitted to pass through one intervening room to reach the exit access corridor.

Exception No. 3: Exit access from a special nursing suite shall be permitted to pass through one intervening room to reach the exit access corridor where the arrangement allows for direct and constant visual supervision by nursing personnel.

Exception No. 4: Exit access from a suite of rooms, other than patient sleeping rooms, shall be permitted to pass through not more than two adjacent rooms to reach the exit access corridor where the travel distance within the suite is in accordance with 18.2.5.8.

18.2.5.2 Any patient sleeping room, or any suite that includes patient sleeping rooms, of more than 1000 ft² (93 m²) shall have not less than two exit access doors remotely located from each other.

18.2.5.3 Any room or any suite of rooms, other than patient sleeping rooms, of more than 2500 ft² (230 m²) shall have not less than two exit access doors remotely located from each other.

18.2.5.4 Any suite of rooms that complies with the requirements of 18.2.5 shall be permitted to be subdivided with non-fire-rated, noncombustible, or limited-combustible partitions.

18.2.5.5 Intervening rooms shall not be hazardous areas as defined by 18.3.2.

18.2.5.6 Suites of sleeping rooms shall not exceed 5000 ft² (460 m²).

18.2.5.7 Suites of rooms, other than patient sleeping rooms, shall not exceed 10,000 ft² (930 m²).

18.2.5.8 Suites of rooms, other than patient sleeping rooms, shall be permitted to have one intervening room if the travel distance within the suite to the exit access door does not exceed 100 ft (30 m) and shall be permitted to have two intervening rooms where the travel distance within the suite to the exit access door does not exceed 50 ft (15 m).

19.2.5 Arrangement of Means of Egress.

19.2.5.1 Every habitable room shall have an exit access door leading directly to an exit access corridor.

Exception No. 1: If there is an exit door opening directly to the outside from the room at ground level.

Exception No. 2: Exit access from a patient sleeping room with not more than eight patient beds shall be permitted to pass through one intervening room to reach the exit access corridor.

Exception No. 3: Exit access from a special nursing suite shall be permitted to pass through one intervening room to reach the exit access corridor where the arrangement allows for direct and constant visual supervision by nursing personnel.

Exception No. 4: Exit access from a suite of rooms, other than patient sleeping rooms, shall be permitted to pass through not more than two adjacent rooms to reach the exit access corridor where the travel distance within the suite is in accordance with 19.2.5.8.

19.2.5.2 Any patient sleeping room, or any suite that includes patient sleeping rooms, of more than 1000 ft² (93 m²) shall have not less than two exit access doors remotely located from each other.

19.2.5.3 Any room or any suite of rooms, other than patient sleeping rooms, of more than 2500 ft² (230 m²) shall have not less than two exit access doors remotely located from each other.

19.2.5.4 Any suite of rooms that complies with the requirements of 19.2.5 shall be permitted to be subdivided with non-fire-rated, noncombustible, or limited-combustible partitions.

19.2.5.5 Intervening rooms shall not be hazardous areas as defined by 19.3.2.

19.2.5.6 Suites of sleeping rooms shall not exceed 5000 ft² (460 m²).

19.2.5.7 Suites of rooms, other than patient sleeping rooms, shall not exceed 10,000 ft² (930 m²).

19.2.5.8 Suites of rooms, other than patient sleeping rooms, shall be permitted to have one intervening room if the travel distance within the suite to the exit access door does not exceed 100 ft (30 m) and shall be permitted to have two intervening rooms where the travel distance within the suite to the exit access door does not exceed 50 ft (15 m).

CHAPTER 18 • New

18.2.5.9 Every corridor shall provide access to not less than two approved exits in accordance with Sections 7.4 and 7.5 without passing through any intervening rooms or spaces other than corridors or lobbies. *IBC REQUIRS ii u 4 TO HAVE SAME CONST. REQ'TS AS CORRIDORS.*

18.2.5.10 Every exit or exit access shall be arranged so that no corridor, aisle, or passageway has a pocket or dead end exceeding 30 ft (9.1 m).

CHAPTER 19 • Existing

19.2.5.9* Every corridor shall provide access to not less than two approved exits in accordance with Sections 7.4 and 7.5 without passing through any intervening rooms or spaces other than corridors or lobbies.

A.19.2.5.9 Every exit or exit access should be arranged, if practical and feasible, so that no corridor, passageway, or aisle has a pocket or dead end exceeding 30 ft (9.1 m). *(See also Table A.7.6.1.)*

19.2.5.10 Existing dead-end corridors shall be permitted to be continued to be used if it is impractical and unfeasible to alter them so that exits are accessible in not less than two different directions from all points in aisles, passageways, and corridors.

The term *habitable room* is used in 18/19.2.5.1 in lieu of *patient sleeping room* to clarify that all occupied rooms in a health care facility must have access to a corridor leading to an exit.

Exhibit 18/19.8 illustrates the intent of 18/19.2.5.1 and Exception Nos. 1 and 4. The intervening room is permitted between room A and the corridor because room A has an exit door directly to the outside at ground level. The intervening room is permitted between the examination room B and the corridor because room B is not used for patient sleeping.

Exhibit 18/19.9 illustrates Exception No. 2 to 18/19.2.5.1. Exit access from a patient sleeping room to the corridor is permitted to pass through an intervening room in accordance with Exception No. 2 to 18/19.2.5.1. Locking hardware on the two doors in

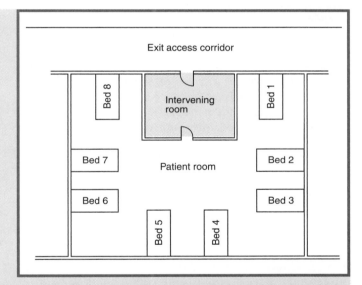

Exhibit 18/19.9 Intervening room between patient room and corridor.

the path to the corridor is permitted only under the special conditions addressed by the exceptions to 18/19.2.2.2.2. If the maximum eight-bed patient room (including the intervening room) exceeds 1000 ft^2 (93 m^2), a second exit access door, remote from the first, is required in accordance with 18/19.2.5.2.

Exception No. 3 to 18/19.2.5.1 permits an intervening room between a special nursing suite and the corridor. Exhibits 18/19.10(a) and (b) depict nursing suites; Exhibit 18/19.10(b) utilizes the intervening room permitted by Exception No. 3.

Various treatment areas are frequently arranged

Exhibit 18/19.8 Direct access to corridor from habitable rooms.

with an intervening workroom located between the exit access corridor and the treatment room. Exception No. 4 to 18/19.2.5.1, in combination with 18/19.2.5.8, allows egress through spaces that are closely related in function to the treatment room and, therefore, are under the immediate control of staff who, along with patients, would be forced to travel through such rooms. Where such an arrangement is used, locking hardware on doors is permitted only under the special conditions addressed by the exceptions to 18/19.2.2.2.2.

Maximum travel distance limitations to the exit access door of nonsleeping suites are specified in 18/19.2.5.8. For sleeping suites, see 18/19.2.6.2.4. Where applying Exception Nos. 2, 3, and 4 of 18/19.2.5.1, 18/19.2.5.5 prohibits intervening rooms from being hazardous areas.

Per 18/19.2.5.2, patient sleeping rooms or sleeping suites larger than 1000 ft² (93 m²) require two exit access doors. The doors are permitted to open onto a common corridor but are required to be remotely located from each other (see 7.5.1.3 and 7.5.1.4). Rooms or suites not used for patient sleeping purposes are permitted to be up to 2500 ft² (230 m²) in area and require only one exit access door, based on the premise that occupants are alert, ambulatory, or, in most instances, accompanied by staff who can assist in evacuating the space during fire or other emergency. For sleeping suites, refer to 18/19.2.5.1, 18/19.2.5.2, and 18/19.2.5.4 through 18/19.2.5.6 for requirements. For nonsleeping suites, refer to 18/19.2.5.1, 18/19.2.5.3 through 18/19.2.5.5, 18/19.2.5.7, and 18/19.2.5.8. Exhibits 18/19.10(a) and 18/19.10(b) illustrate the requirements for sleeping suites. Exhibits 18/19.11(a), 18/19.11(b), and 18/19.11(c) illustrate the requirements for nonsleeping suites.

In Exhibit 18/19.10(a), the arrangement within the sleeping suite is not required to comply with 18/19.2.3.3 relative to exit access minimum width, or with 18/19.3.6 relative to corridor walls and doors. However, the corridors outside the suite must comply with 18/19.3.6. The maximum area of the suite cannot exceed 5000 ft² (460 m²). If the area of the sleeping suite exceeds 1000 ft² (93 m²), two separate, remotely located exit access doors—as shown in the exhibit—are required. In new construction, their separation distance d must be at least $\frac{1}{3}D$ (see 7.5.1.4), based on the requirement that the new construction be sprinklered. In existing installations, the remoteness of the

exit accesses is to be judged by the qualitative provisions of 7.5.1.3.

In Exhibit 18/19.10(b), all the points made for Ex-

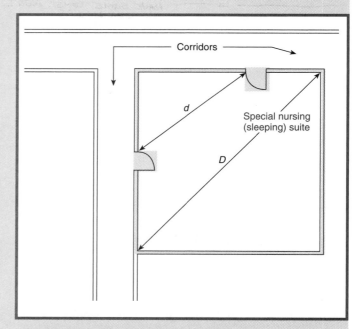

Exhibit 18/19.10(a) *Patient sleeping suite.*

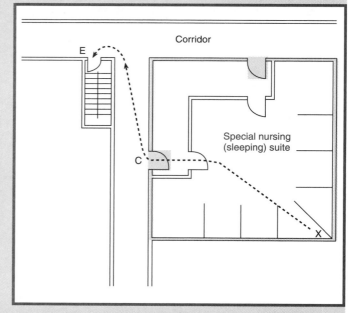

Exhibit 18/19.10(b) *Patient sleeping suite with intervening room to corridor.*

hibit 18/19.10(a) also apply. For example, interior corridors or circulation space within sleeping suites in new construction are not required to be 8 ft (2.4 m) wide. Doors to individual cubicles may be sliding doors or open doorways without a door leaf. Further, the suite is subdivided by cubicle walls using noncombustible or limited-combustible materials such as metal panels with glass or gypsum wallboard on steel studs. One intervening room is positioned between the special nursing (sleeping) suite and the corridor in accordance with Exception No. 3 to 18/19.2.5.1, which imposes a requirement for constant visual supervision by nursing personnel. If the individual cubicles were to be enclosed so as to constitute rooms, then the intervening room to the corridor would be prohibited so as not to violate the single intervening room criterion. However, if those individual cubicles were truly to be enclosed, it is doubtful that the requirement for constant visual supervision could be met.

Travel distance within the patient sleeping suite [that is, distance X to C in Exhibit 18/19.10(b)] is addressed by 18/19.2.6.2.4 and is permitted to be 100 ft (30 m) rather than the 50-ft (15-m) limit imposed on a typical health care sleeping room. However, the total travel distance [that is, distance X to E in Exhibit 18/19.10(b)], including the sum of the travel within the suite and that from the suite door to the exit (that is, corridor travel), is limited by 18/19.2.6.2.2. Thus, if the travel within the suite is between 50 ft and 100 ft (15 m and 30 m), the corridor travel allowance of 18/19.2.6.1 cannot be fully used. If it were fully used, the total travel distance specified in 18/19.2.6.2.2 would be exceeded. The concept permits extra travel within the suite by limiting the corridor travel so that the total travel distance is not excessive.

The concept employed in permitting the sleeping suite is one of ensuring sufficient openness to allow for staff awareness of conditions throughout the suite. Due to an editorial reformatting of these provisions in the 1991 edition of the *Code*, the current wording makes this concept less evident. It was never the intent to permit the patient sleeping suite to include separate television rooms, day rooms, activity alcoves, or similar nonsleeping areas within the suite. Rather, the sleeping suite provisions were intended to permit functions such as a critical care unit or a cardiac care unit with the minimum subdivision needed for privacy and effective functioning but with-

out imposing the requirements of 18/19.2.3.3 relative to exit access minimum width or 18/19.3.6 relative to corridor walls and doors.

In Exhibit 18/19.11(a), the arrangement within the treatment (nonsleeping) suite—such as a surgical suite—is not required to comply with 18/19.2.3.3 relative to exit access minimum width or with 18/19.3.6 relative to corridor walls and doors. However, the corridors outside the suite must comply with 18/19.3.6. The maximum area of the suite cannot exceed 10,000 ft² (930 m²). If the area of the sleeping suite exceeds 2500 ft² (230 m²), two separate, remotely located exit access doors—as shown in the exhibit—are required. In new construction, their separation distance d must be at least $\frac{1}{3}D$ (see 7.5.1.4), based on the requirement that the new construction be sprinklered. In existing installations, the remoteness of the exit accesses is to be judged by the qualitative provisions of 7.5.1.3.

In Exhibit 18/19.11(b), all the points made for Exhibit 18/19.10(a) also apply. For example, interior corridors or circulation space within treatment suites in new construction are not required to be 8 ft (2.4 m) wide. Doors to individual rooms can be sliding doors or open doorways without a door leaf. Further, the suite is subdivided by walls using noncombustible or limited-combustible materials such as metal panels with glass or gypsum wallboard on steel studs. Unlike the sleeping suite, the treatment suite does not require constant visual supervision by staff. For the

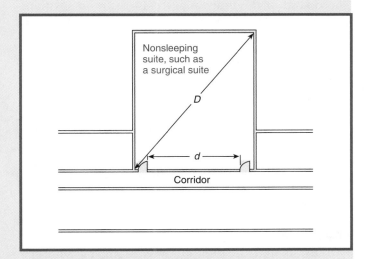

Exhibit 18/19.11(a) *Treatment (nonsleeping) suite.*

CHAPTER 18 • New	CHAPTER 19 • Existing

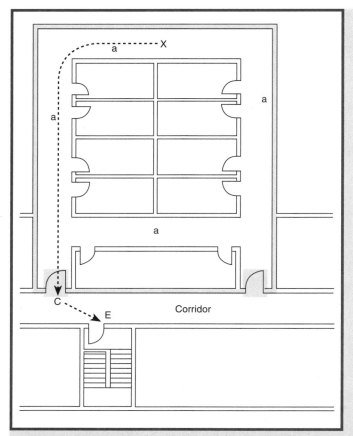

Exhibit 18/19.11(b) *Treatment (nonsleeping) suite with one intervening room to corridor.*

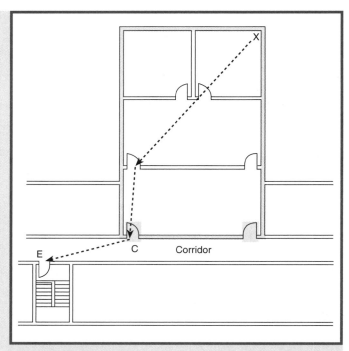

Exhibit 18/19.11(c) *Treatment (nonsleeping) suite with two intervening rooms to corridor.*

occupants of the individual treatment rooms within the suite, aisle *a* depicted in Exhibit 18/19.1(b) is the equivalent of an intervening room. Provided that there is only one intervening room between any treatment room and the corridor, the travel distance within the suite (that is, the distance from X to C) is permitted to be 100 ft (30 m) in accordance with 18/19.2.5.8. If the treatment suite were to exceed 10,000 ft² (930 m²) in area, it would cease to qualify for the suite provisions of 18/19.2.5. As such, this group of rooms and aisles would be required to comply with 18/19.2.3.3 relative to exit access minimum width and 18/19.3.6 relative to corridor walls and doors. This means that the treatment room walls and doors that face onto aisles *a* would become corridor walls. Similarly, aisles a would become corridors.

In Exhibit 18/19.11(c), the treatment suite is shown with two intervening rooms between the innermost room and the corridor. A maximum of two

intervening rooms is permitted by 18/19.2.5.8 but—unlike the treatment suite with a single intervening room and 100 ft (30 m) of permitted travel within the suite—the travel within the suite (that is, distance X to C) is limited to 50 ft (15 m). The decrease in allowable travel within the suite is in consideration that with two intervening rooms an occupant's awareness of fire within the suite decreases. Allowing for a delay in becoming aware of a fire within the suite, it is important that the suite occupants not have far to travel to reach the safety afforded by the corridor.

Paragraph 18/19.2.5.9 specifically prohibits an exit access arrangement that takes an occupant into a corridor and then requires passage through an occupiable space, such as another patient sleeping or treatment room, to gain access to a required exit. Once an occupant reaches the exit access corridor, that corridor is thought to be a safer portion of the exit access than an occupiable room because of the features required by 18/19.3.6. The occupant must be able to reach an exit without having to leave the safety provided by the corridor.

Exhibit 18/19.12 illustrates the maximum 30-ft (9.1-m) dead-end corridor limitation imposed on new construction in health care occupancies.

CHAPTER 18 • New **CHAPTER 19 • Existing**

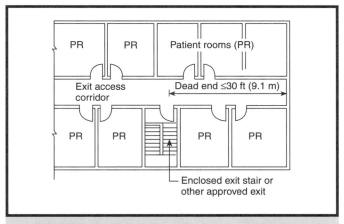

Exhibit 18/19.12 *Dead-end corridor in a new health care occupancy.*

18.2.6 Travel Distance to Exits.

18.2.6.1 Travel distance shall be measured in accordance with Section 7.6.

18.2.6.2 Travel distance shall comply with 18.2.6.2.1 through 18.2.6.2.4.

18.2.6.2.1 The travel distance between any room door required as an exit access and an exit shall not exceed 150 ft (45 m).

18.2.6.2.2 The travel distance between any point in a room and an exit shall not exceed 200 ft (60 m).

18.2.6.2.3 The travel distance between any point in a health care sleeping room and an exit access door in that room shall not exceed 50 ft (15 m).

18.2.6.2.4 The travel distance between any point in a suite of sleeping rooms as permitted by 18.2.5 and an exit access door of that suite shall not exceed 100 ft (30 m) and shall meet the requirements of 18.2.6.2.2.

19.2.6 Travel Distance to Exits.

19.2.6.1 Travel distance shall be measured in accordance with Section 7.6.

19.2.6.2 Travel Distance. Travel distance shall comply with 19.2.6.2.1 through 19.2.6.2.4.

19.2.6.2.1 The travel distance between any room door required as an exit access and an exit shall not exceed 100 ft (30 m).

Exception: The maximum travel distance shall be permitted to be increased by 50 ft (15 m) in buildings protected throughout by an approved, supervised automatic sprinkler system.

19.2.6.2.2 The travel distance between any point in a room and an exit shall not exceed 150 ft (45 m).

Exception: The maximum travel distance shall be permitted to be increased by 50 ft (15 m) in buildings protected throughout by an approved, supervised automatic sprinkler system.

19.2.6.2.3 The travel distance between any point in a health care sleeping room and an exit access door in that room shall not exceed 50 ft (15 m).

19.2.6.2.4 The travel distance between any point in a suite of sleeping rooms as permitted by 19.2.5 and an exit access door of that suite shall not exceed 100 ft (30 m) and shall meet the requirements of 19.2.6.2.2.

The travel distance limitations set by 18/19.2.6.2 can be illustrated using Exhibit 18/19.13. Travel distance is measured only to the nearest exit (point E on the exhibit), not to the second exit required by 18/19.2.4.1. The smoke barrier depicted is not an exit although travel through the cross-corridor doors in the smoke barrier will eventually lead to the second required exit.

In evaluating travel distance for sleeping rooms, the following three tests are required.

(a) *Is the travel distance within the sleeping room excessive?* Regardless of the presence of sprinklers, this distance (X to C in Exhibit 18/19.13) is limited to 50 ft (15 m) by 18/19.2.6.2.3. If the fire were to start in a patient sleeping room, the ability to leave the room quickly would be important. Limiting the travel to 50 ft (15 m) does limit the room size. It should be possible to learn quickly of the fire within such a room and move, or be moved, to the corridor before the fire grows to such size that it would block patient and staff access to the door to the corridor. The 50-ft (15-m) travel distance restriction within a room applies only to sleeping rooms.

(b) *Is the travel distance from the room door to the nearest exit excessive?* This portion of the overall travel distance (C to E in Exhibit 18/19.13) will typically involve exit access corridor travel. For new construction and for sprinklered existing buildings such travel is limited to 150 ft (45 m) by 18/19.2.6.2.1. For non-sprinklered existing buildings, the distance is limited to 100 ft (30 m) by 19.2.6.2.1.

(c) *Is the overall travel distance excessive?* For new construction and for sprinklered existing buildings such travel is limited to 200 ft (60 m) by 18/19.2.6.2.2. For nonsprinklered existing buildings, the distance is limited to 150 ft (45 m) by 19.2.6.2.2. For a sleeping room, but not a sleeping suite, this consideration is relatively unimportant because compliance with paragraphs (a) and (b) will automatically allow compliance with the overall travel distance limitation. However, the limitation on overall travel distance is important for sleeping suites that avail themselves of more than 50 ft (15 m) of travel within the suite. This issue is explained further in the following paragraph.

For travel distance limitations where suites of rooms are involved, see Exhibits 18/19.10(b), 18/19.11(b), and 18/19.11(c). For new construction and sprinklered existing buildings, where sleeping and nonsleeping suites avail themselves of more than 50 ft (15 m) of the permitted 100 ft (30 m) of travel within the suite, the corridor portion of travel distance might have to be limited to less than the 150 ft (45 m) permitted by 18/19.2.6.2.1 so that the total travel distance does not exceed the 200-ft (60-m) limitation established by 18/19.2.6.2.2. For nonsprinklered existing buildings, where sleeping and nonsleeping suites avail themselves of more than 50 ft (15 m) of the permitted 100 ft (30 m) of travel within the suite, the corridor portion of travel distance might have to be limited to less than the 100 ft (30 m) permitted by 19.2.6.2.1 so that the total travel distance does not exceed the 150-ft (45-m) limitation established by 19.2.6.2.2.

In evaluating travel distance for nonsleeping rooms, only two tests are required.

(a) *Is the travel distance from the room door to the nearest exit excessive?* This portion of the overall travel distance (C to E in Exhibit 18/19.13) will typically involve exit access corridor travel. For new construction and for sprinklered existing buildings such travel is limited to 150 ft (45 m) by 18/19.2.6.2.1. For non-sprinklered existing buildings it is limited to 100 ft (30 m) by 19.2.6.2.1.

(b) *Is the overall travel distance excessive?* For new construction and for sprinklered existing buildings such travel is limited to 200 ft (60 m) by 18/19.2.6.2.2. For nonsprinklered existing buildings, it is limited to 150 ft (45 m) by 19.2.6.2.2. Thus, if the corridor travel addressed in paragraph (a) is not utilized to its maximum, the travel within the nonsleeping room itself might be more than the 50-ft (15-m) limit imposed on sleeping rooms.

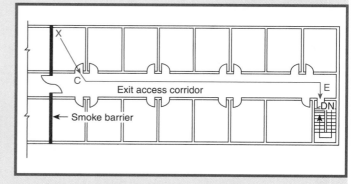

Exhibit 18/19.13 *Travel distance limitations.*

18.2.7 Discharge from Exits.

Discharge from exits shall be arranged in accordance with Section 7.7.

18.2.8 Illumination of Means of Egress.

Means of egress shall be illuminated in accordance with Section 7.8.

18.2.9 Emergency Lighting.

18.2.9.1 Emergency lighting shall be provided in accordance with Section 7.9.

18.2.9.2 Buildings equipped with or in which patients require the use of life-support systems *(see 18.5.1.3)* shall have emergency lighting equipment supplied by the life safety branch of the electrical system as described in NFPA 99, *Standard for Health Care Facilities.*

18.2.10 Marking of Means of Egress.

18.2.10.1 Means of egress shall have signs in accordance with Section 7.10.

18.2.10.2 Buildings equipped with or in which patients require the use of life-support systems *(see 18.5.1.3)* shall have illumination of the required exit and directional signs supplied by the life safety branch of the electrical system as described in NFPA 99, *Standard for Health Care Facilities.*

Exception: Self-luminous exit signs as permitted by 7.10.4.

19.2.7 Discharge from Exits.

Discharge from exits shall be arranged in accordance with Section 7.7.

19.2.8 Illumination of Means of Egress.

Means of egress shall be illuminated in accordance with Section 7.8.

19.2.9 Emergency Lighting.

19.2.9.1 Emergency lighting shall be provided in accordance with Section 7.9.

19.2.10 Marking of Means of Egress.

19.2.10.1 Means of egress shall have signs in accordance with Section 7.10.

Exception: Where the path of egress travel is obvious, signs shall not be required in one-story buildings with an occupant load of fewer than 30 persons.

Each new health care facility equipped with or requiring the use of life-support systems is required to have the marking of the means of egress and emergency lighting supplied by the life safety branch of the electrical systems described in Chapter 3 of NFPA 99, *Standard for Health Care Facilities.*[5]

A facility would not be required to have an emergency generator if the building is a freestanding unit in which, as a normal practice, all the following apply:

(1) Management maintains admitting and discharge policies that preclude the provision of care for any patient or resident who might need to be sustained by electrical life-support equipment, such as respirators or suction apparatus.
(2) No surgical treatment requiring general anesthesia is offered.
(3) Battery-operated systems or equipment are provided to maintain power to exit lights and illumination of egress corridors, stairways, medical preparation areas, and the like, for a minimum of $1^{1}/_{2}$ hours.

Additionally, battery power would be required to be supplied to all alarm systems. For additional information, refer to NFPA 99, *Standard for Health Care Facilities.*

NFPA 99 requires that emergency power supplies be arranged and protected to minimize the possibility of a single incident affecting both normal and emergency power supplies simultaneously. Circuits are to be run separately. Emergency and normal circuits are "joined" at the transfer switch, so damage to the transfer switch would interrupt normal and emergency power supplies simultaneously. The transfer switch is therefore a critical item and should be separated from any potential source of fire, including the emergency generator and attendant fuel supply.

NFPA 99, *Standard for Health Care Facilities,* specifies that emergency generators must be inspected at least weekly and exercised under load for a minimum of 30 minutes each month. See also 9.1.3.

CHAPTER 18 • New	CHAPTER 19 • Existing

18.2.11 Special Means of Egress Features.

(Reserved.)

19.2.11 Special Means of Egress Features.

(Reserved.)

Section 18.3 Protection

18.3.1 Protection of Vertical Openings.

18.3.1.1 Any vertical opening shall be enclosed or protected in accordance with 8.2.5.

Exception No. 1:   Unprotected vertical openings in accordance with 8.2.5.8 shall be permitted.

Exception No. 2:   Exception No. 1 to 8.2.5.6(1) shall not apply to patient sleeping and treatment rooms.

Exception No. 3:   Multilevel patient sleeping areas in psychiatric facilities shall be permitted without enclosure protection between levels, provided that all the following conditions are met:

(a) The entire normally occupied area, including all communicating floor levels, is sufficiently open and unobstructed so that a fire or other dangerous condition in any part shall be obvious to the occupants or supervisory personnel in the area.

(b) Egress capacity is sufficient to provide simultaneously for all the occupants of all communicating levels and areas, with all communicating levels in the same fire area being considered as a single floor area for purposes of determination of required egress capacity.

(c) The height between the highest and lowest finished floor levels shall not exceed 13 ft (4 m); the number of levels shall not be restricted.

Exception No. 4:   Unprotected openings in accordance with 8.2.5.5 shall not be permitted.

18.3.1.2 A door in a stair enclosure shall be self-closing and shall normally be kept in the closed position.

Exception: Doors in stair enclosures held open under the conditions specified by 18.2.2.2.6 and 18.2.2.2.7.

Section 19.3 Protection

19.3.1 Protection of Vertical Openings.

19.3.1.1 Any vertical opening shall be enclosed or protected in accordance with 8.2.5. Where enclosure is provided, the construction shall have not less than a 1-hour fire resistance rating.

Exception No. 1:   Unprotected vertical openings in accordance with 8.2.5.8 shall be permitted.

Exception No. 2:   Exception No. 1 to 8.2.5.6(1) shall not apply to patient sleeping and treatment rooms.

Exception No. 3:   Multilevel patient sleeping areas in psychiatric facilities shall be permitted without enclosure protection between levels, provided that all the following conditions are met:

(a) The entire normally occupied area, including all communicating floor levels, is sufficiently open and unobstructed so that a fire or other dangerous condition in any part is obvious to the occupants or supervisory personnel in the area.

(b) Egress capacity is sufficient to provide simultaneously for all the occupants of all communicating levels and areas, with all communicating levels in the same fire area being considered as a single floor area for purposes of determination of required egress capacity.

(c) The height between the highest and lowest finished floor levels shall not exceed 13 ft (4 m); the number of levels shall not be restricted.

Exception No. 4:   Unprotected openings in accordance with 8.2.5.5 shall not be permitted.

Exception No. 5:   Where a full enclosure of a stairway that is not a required exit is impracticable, the required enclosure shall be permitted to be limited to that necessary to prevent a fire originating in any story from spreading to any other story.

19.3.1.2 A door in a stair enclosure shall be self-closing and shall normally be kept in the closed position.

Exception: Doors in stair enclosures held open under the conditions specified by 19.2.2.2.6 and 19.2.2.2.7.

Paragraph 18/19.3.1.1 specifies protection levels required to maintain floor-to-floor separation in health care facilities. For new construction, the reference is to 8.2.5, which requires 2-hour enclosures around vertical openings connecting more than three stories in buildings. One-hour enclosure of vertical openings is required in all other new health care occupancies. For existing health care occupancies, 1-hour enclosure of vertical openings is required. Note that this requirement is more than the $^1/_2$-hour required by 8.2.5.4 for existing enclosures of vertical openings. Health care occupancies employ a defend-in-place strategy that recognizes the difficulty in evacuating patients to the outside. Thus, the $^1/_2$-hour typically permitted for existing enclosures in existing buildings is not applicable to existing health care occupancies.

Although stairs, if not properly enclosed, create vertical openings, they are often enclosed to qualify as an exit. For existing exit stair enclosures, both the requirements of 7.1.3.2 applicable to exit enclosure and the requirements of 19.3.1.1 applicable to vertical opening protection must be met. For exit stair enclosures connecting more than three stories, the enclosure requirements of 7.1.3.2 are stricter than those of 19.3.1.1. Therefore, a four-story exit stair enclosure would require 2-hour fire resistance–rated enclosure instead of the 1-hour enclosure required for existing vertical openings in health care occupancies.

If a stairway is within the exit access or not used for egress, and full enclosure is not possible, the enclosure is permitted to be limited to that necessary to prevent fire or smoke originating in any one story from spreading to another story. For example, in a two-story building, the stair might be enclosed at the first floor level and left open at the second floor level.

Exception No. 1 to 18/19.3.1.1 references the convenience opening described in 8.2.5.8 and illustrated in Exhibit 18/19.14. This exception applies to any non-concealed vertical opening, not only to a convenience stair. This exception would allow a light well to connect two stories or allow a stair to connect two levels

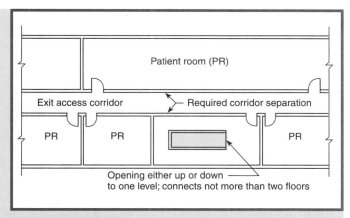

Exhibit 18/19.14 *Permitted convenience opening.*

of a medical library, a file storage area, or an administrative office, for example. The exception would not allow omission of firestopping around pipe penetrations of a floor slab or omission of protection for duct penetrations.

Exception No. 2 to 18/19.3.1.1 modifies the atrium provisions of 8.2.5.6 for applicability to health care occupancies. Patient sleeping and treatment rooms must be separated from the atrium by partitions complying with 8.2.5.6(1) or Exception No. 2 to 8.2.5.6(1)—either 1-hour-rated walls or glass protected by closely spaced sprinklers.

Exception No. 3 to 18/19.3.1.1 recognizes the vertical openings inherent in multilevel patient sleeping areas similar to those described for detention and correctional occupancies in 22.4.4.6 and 23.3.1.2.

Paragraph 18/19.3.1.2 requires fire doors protecting openings in stairway enclosures to be self-closing and normally maintained in a closed position. However, the exception to 18/19.3.1.2 permits stairway doors meeting specified conditions to be held open by an automatic-closing device. If stair enclosure doors are normally maintained in a closed position, they should be provided with a sign that states in large letters, "Fire Exit—Keep Door Closed."

CHAPTER 18 • New	CHAPTER 19 • Existing

18.3.2 Protection from Hazards.

18.3.2.1* Hazardous Areas. Any hazardous area shall be protected in accordance with Section 8.4. The areas described in Table 18.3.2.1 shall be protected as indicated.

Table 18.3.2.1 Hazardous Area Protection

Hazardous Area Description	Separation/Protection
Boiler and fuel-fired heater rooms	1 hour
Central/bulk laundries larger than 100 ft² (9.3 m²)	1 hour
Laboratories employing flammable or combustible materials in quantities less than those that would be considered a severe hazard	See 18.3.6.3.4
Laboratories that use hazardous materials that would be classified as a severe hazard in accordance with NFPA 99, *Standard for Health Care Facilities*	1 hour
Paint shops employing hazardous substances and materials in quantities less than those that would be classified as a severe hazard	1 hour
Physical plant maintenance shops	1 hour
Soiled linen rooms	1 hour
Storage rooms larger than 50 ft² (4.6 m²) but not exceeding 100 ft² (9.3 m²) storing combustible material	See 18.3.6.3.4
Storage rooms larger than 100 ft² (9.3 m²) storing combustible material	1 hour
Trash collection rooms	1 hour

A.18.3.2.1 Provisions for the enclosure of rooms used for charging linen chutes and waste chutes or for rooms into which these chutes empty are provided in Chapter 9.

18.3.2.2* Laboratories. Laboratories employing quantities of flammable, combustible, or hazardous materials that are considered as a severe hazard shall be protected in accordance with NFPA 99, *Standard for Health Care Facilities.*

19.3.2 Protection from Hazards.

19.3.2.1 Hazardous Areas. Any hazardous areas shall be safeguarded by a fire barrier having a 1-hour fire resistance rating or shall be provided with an automatic extinguishing system in accordance with 8.4.1. The automatic extinguishing shall be permitted to be in accordance with 19.3.5.4. Where the sprinkler option is used, the areas shall be separated from other spaces by smoke-resisting partitions and doors. The doors shall be self-closing or automatic-closing. Hazardous areas shall include, but shall not be restricted to, the following:

(1) Boiler and fuel-fired heater rooms
(2) Central/bulk laundries larger than 100 ft² (9.3 m²)
(3) Paint shops
(4) Repair shops
(5) Soiled linen rooms
(6) Trash collection rooms
(7) Rooms or spaces larger than 50 ft² (4.6 m²), including repair shops, used for storage of combustible supplies and equipment in quantities deemed hazardous by the authority having jurisdiction
(8) Laboratories employing flammable or combustible materials in quantities less than those that would be considered a severe hazard.

Exception: Doors in rated enclosures shall be permitted to have nonrated, factory- or field-applied protective plates extending not more than 48 in. (122 cm) above the bottom of the door.

19.3.2.2* Laboratories. Laboratories employing quantities of flammable, combustible, or hazardous materials that are considered as a severe hazard shall be protected in accordance with NFPA 99, *Standard for Health Care Facilities.*

A.18.3.2.2 The hazard level of a laboratory is considered severe if quantities of flammable, combustible, or hazardous materials are present that are capable of sustaining a fire of sufficient magnitude to breach a 1-hour fire separation. See the NFPA *Fire Protection Handbook* for guidance.

18.3.2.3 Anesthetizing Locations. Anesthetizing locations shall be protected in accordance with NFPA 99, *Standard for Health Care Facilities.*

18.3.2.4 Medical Gas. Medical gas storage and administration areas shall be protected in accordance with NFPA 99, *Standard for Health Care Facilities.*

18.3.2.5 Gift Shops. Gift shops shall be protected as hazardous areas where used for the storage or display of combustibles in quantities considered hazardous. Gift shops not considered hazardous and having separately protected storage shall be permitted to be as follows:

(1) Open to a lobby or corridor if the gift shop does not exceed 500 ft² (46.5 m²)
(2) Separated from a lobby or corridor with non-fire-rated walls

18.3.2.6 Cooking Facilities. Cooking facilities shall be protected in accordance with 9.2.3.

Exception:* Where domestic cooking equipment is used for food-warming or limited cooking, protection or segregation of food preparation facilities shall not be required.

A.18.3.2.6 Exception This exception is intended to permit small appliances used for reheating, such as microwave ovens, hot plates, toasters, and nourishment centers to be exempt from the requirements for commercial cooking equipment.

18.3.2.7 Buildings housing health care occupancies as indicated in 18.1.1.1.2 that have rooftop heliports shall be protected in accordance with NFPA 418, *Standard for Heliports.*

A.19.3.2.2 The hazard level of a laboratory is considered severe if quantities of flammable, combustible, or hazardous materials are present that are capable of sustaining a fire of sufficient magnitude to breach a 1-hour fire separation. See NFPA *Fire Protection Handbook* for guidance.

19.3.2.3 Anesthetizing Locations. Anesthetizing locations shall be protected in accordance with NFPA 99, *Standard for Health Care Facilities.*

19.3.2.4 Medical Gas. Medical gas storage and administration areas shall be protected in accordance with NFPA 99, *Standard for Health Care Facilities.*

19.3.2.5 Gift Shops. Gift shops shall be protected as hazardous areas where used for the storage or display of combustibles in quantities considered hazardous. Gift shops not considered hazardous and having separately protected storage shall be permitted to be as follows:

(1) Open to a lobby or corridor if the gift shop does not exceed 500 ft² (46.5 m²) and is protected throughout by an approved automatic sprinkler system
(2) Separated from a lobby or corridor by non-fire-rated walls if the gift shop is protected throughout by an approved automatic sprinkler system

19.3.2.6 Cooking Facilities. Cooking facilities shall be protected in accordance with 9.2.3.

Exception:* Where domestic cooking equipment is used for food-warming or limited cooking, protection or segregation of food preparation facilities shall not be required.

A.19.3.2.6 Exception This exception is intended to permit small appliances used for reheating, such as microwave ovens, hot plates, toasters, and nourishment centers, to be exempt from the requirements for commercial cooking equipment.

Hazardous areas are spaces containing materials that, due to their basic nature (as in the case of flammable liquids) or because of the quantity of combustible materials involved, represent a significantly higher hazard than would otherwise be typical in the general areas of health care facilities.

A list of typically hazardous areas is included in 18/19.3.2.1. The list is meant to be representative, not inclusive. The general reference in 18/19.3.2.1 to Section 8.4 provides the authority having jurisdiction with the opportunity to regulate any space judged to represent a significantly higher hazard than most spaces.

Chapter 18 requires automatic sprinkler protection throughout all new health care facilities. Therefore, all hazardous spaces in new construction must be sprinklered. Where a hazardous area is judged to represent a severe exposure, such as in the case of boiler rooms, laundries, paint shops, and soiled linen rooms, 1-hour fire resistance–rated separation is also necessary. Hazardous areas that are not judged to be severe also require a separation, but the separation is permitted to use a non-fire-rated enclosure capable of retarding the transfer of smoke. Doors protecting openings in such partitions must be tight-fitting and equipped with a closing device (see 18.3.6.3.4 and Section 8.4). Door openings in 1-hour fire resistance–rated barriers must be protected with $3/4$-hour fire protection–rated door assemblies.

In existing health care occupancies, hazardous areas must be separated from other areas by barriers having a 1-hour fire resistance rating, complete with approved fire doors protecting door openings; otherwise, automatic sprinkler protection must be installed. If automatic sprinkler protection is provided, the hazardous area must still be separated from the rest of the building by nonrated barriers designed to resist the passage of smoke.

Provisions for the enclosure of rooms used for charging linen and waste chutes or for the rooms into which these chutes empty are provided in Chapter 9. In addition to the fire-resistant construction requirements for these rooms, automatic sprinkler protection is considered essential.

If flammable liquids are handled or stored, NFPA 30, *Flammable and Combustible Liquids Code*,[6] must be consulted to establish the minimum criteria necessary to mitigate this hazard. Provisions for the use and storage of flammable gases and oxygen are covered in NFPA 99, *Standard for Health Care Facilities*.

The exception to 19.3.2.1 recognizes the benefit of protective plates for the protection of doors that are frequently assaulted with carts and other wheeled vehicles. Without the exception, the minimum 45-minute fire protection–rated doors to hazardous area rooms would be subject to the requirements of 8.2.3.2.1(a), which—via a mandatory reference—would not permit the field application of protective plates to fire-rated doors. The field application of protective plates needs to avoid reducing the fire performance of the door—such as might result if the door is drilled through its entire thickness for the installation of through-bolts.

Laboratories are addressed in 18/19.3.2.2. Laboratories that contain ordinary combustibles and flammable liquids in sufficient quantity to threaten a 1-hour fire separation [for example, wood-equivalent fuel loads in the range of 5 to 10 lb/ft^2 (25 to 50 kg/m^2)] are considered a severe hazard. Laboratories posing a severe hazard must be protected in accordance with Chapter 10, Laboratories, of NFPA 99, *Standard for Health Care Facilities*. Protection would include 1-hour fire resistance–rated separation and automatic sprinkler protection.

If fuel loads of lesser amounts are involved and quantities of flammable liquids are limited, laboratories would simply be considered hazardous areas and would be adequately protected by the automatic sprinklers required in all new health care occupancies. In existing health care occupancies, either 1-hour separation or automatic sprinkler protection would be required.

Gift shops are addressed in 18/19.3.2.5. Many gift shops, particularly those containing combustible storage and having sizable retail areas, do pose a hazard well beyond what is considered normal to patient-occupied spaces and thus merit special protection. However, it is recognized that many small retail areas [less than 500 ft^2 (46.5 m^2), for example] constitute a relatively minor hazard that is adequately mitigated by automatic sprinkler protection. This paragraph provides the authority having jurisdiction with guidance in judging the degree of hazard and offers the facility some flexibility in the design and operation of gift shops. To use either of the two options offered, the gift shop must be judged as nonhazardous, must be sprinklered, and must have separately protected storage areas.

Commercial cooking equipment is addressed in 18/19.3.2.6. It must be installed and protected in accordance with NFPA 96, *Standard for Ventilation Control and Fire Protection of Commercial Cooking Operations*.[7]

A regularly serviced, fixed, automatic fire-extinguishing system would be required for the protection of cooking surfaces and exhaust and duct systems where cooking operations involve the potential for grease-laden vapors. The exception notes that 18/19.3.2.6 would not apply to a room used as a staff lounge equipped with a domestic-type range or microwave oven. Such a room would be considered similar to a treatment room and would require normal separation from the corridor, as indicated in 18/19.3.6.

18.3.3 Interior Finish.

18.3.3.1 Interior finish shall be in accordance with Section 10.2.

18.3.3.2 Interior Wall and Ceiling Finish. Interior wall and ceiling finish materials complying with 10.2.3 shall be permitted throughout if Class A or Class B. The provisions of 10.2.8.1 shall not apply.

Exception No. 1: Walls and ceilings shall be permitted to have Class A, Class B, or Class C interior finish in individual rooms having a capacity not exceeding four persons.

Exception No. 2: Corridor wall finish not exceeding 4 ft (1.2 m) in height that is restricted to the lower half of the wall shall be permitted to be Class A, Class B, or Class C.

19.3.3 Interior Finish.

19.3.3.1 Interior finish shall be in accordance with Section 10.2.

19.3.3.2 Interior Wall and Ceiling Finish. Interior wall and ceiling finish materials complying with 10.2.3 shall be permitted as follows:

(1) Existing materials—Class A or Class B

Exception: In rooms protected by an approved, supervised automatic sprinkler system, existing Class C interior finish shall be permitted to be continued to be used on walls and ceilings within rooms separated from the exit access corridors in accordance with 19.3.6.

(2) Newly installed materials—Class A

Exception No. 1: Newly installed walls and ceilings shall be permitted to have Class A or Class B interior finish in individual rooms having a capacity not exceeding four persons.

Exception No. 2: Newly installed corridor wall finish not exceeding 4 ft (1.2 m) in height that is restricted to the lower half of the wall shall be permitted to be Class A or Class B.

18.3.3.3 Interior Floor Finish. (No requirements.)

19.3.3.3 Interior Floor Finish. Newly installed interior floor finish complying with 10.2.7 shall be permitted in corridors and exits if Class I. No restrictions shall apply to existing interior floor finish.

Exception: In smoke compartments protected throughout by an approved, supervised automatic sprinkler system in accordance with 19.3.5.2, no interior floor finish requirements shall apply.

New interior finishes on walls and ceilings are limited to Class A or Class B materials. The wall and ceiling

interior finish limitations of 18.3.3.2 were written in recognition of the fact that Chapter 18 requires new health care occupancies to be sprinklered. The provisions of 10.2.8.1—which normally permit a reduction in the interior finish requirement by one class if automatic sprinkler protection is provided—are specifically made not applicable to prevent a "double credit" for automatic sprinklers. Existing interior finish materials are permitted to be Class A or Class B without requiring sprinkler protection.

Exception No. 1 to 18.3.3.2 permits Class C interior wall and ceiling finish materials in rooms with a capacity of four or fewer persons. Exception No. 2 to 18.3.3.2 allows wall finish in corridors to be of Class C materials where located up to 4 ft (1.2 m) or less in height above the floor. This provision recognizes fire research that has shown the finish on the lower half of the wall to be far less significant in its influence on early fire growth than the finish on the upper half.[8] In the case of textile materials on walls or ceilings, 10.2.4.1 would take precedence and require automatic sprinkler protection in conjunction with Class A materials, or such wall and ceiling materials must be proven safe by room/corner fire testing.

Existing interior finishes on walls and ceilings are limited solely on the basis of flame spread. The exception to 10.2.3.2 exempts existing interior finishes from the limitations based on smoke development.

Paragraph 10.2.6.2 makes provision for application of approved, fire-retardant coatings to existing interior finish materials for the purpose of reducing the flame spread characteristics to an acceptable level. The commentary on 10.2.6.2 offers additional guidance.

If rooms are separated from corridors by barriers with a minimum of ½-hour fire resistance rating in accordance with 19.3.6.2.1 and the room is protected by an automatic sprinkler system, existing Class C interior finish materials can continue to be used on walls and ceilings within these rooms. If the entire smoke compartment, rather than just the room, were sprinklered, then the corridor wall requirement would drop to that of a barrier to retard the transfer of smoke in order to permit the existing Class C interior finish to be continued in use.

Alterations are required to be made by 18/19.1.1.4.5, to the extent of being practical, in accordance with the requirements for new construction found in Chapter 18. Chapter 18 now requires automatic sprinkler protection for all new facilities and, therefore, incorporates safeguards appropriate for

fully sprinklered buildings. Because new interior finish is permitted to be added to an existing nonsprinklered building, 19.3.3.2(2) fills a gap by providing reasonable regulation for newly installed wall and ceiling finish materials in existing, nonsprinklered health care occupancies.

New interior finish on walls or ceilings of existing buildings is limited to Class A materials, except in small rooms having four or fewer persons, where Class B materials are allowed. If automatic sprinkler protection is provided, Class B materials can be used where Class A materials are normally required, and similarly, Class C materials can be used where Class B materials would otherwise be required. The reason for these allowances is that the use of 10.2.8.1 is not prohibited for existing health care occupancies.

Exception No. 2 to 19.3.3.2(2) allows new wall finish in nonsprinklered corridors of existing buildings to be of Class B materials where located on the lower half of the wall up to 4 ft (1.2 m). If the corridor area of the existing building is sprinklered, then 10.2.8.1—whose use is not prohibited for existing health care occupancies—permits a reduction in interior finish requirement to Class C.

Textile wall or ceiling materials are regulated by 10.2.4.1, which requires automatic sprinkler protection in conjunction with Class A materials, or such wall and ceiling materials must be proven safe by room/corner fire testing. Use of previously approved, existing Class A materials is permitted to continue to be used without sprinkler protection.

It has been shown that floor coverings will not spread a fire until the fire approaches flashover (see commentary on 10.2.7.1). Automatic sprinklers will activate well in advance of any significant involvement of a floor covering. On the basis of requiring all new health care occupancies to be sprinklered, Chapter 18 does not limit interior floor finish.

Paragraph 19.3.3.3—like 19.3.3.2(2)—is needed, because Chapter 18 does not require all existing health care occupancies to be sprinklered. Any new interior floor finish to be installed in corridors and exits within existing, nonsprinklered health care facilities is required to meet the criteria for Class I materials as indicated in 10.2.7.2. However, existing floor finish materials that have been previously evaluated and judged acceptable are permitted to continue to be used.

18.3.4 Detection, Alarm, and Communications Systems.

18.3.4.1 General. Health care occupancies shall be provided with a fire alarm system in accordance with Section 9.6.

18.3.4.2* Initiation. Initiation of the required fire alarm systems shall be by manual means in accordance with 9.6.2 and by means of any required sprinkler system waterflow alarms, detection devices, or detection systems.

Exception: Manual fire alarm boxes in patient sleeping areas shall not be required at exits if located at all nurses' control stations or other continuously attended staff location, provided that such manual fire alarm boxes are visible and continuously accessible and that travel distances required by 9.6.2.4 are not exceeded.

A.18.3.4.2 It is not the intent of this *Code* to require single-station smoke detectors that might be required by local codes to be connected to or to initiate the building fire alarm system.

18.3.4.3 Notification.

18.3.4.3.1 Occupant Notification. Occupant notification shall be accomplished automatically in accordance with 9.6.3. Exception No. 3 to 9.6.3.2 shall be prohibited.

Exception:* In lieu of audible alarm signals, visible alarm-indicating appliances shall be permitted to be used in critical care areas.

A.18.3.4.3.1 Exception It is the intent of this exception to permit a visible fire alarm signal instead of an audible signal to reduce interference between the fire alarm and medical equipment monitoring alarms.

18.3.4.3.2 Emergency Forces Notification. Fire department notification shall be accomplished in accordance with 9.6.4.

19.3.4 Detection, Alarm, and Communications Systems.

19.3.4.1 General. Health care occupancies shall be provided with a fire alarm system in accordance with Section 9.6.

19.3.4.2* Initiation. Initiation of the required fire alarm systems shall be by manual means in accordance with 9.6.2 and by means of any required sprinkler system waterflow alarms, detection devices, or detection systems.

Exception No. 1: Manual fire alarm boxes in patient sleeping areas shall not be required at exits if located at all nurses' control stations or other continuously attended staff location, provided that such manual fire alarm boxes are visible and continuously accessible and that travel distances required by 9.6.2.4 are not exceeded.

Exception No. 2: Fixed extinguishing systems protecting commercial cooking equipment in kitchens that are protected by a complete automatic sprinkler system shall not be required to initiate the fire alarm system.

Exception No. 3: Detectors required by the exceptions to 19.7.5.2 and 19.7.5.3.

A.19.3.4.2 It is not the intent of this *Code* to require single-station smoke detectors, which might be required by local codes, to be connected to or to initiate the building fire alarm system.

19.3.4.3 Notification.

19.3.4.3.1 Occupant Notification. Occupant notification shall be accomplished automatically in accordance with 9.6.3.

Exception No. 1:* In lieu of audible alarm signals, visible alarm-indicating appliances shall be permitted to be used in critical care areas.

A.19.3.4.3.1 Exception No. 1 It is the intent of this exception to permit a visible fire alarm signal instead of an audible signal to reduce interference between the fire alarm and medical equipment monitoring alarms.

Exception No. 2: Where visual devices have been installed in patient sleeping areas in place of the audible alarm, they shall be permitted where accepted by the authority having jurisdiction.

19.3.4.3.2 Emergency Forces Notification. Fire department notification shall be accomplished in accordance with 9.6.4.

CHAPTER 18 • New	CHAPTER 19 • Existing

Exception: Smoke detection devices or smoke detection systems equipped with reconfirmation features shall not be required to automatically notify the fire department unless the alarm condition is reconfirmed after a period not exceeding 120 seconds.

18.3.4.3.3 Alarm annunciation shall be provided in accordance with 9.6.7.

Exception: The alarm zone shall be permitted to coincide with the permitted area for smoke compartments.

18.3.4.4 Emergency Control. Operation of any activating device in the required fire alarm system shall be arranged to accomplish automatically any control functions to be performed by that device. *(See 9.6.5.)*

18.3.4.5 Detection.

18.3.4.5.1 Detection systems, where required, shall be in accordance with Section 9.6.

18.3.4.5.2 Detection in Spaces Open to Corridors. *(See 18.3.6.1.)*

18.3.4.5.3* Nursing Homes. An approved automatic smoke detection system shall be installed in corridors throughout smoke compartments containing patient sleeping rooms and in spaces open to corridors as permitted in nursing homes by 18.3.6.1.

Exception No. 1: Corridor systems shall not be required where each patient sleeping room is protected by an approved smoke detection system.

Exception No. 2: Corridor systems shall not be required where patient room doors are equipped with automatic door-closing devices with integral smoke detectors on the room side installed in accordance with their listing, provided that the integral detectors provide occupant notification.

Exception: Smoke detection devices or smoke detection systems equipped with reconfirmation features shall not be required to automatically notify the fire department unless the alarm condition is reconfirmed after a period not exceeding 120 seconds.

19.3.4.4 Emergency Control. Operation of any activating device in the required fire alarm system shall be arranged to accomplish automatically any control functions to be performed by that device. *(See 9.6.5.)*

19.3.4.5 Detection.

19.3.4.5.1 Corridors. An approved automatic smoke detection system shall be installed in all corridors of limited care facilities. Such system shall be in accordance with Section 9.6.

Exception No. 1: Where each patient sleeping room is protected by an approved smoke detection system, and a smoke detector is provided at smoke barriers and horizontal exits in accordance with Section 9.6, the corridor smoke detection system shall not be required on the patient sleeping room floors.

Exception No. 2: Smoke compartments protected throughout by an approved, supervised automatic sprinkler system in accordance with 19.3.5.2.

19.3.4.5.2 Detection in Spaces Open to Corridors. *(See 19.3.6.1.)*

A.18.3.4.5.3 The requirement for smoke detectors in spaces open to the corridors eliminates the requirement contained in 18.3.6.1 for direct supervision by the facility staff of nursing homes.

Exception No. 3 to 19.3.4.2 addresses a smoke detector installed for a special purpose. Paragraphs 19.7.5.2 and 19.7.5.3 require that newly introduced upholstered furniture and mattresses be resistant to cigarette ignition and have limited rates of heat release. As exceptions to the requirement for limiting the rate of heat release, either sprinklers must be provided or the room must have a smoke detector. Exception No. 3 to 19.3.4.2 exempts such smoke detectors from having to initiate the building alarm system.

Paragraph 18.3.4.3.1 specifically prohibits new health care occupancies from using Exception No. 3 to 9.6.3.2, which exempts detectors at doors for the exclusive operation of automatic door release from the requirements for occupant notification. By referencing the requirements of 9.6.3, normally all exceptions to 9.6.3.2 would be recognized. For example, the use of Exception Nos. 1 and 2 to 9.6.3.2 is not prohibited. Those exceptions exempt detectors used for recalling elevators or closing dampers from initiating occupant notification. Although such detectors must be arranged to initiate the alarm system in accordance with 18.3.4.2, subsequent occupant notification is not required.

Emergency forces notification is addressed in 18/19.3.4.3.2. An independent study by the National Bureau of Standards (currently the National Institute of Standards and Technology) indicates a high rate of nuisance alarms for smoke detectors installed in health care facilities.[9] The study determined that 4.4 nuisance alarms occurred per 100 smoke detectors per year. Further, approximately 14 nuisance alarms occurred for every actual alarm. Because of the high incidence of nuisance alarms, the exception to 18/19.3.4.3.2 permits delaying fire department notification for up to 120 seconds where smoke detectors or smoke detection systems are equipped with a reconfirmation feature. However, staff notification, as required by 18/19.3.4.3.1, cannot be delayed.

Paragraphs 18/19.3.4.1 through 18/19.3.4.5 address required fire alarm equipment. Reliability is of primary importance; therefore, electrical supervision of the system and system components is specified by reference to Section 9.6. In the event of circuit fault, component failure, or other trouble, continuous trouble indication is required and should be provided at a constantly attended location.

A manual fire alarm system is required by 18/19.3.4.1 and 18/19.3.4.2. Manual fire alarm boxes are normally located along the natural routes of egress and are also located to cover all portions of the building. The exception to 18.3.4.2 and Exception No. 1 to 19.3.4.2 allow manual fire alarm boxes, under certain conditions, to be located only at continuously attended staff positions in sleeping areas. This arrangement provides the opportunity for prompt notification of fire without requiring staff to leave their normal work stations. In new installations, it would normally be desirable to have manual fire alarm boxes at all attended staff locations and at entrances to exits, because the additional cost of the extra fire alarm boxes would be minimal. However, the exceptions recognize that the fire alarm boxes located near the exits might lead to nuisance alarms if patients misuse them.

Manual fire alarm boxes should be located so that those qualified to send an alarm can summon aid without having to leave their zone of ordinary activity or pass out of the sight and hearing of people immediately exposed to, or in direct view of, a fire. The operation of a manual fire alarm box should automatically summon attendants who can assist in removing physically helpless occupants and in helping control mentally disabled occupants.

The system required by 18/19.3.4.2 is permitted to be incorporated into an automatic system equipped to detect a fire and initiate an alarm.

The alarm must automatically transmit to a point outside the facility. Where automatic transmission of the alarm to the fire department legally committed to serve the facility is not permitted, arrangements are to be made for the prompt notification of the fire department or such other assistance as may be available in the case of fire or other emergency. Paragraph 9.6.4 lists various methods acceptable for automatically notifying the fire department. The fire department should also be called manually to verify and confirm the automatic transmission of the alarm.

In larger facilities, this might be the responsibility of the facility telephone operator; in smaller facilities, it might be the responsibility of the nursing staff.

Actuation of the fire alarm must initiate the operation of alerting devices throughout the affected zone or building, as appropriate. See Exception Nos. 1 and 2 to 9.6.3.7, which address occupant notification by zone. Visible alerting devices are permitted to substitute for audible devices in critical care areas. See A.18.3.4.3.1, Exception, and A.19.3.4.3.1, Exception No. 1.

Although 18/19.3.4.3.1 requires occupant notification, coded messages are permitted to be used to notify staff and trained responders. As part of their emergency duties, staff will then keep patients and visitors informed of expected actions.

Paragraph 19.3.4.5.1 requires smoke detectors in the corridors of existing limited care facilities. Staffing levels in hospitals and nursing homes reasonably ensure discovery of a fire at an early stage. In existing hospitals and nursing homes, it is considered reasonable to rely on staff to sound the alert.

Paragraph 18.3.4.5.3 requires corridor smoke detection systems in new nursing homes. The justification provided during the *Code* revision process that produced this requirement stated that corridor smoke detectors are needed for redundancy; for some fire scenarios the corridor detector might be the first device to provide notification of fire; and the cost of installing a corridor smoke detection system as part of new construction is minor.

18.3.5 Extinguishment Requirements.

18.3.5.1* Buildings containing health care facilities shall be protected throughout by an approved, supervised automatic sprinkler system in accordance with Section 9.7.

Exception: In Type I and Type II construction, where approved by the authority having jurisdiction, alternative protection measures shall be permitted to be substituted for sprinkler protection in specified areas where the authority having jurisdiction has prohibited sprinklers, without causing a building to be classified as nonsprinklered.

A.18.3.5.1 In areas where the replenishment of water supplies is not immediately available from on-site sources, alternate provisions for the water-fill rate requirements of NFPA 13, *Standard for the Installation of Sprinkler Systems,* and NFPA 22, *Standard for Water Tanks for Private Fire Protection,* that are acceptable to the authority having jurisdiction should be provided. Appropriate means for the replenishment of these supplies from other sources, such as fire department tankers, public safety organizations, or other independent contractors should be incorporated into the overall fire safety plan of the facility.

With automatic sprinkler protection required throughout new health care facilities and quick-response sprinklers required in smoke compartments containing patient sleeping rooms, a fire and its life-threatening byproducts can be reduced, thereby allowing the defend-in-place concept to continue. The difficulty in maintaining the proper integrity of life safety elements has been considered and it has been judged that the probability of a sprinkler system operating as designed is equal to or greater than other life safety features.

18.3.5.2* Listed quick-response or listed residential sprinklers shall be used throughout smoke compartments containing patient sleeping rooms.

19.3.5 Extinguishment Requirements.

19.3.5.1 Where required by 19.1.6, health care facilities shall be protected throughout by an approved, supervised automatic sprinkler system in accordance with Section 9.7.

Exception: In Type I and Type II construction, where approved by the authority having jurisdiction, alternative protection measures shall be permitted to be substituted for sprinkler protection in specified areas where the authority having jurisdiction has prohibited sprinklers, without causing a building to be classified as nonsprinklered.

19.3.5.2* Where this *Code* permits exceptions for fully sprinklered buildings or smoke compartments, the sprinkler system shall meet the following criteria:

(1) It shall be in accordance with Section 9.7.

(2) It shall be electrically connected to the fire alarm system.

(3) It shall be fully supervised.

Exception: In Type I and Type II construction, where approved by the authority having jurisdiction, alternative protection measures shall be permitted to be substituted for sprinkler protection in specified areas where the authority having jurisdiction has prohibited sprinklers, without causing a building to be classified as nonsprinklered.

A.18.3.5.2 The requirements for use of quick-response sprinklers intend that quick-response sprinklers be the predominant type of sprinkler installed in the smoke compartment. It is recognized, however, that quick-response sprinklers might not be approved for installation in all areas such as those where NFPA 13, *Standard for the Installation of Sprinkler Systems,* requires sprinklers of the intermediate- or high-temperature classification. It is not the intent of the 18.3.5.2 requirements to prohibit the use of standard sprinklers in limited areas of a smoke compartment where intermediate- or high-temperature sprinklers are required.

Where the installation of quick-response sprinklers is impracticable in patient sleeping room areas, appropriate equivalent protection features acceptable to the authority having jurisdiction should be provided. It is recognized that the use of quick-response sprinklers might be limited in facilities housing certain types of patients or by the installation limitations of quick-response sprinklers.

A.19.3.5.2 It is intended that any valve that controls automatic sprinklers in the entire building or portions of the building, including sectional and floor control valves, be electrically supervised. Valves that control isolated sprinkler heads, such as in laundry and trash chutes, are not required to be electrically supervised. Appropriate means should be taken to ensure that valves that are not electrically supervised remain open.

18.3.5.3 (Reserved.)

19.3.5.3* Where this *Code* permits exceptions for fully sprinklered buildings or smoke compartments and specifically references this paragraph, the sprinkler system shall meet the following criteria:

(1) It shall be installed throughout the building in accordance with Section 9.7.

(2) It shall be electrically connected to the fire alarm system.

(3) It shall be fully supervised.

(4) It shall be equipped with listed quick-response or listed residential sprinklers throughout all smoke compartments containing patient sleeping rooms.

Exception No. 1: Standard response sprinklers shall be permitted to be continued to be used in existing approved sprinkler systems where quick-response and residential sprinklers were not listed for use in such locations at the time of installation.

Exception No. 2: Standard response sprinklers shall be permitted for use in hazardous areas protected in accordance with 19.3.2.1.

A.19.3.5.3 The exceptions to 19.3.5.3 are not intended to supplant NFPA 13, *Standard for the Installation of Sprinkler*

CHAPTER 18 • New	CHAPTER 19 • Existing

Systems, which requires that residential sprinklers with more than a 10°F (5.6°C) difference in temperature rating not be mixed within a room. Currently there are no additional prohibitions in NFPA 13 on the mixing of sprinklers having different thermal response characteristics. Conversely, there are no design parameters to make practical the mixing of residential and other types of sprinklers.

18.3.5.4 (Reserved.)

19.3.5.4 Isolated hazardous areas shall be permitted to be protected in accordance with 9.7.1.2. For new installations in existing health care occupancies, where more than two sprinklers are installed in a single area, waterflow detection shall be provided to sound the building fire alarm, or to notify by a signal, any constantly attended location, such as PBX, security, or emergency room, at which the necessary corrective action shall be taken.

18.3.5.5* Sprinklers in areas where cubicle curtains are installed shall be in accordance with NFPA 13, *Standard for the Installation of Sprinkler Systems.*

19.3.5.5* Newly introduced cubicle curtains in sprinklered areas shall be installed in accordance with NFPA 13, *Standard for the Installation of Sprinkler Systems.*

A.18.3.5.5 For the proper operation of sprinkler systems, cubicle curtains and sprinkler locations need to be coordinated. Improperly designed systems might obstruct the sprinkler spray from reaching the fire or might shield the heat from the sprinkler. Many options are available to the designer including, but not limited to, hanging the cubicle curtains 18 in. (46 cm) below the sprinkler deflector; using a ½-in. (1.3-cm) diagonal mesh or a 70 percent open weave top panel that extends 18 in. (46 cm) below the sprinkler deflector; or designing the system to have a horizontal and minimum vertical distance that meets the requirements of NFPA 13, *Standard for the Installation of Sprinkler Systems.* The test data that forms the basis of the NFPA 13 requirements is from fire tests with sprinkler discharge that penetrated a single privacy curtain.

A.19.3.5.5 For the proper operation of sprinkler systems, cubicle curtains and sprinkler locations need to be coordinated. Improperly designed systems might obstruct the sprinkler spray from reaching the fire or might shield the heat from the sprinkler. Many options are available to the designer including, but not limited to, hanging the cubicle curtains 18 in. (46 cm) below the sprinkler deflector; using ½-in. (1.3-cm) diagonal mesh or a 70 percent open weave top panel that extends 18 in. (46 cm) below the sprinkler deflector; or designing the system to have a horizontal and minimum vertical distance that meets the requirements of NFPA 13, *Standard for the Installation of Sprinkler Systems.* The test data that forms the basis of the NFPA 13 requirements is from fire tests with sprinkler discharge that penetrated a single privacy curtain.

18.3.5.6 Portable fire extinguishers shall be provided in all health care occupancies in accordance with 9.7.4.1.

19.3.5.6 Portable fire extinguishers shall be provided in all health care occupancies in accordance with 9.7.4.1.

Paragraph 18.3.5.1 requires automatic sprinkler protection throughout all new health care facilities; 18.3.5.2 requires the use of quick-response or residential sprinklers throughout all smoke compartments containing patient sleeping rooms.

Where sprinkler protection is specified, complete building coverage in accordance with the provisions of NFPA 13, *Standard for the Installation of Sprinkler Systems,*[10] is required. The *Code* does not exempt any area of the building from sprinkler protection (see Section 9.7). However, where automatic sprinkler

protection is omitted from certain spaces in Type I and Type II construction at the mandate of the authority having jurisdiction and the authority having jurisdiction approves alternative protective measures, the building is still considered fully protected throughout in accordance with the exception to 18/19.3.5.1. Sprinklers are permitted to be omitted only from areas in buildings of fire-rated, noncombustible construction, where the building will have sufficient structural fire resistance to outlast most fires. Use of alternative, protective measures to automatic sprinklers should

CHAPTER 18 • New

CHAPTER 19 • Existing

be carefully evaluated to ensure equivalent protection. Where other automatic fire-extinguishing systems are used as an alternative to sprinklers for specific spaces, it is suggested that the spaces also be separated by fire resistance–rated construction.

The term *supervised* means that a distinct, supervisory signal must be provided to a constantly attended location in the event of any malfunction or action that would impair sprinkler performance. Supervision must be provided, for example, for water supply and sprinkler control valves, fire pump power and running conditions, water tank levels and temperatures, pressure in pressure tanks, air pressure in dry-pipe systems, building temperature, and city water pressure. Supervision should include all sprinkler sectional control valves in addition to main control valves. See also 9.7.2.

The intent of 19.3.5.2 is to allow deletion of redundant features of fire protection within an individual smoke compartment that is sprinklered. This paragraph, for example, could be used to allow higher flame spread wall/ceiling finish or could be used to allow nonrated corridor partitions within the sprin-

klered smoke compartment. In a limited care facility, the corridor smoke detection could be eliminated within the sprinklered smoke compartment. However, certain general building protection features must be maintained unless the building is fully sprinklered. For example, no relaxation in exit features (see Section 19.2) or building construction requirements (see 19.1.6) should be granted unless the building is fully protected by automatic sprinklers.

Paragraph 19.3.5.3 allows deletion of a number of redundant features of protection where automatic sprinkler protection is provided and where quick-response sprinklers are used throughout smoke compartments having sleeping rooms. For example, Exception No. 2 to 19.3.7.3 permits elimination of dampers in ducts penetrating smoke barriers where compartments on both sides of the barriers are sprinkler protected under certain conditions. It will permit elimination of dampers where compartments not used for patient sleeping are sprinklered, using either standard or quick-response sprinklers, or where compartments having patient sleeping rooms use quick-response or residential sprinklers.

18.3.6 Corridors.

Subsection 18/19.3.6 essentially stipulates that all areas that contain combustibles in sufficient quantities to produce a life-threatening fire must be separated from exit access corridors by partitions. Corridor partitions in new health care occupancies and sprinklered existing health care occupancies must be able to retard the transfer of smoke but need not be fire-rated. In nonsprinklered existing health care occupancies, the corridor partitions must have a minimum of ½-hour fire resistance rating.

19.3.6 Corridors.

Paragraph 18/19.3.6.1 establishes requirements for the existence and location of corridor partitions.

Paragraph 18/19.3.6.2 establishes construction requirements for corridor partitions.

Paragraph 18/19.3.6.3 establishes requirements for doors in corridor partitions.

Paragraph 18/19.3.6.4 addresses transfer grilles.

Paragraph 18/19.3.6.5 permits miscellaneous openings such as mail slots.

18.3.6.1 Corridors shall be separated from all other areas by partitions complying with 18.3.6.2 through 18.3.6.5. *(See also 18.2.5.9.)*

Exception No. 1: Spaces shall be permitted to be unlimited in area and open to the corridor, provided that the following criteria are met:

(a) The spaces are not used for patient sleeping rooms, treatment rooms, or hazardous areas.

(b) The corridors onto which the spaces open in the

19.3.6.1 Corridors shall be separated from all other areas by partitions complying with 19.3.6.2 through 19.3.6.5. *(See also 19.2.5.9.)*

Exception No. 1: Smoke compartments protected throughout by an approved, supervised automatic sprinkler system in accordance with 19.3.5.3 shall be permitted to have spaces that are unlimited in size open to the corridor, provided that the following criteria are met:

(a) The spaces are not used for patient sleeping rooms, treatment rooms, or hazardous areas.

(b) The corridors onto which the spaces open in the

CHAPTER 18 • New	CHAPTER 19 • Existing

same smoke compartment are protected by an electrically supervised automatic smoke detection system in accordance with 18.3.4, or the smoke compartment in which the space is located is protected throughout by quick-response sprinklers.

(c) The open space is protected by an electrically supervised automatic smoke detection system in accordance with 18.3.4, or the entire space is arranged and located to allow direct supervision by the facility staff from a nurses' station or similar space.

(d) The space does not obstruct access to required exits.

Exception No. 2: Waiting areas shall be permitted to be open to the corridor, provided that the following criteria are met:

(a) The aggregate waiting area in each smoke compartment does not exceed 600 ft² (55.7 m²).

(b) Each area is protected by an electrically supervised automatic smoke detection system in accordance with 18.3.4, or each area is arranged and located to allow direct supervision by the facility staff from a nursing station or similar space.

(c) The area does not obstruct access to required exits.

Exception No. 3:* Spaces for nurses' stations.

A.18.3.6.1 Exception No. 3 A typical nurses' station would normally contain one or more of the following with associated furniture and furnishings:

(1) Charting area
(2) Clerical area
(3) Nourishment station
(4) Storage of small amounts of medications, medical equipment and supplies, clerical supplies, and linens
(5) Patient monitoring and communication equipment

Exception No. 4: Gift shops open to the corridor where protected in accordance with 18.3.2.5.

Exception No. 5: In a limited care facility, group meeting or multipurpose therapeutic spaces shall be permitted to open to the corridor, provided that the following criteria are met:

(a) The space is not a hazardous area.

(b) The space is protected by an electrically supervised automatic smoke detection system in accordance with 18.3.4, or the space is arranged and located to allow direct supervision by the facility staff from the nurses' station or similar location.

---

same smoke compartment are protected by an electrically supervised automatic smoke detection system in accordance with 19.3.4, or the smoke compartment in which the space is located is protected throughout by quick-response sprinklers.

(c) The open space is protected by an electrically supervised automatic smoke detection system in accordance with 19.3.4, or the entire space is arranged and located to allow direct supervision by the facility staff from a nurses' station or similar space.

(d) The space does not obstruct access to required exits.

Exception No. 2: In smoke compartments protected throughout by an approved, supervised automatic sprinkler system in accordance with 19.3.5.3, waiting areas shall be permitted to be open to the corridor, provided that the following criteria are met:

(a) The aggregate waiting area in each smoke compartment does not exceed 600 ft² (55.7 m²).

(b) Each area is protected by an electrically supervised automatic smoke detection system in accordance with 19.3.4, or each area is arranged and located to allow direct supervision by the facility staff from a nursing station or similar space.

(c) The area does not obstruct access to required exits.

Exception No. 3:* Spaces for nurses' stations.

A.19.3.6.1 Exception No. 3 A typical nurses' station would normally contain one or more of the following with associated furniture and furnishings:

(1) Charting area
(2) Clerical area
(3) Nourishment station
(4) Storage of small amounts of medications, medical equipment and supplies, clerical supplies, and linens
(5) Patient monitoring and communication equipment

Exception No. 4: Gift shops open to the corridor where protected in accordance with 19.3.2.5.

Exception No. 5: Limited care facilities in smoke compartments protected throughout by an approved, supervised automatic sprinkler system in accordance with 19.3.5.3 shall be permitted to have group meeting or multipurpose therapeutic spaces open to the corridor, provided that the following criteria are met:

(a) The space is not a hazardous area.

(b) The space is protected by an electrically supervised automatic smoke detection system in accordance with 19.3.4, or the space is arranged and located to allow direct supervision by the facility staff from the nurses' station or similar location.

(c) The area does not obstruct access to required exits.

(c) The area does not obstruct access to required exits.

Exception No. 6:   Spaces other than patient sleeping rooms, treatment rooms, and hazardous areas shall be permitted to be open to the corridor and unlimited in area, provided that the following criteria are met:

(a) The space and the corridors onto which it opens, where located in the same smoke compartment, are protected by an electrically supervised automatic smoke detection system in accordance with 19.3.4.

(b)* Each space is protected by automatic sprinklers, or the furnishings and furniture, in combination with all other combustibles within the area, are of such minimum quantity and arrangement that a fully developed fire is unlikely to occur.

A.19.3.6.1 Exception No. 6(b) A fully developed fire (flashover) occurs if the rate of heat release of the burning materials exceeds the capability of the space to absorb or vent that heat. The ability of common lining (wall, ceiling, and floor) materials to absorb heat is approximately 0.75 Btu (0.79 kJ) per ft^2 of lining. The venting capability of open doors or windows is in excess of 20 Btu (21 kJ) per ft^2 of opening. In a fire that has not reached flashover conditions, fire will spread from one furniture item to another only if the burning item is close to another furniture item. For example, if individual furniture items have heat release rates of 500 Btu per second (525 kW) and are separated by 12 in. (30.5 cm) or more, the fire is not expected to spread from item to item, and flashover is unlikely to occur. *(See also the NFPA Fire Protection Handbook.)*

(c) The space does not obstruct access to required exits.

Exception No. 7:*   Waiting areas shall be permitted to be open to the corridor, provided that the following criteria are met:

(a) Each area does not exceed 600 ft^2 (55.7 m^2).

(b) The area is equipped with an electrically supervised automatic smoke detection system in accordance with 19.3.4.

(c) The area does not obstruct any access to required exits.

A.19.3.6.1 Exception No. 7 This exception permits waiting areas to be located across the corridor from each other, provided that neither area exceeds the 600-ft^2 (55.7-m^2) limitation.

Exception No. 8:   In a limited care facility, group meeting or multipurpose therapeutic spaces, other than hazardous areas, that are under continuous supervision by facility staff shall be permitted to be open to the corridor, provided that the following criteria are met:

CHAPTER 18 • New	CHAPTER 19 • Existing

(a) Each area does not exceed 1500 ft² (140 m²).

(b) Not more than one such space is permitted per smoke compartment.

(c) The area is equipped with an electrically supervised automatic smoke detection system in accordance with 19.3.4.

(d) The area does not obstruct access to required exits.

Paragraph 18/19.3.6.1 requires that all spaces be separated from corridors by partitions. The intent is to limit the risk of exposing the corridor to fire. Exceptions are provided to allow specific areas to be open to the corridor. Exception Nos. 1 through 5 to 18.3.6.1 and Exception Nos. 1 through 8 to 19.3.6.1 specify those areas that are permitted to be open to corridors.

Exception No. 1 to 18/19.3.6.1 contains provisions that allow unlimited size spaces such as recreation/lounge/waiting areas to be open to the corridor. New health care occupancies are offered this exception because they are sprinklered; existing health care occupancies must be sprinklered in order to use the exception. The open space must be visually supervised by staff from a permanent staff location, or equivalent early warning of fire must be provided by an electrically supervised smoke detection system within the open space. Interconnected corridors that are not separated from the space must be equipped with an electrically supervised smoke detection system, or the smoke compartment must be sprinklered throughout using quick-response sprinklers. Exhibit 18/19.15(a) illustrates the provisions of Exception No. 1 to 18/19.3.6.1. The black-filled circles at the left of the figure depict quick-response sprinklers; the unfilled

circles at the right of the figure depict standard response sprinklers. In the smoke compartment at the left, which includes patient sleeping rooms, the open space has direct supervision from the nurses' station located across the corridor. In the smoke compartment at the right, which contains no patient sleeping rooms, neither open space has direct supervision, so each space is equipped with smoke detection; because the sprinklers in this compartment are standard response sprinklers, the required smoke detection must be extended into the corridor of that compartment.

Waiting areas, which in aggregate area are not permitted to exceed 600 ft² (55.7 m²) in any one smoke compartment, are permitted to be open to the corridor in accordance with Exception No. 2 to 18/19.3.6.1. Each waiting area must be located to permit direct visual supervision by the staff or must be equipped with an electrically supervised automatic smoke detection system. In all cases, waiting spaces must be arranged so as not to obstruct access to exits. Exhibit 18/19.15(b) illustrates the provisions of Exception No. 2 to 18/19.3.6.1. The number of waiting spaces is not limited, but their aggregate area cannot exceed 600 ft² (55.7 m²) per smoke compartment. The waiting

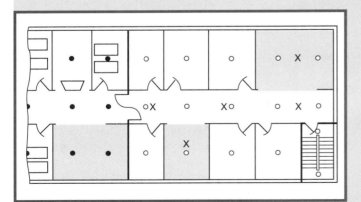

Exhibit 18/19.15(a) *Spaces of unlimited size that are open to the corridor.*

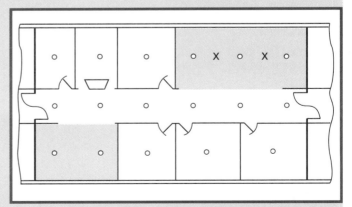

Exhibit 18/19.15(b) *Waiting spaces of limited size that are open to the corridor.*

space at the left of the compartment receives direct supervision from the nurses' station located across the corridor. The waiting space at the right of the compartment has no direct supervision and therefore must be provided with smoke detection.

Exception No. 1 to 18/19.3.6.1 does not permit treatment spaces to be open to corridors, and Exception No. 2 to 18/19.3.6.1 limits the open spaces for use as waiting areas. Exception No. 5 to 18/19.3.6.1, however, permits multipurpose therapeutic spaces to be open to corridors in limited care facilities. These spaces are not permitted to be used for hazardous operations, such as woodworking, involving occupational therapy.

Exception Nos. 1, 2, and 5 to 18/19.3.6.1 require

that the open space be supervised by the staff or protected by a smoke detection system. Staff supervision is important; it allows the staff to see, hear, or smell a developing fire or to prevent the ignition of a fire by virtue of their presence. The use of closed-circuit television or mirrors does not offer all the protection provided by staff and should not be relied on as a substitute for direct supervision. Adequate supervision is not provided if the staff cannot readily supervise the space without extraordinary effort (for example, by looking around a corner).

Areas used for charting and communication by doctors and nurses are permitted to be open to the corridor, as are nurses' stations. See Exception No. 3 to 18/19.3.6.1.

18.3.6.2* Construction of Corridor Walls. Corridor walls shall form a barrier to limit the transfer of smoke. Such walls shall be permitted to terminate at the ceiling where the ceiling is constructed to limit the transfer of smoke. No fire resistance rating is required for corridor walls.

A.18.3.6.2 It is the *Code*'s intent that there be no required fire resistance nor area limitations for vision panels in corridor walls and doors.

An architectural, exposed, suspended-grid acoustical tile ceiling with penetrating items such as sprinkler piping and sprinklers; ducted HVAC supply and return-air diffusers; speakers; and recessed lighting fixtures is capable of limiting the transfer of smoke.

19.3.6.2 Construction of Corridor Walls.

19.3.6.2.1* Corridor walls shall be continuous from the floor to the underside of the floor or roof deck above, through any concealed spaces, such as those above suspended ceilings, and through interstitial structural and mechanical spaces, and they shall have a fire resistance rating of not less than ½ hour.

A.19.3.6.2.1 The intent of the ½-hour fire resistance rating for corridor partitions is to require a nominal fire rating, particularly where the fire rating of existing partitions cannot be documented. Examples of acceptable partition assemblies would include, but are not limited to, ½-in. (1.3-cm) gypsum board, wood lath and plaster, gypsum lath, or metal lath and plaster.

Exception No. 1:* In smoke compartments protected throughout by an approved, supervised automatic sprinkler system in accordance with 19.3.5.2, a corridor shall be permitted to be separated from all other areas by non-fire-rated partitions and shall be permitted to terminate at the

CHAPTER 18 • New	CHAPTER 19 • Existing

ceiling where the ceiling is constructed to limit the transfer of smoke.

A.19.3.6.2.1 Exception No. 1 An architectural, exposed, suspended-grid acoustical tile ceiling with penetrating items such as sprinkler piping and sprinklers; ducted HVAC supply and return-air diffusers; speakers; and recessed lighting fixtures is capable of limiting the transfer of smoke.

Exception No. 2: Existing corridor partitions shall be permitted to terminate at ceilings that are not an integral part of a floor construction if 5 ft (1.5 m) or more of space exists between the top of the ceiling subsystem and the bottom of the floor or roof above, provided that the following criteria are met:

(a) The ceiling shall be part of a fire-rated assembly tested to have a fire resistance rating of not less than 1 hour in compliance with the provisions of 8.2.3.1.

(b) The corridor partitions form smoketight joints with the ceilings (joint filler, if used, shall be noncombustible).

(c) Each compartment of interstitial space that constitutes a separate smoke area is vented, in a smoke emergency, to the outside by mechanical means having sufficient capacity to provide not less than two air changes per hour but, in no case, a capacity less than 5000 ft³/min (2.36 m³/s).

(d) The interstitial space shall not be used for storage.

(e) The space shall not be used as a plenum for supply, exhaust, or return air, except as noted in 19.3.6.2.1(3).

Exception No. 3:* Existing corridor partitions shall be permitted to terminate at monolithic ceilings that resist the passage of smoke where there is a smoketight joint between the top of the partition and the bottom of the ceiling.

A.19.3.6.2.1 Exception No. 3 Monolithic ceilings are continuous horizontal membranes composed of noncombustible or limited-combustible materials, such as plaster or gypsum board, with seams or cracks permanently sealed.

19.3.6.2.2* Corridor walls shall form a barrier to limit the transfer of smoke.

A.19.3.6.2.2 The purpose of extending a corridor wall above a lay-in ceiling or through a concealed space is to provide a barrier to limit the passage of smoke. The intent of 19.3.6.2.2 is not to require light-tight barriers above lay-in ceilings or to require an absolute seal of the room from the corridor. Small holes, penetrations or gaps around items such as ductwork, conduit, or telecommunication lines should not affect the ability of this barrier to limit the passage of smoke.

19.3.6.2.3 Fixed fire window assemblies in accordance with 8.2.3.2.2 shall be permitted in corridor walls.

Exception: There shall be no restrictions in area and fire resistance of glass and frames in smoke compartments protected throughout by an approved, supervised automatic sprinkler system in accordance with 19.3.5.2.

The choice of materials used to construct corridor walls/partitions might be affected by the building construction types addressed by 18/19.1.6.2. For example, corridor construction materials in buildings of Type I or Type II construction must be either noncombustible or limited-combustible as required by 18/19.1.6.3.

In new health care occupancies and sprinklered existing health care occupancies, corridor walls need not be fire rated but must be constructed to resist the passage of smoke. Where suspended ceilings are provided, partitions are permitted to terminate at the suspended ceiling without any additional special protection if the suspended ceiling will resist the passage of smoke. The ability to resist the passage of smoke must be carefully evaluated. There are no restrictions in terms of area or fire resistance for glazing used in these non-fire-rated corridor partitions. In buildings protected throughout by an approved automatic sprinkler system, corridor walls are permitted to terminate at ceilings, provided the wall and ceiling resist the passage of smoke. These requirements are illustrated in Exhibit 18/19.16(a).

Editions of the *Code* prior to 1997 required that corridor walls in nonsprinklered health care occupancies have a minimum 20-minute fire resistance rating. The change to a minimum $^1/_2$-hour fire resistance rating was not meant to implement a more stringent requirement. Rather, Chapter 8 simplified the range of fire resistance ratings to reduce what had previously been 20-minute, $^1/_2$-hour, and $^3/_4$-hour ratings to the single category of a $^1/_2$-hour fire resistance rating. See the explanation in A.8.2.3.1.2(3) for determining that existing walls in good condition, that previously received credit for providing a 20-minute rating, provide a $^1/_2$-hour rating. It is not the intent to throw into noncompliance existing walls that were previously judged to meet the former 20-minute rating criterion.

In nonsprinklered existing health care occupancies, corridor walls must be constructed of assemblies having a minimum fire resistance rating of $^1/_2$ hour. In setting the requirements for $^1/_2$-hour corridor wall partitions, it was intended to accept the separation

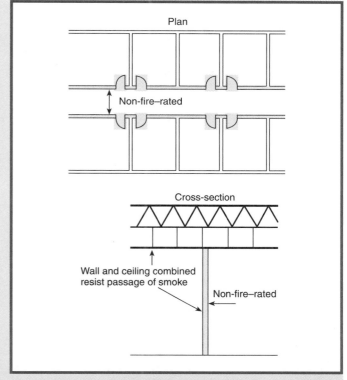

Exhibit 18/19.16(a) *Corridor walls in new health care occupancies and existing, sprinklered health care occupancies.*

provided by existing partitions of any substantial construction that are capable of serving as a barrier for a short period of time—without requiring documentation of a specific fire rating. The $^1/_2$-hour rating is intended to permit partitions of wood lath and plaster, $^1/_2$-in. (1.3-cm) gypsum board, and similar materials. Ordinary glass would not be permitted in corridor walls of nonsprinklered health care occupancies.

Fire-rated existing corridor partitions must be constructed to extend continuously through all concealed spaces—for example, through to the floor or roof deck above a suspended ceiling. This requirement is illustrated in Exhibit 18/19.16(b). Where a monolithic ceiling composed of noncombustible materials, such as plaster or gypsum board with permanently sealed seams forming a continuous horizontal

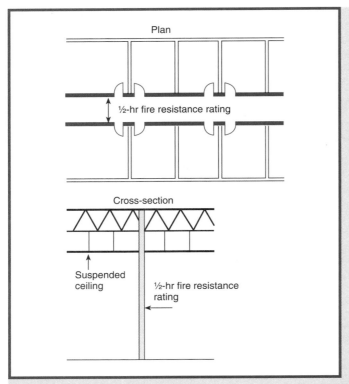

Exhibit 18/19.16(b) *Corridor walls in existing, nonsprinklered health care smoke compartment.*

membrane, is provided, existing partitions are permitted to terminate at the underside of the ceiling in accordance with Exception No. 3 to 19.3.6.2.1.

Openings in corridor partitions in nonsprinklered buildings must be suitably protected to maintain

corridor separation. One-quarter-in. (0.65-cm) thick, fire-rated, wired glass is limited to a maximum of 1296 in.² (0.84 m²) set in approved metal frames. Each wired glass panel is limited to a maximum dimension of 54 in. (140 cm). The glass should be labeled and should be well embedded in putty, with all exposed joints between the metal and the glass struck and pointed (see NFPA 80, *Standard for Fire Doors and Windows*)[11]. A number of wired glass panels can be used in a single partition, provided that each 1296-in.² (0.84-m²) section is separated from adjacent panels by a steel or other approved metal mullion. Fire-rated glazing, other than $1/_4$-in. (0.65-cm) wired glass, should be installed in accordance with the manufacturer's instructions and listing. The use of fire-rated glazing in a partition reduces the fire resistance capability of the partition because of radiant energy transfer through the glass panel. The excessive use of glazing, therefore, should be avoided.

Exception No. 2 to 19.3.6.2.1 specifies criteria for terminating existing corridor partitions at ceilings where the interstitial space above the ceiling meets certain criteria. However, the exception does not exempt the minimum $1/_2$-hour fire resistance rating of the corridor walls. The walls are permitted to terminate at a ceiling that has been tested as a portion of a floor/ceiling or roof/ceiling assembly having a fire resistance rating of 1 hour or more. Each compartment located above such a ceiling must be equipped with an automatic mechanical smoke exhaust system that is capable of providing a minimum of two air changes per hour but exhausting not less than 5000 ft³/min (2.36 m³/sec). See the additional criteria in 19.3.6.2.1, Exception No. 2(a) through (e).

18.3.6.3* Corridor Doors.

A.18.3.6.3 While it is recognized that closed doors serve to maintain tenable conditions in a corridor and adjacent patient rooms, such doors, which under normal or fire conditions are self-closing, might create a special hazard for the personal safety of a room occupant. These closed doors might present a problem of delay in discovery, confining fire products beyond tenable conditions.

Because it is critical for responding staff members to be able to immediately identify the specific room involved, it is suggested that approved automatic smoke detection that is interconnected with the building fire alarm be considered for rooms having doors equipped with closing devices. Such detection is permitted to be located at any approved point

19.3.6.3 Corridor Doors.

within the room. When activated, the detector is required to provide a warning that indicates the specific room of involvement by activation of a fire alarm annunciator, nurse call system, or any other device acceptable to the authority having jurisdiction.

18.3.6.3.1* Doors protecting corridor openings shall be constructed to resist the passage of smoke. Compliance with NFPA 80, *Standard for Fire Doors and Fire Windows,* shall not be required. Clearance between the bottom of the door and the floor covering not exceeding 1 in. (2.5 cm) shall be permitted for corridor doors.

19.3.6.3.1* Doors protecting corridor openings in other than required enclosures of vertical openings, exits, or hazardous areas shall be substantial doors, such as those constructed of 1¾-in. (4.4-cm) thick, solid-bonded core wood or of construction that resists fire for not less than 20 minutes and shall be constructed to resist the passage of smoke. Compliance with NFPA 80, *Standard for Fire Doors and Fire Windows,* shall not be required. Clearance between the bottom of the door and the floor covering not exceeding 1 in. (2.5 cm) shall be permitted for corridor doors.

Exception: Doors to toilet rooms, bathrooms, shower rooms, sink closets, and similar auxiliary spaces that do not contain flammable or combustible materials.

Exception No. 1: Doors to toilet rooms, bathrooms, shower rooms, sink closets, and similar auxiliary spaces that do not contain flammable or combustible materials.

Exception No. 2: In smoke compartments protected throughout by an approved, supervised automatic sprinkler system in accordance with 19.3.5.2, the door construction requirements of 19.3.6.3.1 shall not be mandatory, but the doors shall be constructed to resist the passage of smoke.

A.18.3.6.3.1 Gasketing of doors should not be necessary to achieve resistance to the passage of smoke if the door is relatively tight-fitting.

A.19.3.6.3.1 Gasketing of doors should not be necessary to achieve resistance to the passage of smoke if the door is relatively tight-fitting.

18.3.6.3.2 Doors shall be provided with positive latching hardware. Roller latches shall be prohibited.

19.3.6.3.2* Doors shall be provided with a means suitable for keeping the door closed that is acceptable to the authority having jurisdiction. The device used shall be capable of keeping the door fully closed if a force of 5 lbf (22 N) is applied at the latch edge of the door. Roller latches shall be prohibited on corridor doors in buildings not fully protected by an approved automatic sprinkler system in accordance with 19.3.5.2.

Exception: Doors to toilet rooms, bathrooms, shower rooms, sink closets, and similar auxiliary spaces that do not contain flammable or combustible materials.

Exception No. 1: Doors to toilet rooms, bathrooms, shower rooms, sink closets, and similar auxiliary spaces that do not contain flammable or combustible materials.

Exception No. 2: Existing roller latches demonstrated to keep the door closed against a force of 5 lbf (22 N) shall be permitted to be kept in service.

A.19.3.6.3.2 While it is recognized that closed doors serve to maintain tenable conditions in a corridor and adjacent patient rooms, such doors, which under normal or fire conditions are self-closing, might create a special hazard for the personal safety of a room occupant. These closed doors might present a problem of delay in discovery, confining fire products beyond tenable conditions.

Since it is critical for responding staff members to be able to immediately identify the specific room involved, it is suggested that approved automatic smoke detection that is interconnected with the building fire alarm be considered for rooms having doors equipped with closing devices. Such detection is permitted to be located at any approved point within the room. When activated, the detector is required to provide a warning that indicates the specific room of involvement by activation of a fire alarm annunciator, nurse call system, or any other device acceptable to the authority having jurisdiction.

In existing buildings, use of the following options reasonably ensures that patient room doors will be closed and remain closed during a fire:

(1) Doors should have positive latches and a suitable program that trains staff to close the doors in an emergency should be established.
(2) It is the intent of the *Code* that no new installations of roller latches be permitted, however, repair or replacement of roller latches is not considered a new installation.
(3) Doors protecting openings to patient sleeping or treatment rooms, or spaces having a similar combustible loading might be held closed using a closer exerting a closing force of not less than 5 lbf (22 N) on the door latch stile.

18.3.6.3.3* Hold-open devices that release when the door is pushed or pulled shall be permitted.

A.18.3.6.3.3 Doors should not be blocked open by furniture, door stops, chocks, tie-backs, drop-down or plunger-type devices, or other devices that necessitate manual unlatching or releasing action to close. Examples of hold-open devices that release when the door is pushed or pulled are friction catches or magnetic catches.

18.3.6.3.4 Door-closing devices shall not be required on doors in corridor wall openings other than those serving required exits, smoke barriers, or enclosures of vertical openings and hazardous areas.

18.3.6.3.5 Nonrated, factory- or field-applied protective plates extending not more than 48 in. (122 cm) above the bottom of the door shall be permitted.

18.3.6.3.6 Dutch doors shall be permitted where they conform to 18.3.6.3. In addition, both the upper leaf and lower leaf shall be equipped with a latching device, and the meeting edges of the upper and lower leaves shall be equipped with an astragal, a rabbet, or a bevel.

19.3.6.3.3* Hold-open devices that release when the door is pushed or pulled shall be permitted.

A.19.3.6.3.3 Doors should not be blocked open by furniture, door stops, chocks, tie-backs, drop-down or plunger-type devices, or other devices that necessitate manual unlatching or releasing action to close. Examples of hold-open devices that release when the door is pushed or pulled are friction catches or magnetic catches.

19.3.6.3.4 Door-closing devices shall not be required on doors in corridor wall openings other than those serving required exits, smoke barriers, or enclosures of vertical openings and hazardous areas.

19.3.6.3.5 Nonrated, factory- or field-applied protective plates extending not more than 48 in. (122 cm) above the bottom of the door shall be permitted.

19.3.6.3.6 Dutch doors shall be permitted where they conform to 19.3.6.3. In addition, both the upper leaf and lower leaf shall be equipped with a latching device, and the meeting edges of the upper and lower leaves shall be equipped with an astragal, a rabbet, or a bevel.

Dutch doors protecting openings in enclosures around hazardous areas shall comply with NFPA 80, *Standard for Fire Doors and Fire Windows.*

Dutch doors protecting openings in enclosures around hazardous areas shall comply with NFPA 80, *Standard for Fire Doors and Fire Windows.*

19.3.6.3.7 Door frames shall be labeled, shall be of steel construction, or shall be of other materials in compliance with the provisions of 8.2.3.2.1.

Exception: Door frames in smoke compartments protected throughout by an approved, supervised automatic sprinkler system in accordance with Section 9.7.

19.3.6.3.8 Fixed fire window assemblies in accordance with 8.2.3.2.2 shall be permitted in corridor doors.

Exception: There shall be no restrictions in area and fire resistance of glass and frames in smoke compartments protected throughout by an approved, supervised automatic sprinkler system in accordance with 19.3.5.2.

Paragraph 18/19.3.6.3.1 permits a maximum 1-in. (2.5-cm) clearance between the bottom of non-fire-rated corridor doors and the upper surface of the floor covering material. The paragraph avoids using the word undercut because of the negative connotation that word conjures in many minds. It is not the intent to permit the door to be deliberately undercut for purposes of making the building heating, ventilating, and air conditioning system function. That practice is prohibited by 2-3.11.1 of NFPA 90A, *Standard for the Installation of Air-Conditioning and Ventilating Systems.*[12] Also, see 18/19.3.6.4, which addresses the concept by prohibiting transfer grilles in corridor walls.

Paragraph 18.3.6.3.2 clearly requires positive latching hardware on doors in corridor walls in new health care occupancies. The purpose is to ensure that doors, once closed by staff, remain closed. Roller latches are not permitted in new health care occupancies.

Doors protecting openings in non-fire-rated corridor partitions—as permitted in new and existing, sprinklered health care occupancies—must be able to resist the passage of smoke but are not required to have a fire protection rating. Door-closing devices are not required except on doors protecting openings in exit enclosures, vertical openings, or required enclosures of hazardous contents areas. There are no restrictions—in terms of area or fire rating for glazing used in corridor doors—in new and sprinklered existing health care occupancies.

Patient room corridor doors are not required to have a fire protection rating in new and sprinklered existing health care occupancies. In existing, non-sprinklered health care occupancies the door need not be a true 20-minute fire protection rated assembly; rather, it is permitted to be a substantial door such as those constructed of 1¾-in. (4.4-cm) thick, solid-bonded core wood. Some persons consider these doors to be equivalent to 20-minute fire protection–rated doors for which the self-closer has been omitted. If the doors were truly a 20-minute fire protection–rated assembly, field-applied protective plates would be prohibited. Subparagraph 18/19.3.6.3.5 reminds the user that factory- or field-applied protective plates are permitted. In issuing that reminder, 18/19.3.6.3.5 sets an arbitrary maximum height of 48 in. (122 cm) above which the protective plate cannot extend. Paragraph 18/19.3.6.3.5 gives the proponents for protective plates the specific permission they requested, but in doing so, adds a height restriction that did not exist when the *Code* was silent on the subject of protective plates on "nonrated" corridor doors.

Existing corridor doors are not specifically required to be provided with a positive latch. However, they must be capable of being closed and maintained closed during a fire. Where positive latches are used, doors must be equipped with a latch <u>that cannot be held in the retracted position</u>. The latch should be capable of holding the door in a closed position when subjected to stresses imposed by exposure to fire. In nonsprinklered buildings, roller latches are not allowed, unless the existing roller latches meet the performance criterion of being able to keep the door closed against a force of 5 lbf (22 N).

Corridor doors in nonsprinklered smoke compartments in existing health care occupancies are required to be installed in approved metal or "heavy wood" frames. Fixed, wired-glass vision panels installed in these doors are not permitted to exceed an area of 1296 in.^{2} (0.84 m^2) [maximum dimension of 54 in. (140 cm)] and must be set in approved, metal frames. Other fire-rated glazing must be used in accordance with its listing. Labeled door frames and closing devices are not required except on doors protecting openings in exit enclosures, vertical openings, or required enclosures of hazardous areas.

Paragraph 18/19.3.6.4 addresses transfer grilles in corridor walls. The use of an exit access corridor as an exhaust, supply, or return air plenum for the building air-handling system is not permitted. Corridor doors are not permitted to be deliberately undercut to facilitate transfer of air, but there may be a maximum 1-in. (2.5-cm) clearance at the bottom of the

door in accordance with 18/19.3.6.3.1. Transfer grilles are not allowed in corridor walls (see 18/19.3.6.4) or corridor doors. Also see 2-3.11.1 of NFPA 90A, *Standard for the Installation of Air-Conditioning and Ventilating Systems*. However, sink closets, bathrooms, and toilets can have doors equipped with a fixed grille or louver to allow exhaust air to be "made up" from the corridor (see exception to 18/19.3.6.3.1). Where a door to a sink closet, bathroom, or toilet is equipped with a grille or louver, such spaces are not permitted to be used for the storage of flammable or combustible supplies. When using this exception for sink closets, caution must be exercised because they are often used for storage of combustibles.

Paragraph 18/19.3.6.5 establishes restrictions for miscellaneous openings in corridor walls. For practical reasons, many small openings are required in corridor walls for use as mail slots, as cashier windows, and as pass-throughs to laboratory or pharmacy spaces. Paragraph 18/19.3.6.5 allows for such openings. Openings are not allowed in compartments having sleeping rooms. In other sprinklered compartments, the opening must be limited to a maximum of 80 in.^{2} (520 cm^2) and must be located in the lower half of the partition. In existing, nonsprinklered, nonsleeping, smoke compartments, the opening size is limited to 20 in.^{2} (130 cm^2).

18.3.6.4 Transfer Grilles. Transfer grilles, regardless of whether they are protected by fusible link–operated dampers, shall not be used in these walls or doors.

Exception: Doors to toilet rooms, bathrooms, shower rooms, sink closets, and similar auxiliary spaces that do not contain flammable or combustible materials shall be permitted to have ventilating louvers or to be undercut.

18.3.6.5 Openings. In other than smoke compartments containing patient bedrooms, miscellaneous openings such as mail slots, pharmacy pass-through windows, laboratory pass-through windows, and cashier pass-through windows shall be permitted to be installed in vision panels or doors without special protection, provided that the aggregate area of openings per room does not exceed 80 in.^{2} (520 cm^2) and the openings are installed at or below half the distance from the floor to the room ceiling.

19.3.6.4 Transfer Grilles. Transfer grilles, regardless of whether they are protected by fusible link–operated dampers, shall not be used in these walls or doors.

Exception: Doors to toilet rooms, bathrooms, shower rooms, sink closets, and similar auxiliary spaces that do not contain flammable or combustible materials shall be permitted to have ventilating louvers or to be undercut.

19.3.6.5 Openings. In other than smoke compartments containing patient bedrooms, miscellaneous openings such as mail slots, pharmacy pass-through windows, laboratory pass-through windows, and cashier pass-through windows shall be permitted to be installed in vision panels or doors without special protection, provided that the aggregate area of openings per room does not exceed 20 in.^{2} (130 cm^2), and the openings are installed at or below half the distance from the floor to the room ceiling.

Exception: For rooms protected throughout by an approved, supervised automatic sprinkler system in accordance with 19.3.5.2, the aggregate area of openings per room shall not exceed 80 in.² (520 cm²).

18.3.7* Subdivision of Building Spaces.

A.18.3.7 See A.18.2.2.

18.3.7.1 Buildings containing health care facilities shall be subdivided by smoke barriers as follows:

(1) To divide every story used by inpatients for sleeping or treatment into not less than two smoke compartments
(2) To divide every story having an occupant load of 50 or more persons, regardless of use, into not less than two smoke compartments
(3) To limit the size of each smoke compartment required by (1) and (2) to an area not exceeding 22,500 ft² (2100 m²)

Exception: The area of an atrium separated in accordance with 8.2.5.6 shall not be limited in size.

(4) To limit the travel distance from any point to reach a door in the required smoke barrier to a distance not exceeding 200 ft (60 m).

Exception No. 1: Stories that do not contain a health care occupancy, located totally above the health care occupancy.

Exception No. 2: Areas that do not contain a health care occupancy and that are separated from the health care occupancy by a fire barrier complying with 7.2.4.3.

Exception No. 3: Stories that do not contain health care occupancies and that are more than one story below the health care occupancy.

Exception No. 4: Open-air parking structures protected throughout by an approved, supervised automatic sprinkler system in accordance with Section 9.7.

18.3.7.2 Smoke barriers shall be provided on stories that are usable but unoccupied.

18.3.7.3 Any required smoke barrier shall be constructed in accordance with Section 8.3 and shall have a fire resistance rating of not less than 1 hour.

Exception No. 1: Where an atrium is used, smoke barriers shall be permitted to terminate at an atrium wall constructed in accordance with Exception No. 2 to 8.2.5.6(1). Not less than two separate smoke compartments shall be provided on each floor.

19.3.7 Subdivision of Building Spaces.

19.3.7.1 Smoke barriers shall be provided to divide every story used for sleeping rooms for more than 30 patients into not less than two smoke compartments. The size of any such smoke compartment shall not exceed 22,500 ft² (2100 m²), and the travel distance from any point to reach a door in the required smoke barrier shall not exceed 200 ft (60 m).

Exception No. 1: Where neither the length nor width of the smoke compartment exceeds 150 ft (45 m), the travel distance to reach the smoke barrier door shall not be limited.

Exception No. 2: The area of an atrium separated in accordance with 8.2.5.6 shall not be limited in size.

19.3.7.2 For purposes of the requirements of 19.3.7, the number of health care occupants shall be determined by actual count of patient bed capacity.

19.3.7.3 Any required smoke barrier shall be constructed in accordance with Section 8.3 and shall have a fire resistance rating of not less than ½ hour.

Exception No. 1: Where an atrium is used, smoke barriers shall be permitted to terminate at an atrium wall constructed in accordance with Exception No. 2 to 8.2.5.6(1). Not less than two separate smoke compartments shall be provided on each floor.

CHAPTER 18 • New	CHAPTER 19 • Existing

Exception No. 2:* Dampers shall not be required in duct penetrations of smoke barriers in fully ducted heating, ventilating, and air conditioning systems.

A.18.3.7.3 Exception No. 2 Where the smoke control system design requires dampers in order that the system functions effectively, it is not the intent of the exception to permit the damper to be omitted.

This exception is not intended to prevent the use of plenum returns where ducting is used to return air from a ceiling plenum through smoke barrier walls. Short stubs or jumper ducts are not acceptable. Ducting is required to connect at both sides of the opening and to extend into adjacent spaces away from the wall. The intent is to prohibit open-air transfers at or near the smoke barrier walls.

18.3.7.4 Not less than 30 net ft² (2.8 net m²) per patient in a hospital or nursing home, or not less than 15 net ft² (1.4 net m²) per resident in a limited care facility, shall be provided within the aggregate area of corridors, patient rooms, treatment rooms, lounge or dining areas, and other low hazard areas on each side of the smoke barrier. On stories not housing bed or litterborne patients, not less than 6 net ft² (0.56 net m²) per occupant shall be provided on each side of the smoke barrier for the total number of occupants in adjoining compartments.

18.3.7.5* Doors in smoke barriers shall be substantial doors, such as 1¾-in. (4.4-cm) thick, solid-bonded wood core doors, or shall be of construction that resists fire for not less than 20 minutes. Nonrated factory- or field-applied protective plates extending not more than 48 in. (122 cm) above the bottom of the door shall be permitted. Cross-corridor openings in smoke barriers shall be protected by a pair of swinging doors or a horizontal sliding door complying with 7.2.1.14. Swinging doors shall be arranged so that each door swings in a direction opposite from the other.

The minimum clear width for swinging doors shall be as follows:

(1) Hospitals and nursing homes—41.5 in. (105 cm)
(2) Psychiatric hospitals and limited care facilities—32 in. (81 cm)

The minimum clear width opening for horizontal sliding doors shall be as follows:

(1) Hospitals and nursing homes—83 in. (211 cm)
(2) Psychiatric hospitals and limited care facilities—64 in. (163 cm)

Exception No. 2:* Dampers shall not be required in duct penetrations of smoke barriers in fully ducted heating, ventilating, and air conditioning systems where an approved, supervised automatic sprinkler system in accordance with 19.3.5.3 has been provided for smoke compartments adjacent to the smoke barrier.

A.19.3.7.3 Exception No. 2 Where the smoke control system design requires dampers in order that the system functions effectively, it is not the intent of the exception to permit the damper to be omitted.

This exception is not intended to prevent the use of plenum returns where ducting is used to return air from a ceiling plenum through smoke barrier walls. Short stubs or jumper ducts are not acceptable. Ducting is required to connect at both sides of the opening and to extend into adjacent spaces away from the wall. The intent is to prohibit open-air transfers at or near the smoke barrier walls.

19.3.7.4 Not less than 30 net ft² (2.8 net m²) per patient in a hospital or nursing home, or not less than 15 net ft² (1.4 net m²) per resident in a limited care facility, shall be provided within the aggregate area of corridors, patient rooms, treatment rooms, lounge or dining areas, and other low hazard areas on each side of the smoke barrier. On stories not housing bed or litterborne patients, not less than 6 net ft² (0.56 net m²) per occupant shall be provided on each side of the smoke barrier for the total number of occupants in adjoining compartments.

19.3.7.5 Openings in smoke barriers shall be protected by fire-rated glazing; by wired glass panels and steel frames; by substantial doors, such as 1¾-in. (4.4-cm) thick, solid-bonded wood core doors; or by construction that resists fire for not less than 20 minutes. Nonrated factory- or field-applied protective plates extending not more than 48 in. (122 cm) above the bottom of the door shall be permitted.

Exception: Doors shall be permitted to have fixed fire window assemblies in accordance with 8.2.3.2.2.

A.18.3.7.5 Smoke partition doors are intended to provide access to adjacent zones. The pair of cross-corridor doors are required to be opposite swinging. Access to both zones is required.

18.3.7.6* Doors in smoke barriers shall comply with 8.3.4 and shall be self-closing or automatic-closing in accordance with 18.2.2.2.6.

A.18.3.7.6 Smoke barriers might include walls having door openings other than cross-corridor doors. There is no restriction in the *Code* regarding which doors or how many doors form part of a smoke barrier. For example, doors from the corridor to individual rooms are permitted to form part of a smoke barrier.

18.3.7.7* Vision panels consisting of fire-rated glazing or wire glass panels in approved frames shall be provided in each cross-corridor swinging door and at each cross-corridor horizontal sliding door in a smoke barrier.

A.18.3.7.7 It is not the intent to require the frame to be a listed assembly.

18.3.7.8 Rabbets, bevels, or astragals shall be required at the meeting edges, and stops shall be required at the head and sides of door frames in smoke barriers. Positive latching hardware shall not be required. Center mullions shall be prohibited.

19.3.7.6* Doors in smoke barriers shall comply with 8.3.4 and shall be self-closing or automatic-closing in accordance with 19.2.2.2.6. Such doors in smoke barriers shall not be required to swing with egress travel. Positive latching hardware shall not be required.

A.19.3.7.6 Smoke barriers might include walls having door openings other than cross-corridor doors. There is no restriction in the *Code* regarding which doors or how many doors form part of a smoke barrier. For example, doors from the corridor to individual rooms are permitted to form part of a smoke barrier.

19.3.7.7 Door openings in smoke barriers shall be protected by a swinging door providing a clear width of not less than 32 in. (81 cm) or by a horizontal sliding door complying with 7.2.1.14 and providing a clear width of not less than 32 in. (81 cm).

Exception: *Existing 34-in. (86-cm) doors.*

Paragraph 18.3.7.1 requires that all floors of a building housing a new health care occupancy—other than those meeting one of the four exceptions to 18.3.7.1—be subdivided into smoke compartments.

Paragraph 18.3.7.1(1) requires subdivision of any floor used by inpatients for sleeping or treatment into at least two smoke compartments, regardless of size or number of patients. Paragraph 18.3.7.1(2) requires any floor with an occupant load of 50 or more persons, regardless of size or use, to be subdivided into two smoke compartments, using smoke barriers. However, Exception Nos. 1 through 4 provide exemptions for some non-health care occupancy floors.

Exhibit 18/19.17 illustrates the use of 18.3.7.1(1) and (2) and the four exceptions.

- Floors 10 through 12 do not contain a health care occupancy and are located above the health care

occupancy—per Exception No. 1, they do not require smoke barriers.
- Floors 6B through 9B are health care occupancy floors used for inpatient sleeping or treatment—per 18.3.7.1(1), they must be subdivided by smoke barriers.
- Floors 6A through 9A do not contain a health care occupancy and are separated from the health care occupancy by 2-hour fire resistance–rated barriers complying with the provisions of 7.2.4.3 applicable to horizontal exit fire barriers—per Exception No. 2, they do not require smoke barriers.
- Floor 5 does not contain a health care occupancy and does not meet Exception No. 3 because it is not more than one story below the health care occupancy—per 18.3.7.1(2) it must be subdivided by smoke barriers if it has an occupant load of 50 or more persons.

CHAPTER 18 • New   **CHAPTER 19 • Existing**

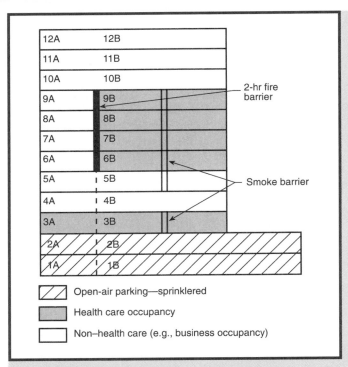

12A   12B
11A   11B
10A   10B
9A   9B   ← 2-hr fire barrier
8A   8B
7A   7B
6A   6B
5A   5B   ← Smoke barrier
4A   4B
3A   3B

[///] Open-air parking—sprinklered

[▓] Health care occupancy

[ ] Non–health care (e.g., business occupancy)

Exhibit 18/19.17 Smoke barriers for new health care occupancy buildings.

• Floor 4 does not contain a health care occupancy and is more than one story below the health care occupancy—per Exception No. 3, it does not require smoke barriers.

• Floor 3 is a health care occupancy floor used for inpatient sleeping or treatment—per 18.3.7.1(1), it must be subdivided by smoke barriers.

• Floors 1 and 2 are used as an open-air parking structure and are protected by a supervised automatic sprinkler system—even though floor 2 is located immediately below a health care occupancy floor, Exception No. 4 exempts these floors from the smoke barrier requirement.

For existing health care occupancies, the first sentence of 19.3.7.1 requires smoke barriers only for the purpose of subdividing stories having sleeping rooms for more than 30 patients. Subdivision is not required on treatment floors (provided there are no sleeping rooms) regardless of area or number of patients. Patient bed capacity is to be used (see 19.3.7.2) to determine the number of patients per story.

Paragraphs 18.3.7.1(3) and (4) and the second sentence of 19.3.7.1 do not present criteria related to whether smoke barriers are required in a building. Rather, they specify dimensional criteria for smoke compartments to establish limits for maximum size, given that smoke barriers are required by 18.3.7.1(1) or (2) or the first sentence of 19.3.7.1. The maximum area of any smoke compartment created by subdividing the floor cannot exceed 22,500 ft² (2100 m²). If the compartment were perfectly square, this would involve a 150 ft × 150 ft (45 m × 45 m) area. However, to provide the facility and designer with flexibility in the arrangement of smoke compartments, the arbitrary 150-ft (45-m) length and width limits of earlier editions were replaced in 1991 by a 200-ft (60-m) travel limitation to a door in the smoke barrier [see 18.3.7.1(4) and the second sentence of 19.3.7.1]. Smoke compartments must be designed so that a person is able to reach a smoke barrier door within a distance of travel of 200 ft (60 m) from any point in a compartment, measured along the natural path of travel in accordance with 7.6.2. However, the travel limitation is exempted for existing smoke compartments where neither the length nor width exceeds 150 ft (45 m) in accordance with Exception No. 1 to 19.3.7.1.

In Exhibit 18/19.18, the construction of one smoke barrier divides the floor into two smoke compartments. If either smoke compartment—one consisting of the combination of areas A and B or the other consisting of area C—exceeds 22,500 ft² (2100 m²) or requires occupant travel in excess of 200 ft (60 m) to reach the doors in the smoke barrier, further subdivision using additional smoke barriers is required. For existing smoke compartments, in lieu of meeting the 200-ft (60-m) travel limitation, the existing arrangement is permitted to be continued if neither the compartment length nor width exceeds 150 ft (45 m). Assuming that the smoke compartment consisting of the combination of areas A and B is too large to meet the specified conditions, a second smoke barrier extending from point X to point Y might provide a logical solution.

Exhibit 18/19.19 illustrates the travel distance limitation to a door in a smoke barrier. Although the room positioned at the top of exhibit between the smoke barrier and the enclosed exit stair has a short travel distance to an exit (distance X to E), the enclosed exit stair is not usable by those incapable of self-preservation. Therefore, the distance of travel to the doors in the smoke barrier (distance X to E to B)

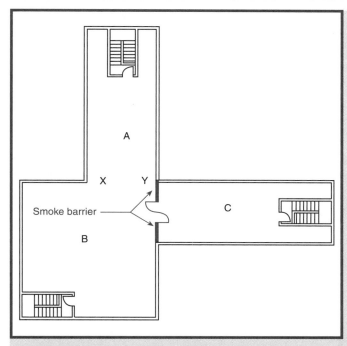

Exhibit 18/19.18 Smoke barrier dividing floor into two smoke compartments.

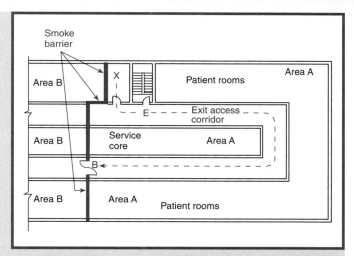

Exhibit 18/19.19 Limited travel distance to door in smoke barrier.

must not exceed 200 ft (60 m). For the existing smoke compartment the 200-ft (60-m) criterion would be exempted if neither the smoke compartment length nor the width exceeds 150 ft (45 m). For this floor plan, an additional pair of doors in the smoke barrier where it crosses the corridor in the top half of the exhibit might provide a logical solution to a travel distance problem.

Horizontal exits are permitted to be substituted for smoke barriers. In such cases, the horizontal exit would also have to be constructed to comply with smoke barrier requirements. See Section 8.3.

Areas open to atriums are not permitted to be used for patient sleeping or treatment areas (see Exception No. 2 to 18/19.3.1.1). Atrium smoke compartments arranged in accordance with 8.2.5.6 are not limited in size.

Paragraph 18/19.3.7.5 addresses smoke barrier doors. Although the cross-corridor smoke barrier doors in new health care occupancies are required to resist the penetration of fire for at least 20 minutes, they are not required to have a true fire protection rating. Similarly, the smoke-barrier doors in existing health care occupancies are not required to have a

true fire protection rating. Yet, some persons incorrectly consider these $1^3/_4$-in. (4.4-cm) thick, solid-bonded wood doors to be 20-minute fire protection–rated doors from which the latch has been omitted. If the door were truly a 20-minute fire protection–rated assembly, field-applied protective plates would be prohibited. The second sentence of 18/19.3.7.5 reminds the user that factory- or field-applied protective plates are permitted. In issuing that reminder, 18/19.3.7.5 sets an arbitrary maximum height of 48 in. (122 cm) above which the protective plate cannot extend. Paragraph 18/19.3.7.5 gives the proponents for protective plates the specific permission they requested—but in doing so, adds a height restriction that did not exist when the *Code* was silent on the subject of protective plates on "nonrated" smoke barrier doors.

During a fire, the emergency evacuation of patients in a health care facility is an inefficient, time-consuming process. Realistically, if patients must be moved, sizable numbers of occupants can be relocated only through horizontal travel. Smoke barriers and horizontal exits used to subdivide a building serve three purposes fundamental to the protection of inpatients:

(1) They limit the spread of fire and smoke.
(2) They limit the number of occupants exposed to a single fire.
(3) They provide for horizontal relocation of patients by creating a safe area on the same floor level.

The smoke barrier requirements result in a floor's area being divided by a barrier into a minimum of two compartments. Although not stated in the *Code*, it would be desirable to subdivide health care facilities in such a way as to have separate banks of elevators in different smoke zones. Should evacuation of the building become necessary, patients can first be moved horizontally to a temporary area of refuge and then be removed from the floor via elevators.

In new health care occupancies the openings between the meeting edges of pairs of smoke barrier doors and between the doors and frames must be minimized to retard the transfer of smoke. Because 18.3.7.5 requires these doors to swing in opposite directions from each other, the protection at the meeting edge does not create a coordination problem and, therefore, is simple to provide. An overlapping astragal plate on the leading edge of one of the doors will usually suffice for compliance with 18.3.7.8.

Dampers are not required in ducted penetrations of smoke barriers in new health care occupancies (see Exception No. 2 to 18.3.7.3). This exception anticipates that fire size will be limited by automatic sprinklers and that duct systems will also inhibit the transfer of smoke. This exception does not prohibit the installation of smoke dampers, nor does it exempt the smoke damper if required for other reasons. For example, if the building has a smoke-control system that needs a smoke damper at the smoke barrier, then it must be installed. An automatic-closing damper, activated by a smoke detector, would be required to protect a transfer grille.

Note that, for existing smoke barriers, the combination fire/smoke dampers required in 8.3.5 are permitted to be omitted in engineered smoke control systems if the system design is such that a damper is not required at that point. Exception No. 2 to 19.3.7.3 also permits deletion of dampers in ducted penetrations of smoke barriers where compartments adjacent to the barrier are protected by automatic sprinklers. This exception would not be permitted if an engineered smoke control system required a damper at this point. Openings for transfer grilles require automatic-closing dampers.

Exhibits 18/19.20(a) and 18/19.20(b) illustrate some of the detailed requirements of 18/19.3.7 for subdividing building spaces through the use of smoke barriers.

In Exhibit 18/19.21, the smoke barrier requirement for a building with an atrium is satisfied by

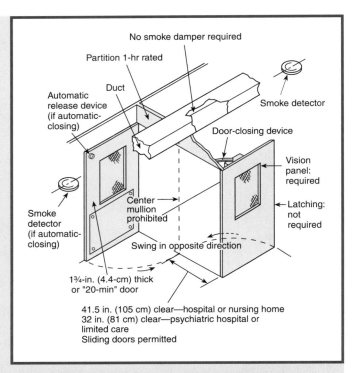

Exhibit 18/19.20(a) *Details of new smoke barrier.*

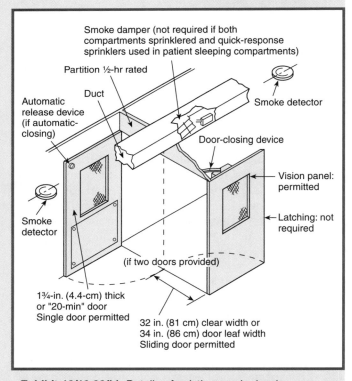

Exhibit 18/19.20(b) *Details of existing smoke barrier.*

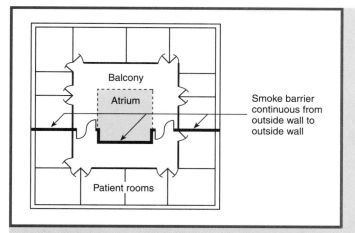

Exhibit 18/19.21 *Smoke compartments in atrium building.*

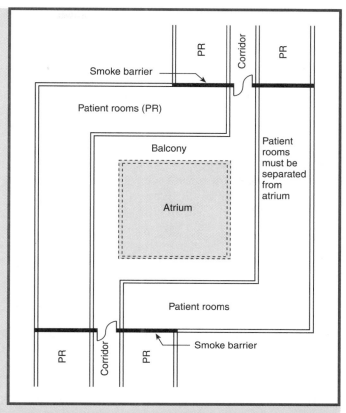

Exhibit 18/19.22 *Atrium smoke compartment with unlimited area.*

running the smoke barrier partition directly through the building from one outside wall to the opposite outside wall and hugging one edge of the open atrium space. In Exhibit 18/19.22, the exception to 18.3.7.1(3) or Exception No. 2 to 19.3.7.1 is used to permit the smoke compartment containing the atrium to be unlimited in size. The patient floor is divided into three smoke compartments by locating two smoke barriers away from the atrium opening and thus preserving the visual impact of the atrium. The center smoke compartment, which includes the atrium, is not limited in size, but the distance of travel from any point to a smoke barrier door is limited to 200 ft (60 m).

18.3.8* Special Protection Features—Outside Window or Door.

Every patient sleeping room shall have an outside window or outside door. The allowable sill height shall not exceed 36 in. (91 cm) above the floor.

Exception No. 1:   Newborn nurseries and rooms intended for occupancy for less than 24 hours, such as those housing obstetrical labor beds, recovery beds, and observation beds in the emergency department.

Exception No. 2:   Windows in atrium walls shall be considered outside windows for the purposes of this requirement.

Exception No. 3:   The window sill in special nursing care areas, such as those housing ICU, CCU, hemodialysis, and neonatal patients, shall not exceed 60 in. (152 cm) above the floor.

19.3.8 Special Protection Features—Outside Window or Door.

Every patient sleeping room shall have an outside window or outside door.

Exception No. 1:   Newborn nurseries and rooms intended for occupancy for less than 24 hours, such as those housing obstetrical labor beds, recovery beds, and observation beds in the emergency department.

Exception No. 2:   Windows in atrium walls shall be considered outside windows for the purposes of this requirement.

CHAPTER 18 • New	CHAPTER 19 • Existing

Exception No. 4:   The window sill in limited care facilities shall not exceed 44 in. (112 cm) above the floor.

A.18.3.8 Individual sleeping cubicles within sleeping suites, as permitted by 18.2.5.3, are not required to have an outside window or outside door in each cubicle, provided that not less than one outside window or outside door is provided in the suite or that the requirements of 18.3.8, Exception No. 3, are met.

Paragraphs 18.3.8.1 and 19.3.8 requires an outside door or outside window in each room where patients sleep. The window is not required to be operable. A maximum allowable sill height of 36 in. (91 cm) is specified for new health care occupancies, except in special nursing care areas (for example, recovery rooms, intensive care units, coronary care units, and dialysis units) where the sill height is permitted to be not more than 60 in. (152 cm) above the floor. Limited care facility designs are frequently similar to residential-type buildings. Sill height has been set at a maximum of 44 in. (112 cm) above the floor in new limited care facilities, consistent with residential construction practices. Sill height is limited in new construction to ensure access to the window should it ever need to be used for ventilation purposes.

Rooms that are occupied for less than 24 hours, such as those used for recovery, child delivery, or emergency care, or rooms used for newborn nurseries need not be provided with a window. These rooms are exempted from the requirements for windows because the high incidence of direct nursing supervision of all patients in these areas reduces the likelihood that patients will be trapped in a smoky fire. However, where it is not possible to provide windows, a conservative design should provide some added protection, such as early warning by smoke detectors, or high-volume exhaust ventilation.

Section 18.4 Special Provisions

18.4.1 Windowless Buildings.

Windowless buildings or windowless portions of buildings shall not be used for patient sleeping rooms. Windowless buildings or windowless portions of buildings shall comply with Section 11.7.

18.4.2 High-Rise Buildings.

High-rise buildings shall comply with Section 11.8.

Section 19.4 Special Provisions

19.4.1 Windowless Buildings.

See Section 11.7 for requirements for windowless buildings.

19.4.2 High-Rise Buildings.

(Reserved.)

Section 18.5 Building Services

18.5.1 Utilities.

18.5.1.1 Utilities shall comply with the provisions of Section 9.1.

18.5.1.2 Power for alarms, emergency communication systems, and illumination of generator set locations shall be in accordance with the essential electrical system requirements of NFPA 99, *Standard for Health Care Facilities.*

Section 19.5 Building Services

19.5.1 Utilities.

Utilities shall comply with the provisions of Section 9.1.

Exception: Existing installations shall be permitted to be continued in service, provided that the systems do not present a serious hazard to life.

18.5.1.3 Any health care occupancy, as indicated in 18.1.1.1.2, that normally uses life-support devices shall have electrical systems designed and installed in accordance with NFPA 99, *Standard for Health Care Facilities*.

Exception: This requirement shall not apply to a facility that uses life-support equipment for emergency purposes only.

18.5.2 Heating, Ventilating, and Air Conditioning.

18.5.2.1 Heating, ventilating, and air conditioning shall comply with the provisions of Section 9.2 and shall be installed in accordance with the manufacturer's specifications.

Exception: As modified in 18.5.2.2.

18.5.2.2* Any heating device other than a central heating plant shall be designed and installed so that combustible material will not be ignited by the device or its appurtenances. If fuel-fired, such heating devices shall be chimney connected or vent connected, shall take air for combustion directly from outside, and shall be designed and installed to provide for complete separation of the combustion system from the atmosphere of the occupied area. Any heating device shall have safety features to immediately stop the flow of fuel and shut down the equipment in case of either excessive temperatures or ignition failure.

Exception No. 1: Approved, suspended unit heaters shall be permitted in locations other than means of egress and patient sleeping areas, provided that such heaters are located high enough to be out of the reach of persons using the area and are equipped with the safety features required by 18.5.2.2.

Exception No. 2: Fireplaces shall be permitted and used only in areas other than patient <u>sleeping areas</u>, provided that such areas are separated from patient sleeping spaces by construction having not less than a 1-hour fire resistance rating and that such fireplaces comply with the provisions of 9.2.2. In addition, the fireplace shall be equipped with a hearth that shall be raised not less than 4 in. (10.2 cm) and a fireplace enclosure guaranteed against breakage up to a temperature of 650°F (343°C) and constructed of heat-tempered glass or other approved material. If, in the opinion of the authority having jurisdiction, special hazards are present, a lock on the enclosure and other safety precautions shall be permitted to be required.

19.5.2 Heating, Ventilating, and Air Conditioning.

19.5.2.1 Heating, ventilating, and air conditioning shall comply with the provisions of Section 9.2 and shall be installed in accordance with the manufacturer's specifications.

Exception: As modified in 19.5.2.2.

19.5.2.2* Any heating device other than a central heating plant shall be designed and installed so that combustible material will not be ignited by the device or its appurtenances. If fuel-fired, such heating devices shall be chimney connected or vent connected, shall take air for combustion directly from the outside, and shall be designed and installed to provide for complete separation of the combustion system from the atmosphere of the occupied area. Any heating device shall have safety features to immediately stop the flow of fuel and shut down the equipment in case of either excessive temperature or ignition failure.

Exception No. 1: Approved, suspended unit heaters shall be permitted in locations other than means of egress and patient sleeping areas, provided that such heaters are located high enough to be out of the reach of persons using the area and are equipped with the safety features required by 19.5.2.2.

Exception No. 2: Fireplaces shall be permitted and used only in areas other than patient sleeping areas, provided that such areas are separated from patient sleeping spaces by construction having not less than a 1-hour fire resistance rating and that such fireplaces comply with the provisions of 9.2.2. In addition, the fireplace shall be equipped with a fireplace enclosure guaranteed against breakage up to a temperature of 650°F (343°C) and constructed of heat-tempered glass or other approved material. If, in the opinion of the authority having jurisdiction, special hazards are present, a lock on the enclosure and other safety precautions shall be permitted to be required.

CHAPTER 18 • New	CHAPTER 19 • Existing

A.18.5.2.2 For both new and existing buildings, it is the intent to permit the installation and use of fireplace stoves and room heaters utilizing solid fuel as defined in NFPA 211, *Standard for Chimneys, Fireplaces, Vents, and Solid Fuel-Burning Appliances,* provided that all such devices are installed, maintained, and used in accordance with the appropriate provisions of that standard and all manufacturers' specifications. These requirements are not intended to permit freestanding solid fuel– burning appliances such as freestanding wood-burning stoves.

A.19.5.2.2 For both new and existing buildings, it is the intent to permit the installation and use of fireplace stoves and room heaters using solid fuel as defined in NFPA 211, *Standard for Chimneys, Fireplaces, Vents, and Solid Fuel-Burning Appliances,* provided that all such devices are installed, maintained, and used in accordance with the appropriate provisions of that standard and all manufacturers' specifications. These requirements are not intended to permit freestanding solid fuel– burning appliances such as freestanding wood-burning stoves.

18.5.3 Elevators, Escalators, and Conveyors.

Elevators, escalators, and conveyors shall comply with the provisions of Section 9.4.

19.5.3 Elevators, Escalators, and Conveyors.

Elevators, escalators, and conveyors shall comply with the provisions of Section 9.4.

Paragraphs 18/19.5.2.1 and 18/19.5.2.2 specify safeguards for air conditioning, ventilating, heating, and other service equipment to minimize the possibility of such devices serving as a source of ignition. Fuel-fired heating devices, except central heating systems, must be designed to provide complete separation of the combustion system from the occupied spaces. Air for combustion must be taken directly from the outside.

A major concern is preventing the ignition of clothing, bedclothes, furniture, and other furnishings by a heating device. Therefore, 18/19.7.8 prohibits portable heating devices in areas used by patients.

Paragraph 18/19.5.3 addresses elevators. Although not counted as required exits for the general populace, elevators might constitute a valuable, supplemental facility for evacuating patients from health care buildings. In some cases, using an elevator might be the only feasible way to move critically ill patients or patients in restraining devices.

Elevators, however, have many inherent weaknesses that tend to limit reliability. Elevator access doors are designed with operating tolerances that permit smoke transfer into the shaft. During a fire, a power failure might cause an elevator to stop between floors, trapping its passengers. Elevators might, during their descent from upper floors, stop automatically at the floor where the fire is burning, allow the doors to open, and expose the occupants to the fire.

Many of these weaknesses can be minimized by providing emergency power, separating the elevator lobby from other building spaces using rated construction, designing detection and alarm equipment to prevent elevators from stopping at a floor exposed to a fire, providing an emergency smoke control system, and pressurizing the elevator shaft and adjacent lobbies. These countermeasures represent good fire protection judgment but are not the result of any requirements of this *Code.*

Through emergency planning and staff training, the potential problem of crowded elevators might be avoided. Emergency plans can make effective use of elevators by transferring patients through a horizontal exit, for example, to a separate fire area. Within the separate fire area, a staged evacuation program could be instituted, with the elevators taking patients to the ground level, permitting horizontal movement to the outside.

18.5.4 Rubbish Chutes, Incinerators, and Laundry Chutes.

18.5.4.1 Rubbish chutes, incinerators, and laundry chutes shall comply with the provisions of Section 9.5.

19.5.4 Rubbish Chutes, Incinerators, and Laundry Chutes.

19.5.4.1 Any existing linen and trash chute, including pneumatic rubbish and linen systems, that opens directly onto any corridor shall be sealed by fire-resistive construction to prevent further use or shall be provided with a fire door assembly having a fire protection rating of 1 hour. All new chutes shall comply with Section 9.5.

18.5.4.2 Any rubbish chute or linen chute, including pneumatic rubbish and linen systems, shall be provided with automatic extinguishing protection in accordance with Section 9.7. *(See Section 9.5.)*

18.5.4.3 Any trash chute shall discharge into a trash collection room used for no other purpose and protected in accordance with Section 8.4.

18.5.4.4 Incinerators shall not be directly flue-fed, nor shall any floor charging chute directly connect with the combustion chamber.

Section 18.6 Reserved

Section 18.7* Operating Features

A.18.7 Health care occupants have, in large part, varied degrees of physical disability, and their removal to the outside or even their disturbance caused by moving is inexpedient or impractical in many cases, except as a last resort. Similarly, recognizing that there might be an operating necessity for the restraint of the mentally ill, often by use of barred windows and locked doors, fire exit drills are usually extremely disturbing, detrimental, and frequently impracticable.

In most cases, fire exit drills, as ordinarily practiced in other occupancies, cannot be conducted in health care occupancies. Fundamentally, superior construction, early discovery and extinguishment of incipient fires, and prompt notification need to be relied on to reduce the occasion for evacuation of buildings of this class to a minimum.

18.7.1 Evacuation and Relocation Plan and Fire Drills.

18.7.1.1 The administration of every health care occupancy shall have, in effect and available to all supervisory personnel, written copies of a plan for the protection of all persons in the event of fire, for their evacuation to areas of refuge, and for their evacuation from the building when necessary. All employees shall be periodically instructed and kept informed with respect to their duties under the plan. A copy of the plan shall be readily available at all times in the telephone operator's position or at the security center.

The provisions of 18.7.1.2 through 18.7.2.3 shall apply.

19.5.4.2 Any rubbish chute or linen chute, including pneumatic rubbish and linen systems, shall be provided with automatic extinguishing protection in accordance with Section 9.7. *(See Section 9.5.)*

19.5.4.3 Any trash chute shall discharge into a trash collection room used for no other purpose and protected in accordance with Section 8.4.

19.5.4.4 Existing flue-fed incinerators shall be sealed by fire-resistive construction to prevent further use.

Section 19.6 Reserved

Section 19.7* Operating Features

A.19.7 Health care occupants have, in large part, varied degrees of physical disability, and their removal to the outside or even their disturbance caused by moving is inexpedient or impractical in many cases, except as a last resort. Similarly, recognizing that there might be an operating necessity for the restraint of the mentally ill, often by use of barred windows and locked doors, fire exit drills are usually extremely disturbing, detrimental, and frequently impracticable.

In most cases, fire exit drills, as ordinarily practiced in other occupancies, cannot be conducted in health care occupancies. Fundamentally, superior construction, early discovery and extinguishment of incipient fires, and prompt notification needs to be relied on to reduce the occasion for evacuation of buildings of this class to a minimum.

19.7.1 Evacuation and Relocation Plan and Fire Drills.

19.7.1.1 The administration of every health care occupancy shall have, in effect and available to all supervisory personnel, written copies of a plan for the protection of all persons in the event of fire, for their evacuation to areas of refuge, and for their evacuation from the building when necessary. All employees shall be periodically instructed and kept informed with respect to their duties under the plan. A copy of the plan shall be readily available at all times in the telephone operator's position or at the security center.

The provisions of 19.7.1.2 through 19.7.2.3 shall apply.

| **CHAPTER 18 • New** | **CHAPTER 19 • Existing** |

18.7.1.2* Fire drills in health care occupancies shall include the transmission of a fire alarm signal and simulation of emergency fire conditions. Drills shall be conducted quarterly on each shift to familiarize facility personnel (nurses, interns, maintenance engineers, and administrative staff) with the signals and emergency action required under varied conditions. When drills are conducted between 9:00 p.m. (2100 hours) and 6:00 a.m. (0600 hours), a coded announcement shall be permitted to be used instead of audible alarms.

Exception: Infirm or bedridden patients shall not be required to be moved during drills to safe areas or to the exterior of the building.

A.18.7.1.2 Many health care occupancies conduct fire drills without disturbing patients by choosing the location of the simulated emergency in advance and by closing the doors to patients' rooms or wards in the vicinity prior to initiation of the drill. The purpose of a fire drill is to test and evaluate the efficiency, knowledge, and response of institutional personnel in implementing the facility fire emergency plan. Its purpose is not to disturb or excite patients. Fire drills should be scheduled on a random basis to ensure that personnel in health care facilities are drilled not less than once in each 3-month period.

Drills should consider the ability to move patients to an adjacent smoke compartment. Relocation can be practiced using simulated patients or empty wheelchairs.

18.7.1.3 Employees of health care occupancies shall be instructed in life safety procedures and devices.

The former requirement for patient beds to be on wheels or casters was deleted from the *Code* in 1991. Ordinary practice in health care occupancies is to move patients through the hospital on narrow beds, on guerneys, on carts, or in wheelchairs. Thus, hospitals have little experience in moving patients in large beds. In addition, the furniture in rooms—chairs, nightstands, food trays/tables, and medical equipment—must be moved out of the way to allow patient

18.7.2 Procedure in Case of Fire.

18.7.2.1* For health care occupancies, the proper protection of patients shall require the prompt and effective response of health care personnel. The basic response required of staff shall include the removal of all occupants directly involved with the fire emergency, transmission of an appropriate fire alarm signal to warn other building occupants and

---

19.7.1.2* Fire drills in health care occupancies shall include the transmission of a fire alarm signal and simulation of emergency fire conditions. Drills shall be conducted quarterly on each shift to familiarize facility personnel (nurses, interns, maintenance engineers, and administrative staff) with the signals and emergency action required under varied conditions. When drills are conducted between 9:00 p.m. (2100 hours) and 6:00 a.m. (0600 hours), a coded announcement shall be permitted to be used instead of audible alarms.

Exception: Infirm or bedridden patients shall not be required to be moved during drills to safe areas or to the exterior of the building.

A.19.7.1.2 Many health care occupancies conduct fire drills without disturbing patients by choosing the location of the simulated emergency in advance and by closing the doors to patients' rooms or wards in the vicinity prior to initiation of the drill. The purpose of a fire drill is to test and evaluate the efficiency, knowledge, and response of institutional personnel in implementing the facility fire emergency plan. Its purpose is not to disturb or excite patients. Fire drills should be scheduled on a random basis to ensure that personnel in health care facilities are drilled not less than once in each 3-month period.

Drills should consider the ability to move patients to an adjacent smoke compartment. Relocation can be practiced using simulated patients or empty wheelchairs.

19.7.1.3 Employees of health care occupancies shall be instructed in life safety procedures and devices.

beds to be turned and moved out of the room. Moving patients in this way requires extra staff time that is usually unavailable during a fire. Emphasis should be placed on the quick movement of patients who are in the room of fire origin, as well as others who are directly exposed to the fire. Patient movement in fire emergencies is often achieved by dragging occupants on bedding, as opposed to moving beds.

19.7.2 Procedure in Case of Fire.

19.7.2.1* For health care occupancies, the proper protection of patients shall require the prompt and effective response of health care personnel. The basic response required of staff shall include the removal of all occupants directly involved with the fire emergency, transmission of an appropriate fire alarm signal to warn other building occupants and summon staff, confinement of the effects of the fire by closing doors to isolate the fire area, and the relocation of patients as detailed in the health care occupancy's fire safety plan.

A.18.7.2.1 Each facility has specific characteristics that vary sufficiently from other facilities to prevent the specification of a universal emergency procedure. The following recommendations, however, contain many of the elements that should be considered and adapted as appropriate to the individual facility.

Upon discovery of fire, personnel should immediately take the following action.

(a) If any person is involved in the fire, the discoverer should go to the aid of that person, calling aloud an established code phrase. The use of a code provides for both the immediate aid of any endangered person and the transmission of an alarm. Any person in the area, upon hearing the code called aloud, should activate the building fire alarm using the nearest manual fire alarm box.

(b) If a person is not involved in the fire, the discoverer should activate the building fire alarm using the nearest manual fire alarm box.

(c) Personnel, upon hearing the alarm signal, should immediately execute their duties as outlined in the facility fire safety plan.

(d) The telephone operator should determine the location of the fire as indicated by the audible signal. In a building equipped with an uncoded alarm system, a person on the floor of fire origin should be responsible for promptly notifying the facility telephone operator of the fire location.

(e) If the telephone operator receives a telephone alarm reporting a fire from a floor, the operator should regard that alarm in the same fashion as an alarm received over the fire alarm system. The operator should immediately notify the fire department and alert all facility personnel of the place of fire and its origin.

(f) If the building fire alarm system is out of order, any person discovering a fire should immediately notify the telephone operator by telephone. The operator should then transmit this information to the fire department and alert the building occupants.

18.7.2.2 A written health care occupancy fire safety plan shall provide for the following:

(1) Use of alarms
(2) Transmission of alarm to fire department
(3) Response to alarms

summon staff, confinement of the effects of the fire by closing doors to isolate the fire area, and the relocation of patients as detailed in the health care occupancy's fire safety plan.

A.19.7.2.1 Each facility has specific characteristics that vary sufficiently from other facilities to prevent the specification of a universal emergency procedure. The following recommendations, however, contain many of the elements that should be considered and adapted as appropriate to the individual facility.

Upon discovery of fire, personnel should immediately take the following action.

(a) If any person is involved in the fire, the discoverer should go to the aid of that person, calling aloud an established code phrase. The use of a code provides for both the immediate aid of any endangered person and the transmission of an alarm. Any person in the area, upon hearing the code called aloud, should activate the building fire alarm using the nearest manual fire alarm box.

(b) If a person is not involved in the fire, the discoverer should activate the building fire alarm using the nearest manual fire alarm box.

(c) Personnel, upon hearing the alarm signal, should immediately execute their duties as outlined in the facility fire safety plan.

(d) The telephone operator should determine the location of the fire as indicated by the audible signal. In a building equipped with an uncoded alarm system, a person on the floor of fire origin should be responsible for promptly notifying the facility telephone operator of the fire location.

(e) If the telephone operator receives a telephone alarm reporting a fire from a floor, the operator should regard that alarm in the same fashion as an alarm received over the fire alarm system. The operator should immediately notify the fire department and alert all facility personnel of the place of fire and its origin.

(f) If the building fire alarm system is out of order, any person discovering a fire should immediately notify the telephone operator by telephone. The operator should then transmit this information to the fire department and alert the building occupants.

19.7.2.2 A written health care occupancy fire safety plan shall provide for the following:

(1) Use of alarms
(2) Transmission of alarm to fire department
(3) Response to alarms

CHAPTER 18 • New	CHAPTER 19 • Existing

(4) Isolation of fire
(5) Evacuation of immediate area
(6) Evacuation of smoke compartment
(7) Preparation of floors and building for evacuation
(8) Extinguishment of fire

18.7.2.3 All health care occupancy personnel shall be instructed in the use of and response to fire alarms. In addition, they shall be instructed in the use of the code phrase to ensure transmission of an alarm under the following conditions:

(1) When the individual who discovers a fire must immediately go to the aid of an endangered person
(2) During a malfunction of the building fire alarm system

Personnel hearing the code announced shall first activate the building fire alarm using the nearest manual fire alarm box and then shall execute immediately their duties as outlined in the fire safety plan.

In addition to the requirements of 18/19.7.2, evacuation plans should stress that the doors of as many patient rooms as possible be closed to block smoke spreading from a fire and, if possible, to confine the fire in a room. This single action taken by the staff (that is, manually closing the doors) achieves the level of safety to life mandated by the *Code* in Chapters 18 and 19. In studies of fires in health care institutions in which the staff closed doors and subsequent responders left the doors closed, the fire spread was

18.7.3 Maintenance of Exits.

Proper maintenance shall be provided to ensure the dependability of the method of evacuation selected. Health care occupancies that find it necessary to lock exits shall, at all times, maintain an adequate staff qualified to release locks and direct occupants from the immediate danger area to a place of safety in case of fire or other emergency.

18.7.4* Smoking.

Smoking regulations shall be adopted and shall include not less than the following provisions:

(1) Smoking shall be prohibited in any room, ward, or compartment where flammable liquids, combustible gases, or oxygen is used or stored and in any other hazardous location, and such areas shall be posted with signs that read NO SMOKING or shall be posted with the international symbol for no smoking.

---

(4) Isolation of fire
(5) Evacuation of immediate area
(6) Evacuation of smoke compartment
(7) Preparation of floors and building for evacuation
(8) Extinguishment of fire

19.7.2.3 All health care occupancy personnel shall be instructed in the use of and response to fire alarms. In addition, they shall be instructed in the use of the code phrase to ensure transmission of an alarm under the following conditions:

(1) When the individual who discovers a fire must immediately go to the aid of an endangered person
(2) During a malfunction of the building fire alarm system

Personnel hearing the code announced shall first activate the building fire alarm using the nearest manual fire alarm box and then shall execute immediately their duties as outlined in the fire safety plan.

readily confined, and either there was no loss of life or loss of life was low.
In many fatality fires in health care facilities, staff either did not close doors or someone reopened them. The fire spread was sizable, and the loss of life was high. Emphasis must be placed on training staff to sound an alarm, to rescue patients (as needed), and then to close all doors. The closing of doors historically has had the most significant effect on limiting the spread of fire and smoke.

19.7.3 Maintenance of Exits.

Proper maintenance shall be provided to ensure the dependability of the method of evacuation selected. Health care occupancies that find it necessary to lock exits shall, at all times, maintain an adequate staff qualified to release locks and direct occupants from the immediate danger area to a place of safety in case of fire or other emergency.

19.7.4* Smoking.

Smoking regulations shall be adopted and shall include not less than the following provisions:

(1) Smoking shall be prohibited in any room, ward, or compartment where flammable liquids, combustible gases, or oxygen is used or stored and in any other hazardous location, and such areas shall be posted with signs that read NO SMOKING or shall be posted with the international symbol for no smoking.

CHAPTER 18 • New	CHAPTER 19 • Existing

Exception: In health care occupancies where smoking is prohibited and signs are prominently placed at all major entrances, secondary signs with language that prohibits smoking shall not be required.

(2) Smoking by patients classified as not responsible shall be prohibited.

Exception: The requirement of 18.7.4(2) shall not apply where the patient is under direct supervision.

(3) Ashtrays of noncombustible material and safe design shall be provided in all areas where smoking is permitted.

(4) Metal containers with self-closing cover devices into which ashtrays can be emptied shall be readily available to all areas where smoking is permitted.

A.18.7.4 The most rigid discipline with regard to prohibition of smoking might not be nearly as effective in reducing incipient fires from surreptitious smoking as the open recognition of smoking, with provision of suitable facilities for smoking. Proper education and training of the staff and attendants in the ordinary fire hazards and their abatement is unquestionably essential. The problem is a broad one, varying with different types and arrangements of buildings; the effectiveness of rules of procedure, which need to be flexible, depends in large part on the management.

18.7.5 Furnishings, Bedding, and Decorations.

18.7.5.1* Draperies, curtains, including cubicle curtains, and other loosely hanging fabrics and films serving as furnishings or decorations in health care occupancies shall be in accordance with the provisions of 10.3.1. *(See 18.3.5.5.)*

Exception: Curtains at showers.

A.18.7.5.1 In addition to the provisions of 10.3.1, which deal with ignition resistance, additional requirements with respect to the location of cubicle curtains relative to sprinkler placement are included in NFPA 13, *Standard for the Installation of Sprinkler Systems.*

18.7.5.2 Newly introduced upholstered furniture within health care occupancies shall meet the criteria specified when tested in accordance with the methods cited in 10.3.2(2) and 10.3.3.

Exception: In health care occupancies where smoking is prohibited and signs are prominently placed at all major entrances, secondary signs with language that prohibits smoking shall not be required.

(2) Smoking by patients classified as not responsible shall be prohibited.

Exception: The requirement of 19.7.4(2) shall not apply where the patient is under direct supervision.

(3) Ashtrays of noncombustible material and safe design shall be provided in all areas where smoking is permitted.

(4) Metal containers with self-closing cover devices into which ashtrays can be emptied shall be readily available to all areas where smoking is permitted.

A.19.7.4 The most rigid discipline with regard to prohibition of smoking might not be nearly as effective in reducing incipient fires from surreptitious smoking as the open recognition of smoking, with provision of suitable facilities for smoking. Proper education and training of the staff and attendants in the ordinary fire hazards and their abatement is unquestionably essential. The problem is a broad one, varying with different types and arrangements of buildings; the effectiveness of rules of procedure, which need to be flexible, depends in large part on the management.

19.7.5 Furnishings, Bedding, and Decorations.

19.7.5.1* Draperies, curtains, including cubicle curtains, and other loosely hanging fabrics and films serving as furnishings or decorations in health care occupancies shall be in accordance with the provisions of 10.3.1. *(See 19.3.5.5.)*

Exception: Curtains at showers.

A.19.7.5.1 In addition to the provisions of 10.3.1, which deal with ignition resistance, additional requirements with respect to the location of cubicle curtains relative to sprinkler placement are included in NFPA 13, *Standard for the Installation of Sprinkler Systems.*

19.7.5.2 Newly introduced upholstered furniture within health care occupancies shall meet the criteria specified when tested in accordance with the methods cited in 10.3.2(2) and 10.3.3.

Exception: Upholstered furniture belonging to the patient in sleeping rooms of nursing homes, provided that a smoke detector is installed in such rooms. Battery-powered single-station smoke detectors shall be permitted.

18.7.5.3 Newly introduced mattresses within health care occupancies shall meet the criteria specified when tested in accordance with the methods cited in 10.3.2(3) and 10.3.4.

18.7.5.4 Combustible decorations shall be prohibited in any health care occupancy unless they are flame-retardant.

Exception: Combustible decorations, such as photographs and paintings, in such limited quantities that a hazard of fire development or spread is not present.

18.7.5.5 Soiled linen or trash collection receptacles shall not exceed 32 gal (121 L) in capacity. The average density of container capacity in a room or space shall not exceed 0.5 gal/ft^2 (20.4 L/m^2). A capacity of 32 gal (121 L) shall not be exceeded within any 64-ft^2 (5.9-m^2) area. Mobile soiled linen or trash collection receptacles with capacities greater than 32 gal (121 L) shall be located in a room protected as a hazardous area when not attended.

Exception: Container size and density shall not be limited in hazardous areas.

19.7.5.3 Newly introduced mattresses within health care occupancies shall meet the criteria specified when tested in accordance with the methods cited in 10.3.2(3) and 10.3.4.

Exception: Mattresses belonging to the patient in sleeping rooms of nursing homes, provided that a smoke detector is installed in such rooms. Battery-powered single-station smoke detectors shall be permitted.

19.7.5.4 Combustible decorations shall be prohibited in any health care occupancy unless they are flame-retardant.

Exception: Combustible decorations, such as photographs and paintings, in such limited quantities that a hazard of fire development or spread is not present.

19.7.5.5 Soiled linen or trash collection receptacles shall not exceed 32 gal (121 L) in capacity. The average density of container capacity in a room or space shall not exceed 0.5 gal/ft^2 (20.4 L/m^2). A capacity of 32 gal (121 L) shall not be exceeded within any 64-ft^2 (5.9-m^2) area. Mobile soiled linen or trash collection receptacles with capacities greater than 32 gal (121 L) shall be located in a room protected as a hazardous area when not attended.

Exception: Container size and density shall not be limited in hazardous areas.

Cigarette ignition-resistance testing—as detailed in 10.3.2—and rate of heat release testing—as detailed in 10.3.3 and 10.3.4—are required by 18/19.7.5.2 and 18/19.7.5.3 for newly introduced upholstered furniture and newly introduced mattresses in health care occupancies, unless the room or space is sprinklered. However, these requirements would seldom apply in new health care occupancies because 18.3.5.1 requires new health care occupancies to be sprinklered. Unlike new health care occupancies—which are required to be sprinklered—many existing facilities are not sprinklered. Yet government regulations require that patients be permitted to bring their own furniture with them to a nursing home. The exception to 19.7.5.2 and the exception to 19.7.5.3 offer nonsprinklered existing health care facilities another option—providing smoke detection within the patient room. If early warning is provided to staff, then an incipient stage fire might be able to be extinguished manually almost as quickly as would occur automatically in a room that is sprinklered.

Paragraph 18/19.7.5.5 establishes maximum trash container sizes and placement densities permitted within a room. Containers larger than that specified, or grouped containers exceeding the density per room criterion, present a hazard greater than that associated with the normal furnishing of a health care occupancy room.

Large, mobile soiled linen or trash receptacles can be moved along the corridor as collections occur but must be attended by staff. If housekeeping staff, for example, must leave the area, the container must be stored in a room designed and maintained as a hazardous area in accordance with 18/19.3.2.1.

Exhibit 18/19.23 illustrates the requirements of 18/19.7.5.5.

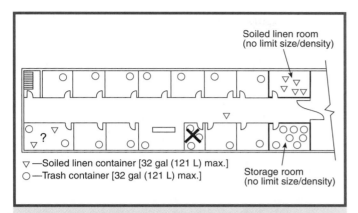

Exhibit 18/19.23 *Allowable soiled linen or trash collection receptacles.*

18.7.6 Maintenance and Testing.

(See 4.6.12.)

18.7.7* Engineered Smoke Control Systems.

New engineered smoke control systems shall be tested in accordance with established engineering principles and shall meet the performance requirements of such testing prior to acceptance. Following acceptance, all engineered smoke control systems shall be tested periodically in accordance with recognized engineering principles. Test documentation shall be maintained on the premises at all times.

A.18.7.7 Two documents that provide recognized engineering principles for the testing of smoke control systems are NFPA 92A, *Recommended Practice for Smoke-Control Systems,* and NFPA 92B, *Guide for Smoke Management Systems in Malls, Atria, and Large Areas.*

18.7.8 Portable Space-Heating Devices.

Portable space-heating devices shall be prohibited in all health care occupancies.

Exception: Portable space-heating devices shall be permitted to be used in nonsleeping staff and employee areas where the heating elements of such devices do not exceed 212°F (100°C).

18.7.9 Construction, Repair, and Improvement Operations.

18.7.9.1 Construction, repair, and improvement operations shall comply with 4.6.10.

19.7.6 Maintenance and Testing.

(See 4.6.12.)

19.7.7* Engineered Smoke Control Systems.

Existing engineered smoke control systems, unless specifically exempted by the authority having jurisdiction, shall be tested in accordance with established engineering principles. Systems not meeting the performance requirements of such testing shall be continued in operation only with the specific approval of the authority having jurisdiction.

A.19.7.7 Two documents that provide recognized engineering principles for the testing of smoke control systems are NFPA 92A, *Recommended Practice for Smoke-Control Systems,* and NFPA 92B, *Guide for Smoke Management Systems in Malls, Atria, and Large Areas.*

19.7.8 Portable Space-Heating Devices.

Portable space-heating devices shall be prohibited in all health care occupancies.

Exception: Portable space-heating devices shall be permitted to be used in nonsleeping staff and employee areas where the heating elements of such devices do not exceed 212°F (100°C).

19.7.9 Construction, Repair, and Improvement Operations.

19.7.9.1 Construction, repair, and improvement operations shall comply with 4.6.10.

CHAPTER 18 • New

CHAPTER 19 • Existing

18.7.9.2 The means of egress in any area undergoing construction, repair, or improvements shall be inspected daily for compliance with 7.1.10.1 and shall also comply with NFPA 241, *Standard for Safeguarding Construction, Alteration, and Demolition Operations.*

19.7.9.2 The means of egress in any area undergoing construction, repair, or improvements shall be inspected daily for compliance with of 7.1.10.1 and shall also comply with NFPA 241, *Standard for Safeguarding Construction, Alteration, and Demolition Operations.*

References Cited in Commentary

1. NFPA 101A, *Guide on Alternative Approaches to Life Safety*, 1998 edition, National Fire Protection Association, Quincy, MA. The edition of NFPA 101A that corresponds with the 2000 *Life Safety Code* will be published in 2001.
2. NFPA 220, *Standard on Types of Building Construction*, 1999 edition, National Fire Protection Association, Quincy, MA.
3. NFPA 241, *Standard for Safeguarding Construction, Alteration, and Demolition Operations*, 1996 edition, National Fire Protection Association, Quincy, MA.
4. NFPA 72, *National Fire Alarm Code®*, 1999 edition, National Fire Protection Association, Quincy, MA.
5. NFPA 99, *Standard for Health Care Facilities*, 1999 edition, National Fire Protection Association, Quincy, MA.
6. NFPA 30, *Flammable and Combustible Liquids Code*, 1996 edition, National Fire Protection Association, Quincy, MA.
7. NFPA 96, *Standard for Ventilation Control and Fire Protection of Commercial Cooking Operations*, 1998 edition, National Fire Protection Association, Quincy, MA.
8. W. J. Christian and T. E. Waterman, "Flame Spread in Corridors: Effects of Location and Area of Wall Finish," *Fire Journal*, Vol. 65, No. 4, pp. 25–32, July 1971.
9. R. W. Bukowski and S. M. Istvan, "A Survey of Field Experience with Smoke Detectors in Health Care Facilities," NBSIR 80-2130, Center for Fire Research, National Bureau of Standards, October 1980.
10. NFPA 13, *Standard for the Installation of Sprinkler Systems*, 1999 edition, National Fire Protection Association, Quincy, MA.
11. NFPA 80, *Standard for Fire Doors and Windows*, 1999 edition, National Fire Protection Association, Quincy, MA.
12. NFPA 90A, *Standard for the Installation of Air-Conditioning and Ventilating Systems*, 1999 edition, National Fire Protection Association, Quincy, MA.

CHAPTERS 20 and 21

New and Existing Ambulatory Health Care Occupancies

Chapters 20 and 21 address the needs of occupants of facilities that provide medical treatment on an outpatient basis. This treatment is not merely a routine medical visit such as to a doctor's office, but rather a procedure that renders the patient incapable of self-preservation. Although this description might sound similar to what one would expect of a hospital, the major difference is that an ambulatory health care facility does not provide care for any individual for an elapsed time of 24 hours or more. Rather, a patient receives treatment and then leaves the facility. Patients suffering complications that would prevent their leaving the ambulatory health care facility would typically be transported and admitted to a hospital that provides care on a 24-hour basis.

There is also an important distinction concerning the number of occupants required to constitute classification as an ambulatory health care occupancy—that number being four or more (see the definition of *ambulatory health care occupancy* in 3.3.134.1). The requirements for ambulatory health care occupancies are based on a combination of requirements—some from those that are applicable to hospitals and some that come from directly referencing the provisions of Chapters 38 and 39 for business occupancies. If a facility does not meet the definition of *ambulatory health care occupancy*, it generally needs to comply only with the requirements for a business occupancy.

Table 20/21.1 differentiates among health care, ambulatory health care, and business occupancies on the basis of patient load and care provided. Incapability of self-preservation might be the result of the use of general anesthesia or a treatment such as dialysis. Based on the scope of each of the chapters listed in the table, this approach would allow a dentist to administer general anesthesia to not more than three patients simultaneously and to be classified as a business occupancy. If the dentist expands the simultaneous administration of general anesthesia to a fourth patient, then the more stringent requirements for ambulatory health care occupancies would be applicable.

Table 20/21.1 Occupancy Classification Comparison

	Chapters 18/19 Health Care Occupancies	Chapters 20/21 Ambulatory Health Care Occupancies	Chapters 38/39 Business Occupancies
Number of patients rendered incapable of self-preservation	4 or more†	4 or more	3 or fewer
Patient care provided on 24-hour basis	Yes	No	No

†Incapability of self-preservation might exist prior to admission and be unrelated to the treatment provided (see 18/19.1.1.1.3).

CHAPTER 20 • New

CHAPTER 21 • Existing

Section 20.1 General Requirements

20.1.1 Application.

20.1.1.1 General.

20.1.1.1.1 The requirements of this chapter apply to the following:

(1) New buildings or portions thereof used as ambulatory health care occupancies *(see 1.4.1)*
(2) Additions made to, or used as, an ambulatory health care occupancy *(see 4.6.6 and 20.1.1.4)*

Exception: Additions classified as occupancies other than ambulatory health care that are properly separated from the ambulatory health care occupancy in accordance with 20.1.2.1 and conform to the requirements for the specific occupancy.

(3) Alterations, modernizations, or renovations of existing ambulatory health care occupancies *(see 4.6.7 and 20.1.1.4*
(4) Existing buildings or portions thereof upon change of occupancy to an ambulatory health care occupancy *(see 4.6.11)*

20.1.1.1.2 Ambulatory health care facilities shall comply with the provisions of Chapter 38 and this chapter, whichever is more stringent.

Ambulatory health care facilities exhibit some of the occupancy characteristics of business occupancies and some of the characteristics of health care occupancies. Chapter 20/21 prescribes a level of life safety from fire that is greater than that typically specified for business occupancies but less than that typically found in hospitals, nursing homes, and limited care facilities. See the commentary for 18/19.1.3.

Ambulatory health care facilities are required to comply with the provisions of Chapter 38/39 pertaining to business occupancies and with the additional provisions contained within Chapter 20/21. Where both Chapter 38/39 and Chapter 20/21 address a feature in different ways, the stricter application (typically that addressed by Chapter 20/21) governs. Chapter 20/21 also addresses features not covered by Chapter 38/39 (for example, subdivision of building space via smoke barriers) but similar to those required for health care occupancies by Chapter 18/19.

As an example, Exhibit 20/21.1 is a plan of a single-story, nonsprinklered, existing office building.

Section 21.1 General Requirements

21.1.1 Application.

21.1.1.1 General.

21.1.1.1.1 The requirements of this chapter apply to existing buildings or portions thereof currently occupied as an ambulatory health care occupancy. *(See also 20.1.1.1.1.)*

21.1.1.1.2 Ambulatory health care facilities shall comply with the provisions of Chapter 39 and this chapter, whichever is more stringent.

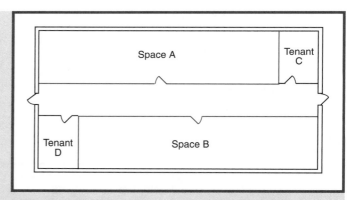

Exhibit 20/21.1 *Occupancy classification dependent on tenant use.*

Tenants C and D occupy a small portion of the floor. Most of the first floor area (spaces A and B located on opposite sides of the corridor) is available for leasing to one or more tenants. A kidney dialysis center (an ambulatory health care occupancy) plans to take space A; a multi-lawyer law practice (a business occupancy) plans to take space B. The previous tenants of both space A and space B used their leased space as offices (business occupancies).

The lawyers' office is classified as a business occupancy; and because its occupancy classification represents no change from that of the previous tenant, it is further classified as an existing business occupancy. The lawyers' office must meet the requirements of Chapter 39, which are applicable to existing business occupancies. The kidney dialysis center, whose treatment will render four or more patients simultaneously incapable of self-preservation, is clas-

sified as an ambulatory health care occupancy; and because its occupancy classification represents a change from that of the previous tenant, it is further classified as a new ambulatory health care occupancy. The kidney dialysis center must meet the requirements of Chapter 20, which are applicable to new ambulatory health care occupancies and those of Chapter 38, which are applicable to new business occupancies.

Table 20/21.2 contrasts the *Code* provisions that apply to the kidney dialysis center and the lawyers' office addressed in the preceding paragraph.

Table 20/21.2 Comparison of Applicable Requirements for Occupancy

Building Feature	Kidney Dialysis Center (new ambulatory health care occupancy)	Lawyers' Office (existing business occupancy)
Occupancy separation	Regulated by 20.1.2.1; corridor wall and partition between space A and tenant C must be 1-hour fire resistance–rated.	No regulation.
Egress door locking	Addressed by 20.1.2.4 and 20.1.1.1.5; doors permitted to be locked if for clinical needs of the patients, but staff must be present to release such locks.	Doors not permitted to be locked while space is occupied in accordance with 7.2.1.5.1.
Minimum construction	Regulated by 20.1.6, but because building is single story, any NFPA 220 construction type is acceptable.	No regulation.
Delayed-egress and access-controlled doors	Limited to exterior doors by 20.2.2.2; must meet 7.2.1.6.	No limitation other than having to meet 7.2.1.6; given that building is not sprinklered, it is doubtful that delayed-egress doors will qualify for use.
Automatic door closing	In addition to release via methods of 7.2.1.8 (smoke detection, power failure, manual action), initiation of the required fire alarm must release the hold-open devices in accordance with 20.2.2.3.	Release hold-open devices via methods of 7.2.1.8 (smoke detection, power failure, manual action).
Door width	Minimum 32-in. (81-cm) clear width in accordance with 20.2.3.3 and 7.2.1.2.3.	Minimum 28 in. (71 cm) door leaf width in accordance with Exception No. 3 to 7.2.1.2.3.
Number of exits	Minimum of two in accordance with 20.2.4.	Single exit permitted by exceptions to 39.2.4.
Number of exit accesses	Minimum of two exit access doors from suite of more than 2500 ft² (232 m²) in accordance with 20.2.4.2, or if common path of travel with single door would be excessive (see 38.2.5.3).	Second exit access door required from suite if common path of travel with single door would be excessive (see 39.2.5.3).
Travel distance	Considered in two pieces in accordance with 20.2.6; room door to exit travel (typically corridor travel) limited to 100 ft (30 m); total travel limited to 150 ft (45 m).	One consideration of total travel distance, which is limited to 200 ft (60 m) in accordance with 39.2.6.

(continues)

CHAPTER 20 • New

CHAPTER 21 • Existing

Table 20/21.2 Continued

Building Feature	Kidney Dialysis Center (new ambulatory health care occupancy)	Lawyers' Office (existing business occupancy)
Emergency lighting	Required within center and its egress paths by 20.2.9.1.	Required by 39.2.9.1 only if the single floor has occupant load of 1000 or more persons.
Alarm system	Required within center by 20.3.4; manual fire alarm boxes; automatic occupant notification; and fire department notification.	Required by 39.3.4 only if the single floor has occupant load of 1000 or more persons; automatic initiation permitted to substitute for manual fire alarm boxes; occupant notification can come from attended location; fire department notification not required.
Smoke compartmentation	Required by 20.3.7; separation required from other tenants; subdivision by smoke barriers within center unless <5000 ft² (<465 m²) and smoke detection, or <10,000 ft² (<930 m²) and sprinklers.	No regulation.
Evacuation and relocation plan	Required by 20.7.1.	No regulation.
Staff procedures in case of fire	Required by 20.7.2.	No regulation.
Control of furnishings	Required by 20.7.5 for curtains, upholstered furniture, mattresses, trash receptacles.	No regulation.

20.1.1.1.3 This chapter establishes life safety requirements, in addition to those required in Chapter 38, for the design of all ambulatory health care occupancies as defined in 3.3.8.

20.1.1.1.4 Buildings, or sections of buildings, that primarily house patients who, in the opinion of the governing body of the facility and the governmental agency having jurisdiction, are capable of judgment and appropriate physical action for self-preservation under emergency conditions shall be permitted to comply with chapters of this *Code* other than Chapter 20.

20.1.1.1.5 It shall be recognized that, in buildings providing treatment for certain types of patients or having detention rooms or a security section, it might be necessary to lock doors and bar windows to confine and protect building inhabitants. In such instances, the authority having jurisdiction shall make appropriate modifications to those sections of this *Code* that would otherwise require means of egress to be kept unlocked.

20.1.1.1.6* The requirements of this chapter are based on the assumption that staff is available in all patient-occupied areas to perform certain fire safety functions as required in other paragraphs of this chapter.

21.1.1.1.3 This chapter establishes life safety requirements, in addition to those required in Chapter 39, for the design of all ambulatory health care occupancies as defined in 3.3.8.

21.1.1.1.4 Buildings, or sections of buildings, that primarily house patients who, in the opinion of the governing body of the facility and the governmental agency having jurisdiction, are capable of judgment and appropriate physical action for self-preservation under emergency conditions shall be permitted to comply with chapters of this *Code* other than Chapter 21.

21.1.1.1.5 It shall be recognized that, in buildings providing treatment for certain types of patients or having detention rooms or a security section, it might be necessary to lock doors and bar windows to confine and protect building inhabitants. In such instances, the authority having jurisdiction shall make appropriate modifications to those sections of this *Code* that would otherwise require means of egress to be kept unlocked.

21.1.1.1.6* The requirements of this chapter are based on the assumption that staff is available in all patient-occupied areas to perform certain fire safety functions as required in other paragraphs of this chapter.

| CHAPTER 20 • New | CHAPTER 21 • Existing |

A.20.1.1.1.6 The *Code* recognizes that certain functions necessary for the life safety of building occupants, such as the closing of corridor doors, the operation of manual fire alarm devices, and the removal of patients from the room of fire origin, require the intervention of facility staff. It is not the intent of 20.1.1.1.6 to specify the levels or locations of staff necessary to meet this requirement.

20.1.1.2* Goals and Objectives. The goals and objectives of Sections 4.1 and 4.2 shall be met with due consideration for functional requirements. This is accomplished by limiting the development and spread of a fire emergency to the room of fire origin and reducing the need for occupant evacuation, except from the room of fire origin.

A.20.1.1.2 This objective is accomplished in the context of the physical facilities, the type of activities undertaken, the provisions for the capabilities of staff, and the needs of all occupants through requirements directed at the following:

(1) Prevention of ignition
(2) Detection of fire
(3) Control of fire development
(4) Confinement of the effects of fire
(5) Extinguishment of fire
(6) Provision of refuge or evacuation facilities, or both
(7) Staff reaction

20.1.1.3 Total Concept. All ambulatory health care facilities shall be designed, constructed, maintained, and operated to minimize the possibility of a fire emergency requiring the evacuation of occupants. Because the safety of ambulatory health care occupants cannot be ensured adequately by dependence on evacuation of the building, their protection from fire shall be provided by appropriate arrangement of facilities, adequate, trained staff, and development of operating and maintenance procedures composed of the following:

(1) Design, construction, and compartmentation
(2) Provision for detection, alarm, and extinguishment
(3) Fire prevention and the planning, training, and drilling programs for the isolation of fire, transfer of occupants to areas of refuge, or evacuation of the building

20.1.1.4 Additions, Conversions, Modernization, Renovation, and Construction Operations.

20.1.1.4.1 Additions. Additions shall be separated from any existing structure not conforming to the provisions within Chapter 21 by a fire barrier having not less than a 2-hour fire resistance rating and constructed of materials as required for the addition. *(See 4.6.3 and 4.6.6.)*

A.21.1.1.1.6 The *Code* recognizes that certain functions necessary for the life safety of building occupants, such as the closing of corridor doors, the operation of manual fire alarm devices, and the removal of patients from the room of fire origin, require the intervention of facility staff. It is not the intent of 21.1.1.1.6 to specify the levels or locations of staff necessary to meet this requirement.

21.1.1.2* Goals and Objectives. The goals and objectives of Sections 4.1 and 4.2 shall be met with due consideration for functional requirements. This is accomplished by limiting the development and spread of a fire emergency to the room of fire origin and reducing the need for occupant evacuation, except from the room of fire origin.

A.21.1.1.2 This objective is accomplished in the context of the physical facilities, the type of activities undertaken, the provisions for the capabilities of staff, and the needs of all occupants through requirements directed at the following:

(1) Prevention of ignition
(2) Detection of fire
(3) Control of fire development
(4) Confinement of the effects of fire
(5) Extinguishment of fire
(6) Provision of refuge or evacuation facilities, or both
(7) Staff reaction

21.1.1.3 Total Concept. All ambulatory health care facilities shall be designed, constructed, maintained, and operated to minimize the possibility of a fire emergency requiring the evacuation of occupants. Because the safety of ambulatory health care occupants cannot be ensured adequately by dependence on evacuation of the building, their protection from fire shall be provided by appropriate arrangement of facilities, adequate, trained staff, and development of operating and maintenance procedures composed of the following:

(1) Design, construction, and compartmentation
(2) Provision for detection, alarm, and extinguishment
(3) Fire prevention and the planning, training, and drilling programs for the isolation of fire, transfer of occupants to areas of refuge, or evacuation of the building

21.1.1.4 Additions, Conversions, Modernization, Renovation, and Construction Operations.

21.1.1.4.1 Additions. Additions shall be separated from any existing structure not conforming to the provisions within Chapter 21 by a fire barrier having not less than a 2-hour fire resistance rating and constructed of materials as required for the addition. *(See 4.6.3 and 4.6.6.)*

20.1.1.4.2 Communicating openings in dividing fire barriers required by 20.1.1.4.1 shall be permitted only in corridors and shall be protected by approved self-closing fire doors. *(See also Section 8.2.)*

20.1.1.4.3 Doors in barriers required by 20.1.1.4.1 shall normally be kept closed.

Exception: Doors shall be permitted to be held open if they meet the requirements of 20.2.2.3.

20.1.1.4.4 Changes of Occupancy. A change from a hospital or nursing home to an ambulatory health care occupancy shall not be considered a change in occupancy or occupancy subclassification.

20.1.1.4.5 Renovations, Alterations, and Modernizations. *(See 4.6.7.)*

20.1.1.4.6 Construction, Repair, and Improvement Operations. *(See 4.6.10.)*

21.1.1.4.2 Communicating openings in dividing fire barriers required by 21.1.1.4.1 shall be permitted only in corridors and shall be protected by approved self-closing fire doors. *(See also Section 8.2.)*

21.1.1.4.3 Doors in barriers required by 21.1.1.4.1 shall normally be kept closed.

Exception: Doors shall be permitted to be held open if they meet the requirements of 21.2.2.3.

21.1.1.4.4 Changes of Occupancy. A change from a hospital or nursing home to an ambulatory health care occupancy shall not be considered a change in occupancy or occupancy subclassification.

21.1.1.4.5 Renovations, Alterations, and Modernizations. *(See 4.6.7.)*

21.1.1.4.6 Construction, Repair, and Improvement Operations. *(See 4.6.10.)*

Paragraph 20/21.1.1.4.1 establishes separation criteria for additions to existing structures that do not conform to the provisions of Chapter 21. However, if an existing building meets the provisions of Chapter 21, the new addition that complies with Chapter 20 would not be required to be separated from the existing portion of the newly enlarged building.

Where additions are required to be separated from existing portions of buildings, barriers must be constructed of assemblies providing a minimum of 2-hour fire resistance rating.

Openings in barriers separating additions complying with Chapter 20 from portions of the building not in compliance with the requirements of Chapter 21 are limited to those that are absolutely necessary—

that is, cross-corridor doors (see 20/21.1.1.4.2). Openings are required to be protected by 1½-hour fire protection–rated door assemblies. The fire doors are required to be self-closing and to remain closed, or they are permitted to be held open by an automatic release device in accordance with 20/21.2.2.3 and 7.2.1.8. No openings other than the cross-corridor doors are permitted in the separating barrier. Thus, there can be no penetrations by ductwork. A convenience door between two rooms on opposite sides of the barrier also would be prohibited. However, if the existing portion of the building is in compliance with the requirements of Chapter 21, no separation is required. Therefore, unlimited openings are permitted.

20.1.2 Mixed Occupancies.

(See also 6.1.14.)

20.1.2.1* Sections of ambulatory health care facilities shall be permitted to be classified as other occupancies, provided that they meet all of the following conditions:

(1) They are not intended to serve ambulatory health care occupants for purposes of treatment or customary access by patients incapable of self-preservation.
(2) They are separated from areas of ambulatory health care occupancies by construction having a fire resistance rating of not less than 1 hour.

21.1.2 Mixed Occupancies.

(See also 6.1.14.)

21.1.2.1* Sections of ambulatory health care facilities shall be permitted to be classified as other occupancies, provided that they meet all of the following conditions:

(1) They are not intended to serve ambulatory health care occupants for purposes of treatment or customary access by patients incapable of self-preservation.
(2) They are separated from areas of ambulatory health care occupancies by construction having a fire resistance rating of not less than 1 hour.

A.20.1.2.1 Doctors' offices and treatment and diagnostic facilities intended solely for outpatient care that are physically separated from facilities for the treatment or care of inpatients, but that are otherwise associated with the management of an institution, might be classified as business occupancies rather than health care occupancies.

20.1.2.2 All means of egress from ambulatory health care occupancies that traverse nonambulatory health care spaces shall conform to requirements of this *Code* for ambulatory health care occupancies.

Exception: Exit through a horizontal exit into other contiguous occupancies that do not conform with ambulatory health care egress provisions, but that do comply with requirements set forth in the appropriate occupancy chapter of this Code, shall be permitted, provided that the occupancy does not contain high hazard contents.

20.1.2.3 Egress provisions for areas of ambulatory health care facilities that correspond to other occupancies shall meet the corresponding requirements of this *Code* for such occupancies. Where the clinical needs of the occupant necessitate the locking of means of egress, staff shall be present for the supervised release of occupants during all times of use.

20.1.2.4 Any area with a hazard of contents classified higher than that of the ambulatory health care occupancy and located in the same building shall be protected as required in 20.3.2.

20.1.2.5 Non-health care–related occupancies classified as containing high hazard contents shall not be permitted in buildings housing ambulatory health care occupancies.

20.1.3 Special Definitions.

   Ambulatory Health Care Occupancy. See 3.3.8.

Prior to the 1981 edition of the *Code,* occupancies that offered medical services on an outpatient basis would have been regulated within the chapter covering business occupancies. The threat to life in an outpatient facility where four or more patients might be subject to medical procedures requiring general anesthesia, treatments such as hemodialysis, or freestanding emergency service is significantly greater than that typical of a business occupancy. Conversely,

20.1.4 Classification of Occupancy.

(See 20.1.3.)

A.21.1.2.1 Doctors' offices and treatment and diagnostic facilities intended solely for outpatient care that are physically separated from facilities for the treatment or care of inpatients, but that are otherwise associated with the management of an institution, might be classified as business occupancies rather than health care occupancies.

21.1.2.2 All means of egress from ambulatory health care occupancies that traverse nonambulatory health care spaces shall conform to the requirements of this *Code* for ambulatory health care occupancies.

Exception: Exit through a horizontal exit into other contiguous occupancies that do not conform with ambulatory health care egress provisions, but that do comply with requirements set forth in the appropriate occupancy chapter of this Code, shall be permitted, provided that the occupancy does not contain high hazard contents.

21.1.2.3 Egress provisions for areas of ambulatory health care facilities that correspond to other occupancies shall meet the corresponding requirements of this *Code* for such occupancies. Where the clinical needs of the occupant necessitate the locking of means of egress, staff shall be present for the supervised release of occupants during all times of use.

21.1.2.4 Any area with a hazard of contents classified higher than that of the ambulatory health care occupancy and located in the same building shall be protected as required in 21.3.2.

21.1.2.5 Non-health care–related occupancies classified as containing high hazard contents shall not be permitted in buildings housing ambulatory health care occupancies.

21.1.3 Special Definitions.

   Ambulatory Health Care Occupancy. See 3.3.8.

application of the requirements for health care facilities that contemplate 24-hour care would be unnecessarily restrictive. In establishing the occupancy classification of an ambulatory health care facility, the intent was to develop requirements that fall between the restrictions applicable to business occupancies and those applicable to health care facilities in terms of the level of life safety provided.

21.1.4 Classification of Occupancy.

(See 21.1.3.)

CHAPTER 20 • New	CHAPTER 21 • Existing

20.1.5 Classification of Hazard of Contents.

The classification of hazard of contents shall be as defined in Section 6.2.

20.1.6 Minimum Construction Requirements.

20.1.6.1 For the purposes of 20.1.6, the number of stories shall be counted starting with the primary level of exit discharge and ending with the highest occupiable level. For the purposes of 20.1.6, the primary level of exit discharge of a building shall be that floor that is level with or above finished grade of the exterior wall line for 50 percent or more of its perimeter.

20.1.6.2 Buildings of one story in height housing ambulatory health care facilities shall be of any construction type in accordance with NFPA 220, *Standard on Types of Building Construction. (See 8.2.1.)*

20.1.6.3 Buildings of two or more stories in height housing ambulatory health care facilities shall be of Type I(443), Type I(332), Type II(222), Type II(111), Type III(211), Type IV(2HH), or Type V(111) construction. *(See 8.2.1.)*

Exception: Buildings constructed of Type II(000), Type III(200), or Type V(000), if protected throughout by an approved, supervised automatic sprinkler system in accordance with Section 9.7.

20.1.6.4 Any level below the level of exit discharge shall be separated from the level of exit discharge by not less than Type II(111), Type III(211), or Type V(111) construction. *(See 8.2.1.)*

Exception: Separation shall not be required for such levels if they are under the control of the ambulatory health care facility and any hazardous spaces are protected in accordance with Section 8.4.

20.1.6.5 Where new ambulatory health care facilities are located in existing buildings, the authority having jurisdiction shall be permitted to accept construction systems of lesser fire resistance than that required by 20.1.6.2 through 20.1.6.4, provided that it can be demonstrated to the authority's satisfaction that prompt evacuation of the facility can be achieved in case of fire or that the exposing occupancies and materials of construction present no threat of fire penetration from such occupancy to the ambulatory health care facility or to the collapse of the structure.

20.1.6.6 All interior walls and partitions in buildings of Type I or Type II construction shall be of noncombustible or limited-combustible materials.

21.1.5 Classification of Hazard of Contents.

The classification of hazard of contents shall be as defined in Section 6.2.

21.1.6 Minimum Construction Requirements.

21.1.6.1 For the purposes of 21.1.6, the number of stories shall be counted starting with the primary level of exit discharge and ending with the highest occupiable level. For the purposes of 21.1.6, the primary level of exit discharge of a building shall be that floor that is level with or above finished grade of the exterior wall line for 50 percent or more of its perimeter.

21.1.6.2 Buildings of one story in height housing ambulatory health care facilities shall be of any construction type in accordance with NFPA 220, *Standard on Types of Building Construction. (See 8.2.1.)*

21.1.6.3 Buildings of two or more stories in height housing ambulatory health care facilities shall be of Type I(443), Type I(332), Type II(222), Type II(111), Type III(211), Type IV(2HH), or Type V(111) construction. *(See 8.2.1.)*

Exception: Buildings constructed of Type II(000), Type III(200), or Type V(000), if protected throughout by an approved, supervised automatic sprinkler system in accordance with Section 9.7.

21.1.6.4 Any level below the level of exit discharge shall be separated from the level of exit discharge by not less than Type II(111), Type III(211), or Type V(111) construction. *(See 8.2.1.)*

Exception: Separation shall not be required for such levels if they are under the control of the ambulatory health care facility and any hazardous spaces are protected in accordance with Section 8.4.

21.1.6.5 In existing buildings, the authority having jurisdiction shall be permitted to accept construction systems of lesser fire resistance than that required by 21.1.6.2 through 21.1.6.4, provided that it can be demonstrated to the authority's satisfaction that prompt evacuation of the facility can be achieved in case of fire or that the exposing occupancies and materials of construction present no threat of fire penetration from such occupancy to the ambulatory health care facility or to the collapse of the structure.

21.1.6.6 All interior walls and partitions in buildings of Type I or Type II construction shall be of noncombustible or limited-combustible materials.

20.1.6.7 All buildings with more than one level below the level of exit discharge shall have all such lower levels separated from the level of exit discharge by not less than Type II(111) construction.

21.1.6.7 All buildings with more than one level below the level of exit discharge shall have all such lower levels separated from the level of exit discharge by not less than Type II(111) construction.

Allowable building construction types are determined as a function of the number of stories in a building. In determining the number of stories, the first story is considered to be the primary level of exit discharge. Only occupiable levels are counted in determining story height. For example, an unoccupied attic would not constitute a story.

Determining story height where a building is located on a sloping grade can be difficult. Paragraph 20/21.1.6.1 notes that a story on a sloping site that is partially below grade should be counted as a story if the floor is level with or above grade along 50 percent or more of the perimeter of the building at the exterior wall. Application of the 50 percent perimeter guideline is illustrated in Exhibit 20/21.2. Because of sloping grade, the primary level of exit discharge is not obvious. The 50 percent perimeter guideline clarifies that for the arrangement illustrated; the first story is the

primary level of exit discharge. The number of stories includes primary level of exit discharge and all occupiable floors located above. This is an example of a two-story building.

Construction types permitted for buildings housing ambulatory health care facilities are detailed in 20/21.1.6.2 through 20/21.1.6.3 and summarized in Table 20/21.3. For additional information on the notations used to designate a particular construction type, see Table A.8.2.1 of this *Code* and NFPA 220, *Standard on Types of Building Construction.*[1]

Paragraph 20/21.1.6.5 permits flexibility in the construction requirements that apply to a new ambulatory health care facility to be placed in an existing building. Adequate supporting data must be supplied to the authority having jurisdiction to justify a reduction in fire-rated construction.

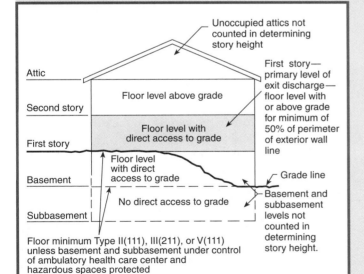

Exhibit 20/21.2 Determining number of stories for application of minimum construction requirements.

Table 20/21.3 Construction Types Permitted in Ambulatory Health Care Occupancies

Construction Type	Stories	
	1	2 or More
I(443), I(332), II(222), II(111) (Fire resistive and protected noncombustible)	X	X
II(000) (Unprotected noncombustible)	X	X†
III(211) (Protected ordinary)	X	X
III(200) (Unprotected ordinary)	X	X†
IV(2HH) (Heavy timber)	X	X
V(111) (Protected wood frame)	X	X
V(000) (Unprotected wood frame)	X	X†

X— Construction types allowed.
†—Automatic sprinkler protection required.

CHAPTER 20 • New

20.1.7 Occupant Load.

(See 38.1.7.)

Section 20.2 Means of Egress Requirements

20.2.1 General.

Every aisle, passageway, corridor, exit discharge, exit location, and access shall be in accordance with Chapter 7.

Exception: As modified by 20.2.2 through 20.2.11.

20.2.2 Means of Egress Components.

20.2.2.1 Components of means of egress shall be limited to the types described in 38.2.2.

20.2.2.2 Special locking arrangements complying with 7.2.1.6 shall be permitted on exterior doors.

20.2.2.3 Any door in an exit passageway, horizontal exit, smoke barrier, stairway enclosure, or hazardous area enclosure shall be permitted to be held open only by an automatic release device that complies with 7.2.1.8.2. The required manual fire alarm system and the systems required by 7.2.1.8.2 shall be arranged to initiate the closing action of all such doors throughout the smoke compartment or throughout the entire facility.

20.2.2.4 Where doors in a stair enclosure are held open by an automatic release device as permitted in 20.2.2.3, initiation of a door-closing action on any level shall cause all doors at all levels in the stair enclosure to close.

The special locking arrangements of 7.2.1.6 include both delayed-egress locks and access-controlled egress doors. Use of these devices is limited by 20/21.2.2.2 to exterior doors. Thus, a door from an ambulatory health care center to a common corridor, for example, is not permitted to be equipped with a delayed-egress lock or an access-controlled door release system.

It is desirable to keep doors in exit enclosures, stair enclosures, horizontal exits, smoke barriers, and hazardous areas closed at all times to impede the spread of smoke and gases caused by a fire. However, some doors will be kept open for reasons of operating efficiency or comfort. Where doors in required fire or smoke barriers are to be held open, they must be equipped with automatic devices designed to close the doors by the methods described in 20/21.2.2.3 and 7.2.1.8.

CHAPTER 21 • Existing

21.1.7 Occupant Load.

(See 39.1.7.)

Section 21.2 Means of Egress Requirements

21.2.1 General.

Every aisle, passageway, corridor, exit discharge, exit location, and access shall be in accordance with Chapter 7.

Exception: As modified by 21.2.2 through 21.2.11.

21.2.2 Means of Egress Components.

21.2.2.1 Components of means of egress shall be limited to the types described in 39.2.2.

21.2.2.2 Special locking arrangements complying with 7.2.1.6 shall be permitted on exterior doors.

21.2.2.3 Any door in an exit passageway, horizontal exit, smoke barrier, stairway enclosure, or hazardous area enclosure shall be permitted to be held open only by an automatic release device that complies with 7.2.1.8.2. The required manual fire alarm system and the systems required by 7.2.1.8.2 shall be arranged to initiate the closing action of all such doors throughout the smoke compartment or throughout the entire facility.

21.2.2.4 Where doors in a stair enclosure are held open by an automatic release device as permitted in 21.2.2.3, initiation of a door-closing action on any level shall cause all doors at all levels in the stair enclosure to close.

The automatic device must cause the doors to close by operation of the manual fire alarm system. The doors must also be designed to close by actuation of smoke detectors in the vicinity of the door opening. See 7.2.1.8.2.

It is especially important in facilities providing ambulatory health care to maintain floor-to-floor separation. Doors protecting openings in a stair enclosure can be held open by an automatic device only if arranged to close as specified earlier. Initiation of any action that causes a door to close at one level must cause all doors protecting openings within that stair enclosure to close. Because the doors in the exit stair enclosure are rated fire door assemblies, they will latch when brought to their closed position.

CHAPTER 20 • New

CHAPTER 20 • New　　　　　**CHAPTER 21 • Existing**

20.2.3 Capacity of Means of Egress.

20.2.3.1 The capacity of any required means of egress shall be determined in accordance with the provisions of 38.2.3 and shall be based on its width as specified in Section 7.3.

20.2.3.2 The clear width of any corridor or passageway required for exit access shall be not less than 44 in. (112 cm).

20.2.3.3 Doors in the means of egress from diagnostic or treatment areas, such as x-ray, surgical, or physical therapy, shall provide a clear width of not less than 32 in. (81 cm).

21.2.3 Capacity of Means of Egress.

21.2.3.1 The capacity of any required means of egress shall be determined in accordance with the provisions of 39.2.3 and shall be based on its width as specified in Section 7.3.

21.2.3.2 The clear width of any corridor or passageway required for exit access shall be not less than 44 in. (112 cm).

21.2.3.3 Doors in the means of egress from diagnostic or treatment areas, such as x-ray, surgical, or physical therapy, shall provide a clear width of not less than 32 in. (81 cm).

Exception: Existing 34-in. (86-cm) doors.

The capacity of the means of egress in ambulatory health care facilities is determined on the basis of provisions in Chapter 38/39 that address business occupancies. Paragraph 38/39.2.3.1 refers to Section 7.3, which requires the capacity of level exit components to be computed on the basis of 0.2 in. (0.5 cm) per person, whereas stair capacity is computed using 0.3 in. (0.8 cm) per person. These capacities are the same as permitted within sprinklered hospitals, nursing homes, and limited care facilities. Even if the ambulatory health care facility is not sprinklered, these capacity factors are considered reasonable based on the assumption that the majority of occupants will be ambulatory.

Corridor widths greater than 44 in. (112 cm) might be required within ambulatory health care facilities for functional purposes. However, the minimum width for corridors used as common exit access is 44 in. (112 cm). The 44-in. (112-cm) width, which is significantly less than required in new hospitals, nursing homes, and limited care facilities, is specified on the assumption that most occupants will be ambulatory.

In many instances, doors wider than 32-in. (81-cm) clear width will be required for functional purposes. This paragraph addresses doors that provide access to common hallways and corridors. The 32-in. (81-cm) minimum clear width, which is significantly less than what is required in new hospitals and nursing homes, is specified on the assumption that most occupants will be ambulatory or moving in wheelchairs. A 32-in. (81-cm) clear width door opening is sufficiently wide to accommodate a wheelchair user.

20.2.4 Number of Exits.

20.2.4.1 Not less than two exits of the types described in 38.2.2 that are remotely located from each other shall be provided for each floor or fire section of the building.

20.2.4.2 Any room and any suite of rooms of more than 2500 ft² (232 m²) shall have not less than two exit access doors remotely located from each other.

20.2.4.3 Not less than two exits of the types described in 38.2.2 shall be accessible from each smoke compartment. Egress shall be permitted through adjacent compartments but shall not require return through the compartment of fire origin.

21.2.4 Number of Exits.

21.2.4.1 Not less than two exits of the types described in 39.2.2 that are remotely located from each other shall be provided for each floor or fire section of the building.

21.2.4.2 Any room and any suite of rooms of more than 2500 ft² (232 m²) shall have not less than two exit access doors remotely located from each other.

21.2.4.3 Not less than two exits of the types described in 39.2.2 shall be accessible from each smoke compartment. Egress shall be permitted through adjacent compartments but shall not require return through the compartment of fire origin.

CHAPTER 20 • New	CHAPTER 21 • Existing

20.2.5 Arrangement of Means of Egress.

(See 38.2.5.)

20.2.6 Travel Distance to Exits.

20.2.6.1 Travel distance shall be measured in accordance with Section 7.6.

20.2.6.2 Travel Distance. Travel distance shall be as follows:

(1) The travel distance between any room door required as an exit access and an exit shall not exceed 100 ft (30 m).
(2) The travel distance between any point in a room and an exit shall not exceed 150 ft (45 m).

Exception: The maximum travel distance in 20.2.6.2(1) or (2) shall be permitted to be increased by 50 ft (15 m) in buildings protected throughout by an approved automatic sprinkler system.

Travel distance is measured only to the nearest exit, not to both exits. The requirements of 20/21.2.6.2 are illustrated in Exhibit 20/21.3.

21.2.5 Arrangement of Means of Egress.

(See 39.2.5.)

21.2.6 Travel Distance to Exits.

21.2.6.1 Travel distance shall be measured in accordance with Section 7.6.

21.2.6.2 Travel Distance. Travel distance shall be as follows:

(1) The travel distance between any room door required as an exit access and an exit shall not exceed 100 ft (30 m).
(2) The travel distance between any point in a room and an exit shall not exceed 150 ft (45 m).

Exception: The maximum travel distance in 21.2.6.2(1) or (2) shall be permitted to be increased by 50 ft (15 m) in buildings protected throughout by an approved automatic sprinkler system.

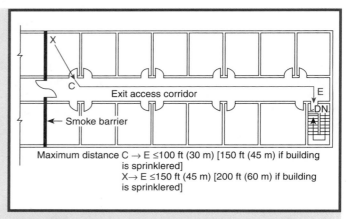

Exhibit 20/21.3 Travel distance limitations for an ambulatory health care facility.

20.2.7 Discharge from Exits.

(See 38.2.7.)

20.2.8 Illumination of Means of Egress.

Means of egress shall be illuminated in accordance with Section 7.8.

20.2.9 Emergency Lighting and Essential Electrical Systems.

20.2.9.1 Emergency lighting shall be provided in accordance with Section 7.9.

21.2.7 Discharge from Exits.

(See 39.2.7.)

21.2.8 Illumination of Means of Egress.

Means of egress shall be illuminated in accordance with Section 7.8.

21.2.9 Emergency Lighting and Essential Electrical Systems.

21.2.9.1 Emergency lighting shall be provided in accordance with Section 7.9.

20.2.9.2 Where general anesthesia or life-support equipment is used, each ambulatory health care facility shall be provided with an essential electrical system in accordance with NFPA 99, *Standard for Health Care Facilities.*

Exception No. 1: Where battery-operated equipment is provided and acceptable to the authority having jurisdiction.

Exception No. 2: This requirement shall not apply to a facility that uses life-support equipment for emergency purposes only.

All ambulatory health care facilities are required to be equipped with emergency lighting. If medical procedures requiring general anesthesia are practiced, or if life-support equipment is used for other than emergency purposes only, ambulatory health care facilities are required to be served by electrical systems meeting the criteria for essential electrical systems as detailed in Chapter 3 of NFPA 99, *Standard for Health Care Facilities.*[2]

A facility would not be required to have an emergency generator if the building is a freestanding unit and if, as a normal practice, the following conditions apply:

20.2.10 Marking of Means of Egress.

Means of egress shall have signs in accordance with Section 7.10.

20.2.11 Special Means of Egress Features.

(Reserved.)

Section 20.3 Protection

20.3.1 Protection of Vertical Openings.

(See 38.3.1.)

20.3.2 Protection from Hazards.

(See 38.3.2.)

20.3.2.1 Laboratories employing quantities of flammable, combustible, or hazardous materials that are considered as a severe hazard shall be protected in accordance with NFPA 99, *Standard for Health Care Facilities.*

20.3.2.2 Anesthetizing locations shall be protected in accordance with NFPA 99, *Standard for Health Care Facilities.*

21.2.9.2 Where general anesthesia or life-support equipment is used, each ambulatory health care facility shall be provided with an essential electrical system in accordance with NFPA 99, *Standard for Health Care Facilities.*

Exception No. 1: Where battery-operated equipment is provided and acceptable to the authority having jurisdiction.

Exception No. 2: This requirement shall not apply to a facility that uses life-support equipment for emergency purposes only.

(1) Management maintains policies that preclude the provision of care for any patient who might need to be sustained by electrical life-support equipment, such as respirators or suction apparatus.
(2) No surgical treatment requiring general anesthesia is offered.
(3) Battery-operated systems or equipment are provided that would maintain power to exit lights and illumination for egress corridors, stairways, medical preparation areas, and the like, for a minimum of 1½ hours. Additionally, battery power would be required to be supplied to all alarm systems.

21.2.10 Marking of Means of Egress.

Means of egress shall have signs in accordance with Section 7.10.

21.2.11 Special Means of Egress Features.

(Reserved.)

Section 21.3 Protection

21.3.1 Protection of Vertical Openings.

(See 39.3.1.)

21.3.2 Protection from Hazards.

(See 39.3.2.)

21.3.2.1 Laboratories employing quantities of flammable, combustible, or hazardous materials that are considered as a severe hazard shall be protected in accordance with NFPA 99, *Standard for Health Care Facilities.*

21.3.2.2 Anesthetizing locations shall be protected in accordance with NFPA 99, *Standard for Health Care Facilities.*

Laboratories that contain ordinary combustibles and flammable liquids in sufficient quantity to threaten a 1-hour fire separation [for example, wood-equivalent fuel loads in the range of 5 lb/ft² to 10 lb/ft² (25 kg/m² to 50 kg/m²)] are considered to be a severe hazard. Laboratories representing a severe hazard must be protected in accordance with Chapter 10 of NFPA 99, *Standard for Health Care Facilities*. Protection would

include 1-hour fire resistance separation and automatic sprinkler protection.

Where fuel loads of lesser amounts are involved and quantities of flammable liquids are limited, laboratories would simply be considered hazardous contents areas and would require either 1-hour separation or automatic sprinkler protection.

20.3.3 Interior Finish.

(See 38.3.3.)

20.3.4 Detection, Alarm, and Communications Systems.

20.3.4.1 General. Ambulatory health care facilities shall be provided with fire alarm systems in accordance with Section 9.6, except as modified by 20.3.4.2 through 20.3.4.5.

20.3.4.2 Initiation. Initiation of the required fire alarm systems shall be by manual means in accordance with 9.6.2 and by means of any detection devices or detection systems required.

20.3.4.3 Occupant Notification. Occupant notification shall be accomplished automatically, without delay, upon operation of any fire alarm activating device by means of an internal audible alarm in accordance with 9.6.3.

20.3.4.4 Emergency Forces Notification. Fire department notification shall be accomplished in accordance with 9.6.4.

Exception: Smoke detection devices or smoke detection systems equipped with reconfirmation features shall not be required to automatically notify the fire department unless the alarm condition is reconfirmed after a period not exceeding 120 seconds.

20.3.4.5 Emergency Control. Operation of any activating device in the required fire alarm system shall be arranged to accomplish automatically, without delay, any control functions required to be performed by that device. *(See 9.6.5.)*

21.3.3 Interior Finish.

(See 39.3.3.)

21.3.4 Detection, Alarm, and Communications Systems.

21.3.4.1 General. Ambulatory health care facilities shall be provided with fire alarm systems in accordance with Section 9.6, except as modified by 21.3.4.2 through 21.3.4.5.

21.3.4.2 Initiation. Initiation of the required fire alarm systems shall be by manual means in accordance with 9.6.2 and by means of any detection devices or detection systems required.

21.3.4.3 Occupant Notification. Occupant notification shall be accomplished automatically, without delay, upon operation of any fire alarm activating device by means of an internal audible alarm in accordance with 9.6.3.

21.3.4.4 Emergency Forces Notification. Fire department notification shall be accomplished in accordance with 9.6.4.

Exception: Smoke detection devices or smoke detection systems equipped with reconfirmation features shall not be required to automatically notify the fire department unless the alarm condition is reconfirmed after a period not exceeding 120 seconds.

21.3.4.5 Emergency Control. Operation of any activating device in the required fire alarm system shall be arranged to accomplish automatically, without delay, any control functions required to be performed by that device. *(See 9.6.5.)*

Paragraphs 20/21.3.4.1 through 20/21.3.4.5 address required fire alarm equipment. Reliability is of prime importance; therefore, electrical supervision of the system and system components is specified by the standards referenced in Section 9.6. In the event of circuit fault, component failure, or other trouble, a

continuous trouble indication signal is required and should be provided at a constantly attended location.

A manual fire alarm system is required by 20/21.3.4.1 and 20/21.3.4.2. Manual fire alarm boxes should be located along the natural routes of egress and cover all portions of the building. Manual fire alarm boxes should be located so that those qualified to send an alarm can summon aid without having to leave their zone of ordinary activities or pass beyond the view and hearing of people immediately exposed to, or in direct view of, a fire. The operation of a manual fire alarm box should automatically summon attendants to assist in removing physically helpless occupants. The system required by 20/21.3.4.2 can be incorporated into an automatic system equipped to detect a fire and initiate an alarm.

Actuation of any required fire or smoke detector, activation of a required sprinkler system, or operation of a manual fire alarm box must automatically, without delay, sound audible alarm devices within the building. Neither presignal systems nor positive alarm sequence is permitted (see 9.6.3.3 and 9.6.3.4).

The alarm must automatically transmit to a point outside the facility. If automatic transmission of the alarm to the fire department legally committed to serve the facility is not permitted, arrangements need to be made for the prompt notification of the fire department or such other assistance as is available in the case of fire or other emergency. Paragraph 9.6.4 lists various methods acceptable for automatically notifying the fire department. The fire department should also be called manually to verify and confirm the automatic transmission of the alarm. In larger facilities this may be the responsibility of the facility telephone operator. In smaller facilities it might be the responsibility of the nursing staff. Actuation of the fire alarm must initiate the operation of audible alerting devices that sound throughout the affected zone or building.

20.3.5 Extinguishment Requirements.

(See 38.3.5.)

20.3.5.1 Isolated hazardous areas shall be permitted to be protected in accordance with 9.7.1.2. Where more than two sprinklers are installed in a single area, waterflow detection shall be provided to sound the building fire alarm, or to notify by a signal, any constantly attended location, such as PBX, security, or emergency room, at which the necessary corrective action shall be taken.

20.3.5.2 Portable fire extinguishers shall be provided in ambulatory health care facilities in accordance with 9.7.4.1.

20.3.6 Corridors.

20.3.6.1 General. *(See 38.3.6.)*

20.3.6.2 Openings. Miscellaneous openings such as mail slots, pharmacy pass-through windows, laboratory pass-through windows, and cashier pass-through windows shall be permitted to be installed in vision panels or doors without special protection, provided that the aggregate area of openings per room does not exceed 20 in.² (135 cm²) and the openings are installed at or below half the distance from the floor to the room ceiling.

Exception: For rooms protected throughout by an approved, supervised automatic sprinkler system in accordance with Section 7.7, the aggregate area of openings per room shall not exceed 80 in.² (520 cm²).

21.3.5 Extinguishment Requirements.

(See 39.3.5.)

21.3.5.1 Isolated hazardous areas shall be permitted to be protected in accordance with 9.7.1.2. For new installations in existing ambulatory health care facilities, where more than two sprinklers are installed in a single area, waterflow detection shall be provided to sound the building fire alarm, or to notify by a signal, any constantly attended location, such as PBX, security, or emergency room, at which the necessary corrective action shall be taken.

21.3.5.2 Portable fire extinguishers shall be provided in ambulatory health care facilities in accordance with 9.7.4.1.

21.3.6 Corridors.

(No requirements.)

20.3.7 Subdivision of Building Space.

20.3.7.1 Ambulatory health care facilities shall be separated from other tenants and occupancies by walls having not less than a 1-hour fire resistance rating. Such walls shall extend from the floor slab below to the floor or roof slab above. Doors shall be constructed of not less than 1¾-in. (4.4-cm) thick, solid-bonded wood core or the equivalent and shall be equipped with positive latches. These doors shall be self-closing and shall be kept in the closed position except when in use. Any vision panels shall be of fixed fire window assemblies in accordance with 8.2.3.2.2.

20.3.7.2 The ambulatory health care facility shall be divided into not less than two smoke compartments.

Exception No. 1: Facilities of less than 5000 ft² (465 m²) and protected by an approved automatic smoke detection system.

Exception No. 2: Facilities of less than 10,000 ft² (930 m²) and protected throughout by an approved, supervised automatic sprinkler system installed in accordance with Section 9.7.

Exception No. 3: An area in an adjoining occupancy shall be permitted to serve as a smoke compartment for the ambulatory health care facility if the following criteria are met:

(a) The separating wall and both compartments meet the requirements of 20.3.7.

(b) The ambulatory health care facility is less than 22,500 ft² (2100 m²).

(c) Access from the ambulatory health care facility to the other occupancy is unrestricted.

20.3.7.3 Any required smoke barrier shall be constructed in accordance with Section 8.3 and shall have a fire resistance rating of not less than 1 hour.

Exception: Dampers shall not be required in duct penetrations of smoke barriers in fully ducted heating, ventilating, and air conditioning systems for buildings protected throughout by an approved, supervised automatic sprinkler system in accordance with Section 9.7.

20.3.7.4 Vision panels in the smoke barrier shall be of fixed fire window assemblies in accordance with 8.2.3.2.2.

20.3.7.5 Not less than 15 net ft² (1.4 net m²) per ambulatory health care facility occupant shall be provided within the aggregate area of corridors, patient rooms, treatment rooms, lounges, and other low hazard areas on each side of the smoke compartment for the total number of occupants in

21.3.7 Subdivision of Building Space.

21.3.7.1 Ambulatory health care facilities shall be separated from other tenants and occupancies by walls having not less than a 1-hour fire resistance rating. Such walls shall extend from the floor slab below to the floor or roof slab above. Doors shall be constructed of not less than 1¾-in. (4.4-cm) thick, solid-bonded wood core or the equivalent and shall be equipped with positive latches. These doors shall be self-closing and shall be kept in the closed position except when in use. Any vision panels shall be of fixed fire window assemblies in accordance with 8.2.3.2.2.

21.3.7.2 The ambulatory health care facility shall be divided into not less than two smoke compartments.

Exception No. 1: Facilities of less than 5000 ft² (465 m²) and protected by an approved automatic smoke detection system.

Exception No. 2: Facilities of less than 10,000 ft² (930 m²) and protected throughout by an approved, supervised automatic sprinkler system installed in accordance with Section 9.7.

Exception No. 3: An area in an adjoining occupancy shall be permitted to serve as a smoke compartment for the ambulatory health care facility if the following criteria are met:

(a) The separating wall and both compartments meet the requirements of 21.3.7.

(b) The ambulatory health care facility is less than 22,500 ft² (2100 m²).

(c) Access from the ambulatory health care facility to the other occupancy is unrestricted.

21.3.7.3 Any required smoke barrier shall be constructed in accordance with Section 8.3 and shall have a fire resistance rating of not less than 1 hour.

Exception: Dampers shall not be required in duct penetrations of smoke barriers in fully ducted heating, ventilating, and air conditioning systems for buildings protected throughout by an approved, supervised automatic sprinkler system in accordance with Section 9.7.

21.3.7.4 Vision panels in the smoke barrier shall be of fixed fire window assemblies in accordance with 8.2.3.2.2.

21.3.7.5 (Reserved.)

adjoining compartments. Smoke barriers shall be provided to limit the size of each smoke compartment to an area not exceeding 22,500 ft^2 (2100 m^2) and to limit the travel distance from any point to reach a door in the required smoke barrier to 200 ft (60 m).

Exception: The area of an atrium separated in accordance with 8.2.5.6 shall not be limited in size.

20.3.7.6* Doors in smoke barriers shall be not less than 1¾-in. (4.4-cm) thick, solid-bonded wood core or the equivalent and shall be self-closing. A vision panel shall be required.

A.20.3.7.6 Smoke barriers might include walls having door openings other than cross-corridor doors. There is no restriction in the *Code* regarding which doors or how many doors form part of a smoke barrier. For example, doors from the corridor to individual rooms are permitted to form part of a smoke barrier.

20.3.7.7 Doors in smoke barriers shall normally be kept closed, or, if held open, they shall be equipped with automatic devices that will release the doors upon activation of the fire alarm system and either one of the following:

(1) A local smoke detector
(2) A complete automatic fire-extinguishing system or complete automatic fire detection system

Ambulatory health care facilities are frequently located within buildings used for a variety of purposes. Placing these facilities within buildings containing hazardous occupancies should be avoided. If located within a building of mixed use, the ambulatory health care facility must be separated from adjacent tenants and occupancies by minimum 1-hour fire resistance–rated partitions in accordance with 20/21.3.7.1. Doors protecting openings in such partitions must be of at least 1¾-in. (4.4-cm) thick, solid-bonded wood core or of equivalent construction that will resist fire for a minimum of 20 minutes. The doors must be equipped with positive latching hardware of a type that cannot be held in the retracted position. Roller latches cannot be used. These doors must be self-closing and normally maintained in the closed position, or, if the doors are to be held open, an automatic device must be used as specified in 20/21.2.2.3.

Glazing within doors and partitions will generally involve a maximum area of 1296 in.^{2} (0.84 m^2) of wired glass, set in approved metal frames. Each wired-glass panel should be limited to a maximum dimension of

21.3.7.6* Doors in smoke barriers shall be not less than 1¾-in. (4.4-cm) thick, solid-bonded wood core or the equivalent and shall be self-closing. A vision panel shall be required.

A.21.3.7.6 Smoke barriers might include walls having door openings other than cross-corridor doors. There is no restriction in the *Code* regarding which doors or how many doors form part of a smoke barrier. For example, doors from the corridor to individual rooms are permitted to form part of a smoke barrier.

21.3.7.7 Doors in smoke barriers shall normally be kept closed, or, if held open, they shall be equipped with automatic devices that will release the doors upon activation of the fire alarm system and either one of the following:

(1) A local smoke detector
(2) A complete automatic fire-extinguishing system or complete automatic fire detection system

54 in. (137 cm). The glass should be labeled, should be ¼ in. (0.6 cm) thick, and should be well embedded in putty, with all exposed joints between the metal and the glass struck and pointed (see NFPA 80, *Standard for Fire Doors and Windows*[3]). A number of wired glass panels can be used in a single partition, provided that each 1296-in.^{2} (0.84-m^2) section is separated from adjacent panels by a metal mullion. The excessive use of wired-glass panels should be avoided. The use of wired glass panels in a partition reduces the effectiveness of the partition because radiant energy transfer through the glass panel readily occurs. Other fire-rated glazing is available and, where used, should be installed in accordance with the manufacturer's instructions and listing.

Partitions separating ambulatory health care facilities from other occupancies must extend from the floor to the floor or roof deck above, extending completely through concealed spaces above suspended ceilings, for example. The partition must form a continuous barrier. Openings around penetrations involving building services should be

CHAPTER 20 • New

CHAPTER 21 • Existing

adequately protected to maintain the 1-hour separation. Special attention should be paid to penetrations involving air-handling ducts. In general, steel ducts will not require a fire damper. Penetrations involving nonmetallic ducts or aluminum ducts should be carefully evaluated. Fire dampers should be provided to protect duct penetrations where the projected fire exposure is judged sufficient to jeopardize the required separation because of the duct penetration. The possible movement of air from space to space under conditions of system operation and conditions of system shutdown should be evaluated for both conditions. If there is a significant potential for the transfer of smoke from an adjacent space to the ambulatory health care facility or from the ambulatory health care facility to a corridor, fire dampers should be provided for duct penetrations, even though the *Code* does not specifically require such protection. See Exhibit 20/21.4.

The requirements of 20/21.3.7.1 through 20/21.3.7.7 for subdividing building spaces through the use of smoke barriers are illustrated in Exhibit 20/21.4 and Exhibit 20/21.5. Smoke barriers are not required if the ambulatory health care center meets either of the following conditions:

(1) Its area is less than 5000 ft^2 (465 m^2) and it is protected by an automatic smoke detection system.

(2) Its area is less than 10,000 ft^2 (930 m^2) and it is protected by an automatic sprinkler system.

Further, Exception No. 3 to 20/21.3.7.2 permits the smoke barrier to be located—under specific criteria—at the wall that separates the ambulatory health care center from a neighboring tenant space of some other occupancy classification.

During a fire, the emergency evacuation of patients in an ambulatory health care facility can be an inefficient, time-consuming process. Realistically, if nonambulatory patients must be moved, any number of occupants can be relocated but only readily through horizontal travel. Smoke barriers used to subdivide a building serve three purposes fundamental to the protection of patients:

(1) They limit the spread of fire and fire-produced contaminants.

(2) They limit the number of occupants exposed to a single fire.

(3) They provide for horizontal relocation of patients by creating an area of refuge on the same floor level.

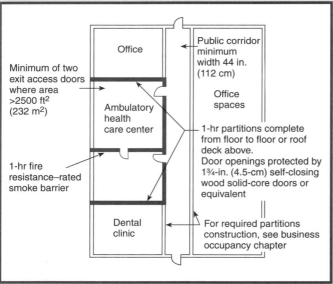

Exhibit 20/21.4 Separation and subdivision requirements for an ambulatory health care facility.

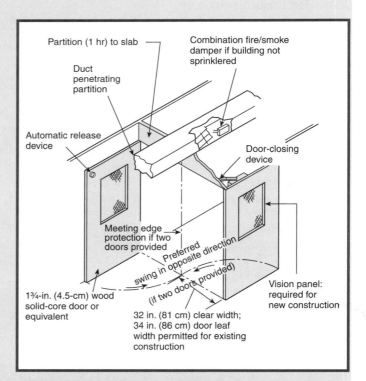

Exhibit 20/21.5 Smoke barrier and associated openings protection for an ambulatory health care facility.

Section 20.4 Special Provisions

(See Section 38.4.)

Section 20.5 Building Services

20.5.1 Utilities.

Utilities shall comply with the provisions of Section 9.1.

20.5.2 Heating, Ventilating, and Air Conditioning.

20.5.2.1 Heating, ventilating, and air conditioning shall comply with the provisions of Section 9.2 and shall be in accordance with the manufacturer's specifications.

Exception: As modified in 20.5.2.2.

20.5.2.2 Any heating device, other than a central heating plant, shall be designed and installed so that combustible material will not be ignited by the device or its appurtenances. If fuel-fired, such heating devices shall be chimney connected or vent connected, shall take air for combustion directly from the outside, and shall be designed and installed to provide for complete separation of the combustion system from the atmosphere of the occupied area. Any heating device shall have safety features to immediately stop the flow of fuel and shut down the equipment in case of either excessive temperature or ignition failure.

Exception: Approved, suspended unit heaters shall be permitted in locations other than means of egress and patient treatment areas, provided that such heaters are located high enough to be out of the reach of persons using the area and are equipped with the safety features required by 20.5.2.2.

20.5.3 Elevators, Escalators, and Conveyors.

Elevators, escalators, and conveyors shall comply with the provisions of Section 9.4.

20.5.4 Rubbish Chutes, Incinerators, and Laundry Chutes.

Rubbish chutes, incinerators, and laundry chutes shall comply with the provisions of Section 9.5.

Section 21.4 Special Provisions

(See Section 39.4.)

Section 21.5 Building Services

21.5.1 Utilities.

Utilities shall comply with the provisions of Section 9.1.

Exception: Existing installations shall be permitted to be continued in service, provided that the systems do not present a serious hazard to life.

21.5.2 Heating, Ventilating, and Air Conditioning.

21.5.2.1 Heating, ventilating, and air conditioning shall comply with the provisions of Section 9.2 and shall be in accordance with the manufacturer's specifications.

Exception: As modified in 21.5.2.2.

21.5.2.2 Any heating device, other than a central heating plant, shall be designed and installed so that combustible material will not be ignited by the device or its appurtenances. If fuel-fired, such heating devices shall be chimney connected or vent connected, shall take air for combustion directly from the outside, and shall be designed and installed to provide for complete separation of the combustion system from the atmosphere of the occupied area. Any heating device shall have safety features to immediately stop the flow of fuel and shut down the equipment in case of either excessive temperature or ignition failure.

Exception: Approved, suspended unit heaters shall be permitted in locations other than means of egress and patient treatment areas, provided that such heaters are located high enough to be out of the reach of persons using the area and are equipped with the safety features required by 21.5.2.2.

21.5.3 Elevators, Escalators, and Conveyors.

Elevators, escalators, and conveyors shall comply with the provisions of Section 9.4.

21.5.4 Rubbish Chutes, Incinerators, and Laundry Chutes.

Rubbish chutes, incinerators, and laundry chutes shall comply with the provisions of Section 9.5.

Paragraphs 20/21.5.2.1 and 20/21.5.2.2 specify safeguards for air conditioning, ventilating, heating, and other service equipment in order to minimize the possibility of such devices serving as a source of ignition. Fuel-fired heating devices, except central heating systems, must be designed to provide complete separation of the combustion system from the occupied spaces. Air for combustion must be taken directly from the outside.

A major concern is preventing the ignition of clothing, bedclothes, furniture, and other furnishings by a heating device. Therefore, 20/21.7.8 prohibits portable heating devices in areas used by patients.

Paragraph 20/21.5.3 addresses elevators. Although not counted as required exits for the general populace, elevators might constitute a valuable, supplemental facility for evacuating ambulatory health care patients from buildings. In some cases, using an elevator might be the only feasible way to move patients who are unable to use the exit stairs.

Elevators, however, have many inherent weaknesses that tend to limit reliability. Elevator access doors are designed with operating tolerances that permit smoke transfer into the shaft. During a fire, a power failure might cause an elevator to stop between floors, trapping its passengers. Elevators might, during their descent from upper floors, stop automatically at the floor where the fire is burning, allow the doors to open, and expose the occupants to the fire.

Many of these weaknesses can be minimized by providing emergency power, separating the elevator lobby from other building spaces using rated construction, designing detection and alarm equipment to prevent elevators from stopping at a floor exposed to a fire, providing an emergency smoke control system, and pressurizing the elevator shaft and adjacent lobbies. This represents good fire protection judgment but is not the result of any requirements of this *Code*.

Through emergency planning and staff training, the potential problem of crowding elevators might be avoided. Emergency plans can make effective use of elevators by transferring patients through a horizontal exit, for example, to a separate fire area. Within the separate fire area, a staged evacuation program could be instituted, with the elevators taking patients to the ground level, thereby permitting horizontal travel to the outside.

Section 20.6 Reserved

Section 21.6 Reserved

Section 20.7* Operating Features

A.20.7 Health care occupants have, in large part, varied degrees of physical disability, and their removal to the outside or even their disturbance caused by moving is inexpedient or impractical in many cases, except as a last resort. Similarly, recognizing that there might be an operating necessity for the restraint of the mentally ill, often by use of barred windows and locked doors, fire exit drills are usually extremely disturbing, detrimental, and frequently impracticable.

In most cases, fire exit drills, as ordinarily practiced in other occupancies, cannot be conducted in health care occupancies. Fundamentally, superior construction, early discovery and extinguishment of incipient fires, and prompt notification need to be relied on to reduce the occasion for evacuation of buildings of this class to a minimum.

Section 21.7* Operating Features

A.21.7 Health care occupants have, in large part, varied degrees of physical disability, and their removal to the outside or even their disturbance caused by moving is inexpedient or impractical in many cases, except as a last resort. Similarly, recognizing that there might be an operating necessity for the restraint of the mentally ill, often by use of barred windows and locked doors, fire exit drills are usually extremely disturbing, detrimental, and frequently impracticable.

In most cases, fire exit drills, as ordinarily practiced in other occupancies, cannot be conducted in health care occupancies. Fundamentally, superior construction, early discovery and extinguishment of incipient fires, and prompt notification needs to be relied on to reduce the occasion for evacuation of buildings of this class to a minimum.

20.7.1 Evacuation and Relocation Plan and Fire Drills.

20.7.1.1 The administration of every ambulatory health care facility shall have, in effect and available to all supervisory personnel, written copies of a plan for the protection of all persons in the event of fire, for their evacuation to areas of refuge, and for their evacuation from the building when necessary. All employees shall be periodically instructed and kept informed with respect to their duties under the plan. A copy of the plan shall be readily available at all times in the telephone operator's position or at the security center.

The provisions of 20.7.1.2 through 20.7.2.3 shall apply.

20.7.1.2* Fire drills in ambulatory health care facilities shall include the transmission of a fire alarm signal and simulation of emergency fire conditions. Drills shall be conducted quarterly on each shift to familiarize facility personnel (nurses, interns, maintenance engineers, and administrative staff) with the signals and emergency action required under varied conditions. When drills are conducted between 9:00 p.m. (2100 hours) and 6:00 a.m. (0600 hours), a coded announcement shall be permitted to be used instead of audible alarms.

Exception: Infirm or bedridden patients shall not be required to be moved during drills to safe areas or to the exterior of the building.

A.20.7.1.2 Many health care occupancies conduct fire drills without disturbing patients by choosing the location of the simulated emergency in advance and by closing the doors to patients' rooms or wards in the vicinity prior to the initiation of the drill. The purpose of a fire drill is to test and evaluate the efficiency, knowledge, and response of institutional personnel in implementing the facility fire emergency plan. Its purpose is not to disturb or excite patients. Fire drills should be scheduled on a random basis to ensure that personnel in health care facilities are drilled not less than once in each 3-month period.

Drills should consider the ability to move patients to an adjacent smoke compartment. Relocation can be practiced using simulated patients or empty wheelchairs.

20.7.1.3 Employees of ambulatory health care facilities shall be instructed in life safety procedures and devices.

20.7.2 Procedure in Case of Fire.

20.7.2.1* For ambulatory health care facilities, the proper protection of patients shall require the prompt and effective response of ambulatory health care personnel. The basic response required of staff shall include the removal of all

21.7.1 Evacuation and Relocation Plan and Fire Drills.

21.7.1.1 The administration of every ambulatory health care facility shall have, in effect and available to all supervisory personnel, written copies of a plan for the protection of all persons in the event of fire, for their evacuation to areas of refuge, and for their evacuation from the building when necessary. All employees shall be periodically instructed and kept informed with respect to their duties under the plan. A copy of the plan shall be readily available at all times in the telephone operator's position or at the security center.

The provisions of 21.7.1.2 through 21.7.2.3 shall apply.

21.7.1.2* Fire drills in ambulatory health care facilities shall include the transmission of a fire alarm signal and simulation of emergency fire conditions. Drills shall be conducted quarterly on each shift to familiarize facility personnel (nurses, interns, maintenance engineers, and administrative staff) with the signals and emergency action required under varied conditions. When drills are conducted between 9:00 p.m. (2100 hours) and 6:00 a.m. (0600 hours), a coded announcement shall be permitted to be used instead of audible alarms.

Exception: Infirm or bedridden patients shall not be required to be moved during drills to safe areas or to the exterior of the building.

A.21.7.1.2 Many health care occupancies conduct fire drills without disturbing patients by choosing the location of the simulated emergency in advance and by closing the doors to patients' rooms or wards in the vicinity prior to initiation of the drill. The purpose of a fire drill is to test and evaluate the efficiency, knowledge, and response of institutional personnel in implementing the facility fire emergency plan. Its purpose is not to disturb or excite patients. Fire drills should be scheduled on a random basis to ensure that personnel in health care facilities are drilled not less than once in each 3-month period.

Drills should consider the ability to move patients to an adjacent smoke compartment. Relocation can be practiced using simulated patients or empty wheelchairs.

21.7.1.3 Employees of ambulatory health care facilities shall be instructed in life safety procedures and devices.

21.7.2 Procedure in Case of Fire.

21.7.2.1* For ambulatory health care facilities, the proper protection of patients shall require the prompt and effective response of ambulatory health care personnel. The basic response required of staff shall include the removal of all occupants directly involved with the fire emergency, transmission of an appropriate fire alarm signal to warn other building occupants and summon staff, confinement of the effects of the fire by closing doors to isolate the fire area, and the relocation of patients as detailed in the facility's fire safety plan.

A.20.7.2.1 Each facility has specific characteristics that vary sufficiently from other facilities to prevent the specification of a universal emergency procedure. The following recommendations, however, contain many of the elements that should be considered and adapted as appropriate to the individual facility.

Upon discovery of fire, personnel should immediately take the following action.

(a) If any person is involved in the fire, the discoverer should go to the aid of that person, calling aloud an established code phrase. The use of a code provides for both the immediate aid of any endangered person and the transmission of an alarm. Any person in the area, upon hearing the code called aloud, should activate the building fire alarm using the nearest manual fire alarm box.

(b) If a person is not involved in the fire, the discoverer should activate the building fire alarm using the nearest manual fire alarm box.

(c) Personnel, upon hearing the alarm signal, should immediately execute their duties as outlined in the facility fire safety plan.

(d) The telephone operator should determine the location of the fire as indicated by the audible signal. In a building equipped with an uncoded alarm system, a person on the floor of fire origin should be responsible for promptly notifying the facility telephone operator of the fire location.

(e) If the telephone operator receives a telephone alarm reporting a fire from a floor, the operator should regard that alarm in the same fashion as an alarm received over the fire alarm system. The operator should immediately notify the fire department and alert all facility personnel of the place of fire and its origin.

(f) If the building fire alarm system is out of order, any person discovering a fire should immediately notify the telephone operator by telephone. The operator should then transmit this information to the fire department and alert the building occupants.

20.7.2.2 A written fire safety plan shall provide for the following:

(1) Use of alarms
(2) Transmission of alarm to fire department
(3) Response to alarms

occupants directly involved with the fire emergency, transmission of an appropriate fire alarm signal to warn other building occupants and summon staff, confinement of the effects of the fire by closing doors to isolate the fire area, and the relocation of patients as detailed in the facility's fire safety plan.

A.21.7.2.1 Each facility has specific characteristics that vary sufficiently from other facilities to prevent the specification of a universal emergency procedure. The following recommendations, however, contain many of the elements that should be considered and adapted as appropriate to the individual facility.

Upon discovery of fire, personnel should immediately take the following action.

(a) If any person is involved in the fire, the discoverer should go to the aid of that person, calling aloud an established code phrase. The use of a code provides for both the immediate aid of any endangered person and the transmission of an alarm. Any person in the area, upon hearing the code called aloud, should activate the building fire alarm using the nearest manual fire alarm box.

(b) If a person is not involved in the fire, the discoverer should activate the building fire alarm using the nearest manual fire alarm box.

(c) Personnel, upon hearing the alarm signal, should immediately execute their duties as outlined in the facility fire safety plan.

(d) The telephone operator should determine the location of the fire as indicated by the audible signal. In a building equipped with an uncoded alarm system, a person on the floor of fire origin should be responsible for promptly notifying the facility telephone operator of the fire location.

(e) If the telephone operator receives a telephone alarm reporting a fire from a floor, the operator should regard that alarm in the same fashion as an alarm received over the fire alarm system. The operator should immediately notify the fire department and alert all facility personnel of the place of fire and its origin.

(f) If the building fire alarm system is out of order, any person discovering a fire should immediately notify the telephone operator by telephone. The operator should then transmit this information to the fire department and alert the building occupants.

21.7.2.2 A written fire safety plan shall provide for the following:

(1) Use of alarms
(2) Transmission of alarm to fire department
(3) Response to alarms

(4) Isolation of fire
(5) Evacuation of immediate area
(6) Evacuation of smoke compartment
(7) Preparation of floors and building for evacuation
(8) Extinguishment of fire

20.7.2.3 All personnel shall be instructed in the use of and response to fire alarms. In addition, they shall be instructed in the use of the code phrase to ensure transmission of an alarm under the following conditions:

(1) When the individual who discovers a fire must immediately go to the aid of an endangered person
(2) During a malfunction of the building fire alarm system

Personnel hearing the code announced shall first activate the building fire alarm using the nearest fire alarm box and then shall execute immediately their duties as outlined in the fire safety plan.

20.7.3 Maintenance of Exits.

Proper maintenance shall be provided to ensure the dependability of the method of evacuation selected. Ambulatory health care occupancies that find it necessary to lock exits shall, at all times, maintain an adequate staff qualified to release locks and direct occupants from the immediate danger area to a place of safety in case of fire or other emergency.

20.7.4* Smoking.

Smoking regulations shall be adopted and shall include not less than the following provisions:

(1) Smoking shall be prohibited in any room, ward, or compartment where flammable liquids, combustible gases, or oxygen is used or stored and in any other hazardous location, and such areas shall be posted with signs that read NO SMOKING or shall be posted with the international symbol for no smoking.

Exception: The requirement of 20.7.4(1) shall not apply where smoking is prohibited and signs are prominently placed at all major entrances, secondary signs with language that prohibits smoking shall not be required.

(2) Smoking by patients classified as not responsible shall be prohibited.

Exception: The requirement of 20.7.4(2) shall not apply where the patient is under direct supervision.

(3) Ashtrays of noncombustible material and safe design shall be provided in all areas where smoking is permitted.

(4) Isolation of fire
(5) Evacuation of immediate area
(6) Evacuation of smoke compartment
(7) Preparation of floors and building for evacuation
(8) Extinguishment of fire

21.7.2.3 All personnel shall be instructed in the use of and response to fire alarms. In addition, they shall be instructed in the use of the code phrase to ensure transmission of an alarm under the following conditions:

(1) When the individual who discovers a fire must immediately go to the aid of an endangered person
(2) During a malfunction of the building fire alarm system

Personnel hearing the code announced shall first activate the building fire alarm using the nearest fire alarm box and then shall execute immediately their duties as outlined in the fire safety plan.

21.7.3 Maintenance of Exits.

Proper maintenance shall be provided to ensure the dependability of the method of evacuation selected. Ambulatory health care occupancies that find it necessary to lock exits shall, at all times, maintain an adequate staff qualified to release locks and direct occupants from the immediate danger area to a place of safety in case of fire or other emergency.

21.7.4* Smoking.

Smoking regulations shall be adopted and shall include not less than the following provisions:

(1) Smoking shall be prohibited in any room, ward, or compartment where flammable liquids, combustible gases, or oxygen is used or stored and in any other hazardous location, and such areas shall be posted with signs that read NO SMOKING or shall be posted with the international symbol for no smoking.

Exception: The requirement of 21.7.4(2) shall not apply where smoking is prohibited and signs are prominently placed at all major entrances, secondary signs with language that prohibits smoking shall not be required.

(2) Smoking by patients classified as not responsible shall be prohibited.

Exception: The requirement of 21.7.4(2) shall not apply where the patient is under direct supervision.

(3) Ashtrays of noncombustible material and safe design shall be provided in all areas where smoking is permitted.

CHAPTER 20 • New	CHAPTER 21 • Existing

(4) Metal containers with self-closing cover devices into which ashtrays can be emptied shall be readily available to all areas where smoking is permitted.

A.20.7.4 The most rigid discipline with regard to prohibition of smoking might not be nearly as effective in reducing incipient fires from surreptitious smoking as the open recognition of smoking, with provision of suitable facilities for smoking. Proper education and training of the staff and attendants in the ordinary fire hazards and their abatement is unquestionably essential. The problem is a broad one, varying with different types and arrangements of buildings; the effectiveness of rules of procedure, which need to be flexible, depends in large part on the management.

20.7.5 Furnishings, Bedding, and Decorations.

20.7.5.1* Draperies, curtains, including cubicle curtains, and other loosely hanging fabrics and films serving as furnishings or decorations in ambulatory health care occupancies shall be in accordance with the provisions of 10.3.1.

Exception: Curtains at showers.

A.20.7.5.1 In addition to the provisions of 10.3.1, which deal with ignition resistance, additional requirements with respect to the location of cubicle curtains relative to sprinkler placement are included in NFPA 13, *Standard for the Installation of Sprinkler Systems.*

20.7.5.2 Newly introduced upholstered furniture shall meet the criteria specified when tested in accordance with the methods cited in 10.3.2(2) and 10.3.3.

20.7.5.3 Newly introduced mattresses shall meet the criteria specified when tested in accordance with the methods cited in 10.3.2(3) and 10.3.4.

20.7.5.4 Combustible decorations shall be prohibited unless they are flame-retardant.

Exception: Combustible decorations, such as photographs and paintings, in such limited quantities that a hazard of fire development or spread is not present.

20.7.5.5 Soiled linen or trash collection receptacles shall not exceed 32 gal (121 L) in capacity. The average density of container capacity in a room or space shall not exceed 0.5 gal/ft^2 (20.4 L/m^2). A capacity of 32 gal (121 L) shall not be exceeded within any 64-ft^2 (5.9-m^2) area. Mobile soiled linen or trash collection receptacles with capacities greater than 32 gal (121 L) shall be located in a room protected as a hazardous area when not attended.

Exception: Container size and density shall not be limited in hazardous areas.

(4) Metal containers with self-closing cover devices into which ashtrays can be emptied shall be readily available to all areas where smoking is permitted.

A.21.7.4 The most rigid discipline with regard to prohibition of smoking might not be nearly as effective in reducing incipient fires from surreptitious smoking as the open recognition of smoking, with provision of suitable facilities for smoking. Proper education and training of the staff and attendants in the ordinary fire hazards and their abatement is unquestionably essential. The problem is a broad one, varying with different types and arrangements of buildings; the effectiveness of rules of procedure, which need to be flexible, depends in large part on the management.

21.7.5 Furnishings, Bedding, and Decorations.

21.7.5.1* Draperies, curtains, including cubicle curtains, and other loosely hanging fabrics and films serving as furnishings or decorations in ambulatory health care occupancies shall be in accordance with the provisions of 10.3.1.

Exception: Curtains at showers.

A.21.7.5.1 In addition to the provisions of 10.3.1, which deal with ignition resistance, additional requirements with respect to the location of cubicle curtains relative to sprinkler placement are included in NFPA 13, *Standard for the Installation of Sprinkler Systems.*

21.7.5.2 Newly introduced upholstered furniture shall meet the criteria specified when tested in accordance with the methods cited in 10.3.2(2) and 10.3.3.

21.7.5.3 Newly introduced mattresses shall meet the criteria specified when tested in accordance with the methods cited in 10.3.2(3) and 10.3.4.

21.7.5.4 Combustible decorations shall be prohibited unless they are flame-retardant.

Exception: Combustible decorations, such as photographs and paintings, in such limited quantities that a hazard of fire development or spread is not present.

21.7.5.5 Soiled linen or trash collection receptacles shall not exceed 32 gal (121 L) in capacity. The average density of container capacity in a room or space shall not exceed 0.5 gal/ft^2 (20.4 L/m^2). A capacity of 32 gal (121 L) shall not be exceeded within any 64-ft^2 (5.9-m^2) area. Mobile soiled linen or trash collection receptacles with capacities greater than 32 gal (121 L) shall be located in a room protected as a hazardous area when not attended.

Exception: Container size and density shall not be limited in hazardous areas.

CHAPTER 20 • New   **CHAPTER 21 • Existing**

Cigarette ignition-resistance testing—as detailed in 10.3.2—and rate of heat release testing—as detailed in 10.3.3 and 10.3.4—are required by 20/21.7.5.2 and 20/21.7.5.3 for newly introduced upholstered furniture and newly introduced mattresses in ambulatory health care occupancies, unless the room or space is sprinklered. Unlike new hospitals and nursing homes—which are required to be sprinklered—many new and existing ambulatory health care facilities will not be sprinklered. Thus, newly introduced upholstered furniture and mattresses will be subject to cigarette ignition resistance and rate of heat release testing.

Paragraph 20/21.7.5.5 establishes maximum trash container sizes and placement densities permitted within a room. Containers larger than those specified, or grouped containers exceeding the density per room criterion, present a hazard greater than that associated with the normal furnishing of an ambulatory health care center room.

Large, mobile soiled linen or trash receptacles can be moved along the corridor as collections occur

but must be attended by staff. If housekeeping staff, for example, must leave the area, the container must be stored in a room designed and maintained as a hazardous area in accordance with 20/21.3.2. Exhibit 20/21.6 illustrates the requirements of 20/21.7.5.5.

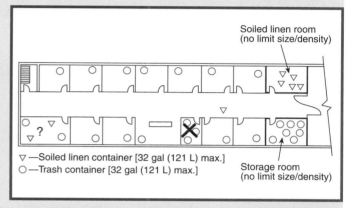

Exhibit 20/21.6 *Allowable soiled linen or trash collection receptacles.*

20.7.6 Maintenance and Testing.

(See 4.6.12.)

20.7.7* Engineered Smoke Control Systems.

New engineered smoke control systems shall be tested in accordance with established engineering principles and shall meet the performance requirements of such testing prior to acceptance. Following acceptance, all engineered smoke control systems shall be tested periodically in accordance with recognized engineering principles. Test documentation shall be maintained on the premises at all times.

A.20.7.7 Two documents that provide recognized engineering principles for the testing of smoke control systems are NFPA 92A, *Recommended Practice for Smoke-Control Systems*, and NFPA 92B, *Guide for Smoke Management Systems in Malls, Atria, and Large Areas*.

20.7.8 Portable Space-Heating Devices.

Portable space-heating devices shall be prohibited.

Exception: Portable space-heating devices shall be permitted to be used in nonsleeping staff and employee areas where the heating elements of such devices do not exceed 212°F (100°C).

21.7.6 Maintenance and Testing.

(See 4.6.12.)

21.7.7* Engineered Smoke Control Systems.

New engineered smoke control systems shall be tested in accordance with established engineering principles and shall meet the performance requirements of such testing prior to acceptance. Following acceptance, all engineered smoke control systems shall be tested periodically in accordance with recognized engineering principles. Test documentation shall be maintained on the premises at all times.

A.21.7.7 Two documents that provide recognized engineering principles for the testing of smoke control systems are NFPA 92A, *Recommended Practice for Smoke-Control Systems*, and NFPA 92B, *Guide for Smoke Management Systems in Malls, Atria, and Large Areas*.

21.7.8 Portable Space-Heating Devices.

Portable space-heating devices shall be prohibited.

Exception: Portable space-heating devices shall be permitted to be used in nonsleeping staff and employee areas where the heating elements of such devices do not exceed 212°F (100°C).

CHAPTER 20 • New   **CHAPTER 21 • Existing**

20.7.9 Construction, Repair, and Improvement Operations.

20.7.9.1 Construction, repair, and improvement operations shall comply with 4.6.10.

20.7.9.2 The means of egress in any area undergoing construction, repair, or improvements shall be inspected daily for compliance with 7.1.10.1 and shall also comply with NFPA 241, *Standard for Safeguarding Construction, Alteration, and Demolition Operations.*

21.7.9 Construction, Repair, and Improvement Operations.

21.7.9.1 Construction, repair, and improvement operations shall comply with 4.6.10.

21.7.9.2 The means of egress in any area undergoing construction, repair, or improvements shall be inspected daily for compliance with 7.1.10.1 and shall also comply with NFPA 241, *Standard for Safeguarding Construction, Alteration, and Demolition Operations.*

References Cited in Commentary

1. NFPA 220, *Standard on Types of Building Construction*, 1999 edition, National Fire Protection Association, Quincy, MA.
2. NFPA 99, *Standard for Health Care Facilities*, 1999 edition, National Fire Protection Association, Quincy, MA.
3. NFPA 80, *Standard for Fire Doors and Windows*, 1999 edition, National Fire Protection Association, Quincy, MA.

New and Existing Detention and Correctional Occupancies

Detention and correctional occupancies apply the total concept approach to life safety—complete with a defend-in-place strategy—much as is done for health care occupancies. Unlike health care occupancies, where the incapability of self-preservation is due to a medical condition, detention and correctional occupancies render occupants incapable of self-preservation because of security restrictions. Security restrictions prevent, to a large extent, free and customary movement and access to other areas of a building. In general, many of the normal features needed in a detention facility are nearly the exact opposite of what the *Code* attempts to provide for other occupancies. The use of locked doors, often with key-operated locks (see 22/23.2.11.2); egress components for which use is restricted or traffic flow is constricted, such as a sally port (see 22/23.2.5.4); and discharge of exits onto other than public ways (see 22/23.2.7.1) are features not usually permitted in other occupancies.

Chapters 22 and 23 impose limitations on the degree of locking that can be used. These limits form a classification scheme based on the appropriate use condition. In general, the amount of restriction (Use Condition I is free egress and Use Condition V is contained; see 22/23.1.4.1) in the detention and correctional facility dictates the use of acceptable locking methods and means of egress features that are not otherwise permitted in other occupancies. As in a health care facility, those unique features necessary to protect the occupants *in place* include construction, compartmentation, alarm and detection, and staff facilitation to help lead or direct occupants to safe areas within the premises of the detention facility campus.

Section 22/23.7 provides routine operating requirements, such as 24-hour staffing, means for resident notification of staff in an emergency, preparation and maintenance of evacuation plans, staff training in the use of portable fire extinguishers, storage of combustible personal property, presence of heat-producing appliances, control of flammability of draperies, curtains, mattresses, and upholstered furniture, and visual and tactile identification of keys necessary for unlocking doors within the means of egress. Because locking doors—which is necessary for the intended function of the facility—is contrary to the basic *Code* tenet that the means of egress system be under the control of building occupants, the presence of properly trained staff is paramount to providing a level of life safety equivalent to that provided in other occupancies. Section 22/23.7 requires the necessary staffing and training that—where combined with the *Code* requirements of the core chapters and the remainder of Chapter 22/23—achieve the necessary level of life safety.

Section 22.1 General Requirements

22.1.1 Application.

22.1.1.1 The requirements of this chapter apply to the following:

Section 23.1 General Requirements

23.1.1 Application.

23.1.1.1 The requirements of this chapter apply to existing buildings or portions thereof currently occupied as detention or correctional occupancies. *(See also 22.1.1.1.)*

CHAPTER 22 • New

CHAPTER 23 • Existing

(1) New buildings or portions thereof used as detention or correctional occupancies *(see 1.4.1)*
(2) Additions made to, or used as, a detention or correctional occupancy *(see 4.6.6 and 22.1.1.6)*
(3) Alterations, modernizations, or renovations of existing detention or correctional occupancies *(see 4.6.7 and 22.1.1.7)*
(4) Existing buildings or portions thereof upon change of occupancy to a detention or correctional occupancy *(see 4.6.11)*

22.1.1.2 This chapter establishes life safety requirements for the design of all new detention and correctional facilities.

Exception No. 1: Use Condition I facilities protected as residential occupancies in accordance with 22.1.4.3.

Exception No. 2:* Facilities determined to have equivalent safety provided in accordance with Section 1.5.

A.22.1.1.2 Exception No. 2 In determining equivalency for conversions, modernizations, renovations, or unusual design concepts of detention and correctional facilities, the authority having jurisdiction is permitted to accept evaluations based on Chapter 4 of NFPA 101A, *Guide on Alternative Approaches to Life Safety,* utilizing the parameters for new construction.

22.1.1.3 Detention and correctional occupancies shall include those used for purposes such as correctional institutions, detention facilities, community residential centers, training schools, work camps, and substance abuse centers where occupants are confined or housed under some degree of restraint or security.

22.1.1.4 Detention and correctional occupancies provide sleeping facilities for four or more residents and are occupied by persons who are generally prevented from taking self-preservation action because of security measures not under the occupants' control.

22.1.1.5 Total Concept. All detention and correctional facilities shall be designed, constructed, maintained, and operated to minimize the possibility of a fire emergency. Because the safety of all occupants in detention and correctional facilities cannot be adequately ensured solely by dependence on evacuation of the building, their protection from fire shall be provided by appropriate arrangement of facilities; adequate, trained staff; and development of operating, security, and maintenance procedures composed of the following:

(1) Design, construction, and compartmentation
(2) Provision for detection, alarm, and extinguishment
(3) Fire prevention and planning, training, and drilling pro-

23.1.1.2 This chapter establishes life safety requirements for all existing detention and correctional facilities.

Exception No. 1: Use Condition I facilities protected as residential occupancies in accordance with 23.1.4.3.

Exception No. 2:* Facilities determined to have equivalent safety provided in accordance with Section 1.5.

A.23.1.1.2 Exception No. 2 In determining equivalency for existing detention and correctional facilities, the authority having jurisdiction is permitted to accept evaluations based on Chapter 4 of NFPA 101A, *Guide on Alternative Approaches to Life Safety,* utilizing the parameters for existing buildings.

23.1.1.3 Detention and correctional occupancies shall include those used for purposes such as correctional institutions, detention facilities, community residential centers, training schools, work camps, and substance abuse centers where occupants are confined or housed under some degree of restraint or security.

23.1.1.4 Detention and correctional occupancies provide sleeping facilities for four or more residents and are occupied by persons who are generally prevented from taking self-preservation action because of security measures not under the occupants' control.

23.1.1.5 Total Concept. All detention and correctional facilities shall be designed, constructed, maintained, and operated to minimize the possibility of a fire emergency. Because the safety of all occupants in detention and correctional facilities cannot be adequately ensured solely by dependence on evacuation of the building, their protection from fire shall be provided by appropriate arrangement of facilities; adequate, trained staff; and development of operating, security, and maintenance procedures composed of the following:

(1) Design, construction, and compartmentation
(2) Provision for detection, alarm, and extinguishment
(3) Fire prevention and planning, training, and drilling pro-

grams for the isolation of fire and the transfer of occupants to areas of refuge, for evacuation of the building, or for protection of the occupants in place

(4) Provision of security to the degree necessary for the safety of the public and the occupants of the facility

22.1.1.6 Additions. Additions shall be separated from any existing structure not conforming with the provisions of Chapter 23 by a fire barrier having not less than a 2-hour fire resistance rating constructed to the requirements of the addition. Doors in these partitions shall normally be kept closed.

Exception: Doors shall be permitted to be held open if they meet the requirements of the exception to 7.2.1.8.

22.1.1.7 Modernizations or Renovations. Modernizations and renovations shall be in accordance with 4.6.7.

Exception: In nonsprinklered existing buildings, modernizations or renovations shall be permitted to comply with the nonsprinklered options contained in 22.4.4 in lieu of the sprinkler requirement of 22.3.5.2.

Although 22/23.1.1.2 states that Chapter 22/23 establishes life safety requirements for detention and correctional facilities, the chapter focuses primarily on life safety requirements for the residential portions of these occupancies. See the commentary associated with 22/23.1.2.1, which explains that the requirements of Chapter 22/23 apply mainly to the residential areas of a detention and correctional occupancy.

Exception No. 1 to 22/23.1.1.2 exempts Use Condition I facilities from the requirements of Chapter 22/23 if such facilities are protected as residential occupancies. In accordance with 22/23.1.4, which defines the five resident user category groups, Use Condition I provides residents with free movement from sleeping areas and other spaces where access or occupancy is permitted to the exterior, by a means of an egress system that meets the same requirements as would be provided for occupants of hotel, dormitory, apartment, or lodging or rooming house occupancies. Because locked doors have not been imposed on the residents of a Use Condition I detention or correctional occupancy, such a facility does not require the protect-in-place strategy and associated requirements of Chapter 22/23. For information on the protection of Use Condition I facilities, Exception No. 1 to 22/23.1.1.2 and Exception No. 1 to 22/23.1.4.3 refer the user to the residential occupancy chapters of the *Code* in lieu of the provisions of Chapter 22/23.

grams for the isolation of fire and the transfer of occupants to areas of refuge, for evacuation of the building, or for protection of the occupants in place

(4) Provision of security to the degree necessary for the safety of the public and the occupants of the facility

23.1.1.6 Additions. Additions shall be separated from any existing structure not conforming with the provisions of Chapter 23 by a fire barrier having not less than a 2-hour fire resistance rating constructed to the requirements of the addition. Doors in these partitions shall normally be kept closed.

Exception: Doors shall be permitted to be held open if they meet the requirements of the exception to 7.2.1.8.

23.1.1.7 Modernizations or Renovations. Modernizations and renovations shall be in accordance with 4.6.7.

Exception: In nonsprinklered existing buildings, modernizations or renovations shall be permitted to comply with the nonsprinklered options contained in 22.4.4 in lieu of the sprinkler requirement of 22.3.5.2.

Exception No. 2 to 22/23.1.1.2 permits the equivalency provisions of Section 1.5 to be used to comply with the intended level of life safety rather than having to meet the requirements of Chapter 22/23. The 2001 edition of NFPA 101A, *Guide on Alternative Approaches to Life Safety,* will provide information on one possible equivalency system for use in detention and correctional occupancies.[1] Its measurement system is calibrated against the requirements of the 2000 edition of the *Life Safety Code,* whereas the fire safety evaluation systems contained in the 1998 edition of NFPA 101A were calibrated against the requirements of the 1997 edition of the *Code.* The 2001 edition of NFPA 101A will be published early in 2001.

The fire safety evaluation system for detention and correctional occupancies contained in NFPA 101A provides a method in which the user assigns numerical values to various building parameters. The individual values are totaled and compared with established values. Using this system, alternative designs can be evaluated as options to literal *Code* compliance. The *Code* does not intend to limit acceptable equivalency evaluations solely to those based on this system. The authority having jurisdiction retains the discretion—in accordance with Section 1.5—to evaluate and approve alternative designs on the basis of appropriate supporting data. Also, Section 4.4 of this *Code* permits the use of the performance-based

CHAPTER 22 • New   **CHAPTER 23 • Existing**

option for the design of a complete life safety system in accordance with Chapter 5.

Both A.6.1.7.1 and 22/23.1.1.3 reflect the current terminology for various forms of detention and correctional occupancies. The terms *adult correctional institutions, adult local detention facilities, juvenile detention facilities, juvenile training schools, adult and juvenile community residential centers, adult and juvenile work camps,* and *adult and juvenile substance abuse centers* are used in place of terms such as *reformatories* and *houses of correction.*

Residents of detention and correctional occupancies and patients in health care occupancies are judged to be incapable of self-preservation during a fire emergency. In the case of a health care occupancy patient, incapability is due to physical or mental illness or infirmity. The detention and correctional occupancy resident, although most likely ambulatory or able-bodied, is incapable of self-preservation due to security measures imposed and beyond the resident's control. In both cases, the occupants might have to await staff action before moving to an exit, another fire compartment, or another smoke compartment. Impediments to adequate egress are further compounded in detention and correctional occupancies by the reluctance of staff to unlock doors leading to the outside. Thus, horizontal movement within the facility to another fire compartment or smoke compartment might be the only means of egress system that the resident is allowed to use in a fire emergency, regardless of how many exit doors to the outside are installed. Therefore, use of the "total concept" described in 22/23.1.1.5 is critical.

The total concept as used in 22/23.1.1.5 establishes a protect-in-place or defend-in-place strategy. This strategy mandates requirements that minimize the need for building evacuation by restricting the development and spread of a fire emergency to the room of fire origin. This concept is desirable because safety cannot be ensured by relying on a means of egress system that is predicated on the use of evacuation but for which locks either cannot or will not be unlocked in a timely manner. The requirements (for example, Section 22/23.7) first try to prevent ignition and, when fires do occur, set out to detect them (for example, 22/23.3.4.4). Other requirements aim to control the speed with which a fire will develop (for example, 22/23.3.3), and still others serve to confine the effects of fire. Extinguishment of fire is facilitated by sprinkler, standpipe, and portable fire extinguisher requirements. Provisions are made for refuge

areas by encouraging the use of horizontal exits and by requiring smoke barriers. Heavy reliance is placed on staff reaction. All these requirements fit together to minimize the need for evacuation. This is the "total concept."

Additions are addressed in 22/23.1.1.6. Buildings that comply with the requirements for existing detention and correctional occupancies in accordance with Chapter 23 do not require separation from new additions.

Note that, unlike similar requirements that apply to health care occupancies, the positioning of doors in the separating fire barriers is not restricted to cross-corridor locations. Doors must be kept closed unless they meet the requirements for automatic closing found in 7.2.1.8.2.

Exhibit 22/23.1 illustrates the requirements of 22/23.1.1.6. If the existing portion of the building meets the requirements of Chapter 23, the new addition could be open to the existing building.

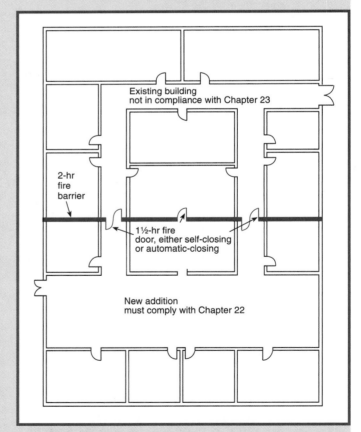

Exhibit 22/23.1 *Separation required between new addition, complying with Chapter 22, and existing building not complying with requirements of Chapter 23.*

22.1.2* Mixed Occupancies.

(See also 6.1.14.)

A.22.1.2 Detention and correctional facilities are a complex of structures, each serving a definite and usually different purpose. In many institutions, all, or almost all, the occupancy-type classifications found in this *Code* are represented. Means of egress and other features are governed by the type of occupancy classification and the hazard of occupancy, unless specific exceptions are made.

All buildings and structures are to be classified using Chapter 22 and Section 6.1 as a guide, subject to the ruling of the authority having jurisdiction where there is a question as to the proper classification of any individual building or structure.

Use condition classification of the institution, as well as individual areas within the complex, is always to be considered by the authority having jurisdiction.

22.1.2.1* Egress provisions for areas of detention and correctional facilities that correspond to other occupancies shall meet the corresponding requirements of this *Code* for such occupancies. Where security operations necessitate the locking of required means of egress, staff shall be provided for the supervised release of occupants during all times of use.

A.22.1.2.1 Key-operated locking hardware should be of institutional grade. Lesser grade hardware might not be suitable for the heavy use that these locks are expected to receive.

22.1.2.2 Sections of detention and correctional facilities shall be permitted to be classified as other occupancies, provided that they meet all of the following conditions:

(1) They are not intended to serve residents for sleeping purposes.
(2) They are separated from areas of detention or correctional occupancies by construction having not less than a 2-hour fire resistance rating.

22.1.2.3 Detention and correctional occupancies in buildings housing other occupancies shall be completely separated from the other occupancies by construction having not less than a 2-hour fire resistance rating, as provided for additions in 22.1.1.6.

22.1.2.4 All means of egress from detention and correctional occupancies that traverse other use areas shall, as a minimum, conform to the requirements of this *Code* for detention and correctional occupancies.

Exception: Egress through a horizontal exit into other contiguous occupancies that do not conform to detention and correctional occupancy egress provisions, but that do comply with requirements set forth in the appropriate occupancy

23.1.2* Mixed Occupancies.

(See also 6.1.14.)

A.23.1.2 Detention and correctional facilities are a complex of structures, each serving a definite and usually different purpose. In many institutions all, or almost all, of the occupancy-type classifications found in this *Code* are represented. Means of egress and other features are governed by the type of occupancy classification and the hazard of occupancy, unless specific exceptions are made.

All buildings and structures are to be classified using Chapter 23 and Section 6.1 as a guide, subject to the ruling of the authority having jurisdiction where there is a question as to the proper classification of any individual building or structure.

Use condition classification of the institution, as well as individual areas within the complex, is always to be considered by the authority having jurisdiction.

23.1.2.1* Egress provisions for areas of detention and correctional facilities that correspond to other occupancies shall meet the corresponding requirements of this *Code* for such occupancies. Where security operations necessitate the locking of required means of egress, staff shall be provided for the supervised release of occupants during all times of use.

A.23.1.2.1 Key-operated locking hardware should be of institutional grade. Lesser grade hardware might not be suitable for the heavy use that these locks are expected to receive.

23.1.2.2 Sections of detention and correctional facilities shall be permitted to be classified as other occupancies, provided that they meet all of the following conditions:

(1) They are not intended to serve residents for sleeping purposes.
(2) They are separated from areas of detention or correctional occupancies by construction having not less than a 2-hour fire resistance rating.

23.1.2.3 Detention and correctional occupancies in buildings housing other occupancies shall be completely separated from the other occupancies by construction having not less than a 2-hour fire resistance rating, as provided for additions in 23.1.1.6.

23.1.2.4 All means of egress from detention and correctional occupancies that traverse other use areas shall, as a minimum, conform to the requirements of this *Code* for detention and correctional occupancies.

Exception: Egress through a horizontal exit into other contiguous occupancies that do not conform to detention and correctional occupancy egress provisions, but that do comply with requirements set forth in the appropriate occupancy

CHAPTER 22 • New

CHAPTER 23 • Existing

chapter of this Code, shall be permitted, provided that the occupancy does not contain high hazard contents. The horizontal exit shall comply with the requirements of 22.2.2.5.

22.1.2.5 Any area with a hazard of contents classified higher than that of the detention or correctional occupancy and located in the same building shall be protected as required in 22.3.2.

22.1.2.6 Nondetention- or noncorrectional-related occupancies classified as containing high hazard contents shall not be permitted in buildings housing detention or correctional occupancies.

chapter of this Code, shall be permitted, provided that the occupancy does not contain high hazard contents. The horizontal exit shall comply with the requirements of 23.2.2.5.

23.1.2.5 Any area with a hazard of contents classified higher than that of the detention or correctional occupancy and located in the same building shall be protected as required in 23.3.2.

23.1.2.6 Nondetention- or noncorrectional-related occupancies classified as containing high hazard contents shall not be permitted in buildings housing detention or correctional occupancies.

Paragraph 22/23.1.2.1 addresses areas of detention and correctional facilities that correspond to other occupancies. Yet, the detailed provisions of Chapter 22/23 apply mainly to the sleeping and living areas of the detention and correctional facility. Although the work areas resemble a typical industrial occupancy, the requirements of Chapter 40, Industrial Occupancies, cannot be applied by themselves because doors within the required means of egress of a detention and correctional occupancy are locked for security. Therefore, the concepts of Chapter 22/23 should be implemented in locked industrial work areas to ensure that the necessary trained staff who control locks are present to facilitate immediate, supervised release of occupants during the event of fire or similar emergency.

In addition, some areas of a large facility might correspond to another occupancy classification. For example, a gymnasium would be considered an assembly occupancy (Chapter 12/13). If locked doors are required, prompt unlocking and release are critical.

Release of locked doors is permitted to be achieved by a remotely activated system capable of unlocking all doors in the means of egress or by a sufficient number of attendants who are continuously on duty, provided with keys, and stationed in the immediate area of all locked means of egress doors. Continuous staff supervision is essential.

Paragraph 22/23.1.2.2 permits portions of a detention and correctional occupancy to be classified as some other occupancy provided that certain safeguards are taken. For example, administrative offices or maintenance areas that are not customarily used by residents as sleeping areas and are separated by 2-hour fire resistance–rated construction could be classified as business or industrial occupancies. In

many cases, "trustees" might be employed in these areas. Their presence in these areas would not be considered a violation of 22/23.1.2.2, provided they have the freedom of egress found in an unlocked environment.

Paragraph 22/23.1.2.3 requires that if a detention or correctional occupancy is located in a building of another classification, the detention or correctional occupancy must be separated from the other occupancy by construction having a fire resistance rating of 2 hours (see 22/23.1.1.6). This requirement would apply to a small detention lockup facility (at least four residents, per 22/23.1.1.4) located in a combination county courthouse/office/police building. In accordance with 22/23.7.1.1, the detention area must be staffed 24 hours per day. The remainder of the building, especially office areas, might not be occupied at night. A fire that originates and develops in an unoccupied area will not threaten the occupants of the detention facility as readily due to the protection provided by the required 2-hour fire resistance–rated barrier.

Note that 22/23.1.2.3 addresses occupancy classification only, not hazard of contents. Hazard of contents is addressed in 22/23.1.2.5.

Paragraph 22/23.1.2.4 addresses detention and correctional occupancy egress paths that traverse other use areas. The means of egress from detention and correctional occupancies that traverse nondetention and noncorrectional spaces must conform to the requirements for detention and correctional occupancies. However, if a 2-hour fire barrier and the associated opening protectives located between a detention or correctional occupancy and another occupancy (for example, business) qualify as a horizontal exit (see 22/23.2.2.5 and 7.2.4), the means of egress system in the business occupancy need comply only

CHAPTER 22 • New   **CHAPTER 23 • Existing**

with the appropriate requirements contained in Chapter 38/39.

Paragraph 22/23.1.2.5 regulates those spaces in a detention and correctional occupancy that have more hazardous contents—in quantity or type—than are usually found in such an occupancy. Spaces, such as rooms used for the storage of highly combustible materials, trash collection rooms, and paint shops, must be protected in accordance with 22/23.3.2.

Paragraph 22/23.1.2.6 prohibits another occupancy with highly hazardous contents—such as flammable liquids storage—from being located in a building housing detention and correctional occu-

pancies. The intent of this paragraph is not to exclude normal storage, but to prevent the conversion of a portion of a detention and correctional facility to a warehouse that contains a larger quantity or a more hazardous type of combustible material than would be normally expected in a detention and correctional occupancy. This requirement applies principally to residential areas. For example, industrial areas that are part of the overall detention and correctional facility but are located in a nonresidential-use building can have flammable liquids as part of the industrial process.

22.1.3 Special Definitions.

Detention and Correctional Residential Housing Area. See 3.3.45.

Sally Port (Security Vestibule). See 3.3.170.

22.1.4 Classification of Occupancy.

22.1.4.1* For application of the life safety requirements of this chapter, the resident user category shall be divided into the following five groups.

(a) *Use Condition I—Free Egress.* Free movement is allowed from sleeping areas and other spaces where access or occupancy is permitted to the exterior via means of egress that meet the requirements of the *Code.*

(b) *Use Condition II—Zoned Egress.* Free movement is allowed from sleeping areas and any other occupied smoke compartment to one or more other smoke compartments.

(c) *Use Condition III—Zoned Impeded Egress.* Free movement is allowed within individual smoke compartments, such as within a residential unit comprised of individual sleeping rooms and a group activity space, with egress impeded by remote-controlled release of means of egress from such a smoke compartment to another smoke compartment.

(d) *Use Condition IV—Impeded Egress.* Free movement is restricted from an occupied space. Remote-controlled release is provided to allow movement from all sleeping rooms, activity spaces, and other occupied areas within the smoke compartment to another smoke compartment.

(e) *Use Condition V—Contained.* Free movement is restricted from an occupied space. Staff-controlled manual release at each door is provided to allow movement from all sleeping rooms, activity spaces, and other occupied areas

23.1.3 Special Definitions.

Detention and Correctional Residential Housing Area. See 3.3.45.

Sally Port (Security Vestibule). See 3.3.170.

23.1.4 Classification of Occupancy.

23.1.4.1* For application of the life safety requirements that follow, the resident user category shall be divided into the following five groups.

(a) *Use Condition I—Free Egress.* Free movement is allowed from sleeping areas and other spaces where access or occupancy is permitted to the exterior via means of egress meeting the requirements of this *Code.*

(b) *Use Condition II—Zoned Egress.* Free movement is allowed from sleeping areas and any other occupied smoke compartment to one or more other smoke compartments.

(c) *Use Condition III—Zoned Impeded Egress.* Free movement is allowed within individual smoke compartments, such as within a residential unit comprised of individual sleeping rooms and a group activity space, with egress impeded by remote-controlled release of means of egress from such a smoke compartment to another smoke compartment.

(d) *Use Condition IV—Impeded Egress.* Free movement is restricted from an occupied space. Remote-controlled release is provided to allow movement from all sleeping rooms, activity spaces, and other occupied areas within the smoke compartment to another smoke compartment.

(e) *Use Condition V—Contained.* Free movement is restricted from an occupied space. Staff-controlled manual release at each door is provided to allow movement from all sleeping rooms, activity spaces, and other occupied areas

CHAPTER 22 • New	CHAPTER 23 • Existing

within the smoke compartment to another smoke compartment.

A.22.1.4.1 Users and occupants of detention and correctional facilities at various times can be expected to include staff, visitors, and residents. The extent and nature of facility utilization will vary according to the type of facility, its function, and its programs.

Figure A.22.1.4.1 illustrates the five use conditions.

within the smoke compartment to another smoke compartment.

A.23.1.4.1 Users and occupants of detention and correctional facilities at various times can be expected to include staff, visitors, and residents. The extent and nature of facility utilization will vary according to the type of facility, its function, and its programs.

Figure A.23.1.4.1 illustrates the five use conditions.

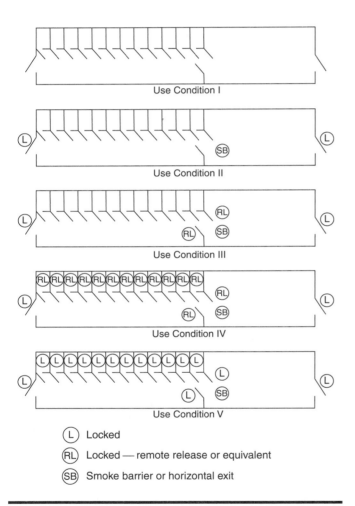

Figure A.22.1.4.1 Detention and correctional use conditions.

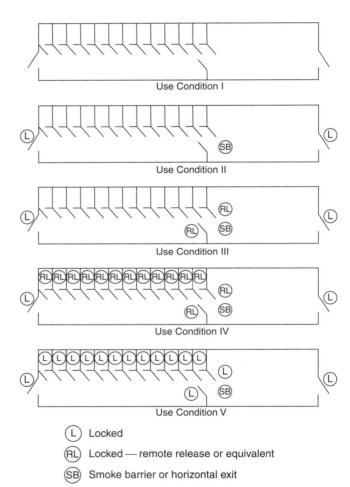

Figure A.23.1.4.1 Detention and correctional use conditions.

22.1.4.2* To be classified as Use Condition III or Use Condition IV, the arrangement, accessibility, and security of the release mechanism(s) used for emergency egress shall be such that the minimum available staff, at any time, can promptly release the locks.

23.1.4.2* To be classified as Use Condition III or Use Condition IV, the arrangement, accessibility, and security of the release mechanism(s) used for emergency egress shall be such that the minimum available staff, at any time, can promptly release the locks.

A.22.1.4.2 Prompt operation is intended to be accomplished in the period of time between detection of fire by either the smoke detector(s) required by 22.3.4 or by other means, whichever comes first, and the advent of intolerable conditions forcing emergency evacuation. Fire tests have indicated that the time available is a function of the volume and height of the space involved and the rate of fire development. In traditional single-story corridor arrangements, the time between detection by smoke detectors and the advent of lethal conditions down to head height can be as short as approximately 3 minutes. In addition, it should be expected that approximately 1 minute will be required to evacuate all the occupants of a threatened smoke compartment once the locks are released. In such a case, a prompt release time would be 2 minutes.

22.1.4.3 Areas housing occupancies corresponding to Use Condition I shall conform to the requirements of residential occupancies under this *Code*.

Exception:* Use Condition I facilities shall be permitted to conform to the requirements of this chapter for Use Condition II facilities, provided that the staffing requirements of Section 22.7 are met.

A.22.1.4.3 Exception If the Use Condition I facility conforms to the requirements of residential occupancies under this *Code*, there are no staffing requirements. If the Use Condition I facility conforms to the requirements of Use Condition II facilities as permitted by this exception, staffing is required in accordance with Section 22.7.

A.23.1.4.2 Prompt operation is intended to be accomplished in the period of time between detection of fire by either the smoke detector(s) required by 23.3.4 or by other means, whichever comes first, and the advent of intolerable conditions forcing emergency evacuation. Fire tests have indicated that the time available is a function of the volume and height of the space involved and the rate of fire development. In traditional single-story corridor arrangements, the time between detection by smoke detectors and the advent of lethal conditions down to head height can be as short as approximately 3 minutes. In addition, it should be expected that approximately 1 minute will be required to evacuate all the occupants of a threatened smoke compartment once the locks are released. In such a case, a prompt release time would be 2 minutes.

23.1.4.3 Areas housing occupancies corresponding to Use Condition I shall conform to the requirements of residential occupancies under this *Code*.

Exception:* Use Condition I facilities shall be permitted to conform to the requirements of this chapter for Use Condition II facilities, provided that the staffing requirements of Section 23.7 are met.

A.23.1.4.3 Exception If the Use Condition I facility conforms to the requirements of residential occupancies under this *Code*, there are no staffing requirements. If the Use Condition I facility conforms to the requirements of Use Condition II facilities as permitted by this exception, staffing is required in accordance with Section 23.7.

Use Condition I facilities have no physical restrictions—such as locks—on the means of egress. The occupants are capable of self-preservation. An example is a work release center whose doors are not locked. See Figure A.22/A.23.1.4.1. Because the means of egress system is kept unlocked, occupants are as free to escape a fire emergency as occupants of any other residential type of occupancy. Therefore, Use Condition I detention and correctional occupancies are exempted from the requirements of Chapter 22/23 by 22/23.1.4.3 and must meet the requirements of some other occupancy chapter, such as Chapter 28/29 for hotels and dormitories. See 22/23.1.4.3 and Exception No. 1 to 22/23.1.1.2.

The residents of a Use Condition II facility have the freedom to move within the building, including the freedom to move from their rooms, across the smoke barrier, and into a separate smoke compartment. Movement through the exit door in the exterior

wall to the outside is impeded by locked doors that are permitted to be unlocked manually at the door. See Figure A.22/A.23.1.4.1.

The residents of a Use Condition III facility are free to move outside their rooms but are confined to the smoke compartment that contains their rooms. Movement to an adjoining smoke compartment is impeded by locked doors within the smoke barrier that must be equipped with remote-control release. Movement through the exit door in the exterior wall to the outside is impeded by locked doors that are permitted to be unlocked manually at the door. See Figure A.22/A.23.1.4.1.

The residents of Use Condition IV facilities are locked in their sleeping rooms. Locks on sleeping room doors must be equipped with remote control release. Movement to an adjoining smoke compartment is impeded by locked doors within the smoke barrier that must be equipped with remote-control release. Movement through the exit door in the exterior wall to the outside is impeded by locked doors that are permitted to be unlocked manually at the door. See Figure A.22/A.23.1.4.1.

In Use Condition V facilities, all locks are manually operated at the individual door. See Figure A.22/A.23.1.4.1. The unlocking process places a heavy demand on staff to open doors in an emergency and severely restricts the movement of residents of Use Condition V facilities. Therefore, the most stringent requirements of Chapter 22/23 are applied to such facilities.

As part of the definitions of Use Condition II through Use Condition V, reference is made to smoke compartments and the type of locking (none, remote release, or manual operation) used for smoke barrier doors. A facility without a smoke barrier can still qualify as meeting the requirements for one of these use conditions by providing for movement to a location judged to be equivalent to a smoke compartment, such as (1) a public way, (2) a building separated from the space in question by either adequate fire resistance–rated construction or distance, or (3) an adequately sized outside holding area located at a safe distance. The locking operation of the door to this alternative location cannot be more stringent than that allowed for the smoke barrier door of the corresponding use condition—no locking for Use Condition II, remote release for Use Condition III and Use Condition IV, and manual operation for Use Condition V. See also 22/23.3.7.

Note that in Figure A.22/A.23.1.4.1, Locked (L) designates manual unlocking operation at the door.

The major requirements noted in paragraph 22/23.1.4.2 are that the area must be under continuous supervision, and a sufficient number of staff must be present and must have the necessary keys readily available to release the locks.

The intent of 22/23.1.4.3 is that detention and cor-

rectional occupancies in which the occupants are not locked in at any time are to be classified as residential occupancies and thus meet the requirements of Chapter 26, 28/29, or 30/31, as appropriate. Those buildings that permit free egress, although used as correctional occupancies, are not classified as detention and correctional occupancies under this *Code*. A facility equipped with locking devices on its doors cannot be classified as Use Condition I because the locks could be used in the future. Instead, depending on the locks' mode of operation—remote or manual—the corresponding use condition should be assigned and the requirements of Chapter 22/23 followed. A facility should be classified as Use Condition I only if the locking devices are physically removed.

In lieu of following the requirements for a normal residential occupancy—as detailed in Chapter 26, 28/29, or 30/31—a Use Condition I facility is permitted to comply with the Chapter 22/23 provisions applicable to a Use Condition II facility. This exception permits the entire facility—which might have a variety of use conditions—to be measured against the requirements of Chapter 22/23 without having to make special use of other occupancy chapters. However—as the language of the exception to A.22/A.23.1.4.3 advises—if the requirements applicable to Use Condition II are used, staffing is required. Proper protection would not be assured by mixing the provisions of a residential occupancy chapter—Chapter 28/29, for example, for which the hotel provisions do not rely on staff action—with those of Chapter 22/23 applicable to Use Condition II facilities, for which heavy reliance is placed on staff action. In other words, the *Code* requires full compliance with either the requirements applicable to a residential occupancy or those applicable to a detention and correctional occupancy—not a self-prescribed mixing of options.

22.1.5 Classification of Hazard of Contents.

The classification of hazard of contents shall be as defined in Section 6.2.

22.1.6 Minimum Construction Requirements.

22.1.6.1 For the purposes of 22.1.6, the number of stories shall be counted starting with the primary level of exit discharge. For the purposes of 22.1.6, the primary level of exit

23.1.5 Classification of Hazard of Contents.

The classification of hazard of contents shall be as defined in Section 6.2.

23.1.6 Minimum Construction Requirements.

23.1.6.1 For the purposes of 23.1.6, the number of stories shall be counted starting with the primary level of exit discharge. For the purposes of 23.1.6, the primary level of exit discharge of a building shall be that floor that is level with or above finished grade on the exterior wall line for 50 percent or more of its perimeter. Building levels below the primary level shall not be counted as a story in determining the height of the building.

22.1.6.2 (Reserved.)

22.1.6.3 Detention and correctional occupancies shall be limited to the types of building construction permitted by Table 22.1.6.3. *(See 8.2.1.)*

discharge of a building shall be that floor that is level with or above finished grade on the exterior wall line for 50 percent or more of its perimeter. Building levels below the primary level shall not be counted as a story in determining the height of the building.

23.1.6.2 A residential housing area complying with 23.3.1.2 shall be considered as a one-story building for purposes of applying 23.1.6.3.

23.1.6.3 Detention and correctional occupancies shall be limited to the types of building construction permitted by Table 23.1.6.3. *(See 8.2.1.)*

Table 22.1.6.3 Construction Type Limitations

Type of Construction	1 Story with Basement	1 Story without Basement	2 Stories	3 Stories	>3 Stories and Not High-Rise	High-Rise
I(443)	X	X	X	X	X	X
I(332)	X	X	X	X	X	X
II(222)	X	X	X	X	X	X
II(111)	X	X	X	NP	NP	NP
III(211)	X	X	X	NP	NP	NP
IV(2HH)	X	X	X	NP	NP	NP
V(111)	X	X	X	NP	NP	NP
II(000)	X	X	X	NP	NP	NP
III(200)	X	X	X	NP	NP	NP
V(000)	X	X	X	NP	NP	NP

X: Permitted types of construction.

NP: Not permitted.

Table 23.1.6.3 Construction Type Limitations

Type of Construction	1 Story with Basement	1 Story without Basement	2 Stories	3 Stories	>3 Stories and Not High-Rise	High-Rise
I(443)	X	X	X	X	X	X[1]
I(332)	X	X	X	X	X	X[1]
II(222)	X	X	X	X	X	X[1]
II(111)	X[2]	X	X[2]	X[1]	X[1]	X[1]
III(211)	X[2]	X	X[2]	X[1]	X[1]	X[1]
IV(2HH)	X[2]	X	X[2]	X[1]	X[1]	X[1]
V(111)	X[2]	X	X[2]	X[1]	X[1]	X[1]
II(000)	X[2]	X[2]	X[1]	X[1]	X[1]	X[1]
III(200)	X[2]	X[2]	X[1]	X[1]	X[1]	X[1]
V(000)	X[2]	X[2]	X[1]	X[1]	X[1]	X[1]

X: Permitted types of construction.

[1]Permitted if the entire building is protected throughout by an approved, supervised automatic sprinkler system in accordance with Section 9.7.

[2]Where Use Condition V is used, permitted if the entire building is protected throughout by an approved, supervised automatic sprinkler system in accordance with Section 9.7.

CHAPTER 22 • New

CHAPTER 23 • Existing

Exception No. 1:   Any building of Type I, Type II(222), or Type II(111) construction shall be permitted to include roofing systems involving combustible or steel supports, decking, or roofing, provided that the following criteria are met:

(a)   The roof covering meets not less than Class C requirements in accordance with NFPA 256, Standard Methods of Fire Tests of Roof Coverings.

(b)   The roof is separated from all occupied portions of the building by a noncombustible floor assembly that includes not less than 2½ in. (6.4 cm) of concrete or gypsum fill. To qualify for this exception, the attic or other space so developed shall be either unoccupied or protected throughout by an approved automatic sprinkler system.

Exception No. 2:   In determining building construction type, exposed steel roof members located 16 ft (4.9 m) or more above the floor of the highest cell shall be disregarded.

22.1.6.4 All interior walls and partitions in Type I or Type II construction shall be of noncombustible or limited-combustible materials.

Exhibit 22/23.2 illustrates the method for counting stories in accordance with 22/23.1.6.1 for use with Table 22/23.1.6.3. If the attic were judged occupiable, the exhibit would depict a four-story building; otherwise the exhibit illustrates a three-story building.

The provisions of 22.4.4.6 and 23.3.1.2 address multilevel housing areas for which the vertical separation between the lowest floor level and the uppermost floor level does not exceed 13 ft (4 m), without limiting the number of levels. See Figure A.22.4.4.6.4 and Figure A.23.3.1.2.3. A multilevel housing area meeting all the requirements of 22.4.4.6 and 23.3.1.2 is treated as a single story in determining required building construction type in accordance with 22/23.1.6.3.

The *Code* recognizes that locked doors to the outside will be reluctantly unlocked, slowly unlocked, or never unlocked. Therefore, the *Code* relies on the defend-in-place or protect-in-place strategy addressed in the commentary on 22/23.1.1.2, which follows the exception to 22/23.2.3.1.1.7. Paragraph 22/23.1.6.3 establishes minimum construction requirements to help ensure the structural integrity of the building for the time required to release residents to the outside or hold them in a safe fire compartment or smoke compartment.

Table 22/23.1.6.3 establishes minimum construc-

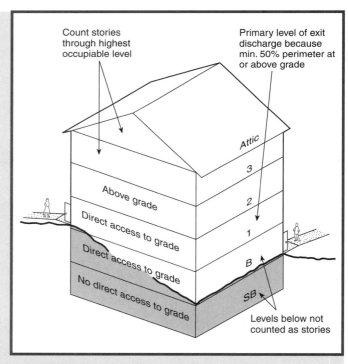

Exhibit 22/23.2 Method for counting stories.

tion types for detention and correctional occupancies. Under some conditions, certain building construction types are prohibited from being constructed and occupied for detention and correctional occupancy use, even if protected by automatic sprinklers. The automatic sprinkler requirements contained in this table are based on construction type. Automatic sprinkler protection also is required for new construction by 22.3.5.2. See NFPA 220, *Standard on Types of Building Construction*, for definitions of types of construction.[2] Also see 8.2.1 and Table A.8.2.1.

Maintaining the integrity of building construction under fire conditions is mandated because detention and correctional facility residents are

incapable of self-preservation due to security requirements imposed by the facility. Thus, although NFPA 220, *Standard on Types of Building Construction*, does not regulate the combustibility of interior non-bearing walls and partitions, 22.1.6.4 allows for credit to be taken for Type I or Type II construction in new detention and correctional occupancies only if such interior walls and partitions are of noncombustible or limited-combustible construction. For definitions of the terms *noncombustible* and *limited-combustible*, see 3.3.131 and 3.3.118 of this *Code* and NFPA 220.

22.1.7 Occupant Load.

The occupant load, in number of persons for whom means of egress and other provisions are required, shall be determined on the basis of the occupant load factors of Table 7.3.1.2 that are characteristic of the use of the space or shall be determined as the maximum probable population of the space under consideration, whichever is greater.

23.1.7 Occupant Load.

The occupant load, in number of persons for whom means of egress and other provisions are required, shall be determined on the basis of the occupant load factors of Table 7.3.1.2 that are characteristic of the use of the space or shall be determined as the maximum probable population of the space under consideration, whichever is greater.

This paragraph references the use of the occupant load factors of Table 7.3.1.2 from which an occupant load can be determined. The means of egress system must be sized to handle whichever is larger: the number of persons intended to occupy the space or the number of persons calculated by using the occupant load factor.

The *Code* intends that the occupant load factor be used only for sizing the means of egress, not for

limiting the number of persons within a space. If a means of egress can accommodate an occupant load larger than that calculated using the occupant load factor characteristic of the use of the space, the *Code* does not prohibit such a load. In a facility with excess means of egress capacity, other considerations such as plumbing codes or sanitary codes, sociological factors, and common sense will help determine the maximum occupant load.

Section 22.2 Means of Egress Requirements

22.2.1 General.

Means of egress shall comply with Chapter 7.

Exception: As otherwise provided or modified in Section 22.2.

22.2.2 Means of Egress Components.

22.2.2.1 Components of means of egress shall be limited to the types described in 22.2.2.2 through 22.2.2.11.

Section 23.2 Means of Egress Requirements

23.2.1 General.

Means of egress shall comply with Chapter 7.

Exception: As otherwise provided or modified in Section 23.2.

23.2.2 Means of Egress Components.

23.2.2.1 Components of means of egress shall be limited to the types described in 23.2.2.2 through 23.2.2.11.

| CHAPTER 22 • New | CHAPTER 23 • Existing |

22.2.2.2 Doors. Doors complying with 7.2.1 shall be permitted.

Exception: As provided in 22.2.11.

22.2.2.3 Stairs.

22.2.2.3.1 Stairs complying with 7.2.2 shall be permitted.

Exception: Noncombustible grated stair treads and landing floors shall be permitted.

22.2.2.3.2 Spiral stairs complying with 7.2.2.2.3 shall be permitted for access to and between staff locations.

22.2.2.4 Smokeproof Enclosures. Smokeproof enclosures complying with 7.2.3 shall be permitted.

22.2.2.5 Horizontal Exits. Horizontal exits complying with 7.2.4 and the modifications of 22.2.2.5.1 through 22.2.2.5.2 shall be permitted.

22.2.2.5.1 Not less than 6 ft^2 (0.56 m^2) of accessible space per occupant shall be provided on each side of the horizontal exit for the total number of people in adjoining compartments.

22.2.2.5.2 Horizontal exits shall be permitted to comprise 100 percent of the exits required, provided that an exit, other than a horizontal exit, located in another (not necessarily adjacent) fire compartment is accessible without returning through the compartment of fire origin.

23.2.2.2 Doors. Doors complying with 7.2.1 shall be permitted.

Exception: As provided in 23.2.11.

23.2.2.3 Stairs.

23.2.2.3.1 Stairs complying with 7.2.2 shall be permitted.

Exception: Noncombustible grated stair treads and landing floors shall be permitted.

23.2.2.3.2 Spiral stairs complying with 7.2.2.2.3 shall be permitted for access to and between staff locations.

23.2.2.4 Smokeproof Enclosures. Smokeproof enclosures complying with 7.2.3 shall be permitted.

23.2.2.5 Horizontal Exits. Horizontal exits complying with 7.2.4 and the modifications of 23.2.2.5.1 through 23.2.2.5.4 shall be permitted.

23.2.2.5.1 Not less than 6 ft^2 (0.56 m^2) of accessible space per occupant shall be provided on each side of the horizontal exit for the total number of people in adjoining compartments.

23.2.2.5.2* Horizontal exits shall be permitted to comprise 100 percent of the exits required, provided that an exit, other than a horizontal exit, located in another (not necessarily adjacent) fire compartment is accessible without returning through the compartment of fire origin.

A.23.2.2.5.2 An exit is not necessary from each individual fire compartment if there is access to an exit through other fire compartments without passing through the fire compartment of fire origin.

23.2.2.5.3* Ducts shall be permitted to penetrate horizontal exits in accordance with Exception No. 2 to 7.2.4.3.3 if protected by combination fire dampers/smoke leakage–rated dampers that meet the smoke damper actuation requirements of 8.3.5.

A.23.2.2.5.3 This provision is intended to promote the use of horizontal exits in detention and correctional occupancies. Horizontal exits provide an especially effective egress system for an occupancy in which the occupants, due to security concerns, are not commonly released to the outside. This provision offers a *Code*-specified equivalent alternative to the Chapter 7 requirement that horizontal exits are not to be penetrated by ducts. The intended continuity of the fire resistance–rated and smoke-resisting barrier is maintained by requiring that duct penetrations of horizontal exits be protected by combination fire damper/smoke leakage–rated

CHAPTER 22 • New	**CHAPTER 23 • Existing**

dampers that will close upon activation of a smoke detector and a heat-actuated mechanism before the barrier's ability to resist the passage of smoke and fire is compromised.

23.2.2.5.4 A door in a horizontal exit shall not be required to swing with egress travel as specified in 7.2.4.3.6.

22.2.2.6 Ramps. Ramps complying with 7.2.5 shall be permitted.

23.2.2.6 Ramps. Ramps complying with 7.2.5 shall be permitted.

22.2.2.7 Exit Passageways. Exit passageways complying with 7.2.6 shall be permitted.

23.2.2.7 Exit Passageways. Exit passageways complying with 7.2.6 shall be permitted.

22.2.2.8 (Reserved.)

23.2.2.8 Fire Escape Stairs. Fire escape stairs complying with 7.2.8 shall be permitted.

22.2.2.9 Fire Escape Ladders. Fire escape ladders complying with 7.2.9 shall be permitted.

23.2.2.9 Fire Escape Ladders. Fire escape ladders complying with 7.2.9 shall be permitted.

22.2.2.10 Alternating Tread Devices. Alternating tread devices complying with 7.2.11 shall be permitted.

23.2.2.10 Alternating Tread Devices. Alternating tread devices complying with 7.2.11 shall be permitted.

22.2.2.11 Areas of Refuge. Areas of refuge complying with 7.2.12 shall be permitted.

23.2.2.11 Areas of Refuge. Areas of refuge complying with 7.2.12 shall be permitted.

Chapter 22/23 recognizes the following means of egress components as described in Chapter 7: doors (7.2.1), stairs (7.2.2), smokeproof enclosures (7.2.3), horizontal exits (7.2.4), ramps (7.2.5), exit passageways (7.2.6), fire escape ladders (7.2.9), alternating tread devices (7.2.11), and areas of refuge (7.2.12). Also, Chapter 23 recognizes existing fire escape stairs (7.2.8). However, Chapter 22/23 often modifies the provisions of Chapter 7 applicable to those means of egress components. For example, although the Chapter 7 provisions that apply to horizontal exits would limit a horizontal exit to providing a maximum of 50 percent of the number of exits or 50 percent of the total egress capacity, Chapter 22/23 encourages the voluntary use of horizontal exits by permitting up to 100 percent of the exits to be reached by way of horizontal exits if additional criteria can be met.

Chapter 7 considers escalators, moving walks, and fire escape stairs as acceptable means of egress only if they are part of an existing occupancy and are specifically recognized by an occupancy chapter. They are not permitted in the means of egress system of a detention and correctional occupancy. Slide escapes are not recognized by Chapter 22/23 as part of an egress system in detention and correctional occupancies. Areas of refuge (see 7.2.12) might be used to provide accessible means of egress as re-

quired for new facilities in accordance with the provisions of 7.5.4.

Older editions of the *Code* contained an exception to 22/23.2.2.3.1 that exempted handrails and guards from the requirement for intermediate rails designed to keep children from falling through the spaces between rails. The exception still applies to detention and correctional occupancies but now appears as Exception No. 2 to 7.2.2.4.6(3). The rationale for this exception is that these facilities are used only by adults or older juveniles, and intermediate railings might impact functional requirements by interfering with visual observation by staff.

Grated stair treads and grated landing floors are recognized as usable in this occupancy because occupant reluctance to walk on such surfaces is not expected. Similarly, the potential for small shoe heels getting caught in the grated surfaces is greatly reduced in this occupancy.

Paragraph 22/23.2.2.3.2 permits spiral stairs conforming to 7.2.2.2.3 for staff use only. These provisions prohibit a spiral stair from being part of the required means of egress system within areas occupied by residents.

Paragraph 22/23.2.2.4 permits a smokeproof enclosure to serve as part of the means of egress system in detention and correctional occupancies only if the smokeproof enclosure meets the requirements of 7.2.3. However, the smokeproof enclosure is not required. An example of an occupancy requiring a smokeproof enclosure can be found in 31.2.11. In that paragraph, nonsprinklered, existing, high-rise apartment buildings are required to be provided with smokeproof enclosures in accordance with 7.2.3.

Horizontal exits are addressed in 22/23.2.2.5. Subsection 7.2.4 requires at least 3 ft² (0.28 m²) of accumulation space per occupant on each side of the horizontal exit. Subsection 22/23.2.2.5.1. requires 6 ft² (0.56 m²) per occupant. The reasons for this requirement include possible conflicts among the residents, the anticipated extended time spent in the refuge area, and the fact that horizontal exits are permitted to comprise 100 percent of required exits in detention and correctional occupancies in accordance with 22/23.2.2.5.2.

Paragraph 22/23.2.2.5.2 permits horizontal exits to comprise 100 percent of the exits from any fire compartment as long as it is not necessary to travel through the compartment of fire origin to reach a door to the outside—that is, the compartment is not "dead-ended."

In Exhibit 22/23.3, horizontal exits correctly comprise 100 percent of total exits from fire compartments B, C, and D. Compartment F would require the addition of an exit door that opens directly to the outside in order to reach the outside of the building without traveling through fire compartment E. Compartments A and E comply with the *Code*, using one horizontal exit and one exit door directly to the exterior of the building.

Due to the practical difficulties of using vertical exit travel to the outside in detention and correctional occupancies, including the reluctance of staff to unlock doors, special recognition is given to horizontal travel and the use of horizontal exits. One hundred percent of the total required egress capacity for a given fire area is permitted to be provided by horizontal exits, as previously explained. In the event a horizontal exit also serves as a smoke barrier, refer to 22/23.2.4.2 and 22/23.3.7.

Paragraph 7.2.4.3.3 states that fire barriers used in creating a horizontal exit are prohibited from penetration by ducts. To promote the use of horizontal exits in detention and correctional occupancies— without burdening a facility with regard to duct penetrations—22/23.2.2.5.3 and the corresponding

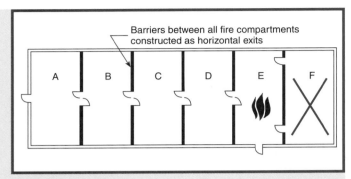

Exhibit 22/23.3 *Horizontal exit fire compartment arrangement.*

Exception No. 2 to 7.2.4.3.3 were developed. If smoke detection is used to shut a combination fire damper/ smoke leakage–rated damper early in a fire, the fire- and smoke-resisting features of the horizontal exit can be reestablished at points where ducts penetrate the barrier.

Paragraphs 22/23.2.2.6, 22/23.2.2.7, and 22/23.2.2.9 do not mandate the use of ramps, exit passageways, or fire escape ladders. Rather, these paragraphs recognize ramps, exit passageways, or fire escape ladders as part of the means of egress system only if they meet the applicable requirements of 7.2.5 through 7.2.9. Further, 23.2.2.8 recognizes the use of existing fire escape stairs in accordance with 7.2.8. Note that 7.2.9 restricts the use of fire escape ladders to spaces such as normally unoccupied roofs and equipment platforms. Further, use is restricted to a maximum of three persons—all capable of using the ladder.

Paragraph 22/23.2.2.10 does not mandate the use of alternating tread devices but does recognize them as part of the means of egress system only if they meet the requirements of 7.2.11. Note that 7.2.11 restricts the use of alternating tread devices to spaces such as normally unoccupied roofs and equipment platforms. Further, use is restricted to a maximum of three persons—all capable of using the device.

Paragraph 22/23.2.2.11 does not mandate the use of areas of refuge but does recognize an area of refuge as part of the means of egress system only if it meets the requirements of 7.2.12. Areas of refuge will often be used to meet the requirements for accessible means of egress mandated for new facilities by 7.5.4 in areas accessible to persons with severe mobility impairments.

CHAPTER 22 • New	CHAPTER 23 • Existing

22.2.3 Capacity of Means of Egress.

22.2.3.1 The capacity of any required means of egress shall be in accordance with Section 7.3.

22.2.3.2 Aisles, corridors, and ramps required for egress shall be not less than 4 ft (1.2 m) in width.

22.2.3.3 For residents' sleeping room door widths, see 22.2.11.3.

22.2.4 Number of Exits.

(See also Section 7.4.)

22.2.4.1 Not less than two separate exits shall meet the following criteria:

(1) They shall be provided on every story.
(2) They shall be accessible from every part of every story, fire compartment, or smoke compartment; however, exit access travel shall be permitted to be common for the distances permitted as common path of travel by 22.2.5.3.

22.2.4.2* Not less than one approved exit shall be accessible from each fire compartment and each required smoke compartment into which residents are potentially moved in a fire emergency, with the exits arranged so that egress is possible without returning through the zone of fire origin.

A.22.2.4.2 An exit is not necessary from each individual fire compartment or smoke compartment if there is access to an exit through other fire compartments or smoke compartments without passing through the fire compartment or smoke compartment of fire origin.

22.2.5 Arrangement of Means of Egress.

(See also Section 7.5.)

22.2.5.1 Every sleeping room shall have a door leading directly to an exit access corridor.

Exception No. 1: If there is an exit door opening directly to the outside from the room at the ground level.

Exception No. 2: One adjacent room, such as a day room, group activity space, or other common space shall be permitted to intervene. Where sleeping rooms directly adjoin a day

23.2.3 Capacity of Means of Egress.

23.2.3.1 The capacity of any required means of egress shall be in accordance with Section 7.3.

23.2.3.2 Aisles, corridors, and ramps required for egress shall be not less than 3 ft (0.9 m) in width.

23.2.3.3 For residents' sleeping room door widths, see 23.2.11.3.

23.2.4 Number of Exits.

(See also Section 7.4.)

23.2.4.1* Not less than two separate exits shall meet the following criteria:

(1) They shall be provided on every story.
(2) They shall be accessible from every part of every story, fire compartment, or smoke compartment; however; exit access travel shall be permitted to be common for the distances permitted as common path of travel by 23.2.5.3.

A.23.2.4.1 Multilevel and multitiered residential housing areas meeting the requirements of 23.3.1.2 and 23.3.1.3 are considered single story. Therefore, two exits are not required from each level; only access to two exits is required.

23.2.4.2* Not less than one approved exit shall be accessible from each fire compartment and each required smoke compartment into which residents are potentially moved in a fire emergency, with the exits arranged so that egress is possible without returning through the zone of fire origin.

A.23.2.4.2 An exit is not necessary from each individual fire compartment and smoke compartment if there is access to an exit through other fire compartments or smoke compartments without passing through the fire compartment or smoke compartment of fire origin.

23.2.5 Arrangement of Means of Egress.

(See also Section 7.5.)

23.2.5.1 Every sleeping room shall have a door leading directly to an exit access corridor.

Exception No. 1: If there is an exit door opening directly to the outside from the room at the ground level.

Exception No. 2: One adjacent room, such as a day room, group activity space, or other common space shall be permitted to intervene. Where sleeping rooms directly adjoin a day

CHAPTER 22 • New

CHAPTER 23 • Existing

room or group activity space that is used for access to an exit, such sleeping rooms shall be permitted to open directly to the day room or space and shall be permitted to be separated in elevation by a one-half or full story height. (See 22.4.4.6.)

22.2.5.2 No exit or exit access shall contain a corridor, hallway, or aisle having a pocket or dead end exceeding 50 ft (15 m) for Use Condition II, Use Condition III, or Use Condition IV and 20 ft (6.1 m) for Use Condition V.

22.2.5.3 A common path of travel shall not exceed 100 ft (30 m).

22.2.5.4 A sally port shall be permitted in a means of egress where there are provisions for continuous and unobstructed travel through the sally port during an emergency egress condition.

room or group activity space that is used for access to an exit, such sleeping rooms shall be permitted to open directly to the day room or space and shall be permitted to be separated in elevation by a one-half or full story height. (See 23.3.1.2.)

23.2.5.2* Existing dead-end corridors are undesirable and shall be altered wherever possible so that exits are accessible in not less than two different directions from all points in aisles, passageways, and corridors.

A.23.2.5.2 Every exit or exit access should be arranged, if feasible, so that no corridor or aisle has a pocket or dead end exceeding 50 ft (15 m) for Use Conditions II, III, and IV and 20 ft (6.1 m) for Use Condition V.

23.2.5.3 A common path of travel shall not exceed 50 ft (15 m).

Exception No. 1: A common path of travel shall be permitted for the first 100 ft (30 m) in smoke compartments protected throughout by an approved automatic sprinkler system in accordance with 23.3.5.3.

Exception No. 2: Multilevel residential housing units in which each floor level, considered separately, has not less than one-half of its individual required egress capacity accessible by exit access leading directly out of that level without traversing another communicating floor level.

Exception No. 3: Existing common paths of travel that exceed 50 ft (15 m) shall be permitted to continue to be used subject to the approval of the authority having jurisdiction and the travel distance requirements of 23.2.6.

23.2.5.4 A sally port shall be permitted in a means of egress where there are provisions for continuous and unobstructed travel through the sally port during an emergency egress condition.

Exhibit 22/23.4 illustrates the use of Exception No. 2 to 22/23.2.5.1, which permits one adjacent room to intervene between a sleeping room and the exit access corridor. Sleeping rooms are permitted to be separated in elevation from the day room by one-half to one story. See Exception No. 2 to 22/23.2.5.1.

Exhibit 22/23.5 illustrates the dead-end corridor requirements of 22.2.5.2 applicable to new detention and correctional facilities. In Use Condition V, resident room doors are individually key-locked and the allowable dead-end corridor length is reduced from 50 ft (15 m) to 20 ft (6.1 m). See 22.2.5.2. For existing

facilities, 23.2.5.2 advises that dead-end corridors are undesirable but sets no maximum depth for existing dead ends.

Exhibit 22/23.6 illustrates a common path of travel. If distance X to C exceeds 50 ft (15 m) [100 ft (30 m), if the smoke compartment is sprinklered as is required of new construction], a second exit access is required for the upper level. If the multilevel housing area is large, the common path of travel limitation might require a remote, second exit access door to the corridor.

Exception Nos. 2 and 3 to 23.2.5.3 introduce crite-

CHAPTER 22 • New   **CHAPTER 23 • Existing**

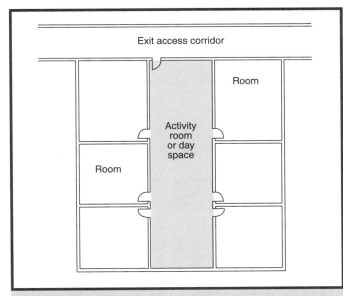

Exhibit 22/23.4 One intervening room between sleeping room and exit access corridor.

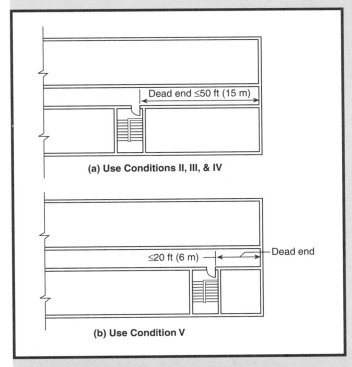

Exhibit 22/23.5 Maximum dead-end corridor for new construction.

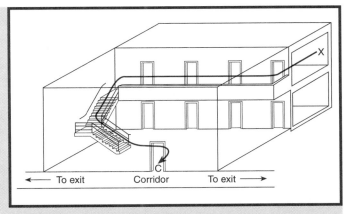

Exhibit 22/23.6 Common path of travel.

ria that recognize existing common paths of travel that exceed the 50-ft (15-m) limitation contained in the base paragraph and the 100-ft (30-m) limitation allowed in sprinklered smoke compartments by Exception No. 1 to 23.2.5.3. Exception No. 2 offers some relief to existing facilities with lengthy common paths of travel on individual levels of multilevel residential housing units, provided that at least half the occupant load of any level can be accommodated by exit access leading directly from that level without traveling on any other level that is open to that housing unit. This affords the residents of any level with an exit access that leads to an exit without being exposed to the fire on another level of the housing unit. Exception No. 3 permits existing, excessively long common paths of travel to continue to be used only if specifically approved by the authority having jurisdiction.

A security vestibule, called a *sally port*, is addressed in 22/23.2.5.4. A sally port is designed so that during routine and non-fire emergency conditions the door at one end of the vestibule is securely locked whenever the door at the opposite end is open. When one door is opened, the door through which entrance is made is closed and locked; the door at the opposite end is then unlocked and opened to provide egress from the vestibule. The sally port acts as a security device that prevents a continuous flow of people from "storming" the exits. Under fire conditions, it would severely restrict the egress flow of occupants and prevent hose lines from being run through the openings. Therefore, if a sally port is to be permitted as part of a required means of egress, the door controls must be capable of being overridden to allow continuous and unobstructed passage in accordance with

CHAPTER 22 • New	CHAPTER 23 • Existing

22/23.2.5.4. Exhibits 22/23.7 depicts a sally port. If the sally port illustrated is part of the required means of egress, both doors of the sally port must be capable of being opened at the same time to provide unobstructed egress.

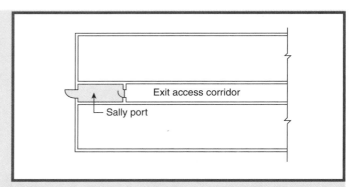

Exhibit 22/23.7 *A sally port or security vestibule.*

22.2.6 Travel Distance to Exits.

Travel distance shall comply with 22.2.6.1 through 22.2.6.3.

22.2.6.1 The travel distance between any room door required as an exit access and an exit shall not exceed 150 ft (45 m).

22.2.6.2 The travel distance between any point in a room and an exit shall not exceed 200 ft (60 m).

22.2.6.3 The travel distance between any point in a sleeping room to the door in that room shall not exceed 50 ft (15 m).

Exception: The maximum travel distance shall be permitted to be increased to 100 ft (30 m) in open dormitories where the enclosing walls of the dormitory space are of smoketight construction. Where travel distance to the exit access door from any point within the dormitory exceeds 50 ft (15 m), not less than two exit access doors remotely located from each other shall be provided.

23.2.6 Travel Distance to Exits.

Travel distance shall comply with 23.2.6.1 through 23.2.6.3.

23.2.6.1 The travel distance between any room door required as an exit access and an exit or smoke barrier shall not exceed 100 ft (30 m).

Exception: The maximum travel distance shall be permitted to be increased by 50 ft (15 m) in buildings protected throughout by an approved automatic sprinkler system or smoke control system.

23.2.6.2 The travel distance between any point in a room and an exit or smoke barrier shall not exceed 150 ft (45 m).

Exception: The maximum travel distance shall be permitted to be increased by 50 ft (15 m) in buildings protected throughout by an approved automatic sprinkler system or smoke control system.

23.2.6.3 The travel distance between any point in a sleeping room to the door of that room shall not exceed 50 ft (15 m).

Exception: The maximum travel distance shall be permitted to be increased to 100 ft (30 m) in open dormitories where the enclosing walls of the dormitory space are of smoketight construction. Where travel distance to the exit access door from any point within the dormitory exceeds 50 ft (15 m), not less than two exit access doors remotely located from each other shall be provided.

Exhibit 22/23.8 illustrates the travel distance requirements of 22/23.2.6. Travel distance is measured to the closest exit only, not to both of the exits required by 22/23.2.4. Travel distance is measured along the natural path of travel (see 7.6.2). The term *sprinklered*, as used in the exhibit, means that the entire building is protected by a complete, approved automatic extinguishing system. New detention and correctional occupancies are required to be sprinklered; thus, they are permitted the longer travel distances. The term *smoke control*, as used in the exhibit, means that the entire building is equipped with a system to control the movement of smoke in accordance with Section 9.3.

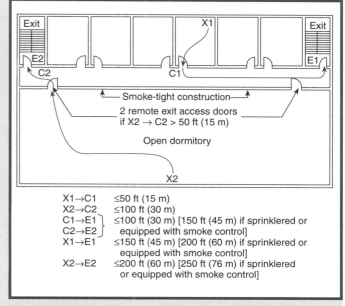

X1→C1	≤50 ft (15 m)
X2→C2	≤100 ft (30 m)
C1→E1 ⎱	≤100 ft (30 m) [150 ft (45 m) if sprinklered or
C2→E2 ⎰	equipped with smoke control]
X1→E1	≤150 ft (45 m) [200 ft (60 m) if sprinklered or
	equipped with smoke control]
X2→E2	≤200 ft (60 m) [250 ft (76 m) if sprinklered
	or equipped with smoke control]

Exhibit 22/23.8 *Travel distance to exits in detention and correctional occupancies.*

22.2.7 Discharge from Exits.

22.2.7.1 Exits shall be permitted to discharge into a fenced or walled courtyard, provided that not more than two walls of the courtyard are the building walls from which egress is being made. Enclosed yards or courts shall be of sufficient size to accommodate all occupants at a distance of not less than 50 ft (15 m) from the building while providing a net area of 15 ft² (1.4 m²) per person.

22.2.7.2 All exits shall be permitted to discharge through the level of exit discharge. The requirements of 7.7.2 shall be waived, provided that not more than 50 percent of the exits discharge into a single fire compartment separated from other compartments by construction having not less than a 1-hour fire resistance rating.

23.2.7 Discharge from Exits.

23.2.7.1 Exits shall be permitted to discharge into a fenced or walled courtyard, provided that not more than two walls of the courtyard are the building walls from which egress is being made. Enclosed yards or courts shall be of sufficient size to accommodate all occupants at a distance of not less than 50 ft (15 m) from the building while providing a net area of 15 ft² (1.4 m²) per person.

23.2.7.2 All exits shall be permitted to discharge through the level of exit discharge. The requirements of 7.7.2 shall be waived, provided that not more than 50 percent of the exits discharge into a single fire compartment separated from other compartments by construction having not less than a 1-hour fire resistance rating.

Exception: Where all exits discharge through areas on the level of discharge, a smoke barrier shall be provided to divide that level into not less than two compartments, with not less than one exit discharging into each compartment, and each smoke compartment shall have an exit discharge to the building exterior. The level of discharge shall be provided with automatic sprinkler protection. Any other portion of the level of discharge with access to the discharge area shall be provided with automatic sprinkler protection or shall be separated from the discharge area in accordance with the requirements for the enclosure of exits. (See 7.1.3.2.1.)

CHAPTER 22 • New   **CHAPTER 23 • Existing**

Exhibits 22/23.9(a) and 22/23.9(b) illustrate the requirements of 22/23.2.7.1.

The provisions of 7.7.2 establish criteria under which up to 50 percent of the required exits, in either number or capacity, are permitted to discharge through the level of exit discharge, with the other 50 percent required to discharge directly to the outside. Because of security concerns and the belief that doors to the exterior will not be readily unlocked in detention and correctional occupancies, 22/23.2.7.2 allows 100 percent of the exits to discharge through the level of exit discharge. This exception is permitted if a minimum 1-hour fire resistance–rated separation that

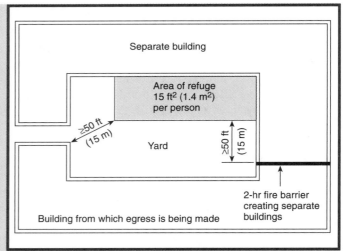

Exhibit 22/23.9(b) Exit discharge into an enclosed yard with minimum separation distance from "building" from which egress is being made.

creates at least two fire compartments is provided on the level of exit discharge. Not more than one-half of the exits are permitted to discharge into any one fire compartment.

The exception to 23.2.7.2 allows a smoke barrier to be substituted for a fire barrier in an existing facility if certain conditions can be met. The travel route along the level of exit discharge must be sprinklered, and the route must be separated from nonsprinklered portions of the level of exit discharge by fire barriers meeting the fire resistance rating requirements applicable to exit enclosures.

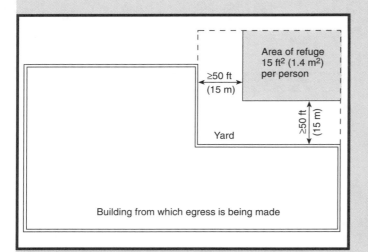

Exhibit 22/23.9(a) Exit discharge into fenced yard with minimum separation distance from building.

22.2.8 Illumination of Means of Egress.

Means of egress shall be illuminated in accordance with Section 7.8.

22.2.9 Emergency Lighting.

Emergency lighting shall be provided in accordance with Section 7.9.

22.2.10 Marking of Means of Egress.

Exit marking shall be provided in areas accessible to the public in accordance with Section 7.10.

23.2.8 Illumination of Means of Egress.

Means of egress shall be illuminated in accordance with Section 7.8.

23.2.9 Emergency Lighting.

Emergency lighting shall be provided in accordance with Section 7.9.

Exception: Emergency lighting of not less than a 1-hour duration shall be permitted to be provided.

23.2.10 Marking of Means of Egress.

Exit marking shall be provided in areas accessible to the public in accordance with Section 7.10.

CHAPTER 22 • New	CHAPTER 23 • Existing

Exception: Exit signs shall not be required in detention and correctional residential housing areas. (See definition in 3.3.145.)

Exception: Exit signs shall not be required in detention and correctional residential housing areas. (See definition of 3.3.145.)

The exemption of exit signs in sleeping areas of detention and correctional occupancies recognizes that persons occupying such areas are familiar with those portions of the facility and know the location of exits.

Other portions of the facility might not be as familiar to residents and visitors and thus must have proper exit marking in accordance with 22/23.2.10.

22.2.11 Special Features.

22.2.11.1 Doors within means of egress shall be in accordance with Chapter 7.

Exception: As provided in 22.2.11.2 through 22.2.11.10.

22.2.11.2 Doors shall be permitted to be locked in accordance with the applicable use condition.

22.2.11.3* Doors to resident sleeping rooms shall be not less than 28 in. (71 cm) in clear width.

A.22.2.11.3 It might be necessary to provide a certain number of resident sleeping rooms with doors providing a clear width of not less than 32 in. (81 cm) *(see 7.2.1.2)* in order to comply with the requirements for the physically handicapped. Such sleeping rooms should be located where there is a direct accessible route to the exterior or to an area of safe refuge. *(See 22.3.7.)*

22.2.11.4 Doors in a means of egress shall be permitted to be of the horizontal sliding type, provided that the force necessary to slide the door to its fully open position does not exceed 50 lbf (222 N) where a force of 50 lbf (222 N) is simultaneously applied perpendicular to the door.

22.2.11.5 Doors from areas of refuge to the exterior shall be permitted to be locked with key locks in lieu of locking methods described in 22.2.11.6. The keys to unlock such doors shall be maintained and available at the facility at all times, and the locks shall be operable from the outside.

22.2.11.6* Any remote-control release used in a means of egress shall be provided with a reliable means of operation to release locks on all doors and shall be remotely located from the resident living areas. The remote location shall provide sight and sound supervision of the resident living areas.

23.2.11 Special Features.

23.2.11.1 Doors within means of egress shall be in accordance with Chapter 7.

Exception: As provided in 23.2.11.2 through 23.2.11.8.

23.2.11.2 Doors shall be permitted to be locked in accordance with the applicable use condition.

23.2.11.3* Doors to resident sleeping rooms shall be not less than 28 in. (71 cm) in clear width.

Exception: Existing doors to resident sleeping rooms housing four or fewer residents shall be permitted to be not less than 19 in. (48.3 cm) in clear width.

A.23.2.11.3 It might be necessary to provide a certain number of resident sleeping rooms with doors providing a clear width of not less than 32 in. (81 cm) *(see 7.2.1.2)* in order to comply with the requirements for the physically handicapped. Such sleeping rooms should be located where there is a direct accessible route to the exterior or to an area of safe refuge. *(See 23.3.7.)*

23.2.11.4 Doors in a means of egress shall be permitted to be of the horizontal sliding type, provided that the force necessary to slide the door to its fully open position does not exceed 50 lbf (222 N) where a force of 50 lbf (222 N) is simultaneously applied perpendicular to the door.

23.2.11.5 Doors from areas of refuge to the exterior shall be permitted to be locked with key locks in lieu of locking methods described in 23.2.11.6. The keys to unlock such doors shall be maintained and available at the facility at all times, and the locks shall be operable from the outside.

23.2.11.6* Any remote-control release used in a means of egress shall be provided with a reliable means of operation to release locks on all doors and shall be remotely located from the resident living area. The remote location shall provide sight and sound supervision of the resident living areas.

Exception: Remote-control locking and unlocking of occupied rooms in Use Condition IV shall not be required, provided that not more than 10 locks need to be unlocked in order to relocate all occupants from one smoke compartment to an area of refuge as promptly as is required where remote-control unlocking is used. Unlocking of all necessary locks shall be accomplished with not more than two separate keys. (See 22.3.7.7 for requirements for smoke barrier doors.)

A.22.2.11.6 A remote position is generally a control point where a number of doors can be unlocked simultaneously, either mechanically or electrically. In areas where there are a number of sleeping rooms, it is impractical for attendants to unlock doors individually. Doors in an exit should be unlocked prior to unlocking sleeping room doors. Sight and sound supervision of resident living areas can be by means of camera and communications systems.

This section of the *Code* does not intend to prohibit Use Condition V facilities, nor does it intend to limit Use Condition V facilities to 10 manually released locks.

22.2.11.7 All remote-control release–operated doors shall be provided with a redundant means of operation as follows:

(1) Power-operated sliding doors or power-operated locks shall be constructed so that, in the event of power failure, a manual mechanical means to release and open the doors is provided at each door, and either emergency power arranged in accordance with 7.9.2.2 is provided for the power operation or a remote-control manual mechanical release is provided.

(2) Mechanically operated sliding doors or mechanically operated locks shall be provided with a manual mechanical means at each door to release and open the door.

22.2.11.8 The provisions of 7.2.1.5.2 for stairway re-entry shall not apply.

22.2.11.9 Doors unlocked by means of remote control under emergency conditions shall not automatically relock when closed unless specific action is taken at the remote-control location to enable doors to relock.

22.2.11.10 Emergency power shall be provided for all electrically power-operated sliding doors and power-operated locks. Power shall be arranged to automatically operate within 10 seconds upon failure of normal power and to

Exception: Remote-control locking and unlocking of occupied rooms in Use Condition IV shall not be required, provided that not more than 10 locks need to be unlocked in order to relocate all occupants from one smoke compartment to an area of refuge as promptly as is required where remote-control unlocking is used. Unlocking of all necessary locks shall be accomplished with not more than two separate keys. (See 23.3.7.7 for requirements for smoke barrier doors.)

A.23.2.11.6 A remote position is generally a control point where a number of doors can be unlocked simultaneously, either mechanically or electrically. In areas where there are a number of sleeping rooms, it is impractical for attendants to unlock doors individually. Doors in an exit should be unlocked prior to unlocking sleeping room doors. Sight and sound supervision of resident living areas can be by means of camera and communications systems.

This section of the *Code* does not intend to prohibit Use Condition V facilities, nor does it intend to limit Use Condition V facilities to 10 manually released locks.

23.2.11.7 All remote-control release–operated doors shall be provided with a redundant means of operation as follows:

(1) Power-operated sliding doors or power-operated locks shall be constructed so that, in the event of power failure, a manual mechanical means to release and open the doors is provided at each door, and either emergency power arranged in accordance with 7.9.2.2 is provided for the power operation or a remote-control manual mechanical release is provided.

Exception: The combination of emergency power-operated release of selected individual doors and remote-control manual mechanical ganged release shall be permitted without mechanical release means at each door.

(2) Mechanically operated sliding doors or mechanically operated locks shall be provided with a manual mechanical means at each door to release and open the door.

23.2.11.8 The provisions of 7.2.1.5.2 for stairway re-entry shall not apply.

maintain the necessary power source for not less than 1½ hours.

Exception: This provision shall not be applicable for facilities with 10 or fewer locks complying with the exception to 22.2.11.6.

The provision of 22/23.2.11.2 overrides the Chapter 7 requirement that all doors within the required means of egress be unlocked from the side from which egress is to be made and fully under the control of the building occupants. It recognizes that, to function as intended, a detention and correctional occupancy uses various means of locking. Paragraph 22/23.2.11.2 allows only that degree of locking that is appropriate to a specific use condition. Therefore, a Use Condition II facility, which has more lenient life safety requirements than a Use Condition V facility, cannot contain sleeping rooms that must be individually locked by key. A Use Condition V facility must comply with a more stringent set of requirements than a Use Condition II facility and is permitted to have individual doors manually locked by key.

Paragraph 7.2.1.4.1 requires that all doors in a means of egress be side-hinged or pivoted-swinging. Paragraph 22/23.2.11.4 allows the use of sliding doors if they meet the specified requirements. In addition, Exception No. 3 to 7.2.1.4.1 recognizes the limited use of other horizontal sliding doors in accordance with the provisions of 7.2.1.14.

Paragraph 22/23.2.11.5 requires that keys be maintained and available. The term *available* means that keys should be readily accessible to staff for use at any time for evacuation of occupants. The following requirements are important:

(1) The keys required to evacuate occupants are accessible at all times.
(2) The staff is trained in the location and use of keys.
(3) The staff has authorization and standing orders to immediately unlock doors that lead from smoke compartments to the exterior during fire emergency conditions.

Authorizing staff to unlock doors avoids lost time that would occur if awaiting authorization from administrative authorities before doors can be unlocked.

In 22/23.2.11.6, use of the term *remote* means outside the area where occupants are restrained. It is not necessary to have the remote unlocking mecha-nism in a separate fire area, although this precaution might be beneficial. Doors within the exit should be unlocked prior to unlocking sleeping room doors. This precaution prevents jamming of the exit door caused by several persons exerting pressure on it.

The exception to 22/23.2.11.6 applies to facilities that are seeking classification as Use Condition IV but that have need for up to 10 locks that must be manually released at the door. Where remote locking is required by Use Condition IV, it must be provided, except as addressed by the exception. The exception permits up to 10 manual locks to allow occupants to move to another fire compartment or smoke compartment while permitting the facility to qualify as having provided remote release. The use of a limited number (a maximum of 10) of manual locks, in addition to the possibility of hundreds of remotely released locks within the same facility, does not impose a Use Condition V classification. This exception might apply in situations involving fewer than 10 doors if a door is secured with more than one lock.

Exhibits 22/23.10(a) and 22/23.10(b) depict two

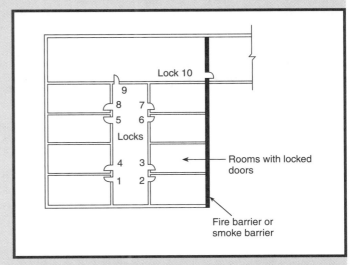

Exhibit 22/23.10(a) *Example of manually unlocked locks permitted within smoke compartment of Use Condition IV facility.*

CHAPTER 22 • New   **CHAPTER 23 • Existing**

Rooms with doors not locked or capable of being unlocked remotely

Lock 2   Lock 1

Day space

Lock 3   Smoke barrier

Lock 4   Lock 5

Rooms with doors not locked or capable of being unlocked remotely

Locks
6 7 8 9

Rooms with locked doors

Exhibit 22/23.10(b) Another example of manually unlocked locks permitted within smoke compartment of Use Condition IV facility.

typical arrangements that illustrate this exception. In Exhibit 22/23.10(a) each door is equipped with a single key-operated lock. In Exhibit 22/23.10(b) multiple door areas are secured by a door with a single key-operated lock. One manual lock, in addition to the 9

shown in the exhibit, would be permitted but it cannot be on the smoke barrier door if the smoke compartment contains more than 20 persons in accordance with 22/23.3.7.7.

The exception to 22/23.2.11.6 has been misinterpreted to mean that a Use Condition V detention/correctional facility (which, by definition, permits manual unlocking of each door) is limited to a maximum of 10 such manual locks. A Use Condition V facility is permitted to have an unlimited number of manual locks. In fact, the exception to 22/23.2.11.6 applies only to Use Condition IV facilities and allows a facility to retain its classification as Use Condition IV (that is, remote release), provided that there are 10 or fewer manually released locks and that unlocking can be achieved with a maximum of two keys.

The speed with which the doors can be unlocked and the occupants moved to a safe location is critical. If the 10 locks cannot be rapidly released by manual unlocking due to staffing restrictions or for any other reason, remote unlocking must be used. If doors are equipped with locking devices, it is assumed that the locks will be used, and they must be counted as part of the total number of locks.

Paragraph 22.2.11.8, applicable to new facilities, requires that, once doors are remotely unlocked under emergency conditions, they cannot automatically relock if they reclose unless deliberate action is taken to lock them. This deliberate action can be taken at the individual door or at the remote location. This safety measure prevents occupants from being mistakenly locked into a room during emergency egress.

Section 22.3 Protection

22.3.1 Protection of Vertical Openings.

22.3.1.1 Any vertical opening shall be enclosed or protected in accordance with 8.2.5.

Exception No. 1: Unprotected vertical openings in accordance with 8.2.5.8 shall be permitted.

Exception No. 2:* In residential housing area smoke compartments, unprotected vertical openings shall be permitted in accordance with the conditions of 8.2.5.5, provided that the height between the lowest and highest finished floor levels does not exceed 23 ft (7 m). The number of levels shall not be restricted. Residential housing areas subdivided in accordance with 22.3.8 shall be permitted to be considered

Section 23.3 Protection

23.3.1 Protection of Vertical Openings.

23.3.1.1 Any vertical opening shall be enclosed or protected in accordance with 8.2.5.

Exception No. 1: Unprotected vertical openings in accordance with 8.2.5.8 shall be permitted.

Exception No. 2: In residential housing area smoke compartments protected throughout by an approved automatic sprinkler system, unprotected vertical openings shall be permitted in accordance with the conditions of 8.2.5.5, provided that the height between the lowest and highest finished floor levels does not exceed 23 ft (7 m). The number of levels shall not be restricted. Residential housing areas subdivided as part of the communicating space. The separation shall not be required to have a fire resistance rating. (See Exception No. 2 to 8.2.5.5(4).)

A.22.3.1.1 Exception No. 2 For purposes of providing control valves and waterflow devices, multilevel residential housing areas complying with this exception are considered to be single story.

in accordance with 23.3.8 shall be permitted to be considered as part of the communicating space. The separation shall not be required to have a fire resistance rating. (See Exception No. 2 to 8.2.5.5(4).)

Exception No. 3: Multilevel residential housing areas in accordance with 23.3.1.2.

Exception No. 4: Where full enclosure is impractical, the required enclosure shall be permitted to be limited to that necessary to prevent a fire originating in any story from spreading to any other story.

Exception No. 5: The fire resistance rating of enclosures in detention and correctional occupancies protected throughout by an approved automatic sprinkler system shall be not less than 1 hour.

23.3.1.2 Multilevel residential housing areas without enclosure protection between levels shall be permitted, provided that the conditions of 23.3.1.2.1 through 23.3.1.2.3 are met.

23.3.1.2.1* The entire normally occupied area, including all communicating floor levels, shall be sufficiently open and unobstructed so that a fire or other dangerous condition in any part is obvious to the occupants or supervisory personnel in the area.

A.23.3.1.2.1 It is not the intent of this requirement to restrict room face separations, which restrict visibility from the common space into individual sleeping rooms.

23.3.1.2.2 Egress capacity shall simultaneously accommodate all occupants of all communicating levels and areas, with all communicating levels in the same fire area considered as a single floor area for purposes of determining required egress capacity.

23.3.1.2.3* The height between the highest and lowest finished floor levels shall not exceed 13 ft (4 m). The number of levels shall not be restricted.

A.23.3.1.2.3 The vertical separation between the lowest floor level and the uppermost floor level is not to exceed 13 ft (4 m). Figure A.23.3.1.2.3 illustrates how the height is to be determined.

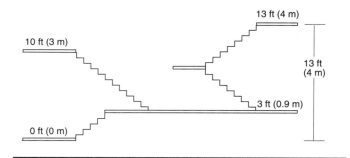

Figure A.23.3.1.2.3 *Vertical height measurement.*

23.3.1.3* A multitiered, open cell block shall be considered as a single-story building, where one of the following criteria are met:

(1) A smoke control system is provided *(see recommended design criteria in A.23.3.1.3)* to maintain the level of smoke from potential cell fires at not less than 5 ft (152 cm) above the floor level of any occupied tier involving space that is classified as follows:
   a. Use Condition IV or Use Condition V
   b. Use Condition III, unless all persons housed in such space can pass through a free access smoke barrier or freely pass below the calculated smoke level with not more than 50 ft (15 m) of travel from their cells
(2) The entire building, including cells, is provided with complete automatic sprinkler protection in accordance with 23.3.5.

A.23.3.1.3 A recommended method of calculating the expected level of smoke in a smoke removal–equipped cell block follows.

This method for calculating the expected level of smoke has been developed from data experimentally produced in full-scale burnouts of test cells. The test cells were sized, loaded with fuel, and constructed to represent severe conditions of heavily fuel-loaded (approximately 6 lb/ft² (29 kg/ m²)) cells as found in prison locations. The filling rate and temperature of the effluent gas and smoke have been calculated using the data from these tests and established formulae from plume dynamics.

The application of the method described in A.23.3.1.3 should be limited to situations where there is not less than 10 ft (3 m) from the floor level to the lowest acceptable level of smoke accumulation (Z); the reservoir above the lowest acceptable level for Z is at least 20 percent of the Z dimension, the length of the cell block is not less than Z, and the fan is not less than 10 ft (3 m) higher than the floor of the highest cell.

The determination of smoke removal requirements is based on the dimensions of the cell opening. Where more than one cell opening is involved, the larger size on the level being calculated should be used.

The fan size, temperature rating, and operations means can be determined by the following procedure.

(a) *Acceptable Smoke Level.* Determine the lowest acceptable level of smoke accumulation in accordance with 23.3.1.3. The vertical distance between that level and the floor level of the lowest open cell is the value of Z to be used in connection with Figure A.23.3.1.3(a).

(b) *Characteristic Cell Opening.* Determine the opening of the cell face. Where there is more than one size of cell opening, use the largest. Match the actual opening to those shown in Figure A.23.3.1.3(b), and use the corresponding curve from Figure A.23.3.1.3(a). If there is no match between the size and shape of the opening and Figure A.23.3.1.3(a), interpolate between the curves. If the opening

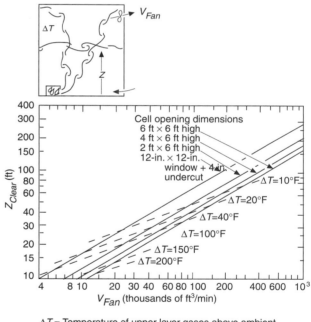

ΔT = Temperature of upper layer gases above ambient
V_{Fan} = Fan discharge capacity (as installed)
Z_{Clear} = Distance from cell floor to smoke layer

Solid line: Ventilation rate curves
Dashed line: Constant temperature rise curves

For SI units, ft × 0.3048 = m; ft³/min × 0.00047 = m³/s; (°F − 32) × 1.8 = °C; 1 in. = 2.54 cm.

Figure A.23.3.1.3(a) *Cell block smoke control ventilation curves.*

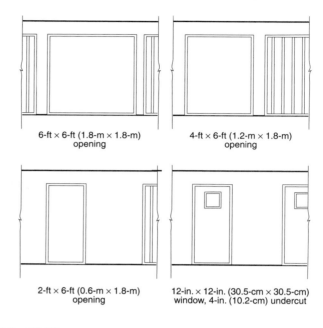

6-ft × 6-ft (1.8-m × 1.8-m) opening

4-ft × 6-ft (1.2-m × 1.8-m) opening

2-ft × 6-ft (0.6-m × 1.8-m) opening

12-in. × 12-in. (30.5-cm × 30.5-cm) window, 4-in. (10.2-cm) undercut

Figure A.23.3.1.3(b) Typical cell openings.

exceeds 6 ft × 6 ft (1.8 m × 1.8 m), use the curve for a 6-ft × 6-ft (1.8-m × 1.8-m) opening. This curve represents the maximum burning situation, and increasing the size of the opening will not increase the actual burning rate.

(c) *Exhaust Fan Rate.* Determine the exhaust fan capacity needed to extract smoke at a rate that will maintain the smoke level at a point higher than Z. This is the rate shown on the baseline of Figure A.23.3.1.3(a) corresponding to the level of Z on the vertical axis for the solid line (ventilation rate) curve appropriate to the cell door size. This exhaust capability needs to be provided at a point higher than Z.

(d) *Intake Air.* Provide intake air openings that either exist or are automatically provided at times of emergency smoke removal. These openings are to be located at or near the baseline of the cell block to allow for intake air at the rate to be vented by the fan. The openings provided shall be sufficient to avoid a friction load that can reduce the exhaust efficiency. Standard air-handling design criteria are used in making this calculation.

(e) *Fan Temperature Rating.* Determine the potential temperature of gases that the fan might be required to handle by measuring the distance from the floor of the highest cell to the centerline of the fan, or fan ports if the fan is in a duct or similar arrangement. Determine the intersection of the new Z value with the appropriate ventilation rate curve (solid line) from Figure A.23.3.1.3(a). Estimate the temperature rise by interpolating along the appropriate ventilation rate curve and between the constant temperature rise curves (dashed lines) from Figure A.23.3.1.3(a). Provide all elements of the exhaust system that are to be above the acceptable smoke level with the capability to effectively operate with the indicated increase in temperature.

(f) *Operation of Exhaust System.* The emergency exhaust system should be arranged to initiate automatically on detection of smoke, on operation of a manual fire alarm system, or by direct manual operation. The capability to manually start the automatic exhaust system should be provided in a guard post in the cell block, at another control location, or both. Where appropriate, the emergency exhaust fans are permitted to be used for comfort ventilation as well as serving their emergency purposes.

Subsection 22/23.3.1 specifies the protection required to maintain floor-to-floor separation, which helps to prevent the products of combustion from moving vertically through the building.

The convenience stair addressed by 8.2.5.8 and recognized by Exception No. 1 to 22/23.3.1.1 is illustrated in Exhibits 22/23.11(a) and 22/23.11(b).

Paragraph 8.2.5.5 addresses a vertical opening that is permitted to connect not more than three floor levels. Exception No. 2 to 22/23.3.1.1 addresses typical, multilevel housing areas that use staggered, partial levels as depicted in Exhibit 22/23.12. The exception modifies the three-floor restriction of 8.2.5.5 by allowing a 23-ft (7-m) height limitation be-

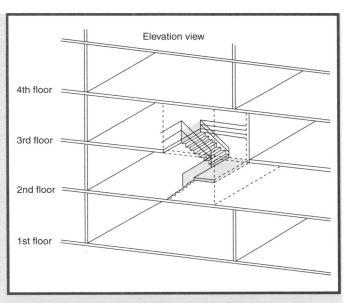

Exhibit 22/23.11(b) *Elevation view of convenience stair.*

tween the lowest and highest finished floor levels to permit greater flexibility in the design and use of detention and correctional occupancies. The exception applies only to facilities whose residential housing areas are protected throughout by automatic sprinklers.

Exception No. 2 to 22/23.3.1.1 clarifies that a residential housing unit that complies with the requirements of Table 22/23.3.8 is considered to be part of the communicating space addressed by 8.2.5.5. This clarification prevents the *Code* user from needlessly complying with 8.2.5.5(4), which would require a fully

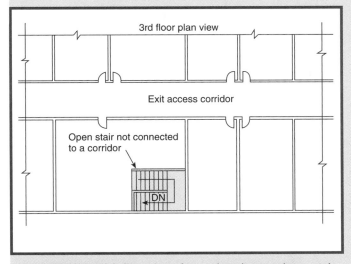

Exhibit 22/23.11(a) *Plan view of unenclosed convenience stair.*

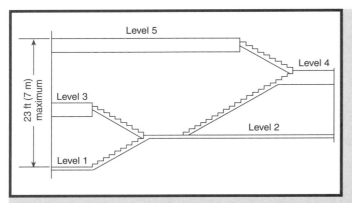

Exhibit 22/23.12 *Unprotected vertical openings in sprinklered housing area.*

sprinklered residential area to be separated from all rooms abutting a communicating space (for example, a day room with a high ceiling) by means of smoke-resisting construction. If this clarification were not made, all openings, including doors, from resident sleeping rooms to the day space would be required to have smoke-resistant opening protectives. Such a requirement would place an undue burden on such facilities. Instead of requiring smoke-resistant separations between each resident sleeping room and the day space, the *Code* judges that adequate life safety is provided if the residential housing unit is subdivided in accordance with the provisions of 22/23.3.8.

Also, compliance with 8.2.5.5(8) would then be impractical. Exception No. 2 was added to 8.2.5.5(4) to prevent this portion of Exception No. 2 to 22/23.3.1.1 from conflicting with the provisions of 8.2.5.5(4).

Whereas 22/23.3.1.1, Exception No. 2, allows multilevel housing areas with a maximum 23-ft (7-m) height between the lowest and the highest finished floor levels if the housing areas are fully sprinklered, 23.3.1.2 allows similar vertical openings in nonsprinklered, existing multilevel housing areas but limits the height of the area served by the openings to 13 ft (4 m).

Paragraph 23.3.1.3 addresses an existing multitiered open cell block. A multitiered open cell block in excess of 23 ft (7 m) in height, measured between the lowest and highest finished floor levels (see Exception No. 2 to 23.3.1.1), could not be built in compliance with the *Life Safety Code*. However, the provisions of 23.3.1.3 continue to recognize existing, multitiered open cell blocks if (1) automatic sprinkler protection is provided or (2) smoke control is provided to deal with the limited amount of smoke that a sprinkler-controlled fire generates. In addition to the information on smoke control provided in A.23.3.1.3, see the detailed commentary following 8.2.5.6(6) on the subject of atrium smoke control. The physics associated with smoke development, spread, and control in a multitiered open cell block is similar to that of an atrium.

22.3.2 Protection from Hazards.

22.3.2.1* Hazardous Areas. Any hazardous area shall be protected in accordance with Section 8.4. The areas described in Table 22.3.2.1 shall be protected as indicated.

A.22.3.2.1 Furnishings are usually the first items ignited in a detention and correctional environment. The type, quantity, and arrangement of furniture and other combustibles are important factors in determining how fast the fire will develop. Furnishings, including upholstered items and wood items such as wardrobes, desks, and bookshelves, might provide sufficient fuel to result in room flashover, which is the full fire involvement of all combustibles within a room once sufficient heat has been built up within the room.

Combustible loading in any room opening onto a residential housing area should be limited to reduce the potential for room flashover. Rooms in which fuel loads are not controlled, thereby creating a potential for flashover, should be

23.3.2 Protection from Hazards.

23.3.2.1* Hazardous Areas. Any hazardous area shall be protected in accordance with Section 8.4. The areas described in Table 23.3.2.1 shall be protected as indicated.

A.23.3.2.1 It is strongly recommended that padded cells not be used due to their fire record. However, recognizing that they will be used in some cases, provisions for the protection of padded cells are provided. It is recognized that the ¾-hour fire door will be violated with the "plant on" of the padding, but a ¾-hour fire door should be the base of the assembly.

CHAPTER 22 • New | **CHAPTER 23 • Existing**

Table 22.3.2.1 Hazardous Area Protection

Hazardous Area Description	Separation/Protection
Areas not incidental to resident housing	2 hours
Boiler and fuel-fired heater rooms	1 hour
Central or bulk laundries >100 ft² (>9.3 m²)	1 hour
Commercial cooking equipment	In accordance with 9.2.3
Commissaries	Smoke resistant
Employee locker rooms	Smoke resistant
Hobby/handicraft shops	Smoke resistant
Maintenance shops	Smoke resistant
Padded cells	1 hour
Soiled linen rooms	1 hour
Storage rooms >50 ft² (>4.6 m²) in area but ≤100 ft² (≤9.3 m²) in area storing combustible material	Smoke resistant
Storage rooms >100 ft² (>9.3 m²) storing combustible materials	1 hour
Trash collection rooms	1 hour

Table 23.3.2.1 Hazardous Area Protection

Hazardous Area Description	Separation/Protection
Areas not incidental to resident housing	2 hours
Boiler and fuel-fired heater rooms	1 hour or sprinklers
Central or bulk laundries >100 ft² (>9.3 m²)	1 hour or sprinklers
Commercial cooking equipment	In accordance with 9.2.3
Commissaries	1 hour or sprinklers
Employee locker rooms	1 hour or sprinklers
Hobby/handicraft shops	1 hour or sprinklers
Maintenance shops	1 hour or sprinklers
Padded cells	1 hour and sprinklers
Soiled linen rooms	1 hour or sprinklers
Storage rooms >50 ft² (>4.6 m²) in area storing combustible material	1 hour or sprinklers
Trash collection rooms	1 hour or sprinklers

considered hazardous areas. Where fire-rated separation is provided, doors to such rooms, including sleeping rooms, should be self-closing.

It is strongly recommended that padded cells not be used due to their fire record. However, recognizing that they will be used in some cases, provisions for the protection of padded cells are provided. It is recognized that the ¾-hour fire door will be violated with the "plant on" of the padding, but a ¾-hour fire door should be the base of the assembly.

22.3.2.2 Hazardous areas determined by the authority having jurisdiction as not incidental to residents' housing shall be separated by 2-hour fire resistance–rated barriers in conjunction with automatic sprinkler protection.

22.3.2.3 Where cooking facilities are protected in accordance with 9.2.3, kitchens shall not be required to be provided with roomwide protection.

23.3.2.2 Hazardous areas determined by the authority having jurisdiction as not incidental to residents' housing shall be separated by 2-hour fire resistance–rated barriers in conjunction with automatic sprinkler protection.

23.3.2.3 Where cooking facilities are protected in accordance with 9.2.3, kitchens shall not be required to be provided with roomwide protection.

Hazardous areas in detention and correctional occupancies are spaces with contents that, due to their nature—as in the case of flammable liquids—or because of the quantity of combustible materials involved, represent a significantly higher hazard than would otherwise be typical of detention and correctional occupancies. Paragraph 22/23.3.2.1 requires hazardous areas to be protected. The protection required by Table 22.3.2.1 for hazardous areas in new facilities was specified knowing that new facilities must be sprinklered. Thus, where Table 22.3.2.1 requires smoke-resistant separation—for example, for employee locker rooms—the actual protection is that provided by both the sprinkler system and the smoke-resistant walls. Similarly, where Table 22.3.2.1 requires 1-hour fire resistance–rated separation, the actual protection is that provided by both the sprinkler system and the fire–rated walls. For existing facilities, the areas listed in Table 23.3.2.1 must be protected by the specified fire resistance–rated separation, sprinklering, or combination of separation and sprinklering.

Padded cells are considered to be severe hazard areas due to high heat release, high rate of combustion, and the quantity of smoke produced by padding materials. Therefore, padded cells must be protected

by automatic sprinklers and separated by 1-hour construction.

Where flammable liquids are handled or stored, NFPA 30, *Flammable and Combustible Liquids Code*, should be consulted to establish the minimum criteria necessary to mitigate this hazard.[3] See also 8.4.3.

Even typical housing area furnishings can provide the combustible loading that will allow room flashover to occur. The potential for flashover should be considered, particularly for nonsprinklered, multi-level housing areas allowed by 23.3.1.2. Flashover on a lower level could rapidly deteriorate the tenability of conditions on upper levels, as the products of combustion bank down from the ceiling of the housing area, affecting residents of the upper levels before they can use the means of egress system.

22.3.3 Interior Finish.

22.3.3.1 Interior finish shall be in accordance with Section 10.2.

22.3.3.2 Interior Wall and Ceiling Finish. Interior wall and ceiling finish complying with 10.2.3 shall be Class A or Class B in corridors, in exits, and in any space not separated from corridors and exits by partitions capable of retarding the passage of smoke; and Class A, Class B, or Class C in all other areas. The provisions of 10.2.8.1 shall not apply.

22.3.3.3 Interior Floor Finish. Interior floor finish complying with 10.2.7 shall be Class I or Class II in corridors and exits. The provisions of 10.2.8.2 shall not apply.

23.3.3 Interior Finish.

23.3.3.1 Interior finish shall be in accordance with Section 10.2.

23.3.3.2 Interior Wall and Ceiling Finish. Interior wall and ceiling finish complying with 10.2.3 shall be Class A or Class B in corridors, in exits, and in any space not separated from corridors and exits by partitions capable of retarding the passage of smoke; and Class A, Class B, or Class C in all other areas.

23.3.3.3 Interior Floor Finish. Interior floor finish complying with 10.2.7 shall be Class I or Class II in corridors and exits.

Exception: Existing floor finish material of Class A or Class B in nonsprinklered smoke compartments and Class A, Class B, or Class C in sprinklered smoke compartments shall be permitted to be continued to be used, provided that it has been evaluated based on tests performed in accordance with 10.2.7.

Paragraph 22/23.3.3.2 imposes stricter interior wall and ceiling finish requirements in exits, corridors, and spaces not separated from the corridor than it does in other use areas. To apply the less stringent requirements within the use areas, the required separation need be only a partition capable of retarding the passage of smoke. The partition must be of substantial construction but is not required to have a fire resistance rating.

The exception to 23.3.3.3 recognizes existing interior floor finish materials that have been tested in a accordance with NFPA 255, *Standard Method of Test of Surface Burning Characteristics of Building Materials*,[4] as an exemption to the requirement of 10.2.7 that testing of floor finish materials be performed per NFPA 253, *Standard Method of Test for Critical Radiant Flux of Floor Covering Systems Using a Radiant Heat Energy Source*.[5] NFPA 255 contains the flame spread and smoke development measurement method currently used to evaluate interior wall and ceiling finish materials in accordance with the requirements of Section 10.2. Prior to the 1981 edition of the *Code*, floor finish was

tested in accordance with NFPA 255. This exception allows material that was tested and approved by this method to remain in use.

22.3.4 Detection, Alarm, and Communications Systems.

22.3.4.1 General.

22.3.4.1.1 Detention and correctional occupancies shall be provided with a fire alarm system in accordance with Section 9.6, except as modified by 22.3.4.1.2 through 22.3.4.4.

22.3.4.1.2 All fire alarm systems and detection systems required in 22.3.4 shall be provided with a secondary power supply, and the installation shall be in accordance with NFPA 72, *National Fire Alarm Code.*

22.3.4.2 Initiation. Initiation of the required fire alarm system shall be by manual means in accordance with 9.6.2, by means of any required detection devices or detection systems, and by means of waterflow alarm in the sprinkler system required by 22.3.5.2.

Exception No. 1: Manual fire alarm boxes shall be permitted to be locked, provided that staff is present within the area when it is occupied and staff has keys readily available to unlock the boxes.

Exception No. 2: Manual fire alarm boxes shall be permitted to be located in a staff location, provided that the staff location is attended when the building is occupied and that the staff attendant has direct supervision of the sleeping area.

22.3.4.3 Notification.

22.3.4.3.1 Occupant Notification. Occupant notification shall be accomplished automatically in accordance with 9.6.3. A positive alarm sequence shall be permitted in accordance with 9.6.3.4.

Exception: * *Any smoke detectors required by this chapter shall be permitted to be arranged to alarm at a constantly attended location only and shall not be required to accomplish general occupant notification.*

23.3.4 Detection, Alarm, and Communications Systems.

23.3.4.1 General.

23.3.4.1.1 Detention and correctional occupancies shall be provided with a fire alarm system in accordance with Section 9.6, except as modified by 23.3.4.1.2 through 23.3.4.4.

Exception: Existing systems lacking the monitoring of wiring required by 9.6.1.6 shall be permitted to be continued in use in buildings protected by a complete automatic extinguishing system.

23.3.4.1.2 All fire alarm systems and detection systems required in 23.3.4 shall be provided with a secondary power supply, and the installation shall be in accordance with NFPA 72, *National Fire Alarm Code.*

23.3.4.2 Initiation. Initiation of the required fire alarm system shall be by manual means in accordance with 9.6.2 and by means of any required detection devices or detection systems.

Exception No. 1: Manual fire alarm boxes shall be permitted to be locked, provided that staff is present within the area when it is occupied and staff has keys readily available to unlock the boxes.

Exception No. 2: Manual fire alarm boxes shall be permitted to be located in a staff location, provided that the staff location is attended when the building is occupied and that the staff attendant has direct supervision of the sleeping area.

23.3.4.3 Notification.

23.3.4.3.1 Occupant Notification. Occupant notification shall be accomplished automatically in accordance with 9.6.3. A positive alarm sequence shall be permitted in accordance with 9.6.3.4.

Exception: * *Any smoke detectors required by this chapter shall be permitted to be arranged to alarm at a constantly attended location only and shall not be required to accomplish general occupant notification.*

A.22.3.4.3.1 Exception The staff at the constantly attended location should have the capability to promptly initiate the general alarm function and contact the fire department or have direct communication with a control room or other location that can initiate the general alarm function and contact the fire department.

22.3.4.3.2 Emergency Forces Notification. Fire department notification shall be accomplished in accordance with 9.6.4. A positive alarm sequence shall be permitted in accordance with 9.6.3.4.

Exception No. 1: Any smoke detectors required by this chapter shall not be required to transmit an alarm to the fire department.

Exception No. 2: This requirement shall not apply where staff is provided at a constantly attended location that has the capability to promptly notify the fire department or has direct communication with a control room having direct access to the fire department. The fire plan, as required by 22.7.1.3, shall include procedures for logging of alarms and immediate notification of the fire department.

22.3.4.4* Detection. An approved automatic smoke detection system shall be in accordance with Section 9.6, as modified by 22.3.4.4.1 through 22.3.4.4.3, throughout all resident sleeping areas and adjacent day rooms, activity rooms, or contiguous common spaces.

A.22.3.4.4 Examples of contiguous common spaces are galleries and corridors.

22.3.4.4.1 Smoke detectors shall not be required in sleeping rooms with four or fewer occupants.

22.3.4.4.2 Other arrangements and positioning of smoke detectors shall be permitted to prevent damage or tampering, or for other purposes. Such arrangements shall be capable of detecting any fire, and the placement of detectors shall be such that the speed of detection is equivalent to that provided by the spacing and arrangements required by the installation standards referenced in Section 9.6. Detectors shall be permitted to be located in exhaust ducts from cells, behind grilles, or in other locations. The equivalent performance of the design, however, shall be acceptable to the authority having jurisdiction in accordance with the equivalency concepts specified in Section 1.5.

A.23.3.4.3.1 Exception The staff at the constantly attended location should have the capability to promptly initiate the general alarm function and contact the fire department or have direct communication with a control room or other location that can initiate the general alarm function and contact the fire department.

23.3.4.3.2 Emergency Forces Notification. Fire department notification shall be accomplished in accordance with 9.6.4. A positive alarm sequence shall be permitted in accordance with 9.6.3.4.

Exception No. 1: Any smoke detectors required by this chapter shall not be required to transmit an alarm to the fire department.

Exception No. 2: This requirement shall not apply where staff is provided at a constantly attended location that has the capability to promptly notify the fire department or has direct communication with a control room having direct access to the fire department. The fire plan, as required by 23.7.1.3, shall include procedures for logging of alarms and immediate notification of the fire department.

23.3.4.4 Detection. An approved automatic smoke detection system shall be in accordance with Section 9.6, as modified by 23.3.4.4.1 through 23.3.4.4.4, throughout all resident housing areas.

23.3.4.4.1 Smoke detectors shall not be required in sleeping rooms with four or fewer occupants in Use Condition II or Use Condition III.

23.3.4.4.2 Other arrangements and positioning of smoke detectors shall be permitted to prevent damage or tampering, or for other purposes. Such arrangements shall be capable of detecting any fire, and the placement of detectors shall be such that the speed of detection is equivalent to that provided by the spacing and arrangements required by the installation standards referenced in Section 9.6. Detectors shall be permitted to be located in exhaust ducts from cells, behind grilles, or in other locations. The equivalent performance of the design, however, shall be acceptable to the authority having jurisdiction in accordance with the equivalency concepts specified in Section 1.5.

22.3.4.4.3* Smoke detectors shall not be required in Use Condition II open dormitories where staff is present within the dormitory whenever the dormitory is occupied.

A.22.3.4.4.3 An open dormitory is a dormitory that is arranged to allow staff to observe the entire dormitory area at one time.

Given that new detention and correctional facilities must be sprinklered, 22.3.4.2 requires waterflow alarm as one of the means for initiating the fire alarm system.

By being silent on the subject, 22/23.3.4.3.1 does not permit presignal systems. Rather, notification must be provided without delay in accordance with 9.6.3, or the more reliable form of presignal—called positive alarm sequence—can be used if complying with 9.6.3.4. However, to avoid numerous nuisance alarms, the exception does exempt smoke detectors from sounding a general alarm.

Where the fire department is not equipped to receive alarms or where direct transmission to the fire department is not permitted, the provisions of 22/23.3.4.3.2 require that arrangements be made for the prompt notification of the fire department. One means of notification is by an approved central station

22.3.5 Extinguishment Requirements.

22.3.5.1 High-rise buildings shall comply with 22.4.3.

22.3.5.2 All buildings classified as Use Condition II, Use Condition III, Use Condition IV, or Use Condition V shall be protected throughout by an approved, supervised automatic sprinkler system in accordance with Section 9.7.

23.3.4.4.3* Smoke detectors shall not be required in Use Condition II open dormitories where staff is present within the dormitory whenever the dormitory is occupied and the building is protected throughout by an approved, supervised automatic sprinkler system in accordance with Section 9.7.

A.23.3.4.4.3 An open dormitory is a dormitory that is arranged to allow staff to observe the entire dormitory area at one time.

23.3.4.4.4 In smoke compartments protected throughout by an approved automatic sprinkler system in accordance with 23.3.5.3, smoke detectors shall not be required, except in corridors, common spaces, and sleeping rooms with more than four occupants.

alarm system. Paragraph 9.6.4 provides several options for notifying the fire department automatically. Where smoke detectors are provided, they are not required to sound the fire alarm or to transmit a signal to the fire department but are required to sound an alarm at a constantly attended location, unless otherwise specified.

Paragraph 22/23.3.4.4.3 is a new exemption to the smoke detection system requirement. It applies to Use Condition II open dormitories where staff are present within the dormitory whenever the dormitory is occupied. Note that Use Condition II facilities must permit free movement from sleeping areas to another smoke compartment. The concept employed is one of relying on awake and alert staff within the dormitory to act as human fire detectors, provide early warning, and permit residents to move into a safe smoke compartment.

23.3.5 Extinguishment Requirements.

23.3.5.1 High-rise buildings shall comply with 23.4.3.

23.3.5.2* Where required by 23.1.6, facilities shall be protected throughout by an approved, supervised automatic sprinkler system in accordance with Section 9.7.

A.23.3.5.2 Where the openings in ceilings or partitions are ¼ in. (0.6 cm) or larger in the smallest dimension, where the thickness or depth of the material does not exceed the smallest dimension of the openings, and where such openings constitute not less than 70 percent of the area of the ceiling or partition material, the disruption of sprinkler spray patterns is permitted to be disregarded.

CHAPTER 22 • New	CHAPTER 23 • Existing

22.3.5.3 The automatic sprinkler system required by 22.3.5.2 shall be as follows:

(1) In accordance with Section 9.7
(2) Electrically connected to the fire alarm system
(3) Fully supervised

22.3.5.4 Portable fire extinguishers shall be provided in accordance with 9.7.4.1.

Exception No. 1:* Access to portable fire extinguishers shall be permitted to be locked.

A.22.3.5.4 Exception No. 1 Where access to portable fire extinguishers is locked, staff should be present on a 24-hour basis and should have keys readily available to unlock access to the extinguishers. Where supervision of sleeping areas is from a 24-hour attended staff location, portable fire extinguishers are permitted to be provided at the staff location in lieu of the sleeping area.

Exception No. 2: Portable fire extinguishers shall be permitted to be located at staff locations only.

22.3.5.5 Standpipe and hose systems shall be provided in accordance with 9.7.4.2 as follows:

(1) Class I standpipe systems shall be provided for any building over two stories in height.
(2) Class III standpipe and hose systems shall be provided for all nonsprinklered buildings over two stories in height.

Exception No. 1: One-inch (2.5-cm) diameter formed hose on hose reels shall be permitted to provide Class II service.

Exception No. 2: Separate Class I and Class II systems shall be permitted in lieu of a Class III system.

23.3.5.3 Where this *Code* permits exceptions for fully sprinklered detention and correctional occupancies or sprinklered smoke compartments, the sprinkler system shall be as follows:

(1) In accordance with Section 9.7
(2) Electrically connected to the fire alarm system
(3) Fully supervised

23.3.5.4 Portable fire extinguishers shall be provided in accordance with 9.7.4.1.

Exception No. 1:* Access to portable fire extinguishers shall be permitted to be locked.

A.23.3.5.4 Exception No. 1 Where access to portable fire extinguishers is locked, staff should be present on a 24-hour basis and should have keys readily available to unlock access to the extinguishers. Where supervision of sleeping areas is from a 24-hour attended staff location, portable fire extinguishers are permitted to be provided at the staff location in lieu of the sleeping area.

Exception No. 2: Portable fire extinguishers shall be permitted to be located at staff locations only.

23.3.5.5 Standpipe and hose systems shall be provided in accordance with 9.7.4.2 as follows:

(1) Class I standpipe systems shall be provided for any building over two stories in height.
(2) Class III standpipe and hose systems shall be provided for all nonsprinklered buildings over two stories in height.

Exception No. 1: One-inch (2.5-cm) diameter formed hose on hose reels shall be permitted to provide Class II service.

Exception No. 2: Separate Class I and Class II systems shall be permitted in lieu of a Class III system.

Paragraph 22.3.5.1, applicable to new facilities in high-rise buildings, refers to 22.4.3, which in turn mandatorily references 11.8.2—which addresses those high-rise building provisions applicable to automatic sprinkler systems and standpipes. Paragraph 23.3.5.1, applicable to existing facilities in high-rise buildings, refers to 23.4.3, which in turn mandates an automatic sprinkler system, but not standpipes. For both new and existing facilities, a sprinkler control valve and waterflow device must be provided for each floor.

Paragraph 22.3.5.2 requires that new detention and correctional occupancies be protected through-

out by approved, supervised automatic sprinkler systems. However, in establishing the sprinkler requirement, the Technical Committee on Detention and Correctional Occupancies realized that some jurisdictions follow policies—often established at the state level—that do not permit automatic sprinklers in detention and correctional facilities. Thus, 22.4.4 provides additional criteria needed for the proper protection of nonsprinklered existing building renovations.

Where automatic sprinklers are installed to comply with the *Code*, the system must be a complete, approved automatic sprinkler system installed in accordance with NFPA 13, *Standard for the Installation of Sprinkler Systems.*[6] The use of manually operated sprinklers is not recognized by the *Code.* Informal surveys of detention and correctional occupancy staff indicate no significant problems with the installation, maintenance, and use of automatic sprinkler systems in detention and correctional facilities. The system must also be supervised in accordance with the requirements of 9.7.2 to comply with the *Code.* Exhibit 22/23.13 illustrates a typical institutional sprinkler.

Exception No. 1 to 22/23.3.5.4 permits fire extinguishers to be locked. Time is critical when using extinguishers; therefore, keys must be carried by the staff or be readily accessible.

The requirements of 22/23.3.5.5 for standpipes intend that 2½-in. (6.2-cm) hose connections be available for fire department use in any detention and correctional occupancy more than two stories in height. In addition, if such buildings are nonsprinklered, there should also be 1½-in. (3.8-cm) connections and hose for staff and resident use.

Exception No. 1 to 22/23.3.5.5 permits the use of 1-in. (2.5-cm) formed rubber hose in place of the fabric-jacketed, rubber-lined hose normally required in standpipe systems. The rubber hose is normally stored on reels and is easier to use.

Exhibit 22/23.13 Typical institutional sprinkler.

22.3.6 Corridors.

(See 22.3.8.)

22.3.7 Subdivision of Building Spaces.

22.3.7.1 Smoke barriers shall be provided to divide every story used for sleeping by residents, or any other story having an occupant load of 50 or more persons, into not less than two compartments.

Exception No. 1: Protection shall be permitted to be accomplished using horizontal exits. (See 7.2.4.)

Exception No. 2:* The requirement for subdivision of building space shall be permitted to be fulfilled by one of the following:

23.3.6 Corridors.

(See 23.3.8.)

23.3.7 Subdivision of Building Spaces.

23.3.7.1* Smoke barriers shall be provided to divide every story used for sleeping by 10 or more residents, or any other story having an occupant load of 50 or more persons, into not less than two compartments.

A.23.3.7.1 Consideration can be given for large open areas that might be permitted to function as smoke sinks as an alternative to the installation of more than one smoke barrier as required by 23.3.7. Vertical movement downward to an area of refuge might be permitted by the authority having jurisdiction in lieu of horizontal movement.

Exception No. 1: Protection shall be permitted to be accomplished using horizontal exits. (See 7.2.4.)

Exception No. 2:* The requirement for subdivision of building space shall be permitted to be fulfilled by one of the following:

(a) Smoke compartments having exit to a public way where such exit serves only one area and has no openings to other areas

(b) A building separated from the resident housing area by a 2-hour fire resistance rating or 50 ft (15 m) of open space

(c) A secured, open area having a holding space located 50 ft (15 m) from the housing area that provides 15 ft² (1.4 m²) or more of refuge area for each person (resident, staff, visitors) potentially present at the time of a fire

Doors used to access the areas specified in (a), (b), and (c) of this exception shall meet the requirements for doors at smoke barriers for the applicable use condition.

A.22.3.7.1 Exception No. 2 A door to the outside, by itself, does not meet the intent of the exception if emergency operating procedures do not provide for the door to be unlocked when needed. In cases where use of the door is not ensured, a true smoke barrier per the base requirement of 22.3.7.1 would be needed.

22.3.7.2 Where smoke barriers are required by 22.3.7.1, they shall be provided as follows:

(1) They shall limit the occupant load to not more than 200 residents in any smoke compartment.
(2) They shall limit the travel distance to a door in a smoke barrier as follows:
  a. The distance from any room door required as exit access shall not exceed 150 ft (45 m).
  b. The distance from any point in a room shall not exceed 200 ft (60 m).

22.3.7.3* Any required smoke barrier shall be constructed in accordance with Section 8.3. Barriers shall be of substantial construction and shall have structural fire resistance.

A.22.3.7.3 Structural fire resistance is defined as the ability of the assembly to stay in place and maintain structural integrity without consideration of heat transmission. Twelve-gauge steel plate suitably framed and stiffened meets this requirement.

(a) Smoke compartments having exit to a public way where such exit serves only one area and has no openings to other areas

(b) A building separated from the resident housing area by a 2-hour fire resistance rating or 50 ft (15 m) of open space

(c) A secured, open area having a holding space located 50 ft (15 m) from the housing area that provides 15 ft² (1.4 m²) or more of refuge area for each person (resident, staff, visitors) potentially present at the time of a fire

Doors used to access the areas specified in (a), (b), and (c) of this exception shall meet the requirements for doors at smoke barriers for the applicable use condition.

A.23.3.7.1 Exception No. 2 A door to the outside, by itself, does not meet the intent of the exception if emergency operating procedures do not provide for the door to be unlocked when needed. In cases where use of the door is not ensured, a true smoke barrier per the base requirement of 23.3.7.1 would be needed.

23.3.7.2 Where smoke barriers are required by 23.3.7.1, they shall be provided as follows:

(1) They shall limit the occupant load to not more than 200 residents in any smoke compartment.
(2)* They shall limit the travel distance to a door in a smoke barrier as follows:
  a. The distance from any room door required as exit access shall not exceed 100 ft (30 m).
  b. The distance from any point in a room shall not exceed 150 ft (45 m).

Exception: The maximum travel distance shall be permitted to be increased by 50 ft (15 m) in smoke compartments protected throughout by an approved automatic sprinkler system or automatic smoke control system.

A.23.3.7.2(2) Consideration should be given to increasing the travel distance to a smoke barrier to coincide with existing range lengths and exits.

23.3.7.3* Any required smoke barrier shall be constructed in accordance with Section 8.3. Barriers shall be of substantial construction and shall have a structural fire resistance.

A.23.3.7.3 Structural fire resistance is defined as the ability of the assembly to stay in place and maintain structural integrity without consideration of heat transmission. Twelve-gauge steel plate suitably framed and stiffened meets this requirement.

CHAPTER 22 • New

CHAPTER 23 • Existing

22.3.7.4 Openings in smoke barriers shall be protected in accordance with Section 8.3.

Exception No. 1:* *There shall be no restriction on the total number of vision panels in any barrier.*

A.22.3.7.4 Exception No. 1 As an example, a smoke barrier is permitted to consist of fire-rated glazing panels mounted in a security grille arrangement.

Exception No. 2: *Sliding doors in smoke barriers that are designed to normally be kept closed and are remotely operated from a continuously attended location shall not be required to be self-closing.*

22.3.7.5 Not less than 6 net ft² (0.56 net m²) per occupant shall be provided on each side of the smoke barrier for the total number of occupants in adjoining compartments. This space shall be readily available wherever occupants are moved across the smoke barrier in a fire emergency.

22.3.7.6 Doors shall provide resistance to the passage of smoke. Swinging doors shall be self-latching, or the opening resistance of the door shall be not less than 5 lbf (22 N).

22.3.7.7 Doors in smoke barriers shall conform with the requirements for doors in means of egress as specified in Section 22.2 and shall have locking and release arrangements according to the applicable use condition. The provisions of the exception to 22.2.11.6 shall not be used for smoke barrier doors serving a smoke compartment containing more than 20 persons.

22.3.7.8 Vision panels shall be provided in smoke barriers at points where the barrier crosses an exit access corridor.

22.3.7.9 Smoke dampers shall be provided in accordance with 8.3.5.

Exception: *Other arrangements and positioning of smoke detectors shall be permitted to prevent damage or tampering, or for other purposes. Such arrangements shall be capable of detecting any fire, and the placement of detectors shall be such that the speed of detection is equivalent to that provided by the spacing and arrangement required by NFPA 72, National Fire Alarm Code, as referenced in 8.3.5.3.*

23.3.7.4 Openings in smoke barriers shall be protected in accordance with Section 8.3.

Exception No. 1:* *There shall be no restriction on the total number of vision panels in any barrier.*

A.23.3.7.4 Exception No. 1 As an example, a smoke barrier is permitted to consist of fire-rated glazing panels mounted in a security grille arrangement.

Exception No. 2: *Sliding doors in smoke barriers that are designed to normally be kept closed and are remotely operated from a continuously attended location shall not be required to be self-closing.*

23.3.7.5 Not less than 6 net ft² (0.56 net m²) per occupant shall be provided on each side of the smoke barrier for the total number of occupants in adjoining compartments. This space shall be readily available wherever occupants are moved across the smoke barrier in a fire emergency.

23.3.7.6 Doors shall provide resistance to the passage of smoke. Swinging doors shall be self-latching, or the opening resistance of the door shall be not less than 5 lbf (22 N). Such doors shall not be required to swing in the direction of egress travel.

23.3.7.7 Doors in smoke barriers shall conform with the requirements for doors in means of egress as specified in Section 23.2 and shall have locking and release arrangements according to the applicable use condition. The provisions of the exception to 23.2.11.6 shall not be used for smoke barrier doors serving a smoke compartment containing more than 20 persons.

23.3.7.8 Vision panels shall be provided in smoke barriers at points where the barrier crosses an exit access corridor.

23.3.7.9 Smoke dampers shall be provided in accordance with 8.3.5.

Exception: *Other arrangements and positioning of smoke detectors shall be permitted to prevent damage or tampering, or for other purposes. Such arrangements shall be capable of detecting any fire and the placement of detectors shall be such that the speed of detection is equivalent to that provided by the spacing and arrangement required by NFPA 72, National Fire Alarm Code, as referenced in 8.3.5.3.*

Smoke barriers and horizontal exits used to subdivide a building serve three purposes that are fundamental to the protection of occupants:

(1) They limit the spread of fire and fire-produced contaminants.
(2) They limit the number of occupants exposed to a single fire.
(3) They provide for horizontal relocation of occupants by creating a safe area on the same floor.

The requirements of 22/23.3.7.1 and 22/23.3.7.2 for subdividing building spaces are illustrated in Exhibit 22/23.14. Exhibit 22/23.15 illustrates the requirements of Exception No. 2 to 22/23.3.7.1. In Exhibit 22/23.15, the door from resident housing building to yard can be locked only to the degree that a smoke barrier door can be locked for the applicable use condition.

Paragraph 22/23.3.7.3 requires smoke barriers to have structural fire resistance. However, the specific fire resistance in hours is omitted. The intent is to eliminate the use of highly combustible or flimsy materials, such as plastic sheeting, that might possibly limit smoke movement but have little structural integrity.

The doors in the required smoke barriers must resist the passage of smoke for the same reason that smoke barriers must resist the passage of smoke. The door constructed of materials that resist the passage of smoke will stop smoke from traveling across the door opening only if the door remains tightly closed. Therefore, 22/23.3.7.6 requires that the door, which 8.3.4.3 requires to be either self-closing or automatic-closing, also must be self-latching or offer a 5-lbf (22-N) resistance to opening, as a minimum. This combination of requirements should help to ensure that the door will be closed under smoke conditions and remain closed, even under the pressures generated by a fire, to resist the passage of smoke.

The provisions of the exception to 22/23.2.11.6 allow up to 10 locks to require manual unlocking in a timely fashion and still be considered as providing the degree of remote unlocking necessary to satisfy the requirements of a Use Condition IV facility—as opposed to a Use Condition V facility. However, 22/23.3.7.7 does not allow locks on smoke barrier doors to be part of the maximum 10 manually unlocked locks where a smoke compartment houses more than 20 persons. This limitation emphasizes the importance of maintaining a means of egress system

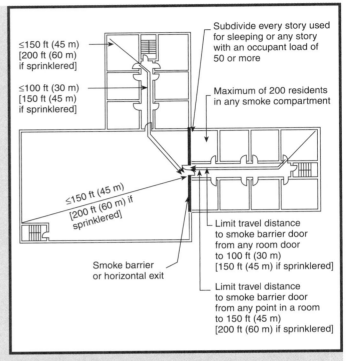

Exhibit 22/23.14 *Subdivision of building spaces into smoke compartments using smoke barriers.*

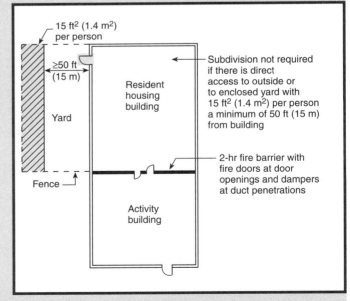

Exhibit 22/23.15 *Alternatives to subdivision by smoke barriers.*

within a Use Condition IV facility (that is, where re-mote release is required), with more than 20 persons per smoke compartment, that allows resident move-ment to another smoke compartment without having to manually release the lock on the smoke barrier

door. A manually released lock on the smoke barrier door would force a reclassification of the facility to Use Condition V and compliance with the more strin-gent requirements applicable to that classification.

22.3.8* Special Protection Features—Subdivision of Resident Housing Spaces.

Subdivision of facility spaces shall comply with Table 22.3.8.

23.3.8* Special Protection Features—Subdivision of Resident Housing Spaces.

Subdivision of facility spaces shall comply with Table 23.3.8.

Table 22.3.8 Subdivision of Resident Housing Spaces

Feature	Use Condition			
	II	III	IV	V
Room to room separation	NR	NR	NR	SR
Room face to corridor separation	NR	NR	NR	SR
Room face to common space separation	NR	NR SR ≤50 ft >50 ft (≤15 m)† (>15 m)†	NR SR ≤50 ft >50 ft (≤15 m)† (>15 m)†	SR
Common space to corridor separation	NR	NR	NR	SR
Total openings in solid room face where room face is required to be smoke resistant or fire rated‡	120 in.² (0.08 m²)	120 in.² (0.08 m²)	120 in.² (0.08 m²)	120 in.² (0.08 m²), closable from in-side, or 120 in.² (0.08 m²) with smoke control

NR: No requirement

SR: Smoke resistant.

Notes:

1. Doors in openings in partitions required to be smoke resistant (SR) in accordance with Table 22.3.8 shall be substantial doors of construction that resists the passage of smoke. Latches and door closers shall not be required on cell doors.

2. Under Use Condition II, Use Condition III, or Use Condition IV, a space subdivided by open construction (any combination of grating doors and grating walls or solid walls) shall be permitted to be considered one room if housing not more than 16 persons. The perimeter walls of such space shall be of smoke-resistant construction. Smoke detection shall be provided in such space. Under Use Condition IV, common walls between sleeping areas within the space shall be smoke resistant, and grating doors and fronts shall be permitted to be used. Under Use Condition II and Use Condition III, open dormitories shall be permitted to house more than 16 persons as permitted by other sections of this chapter.

3. Where barriers are required to be smoke resistant (SR), the provisions of 8.2.4 shall not apply.

†Travel distance through the common space to the exit access corridor.

‡"Total openings in solid room face" includes all openings (for example, undercuts, food passes, grilles), the total of which shall not exceed 120 in.² (0.08 m²). All openings shall be 36 in. (91 m) or less above the floor.

Table 23.3.8 Subdivision of Resident Housing Spaces

Feature	II	III			IV		V	
	NS	NS	NS	AS	NS	AS	NS	AS
Room to room separation	NR	NR	NR	NR	SR	NR	SR	SR†
Room face to corridor separation	NR	NR	SR‡	NR	SR‡	NR	FR‡	SR†
Room face to common space separation	NR	NR	NR SR‡ ≤50 ft >50 ft (≤15 m)§ (>15 m)§	NR SR‡ ≤50 ft >50 ft (≤15 m)§ (>15 m)§	SR‡	NR SR‡ ≤50 ft >50 ft (≤15 m)§ (>15 m)§	SR‡	SR†
Common space to corridor separation	SR	NR	SR	NR	SR	NR	FR	SR†
Total openings in solid room face where room face is required to be smoke resistant or fire rated#	120 in.² (0.08 m²)	120 in.² (0.08 m²)			120 in.² (0.08 m²)		120 in.² (0.08 m²), closable from inside, or 120 in.² (0.08 m²) with smoke control	

(Header: Use Condition)

NS: Not protected by automatic sprinklers.

AS: Protected by automatic sprinklers.

NR: No requirement.

SR: Smoke resistant.

FR: Fire rated—1 hour.

Notes:

1. Doors in openings in partitions required to be fire rated (FR) in accordance with Table 23.3.8 in other than required enclosures of exits of hazardous areas shall be substantial doors of construction that resists fire for not less than 20 minutes. Vision panels with wired glass or glass with not less than 45-minute fire-rated glazing shall be permitted. Latches and door closers shall not be required on cell doors.

2. Doors in openings in partitions required to be smoke resistant (SR) in accordance with Table 23.3.8 shall be substantial doors of construction that resists the passage of smoke. Latches and door closers shall not be required on cell doors.

3. Under Use Condition II, Use Condition III, or Use Condition IV, a space subdivided by open construction (any combination of grating doors and grating walls or solid walls) shall be permitted to be considered one room if housing not more than 16 persons. The perimeter walls of such space shall be of smoke-resistant construction. Smoke detection shall be provided in such space. Under Use Condition IV, common walls between sleeping areas within the space shall be smoke resistant, and grating doors and fronts shall be permitted to be used. Under Use Condition II and Use Condition III, open dormitories shall be permitted to house more than 16 persons as permitted by other sections of this chapter.

4. Where barriers are required to be smoke resistant (SR), the provisions of 8.2.4 shall not apply.

†Might be no requirement (NR) where one of the following is provided:

(1) An approved automatic smoke detection system installed in all corridors and common spaces.

(2) Multitiered cell blocks meeting the requirements of 23.3.1.3

‡Might be no requirement (NR) in multitiered, open cell blocks meeting the requirements of 23.3.1.3.

§Travel distance through the common space to the exit access corridor.

#"Total openings in solid room face" includes all openings (for example, undercuts, food passes, grilles), the total of which shall not exceed 120 in.² (0.08 m²). All openings shall be 36 in. (91 cm) or less above the floor.

A.22.3.8 The requirements in Table 22.3.8 for smoke-resistant separations include taking the necessary precautions to restrict the spread of smoke through the air-handling system. However, the intent is not that smoke dampers are required to be provided for each opening. Smoke dampers would be one acceptable method; however, other techniques, such as allowing the fans to continue to run with 100 percent supply and 100 percent exhaust, would be acceptable.

A.23.3.8 The requirements in Table 23.3.8 for smoke-resistant and fire-rated separations include taking the necessary precautions to restrict the spread of smoke through the air-handling system. However, the intent is not that smoke dampers are required to be provided for each opening. Smoke dampers would be one acceptable method; however, other techniques, such as allowing the fans to continue to run with 100 percent supply and 100 percent exhaust, would be acceptable.

Paragraph 22/23.3.8 provides for the separation of areas where residents are housed. This separation serves two basic needs: (1) It keeps a fire and its products confined to the area of origin, and (2) it protects those occupants located outside the area of origin. Table 22/23.3.8 establishes individual requirements based on the use condition involved. Where a common wall is used for different purposes, such as "room face to corridor" and "common space to corridor," the most restrictive requirement needs to be applied to the entire wall. Table 22/23.3.8 and its notes specify a wide variety of options in addition to the locking options previously detailed in the chapter. Note 2 to Table 22.3.8 and Note 3 to Table 23.3.8 also allow a space that has been subdivided to be treated as a single room. In combination with the various locking options, this can be quite useful.

Section 22.4 Special Provisions

22.4.1 Windowless Structures.

The provisions of Section 11.7 for windowless structures shall not apply.

Section 23.4 Special Provisions

23.4.1 Windowless Structures.

23.4.1.1 Windowless structures used as detention and correctional occupancies shall comply with 23.4.1.2. The provisions of Section 11.7 for windowless structures shall not apply.

Exception: Buildings protected throughout by an approved automatic sprinkler system in accordance with 23.3.5.3.

23.4.1.2 Means shall be provided to evacuate smoke from the smoke compartment of fire origin. Any of the following means shall be acceptable:

(1)   Operable windows on not less than two sides of the building, spaced not more than 30 ft (9.1 m) apart, that provide openings with dimensions of not less than 22 in. (56 cm) in width and 24 in. (61 cm) in height
(2)*   Manual or automatic smoke vents

A.23.4.1.2(2) The automatic smoke venting should be in accordance with NFPA 204, *Guide for Smoke and Heat Venting*, for light hazard occupancies.

(3)   Engineered smoke control system
(4)   Mechanical exhaust system providing not less than 6 air changes per hour
(5)   Other method acceptable to the authority having jurisdiction

| CHAPTER 22 • New | CHAPTER 23 • Existing |

22.4.2 Underground Buildings.

See Section 11.7 for requirements for underground buildings.

22.4.3 High-Rise Buildings.

High-rise buildings shall comply with 11.8.2.

23.4.2 Underground Buildings.

See Section 11.7 for requirements for underground buildings.

23.4.3 High-Rise Buildings.

Existing high-rise buildings shall be protected throughout by an approved, supervised automatic sprinkler system in accordance with Section 9.7. A sprinkler control valve and a waterflow device shall be provided for each floor.

Paragraph 23.4.1.2 provides a variety of options for evacuating smoke from the smoke compartment of fire origin in windowless buildings.

Paragraph 23.4.3 retroactively requires existing, high-rise detention and correctional occupancy buildings to be protected throughout by approved, supervised automatic sprinkler systems. Addition-

ally, a sprinkler control valve and waterflow device must be provided for each floor. Levels of a multilevel housing area complying with 23.3.1.2 and 23.3.1.3 do not constitute multiple floors and, thus, are not required to be provided with individual control valves and waterflow devices on each level.

22.4.4 Nonsprinklered Existing Building Renovations.

22.4.4.1 General. Modernizations or renovations of nonsprinklered existing buildings shall be permitted to meet the requirements of this chapter as modified by 22.4.4.2 through 22.4.4.13 in lieu of the sprinkler requirement of 22.3.5.2.

Chapter 22 requires that new detention and correctional occupancies be protected throughout by approved, supervised automatic sprinkler systems. See 22.3.5.2. However, some jurisdictions follow policies—often established at the state level—that do not permit automatic sprinklers in detention and correctional facilities. Also, 4.6.7 requires that renovations meet as nearly as practicable the requirements for new construction. In jurisdictions that do not permit sprinklering, if the requirements of Chapter 22 were followed for renovations, but sprinklers were not installed, some needed safeguards might be overlooked. Thus, 22.4.4 presents those additional safeguards that are needed if the facility is not sprinklered. For example, 22.4.4.5.2 establishes for nonsprinklered buildings a maximum travel distance of 150 ft (45 m) between any point in a room and an exit. Had the renovation in the nonsprinklered building been predicated on the provisions of 22.2.6.2, the travel distance limitation would have mistakenly been interpreted to be 200 ft (60 m) between any point

in a room and an exit. The 200-ft (60-m) allowance is intended to apply only to sprinklered buildings.

Subsection 22.4.4 serves as a repository for provisions that were contained in Chapter 22 before sprinklers were mandated for new construction. Its provisions remind the user that the requirements interspersed throughout Chapter 22 are predicated on the presence of sprinkler protection. If sprinklers are not installed, additional requirements must be met in an attempt to achieve a level of life safety approaching that provided in a sprinklered building. However, even if all the former specifications for nonsprinklered buildings are met, the overall level of life safety will not necessarily be the same as that provided in a sprinklered facility. When the 1997 edition of the *Code* presented the first requirement for sprinklering of all new detention and correctional occupancies, the overall level of life safety was elevated from that provided by compliance with the nonsprinklered building option.

22.4.4.2 Minimum Construction Requirements (Nonsprinklered Buildings).

22.4.4.2.1 Detention and correctional occupancies in nonsprinklered buildings shall be limited to the types of building construction permitted by Table 22.4.4.2.1. *(See 8.2.1.)*

Table 22.4.4.2.1 Construction Type Limitations—Nonsprinklered Buildings

Type of Construction	1 Story with Basement	1 Story without Basement	2 Stories	3 Stories	>3 Stories and Not High-Rise	High-Rise
I(443)	X	X	X	X	X	NP
I(332)	X	X	X	X	X	NP
II(222)	X	X	X	X	X	NP
II(111)	X*	X	X*	NP	NP	NP
III(211)	X*	X*	X*	NP	NP	NP
IV(2HH)	X*	X*	X*	NP	NP	NP
V(111)	X*	X*	X*	NP	NP	NP
II(000)	NP	NP	NP	NP	NP	NP
III(200)	NP	NP	NP	NP	NP	NP
V(000)	NP	NP	NP	NP	NP	NP

X: Permitted types of construction.

NP: Not permitted.

*Permitted for other than Use Condition V.

22.4.4.2.2 A residential housing area complying with 22.4.4.6 shall be considered as a one-story building for purposes of applying 22.4.4.2.

22.4.4.3* Horizontal Exit Duct Penetrations (Nonsprinklered Buildings).
Ducts shall be permitted to penetrate horizontal exits in accordance with Exception No. 2 to 7.2.4.3.3 if protected by combination fire dampers/smoke leakage–rated dampers that meet the smoke damper actuation requirements of 8.3.5.

A.22.4.4.3 This provision is intended to promote the use of horizontal exits in detention and correctional occupancies. Horizontal exits provide an especially effective egress system for an occupancy in which the occupants, due to security concerns, are not commonly released to the outside. This provision offers a *Code*-specified equivalent alternative to the Chapter 7 requirement that horizontal exits are not to be penetrated by ducts in nonsprinklered buildings. The intended continuity of the fire resistance–rated and smoke-resisting barrier is maintained by requiring that duct penetrations of horizontal exits be protected by combination fire damper/smoke leakage–rated dampers that will close upon activation of a smoke detector and a heat-actuated mechanism before the barrier's ability to resist the passage of smoke and fire is compromised.

22.4.4.4 Common Path of Travel (Nonsprinklered Buildings). A common path of travel shall not exceed 50 ft (15 m).

22.4.4.5 Travel Distance to Exits (Nonsprinklered Buildings).

22.4.4.5.1 The travel distance between any room door required as an exit access and an exit shall not exceed 100 ft (30 m).

22.4.4.5.2 The travel distance between any point in a room and an exit shall not exceed 150 ft (45 m).

22.4.4.6 Protection of Vertical Openings (Nonsprinklered Buildings).

22.4.4.6.1 Multilevel residential housing areas without enclosure protection between levels shall be permitted, provided that the conditions of 22.4.4.6.2 through 22.4.4.6.4 are met.

22.4.4.6.2* The entire normally occupied area, including all communicating floor levels, shall be sufficiently open and unobstructed so that a fire or other dangerous condition in any part is obvious to the occupants or supervisory personnel in the area.

A.22.4.4.6.2 It is not the intent of this requirement to restrict room face separations, which restrict visibility from the common space into individual sleeping rooms.

22.4.4.6.3 Egress capacity shall simultaneously accommodate all occupants of all communicating levels and areas, with all communicating levels in the same fire area considered as a single floor area for purposes of determining required egress capacity.

22.4.4.6.4* The height between the highest and lowest finished floor levels shall not exceed 13 ft (4 m). The number of levels shall not be restricted.

A.22.4.4.6.4 The vertical separation between the lowest floor level and the uppermost floor level is not to exceed 13 ft (4 m). Figure A.22.4.4.6.4 illustrates how the height is to be determined.

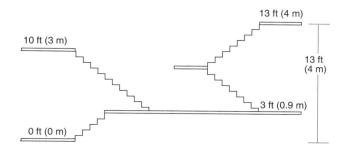

Figure A.22.4.4.6.4 Vertical height measurement.

22.4.4.7 Hazardous Areas (Nonsprinklered Buildings). Any hazardous area shall be protected in accordance with Section 8.4. The areas described in the Table 22.4.4.7 shall be protected as indicated.

Table 22.4.4.7 Hazardous Area Protection—
Nonsprinklered Buildings

Hazardous Area Description	Separation/Protection
Areas not incidental to resident housing	2 hours
Boiler and fuel-fired heater rooms	2 hours or 1 hour and sprinklers
Central or bulk laundries >100 ft² (>9.3 m²)	2 hours or 1 hour and sprinklers
Commercial cooking equipment	In accordance with 9.2.3
Commissaries	1 hour or sprinklers
Employee locker rooms	1 hour or sprinklers
Hobby/handicraft shops	1 hour or sprinklers
Maintenance shops	1 hour or sprinklers
Padded cells	2 hours or 1 hour and sprinklers
Soiled linen rooms	2 hours or 1 hour and sprinklers
Storage rooms >50 ft² (>4.6 m²) in area but ≤100 ft² (≤9.3 m²) in area storing combustible material	1 hour or sprinklers
Storage rooms >100 ft² (>9.3 m²) storing combustible materials	2 hours or 1 hour and sprinklers
Trash collection rooms	2 hours or 1 hour and sprinklers

22.4.4.8 Interior Finish (Nonsprinklered Buildings).

22.4.4.8.1 Interior Wall and Ceiling Finish. Interior wall and ceiling finish complying with 10.2.3 shall be Class A in corridors, in exits, and in any space not separated from corridors and exits by partitions capable of retarding the passage of smoke; and Class A, Class B, or Class C in all other areas.

22.4.4.8.2 Interior Floor Finish. Interior floor finish complying with 10.2.7 shall be Class I in corridors and exits.

22.4.4.9 Detection, Alarm, and Communications Systems (Nonsprinklered Buildings).

22.4.4.9.1 Initiation. Initiation of the fire alarm system required by 22.3.4.1.1 shall be by manual means in accordance with 9.6.2 and by means of any required detection devices or detection systems.

Exception No. 1: Manual fire alarm boxes shall be permitted to be locked, provided that staff is present within the area when it is occupied and staff has keys readily available to unlock the boxes.

Exception No. 2: Manual fire alarm boxes shall be permitted to be located in a staff location, provided that the staff location is attended when the building is occupied and that the staff attendant has direct supervision of the sleeping area.

22.4.4.9.2 Detection. An approved automatic smoke detection system shall be in accordance with Section 9.6, as modified by 22.4.4.9.2.1 and 22.4.4.9.2.2, throughout all resident sleeping areas and adjacent day rooms, activity rooms, or contiguous common spaces.

22.4.4.9.2.1 Smoke detectors shall not be required in sleeping rooms with four or fewer occupants in Use Condition II or Use Condition III.

22.4.4.9.2.2 Other arrangements and positioning of smoke detectors shall be permitted to prevent damage or tampering, or for other purposes. Such arrangements shall be capable of detecting any fire, and the placement of detectors shall be such that the speed of detection is equivalent to that provided by the spacing and arrangements required by the installation standards referenced in Section 9.6. Detectors shall be permitted to be located in exhaust ducts from cells, behind grilles, or in other locations. The equivalent performance of the design, however, shall be acceptable to the authority having jurisdiction in accordance with the equivalency concepts specified in Section 1.5.

22.4.4.10 Subdivision of Building Spaces (Nonsprinklered Buildings). Where smoke barriers are required by 22.3.7.1, they shall be provided as follows:

(1) They shall limit the occupant load to not more than 200 residents in any smoke compartment.

(2) They shall limit the travel distance to a door in a smoke barrier as follows:

　a. The distance from any room door required as exit access shall not exceed 100 ft (30 m).

　b. The distance from any point in a room shall not exceed 150 ft (45 m).

22.4.4.11* Subdivision of Resident Housing Spaces (Non-sprinklered Buildings). Subdivision of facility spaces shall comply with Table 22.4.4.11.

Table 22.4.4.11 Subdivision of Resident Housing Spaces — Nonsprinklered Buildings

Feature	Use Condition			
	II	**III**	**IV**	**V**
Room to room separation	NR	NR	SR	FR(½)
Room face to corridor separation	SR	SR	SR	FR
Room face to common space separation	NR	NR　　　　SR ≤50 ft　　>50 ft (≤15 m)†　(>15 m)†	SR	FR
Common space to corridor separation	FR	FR	FR	FR
Total openings in solid room face where room face is required to be smoke resistant or fire rated‡	120 in.² (0.08 m²)	120 in.² (0.08 m²)	120 in.² (0.08 m²)	120 in.² (0.08 m²), closable from inside, or 120 in.² (0.08 m²) with smoke control

NR: No requirement.

SR; Smoke resistant.

FR(½): Fire rated—½ hour.

FR: Fire rated—1 hour.

Notes:

1. Doors in openings in partitions required to be fire rated (FR(½), FR) in accordance with Table 22.4.4.11 in other than required enclosures of exits or hazardous areas shall be substantial doors of construction that resists fire for not less than 20 minutes. Vision panels with wired glass or glass with not less than 45-minute fire-rated glazing shall be permitted. Latches and door closers shall not be required on cell doors.

2. Doors in openings in partitions required to be smoke resistant (SR) in accordance with Table 22.4.4.11 shall be substantial doors of construction that resists the passage of smoke. Latches and door closers shall not be required on cell doors.

3. Under Use Condition II, Use Condition III, or Use Condition IV, a space subdivided by open construction (any combination of grating doors and grating walls or solid walls) shall be permitted to be considered one room if housing not more than 16 persons. The perimeter walls of such space shall be of smoke-resistant construction. Smoke detection shall be provided in such space. Under use Condition IV, common walls between sleeping areas within the space shall be smoke resistant, and grating doors and fronts shall be permitted to be used. In Condition II and Use Condition III, open dormitories shall be permitted to house more than 16 persons as permitted by other sections of this chapter.

4. Where barriers are required to be smoke resistant (SR), the provisions of 8.2.4 shall not apply.

†Travel distance through the common space to the exit access corridor.

‡"Total openings in solid room face" includes all openings (for example, undercuts, food passes, grilles), the total of which shall not exceed 120 in.² (0.08 m²). All openings shall be 36 in. (91 cm) or less above the floor.

A.22.4.4.11 The requirements in Table 22.4.4.11 for smoke-resistant and fire-rated separations include taking the necessary precautions to restrict the spread of smoke through the air-handling system. However, the intent is that smoke dampers are required to be provided for each opening. Smoke dampers would be one acceptable method; however, other techniques, such as allowing the fans to continue to run with 100 percent supply and 100 percent exhaust, would be acceptable.

22.4.4.12 Windowless Structures (Nonsprinklered Buildings).

22.4.4.12.1 Windowless structures used as detention and correctional occupancies shall comply with 22.4.4.12.2. The provisions of Section 11.7 for windowless structures shall not apply.

22.4.4.12.2 Means shall be provided to evacuate smoke from the smoke compartment of fire origin. Any of the following means shall be acceptable:

(1) Operable windows on not less than two sides of the building, spaced not more than 30 ft (9.1 m) apart, that provide openings with dimensions of not less than 22 in. (56 cm) in width and 24 in. (61 cm) in height

(2)* Manual or automatic smoke vents

A.22.4.4.12.2(2) The automatic smoke venting should be in accordance with NFPA 204, *Guide for Smoke and Heat Venting*, for light hazard occupancies.

(3) Engineered smoke control system

(4) Mechanical exhaust system providing not less than 6 air changes per hour

(5) Other method acceptable to the authority having jurisdiction

22.4.4.13* Furnishings, Bedding, and Decorations (Nonsprinklered Buildings).

A.22.4.4.13 Personal property provides combustible contents for fire development. Therefore, adequate controls are needed to limit the quantity and combustibility of fuels available to burn to reduce the probability of room flashover. The provisions of 22.4.4.13 will not, by themselves, prevent room flashover if personal property controls are not provided.

22.4.4.13.1 Newly introduced upholstered furniture within detention and correctional occupancies shall be tested in accordance with the provisions of 10.3.2(2) and 10.3.3.

22.4.4.13.2* Newly introduced mattresses within detention and correctional occupancies shall be tested in accordance with the provisions of 10.3.2(3) and 10.3.4.

A.22.4.4.13.2 Mattresses used in detention and correctional facilities should be evaluated with regard to the fire hazards of the environment. The potential for vandalism and excessive wear and tear also should be taken into account when evaluating the fire performance of the mattress.

Section 22.5 Building Services

22.5.1 Utilities.

22.5.1.1 Utilities shall comply with the provisions of Section 9.1.

22.5.1.2 Alarms, emergency communication systems, and the illumination of generator set locations shall be provided with emergency power in accordance with NFPA 70, *National Electrical Code.*

22.5.2 Heating, Ventilating, and Air Conditioning.

22.5.2.1 Heating, ventilating, and air conditioning equipment shall comply with the provisions of Section 9.2 and shall be installed in accordance with the manufacturer's specifications.

Exception: As modified in 22.5.2.2.

22.5.2.2 Portable space-heating devices shall be prohibited. Any heating device other than a central heating plant shall be designed and installed so that combustible material shall not be ignited by the device or its appurtenances. If fuel-fired, such heating devices shall be chimney connected or vent connected, shall take air for combustion directly from outside, and shall be designed and installed to provide for complete separation of the combustion system from the atmosphere of the occupied area. The heating system shall have safety devices to immediately stop the flow of fuel and shut down the equipment in case of either excessive temperatures or ignition failure.

Exception: Approved, suspended unit heaters shall be permitted in locations other than means of egress and sleeping areas, provided that such heaters are located high enough to be out of the reach of persons using the area and are vent connected and equipped with the safety devices required by 22.5.2.2.

Section 23.5 Building Services

23.5.1 Utilities.

23.5.1.1 Utilities shall comply with the provisions of Section 9.1.

23.5.1.2 Alarms, emergency communication systems, and the illumination of generator set installations shall be provided with emergency power in accordance with NFPA 70, *National Electrical Code.*

Exception: Systems complying with earlier editions of NFPA 70, National Electrical Code, and not presenting a life safety hazard shall be permitted to continue to be used.

23.5.2 Heating, Ventilating, and Air Conditioning.

23.5.2.1 Heating, ventilating, and air conditioning equipment shall comply with the provisions of Section 9.2 and shall be installed in accordance with the manufacturer's specifications.

Exception No. 1: As modified in 23.5.2.2.

Exception No. 2: Systems complying with earlier editions of the applicable codes and not presenting a life safety hazard shall be permitted to continue to be used.

23.5.2.2 Portable space-heating devices shall be prohibited. Any heating device other than a central heating plant shall be designed and installed so that combustible material shall not be ignited by the device or its appurtenances. If fuel-fired, such heating devices shall be chimney connected or vent connected, shall take air for combustion directly from outside, and shall be designed and installed to provide for complete separation of the combustion system from the atmosphere of the occupied area. The heating system shall have safety devices to immediately stop the flow of fuel and shut down the equipment in case of either excessive temperatures or ignition failure.

Exception: Approved, suspended unit heaters shall be permitted in locations other than means of egress and sleeping areas, provided that such heaters are located high enough to be out of the reach of persons using the area and are vent connected and equipped with the safety devices required by 23.5.2.2.

22.5.2.3 Combustion and ventilation air for boiler, incinerator, or heater rooms shall be taken directly from and discharged directly to the outside.

22.5.3 Elevators, Escalators, and Conveyors.

Elevators, escalators, and conveyors shall comply with the provisions of Section 9.4.

22.5.4 Rubbish Chutes, Incinerators, and Laundry Chutes.

22.5.4.1 Rubbish chutes, incinerators, and laundry chutes shall comply with the provisions of Section 9.5.

22.5.4.2 Any rubbish chute or linen chute, including pneumatic rubbish and linen systems, shall be provided with automatic extinguishing protection in accordance with Section 9.7.

22.5.4.3 Any trash chute shall discharge into a trash collection room used for no other purpose and protected in accordance with Section 8.4.

22.5.4.4 Any incinerator shall not be directly flue-fed, nor shall any floor chute directly connect with the combustion chamber.

Section 22.6 Reserved

Section 22.7 Operating Features

22.7.1 Attendants, Evacuation Plan, Fire Drills.

22.7.1.1 Detention and correctional facilities, or those portions of facilities having such occupancy, shall be provided with 24-hour staffing. Staff shall be within three floors or a 300-ft (91-m) horizontal distance of the access door of each resident housing area.

In addition, for Use Condition III, Use Condition IV, and Use Condition V, the arrangement shall be such that the staff involved starts the release of locks necessary for emergency evacuation or rescue and initiates other necessary emergency actions within 2 minutes of alarm.

Exception: For areas in which all locks are unlocked remotely in compliance with 22.2.11.6, staff shall not be required to be within three floors or 300 ft (104 m) of the access door. The exception to 22.2.11.6 shall not be used in conjunction with this exception.

23.5.2.3 Combustion and ventilation air for boiler, incinerator, or heater rooms shall be taken directly from and discharged directly to the outside.

23.5.3 Elevators, Escalators, and Conveyors.

Elevators, escalators, and conveyors shall comply with the provisions of Section 9.4.

23.5.4 Rubbish Chutes, Incinerators, and Laundry Chutes.

23.5.4.1 Rubbish chutes, incinerators, and laundry chutes shall comply with the provisions of Section 9.5.

23.5.4.2 Any rubbish chute or linen chute, including pneumatic rubbish and linen systems, shall be provided with automatic extinguishing protection in accordance with Section 9.7.

23.5.4.3 Any trash chute shall discharge into a trash collection room used for no other purpose and protected in accordance with Section 8.4.

23.5.4.4 Any incinerator shall not be directly flue-fed, nor shall any floor chute directly connect with the combustion chamber.

Section 23.6 Reserved

Section 23.7 Operating Features

23.7.1 Attendants, Evacuation Plan, Fire Drills.

23.7.1.1 Detention and correctional facilities, or those portions of facilities having such occupancy, shall be provided with 24-hour staffing. Staff shall be within three floors or a 300-ft (91-m) horizontal distance of the access door of each resident housing area.

In addition, for Use Condition III, Use Condition IV, and Use Condition V, the arrangement shall be such that the staff involved starts the release of locks necessary for emergency evacuation or rescue and initiates other necessary emergency actions within 2 minutes of alarm.

Exception: For areas in which all locks are unlocked remotely in compliance with 23.2.11.6, staff shall not be required to be within three floors or 300 ft (194 m) of the access door. The exception to 23.2.11.6 shall not be used in conjunction with this exception.

22.7.1.2* Provisions shall be made so that residents in Use Condition III, Use Condition IV, and Use Condition V shall be able to notify staff of an emergency.

A.22.7.1.2 This requirement is permitted to be met by electronic or oral monitoring systems, visual monitoring, call signals, or other means.

22.7.1.3* The administration of every detention or correctional facility shall have, in effect and available to all supervisory personnel, written copies of a plan for the protection of all persons in the event of fire, for their evacuation to areas of refuge, and for evacuation from the building when necessary. All employees shall be instructed and drilled with respect to their duties under the plan. The plan shall be coordinated with and reviewed by the fire department legally committed to serve the facility.

A.22.7.1.3 Periodic, coordinated training should be conducted and should involve detention and correctional facility personnel and personnel of the fire department legally committed to serving the facility.

22.7.1.4 Employees of detention and correctional occupancies shall be instructed in the proper use of portable fire extinguishers and other manual fire suppression equipment. Such training shall be provided to new staff promptly upon commencement of duty. Refresher training shall be provided to existing staff at not less than annual intervals.

22.7.2 Books, clothing, and other combustible personal property allowed in sleeping rooms shall be stored in closable metal lockers or a fire-resistant container.

22.7.3 The number of heat-producing appliances, such as toasters and hot plates, and the overall use of electrical power within a sleeping room shall be controlled by facility administration.

22.7.4* Furnishings, Bedding, and Decorations.

A.22.7.4 Personal property provides combustible contents for fire development. Therefore, adequate controls are needed to limit the quantity and combustibility of the fuels available to burn to reduce the probability of room flashover. The provisions of 22.7.4 will not, by themselves, prevent room flashover if personal property controls are not provided.

22.7.4.1 Draperies and curtains, including privacy curtains, in detention and correctional occupancies shall be in accordance with the provisions of 10.3.1.

23.7.1.2* Provisions shall be made so that residents in Use Condition III, Use Condition IV, and Use Condition V shall be able to notify staff of an emergency.

A.23.7.1.2 This requirement is permitted to be met by electronic or oral monitoring systems, visual monitoring, call signals, or other means.

23.7.1.3* The administration of every detention or correctional facility shall have, in effect and available to all supervisory personnel, written copies of a plan for the protection of all persons in the event of fire, for their evacuation to areas of refuge, and for evacuation from the building when necessary. All employees shall be instructed and drilled with respect to their duties under the plan. The plan shall be coordinated with and reviewed by the fire department legally committed to serve the facility.

A.23.7.1.3 Periodic, coordinated training should be conducted and should involve detention and correctional facility personnel and personnel of the fire department legally committed to serving the facility.

23.7.1.4 Employees of detention and correctional occupancies shall be instructed in the proper use of portable fire extinguishers and other manual fire suppression equipment. Such training shall be provided to new staff promptly upon commencement of duty. Refresher training shall be provided to existing staff at not less than annual intervals.

23.7.2 Books, clothing, and other combustible personal property allowed in sleeping rooms shall be stored in closable metal lockers or a fire-resistant container.

23.7.3 The number of heat-producing appliances, such as toasters and hot plates, and the overall use of electrical power within a sleeping room shall be controlled by facility administration.

23.7.4* Furnishings, Bedding, and Decorations.

A.23.7.4 Personal property provides combustible contents for fire development. Therefore, adequate controls are needed to limit the quantity and combustibility of the fuels available to burn to reduce the probability of room flashover. The provisions of 23.7.4 will not, by themselves, prevent room flashover if personal property controls are not provided.

23.7.4.1 Draperies and curtains, including privacy curtains, in detention and correctional occupancies shall be in accordance with the provisions of 10.3.1.

CHAPTER 22 • New

CHAPTER 23 • Existing

22.7.4.2 (Reserved.)

22.7.4.3 (Reserved.)

22.7.4.4 Combustible decorations shall be prohibited in any detention or correctional occupancy unless flame-retardant.

22.7.4.5 Wastebaskets and other waste containers shall be of noncombustible or other approved materials. Waste containers with a capacity exceeding 20 gal (76 L) shall be provided with a noncombustible lid or lid of other approved material.

22.7.5 Keys.

All keys necessary for unlocking doors installed in a means of egress shall be individually identified by both touch and sight.

22.7.6 Portable Space-Heating Devices.

Portable space-heating devices shall be prohibited in all detention and correctional occupancies.

23.7.4.2 Newly introduced upholstered furniture within detention and correctional occupancies shall be tested in accordance with the provisions of 10.3.2(2) and 10.3.3.

23.7.4.3* Newly introduced mattresses within detention and correctional occupancies shall be tested in accordance with the provisions of 10.3.2(3) and 10.3.4.

A.23.7.4.3 Mattresses used in detention and correctional facilities should be evaluated with regard to the fire hazards of the environment. The potential for vandalism and excessive wear and tear also should be taken into account when evaluating the fire performance of the mattress.

23.7.4.4 Combustible decorations shall be prohibited in any detention or correctional occupancy unless flame-retardant.

23.7.4.5 Wastebaskets and other waste containers shall be of noncombustible or other approved materials. Waste containers with a capacity exceeding 20 gal (76 L) shall be provided with a noncombustible lid or lid of other approved material.

23.7.5 Keys.

All keys necessary for unlocking doors installed in a means of egress shall be individually identified by both touch and sight.

23.7.6 Portable Space-Heating Devices.

Portable space-heating devices shall be prohibited in all detention and correctional occupancies.

Paragraph 22/23.7.1.2 requires that residents be able to notify staff of an emergency. Use Condition IV and Use Condition V facilities rely on staff action to release locks to allow residents to leave their rooms; Use Condition III, Use Condition IV, and Use Condition V facilities rely on staff action to release locks to allow residents to move to an adjacent smoke compartment. The staff needs to be made aware of fire conditions early in a fire. Thus, residents might discover a fire before automatic detection devices are initiated and need a means of notifying staff.

A properly designed and well-tested fire emergency plan, as required by 22/23.7.1.3, is important in detention and correctional occupancies where residents depend heavily on staff performance for safety under fire conditions.

The provisions of 22/23.7.4 make use of the menu of provisions in Section 10.3 that apply to furnishings and contents, particularly those that address uphol-

stered furniture and mattresses. Nevertheless, to prevent the occurrence of room flashover in the small room spaces characteristic of detention and correctional occupancies, the control of combustible personal property is also very important.

The provisions of 22/23.7.4.1 through 22/23.7.4.5—and the corresponding provisions applicable to health care occupancies—present the most vigorous regulations of contents and furnishings by this *Code*. It is appropriate that this be done for detention and correctional occupancies in consideration of the protect-in-place strategy required of this occupancy by the *Code* and the reluctance of staff to unlock doors to allow residents to move to the outside.

Draperies and curtains must be flame resistant. Paragraphs 23.7.4.2 and 23.7.4.3 require newly introduced upholstered furniture and mattresses to be resistant to cigarette ignition and have limited rates of heat release if the space is not sprinklered. Paragraphs 22.7.4.2 and 22.7.4.3 are shown as reserved because new detention and correctional occupancies are required to be sprinklered. Therefore, in a sprinklered detention and correctional occupancy space, neither upholstered furniture nor mattresses are regulated on the assumption that the sprinklers will prevent room flashover.

References Cited in Commentary

1. NFPA 101A, *Guide on Alternative Approaches to Life Safety*, National Fire Protection Association, Quincy, MA. (The edition of NFPA 101A that corresponds with the 2000 *Life Safety Code* will be published in 2001.)

2. NFPA 220, *Standard on Types of Building Construction*, 1999 edition, National Fire Protection Association, Quincy, MA.
3. NFPA 30, *Flammable and Combustible Liquids Code*, 1996 edition, National Fire Protection Association, Quincy, MA.
4. NFPA 255, *Standard Method of Test of Surface Burning Characteristics of Building Materials*, 2000 edition, National Fire Protection Association, Quincy, MA.
5. NFPA 253, *Standard Method of Test for Critical Radiant Flux of Floor Covering Systems Using a Radiant Heat Energy Source*, 2000 edition, National Fire Protection Association, Quincy, MA.
6. NFPA 13, *Standard for the Installation of Sprinkler Systems*, 1999 edition, National Fire Protection Association, Quincy, MA.

CHAPTER 24

One- and Two-Family Dwellings

Although most people feel safest in their homes, fire deaths in the home account for some 65 percent of all fatalities attributable to fire in the United States. Chapter 24 highlights a number of factors that significantly mitigate the fire problem. A key and unique component that is addressed in this chapter, and that is selectively applied to the other residential chapters, is the means of escape (see Section 24.2). The concept of means of escape focuses on providing a second way out of an occupied room or space within a living unit, regardless of whether it is a single family home or a dwelling unit within an apartment building. Means of escape features do not need to meet the high standards and criteria that apply to the means of egress. In short, means of escape is an important yet broadly applied concept that is intended to reduce the chance of occupants becoming trapped in a room or space if the primary egress route is unavailable.

As in other occupancy chapters, the provisions of Chapter 24 achieve their intended level of safety by regulating the interior wall and ceiling finish and mandating the installation of smoke alarms. As is the case in other residential occupancies, a few carefully implemented features greatly improve the safety of occupants.

Section 24.1 General Requirements

24.1.1 Application.

24.1.1.1* This chapter establishes life safety requirements for all one- and two-family dwellings. One- and two-family dwellings include buildings containing not more than two dwelling units in which each dwelling unit is occupied by members of a single family with not more than three outsiders, if any, accommodated in rented rooms.

A.24.1.1.1 The *Code* specifies that wherever there are three or more living units in a building, the building is considered an apartment building and is required to comply with either Chapter 30 or Chapter 31, as appropriate. A townhouse unit is considered to be an apartment building if there are three or more units in the building. The type of wall required between units in order to consider them as separate buildings is normally established by the authority having jurisdiction. If the units be separated by a wall of sufficient fire resistance and structural integrity to be considered as separate buildings, then the provisions of Chapter 24 apply to each townhouse. Condominium is a form of ownership, not occupancy; for example, there are condominium warehouses, condominium apartments, and condominium offices.

The provisions of 24.1.1.1 state that, in one- and two-family dwellings, each dwelling unit can be "occupied by members of a single family with not more than three outsiders." The *Code* does not define the term family. The definition of family is subject to federal, state, and local regulations and might not be restricted to a person or a couple (two people) and their children. The following examples aid in differentiating between a single-family dwelling and a lodging or rooming house:

(1) An individual or a couple (two people) who rent a house from a landlord and then sublease space for up to three individuals should be considered a family renting to a maximum of three outsiders, and the house should be regulated as a single-family dwelling in accordance with Chapter 24.

(2) A house rented from a landlord by an individual or a couple (two people) in which space is subleased to four or more individuals, but not more than 16, should be considered and regulated as a lodging or rooming house in accordance with Chapter 26.

(3) A residential building that is occupied by four or more individuals, but not more than 16, each renting from a landlord, without separate cooking facilities, should be

considered and regulated as a lodging or rooming house in accordance with Chapter 26.

Considerable debate has centered on the term *family*. It is not the intent of 24.1.1.1 to define the term; however, A.24.1.1.1 provides assistance in determining where the term family is inappropriate and another chapter of the *Code* is to be used. If more than three outsiders are accommodated in a building, the building should be classified as a lodging or rooming house and should be arranged to meet the requirements of Chapter 26. The reasoning behind this classification guideline is that outsiders keep each other less informed about conditions within the building and more often keep their room doors closed when occupying their rooms than do family members. The lack of communication and reduced openness and awareness justify the additional alarm system, vertical opening, and corridor wall and door requirements that apply to lodging and rooming houses.

24.1.1.2 The requirements of this chapter apply to new buildings and to existing or modified buildings according to the provisions of 1.4.1 of this *Code*.

24.1.2 Mixed Occupancies.

24.1.2.1 Where another type of occupancy exists in the same building as a residential occupancy, the requirements of 6.1.14 of this *Code* shall apply.

24.1.2.2 No dwelling unit of a residential occupancy shall have its sole means of egress pass through any nonresidential occupancy in the same building.

24.1.2.3 No multiple-dwelling unit of a residential occupancy shall be located above any nonresidential occupancy.

Exception No. 1: Where the dwelling unit of the residential occupancy and exits therefrom are separated from the non-residential occupancy by construction having a fire resistance rating of not less than 1 hour.

Exception No. 2: Where the nonresidential occupancy is protected throughout by an approved, supervised automatic sprinkler system in accordance with Section 9.7.

Exception No. 3: Where the nonresidential occupancy is protected by an automatic fire detection system in accordance with Section 9.6.

One- and two-family dwellings are commonly found above stores, offices, and restaurants. Locating these occupancies in proximity to each other presents a life

safety challenge for the occupants of the residential dwellings. The typical configuration of these buildings creates the potential for a significant time lapse before occupants of the residential dwellings become aware of an emergency in another part of the building and take the necessary action. The provisions of 24.1.2.2 and 24.1.2.3 are intended to provide added protection for the residential occupancy during that lapse. Therefore, these requirements are intended to apply wherever such a mixture of occupancies exists, whether in new construction or existing buildings.

24.1.3 Definitions.

Terms applicable to this chapter are defined in Chapter 3 of this *Code;* where necessary, other terms are defined in the text.

24.1.4 Classification of Occupancy.

(See 24.1.1.1.)

24.1.5 Classification of Hazard of Contents.

The contents of residential occupancies shall be classified as ordinary hazard in accordance with 6.2.2.

NFPA 13, *Standard for the Installation of Sprinkler Systems,* classifies the contents of a dwelling as light hazard for the purpose of designing automatic sprinkler systems.[1] The difference in classification in the *Code* is based on the threat to life or life safety (ordinary), as opposed to the challenge to the extinguishing capability of the automatic sprinkler system (light).

24.1.6 Minimum Construction Requirements.

(No special requirements.)

24.1.7 Occupant Load.

(No requirements.)

24-2* Means of Escape Requirements

A.24.2 The phrase "means of escape" indicates a way out of a residential unit that does not conform to the strict definition of means of egress but does meet the intent of the definition by providing an alternative way out of a building. *(See A.7.1.1 and means of escape in 3.3.122.)*

24.2.1 General.

The provisions of Chapter 7 shall not apply to means of escape unless specifically referenced in this chapter.

In 24.2.1, the term *means of escape* is used in contrast to the usual *means of egress*, because the escape paths required for a dwelling need not be the true exit access, exit, and exit discharge required for public buildings. The concept of means of escape is fully developed in Section 24.2. The intent is that at least one means of escape (primary) be of a high degree of quality that is similar to the means of egress components described in Chapter 7. Homes rarely have an exit arrangement complying with Chapter 7. The door through which occupants normally enter and leave the dwelling can typically serve as the primary means of escape. Another way out of the dwelling, such as through a large, operable window, is needed as the secondary means of escape. A secondary means of escape needs to be available for use if the route involving the primary means of escape becomes unusable during a fire or similar emergency.

Unless Chapter 24 specifically references a means of egress provision of Chapter 7, only the means of escape requirements of Chapter 24 are required to be met. See 24.2.5.1, which mandatorily references the use of the provisions of 7.2.2 and 7.2.5 for stairs, ramps, and associated guards and handrails.

24.2.2 Number and Types of Means of Escape.

24.2.2.1 Number of Means of Escape.
In any dwelling or dwelling unit of two rooms or more, every sleeping room and every living area shall have not less than one primary means of escape and one secondary means of escape.

See the definition of *living area* in 3.3.119.

Exception: A secondary means of escape shall not be required where one of the following conditions are met:

(a) The bedroom or living area has a door leading directly to the outside of the building at or to grade level.

(b) The dwelling unit is protected throughout by an approved automatic sprinkler system in accordance with 24.3.5.

The benefit of two means of escape is based on the same concept as the requirements for two means of egress in other occupancies. Two separate means of escape reduce the possibility of a person becoming trapped if one of the paths is obstructed by fire.

A secondary means of escape from each bedroom or living area is not required if the bedroom or living area has a door opening directly to the outside of the building, at or to grade level, or if the dwelling unit is protected throughout by an approved automatic sprinkler system. In order to be acceptable, the sprinkler system must be installed in accordance with one of the following:

(1) NFPA 13, *Standard for the Installation of Sprinkler Systems*
(2) NFPA 13D, *Standard for the Installation of Sprinkler Systems in One- and Two-Family Dwellings and Manufactured Homes*[2]
(3) NFPA 13R, *Standard for the Installation of Sprinkler Systems in Residential Occupancies up to and Including Four Stories in Height*[3]

The sprinkler exception in subpart (b) of the exception to 24.2.2.1 is probably the most practical and common way to avoid providing a secondary means of escape. The exception might be used, for example, in an underground dwelling without windows or in a dwelling where the windows do not comply with 24.2.2.3(c).

24.2.2.2 Primary Means of Escape.
The primary means of escape shall be a door, stairway, or ramp providing a means of unobstructed travel to the outside of the dwelling unit at street or ground level.

Note that a door, stairway, or ramp providing a means of unobstructed travel to the outside is usually provided for the functional purposes of entering and leaving the dwelling. Therefore, the requirement for a primary means of escape is almost automatically met in a typical dwelling.

An attic bedroom, for example, that is accessible only by means of a trap door or folding ladder, would not have a *Code*-complying primary means of escape. See 24.2.5.4. Direct stair access would be required.

24.2.2.3* Secondary Means of Escape.
The secondary means of escape shall be one of the following.

A.24.2.2.3 For use of emergency escape devices, refer to A.7.1.1.

(a) It shall be a door, stairway, passage, or hall providing a way of unobstructed travel to the outside of the dwelling at street or ground level that is independent of and remote from the primary means of escape.

(b) It shall be a passage through an adjacent nonlockable space, independent of and remote from the primary means of escape, to any approved means of escape.

(c)* It shall be an outside window or door operable from the inside without the use of tools, keys, or special effort and shall provide a clear opening of not less than 5.7 ft² (0.53 m²). The width shall be not less than 20 in. (51 cm), and the height shall be not less than 24 in. (61 cm). The bottom of the opening shall be not more than 44 in. (112 cm) above the floor. Such means of escape shall be acceptable where one of the following criteria are met:

(1) The window shall be within 20 ft (6.1 m) of grade.
(2) The window shall be directly accessible to fire department rescue apparatus as approved by the authority having jurisdiction.
(3) The window or door shall open onto an exterior balcony.
(4) The window shall have a sill height below the adjacent ground level and shall be provided with a window well meeting the following criteria:

   a. The window well shall have horizontal dimensions that allow the window to be fully opened.
   b. The window well shall have an accessible net clear opening of not less than 9 ft² (0.82 m²) with a length and width of not less than 36 in. (91.4 cm).
   c. A window well with a vertical depth of more than 44 in. (112 cm) shall be equipped with an approved permanently affixed ladder or with steps meeting the following criteria:

      1. The ladder or steps shall not encroach more than 6 in. (15.2 cm) into the required dimensions of the window well.
      2. The ladder or steps shall not be obstructed by the window.

Ladders or steps that comply with the requirements of 24.2.2.3(c)(4)c shall be exempt from the requirements of 7.2.2.

Exception: Existing approved means of escape.

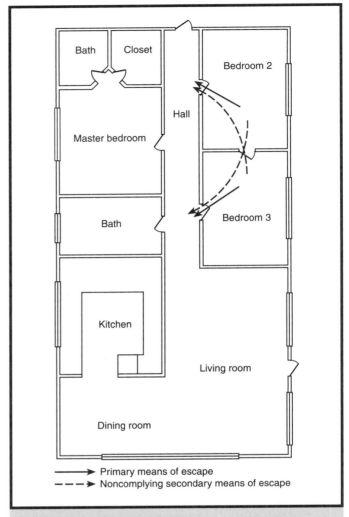

Exhibit 24.1 *Noncomplying secondary means of escape arrangement.*

The purpose of the secondary means of escape is to provide an occupant with an alternate escape route when fire or smoke blocks the normal means of escape from the dwelling unit. Paragraph 24.2.2.3 permits the use of the following three types of secondary means of escape.

(a) It is the intent of 24.2.2.3(a) that the door, stairway, passage, or hall serving as the secondary means of escape be independent of, and remote from, the primary means of escape required by 24.2.2.2. Exhibit 24.1 illustrates a dwelling unit where none of the windows complies with the requirements of 24.2.2.3(c) and a nonlockable door is located between bedrooms 2 and 3. As a result, both the primary and secondary means of escape from bedrooms 2 and 3 lead into the same hallway. A fire in or near this hallway would impact both means of escape for these rooms. If the hallway within the dwelling unit is separated from all living spaces and leads to two separate ways out of the dwelling unit, it might be judged that the hallway does, in fact, lead to two separate, independent, and remote means of escape.

Two doors leading out of a sleeping room might not be practical or effective in most single-family dwellings. In the apartment illustrated in Exhibit 24.2, bedrooms 1 and 2 each have a window (WNC) that does not comply as a secondary means of escape. In bedroom 1, a door that meets the criteria of being independent and remote from the main door provides the secondary means of escape. Bedrooms 2 and 3 are provided with compliant windows (W) as

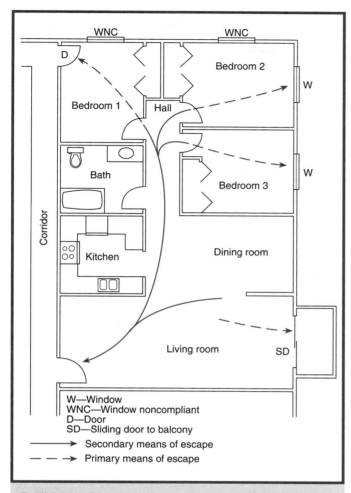

Exhibit 24.2 *Secondary means of escape arrangement complying with 24.2.2.*

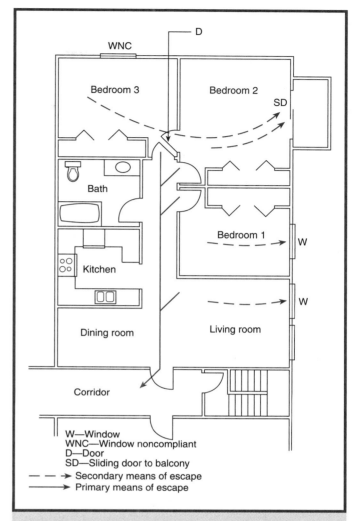

Exhibit 24.3 *Alternative secondary means of escape arrangement complying with 24.2.2.*

their secondary means of escape, and the living space has a compliant sliding glass door to the balcony.

(b) Passage through an adjacent nonlockable space, as addressed by 24.2.2.3(b), is illustrated in Exhibit 24.3. In this illustration bedroom 3 has a window (WNC) that does not comply with the provisions of 24.2.2.3(c); however, there is a compliant door (D) between bedrooms 3 and 2 that provides a secondary means of escape using the compliant sliding door in bedroom 2 to the balcony.

(c) The use of an operable window providing an opening of the minimum dimensions specified in 24.2.2.3(c) is the secondary means of escape most often provided. Exhibit 24.4 illustrates the minimum dimensions required for escape windows. Note that a window providing only the minimum width and minimum height dimensions specified by 24.2.2.3(c) does not provide the required minimum area; if ei-

ther the minimum width or minimum height dimension is used, the other dimension must be increased to achieve the minimum area requirement. This too is illustrated in Exhibit 24.4.

The outside window addressed in 24.2.2.3(c) must comply with one of the following four accessibility arrangements.

(a) The first arrangement makes it possible for an occupant to drop from the window because the window must be within 20 ft (6.1 m) of grade.

(b) The second arrangement relies on the fire department to rescue an occupant from a window that is within reach of rescue apparatus. Such rescue can be achieved either by means of truck-mounted

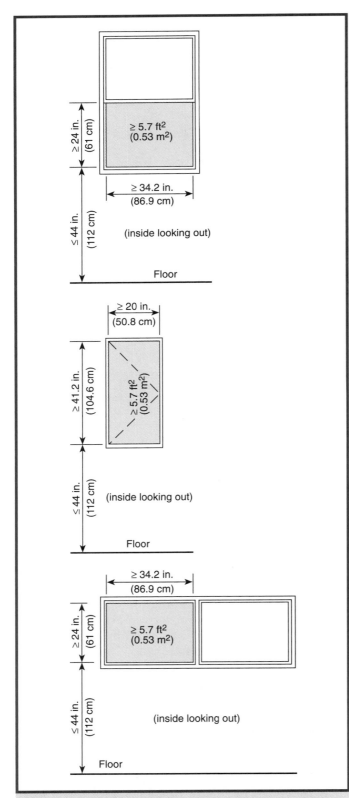

Exhibit 24.4 *Escape window minimum opening dimensions.*

aerial ladders, ground ladders, or other means acceptable to the authority having jurisdiction.

(c) The third arrangement allows an occupant to reach an exterior balcony to breathe fresh air while awaiting either rescue or fire extinguishment. This method could be used where the balcony is not within reach of rescue apparatus. See Exhibits 24.2 and 24.3.

(d) The fourth arrangement recognizes the increasing trend of developing or converting basements into living space such as home offices, playrooms, or sleeping areas. Fire in these areas or the areas above them could easily block the primary means of escape, which is usually a single stair to the upper level. This option provides requirements for the size of the window well, in addition to the window size, to provide sufficient space to operate the window and move up to grade level.

The exception to 24.2.2.3 allows an existing means of escape—approved by the authority having jurisdiction—to continue to be used. Other than in those instances where the means of escape is of extremely poor quality, this exception limits the impact on existing buildings where they are required to comply with 24.2.2.3.

A.24.2.2.3(c) A window with dimensions of 20 in. $\times$ 24 in. (51 cm $\times$ 61 cm) has an opening of 3.3 ft^2 (0.31 m^2), which is less than the required 5.7 ft^2 (0.53 m^2). Therefore, either the height or width needs to exceed the minimum requirement to provide the required clear area. *(See Figure A.24.2.2.3(c)).*

24.2.2.4 Every story more than 2000 ft^2 (185 m^2) in area or with a travel distance to the primary means of escape of more than 75 ft (23 m) shall be provided with two primary means of escape remotely located from each other.

Exception No. 1: Existing one- and two-family dwellings shall be permitted to have a single primary means of escape.

Exception No. 2: Buildings protected throughout by an approved, supervised automatic sprinkler system in accordance with 24.3.5.

24.2.3 Arrangement of Means of Escape.

Any required path of travel in a means of escape from any room to the outside shall not pass through another room or apartment not under the immediate control of the occupant of the first room or through a bathroom or other space subject to locking.

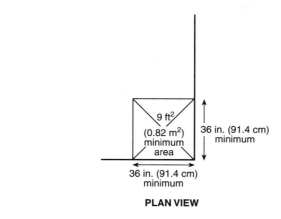

PLAN VIEW

9 ft²
(0.82 m²)
minimum
area

36 in. (91.4 cm)
minimum

36 in. (91.4 cm)
minimum

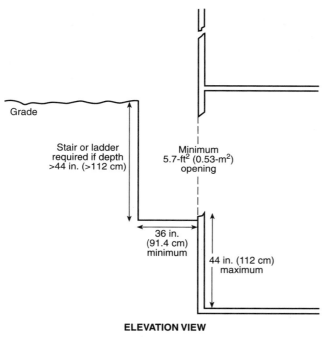

Grade

Stair or ladder
required if depth
>44 in. (>112 cm)

Minimum
5.7-ft² (0.53-m²)
opening

36 in.
(91.4 cm)
minimum

44 in. (112 cm)
maximum

ELEVATION VIEW

Figure A.24.2.2.3(c) Escape window utilizing a window well.

Paragraph 24.2.3 sets criteria in recognition that a means of escape that relies on travel through an adjacent space might not be usable if the door separating the spaces is locked against escape. One- and two-family dwellings can have rooms occupied by up to three outsiders or could be arranged so that a second family must escape through the living space of the first family. This arrangement is often found in older homes that were not originally built as duplexes but that were later converted to this arrangement. Such situations create the potential for doors to be locked

against escape. Any spaces through which escape will occur must be under the control of the person escaping.

24.2.4 Doors.

24.2.4.1 Doors in the path of travel of a means of escape shall be not less than 28 in. (71 cm) wide.

Exception: Bathroom doors shall be not less than 24 in. (61 cm) wide.

Although Chapter 7 requires 32-in. (81-cm) clear width doors in new construction and 28-in. (71-cm) wide doors in existing buildings, 24.2.4.1 allows the use of 28-in. (71-cm) wide doors [24 in. (61 cm) for bathrooms] in both new and existing buildings. This measurement, as illustrated in Exhibit 24.5, is a leaf width measurement of the door, not a clear width measurement of the door opening. This requirement applies to doors in one- and two-family dwellings and within the guest rooms and guest suites of lodging and rooming houses, hotels and dormitories, and dwelling units of apartment buildings.

The 28-in. (71-cm) wide doors specified in 24.2.4.1 are used in some dwelling designs, but ease of access and the need to move furniture and appliances usually dictate a larger size.

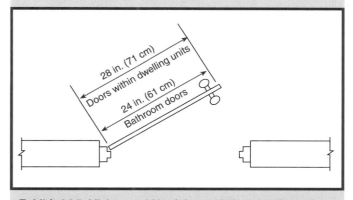

Exhibit 24.5 *Minimum width of doors within a dwelling unit.*

24.2.4.2 Doors shall be not less than 6 ft 6 in. (2 m) in nominal height.

24.2.4.3 Every closet door latch shall be such that children can open the door from inside the closet.

24.2.4.4 Every bathroom door shall be designed to allow opening from the outside during an emergency when locked.

Paragraphs 24.2.4.3 and 24.2.4.4 recognize that, during a fire, children will often seek refuge in bathrooms and closets. The provisions for releasing the latch from the inside and the lock from the outside of closet and bathroom doors allow escape and facilitate rescue by parents or by fire department personnel.

24.2.4.5 Doors shall be swinging or sliding.

24.2.4.6* No door in any means of escape shall be locked against egress when the building is occupied. All locking devices that impede or prohibit egress or that cannot be easily disengaged shall be prohibited.

A.24.2.4.6 It is the intent of this requirement that security measures, where installed, do not prevent egress.

Paragraph 24.2.4.6 prohibits a dwelling unit from having any door locked against egress while the dwelling unit is occupied. This requirement permits a door to have a locking device that allows the door to be opened from within the building for the purpose of escape but that does not allow the door to be opened from outside the building. Ordinary double-cylinder locks and key-operated chain locks do not meet this requirement. Several multiple-death fires have occurred when a door lock could not be released because the key could not be found.

The prohibition on locking applies only to doors or windows that are part of the required means of escape system. Often the rear door of a dwelling is not part of the required escape system and, therefore, such a door is permitted to be equipped with a double-cylinder key-operated lock.

24.2.5 Stairs, Landings, Ramps, Balconies, or Porches.

24.2.5.1 Stairs, ramps, guards, and handrails shall be in accordance with 7.2.2 for stairs and 7.2.5 for ramps.

Exception No. 1: The provisions of 7.2.2.5, 7.2.5.5, and 7.7.3 shall not apply.

Exception No. 2: If serving as a secondary means of escape, stairs complying with the fire escape requirements of Table 7.2.8.4.1(a) or Table 7.2.8.4.1(b) shall be permitted.

Exception No. 3: If serving as a secondary means of escape, ramps complying with the existing ramp requirements of 7.2.5.2(2) shall be permitted.

Exception No. 4: Riser heights not exceeding 7¾ in. (19.7 cm) and tread depths of not less than 10 in. (25.4 cm) shall be permitted for stairs in new construction.

The Chapter 7 requirement that restricts the use of Class B stairs [maximum 8-in. (20.3-cm) riser height and minimum 9-in. (22.9-cm) tread depth] to existing buildings is referenced in Chapter 24. This requirement permits Class B stairs only within existing dwelling units. For new stairs within dwelling units, Exception No. 4 to 24.2.5.1 permits a geometry where the riser height is permitted to be as high as 7¾ in. (19.7 cm) and the tread depth is permitted to be as shallow as 10 in. (25.4 cm). It is important to keep in mind that carpeting might be installed on the stairs in the future. Carpeting might have an impact on the effective tread depth. Exhibit 24.6 illustrates the effect of carpeting on the stepping surface of the stair. Designing the stairs to the minimum geometry is insufficient; consideration must be given to floor coverings. Such consideration might result in a design that exceeds the minimum geometry established in Exception No. 4 but that is still less than the requirements of 7.2.2.

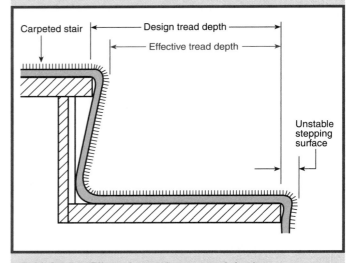

Exhibit 24.6 *Effect of carpeting on tread depth.*

24.2.5.2 The clear width of stairs, landings, ramps, balconies, and porches shall be not less than 36 in. (91 cm), measured in accordance with 7.3.2.

24.2.5.3 Spiral stairs and winders in accordance with 7.2.2.2.3 and 7.2.2.2.4 shall be permitted within a single dwelling unit.

24.2.5.4 No sleeping rooms or living rooms shall be accessible only by a ladder, a stair ladder, an alternating tread device, or folding stairs or through a trap door.

24.2.6 Hallways.

The width of hallways shall be not less than 36 in. (91 cm). The height of hallways shall be not less than 7 ft (2.1 m) nominal, with clearance below projections from the ceiling of not less than 6 ft 8 in. (203 cm) nominal.

Exception: Existing approved hallways shall be permitted to be continued to be used.

Within the dwelling unit, headroom is regulated only in the hallways. Such regulation helps to ensure that the space above head height can accumulate smoke early in the fire to permit safe escape through the hallway, which will help to prevent the need for occupants to crawl near floor level to avoid the descending smoke layer.

Section 24.3 Protection

24.3.1 Protection of Vertical Openings.

(No requirements.)

24.3.2 (Reserved.)

24.3.3 Interior Finish.

24.3.3.1 Interior Wall and Ceiling Finish. Interior finish on walls and ceilings of occupied spaces shall be Class A, Class B, or Class C as defined in Section 10.2.

24.3.3.2 Interior Floor Finish. (No requirements.)

24.3.4 Detection, Alarm, and Communications Systems.

Approved, single-station smoke alarms shall be installed in accordance with 9.6.2.10 in the following locations:

(1) All sleeping rooms

Exception: Smoke alarms shall not be required in sleeping rooms in existing one- and two-family dwellings.

(2) Outside of each separate sleeping area, in the immediate vicinity of the sleeping rooms
(3) On each level of the dwelling unit, including basements

Exception No. 1: Dwelling units protected by an approved smoke detection system in accordance with Section 9.6 and equipped with an approved means of occupant notification.

Exception No. 2: In existing one- and two-family dwellings approved smoke alarms powered by batteries shall be permitted.

The reference to 9.6.2.10 requires smoke alarms to be hard-wired into the electrical system of the home or to be a plug-in alarm. Exception No. 2 to 24.3.4, which permits battery-powered smoke alarms in existing dwellings, gives dwelling occupants relief from retrofit requirements while providing needed protection. However, occupants of dwellings that use battery-operated smoke alarms must ensure that they are tested and maintained properly. NFPA analysis has shown that 30 percent of smoke alarms were inoperative in homes that had smoke alarms and that had experienced fire. The primary reason for smoke alarm failure is that the battery was removed to avoid nuisance alarms. NFPA public education programs, such as the Learn Not to Burn® program, are effective tools for promoting proper smoke alarm maintenance.

Regardless of the power source, it is important that smoke alarms be properly located. Exhibits 24.7 and 24.8 illustrate the required locations of the smoke alarms per 24.3.4.5. The reference to 9.6.2.10 directs the user to NFPA 72, *National Fire Alarm Code*.[4] Further information on the mounting, location, spacing, and performance of smoke alarms is found in Chapter 8 of NFPA 72.

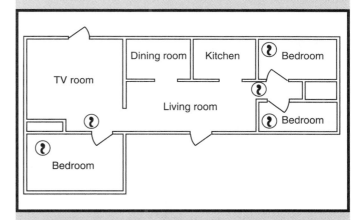

Exhibit 24.7 *Required smoke alarm locations.*

24.3.5 Extinguishment Requirements.

Where an automatic sprinkler system is required or is used as an alternative method of protection, either for total or partial building coverage, the system shall be in accordance with Section 9.7. In buildings up to and including four stories in height, systems in accordance with NFPA 13R, *Standard for the Installation of Sprinkler Systems in Residential Occupancies up to and Including Four Stories in Height,* shall be permitted. Systems in accordance with NFPA 13D, *Stan-*

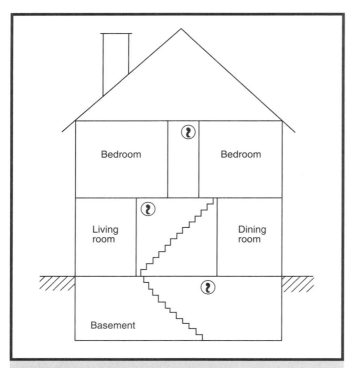

Exhibit 24.8 *Required smoke alarm placement per level.*

dard for the Installation of Sprinkler Systems in One- and Two-Family Dwellings and Manufactured Homes, *shall also be permitted.*

NFPA 13D, *Standard for the Installation of Sprinkler Systems in One- and Two-Family Dwellings and Manufactured Homes*, was developed after extensive research that included full-scale fire tests. It introduced the concept of a quick-response residential sprinkler. Unlike its industrial standard spray sprinkler counterpart, which is inherently slow to fuse its relatively massive eutectic solder element, a quick-response, residential sprinkler operates very quickly once its rated temperature is sensed. Quick-response sprinklers begin to control a fire early in its growth. In addition to being quick to respond, residential sprinklers (as mandated by NFPA 13D) have a specifically designed spray pattern that delivers water to nearly the full height of the walls of small rooms that are typical of residential occupancies.

NFPA 13R, *Standard for the Installation of Sprinkler*

Systems in Residential Occupancies up to and Including Four Stories in Height, was first published in 1989. It addresses residential sprinklers, which incorporate the quick-response sprinkler technology described in the preceding paragraph in the commentary on NFPA 13D. NFPA 13R thus extends the technological and economic benefits of an NFPA 13D-type system to larger residential buildings, while requiring additional provisions that are commensurate with increased building size that will help to ensure improved protection against injury and life loss to building residents—including those occupying the room of fire origin.

Section 24.4 Reserved

Section 24.5 Building Services

24.5.1 Heating, Ventilating, and Air Conditioning.

24.5.1.1 Heating, ventilating, and air conditioning equipment shall comply with the provisions of Section 9.2.

24.5.1.2 Unvented fuel-fired heaters shall not be used.

Exception: Listed and approved unvented fuel-fired heaters in one- and two-family dwellings.

References Cited in Commentary

1. NFPA 13, *Standard for the Installation of Sprinkler Systems*, 1999 edition, National Fire Protection Association, Quincy, MA.
2. NFPA 13D, *Standard for the Installation of Sprinkler Systems in One- and Two-Family Dwellings and Manufactured Homes*, 1999 edition, National Fire Protection Association, Quincy, MA.
3. NFPA 13R, *Standard for the Installation of Sprinkler Systems in Residential Occupancies up to and Including Four Stories in Height*, 1999 edition, National Fire Protection Association, Quincy, MA.
4. NFPA 72, *National Fire Alarm Code®*, 1999 edition, National Fire Protection Association, Quincy, MA.

CHAPTER 25

Reserved

Typically, the occupancy chapters are paired so that the even-numbered chapter in the pair addresses new facilities of the occupancy type and the odd-numbered chapter addresses existing facilities of the occupancy type. Chapter 24, which precedes this chapter, addresses both new and existing one- and two-family dwellings in a single chapter. Chapter 25 has been reserved to permit the chapter on lodging or rooming houses to be assigned an even number (that is, Chapter 26). The reserved chapter number might be used at a future date if the requirements for one- and two-family dwellings are split into a pair of chapters—one for new construction and one for existing buildings.

CHAPTER 26

Lodging or Rooming Houses

Chapter 26 addresses the requirements for both new and existing lodging or rooming houses. These facilities provide accommodation for 16 or fewer occupants on a transient basis. While some users of the *Code* might confuse lodging or rooming facilities with a hotel occupancy—or a board and care facility—the primary differences among the occupancies center on the total number of occupants served and the nature of any personal care that is provided. While some of these facilities might provide what appears to be longer-term, daily living accommodations, other facilities, such as a bed and breakfast facility, might serve on a short-term basis. If a bed and breakfast facility provides accommodations for more than 16 occupants, it would be appropriate to use Chapters 28 and 29 for hotels and dormitories to evaluate the requisite life safety features.

Table 26.1 is a guide to the appropriate chapter for multi-tenant residential occupancies.

Section 26.1 General Requirements

26.1.1 Application.

26.1.1.1* This chapter applies to buildings that provide sleeping accommodations for a total of 16 or fewer persons on either a transient or permanent basis, with or without meals, but without separate cooking facilities for individual occupants, except as provided in Chapter 24.

A.26.1.1.1 Bed and breakfast occupancies with more than 3, but fewer than 16, occupants are considered lodging and rooming houses.

If sleeping accommodations for more than 16 people are provided, the occupancy should be classified as a hotel or dormitory. The reference to Chapter 24 concerns the provision that allows rooms to be occupied by a maximum of three outsiders in addition to

Table 26.1 Comparative Factors for Classification of Residential Occupancies

	Chapter 26 Lodging or Rooming Houses	Chapters 28 and 29 Hotels and Dormitories	Chapters 30 and 31 Apartment Buildings	Chapters 32 and 33 Residential Board and Care
Occupants of a transient nature?	Yes	Yes	No	No
Number of occupants in facility?	16 or fewer	More than 16	As few as 3. Application is based on presence of 3 or more independent living units	4 or more
Personal care services provided?	No	No	No	Yes

family members in one- and two-family dwellings without changing the occupancy classification. Many of the facilities that house more than three outsiders but fewer than 16 people ordinarily would not be considered lodging or rooming houses but, nevertheless, do meet the definition—for example, a fire station that has a bunk room. The fire station with bunking facilities would normally be considered a mixed occupancy, depending on the arrangement of the facility. For example, in Exhibit 26.1(a), the fire station would be classified as a mixed occupancy because it contains assembly, business, lodging and rooming, industrial, and storage occupancies. By applying the most restrictive requirements, this building would require automatic sprinklers via the provisions of 26.3.5.2. If additional exits are added to provide separate means of egress for the bunk room, equipment shop, assembly hall, and apparatus bay and separation from the assembly hall as shown in Exhibit 26.1(b), the building is no longer considered a mixed occupancy, and the provisions for the occupancy within each space would be applied separately.

26.1.1.2 The requirements of this chapter apply to new buildings and to existing or modified buildings according to the provisions of 1.4.1 of this *Code*.

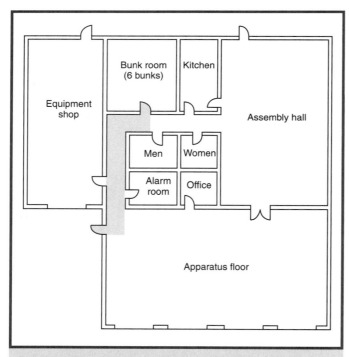

Exhibit 26.1(a) *Fire station that is a mixed occupancy.*

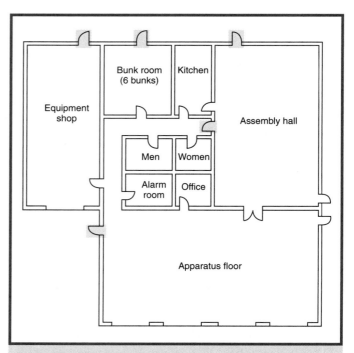

Exhibit 26.1(b) *Fire station that is not a mixed occupancy.*

26.1.2 Mixed Occupancies.

26.1.2.1 Where another type of occupancy exists in the same building as a residential occupancy, the requirements of 6.1.14 of this *Code* shall apply.

26.1.2.2 No dwelling unit of a residential occupancy shall have its sole means of egress pass through any nonresidential occupancy in the same building.

26.1.2.3 No multiple-dwelling unit of a residential occupancy shall be located above any nonresidential occupancy.

Exception No. 1: Where the dwelling unit of the residential occupancy and exits therefrom are separated from the nonresidential occupancy by construction having a fire-resistance rating of not less than 1 hour.

Exception No. 2: Where the nonresidential occupancy is protected throughout by an approved, supervised automatic sprinkler system in accordance with Section 9.7.

Exception No. 3: A building with not more than two dwelling units above a nonresidential occupancy shall be permitted, provided that the nonresidential occupancy is protected by an automatic fire detection system in accordance with Section 9.6.

Paragraph 26.1.2.3 recognizes that a nonresidential occupancy might be located below a lodging or rooming house. The location of such an occupancy presents a life safety challenge for the occupants of the residential dwelling. The typical configuration of these buildings creates the potential for a significant time lapse before occupants of the residential occupancy become aware of an emergency in another part of the building and take the necessary action. The provisions of 26.1.2.2 and 26.1.2.3 are intended to provide added protection for the residential occupancy during that lapse. Therefore, these requirements are intended to apply wherever this mixture of occupancies exists, whether in new construction or in existing buildings.

26.1.3 Definitions.

Terms applicable to this chapter are defined in Chapter 3 of this *Code;* where necessary, other terms are defined in the text.

26.1.4 Classification of Occupancy.

(See 26.1.1.1.)

26.1.5 Classification of Hazard of Contents.

The contents of residential occupancies shall be classified as ordinary hazard in accordance with 6.2.2.

NFPA 13, *Standard for the Installation of Sprinkler Systems,* classifies the contents of a lodging or rooming house as light hazard for the purpose of designing automatic sprinkler systems.[1] The difference in classification in the *Code* is based on the threat to life or life safety (ordinary), as opposed to the challenge to the extinguishing capability of the automatic sprinkler system (light).

26.1.6 Minimum Construction Requirements.

(No special requirements.)

26.1.7 Occupant Load.

(See 26.1.1.1.)

Section 26.2 Means of Escape Requirements

26.2.1 Number and Types of Means of Escape.

26.2.1.1 Every sleeping room and living area shall have access to a primary means of escape complying with Chapter

24 and located to provide a safe path of travel to the outside. Where the sleeping room is above or below the level of exit discharge, the primary means of escape shall be an interior stair in accordance with 26.2.2, an exterior stair, a horizontal exit in accordance with 7.2.4, or an existing fire escape stair in accordance with 7.2.8.

The concept of means of escape has been fully developed in Chapter 24. The provisions for means of escape are used in 26.2.1.1, because the escape paths required for a lodging or rooming house are more similar to those provided for a dwelling than for public buildings. The *Code* requires that at least one means of escape from levels above or below the level of exit discharge is to be an enclosed interior stair, an exterior stair, a horizontal exit, or an existing fire escape. The intent is that at least one means of escape (primary) be of a high degree of quality that is similar to the means of egress components described in Chapter 7. Most lodging or rooming houses are converted homes that rarely have an exit arrangement complying with Chapter 7. However, the *Code* recognizes the issue of public liability associated with lodging guests and includes requirements in Chapter 26 that provide a level of escape quality higher than that normally found in a single-family home.

The protection of the primary means of escape as required by 26.2.1.1—often accomplished by the protection of vertical openings in accordance with 26.2.2 and 26.3.1.1—is the major distinction between the requirements applicable to one- and two-family dwellings and those applicable to lodging or rooming houses. Another distinction is the requirement in 26.3.5.2 for the provision of automatic sprinklers in new lodging or rooming houses. By protecting the escape path from exposure to unprotected vertical openings—such as the unenclosed stairs normally found in single-family dwellings—the *Code* helps to ensure that the occupants of a lodging or rooming house can reach a point of safety. This protection is important, because the occupants of a lodging or rooming house characteristically occupy their rooms with the doors closed. Therefore, they lack the awareness of emergency conditions that is experienced by members of a family who live together within a dwelling where doors are usually open.

Exhibits 26.2, 26.3, 26.4, 26.5, 26.6, and 26.7, which appear throughout the rest of the commentary on this chapter, illustrate six possible methods of complying with the means of escape provisions of 26.2.1.1, as affected by the provisions of 26.2.2 and 26.3.1.1.

26.2.1.2 In addition to the primary route, each sleeping room and living area shall have a second means of escape in accordance with 24.2.2.

Exception: If the sleeping room or living area has a door leading directly outside the building with access to grade or to a stairway that meets the requirements for exterior stairs in 26.2.1.1, that means of escape shall be considered as meeting all of the escape requirements for that sleeping room or living area.

The *Code* specifies that the secondary means of escape must comply with 24.2.2. Paragraph 24.2.2.4 exempts a secondary means of escape if the building is sprinklered in accordance with either NFPA 13, *Standard for the Installation of Sprinkler Systems*, or NFPA 13R, *Standard for the Installation of Sprinkler Systems in Residential Occupancies up to and Including Four Stories in Height.*[2] Because most new lodging or rooming houses are required to be protected with sprinklers in accordance with 26.3.5.2, a secondary means of escape will seldom be needed. Where existing, nonsprinklered lodging or rooming houses are deficient with respect to secondary means of escape, protection of vertical openings, or required door closers on sleeping room doors, sprinklering becomes a viable alternative to correcting such deficiencies individually.

26.2.1.3 Every story more than 2000 ft² (185 m²) in area or with travel distance to the primary means of escape more than 75 ft (23 m) shall be provided with two primary means of escape remotely located from each other.

Exception No. 1: Existing lodging or rooming houses shall be permitted to have a single primary means of escape.

Exception No. 2: Buildings protected throughout by an approved, supervised automatic sprinkler system in accordance with 26.3.5.

26.2.2 Interior stairways shall be enclosed by½-hour fire barriers with all openings protected with smoke-actuated automatic-closing or self-closing doors having a fire resistance comparable to that required for the enclosure. The stairway shall comply with 7.2.2.5.3.

Exception No. 1: Where an interior stair connects the street floor with the story next above or below only, but not with both, the interior stair shall be required to be enclosed only on the street floor.

Exception No. 2: Stairways shall be permitted to be unenclosed in accordance with the exceptions to 26.3.1.1.

In Exhibit 26.2, an enclosed interior stair in accordance with 26.2.2 is shown on the first floor. The stair discharges directly to the outside and serves as the primary means of escape for this nonsprinklered rooming house. The entry foyer is separated from the rest of the first floor by walls with a ½-hour fire resistance rating, and the doors are self-closing with a 20-minute fire protection rating. The entry foyer cannot be used for any other purpose, such as a lounge for the occupants. Walls with a ½-hour fire resistance rating and a self-closing door with a 20-minute fire protection rating also enclose the stairs on the second floor. The walls and door provide

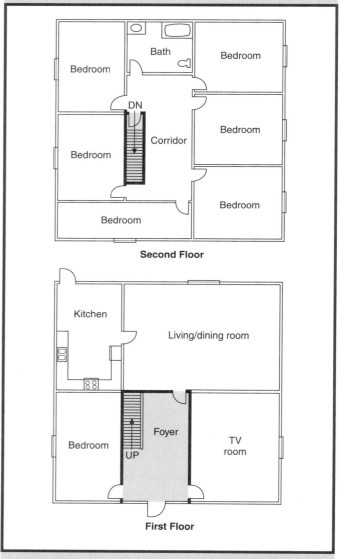

Exhibit 26.2 *Means of escape—existing nonsprinklered lodging or rooming house.*

the necessary separation between the second floor corridor and the vertical opening. Compliant windows in all sleeping and living spaces provide the secondary means of escape.

Exhibit 26.3 illustrates the use of Exception No. 1 to 26.2.2. To meet the criteria for the exception, stairs A and B connect only two floors and are separated from the rest of the first floor. Stair A cannot extend to the second floor and Stair B cannot extend to the basement. The arrangement of stair A protects the residents on the first and second floors from fire and smoke in the basement. The arrangement of stair B protects the residents on the second floor from fire and smoke on the street floor.

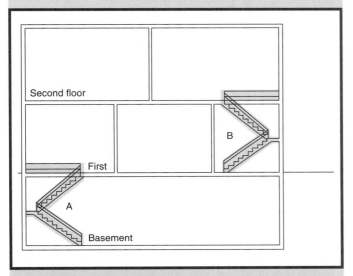

Second floor

B

First

A

Basement

Exhibit 26.3 *A two-story stairway.*

See the commentary following 26.3.3.1.1 for an explanation of the provisions for unenclosed stairways permitted by 26.2.2, Exception No. 2.

26.2.3 Doors and paths of travel in a means of escape shall be not less than 28 in. (71 cm) wide.

Exception: Bathroom doors shall be not less than 24 in. (61 cm) wide.

26.2.4 Every closet door latch shall be such that it can be readily opened from the inside in case of emergency.

26.2.5 Every bathroom door shall be designed to allow opening from the outside during an emergency when locked.

26.2.6 Winders in accordance with 7.2.2.2.4 shall be permitted.

26.2.7* No door in any means of escape shall be locked against egress when the building is occupied.

Exception: Delayed-egress locks complying with 7.2.1.6.1 shall be permitted, provided that not more than one such device is located in any one escape path.

A.26.2.7 It is the intent of this requirement that security measures, where installed, do not prevent egress.

Subsection 26.2.7 prohibits a lodging or rooming house from having any door locked against egress (escape) while the building is occupied. This requirement permits a door to have a locking device that allows the door to be opened from within the building for the purpose of escape but does not permit the door to be opened from outside the building. Ordinary double-cylinder locks and chain locks do not meet these provisions.

The language of 7.2.1.5.1 is clear. It requires that locks, if provided, are not to require the use of a key, a tool, or special knowledge or effort for operation from the egress side. This requirement eliminates double-cylinder locks and chain locks that require a key to operate the door from the inside. Subparagraph 7.2.1.5.4 requires the use of a simple operation to open a door; locks that require two-handed knobs and similar operations are prohibited.

Chapter 7 recognizes the need for security chains or rods on guest room doors and allows one releasing device in addition to the door knob or lever. The typical guest room door has three devices: a latch, a lock, and a security chain or rod. However, the *Code* allows only two releasing actions for new installations. This requirement is met by using a latch and lockset equipped with a lock bolt that automatically retracts when the latch handle is turned from the inside; therefore, only one releasing action is needed for the two devices. The second action is the release of the security chain or rod. However, neither device requires the use of a key, a tool, or special knowledge or effort. In existing installations, three releasing devices are permitted: the security device, the lock, and the latch.

The exception to 26.2.7 recognizes the use of the delayed-egress lock detailed in 7.2.1.6.1. Use of a delayed-egress lock requires that the building be protected throughout by either an automatic sprinkler system or a fire detection system. The 15-second or 30-second delay permitted by 7.2.1.6.1 does not affect the immediate release of the lock upon activation of the sprinklers or detectors, or upon loss of power to the lock. This device helps provide the security needed for doors that are used infrequently in lodging or rooming houses. At the same time, doors remain available for emergency use. Chains and padlocks do not to provide this protection.

26.2.8 Doors serving a single dwelling unit shall be permitted to be provided with a lock in accordance with Exception No. 3 to 7.2.1.5.1.

Section 26.3 Protection

26.3.1 Protection of Vertical Openings.

26.3.1.1 Vertical openings shall be protected so that no primary escape route is exposed to an unprotected vertical opening. The vertical opening shall be considered protected if the opening is cut off and enclosed in a manner that provides a smoke- and fire-resisting capability of not less than ½ hour. Any doors or openings shall have a smoke- and fire-resisting capability equivalent to that of the enclosure and shall be automatic-closing on detection of smoke or shall be self-closing.

Exception No. 1: In buildings three or fewer stories in height that are protected throughout by an approved automatic sprinkler system in accordance with 26.3.5, unprotected vertical openings shall be permitted. However, in such cases, a primary means of escape from each sleeping area shall be provided. Such means of escape shall not pass through a portion of a lower floor unless such portion is separated from all spaces on that floor by construction having a ½-hour fire resistance rating.

Exception No. 2: In buildings two or fewer stories in height protected throughout by an approved, supervised automatic sprinkler system in accordance with 26.3.5.1, stair enclosures shall not be required. The exception to 24.2.2.1(b) shall not be used.

An outside stair is used as the primary means of escape in Exhibit 26.4. Compliant windows in each of the bedrooms provide the secondary means of escape. The interior stair in this arrangement is just a convenience stair, independent of the required means of escape. If no sprinkler system is provided, the stairs must be enclosed in accordance with 26.3.1.1, as depicted in Exhibit 26.4. If a sprinkler system is provided, either of the two exceptions to 26.3.1.1 is permitted to be applied.

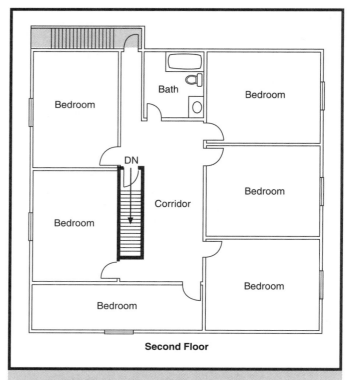

Exhibit 26.4 *Means of escape—outside stair use.*

Exception No.1 to 26.3.1.1 permits a vertical opening of up to three stories to be unprotected in a fully sprinklered, maximum three-story, lodging or rooming house, provided that the primary means of escape is separated on the lower floor(s). Exhibit 26.5 illustrates a three-story, fully sprinklered lodging or rooming house. The stairs are open from the first to the third floor. However the walls separating the living spaces from the stairs on floors one and two are of a construction with a ½-hour fire resistance rating.

In bed and breakfast facilities, it is often important to retain the historical integrity or homelike ambience of the building. Separation or enclosure of a decorative main stair would effectively eliminate the characteristics that draw people to these facilities. On the other hand, it is necessary to provide appropriate protection to the guests. Exhibit 26.6 illustrates a two-story bed and breakfast facility that is protected with automatic sprinklers. Once again, the stair serves as the primary means of escape. In this case, Exception No. 2 to 26.3.1.1 is used. It is important to note that the use of this exception has an impact on the secondary means of escape. Even though 24.2.2.1(b) permits the elimination of the secondary means of escape in fully sprinklered buildings, Exception No. 2 to 26.3.1.1 specifically prohibits the use

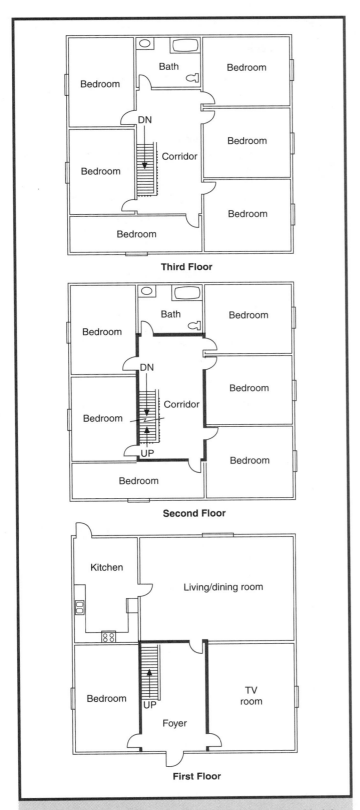

Third Floor

Second Floor

First Floor

Exhibit 26.5 Means of escape—three-story sprinklered lodging or rooming house.

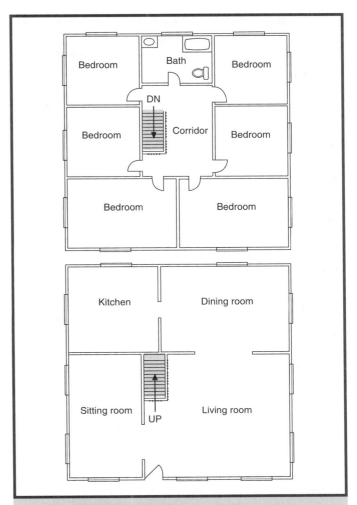

Exhibit 26.6 Means of escape—two-story, sprinklered bed and breakfast facility.

of 24.2.2.1(b) if the automatic sprinklers are used for the purpose of protecting the vertical opening. The result is that all windows from the sleeping rooms or living areas must comply as a secondary means of escape if this arrangement is to be permitted.

26.3.1.2 Exterior stairs shall be reasonably protected against blockage caused by fire that would simultaneously expose both the interior and exterior means of escape. Such protection shall be permitted to be accomplished through separation by physical distance, arrangement of the stairs, protection of the openings exposing the stairs, or other means acceptable to the authority having jurisdiction.

26.3.2 Interior Finish.

26.3.2.1 Interior finish shall be in accordance with Section 10.2.

26.3.2.2 Interior Wall and Ceiling Finish. Interior wall and ceiling finish materials complying with 10.2.3 shall be Class A, Class B, or Class C in occupied spaces.

26.3.2.3 Interior Floor Finish. (No requirements.)

26.3.3 Detection, Alarm, and Communications Systems.

26.3.3.1 General. Lodging and rooming houses shall be provided with a fire alarm system in accordance with Section 9.6.

Exception: Existing lodging and rooming houses that have an existing smoke detection system meeting or exceeding the requirements of 26.3.3.5 where that detection system includes not less than one manual fire alarm box per floor arranged to initiate the smoke detection alarm.

The exception to 26.3.3.1 allows multiple-station smoke detectors and a manual fire alarm box arranged as a system to substitute for a standard fire alarm system in accordance with NFPA 72, *National Fire Alarm Code.*[3]

26.3.3.2 Initiation. Initiation of the required fire alarm system shall be by manual means in accordance with 9.6.2.

Exception: Buildings protected throughout by an approved automatic sprinkler system in accordance with 26.3.5, with alarm initiation in accordance with 9.6.2.1(3).

26.3.3.3 Notification. Occupant notification shall be provided automatically in accordance with 9.6.3.

Exception No. 1:   *Visible signals for the hearing impaired shall not be required where the proprietor resides in the building and there are five or fewer rooms for rent.*

A.26.3.3.3 Exception No. 1 The proprietor is the owner or owner's agent with responsible charge.

Exception No. 2:   Positive alarm sequence in accordance with 9.6.3.4 shall be permitted.

26.3.3.4 Detection. (Reserved.)

26.3.3.5 Smoke Alarms. Approved single-station smoke alarms shall be installed in accordance with 9.6.2.10 in every sleeping room. Such smoke alarms shall not be required to be interconnected.

Exception: Existing battery-powered smoke alarms, rather than house electric-powered smoke alarms, shall be permitted where the facility has demonstrated to the authority having jurisdiction that the testing, maintenance, and battery

replacement programs will ensure reliability of power to the smoke alarms.

Paragraph 26.3.3.5 requires the installation of a smoke alarm in each sleeping room. This requirement applies retroactively to existing lodging or rooming houses, as well as to new construction.

While the exception to 26.3.3.5 allows existing battery-powered smoke alarms to remain in place if approved by the authority having jurisdiction, newly installed smoke alarms must be powered by the building electrical service. This requirement applies to both new and existing lodging or rooming houses in accordance with 9.6.2.10.

26.3.4 Separation of Sleeping Rooms.

All sleeping rooms shall be separated from escape route corridors by walls and doors that are smoke resistant. There shall be no louvers or operable transoms. Air passages shall not penetrate the wall unless they are properly installed heating and utility installations other than transfer grilles. Transfer grilles shall be prohibited. Doors shall be provided with latches or other mechanisms suitable for keeping the doors closed. Doors shall not be arranged to prevent the occupant from closing the door. Doors shall be self-closing or automatic-closing upon detection of smoke.

Exception: Door-closing devices shall not be required in buildings protected throughout by an approved automatic sprinkler system in accordance with 26.3.5.

The requirement of 26.3.4 is similar to that requiring corridor walls and doors in hotels and apartment buildings; however, no fire resistance rating is required. Unlike hotels and apartment buildings, door closers are exempted in sprinklered lodging or rooming houses. See Exhibit 26.7.

26.3.5 Extinguishment Requirements.

26.3.5.1* Where an automatic sprinkler system is required or is used as an alternative method of protection, either for total or partial building coverage, the system shall be in accordance with Section 9.7 and shall actuate the fire alarm system in accordance with Section 9.6. In buildings up to and including four stories in height, systems in accordance with NFPA 13R, *Standard for the Installation of Sprinkler Systems in Residential Occupancies up to and Including Four Stories in Height,* shall be permitted. The use of NFPA 13D, *Standard for the Installation of Sprinkler Systems in One- and Two-Family Dwellings and Manufactured Homes,* shall be permitted where the lodging or rooming house is

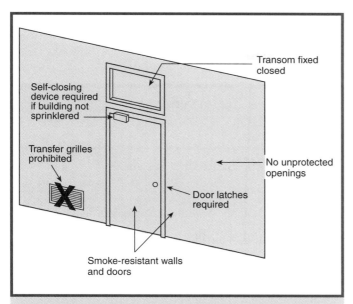

Exhibit 26.7 Sleeping room/escape route separation.

not part of a mixed occupancy. Entrance foyers shall be sprinklered. Lodging and rooming houses with sleeping accommodations for more than eight occupants shall be treated as two-family dwellings with regard to the water supply.

Exception No. 1: In buildings sprinklered in accordance with NFPA 13, Standard for the Installation of Sprinkler Systems, closets less than 12 ft² (1.1 m²) in area in individual dwelling units shall not be required to be sprinklered. Closets that contain equipment such as washers, dryers, furnaces, or water heaters shall be sprinklered regardless of size.

Exception No. 2: In existing lodging and rooming houses, sprinkler installations shall not be required in closets not exceeding 24 ft² (2.2 m²) and in bathrooms not exceeding 55 ft² (5.1 m²).

A.26.3.5.1 The decision to permit the use of the criteria from NFPA 13D, *Standard for the Installation of Sprinkler Systems in One- and Two-Family Dwellings and Manufactured Homes,* in these occupancies is based on the following:

(1) The desire to obtain a level of fire suppression and control that is approximately equivalent to that delivered by residential facilities protected by such systems *(see the appendix statement in NFPA 13D, Standard for the Installation of Sprinkler Systems in One- and Two-Family Dwellings and Manufactured Homes)*

(2) The fact that potential fire exposure and challenge to the suppression system in a small lodging and rooming occupancy is of the same nature and no more severe than that found in residences

Because there is such a wide variety of buildings that might fall into the classification of lodging or rooming houses, it is necessary to provide references to all three of the standards for the installation of automatic sprinkler systems.

The use of NFPA 13R, *Standard for the Installation of Sprinkler Systems in Residential Occupancies up to and Including Four Stories in Height,* is appropriate for many lodging or rooming houses.

In certain lodging or rooming house occupancies, the use of NFPA 13D, *Standard for the Installation of Sprinkler Systems in One- and Two-Family Dwellings and Manufactured Homes,* is also appropriate.[4] Some lodging or rooming houses might be closer in similarity to a one- or two-family dwelling, whereas others are not. For example, an NFPA 13D system would be appropriate for a single-family dwelling that is used as a bed and breakfast (lodging or rooming house classification for purposes of applying this *Code*) but not for a fire station with a bunk room. Paragraph 26.3.5.1 contains the following three provisions for the use of an NFPA 13D system in these types of lodging or rooming houses:

(1) The system must not be part of a mixed occupancy.
(2) The entrance foyer must be sprinklered (not a requirement in NFPA 13D).
(3) If the lodging and rooming house contains sleeping accommodations for more than eight occupants, the sprinkler system water supply must be designed in accordance with NFPA 13D criteria for two-family dwellings.

NFPA 13D requires the water supply for two-family dwellings with a common water main to be designed for a 30-minute duration rather than the 10-minute duration permitted for single-family dwellings.

26.3.5.2 All new lodging or rooming houses shall be protected throughout by an approved automatic sprinkler system in accordance with 26.3.5.1.

Exception: Where every sleeping room has a door opening directly to the outside of the building at street or ground level, or has a door opening directly to the outside leading to an exterior stairway that meets the requirements of 26.2.1.1.

Exhibit 26.8 illustrates an arrangement where each room has a door leading directly to an exterior balcony and exterior stairs to grade. In this design, the exception to 26.2.1.2 eliminates the requirement for

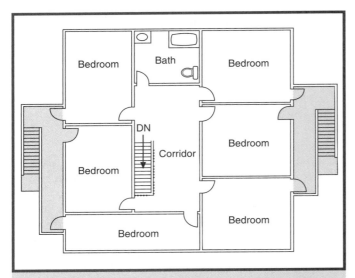

Exhibit 26.8 *Means of escape—nonsprinklered lodging or rooming house.*

a secondary means of escape. Therefore, no protection of the interior stairs is required. If no sleeping rooms are located on the first floor, or if the first floor sleeping rooms are arranged to discharge directly outside, automatic sprinklers are not required in this building.

With the exception of those lodging or rooming houses in which each sleeping room has a door providing direct access to the exterior at grade or to an exterior stairway, new lodging or rooming houses must be protected throughout with an approved automatic sprinkler system.

If a new lodging or rooming house is part of another occupancy and is treated as a mixed occupancy, the entire mixed occupancy is required to be sprinklered. To waive this requirement, the occupancies would have to be arranged so that the lodging or rooming house is treated as a separate occupancy. This arrangement would require the egress system for each occupancy to be separate. Doors that open

directly to the outside from each of the occupancies usually achieve this separate egress.

Section 26.4 Reserved

Section 26.5 Building Services

26.5.1 Utilities.

Utilities shall comply with the provisions of Section 9.1.

26.5.2 Heating, Ventilating, and Air Conditioning.

26.5.2.1 Heating, ventilating, and air conditioning equipment shall comply with the provisions of Section 9.2.

26.5.2.2 Unvented fuel-fired heaters shall not be used.

Exception: Gas space heaters in compliance with NFPA 54, National Fuel Gas Code.

26.5.3 Elevators, Escalators, and Conveyors.

Elevators, escalators, and conveyors shall comply with the provisions of Section 9.4.

References Cited in Commentary

1. NFPA 13, *Standard for the Installation of Sprinkler Systems*, 1999 edition, National Fire Protection Association, Quincy, MA.
2. NFPA 13R, *Standard for the Installation of Sprinkler Systems in Residential Occupancies up to and Including Four Stories in Height*, 1999 edition, National Fire Protection Association, Quincy, MA.
3. NFPA 72, *National Fire Alarm Code®*, 1999 edition, National Fire Protection Association, Quincy, MA.
4. NFPA 13D, *Standard for the Installation of Sprinkler Systems in One- and Two-Family Dwellings and Manufactured Homes*, 1999 edition, National Fire Protection Association, Quincy, MA.

CHAPTER 27

Reserved

Typically, the occupancy chapters are paired so that the even-numbered chapter in the pair addresses new facilities of the occupancy type and the odd-numbered chapter addresses existing facilities of the occupancy type. Chapter 26, which precedes this chapter, addresses both new and existing lodging or rooming houses in a single chapter. Chapter 27 has been reserved to permit the chapter on new hotels and dormitories to be assigned an even number (that is, Chapter 28). The reserved chapter number might be used at a future date if the requirements for lodging or rooming houses are split into a pair of chapters—one for new construction and one for existing buildings.

CHAPTERS 28 and 29

New and Existing Hotels and Dormitories

Chapters 28 and 29 address residential occupancies that are primarily transient in nature. Hotel and motel accommodations that are mainly used for stays of relatively short duration fit into this category. Dormitory occupancies, although typically used for up to nine months of near continuous occupancy in the case of a college dormitory, are also regulated by these chapters.

Hotels and dormitories are one of five residential occupancy types addressed by the *Life Safety Code*. Other residential occupancies include one- and two-family dwellings, lodging or rooming houses, apartment buildings, and residential board and care facilities. Sleeping accommodations are a feature common to all residential occupancies.

Paragraph 6.1.8.1 highlights the common principle of life safety that is applied to all residential occupancies addressed by Chapters 24 through 33. Paragraph 6.1.8.1 states that residential occupancies are those occupancies in which sleeping accommodations are provided for purposes other than health care or detention and correction. The presence of sleeping occupants is central to the provisions of Chapters 24 through 33, because occupants who are asleep will be unaware of a developing fire and, when awakened to be alerted to the emergency, might be somewhat confused. Paragraph 6.1.8.1 also differentiates between sleeping occupants in residential occupancies and those in health care or detention and correctional occupancies, which are also characterized by the occupants' incapability of self-preservation. The provisions of Chapters 24 through 33 are also based on the presence of hazards (such as cooking and heating equipment) in residential occupanc-

ies and the degree to which occupants are familiar with their living space. Occupants might have little or no familiarity, as in the case of the transient residents of hotels, or they might have the total familiarity that is common to residents of single-family dwellings.

Unfamiliar surroundings and the possibility of being asleep when a fire occurs are factors that jeopardize the safety of hotel guests in particular. Hotels pose an additional problem, because typical hotel building configurations often require escaping guests to traverse an interior corridor, which subsequently might expose them to the heat and smoke of corridor and room fires. In recognition of these potential hazards, the *Code* requires most new hotels and dormitories to be protected throughout by an approved, supervised automatic sprinkler system.

In recent years, hotels and motels have experienced a steady reduction in the number of fires, civilian casualties, and civilian injuries. From 1992 to 1996, hotels and motels averaged 5400 structure fires a year as reported to U.S. fire departments. These fires resulted in an average of 38 civilian deaths and 340 civilian injuries per year. These figures do not include lodging or rooming houses and residential board and care facilities, which are defined for fire reporting purposes as facilities limited to fewer than 16 occupants. During the same period, dormitories experienced an average of 2300 fires, 3 civilian deaths, and 103 civilian injuries per year.

Part of the explanation for these reductions is the increasing percentage of hotels that use smoke detection and automatic sprinklers.

| CHAPTER 28 • New | CHAPTER 29 • Existing |

Section 28.1 General Requirements

28.1.1 Application.

28.1.1.1 The requirements of this chapter apply to the following:

(1) New buildings or portions thereof used as hotel or dormitory occupancies *(see 1.4.1)*
(2) Additions made to, or used as, a hotel or dormitory occupancy *(see 4.6.6)*
(3) Alterations, modernizations, or renovations of existing hotel or dormitory occupancies *(see 4.6.7)*
(4) Buildings or portions thereof upon change of occupancy to a hotel or dormitory occupancy *(see 4.6.11)*

Exception: Any dormitory divided into suites of rooms, with one or more bedrooms opening into a living room or study that has a door opening into a common corridor serving a number of suites, shall be classified as an apartment building.

28.1.1.2 The term *hotel,* wherever used in this *Code,* shall include a hotel, inn, club, motel, bed and breakfast, or any other structure meeting the definition of *hotel.*

Chapters 28 and 29 apply to various operations that do not specifically use the term *hotel* but are considered such by definition. The terms *dormitory* and *hotel* are defined in 3.3.46 and 3.3.105. In some cases, Chapters 28 and 29 apply even if the identification of the occupancy suggests the application of a different chapter. For example, a lodging or rooming house that accommodates more than 16 people is considered a hotel.

Conversely, some operations that would be expected to be covered by Chapters 28 and 29 are not. For example, the exception to 28/29.1.1.1 recognizes that the common dormitory design in which a group of bedrooms opens into a study or living room duplicates a typical apartment design in which several bedrooms open into a living room or kitchen. Because the design and the risk of fire are the same, the *Code* treats this arrangement as that of an apartment build-

Section 29.1 General Requirements

29.1.1 Application.

29.1.1.1 The requirements of this chapter apply to existing buildings or portions thereof currently occupied as hotel or dormitory occupancies. *(See also 28.1.1.)*

Exception: Any dormitory divided into suites of rooms, with one or more bedrooms opening into a living room or study that has a door opening into a common corridor serving a number of suites, shall be classified as an apartment building.

29.1.1.2 The term *hotel,* wherever used in this *Code*, shall include a hotel, inn, club, motel, bed and breakfast, or any other structure meeting the definition of *hotel.*

ing. Exhibit 28/29.1 illustrates the arrangement of a dormitory suite that would be treated as an apartment.

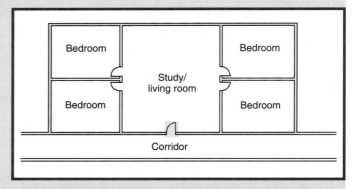

Exhibit 28/29.1 *Dormitory suite apartment.*

28.1.2 Mixed Occupancies.

28.1.2.1 Where another type of occupancy exists in the same building as a residential occupancy, the requirements of 6.1.14 of this *Code* shall apply.

29.1.2 Mixed Occupancies.

29.1.2.1 Where another type of occupancy exists in the same building as a residential occupancy, the requirements of 6.1.14 of this *Code* shall apply.

CHAPTER 28 • New   **CHAPTER 29 • Existing**

28.1.2.2 No dwelling unit of a residential occupancy shall have its sole means of egress pass through any nonresidential occupancy in the same building.

28.1.2.3 No multiple-dwelling unit of a residential occupancy shall be located above any nonresidential occupancy.

Exception No. 1:   Where the dwelling unit of the residential occupancy and exits therefrom are separated from the non-residential occupancy by construction having a fire resistance rating of not less than 1 hour.

Exception No. 2:   Where the nonresidential occupancy is protected throughout by an approved, supervised automatic sprinkler system in accordance with Section 9.7.

29.1.2.2 No dwelling unit of a residential occupancy shall have its sole means of egress pass through any nonresidential occupancy in the same building.

29.1.2.3 No multiple-dwelling unit of a residential occupancy shall be located above any nonresidential occupancy.

Exception No. 1:   Where the dwelling unit of the residential occupancy and exits therefrom are separated from the non-residential occupancy by construction having a fire resistance rating of not less than 1 hour.

Exception No. 2:   Where the nonresidential occupancy is protected throughout by an approved, supervised automatic sprinkler system in accordance with Section 9.7.

Exception No. 3:   A building with not more than two dwelling units above a nonresidential occupancy shall be permitted, provided that the nonresidential occupancy is protected by an automatic fire detection system in accordance with Section 9.6.

Residential occupancies often exist in buildings that also house assembly, mercantile, or business occupancies. These nonresidential occupancies might pose an additional threat, because they are not constantly occupied. An undetected fire in an unoccupied area has the potential to affect the tenability of the residential portion of the building before occu-

pants can be awakened and take the appropriate actions for safe egress. Therefore, the requirements of 28.1.2 and 29.1.2 help to ensure that it is safe to have hotels or dormitories within these mixed occupancy buildings by providing the necessary protection and separation.

28.1.3 Definitions.

Terms applicable to this chapter are defined in Chapter 3 of this *Code*; where necessary, other terms are defined in the text.

> **Dormitory.** See 3.3.46.
> **Guest Room.** See 3.3.94.
> **Guest Suite.** See 3.3.95.
> **Hotel.** See 3.3.105.

29.1.3 Definitions.

Terms applicable to this chapter are defined in Chapter 3 of this *Code*; where necessary, other terms are defined in the text.

> **Dormitory.** See 3.3.46.
> **Guest Room.** See 3.3.94.
> **Guest Suite.** See 3.3.95.
> **Hotel.** See 3.3.105.

In the definition of *dormitory* in 3.3.46, the wording "without individual cooking facilities" refers to the absence of cooking equipment in any room or unit of a dormitory. If such equipment is present throughout a facility, the occupancy should be classified as an apartment building. The wording "with or without meals" indicates the *Code*'s acceptance of a central cafeteria used to serve meals for the occupants of a dormitory.

The requirements of Chapters 28 and 29 often are worded to apply specifically within a guest room or guest suite. The first sentence of A.3.3.46 clarifies that, where the chapter uses the terms *guest room* and *guest suite*, the intent is that the requirement also be applied to dormitory rooms used for sleeping and living purposes.

A residential occupancy called a lodging house or rooming house by its operators but with sleeping accommodations for more than 16 persons is classified as a hotel and is regulated under the provisions of Chapter 28 or 29. In the A.3.3.105 annex verbiage on the definition of the term *hotel*, the reference to a 30-day time period helps to define *transient*. Where guest rooms or guest suites have individual cooking facilities the appropriate classification is "apartment building." However, certain facilities (for example, extended-stay hotels) might contain the potential for

hazards associated with both a hotel (unfamiliarity with surroundings) and an apartment building (higher fuel load, greater number of ignition sources, and travel through multiple rooms). In such cases, the authority having jurisdiction might permit the building to be classified as a mixed occupancy (hotel and apartment building) and apply the more restrictive requirements.

28.1.4 Classification of Occupancy.

(See 28.1.3.)

28.1.5 Classification of Hazard of Contents.

The contents of residential occupancies shall be classified as ordinary hazard in accordance with 6.2.2. For the design of automatic sprinkler systems, the classification of contents in NFPA 13, *Standard for the Installation of Sprinkler Systems,* shall apply.

NFPA 13, *Standard for the Installation of Sprinkler Systems,* classifies the contents of a hotel or dormitory occupancy building as light hazard for the purpose of designing automatic sprinkler systems.[1] The differ-

29.1.4 Classification of Occupancy.

(See 29.1.3.)

29.1.5 Classification of Hazard of Contents.

The contents of residential occupancies shall be classified as ordinary hazard in accordance with 6.2.2. For the design of automatic sprinkler systems, the classification of contents in NFPA 13, *Standard for the Installation of Sprinkler Systems,* shall apply.

ence in classification in the *Code* is based on the threat to life or life safety (ordinary) versus the challenge to the extinguishing capability of the automatic sprinkler system (light).

28.1.6 Minimum Construction Requirements.

(No special requirements.)

Although Chapters 28 and 29 do not establish minimum construction requirements, if the hotel contains an assembly occupancy, Chapters 12 and 13 do estab-

29.1.6 Minimum Construction Requirements.

(No special requirements.)

lish minimum construction requirements based on the location of the assembly occupancy within the building.

28.1.7 Occupant Load.

The occupant load, in number of persons for whom means of egress and other provisions are required, shall be determined on the basis of the occupant load factors of Table 7.3.1.2 that are characteristic of the use of the space or shall be determined as the maximum probable population of the space under consideration, whichever is greater.

The amount of material presented in 28/29.1.7 has been reduced for the 2000 edition of the *Code*, because all occupant load factors have been moved to Table

29.1.7 Occupant Load.

The occupant load, in number of persons for whom means of egress and other provisions are required, shall be determined on the basis of the occupant load factors of Table 7.3.1.2 that are characteristic of the use of the space or shall be determined as the maximum probable population of the space under consideration, whichever is greater.

7.3.1.2 in the chapter addressing means of egress. Note that the occupant load factors in Table 7.3.1.2 for residential use do not preclude the need for providing egress capacity from concentrated sleeping areas (bunk rooms) based on the maximum probable population rather than on the calculated occupant load using floor area. If the actual population of a bunk room exceeds 1 person per 200 ft² (18.6 m²), the egress capacity features (for example, door widths) must be designed based on the actual number of occupants.

See Section 7.3 for further details on the use of occupant load for determining the capacity of the means of egress.

The occupant load calculations for areas of hotels used for nonresidential purposes should be based on the occupant load factors applicable to the use of the area.

Section 28.2 Means of Egress Requirements

28.2.1 General.

Means of egress from guest rooms or guest suites to the outside of the building shall be in accordance with Chapter 7 and this chapter. Means of escape within the guest room or guest suite shall comply with the provisions of Section 24.2 for one- and two-family dwellings. For the purpose of application of the requirements of Chapter 24, the terms *guest room* and *guest suite* shall be synonymous with the terms *dwelling or living unit*.

Subsection 28/29.2.1 requires that every guest room or guest suite is to comply with Section 24.2, which addresses means of escape in one- and two-family dwellings. This mandatory reference to Chapter 24 is important for several reasons. First, it establishes a requirement for two means of escape from every sleeping room and living area of a guest suite having two rooms or more. Subsection 24.2.2 establishes several acceptable types of secondary means of escape, the most common of which is an operable window with specified minimum opening dimensions. A secondary means of escape is exempted if a guest suite is protected by an automatic sprinkler system. Note that 24.2.2 does not require the entire building to be sprinklered but only the guest suite that is deficient with respect to the secondary means of escape. However, a mandate for complete building sprinkler protection, such as that in 28.3.5.2, might be specified elsewhere.

28.2.2 Means of Egress Components.
28.2.2.1 General.
28.2.2.1.1 Components of means of egress shall be limited to the types described in 28.2.2.2 through 28.2.2.12.

Section 29.2 Means of Egress Requirements

29.2.1 General.

Means of egress from guest rooms or guest suites to the outside of the building shall be in accordance with Chapter 7 and this chapter. Means of escape within the guest room or guest suite shall comply with the provisions of Section 24.2 for one- and two-family dwellings. For the purpose of application of the requirements of Chapter 24, the terms *guest room* and *guest suite* shall be synonymous with the terms *dwelling* or *living unit*.

A second important provision of Section 24.2 is that the means of egress provisions of Chapter 7 do not apply within the guest room or guest suite unless they are specifically referenced. For example, the minimum width of means of escape doors within a guest room or guest suite is 28 in. (71 cm), rather than the 32-in. (81-cm) minimum width specified for means of egress by Chapter 7. The requirement of Chapter 7 applies to the door from the room or suite to the common corridor, because this door is the transition point at which means of escape ends and the standard means of egress begins. Chapter 24 also permits the use of winders and spiral stairs within a guest room or guest suite, and the provisions of Chapter 24 for headroom apply within the guest room or suite, superceding those of Chapter 7. See the commentary on Chapter 24 for additional information on means of escape from living units.

29.2.2 Means of Egress Components.
29.2.2.1 General.
29.2.2.1.1 Components of means of egress shall be limited to the types described in 29.2.2.2 through 29.2.2.12.

28.2.2.1.2 In buildings protected throughout by an approved, supervised automatic sprinkler system in accordance with 28.3.5, exit enclosures shall have a fire resistance rating of not less than 1 hour, and the fire protection rating of doors shall be not less than 1 hour.

29.2.2.1.2 In buildings protected throughout by an approved automatic sprinkler system in accordance with 29.3.5, exit enclosures shall have a fire resistance rating of not less than 1 hour, and the fire protection rating of doors shall be not less than 1 hour.

The general provisions for the means of egress components in hotels and dormitories modify the provisions of Chapter 7 in the following two areas:

(1) Limits on the components of the means of egress
(2) Protection of the means of egress

First, a general reference to the components of the means of egress in Chapter 7 is made in place of repeating its myriad provisions. Most of these components are permitted in both new and existing hotels and dormitories. Some of the components are permitted to be used in accordance with the provisions of Chapter 7 and the additional provisions of Chapters 28 and 29. For example, delayed-egress locks are permitted by Exception No. 1 to 28.2.2.2.2 and Exception No. 1 to 29.2.2.2.2, which allow their use in accordance with 7.2.1.6.1 if not more than one device is located in any single egress path.

If not permitted, no reference to an egress component is made in the specific occupancy chapter. For example, escalators and fire escape stairs are only permitted in existing hotels. Therefore, 29.2.2.8 and 29.2.2.9 contain specific references to Chapter 7, while 28.2.2.8 and 28.2.2.9 are reserved and contain no such reference. Neither chapter permits the use of slide escapes; consequently, no reference to slide escapes is made within the means of egress sections of either chapter.

Second, Chapters 28 and 29 recognize the relatively low fuel loads of hotels and permit a fire resistance rating of 1 hour for exit enclosures and other vertical openings (see Exception No. 2 to 28.3.1.1 and Exception No. 2 to 29.3.1.1) in buildings protected throughout by an approved, supervised automatic sprinkler system.

Because the *Code* currently requires that most new hotels and dormitories be protected throughout by an approved automatic sprinkler system, a 1-hour fire resistance–rated exit enclosure will typically be permitted in new construction. However, if the exception to 28.3.5.2—which exempts certain building ar-

rangements from the sprinkler requirement—is exercised, the 1-hour rated enclosure option of 28.2.2.1.2 is not permitted. This situation dictates a default to the Chapter 7 exit enclosure requirements, which, because they are based on the number of stories connected by the exit enclosure, might require 2-hour fire resistance–rated enclosures. See 7.1.3.2.

The reduction to a 1-hour fire resistance–rated enclosure for exits is not permitted for assembly, mercantile, or business occupancies and, therefore, cannot be used where mixed hotel/assembly, hotel/mercantile, or hotel/business occupancies are involved. In facilities of four or more stories, where hotel occupancies and other occupancies are adequately separated and treated independently, a 1-hour exit enclosure in the hotel portion and a 2-hour enclosure elsewhere might be permitted.

Exhibit 28/29.2 illustrates the modification to the requirements for protection of exit enclosures and other vertical openings in a fully sprinklered building. The provision for the 1-hour exit enclosure does not apply to other occupancies in a hotel complex or in mixed occupancies.

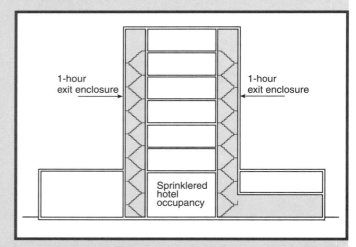

Exhibit 28/29.2 *Exit enclosure separation—sprinklered building.*

28.2.2.2 Doors.

28.2.2.2.1 Doors complying with 7.2.1 shall be permitted.

28.2.2.2.2 No door in any means of egress shall be locked against egress when the building is occupied.

Exception No. 1: Delayed-egress locks complying with 7.2.1.6.1 shall be permitted, provided that not more than one such device is located in any one egress path.

Exception No. 2: Access-controlled egress doors complying with 7.2.1.6.2 shall be permitted.

29.2.2.2 Doors.

29.2.2.2.1 Doors complying with 7.2.1 shall be permitted.

29.2.2.2.2 No door in any means of egress shall be locked against egress when the building is occupied.

Exception No. 1: Delayed-egress locks complying with 7.2.1.6.1 shall be permitted, provided that not more than one such device is located in any one egress path.

Exception No. 2: Access-controlled egress doors complying with 7.2.1.6.2 shall be permitted.

Hotels and dormitories are prohibited from having any door locked against egress while the building is occupied. This requirement permits a door to be equipped with a locking device that allows the door to be opened from within the building for the purpose of egress but does not allow the door to be opened from outside the building. Ordinary double-cylinder locks and chain locks do not meet these criteria, because they require keys for operation.

The language of 7.2.1.5.1 is clear. Paragraph 7.2.1.5.1 states that locks, if provided, are not to require the use of a key, a tool, or special knowledge or effort for operation from the egress side of the building. This requirement prohibits double-cylinder locks and chain locks that require a key to operate the door from the inside. Paragraph 7.2.1.5.4 requires the use of a simple operation to open a door; locks that require two-handed knobs and similar operations are prohibited.

Hotel room doors provide security for the occupants in the room. Recognizing this additional function, Chapter 7 permits the use of security chains or rods, as well as locks, on hotel room doors and also permits releasing devices in addition to the doorknob or lever. The permitted number of additional releasing actions differs for new and existing buildings. One additional releasing action is permitted for new construction and two additional actions are permitted in existing buildings. The typical hotel room door has three devices: a latch, a lock, and a security chain or rod. This arrangement is permitted in existing buildings, provided that only two additional releasing operations are needed for unlocking. This arrangement would also be permitted in new construction, provided that the latch and lock set are interconnected

so that the lock bolt and the latch will retract simultaneously when the latch handle is turned from the inside; thus, only one releasing action is needed for the two devices. The second action is the release of the security chain or rod. The overriding requirement for any of these devices is that they not require the use of a key, a tool, or special knowledge or effort to operate.

Exception No. 1 to 28.2.2.2.2 and Exception No. 1 to 29.2.2.2.2 recognize the use of the delayed-egress lock detailed in 7.2.1.6.1 if not more than one such lock is located in any single egress path. The use of a delayed-egress lock requires that the building be protected throughout by either an automatic sprinkler or automatic fire detection system. The 15-second or 30-second delay permitted by 7.2.1.6.1 does not affect the immediate release of the lock upon activation of sprinklers or detectors or upon loss of power to the lock. The delay device provides the security needed for doors that are used infrequently. At the same time, the door remains available for emergency use. Chains and padlocks do not provide these safety features.

Exception No. 1 to 7.2.1.5.2 permits selected exit stair enclosure doors to be locked from the stairwell side, while other stair enclosure doors must remain unlocked. If the selected re-entry provisions are not used, one of the other two options specified by 7.2.1.5.2 must be used for stair enclosures serving five or more stories. Doors are permitted to be locked from the stairwell side if initiation of the building fire alarm system automatically unlocks the door; otherwise, all stair enclosure doors must remain unlocked at all times.

CHAPTER 28 • New

CHAPTER 29 • Existing

28.2.2.2.3 Revolving doors complying with 7.2.1.10 shall be permitted.

28.2.2.2.4 Horizontal sliding doors, as permitted by 7.2.1.14, shall not be used across corridors.

Note that the special form of horizontal sliding door detailed in 7.2.1.14 is prohibited for cross-corridor

28.2.2.3 Stairs. Stairs complying with 7.2.2 shall be permitted.

28.2.2.4 Smokeproof Enclosures. Smokeproof enclosures complying with 7.2.3 shall be permitted.

28.2.2.5 Horizontal Exits. Horizontal exits complying with 7.2.4 shall be permitted.

28.2.2.6 Ramps. Ramps complying with 7.2.5 shall be permitted.

28.2.2.7 Exit Passageways. Exit passageways complying with 7.2.6 shall be permitted.

28.2.2.8 (Reserved.)

28.2.2.9 (Reserved.)

28.2.2.10 Fire Escape Ladders. Fire escape ladders complying with 7.2.9 shall be permitted.

28.2.2.11 Alternating Tread Devices. Alternating tread devices complying with 7.2.11 shall be permitted.

28.2.2.12* Areas of Refuge. Areas of refuge complying with 7.2.12 shall be permitted.

Exception: In buildings protected throughout by an approved, supervised automatic sprinkler system in accordance with 28.3.5, the two accessible rooms or spaces separated from each other by smoke-resistive partitions in accordance

29.2.2.2.3 Revolving doors complying with 7.2.1.10 shall be permitted.

29.2.2.2.4 Horizontal sliding doors, as permitted by 7.2.1.14, shall not be used across corridors.

installations in both new and existing hotels and dormitories.

29.2.2.3 Stairs. Stairs complying with 7.2.2 shall be permitted.

29.2.2.4 Smokeproof Enclosures. Smokeproof enclosures complying with 7.2.3 shall be permitted.

29.2.2.5 Horizontal Exits. Horizontal exits complying with 7.2.4 shall be permitted.

29.2.2.6 Ramps. Ramps complying with 7.2.5 shall be permitted.

29.2.2.7 Exit Passageways. Exit passageways complying with 7.2.6 shall be permitted.

29.2.2.8* Escalators. Escalators previously approved as a component in a means of egress shall be permitted to continue to be considered in compliance.

A.29.2.2.8 Due to the nature of escalators, they are no longer acceptable as a component in a means of egress. However, since many escalators have been used for exit access and exit discharge in the past, they are permitted to continue to be considered in compliance. Very few escalators have ever been installed in a manner to qualify as an exit. For information on escalator protection and requirements, see previous editions of the *Code.*

29.2.2.9 Fire Escape Stairs. Fire escape stairs complying with 7.2.8 shall be permitted.

29.2.2.10 Fire Escape Ladders. Fire escape ladders complying with 7.2.9 shall be permitted.

29.2.2.11 Alternating Tread Devices. Alternating tread devices complying with 7.2.11 shall be permitted.

29.2.2.12* Areas of Refuge. Areas of refuge complying with 7.2.12 shall be permitted.

Exception: In buildings protected throughout by an approved, supervised automatic sprinkler system in accordance with 29.3.5, the two accessible rooms or spaces separated from each other by smoke-resistive partitions in accordance with the definition of area of refuge in 3.3.14 shall not be required.

A.28.2.2.12 The provision of 28.2.2.12 permits the entire floor to serve as an area of refuge where it is protected in accordance with 28.3.5. The provision is acceptable because supervised automatic sprinkler systems have built-in signals for monitoring features of the system, such as the opening and closing of water control valves. Such systems also monitor pump power supplies, water tank levels, and conditions that will impair the satisfactory operation of the sprinkler system. Because of these monitoring features, supervised automatic sprinkler systems have a high level of satisfactory performance and response to fire conditions.

Paragraph 7.5.4.1 requires that areas accessible to persons with severe mobility impairment be provided with accessible means of egress. For stories above the level of exit discharge, where providing ramps is usually not feasible, areas of refuge (see 7.2.12) will typically be used to meet the requirements for accessible means of egress. The exception to 28.2.2.12 allows a sprinklered story of a hotel or dormitory to be considered an area of refuge, even if an occupant does not have access to any of the guest rooms and is confined to the exit access corridor. Due to the effectiveness of the sprinkler system, an occupant with mobility impairment should be able to remain on the floor without experiencing untenable conditions. However, because locked guest room doors create inaccessibility to spaces other than the corridor, the corridor effectively serves as the area

with the definition of area of refuge in 3.3.14 shall not be required.

A.29.2.2.12 The provision of 29.2.2.12 permits the entire floor to serve as an area of refuge where it is protected in accordance with 29.3.5. The provision is acceptable because supervised automatic sprinkler systems have built-in signals for monitoring features of the system, such as the opening and closing of water control valves. Such systems also monitor pump power supplies, water tank levels, and conditions that will impair the satisfactory operation of the sprinkler system. Because of these monitoring features, supervised automatic sprinkler systems have a high level of satisfactory performance and response to fire conditions.

of refuge. The authority having jurisdiction might choose to require demonstrations of tenability, as required by 7.2.12.3.2, if the aggregate corridor area on the story is less than 1000 ft² (93 m²), regardless of the area of the entire floor.

Existing hotels are exempt from the provisions of 7.5.4.1, which require that areas accessible to persons with severe mobility impairment be provided with accessible means of egress. Therefore, areas of refuge are not required but are permitted to serve within the means of egress. If an area of refuge is used within an existing hotel, the exception to 29.2.2.12 allows a sprinklered story of a hotel or dormitory to be considered an area of refuge, even if an occupant does not have access to any of the guest rooms and is confined to the exit access corridor.

28.2.3 Capacity of Means of Egress.

28.2.3.1 The capacity of means of egress shall be in accordance with Section 7.3.

28.2.3.2 Street floor exits shall be sufficient for the occupant load of the street floor plus the required capacity of stairs and ramps discharging onto the street floor.

When occupants from upper floors are discharged from exit stair enclosures onto the street floor (in accordance with 7.7.2) and mix with occupants of the street floor in attempting egress to the exterior, the result is an increased demand on street floor egress components, such as exit doors. Therefore, the *Code*

29.2.3 Capacity of Means of Egress.

29.2.3.1 The capacity of means of egress shall be in accordance with Section 7.3.

29.2.3.2 Street floor exits shall be sufficient for the occupant load of the street floor plus the required capacity of stairs and ramps discharging onto the street floor.

requires that street floor exits be sized to handle the combined capacity.

Exhibit 28/29.3 illustrates the traditional, grand lobby design found in many hotels in which multiple exit stairs and street floor exits converge at one or two exterior door locations. The required aggregate

CHAPTER 28 • New	CHAPTER 29 • Existing

capacity of doors A and B is based on the number of people expected to use them. Assuming that the street floor has an occupant load of 400 persons and each of the two enclosed exit stairs (that is, stair 1 and stair 2) discharging into the street floor has a required capacity of 200 persons (that is, a maximum of 50 percent of the 400-person occupant load of the second or third floor via stair 1 and a maximum of 50 percent of the 400-person occupant load of the basement via stair 2), the required egress capacity for the street floor would be 800 persons. The unobstructed door or level travel width required to accommodate 800 persons is 160 in. (406 cm). The opening provided by each pair of doors, A and B, needs to be 80 in. (203 cm) in clear, unobstructed width.

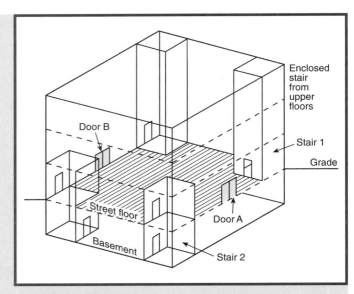

Exhibit 28/29.3 *Egress capacity for street floor.*

28.2.3.3 The corridor width shall be sufficient to accommodate the required occupant load, but shall be not less than 44 in. (112 cm).

Exception:* Corridors within individual guest rooms or individual guest suites.

A.28.2.3.3 Exception This exception applies to corridors within an individual room or suite and does not apply where a suite can be subdivided and rented separately.

28.2.4 Number of Exits.

Not less than two separate exits shall be provided on each story. *(See also Section 7.4.)*

Exception: Buildings of four stories or less protected throughout by an approved, supervised automatic sprinkler system in accordance with 28.3.5, with not more than four guest rooms or guest suites per floor, shall be permitted to have a single exit under the following conditions:

(a) The stairway is completely enclosed or separated by barriers having a fire resistance rating of not less than 1 hour, with self-closing 1-hour fire protection–rated doors protecting all openings between the stairway enclosure and the building.

(b) The stairway does not serve more than one-half of a story below the level of exit discharge.

29.2.4 Number of Exits.

Not less than two exits shall be accessible from every floor, including floors below the level of exit discharge and floors occupied for public purposes.

Exception: Buildings of four stories or less protected throughout by an approved, supervised automatic sprinkler system in accordance with 29.3.5, with not more than four guest rooms or guest suites per floor, shall be permitted to have a single exit under the following conditions:

(a) The stairway is completely enclosed or separated by barriers having a fire resistance rating of not less than 1 hour with self-closing 1-hour fire protection–rated doors protecting all openings between the stairway enclosure and the building.

(b) The stairway does not serve more than one-half of a story below the level of exit discharge.

| CHAPTER 28 • New | CHAPTER 29 • Existing |

(c) All corridors serving as access to exits have not less than a 1-hour fire resistance rating.

(d) The travel distance from the entrance door of any guest room or guest suite to an exit does not exceed 35 ft (10.7 m).

(e) Horizontal and vertical separation with a fire rating of not less than ½ hour is provided between guest rooms or guest suites.

(c) All corridors serving as access to exits have not less than a 1-hour fire resistance rating.

(d) The travel distance from the entrance door of any guest room or guest suite to an exit does not exceed 35 ft (10.7 m).

(e) Horizontal and vertical separation with a fire rating of not less than ½ hour is provided between guest rooms or guest suites.

Although 28.2.4 and 29.2.4 require a minimum of two separate exits from each floor, 7.4.1.2 requires a third exit when the occupant load of a floor exceeds 500 and a fourth exit when it exceeds 1000. The requirement of 7.4.1.2 will probably have little effect on modern hotel design practices, because floors large enough to accommodate more than 500 persons would probably be provided with more than two exits based on travel distance limit considerations.

28.2.5 Arrangement of Means of Egress.

28.2.5.1 Access to all required exits shall be in accordance with Section 7.5.

Exception: The distance between exits addressed by 7.5.1.4 shall not apply to common nonlooped exit access corridors in buildings that have corridor doors from the guest room or guest suite that are arranged such that the exits are located in opposite directions from such doors.

28.2.5.2 Common paths of travel shall not exceed 35 ft (10.7 m). Travel within a guest room or guest suite shall not be included when calculating common path of travel.

Exception: In buildings protected throughout by an approved, supervised automatic sprinkler system in accordance with 28.3.5, common path of travel shall not exceed 50 ft (15 m).

28.2.5.3 Dead-end corridors shall not exceed 35 ft (10.7 m).

Exception: In buildings protected throughout by an approved, supervised automatic sprinkler system in accordance with 28.3.5, dead-end corridors shall not exceed 50 ft (15 m).

28.2.5.4 Any guest room or any guest suite of rooms in excess of 2000 ft² (185 m²) shall be provided with not less than two exit access doors remotely located from each other.

29.2.5 Arrangement of Means of Egress.

29.2.5.1 Access to all required exits shall be in accordance with Section 7.5.

29.2.5.2 Common paths of travel shall not exceed 35 ft (10.7 m). Travel within a guest room or guest suite shall not be included when calculating common path of travel.

Exception: In buildings protected throughout by an approved, supervised automatic sprinkler system in accordance with 29.3.5, common path of travel shall not exceed 50 ft (15 m).

29.2.5.3 Dead-end corridors shall not exceed 50 ft (15 m).

The provisions for the arrangement of the means of egress for hotels differ significantly from the provisions in Chapter 7. The first difference appears in 28.2.5.1, which addresses the remoteness of exits.

Applying the remoteness of exits provisions of 7.5.1.4 could result in a corridor that is longer than is necessary for the efficient use of the space. The exception to 28.2.5.1 offers some relief. Exhibit 28/29.4 helps

CHAPTER 28 • New	CHAPTER 29 • Existing

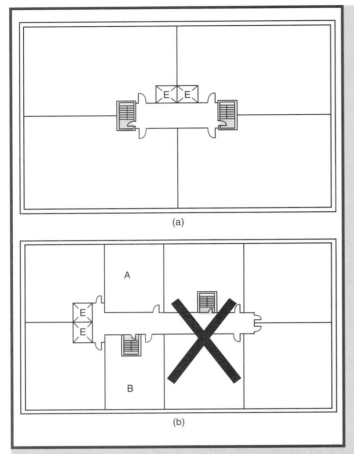

Exhibit 28/29.4 New hotels/dormitories—exit remoteness.

to clarify the intent of the exception to 28.2.5.1. In illustration (a) of Exhibit 28/29.4, all four guest rooms/ guest suites have access to two exits immediately upon leaving the guest room/guest suite and entering the exit access corridor. This arrangement meets the provisions of the exception. Contrast this arrangement with that depicted in illustration (b) of Exhibit 28/29.4, where only guest rooms/guest suites A and B have access to two exits immediately upon leaving the guest room/guest suite and entering the exit access corridor. The other guest rooms/guest suites do not have immediate access to two exits. This arrangement does not meet the provisions of the exception to 28.2.5.1.

The concepts underlying the limitations imposed on common paths of travel and dead-end corridors

are similar but not identical to those explained in the commentary on 7.5.1.6. Because of modifications made by Chapters 28 and 29 in defining where common path of travel begins, the difference between common paths of travel and dead-end corridors is less pronounced for hotels and dormitories. For most other occupancies, common path of travel is measured from the most remote point subject to occupancy to the point where occupants have a choice of traveling in independent directions (see Exception No. 2 to 7.5.1.2 and the definition of *common path of travel* in 3.3.32). For hotels, the travel within the guest room, though regulated by 28.2.6.1 and 29.2.6.1 for distance, is not included as part of the common path of travel. Therefore, common path of travel, as illustrated by the solid arrows in Exhibit 28/29.5, is measured from the room door to the point where occupants have a choice of traveling in independent directions. This depiction can be thought of as a modified common path of travel, because measurement does not extend into the guest room or guest suite.

The distances permitted for common path of travel in new and existing hotels also differs. Because most new hotels are required to be sprinklered (see 28.3.5.2), the 35-ft (10.7-m) modified common path of travel and dead-end corridor limitations permitted

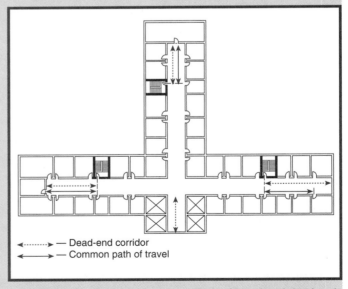

— - - - - - ▷ — Dead-end corridor
◄━━━━━▶ — Common path of travel

Exhibit 28/29.5 Modified common path of travel and dead-end corridors in a hotel.

by 28.2.5.2 and 28.2.5.3 will usually be supplanted by the 50-ft (15-m) limitation permitted by the exceptions to 28.2.5.2 and 28.2.5.3. However, if a building can comply with the exception to 28.3.5.2, which exempts sprinklers, the 35-ft (10.7-m) common path of travel and dead-end corridor limitations would apply.

In existing hotels, automatic sprinklers are not required. However, if the building is protected throughout by an approved, supervised automatic

sprinkler system, the common path of travel is permitted to be 50 ft (15 m), which is the same distance permitted for the length of existing dead-end corridors, regardless of sprinkler system considerations.

While not considered part of the common path of travel, travel within a guest room or a guest suite in a new hotel is regulated by 28.2.5.4, which limits single exit access to rooms and suites not larger than 2000 ft² (185 m²).

28.2.6 Travel Distance to Exits.

28.2.6.1 Travel distance within a guest room or guest suite to a corridor door shall not exceed 75 ft (23 m).

Exception: A travel distance not exceeding 125 ft (38 m) shall be permitted in buildings protected by an approved, supervised automatic sprinkler system in accordance with 28.3.5.

28.2.6.2 Travel distance from the corridor door of any guest room or guest suite to the nearest exit, measured in accordance with Section 7.6, shall not exceed 100 ft (30 m).

Exception No. 1: The permitted travel distance to exits shall not exceed 200 ft (60 m) for exterior ways of exit access arranged in accordance with 7.5.3.

Exception No. 2: The permitted travel distance to exits shall not exceed 200 ft (60 m) where the exit access and any portion of the building that is tributary to the exit access are protected throughout by an approved, supervised automatic sprinkler system in accordance with 28.3.5. In addition, the portion of the building in which the 200-ft (60-m) travel distance is permitted shall be separated from the remainder of the building by construction having a fire resistance rating of not less than 1 hour, for buildings not more than three stories in height, and 2 hours for buildings more than three stories in height.

29.2.6 Travel Distance to Exits.

29.2.6.1 Travel distance within a guest room or guest suite to a corridor door shall not exceed 75 ft (23 m).

Exception: A travel distance not exceeding 125 ft (38 m) shall be permitted in buildings protected by an approved automatic sprinkler system in accordance with 29.3.5.

29.2.6.2 Travel distance from the corridor door of any guest room or guest suite to the nearest exit, measured in accordance with Section 7.6, shall not exceed 100 ft (30 m).

Exception No. 1: The permitted travel distance to exits shall not exceed 200 ft (60 m) for exterior ways of exit access arranged in accordance with 7.5.3.

Exception No. 2: The permitted travel distance to exits shall not exceed 200 ft (60 m) where the exit access and any portion of the building that is tributary to the exit access are protected throughout by an approved automatic sprinkler system in accordance with 29.3.5. In addition, the portion of the building in which the 200-ft (60-m) travel distance is permitted shall be separated from the remainder of the building by construction having a fire resistance rating of not less than 1 hour, for buildings not more than three stories in height, and 2 hours, for buildings more than three stories in height.

Travel distance limitations are divided into the following two portions of the overall travel distance:

(1) Travel within a room or suite of rooms to the room door
(2) Travel from the corridor door to the nearest exit

This concept and the distance limitations specified in 28/29.2.6.2 are illustrated in Exhibit 28/29.6. If

the travel distance within a room or suite or rooms is excessive, an additional remote door to the corridor can usually be added to correct the deficiency. Excessive travel distance within the corridor can usually be corrected by adding another exit.

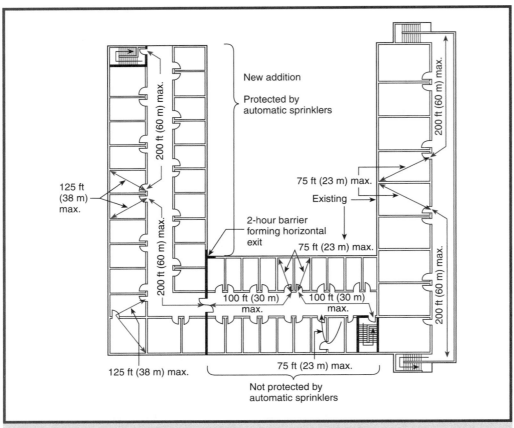

Exhibit 28/29.6 *Travel distance measurement and limitations in hotels.*

28.2.7 Discharge from Exits.

28.2.7.1 Exit discharge shall comply with Section 7.7.

28.2.7.2* Any required exit stair that is located so that it is necessary to pass through the lobby or other open space to reach the outside of the building shall be continuously enclosed down to a level of exit discharge or to a mezzanine within a lobby at a level of exit discharge.

A.28.2.7.2 Where open stairways are permitted, they are considered as exit access to exits rather than as exits, and the requirements for travel distance to exits include the travel on such stairs. *(See 7.6.2.)*

28.2.7.3 The distance of travel from the termination of the exit enclosure to an exterior door leading to a public way shall not exceed 100 ft (30 m).

29.2.7 Discharge from Exits.

29.2.7.1 Exit discharge shall comply with Section 7.7.

29.2.7.2* Any required exit stair that is located so that it is necessary to pass through the lobby or other open space to reach the outside of the building shall be continuously enclosed down to a level of exit discharge or to a mezzanine within a lobby at a level of exit discharge.

A.29.2.7.2 Where open stairways or escalators are permitted, they are considered as exit access to exits rather than as exits, and the requirements for travel distance to exits include the travel on such stairs and escalators. *(See 7.6.2.)*

29.2.7.3 The distance of travel from the termination of the exit enclosure to an exterior door leading to a public way shall not exceed 150 ft (45 m) in buildings protected throughout by an approved automatic sprinkler system in accordance with 29.3.5 and shall not exceed 100 ft (30 m) in all other buildings.

Section 7.7 allows a maximum of 50 percent of the number and capacity of exits to discharge through the street floor under limited conditions (see 7.7.2). Paragraph 28/29.2.7.2 modifies the restrictions of Section 7.7 by treating an exit that discharges onto a mezzanine within the lobby of a hotel (with subsequent open stair travel to the lobby floor on the level of exit discharge) as equivalent to an exit that discharges directly into the lobby at the level of exit discharge. Therefore, 50 percent of the exits can discharge onto a mezzanine; the other 50 percent must discharge directly outside. Occupants then travel across the mezzanine, along open stairs to the lobby level, and to the outside. However, the distance from the termination of the exit enclosure to the exterior door is limited to a maximum of 100 ft (30 m) in new buildings. In existing buildings the same 100-ft (30-m) limitation applies, unless the building is protected with automatic sprinklers, in which case the distance can be extended to 150 ft (45 m). The part of the exit

discharge that occurs within the building is depicted in Exhibit 28/29.7 by the arrow that connects the door at Stair 1 with the lobby door to the outside. See also the commentary on 7.7.2.

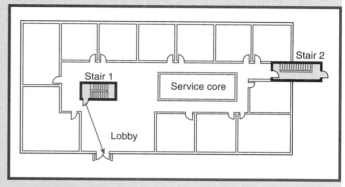

Exhibit 28/29.7 *Exit discharge through street floor.*

28.2.8 Illumination of Means of Egress.

Means of egress shall be illuminated in accordance with Section 7.8.

28.2.9 Emergency Lighting.

Emergency lighting in accordance with Section 7.9 shall be provided in all buildings with more than 25 rooms.

Exception: Where each guest room or guest suite has an exit direct to the outside of the building at street or ground level.

28.2.10 Marking of Means of Egress.

Means of egress shall have signs in accordance with Section 7.10.

28.2.11 Special Means of Egress Features.

(Reserved.)

Section 28.3 Protection

28.3.1 Protection of Vertical Openings.

28.3.1.1 Any vertical opening shall be enclosed or protected in accordance with 8.2.5.

29.2.8 Illumination of Means of Egress.

Means of egress shall be illuminated in accordance with Section 7.8.

29.2.9 Emergency Lighting.

Emergency lighting in accordance with Section 7.9 shall be provided in all buildings with more than 25 rooms.

Exception: Where each guest room or guest suite has an exit direct to the outside of the building at street or ground level.

29.2.10 Marking of Means of Egress.

Means of egress shall have signs in accordance with Section 7.10.

29.2.11 Special Means of Egress Features.

(Reserved.)

Section 29.3 Protection

29.3.1 Protection of Vertical Openings.

29.3.1.1 Any vertical opening shall be enclosed or protected in accordance with 8.2.5.

Exception No. 1:   Openings in accordance with 8.2.5.8 shall be permitted.

Exception No. 2:   In buildings protected throughout by an approved, supervised automatic sprinkler system in accordance with 28.3.5, the fire resistance of walls shall be not less than 1 hour and the fire protection rating of doors shall be not less than 1 hour.

Exception No. 1:   Openings in accordance with 8.2.5.8 shall be permitted.

Exception No. 2:   In buildings protected throughout by an approved automatic sprinkler system in accordance with 29.3.5, and in which exits and required ways of travel thereto are adequately safeguarded against fire and smoke within the building, or where every individual room has direct access to an exterior exit without passing through any public corridor, the protection of vertical openings that are not part of required exits shall not be required where approved by the authority having jurisdiction. The exemption shall be permitted only where such openings do not endanger required means of egress.

Exception No. 3:   In buildings not more than two stories in height, unprotected openings shall be permitted by the authority having jurisdiction to continue to be used where the building is protected throughout by an approved automatic sprinkler system in accordance with 29.3.5.

New hotels, except those in low-rise buildings where all guest sleeping rooms have a door to the exterior at grade or to an exterior exit access balcony, must be protected throughout by an approved, supervised automatic sprinkler system (see 28.3.5.2 and its exception). Therefore, most new hotels, by virtue of their compliance with the sprinkler requirements of 28.3.5.2, are permitted to use the 1-hour vertical enclosure protection option in accordance with Exception No. 2 to 28.3.1.1, regardless of the number of stories the vertical opening connects. See also the commentary following A.28/A.29.2.2.1.2.

The enclosure of vertical openings in existing hotels is provided by means of a performance approach. Openings must be either enclosed in accordance with 8.2.5, or they must satisfy the objectives of 4.5.5. Note, however, that no such performance approach is provided for new hotels.

The first exception to 28.3.1.1 and 29.3.1.1 is the same. Exception No. 1 permits an open stair connecting a maximum of two levels within a guest suite. This stair is permitted to serve as a means of escape.

Exception No. 2 to 29.3.1.1 allows existing unprotected openings under the following conditions:

(1) Openings are approved by the authority having jurisdiction.
(2) The building is totally sprinklered.
(3) Exits and exit accesses are adequately separated from the remainder of the building.
(4) In lieu of condition (3), every room has direct access to an exterior exit that does not require travel through a public corridor.
(5) Shafts that enclose required exit stairs are protected.

Exception No. 3 to 29.3.1.1 allows existing unprotected vertical openings under the following conditions:

(1) Openings are approved by the authority having jurisdiction.
(2) The building is not more than two stories.
(3) The building is totally sprinklered.

Therefore, unless an existing unprotected vertical opening complies with Exception No. 3 to 29.3.1.1, a building with a vertical opening is required to be either fully sprinklered or at least partially sprinklered.

28.3.1.2 No floor below the level of exit discharge used only for storage, heating equipment, or purposes other than residential occupancy shall have unprotected openings to floors used for residential purposes.

29.3.1.2 No floor below the level of exit discharge used only for storage, heating equipment, or purposes other than residential occupancy shall have unprotected openings to floors used for residential purposes.

CHAPTER 28 • New   **CHAPTER 29 • Existing**

28.3.2 Protection from Hazards.

28.3.2.1 Any room containing high-pressure boilers, refrigerating machinery, transformers, or other service equipment subject to possible explosion shall not be located directly under or directly adjacent to exits. All such rooms shall be effectively cut off from other parts of the building as specified in Section 8.4.

28.3.2.2 Hazardous Areas. Any hazardous area shall be protected in accordance with Section 8.4. The areas described in Table 28.3.2.2 shall be protected as indicated. Where sprinkler protection without fire-rated separation is used, areas shall be separated from other spaces by smoke partitions complying with 8.2.4.

29.3.2 Protection from Hazards.

29.3.2.1 Any room containing high pressure boilers, refrigerating machinery, transformers, or other service equipment subject to possible explosion shall not be located directly under or directly adjacent to exits. All such rooms shall be effectively cut off from other parts of the building as specified in Section 8.4.

29.3.2.2 Hazardous Areas. Any hazardous area shall be protected in accordance with Section 8.4. The areas described in Table 29.3.2.2 shall be protected as indicated. Where sprinkler protection without fire-rated separation is used, areas shall be separated from other spaces by smoke partitions complying with 8.2.4.

Table 28.3.2.2 Hazardous Area Protection

Hazardous Area Description	Separation/Protection
Boiler and fuel-fired heater rooms serving more than a single guest room or guest suite	1 hour and sprinklers
Employee locker rooms	1 hour or sprinklers
Gift or retail shops	1 hour or sprinklers
Bulk laundries	1 hour and sprinklers
Guest laundries ≤100 ft² (≤9.3 m²) outside of guest rooms or guest suites	1 hour or sprinklers†
Guest laundries >100 ft² (>9.3 m²) outside of guest rooms or guest suites	1 hour and sprinklers
Maintenance shops	1 hour and sprinklers
Storage rooms‡	1 hour or sprinklers
Trash collection rooms	1 hour and sprinklers

†Where automatic sprinkler protection is provided, no enclosure shall be required.

‡Where storage areas not exceeding 24 ft² (2.2 m²) are directly accessible from the guest room or guest suite, no separation or protection shall be required.

Table 29.3.2.2 Hazardous Area Protection

Hazardous Area Description	Separation/Protection
Boiler and fuel-fired heater rooms serving more than a single guest room or guest suite	1 hour or sprinklers
Employee locker rooms	1 hour or sprinklers
Gift or retail shops >100 ft² (>9.3m²)	1 hour or sprinklers†
Bulk laundries	1 hour or sprinklers
Guest laundries >100 ft² (>9.3m²) outside of guest rooms or guest suites	1 hour or sprinklers†
Maintenance shops	1 hour and sprinklers
Rooms or spaces used for storage of combustible supplies and equipment in quantities deemed hazardous by the authority having jurisdiction‡	1 hour or sprinklers
Trash collection rooms	1 hour and sprinklers

†Where automatic sprinkler protection is provided, no enclosure shall be required.

‡Where storage areas not exceeding 24 ft² (2.2 m²) are directly accessible from the guest room or guest suite, no separation or protection shall be required.

Note the differences in the hazardous area protection requirements for new and existing hotels. Particular attention should be given to the fact that automatic sprinklers are often used as an alternative to providing a rated separation. In new construction, many of the areas are required to be separated by construction with a 1-hour fire resistance rating and are also required to be protected by automatic sprinklers. In existing construction, automatic sprinklers are used as an alternative to rated construction, with the exception of trash collection rooms and maintenance shops, where both protection methods would be required.

While the list that appears in Table 28/29.3.2.2 provides specific direction for certain hazardous contents areas, it is not all-inclusive. Other areas that are deemed hazardous need to be provided with the appropriate level of protection in accordance with Section 8.4.

28.3.3 Interior Finish.

28.3.3.1 Interior finish shall be in accordance with Section 10.2.

28.3.3.2 Interior Wall and Ceiling Finish. Interior wall and ceiling finish materials complying with 10.2.3 shall be permitted as follows:

(1) Exit enclosures—Class A
(2) Lobbies and corridors—Class A or Class B
(3) Other spaces—Class A, Class B, or Class C

28.3.3.3 Interior Floor Finish. Interior floor finish in accordance with 10.2.7 shall be in accordance with Table 28.3.3.3.

Table 28.3.3.3 Interior Floor Finish

Location	Sprinklered	Nonsprinklered
Corridors	No requirement	Class II
Exits	No requirement	Class II

28.3.3.4* Furnishings and Decorations. New draperies, curtains, and other similar loosely hanging furnishings and decorations in hotels and dormitories shall be in accordance with the provisions of 10.3.1.

A.28.3.3.4 In nonsprinklered hotels, dormitories, or apartment buildings, new upholstered furniture located in corridors or areas not separated from corridors by corridor walls, as specified in the *Code*, should be tested in accordance with NFPA 261, *Standard Method of Test for Determining Resistance of Mock-Up Upholstered Furniture Material Assemblies to Ignition by Smoldering Cigarettes.* The char length is not to exceed 1½ in. (3.8 cm) and should be labeled to indicate such compliance.

Tables 28/29.3.3.3 are included to directly incorporate the provisions of 10.2.8.2 into the occupancy chapters,

29.3.3 Interior Finish.

29.3.3.1 Interior finish shall be in accordance with Section 10.2.

29.3.3.2 Interior Wall and Ceiling Finish. Interior wall and ceiling finish materials complying with 10.2.3 shall be permitted as follows:

(1) Exit enclosures—Class A or Class B
(2) Lobbies and corridors that are part of an exit access—Class A or Class B
(3) Other spaces—Class A, Class B, or Class C

29.3.3.3 Interior Floor Finish. Interior floor finish in accordance with 10.2.7 shall be in accordance with Table 29.3.3.3.

Exception: Previously installed and approved floor covering.

Table 29.3.3.3 Interior Floor Finish

Location	Sprinklered	Nonsprinklered
Corridors	No requirement	Class II
Exits	No requirement	Class II

29.3.3.4* Furnishings and Decorations. New draperies, curtains, and other similar loosely hanging furnishings and decorations in hotels and dormitories shall be in accordance with the provisions of 10.3.1.

A.29.3.3.4 In nonsprinklered hotels, dormitories, or apartment buildings, new upholstered furniture located in corridors or areas not separated from corridors by corridor walls, as specified in the *Code*, should be tested in accordance with NFPA 261, *Standard Method of Test for Determining Resistance of Mock-Up Upholstered Furniture Material Assemblies to Ignition by Smoldering Cigarettes.* The char length is not to exceed 1½ in. (3.8 cm), and should be labeled to indicate such compliance.

which relieves the *Code* user from referencing the provision of 10.2.8.2 itself.

Although there are no mandatory references to the upholstered furniture and mattress provisions of 10.3.2 through 10.3.4, most new hotels and dormitories will be sprinklered in accordance with the requirements of Chapter 28. Sprinklered building spaces are exempted from the provisions of 10.3.2 through 10.3.4 for upholstered furniture and mattresses, based on the assumption that the sprinklers will prevent room flashover. Existing hotels and dormitories are permitted to install sprinklers to take advantage of these exceptions. For nonsprinklered hotels and dormitories, A.28/A.29.3.3.4 recommends that—as a minimum—the cigarette ignition resistance of new furniture be proven by testing.

28.3.4 Detection, Alarm, and Communications Systems.

28.3.4.1 General. A fire alarm system in accordance with Section 9.6, except as modified by 28.3.4.2 through 28.3.4.5, shall be provided.

28.3.4.2 Initiation. The required fire alarm system shall be initiated by the following:

(1) Manual means in accordance with 9.6.2

(2) A manual fire alarm box located at the hotel desk or other convenient central control point under continuous supervision by responsible employees
(3) Any automatic sprinkler system
(4) Any required automatic detection system

Exception: The requirement of 28.3.4.2(4) shall not apply to sleeping room smoke detectors.

28.3.4.3 Notification.

28.3.4.3.1* Occupant notification shall be provided automatically in accordance with 9.6.3. Positive alarm sequence in accordance with 9.6.3.4 shall be permitted.

A.28.3.4.3.1 Visible signaling appliances might be governed by provisions of federal regulations in 28 *CFR* 36, Appendix A (Americans with Disabilities Act Accessibility Guidelines — ADAAG), Section 4.28, Alarms.

28.3.4.3.2* Guest rooms and guest suites specifically required and equipped to accommodate hearing impaired individuals shall be provided with a visible notification appliance.

29.3.4 Detection, Alarm, and Communications Systems.

29.3.4.1 General. A fire alarm system in accordance with Section 9.6, except as modified by 29.3.4.2 through 29.3.4.5, shall be provided.

Exception: Buildings where each guest room has exterior exit access in accordance with 7.5.3, and the building does not exceed three stories in height.

29.3.4.2 Initiation. The required fire alarm system shall be initiated by the following:

(1) Manual means in accordance with 9.6.2

Exception: Manual means as specified in 9.6.2, other than as required by 29.3.4.2(2), shall not be required where there are other effective means to activate the fire alarm system, such as complete automatic sprinkler or automatic detection systems.

(2) A manual fire alarm box located at the hotel desk or other convenient central control point under continuous supervision by responsible employees
(3) Any required automatic sprinkler system
(4) Any required automatic detection system

Exception: The requirements of 29.3.4.2(4) shall not apply to sleeping room smoke detectors.

29.3.4.3 Notification.

29.3.4.3.1 Occupant notification shall be provided automatically in accordance with 9.6.3. Positive alarm sequence in accordance with 9.6.3.4 shall be permitted. A presignal system in accordance with 9.6.3.3 shall be permitted.

29.3.4.3.2* Provisions shall be made for the immediate notification of the public fire department by telephone or other means in case of fire. Where there is no public fire department, notification shall be made to the private fire brigade.

CHAPTER 28 • New　　　　　　　　　　**CHAPTER 29 • Existing**

A.28.3.4.3.2 A quantity of such rooms and suites might be required to be equipped to accommodate hearing impaired individuals based on the total number of rooms in a transient lodging facility. *(See 28 CFR 36, Appendix A (Americans with Disabilities Act Accessibility Guidelines — ADAAG), Sections 9.1.3, 9.1.5, and 9.2.2(8).)*

28.3.4.3.3 In occupiable areas, other than guest rooms and guest suites, visible notification appliances shall be provided.

28.3.4.3.4 Annunciation in accordance with 9.6.7 shall be provided.

Exception: Buildings not more than two stories in height and with not more than 50 rooms.

28.3.4.3.5* Provisions shall be made for the immediate notification of the public fire department by telephone or other means in case of fire. Where there is no public fire department, notification shall be made to the private fire brigade.

A.28.3.4.3.5 The provision for immediate notification of the public fire department is intended to include, but is not limited to, all of the arrangements in 9.6.4. Other arrangements that depend on a clerk or other member of the staff to notify the fire department might also be permitted. In such cases, however, it is essential that a trained staff member and an immediately available means of calling the fire department are continuously available. If a telephone is to be used, it should not be of any type or arrangement that requires a coin or the unlocking of a device to contact the fire department.

A.29.3.4.3.2 The provision for immediate notification of the public fire department is intended to include, but is not limited to, all of the arrangements in 9.6.4. Other arrangements that depend on a clerk or other member of the staff to notify the fire department might also be permitted. In such cases, however, it is essential that a trained staff member and an immediately available means of calling the fire department are continuously available. If a telephone is to be used, it should not be of any type or arrangement that requires a coin or the unlocking of a device to contact the fire department.

The *Code* requires that, in addition to the normal distribution of manual fire alarm stations (see 9.6.2), the front desk, telephone operator's location, or similar location must also be equipped with a manual pull station. The intent is that a pull station is to be available at the location where guests phone in an emergency.

The *Code* exempts sleeping room smoke alarms from initiating the building fire alarm system. The smoke alarms installed in sleeping rooms are usually single-station alarms that are provided for the sole purpose of notifying the occupants of a smoky condition within that room. Thus, the alarms are not a part of a required automatic detection system and are not required to initiate the building alarm system. The *Code* does not prohibit room alarms from activating the system; however, this is discouraged to prevent numerous activations that could pose a nuisance alarm problem in hotels. There are alarms available that annunciate at a central point, alert the occupants of the room, and notify management of a problem in that room without sounding an alarm throughout the facility.

The exception to 29.3.4.2(1) eliminates the requirements for manual fire alarm boxes to be located so that all portions of a building are within 200 ft (60 m) of a manual fire alarm box (see Section 9.6) in existing hotels where an automatic sprinkler system or an automatic fire detection system is provided throughout the building. The alarm system is still required; only the requirement for additional manual fire alarm boxes is eliminated.

The location of audible alarm devices in hotels affects their audibility. In most new construction, corridor walls are of such character (soundproof) that a sounding device would be needed in each guest room or guest suite to meet the performance criterion for audibility throughout the building. The use of sounding devices only in the corridor might necessitate their operation at dangerous sound levels to awaken guests in their rooms. See Supplement 2 of this handbook.

The permitted use of positive alarm sequence by 28/29.3.4.3.1 recognizes a technology similar to a presignal system but with additional fail-safe features. See the commentary on 9.6.3.4.

Presignal systems have repeatedly been involved in delaying alarms in multiple-death fires and are not permitted in new construction. However, the occurrence of nuisance alarms in hotels is real, and presignal systems continue to be permitted in existing buildings. Therefore, if the presignal is to be transmitted to a building staff location (for example, front desk), 9.6.3.3 specifies that it must be received by trained staff. As a result, hotel employees assigned to signal-receiving locations must be well trained with respect to fire alarm signals and proper staff response to an alarm.

Neither 28.3.4.3.5 nor 29.3.4.3.2 requires a direct fire alarm connection to the fire department; however, direct connection is an excellent method of complying. The telephone addressed in A.28.3.4.3.5 and A.29.3.4.3.2 needs to be equipped for direct outside dial without going through a switchboard and should not be a pay phone.

House-powered, single-station smoke alarms are required in each sleeping room and living area located in a guest room or guest suite. The intent is to alert the occupant of the room to the presence of a fire originating in that room or suite. Normally, the alarms are not tied into the building fire alarm [see the exception to 28.3.4.2(4) and the exception to 29.3.4.2(4)]. The expected course of action is as follows:

(1) The smoke alarm alerts occupant of room; the occupant leaves the room.
(2) The self-closing device on the corridor door returns the door to its closed and latched position.
(3) The occupant pulls a manual alarm station, thereby initiating the building alarm system; occupant enters exit and leaves building.
(4) If the occupant fails to sound the alarm manually, compensation is provided in new construction by corridor smoke detectors or by automatic sprinklers (see the exception to 28.3.4.4).

In addition to requiring a smoke alarm in each sleeping room, a smoke alarm is required in each living area within the guest room or guest suite. These alarms are required for the following two reasons:

(1) The living area is often used for sleeping, even if such use was not the original intent.
(2) Most sleeping rooms are arranged so that a fire in the living area will rapidly block escape from the sleeping area.

If a corridor smoke detection system is provided, it must be maintained, since the system is required for new construction, unless the building is sprinklered. Removal of the system would be considered a renovation, and renovations must comply with the requirements for new construction to the extent practical.

28.3.4.4 Detection. A corridor smoke detection system in accordance with Section 9.6 shall be provided.

Exception: Buildings protected throughout by an approved, supervised automatic sprinkler system in accordance with 28.3.5.1.

28.3.4.5* Smoke Alarms. An approved single-station smoke alarm shall be installed in accordance with 9.6.2.10 in every guest room and every living area and sleeping room within a guest suite.

29.3.4.4 Detection. (Reserved.)

29.3.4.5* Smoke Alarms. An approved single-station smoke alarm shall be installed in accordance with 9.6.2.10 in every guest room and every living area and sleeping room within a guest suite. These alarms shall not be required to be interconnected. Single-station smoke alarms without a secondary (standby) power source shall be permitted.

A.28.3.4.5 Caution needs to be exercised in locating smoke detectors with regard to their proximity to bathrooms, cooking facilities, and HVAC outlets in order to prevent nuisance alarms.

28.3.5 Extinguishment Requirements.

28.3.5.1 Where an automatic sprinkler system is installed, either for total or partial building coverage, the system shall be in accordance with Section 9.7. In buildings up to and including four stories in height, systems in accordance with NFPA 13R, *Standard for the Installation of Sprinkler Systems in Residential Occupancies up to and Including Four Stories in Height,* shall be permitted.

Exception: The provisions for draft stops and closely spaced sprinklers in NFPA 13, Standard for the Installation of Sprinkler Systems, shall not be required for openings complying with 8.2.5.8 where the opening is within the guest room or guest suite.

28.3.5.2 All buildings shall be protected throughout by an approved, supervised automatic sprinkler system in accordance with 28.3.5.1.

Exception: Buildings other than high-rise buildings, where all guest sleeping rooms have a door that opens directly to the outside at street or ground level, or to exterior exit access arranged in accordance with 7.5.3.

28.3.5.3 Listed quick-response or listed residential sprinklers shall be used throughout guest rooms and guest room suites.

28.3.5.4 Open parking structures complying with NFPA 88A, *Standard for Parking Structures,* that are contiguous with hotels or dormitories shall be exempt from the sprinkler requirements of 28.3.5.2.

A.29.3.4.5 Caution needs to be exercised in locating smoke detectors with regard to their proximity to bathrooms, cooking facilities, and HVAC outlets in order to prevent nuisance alarms.

29.3.5 Extinguishment Requirements.

29.3.5.1* Where an automatic sprinkler system is installed, either for total or partial building coverage, the system shall be in accordance with Section 9.7. In buildings up to and including four stories in height, systems in accordance with NFPA 13R, *Standard for the Installation of Sprinkler Systems in Residential Occupancies up to and Including Four Stories in Height,* shall be permitted.

Exception No. 1: The provisions for draft stops and closely spaced sprinklers in NFPA 13, Standard for the Installation of Sprinkler Systems, shall not be required for openings complying with 8.2.5.8 where the opening is within the guest room or guest suite.

Exception No. 2: In guest rooms and in guest room suites, sprinkler installations shall not be required in closets not exceeding 24 ft² (2.2 m²) and in bathrooms not exceeding 55 ft² (5.1 m²).

A.29.3.5.1 Although not required by the *Code,* the use of residential sprinklers or quick-response sprinklers is encouraged for new installations of sprinkler systems within dwelling units, apartments, and guest rooms. Caution should be exercised, as the system needs to be designed for the sprinkler being used.

29.3.5.2 All high-rise buildings shall be protected throughout by an approved, supervised automatic sprinkler system in accordance with 29.3.5.1.

Exception: Where each guest room or guest suite has exterior exit access in accordance with 7.5.3.

29.3.5.3 (Reserved.)

29.3.5.4 (Reserved.)

28.3.5.5 Portable fire extinguishers shall be provided as specified in 9.7.4.1 in hazardous areas addressed by 28.3.2.2.

Exception: In buildings protected throughout with an approved, supervised automatic sprinkler system in accordance with Section 9.7.

New hotel and dormitory buildings must be protected throughout by an approved, supervised automatic sprinkler system—unless the building is a low-rise structure and all guest rooms have doors to the exterior at grade or to exterior exit access balconies. The disproportionate percentage of deaths associated with residential occupancies and the conditions precipitating these fatalities in hotel settings (waking sleeping occupants, and escape in unfamiliar surroundings) prompted the *Code* to mandate that most new hotels have an automatic sprinkler system installed. See also 3.3.101 for the definition of *high-rise building*.

Automatic sprinklers are not required in existing hotels and dormitories. Paragraph 29.3.5.1 specifies requirements for such systems where they are installed. Other portions of Chapter 29 offer significant incentives for installing sprinklers. Examples include a reduction in the fire resistance rating of exit enclosures (29.2.2.1.2) and an increase in common path of travel (29.2.5.2) and travel distance (29.2.6.1 and

28.3.6 Corridors.

28.3.6.1 Walls. Exit access corridor walls shall consist of fire barriers in accordance with 8.2.3 that have not less than a 1-hour fire resistance rating.

Exception: In buildings protected throughout by an approved, supervised automatic sprinkler system in accordance with 28.3.5, corridor walls shall have not less than a ½-hour fire resistance rating.

28.3.6.2 Doors. Doors that open onto exit access corridors shall have not less than a 20-minute fire protection rating in accordance with 8.2.3.2.

29.3.5.5 Portable fire extinguishers shall be provided as specified in 9.7.4.1 in hazardous areas addressed by 29.3.2.2.

Exception: In buildings protected throughout with an approved automatic sprinkler system in accordance with Section 9.7.

29.2.6.2). In addition, other subsections address exit discharge (29.2.7), vertical openings (29.3.1), hazardous areas (29.3.2), interior finish (29.3.3), corridor walls (29.3.6), and smoke barriers (29.3.7).

An automatic sprinkler system is required in existing high-rise hotels and dormitories. However, the exception to 29.3.5.2 allows existing, nonsprinklered high-rise hotels to remain nonsprinklered if every guest room or guest suite has exterior exit access. Exterior exit access eliminates traversing the corridor where conditions might not remain tenable.

Subsection 4.2.1 states the *Code* objective of protecting occupants who are not intimate with the initial fire development from loss of life and improving the survivability of those who are intimate with the fire development. Based on this objective, new hotels are required to use quick-response or residential sprinklers throughout guest rooms and guest suites. The technology associated with quick-response and residential sprinklers helps to maintain tenability within the room of fire origin.

29.3.6 Corridors.

29.3.6.1 Walls. Exit access corridor walls shall consist of fire barriers in accordance with 8.2.3 that have not less than a ½-hour fire resistance rating.

Exception: In buildings protected throughout by an approved automatic sprinkler system in accordance with 29.3.5, no fire resistance rating shall be required, but the walls and all openings therein shall resist the passage of smoke.

29.3.6.2 Doors. Doors that open onto exit access corridors shall have not less than a 20-minute fire protection rating in accordance with 8.2.3.2.

Exception No. 1: Doors complying with 8.2.3.2.3.

Exception No. 2: Where automatic sprinkler protection is provided in the corridor in accordance with 31.3.5.2 through 31.3.5.4, doors shall not be required to have a fire protection

CHAPTER 28 • New

28.3.6.3 Doors that open onto exit access corridors shall be self-closing and self-latching.

28.3.6.4 Unprotected openings shall be prohibited in exit access corridor walls and doors.

Exception: Such spaces shall be permitted to be unlimited in area and open to the corridor, provided that the following criteria are met:

(a) The spaces are not used for guest rooms or guest suites or hazardous areas.

(b) The building is protected throughout by an approved, supervised automatic sprinkler system in accordance with 28.3.5.

(c) The space does not obstruct access to required exits.

28.3.6.5 Transoms, louvers, or transfer grilles shall be prohibited in walls or doors of exit access corridors.

CHAPTER 29 • Existing

rating but shall resist the passage of smoke. Doors shall be equipped with latches to keep doors tightly closed.

29.3.6.3 Doors that open onto exit access corridors shall be self-closing and self-latching.

29.3.6.4 Unprotected openings shall be prohibited in exit access corridor walls and doors.

Exception: Such spaces shall be permitted to be unlimited in area and open to the corridor, provided that the following criteria are met:

(a) The spaces are not used for guest rooms or guest suites or hazardous areas.

(b) The space is protected by an approved automatic sprinkler system in accordance with 29.3.5.

(c) The space does not obstruct access to required exits.

29.3.6.5 Transoms, louvers, or transfer grilles shall be prohibited in walls or doors of exit access corridors.

Exception No. 1: Existing transoms shall be permitted but shall be fixed in the closed position and shall be covered or otherwise protected to provide a fire resistance rating not less than that of the wall in which they are installed.

Exception No. 2: This requirement shall not apply where a corridor smoke detection system is provided that, when sensing smoke, sounds the building alarm and shuts down return or exhaust fans that draw air into the corridor from the guest rooms. The transfer grille or louver shall be located in the lower one-third of the wall or door height.

Exception No. 3: This requirement shall not apply to buildings protected throughout by an approved automatic sprinkler system complying with 29.3.5 or buildings with corridor sprinkler protection in accordance with 31.3.5.2 through 31.3.5.4. The transfer grille or louver shall be located in the lower one-third of the wall or door height.

The provisions of 28/29.3.6 reflect the concern for providing safety to persons occupying guest rooms during a fire. The minimum 1-hour fire resistance rating (½ hour for existing hotels and dormitories) required for corridor wall construction is intended to prevent fire from moving from the corridor to a room or to prevent fire from spreading from a room to the corridor.

Although the reduction to a ½-hour fire resistance rating—as allowed by the exception to 28.3.6.1—would result in little savings in new construction, it could be useful in rehabilitation, renovations, or conversions of existing structures that are required to meet the provisions for new construction (see 4.6.7). Most existing lath and plaster walls provide 20-minute to 30-minute fire resistance ratings. If automatic sprinkler protection is provided through-out the building, the existing walls should not have to be replaced.

Corridor walls are required only to resist the passage of smoke in existing buildings with automatic sprinklers.

The fire-rated corridor door required by 28/29.3.6 provides a level of protection commensurate with the expected fuel load in the room and the fire resistance of the corridor wall construction. The purpose is to box a fire out of a room or to box it within the room by means of corridor wall and door construction. Fuel load studies conducted by the National Bureau of Standards (currently the National Institute of Standards and Technology) demonstrated that residential occupancies typically have fuel loads capable of sustaining a fire for approximately 20 to 30 minutes.

Exception No. 2 to 29.3.6.2 also allows a nonrated door that resists the passage of smoke in buildings that have corridor sprinkler protection installed in accordance with Option 3 for apartment buildings. See 31.3.5.2 and its commentary for information on apartment building Option 3 corridor sprinkler requirements. In Exhibits 28/29.8(a) and (b), the self-closing door is needed to complete the separation established by the fire resistance–rated corridor wall. No exceptions or options permit omission of the self-closing device on the door. Although an existing wall is not required to be fire rated if sprinkler protection is provided, the wall needs to be solid and resist the passage of smoke.

A 20-minute fire protection rating is required for guest room corridor doors. NFPA 80, *Standard for Fire Doors and Fire Windows,* requires a fire-rated door to be self-closing; however, the requirement for self-closing doors is important enough to be repeated in 28/29.3.6.3, rather than relying only on the referenced document.[2]

NFPA 90A, *Standard for the Installation of Air-Conditioning and Ventilating Systems,* prohibits corridors in hotels from being used as a portion of the system for supply, return, or exhaust air.[3]

Operable transoms are prohibited in hotels based on multiple-death fires in which transoms allowed fire and smoke to move through corridors and into occupied rooms. However, existing hotels built prior to 1950 often use corridors for supply or return air. The *Code* continues to recognize this practice for existing hotels if the specific conditions of the exceptions to 29.3.6.5 are met.

Exhibit 28/29.8(a) illustrates the requirements of 28.3.6 for corridors in new hotels and dormitories; Exhibit 28/29.8(b) illustrates the requirements of 29.3.6 for existing hotels and dormitories.

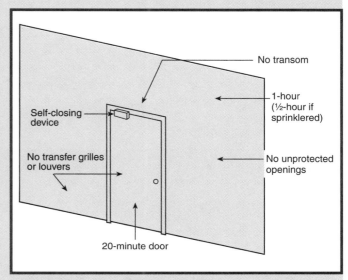

Exhibit 28/29.8(a) *Protection of guest room corridors and openings in new hotels.*

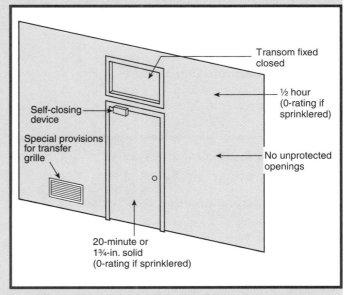

Exhibit 28/29.8(b) *Protection of guest room corridors and openings in existing hotels.*

28.3.7 Subdivision of Building Spaces.

(Reserved.)

29.3.7 Subdivision of Building Spaces.

Every guest room floor shall be divided into not less than two smoke compartments of approximately the same size by smoke barriers in accordance with Section 8.3. Smoke dampers shall not be required.

Additional smoke barriers shall be provided so that the travel distance from a guest room corridor door to a smoke barrier shall not exceed 150 ft (45 m).

Exception No. 1: Buildings protected throughout by an approved automatic sprinkler system in accordance with 29.3.5 or a corridor sprinkler system conforming to 31.3.5.2 through 31.3.5.4.

Exception No. 2: Smoke barriers shall not be required where each guest room is provided with exterior ways of exit access arranged in accordance with 7.5.3.

Exception No. 3: Smoke barriers shall not be required where the aggregate corridor length on each floor is not more than 150 ft (45 m).

Paragraph 29.3.7 requires all but relatively small floors of existing buildings to be subdivided into two smoke compartments. This requirement provides for horizontal movement of occupants, limits the number of rooms and, therefore, limits the number of occupants exposed to a single fire that might block a corridor. Because no fire rating is required for the barrier and smoke dampers are not required, the require-

ment is not overly burdensome in typical hotel or dormitory construction. The exception for automatic sprinklers reflects the excellent life loss record of buildings equipped with sprinkler protection.

A horizontal exit is permitted to be used to comply with 29.3.7 and, thereby, to serve more than one function.

28.3.8 Special Protection Features.

(Reserved.)

29.3.8 Special Protection Features.

(Reserved.)

Section 28.4 Special Provisions

28.4.1 High-Rise Buildings.

High-rise buildings shall comply with Section 11.8.

Section 29.4 Special Provisions

29.4.1 High-Rise Buildings.

High-rise buildings shall comply with 29.3.5.2.

Section 28.5 Building Services

28.5.1 Utilities.

Utilities shall comply with the provisions of Section 9.1.

28.5.2 Heating, Ventilating, and Air Conditioning.

28.5.2.1 Heating, ventilating, and air conditioning equipment shall comply with the provisions of Section 9.2, except as otherwise required in this chapter.

28.5.2.2 Unvented fuel-fired heaters shall not be used.

Exception: Gas space heaters in compliance with NFPA 54, National Fuel Gas Code.

28.5.3* Elevators, Escalators, and Conveyors.

Elevators, escalators, and conveyors shall comply with the provisions of Section 9.4. In high-rise buildings, one elevator shall be provided with a protected power supply and shall be available for use by the fire department in case of emergency.

A.28.5.3 "Protected power supply" means a source of electrical energy of sufficient capacity to allow proper operation of the elevator and its associated control and communications systems. The power supply's point of origin, system of distribution, type and size of overcurrent protection, degree of isolation from other portions of the building electrical system, and degree of mechanical protection should be such that it is unlikely that the supply would be disrupted at any but the advanced stages of building fire involvement or by structural collapse.

A protected power supply might consist of, and should provide, not less than the level of reliability associated with an electrical distribution system with service equipment located and installed in accordance with Section 230-72(b) and Section 230-82(5) of NFPA 70, *National Electrical Code.* The distribution system is not to have any other connection to the building electrical distribution system. A protected power supply is not required to incorporate two sources of energy or automatic transfer capability from a normal to an emergency source, for example, an alternate set of service conductors.

The number and type of elevators to be connected to a protected power supply should be limited, or the characteristics of the protected power supply should be selected to ensure conformance with Section 230-95 of NFPA 70, *National Electrical Code,* without the provision of ground fault protection for the supply.

An elevator installation supplied by a protected power supply should comply with Article 620 of NFPA 70, *National*

Section 29.5 Building Services

29.5.1 Utilities.

Utilities shall comply with the provisions of Section 9.1.

29.5.2 Heating, Ventilating, and Air Conditioning.

29.5.2.1 Heating, ventilating, and air conditioning equipment shall comply with the provisions of Section 9.2, except as otherwise required in this chapter.

29.5.2.2 Unvented fuel-fired heaters shall not be used.

Exception: Gas space heaters in compliance with NFPA 54, National Fuel Gas Code.

29.5.3 Elevators, Escalators, and Conveyors.

Elevators, escalators, and conveyors shall comply with the provisions of Section 9.4.

Electrical Code, except that the energy absorption means required by Section 620-91 should always be connected on the load side of the disconnecting means. The energy absorption means should not consist of loads likely to become inoperative or disconnected under the conditions assumed to exist when the elevator is under the control of fire department personnel. Examples of such loads include light and power loads external to the elevator equipment room.

28.5.4 Rubbish Chutes, Incinerators, and Laundry Chutes.

Rubbish chutes, incinerators, and laundry chutes shall comply with the provisions of Section 9.5.

29.5.4 Rubbish Chutes, Incinerators, and Laundry Chutes.

Rubbish chutes, incinerators, and laundry chutes shall comply with the provisions of Section 9.5.

Section 28.6 Reserved

Section 29.6 Reserved

Section 28.7 Operating Features

28.7.1 Hotel Emergency Organization.

28.7.1.1* Employees of hotels shall be instructed and drilled in the duties they are to perform in the event of fire, panic, or other emergency.

A.28.7.1.1 Employers are obligated to determine the degree to which employees are to participate in emergency activities. Regulations of the U.S. Department of Labor (OSHA) govern these activities and provide options for employers, from total evacuation to aggressive structural fire fighting by employee brigades. *(For additional information, see OSHA Regulations for Emergency Procedures and Fire Brigades, 29 CFR 1910, E and L.)*

28.7.1.2* Drills of the emergency organization shall be held at quarterly intervals and shall cover such points as the operation and maintenance of the available first aid fire appliances, the testing of devices to alert guests, and a study of instructions for emergency duties.

A.28.7.1.2 Emergencies should be assumed to have arisen at various locations in the occupancy in order to train employees in logical procedures.

28.7.2 Emergency Duties.

Upon discovery of a fire, employees shall carry out the following duties:

Section 29.7 Operating Features

29.7.1 Hotel Emergency Organization.

29.7.1.1* Employees of hotels shall be instructed and drilled in the duties they are to perform in the event of fire, panic, or other emergency.

A.29.7.1.1 Employers are obligated to determine the degree to which employees are to participate in emergency activities. Regulations of the U.S. Department of Labor (OSHA) govern these activities and provide options for employers, from total evacuation to aggressive structural fire fighting by employee brigades. *(For additional information, see OSHA Regulations for Emergency Procedures and Fire Brigades, 29 CFR 1910, E and L.)*

29.7.1.2* Drills of the emergency organization shall be held at quarterly intervals and shall cover such points as the operation and maintenance of the available first aid fire appliances, the testing of devices to alert guests, and a study of instructions for emergency duties.

A.29.7.1.2 Emergencies should be assumed to have arisen at various locations in the occupancy in order to train employees in logical procedures.

29.7.2 Emergency Duties.

Upon discovery of a fire, employees shall carry out the following duties:

CHAPTER 28 · New

(1) Activate the facility fire protection signaling system, if provided
(2) Notify the public fire department
(3) Take other action as previously instructed

28.7.3 Drills in Dormitories.

Emergency egress and relocation drills shall be regularly conducted in accordance with Section 4.7.

28.7.4 Emergency Instructions for Residents or Guests.

28.7.4.1* A floor diagram reflecting the actual floor arrangement, exit locations, and room identification shall be posted in a location and manner acceptable to the authority having jurisdiction on, or immediately adjacent to, every guest room door in hotels and in every resident room in dormitories.

A.28.7.4.1 Floor diagrams should reflect the actual floor arrangement and should be oriented with the actual direction to the exits.

The manner in which the information is to be posted and the nature of its contents are at the discretion of

28.7.4.2* Fire safety information shall be provided to allow guests to make the decision to evacuate to the outside, to evacuate to an area of refuge, to remain in place, or to employ any combination of the three options.

A.28.7.4.2 Factors for developing the fire safety information include such items as construction type, suppression systems, alarm and detection systems, building layout, and building HVAC systems.

References Cited in Commentary

1. NFPA 13, *Standard for the Installation of Sprinkler Systems*, 1999 edition, National Fire Protection Association, Quincy, MA.
2. NFPA 80, *Standard for Fire Doors and Fire Windows*,

CHAPTER 29 · Existing

(1) Activate the facility fire protection signaling system, if provided
(2) Notify the public fire department
(3) Take other action as previously instructed

29.7.3 Drills in Dormitories.

Emergency egress and relocation drills shall be regularly conducted in accordance with Section 4.7.

29.7.4 Emergency Instructions for Residents or Guests.

29.7.4.1* A floor diagram reflecting the actual floor arrangement, exit locations, and room identification shall be posted in a location and manner acceptable to the authority having jurisdiction on, or immediately adjacent to, every guest room door in hotels and in every resident room in dormitories.

A.29.7.4.1 Floor diagrams should reflect the actual floor arrangement and should be oriented with the actual direction to the exits.

the authority having jurisdiction and depend on the building, its layout, and the protection provided.

29.7.4.2* Fire safety information shall be provided to allow guests to make the decision to evacuate to the outside, to evacuate to an area of refuge, to remain in place, or to employ any combination of the three options.

A.29.7.4.2 Factors for developing the fire safety information include such items as construction type, suppression systems, alarm and detection systems, building layout, and building HVAC systems.

1999 edition, National Fire Protection Association, Quincy, MA.
3. NFPA 90A, *Standard for the Installation of Air-Conditioning and Ventilating Systems*, 1999 edition, National Fire Protection Association, Quincy, MA.

CHAPTERS 30 and 31

New and Existing Apartment Buildings

Apartment buildings are one of five residential occupancy types addressed by the *Life Safety Code*. Other residential occupancies include one- and two-family dwellings, lodging or rooming houses, hotels and dormitories, and residential board and care facilities. Sleeping accommodations are a feature common to all residential occupancies.

Paragraph 6.1.8.1 highlights the common principle of life safety that is applied to all residential occupancies addressed by Chapters 24 through 33. Paragraph 6.1.8.1 states that residential occupancies are those occupancies in which sleeping accommodations are provided for purposes other than health care or detention and correction. The presence of sleeping occupants is central to the provisions of Chapters 24 through 33, because occupants who are asleep will be unaware of a developing fire and, when awakened to be alerted to the emergency, might be somewhat confused. Paragraph 6.1.8.1 also differentiates between sleeping occupants in residential occupancies and those in health care or detention and correctional occupancies, which are also characterized by the occupants' incapability of self preservation. The provisions of Chapters 24 through 33 are also based on the presence of hazards (such as cooking and heating equipment) in residential occupancies and the degree to which occupants are familiar with their living space. Occupants might have little or no familiarity, as in the case of the transient residents of hotels, or they might have the total familiarity that is common to residents of single-family dwellings.

Apartment buildings pose an additional problem, because the typical building configuration often requires an escaping resident to traverse an interior corridor, which subsequently might expose the resident to the heat and smoke of a corridor or dwelling unit fire. In recognition of these potential hazards, the *Code* requires most new apartment buildings to be protected throughout by an approved, supervised automatic sprinkler system.

Apartments, townhouses, flats, and condominiums accounted for 103,300 structure fires per year, as reported to U.S. fire departments from 1992 to 1996. Table 30/31.1 provides a breakdown of the contribution of apartment building fires to the overall home structure fire record from 1992 to 1996.

The causes of apartment building fires differ significantly from one- and two-family dwelling fires in building equipment areas. Heating and electrical equipment accounted for 27 percent of the fires in one- and two-family dwellings, while accounting for only 11 percent of the fires in apartment buildings. This difference is most likely due to the centralized arrangement of the heating and electrical systems typical of most apartment buildings. Equipment fires are usually the result of poor maintenance or human error. Heating and electrical systems tend to be more closely regulated, maintained, and supervised in apartment buildings, which results in a reduced chance of equipment malfunction.

The numbers of fires caused by occupants (for example, those due to cooking and smoking) is high in both categories of home structures.

These data demonstrate the importance of applying the *Life Safety Code* to apartment buildings to help ensure fire safety, but they also demonstrate the continuing need for public education regarding the causes and prevention of home fires.

CHAPTER 30 • New　　　　　　　　　　　　　　　　**CHAPTER 31 • Existing**

Table 30/31.1 Home Structure Fires, 1992–1996 Annual Averages

Occupancy	Fires	Civilian Deaths	Civilian Injuries
All home structure fires	436,200	3,777	19,872
Apartment, condominium, or tenement	103,300	692	6,527
One or two living units with business	3,500	36	195
Three to six units	29,000	267	1,897
Seven to twenty units	25,800	142	1,702
Over twenty units	33,500	183	2,192
Unclassified/unknown	11,500	64	542

Source: National estimates based on NFIRS and NFPA surveys.

Section 30.1 General Requirements

30.1.1 Application.

30.1.1.1 The requirements of this chapter apply to the following:

(1) New buildings or portions thereof used as apartment occupancies *(see 1.4.1)*
(2) Additions made to, or used as, an apartment occupancy *(see 4.6.6)*
(3) Alterations, modernizations, or renovations of existing apartment occupancies *(see 4.6.7)*
(4) Buildings or portions thereof upon change of occupancy to an apartment occupancy *(see 4.6.11)*

30.1.1.2 The term *apartment building,* wherever used in this *Code,* shall include an apartment house, tenement, garden apartment, or any other structure meeting the definition of *apartment building.*

30.1.2 Mixed Occupancies.

Due to the disproportionate percentage of deaths associated with residential occupancies, the *Code,* with some exceptions, mandates sprinkler protection in new apartment buildings. For existing apartment buildings the *Code* provides four alternative packages referred to as *options.*

The options specify the varying degrees to which

Section 31.1* General Requirements

A.31.1 See Table A.31.1.

31.1.1 Application.

31.1.1.1 The requirements of this chapter apply to existing buildings or portions thereof currently occupied as apartment occupancies *(see also 30.1.1).* In addition, the building shall meet the requirements of one of the following options:

(1) Option 1—Buildings without fire suppression or detection systems
(2) Option 2—Buildings provided with a complete automatic fire detection and notification system
(3) Option 3—Buildings provided with automatic sprinkler protection in selected areas
(4) Option 4—Buildings protected throughout by an approved automatic sprinkler system

31.1.1.2 The term *apartment building,* wherever used in this *Code,* shall include an apartment house, tenement, garden apartment, or any other structure meeting the definition of *apartment building.*

31.1.2 Mixed Occupancies.

an apartment building is protected by fire detection or fire suppression systems as follows:

(1) Option 1—no suppression or detection systems
(2) Option 2—total automatic fire detection (although 31.3.4.5 requires single-station smoke detectors within each apartment unit, such detectors

Table A.31.1 Alternate Requirements for Existing Apartment Buildings According to Protection Provided

	No Suppression or Detection System Option No. 1	Total Automatic Fire Detection Option No. 2	Sprinkler Protection in Selected Areas Option No. 3	Auto Extinguishing per NFPA 13 (with exceptions) Option No. 4
Exit Access				
Travel distance from apartment door to exit	100 ft (30 m)	150 ft (45 m)	150 ft (45 m)	200 ft (60 m)
Travel distance within apartment	75 ft (23 m)	125 ft (38 m)	75 ft (23 m)	125 ft (38 m)
Smoke barrier req. *(See 31.3.7.)*	R	R	R	NR
Max. single path corridor distance	35 ft (10.7 m)	35 ft (10.7 m)	35 ft (10.7 m)	35 ft (10.7 m)
Max. dead end	50 ft (15 m)	50 ft (15 m)	50 ft (15 m)	50 ft (15 m)
Corridor fire resistance				
Walls	½ hr	½ hr	½ hr	½ hr
Doors (fire protection rating)	20 min. or 1¾-in. (4.4-cm) thick	20 min. or 1¾-in. (4.4-cm) thick	smoke-resisting	smoke-resisting
Interior Finish				
Lobbies and corridors	A or B	A or B	A or B	A, B, or C
Other spaces	A, B, or C	A, B, or C	A, B, or C	A, B, or C
Floors in corridors	I or II	I or II	NR	NR
Exits				
Wall fire resistance				
1–3 stories	1 hr	1 hr	1 hr	1 hr
>3 stories	2 hr	2 hr	2 hr	1 hr
Smokeproof enclosures				
Not high-rise	NR	NR	NR	NR
High-rise	R	R	R	NR
Door fire resistance				
1–3 stories	1 hr	1 hr	1 hr	1 hr
>3 stories	1½ hr	1½ hr	1½ hr	1 hr
Interior finish				
Walls and ceilings	A or B	A or B	A or B	A, B, or C
Floors	I or II	I or II	I or II	NR
Within Living Unit (Apartment)				
Escape windows, per Section 24.2 *(See 31.2.1.)*	R	R	R	NR
Alarm System				
>3 stories or >11 units	Manual initiation	Manual & auto initiation	Manual & auto initiation	Manual & auto initiation
>2 stories or >50 units	Annunciator panel	Annunciator panel	Annunciator panel	Annunciator panel

R: Required *(see Code for details and exceptions).*
NR: No requirements.

are not part of a system and are not located in all areas of the building; therefore, their presence does not constitute an Option 2 apartment building)

(3) Option 3—partial sprinkler protection (mainly corridor sprinklers—see 31.3.5.2)
(4) Option 4—protection throughout by means of a supervised automatic sprinkler system

CHAPTER 30 • New

CHAPTER 31 • Existing

In recognition of the life safety benefits associated with a properly installed and maintained sprinkler system, an Option 4 apartment building is exempted from the various *Code* provisions required of Option 1 through Option 3 apartment buildings. The exemptions and reductions permitted for an Option 4 apartment building include the following:

(1) Increased travel distance allowances
(2) Reduction in required corridor fire resistance ratings
(3) Decreased interior finish requirements
(4) Exemption from the smoke barrier requirement

The protection requirements for new apartment buildings are equivalent to Option 4.

Table A.31.1 summarizes the different protection packages required, depending on whether the apartment building follows Option 1, Option 2, Option 3, or Option 4.

This comprehensive approach provides an attempt at codifying system design. Although a total system would consist of many alternatives, the systems detailed in Options 1 through 4 are more limited, because only four options are available. However, the user can identify the most appropriate option based on the existing building's size, height, and arrangement. The options provide an opportunity to coordinate the safety approach that best fits a building, rather than adapting a building to a single codified set of criteria.

30.1.2.1 Where another type of occupancy exists in the same building as a residential occupancy, the requirements of 6.1.14 of this *Code* shall apply.

30.1.2.2 No dwelling unit of a residential occupancy shall have its sole means of egress pass through any nonresidential occupancy in the same building.

30.1.2.3 No multiple-dwelling unit of a residential occupancy shall be located above any nonresidential occupancy.

Exception No. 1:   Where the dwelling unit of the residential occupancy and exits therefrom are separated from the nonresidential occupancy by construction having a fire resistance rating of not less than 1 hour.

Exception No. 2:   Where the nonresidential occupancy is protected throughout by an approved, supervised automatic sprinkler system in accordance with Section 9.7.

31.1.2.1 Where another type of occupancy exists in the same building as a residential occupancy, the requirements of 6.1.14 of this *Code* shall apply.

31.1.2.2 No dwelling unit of a residential occupancy shall have its sole means of egress pass through any nonresidential occupancy in the same building.

31.1.2.3 No multiple-dwelling unit of a residential occupancy shall be located above any nonresidential occupancy.

Exception No. 1:   Where the dwelling unit of the residential occupancy and exits therefrom are separated from the nonresidential occupancy by construction having a fire resistance rating of not less than 1 hour.

Exception No. 2:   Where the nonresidential occupancy is protected throughout by an approved, supervised automatic sprinkler system in accordance with Section 9.7.

Exception No. 3:   A building with not more than two dwelling units above a nonresidential occupancy shall be permitted, provided that the nonresidential occupancy is protected by an automatic fire detection system in accordance with Section 9.6.

Residential occupancies often exist in buildings that also house assembly, mercantile, or business occupancies. These nonresidential occupancies might pose an additional threat, because they are not constantly occupied. An undetected fire in an unoccupied area has the potential to affect the tenability of

the residential portion of the building before occupants can be awakened and take the appropriate actions for safe egress. Therefore, the requirements of 30.1.2 and 31.1.2 help to ensure that it is safe to have apartments within these mixed occupancy buildings by providing the necessary protection and separation.

CHAPTER 30 • New

30.1.3 Definitions.

Terms applicable to this chapter are defined in Chapter 3 of this *Code*; where necessary, other terms are defined in the text.

   Apartment Building. See 3.3.12.

30.1.4 Classification of Occupancy.

(See 30.1.3.)

30.1.5 Classification of Hazard of Contents.

The contents of residential occupancies shall be classified as ordinary hazard in accordance with 6.2.2.

30.1.6 Minimum Construction Requirements.

(No special requirements.)

30.1.7 Occupant Load.

The occupant load, in number of persons for whom means of egress and other provisions are required, shall be determined on the basis of the occupant load factors of Table 7.3.1.2 that are characteristic of the use of the space or shall be determined as the maximum probable population of the space under consideration, whichever is greater.

The annex text to the definition of *apartment building* in 3.3.25.1 clarifies how town house–type apartments—particularly those under condominium ownership—should be classified for application of the *Code*. It is often mistakenly believed that condominiums are a form of occupancy rather than a form of ownership.

NFPA 13, *Standard for the Installation of Sprinkler Systems*, classifies the contents of an apartment building as light hazard for the purpose of designing automatic sprinkler systems.[1] Subsection 30.1.5 classifies the contents of an apartment building as ordinary hazard for the purposes of applying the *Code*. The

Section 30.2 Means of Egress Requirements

30.2.1 General.

Means of egress from dwelling units to the outside of the building shall be in accordance with Chapter 7 and this

CHAPTER 31 • Existing

31.1.3 Definitions.

Terms applicable to this chapter are defined in Chapter 3 of this *Code*; where necessary, other terms are defined in the text.

   Apartment Building. See 3.3.12.

31.1.4 Classification of Occupancy.

(See 31.1.3.)

31.1.5 Classification of Hazard of Contents.

The contents of residential occupancies shall be classified as ordinary hazard in accordance with 6.2.2.

31.1.6 Minimum Construction Requirements.

(No special requirements.)

31.1.7 Occupant Load.

The occupant load, in number of persons for whom means of egress and other provisions are required, shall be determined on the basis of the occupant load factors of Table 7.3.1.2 that are characteristic of the use of the space or shall be determined as the maximum probable population of the space under consideration, whichever is greater.

difference in classification is based on the threat to life or life safety (ordinary) versus the challenge to the extinguishing capability of the automatic sprinkler system (light).

The amount of material presented in 30/31.1.7 has been reduced for the 2000 edition of the *Code*, because all occupant load factors have been moved to Table 7.3.1.2 in the chapter addressing means of egress.

The occupant load calculations for areas of apartment buildings used for nonresidential purposes should be based on the occupant load factors applicable to the use of the area.

Section 31.2 Means of Egress Requirements

31.2.1 General.

Means of egress from dwelling units to the outside of the building shall be in accordance with Chapter 7 and this chapter. Means of escape within the dwelling unit shall comply with the provisions of Section 24.2 for one- and two-family dwellings.

Subsection 30/31.2.1 requires that every dwelling unit is to comply with Section 24.2, which addresses means of escape in one- and two-family dwellings. This mandatory reference to Chapter 24 is important for several reasons. First, it establishes a requirement for two means of escape from every sleeping room and living area of a dwelling unit having two rooms or more. Subsection 24.2.2 establishes several acceptable types of secondary means of escape, the most common of which is an operable window with specified minimum opening dimensions. A secondary means of escape is exempted if a dwelling unit is protected by an automatic sprinkler system. Note that 24.2.2 does not require the entire building to be sprinklered but only the dwelling unit that is deficient with respect to the secondary means of escape. However, a mandate for complete building sprinkler protection, such as that in 30.3.5.2, might be specified elsewhere.

A second important provision of Section 24.2 is that the means of egress provisions of Chapter 7 do not apply within the dwelling units unless they are specifically referenced. For example, the minimum width of means of escape doors within a dwelling unit is 28 in. (71 cm), rather than the 32-in. (81-cm) minimum width specified for means of egress by Chapter 7. The requirement of Chapter 7 applies to the door from the dwelling unit to the common corri-

30.2.2 Means of Egress Components.

30.2.2.1 General.

30.2.2.1.1 Components of means of egress shall be limited to the types described in 30.2.2.2 through 30.2.2.12.

30.2.2.1.2 In buildings protected throughout by an approved, supervised automatic sprinkler system in accordance with 30.3.5, exit enclosures shall have a fire resistance rating of not less than 1 hour, and doors shall have a fire protection rating of not less than 1 hour.

chapter. Means of escape within the dwelling unit shall comply with the provisions of Section 24.2 for one- and two-family dwellings.

dor, because this door is the transition point at which means of escape ends and the standard means of egress begins. Chapter 24 also permits the use of winders and spiral stairs within a dwelling unit, and the provisions of Chapter 24 for headroom apply within the dwelling unit, superceding those of Chapter 7. See the commentary on Chapter 24 for additional information on means of escape from living units.

The means of egress provisions of Chapter 7 are applied from the dwelling unit to the outside of the building. Many of the items contained in Section 30/31.2 are provisions that Chapter 7 provides as options that might be specifically recognized by an occupancy chapter, such as Exception No. 1 to 30/31.2.2.2.2, which allows the use of delayed-egress locks in accordance with 7.2.1.6.1. In other cases, a feature addressed by Chapter 7 is not permitted to be used in the means of egress of apartment buildings, because it is not specifically permitted by Section 30/31.2. The absence of slide escapes in the list of acceptable means of egress components in 30/31.2.2 is an example of a component that is not permitted. Also, Section 30/31.2 limits the degree to which Chapter 7 features can be used, such as the provision of maximum lengths for dead-end corridors and common paths of travel addressed in 30/31.2.5.

31.2.2 Means of Egress Components.

31.2.2.1 General.

31.2.2.1.1 Components of means of egress shall be limited to the types described in 31.2.2.2 through 31.2.2.12.

31.2.2.1.2 In buildings using Option 4, exit enclosures shall have a fire resistance rating of not less than 1 hour, and doors shall have a fire protection rating of not less than 1 hour.

31.2.2.1.3 In non-high-rise buildings using Option 2, Option 3, or Option 4, exit stair doors shall be permitted to be 1¾-in. (4.4-cm) thick, solid-bonded wood core doors, self-closing and self-latching, and in wood frames not less than ¾ in. (1.9 cm) thick. In buildings using Option 3, sprinklers shall also be provided within the exit enclosure in accordance with NFPA 13, *Standard for the Installation of Sprinkler Systems.*

CHAPTER 30 • New

The general provisions for the means of egress components in apartment buildings modify the provisions of Chapter 7 in the following two areas:

(1) Limits on the components of the means of egress
(2) Protection of the means of egress

First, a general reference to the components of the means of egress in Chapter 7 is made in place of repeating its myriad provisions. Most of these components are permitted in both new and existing apartment buildings. Some of the components are permitted to be used in accordance with the provisions of Chapter 7 and the additional provisions of Chapters 30 and 31. For example, delayed-egress locks are permitted by Exception No. 1 to 30.2.2.2.2 and Exception No. 1 to 31.2.2.2.2, which allow their use in accordance with 7.2.1.6.1 if not more than one device is located in any single egress path.

If not permitted, no reference to an egress component is made in the specific occupancy chapter. For example, escalators and fire escape stairs are only permitted in existing apartment buildings. Therefore, 31.2.2.8 and 31.2.2.9 contain specific references to Chapter 7, while 30.2.2.8 and 30.2.2.9 are reserved and contain no such reference. Neither chapter permits the use of slide escapes; consequently, no reference to slide escapes is made within the means of egress sections of either chapter.

Second, Chapters 30 and 31 recognize the relatively low fuel loads of apartment buildings and permit a fire resistance rating of 1 hour for exit enclosures and other vertical openings (see Exception No. 2 to 30.3.1.1 and Exception No. 2 to 31.3.1.1) in buildings protected throughout by an approved, supervised automatic sprinkler system.

Because the *Code* requires that most new apartment buildings be protected throughout by an approved automatic sprinkler system, a 1-hour fire resistance–rated exit enclosure will typically be permitted in new construction. However, if the exception to 30.3.5.2—which exempts certain building arrangements from the sprinkler requirement—is exercised,

CHAPTER 31 • Existing

the 1-hour rated enclosure option of 30.2.2.1.2 is not permitted. This situation dictates a default to the Chapter 7 exit enclosure requirements, which, because they are based on the number of stories connected by the exit enclosure, might require 2-hour fire resistance–rated enclosures. See 7.1.3.2.

The reduction to a 1-hour fire resistance–rated enclosure for exits is not permitted for assembly, mercantile, or business occupancies and, therefore, cannot be used where mixed apartment/assembly, apartment/mercantile, or apartment/business occupancies are involved. In facilities of four or more stories, where apartment occupancies and other occupancies are adequately separated and treated independently, a 1-hour exit enclosure in the apartment portion and a 2-hour enclosure elsewhere might be permitted.

Exhibit 30/31.1 illustrates the modification to the requirements for protection of exit enclosures and other vertical openings in a fully sprinklered apartment building. The provision for the 1-hour exit enclosure does not apply to other occupancies in an apartment complex or in mixed occupancies.

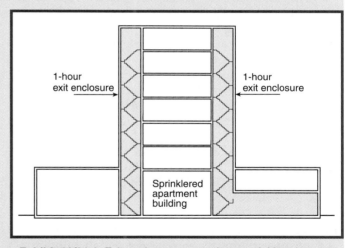

Exhibit 30/31.1 *Exit enclosure separation—sprinklered apartment building.*

30.2.2.2 Doors.

30.2.2.2.1 Doors complying with 7.2.1 shall be permitted.

30.2.2.2.2* No door in any means of egress shall be locked against egress when the building is occupied.

31.2.2.2 Doors.

31.2.2.2.1 Doors complying with 7.2.1 shall be permitted.

31.2.2.2.2 No door in any means of egress shall be locked against egress when the building is occupied.

CHAPTER 30 • New

Exception No. 1: Delayed-egress locks complying with 7.2.1.6.1 shall be permitted, provided that not more than one such device is located in any one egress path.

Exception No. 2: Access-controlled egress doors complying with 7.2.1.6.2 shall be permitted.

A.30.2.2.2.2 It is the intent of this requirement that security measures, where installed, should not prevent egress.

30.2.2.2.3 Revolving doors complying with 7.2.1.10 shall be permitted.

30.2.2.2.4 Horizontal sliding doors, as permitted by 7.2.1.14, shall not be used across corridors.

Apartment buildings are prohibited from having any door locked against egress while the building is occupied. This requirement permits a door to be equipped with a locking device that allows the door to be opened from within the building for the purpose of egress but does not allow the door to be opened from outside the building. Ordinary double-cylinder locks and chain locks do not meet these criteria, because they require keys for operation.

The language of 7.2.1.5.1 is clear. Paragraph 7.2.1.5.1 states that locks, if provided, are not to require the use of a key, a tool, or special knowledge or effort for operation from the egress side of the building. This requirement prohibits double-cylinder locks and chain locks that require a key to operate the door from the inside. Paragraph 7.2.1.5.4 requires the use of a simple operation to open a door; locks that require two-handed knobs and similar operations are prohibited.

Apartment doors provide security for the occupants in the unit. Recognizing this additional function, Chapter 7 permits the use of security chains or rods, as well as locks, on apartment doors and also permits releasing devices in addition to the doorknob or lever. The permitted number of additional releasing actions differs for new and existing buildings. One additional releasing action is permitted for new apartment buildings and two additional actions are permitted in existing apartment buildings. The typical apartment door has three devices: a latch, a lock, and a security chain or rod. This arrangement is permitted in existing buildings, provided that only two additional releasing operations are necessary. This arrangement would also be permitted in new construction, provided that the latch and lock set are interconnected so that the lock bolt and the latch will

CHAPTER 31 • Existing

Exception No. 1: Delayed-egress locks complying with 7.2.1.6.1 shall be permitted, provided that not more than one such device is located in any one egress path.

Exception No. 2: Access-controlled egress doors complying with 7.2.1.6.2 shall be permitted.

31.2.2.2.3 Revolving doors complying with 7.2.1.10 shall be permitted.

31.2.2.2.4 Horizontal sliding doors, as permitted by 7.2.1.14, shall not be used across corridors.

retract simultaneously when the latch handle is turned from the inside; thus, only one releasing action is needed for the two devices. The second action is the release of the security chain or rod. The overriding requirement for any of these devices is that they not require the use of a key, a tool, or special knowledge or effort to operate.

Exception No. 1 to 30.2.2.2.2 and Exception No. 1 to 31.2.2.2.2 recognize the use of the delayed-egress lock detailed in 7.2.1.6.1 if not more than one such lock is located in any single egress path. The use of a delayed-egress lock requires that the building be protected throughout by either an automatic sprinkler or automatic fire detection system. The 15-second or 30-second delay permitted by 7.2.1.6.1 does not affect the immediate release of the lock upon activation of sprinklers or detectors or upon loss of power to the lock. The delay device provides the security needed for doors that are used infrequently. At the same time, the door remains available for emergency use. Chains and padlocks do not provide these safety features.

Exception No. 1 to 7.2.1.5.2 permits selected exit stair enclosure doors to be locked from the stairwell side, while other stair enclosure doors must remain unlocked. If the selected re-entry provisions are not used, one of the other two options specified by 7.2.1.5.2 must be used for stair enclosures serving five or more stories. Doors are permitted to be locked from the stairwell side if initiation of the building fire alarm system automatically unlocks the door; otherwise, all doors must remain unlocked at all times.

Note that 30/31.2.2.2.4 restricts the use of the special form of horizontal sliding door to a greater extent than 7.2.1.14 by prohibiting cross-corridor installations.

CHAPTER 30 • New

30.2.2.3 Stairs.

30.2.2.3.1 Stairs complying with 7.2.2 shall be permitted.

30.2.2.3.2 Within any individual dwelling unit, stairs more than one story above or below the entrance floor level of the dwelling unit shall not be permitted.

30.2.2.3.3 Spiral stairs complying with 7.2.2.2.3 shall be permitted within a single dwelling unit.

30.2.2.3.4 Winders complying with 7.2.2.2.4 shall be permitted within a single dwelling unit.

Paragraph 30/31.2.2.3.2 requires that no level of an apartment unit be located farther than one story away from an entrance. This requirement would usually prohibit an apartment unit from encompassing more than three stories: main, upper, and lower. However, if an apartment has entrances at more than one level,

30.2.2.4 Smokeproof Enclosures. Smokeproof enclosures complying with 7.2.3 shall be permitted.

30.2.2.5 Horizontal Exits. Horizontal exits complying with 7.2.4 shall be permitted.

30.2.2.6 Ramps. Ramps complying with 7.2.5 shall be permitted.

30.2.2.7 Exit Passageways. Exit passageways complying with 7.2.6 shall be permitted.

30.2.2.8 (Reserved.)

30.2.2.9 (Reserved.)

30.2.2.10 Fire Escape Ladders. Fire escape ladders complying with 7.2.9 shall be permitted.

30.2.2.11 Alternating Tread Devices. Alternating tread devices complying with 7.2.11 shall be permitted.

CHAPTER 31 • Existing

31.2.2.3 Stairs.

31.2.2.3.1 Stairs complying with 7.2.2 shall be permitted.

31.2.2.3.2 Within any individual dwelling unit, stairs more than one story above or below the entrance floor level of the dwelling unit shall not be permitted.

31.2.2.3.3 Spiral stairs complying with 7.2.2.2.3 shall be permitted within a single dwelling unit.

31.2.2.3.4 Winders complying with 7.2.2.2.4 shall be permitted.

more than three stories are permitted. Because Exception No. 1 to 30/31.3.1.1 allows only two levels within an apartment unit to be open to each other in accordance with 8.2.5.8, the third level must be separated in accordance with 8.2.4.

31.2.2.4 Smokeproof Enclosures. Smokeproof enclosures complying with 7.2.3 shall be permitted. *(See also 31.2.11.)*

31.2.2.5 Horizontal Exits. Horizontal exits complying with 7.2.4 shall be permitted.

31.2.2.6 Ramps. Ramps complying with 7.2.5 shall be permitted.

31.2.2.7 Exit Passageways. Exit passageways complying with 7.2.6 shall be permitted.

31.2.2.8* Escalators. Escalators previously approved as a component in the means of egress shall be permitted to continue to be considered as in compliance.

A.31.2.2.8 Due to the nature of escalators, they are no longer acceptable as a component in a means of egress. However, since many escalators have been used for exit access and exit discharge in the past, they are permitted to continue to be considered in compliance. Very few escalators have ever been installed in a manner to qualify as an exit. For information on escalator protection and requirements, see previous editions of the *Code.*

31.2.2.9 Fire Escape Stairs. Fire escape stairs complying with 7.2.8 shall be permitted.

31.2.2.10 Fire Escape Ladders. Fire escape ladders complying with 7.2.9 shall be permitted.

31.2.2.11 Alternating Tread Devices. Alternating tread devices complying with 7.2.11 shall be permitted.

CHAPTER 30 • New

30.2.2.12* Areas of Refuge. Areas of refuge complying with 7.2.12 shall be permitted.

Exception: In buildings protected throughout by an approved, supervised automatic sprinkler system in accordance with 30.3.5, the two accessible rooms or spaces separated from each other by smoke-resistive partitions in accordance with the definition of area of refuge in 3.3.14 shall not be required.

A.30.2.2.12 The provision of 30.2.2.12 permits the entire floor to serve as an area of refuge where it is protected in accordance with 30.3.5. The provision is acceptable because supervised automatic sprinkler systems have built-in signals for monitoring features of the system, such as the opening and closing of water control valves. Such systems also monitor pump power supplies, water tank levels, and conditions that will impair the satisfactory operation of the sprinkler system. Because of these monitoring features, supervised automatic sprinkler systems have a high level of satisfactory performance and response to fire conditions.

Paragraph 7.5.4.1 requires that areas accessible to persons with severe mobility impairment be provided with accessible means of egress. Existing apartment buildings are exempt from the provisions of 7.5.4.1. Therefore, areas of refuge are not required in existing apartment buildings but are permitted to serve within the means of egress.

For stories above the level of exit discharge, where providing ramps is usually not feasible, areas of refuge (see 7.2.12) will typically be used to meet the requirements for accessible means of egress in new apartment buildings. The exception to 30/31.2.2.12 allows a sprinklered story of an apartment building

30.2.3 Capacity of Means of Egress.

30.2.3.1 The capacity of means of egress shall be in accordance with Section 7.3.

30.2.3.2 Street floor exits shall be sufficient for the occupant load of the street floor plus the required capacity of stairs and ramps discharging onto the street floor.

30.2.3.3 The corridor width shall be sufficient to accommodate the required occupant load, but shall be not less than 44 in. (112 cm).

Exception: Corridors with a required capacity not exceeding 50 persons as defined in Section 7.3 shall be not less than 36 in. (91 cm) in width.

CHAPTER 31 • Existing

31.2.2.12* Areas of Refuge. Areas of refuge complying with 7.2.12 shall be permitted.

Exception: In buildings protected throughout by an approved, supervised automatic sprinkler system in accordance with 31.3.5, the two accessible rooms or spaces separated from each other by smoke-resistive partitions in accordance with the definition of area of refuge in 3.3.14 shall not be required.

A.31.2.2.12 The provision of 31.2.2.12 permits the entire floor to serve as an area of refuge where it is protected in accordance with 31.3.5. The provision is acceptable because supervised automatic sprinkler systems have built-in signals for monitoring features of the system, such as the opening and closing of water control valves. Such systems also monitor pump power supplies, water tank levels, and conditions that will impair the satisfactory operation of the sprinkler system. Because of these monitoring features, supervised automatic sprinkler systems have a high level of satisfactory performance and response to fire conditions.

to be considered an area of refuge, even if an occupant does not have access to any of the apartment units. Due to the effectiveness of the sprinkler system, an occupant with mobility impairment should be able to remain on the floor without experiencing untenable conditions. However, because locked apartment unit doors create inaccessibility to spaces other than the corridor, the corridor effectively serves as the area of refuge. The authority having jurisdiction might choose to require demonstration of tenability, as required by 7.2.12.3.2, if the aggregate corridor area on the story is less than 1000 ft^2 (93 m^2), regardless of the area of the entire floor.

31.2.3 Capacity of Means of Egress.

31.2.3.1 The capacity of means of egress shall be in accordance with Section 7.3.

31.2.3.2 Street floor exits shall be sufficient for the occupant load of the street floor plus the required capacity of stairs and ramps discharging onto the street floor.

When occupants from upper floors are discharged from exit stair enclosures onto the street floor (in accordance with 7.7.2) and mix with occupants of the street floor in attempting egress to the exterior, the result is an increased demand on street floor egress components, such as exit doors. Therefore, the *Code* requires that street floor exits be sized to handle the combined capacity.

Exhibit 30/31.2 illustrates a lobby design that might be found in apartment buildings in which multiple exit stairs and street floor exits converge at one or two exterior door locations. The required aggregate capacity of doors A and B is based on the number of people expected to use them. Assuming that the street floor has an occupant load of 400 persons and each of the two enclosed exit stairs (that is, stair 1 and stair 2) discharging into the street floor has a required capacity of 200 persons (that is, a maximum of 50 percent of the 400-person occupant load of the second or third floor via stair 1 and a maximum of 50 percent of the 400-person occupant load of the basement via stair 2), the required egress capacity for the street floor would be 800 persons. The unobstructed door or level travel width required to accom-

modate 800 persons is 160 in. (406 cm). The opening provided by each pair of doors, A and B, needs to be 80 in. (203 cm) in clear, unobstructed width.

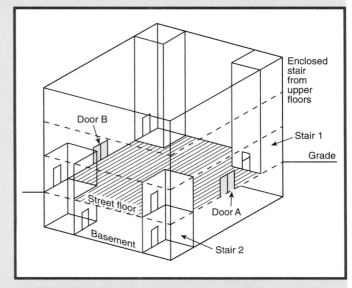

Exhibit 30/31.2 *Egress capacity for street floor.*

30.2.4 Number of Exits.

Every dwelling unit shall have access to not less than two separate exits remotely located from each other as required by 7.5.1. *(See also Section 7.4.)*

Exception No. 1: Any dwelling unit shall be permitted to have a single exit, provided that one of the following criteria is met:

(a) The dwelling unit has an exit door opening directly to the street or yard at ground level.

(b) The dwelling unit has direct access to an outside stair complying with 7.2.2 that serves not more than two units, both of which are located on the same floor.

(c) The dwelling unit has direct access to an interior stair serving only that unit, and such stair is separated from all other portions of the building by fire barriers having not less than a 1-hour fire resistance rating with no opening therein.

Exception No. 2: Buildings of four stories or less protected throughout by an approved, supervised automatic sprinkler system in accordance with 30.3.5, with not more than four dwelling units per story, shall be permitted to have a single exit under the following conditions:

31.2.4 Number of Exits.

Every dwelling unit shall have access to not less than two separate exits remotely located from each other as required by 7.5.1. *(See also Section 7.4.)*

Exception No. 1: Any dwelling unit shall be permitted to have a single exit, provided that one of the following criteria is met:

(a) The dwelling unit has an exit door opening directly to the street or yard at ground level.

(b) The dwelling unit has direct access to an outside stair complying with 7.2.2 that serves not more than two units, both of which are located on the same floor.

(c) The dwelling unit has direct access to an interior stair serving only that unit, and such stair is separated from all other portions of the building by fire barriers having not less than a 1-hour fire resistance rating with no opening therein.

Exception No. 2: Buildings of four stories or less protected throughout by an approved, supervised automatic sprinkler system in accordance with 31.3.5.1 shall be permitted to have a single exit under the following conditions:

(a) The stairway is separated from the rest of the building by barriers having not less than a 1-hour fire resistance rating, with self-closing doors having not less than a 1-hour fire protection rating protecting all openings between the stairway enclosure and the building.

(b) The stairway does not serve more than one-half of a story below the level of exit discharge.

(c) All corridors serving as access to exits have not less than a 1-hour fire resistance rating.

(d) The travel distance from the entrance door of any dwelling unit to an exit does not exceed 35 ft (10.7 m).

(e) Horizontal and vertical separation with a fire rating of not less than ½ hour is provided between dwelling units.

(a) The stairway is separated from the rest of the building by barriers having not less than a 1-hour fire resistance rating, with self-closing doors having not less than a 1-hour fire protection rating protecting all openings between the stairway enclosure and the building.

(b) The stairway does not serve more than one-half of a story below the level of exit discharge.

(c) All corridors serving as access to exits have not less than a ½-hour fire resistance rating.

(d) The travel distance from the entrance door of any dwelling unit to an exit does not exceed 35 ft (10.7 m).

(e) Horizontal and vertical separation with a fire rating of not less than ½ hour is provided between dwelling units.

Exception No. 3: Any building of three stories or less in its entirety shall be permitted to have a single exit under the following conditions:

(a) The stairway is separated from the rest of the building by barriers having not less than a 1-hour fire resistance rating, with self-closing doors having not less than a 1-hour fire protection rating protecting all openings between the stairway enclosure and the building.

(b) The stairway does not serve more than one-half of a story below the level of exit discharge.

(c) All corridors serving as access to exits have not less than a 20-minute fire resistance rating.

(d) The travel distance from the entrance door of any dwelling unit to an exit does not exceed 35 ft (10.7 m).

(e) Horizontal and vertical separation with a fire rating of not less than ½ hour is provided between dwelling units.

Exception No. 4: A building of any height, with not more than four dwelling units per floor, with a smokeproof enclosure or outside stair in accordance with the requirements of 7.2.3 as the exit, where such exit is immediately accessible to all dwelling units served thereby, shall be permitted to have a single exit. "Immediately accessible" means that the travel distance from the entrance door of any dwelling unit to an exit shall not exceed 20 ft (6.1 m).

Exception No. 1 to 30/31.2.4 allows a single means of egress under the following conditions:

(a) The living unit has an exit leading directly to the street or yard at ground level. This arrangement is common in the case of town houses or row houses. Under this arrangement, the front door is the only

required exit, so no provisions for a rear door are required. If a rear door is provided, it does not have to meet the locking or other requirements of the *Code*.

(b) The apartment has direct access to an outside stair serving a maximum of two apartments, and both of these apartments are on the same floor. The outside stair must be separated from the interior of the building as detailed in 7.2.2.6.3. This arrangement is detailed in Exhibit 30/31.3(a).

(c) The single exit is a private stairway serving one apartment only and is separated from all abutting apartment units, including those on lower floors, by 1-hour rated construction. Note that this stairway is required to be separated only from other spaces by the required 1-hour construction; it is not required to be separated from the apartment unit that it serves. This arrangement is detailed in Exhibit 30/31.3(b).

Exception No. 2 to 30.2.4 addresses garden-type apartment buildings where the apartment unit entrance doors open either directly into a single-exit stair enclosure or into a vestibule or short corridor leading to a single, enclosed exit stair. In other situations, the stair is open to the exterior or is enclosed by glass at the front of the building. Exception No. 2

allows a single exit under this arrangement if additional conditions can be met.

Exhibit 30/31.4(a) illustrates the following provisions of Exception No. 2 to 30.2.4:

(1) The building must be sprinklered in accordance with 30.3.5.
(2) The building must be not more than four stories high.
(3) The building must have not more than four apartment units per floor.
(4) The single exit stair must be separated from the building by construction with a minimum 1-hour fire resistance rating.
(5) The exit enclosure doors (E) must be 1-hour fire protection–rated and self-closing, including apartment unit doors if they open directly into the exit enclosure.
(6) If the apartment unit doors (A) open into a corridor, they must be 20-minute fire protection–rated.

A frequent violation of this exception is the use of a nonrated door and the lack of a door closer. The travel distance from the apartment unit door to the exit enclosure door (A-E) cannot exceed 35 ft (10.7 m). Both horizontal and vertical 30-minute fire resistance–rated separation are required between apartment units.

For existing apartment buildings, Exception No. 2 to 31.2.4 differs by not limiting the number of apartment units per floor, as depicted in Exhibit 30/31.4(b), and permitting the corridor fire resistance rating to be ½ hour instead of 1 hour.

Exception No. 3 to 31.2.4 is similar to Exception

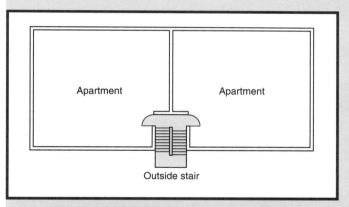

Exhibit 30/31.3(a) *Outside stair serving two apartment units.*

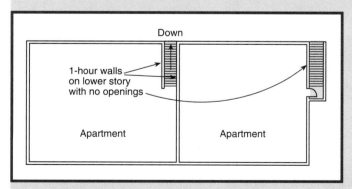

Exhibit 30/31.3(b) *Stair serving one apartment unit.*

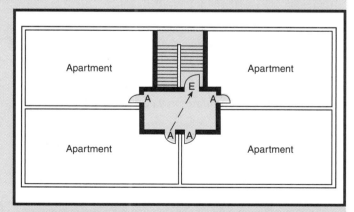

Exhibit 30/31.4(a) *New apartment building—single-exit arrangement.*

No. 2 in that it permits a single exit from a typical garden-type apartment building. However, the apartment building is not required to be sprinklered and is limited to being not more than three stories high.

Exception No. 4 to 31.2.4 for existing buildings describes an uncommon arrangement. Note that there are no height limitations, but only four apartment units per floor are permitted. Furthermore, apartments must have immediate access to a smokeproof enclosure or to an outside stair that meets the requirements of a smokeproof enclosure. The exceptions to the requirements for outside stairs in Chapter 7 for unprotected openings that expose a stair would not apply in this case, because the *Code* specifically references 7.2.3 on smokeproof enclosures. Subsection 7.2.3 does not permit unprotected openings that expose the stair.

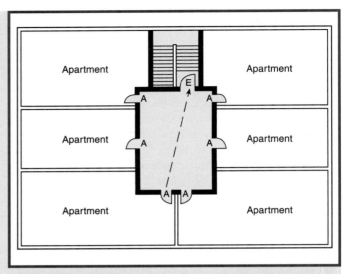

Exhibit 30/31.4(b) *Existing apartment building—single-exit arrangement.*

30.2.5 Arrangement of Means of Egress.

30.2.5.1 Access to all required exits shall be in accordance with Section 7.5.

Exception: The distance between exits addressed by 7.5.1.4 shall not apply to nonlooped exit access corridors in buildings that have corridor doors from the dwelling units that are arranged such that the exits are located in opposite directions from such doors.

30.2.5.2 Common paths of travel shall not exceed 35 ft (10.7 m). Travel within a dwelling unit shall not be included when calculating common path of travel.

Exception: In buildings protected throughout by an approved, supervised automatic sprinkler system in accordance with 30.3.5, common path of travel shall not exceed 50 ft (15 m).

30.2.5.3 Dead-end corridors shall not exceed 35 ft (10.7 m).

Exception: In buildings protected throughout by an approved, supervised automatic sprinkler system in accordance with 30.3.5, dead-end corridors shall not exceed 50 ft (15 m).

31.2.5 Arrangement of Means of Egress.

31.2.5.1 Access to all required exits shall be in accordance with Section 7.5.

31.2.5.2 Common paths of travel shall not exceed 35 ft (10.7 m). Travel within a dwelling unit shall not be included when calculating common path of travel.

Exception: In buildings protected throughout by an approved, supervised automatic sprinkler system in accordance with 31.3.5, common path of travel shall not exceed 50 ft (15 m).

31.2.5.3 Dead-end corridors shall not exceed 50 ft (15 m).

The provisions for the arrangement of the means of egress in apartment buildings differ significantly from the provisions in Chapter 7. The first difference

appears in 30.2.5.1, which addresses the remoteness of exits. Applying the remoteness of exits provisions of 7.5.1.4 could result in a corridor that is longer than is necessary for the efficient use of the space. The exception to 30.2.5.1 offers some relief. Exhibit 30/31.5 helps to clarify the intent of the exception to 30.2.5.1. In illustration (a) of Exhibit 30/31.5, all four dwelling units have access to two exits immediately upon leaving the dwelling unit and entering the exit access corridor. This arrangement meets the provisions of the exception. Contrast this arrangement with that depicted in illustration (b) of Exhibit 30/31.5, where only dwelling units A and B have access to two exits immediately upon leaving the dwelling unit and entering the exit access corridor. The other dwelling units do not have immediate access to two exits. This arrangement does not meet the provisions of the exception to 30.2.5.1.

The concepts underlying the limitations imposed on common paths of travel and dead-end corridors are similar but not identical to those explained in

the commentary on 7.5.1.6. Because of modifications made by Chapters 30 and 31 in defining where common path of travel begins, the difference between common paths of travel and dead-end corridors is less pronounced for apartment buildings. For most other occupancies, common path of travel is measured from the most remote point subject to occupancy to the point where occupants have a choice of traveling in independent directions (see Exception No. 2 to 7.5.1.2 and the definition of *common path of travel* in 3.3.32). For apartment buildings, the travel within the dwelling unit, though regulated by 30.2.6.1 and 31.2.6.1 for distance, is not included as part of the common path of travel. Therefore, common path of travel, as illustrated by the solid arrows in Exhibit 30/31.6, is measured from the room door to the point where occupants have a choice of traveling in independent directions. This depiction can be thought of as a modified common path of travel, because measurement does not extend into the dwelling unit.

The distances permitted for common path of travel in new and existing apartment buildings also differs. Because most new apartment buildings are required to be sprinklered (see 30.3.5.2), the 35-ft (10.7-m) modified common path of travel and dead-end corridor limitations permitted by 30.2.5.2 and 30.2.5.3 will usually be supplanted by the 50-ft (15-m) limitation permitted by the exceptions to

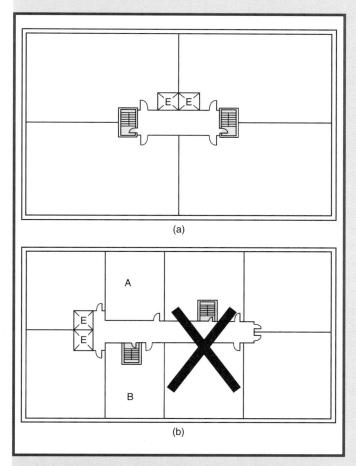

(a)

(b)

Exhibit 30/31.5 New apartment buildings—exit remoteness.

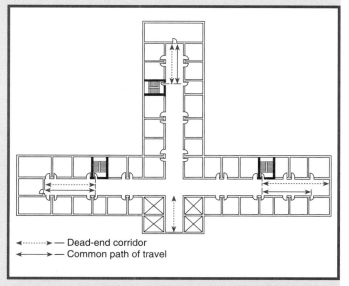

◄┈┈┈► — Dead-end corridor
◄────► — Common path of travel

Exhibit 30/31.6 Modified common path of travel and dead-end corridors in an apartment building.

CHAPTER 30 • New	CHAPTER 31 • Existing

30.2.5.2 and 30.2.5.3. However, if a building can comply with the exception to 30.3.5.2, which exempts sprinklers, the 35-ft (10.7-m) common path of travel and dead-end corridor limitations would apply.

In existing apartment buildings, automatic sprinklers are not required. However, if the building is protected throughout by an approved, supervised automatic sprinkler system, the common path of travel is permitted to be 50 ft (15 m), which is the same distance permitted for the length of existing dead-end corridors, regardless of sprinkler system considerations.

30.2.6 Travel Distance to Exits.

30.2.6.1 Travel distance within a dwelling unit (apartment) to a corridor door shall not exceed 75 ft (23 m).

Exception: In buildings protected throughout by an approved, supervised automatic sprinkler system in accordance with 30.3.5, the travel distance shall not exceed 125 ft (38 m).

30.2.6.2 The travel distance from a dwelling unit (apartment) entrance door to the nearest exit shall not exceed 100 ft (30 m).

Exception No. 1: In buildings protected throughout by an approved, supervised automatic sprinkler system in accordance with 30.3.5, the travel distance shall not exceed 200 ft (60 m).

Exception No. 2: Travel distance to exits shall not exceed 200 ft (60 m) for exterior ways of exit access arranged in accordance with 7.5.3.

30.2.6.3 The travel distance from areas other than those within living units to the exit, measured in accordance with Section 9.6, shall not exceed 200 ft (67 m).

Exception: Travel distance shall not exceed 250 ft (83 m) in buildings protected throughout by an approved, supervised automatic sprinkler system in accordance with Section 9.7.

31.2.6 Travel Distance to Exits.

31.2.6.1 Travel distance within a dwelling unit (apartment) to a corridor door shall not exceed the following limits:

(1) For buildings using Option 1 or Option 3—75 ft (23 m)
(2) For buildings using Option 2 or Option 4—125 ft (38 m)

31.2.6.2 The travel distance from a dwelling unit (apartment) entrance door to the nearest exit shall not exceed the following limits:

(1) For buildings using Option 1—100 ft (30 m)
(2) For buildings using Option 2 or Option 3—150 ft (45 m)
(3) For buildings using Option 4—200 ft (60 m)

Exception: Travel distance to exits shall not exceed 200 ft (60 m) for exterior ways of exit access arranged in accordance with 7.5.3.

The travel distance limitations specified in 30/31.2.6.1 and 30/31.2.6.2 divide the measurement into the following two portions of the overall travel distance:

(1) Travel within an apartment unit to the door to the common space of the building
(2) Travel from the corridor door to the nearest exit

If the travel distance within an apartment unit is excessive, an additional remote door to the corridor can usually be added to correct the deficiency. The presence of automatic sprinklers or the use of exterior ways of exit access modifies travel distance. In existing buildings, the presence of a fire detection and notification system or a partial sprinkler system (Option 2 and Option 3) also modifies travel distances, though not to the extent of a complete automatic sprinkler system (Option 4).

Paragraph 30.2.6.3 establishes travel distance limitations from areas other than those within living units of new apartment buildings. For example, many apartment buildings have common activity rooms, lounges, lobbies, and similar spaces that are neither living units, as addressed by 30.2.6.1, nor exit access corridor–like spaces, as addressed by 30.2.6.2. The maximum 200-ft (67-m) travel distance allowance, which can be increased to 250 ft (83 m) in sprinklered

CHAPTER 30 • New   **CHAPTER 31 • Existing**

buildings, treats the travel distance in one continuous measurement. For example, the travel distance limitation would apply to the full distance of travel

through an activity room and the associated exit access corridors to the exit.

30.2.7 Discharge from Exits.

Exit discharge shall comply with Section 7.7.

31.2.7 Discharge from Exits.

31.2.7.1 Exit discharge shall comply with Section 7.7.

31.2.7.2 Any required exit stair that is located so that it is necessary to pass through the lobby or other open space to reach the outside of the building shall be continuously enclosed to a level of exit discharge or to a mezzanine within a lobby at a level of exit discharge.

31.2.7.3 The distance of travel from the termination of the exit enclosure to an exterior door leading to a public way shall not exceed 150 ft (45 m) in buildings protected throughout by an approved automatic sprinkler system and shall not exceed 100 ft (30 m) in all other buildings.

Section 7.7 allows a maximum of 50 percent of both the number and capacity of exits to discharge through the street floor under limited conditions (see 7.7.2).

Paragraphs 31.2.7.2 and 31.2.7.3 modify the restrictions of Section 7.7 for existing apartment buildings. In this arrangement, an exit that discharges onto a mezzanine within the lobby of an apartment building (with subsequent open stair travel to the lobby floor on the level of exit discharge) is considered equivalent to an exit that discharges directly into the lobby at the level of exit discharge. Therefore, 50 percent of the exits can discharge onto a mezzanine; the other 50 percent must discharge directly outside. Occupants then travel across the mezzanine, along open stairs to the lobby level, and to the outside. However, the distance from the termination of the exit enclosure to the exterior door is limited to a maximum of 100 ft (30 m) unless the building is protected with automatic sprinklers, in which case the distance

can be extended to 150 ft (45 m). The part of the exit discharge that occurs within the building is depicted in Exhibit 30/31.7 by the arrow that connects the door at Stair 1 with the lobby door to the outside. See also the commentary on 7.7.2.

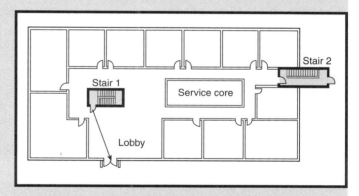

Exhibit 30/31.7 *Exit discharge through street floor.*

30.2.8 Illumination of Means of Egress.

Means of egress shall be illuminated in accordance with Section 7.8.

30.2.9 Emergency Lighting.

Emergency lighting in accordance with Section 7.9 shall be provided in all buildings with more than 12 dwelling units or more than three stories in height.

31.2.8 Illumination of Means of Egress.

Means of egress shall be illuminated in accordance with Section 7.8.

31.2.9 Emergency Lighting.

Emergency lighting in accordance with Section 7.9 shall be provided in all buildings with more than 12 dwelling units or more than three stories in height.

CHAPTER 30 • New	CHAPTER 31 • Existing

Exception: Where every dwelling unit has a direct exit to the outside of the building at grade level.

Exception: Where every dwelling unit has a direct exit to the outside of the building at grade level.

30.2.10 Marking of Means of Egress.

Means of egress shall have signs in accordance with Section 7.10 in all buildings requiring more than one exit.

31.2.10 Marking of Means of Egress.

Means of egress shall have signs in accordance with Section 7.10 in all buildings requiring more than one exit.

30.2.11 Special Means of Egress Features.

(Reserved.)

31.2.11* Special Means of Egress Features.

In high-rise buildings using Option 1, Option 2, or Option 3, smokeproof enclosures shall be provided in accordance with 7.2.3.

A.31.2.11 The provision of 31.2.11 recognizes the need to provide smoke control in existing buildings. Smokeproof enclosures can be accomplished without the use of a vestibule in accordance with 7.2.3.

The exception to 30/31.2.9 does not apply to all apartment buildings with exterior exit access but only to those where each apartment unit has direct exit at grade (no vertical travel).
   Subsection 31.2.11 impacts existing, nonsprin-

klered high-rise apartment buildings. If smokeproof enclosures are not already provided, it might be more realistic to add sprinkler protection than to modify stairs to meet the requirements for smokeproof enclosures.

Section 30.3 Protection

30.3.1 Protection of Vertical Openings.

30.3.1.1 Any vertical opening shall be enclosed or protected in accordance with 8.2.5. Where the provisions of 8.2.5.5 are used, the requirements of 30.3.5.5 shall be met.

Exception No. 1:   Openings in accordance with 8.2.5.8 shall be permitted.

Exception No. 2:   In buildings protected throughout by an approved, supervised automatic sprinkler system in accordance with 30.3.5, the fire resistance of walls shall be not less than 1 hour, and the fire protection rating of doors shall be not less than 1 hour.

30.3.1.2 No floor below the level of exit discharge used only for storage, heating equipment, or purposes other than residential occupancy open to the public shall have unprotected openings to floors used for residential purposes.

30.3.1.3 No unenclosed vertical opening shall be permitted in any building or fire section with only one exit.

Section 31.3 Protection

31.3.1 Protection of Vertical Openings.

31.3.1.1 Any vertical opening shall be enclosed or protected in accordance with 8.2.5.

Exception No. 1:   Openings in accordance with 8.2.5.8 shall be permitted.

Exception No. 2:   In buildings protected throughout by an approved automatic sprinkler system in accordance with 31.3.5, and in which exits and required ways of travel thereto are adequately safeguarded against fire and smoke within the building, or where every individual room has direct access to an exterior exit without passing through any public corridor, the protection of vertical openings that are not part of required exits shall not be required.

31.3.1.2 No floor below the level of exit discharge used only for storage, heating equipment, or purpose other than residential occupancy open to the public shall have unprotected openings to floors used for residential purposes.

CHAPTER 30 • New   **CHAPTER 31 • Existing**

The protection of vertical openings is provided by a reference to 8.2.5 for both new and existing apartment buildings. However, automatic sprinkler protection is required throughout new apartment buildings where the building has a communicating space in accordance with 8.2.5.5.

Exception No. 1 to 30/31.3.1.1 has traditionally permitted an unenclosed stair to be located within an apartment unit (living unit) for the purpose of connecting two adjacent stories. The open stair typically served as means of escape for occupants of a living unit. The provisions of 8.2.5.8 do not permit the opening to serve as required means of egress. It is not the intent to prohibit an open stair from serving as means of escape for occupants of a living unit.

In the case of a three-story apartment unit, only two of the three stories can be connected by an open stair. The stair connecting the third level must be enclosed in accordance with 8.2.5.

Atriums are permitted in both new and existing apartment buildings (see 8.2.5.6). However, 8.2.5.6 requires total automatic sprinkler protection in buildings with atriums. Therefore, an existing apartment building would be permitted to have an atrium only where Option 4 is used.

New apartment buildings, other than those meeting the provisions of the exception to 30.3.5.2, must be protected throughout by an approved, supervised automatic sprinkler system. Therefore, most new apartment buildings, by virtue of their compliance with the sprinkler requirements of 30.3.5.2, are permitted to use the 1-hour vertical enclosure protection option in accordance with Exception No. 2 to 30.3.1.1, regardless of the number of stories connected by the vertical opening. See also the commentary that addresses 30/31.2.2.1.2.

30.3.2 Protection from Hazards.

30.3.2.1 Hazardous Areas. Any hazardous area shall be protected in accordance with Section 8.4. The areas described in Table 30.3.2.1 shall be protected as indicated. Where sprinkler protection without fire-rated separation is used, areas shall be separated from other spaces by smoke partitions complying with 8.2.4.

31.3.2 Protection from Hazards.

31.3.2.1 Hazardous Areas. Any hazardous area shall be protected in accordance with Section 8.4. The areas described in Table 31.3.2.1 shall be protected as indicated. Where sprinkler protection without fire-rated separation is used, areas shall be separated from other spaces by smoke partitions complying with 8.2.4.

Table 30.3.2.1 Hazardous Area Protection

Hazardous Area Description	Separation/Protection
Boiler and fuel-fired heater rooms serving more than a single dwelling unit	1 hour and sprinklers
Employee locker rooms	1 hour or sprinklers
Gift or retail shops	1 hour or sprinklers
Bulk laundries	1 hour and sprinklers
Laundries ≤ 100 ft^2 (≤ 9.3 m^2) outside of dwelling units	1 hour or sprinklers†
Laundries >100 ft^2 (>9.3 m^2) outside of dwelling units	1 hour and sprinklers
Maintenance shops	1 hour and sprinklers
Storage rooms outside of dwelling units	1 hour or sprinklers
Trash collection rooms	1 hour and sprinklers

†Where sprinklers are provided, separation shall not be required.

Table 31.3.2.1 Hazardous Area Protection

Hazardous Area Description	Separation/Protection
Boiler and fuel-fired heater rooms serving more than a single dwelling unit	1 hour or sprinklers
Employee locker rooms	1 hour or sprinklers
Gift or retail shops >100 ft^2 (>9.3 m^2)	1 hour or sprinklers†
Bulk laundries	1 hour or sprinklers
Laundries >100 ft^2 (>9.3 m^2) outside of dwelling units	1 hour or sprinklers†
Maintenance shops	1 hour or sprinklers
Rooms or spaces used for storage of combustible supplies and equipment in quantities deemed hazardous by the authority having jurisdiction	1 hour or sprinklers
Trash collection rooms	1 hour or sprinklers

†Where sprinklers are provided, separation shall not be required.

CHAPTER 30 • New

CHAPTER 31 • Existing

Note the differences in the hazardous area protection requirements for new and existing apartment buildings. Particular attention should be given to the fact that automatic sprinklers are often used as an alternative to providing a rated separation. In new apartment buildings, many of the areas are required to be separated by construction with a 1-hour fire resistance rating and are also required to be protected by automatic sprinklers. In existing apartment buildings, au-

tomatic sprinklers are used as an alternative to the separation requirement.

While the list that appears in Table 30/31.3.2.1 provides specific direction for certain hazardous contents areas, it is not all-inclusive. Other areas that are deemed hazardous need to be provided with the appropriate level of protection in accordance with Section 8.4.

30.3.3 Interior Finish.

30.3.3.1 Interior finish shall be in accordance with Section 10.2.

30.3.3.2 Interior Wall and Ceiling Finish. Interior wall and ceiling finish materials complying with 10.2.3 shall be permitted as follows:

(1) Exit enclosures—Class A
(2) Lobbies and corridors—Class A or Class B
(3) Other spaces—Class A, Class B, or Class C

30.3.3.3 Interior Floor Finish. Interior floor finish in accordance with 10.2.7 shall be in accordance with Table 30.3.3.3.

Table 30.3.3.3 Interior Floor Finish

Location	Sprinklered	Nonsprinklered
Corridors	No requirement	Class II
Exits	No requirement	Class II

31.3.3 Interior Finish.

31.3.3.1 Interior finish shall be in accordance with Section 10.2.

31.3.3.2 Interior Wall and Ceiling Finish. Interior wall and ceiling finish materials complying with 10.2.3 shall be permitted as follows:

(1) Exit enclosures—Class A or Class B
(2) Lobbies and corridors—Class A or Class B
(3) Other spaces—Class A, Class B, or Class C

31.3.3.3 Interior Floor Finish. Interior floor finish in accordance with 10.2.7 shall be in accordance with Table 31.3.3.3.

Table 31.3.3.3 Interior Floor Finish

Location	Option 3 and Option 4	Option 1 and Option 2
Corridors	No requirement	Class II
Exits	No requirement	Class II

Exception: Previously installed and approved floor coverings.

30.3.4 Detection, Alarm, and Communications Systems.

30.3.4.1 General. Apartment buildings with more than three stories or with more than 11 dwelling units shall be provided with a fire alarm system in accordance with Section 9.6, except as modified by 30.3.4.2 through 30.3.4.5.

Exception No. 1: Where each dwelling unit is separated from other contiguous dwelling units by fire barriers (see 8.2.3) having a fire resistance rating of not less than 1 hour, and where each dwelling unit has either its own independent

31.3.4 Detection, Alarm, and Communications Systems.

31.3.4.1 General. Apartment buildings with more than three stories or with more than 11 dwelling units shall be provided with a fire alarm system in accordance with Section 9.6, except as modified by 31.3.4.2 through 31.3.4.5.

Exception: Where each dwelling unit is separated from other contiguous dwelling units by fire barriers (see 8.2.3) having a fire resistance rating of not less than ½ hour, and where each dwelling unit has either its own independent exit or its own independent stairway or ramp discharging at grade.

Exception No. 2: Buildings that are protected throughout by an approved, automatic sprinkler system in accordance with 30.3.5.1, that do not exceed four stories in height, and that contain not more than 16 dwelling units.

The intent of Exception No. 1 to 30/31.3.4.1 is to exempt town house–type apartment buildings from the requirement for a fire alarm system because, during a fire, each apartment unit retains safe egress routes for longer than is typical of standard apartment build-

---

exit or its own independent stairway or ramp discharging at grade.

ings with interior exit access corridors. The safe egress route helps to ensure that any delay in occupant notification resulting from the absence of an alarm system can be tolerated without undue risk.

30.3.4.2 Initiation.

30.3.4.2.1 Initiation of the required fire alarm system shall be by manual means in accordance with 9.6.2.

Exception: Buildings that are protected throughout by an approved, supervised automatic sprinkler system in accordance with 30.3.5.1, that do not exceed four stories in height, and that contain not more than 16 dwelling units.

30.3.4.2.2 In buildings protected throughout by an approved, supervised automatic sprinkler system in accordance with 30.3.5, required fire alarm systems shall be initiated upon operation of the automatic sprinkler system.

31.3.4.2 Initiation.

31.3.4.2.1 Initiation of the required fire alarm system shall be by manual means in accordance with 9.6.2.

Exception: Buildings that are protected throughout by an approved, supervised automatic sprinkler system in accordance with 31.3.5.1, that do not exceed four stories in height, and that contain not more than 16 dwelling units.

31.3.4.2.2 In buildings using Option 2, the required fire alarm system shall be initiated by the automatic fire detection system in addition to the manual initiation means of 31.3.4.2.1.

31.3.4.2.3 In buildings using Option 3, the required fire alarm system shall be initiated upon operation of the automatic sprinkler system in addition to the manual initiation means of 31.3.4.2.1.

31.3.4.2.4 In buildings using Option 4, the required fire alarm system shall be initiated upon operation of the automatic sprinkler system in addition to the manual initiation means of 31.3.4.2.1.

30.3.4.3 Notification.

30.3.4.3.1 Occupant notification shall be provided automatically in accordance with Section 9.6. Visible signals shall be installed in units designed for the hearing impaired. Positive alarm sequence in accordance with 9.6.3.4 shall be permitted.

30.3.4.3.2 Annunciation in accordance with 9.6.7 shall be provided.

31.3.4.3 Notification.

31.3.4.3.1 Occupant notification shall be provided automatically in accordance with Section 9.6. Visible signals shall be installed in units designed for the hearing impaired. Positive alarm sequence in accordance with 9.6.3.4 shall be permitted. Existing approved presignal systems shall be permitted in accordance with 9.6.3.3.

31.3.4.3.2 An annunciator panel connected with the required fire alarm system shall be provided. The location of the annunciator panel shall be approved by the authority having jurisdiction.

CHAPTER 30 • New	CHAPTER 31 • Existing

Exception No. 1: Buildings not more than two stories in height and having not more than 50 dwelling units.

Exception No. 2: Buildings that are protected throughout by an approved, supervised automatic sprinkler system in accordance with 30.3.5.1, that do not exceed four stories in height, and that contain not more than 16 dwelling units.

30.3.4.4 Detection. (Reserved.)

30.3.4.5 Smoke Alarms.

30.3.4.5.1* Approved single-station smoke alarms shall be installed in accordance with 9.6.2.10 outside every sleeping area in the immediate vicinity of the bedrooms and on all levels of the dwelling unit, including basements.

A.30.3.4.5.1 Previous editions of the *Code* permitted the single-station smoke detector required by 30.3.4.5.1 to be omitted from each apartment where a complete automatic smoke detection system was installed throughout the building. With such a system, when one detector is activated, an alarm is sounded throughout the building. Experience with complete smoke detection systems in apartment buildings has shown that numerous nuisance alarms are likely to occur. Where there is a problem with frequent nuisance alarms, occupants ignore the alarm, or the system is either disconnected or otherwise rendered inoperative.

30.3.4.5.2 Approved single-station smoke alarms shall be installed in accordance with 9.6.2.10 in every sleeping room.

Exception: In buildings protected throughout by an approved, supervised automatic sprinkler system in accordance with 30.3.5.

Exception No. 1: Buildings not more than two stories in height and having not more than 50 dwelling units.

Exception No. 2: Buildings that are protected throughout by an approved, supervised automatic sprinkler system in accordance with 31.3.5.1, that do not exceed four stories in height, and that contain not more than 16 dwelling units.

31.3.4.4 Detection. In buildings using Option 2, a complete automatic fire detection system in accordance with 9.6.1.4 shall be required.

31.3.4.5 Smoke Alarms.

31.3.4.5.1 Approved single-station smoke alarms shall be installed in accordance with 9.6.2.10 outside every sleeping area in the immediate vicinity of the bedrooms and on all levels of the dwelling unit, including basements.

Exception No. 1: The single-station smoke alarm shall not be required where the building is equipped throughout with an existing, complete automatic smoke detection system.

Exception No. 2: Single-station smoke alarms without a secondary (standby) power source shall be permitted.

Existing apartment buildings using Option 2 are protected throughout by a fire detection system (see 31.3.4.4). The increased travel distance permitted in an Option 2 apartment building (see 31.2.6.1 and 31.2.6.2) is based on early occupant notification of fire. Therefore, the detectors must initiate the alarm system in addition to the initiation provided by manual fire alarm boxes.

The corridors of existing apartment buildings using Option 3 are protected by sprinklers (see 31.3.5.2). The activation of the sprinkler system must initiate the alarm system in addition to the initiation provided by manual fire alarm boxes.

Existing apartment buildings using Option 4 are protected throughout by automatic sprinkler systems (see 31.3.5.5). The activation of the sprinkler system must initiate the alarm system in addition to the initiation provided by manual fire alarm boxes.

Exception No. 2 to 30/31.3.4.3.2 exempts automatic annunciation based on automatic sprinklers and small building size. Given the additional limitation on building height and number of units, it is believed that fire in a fully sprinklered building can be controlled to a level that permits a delay by responding emergency forces in locating a fire.

In existing apartment buildings using Option 2, a total automatic fire detection system is required and must be interconnected with the building fire alarm system in accordance with 31.3.4.2.2. This system is required in addition to the single-station smoke alarms required by 31.3.4.5. Note that 31.3.4.4 does not require the fire detection system to be comprised solely of smoke detectors but, instead, allows the use of either heat or smoke detectors, or combinations of the two. Heat detectors are allowed by 31.3.4.4 because they are used as part of a system that is separate from the single-station smoke alarms addressed in 31.3.4.5. The single-station smoke alarms will alert occupants within an apartment of a fire originating within that unit. When an occupant leaves the apartment, the door closes and latches behind the occupant (see 31.3.6.3), and the occupant pulls a manual fire alarm box. If the occupant fails to sound the alarm manually and the fire continues to develop in the apartment, the heat detectors initiate the building fire alarm system prior to the fire becoming a threat to other apartment units. Fire detection systems have proved very effective where used. In addition, because the system is required to be tied into the building fire alarm system, the use of heat detectors instead of system smoke detectors would eliminate many nuisance alarms that might occur because of cooking or smoking.

The smoke alarm(s) required by 30.3.4.5.1 and 31.3.4.5.1 should be located in the hall area(s) that provides access to rooms used for sleeping. In multi-level living units, the smoke alarm covering the upper level should normally be located at the top of the stairs. The smoke alarm(s) should be mounted on the ceiling or on the wall within 12 in. (30.5 cm) of, but no closer than 6 in. (15.2 cm) to, the ceiling. The smoke

alarm should be remotely located from the cooking area. Where unusual factors such as room configuration, air movement, or stagnant air pockets must be considered, the authority having jurisdiction and the designer should determine the placement of the smoke alarms. See NFPA 72, *National Fire Alarm Code*, for additional details. [2]

Note that 9.6.2.10 requires a smoke alarm to be powered by house current, which should be achieved by using directly wired or plug-in type smoke detectors. Battery-powered units do not meet the requirements of 9.6.2.10.

It is not the intent to prohibit interconnecting smoke alarms within a single apartment. If the apartment needs more than one smoke alarm, interconnection will probably be required to meet the performance criterion for audibility detailed in 9.6.2.10.3.

In new apartment buildings, 30.3.4.5.2 supplements the smoke alarms required by 30.3.4.5.1 within individual apartment units by requiring the installation of smoke alarms within every sleeping room of each unit. Such installation provides rapid notification to those occupants intimate with a fire originating within a sleeping room. Smoke alarms are required in the bedrooms of nonsprinklered apartment units, regardless of direct egress arrangements. In sprinklered buildings, sleeping room detectors are exempted by the exception to 30.3.4.5.2. The exception does not equate sprinklers with smoke detectors; instead, it emphasizes that alarms are needed as well as exits direct to grade level.

30.3.5 Extinguishment Requirements.

30.3.5.1 Where an automatic sprinkler system is installed, either for total or partial building coverage, the system shall be in accordance with Section 9.7. In buildings up to and including four stories in height, systems in accordance with NFPA 13R, *Standard for the Installation of Sprinkler Systems in Residential Occupancies up to and Including Four Stories in Height*, shall be permitted.

Exception No. 1: In buildings sprinklered in accordance with NFPA 13, Standard for the Installation of Sprinkler Systems, closets less than 12 ft² (1.1 m²) in area in individual dwelling units shall not be required to be sprinklered. Closets that contain equipment such as washers, dryers, furnaces, or water heaters shall be sprinklered regardless of size.

31.3.5 Extinguishment Requirements.

31.3.5.1* Where an automatic sprinkler system is installed, either for total or partial building coverage, the system shall be in accordance with Section 9.7. In buildings up to and including four stories in height, systems in accordance with NFPA 13R, *Standard for the Installation of Sprinkler Systems in Residential Occupancies up to and Including Four Stories in Height*, shall be permitted.

Exception No. 1: In individual dwelling units, sprinkler installation shall not be required in closets not exceeding 24 ft² (2.2 m²) and in bathrooms not exceeding 55 ft² (5.1 m²). Closets that contain equipment such as washers, dryers, furnaces, or water heaters shall be sprinklered regardless of size.

Exception No. 2: The provisions for draft stops and closely spaced sprinklers in NFPA 13, Standard for the Installation of Sprinkler Systems, shall not be required for openings complying with 8.2.5.8 where the opening is within the dwelling unit.

30.3.5.2 All buildings shall be protected throughout by an approved, supervised automatic sprinkler system in accordance with 30.3.5.1.

Exception: Buildings where every dwelling unit is provided with one of the following:

(a) An exit door opening directly to the street or yard at ground level

(b) Direct access to an outside stair complying with 7.2.2 that serves not more than two units, both of which are located on the same floor

(c) Direct access to an interior stair serving only that unit, and such stair is separated from all other portions of the building by fire barriers having a 1-hour fire resistance rating with no openings therein

30.3.5.3 Listed quick-response or listed residential sprinklers shall be used throughout all dwelling units.

30.3.5.4 Open parking structures complying with NFPA 88A, *Standard for Parking Structures,* that are contiguous with apartment buildings shall be exempt from the sprinkler requirements of 30.3.5.2.

30.3.5.5 Buildings with unprotected openings in accordance with 8.2.5.5 shall be protected throughout by an approved, supervised automatic sprinkler system in accordance with 30.3.5.

30.3.5.6 (Reserved.)

Exception No. 2: The provisions for draft stops and closely spaced sprinklers in NFPA 13, Standard for the Installation of Sprinkler Systems, shall not be required for openings complying with 8.2.5.8 where the opening is within the dwelling unit.

A.31.3.5.1 Although not required by the *Code,* the use of residential sprinklers or quick-response sprinklers is encouraged for new installations of sprinkler systems within dwelling units, apartments, and guest rooms. Caution should be exercised, as the system needs to be designed for the sprinkler being used.

31.3.5.2 Buildings using Option 3 shall be provided with the following:

(1) Automatic sprinklers in the corridor along the corridor ceiling

(2) An automatic sprinkler within any dwelling unit that has a door opening to the corridor, with such sprinkler positioned over the center of the door

Exception: The sprinkler inside dwelling units shall not be required if the door to the dwelling unit has not less than a 20-minute fire protection rating and is self-closing.

31.3.5.3 The sprinkler installation required in 31.3.5.2 shall meet the requirements of Section 9.7 in terms of workmanship and materials.

31.3.5.4 The installation of the corridor sprinklers required in 31.3.5.2 shall not exceed the maximum spacing and protection area requirements of the installation standards referenced in Section 9.7.

31.3.5.5 Buildings using Option 4 shall be protected throughout by an approved automatic sprinkler system in accordance with 31.3.5.1. The automatic sprinkler system shall meet the requirements of Section 9.7 for supervision for buildings more than six stories in height.

31.3.5.6 All high-rise buildings shall be protected throughout by an approved, supervised automatic sprinkler system in accordance with 31.3.5.1.

Exception No. 1: Where every dwelling unit has exterior exit access in accordance with 7.5.3.

Exception No. 2:* Buildings in which an engineered life safety system has been approved by the authority having jurisdiction.

CHAPTER 30 • New   **CHAPTER 31 • Existing**

A.31.3.5.6 Exception No. 2 This system might consist of a combination of any or all of the following systems:

(1) Partial automatic sprinkler protection
(2) Smoke detection alarms
(3) Smoke control
(4) Compartmentation or other approved systems, or both

30.3.5.7 Portable fire extinguishers in accordance with 9.7.4.1 shall be provided in hazardous areas addressed by 30.3.2.1.

Exception: In buildings protected throughout with an approved, supervised automatic sprinkler system in accordance with Section 9.7.

31.3.5.7 Portable fire extinguishers in accordance with 9.7.4.1 shall be provided in hazardous areas addressed by 31.3.2.1.

Exception: In buildings protected throughout with an approved automatic sprinkler system in accordance with Section 9.7.

The *Code* permits NFPA 13R, *Standard for the Installation of Sprinkler Systems in Residential Occupancies up to and Including Four Stories in Height,* to be used, within its scope, in place of NFPA 13,[3] *Standard for the Installation of Sprinkler Systems.* However, the provision of 30.3.5.3, which requires the use of listed quick-response sprinklers or listed residential sprinklers within dwelling units, supersedes any sprinkler choice options permitted by NFPA 13R or NFPA 13.

Exception No. 1 to 30/31.3.5.1 exempts small closets from being sprinklered because of the limited fuel load characteristics of apartment unit closets. The closets exempted are limited to those within a living unit; closets in common building areas are not exempted.

In the 1997 edition of the *Code,* it was the intent that Exception No. 1 to 30.3.5.1 override the requirements in both NFPA 13 and NFPA 13R. Subsequent changes to NFPA 13R make this exception to that standard unnecessary. Therefore, the first sentence of the exception now applies only where the sprinkler system is designed in accordance with NFPA 13. The last sentence clarifies that the unsprinklered closet cannot contain mechanical equipment and its associated ignition sources and potential for fire spread.

Those features that define residential occupancies also contribute to their associated poor life loss statistics. Approximately 82 percent of all fire deaths that occurred in the United States from 1993 to 1997 occurred in residential settings. More specifically, almost 15 percent of all deaths took place in apartment building fires. In recognition of the fire problem in residential occupancies and the proven life safety benefit of properly installed and maintained sprinkler systems, the *Code* requires sprinklers in new

apartment buildings, unless the provisions of the exception to 30.3.5.2 are met.

The exception can be applied only where each living unit within a building is provided with one of the following:

(1) A door opening to the outside at grade level
(2) Direct access to an outside stair that is permitted to serve no more than two units that must access the stair on the same story
(3) Access to an interior stair that serves only the unit itself and that is properly separated from the remainder of the building

The direct access required from each living unit to the outside, in combination with the early warning provided by the sleeping room smoke detectors required by 30.3.4.5.2, provides an acceptable alternative to sprinklers. The conditions under which this exception is permitted are equivalent to those that allow a single exit in accordance with Exception No. 1 to 30.2.4.

Exhibit 30/31.8 depicts egress arrangements for two-story nonsprinklered apartment buildings with outside stairs. Illustration (a) depicts a two-story apartment building with two units on the second floor that have direct access to the outside stair. Illustration (b) depicts a two-story apartment building with four units on the second floor. In this case, the stairs are separated by a barrier so that each serves only two dwelling units.

Exhibit 30/31.9 depicts an egress arrangement for a three-story, nonsprinklered apartment building meeting the provisions of the exception to 30.3.5.2. Each apartment has its own egress system direct to ground.

CHAPTER 30 • New	CHAPTER 31 • Existing

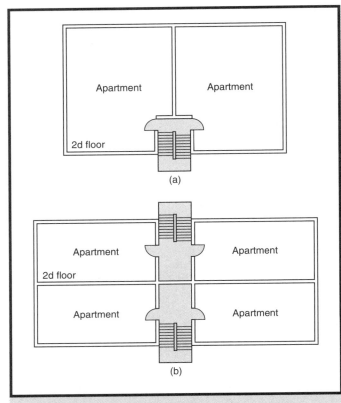

Exhibit 30/31.8 *Two-story apartment building—exempt from building sprinkler system requirement.*

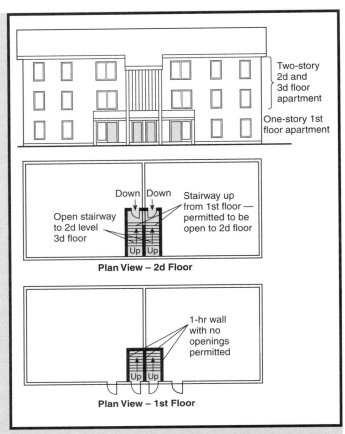

Exhibit 30/31.9 *Three-story apartment building—exempt from building sprinkler system requirement.*

In existing apartment buildings, Option 3 and Option 4 require automatic sprinkler installation. Exhibit 30/31.10 illustrates the sprinkler location requirements for an Option 3 existing apartment building. The exception to 31.3.5.2 permits a 20-minute fire protection–rated, self-closing corridor door to serve in lieu of the sprinklers positioned inside each apartment unit in the vicinity of the corridor door; however, the corridor sprinklers must still be provided.

The *Code* provides numerous incentives for existing apartment buildings to use Option 4 sprinkler protection, as detailed in 31.3.5.5. Some of the more significant incentives that apply to existing apartment buildings are provided in Exception No. 2 to 31.2.4, 31.2.6, 31.2.11, Exception No. 2 to 31.3.6.2, and Exception No. 1 to 31.3.7. However, to take advantage of these incentives, the building must be sprinklered in accordance with Option 4, as detailed in 31.3.5.5.

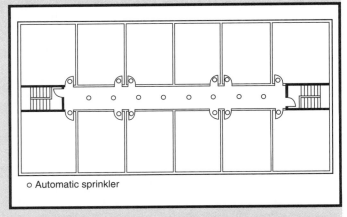

Exhibit 30/31.10 *Option 3 sprinkler protection for existing apartment buildings.*

CHAPTER 30 • New   **CHAPTER 31 • Existing**

One of the objectives of the *Code* is to provide a structure that will protect occupants who are not intimate with the initial fire development for the time needed to evacuate (see 4.2.1). Based on this objective, new apartment buildings are required to use quick-response or residential sprinklers throughout apartment units. The annex text of A.31.3.5.1 encourages the use of approved residential or quick-response sprinklers within dwelling units of existing apartment buildings. The intent is to obtain the quick response provided by these sprinklers as well as the high-spray pattern provided by residential sprinklers. The technology associated with quick-response and residential sprinklers helps to maintain tenability within the room of fire origin.

Designers of sprinkler systems must use caution, as residential and quick-response sprinklers cannot always be installed in a system that was originally designed for standard sprinklers. Situations also exist where residential or quick-response sprinklers might

not be listed for use, such as use for vaulted ceilings. In such cases, the designer could provide the best alternative sprinkler.

Paragraph 31.3.5.6 requires approved supervised sprinkler systems throughout high-rise apartment buildings. However, the *Code* does provide two alternatives. The first exempts sprinklers throughout if each living unit has direct exterior exit access. In lieu of installing sprinklers throughout, the *Code* also permits the application of an approved, engineered life safety system. Although not required, the annex note suggests that this engineered life safety system should include some combination of automatic sprinkler protection, detection, smoke control, and compartmentation. The *Code* further requires that this alternative approach be approved by the authority having jurisdiction. During the planning phase, the enforcer should determine whether a system is acceptable. See the definition of *high-rise building* in 3.3.101.

30.3.6 Corridors.

30.3.6.1 Walls. Exit access corridor walls shall consist of fire barriers in accordance with 8.2.3 that have not less than a 1-hour fire resistance rating.

Exception: In buildings protected throughout by an approved, supervised automatic sprinkler system in accordance with 30.3.5, corridor walls shall have not less than a ½-hour fire resistance rating.

30.3.6.2 Doors. Doors that open onto exit access corridors shall have not less than a 20-minute fire protection rating in accordance with 8.2.3.2.

30.3.6.3 Doors that open onto exit access corridors shall be self-closing and self-latching.

30.3.6.4 Unprotected openings shall be prohibited in exit access corridor walls and doors.

31.3.6 Corridors.

31.3.6.1* Walls. Exit access corridor walls shall consist of fire barriers in accordance with 8.2.3 that have not less than a ½-hour fire resistance rating.

A.31.3.6.1 The intent is to recognize that existing partitions of sound wood lath and plaster, wire lath and plaster, or gypsum lath and plaster construction have demonstrated the ability to contain most room fires. Recent data on archaic construction methods have established the fire resistance rating of such construction at about 20 minutes. Such construction meets the intent of 31.3.6.1.

31.3.6.2 Doors. Doors that open onto exit access corridors shall have not less than a 20-minute fire protection rating in accordance with 8.2.3.2.

Exception No. 1: Doors complying with 8.2.3.2.3.

Exception No. 2: In buildings using Option 3 or Option 4, doors shall be constructed to resist the passage of smoke.

31.3.6.3 Doors that open onto exit access corridors shall be self-closing and self-latching.

31.3.6.4 Unprotected openings shall be prohibited in exit access corridor walls and doors.

CHAPTER 30 • New

CHAPTER 31 • Existing

Exception: Such spaces shall be permitted to be unlimited in area and open to the corridor, provided that the following criteria are met:

(a) The spaces are not used for dwelling units or hazardous areas.

(b) The space is protected by an approved, supervised automatic sprinkler system in accordance with 30.3.5.

(c) The space does not obstruct access to required exits.

30.3.6.5 Transoms, louvers, or transfer grilles shall be prohibited in walls or doors of exit access corridors.

Exception: Such spaces shall be permitted to be unlimited in area and open to the corridor, provided that the following criteria are met:

(a) The spaces are not used for dwelling units or hazardous areas.

(b) The space is protected by an approved automatic sprinkler system in accordance with 31.3.5.

(c) The space does not obstruct access to required exits.

31.3.6.5 Transoms, louvers, or transfer grilles shall be prohibited in walls or doors of exit access corridors.

The provisions of 30/31.3.6 reflect concern for providing safety for occupants in their apartments during a fire. The minimum 1-hour fire resistance rating required for corridor wall construction in new apartment buildings is intended to prevent fire from moving from the corridor to an apartment or to prevent fire from spreading from an apartment to the corridor.

The minimum ½-hour fire resistance rating required for corridor wall construction in existing apartment buildings recognizes that most existing lath and plaster walls provide a 30-minute fire resistance rating.

The exception to 30.3.6.1 also permits a reduction to a ½-hour fire resistance rating in new sprinklered apartment buildings. Although this reduction would result in little savings in new construction, it could be useful in rehabilitation, renovations, or conversions of existing structures that are required to meet the provisions for new construction (see 4.6.7). If automatic sprinkler protection is provided throughout the building, the existing corridor walls should not have to be replaced.

The installation and proper maintenance of the required self-closing device on the door between an apartment and the common corridor could lead to a significant reduction in fatalities caused by fire in apartment buildings. Studies of typical apartment fires indicate that fire spreads beyond the apartment of origin because doors are left open as occupants escape.

In other cases, fatalities occur when occupants who suspect a fire open the door to a room fully involved with fire or cause full fire involvement of the room by introducing oxygen through the open door. Spring-loaded hinges or closers will cause these doors to close and latch, preventing smoke or fire

from spreading down the corridor and exposing other occupants.

The door required by 30/31.3.6.2 provides a level of protection commensurate with the expected fuel load in the apartment unit and the fire resistance of the corridor wall construction. The purpose is to box a fire out of an apartment unit or to box it within the apartment unit by means of corridor wall and door construction. Fuel load studies conducted by the National Bureau of Standards (currently the National Institute of Standards and Technology) demonstrated that residential occupancies typically have fuel loads capable of sustaining a fire for approximately 20 to 30 minutes.

Exhibits 30/31.11 and 30/31.12 detail the wall construction and opening protection requirements of 30/31.3.6.

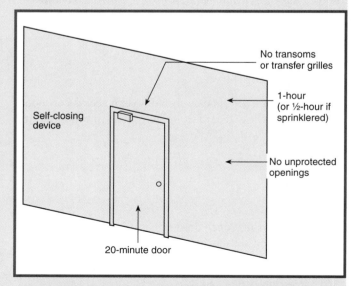

Exhibit 30/31.11 Corridor wall construction in new apartment building.

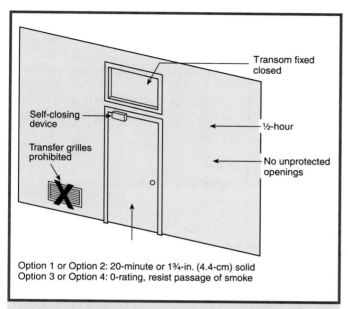

Transom fixed
closed

Self-closing
device

½-hour

Transfer grilles
prohibited

No unprotected
openings

Option 1 or Option 2: 20-minute or 1¾-in. (4.4-cm) solid
Option 3 or Option 4: 0-rating, resist passage of smoke

Exhibit 30/31.12 *Corridor wall construction in existing apartment building.*

30.3.7 Subdivisions of Building Spaces.

(Reserved.)

31.3.7 Subdivision of Building Spaces— Smoke Barriers.

Smoke barriers in accordance with Section 8.3 shall be provided in exit access corridors to establish not less than two compartments approximately equal in size. The length of each smoke compartment, measured along the corridor, shall not exceed 200 ft (60 m). Smoke dampers shall not be required.

Exception No. 1: Buildings using Option 4.

Exception No. 2: Exterior exit access in accordance with 7.5.3 that provides access to two exits.

Exception No. 3: Buildings complying with one of the exceptions to 31.2.4.

Exception No. 4: Buildings with exits not more than 50 ft (15 m) apart.

Exception No. 5: Where each dwelling unit has direct access to the exterior at grade.

The smoke barriers required for existing apartment building by 31.3.7 are relatively easy to provide, because no fire resistance rating is required and smoke dampers are exempted where ducts penetrate the barrier. In most cases, installing a set of cross-corridor doors with smoke-actuated automatic closers will meet the requirement. Exemptions to the requirement include sprinklered buildings (Exception

No. 1), buildings with a single exit (Exception No. 3), and buildings that do not use corridors as required exit access (Exception No. 2 and Exception No. 5).

Exception No. 4 does not require smoke barriers every 50 ft (15 m) but exempts a smoke barrier located on a floor where the exit stairs are spaced no farther than 50 ft (15 m) apart, measured along the corridor.

30.3.8 Special Protection Features.

(Reserved.)

31.3.8 Special Protection Features.

(Reserved.)

Section 30.4 Special Provisions

30.4.1 High-Rise Buildings.

High-rise buildings shall comply with Section 11.8. Exception No. 1 and Exception No. 2 to 30.3.5.1 shall be permitted.

Section 31.4 Special Provisions

31.4.1 High-Rise Buildings.

High-rise buildings shall comply with 31.2.11 and 31.3.5.6.

Section 30.5 Building Services

30.5.1 Utilities.

Utilities shall comply with the provisions of Section 9.1.

30.5.2 Heating, Ventilating, and Air Conditioning.

30.5.2.1 Heating, ventilating, and air conditioning equipment shall comply with the provisions of Section 9.2.

Section 31.5 Building Services

31.5.1 Utilities.

Utilities shall comply with the provisions of Section 9.1.

31.5.2 Heating, Ventilating, and Air Conditioning.

31.5.2.1 Heating, ventilating, and air conditioning equipment shall comply with the provisions of Section 9.2.

NFPA 90A, *Standard for the Installation of Air-Conditioning and Ventilating Systems*, prohibits the use of public

corridors in residential occupancies as part of the system for supply, return, or exhaust air. [4]

30.5.2.2 Unvented fuel-fired heaters shall not be used.

Exception: Gas space heaters in compliance with NFPA 54, National Fuel Gas Code.

30.5.3 Elevators, Escalators, and Conveyors.

Elevators, escalators, and conveyors shall comply with the provisions of Section 9.4.

30.5.4 Rubbish Chutes, Incinerators, and Laundry Chutes.

Rubbish chutes, incinerators, and laundry chutes shall comply with the provisions of Section 9.5.

31.5.2.2 Unvented fuel-fired heaters shall not be used.

Exception: Gas space heaters in compliance with NFPA 54, National Fuel Gas Code.

31.5.3 Elevators, Escalators, and Conveyors.

Elevators, escalators, and conveyors shall comply with the provisions of Section 9.4.

31.5.4 Rubbish Chutes, Incinerators, and Laundry Chutes.

Rubbish chutes, incinerators, and laundry chutes shall comply with the provisions of Section 9.5.

Section 30.6 Reserved

Section 31.6 Reserved

Section 30.7 Operating Features

30.7.1 Emergency Instructions for Residents of Apartment Buildings.

Emergency instructions shall be provided annually to each dwelling unit to indicate the location of alarms, egress paths, and actions to be taken, both in response to a fire in the dwelling unit and in response to the sounding of the alarm system.

The manner in which the information is posted and the nature of its contents are at the discretion of the authority having jurisdiction and depend on the building, its layout, and the protection provided.

References Cited in Commentary

1. NFPA 13, *Standard for the Installation of Sprinkler Systems*, 1999 edition, National Fire Protection Association, Quincy, MA.

Section 31.7 Operating Features

31.7.1 Emergency Instructions for Residents of Apartment Buildings.

Emergency instructions shall be provided annually to each dwelling unit to indicate the location of alarms, egress paths, and actions to be taken, both in response to a fire in the dwelling unit and in response to the sounding of the alarm system.

2. NFPA 72, *National Fire Alarm Code®*, 1999 edition, National Fire Protection Association, Quincy, MA.
3. NFPA 13R, *Standard for the Installation of Sprinkler Systems in Residential Occupancies up to and Including Four Stories in Height*, 1999 edition, National Fire Protection Association, Quincy, MA.
4. NFPA 90A, *Standard for the Installation of Air-Conditioning and Ventilating Systems*, 1999 edition, National Fire Protection Association, Quincy, MA.

CHAPTERS 32 and 33

New and Existing Residential Board and Care Occupancies

The primary characteristic that differentiates a residential board and care occupancy from the other residential occupancies is the availability of personal care services. *Personal care*, as defined in 3.3.145, includes assistance with many of the activities of daily living. Personal care services might include assisting residents with bathing and dressing and helping residents with bill payment and similar household maintenance–related tasks. Personal care does not include nursing home–type care, nor does it include medical care.

Once it has been determined whether personal care services are provided, the level of evacuation capability must be determined. Chapter 32/33 establishes three levels of evacuation capability—prompt, slow, and impractical. In cases where an evacuation capability of prompt has been established, the requirements for the residents are based on provisions similar to the rules for a lodging or rooming house or a hotel. If the evacuation capability is determined to be impractical, the requirements imposed share some of the defend-in-place features used for health care occupancies.

Chapter 32/33 further classifies residential board and care occupancies based on the number of residents. For this purpose, the chapters are further subdivided to address requirements for small (16 or fewer residents) and large (more than 16 residents) facilities. As the number of residents put at risk by fire increases, the requirements naturally become stricter.

Of the three determinations that must be made to classify a residential board and care occupancy (that is, availability of personal care, evacuation capability, and number of residents), the most difficult is that of determining the evacuation capability. Evacuation capability is to be established based on the occupants' (that is, residents and staff, working together) ability to move to a safe location, such as an enclosed exit stair or a point outside of the structure. The annex text for the definition of *evacuation capability* in A.3.3.56 provides guidance on classifying evacuation capability. A substantial change to Chapter 32/33 for the 2000 edition is the requirement of 32/33.2.1.2.2 and 32/33.3.1.2.3 that facility management furnish the authority having jurisdiction with an evacuation capability determination conducted using a procedure acceptable to the authority having jurisdiction. If such documentation is not furnished, the evacuation capability is set, by default, as impractical.

Protection features for residential board and care occupancies range from regulating the allowable types of construction, to mandating alarm and detection systems, to mandating automatic sprinkler protection for all new facilities.

Another unique portion of Chapter 32/33 is Section 32/33.4, which addresses the location of a residential board and care occupancy within an apartment building. The apartment building itself is evaluated on its suitability to house the residential board and care occupancy. The apartment units used as a residential board and care occupancy are judged individually based on the requirements of Section 32/33.2, which applies to small residential board and care occupancies.

As in the case of other occupancy chapters that address occupants with limited self-preservation capability, Chapter 32/33 relies on staff intervention and staff support to assist the residents during fire and similar emergencies. It is the responsibility of the staff to understand and implement the emergency plan for the facility. The plan must include a method for familiarizing residents with the procedures to be followed during a fire.

Section 32.1 General Requirements

32.1.1* Application.

A.32.1.1 The requirements of Chapter 32 are designed to accommodate typical changes in the capabilities of the resident, such as those due to accidents, temporary illness, cyclical variations in capabilities, and gradual aging. This approach is based on the assumption that the capabilities of the resident will be evaluated not less than annually, and for residents with geriatric problems or degenerative diseases, not less than every 6 months. Also, residents should be reevaluated after each accident or illness that requires hospitalization.

The requirements of Chapter 32 were developed on the assumption that the occupants will normally evacuate the building in fire emergencies. During fire exit drills, all occupants should evacuate the building with staff assistance as needed. Exceptions can be made in facilities with an evacuation capability rating of impractical *(see 32.7.3)*. Managers of board and care homes with nursing home backgrounds sometimes are not aware of the differences between the requirements of 18.7.1 and 32.7.3.

32.1.1.1 The requirements of this chapter apply to the following:

(1) New buildings or portions thereof used as residential board and care occupancies *(see 1.4.1)*
(2) Additions made to, or used as, residential board and care occupancies *(see 4.6.6)*
(3) Alterations, modernizations, or renovations of residential board and care occupancies *(see 4.6.7)*
(4) Buildings or portions thereof upon change of occupancy to a residential board and care occupancy *(see 4.6.11)*

32.1.1.2 This chapter is divided into five sections as follows:

(1) Section 32.1—General Requirements
(2) Section 32.2—Small Facilities (that is, sleeping accommodations for not more than 16 residents)
(3) Section 32.3—Large Facilities (that is, sleeping accommodations for more than 16 residents)
(4) Section 32.4—Suitability of an Apartment Building to House a Board and Care Occupancy
(5) Section 32.7—Operating Features *(Sections 32.5 and 32.6 are reserved.)*

32.1.1.3 Conversion. For the purposes of this chapter, exceptions for conversions shall apply only for a change of occupancy from an existing residential or health care occupancy to a residential board and care occupancy.

Section 33.1 General Requirements

33.1.1* Application.

A.33.1.1 The requirements of Chapter 33 are designed to accommodate typical changes in the capabilities of the resident, such as those due to accidents, temporary illness, cyclical variations in capabilities, and gradual aging. This approach is based on the assumption that the capabilities of the resident will be evaluated not less than annually, and for residents with geriatric problems or degenerative diseases, not less than every 6 months. Also, residents should be reevaluated after each accident or illness that requires hospitalization.

The requirements of Chapter 33 were developed on the assumption that the occupants will normally evacuate the building in fire emergencies. During fire exit drills, all occupants should evacuate the building with staff assistance as needed. Exceptions can be made in facilities with an evacuation capability rating of impractical *(see 33.7.3)*. Managers of board and care homes with nursing home backgrounds sometimes are not aware of the differences between the requirements of 19.7.1 and 33.7.3.

33.1.1.1 The requirements of this chapter apply to existing buildings or portions thereof currently occupied as residential board and care occupancies *(see also 32.1.1)*.

33.1.1.2 This chapter is divided into five sections as follows:

(1) Section 33.1—General Requirements
(2) Section 33.2—Small Facilities (that is, sleeping accommodations for not more than 16 residents)
(3) Section 33.3—Large Facilities (that is, sleeping accommodations for more than 16 residents)
(4) Section 33.4—Suitability of an Apartment Building to House a Board and Care Occupancy
(5) Section 33.7—Operating Features *(Sections 33.5 and 33.6 are reserved.)*

33.1.1.3 Conversion. For the purposes of this chapter, exceptions for conversions shall apply only for a change of occupancy from an existing residential or health care occupancy to a residential board and care occupancy.

Residential board and care occupancies are also known as assisted living facilities, halfway houses, retirement homes, rooming houses, and community living centers, among others. Regardless of the label, the level of care that is provided is the key to identifying a residential board and care facility.

In recent years, the number of retirement community facilities has grown. These facilities might provide different living arrangements for the elderly within the same building or group of buildings. They also might offer any combination of independent living facilities (apartments), board and care facilities, and full nursing facilities. It is important that the occupancy classification for each building or area is properly identified and that proper separation between the occupancies is provided as necessary.

During the 1990s, NFPA documented fires in 18 board and care occupancies resulting in 100 deaths. Table 32/33.1 is a partial list of multiple-death fires in residential board and care occupancies that occurred between 1990 and 1998.

Table 32/33.1 Residential Board and Care Multiple-Death Fires

Year	Location	Fatalities
1990	Bessemer, AL	4
1991	Colorado Springs, CO	9
1992	Detroit, MI	10
1994	Broward County, FL	5
1995	Mississauga, Ont.	8
1996	Laurinberg, NC	8
1996	Shelby County, TN	4
1996	Ste. Genevieve, Que.	7
1997	Harveys Lake, PA	10
1998	Arlington, WA	8

The following were major contributing factors in these multiple-death fires:

(1) Lack of automatic sprinklers
(2) Doors open to the room of fire origin
(3) Doors open to stairs or unprotected vertical openings
(4) Ineffective staff or resident training or response

Chapter 32/33 addresses basic fire protection features while maintaining the ability to operate such a facility in a noninstitutional environment. The requirements for small board and care facilities are similar to the provisions for one- and two-family dwellings and lodging or rooming houses. The requirements for large facilities, other than those in which residents are classified as impractical to evacuate, are similar to the requirements for new hotels. Large facilities in which residents are classified as impractical to evacuate are required to comply with the requirements of Chapter 18/19. While the provisions of Chapter 32/33 might be similar to other residential occupancies, certain requirements differ due to the unique characteristics of board and care facilities—such as the varying degrees to which occupants are able to respond to a fire emergency.

The requirements of Chapter 32/33 are based on two main concepts as follows:

(1) Larger buildings are more difficult to evacuate than smaller buildings and require more built-in fire protection.
(2) Occupants who are more difficult to evacuate require more built-in fire protection than occupants who are easier to evacuate.

It is also anticipated that a small facility typically will be located in a structure that has the appearance of, and that operates in a manner similar to, a dwelling. The operation and size of a small facility also demands unique consideration with respect to the fire protection features provided. Certain fire protection features that are appropriate for large facilities, such as smoke barriers, might not be appropriate and might not provide adequate protection in small facilities. For this reason, Exception No. 2 to 33.2.1.2.1, which permits small facilities to comply with the requirements for large facilities, applies only to those facilities that have previously met the criteria for the exception. The 1985 edition of the *Code* permitted small facilities to comply with the requirements for large facilities in lieu of the provisions for small facilities. As stated in Exception No. 2 to 33.2.1.2.1, a small facility that has previously been approved, based on the requirements for a large facility, is permitted to continue to be evaluated as a large facility. However, any other small facility must meet the provisions for a small facility and is not permitted to meet the provisions for a large facility as an alternative.

Several requirements in Chapter 32 permit exceptions for conversions. Where a building previously occupied as another type of residential occupancy or a health care occupancy is converted to a board and care facility, such change of use must

CHAPTER 32 • New	CHAPTER 33 • Existing

comply with the requirements for new construction in accordance with 4.6.11. This requirement would apply where a hotel, apartment building, lodging or rooming house, dwelling, hospital, nursing home, or limited care facility is converted to a residential board and care facility. However, certain provisions of Chapter 32 are intended to eliminate undue hardship while maintaining a reasonable degree of life safety.

In such cases, the specific wording of Chapter 32 exempts the existing building from meeting a requirement that would otherwise apply to a new board and care facility. For example, Exception No. 2 to 32.2.2.5.1 permits existing 28-in. (71-cm) wide doors in converted facilities to remain in use rather than being replaced with the 32-in. (81-cm) wide doors normally required in new board and care facilities.

32.1.2 Mixed Occupancies.

32.1.2.1 Where another type of occupancy exists in the same building as a residential board and care occupancy, the requirements of 6.1.14 of this *Code* shall apply.

Exception No. 1: Occupancies that are completely separated from all portions of the building used for a residential board and care facility and its egress system by construction having a fire resistance rating of not less than 2 hours.

Exception No. 2: This requirement shall not apply to apartment buildings housing residential board and care occupancies in conformance with Section 32.4. In such facilities, any safeguards required by Section 32.4 that are more restrictive than those for other housed occupancies shall apply only to the extent prescribed by Section 32.4.

32.1.2.2 No board and care occupancy shall have its sole means of egress pass through any nonresidential or non-health care occupancy in the same building.

32.1.2.3 No board and care occupancy shall be located above a nonresidential or non-health care occupancy.

Exception: Where the board and care occupancy and exits therefrom are separated from the nonresidential or non-health care occupancy by construction having a fire resistance rating of not less than 2 hours.

33.1.2 Mixed Occupancies.

33.1.2.1 Where another type of occupancy exists in the same building as a residential board and care occupancy, the requirements of 6.1.14 of this *Code* shall apply.

Exception No. 1: Occupancies that are completely separated from all portions of the building used for a residential board and care facility and its egress system by construction having a fire resistance rating of not less than 2 hours.

Exception No. 2: This requirement shall not apply to apartment buildings housing residential board and care occupancies in conformance with Section 33.4. In such facilities, any safeguards required by Section 33.4 that are more restrictive than those for other housed occupancies shall apply only to the extent prescribed by Section 33.4.

33.1.2.2 No board and care occupancy shall have its sole means of egress pass through any nonresidential or non-health care occupancy in the same building.

33.1.2.3 No board and care occupancy shall be located above a nonresidential or non-health care occupancy.

Exception No. 1: Where the board and care occupancy and exits therefrom are separated from the nonresidential or non-health care occupancy by construction having a fire resistance rating of not less than 2 hours.

Exception No. 2: Where a nonresidential or non-health care occupancy is protected throughout by an approved, supervised automatic sprinkler system in accordance with Section 9.7 and is separated therefrom by construction with a fire-resistance rating of 1 hour.

The location of a board and care occupancy in a building with mixed occupancies presents a life safety challenge for the occupants of the board and care occupancy. The typical configuration of such build-

ings creates the potential for significant time to elapse before occupants of the board and care occupancy become aware of an emergency in another part of the building and take the necessary action. The requirements of 32/33.1.2 help to ensure that it is safe to locate residential occupancies within these mixed occupancy buildings by providing the necessary protection and separation.

Exception No. 1 to 32/33.1.2.1 requires that the residential board and care facility and its exit system be separated from the other occupancy if requirements applicable to the mixed occupancy are not provided throughout the building. Therefore, if the residential board and care occupancy is located on the second floor and Exception No. 1 to 32/33.1.2.1 is to be applied, the exit stair must have a 2-hour fire-rated enclosure, even though 7.1.3.2 permits a 1-hour fire-rated enclosure. Where the residential board and care occupancy is located on the same floor as the other occupancy, the required 2-hour rated separation might also serve as a horizontal exit, if the provisions of 7.2.4 are met.

Exception No. 2 to 32/33.1.2.1 clarifies that board and care facilities located within an apartment building need not comply with the requirements for a mixed apartment/board and care occupancy. The provisions of Section 32/33.4 apply to the entire building and supplement the provisions of Chapters 30 and 31 for apartment buildings. In addition, the apartment unit housing a board and care facility must comply with the provisions of Section 32/33.2 (see 32/33.4.1.2).

The provisions of 32/33.1.2.2 and 32/33.1.2.3 are intended to provide added protection for the board and care occupancy during evacuation. Therefore, these requirements are intended to apply wherever this mixture of board and care and nonresidential or non-health care occupancies exists, be it in new or existing buildings.

32.1.3 Definitions.

Evacuation Capability. See 3.3.56.

Impractical Evacuation Capability. See 3.3.108.

Personal Care. See 3.3.145.

Point of Safety. See 3.3.151.

Prompt Evacuation Capability. See 3.3.154.

Residential Board and Care Occupancy. See 3.3.163.

Residential Board and Care Resident. See 3.3.164.

Slow Evacuation Capability. See 3.3.180.

Staff (Residential Board and Care). See 3.3.190.

Thermal Barrier. See 3.3.202.

32.1.4 Acceptability of Means of Egress or Escape.

No means of escape or means of egress shall be considered as complying with the minimum criteria for acceptance unless emergency evacuation drills are regularly conducted using that route in accordance with the requirements of 32.7.3.

32.1.5* Fire resistance–rated assemblies shall comply with 8.2.3.

A.32.1.5 The provisions of 8.2.3.1.2(3) address a ½-hour fire resistance rating. The information in A.8.2.3.1.2(3) addresses common materials used in ½-hour fire resistance–rated barriers.

33.1.3 Definitions.

Evacuation Capability. See 3.3.56.

Impractical Evacuation Capability. See 3.3.108.

Personal Care. See 3.3.145.

Point of Safety. See 3.3.151.

Prompt Evacuation Capability. See 3.3.154.

Residential Board and Care Occupancy. See 3.3.163.

Residential Board and Care Resident. See 3.3.164.

Slow Evacuation Capability. See 3.3.180.

Staff (Residential Board and Care). See 3.3.190.

Thermal Barrier. See 3.3.202.

33.1.4 Acceptability of Means of Egress or Escape.

No means of escape or means of egress shall be considered as complying with the minimum criteria for acceptance unless emergency evacuation drills are regularly conducted using that route in accordance with the requirements of 33.7.3.

33.1.5* Fire resistance–rated assemblies shall comply with 8.2.3.

A.33.1.5 The provisions of 8.2.3.1.2(3) address a ½-hour fire resistance rating. The information in A.8.2.3.1.2(3) addresses common materials used in ½-hour fire resistance–rated barriers.

CHAPTER 32 • New	CHAPTER 33 • Existing

32.1.6 (Reserved.)

32.1.7 (Reserved.)

33.1.6 Changes in Facility Size.

A change in facility size from small to large shall be considered a change in occupancy subclassification and shall require compliance with the provisions applicable to new construction.

33.1.7* Changes in Group Evacuation Capability.

A change in evacuation capability shall be permitted where the facility conforms to the requirements applicable to new construction, conversions, and the new evacuation capability.

Exception: Where the evacuation capability changes to a faster level.

A.33.1.7 When the group evacuation capability changes to a level of greater risk, the owner/operator of the facility needs to take such action as is necessary, within a reasonable time frame, to restore the evacuation capability of the facility to that for which it was approved. If subsequent evaluations indicate that the original evacuation capability of the facility cannot or is not being maintained at the original level of risk, the facility would be considered as having changed the occupancy subclassification to one of greater risk, and the safeguards required for the level of greater risk would apply. If a facility improves its original evacuation capability to one of less risk, a re-evaluation and upgrading to the requirements for new construction is not needed.

A number of key terms, such as *evacuation capability, personal care,* and *point of safety,* are referenced in 32/33.1.3. The user needs to understand these terms to make effective use of the requirements for board and care facilities.

Evacuation capability (see definition in 3.3.56) is an underlying factor for various provisions of the occupancy chapters. However, in most occupancy chapters, the *Code* assumes that the building occupants have an evacuation capability similar to that of others within that occupancy, and the requirements are based on the ability of occupants to reach safety by means of exits. In the institutional occupancy chapters, the *Code* assumes that many of the building occupants will be incapable of evacuating the building, and the protection of life from fire is achieved by the defend-in-place method. In large residential buildings (hotels and apartment buildings), where evacuation capability might be affected due to the large size of the building, substantial, built-in fire protection is required.

In Chapter 32/33, evacuation capability must be determined before proceeding to identify applicable requirements. The numerous and diverse types of facilities that are included in residential board and care facilities preclude all occupants from having the same evacuation capability. For example, the occupants in an orphanage, a shelter for battered spouses, a group home for highly functioning mentally handicapped persons, or a halfway house for prison parolees, might have normal evacuation capability. In facilities housing elderly, physically-impaired persons, occupants might be slow moving or might need assistance in recognizing the need for evacuation. In some facilities, evacuation of the building might not be practical at all.

Evacuation capability for an entire facility is not determined based on the resident who is least capable. A facility that houses one impaired resident might have excellent evacuation capability if the staff or an assigned resident "buddy" is able to provide the assistance needed to effect a prompt evacuation of the entire group. Evacuation capability is based on the ability to relocate to a point of safety that is not necessarily a public way (see the definition of point of safety in 3.3.151). The protection features required by Chapter 32/33 are intended to coordinate with the evacuation capability of the occupants. As such, the fire endurance of the structure, the interior finish materials, and the types and arrangement of means of escape and exits, as well as the corridor enclosure provisions, vary based on whether a facility houses occupants who are prompt, slow, or impractical to evacuate. Facilities that are impractical to evacuate use the defend-in-place concept. In small facilities, this concept is achieved by improving the protection of vertical openings. In large facilities, the concept is achieved by mandating the use of the health care provisions of Chapter 18/19.

Personal care (see definition in 3.3.145) is significant, because the occupants of a board and care facility require care. Personal care is not medical care, as might be provided in a hospital or nursing home but, rather, it is a form of assistance in meeting the demands of daily living. The term *transient medical care*, as used in A.3.3.145, refers to the kind of medical care that is normally provided in the home by one family member for another. Transient medical care does not refer to skilled nursing or acute medical care.

Point of safety (see definition in 3.3.151) is another term that is specifically used in Chapter 32/33. It is well recognized that there are many buildings from which evacuation of all occupants to the outside cannot be achieved within a reasonable amount of time.

Chapter 32/33 establishes the criteria for a point of safety within the building. Essentially, point of safety is an area where residents can remain in safety until the fire is extinguished or until outside assistance can arrive to complete evacuation to the exterior.

Several sections of editions of the *Code* published in the 1980s referred to a finish rating of 15 or 20 minutes. The term *finish rating* is similar to, but not as widely used as, the term *thermal barrier* (see definition in 3.3.202). For this reason, Chapter 32/33 uses the term thermal barrier in lieu of finish rating in specifying the protection of structural elements and the separation of areas where automatic sprinkler protection is omitted. As noted in A.3.3.21, finish ratings might be used to determine a material's acceptability as a thermal barrier.

Subsection 32/33.1.4 addresses the acceptability of the means of egress or escape. Exits and means of escape are worthless unless residents are familiar with them and are comfortable using them. An exit or means of escape that is never used in drills will probably not be used in an emergency evacuation. This does not mean that, if windows serve as a secondary means of escape, a resident must practice escaping via the window during a drill. However, during drills it would be important to identify the appropriate windows and ensure that residents are familiar with the operation of the windows and their proper use during escape.

Subsections 33.1.6 and 33.1.7 address changes that might occur during the life of a board and care occupancy. Physical/structural growth will be easily identified, since permits for changes would normally be required. Changes in evacuation capability might be more subtle and will require a close review of the facility's fire drill records.

Section 32.2 Small Facilities

32.2.1 General.

32.2.1.1 Scope. Section 32.2 applies to residential board and care occupancies providing sleeping accommodations for not more than 16 residents. Where there are sleeping accommodations for more than 16 residents, the occupancy shall be classified as a large facility in accordance with Section 32.3.

Section 33.2 Small Facilities

33.2.1 General.

33.2.1.1 Scope. Section 32.2 applies to residential board and care occupancies providing sleeping accommodations for not more than 16 residents. Where there are sleeping accommodations for more than 16 residents, the occupancy shall be classified as a large facility in accordance with Section 33.3.

CHAPTER 32 • New	CHAPTER 33 • Existing

32.2.1.2 Requirements Based on Evacuation Capability.

32.2.1.2.1 Small facilities shall comply with the requirements of Section 32.2 as indicated for the appropriate evacuation capability. The ability of all occupants, residents, staff, and family members shall be considered in determining evacuation capability.

Exception:*   *Facilities where the authority having jurisdiction has determined equivalent safety is provided in accordance with Section 1.5.*

A.32.2.1.2.1 Exception In determining equivalency for conversions, modernizations, renovations, or unusual design concepts, the authority having jurisdiction might permit evaluations based on NFPA 101A, *Guide on Alternative Approaches to Life Safety,* Chapter 6.

32.2.1.2.2 Facility management shall furnish to the authority having jurisdiction, upon request, an evacuation capability determination using a procedure acceptable to the authority having jurisdiction. Where such documentation is not furnished, the evacuation capability shall be classified as impractical.

33.2.1.2 Requirements Based on Evacuation Capability.

33.2.1.2.1 Small facilities shall comply with the requirements of Section 33.2 as indicated for the appropriate evacuation capability. The ability of all occupants, residents, staff, and family members shall be considered in determining evacuation capability.

Exception No. 1:*   *Facilities where the authority having jurisdiction has determined equivalent safety is provided in accordance with Section 1.5.*

A.33.2.1.2.1 Exception No. 1 In determining equivalency for existing buildings, conversions, modernizations, renovations, or unusual design concepts, the authority having jurisdiction might permit evaluations based on NFPA 101A, *Guide on Alternative Approaches to Life Safety,* Chapter 6.

Exception No. 2:   Facilities that were previously approved as complying with the requirements for a large facility having the same evacuation capability.

33.2.1.2.2 Facility management shall furnish to the authority having jurisdiction, upon request, an evacuation capability determination using a procedure acceptable to the authority having jurisdiction. Where such documentation is not furnished, the evacuation capability shall be classified as impractical.

The importance of an accurate evaluation of evacuation capabilities cannot be overstated. Ineffective resident or staff response was a contributing factor in the majority of the multiple-death fires listed in Table 32/33.1.

Determining the evacuation capability is not simply a matter of timing a fire drill in the middle of the day. Many variables impact a resident's capability to evacuate, and these variables must be carefully considered and factored into the documentation presented to the authority having jurisdiction for approval. Some variables that should be considered follow.

(a) *Time of Day.* An occupant's ability to evacuate might be slowed dramatically when the person must be awakened. In such a situation, the occupant must process the information that evacuation is necessary and then begin evacuating.

(b) *Medication.* Many individuals in board and care occupancies take various medications for behavior control or as a sleeping aid. If an individual is

medicated, he or she might need additional assistance in responding and evacuating.

(c) *Mobility and Location of Occupants.* Once individuals become aware of an emergency and take action, their ability to move through the building must be considered. Individuals using wheelchairs, walkers, or canes are further slowed when using stairs or ramps or when opening doors.

(d) *Staff Assistance.* Though the *Code* does not specify minimum staffing levels, staffing levels should be considered, especially where high resident-to-staff ratios exist. Given the additional needs mentioned in (a) through (c), the staff will be limited in their ability to impact evacuation time where multiple residents need assistance.

The evacuation capability of the population of a board and care occupancy might vary over time. The required documentation should be reviewed regularly to ensure that it accurately represents the current evacuation capability of the residents and staff.

When determining equivalency in accordance with the exception to 32.2.1.2.1 or Exception No. 1 to 33.2.1.2.1, it is important to note that the equivalency measurement systems of the 1998 edition of NFPA 101A, *Guide on Alternative Approaches to Life Safety*, were calibrated against the requirements of the 1997 edition of NFPA *101* and might not accurately evaluate equivalency with the requirements of the 2000 edition of the *Life Safety Code*.[1] At the time this handbook went to press, the 2001 edition of NFPA 101A was being prepared. Once issued, the 2001 edition

of NFPA 101A can be used to measure equivalency against the requirements of the 2000 edition of the *Code*.

Exception No. 2 to 33.2.1.2.1 continues to recognize an existing situation that resulted from compliance with a provision of the 1985 edition of the *Code* that permitted small board and care facilities to comply with the requirements for large facilities. The protection features applicable to large facilities might not necessarily provide adequate protection for small facilities. See the commentary on 33.1.1.3.

32.2.1.3 Minimum Construction Requirements. (No special requirements.)

33.2.1.3 Minimum Construction Requirements.

33.2.1.3.1 Prompt Evacuation Capability. (No special requirements.)

33.2.1.3.2 Slow Evacuation Capability. The facility shall be housed in a building where the interior is fully sheathed with lath and plaster or other material providing a 15-minute thermal barrier, including all portions of bearing walls, bearing partitions, floor construction, and roofs. All columns, beams, girders, and trusses shall be similarly encased or otherwise shall provide not less than a ½-hour fire resistance rating.

Exception No. 1: Exposed steel or wood columns, girders, and beams (but not joists) located in the basement.

Exception No. 2: Buildings of Type I, Type II(222), Type II(111), Type III(211), Type IV, or Type V(111) construction. (See 8.2.1.)

Exception No. 3: Areas protected by approved automatic sprinkler systems in accordance with 33.2.3.5.

Exception No. 4: Unfinished, unused, and essentially inaccessible loft, attic, or crawl spaces.

Exception No. 5: Where the facility can demonstrate to the authority having jurisdiction that the group is capable of evacuating the building in 8 minutes or less or achieves an E-score of three or less using the board and care occupancies evacuation capability determination methodology of NFPA 101A, Guide on Alternative Approaches to Life Safety.

33.2.1.3.3 Impractical Evacuation Capability. Buildings shall be of any construction type in accordance with 8.2.1 other than Type II(000), Type III(200), or Type V(000) construction.

Exception: Buildings protected throughout by an approved, supervised automatic sprinkler system in accordance with 33.2.3.5 shall be permitted to be of any type of construction.

Because 32.2.3.5.1 requires new small board and care facilities to be sprinklered, no additional requirements with respect to minimum building construction types apply for new construction. However, no sprinkler mandate is specified for existing board and care occupancies. Therefore, 33.2.1.3.2 and 33.2.1.3.3 establish minimum construction requirements to provide an adequate level of safety for existing small facilities with slow or impractical evacuation capability.

Exhibit 32/33.1 illustrates the concept of sheathing the interior of a small board and care facility building with a slow evacuation capability to achieve the 15-minute thermal barrier that is required by 33.2.1.3.2. The nonsprinklered areas (A, C, and D) are required to have sheathing to protect bearing walls, floor construction, and roofs. The heavy timber columns and girders in area A do not require sheathing but must provided a minimum fire resistance rating of 30 minutes. As permitted by Exception No. 3, the sprinklered areas of the building are exempt from the sheathing requirement.

Exception No. 5 to 33.2.1.3.2 is intended to allow unsheathed, unsprinklered wood frame construction in facilities that house groups capable of evacuation to a point of safety within 8 minutes. For such groups, the additional evacuation time provided by fire-resistant sheathing is not necessary.

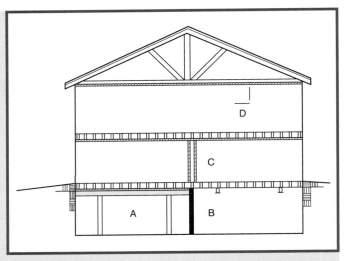

Exhibit 32/33.1 Sheathing requirements in a small facility with slow evacuation capability.

Subparagraph 33.2.3.5.3 mandates that all existing small facilities with impractical evacuation capability are to be protected with a supervised automatic sprinkler system. The exception to 33.2.1.3.3 is permitted if the entire building, not only the residential board and care facility, is protected with a supervised automatic sprinkler system.

32.2.2 Means of Escape.

32.2.2.1 Number of Means of Escape. Each normally occupied story of the facility shall have not less than two remotely located means of escape that do not involve using windows. Not less than one of these means of escape shall be in accordance with 32.2.2.2. The provisions of Chapter 7 shall not apply to means of escape unless specifically referenced in this chapter.

Exception No. 1: In prompt evacuation capability facilities, one means of escape shall be permitted to involve windows complying with 32.2.2.3(c).

Exception No. 2: A second means of escape from each story shall not be required where the entire building is protected throughout by an approved automatic sprinkler system complying with 32.2.3.5 and the facility has two means of escape.

33.2.2 Means of Escape.

33.2.2.1 Number of Means of Escape. Each normally occupied story of the facility shall have not less than two remotely located means of escape that do not involve using windows. Not less than one of these means of escape shall be in accordance with 33.2.2.2. The provisions of Chapter 7 shall not apply to means of escape unless specifically referenced in this chapter.

Exception No. 1: In prompt evacuation capability facilities, one means of escape shall be permitted to involve windows complying with 33.2.2.3(c).

Exception No. 2: A second means of escape from each story shall not be required where the entire building is protected throughout by an approved automatic sprinkler system complying with 33.2.3.5 and the facility has two means of escape. This exception shall not be permitted to be used in conjunction with Exception No. 2 to 33.2.2.3.

32.2.2.2 Primary Means of Escape. Every sleeping room and living area shall have access to a primary means of escape located to provide a safe path of travel to the outside. Where sleeping rooms or living areas are above or below the level of exit discharge, the primary means of escape shall be an interior stair in accordance with 32.2.2.4, an exterior stair, a horizontal exit, or a fire escape stair.

32.2.2.3 Secondary Means of Escape from Sleeping Rooms. In addition to the primary route, each sleeping room in facilities that use Exception No. 1 to 32.2.3.5.1 shall have a second means of escape that consists of one of the following.

(a) It shall be a door, stairway, passage, or hall providing a way of unobstructed travel to the outside of the dwelling at street or ground level that is independent of and remotely located from the primary means of escape.

(b) It shall be a passage through an adjacent nonlockable space, independent of and remotely located from the primary means of escape, to any approved means of escape.

(c)* It shall be an outside window or door operable from the inside without the use of tools, keys, or special effort that provides a clear opening of not less than 5.7 ft² (0.53 m²). The width shall be not less than 20 in. (51 cm), and the height shall be not less than 24 in. (61 cm). The bottom of the opening shall be not more than 44 in. (112 cm) above the floor. Such means of escape shall be acceptable where one of the following criteria are met:

(1) The window shall be within 20 ft (6.1 m) of grade.
(2) The window shall be directly accessible to fire department rescue apparatus as approved by the authority having jurisdiction.
(3) The window or door shall open onto an exterior balcony.

Exception: If the sleeping room has a door leading directly to the outside of the building with access to grade or to a stairway that meets the requirements of exterior stairs in 32.2.3.1.2, that means of escape shall be considered as meeting all the escape requirements for the sleeping room.

33.2.2.2 Primary Means of Escape.

33.2.2.2.1 Every sleeping room and living area shall have access to a primary means of escape located to provide a safe path of travel to the outside. Where sleeping rooms or living areas are above or below the level of exit discharge, the primary means of escape shall be an interior stair in accordance with 33.2.2.4, an exterior stair, a horizontal exit, or a fire escape stair.

33.2.2.2.2 In slow and impractical evacuation capability facilities, the primary means of escape for each sleeping room shall not be exposed to living areas and kitchens.

Exception: Buildings equipped with quick-response or residential sprinklers throughout. Standard response sprinklers shall be permitted for use in hazardous areas in accordance with 33.2.3.2.

33.2.2.3 Secondary Means of Escape from Sleeping Rooms. In addition to the primary route, each sleeping room shall have a second means of escape that consists of one of the following.

(a) It shall be a door, stairway, passage, or hall providing a way of unobstructed travel to the outside of the dwelling at street or ground level that is independent of and remotely located from the primary means of escape.

(b) It shall be a passage through an adjacent nonlockable space, independent of and remotely located from the primary means of escape, to any approved means of escape.

(c)* It shall be an outside window or door operable from the inside without the use of tools, keys, or special effort that provides a clear opening of not less than 5.7 ft² (0.53 m²). The width shall be not less than 20 in. (51 cm), and the height shall be not less than 24 in. (61 cm). The bottom of the opening shall be not more than 44 in. (112 cm) above the floor. Such means of escape shall be acceptable where the following criteria are met:

(1) The window shall be within 20 ft (6.1 m) of grade.
(2) The window shall be directly accessible to fire department rescue apparatus as approved by the authority having jurisdiction.
(3) The window or door shall open onto an exterior balcony.

Exception No. 1: If the sleeping room has a door leading directly to the outside of the building with access to grade or to a stairway that meets the requirements of exterior stairs in 33.2.3.1.2, that means of escape shall be considered as meeting all the escape requirements for the sleeping room.

Exception No. 2: A second means of escape from each sleeping room shall not be required where the facility is

CHAPTER 32 • New | **CHAPTER 33 • Existing**

protected throughout by an approved automatic sprinkler system in accordance with 33.2.3.5.

Exception No. 3:   Existing approved means of escape shall be permitted to continue to be used.

A.32.2.2.3(c) A window with dimensions of 20 in. × 24 in. (51 cm × 61 cm) has an opening of 3.3 ft² (0.31 m²), which is less than the required 5.7 ft² (0.53 m²). Therefore, either the height or width needs to exceed the minimum requirement to provide the required clear area.

A.33.2.2.3(c) A window with dimensions of 20 in. × 24 in. (51 cm × 61 cm) has an opening of 3.3 ft² (0.31 m²), which is less than the required 5.7 ft² (0.53 m²). Therefore, either the height or width needs to exceed the minimum requirement to provide the required clear area.

The provisions of 32/33.2.2.1, 32/33.2.2.2, and 32/33.2.2.3 establish the criteria for acceptable means of escape in small board and care facilities. Paragraph 32/33.2.2.1 mandates that each story of the facility is to be provided with at least two means of escape. Only one of the means of escape must meet the provisions for a primary means of escape. The second means of escape is permitted to be a window, provided that the window complies with 32/33.2.2.3(c) and the facility evacuation capability is prompt.

The second means of escape from each floor is not required if the entire building housing the residential board and care facility is protected throughout by an automatic sprinkler system in accordance with 32/33.2.3.5. In this instance, the single means of escape must meet the criteria for a primary means of escape specified in 32/33.2.2.2. However, the facility itself must have at least two means of escape.

Where a window is considered as a secondary means of escape within a sleeping room, the window must meet the criteria detailed in 32/33.2.2.3(c), but use of the window is not limited to any specific evacuation capability. Windows are not permitted to serve as a primary means of escape.

The provisions of 32/33.2.2.2 specify a primary means of escape that is arranged so that an occupant can travel safely to the outside at grade level. The intent of the requirement is to ensure that use of the primary means of escape will not be lost due to fire from another floor. Exhibit 32/33.2 depicts an exterior stair (A) that serves as the primary means of escape for the second floor. Occupants of the second floor can travel safely to the outside at grade, because the interior stair (B) is separated from the second floor by enclosing construction on the second floor.

The primary means of escape from rooms above or below grade level will involve vertical travel, such as stairs. For this reason, the *Code* establishes a higher

level of reliability by requiring the primary means of escape to be an enclosed interior stair, an exterior stair, a horizontal exit, or an existing fire escape stair. In Exhibit 32/33.2, this requirement is met by using the exterior stair as the primary means of escape from the second floor, even if the partially enclosed (top only) interior stair is used for day-to-day travel between floors.

In existing board and care occupancies with slow and impractical evacuation capability, and without quick-response or residential sprinklers throughout,

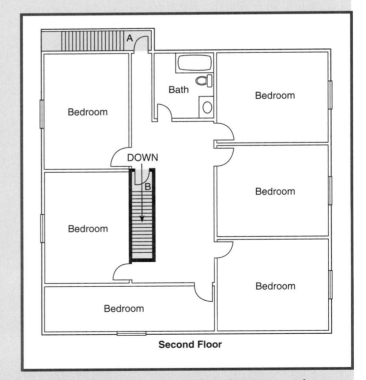

Exhibit 32/33.2 *Exterior stair used as primary means of escape.*

33.2.2.2.2 requires a further enhancement for the primary means of escape. The primary means of escape cannot be exposed to common living spaces and kitchens. Therefore, the primary means of escape from a sleeping room is not permitted to include travel through a day room, a common use space, or a space that is open to a common living space. Exhibit 32/33.3 depicts one example of meeting this requirement. By arranging the outside balconies and exterior stairs as the primary means of escape for the second floor of a small facility with slow or impractical evacuation capability, the means of escape can be used by occupants of the second floor without exposing them to a fire involving the contents of a common living area. Regardless of whether the interior stair is enclosed, the primary means of escape cannot be arranged to force occupants to travel from their rooms into the common living area of the second floor.

The objective of 33.2.2.2.2 is to reduce the probability that smoke and heat from a fire involving the contents of a common living area will adversely affect the use of the primary means of escape. The requirement is based, in part, on historical fire experience, which indicates that fires in residential board and care facilities frequently originate in the furniture and contents of common living spaces.

In recognition of the fact that an automatic sprinkler system using quick-response or residential sprinklers provides a high level of protection, the exception to 33.2.2.2.2 permits the primary means of escape to be exposed to common living areas where such sprinkler protection is provided. Furthermore, the exception permits standard response sprinklers to be used, in lieu of quick-response or residential sprinklers, in hazardous areas that are required to be separated from other parts of the building by the requirements of 33.2.3.2. The exception is allowed because hazardous areas are not occupied by sleeping residents.

A secondary means of escape is required for existing small board and care facilities and new non-sprinklered small board and care facilities (as permitted for conversions by Exception No. 1 to 32.2.3.5.1). The main purpose for the secondary means of escape is to provide the occupants with a reasonable escape alternative when fire or smoke blocks the primary means of escape. Paragraph 32/33.2.2.3(a) through (c) outline three acceptable methods for providing a secondary means of escape. Exhibit 32/33.4 illustrates these three methods.

The doors marked A in Exhibit 32/33.4 meet the intent of 32/33.2.2.3(a), because they are independent of and remotely located from the primary means of escape required by 32/33.2.2.2. If the sleeping room has a second door that leads to the same hallway as the door serving as a primary means of escape, little additional protection is provided, because fire or smoke could affect use of both doors at approximately the same time. If the corridor within the facility into which a sleeping room door opens is separated from all common living spaces, it might be determined that the arrangement is acceptable, provided that the corridor does actually lead to two separate, independent, and remote means of escape. This arrangement is similar to that permitted in other occupancies in which protected corridors are provided. In this case, requiring two doors from the sleeping room to the corridor would provide little additional safety.

The doors marked B in Exhibit 32/33.4 provide a secondary means of escape that passes through an adjacent space, such as another sleeping room. The unlocked doors that lead from bedroom 2 into bedroom 4, and from bedroom 3 into bedroom 5, provide free and unobstructed access in accordance with 32/33.2.2.3(b). Once a resident reaches bedroom 4 or bedroom 5, the secondary means of escape is window C in accordance with 32/33.2.2.3(c).

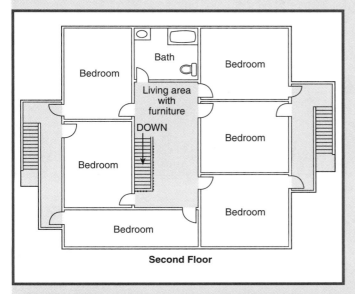

Second Floor

Exhibit 32/33.3 *Alternate arrangement for exterior stairs used as primary means of escape in existing facilities.*

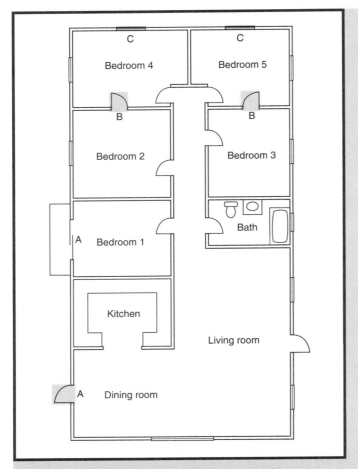

Exhibit 32/33.4 *Secondary means of escape options.*

The windows marked C in Exhibit 32/33.4 comply with the minimum dimensions specified in 32/33.2.2.3(c) and are permitted as a secondary means of escape from a story of a small facility only if the evacuation capability is prompt (see Exception No. 1 to 32/33.2.2.1). However, the use of an operable window of the minimum dimensions specified in 32/33.2.2.3(c) is permitted as a secondary means of escape from a sleeping room, regardless of the residents' evacuation capability.

Exhibit 32/33.5 illustrates the minimum dimensions required for secondary means of escape windows. Note that the minimum width dimension cannot be simultaneously used with the minimum height dimension, because the minimum area requirement will not be satisfied. If either the minimum height or minimum width dimension is used, the

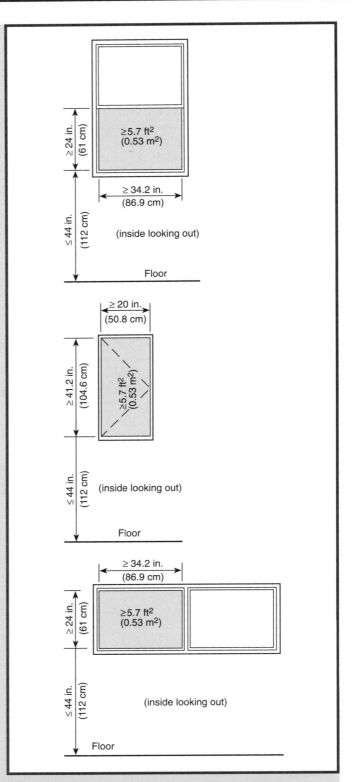

Exhibit 32/33.5 *Minimum dimensions for escape windows.*

other dimension must be increased to create the required opening area.

In addition to the minimum size of the window, the utility of the window must be ensured by one of the following three alternatives:

(1) The window must be within 20 ft (6.1 m) of grade so that dropping from the open window is possible.
(2) The fire department must be capable of rescuing the occupant from the window. (Authority having jurisdiction must determine acceptable means of fire department rescue, such as aerial ladder apparatus or ground ladders, and additional criteria necessary for approval, such as fire department vehicle accessibility.)
(3) The occupant must be capable of reaching an exterior balcony to breathe fresh air while awaiting either rescue or fire extinguishment.

A facility is not required to provide a secondary means of escape from sleeping rooms by meeting one of three conditions. Two of these conditions apply only to existing facilities. First, the exception to 32.2.2.3 and Exception No. 1 to 33.2.2.3 exempt the

secondary means of escape if the sleeping room has a door leading directly to the outside of the building with access to grade. In this case, the door to the outside serves as the equivalent of both the primary and the secondary means of escape. Exhibit 32/33.3 illustrates such an arrangement.

Second, the secondary means of escape is exempted where an existing residential board and care facility is protected throughout with an automatic sprinkler system in accordance with 33.2.3.5. However, Exception No. 2 to 33.2.2.3 is not permitted to be used in conjunction with Exception No. 2 to 33.2.2.1, because the result would be a single means of escape from each room and each floor. Therefore, the secondary means of escape from sleeping rooms is exempted only if a secondary means of escape is provided from each floor and the facility is protected by an automatic sprinkler system.

Third, the secondary means of escape is exempted where an existing board and care facility is provided with a means of escape arrangement that has been approved by the authority having jurisdiction.

32.2.2.4 Interior Stairs Used for Primary Means of Escape. Interior stairs shall be enclosed with ½-hour fire barriers, with all openings equipped with smoke-actuated automatic-closing or self-closing doors having a fire protection rating comparable to that required for the enclosure. Stairs shall comply with 7.2.2.5.3. The entire primary means of escape shall be arranged so that it is not necessary for occupants to pass through a portion of a lower story unless that route is separated from all spaces on that story by construction having not less than a ½-hour fire resistance rating.

In buildings of construction other than Type II(000), Type III(200), or Type V(000), the supporting construction shall be protected to afford the required fire resistance rating of the supported wall.

Exception No. 1: Stairs that connect a story at street level to only one other story shall be permitted to be open to the story that is not at street level.

Exception No. 2: Stair enclosures shall not be required for prompt and slow evacuation capability facilities in buildings of three or fewer stories that are protected with an approved automatic sprinkler system in accordance with 32.2.3.5. This exception shall be permitted only if a primary means of

33.2.2.4 Interior Stairs Used for Primary Means of Escape. Interior stairs shall be enclosed with ½-hour fire barriers, with all openings equipped with smoke-actuated automatic-closing or self-closing doors having a fire protection rating comparable to that required for the enclosure. Stairs shall comply with 7.2.2.5.3. The entire primary means of escape shall be arranged so that it is not necessary for occupants to pass through a portion of a lower story unless that route is separated from all spaces on that story by construction having not less than a ½-hour fire resistance rating.

In buildings of construction other than Type II(000), Type III(200), or Type V(000), the supporting construction shall be protected to afford the required fire resistance rating of the supported wall.

Exception No. 1: Stairs that connect a story at street level to only one other story shall be permitted to be open to the story that is not at street level.

Exception No. 2: Stair enclosures shall not be required in buildings of three or fewer stories that house prompt or slow evacuation capability facilities protected throughout by an approved automatic sprinkler system in accordance with 33.2.3.5 that uses quick-response or residential sprinklers.

CHAPTER 32 • New

CHAPTER 33 • Existing

escape from each sleeping area still exists that does not pass through a portion of a lower floor, unless that route is separated from all spaces on that floor by construction having a ½-hour fire resistance rating.

Exception No. 3:   Stair enclosures shall not be required in buildings of two or fewer stories that house prompt evacuation capability facilities with not more than eight residents. The exception to 32.2.3.4.3.1 shall not be used in conjunction with this exception. Exception No. 1 to 32.2.3.5.1 shall not be used in conjunction with this exception.

This exception shall be permitted only if a primary means of escape from each sleeping area still exists that does not pass through a portion of a lower floor, unless that route is separated from all spaces on that floor by construction having a ½hour fire resistance rating.

Exception No. 3:   Stair enclosures shall not be required in buildings of two or fewer stories that house prompt evacuation capability facilities with not more than eight residents and are protected by an approved automatic sprinkler system in accordance with 33.2.3.5 that uses quick-response or residential sprinklers. Exception No. 2 to 33.2.2.3 shall not be used in conjunction with this exception. The exceptions to 33.2.3.4.3 shall not be used in conjunction with this exception.

Exception No. 4:   In buildings of three or fewer stories that house prompt or slow evacuation capability facilities protected by an approved automatic sprinkler system in accordance with 33.2.3.5, stairs shall be permitted to be open at the topmost story only. The entire primary means of escape of which the stairs are a part shall be separated from all portions of lower stories.

The intent of paragraph 32/33.2.2.4 is to require that an interior stair be enclosed if the stair serves as primary means of escape. Paragraph 32/33.2.2.4 does not require an interior stair used for day-to-day use, but not used as a primary means of escape, to be enclosed. However, the stair might require separation from the floor to prevent exposure of occupants to unsafe conditions while they travel through the primary means of escape (see 32/33.2.2.1, 32/33.2.3.1.1, and Exhibit 32/33.2 and its associated commentary).

If the interior stair serves as primary means of escape, it must be arranged so that occupants are not required to pass through occupied or furnished portions of lower floors. Passage through unfurnished vestibule-like areas on lower floors is permitted if such vestibules are separated from the occupied or furnished areas, or both, by walls and doors. These vestibules provide safety equivalent to that provided by an enlarged stair enclosure.

It is the intent of the *Code* that interior stairs in accordance with 32/33.2.2.4, and all its associated exceptions, qualify as enclosed interior stairs permitted to serve as the primary means of escape by 32/33.2.2.2.

The intent of Exception No. 1 to 32/33.2.2.4 is to permit a stair that connects the first floor to the second floor to be open to the second floor but separated

from the effects of fire on the first floor. This exception also permits a stair that connects the basement level to the first floor to be open to the basement level but separated from the effects of fire on the first floor. This partially enclosed interior stair can serve as a primary means of escape in accordance with 32.2.2.2 and 33.2.2.2.1. Exhibit 32/33.6 illustrates a partially enclosed (separated from ground floor) interior stair in accordance with Exception No. 1 to 32/33.2.2.4 that serves as the primary means of escape for second floor. The partially enclosed interior stair meeting the criteria of this exception is considered to be the equivalent of an enclosed interior stair. The separating walls and doors on the first floor serve the dual purposes of enclosing the stair on that floor and providing a route that does not expose occupants to areas of the first floor that are occupied or furnished, or both. Thus, the first floor stair "lobby" cannot be used as a lounge and cannot contain furniture and furnishings.

The intent of Exception No. 2 to 32/33.2.2.4 is to permit an unenclosed interior stair to serve as the equivalent of an enclosed interior stair in small facilities with prompt or slow evacuation capability. However, the buildings must be of three or fewer stories and must be protected throughout with an automatic

CHAPTER 32 • New   **CHAPTER 33 • Existing**

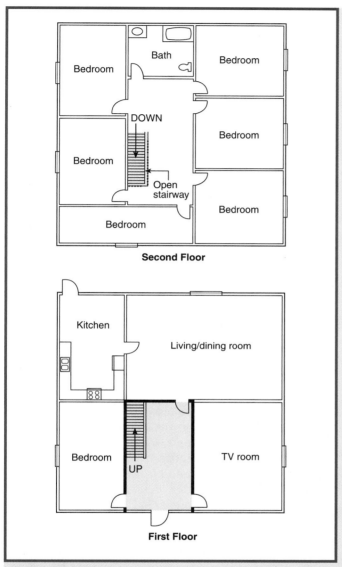

Bedroom

Bath

Bedroom

DOWN

Bedroom

Bedroom

Open stairway

Bedroom

Bedroom

Second Floor

Kitchen

Living/dining room

Bedroom

UP

TV room

First Floor

Exhibit 32/33.6 Partially enclosed interior stair.

sprinkler system using quick-response or residential sprinklers. An unenclosed interior stair meeting the criteria of this exception is considered the equivalent of an enclosed interior stair. Exhibit 32/33.6 can also be used to illustrate the provisions of Exception No. 2. Although the enclosing walls around the vestibule on the first floor serve as the stair enclosure on that floor in accordance with Exception No. 1, the same enclosing walls serve to protect the escape path from the areas that are occupied or furnished on the first

floor in accordance with Exception No. 2. Additionally, based on the presence of sprinklers and other criteria of Exception No. 2, the open stair can extend to a third level.

Exception No. 3 to 32/33.2.2.4 permits a two-story open stair (and its associated exposure to the areas that are occupied or furnished, or both, on the ground floor) to serve as primary means of escape for the smallest facilities (not more than eight residents) with prompt evacuation capability, if the facility is sprinklered using quick-response or residential sprinklers. This exception, in effect, equates such a board and care facility with a one- or two-family dwelling. An unenclosed interior stair meeting the criteria of this exception is considered the equivalent of an enclosed interior stair.

The *Code* prohibits the use of other exceptions in conjunction with Exception No. 3 to 32/33.2.2.4 in both new and existing buildings. Multiple use of these exceptions that are intended for application to sprinklered buildings could result in a level of life safety less than that required by Chapter 32/33.

The following exceptions are not permitted in conjunction with Exception No. 3 to 32/33.2.2.4:

(1) Exception to 32.2.3.4.3.1, which exempts smoke alarms if the building is sprinklered
(2) Exception No. 1 to 32.2.3.5.1, which exempts sprinklers in conversions of small board and care facilities serving eight or fewer residents with a prompt evacuation capability rating
(3) Exception No. 2 to 33.2.2.3, which exempts bedrooms from a required secondary means of escape if the building is sprinklered
(4) Exception No. 1 and Exception No. 2 to 33.2.3.4.3, which exempt common space smoke detectors where the building is sprinklered and the bedrooms are provided with smoke detectors

In existing buildings, Exception No. 4 to 33.2.2.4 permits stairs to be open at the topmost story only where the entire primary means of escape associated with the stairs is separated from all portions of lower stories. In addition, this exception requires the following:

(1) Buildings are to be of three or fewer stories.
(2) Buildings are to house facilities with prompt or slow evacuation capability.
(3) Buildings are to be protected by an approved automatic sprinkler system in accordance with 33.2.3.5.

CHAPTER 32 • New	**CHAPTER 33 • Existing**

32.2.2.5 Doors.

32.2.2.5.1 Doors or paths of travel to a means of escape shall be not less than 32 in. (81 cm) wide.

Exception No. 1: Bathroom doors shall be not less than 24 in. (61 cm) wide.

Exception No. 2: In conversions (see 32.1.1.3), 28-in. (71-cm) doors shall be permitted to continue to be used.

32.2.2.5.2 Doors shall be swinging or sliding.

32.2.2.5.3 Every closet door latch shall be readily opened from the inside in case of an emergency.

32.2.2.5.4 Every bathroom door shall be designed to allow opening from the outside during an emergency when locked.

32.2.2.5.5 No door in any means of escape shall be locked against egress when the building is occupied.

Exception: Delayed-egress locks complying with 7.2.1.6.1 shall be permitted on exterior doors.

32.2.2.5.6 Doors shall comply with 7.2.1.4.5.

32.2.2.5.7 Doors shall comply with 7.2.1.5.4.

33.2.2.5 Doors.

33.2.2.5.1 Doors or paths of travel to a means of escape shall be not less than 28 in. (71 cm) wide.

Exception: Bathroom doors shall be not less than 24 in. (61 cm) wide.

33.2.2.5.2 Doors shall be swinging or sliding.

33.2.2.5.3 Every closet door latch shall be readily opened from the inside in case of an emergency.

33.2.2.5.4 Every bathroom door shall be designed to allow opening from the outside during an emergency when locked.

33.2.2.5.5 No door in any means of escape shall be locked against egress when the building is occupied.

Exception: Delayed-egress locks complying with 7.2.1.6.1 shall be permitted on exterior doors.

33.2.2.5.6 Doors shall comply with 7.2.1.4.5.

33.2.2.5.7 Doors shall comply with 7.2.1.5.4.

If an existing dwelling were converted to a small board and care facility, the provisions of 4.6.11 would require that such changes of occupancy meet the requirements of Chapter 32 for new board and care facilities. Exception No. 2 to 32.2.2.5.1 recognizes the hardship and minor improvement that would be realized if existing 28-in. (71-cm) wide doors were required to be replaced by 32-in. (81-cm) wide doors.

Subparagraph 32/33.2.2.5.5 prohibits a residential board and care facility from having any door in the means of escape locked against egress while the building is occupied. This prohibition is consistent with a fundamental means of egress provision of Chapter 7. Chapter 7 permits a door to have a locking device that allows the door to be opened from within the facility for the purpose of egress but does not allow the door to be opened from outside the facility. Ordinary double-cylinder locks and chain locks do not meet these provisions.

Although resident sleeping room doors are doors that are located in the means of escape, it is the intent of 32/33.2.2.5.7 that the multiple latching/locking devices addressed by Exception No. 1 to 7.2.1.5.4 be permitted.

32.2.2.6 Stairs.

32.2.2.6.1 Stairs shall comply with 7.2.2.

32.2.2.6.2 Winders complying with 7.2.2.2.4 shall be permitted.

32.2.3 Protection.

32.2.3.1 Protection of Vertical Openings.

32.2.3.1.1 Vertical openings shall be protected so as not to expose a primary means of escape. Vertical openings shall

33.2.2.6 Stairs.

33.2.2.6.1 Stairs shall comply with 7.2.2.

33.2.2.6.2 Winders complying with 7.2.2.2.4 shall be permitted.

33.2.3 Protection.

33.2.3.1 Protection of Vertical Openings.

33.2.3.1.1 Vertical openings shall be protected so as not to expose a primary means of escape. Vertical openings shall be considered protected if separated by smoke partitions in accordance with 8.2.4 that prevent the passage of smoke from one story to any primary means of escape on another story. Smoke partitions shall have a fire resistance rating of not less than ½ hour. Any doors or openings to the vertical opening shall be capable of resisting fire for not less than 20 minutes.

Exception: Stairs shall be permitted to be open where complying with Exception No. 2 or Exception No. 3 to 32.2.2.4.

32.2.3.1.2 Exterior stairs shall be reasonably protected against blockage caused by fire that would simultaneously expose both the interior and the exterior means of escape. Such protection shall be accomplished through separation by physical distance, arrangement of the stairs, protection of the openings exposing the stairs, or other means acceptable to the authority having jurisdiction.

be considered protected if separated by smoke partitions in accordance with 8.2.4 that prevent the passage of smoke from one story to any primary means of escape on another story. Smoke partitions shall have a fire resistance rating of not less than ½ hour. Any doors or openings to the vertical opening shall be capable of resisting fire for not less than 20 minutes.

Exception: Stairs shall be permitted to be open where complying with Exception No. 2 or Exception No. 3 to 33.2.2.4.

33.2.3.1.2 Exterior stairs shall be reasonably protected against blockage caused by fire that would simultaneously expose both the interior and the exterior means of escape. Such protection shall be accomplished through separation by physical distance, arrangement of the stairs, protection of the openings exposing the stairs, or other means acceptable to the authority having jurisdiction.

Vertical openings are permitted to be unenclosed, except in cases where, by leaving the vertical opening unenclosed, the primary means of escape route is exposed to the unprotected vertical opening. Exhibit 32/33.7 illustrates an interior stair that, if it were not enclosed, would create an unprotected vertical opening. The interior stair is not part of the primary means of escape, but the vertical opening it creates must be enclosed, so that the route to the exterior stair (which serves as the primary means of escape for the second floor) is not exposed to an unprotected vertical opening. The enclosure around the vertical opening must be, as a minimum, a smoke partition in accordance with 8.2.4. A smoke partition is a continuous membrane designed to form a barrier to limit the transfer of smoke. See the definition of *smoke partition* in 3.3.185.

A smoke partition that limits the transfer of smoke is different from a smoke barrier that restricts smoke movement from one side of a barrier to the other. A smoke partition should be thought of as a barrier that reasonably limits, but doesn't prevent, smoke transfer. As such, suspended ceiling systems and monolithic surfaced ceilings are available that provide resistance to smoke transfer that is approximately equal to the traditional nonrated corridor wall or partition. See 8.2.4 and its commentary for more on smoke partitions.

In Exhibit 32/33.8, the vertical opening created by the interior stair does not expose the primary means of escape. Exposure is avoided, because the

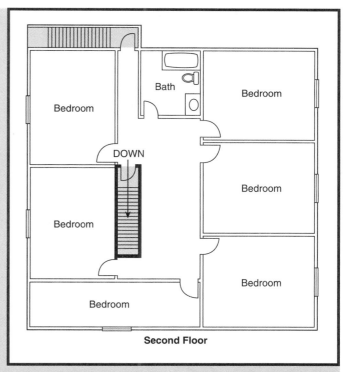

Exhibit 32/33.7 *Vertical opening protected so as not to expose the primary means of escape.*

primary means of escape is the direct route from each bedroom to the exterior balconies and stairs.

The intent of the exception to 32/33.2.3.1.1 is to

CHAPTER 32 • New

CHAPTER 33 • Existing

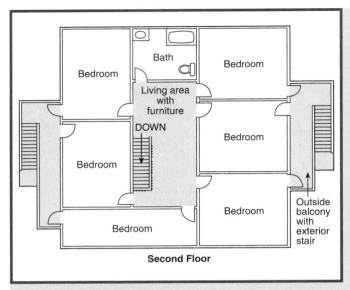

Exhibit 32/33.8 *Vertical opening not exposing the primary means of escape.*

permit the alternative arrangements for stair enclosures found in Exception No. 2 and Exception No. 3 to 32/33.2.2.4 to be considered appropriate vertical opening protection.

Subparagraph 32/33.2.3.1.2 does not mandate compliance with the provisions of Chapter 7 for outside stairs. However, if the exterior stair is to be used as a primary means of escape, protection should be provided to reduce the likelihood that a fire within the facility will render the stair useless. Although this provision applies to small board and care facilities, note that Exception No. 2 to 7.2.2.6.3 exempts outside stairs that serve a two-story building from the protection requirements of 7.2.2.6.3 if a remotely located second exit is provided. In such a case, the presence of an additional remote means of escape might be judged as adequate to eliminate the need to protect the exterior stair from a fire within the building.

32.2.3.2 Protection from Hazards. Any hazardous area shall be protected in accordance with 32.2.3.2.1 and 32.2.3.2.3.

32.2.3.2.1 Any space where there is storage or activity having fuel conditions exceeding that of a one- or two-family dwelling and that possesses the potential for a fully involved fire shall be protected in accordance with 32.2.3.2.2 and 32.2.3.2.3. Areas shall include, but shall not be limited to, areas for cartoned storage, food or household maintenance items in wholesale or institutional-type quantities and concentrations, or mass storage of residents' belongings. Areas containing approved, properly installed and maintained furnaces and heating equipment, furnace rooms, and cooking and laundry facilities shall not be classified as hazardous areas solely on the basis of such equipment.

32.2.3.2.2 Any hazardous area that is on the same floor as, and is in or abuts, a primary means of escape or a sleeping room shall be protected by one of the following means.

(a) Protection shall be an enclosure with a fire resistance rating of not less than 1 hour, with a self-closing or automatic-closing fire door in accordance with 7.2.1.8 that has a fire protection rating of not less than ¾ hour. The enclosure shall be protected by an automatic fire detection system connected to the fire alarm system provided in 32.2.3.4.1.

33.2.3.2 Protection from Hazards. Any hazardous area shall be protected in accordance with 33.2.3.2.1 and 33.2.3.2.3.

33.2.3.2.1 Any space where there is storage or activity having fuel conditions exceeding that of a one- or two-family dwelling and that possesses the potential for a fully involved fire shall be protected in accordance with 33.2.3.2.2 and 33.2.3.2.3. Areas shall include, but shall not be limited to, areas for cartoned storage, food or household maintenance items in wholesale or institutional-type quantities and concentrations, or mass storage of residents' belongings. Areas containing approved, properly installed and maintained furnaces and heating equipment, furnace rooms, and cooking and laundry facilities shall not be classified as hazardous areas solely on the basis of such equipment.

33.2.3.2.2 Any hazardous area that is on the same floor as, and is in or abuts, a primary means of escape or a sleeping room shall be protected by one of the following means.

(a) Protection shall be an enclosure with a fire resistance rating of not less than 1 hour, with a self-closing or automatic-closing fire door in accordance with 7.2.1.8 that has a fire protection rating of not less than ¾ hour.

(b) Protection shall be automatic sprinkler protection, in accordance with 32.2.3.5, and a smoke partition, in accordance with 8.2.4, located between the hazardous area and the sleeping area or primary escape route. Any doors in such separation shall be self-closing or automatic-closing in accordance with 7.2.1.8.

32.2.3.2.3 Other hazardous areas shall be protected by one of the following:

(1) An enclosure having a fire resistance rating of not less than ½ hour, with a self-closing or automatic-closing door in accordance with 7.2.1.8 that is equivalent to not less than 1¾-in. (4.4-cm) thick, solid-bonded wood core construction and is protected by an automatic fire detection system connected to the fire alarm system provided in 32.2.3.4.1
(2) Automatic sprinkler protection in accordance with 32.2.3.5, regardless of enclosure

(b) Protection shall be automatic sprinkler protection, in accordance with 33.2.3.5, and a smoke partition, in accordance with 8.2.4, located between the hazardous area and the sleeping area or primary escape route. Any doors in such separation shall be self-closing or automatic-closing in accordance with 7.2.1.8.

33.2.3.2.3 Other hazardous areas shall be protected by one of the following:

(1) An enclosure having a fire resistance rating of not less than ½ hour, with a self-closing or automatic-closing door in accordance with 7.2.1.8 that is equivalent to not less than a 1 ¾-in. (4.4-cm) thick, solid-bonded wood core construction
(2) Automatic sprinkler protection in accordance with 33.2.3.5, regardless of enclosure

It is recognized that small board and care facilities closely resemble a one- and two-family dwelling. One of the most notable differences is the type of hazards that might be present in a small board and care facility. Greater quantities of household maintenance and cleaning products, cartoned food, and mass storage of residents' belongings result in areas where a fire could quickly grow to full involvement. These are the areas that 32/33.2.3.2.1 intends to be separated in accordance with 32/33.2.3.2.2 and 32/33.2.3.2.3. It is not the intent of 32/33.2.3.2.1 to require areas such as kitchens, laundry rooms, and furnace rooms to be separated. The proper installation and maintenance of the equipment in these areas does not represent an increased hazard to the occupants of the facility.

The protection of hazardous contents areas is based on the potential impact that a fire in the hazardous contents would have on a primary means of escape or on sleeping rooms. If the hazardous area is located on the same floor as sleeping rooms or a primary means of escape, and if a room or means of escape is exposed to the hazardous area, one of the following two protection options is permitted:

(1) The hazardous contents room must be separated from the remainder of the floor by construction with at least a 1-hour fire rating, and automatic fire detection connected to the alarm system must be provided.
(2) Automatic sprinkler protection must be provided within the hazardous contents room, and the sep-

arating construction must be capable of resisting smoke spread outside the area but is not required to be fire rated.

If the hazardous area is located on a different floor or does not abut a primary means of escape or sleeping rooms, it is considered less endangering and can be protected using one of the following two methods:

(1) The hazardous contents room must be separated from the remainder of the floor by construction with at least a ½-hour fire rating, and automatic fire detection connected to the alarm system must be provided.
(2) Automatic sprinkler protection must be provided within the hazardous contents room, and no smoke-resisting separating construction is required.

For example, if a basement in a wood frame building housing a small board and care facility is used only for the storage of combustible materials, the basement is not a required means of escape. If the basement storage area does not abut a sleeping area on the same floor, sheathing the ceiling to provide fire resistance separation is not required if the basement is sprinklered. In applying the provisions of 32/33.2.3.2, note that the sprinkler protection required in nearly all new small board and care facilities by 32.2.3.5.1 should make the protection of hazardous contents areas relatively easy.

32.2.3.3 Interior Finish.

32.2.3.3.1 Interior finish shall be in accordance with Section 10.2.

32.2.3.3.2 Interior Wall and Ceiling Finish. Interior wall and ceiling finish materials complying with 10.2.3 shall be Class A or Class B.

Exception: Class C interior wall and ceiling finish shall be permitted in prompt evacuation capability facilities.

32.2.3.3.3 Interior Floor Finish. (No requirements.)

32.2.3.4 Detection, Alarm, and Communications Systems.

32.2.3.4.1 Fire Alarm Systems. A manual fire alarm system shall be provided in accordance with Section 9.6.

32.2.3.4.2 Occupant Notification. Occupant notification shall be provided automatically, without delay, in accordance with 9.6.3.

32.2.3.4.3 Smoke Alarms.

32.2.3.4.3.1 Approved smoke alarms shall be provided in accordance with 9.6.2.10. Smoke alarms shall be installed on all levels, including basements but excluding crawl spaces and unfinished attics. Additional smoke alarms shall be installed for all living areas as defined in 3.3.119.

Exception: Smoke alarms shall not be required in buildings protected throughout by an approved automatic sprinkler system in accordance with 32.2.3.5.

32.2.3.4.3.2 Each sleeping room shall be provided with an approved, listed single-station smoke alarm in accordance with 9.6.2.10.

33.2.3.3 Interior Finish. Interior wall and ceiling finish shall be Class A or Class B in accordance with Section 10.2. There shall be no requirements for interior floor finish.

Exception: Class C interior wall and ceiling finish shall be permitted in prompt evacuation capability facilities.

33.2.3.4 Detection, Alarm, and Communications Systems.

33.2.3.4.1 Fire Alarm Systems. A manual fire alarm system shall be provided in accordance with Section 9.6.

Exception No. 1: Where there are interconnected smoke detectors meeting the requirements of 33.2.3.4.3 and there is not less than one manual fire alarm box per floor arranged to continuously sound the smoke detector alarms.

Exception No. 2: Other manually activated continuously sounding alarms acceptable to the authority having jurisdiction.

33.2.3.4.2 Occupant Notification. Occupant notification shall be in accordance with 9.6.3.

33.2.3.4.3* Smoke Alarms. Approved smoke alarms shall be provided in accordance with 9.6.2.10. These alarms shall be powered from the building electrical system and, when activated, shall initiate an alarm that is audible in all sleeping areas. Smoke alarms shall be installed on all levels, including basements but excluding crawl spaces and unfinished attics. Additional smoke alarms shall be installed for living rooms, dens, day rooms, and similar spaces.

Exception No. 1: Buildings protected throughout by an approved automatic sprinkler system, in accordance with 33.2.3.5, that uses quick-response or residential sprinklers, and protected with approved smoke alarms installed in each sleeping room, in accordance with 9.6.2.10, that are powered by the building electrical system.

Exception No. 2: Where buildings are protected throughout by an approved automatic sprinkler system, in accordance with 33.2.3.5, that uses quick-response or residential sprinklers, with existing battery-powered smoke alarms in each sleeping room, and where, in the opinion of the authority

CHAPTER 32 • New   **CHAPTER 33 • Existing**

having jurisdiction, the facility has demonstrated that testing, maintenance, and a battery replacement program ensure the reliability of power to the smoke alarms.

A.33.2.3.4.3 Most often smoke alarms sounding an alarm at 85 dBA or greater, installed outside the bedroom area, will meet the intent of this requirement. Smoke alarms remotely located from the bedroom might not be loud enough to awaken the average person. In such cases, it is recommended that smoke alarms be interconnected so that the activation of any smoke alarm will cause all smoke alarms to activate.

In both new and existing board and care facilities, a means of manually initiating the fire alarm system is required. However, 33.2.3.4.1 contains two exceptions for existing facilities. Exception No. 1 permits the use of a "system" of interconnected, multiple-station smoke detectors to meet the manual fire alarm box requirement by providing one manual fire alarm box that is integrated with the smoke detectors on each floor. Exception No. 2 recognizes that, in a small existing building, a sophisticated fire-protective signaling system that employs components "listed" for use in fire-protective signaling systems might not be necessary. The requirements can be satisfied by the installation of electric bells activated by a clearly identified switch on each floor where approved by the authority having jurisdiction.

The requirement of 32.2.3.4.3.1 does not mandate a system of smoke detectors in a small facility. If the building is small enough, single-station smoke alarms might meet the criterion of audibility in all sleeping areas. However, if the building is of significant size or consists of multiple levels, interconnected multiple-station smoke alarms will probably be needed. Additional smoke alarms are required in living rooms and day rooms.

To waive the requirement for common space smoke alarms in new small board and care facilities, the entire building must be protected with an automatic sprinkler system using quick-response or residential sprinklers in accordance with 32.2.3.5, as permitted by the exception to 32.2.3.4.3.1. However, if the sprinkler exception is used to exempt smoke detectors from each level and from living areas, smoke alarms must be provided in each sleeping room in accordance with 32.2.3.4.3.2. Therefore, a sprinkler system that uses quick-response or residential sprinklers permits some, but not all, smoke alarms to be omitted from a small board and care facility.

The same conditions for exemption apply to existing small board and care facilities. To waive the requirement for common space smoke alarms as permitted by Exception No. 1 and Exception No. 2 to 33.2.3.4.3, the entire building must be protected with an automatic sprinkler system using quick-response or residential sprinklers in accordance with 33.2.3.5, and the bedrooms must be provided with smoke alarms. If the existing smoke alarms in the bedrooms are battery powered, they do not need to be replaced with house-powered detectors if the authority having jurisdiction judges that the facility has an adequate testing, maintenance, and battery replacement program.

32.2.3.5 Automatic Extinguishing Systems.

32.2.3.5.1 All facilities shall be protected throughout by an approved automatic sprinkler system in accordance with 32.2.3.5.2. Quick-response or residential sprinklers shall be provided.

33.2.3.5 Automatic Extinguishing Systems.

33.2.3.5.1 (Reserved.)

Exception No. 1:   In conversions, sprinklers shall not be required in small board and care homes with a rating of prompt evacuation capability and serving eight or fewer residents.

Exception No. 2:   Standard response sprinklers shall be permitted for use in hazardous areas in accordance with 32.2.3.2.

32.2.3.5.2* Where an automatic sprinkler system is installed, for either total or partial building coverage, the system shall be in accordance with Section 9.7 and shall initiate the fire alarm system in accordance with 32.2.3.4.1. The adequacy of the water supply shall be documented to the authority having jurisdiction.

Exception No. 1:*   In prompt evacuation capability facilities, an automatic sprinkler system in accordance with NFPA 13D, Standard for the Installation of Sprinkler Systems in One- and Two-Family Dwellings and Manufactured Homes, shall be permitted. Facilities with more than eight residents shall be treated as two-family dwellings with regard to water supply. Additionally, entrance foyers shall be sprinklered.

A.32.2.3.5.2 Exception No. 1 NFPA 13D, *Standard for the Installation of Sprinkler Systems in One- and Two-Family Dwellings and Manufactured Homes,* contains additional requirements for a piping system serving both sprinkler and domestic needs.

Exception No. 2:   In slow and impractical evacuation capability facilities, an automatic sprinkler system in accordance with NFPA 13D, Standard for the Installation of Sprinkler Systems in One- and Two-Family Dwellings and Manufactured Homes, with a 30-minute water supply, shall be permitted. All habitable areas and closets shall be sprinklered. Facilities with more than eight residents shall be treated as two-family dwellings with regard to water supply.

Exception No. 3:   In prompt and slow evacuation capability facilities, where an automatic sprinkler system is in accordance with NFPA 13, Standard for the Installation of Sprinkler Systems, automatic sprinklers shall not be required in closets not exceeding 24 ft² (2.2 m²) and in bathrooms not exceeding 55 ft² (5.1 m²), provided that such spaces are finished with lath and plaster or material providing a 15-minute thermal barrier.

Exception No. 4:   In prompt and slow evacuation capability facilities up to and including four stories in height, systems in accordance with NFPA 13R, Standard for the Installation

33.2.3.5.2* Where an automatic sprinkler system is installed, for either total or partial building coverage, the system shall be in accordance with Section 9.7 and shall activate the fire alarm system in accordance with 33.2.3.4.1. The adequacy of the water supply shall be documented to the authority having jurisdiction.

Exception No. 1:   In prompt evacuation capability facilities, an automatic sprinkler system in accordance with NFPA 13D, Standard for the Installation of Sprinkler Systems in One- and Two-Family Dwellings and Manufactured Homes, shall be permitted. Automatic sprinklers shall not be required in closets not exceeding 24 ft² (2.2 m²) and in bathrooms not exceeding 55 ft² (5.1 m²), provided that such spaces are finished with lath and plaster or materials providing a 15-minute thermal barrier.

Exception No. 2:   In slow and impractical evacuation capability facilities, an automatic sprinkler system in accordance with NFPA 13D, Standard for the Installation of Sprinkler Systems in One- and Two-Family Dwellings and Manufactured Homes, with a 30-minute water supply, shall be permitted. All habitable areas and closets shall be sprinklered. Automatic sprinklers shall not be required in bathrooms not exceeding 55 ft² (5.1 m²), provided that such spaces are finished with lath and plaster or materials providing a 15-minute thermal barrier.

Exception No. 3:   In prompt and slow evacuation facilities, where an automatic sprinkler system is in accordance with NFPA 13, Standard for the Installation of Sprinkler Systems, sprinklers shall not be required in closets not exceeding 24 ft² (2.2 m²) and in bathrooms not exceeding 55 ft² (5.1 m²), provided that such spaces are finished with lath and plaster or materials providing a 15-minute thermal barrier.

Exception No. 4:   In prompt and slow evacuation capability facilities up to and including four stories in height, systems installed in accordance with NFPA 13R, Standard for the

CHAPTER 32 • New　　　　　　　　　　　　　　**CHAPTER 33 • Existing**

of Sprinkler Systems in Residential Occupancies up to and Including Four Stories in Height, shall be permitted.

Exception No. 5: In impractical evacuation capability facilities up to and including four stories in height, systems in accordance with NFPA 13R, Standard for the Installation of Sprinkler Systems in Residential Occupancies up to and Including Four Stories in Height, shall be permitted. All habitable areas and closets shall be sprinklered.

Exception No. 6: Initiation of the fire alarm system shall not be required for existing installations in accordance with 32.2.3.5.5.

A.32.2.3.5.2 The decision to permit the use of the criteria from NFPA 13D, *Standard for the Installation of Sprinkler Systems in One- and Two-Family Dwellings and Manufactured Homes,* in these occupancies is based on the following:

(1) The desire to obtain a level of fire suppression and control approximately equivalent to that delivered by residential facilities protected by such systems (see the appendix statement in NFPA 13D, *Standard for the Installation of Sprinkler Systems in One- and Two-Family Dwellings and Manufactured Homes)*
(2) The fact that potential fire exposure and challenge to the suppression system in a small board and care facility are of the same nature and are no more severe than those found in residences

Chapter 32 permits the use of NFPA 13D, *Standard for the Installation of Sprinkler Systems in One- and Two-Family Dwellings and Manufactured Homes,* and NFPA 13R, *Standard for the Installation of Sprinkler Systems in Residential Occupancies up to and Including Four Stories in Height,* outside of their scopes. This permission based on a review of the occupancy and a recognition that the fires in board and care facilities is similar to those of other residential occupancies and that the level of protection is appropriate. In some circumstances, such as those for impractical evacuation capabilities, the requirements of NFPA 13D and NFPA 13R have been supplemented with requirements for additional water supplies to compensate for the special needs of the board and care occupancy.

32.2.3.5.3 Automatic sprinkler systems installed in prompt and slow evacuation capability facilities shall have valve supervision by one of the following methods:

Installation of Sprinkler Systems in Residential Occupancies up to and Including Four Stories in Height, shall be permitted.

Exception No. 5: In impractical evacuation capability facilities up to and including four stories in height, systems installed in accordance with NFPA 13R, Standard for the Installation of Sprinkler Systems in Residential Occupancies up to and Including Four Stories in Height, shall be permitted. All habitable areas and closets shall be sprinklered. Automatic sprinklers shall not be required in bathrooms not exceeding 55 ft² (5.1 m²), provided that such spaces are finished with lath and plaster or materials providing a 15-minute thermal barrier.

Exception No. 6: Initiation of the fire alarm system shall not be required for existing installations in accordance with 33.2.3.5.5.

A.33.2.3.5.2 The decision to permit the use of the criteria from NFPA 13D, *Standard for the Installation of Sprinkler Systems in One- and Two-Family Dwellings and Manufactured Homes,* in these occupancies is based on the following:

(1) The desire to obtain a level of fire suppression and control approximately equivalent to that delivered by residential facilities protected by such systems (see the appendix statement in NFPA 13D, *Standard for the Installation of Sprinkler Systems in One- and Two-Family Dwellings and Manufactured Homes)*
(2) The fact that potential fire exposure and challenge to the suppression system in a small board and care facility are of the same nature and are no more severe than those found in residences.

Chapter 33 permits the use of NFPA 13D and NFPA 13R, *Standard for the Installation of Sprinkler Systems in Residential Occupancies up to and Including Four Stories in Height,* outside of their scopes. This permission is based on a review of the occupancy and a recognition that the fires in board and care facilities are similar to those of other residential occupancies and that the level of protection is appropriate. In some circumstances, such as those for impractical evacuation capabilities, the requirements of NFPA 13D and NFPA 13R have been supplemented with requirements for additional water supplies to compensate for the special needs of the board and care occupancy.

33.2.3.5.3 Impractical Evacuation Capability. All impractical evacuation capability facilities shall be protected throughout by an approved, supervised automatic sprinkler system in accordance with 33.2.3.5.2.

(1) A single listed control valve that shuts off both domestic and sprinkler systems and a separate shutoff for the domestic system only
(2) Central station, proprietary, or remote station alarm in accordance with Section 9.6
(3) Valve closure that causes the sounding of an audible signal in the facility

32.2.3.5.4 Automatic sprinkler systems installed in impractical evacuation capability facilities shall be supervised in accordance with Section 9.7.

32.2.3.5.5 Sprinkler piping serving not more than six sprinklers for any isolated hazardous area shall be permitted to be installed in accordance with 9.7.1.2. In new installations, where more than two sprinklers are installed in a single area, waterflow detection shall be provided to initiate the fire alarm system required by 32.2.3.4.1. Duration of water supplies shall be as required for the sprinkler systems addressed in 32.2.3.5.2.

33.2.3.5.4 (Reserved.)

33.2.3.5.5 Sprinkler piping serving not more than six sprinklers for any isolated hazardous area shall be permitted to be installed in accordance with 9.7.1.2. In new installations, where more than two sprinklers are installed in a single area, waterflow detection shall be provided to initiate the fire alarm system required by 33.2.3.4.1. Duration of water supplies shall be as required for the sprinkler systems addressed in 33.2.3.5.2.

Subparagraph 32.2.3.5.1 requires that new small board and care facilities be protected by an automatic sprinkler system using quick-response or residential sprinklers. This requirement recognizes the ability of quick-response and residential sprinklers to maintain tenability in the room of origin during most fire scenarios.

Exception No. 1 to 32.2.3.5.1 recognizes the difficulties in retrofitting buildings that are converted to small board and care facilities and provides some relief in these situations.

Exception No. 2 to 32.2.3.5.1 permits standard response sprinklers to be installed in hazardous areas, since such areas are not occupied by sleeping residents.

If sprinkler protection is provided only in the board and care facility, and not throughout the building, the exceptions for sprinklers that require total building sprinkler protection (that is, Exception No. 2 to 32.2.2.1, Exception No. 2 to 32.2.2.4, the exception to 32.2.3.4.3.1, and the exception to 32.2.3.6.4) are not permitted to be used.

Subparagraph 33.2.3.5.2 does not require the installation of automatic sprinkler systems in existing small board and care facilities. Rather, it establishes the criteria for installing automatic sprinkler systems that are provided voluntarily for the purpose of applying one of the sprinkler exceptions to another *Code* requirement.

Although a small board and care facility is of a different occupancy classification than a dwelling or mobile home, Exception No. 1 and Exception No. 2 to 32/33.2.5.2 permit the use of residential sprinkler systems installed in accordance with NFPA 13D, *Standard for the Installation of Sprinkler Systems in One- and Two-Family Dwellings and Manufactured Homes,* for the reasons explained in A.32/A.33.2.3.5.2.[2] Although NFPA 13D does not require sprinklers in small closets and bathrooms of the same maximum sizes as specified in Exception No. 1 and Exception No. 2 to 32/33.2.3.5.2, the *Code* requires that the wall and ceiling surfaces provide a 15-minute thermal barrier. Because facilities with impractical evacuation capability will not be immediately evacuated, the normal 10-minute water supply duration specified in NFPA 13D is required to be increased to 30 minutes. Also, in impractical evacuation capability facilities, sprinklers are required in closets and other habitable areas, other than the bathrooms addressed earlier in this paragraph.

The exemption for sprinklers in bathrooms and closets as permitted by Exception No. 3 to 32/33.2.3.5.2 supplements the requirements of NFPA 13, *Standard for the Installation of Sprinkler Systems.*[3] In addition to meeting the size limitation requirements, the walls and ceilings of bathroom and closet spaces must have a 15-minute thermal barrier rating to qualify for the sprinkler exemption. The 15-minute thermal barrier rating includes walls and ceilings behind fixtures such as prefabricated tub and shower enclosures.

Exception No. 4. and Exception No. 5 to 32/33.2.5.2 recognize the use of sprinkler systems installed in accordance with NFPA 13R, *Standard for the Installation of Sprinkler Systems in Residential Occupancies up to and Including Four Stories in Height.*[4] Closets and habitable areas (other than existing small bathrooms) must be sprinklered.

In facilities with prompt and slow evacuation capability, the sprinkler systems might need to be supervised, depending on the requirements of the sprinkler system installation standard used. For new small board and care facilities, 32.2.3.5.3 requires supervision, regardless of the installation standard used.

Subparagraphs 32.2.3.5.1 and 33.2.3.5.3 require that all small facilities with impractical evacuation capability be fully sprinklered. If sprinkler protection is provided only in the board and care facility, and not throughout the building, any exceptions predicated on complete building sprinkler coverage are not permitted to be used.

The importance of the role of the sprinkler system in protecting occupants who cannot readily evacuate

the building (defend-in-place strategy) requires that sprinkler systems in facilities with impractical evacuation capability be supervised in accordance with 9.7.2. Note that 9.7.2 requires electrical supervision of control valves and the transmission of waterflow alarms to a monitoring station. NFPA 13D and NFPA 13R permit the sprinkler systems to be installed with the domestic water supply valve as the only means to shut off the sprinklers; no valves control only the sprinkler system. This arrangement might satisfy the supervision requirements of 9.7.2. However, waterflow upon sprinkler activation would still need to be transmitted to a monitoring station.

The provision of 32/33.2.3.5.5 that requires water supply duration to be in accordance with 32/33.2.3.5.2 affects facilities where unlimited public water is not available and captive sources such as tanks are used. Either a 10-minute or 30-minute water supply duration is needed, depending on whether the facility is of prompt, slow, or impractical evacuation capability. Because 9.7.1.2 requires 0.15 gpm/ft² (6.1 L/min/m²) for up to six sprinklers protecting an isolated hazardous area, a significant water reserve might be necessary.

32.2.3.6 Construction of Corridor Walls.

32.2.3.6.1 The separation walls of sleeping rooms shall be capable of resisting fire for not less than ½ hour, which is considered to be achieved if the partitioning is finished on both sides with lath and plaster or materials providing a 15-minute thermal barrier. Sleeping room doors shall be substantial doors, such as those of 1 ¾-in. (4.4-cm) thick, solid-bonded wood core construction or other construction of equal or greater stability and fire integrity. Any vision panels shall be fixed fire window assemblies in accordance with 8.2.3.2.2 or shall be wired glass not exceeding 1296 in.² (0.84 m²) each in area and installed in approved frames.

Exception No. 1: In prompt evacuation capability facilities, all sleeping rooms shall be separated from the escape route by smoke partitions in accordance with 8.2.4. Door closing shall be regulated by 32.2.3.6.4.

Exception No. 2: This requirement shall not apply to corridor walls that are smoke partitions in accordance with 8.2.4 and that are protected by automatic sprinklers in accordance with 32.2.3.5 on both sides of the wall and door. In such instances, there shall be no limitation on the type or size of glass panels. Door closing shall be regulated by 32.2.3.6.4.

33.2.3.6 Construction of Corridor Walls.

33.2.3.6.1 The separation walls of sleeping rooms shall be capable of resisting fire for not less than ½ hour, which is considered to be achieved if the partitioning is finished on both sides with lath and plaster or materials providing a 15-minute thermal barrier. Sleeping room doors shall be substantial doors, such as those of 1¾-in. (4.4-cm) thick, solid-bonded wood core construction or other construction of equal or greater stability and fire integrity. Any vision panels shall be fixed fire window assemblies in accordance with 8.2.3.2.2 or shall be wired glass not exceeding 1296 in.² (0.84 m²) each in area and installed in approved frames.

Exception No. 1: In prompt evacuation capability facilities, all sleeping rooms shall be separated from the escape route by smoke partitions in accordance with 8.2.4. Door closing shall be regulated by 33.2.3.6.4.

Exception No. 2: This requirement shall not apply to corridor walls that are smoke partitions in accordance with 8.2.4 and that are protected by automatic sprinklers in accordance with 33.2.3.5 on both sides of the wall and door. In such instances, there shall be no limitation on the type or size of glass panels. Door closing shall be regulated by 33.2.3.6.4.

CHAPTER 32 • New   **CHAPTER 33 • Existing**

Exception No. 3: Sleeping arrangements that are not lo-cated in sleeping rooms shall be permitted for nonresident staff members, provided that the audibility of the alarm in the sleeping area is sufficient to awaken staff who might be sleeping.

Exception No. 3: Sleeping arrangements that are not lo-cated in sleeping rooms shall be permitted for nonresident staff members, provided that the audibility of the alarm in the sleeping area is sufficient to awaken staff who might be sleeping.

Exception No. 4: In previously approved facilities, where the facility has demonstrated to the authority having jurisdic-tion that the group is capable of evacuating the building in 8 minutes or less, or where the group achieves an E-score of three or less using the board and care occupancies evacua-tion capability determination methodology of NFPA 101A, Guide on Alternative Approaches to Life Safety, sleeping rooms shall be separated from escape routes by walls and doors that are smoke resistant.

32.2.3.6.2 No louvers or operable transoms or other air pas-sages shall penetrate the wall, except properly installed heat-ing and utility installations other than transfer grilles. Transfer grilles shall be prohibited.

33.2.3.6.2 No louvers or operable transoms or other air pas-sages shall penetrate the wall, except properly installed heat-ing and utility installations other than transfer grilles. Transfer grilles shall be prohibited.

32.2.3.6.3 Doors shall be provided with latches or other mechanisms suitable for keeping the doors closed. No doors shall be arranged to prevent the occupant from closing the door.

33.2.3.6.3 Doors shall be provided with latches or other mechanisms suitable for keeping the doors closed. No doors shall be arranged to prevent the occupant from closing the door.

32.2.3.6.4 Doors shall be self-closing or automatic-closing in accordance with 7.2.1.8.

33.2.3.6.4 Doors shall be self-closing or automatic-closing in accordance with 7.2.1.8.

Exception: Door-closing devices shall not be required in buildings protected throughout by an approved automatic sprinkler system in accordance with 32.2.3.5.1.

Exception: Door-closing devices shall not be required in buildings protected throughout by an approved automatic sprinkler system in accordance with 33.2.3.5.2.

The intent of 32/33.2.3.6.1 in requiring corridor walls to have a ½-hour fire resistance rating is to require a nominal resistance to burn-through, particularly where the fire rating of existing partitions cannot be documented. Examples of acceptable partition as-semblies include, but are not limited to, ½-in. (1.3-cm) thick gypsum board, wood lath and plaster, or metal lath and plaster.

The intent of the Exception No. 2 to 32/33.2.3.6.1 is that fire resistance–rated materials are not required where sprinkler protection is provided on both sides of the corridor wall and door. Complete sprinkler protection, as required for new construction by 32.2.3.5.1 and permitted for existing facilities by 33.2.3.5, would clearly meet this criterion. Therefore, the exception represents the most typical case where corridor walls and doors are required only to be smoke resisting.

Exception No. 3 to 32/33.2.3.6.1 recognizes that

there are many board and care homes that employ sleep-in staff. The exception is intended to permit staff members to sleep in locations that are not sepa-rated from the corridors. Placing a staff cot in the supervisor's station, living room, or other room does not reclassify that room as a sleeping room.

Exception No. 4 to 33.2.3.6.1 allows a previously approved situation to continue to be recognized in existing small facilities with residents who perform in the faster half of the overall slow evacuation capa-bility category. The exception cannot be used for a first-time evaluation of the adequacy of smoke-resisting corridor walls.

Doors in corridor walls are required by 32/33.2.3.6.4 to be self-closing or automatic-closing. In order to waive this requirement under the ex-ception to 32/33.2.3.6.4, the entire building must be protected throughout by an approved automatic sprinkler system.

CHAPTER 32 • New   **CHAPTER 33 • Existing**

32.2.4 (Reserved.)

32.2.5 Building Services.

32.2.5.1 Utilities. Utilities shall comply with Section 9.1.

32.2.5.2 Heating, Ventilating, and Air Conditioning.

32.2.5.2.1 Heating, ventilating, and air conditioning equipment shall comply with the provisions of 9.2.1 and 9.2.2, except as otherwise required in this chapter.

32.2.5.2.2 No stove or combustion heater shall be located to block escape in case of fire caused by the malfunction of the stove or heater.

32.2.5.2.3 Unvented fuel-fired heaters shall not be used in any residential board and care facility.

32.2.5.3 Elevators, Escalators, and Conveyors. Any elevators, escalators, and conveyors installed shall comply with the provisions of Section 9.4.

Subparagraph 32/33.2.5.2.2 does not require a kitchen containing a stove to be completely separated by smoke partitions, only that the stove be located so that a malfunction does not result in a blockage of the means of escape. If, in the opinion of the authority having jurisdiction, the location of the stove causes blocking of the means of escape in the event of a

Section 32.3 Large Facilities

32.3.1 General.

32.3.1.1 Scope. Section 32.3 applies to residential board and care occupancies providing sleeping accommodations for more than 16 residents. Facilities having sleeping accommodations for not more than 16 residents shall be evaluated in accordance with Section 32.2.

32.3.1.2 Requirements Based on Evacuation Capability.

32.3.1.2.1 Prompt and Slow. Large facilities classified as prompt or slow evacuation capability shall comply with the requirements of Section 32.3 as indicated for the appropriate evacuation capability.

33.2.4 (Reserved.)

33.2.5 Building Services.

33.2.5.1 Utilities. Utilities shall comply with Section 9.1.

33.2.5.2 Heating, Ventilating, and Air Conditioning.

33.2.5.2.1 Heating, ventilating, and air conditioning equipment shall comply with the provisions of 9.2.1 and 9.2.2, except as otherwise required in this chapter.

33.2.5.2.2 No stove or combustion heater shall be located to block escape in case of fire caused by the malfunction of the stove or heater.

33.2.5.2.3 Unvented fuel-fired heaters shall not be used in any residential board and care facility.

malfunction, the application of either 32/33.2.3.2 or 32/33.2.5.2.2 might be appropriate for mitigating the hazard.

Subparagraph 32/33.2.5.2.3 prohibits the use of a typical kerosene portable heater, as well as other fuel-fired, nonvented heaters.

Section 33.3 Large Facilities

33.3.1 General.

33.3.1.1 Scope. Section 33.3 applies to residential board and care occupancies providing sleeping accommodations for more than 16 residents. Facilities having sleeping accommodations for not more than 16 residents shall be evaluated in accordance with Section 33.2. However, facilities meeting the requirements of this section shall be considered to meet the requirements of Section 33.2 for prompt evacuation capability or slow evacuation capability.

33.3.1.2 Requirements Based on Evacuation Capability.

33.3.1.2.1 Prompt and Slow. Large facilities classified as prompt or slow evacuation capability shall comply with the requirements of Section 33.3 as indicated for the appropriate evacuation capability.

CHAPTER 32 • New

CHAPTER 33 • Existing

Exception:*   Facilities where the authority having jurisdiction has determined equivalent safety is provided in accordance with Section 1.5.

A.32.3.1.2.1 Exception In determining equivalency for conversions, modernizations, renovations, or unusual design concepts, the authority having jurisdiction might permit evaluations based on NFPA 101A, *Guide on Alternative Approaches to Life Safety,* Chapter 6.

32.3.1.2.2 Impractical. Large facilities classified as impractical evacuation capability shall meet the requirements for limited care facilities in Chapter 18.

Exception:*   Facilities where the authority having jurisdiction has determined equivalent safety is provided in accordance with Section 1.5.

A.32.3.1.2.2 Exception In determining equivalency for conversions, modernizations, renovations, or unusual design concepts, the authority having jurisdiction might permit evaluations based on NFPA 101A, *Guide on Alternative Approaches to Life Safety,* Chapter 3, using the mandatory safety requirements for nursing homes.

Exception No. 1:*   Facilities where the authority having jurisdiction has determined equivalent safety is provided in accordance with Section 1.5.

A.33.3.1.2.1 Exception No. 1 In determining equivalency for existing buildings, conversions, modernizations, renovations, or unusual design concepts, the authority having jurisdiction might permit evaluations based on NFPA 101A, *Guide on Alternative Approaches to Life Safety,* Chapter 6.

Exception No. 2:   Facilities that were previously approved as complying with 33.3.1.2.2.

33.3.1.2.2 Impractical. Large facilities classified as impractical evacuation capability shall meet the requirements for limited care facilities in Chapter 19.

Exception:*   Facilities where the authority having jurisdiction has determined equivalent safety is provided in accordance with Section 1.5.

A.33.3.1.2.2 Exception In determining equivalency for existing buildings, the authority having jurisdiction might permit evaluations based on NFPA 101A, *Guide on Alternative Approaches to Life Safety,* Chapter 3, substituting Table A.33.3.1.2.2 mandatory safety requirements values for those contained in NFPA 101A.

Table A.33.3.1.2.2 Substitute Mandatory Safety Requirements Values

Zone Location	Containment S_a	Extinguishment S_b	People Movement S_c
First floor	5	6	3
Above or below first floor	9	8	5
Over 75 ft (23 m) in height	9	8	5

32.3.1.2.3 Facility management shall furnish to the authority having jurisdiction, upon request, an evacuation capability determination using a procedure acceptable to the authority having jurisdiction. Where such documentation is not furnished, the evacuation capability shall be classified as impractical.

33.3.1.2.3 Facility management shall furnish to the authority having jurisdiction, upon request, an evacuation capability determination using a procedure acceptable to the authority having jurisdiction. Where such documentation is not furnished, the evacuation capability shall be classified as impractical.

The importance of an accurate evaluation of evacuation capabilities cannot be overstated. Ineffective resident or staff response was a contributing factor in the majority of the multiple-death fires listed in Table 32/33.1.

Determining the evacuation capability is not simply a matter of timing a fire drill in the middle of the day. Many variables impact a resident's capability to evacuate, and these variables must be carefully considered and factored into the documentation presented to the authority having jurisdiction for approval. Some variables that should be considered follow.

(a) *Time of Day.* An occupant's ability to evacuate might be slowed dramatically when the person must be awakened. In such a situation, the occupant must process the information that evacuation is necessary and then begin evacuating.

(b) *Medication.* Many individuals in board and care occupancies take various medications for behavior control or as a sleeping aid. If an individual is medicated, he or she might need additional assistance in responding and evacuating.

(c) *Mobility and Location of Occupants.* Once individuals become aware of an emergency and take action, their ability to move through the building must be considered. Individuals using wheelchairs, walkers, or canes are further slowed when using stairs or ramps or when opening doors.

(d) *Staff Assistance.* Though the *Code* does not specify minimum staffing levels, staffing levels should be considered, especially where high resident-to-staff ratios exist. Given the additional needs

mentioned in (a) through (c), the staff will be limited in their ability to impact evacuation time where multiple residents need assistance.

The evacuation capability of the population of a board and care occupancy might vary over time. The required documentation should be reviewed regularly to ensure that it accurately represents the current evacuation capability of the residents and staff.

When determining equivalency in accordance with the exception to 32/33.3.1.2.1 or 32/33.3.1.2.2, it is important to note that the equivalency measurement systems of the 1998 edition of NFPA 101A, *Guide on Alternative Approaches to Life Safety,* were calibrated against the requirements of the 1997 edition of NFPA *101* and might not accurately evaluate equivalency with the requirements of the 2000 edition of the *Life Safety Code.* At the time this handbook went to press, the 2001 edition of NFPA 101A was being prepared. Once issued, the 2001 edition of NFPA 101A can be used to measure equivalency against the requirements of the 2000 edition of the *Code.*

The difficulty in moving occupants to the outside of a facility with an impractical evacuation capability is comparable to that of a health care facility. Therefore, 32/33.3.1.2.2 requires that large board and care facilities with impractical evacuation capability are to be subject to the requirements of Chapter 18/19 rather than Chapter 32/33. Chapter 18/19 employs a detailed defend-in-place strategy. If the equivalency methodologies of NFPA 101A, *Guide on Alternative Approaches to Life Safety,* are to be applied to a large board and care facility with impractical evacuation capability, the health care FSES must be used instead of the board and care FSES.

32.3.1.3 Minimum Construction Requirements.

32.3.1.3.1 Construction requirements for large facilities shall be as required by 32.3.1.3. Where noted as "fully sheathed," the interior shall be covered with lath and plaster or materials providing a 15-minute thermal barrier.

32.3.1.3.2 For the purpose of construction requirements, stories shall be counted starting with the primary level of exit discharge and ending with the highest occupied level. Where the primary level of exit discharge is not readily apparent, the primary level of exit discharge of a building shall be that story that is level with or above finished grade of the exterior wall line for 50 percent or more of its perimeter.

33.3.1.3 Minimum Construction Requirements.

33.3.1.3.1 Construction requirements for large facilities shall be as required by 33.3.1.3. Where noted as "fully sheathed," the interior shall be covered with lath and plaster or materials providing a 15-minute thermal barrier.

33.3.1.3.2 For the purpose of construction requirements, stories shall be counted starting with the primary level of exit discharge and ending with the highest occupied level. Where the primary level of exit discharge is not readily apparent, the primary level of exit discharge of a building shall be that story that is level with or above finished grade of the exterior wall line for 50 percent or more of its perimeter.

CHAPTER 32 • New

CHAPTER 33 • Existing

Building levels below the primary level shall not be counted as a story in determining the height of the building.

32.3.1.3.3 The minimum construction requirements *(see 8.2.1)*, based on the highest story normally used by board and care residents, shall be as follows.

(a) *One- or Two-Story Facilities.* Any construction type that meets the requirements for a 1-hour or greater fire resistance rating, that is Type IV(2HH), that is fully sheathed, or that is protected throughout by an approved, supervised automatic sprinkler system in accordance with 32.3.3.5.

Exception: One-story prompt evacuation capability facilities having 30 or fewer residents shall be permitted to be of any type construction.

Because evacuation strategies might be limited to moving residents to a point of safety, the *Code* regulates construction type to ensure building stability if the residents are to remain inside. The stability of the building is maintained either by the use of an automatic sprinkler system (as required for new construction by 32.3.3.5.1) or by the use of fire-resistant

Building levels below the primary level shall not be counted as a story in determining the height of the building.

33.3.1.3.3 The minimum construction requirements *(see 8.2.1)*, based on the highest story normally used by board and care residents, shall be as follows.

(a) *One- or Two-Story Facilities.* Any construction type that meets the requirements for 1-hour or greater fire resistance rating, that is Type IV(2HH), that is fully sheathed, or that is protected throughout by an approved automatic sprinkler system in accordance with 33.3.3.5.

Exception: One-story prompt evacuation capability facilities having 30 or fewer residents shall be permitted to be of any type construction.

construction. Table 32.2 summarizes the permissible building construction types for large residential board and care facilities. Note that, in the exception to (a), buildings from which there is a reasonable expectation of prompt evacuation to the exterior are exempted from the minimum construction requirements.

Table 32/33.2 Minimum Construction Requirements for Large Facilities with Prompt or Slow Evacuation Capability

Construc- tion Type	Number of Stories						
	1	2	3	4	5	6	≥7
Type I	X	X	X	X	X	X	X
Type II(222)	X	X	X	X	X	X	X
Type II(111)		X	X		X	X	AS
Type II(000)†	AS‡	AS‡	AS§	AS§	AS§	AS§	NP
Type III(211)	X	X	X	X	X	X	AS
Type III(200)†	AS‡	AS‡	AS§	AS§	AS§	AS§	NP
Type IV(2HH)	X	X	AS	AS	AS	AS	AS
Type V(111)	X	X	AS§	AS§	AS§	AS§	NP
Type V(000)†	AS‡	AS‡	AS§	AS§	NP	NP	NP

X = Permitted.

AS = Permitted if sprinklered as required by 32.3.3.5.

NP = Not permitted.

† = Permitted up to one story, unsheathed and unsprinklered if housing 30 or fewer residents with prompt evacuation capability.

‡ = Permitted if sheathed or sprinklered (sprinklers required by 32.3.3.5).

§ = Permitted if sheathed and sprinklered.

(b) Three- to Six-Story Facilities. Type I, Type II, or Type III construction that meets the requirements for a 1-hour or greater fire resistance rating; Type IV construction that is protected throughout by an approved automatic sprinkler system in accordance with 32.3.3.5; or any other type of construction that is both sheathed and protected throughout by an approved, supervised automatic sprinkler system in accordance with 32.3.3.5, other than Type V(000).

Exception: Three- to four-story facilities of Type V(000) construction that are both fully sheathed and protected throughout by an approved, supervised automatic sprinkler system in accordance with 32.3.3.5.

(c) Facilities More than Six Stories High. Any Type I or Type II(222) construction, and any Type II(111), Type III(211), or Type IV(2HH) construction that is protected throughout by an approved, supervised automatic sprinkler system in accordance with 32.3.3.5.

Exception: Any building of Type I, Type II(222), or Type II(111) construction shall be permitted to include roofing systems involving combustible supports, decking, or roofing, provided that the following criteria are met:

(a) The roof covering meets Class A requirements in accordance with NFPA 256, Standard Methods of Fire Tests of Roof Coverings.

(b) The roof is separated from all occupied portions of the building by a noncombustible floor assembly having not less than a 2-hour fire resistance rating that includes not less than 2½ in. (6.4 cm) of concrete or gypsum fill. To qualify for this exception, the attic or other space so developed shall be either unused or protected throughout by an approved, supervised automatic sprinkler system in accordance with 32.3.3.5.1.

32.3.1.4 Occupant Load. The occupant load, in number of persons for whom means of egress and other provisions are required, shall be determined on the basis of the occupant load factors of Table 7.3.1.2 that are characteristic of the use of the space or shall be determined as the maximum probable population of the space under consideration, whichever is greater.

If the actual occupant load of the facility exceeds the occupant load calculated on the basis of one person per 200 ft² (18.6 m²), as stipulated in Table 7.3.1.2, the egress capacity must be designed to meet the actual (larger) occupant load. The determination of actual occupant load should be based on the total number

(b) Three- to Six-Story Facilities. Type I, Type II, or Type III construction that meets the requirements for 1-hour or greater fire resistance rating; Type IV construction that is protected throughout by an approved automatic sprinkler system in accordance with 33.3.3.5; or any other type of construction that is both sheathed and protected throughout by an approved automatic sprinkler system installed in accordance with 33.3.3.5, other than Type V(000).

Exception: Three- to four-story facilities of Type V(000) construction that are both fully sheathed and protected throughout by an approved, supervised automatic sprinkler system in accordance with 33.3.3.5.

(c) Facilities More than Six Stories High. Any Type I or Type II(222) construction, and any Type II(111), Type III(211), or Type IV(2HH) construction that is protected throughout by an approved automatic sprinkler system in accordance with 33.3.3.5.

Exception: Any building of Type I, Type II(222), or Type II(111) construction shall be permitted to include roofing systems involving combustible supports, decking, or roofing, provided that the following criteria are met:

(a) The roof covering meets Class A requirements in accordance with NFPA 256, Standard Methods of Fire Tests of Roof Coverings.

(b) The roof is separated from all occupied portions of the building by a noncombustible floor assembly having not less than a 2-hour fire resistance rating that includes not less than 2½ in. (6.4 cm) of concrete or gypsum fill. To qualify for this exception, the attic or other space so developed shall be either unused or protected throughout by an approved automatic sprinkler system in accordance with 33.3.3.5.1.

33.3.1.4 Occupant Load. The occupant load, in number of persons for whom means of egress and other provisions are required, shall be determined on the basis of the occupant load factors of Table 7.3.1.2 that are characteristic of the use of the space or shall be determined as the maximum probable population of the space under consideration, whichever is greater.

of residents, staff, and visitors. However, if the actual occupant load is smaller than the calculated occupant load, the minimum egress capacity must not be less than that required for the calculated (larger) occupant load.

32.3.2 Means of Egress.

32.3.2.1 Means of egress shall be in accordance with Chapter 7.

32.3.2.2 Means of Egress Components.

32.3.2.2.1 Components of means of egress shall be limited to the types described in 32.3.2.2.2 through 32.3.2.2.10.

32.3.2.2.2 Doors. Doors in means of egress shall be as follows:

(1) Doors complying with 7.2.1 shall be permitted.
(2) Doors within individual rooms and suites of rooms shall be permitted to be swinging or sliding.
(3) No door in any means of egress shall be locked against egress when the building is occupied.

Exception No. 1:   The requirement of 32.3.2.2.2(3) shall not apply to delayed-egress locks in accordance with 7.2.1.6.1, provided that not more than one device exists in a means of egress.

Exception No. 2:   The requirement of 32.3.2.2.2(3) shall not apply to access-controlled egress doors in accordance with 7.2.1.6.2.

(4) Revolving doors complying with 7.2.1.10 shall be permitted.
(5) Every bathroom door shall be designed to allow opening from the outside during an emergency when locked.

32.3.2.2.3 Stairs. Stairs complying with 7.2.2 shall be permitted.

32.3.2.2.4 Smokeproof Enclosures. Smokeproof enclosures complying with 7.2.3 shall be permitted.

32.3.2.2.5 Horizontal Exits. Horizontal exits complying with 7.2.4 shall be permitted.

32.3.2.2.6 Ramps. Ramps complying with 7.2.5 shall be permitted.

32.3.2.2.7 Exit Passageways. Exit passageways complying with 7.2.6 shall be permitted.

32.3.2.2.8 Fire Escape Ladders. Fire escape ladders complying with 7.2.9 shall be permitted.

32.3.2.2.9 Alternating Tread Devices. Alternating tread devices complying with 7.2.11 shall be permitted.

32.3.2.2.10 Areas of Refuge. Areas of refuge complying with 7.2.12 shall be permitted.

33.3.2 Means of Egress.

33.3.2.1 Means of egress shall be in accordance with Chapter 7.

33.3.2.2 Means of Egress Components.

33.3.2.2.1 Components of means of egress shall be limited to the types described in 33.3.2.2.2 through 33.3.2.2.10.

33.3.2.2.2 Doors. Doors in means of egress shall be as follows:

(1) Doors complying with 7.2.1 shall be permitted.
(2) Doors within individual rooms and suites of rooms shall be permitted to be swinging or sliding.
(3) No door in any means of egress shall be locked against egress when the building is occupied.

Exception No. 1:   The requirement of 33.3.2.2.2(3) shall not apply to delayed-egress locks in accordance with 7.2.1.6.1, provided that not more than one device exists in a means of egress.

Exception No. 2:   The requirement of 33.3.2.2.2(3) shall not apply to access-controlled egress doors in accordance with 7.2.1.6.2.

(4) Revolving doors complying with 7.2.1.10 shall be permitted.

33.3.2.2.3 Stairs. Stairs complying with 7.2.2 shall be permitted.

33.3.2.2.4 Smokeproof Enclosures. Smokeproof enclosures complying with 7.2.3 shall be permitted.

33.3.2.2.5 Horizontal Exits. Horizontal exits complying with 7.2.4 shall be permitted.

33.3.2.2.6 Ramps. Ramps complying with 7.2.5 shall be permitted.

33.3.2.2.7 Exit Passageways. Exit passageways complying with 7.2.6 shall be permitted.

33.3.2.2.8 Fire Escape Ladders. Fire escape ladders complying with 7.2.9 shall be permitted.

33.3.2.2.9 Alternating Tread Devices. Alternating tread devices complying with 7.2.11 shall be permitted.

33.3.2.2.10 Areas of Refuge. Areas of refuge complying with 7.2.12 shall be permitted.

Paragraph 32/33.3.2.1 makes a general reference to Chapter 7 instead of repeating specific provisions. Many of the requirements contained in 32/33.3.2 are Chapter 7 provisions that require occupancy chapter permission such as Exception No. 1 to 32/33.3.2.2.2(3), which allows the use of delayed-egress locks in accordance with 7.2.1.6.1. The limits placed on travel distance in 32/33.3.2.6 are another example of a provision for which the occupancy chapters are permitted to establish restrictions.

Paragraph 32/33.3.2.2.2(3) prohibits a facility from having any door locked against egress while the building is occupied. This is consistent with a fundamental means of egress provision of Chapter 7. This requirement permits a door to have a locking device that allows the door to be opened from within the facility for the purpose of egress but does not allow the door to be opened from outside the facility. Ordinary double-cylinder locks and chain locks do not meet these provisions.

Although resident sleeping room doors are doors in the means of escape, it is the intent of 32/33.3.2.2.2 that the multiple latching/locking devices addressed by Exception No. 1 to 7.2.1.5.4 be permitted.

Exception No. 1 to 32/33.3.2.2.2(3) permits the use of delayed-egress locks that comply with 7.2.1.6.1, provided that not more than one delayed-egress device is encountered in any means of egress path. This provision requires that the building be either protected throughout by automatic sprinklers or equipped throughout with an automatic fire detection system. The 15-second or 30-second delay permitted by 7.2.1.6.1 does not affect the immediate release of the lock upon activation of the sprinklers or detectors or upon loss of power to the lock. The delayed-egress device helps provide security for infrequently used doors or stairs in board and care facilities, while doors remain available for emergency use. Chains and padlocks do not provide this feature.

In new residential board and care facilities, 32.3.2.2.2(5) requires bathroom doors to have an additional safety feature that allows staff to access the bathroom when the door is locked. This feature can be useful for releasing individuals who might mistakenly lock themselves in the bathroom instead of evacuating.

32.3.2.3 Capacity of Means of Egress.

32.3.2.3.1 The capacity of means of egress shall be in accordance with Section 7.3.

32.3.2.3.2 Street floor exits shall be sufficient for the occupant load of the street floor plus the required capacity of stairs and ramps discharging onto the street floor.

32.3.2.3.3 The width of corridors shall be sufficient for the occupant load served but shall be not less than 44 in. (112 cm).

Exception: Corridors serving an occupant load fewer than 50 shall be not less than 36 in. (91 cm) wide.

32.3.2.4 Number of Exits. Not less than two exits shall be accessible from every story, including floors below the level of exit discharge and floors occupied for public purposes.

32.3.2.5 Arrangement of Means of Egress.

32.3.2.5.1 Access to all required exits shall be in accordance with Section 7.5.

32.3.2.5.2 Common paths of travel shall not exceed 125 ft (38.1 m).

33.3.2.3 Capacity of Means of Egress.

33.3.2.3.1 The capacity of means of egress shall be in accordance with Section 7.3.

33.3.2.3.2 Street floor exits shall be sufficient for the occupant load of the street floor plus the required capacity of stairs and ramps discharging onto the street floor.

33.3.2.3.3 The width of corridors shall be sufficient for the occupant load served but shall be not less than 44 in. (112 cm).

Exception: Corridors serving an occupant load fewer than 50 shall be not less than 36 in. (91 cm) wide.

33.3.2.4 Number of Exits. Not less than two exits shall be accessible from every story, including floors below the level of exit discharge and floors occupied for public purposes.

33.3.2.5 Arrangement of Means of Egress.

33.3.2.5.1 Access to all required exits shall be in accordance with Section 7.5.

33.3.2.5.2 Common paths of travel shall not exceed 110 ft (33.5 m).

32.3.2.5.3 Dead-end corridors shall not exceed 50 ft (15 m).

32.3.2.5.4 Any room or any suite of rooms exceeding 2000 ft² (185 m²) shall be provided with not less than two exit access doors remotely located from each other.

32.3.2.6 Travel Distance to Exits.

32.3.2.6.1 Travel distance within a room, suite, or living unit to a corridor door shall not exceed 125 ft (38.1 m).

32.3.2.6.2 Travel distance from the corridor door of any room to the nearest exit, measured in accordance with Section 7.6, shall not exceed 200 ft (60 m).

32.3.2.7 Discharge from Exits. Exit discharge shall comply with Section 7.7.

32.3.2.8 Illumination of Means of Egress. Means of egress shall be illuminated in accordance with Section 7.8.

32.3.2.9 Emergency Lighting. Emergency lighting in accordance with Section 7.9 shall be provided in all buildings with more than 25 rooms.

Exception: Where each sleeping room has a direct exit to the outside of the building at ground level, no emergency lighting shall be required.

32.3.2.10 Marking of Means of Egress. Means of egress shall be marked in accordance with Section 7.10.

32.3.2.11 Special Means of Egress Features. (Reserved.)

Exception: In buildings protected throughout by automatic sprinkler systems in accordance with 33.3.3.5, common path of travel shall not exceed 160 ft (48.8 m).

33.3.2.5.3 Dead-end corridors shall not exceed 50 ft (15 m).

33.3.2.6 Travel Distance to Exits.

33.3.2.6.1 Travel distance from the door within a room, suite, or living unit to a corridor door shall not exceed 75 ft (23 m).

Exception: Travel distance shall not exceed 125 ft (48 m) in buildings protected throughout by an approved automatic sprinkler system in accordance with 33.3.3.5.

33.3.2.6.2 Travel distance from the corridor door of any room to the nearest exit, measured in accordance with Section 7.6, shall not exceed 100 ft (30 m).

Exception No. 1: Travel distance to exits shall not exceed 200 ft (60 m) for exterior ways of exit access arranged in accordance with 7.5.3.

Exception No. 2: Travel distance to exits shall not exceed 200 ft (60 m) if the exit access and any portion of the building that is tributary to the exit access are protected throughout by approved automatic sprinkler systems. In addition, the portion of the building in which the 200-ft (60-m) travel distance is permitted shall be separated from the remainder of the building by construction having a fire resistance rating of not less than 1 hour for buildings not more than three stories in height and not less than 2 hours for buildings more than three stories in height.

33.3.2.7 Discharge from Exits. Exit discharge shall comply with Section 7.7.

33.3.2.8 Illumination of Means of Egress. Means of egress shall be illuminated in accordance with Section 7.8.

33.3.2.9 Emergency Lighting. Emergency lighting in accordance with Section 7.9 shall be provided in all buildings with more than 25 rooms.

Exception: Where each sleeping room has a direct exit to the outside of the building at ground level, no emergency lighting shall be required.

33.3.2.10 Marking of Means of Egress. Means of egress shall be marked in accordance with Section 7.10.

33.3.2.11 Special Means of Egress Features. (Reserved.)

CHAPTER 32 • New   **CHAPTER 33 • Existing**

Subparagraph 32/33.3.2.3.2 requires street-floor egress capacity that is sufficient to accommodate the convergence of first-floor occupants with occupants leaving exit enclosures from the upper and lower floors and traversing areas of the first floor. This concept is common in hotel, apartment, business, and mercantile occupancies. See the commentary on 28/29.2.7.3 and Exhibit 28/29.7.

Paragraph 32/33.3.2.4 contains provisions similar to those for hotels. No exceptions permit a building with a single exit. Note that 7.4.1.2 requires three or four exits for floors with more than 500 and 1000 people. This requirement will probably have minimal impact on board and care facilities, because such large floors would probably need additional exits to meet travel distance limitations.

Common path of travel is measured in the usual manner outlined in A.7.5.1.6. Prior to the mid-1990s the board and care occupancies chapters used a modified corridor common path of travel similar to that currently used in the hotel and apartment occupancy chapters.

Travel distance is addressed in 32/33.3.2.6. Exhibit 32/33.9 illustrates three separate sections of a board and care facility. Areas B and C are nonsprinklered existing portions of the building, and Section A is a proposed new addition. The travel distance limitations of 32/33.3.2.6 are divided into two segments: within a room/suite and within the common corridor system or along the exterior exit access balcony. In the existing areas (B and C), 33.3.2.6.1 limits the travel distance within the room/suite to 75 ft (23 m), or to 125 ft (38.1 m) if the building is protected by an automatic sprinkler system. For new facilities that must be sprinklered in accordance with 32.3.3.51, the travel distance within the room/suite is permitted to be 150 ft (38 m). Once outside the room/suite,

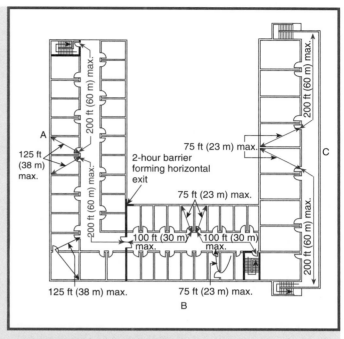

Exhibit 32/33.9 *Travel distance limitations.*

33.3.2.6.2 limits the travel distance to an exit to 100 ft (30 m). However, the distance is permitted to be increased to 200 ft (60 m) if the travel is an exterior exit access (area C) or if the building is protected by an automatic sprinkler system. Automatic sprinklers are required in all new board and care facilities. Therefore, 32.3.2.6.2 permits the 200-ft (60-m) travel distance outside the room/suite.

The exception to 32/33.3.2.9 does not apply to facilities with exterior balconies that require travel on stairs to reach ground level but applies only to facilities that have doors opening directly at ground level.

32.3.3 Protection.

32.3.3.1 Protection of Vertical Openings.

32.3.3.1.1 Any vertical opening shall be enclosed or protected in accordance with 8.2.5.

33.3.3 Protection.

33.3.3.1 Protection of Vertical Openings.

33.3.3.1.1 Any vertical opening shall be enclosed or protected in accordance with 8.2.5.

Exception No. 1:   Unprotected vertical openings not part of required egress shall be permitted to be waived by the authority having jurisdiction where such openings do not endanger required means of egress. This exception shall apply only in buildings protected throughout by an approved

automatic sprinkler system in accordance with 33.3.3.5.1 and in which exits and required ways of travel thereto are adequately safeguarded against fire and smoke within the building, or in which every individual room has direct access to an exterior exit without passing through a public corridor.

Exception No. 2: In buildings not more than two stories in height, unprotected vertical openings shall be permitted by the authority having jurisdiction if the building is protected throughout by an approved automatic sprinkler system in accordance with 33.3.3.5.1.

32.3.3.1.2 No floor below the level of exit discharge used only for storage, heating equipment, or purposes other than residential occupancy shall have unprotected openings to floors used for residential occupancy.

33.3.3.1.2 No floor below the level of exit discharge used only for storage, heating equipment, or purposes other than residential occupancy shall have unprotected openings to floors used for residential occupancy.

Because 32.3.3.5.1 requires an automatic sprinkler system in all new large board and care facilities, a communicating space is permitted to be separated from the remainder of the building by a smoke barrier in accordance with 8.2.5.5, rather than by a 1-hour barrier.

Automatic sprinklers are not required in existing board and care facilities. However, if automatic sprinklers are installed, Exception No. 1 and Exception No. 2 to 33.3.3.1.1 permit the authority having jurisdiction to waive the requirements for protection of vertical openings in certain circumstances.

32.3.3.2 Protection from Hazards.

32.3.3.2.1 Any room containing high-pressure boilers, refrigerating machinery, transformers, or other service equipment subject to possible explosion shall not be located directly under or adjacent to exits. All such rooms shall be effectively separated from other parts of the building as specified in Section 8.4.

32.3.3.2.2 Every hazardous area shall be separated from other parts of the building by a smoke partition in accordance with 8.2.4. Hazardous areas shall include, but shall not be limited to the following:

(1) Boiler and heater rooms
(2) Laundries
(3) Repair shops
(4) Rooms or spaces used for storage of combustible supplies and equipment in quantities deemed hazardous by the authority having jurisdiction

33.3.3.2 Protection from Hazards.

33.3.3.2.1 Any room containing high-pressure boilers, refrigerating machinery, transformers, or other service equipment subject to possible explosion shall not be located directly under or adjacent to exits. All such rooms shall be effectively separated from other parts of the building as specified in Section 8.4.

33.3.3.2.2 Every hazardous area shall be separated from other parts of the building by construction having a fire resistance rating of not less than 1 hour, with communicating openings protected by approved self-closing fire doors, or such area shall be equipped with automatic fire extinguishing systems. Hazardous areas shall include, but shall not be limited to the following:

(1) Boiler and heater rooms
(2) Laundries
(3) Repair shops
(4) Rooms or spaces used for storage of combustible supplies and equipment in quantities deemed hazardous by the authority having jurisdiction

CHAPTER 32 • New

CHAPTER 33 • Existing

The list that appears in 32/33.3.3.2.2 is not all-inclusive. Hazardous areas are those that contain materials that, because of their basic nature or the quantity of combustible materials involved, represent a significantly higher hazard than would otherwise be typical

of the contents of a residential board and care facility. Because sprinklers are mandated for new board and care facilities by 32.3.3.5.1, a 1-hour separation will seldom be needed between the hazardous contents area room and the remainder of a new facility.

32.3.3.3 Interior Finish.

32.3.3.3.1 Interior finish shall be in accordance with Section 10.2.

32.3.3.3.2 Interior Wall and Ceiling Finish. Interior wall and ceiling finish materials complying with 10.2.3 shall be permitted as follows:

(1) Exit enclosures—Class A
(2) Lobbies and corridors—Class A or Class B
(3) Other spaces—Class A or Class B

32.3.3.3.3 Interior Floor Finish. Interior floor finish in accordance with 10.2.7 shall be Class I or Class II in corridors and exits.

32.3.3.4 Detection, Alarm, and Communications Systems.

32.3.3.4.1 General. A fire alarm system in accordance with Section 9.6 shall be provided.

32.3.3.4.2 Initiation. The required fire alarm system shall be initiated by the following means:

(1) Manual means in accordance with 9.6.2

(2) A manual fire alarm box located at a convenient central control point under continuous supervision of responsible employees
(3) The automatic sprinkler system

(4) Any required detection system

33.3.3.3 Interior Finish. Interior wall and ceiling finish shall be Class A or Class B in accordance with Section 10.2. Interior floor finish in accordance with 10.2.7 shall be Class I or Class II in corridors and exits.

Exception: Previously installed floor coverings, subject to the approval of the authority having jurisdiction.

33.3.3.4 Detection, Alarm, and Communications Systems.

33.3.3.4.1 General. A fire alarm system in accordance with Section 9.6 shall be provided.

Exception: Where each sleeping room has exterior exit access in accordance with 7.5.3 and the building is not more than three stories in height.

33.3.3.4.2 Initiation. The required fire alarm system shall be initiated by the following means:

(1) Manual means in accordance with 9.6.2

Exception: A manual means, as specified in 9.6.2, in excess of the manual fire alarm box at a constantly attended location per 33.3.3.4.2(2) below shall not be required where there are other effective means (such as a complete automatic sprinkler or automatic detection system) for notification of fire as required.

(2) A manual fire alarm box located at a convenient central control point under continuous supervision of responsible employees
(3) Any automatic sprinkler system

Exception: Automatic sprinkler systems that are not required by another section of this Code shall not be required to initiate the fire alarm system.

(4) Any required detection system

Exception: Sleeping room smoke alarms shall not be required to initiate the building fire alarm system.

33.3.3.4.3 (Reserved.)

32.3.3.4.3 Annunciator Panel. An annunciator panel connected with the fire alarm system shall be provided. The location of the annunciator shall be approved by the authority having jurisdiction.

Exception: Buildings not more than two stories in height and with not more than 50 sleeping rooms.

32.3.3.4.4 Occupant Notification. Occupant notification shall be provided automatically, without delay, in accordance with 9.6.3.

33.3.3.4.4 Occupant Notification. Occupant notification shall be provided automatically, without delay, by internal audible alarm in accordance with 9.6.3.

32.3.3.4.5 High-rise buildings shall be provided with an approved means of voice communication in accordance with 9.6.3.

33.3.3.4.5 (Reserved.)

Exception: Buildings equipped with a public address system.

32.3.3.4.6* Fire Department Notification. In case of a fire, provisions shall be made for the immediate notification of the public fire department by either telephone or other means. Where there is no public fire department, this notification shall be made to the private fire brigade.

33.3.3.4.6* Fire Department Notification. In case of a fire, provisions shall be made for the immediate notification of the public fire department by either telephone or other means. Where there is no public fire department, this notification shall be made to the private fire brigade.

A.32.3.3.4.6 See A.28.3.4.3.5.

A.33.3.3.4.6 See A.29.3.4.3.2.

32.3.3.4.7 Smoke Alarms. Each sleeping room shall be provided with an approved smoke alarm in accordance with 9.6.2.10 that is powered from the building electrical system.

33.3.3.4.7 Smoke Alarms. Each sleeping room shall be provided with an approved smoke alarm in accordance with 9.6.2.10 that is powered from the building electrical system.

Exception No. 1: Existing battery-powered smoke alarms, rather than building electrical service–powered smoke alarms, shall be accepted where, in the opinion of the authority having jurisdiction, the facility has demonstrated that testing, maintenance, and battery replacement programs ensure the reliability of power to the smoke alarms.

Exception No. 2: Facilities having an existing corridor smoke detection system in accordance with Section 9.6 that is connected to the building fire alarm system.

32.3.3.4.8 Smoke Detection Systems. All living areas as defined in 3.3.119 and corridors shall be provided with smoke detectors in accordance with NFPA 72, *National Fire Alarm Code*, that are arranged to initiate an alarm that is audible in all sleeping areas.

33.3.3.4.8 Smoke Detection Systems. All living areas as defined in 3.3.119 and corridors shall be provided with smoke detectors in accordance with NFPA 72, *National Fire Alarm Code*, that are arranged to initiate an alarm that is audible in all sleeping areas.

Exception No. 1: Detectors shall not be required in living areas in facilities protected throughout by an approved, supervised automatic sprinkler system in accordance with 32.3.3.5.

Exception No. 1: Detectors shall not be required in living areas and kitchens in facilities protected throughout by an approved automatic sprinkler system installed in accordance with 33.3.3.5.

Exception No. 2:   Unenclosed corridors, passageways, balconies, colonnades, or other arrangements with one or more sides along the long dimension fully or extensively open to the exterior at all times.

Exception No. 2:   Unenclosed corridors, passageways, balconies, colonnades, or other arrangements with one or more sides along the long dimension fully or extensively open to the exterior at all times.

Subparagraph 32/33.3.3.4.2(2) requires that, in addition to the normal distribution of manual fire alarm boxes (see 9.6.2), locations such as that of the telephone operator must also be equipped with a manual fire alarm box. The intent is that a manual fire alarm box is to be available at the location where residents/staff phone in an emergency.

Sleeping room smoke alarms are exempt from activating the building fire-protective signaling system. The smoke alarms installed in the sleeping rooms are usually single-station or multiple-station smoke alarms and are not part of a required automatic detection system. Therefore, such smoke alarms are automatically exempted and are intended to notify the occupants of the room of a smoke condition. The exception to 33.3.3.4.2(4) emphasizes this intention. The *Code* does not prohibit room smoke alarms from activating the system; however, such activation should be discouraged to prevent numerous nuisance alarms, which could pose a particular problem in large board and care facilities. Because the purpose of the sleeping room smoke alarms is to warn the occupants of an individual room, the notification of the management and other occupants is the responsibility of the occupant. As such, manual alarm initiation should be emphasized in the required training for residents. See 32/33.7.2.

The location of audible alarm–notification devices in residential board and care facilities affects their audibility. In most new construction, corridor walls are of such character (soundproof) that a sounding device would be needed in each room to meet the performance criterion for alarm audibility throughout the building. If sounding devices are used only in the corridor, they might have to operate at dangerous sound levels to awaken residents in their rooms.

Subparagraph 32/33.3.3.4.6 does not require a direct fire alarm connection to the fire department, although such connection is the preferable method of providing fire department notification. If a telephone is provided, the telephone must be equipped for direct outside dial without going through a switchboard; the telephone is not permitted to be a pay phone.

The purpose of placing smoke alarms in each sleeping room, as required by 32/33.3.3.4.7, is to alert the occupants of a room to the presence of smoke within that room. The alarms are not normally tied to the building fire-protective signaling system as previously discussed. When an occupant leaves a room, the door automatically closes behind the occupant, and the occupant is expected to pull a manual fire alarm box. If the occupant fails to sound the alarm manually, compensation is provided by corridor smoke detectors or by automatic sprinklers. See 32/33.3.3.4.8 and 32/33.3.3.5.

In existing board and care facilities, Exception No. 1 to 33.3.3.4.7 applies only to existing battery-powered alarms and not to newly installed alarms in existing facilities. Battery-powered alarms are to be permitted only if they already exist and the facility can document that they are properly maintained and tested to ensure their reliability.

Exception No. 2 to 33.3.3.4.7 recognizes that corridor smoke detection systems, rather than bedroom smoke alarms, were earlier *Code* requirements. Note that the installation of a new corridor smoke detection system does not waive the need for single-station smoke alarms in each room. However, if a building already has a corridor smoke detection system, single-station smoke alarms in bedrooms are not required.

Subparagraph 32/33.3.3.4.8 requires a system of smoke detectors in the living areas of any facility that is not fully sprinklered. Note that Exception No. 1 to 32/33.3.3.4.8 does not exempt the requirement of 32/33.3.3.4.7 for the provision of single-station smoke alarms in each sleeping room even when automatic sprinklers are installed. The *Code* is not equating sprinklers with smoke detectors but establishes that a fully sprinklered building is an adequate alternative to smoke detection in common spaces. Because 32.3.3.5.1 requires almost all new large board and care facilities to be sprinklered, smoke detectors in common living spaces will not typically be required in new construction. If the facility uses exterior access corridors in the motel style, smoke detection is not required in the exterior corridors in accordance with Exception No. 2 to 32/33.3.3.4.8.

CHAPTER 32 • New	CHAPTER 33 • Existing

32.3.3.5 Extinguishment Requirements.

32.3.3.5.1* All buildings shall be protected throughout by an approved automatic sprinkler system in accordance with Section 9.7. Quick-response or residential sprinklers shall be provided throughout.

Exception No. 1: In buildings not more than four stories in height, a sprinkler system complying with NFPA 13R, Standard for the Installation of Sprinkler Systems in Residential Occupancies up to and Including Four Stories in Height, shall be permitted.

Exception No. 2: Automatic sprinklers shall not be required in small clothes closets where the smallest dimension does not exceed 3 ft (0.9 m), the area does not exceed 24 ft² (2.2 m²), and the walls and ceiling are finished with noncombustible or limited-combustible materials.

Exception No. 3: Standard response sprinklers shall be permitted for use in hazardous areas in accordance with 32.3.3.2.

A.32.3.3.5.1 It is intended that this requirement apply to existing small facilities that are converted to large facilities.

Chapter 32 permits the use of NFPA 13D, *Standard for the Installation of Sprinkler Systems in One- and Two-Family Dwellings and Manufactured Homes,* and NFPA 13R, *Standard for the Installation of Sprinkler Systems in Residential Occupancies up to and Including Four Stories in Height,* outside of their scopes. This permission is based on a review of the occupancy and a recognition that the fires in board and care facilities are similar to those of other residential occupancies and that the level of protection is appropriate. In some circumstances, such as those for impractical evacuation capabilities, the requirements of NFPA 13D and NFPA 13R have been supplemented with requirements for additional water supplies to compensate for the special needs of the board and care occupancy.

32.3.3.5.2 (Reserved.)

33.3.3.5 Extinguishment Requirements.

33.3.3.5.1* Automatic Extinguishment Systems. Where an automatic sprinkler system is installed either for total or partial building coverage, the system shall be installed in accordance with Section 9.7.

Exception No. 1: In buildings not more than four stories in height, a sprinkler system complying with NFPA 13R, Standard for the Installation of Sprinkler Systems in Residential Occupancies up to and Including Four Stories in Height, shall be permitted.

Exception No. 2: Automatic sprinklers shall not be required in closets not exceeding 24 ft² (2.2 m²) and in bathrooms not exceeding 55 ft² (5.1 m²), provided that such spaces are finished with lath and plaster or materials with a 15-minute thermal barrier.

Exception No. 3: Initiation of the fire alarm system shall not be required for existing installations in accordance with 33.3.3.5.4.

A.33.3.3.5.1 It is intended that this requirement apply to existing small facilities that are converted to large facilities.

Chapter 33 permits the use of NFPA 13D, *Standard for the Installation of Sprinkler Systems in One- and Two-Family Dwellings and Manufactured Homes,* and NFPA 13R, *Standard for the Installation of Sprinkler Systems in Residential Occupancies up to and Including Four Stories in Height,* outside of their scopes. This permission is based on a review of the occupancy and a recognition that the fires in board and care facilities are similar to those of other residential occupancies and that the level of protection is appropriate. In some circumstances, such as those for impractical evacuation capabilities, the requirements of NFPA 13D and NFPA 13R have been supplemented with requirements for additional water supplies to compensate for the special needs of the board and care occupancy.

33.3.3.5.2 All high-rise buildings shall be protected throughout by an approved, supervised automatic sprinkler system in accordance with Section 9.7. Such systems shall initiate the fire alarm system in accordance with Section 9.6.

Exception: Automatic sprinklers shall not be required in small clothes closets where the smallest dimension does not exceed 3 ft (0.9 m), the area does not exceed 24 ft² (2.2 m²), and the walls and ceiling are finished with noncombustible or limited-combustible materials.

32.3.3.5.3 Automatic sprinkler systems shall be supervised in accordance with Section 9.7.

32.3.3.5.4 (Reserved.)

32.3.3.5.5 Portable Fire Extinguishers. Portable fire extinguishers in accordance with 9.7.4.1 shall be provided near hazardous areas.

33.3.3.5.3 Automatic sprinkler systems shall be supervised in accordance with Section 9.7. Waterflow alarms shall not be required to be transmitted off-site.

33.3.3.5.4 Sprinkler piping serving not more than six sprinklers for any isolated hazardous area in accordance with 9.7.1.2 shall be permitted. In new installations where more than two sprinklers are installed in a single area, waterflow detection shall be provided to initiate the fire alarm system required by 33.3.3.4.1.

33.3.3.5.5 Portable Fire Extinguishers. Portable fire extinguishers in accordance with 9.7.4.1 shall be provided near hazardous areas.

Automatic sprinklers are required in all new large residential board and care facilities, and there are incentives for installing sprinklers in existing facilities. Exception No. 1 to 32/33.3.3.5.1 applies to sprinkler systems installed in accordance with NFPA 13R, *Standard for the Installation of Sprinkler Systems in Residential Occupancies up to and Including Four Stories in Height.*

Exception No. 2 to 32/33.3.3.5.1 applies to sprinkler systems installed in accordance with NFPA 13R and NFPA 13, *Standard for the Installation of Sprinkler Systems.* The requirement for wall and ceiling surfaces to provide a 15-minute thermal barrier includes the wall and ceiling sections behind prefabricated tub and shower enclosures. This provision helps to confine a fire that originates in a bathroom.

Subparagraph 32.3.3.5.1 requires that new large

board and care facilities and the buildings that house such facilities are to be sprinklered. The automatic sprinkler system is required to use quick-response or residential sprinklers. This requirement recognizes the ability of quick-response and residential sprinklers to maintain tenability in the room of origin during most fire scenarios.

Standard sprinklers are permitted to be installed in hazardous areas, because such areas are not occupied by sleeping residents.

Subparagraph 33.3.3.5.1 does not contain the same requirement for quick-response or residential sprinklers. However, recent changes to NFPA 13R and NFPA 13 require quick-response sprinklers. Such sprinklers would be required if a sprinkler system is installed in the areas of a board and care facility designated as light hazard by these standards.

32.3.3.6 Corridors and Separation of Sleeping Rooms.

32.3.3.6.1 Access shall be provided from every resident use area to not less than one means of egress that is separated from all sleeping rooms by walls complying with 32.3.3.6.3 through 32.3.3.6.6.

33.3.3.6 Corridors and Separation of Sleeping Rooms.

33.3.3.6.1 Access shall be provided from every resident use area to not less than one means of egress that is separated from all other rooms or spaces by walls complying with 33.3.3.6.3 through 33.3.3.6.6.

Exception No. 1: Rooms or spaces, other than sleeping rooms, protected throughout by an approved automatic sprinkler system in accordance with 33.3.3.5.

Exception No. 2: Prompt evacuation capability facilities in buildings not over two stories in height where not less than one required means of egress from each sleeping room provides a path of travel to the outside without traversing any corridor or other spaces exposed to unprotected vertical openings, living areas, and kitchens.

Exception No. 3: Rooms or spaces, other than sleeping rooms, provided with a smoke detection and alarm system connected to activate the building evacuation alarm. Furnishings, finishes, and furniture, in combination with all other combustibles within the spaces, shall be of minimum quantity and arranged so that a fully developed fire is unlikely to occur.

32.3.3.6.2 Sleeping rooms shall be separated from corridors, living areas, and kitchens by walls complying with 32.3.3.6.3 through 32.3.3.6.6.

33.3.3.6.2 Sleeping rooms shall be separated from corridors, living areas, and kitchens by walls complying with 33.3.3.6.3 through 33.3.3.6.6.

32.3.3.6.3 Walls required by 32.3.3.6.1 or 32.3.3.6.2 shall have a fire resistance rating of not less than ½ hour.

33.3.3.6.3 Walls required by 33.3.3.6.1 or 33.3.3.6.2 shall have a fire resistance rating of not less than ½ hour.

Exception: In conversions (see 32.1.1.3), no fire resistance rating shall be required, but the wall shall be a smoke partition in accordance with 8.2.4. The provisions of 8.2.4.3.5 shall not apply.

Exception No. 1: In buildings protected throughout by an approved automatic sprinkler system in accordance with 33.3.3.5, walls shall be smoke partitions in accordance with 8.2.4. The provisions of 8.2.4.3.5 shall not apply.

Exception No. 2: In buildings not more than two stories in height that are classified as prompt evacuation capability and that house not more than 30 residents, walls shall be smoke partitions in accordance with 8.2.4. The provisions of 8.2.4.3.5 shall not apply.

32.3.3.6.4 Doors in walls required by 32.3.3.6.1 or 32.3.3.6.2 shall have a fire protection rating of not less than 20 minutes.

33.3.3.6.4 Doors in walls required by 33.3.3.6.1 or 33.3.3.6.2 shall have a fire protection rating of not less than 20 minutes.

Exception: Doors in renovations and conversions (see 32.1.1.3) that are nonrated doors that resist the passage of smoke shall be permitted to continue to be used.

Exception No. 1: Solid-bonded wood core doors of not less than 1¾ in. (4.4 cm) thickness shall be permitted to continue to be used.

Exception No. 2: In buildings protected throughout by an approved automatic sprinkler system in accordance with 33.3.3.5, doors that are nonrated shall be permitted to continue to be used.

Exception No. 3: Where automatic sprinkler protection is provided in the corridor in accordance with 31.3.5.2 through 31.3.5.4, doors shall not be required to have a fire protection rating but shall be in accordance with 8.2.4.3. The provisions of 8.2.4.3.5 shall not apply. Doors shall be equipped with latches for keeping the doors tightly closed.

32.3.3.6.5 Walls and doors required by 32.3.3.6.1 and 32.3.3.6.2 shall be constructed as smoke partitions in accordance with 8.2.4. The provisions of 8.2.4.3.5 shall not apply. No louvers, transfer grilles, operable transoms, or other air passages shall penetrate such walls or doors, except properly installed heating and utility installations.

33.3.3.6.5 Walls and doors required by 33.3.3.6.1 and 33.3.3.6.2 shall be constructed as smoke partitions in accordance with 8.2.4. The provisions of 8.2.4.3.5 shall not apply. No louvers, transfer grilles, operable transoms, or other air passages shall penetrate such walls or doors, except properly installed heating and utility installations.

CHAPTER 32 • New   **CHAPTER 33 • Existing**

32.3.3.6.6 Doors to hazardous areas, vertical openings, exits, and exit passageways shall be self-closing or automatic-closing.

33.3.3.6.6 Doors in walls required by 33.3.3.6.1 and 33.3.3.6.2 shall be self-closing or automatic-closing in accordance with 7.2.1.8. Doors in walls separating sleeping rooms from corridors shall be automatic-closing in accordance with 7.2.1.8.

Exception No. 1:   Doors to sleeping rooms that have occupant-control locks such that access is normally restricted to the occupants or staff personnel shall be permitted to be self-closing.

Exception No. 2:   In buildings protected throughout by an approved automatic sprinkler system installed in accordance with 33.3.3.5, doors, other than doors to hazardous areas, vertical openings, and exit enclosures, shall not be required to be self-closing or automatic-closing.

Subparagraph 32/33.3.3.6.1 requires the provision of access to at least one exit that is separate from sleeping rooms. For existing board and care facilities, 33.3.3.6.1 contains three exceptions that address special circumstances for an access to an exit that passes through a sitting room, television room, living room, or other common use space. Exhibit 32/33.10 illustrates arrangements requiring egress travel through furnished day rooms that would be prohibited in existing board and care facilities, unless the space is sprinklered or provided with a combination of a smoke detection and alarm system and the combustibility of furnishings is controlled. See 33.3.3.6.1 and its exceptions.

Subparagraph 32/33.3.3.6.3 requires sleeping rooms in new large board and care facilities to be separated from corridors by construction having a fire resistance rating of at least ½ hour. In buildings that are converted from another occupancy to a board and care facility, sleeping rooms must be separated from corridors by smoke partitions in accordance with 8.2.4; however, the provision for self-closing doors in 8.2.4.3.5 does not apply.

In existing buildings, the corridor walls are permitted to be smoke partitions if the building is protected throughout by an automatic sprinkler system (Exception No. 1 to 33.3.3.6.3), or if the facility is moderately sized with prompt evacuation capability (Exception No. 2 to 33.3.3.6.3).

The intent of Exception No. 1 to 33.3.3.6.4 is to minimize the impact of converting a health care facil-

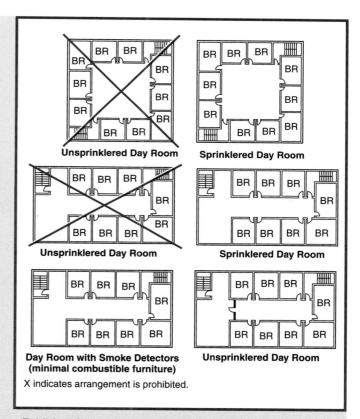

Unsprinklered Day Room   Sprinklered Day Room

Unsprinklered Day Room   Sprinklered Day Room

Day Room with Smoke Detectors (minimal combustible furniture)   Unsprinklered Day Room

X indicates arrangement is prohibited.

Exhibit 32/33.10 *Alternate egress arrangements.*

ity or hotel to a board and care facility by permitting existing doors to remain in use under a variety of conditions.

CHAPTER 32 • New

CHAPTER 33 • Existing

Existing sleeping room doors are required to be automatic-closing in accordance with 33.3.3.6.6 if the building is not sprinklered. In nonsprinklered facilities in which the residents control the privacy lock on their own sleeping room doors, a self-closer (such

as spring hinges or a hydraulic door check) is acceptable. Such a device is permitted because, in practice, such doors are usually kept closed. Therefore, the likelihood that the door will be chocked or held open is minimal.

32.3.3.7 Subdivision of Building Spaces. (Reserved.)

33.3.3.7 Subdivision of Building Spaces. Every sleeping room floor shall be divided into not less than two smoke compartments of approximately the same size, with smoke barriers in accordance with Section 8.3. Smoke dampers shall not be required.

Additional smoke barriers shall be provided such that the travel distance from a sleeping room corridor door to a smoke barrier shall not exceed 150 ft (45 m).

Exception No. 1: Buildings protected throughout by an approved automatic sprinkler system installed in accordance with 33.3.3.5.

Exception No. 2: Where each sleeping room is provided with exterior ways of exit access arranged in accordance with 7.5.3.

Exception No. 3: Smoke barriers shall not be required where the aggregate corridor length on each floor is not more than 150 ft (45 m).

Smoke barriers are not required in new residential board and care facilities due to the mandatory sprinkler provisions of 32.3.3.5.1.

The smoke barrier required by 33.3.3.7 for some existing facilities provides for horizontal movement of occupants and limits the number of rooms and, therefore, the number of occupants exposed to a single fire that might block a corridor. Because no fire rating is required for the barrier, and because smoke dampers are not required, the provision of smoke barriers is not overly burdensome. The exception for buildings equipped with automatic sprinklers reflects the excellent life loss record associated with sprinkler protection.

A horizontal exit is permitted to be used to comply with 33.3.3.7 and, therefore, might serve more than one function. In addition, the smoke compartment is permitted to be considered a point of safety under the following conditions:

(1) The smoke barrier has at least a ½-hour fire-resistance rating.
(2) Protection is provided by an automatic sprinkler system throughout the building.
(3) The smoke compartment has access to an exit that does not require return to the fire area. See the definition of *point of safety* in 3.3.151.

32.3.4 Special Provisions.

(Reserved.)

33.3.4 Special Provisions.

(Reserved.)

32.3.5 (Reserved.)

33.3.5 (Reserved.)

32.3.6 Building Services.

32.3.6.1 Utilities. Utilities shall comply with the provisions of Section 9.1.

32.3.6.2 Heating, Ventilating, and Air Conditioning.

32.3.6.2.1 Heating, ventilating, and air conditioning equipment shall comply with the provisions of Section 9.2.

32.3.6.2.2 No stove or combustion heater shall be located to block escape in case of fire caused by the malfunction of the stove or heater.

32.3.6.2.3 Unvented fuel-fired heaters shall not be used in any board and care occupancy.

32.3.6.3 Elevators, Dumbwaiters, and Vertical Conveyors.

32.3.6.3.1 Elevators, dumbwaiters, and vertical conveyors shall comply with the provisions of Section 9.4.

32.3.6.3.2* In high-rise buildings, one elevator shall be provided with a protected power supply and shall be available for use by the fire department in case of emergency.

A.32.3.6.3.2 See A.28.5.3.

32.3.6.4 Rubbish Chutes, Incinerators, and Laundry Chutes. Rubbish chutes, incinerators, and laundry chutes shall comply with the provisions of Section 9.5.

Section 32.4* Suitability of an Apartment Building to House a Board and Care Occupancy

A.32.4 Board and care occupancies in apartment buildings will usually be small facilities housing 16 or fewer residents. It is intended that the board and care occupancy conform to the requirements of Section 32.2 for small board and care facilities. In the unusual case where an apartment houses a large board and care facility, it would be reasonable for the authority having jurisdiction, using 4.6.1, to apply the provisions of Section 32.3 to the apartment. In addition, the apartment building in which the facility is housed needs to comply with the requirements for apartment buildings in Chapters 30 and 31 and the additional criteria presented in Section 32.4.

33.3.6 Building Services.

33.3.6.1 Utilities. Utilities shall comply with the provisions of Section 9.1.

33.3.6.2 Heating, Ventilating, and Air Conditioning.

33.3.6.2.1 Heating, ventilating, and air conditioning equipment shall comply with the provisions of Section 9.2.

33.3.6.2.2 No stove or combustion heater shall be located to block escape in case of fire caused by the malfunction of the stove or heater.

33.3.6.2.3 Unvented fuel-fired heaters shall not be used in any board and care occupancy.

33.3.6.3 Elevators, Dumbwaiters, and Vertical Conveyors. Elevators, dumbwaiters, and vertical conveyors shall comply with the provisions of Section 9.4.

33.3.6.4 Rubbish Chutes, Incinerators, and Laundry Chutes. Rubbish chutes, incinerators, and laundry chutes shall comply with the provisions of Section 9.5.

Section 33.4* Suitability of an Apartment Building to House a Board and Care Occupancy

A.33.4 Board and care occupancies in apartment buildings will usually be small facilities housing 16 or fewer residents. It is intended that the board and care occupancy conform to the requirements of Section 33.2 for small board and care facilities. In the unusual case where an apartment houses a large board and care facility, it would be reasonable for the authority having jurisdiction, using 6.1.14, to apply the provisions of Section 33.3 to the apartment. In addition, the apartment building in which the facility is housed needs to comply with the requirements for apartment buildings in Chapters 30 and 31 and the additional criteria presented in Section 33.4.

CHAPTER 32 • New

CHAPTER 33 • Existing

A board and care facility located within an apartment building is usually a small facility housing 16 or fewer residents. It is intended that the board and care facility within the apartment building conform to the requirements of Section 32/33.2 for small board and care facilities. In the unusual case where an apartment building houses a large board and care facility,

it is reasonable for the authority having jurisdiction, in accordance with Section 1.5, to apply the provisions of Section 32/33.3 to the apartment unit. In addition, the apartment building in which the facility is housed is required to comply with the requirements for apartment buildings in Chapter 30/31 and the additional criteria provided in Section 32/33.4.

32.4.1 General.

32.4.1.1 Scope. Section 32.4 applies to apartment buildings that have one or more individual apartments used as a board and care occupancy. Section 32.4 determines the suitability of such buildings to house a residential board and care facility. The suitability of such buildings for apartments not used for board and care occupancies is covered in Chapter 30.

Exception: If a new board and care occupancy is created in an existing apartment building, the suitability of such buildings for apartments not used for board and care occupancies shall be covered by Chapter 31.

32.4.1.2 Requirements for individual apartments used as residential board and care occupancies shall be as specified in Section 32.2. Egress from the apartment into the common building corridor shall be considered acceptable egress from the board and care facility.

32.4.1.3 Requirements Based on Evacuation Capability.

32.4.1.3.1 Apartment buildings housing board and care facilities shall comply with the requirements of Section 32.4.

Exception:*   Facilities where the authority having jurisdiction has determined that equivalent safety for housing a residential board and care facility is provided in accordance with Section 1.5.

A.32.4.1.3.1 Exception In determining equivalency for conversions, modernizations, renovations, or unusual design concepts, the authority having jurisdiction might permit evaluations based on NFPA 101A, *Guide on Alternative Approaches to Life Safety,* Chapter 6.

32.4.1.3.2 All facilities shall meet the requirements of Chapter 30 and the additional requirements of Section 32.4.

32.4.1.4 Minimum Construction Requirements. In addition to the requirements of Chapter 30, apartment buildings housing residential board and care facilities for groups classified as prompt or slow evacuation capability shall meet the

33.4.1 General.

33.4.1.1 Scope. Section 33.4 applies to apartment buildings that have one or more individual apartments used as a board and care occupancy. Section 33.4 determines the suitability of such buildings to house a residential board and care facility. The suitability of such buildings for apartments not used for board and care occupancies is covered in Chapter 31.

33.4.1.2 Requirements for individual apartments used as residential board and care occupancies shall be as specified in Section 33.2. Egress from the apartment into the common building corridor shall be considered acceptable egress from the board and care facility.

33.4.1.3 Requirements Based on Evacuation Capability.

33.4.1.3.1 Apartment buildings housing board and care facilities shall comply with the requirements of Section 33.4.

Exception:*   Facilities where the authority having jurisdiction has determined that equivalent safety for housing a residential board and care facility is provided in accordance with Section 1.5.

A.33.4.1.3.1 Exception In determining equivalency for existing buildings, conversions, modernizations, renovations, or unusual design concepts, the authority having jurisdiction might permit evaluations based on NFPA 101A, *Guide on Alternative Approaches to Life Safety,* Chapter 6.

33.4.1.3.2 All facilities shall meet the requirements of Chapter 31 and the additional requirements of Section 33.4.

33.4.1.4 Minimum Construction Requirements. In addition to the requirements of Chapter 31, apartment buildings housing residential board and care facilities for groups classified as prompt or slow evacuation capability shall meet the

| **CHAPTER 32 • New** | **CHAPTER 33 • Existing** |

construction requirements of 32.3.1.3, and those for groups classified as impractical evacuation capability shall meet the construction requirements of 18.1.6. In applying the construction requirements, the height shall be determined by the height of the residential board and care facility measured above the primary level of exit discharge.

Exception: If the new board and care occupancy is created in an existing apartment building, the construction requirements of 33.3.1.3 shall apply for prompt or slow evacuation capability, and the construction requirements of 19.1.6 shall apply for impractical evacuation capability.

32.4.2 Means of Egress.

The requirements of Section 30.2 shall apply only to the parts of means of egress serving the apartment(s) used as a residential board and care occupancy.

Exception: If the new board and care occupancy is created in an existing apartment building, the requirements of Section 31.2 shall apply to the parts of the means of egress serving the apartment(s) used as a residential board and care occupancy.

32.4.3 Protection.

32.4.3.1 Interior Finish. The requirements of 30.3.3 shall apply only to the parts of means of egress serving the apartment(s) used as a residential board and care occupancy.

Exception: If the new board and care occupancy is created in an existing apartment building, the requirements of 31.3.3 shall apply to the parts of the means of egress serving the apartment(s) used as a residential board and care occupancy.

32.4.3.2 Construction of Corridor Walls. The requirements of 30.3.6 shall apply only to corridors serving the residential board and care facility, including that portion of the corridor wall separating the residential board and care facility from the common corridor.

Exception: If the new board and care occupancy is created in an existing apartment building, the requirements of 31.3.6 shall apply to the corridor serving the residential board and care facility.

32.4.3.3 Subdivision of Building Spaces. (Reserved.)

construction requirements of 33.3.1.3, and those for groups classified as impractical evacuation capability shall meet the construction requirements of 19.1.6. In applying the construction requirements, the height shall be determined by the height of the residential board and care facility measured above the primary level of exit discharge.

33.4.2 Means of Egress.

The requirements of Section 31.2 shall apply only to the parts of means of egress serving the apartment(s) used as a residential board and care occupancy.

33.4.3 Protection.

33.4.3.1 Interior Finish. The requirements of 31.3.3 shall apply only to the parts of means of egress serving the apartment(s) used as a residential board and care occupancy.

33.4.3.2 Construction of Corridor Walls. The requirements of 31.3.6 shall apply only to corridors serving the residential board and care facility, including that portion of the corridor wall separating the residential board and care facility from the common corridor.

33.4.3.3 Subdivision of Building Spaces. The requirements of 31.3.7 shall apply to those stories with an apartment(s) used as a residential board and care occupancy.

CHAPTER 32 • New

CHAPTER 33 • Existing

Section 32.5 Reserved

Section 33.5 Reserved

Section 32.6 Reserved

Section 33.6 Reserved

Section 32.7 Operating Features

32.7.1 Emergency Plan.

The administration of every residential board and care facility shall have, in effect and available to all supervisory personnel, written copies of a plan for protecting all persons in the event of fire, for keeping persons in place, for evacuating persons to areas of refuge, and for evacuating persons from the building when necessary. The plan shall include special staff response, including the fire protection procedures needed to ensure the safety of any resident, and shall be amended or revised whenever any resident with unusual needs is admitted to the home. All employees shall be periodically instructed and kept informed with respect to their duties and responsibilities under the plan. Such instruction shall be reviewed by the staff not less than every 2 months. A copy of the plan shall be readily available at all times within the facility.

32.7.2 Resident Training.

All residents participating in the emergency plan shall be trained in the proper actions to be taken in the event of fire. This training shall include actions to be taken if the primary escape route is blocked. If the resident is given rehabilitation or habilitation training, training in fire prevention and the actions to be taken in the event of a fire shall be a part of the training program. Residents shall be trained to assist each other in case of fire to the extent that their physical and mental abilities permit them to do so without additional personal risk.

32.7.3 Emergency Egress and Relocation Drills.

Emergency egress and relocation drills shall be conducted not less than six times per year on a bimonthly basis, with not less than two drills conducted during the night when residents are sleeping. The drills shall be permitted to be announced in advance to the residents. The drills shall involve the actual evacuation of all residents to an assembly point as specified in the emergency plan and shall provide residents with experience in egressing through all exits and

Section 33.7 Operating Features

33.7.1 Emergency Plan.

The administration of every residential board and care facility shall have, in effect and available to all supervisory personnel, written copies of a plan for protecting all persons in the event of fire, for keeping persons in place, for evacuating persons to areas of refuge, and for evacuating persons from the building when necessary. The plan shall include special staff response, including the fire protection procedures needed to ensure the safety of any resident, and shall be amended or revised whenever any resident with unusual needs is admitted to the home. All employees shall be periodically instructed and kept informed with respect to their duties and responsibilities under the plan. Such instruction shall be reviewed by the staff not less than every 2 months. A copy of the plan shall be readily available at all times within the facility.

33.7.2 Resident Training.

All residents participating in the emergency plan shall be trained in the proper actions to be taken in the event of fire. This training shall include actions to be taken if the primary escape route is blocked. If the resident is given rehabilitation or habilitation training, training in fire prevention and the actions to be taken in the event of a fire shall be a part of the training program. Residents shall be trained to assist each other in case of fire to the extent that their physical and mental abilities permit them to do so without additional personal risk.

33.7.3 Emergency Egress and Relocation Drills.

Emergency egress and relocation drills shall be conducted not less than six times per year on a bimonthly basis, with not less than two drills conducted during the night when residents are sleeping. The drills shall be permitted to be announced in advance to the residents. The drills shall involve the actual evacuation of all residents to an assembly point as specified in the emergency plan and shall provide residents with experience in egressing through all exits and

CHAPTER 32 • New

means of escape required by the *Code*. Exits and means of escape not used in any drill shall not be credited in meeting the requirements of this *Code* for board and care facilities.

Exception No. 1: Actual exiting from windows shall not be required to comply with 32.7.3; opening the window and signaling for help shall be an acceptable alternative.

Exception No. 2: If the board and care facility has an evacuation capability classification of impractical, those residents who cannot meaningfully assist in their own evacuation or who have special health problems shall not be required to actively participate in the drill. Section 18.7 shall apply in such instances.

32.7.4 Smoking.

32.7.4.1* Smoking regulations shall be adopted by the administration of board and care occupancies.

A.32.7.4.1 Smoking regulations should include the following.

(a) Smoking should be prohibited in any room, compartment or area where flammable or combustible liquids, combustible gases, or oxygen is used or stored and in any other hazardous location. Such areas should be posted with signs that read NO SMOKING or the international symbol for no smoking. In residential board and care facilities where smoking is totally prohibited and signs so indicating are placed at all major entrances, secondary signs with language that prohibits smoking are not required.

(b) Smoking by residents classified as not responsible with regard to their ability to safely use and dispose of smoking materials should be prohibited. Where the resident is under direct supervision by staff or by a person approved by the administration, smoking might be permitted.

(c) Smoking materials should not be provided to residents or maintained by residents without the approval of the administration.

(d) Areas where smoking is permitted should be clearly identified.

(e) Ashtrays of noncombustible material and safe design should be provided and required to be used in all areas where smoking is permitted.

(f) Self-closing cover devices into which ashtrays can be emptied should be made available to all areas where smoking is permitted and should be required to be used.

32.7.4.2 Where smoking is permitted, noncombustible safety-type ashtrays or receptacles shall be provided in convenient locations.

CHAPTER 33 • Existing

means of escape required by this *Code*. Exits and means of escape not used in any drill shall not be credited in meeting the requirements of this *Code* for board and care facilities.

Exception No. 1: Actual exiting from windows shall not be required to comply with 33.7.3; opening the window and signaling for help shall be an acceptable alternative.

Exception No. 2: If the board and care facility has an evacuation capability classification of impractical, those residents who cannot meaningfully assist in their own evacuation or who have special health problems shall not be required to actively participate in the drill. Section 19.7 shall apply in such instances.

33.7.4 Smoking.

33.7.4.1* Smoking regulations shall be adopted by the administration of board and care occupancies.

A.33.7.4.1 Smoking regulations should include the following:

(a) Smoking should be prohibited in any room, compartment or area where flammable or combustible liquids, combustible gases, or oxygen is used or stored and in any other hazardous location. Such areas should be posted with signs that read NO SMOKING or the international symbol for no smoking. In residential board and care facilities where smoking is totally prohibited and signs so indicating are placed at all major entrances, secondary signs with language that prohibits smoking are not required.

(b) Smoking by residents classified as not responsible with regard to their ability to safely use and dispose of smoking materials should be prohibited. Where the resident is under direct supervision by staff or by a person approved by the administration, smoking might be permitted.

(c) Smoking materials should not be provided to residents or maintained by residents without the approval of the administration.

(d) Areas where smoking is permitted should be clearly identified.

(e) Ashtrays of noncombustible material and safe design should be provided and required to be used in all areas where smoking is permitted.

(f) Self-closing cover devices into which ashtrays can be emptied should be made available to all areas where smoking is permitted and should be required to be used.

33.7.4.2 Where smoking is permitted, noncombustible safety-type ashtrays or receptacles shall be provided in convenient locations.

32.7.5* Furnishings, Bedding, and Decorations.

A.32.7.5 The requirements applicable to draperies/curtains, upholstered furniture, and mattresses apply only to new draperies/curtains, new upholstered furniture, and new mattresses. The word new means unused, normally via procurement from the marketplace, either by purchase or donation, of items not previously used. Many board and care facilities allow residents to bring into the board and care home upholstered furniture items from the resident's previous residence. Such an item is not new and, thus, is not regulated. On the other hand, some of the larger board and care homes purchase contract furniture, as is done in hotels. Such new, unused furniture, whether purchased or received as a donation, is regulated by the requirements of 32.7.5.2. By federal law, mattresses manufactured and sold within the United States must pass testing per FF4-72, *Standard for the Flammability of Mattresses.*

32.7.5.1 New draperies, curtains, and other similar loosely hanging furnishings and decorations in board and care facilities shall be in accordance with the provisions of 10.3.1.

32.7.5.2* New upholstered furniture within board and care facilities shall be tested in accordance with the provisions of 10.3.2(1) and 10.3.3.

Exception: Upholstered furniture belonging to the resident in sleeping rooms, provided that a smoke alarm is installed in such rooms. Battery-powered single-station smoke alarms shall be permitted.

A.32.7.5.2 New upholstered furniture within board and care homes should be tested for rates of heat release in accordance with 10.3.3.

32.7.5.3* New mattresses within board and care facilities shall be tested in accordance with the provisions of 10.3.2(3) and 10.3.4.

Exception: Mattresses belonging to the resident in sleeping rooms, provided that a smoke alarm is installed in such rooms. Battery-powered single-station smoke alarms shall be permitted.

A.32.7.5.3 New mattresses within board and care homes should be tested for rates of heat release in accordance with 10.3.4.

The provisions of 32.7.5 extend the level of life safety provided to a residential board and care facility by further attempting to prevent room flashover. However, rather than impose these requirements retroac-

33.7.5* Furnishings, Bedding, and Decorations.

A.33.7.5 The requirements applicable to draperies/curtains, upholstered furniture, and mattresses apply only to new draperies/curtains, new upholstered furniture, and new mattresses. The word new means unused, normally via procurement from the marketplace, either by purchase or donation, of items not previously used. Many board and care facilities allow residents to bring into the board and care home upholstered furniture items from the resident's previous residence. Such an item is not new and, thus, is not regulated. On the other hand, some of the larger board and care homes purchase contract furniture, as is done in hotels. Such new, unused furniture, whether purchased or received as a donation, is regulated by the requirements of 33.7.5.2. By federal law, mattresses manufactured and sold within the United States must pass testing per FF4-72, *Standard for the Flammability of Mattresses.*

33.7.5.1 New draperies, curtains, and other similar loosely hanging furnishings and decorations in board and care facilities shall be in accordance with the provisions of 10.3.1.

33.7.5.2* New upholstered furniture within board and care facilities shall be tested in accordance with the provisions of 10.3.2(1) and 10.3.3.

Exception: Upholstered furniture belonging to the resident in sleeping rooms, provided that a smoke alarm is installed in such rooms. Battery-powered single-station smoke alarms shall be permitted.

A.33.7.5.2 New upholstered furniture within board and care homes should be tested for rates of heat release in accordance with 10.3.3.

33.7.5.3* New mattresses within board and care facilities shall be tested in accordance with the provisions of 10.3.2(3) and 10.3.4.

Exception: Mattresses belonging to the resident in sleeping rooms, provided that a smoke alarm is installed in such rooms. Battery-powered single-station smoke alarms shall be permitted.

A.33.7.5.3 New mattresses within board and care homes should be tested for rates of heat release in accordance with 10.3.4.

tively, the requirement is applicable to new upholstered furniture and mattresses. The annex note sufficiently details the meaning of the term *new* in this context. Where the annex note references testing in accordance with FF4-72, *Standard for the Flammability of Mattresses,*[5] such testing is the same as that referenced in 10.3.2(3) using 16 CFR 1632, *Standard for the Flammability of Mattresses and Mattress Pads.*[6]

Draperies must be flame resistant in accordance with 10.3.1. New upholstered furniture and mattresses must be resistant to cigarette ignition in accordance with 10.3.2. New upholstered furniture and mattresses must have limited rates of heat release in accordance with 10.3.3 and 10.3.4. See the commentary on Section 10.3.

References Cited in Commentary

1. NFPA 101A, *Guide on Alternative Approaches to Life Safety,* 1998 edition, National Fire Protection Association, Quincy, MA. (The edition of NFPA 101A that corresponds with the 2000 edition of NFPA 101®, *Life Safety Code®,* will be published in 2001.)

2. NFPA 13D, *Standard for the Installation of Sprinkler Systems in One- and Two- Family Dwellings and Manufactured Homes,* 1999 edition, National Fire Protection Association, Quincy, MA.

3. NFPA 13, *Standard for the Installation of Sprinkler Systems,* 1999 edition, National Fire Protection Association, Quincy, MA.

4. NFPA 13R, *Standard for the Installation of Sprinkler Systems in Residential Occupancies up to and Including Four Stories in Height,* 1999 edition, National Fire Protection Association, Quincy, MA.

5. FF4-72, *Standard for the Flammability of Mattresses,* U.S. Government Printing Office, Washington, DC.

6. Title 16 CFR 1632, *Standard for the Flammability of Mattresses and Mattress Pads, Code of Federal Regulations,* volume 16, Part 1632, U.S. Government Printing Office, Washington, DC, published annually.

CHAPTER 34

Reserved

In this 2000 edition, Chapter 34 has been reserved for future use.

CHAPTER 35

Reserved

In this 2000 edition, Chapter 35 has been reserved for future use.

New and Existing Mercantile Occupancies

Mercantile occupancies include stores, markets, and other rooms, buildings, or structures used for the display and sale of merchandise. This occupancy group includes the following:

(1) Supermarkets
(2) 24-hour convenience stores
(3) Department stores
(4) Hardware stores
(5) Video sales and rentals
(6) Drugstores
(7) Rental equipment centers
(8) Automobile sales showrooms
(9) Flea markets and craft centers
(10) Building materials/supplies centers
(11) Shopping centers/malls

Minor merchandising operations in buildings that house other predominant occupancies, such as a newsstand in an office building, must meet the *Code* requirements of the predominant occupancy.

The life safety provisions for mercantile occupancies are based on their characteristic of displaying merchandise for sales purposes, which introduces significant quantities of fuel in sales areas occupied by persons who are mostly unfamiliar with the building. Mercantile occupancies are also characterized by the use of layouts of merchandise displays and store fixtures that confuse the egress path. Fires in department stores, covered mall buildings, and similar mercantile occupancies that resulted in occupant fatalities were practically unheard of in the United States in the 1990s. While some serious fires have occurred in such properties, the established *Code* provisions have served the life safety needs of the occupants very well.

As marketing techniques changed to meet consumer demands—beginning in the 1960s when the first covered shopping malls were built—store design and layout have also changed. Consumers are offered choices that include everything from one-stop shopping to unique specialty stores. As the hypermarket, or big-box store, concept became popular in the early 1980s, the general public found itself shopping in warehouse-type surroundings. The *Code* provisions that apply to mercantile occupancies have recognized these new challenges to providing adequate life safety via a combination of flexible general requirements and specialized provisions such as those contained in 36/37.4.4 for covered mall buildings and 36/37.4.5 for bulk merchandising retail buildings.

The life safety measures needed for mercantile occupancies are as diverse as the types of mercantile facilities. While the nature of the actual store design—as well as the merchandise that is found in the stores—drives much of the *Code* criteria, the ongoing need to prevent the theft of merchandise also affects the protection requirements.

The features of a mercantile occupancy that determine the needed protection include the items for sale, the location of the areas occupied by the public with respect to the level of exit discharge, and the size (that is, gross area) of the facility. Paragraph 36/37.1.4.2 guides the decision process for establishing the appropriate subclassification for the mercantile occupancy.

Establishing and controlling the width of aisles that lead to exits is an important consideration. Paragraph 36/37.2.5.4, as an example, establishes minimum widths. These widths are based on the clear width to prevent boxed or loose merchandise from obstructing the egress path. In certain larger stores, minimum 5-ft (1.5-m) aisles might be the norm. Such larger aisles can accommodate shopping carts, as well as large numbers of occupants.

Automatic sprinkler protection and a manual fire alarm system complement the major features of the protection package for the larger Class A stores. One of the more popular options for notification of the occupants is through the use of a voice communication system as permitted in 36/37.3.4.3.1. Voice communication systems permit specific instructions to be given to the occupants if a fire occurs.

Subsection 36/37.4.5 was added to the *Code* in the 1997 edition and focuses on bulk merchandising retail operations. This subsection establishes criteria that meet the special needs of such stores. The typical bulk merchandising retail store includes display and storage racks that are often more than 20 ft (6.1 m)

high. Display merchandise is typically maintained at the lower levels, while the excess inventory of merchandise is stored on the upper tiers of the rack systems. In such cases, the range of materials in the occupancies is extensive and can include building materials, paint, electrical equipment, and indoor/outdoor power equipment and appliances. In some cases, the store inventory might consist of food stuffs as well as household goods. Due to the crossover nature of such occupancies—which are part warehouse and part store—36/37.4.5.3.1 establishes requirements for providing the fire protection measures needed for a warehouse and the egress measures needed for an occupancy with a large occupant load.

Section 36.1 General Requirements

36.1.1 Application.

36.1.1.1 The requirements of this chapter apply to the following:

(1) New buildings or portions thereof used as mercantile occupancies *(see 1.4.1)*
(2) Additions made to, or used as, a mercantile occupancy *(see 4.6.6 and 36.1.1.3)*
(3) Alterations, modernizations, or renovations of existing mercantile occupancies *(see 4.6.7)*
(4) Existing buildings or portions thereof upon change of occupancy to a mercantile occupancy *(see 4.6.11)*

36.1.1.2 This chapter establishes life safety requirements for all new mercantile buildings. Specific requirements for suboccupancy groups such as Class A, Class B, and Class C mercantile occupancies; covered malls; and bulk merchandising retail buildings are contained in paragraphs pertaining thereto.

36.1.1.3 Additions to existing buildings shall conform to the requirements for new construction. Existing portions of the structure are not required to be modified, provided that the new construction has not diminished the fire safety features of the facility. Existing portions shall be upgraded if the addition results in a change of mercantile subclassification. *(See 36.1.4.2.)*

36.1.1.4 When a mercantile occupancy changes from Class C to Class A or Class B, or from Class B to Class A, the provisions of this chapter shall apply.

Section 37.1 General Requirements

37.1.1 Application.

37.1.1.1 The requirements of this chapter apply to existing buildings or portions thereof currently occupied as mercantile occupancies. *(See also 36.1.1.1.)*

37.1.1.2 This chapter establishes life safety requirements for all existing mercantile buildings. Specific requirements for suboccupancy groups such as Class A, Class B, and Class C mercantile occupancies; covered malls; and bulk merchandising retail buildings are contained in paragraphs pertaining thereto.

37.1.1.3 Additions to existing buildings shall conform to the requirements for new construction. Existing portions of the structure are not required to be modified, provided that the new construction has not diminished the fire safety features of the facility. Existing portions shall be upgraded if the addition results in a change of mercantile subclassification. *(See 37.1.4.2.)*

37.1.1.4 When a mercantile occupancy changes from Class A to Class B or Class C, or from Class B to Class C, the provisions of this chapter shall apply. When a mercantile occupancy changes from Class C to Class A or Class B, or from Class B to Class A, the provisions of Chapter 36 shall apply.

CHAPTER 36 • New

CHAPTER 37 • Existing

To understand the full intent and scope of 37.1.1.1, it is necessary to review it concurrently with 1.4.1 and Section 1.5. Although a building code might permit existing buildings to be excluded from coverage under some form of a grandfather clause, the *Life Safety Code,* by virtue of its interest in safety to life, requires that existing building arrangements comply with the *Code* requirements that apply to existing buildings. The requirements applicable to existing mercantile occupancies are contained in Chapter 37.

If a building complies with an earlier edition of the *Code,* it is not grandfathered and, thereby, exempted from compliance with a more current edition that has been adopted as law in the building's jurisdiction. The committees on safety to life are especially careful to avoid adopting requirements for existing buildings that become more stringent from one edition of the *Code* to the next, unless the change is absolutely necessary to meet the level of safety to life intended. Thus, the old adage of "once in compliance, always in compliance" does not hold.

For the definitions of Class A, Class B, and Class C mercantile occupancies, see 36/37.1.4.2.1 and its associated commentary, and also see Table 36/37.1.

Table 36/37.1 Subclassification of Mercantile Occupancies

Store Class	By Height	By Aggregate Gross Area[1] ft² (m²)
A	>3 Stories[2]	>30,000 (2800)
B	≤3 Stories[2]	>3,000 (280) and ≤30,000 (2800)
C	One story only[3]	≤3,000 (280)

[1]Sections of floors not used for sales purposes are not counted in the area classification.

[2]Stories not used for sales above or below sales floor are not counted in the height classification.

[3]A mezzanine ≤ one-third the area of the floor below is permitted.

Paragraph 36/37.1.1.3 specifies that additions to existing mercantile occupancies must conform to the requirements for new construction. However, the existing portion of the occupancy generally is permitted to continue to be used without an upgrade to meet the requirements for new construction if the existing portion complies with the provisions for existing mercantile occupancies contained in Chapter 37. However, if the addition results in a change in the

mercantile occupancy subclassification (see 36/37.1.4.2)—such as a change from Class C to Class B or from Class B to Class A—the existing portion of the enlarged, overall facility, as well as the newly constructed portion, must be upgraded to meet the provisions that apply to new construction. The provisions of 36/37.1.1.3 are illustrated in the following paragraphs and in Exhibit 36/37.1.

In Exhibit 36/37.1, illustration (a), the new construction, which includes 10,000 ft² (930 m²) of additional sales area and approximately 2000 ft² (186 m²) of new storage area, is added to an existing Class B mercantile occupancy with 5000 ft² (465 m²) of existing sales area. The size and placement of the new addition neither change the Class B mercantile subclassification of the enlarged overall facility nor diminish

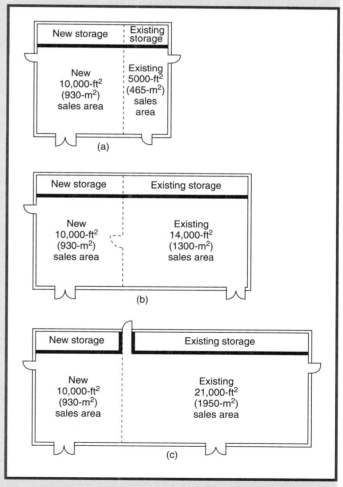

Exhibit 36/37.1 Additions to existing mercantile occupancies.

the fire safety features of the existing portion of the facility. Therefore, the addition is constructed in accordance with the requirements of Chapter 36 and the existing portion of the building is allowed to continue to be used, without upgrade, if it meets the requirements of Chapter 37. If the existing portion of the building does not meet the requirements of Chapter 37, it must be upgraded to meet those requirements.

Exhibit 36/37.1, illustration (b) depicts new construction, identical to that of illustration (a), that is added to an existing Class B mercantile occupancy with 14,000 ft² (1300 m²) of existing sales area. Although the size of the addition does not change the Class B mercantile subclassification of the overall facility, the placement of the new addition appears to have diminished the fire safety of the existing portion of the building with respect to travel distance. The broken line in illustration (b) represents what had been an exterior wall and exit door in the existing mercantile occupancy prior to construction of the addition. The door allowed occupants in the upper left portion of the existing building to reach an exit within the allowable 150-ft (45-m) travel distance specified for existing nonsprinklered mercantile occupancies in accordance with 37.2.6. Without the exit door, occu-

pants of the existing portion of the building must be able to reach an exit—one of the three doors in the perimeter of the enlarged facility—within the same 150-ft (45-m) travel distance limitation. If this is not possible, an additional exit within that distance must be constructed, or the building must be sprinklered to increase the allowable travel distance to 200 ft (60 m). Because the new construction must meet the provisions of Chapter 36, the entire building—new and existing portions—must be sprinklered in accordance with 36.3.5.1, because the building exceeds 12,000 ft² (1115 m²) in gross area [see 36.3.5.1(2)].

Exhibit 36/37.1, illustration (c), depicts new construction, identical to that of illustrations (a) and (b), that is added to an existing Class B mercantile occupancy with 21,000 ft² (1950 m²) of existing sales area. The size of the new sales area, when added to that of the existing mercantile occupancy, exceeds 30,000 ft² (2800 m²) and results in a change in mercantile subclassification from Class B to Class A [see 36/37.1.4.2.1(a)]. In accordance with the provisions of the first and last sentences of 36/37.1.1.3 and the clarification of intent offered in 36/37.1.1.4, the entire building—new and existing portions—must meet the requirements for new mercantile occupancies as detailed in Chapter 36.

36.1.2 Mixed Occupancies.

36.1.2.1 Mixed occupancies shall comply with 6.1.14.

36.1.2.2 Combined Mercantile Occupancies and Parking Structures. Walls separating parking structures from mercantile occupancies shall have a fire resistance rating of not less than 2 hours.

Exception: In enclosed parking structures that are protected throughout by an approved, supervised automatic sprinkler system in accordance with Section 9.7, or in open-air parking structures, nonrated glazing and nonrated opening protectives shall be permitted if all of the following conditions are met:

(a) The openings do not exceed 25 percent of the area of the wall in which they are located.

(b) The openings are used as the main entrance and for associated sidelight functions.

(c) The enclosed connecting mercantile building is protected throughout by an approved, supervised automatic sprinkler system in accordance with Section 9.7.

37.1.2 Mixed Occupancies.

37.1.2.1 Mixed occupancies shall comply with 6.1.14.

37.1.2.2 Combined Mercantile Occupancies and Parking Structures. Walls separating parking structures from mercantile occupancies shall have a fire resistance rating of not less than 2 hours.

Exception: In enclosed parking structures that are protected throughout by an approved automatic sprinkler system in accordance with Section 9.7, or in open-air parking structures, nonrated glazing and nonrated opening protectives shall be permitted if all of the following conditions are met:

(a) The openings do not exceed 25 percent of the area of the wall in which they are located.

(b) The openings are used as the main entrance and for associated sidelight functions.

(c) The enclosed connecting mercantile building is protected throughout by an approved automatic sprinkler system in accordance with Section 9.7.

(d) The floor elevation of the mercantile occupancy is not less than 4 in. (10.2 cm) above the floor level of the parking structure.

(e) No vehicle is able to park or drive within 10 ft (3 m) of the openings.

(f) The openings are protected by not less than a glass membrane.

(g) Any doors in the glass membrane are self-closing.

The provisions of 36/37.1.2.2 address combined mercantile occupancies and parking structures and are very similar to the requirements of 38/39.1.2.2, which address new combined business occupancies and parking structures. It is common for multistory mercantile occupancies (such as department stores and shopping mall buildings) and multistory business occupancies (such as office buildings) to be attached to multistory parking garages. Such garages provide access to the mercantile or business occupancy at multiple levels. To allow flexibility in the number and type of openings and in the degree of stringency required for opening protectives such as fire doors and fire windows, the exception to 36/37.1.2.2 outlines a set of provisions that, where applied in total, will safely allow a reduction in the 2-hour fire resistance

36.1.3 Special Definitions.

Anchor Store. See 3.3.11.

Bulk Merchandising Retail Building. See 3.3.26.

Gross Leasable Area. See 3.3.92.

Open-Air Mercantile Operation. See 3.3.138.

The term *anchor store* is defined in 3.3.11. From a merchandising viewpoint, a shopping mall developer or operator might refer to any of the major tenants that have vast expanses of floor space and instant name recognition—and that are often positioned at the ends and corners of the covered mall building—as anchor stores. However, the *Code* reserves the use of the term anchor store for those stores with means of egress that is independent from the covered mall. See Exhibit 36/37.2, which illustrates the difference between an anchor store and a store that, while large, is not an anchor store. Required egress from an an-

(d) The floor elevation of the mercantile occupancy is not less than 4 in. (10.2 cm) above the floor level of the parking structure.

(e) No vehicle is able to park or drive within 10 ft (3 m) of the openings.

(f) The openings are protected by not less than a glass membrane.

(g) Any doors in the glass membrane are self-closing.

rating required by 36/37.1.2.2. The reduction allows the use of nonrated glazing and opening protectives. This reduction permits the use of glass doors and sidelights in the barrier between the mercantile occupancy and the garage. Security in the garage is thereby increased, because customers and staff can view the parking area through the glass doors or sidelights.

Note that all eight requirements mandated by the exception to 36/37.1.2.2—the sprinkler requirement for enclosed garages in the base paragraph and the seven requirements of subparts (a) through (g)—must be met as a whole to apply the exception to the rule. Otherwise, a continuous 2-hour fire resistance–rated separation between the mercantile occupancy and the parking structure is required.

37.1.3 Special Definitions.

Anchor Store. See 3.3.11.

Bulk Merchandising Retail Building. See 3.3.26.

Gross Leasable Area. See 3.3.92.

Open-Air Mercantile Operation. See 3.3.138.

chor store is not permitted to pass through the covered mall. The store at the left of the figure satisfies this requirement and, therefore, is an anchor store. The opening between the anchor store and the covered mall is permitted, over and above the egress width satisfied by the store's required means of egress. The store at the right of the figure relies on exits from the covered mall as part of its required egress capacity and, therefore, is not an anchor store.

The term *bulk merchandising retail building* (see definition in 3.3.26) applies to the special provisions of 36/37.4.5 for mercantile occupancies characterized

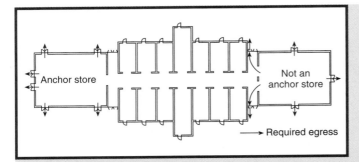

Exhibit 36/37.2 Anchor store and non-anchor store.

by warehouse-type sales areas where merchandise is stored on pallets, in solid piles, or in racks extending far above head height. The storage arrangement and quantities of combustible materials pose challenges that differ from those characteristic of department stores and supermarkets, and they warrant special protection criteria.

The terms *covered mall* (see definition in 3.3.35) and *covered mall building* (see definition in 3.3.36) are different from each other to permit certain requirements to apply to only the covered pedestrian way (the covered mall), while other requirements apply to the entire building, including all tenant spaces and common areas (the covered mall building). For example, the provisions of 36/37.4.4 require automatic sprinkler protection throughout the covered mall building but require an alarm system—and, under certain conditions, a smoke control system—only within the covered mall.

The term *gross leasable area* is defined (see 3.3.92) to provide a criterion under which an occupant load can be calculated for use in sizing the means of egress system for the covered mall only. See 7.3.1.2.

Open-air mercantile operations (see definition in 3.3.138) are addressed in 36/37.4.3.

36.1.4 Classification of Occupancy.

36.1.4.1 Mercantile occupancies shall include all buildings and structures or parts thereof with occupancy as defined in 6.1.10.

36.1.4.2 Subclassification of Occupancy.

36.1.4.2.1 Mercantile occupancies shall be subclassified as follows.

(a) *Class A.* All mercantile occupancies having an aggregate gross area of more than 30,000 ft² (2800 m²) or using more than three levels, excluding mezzanines, for sales purposes.

(b) *Class B.* All mercantile occupancies of more than 3000 ft² (280 m²) but not more than 30,000 ft² (2800 m²) aggregate gross area, or using floors above or below the street floor level for sales purposes (mezzanines permitted). *(See 36.1.4.2.3.)*

Exception: If more than three floors, excluding mezzanines, are used, the mercantile occupancy shall be Class A, regardless of area.

(c) *Class C.* All mercantile occupancies of not more than 3000 ft² (280 m²) gross area used for sales purposes on one story only, excluding mezzanines.

36.1.4.2.2 For the purpose of the classification required in 36.1.4.2.1, the aggregate gross area shall be the total gross

37.1.4 Classification of Occupancy.

37.1.4.1 Mercantile occupancies shall include all buildings and structures or parts thereof with occupancy as defined in 6.1.10.

37.1.4.2 Subclassification of Occupancy.

37.1.4.2.1 Mercantile occupancies shall be subclassified as follows.

(a) *Class A.* All mercantile occupancies having an aggregate gross area of more than 30,000 ft² (2800 m²) or using more than three levels, excluding mezzanines, for sales purposes.

(b) *Class B.* All mercantile occupancies of more than 3000 ft² (280 m²) but not more than 30,000 ft² (2800 m²) aggregate gross area, or using floors above or below the street floor level for sales purposes (mezzanines permitted). *(See 37.1.4.2.3.)*

Exception: If more than three floors, excluding mezzanines, are used, the mercantile occupancy shall be Class A, regardless of area.

(c) *Class C.* All mercantile occupancies of not more than 3000 ft² (280 m²) gross area used for sales purposes on one story only, excluding mezzanines.

37.1.4.2.2 For the purpose of the classification required in 37.1.4.2.1, the aggregate gross area shall be the total gross area of all floors used for mercantile purposes. Where a mercantile occupancy is divided into sections, regardless of fire separation, the aggregate gross area shall include the area of all sections used for sales purposes. Areas of floors not used for sales purposes, such as an area used only for storage and not open to the public, shall not be counted for the purposes of the classifications in 36.1.4.2.1(a) through (c). However, means of egress shall be provided for such nonsales areas in accordance with their occupancy as specified by other chapters of this *Code*.

36.1.4.2.3 Mezzanines shall comply with 8.2.6.

36.1.4.2.4 Where a number of tenant spaces under different management are located in the same building, the aggregate gross area (see 36.1.4.2.2) of all such tenant spaces shall be used in determining classification per 36.1.4.2.1.

Exception No. 1:   Covered mall buildings. (See 36.4.4.)

Exception No. 2:   Where individual tenant spaces are separated by fire barriers with a 2-hour fire resistance rating.

Exception No. 3:   Where tenant spaces are separated by fire barriers with a 1-hour fire resistance rating and the building is protected throughout by an approved, supervised automatic sprinkler system in accordance with Section 9.7.

area of all floors used for mercantile purposes. Where a mercantile occupancy is divided into sections, regardless of fire separation, the aggregate gross area shall include the area of all sections used for sales purposes. Areas of floors not used for sales purposes, such as an area used only for storage and not open to the public, shall not be counted for the purposes of the classifications in 37.1.4.2.1(a) through (c). However, means of egress shall be provided for such nonsales areas in accordance with their occupancy as specified by other chapters of this *Code*.

37.1.4.2.3 The floor area of a mezzanine, or the aggregate floor area of multiple mezzanines, shall not exceed one-half of the floor area of the room or story in which the mezzanines are located. A mezzanine or aggregated mezzanines that exceed the one-half area limitation shall be treated as floors.

37.1.4.2.4 Where a number of tenant spaces under different management are located in the same building, the aggregate gross area *(see 37.1.4.2.2)* of all such tenant spaces shall be used in determining classification per 37.1.4.2.1.

Exception No. 1:   Covered mall buildings. (See 37.4.4.)

Exception No. 2:   Where individual tenant spaces are separated by fire barriers with a 1-hour fire resistance rating.

Paragraph 36/37.1.4.1 refers to 6.1.10 for additional guidance on the classification of a mercantile occupancy. It is important to review the *Code*'s definition (see 6.1.10) of a mercantile occupancy. Note that, per the exception to 6.1.14.2, the definition does not include minor merchandising operations in buildings that house other predominant occupancies, such as a newsstand in an office building. Such occupancies are subject to the requirements of the predominant occupancy. A newsstand located in an office building would be treated under the same business occupancy requirements (Chapter 38/39) as the office building.

Mezzanines are addressed by the one-third area rule of 36.1.4.2.3 and 8.2.6.2.1 for new construction and the one-half area rule of 37.1.4.2.3 for existing mercantile occupancies. Mezzanines with an area that does not exceed the applicable one-third or one-half area rule do not constitute a story and, therefore, are not a factor in determining mercantile occupancy subclassification based on the number of floors used

for sales purposes. The area of such mezzanines used for sales purposes (see 36/37.1.4.2.2) is, however, a factor in determining occupancy subclassification based on floor area devoted to sales purposes. For example, a new mercantile occupancy with a 2100-ft² (195-m²) main sales floor and a 700-ft² (65-m²) sales mezzanine is a Class C mercantile occupancy, while a store with a 2400-ft² (225-m²) main sales floor and a 800-ft² (75-m²) sales mezzanine is a Class B mercantile occupancy. In each case, the mezzanine meets the maximum one-third area rule and is not treated as a story. In the second case, the area of the 800-ft² (75-m²) sales mezzanine, when added to the 2400-ft² (225-m²) main sales floor, exceeds the maximum 3000-ft² (280-m²) sales area for Class C mercantile occupancies and is therefore a Class B mercantile occupancy.

Mezzanines with areas in excess of the maximum one-third area rule (or one-half area rule for existing mercantile occupancies) constitute stories and, thus, sales levels. Therefore, such mezzanines must be considered when determining mercantile occupancy subclassification. For example, a set of plans might show a proposed store with three floor levels of 8000 ft² (740 m²) each that are used for sales purposes and a single 4000-ft² (370-m²) sales mezzanine. The store will actually use four floor levels for sales purposes, because the so-called mezzanine is not a mezzanine based on the maximum one-third area rule of 8.2.6.2.1 referenced by 36.1.4.2.3, which applies to new mercantile occupancies. Although the 30,000-ft² (2800-m²) sales area limitation associated with Class A mercantile occupancies is not exceeded, the four floor levels used for sales purposes result in a Class A mercantile occupancy subclassification in accordance with the definition in 36/37.1.4.2.1(a).

To qualify as a Class A, Class B, or Class C mercantile occupancy, a store must meet the requirements of 36/37.1.4.2.1, which are summarized in Table 36/37.1. The classification process is important, because specific life safety requirements vary for each mercantile class. The criteria vary in degree of stringency, depending on a store's classification, which, while based directly on the size of the sales areas, is indirectly a measure of the number of occupants at risk from any given fire.

Some mercantile occupancies locate their sales and storage areas together (for example, furniture warehouse sales areas). In such cases, the mercantile occupancy subclassification should be determined using the total aggregate gross area that is open to public use. The same procedure should be followed for bulk merchandising retail buildings.

The mezzanine measurement provisions of 37.1.4.2.3 for existing mercantile occupancies use a one-half area rule, whereas the provisions of 36.1.4.2.3 for new mercantile occupancies use a one-third area rule. The one-third rule for new mercantile occupancy mezzanines correlates with the definition of the term *mezzanine* in 3.3.126. Because the one-half area rule was applied to mercantile occupancies long before the general definition of mezzanine was added to Chapter 3, it has been retained only for existing (but not new) mercantile occupancies to prevent the abrupt noncompliance of existing buildings due to an issue that does not significantly lower the level of safety to life. Therefore, mezzanines in existing mercantile occupancies continue to be evaluated based on the historical one-half area criteria.

Examples of mezzanine arrangements to which the maximum one-third area rule can be applied are

depicted in Exhibit 36/37.3(a), illustrations (a) through (f). Examples of mezzanine arrangements to which the maximum one-half area rule of 37.1.4.2.3 for existing mercantile occupancies can be applied are depicted in Exhibit 36/37.3(b), illustrations (a) through (f). For purpose of illustration, assume that all the mezzanines, as well as the entire main floor level, are used for sales purposes. Illustrations (a), (b), (c), and (d) of Exhibit 36/37.3(a) depict a new single story or single floor level with mezzanine, because the aggregate areas of the mezzanines [3000 ft² (280 m²)] do not exceed one-third of the floor area [10,000 ft² (930 m²)] of the room or story in which the

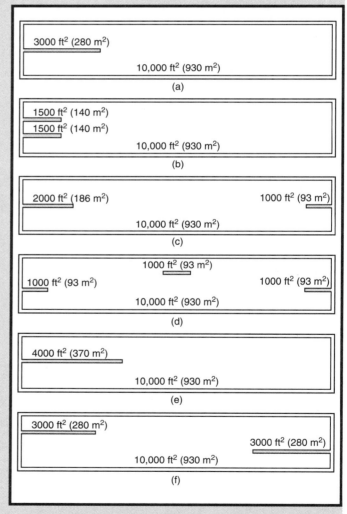

Exhibit 36/37.3(a) *Elevation views of new mercantile occupancy mezzanine arrangements.*

mezzanine is located. Illustrations (a), (b), (c), and (d) of Exhibit 36/37.3(b) depict an existing single story or single floor level with mezzanine because the aggregate areas of the mezzanines [5000 ft² (465 m²)] do not exceed one-half of the floor area [10,000 ft² (930 m²)] of the room or story in which the mezzanine is located.

In illustration (e) of Exhibit 36/37.3(a), the new single 4000-ft² (370-m²) intermediate level referred to by occupants as a mezzanine exceeds the one-third area rule. Similarly, in illustration (e) of Exhibit 36/37.3(b), the existing single 6000-ft² (560-m²) intermediate level referred to by occupants as a mezzanine

exceeds the one-half area rule. Therefore, in both cases, the intermediate level is not a mezzanine for *Life Safety Code* purposes but is a story by itself. Illustration (e) of Exhibit 36/37.3(a) and illustration (e) of Exhibit 36/37.3(b), therefore, depict two-story mercantile occupancies.

In illustration (f) of Exhibit 36/37.3(a), one of the 3000-ft² (280-m²) mezzanines fits within the maximum one-third area allowance for new mezzanines and can be called a mezzanine without constituting a floor level. Similarly, in illustration (f) of Exhibit 36/37.3(b), one of the 4000-ft² (370-m²) mezzanines fits within the maximum one-half area allowance for existing mercantile occupancies and can be called a mezzanine without constituting a floor level. The other mezzanine, although of the same size and thus by itself not in excess of the one-third or one-half area rule, does create a story, because the sum of the areas of the two mezzanines [6000 ft² (560 m²) in illustration (f) of Exhibit 36/37.3(a) and 8000 ft² (745 m²) in illustration (f) of Exhibit 36/37.3(b)] exceeds one-third or one-half of the 10,000-ft² (930-m²) lower floor level. Thus, illustration (f) of Exhibit 36/37.3(a) and illustration (f) of Exhibit 36/37.3(b) depict two-story mercantile occupancies with a mezzanine.

Although the mezzanines in illustrations (a) through (d) of Exhibit 36/37.3(a) and illustrations (a) through (d) of Exhibit 36/37.3(b) do not establish separate stories, their areas, because they are used for sales, are included in the total gross sales area used to establish mercantile occupancy subclassification in accordance with 36/37.1.4.2.1. Illustrations (a) through (d) of Exhibit 36/37.3(a) show 13,000 ft² (1200 m²) of sales area and would be classified as Class B mercantile occupancies. Similarly, illustrations (a) through (d) of Exhibit 36/37.3(b) show 15,000 ft² (1400 m²) of sales area and would be classified as Class B mercantile occupancies.

In addition to the maximum one-third and one-half area limitations of 36/37.1.4.2.3, the provisions of 8.2.6 are also applicable to mezzanines. For example, a mezzanine used for sales purposes that meets the one-third or one-half area rule, would not affect the mercantile occupancy subclassification with respect to number of stories used for sales purposes. However, the mezzanine would be required to be sufficiently open, in accordance with 8.2.6.3, to avoid treatment as a separate floor in terms of number of means of egress (see 36/37.2.4) and the other egress arrangement requirements that apply to floors or stories.

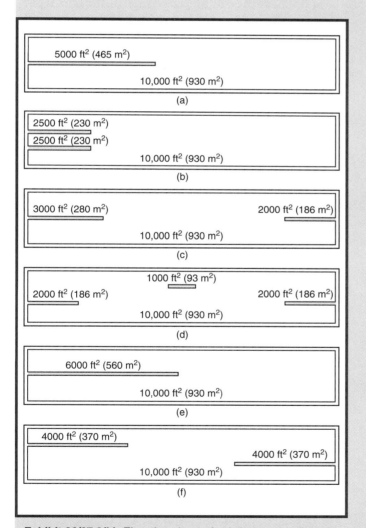

Exhibit 36/37.3(b) *Elevation views of existing mercantile occupancy mezzanine arrangements.*

Note that, for existing mercantile occupancies (see Exception No. 2 to 37.1.4.2.4), the fire resistance–rated separation required to waive aggregate gross area is 1 hour, rather than the 2-hour rating required for new mercantile occupancies via the provision of Exception No. 2 to 36.1.4.2.4. The same 1-hour rating applies to new construction only if the building is sprinklered (see Exception No. 3 to 36.1.4.2.4).

Paragraphs 36/37.1.4.2.1 through 36/37.1.4.2.4 further clarify the subclassification of stores as Class A, Class B, or Class C. Most of these provisions are included in the footnotes to Table 36/37.1. Also, the user should note the following:

(1) The aggregate gross area is the sum of the gross areas of all floors used for mercantile (sales) purposes.
(2) If the store is divided so that some portions are not used for sales purposes, such as shipping/ receiving/storage areas, only the sales areas should be included in the aggregate gross area.
(3) With the exception of covered mall buildings (see 36/37.4.4), the aggregate gross area of stores must be used in subclassifying a mercantile occupancy in accordance with 36/37.1.4.2.1 under the following conditions:
   a. Where stores are contiguous to one another (even if under different ownership to management and occupying numerous buildings)
   b. Where sections or floors used for sales within any building are considered as separate stores (for example, because they are under different management)
   c. Where the contiguous or intermixed stores described in items a and b are not separated from each other by the 2-hour or 1-hour fire resistance–rated fire barriers specified in the exceptions to 36/7.1.4.2.4.

36.1.5 Classification of Hazard of Contents.

36.1.5.1 The contents of mercantile occupancies shall be classified as ordinary hazard in accordance with Section 6.2, except as modified by 36.1.5.2.

36.1.5.2 Mercantile occupancies shall be classified as high hazard if high hazard commodities are displayed or handled without protective wrappings or containers, in which case the following additional provisions shall apply:

(1) Exits shall be located so that not more than 75 ft (23 m) of travel from any point is needed to reach the nearest exit.
(2) From every point, there shall be not less than two exits accessible by travel in different directions (no common path of travel).
(3) All vertical openings shall be enclosed.

36.1.6 Minimum Construction Requirements.

(No special requirements.)

36.1.7 Occupant Load.

The occupant load, in number of persons for whom means of egress and other provisions are required, shall be determined on the basis of the occupant load factors of Table 7.3.1.2 that are characteristic of the use of the space or shall be determined as the maximum probable population of the space under consideration, whichever is greater.

37.1.5 Classification of Hazard of Contents.

37.1.5.1 The contents of mercantile occupancies shall be classified as ordinary hazard in accordance with Section 6.2, except as modified by 37.1.5.2.

37.1.5.2 Mercantile occupancies shall be classified as high hazard if high hazard commodities are displayed or handled without protective wrappings or containers, in which case the following additional provisions shall apply:

(1) Exits shall be located so that not more than 75 ft (23 m) of travel from any point is needed to reach the nearest exit.
(2) From every point, there shall be not less than two exits accessible by travel in different directions (no common path of travel).
(3) All vertical openings shall be enclosed.

37.1.6 Minimum Construction Requirements.

(No special requirements.)

37.1.7 Occupant Load.

The occupant load, in number of persons for whom means of egress and other provisions are required, shall be determined on the basis of the occupant load factors of Table 7.3.1.2 that are characteristic of the use of the space or shall be determined as the maximum probable population of the space under consideration, whichever is greater.

Hazard of contents is addressed in 36/37.1.5. Most occupancy chapters refer to Section 6.2 for classification of hazard of contents. However, the requirement of 36/37.1.5.1 emphasizes that, unless an extraordinarily hazardous situation exists, the contents of mercantile occupancies must be classed as ordinary hazard. This requirement is intended to prevent the user from classifying the hazard of contents as high hazard unless a situation exists that is equivalent to dispensing explosives in bulk. Because the total package of life safety provided by the Chapter 36/37 requirements anticipates the display of significant quantities of combustibles, it should provide an acceptable level of safety without making it necessary to classify the typical mercantile occupancy environment as highly hazardous. Specifically, the Chapter 36/37 requirements should be adequate without imposing the stringent high hazard contents requirements of 36/37.1.5.2 on all but the most hazardous of mercantile occupancies.

Operations that would require classification of a mercantile occupancy as highly hazardous include dispensing gunpowder or other explosives in bulk or dispensing gasoline or flammable solvents by pouring them into open containers. The sale of flammable liquids such as camp stove fuel and rubbing alcohol should be controlled by NFPA 30, *Flammable and Combustible Liquids Code*, with regard to display configuration, total amount, and separation from ignition sources.[1]

Exhibit 36/37.4 illustrates an egress arrangement from a highly hazardous area of a mercantile occupancy that meets the requirements of 36/37.1.5.2(1) and (2), which address limited travel distance and the exclusion of common path of travel. Doors 1 and 2 lead to remote corridor segments that provide access to independent and remote exits. Travel in two independent directions is possible from any point within the high hazard contents room. Travel distance from any point within the high hazard contents room to the nearest exit does not exceed 75 ft (23 m). Although mercantile occupancy requirements are generally lenient in allowing vertical openings (see 36/37.3.1), all vertical openings in high hazard mercantile occupancies are required to be fully enclosed (see 8.2.5) in accordance with 36/37.1.5.2(3).

The phrase "minimum construction," as used in 36/37.1.6, describes the construction of the building housing the occupancy. Some occupancy chapters such as Chapters 18 and 19—which address the life

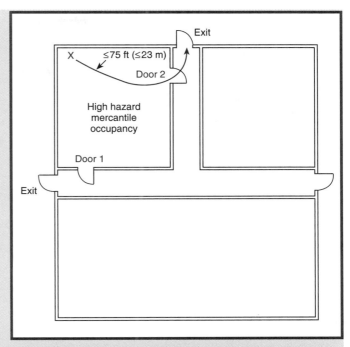

Exhibit 36/37.4 *Egress arrangement from area of mercantile occupancy defined as highly hazardous.*

safety needs of nonambulatory occupants of health care occupancies—require a minimum building construction type to help ensure structural integrity for a prolonged evacuation or for safe refuge within the building. Because mercantile occupancies characteristically are used by ambulatory customers and employees and do not provide sleeping accommodations, no minimum construction requirements are imposed.

The occupant load factors for mercantile uses specified in Table 7.3.1.2 are based on the observation that, during the normal use of a mercantile occupancy, the largest number of customers usually occupy the street floor or a basement sales area. In assigning a higher occupant load to the street floor, the *Code* recognizes merchandising techniques that arrange merchandise to take advantage of the heavy flow of traffic on the street floor. Customers are attracted to merchandise displays as they walk through portions of the street floor to reach escalators, elevators, and stairs to other floors. Thus, larger numbers of occupants are expected to occupy the street floor.

The street floor, as distinguished from other sales floors, is any floor that has an entrance/exit that is

CHAPTER 36 • New	CHAPTER 37 • Existing

directly accessible from the street with not more than three risers of ascent or descent. The term *street floor* is defined in 3.3.196. If differences in the ground level on different sides of a store create several floors of this nature, the *Code* treats them all as street floors; however, a slightly different occupant load factor is used in accordance with the section symbol (§) footnote to Table 7.3.1.2. If the only access to a store from the street is by means of stairs or escalators, the principal sales floor, rather than the street level, must be considered the street floor for the purpose of choosing an occupant load factor and calculating the occupant load.

The terms *covered mall* and *covered mall building* have different meanings (see commentary following 36/37.1.3). Therefore, the intent of the number symbol (#) footnote to Table 7.3.1.2 is that the egress capacity of the overall covered mall building is to be sized to handle an occupant load that is calculated in two steps. First, the occupant load is calculated individually for each store and tenant space using the occupant load factors of Table 7.3.1.2. Second, the required egress capacity for the covered mall itself (the covered pedestrian way) is calculated using the values shown in Figure 7.3.1.2. Each store or tenant space must have sufficient egress capacity for its occupant load. The egress capacity of the covered mall must be

based on Figure 7.3.1.2, which, in effect, automatically accounts for those persons who are in the covered mall (the covered pedestrian way) and those persons discharged from stores into the covered mall as part of the stores' means of egress.

For example, consider a covered mall building with 21 tenant stores located on the street floor. Each store uses 6000 ft² (560 m²) of the 7500 ft² (700 m²) of gross leasable area as sales area [assume that the other 1500 ft² (140 m²) is storage area]. Using an occupant load factor of 30 ft² (2.8 m²) per person for the sales areas and 300 ft² (27.9 m²) for the storage areas, in accordance with Table 7.3.1.2, each store must size its means of egress system to handle 205 persons (6000/30 + 1500/300 = 200 + 5 = 205). Store occupants use the covered mall as part of the required means of egress from each store. Based on the 21 tenant stores, each with 7500 ft² (700 m²) of gross leasable area, the covered mall has a gross leasable area of 21 × 7500 ft² (700 m²) or 157,500 ft² (14,700 m²) that is the basis on which the means of egress from the covered mall must be sized. Figure 7.3.1.2 indicates that, for a gross leasable area of 157,500 ft² (14,700 m²), the occupant load factor is 36 ft² (3.3 m²) per person. The covered mall must provide a means of egress system for 157,500 ft² / 36 ft² per person (14,700 m² / 3.3 m² per person), or 4375 persons.

Section 36.2 Means of Egress Requirements

36.2.1 General.

36.2.1.1 All means of egress shall be in accordance with Chapter 7 and this chapter.

36.2.1.2 No inside open stairway or inside open ramp shall be permitted to serve as a component of the required means of egress system for more than one floor.

36.2.1.3 Where there are two or more floors below the street floor, the same stair or other exit shall be permitted to serve all floors, but all required exits from such areas shall be independent of any open stairways between the street floor and the floor below it.

36.2.1.4 Where a level, outside exit from upper floors is possible owing to hills, such outside exits shall be permitted to serve instead of horizontal exits. If, however, such outside

Section 37.2 Means of Egress Requirements

37.2.1 General.

37.2.1.1 All means of egress shall be in accordance with Chapter 7 and this chapter.

37.2.1.2 No inside open stairway, inside open escalator, or inside open ramp shall be permitted to serve as a component of the required means of egress system for more than one floor.

37.2.1.3 Where there are two or more floors below the street floor, the same stair or other exit shall be permitted to serve all floors, but all required exits from such areas shall be independent of any open stairways between the street floor and the floor below it.

37.2.1.4 Where a level, outside exit from upper floors is possible owing to hills, such outside exits shall be permitted to serve instead of horizontal exits. If, however, such outside

CHAPTER 36 • New	**CHAPTER 37 • Existing**

exits from the upper floor also serve as an entrance from a principal street, the upper floor shall be classified as a street floor in accordance with the definition of street floor in 3.3.196 and shall be subject to the requirements of this chapter for street floors.

36.2.1.5 For special considerations for high hazard contents, see 36.1.5.2.

Paragraph 36/37.2.1.2 prohibits the use of unenclosed interior stairs or unenclosed interior ramps as exit access for more than one floor; it does not establish permission for the existence of an open stairway or ramp. See 36/37.3.1 to determine if the stair or ramp is permitted to be unenclosed.

Paragraph 36/37.2.1.4 addresses street floors. Exhibit 36/37.5 illustrates a case where two floors qualify as street floors because each has one side located at a ground level. Note, however, that each street floor has its other sides located either above or below the building's other ground level. As a result, these floors must have their exits arranged to allow horizontal travel to the exterior at one end of the floor and vertical travel (either up or down to ground level) at the other end of the floor. The egress capacity of the doors to the exterior on floor 1 must accommodate that portion of the occupant load from an upper floor that is expected to travel down to and through the exits to the exterior from floor 1. This egress capacity is in addition to the assigned portion of the floor 1 occupant load. The reverse is true for floor 2, which must increase the size of its exterior exit door capacity to accommodate occupants traveling up from floor 1 as well as those traveling down to and through the exterior exits on floor 2. Paragraphs 7.3.1.5, 7.3.1.6 and 36/37.2.3.2 explain how to add egress capacity based on the number of occupants expected to discharge from floors above and below the street floor. Exhibit

exits from the upper floor also serve as an entrance from a principal street, the upper floor shall be classified as a street floor in accordance with the definition of street floor in 3.3.196 and shall be subject to the requirements of this chapter for street floors.

37.2.1.5 For special considerations for high hazard contents, see 37.1.5.2.

36/37.9, which accompanies the commentary associated with 36/37.2.3.2, provides an example of how to calculate exit capacity for a street floor similar to that illustrated by floor 2 in Exhibit 36/37.5.

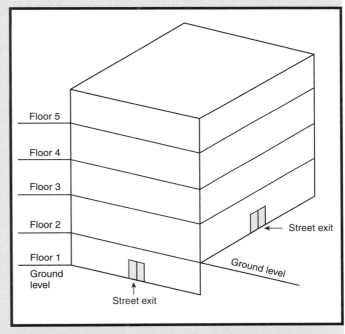

Exhibit 36/37.5 *Mercantile occupancy with two street floors.*

36.2.2 Means of Egress Components.

36.2.2.1 Components of means of egress shall be limited to the types described in 36.2.2.2 through 36.2.2.12.

36.2.2.2 Doors.

36.2.2.2.1 Doors complying with 7.2.1 shall be permitted.

36.2.2.2.2* Locks complying with Exception No. 2 to 7.2.1.5.1 shall be permitted only on principal entrance/exit doors.

37.2.2 Means of Egress Components.

37.2.2.1 Components of means of egress shall be limited to the types described in 37.2.2.2 through 37.2.2.12.

37.2.2.2 Doors.

37.2.2.2.1 Doors complying with 7.2.1 shall be permitted.

37.2.2.2.2* Locks complying with Exception No. 2 to 7.2.1.5.1 shall be permitted only on principal entrance/exit doors.

CHAPTER 36 • New	CHAPTER 37 • Existing

A.36.2.2.2.2 The words "principal entrance/exit doors" describe doors that the authority having jurisdiction can reasonably expect to be unlocked in order for the facility to do business.

A.37.2.2.2.2 The words "principal entrance/exit doors" describe doors that the authority having jurisdiction can reasonably expect to be unlocked in order for the facility to do business.

36.2.2.2.3 (Reserved.)

37.2.2.2.3 The re-entry provisions of 7.2.1.5.2 shall not apply. *(See 7.2.1.5.2, Exception No. 1.)*

36.2.2.2.4 Delayed-egress locks complying with 7.2.1.6.1 shall be permitted.

37.2.2.2.4 Delayed-egress locks complying with 7.2.1.6.1 shall be permitted.

36.2.2.2.5 Access-controlled egress doors complying with 7.2.1.6.2 shall be permitted in buildings protected throughout by an approved, supervised fire detection system in accordance with Section 9.6 or an approved automatic sprinkler system in accordance with Section 9.7.

37.2.2.2.5 Access-controlled egress doors complying with 7.2.1.6.2 shall be permitted in buildings protected throughout by an approved, supervised fire detection system in accordance with Section 9.6 or an approved automatic sprinkler system in accordance with Section 9.7.

36.2.2.2.6 Where horizontal or vertical security grilles or doors are used as a part of the required means of egress from a tenant space, such grilles or doors shall comply with Exception No. 2 to 7.2.1.4.1.

37.2.2.2.6 Where horizontal or vertical security grilles or doors are used as a part of the required means of egress from a tenant space, such grilles or doors shall comply with Exception No. 2 to 7.2.1.4.1.

36.2.2.2.7 All doors at the foot of stairs from upper floors or at the head of stairs leading to floors below the street floor shall swing in the direction of egress travel.

37.2.2.2.7 All doors at the foot of stairs from upper floors or at the head of stairs leading to floors below the street floor shall swing in the direction of egress travel.

36.2.2.2.8 Revolving doors complying with 7.2.1.10 shall be permitted.

37.2.2.2.8 Revolving doors complying with 7.2.1.10 shall be permitted.

37.2.2.2.9 In Class C mercantile occupancies, doors shall be permitted to swing inward against the direction of egress travel where such doors serve only the street floor area.

36.2.2.3 Stairs.

37.2.2.3 Stairs.

36.2.2.3.1 Stairs complying with 7.2.2 shall be permitted.

37.2.2.3.1 Stairs complying with 7.2.2 shall be permitted.

36.2.2.3.2 Spiral stairs complying with 7.2.2.2.3 shall be permitted.

37.2.2.3.2 Spiral stairs complying with 7.2.2.2.3 shall be permitted.

37.2.2.3.3 Winders complying with 7.2.2.2.4 shall be permitted.

36.2.2.4 Smokeproof Enclosures. Smokeproof enclosures complying with 7.2.3 shall be permitted.

37.2.2.4 Smokeproof Enclosures. Smokeproof enclosures complying with 7.2.3 shall be permitted.

36.2.2.5 Horizontal Exits. Horizontal exits complying with 7.2.4 shall be permitted.

37.2.2.5 Horizontal Exits. Horizontal exits complying with 7.2.4 shall be permitted.

36.2.2.6 Ramps. Ramps complying with 7.2.5 shall be permitted.

37.2.2.6 Ramps. Ramps complying with 7.2.5 shall be permitted.

36.2.2.7 Exit Passageways. Exit passageways complying with 7.2.6 shall be permitted.

37.2.2.7 Exit Passageways. Exit passageways complying with 7.2.6 shall be permitted.

Exception:* In lieu of the provisions of 7.2.6.4, an exit passageway in a covered mall building shall be permitted to accommodate the following independently:

Exception:* In lieu of the provisions of 7.2.6.4, an exit passageway in a covered mall building shall be permitted to accommodate the following independently:

(a) The portion of the occupant load assigned to the exit passageway from only the covered mall/pedestrian way

(b) The largest occupant load assigned to the exit passageway from a single tenant space

A.36.2.2.7 Exception To design egress from a covered mall building, the following steps should be used.

(a) The covered mall/pedestrian way has been assigned no occupant load, but it is required to be provided with means of egress sized to accommodate the total occupant load of the covered mall building based on the gross leasable area. The exits for the covered mall/pedestrian way are permitted to be provided by a combination of exterior exit doors and exit passageways.

(b) After completion of step (a), each tenant space is to be judged individually for occupant load and egress capacity. This step normally sends a portion or all (per 36.4.4.2.2) of the tenant space's occupant load into the covered mall. Any remaining occupants are sent through the back of the tenant space into an exit passageway that might serve multiple tenant spaces and the covered mall.

(c) The width of the exit passageway is required to be sized for the most restrictive of the following:

(1) For a width of not less than 66 in. (168 cm) per 36.4.4.1 Exception (b)
(2) For the portion of the egress capacity from the largest single tenant space being served by the exit passageway
(3) For the portion of the egress capacity from the covered mall being provided by the exit passageway

The concepts used in steps (a) through (c) include the following:

(1) After proper egress capacity is provided for the covered mall/pedestrian way, each tenant space is then required to independently provide egress capacity for its occupants.
(2) The covered mall required exit passageway width and the tenant space required exit passageway width are not required to be added together.
(3) The required exit passageway width for a tenant space is not required to be added to that of other tenant spaces using the same exit passageway.

36.2.2.8 (Reserved.)

36.2.2.9 (Reserved.)

36.2.2.10 Fire Escape Ladders. Fire escape ladders complying with 7.2.9 shall be permitted.

(a) The portion of the occupant load assigned to the exit passageway from only the covered mall/ pedestrian way

(b) The largest occupant load assigned to the exit passageway from a single tenant space

A.37.2.2.7 Exception To design egress from a covered mall building, the following steps should be used.

(a) The covered mall/pedestrian way has been assigned no occupant load, but it is required to be provided with means of egress sized to accommodate the total occupant load of the covered mall building based on the gross leasable area. The exits for the covered mall/pedestrian way are permitted to be provided by a combination of exterior exit doors and exit passageways.

(b) After completion of step (a), each tenant space is to be judged individually for occupant load and egress capacity. This step normally sends a portion or all (per 37.4.4.2.2) of the tenant space's occupant load into the covered mall. Any remaining occupants are sent through the back of the tenant space into an exit passageway that might serve multiple tenant spaces and the covered mall.

(c) The width of the exit passageway is required to be sized for the most restrictive of the following:

(1) For a width of not less than 66 in. (168 cm) per 37.4.4.1 Exception (b)
(2) For the portion of the egress capacity from the largest single tenant space being served by the exit passageway
(3) For the portion of the egress capacity from the covered mall being provided by the exit passageway

The concepts used in steps (a) through (c) include the following:

(1) After proper egress capacity is provided for the covered mall/pedestrian way, each tenant space is then required to independently provide egress capacity for its occupants.
(2) The covered mall required exit passageway width and the tenant space required exit passageway width are not required to be added together.
(3) The required exit passageway width for a tenant space is not required to be added to that of other tenant spaces using the same exit passageway.

37.2.2.8 Escalators and Moving Walks. Escalators and moving walks complying with 7.2.7 shall be permitted.

37.2.2.9 Fire Escape Stairs. Fire escape stairs complying with 7.2.8 shall be permitted.

37.2.2.10 Fire Escape Ladders. Fire escape ladders complying with 7.2.9 shall be permitted.

CHAPTER 36 • New	CHAPTER 37 • Existing

36.2.2.11 Alternating Tread Devices. Alternating tread devices complying with 7.2.11 shall be permitted.

36.2.2.12 Areas of Refuge. Areas of refuge complying with 7.2.12 shall be permitted.

Exception: In buildings protected throughout by an approved, supervised automatic sprinkler system in accordance with Section 9.7, two rooms or spaces separated from each other by smoke-resistant partitions in accordance with the definition of area of refuge in 3.3.14 shall not be required.

37.2.2.11 Alternating Tread Devices. Alternating tread devices complying with 7.2.11 shall be permitted.

37.2.2.12 Areas of Refuge. Areas of refuge complying with 7.2.12 shall be permitted.

Exception: In buildings protected throughout by an approved, supervised automatic sprinkler system in accordance with Section 9.7, two rooms or spaces separated from each other by smoke-resistant partitions in accordance with the definition of area of refuge in 3.3.14 shall not be required.

Subparagraph 36/37.2.2.2.2 permits only the principal entrance/exit doors of a mercantile occupancy to be equipped with the special key-operated dead bolt lock described by the provisions of Exception No. 2 to 7.2.1.5.1. It must be easy to determine that the device is locked by using means such as a flag indicator that can be seen at a distance from the door. Other doors along the perimeter of the building are prohibited from being equipped with a key-operated dead bolt lock, because it cannot be guaranteed that these locks will be disengaged simultaneously when the principal entrance/exit door is unlocked each day at the opening of business. See Exhibit 36/37.6.

Although Chapter 36 does not address stairwell re-entry—as contrasted with 37.2.2.2.3, which exempts existing mercantile occupancies from the stairwell re-entry provisions—the re-entry provisions of 7.2.1.5.2 apply. Subparagraph 7.2.1.5.2 requires stairs serving five or more stories to provide either re-entry

from the stairwell back onto all floors at any time, or similar re-entry following automatic release of locking devices initiated by the building fire alarm system. Exception No. 1 to 7.2.1.5.2 allows some stairwell doors to remain locked from the stairwell side of the door to provide building security, while other doors must allow re-entry. The location and number of re-entry points provide the same overall level of life safety for this type of occupancy as that intended by the base provisions of 7.2.1.5.2.

Use of the delayed-egress locking device covered by 7.2.1.6.1 is allowed by 36/37.2.2.2.4 on any door in recognition of the security needs of a mercantile occupancy. The building must be protected throughout by an approved, supervised automatic sprinkler system or approved, supervised automatic fire detection system to apply the delayed-egress locking provisions. In effect, the allowable 15-second or 30-second delay will be experienced only under nonfire conditions or very early in a fire's growth, because the door must be usable immediately upon sprinkler operation, smoke or heat detection, or loss of power that controls the locking mechanism.

Subparagraph 36/37.2.2.2.5 recognizes access-controlled egress doors in mercantile occupancies with either complete sprinkler or fire detection systems as security measures that do not compromise the use of the means of egress system.

Although Exception No. 2 to 7.2.1.4.1 establishes provisions for the arrangement and use of horizontal or vertical security grilles or doors, it requires that an occupancy chapter specifically recognize the use of these security grilles or doors. Subparagraph 36/37.2.2.2.6 provides this recognition for mercantile occupancies.

The provision of 36/37.2.2.2.7 supplements the door provisions of 7.2.1.4 by requiring doors that otherwise would not have to swing in the direction of

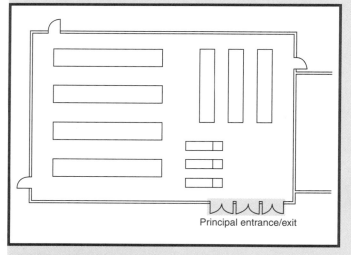

Exhibit 36/37.6 Principal entrance/exit.

Principal entrance/exit

egress travel to do so, based on their location. The queuing and accumulation of people at doors in locations such as at the foot of stairs from upper floors makes it difficult for occupants to step back to allow the door to swing inward.

Subparagraph 36/37.2.2.2.8 addresses revolving doors. The provisions of 7.2.1.10 specify that the use of a revolving door, regardless of whether it is permitted as part of the required means of egress, requires a conforming side-hinged swinging door to be positioned and usable within the same wall as, and to be located within 10 ft (3 m) of, the revolving door. This requirement helps to ensure that, once people move toward the door, if the collapsibility and other safety features of the door fail and render it unusable, egress from the vicinity would still be possible without retracing steps and requiring travel toward the fire. Existing revolving doors are permitted to continue to be used without having to meet some of the more stringent requirements that apply to new revolving doors. See the exceptions to 7.2.1.10.1.

Paragraph 36/37.2.2.4 does not mandate the use of smokeproof enclosures, but it does recognize a smokeproof enclosure as part of the means of egress system in a mercantile occupancy only if the smokeproof enclosure meets the requirements of 7.2.3. For an example of an occupancy requiring a smokeproof enclosure, see 31.2.11, in which existing nonsprinklered high-rise apartment buildings are required to be provided with smokeproof enclosures in accordance with 7.2.3. See 36/37.2.2.1.

Exit passageways are addressed in 36/37.2.2.7. Exit passageways are frequently used within the means of egress system of covered mall buildings as a way of meeting the travel distance limitations or as a method of avoiding numerous exit doors along exterior walls located at the rear of tenant spaces. In effect, the exit passageway labeled A in Exhibit 36/37.7 moves the exit closer to the occupants to create a building arrangement that would otherwise require occupants to travel farther than allowable to reach an exit door in an exterior wall. The exit passageway labeled B in Exhibit 36/37.7 runs along the rear of multiple-tenant spaces and provides access to the exterior only at each end of the exit passageway for security reasons. In both cases, the exit passageway is a *Code*-complying exit in accordance with 7.2.6 and provides the same degree of safety that an exit stair enclosure would provide an occupant of an upper floor in a multistory building.

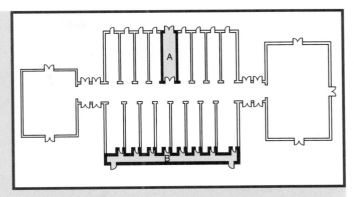

Exhibit 36/37.7 *Typical uses of exit passageways in covered mall buildings.*

Although the provisions of 7.2.6.2 require an exit passageway to be sized to accommodate the aggregate required capacity of all means of egress discharging through the exit passageway, the exception to 36/37.2.2.7 allows some reduction in the required width of exit passageways in covered mall buildings. The exception recognizes that the sizing of the means of egress from the covered mall—calculated in accordance with the provisions of Figure 7.3.1.2—provides egress capacity for occupants of the covered mall and occupants of the adjoining tenant spaces within the covered mall building. Requiring an exit passageway in a covered mall building to be of sufficient size to accommodate both its assigned covered mall occupant load and the occupant load of all tenant spaces discharging through the exit passageway would be equivalent to counting a portion of the building's occupants twice and, thereby, needlessly oversizing the means of egress system.

Paragraph 37.2.2.8 recognizes existing escalators and moving walks as part of the means of egress. Note that, to be permitted to remain within the required means of egress, existing escalators and moving walks must meet the requirements of 7.2.7. To qualify as exits, existing escalators and moving walks must also meet the requirements of 7.2.2.5 that address enclosure.

Paragraph 37.2.2.9 recognizes existing fire escape ladders as part of the means of egress. Note that 7.2.8.1.2 allows only those occupancy chapters that apply to existing buildings to permit a fire escape stair within the required means of egress. Furthermore, Exception No. 1 to 7.2.8.1.2 permits existing buildings to use or to continue to use fire escape stairs for no

CHAPTER 36 • New	CHAPTER 37 • Existing

more than 50 percent of the building's required egress capacity.

In accordance with the provisions of 36/37.2.2.10 and 36/37.2.2.11, both fire escape ladders and alternating tread devices are allowed within the means of egress of mercantile occupancies, but only as permit-

ted by the relatively narrow provisions of 7.2.9 and 7.2.11. The provisions of 7.2.11, in effect, restrict the use of alternating tread devices to locations where the *Code* recognizes the use of fire escape ladders. See 36/37.2.2.11, 7.2.9, and 7.2.11.

36.2.3 Capacity of Means of Egress.

36.2.3.1 The capacity of means of egress shall be in accordance with Section 7.3.

36.2.3.2 In Class A and Class B mercantile occupancies, street floor exits shall be sufficient for the occupant load of the street floor plus the required capacity of stairs and ramps discharging through the street floor.

37.2.3 Capacity of Means of Egress.

37.2.3.1 The capacity of means of egress shall be in accordance with Section 7.3.

37.2.3.2 In Class A and Class B mercantile occupancies, street floor exits shall be sufficient for the occupant load of the street floor plus the required capacity of stairs, ramps, escalators, and moving walks discharging through the street floor.

The provisions of 7.3.1.6 mandate that any required egress capacity from a mezzanine that passes through the room below must be added to the required egress capacity of the room through which the egress passes.

Exhibit 36/37.8 illustrates a case in which a mezzanine is open to the street floor. The exits from the street floor must accommodate the following:

(1) Occupant load of the street floor
(2) Occupant load of the mezzanine in accordance with 7.3.1.6
(3) Required capacity provided by the stairs from other floors discharging through the street floor in accordance with 36/37.2.3.2

To determine the egress capacity for the street floor, the occupant load of the mezzanine (1000 persons) is added to the occupant load of the street floor (2000 persons). In addition, because one-half of the exits from the upper floors discharge through the street floor, the egress capacity of the street floor must accommodate the capacity of the exit stair enclosure that discharges through that floor. The maximum occupant load on any upper floor is 2000 (second floor), and 36/37.2.7.2 permits a maximum of one-half of the exits or one-half of the egress capacity to discharge through the street floor, provided that the building is sprinklered. Therefore, the street floor must be provided with egress capacity for 4000 persons or 800 in. (2030 cm) of exit width using the factor of 0.2 in. (0.5 cm) per person for level exit components found

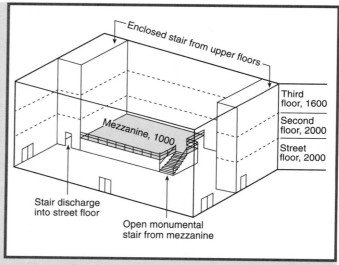

Exhibit 36/37.8 *Mercantile occupancy with mezzanine open to the street floor.*

in Table 7.3.3.1 (2000 for street floor + 1000 for mezzanine + 1000 for upper floors = 4000).

Paragraph 36/37.2.3.2 requires that the exits for the street floor of a Class A or Class B mercantile occupancy have sufficient capacity to handle the occupant load of the street floor and the capacity of the exits discharging through the street floor, such as an enclosed exit stair that accommodates occupants who, when exiting the building during an emergency, must travel up from the basement sales area or down from the upper sales floors and mix with the customers already occupying the street floor.

Because people move more quickly in the horizontal direction than in the vertical direction, it is permissible to provide less door width than stair width within any given egress path. For example, in mercantile occupancies, in accordance with the egress capacity factors of Table 7.3.3.1, level components and ramps require only 0.2 in. (0.5 cm) of width per person, whereas stairs require 0.3 in. (0.8 cm) of width per person. As a rough approximation, for every 44 in. (112 cm) of stair discharging through the street floor, an additional 30 in. (76 cm) of door width opening to the outside must be added to the street floor. Exhibit 36/37.9 illustrates the following example of the calculation method for determining the required exit capacity for the street floor.

Street floor occupant load alone	1000
Maximum upper floor occupant load discharging back through street floor (500 / 2)	+ 250
Basement occupant load discharging back through street floor (400 / 2)	+ 200
	1450 Total occupant load

1450 persons × 0.2 in. (0.5 cm) per person for level exit components per 7.3.3.1 = 290 in. (737 cm) of exit width required from the street floor egress system

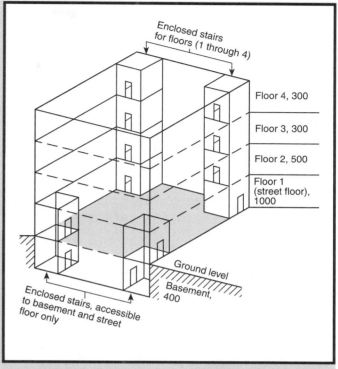

Exhibit 36/37.9 *Calculation of exit capacity required for a street floor in accordance with 36/37.2.3.2.*

36.2.4 Number of Exits.

Not less than two separate exits shall meet the following criteria *(see also Section 7.4):*

(1) They shall be provided on every story.
(2) They shall be accessible from every part of every story or mezzanine.

Exception No. 1:   Exit access travel shall be permitted to be common for the distances permitted as common paths of travel by 36.2.5.3.

Exception No. 2:   A single means of egress shall be permitted in a Class C mercantile occupancy, provided that one of the following conditions is met:

(a) The travel distance to the exit or to a covered mall (if it is considered a pedestrian way) does not exceed 75 ft (23 m).

37.2.4 Number of Exits.

Not less than two separate exits shall meet the following criteria:

(1) They shall be provided on every story.
(2) They shall be accessible from every part of every story or mezzanine.

Exception No. 1:   Exit access travel shall be permitted to be common for the distances permitted as common paths of travel by 37.2.5.3.

Exception No. 2:   A single means of egress shall be permitted in a Class C mercantile occupancy, provided that one of the following conditions is met:

(a) The travel distance to the exit or to a covered mall (if it is considered a pedestrian way) does not exceed 75 ft (23 m).

(b) The travel distance to the exit or to a covered mall (if it is considered a pedestrian way) does not exceed 100 ft (30 m), and the story on which the occupancy is located and all communicating levels that are traversed to reach the exit or covered mall are protected throughout by an approved, supervised automatic sprinkler system in accordance with Section 9.7.

Exception No. 3:   A single means of egress to an exit or to a covered mall (if it is considered a pedestrian way) shall be permitted from a mezzanine within any Class A, Class B, or Class C mercantile occupancy, provided that the common path of travel does not exceed 75 ft (23 m), or does not exceed 100 ft (30 m) if protected throughout by an approved, supervised automatic sprinkler system in accordance with Section 9.7.

(b) The travel distance to the exit or to a covered mall (if it is considered a pedestrian way) does not exceed 100 ft (30 m), and the story on which the occupancy is located and all communicating levels that are traversed to reach the exit or covered mall are protected throughout by an approved automatic sprinkler system in accordance with Section 9.7.

Exception No. 3:   A single means of egress to an exit or to a covered mall (if it is considered a pedestrian way) shall be permitted from a mezzanine within any Class A, Class B, or Class C mercantile occupancy, provided that the common path of travel does not exceed 75 ft (23 m), or does not exceed 100 ft (30 m) if protected throughout by an approved automatic sprinkler system in accordance with Section 9.7.

The provisions of 36/37.2.4, which apply to the required number of exits for mercantile occupancies, clarify that any level that constitutes a story must have at least two exits located on that story. This means that the occupants of the story must be able to enter an exit (such as an enclosed exit stair on an upper floor of a multistory building) without having to travel to another story to reach the entrance to the exit. Because a mezzanine that meets the maximum one-third or one-half area rule of 36/37.1.4.2.3 does not constitute a story (see the commentary associated with 36/37.1.4.2.3), two exits are not required on the mezzanine, but the criteria of 36/37.2.4(2) must be met with respect to providing access to two separate exits, or the provisions of the Exception No. 1 to 36/37.2.4 or Exception No. 2 to 36/37.2.4 must be met.

Exception No. 1 to 36/37.2.4 applies only to 36/37.2.4(2), which requires access to two separate exits from every part of every level (story or mezzanine). Exception No. 1 indicates that 36/37.2.5.3 allows the occupant to travel in one direction for a maximum distance (the common path allowance) before requiring access in two separate directions. Therefore, although the story or mezzanine must eventually provide access to two exits in accordance with 36/37.2.4(2), the access is required to be available only at the point where the allowable common path is expended.

Although the basic requirement of 36/37.2.4 mandates that a mercantile occupancy is to be provided with at least two remotely located exits, Exception No. 2 permits a single exit for Class C (small) mercantile stores, such as tobacco shops, newsstands, and small 24-hour convenience stores. If the travel distance

from any point in such a store to an exit is 75 ft (23 m) or less, the likelihood that a fire might surprise and overcome the customers before they could escape is low (see Exhibit 36/37.10). The exception also

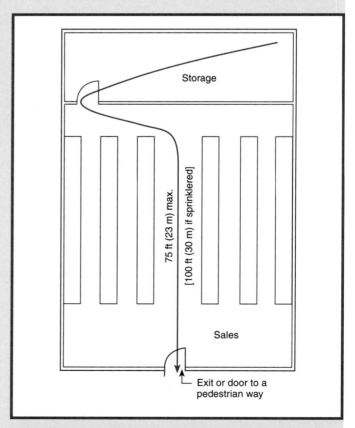

Exhibit 36/37.10 Single exit permitted in a Class C mercantile occupancy if travel distance is limited.

CHAPTER 36 • New

CHAPTER 37 • Existing

allows a single exit in small sprinklered mercantile occupancies if travel to an exit is not more than 100 ft (30 m). Furthermore, Exception No. 2 permits a single exit in Class C occupancies where travel distance to a covered mall that qualifies as a pedestrian way in accordance with the provisions of the exception to 36/37.4.4.1 does not exceed 100 ft (30 m). The provisions of the exception to 36/37.4.4.1 include an

automatic sprinkler system requirement for the entire covered mall building. Exception No. 2 provides additional flexibility and a potential increase in security for those small stores protected by means of automatic sprinkler installations within the store and for those portions of the overall building that occupants must traverse to reach an exit or pedestrian way.

36.2.5 Arrangement of Means of Egress.

36.2.5.1 Means of egress shall be arranged in accordance with Section 7.5.

36.2.5.2 Dead-end corridors shall not exceed 20 ft (6.1 m).

Exception: In buildings protected throughout by an approved, supervised automatic sprinkler system in accordance with Section 9.7, dead-end corridors shall not exceed 50 ft (15 m).

36.2.5.3 Common paths of travel shall not exceed 75 ft (23 m).

Exception: A common path of travel shall be permitted for the first 100 ft (30 m) in a building protected throughout by an approved, supervised automatic sprinkler system in accordance with Section 9.7.

37.2.5 Arrangement of Means of Egress.

37.2.5.1 Means of egress shall be arranged in accordance with Section 7.5.

37.2.5.2* Dead-end corridors shall not exceed 50 ft (15 m).

A.37.2.5.2 The purpose of 37.2.5.2 is to avoid pockets or dead ends of such size that they pose an undue danger of persons becoming trapped in case of fire.

It is recognized that dead ends exceeding the permitted limits exist and, in some cases, are impractical to eliminate. The authority having jurisdiction might permit such dead ends to continue to exist, taking into consideration any or all of the following:

(1) Tenant arrangement
(2) Automatic sprinkler protection
(3) Smoke detection
(4) Exit remoteness

37.2.5.3* Common paths of travel shall not exceed 75 ft (23 m).

Exception: A common path of travel shall be permitted for the first 100 ft (30 m) on a story protected throughout by an approved automatic sprinkler system in accordance with Section 9.7.

A.37.2.5.3 It is recognized that common paths of travel exceeding the permitted limits exist and, in some cases, are impractical to eliminate. The authority having jurisdiction might permit such paths of travel to continue to exist, taking into consideration any or all of the following:

(1) Tenant arrangement
(2) Automatic sprinkler protection
(3) Smoke detection
(4) Exit remoteness

36.2.5.4 Aisles leading to each exit shall be required. The aggregate width of such aisles shall be not less than the required width of the exit.

37.2.5.4 Aisles leading to each exit shall be required. The aggregate width of such aisles shall be not less than the required width of the exit.

CHAPTER 36 • New

36.2.5.5 Required aisles shall be not less than 36 in. (91 cm) in clear width.

36.2.5.6 In Class A mercantile occupancies, not less than one aisle of a 5-ft (1.5-m) minimum width shall lead directly to an exit.

36.2.5.7 If the only means of customer entrance is through one exterior wall of the building, two-thirds of the required egress width shall be located in such wall.

Exception: Bulk merchandising retail buildings. (See 36.4.5.2.)

36.2.5.8 Not less than one-half of the required exits shall be located so as to be reached without passing through checkout stands. In no case shall checkout stands or associated railings or barriers obstruct exits, required aisles, or approaches thereto.

36.2.5.9* Where wheeled carts or buggies are used by customers, adequate provision shall be made for the transit and parking of such carts to minimize the possibility that they might obstruct means of egress.

A.36.2.5.9 In order to eliminate the obstruction to the means of egress of the interior exit access and the exterior exit discharge, it is the intent to provide adequate area for transit and parking of wheeled carts or buggies used by customers. This area includes corral areas adjacent to exits that are constructed to restrict the movement of wheeled carts or buggies therefrom.

36.2.5.10 Exit access in Class A and Class B mercantile occupancies that are protected throughout by an approved, supervised automatic sprinkler system and exit access in all Class C mercantile occupancies shall be permitted to pass through storerooms, provided that the following conditions are met:

(1) Not more than 50 percent of exit access shall be provided through the storeroom.
(2) The storeroom shall not be subject to locking.
(3) The main aisle through the storeroom shall be not less than 44 in. (112 cm) wide.
(4) The path of travel through the storeroom, defined with fixed barriers, shall be direct and continuously maintained in an unobstructed condition.

The exception to 36.2.5.2 recognizes the additional level of safety to life provided by a complete automatic sprinkler system and permits added flexibility when designing the location of corridors and exits

CHAPTER 37 • Existing

37.2.5.5 Required aisles shall be not less than 28 in. (71 cm) in clear width.

37.2.5.6 In Class A mercantile occupancies, not less than one aisle of a 5-ft (1.5-m) minimum width shall lead directly to an exit.

37.2.5.7 If the only means of customer entrance is through one exterior wall of the building, two-thirds of the required egress width shall be located in such wall.

Exception: Bulk merchandising retail buildings. (See 37.4.5.2.)

37.2.5.8 Not less than one-half of the required exits shall be located so as to be reached without passing through checkout stands. In no case shall checkout stands or associated railings or barriers obstruct exits, required aisles, or approaches thereto.

37.2.5.9* Where wheeled carts or buggies are used by customers, adequate provision shall be made for the transit and parking of such carts to minimize the possibility that they might obstruct means of egress.

A.37.2.5.9 In order to eliminate the obstruction to the means of egress of the interior exit access and the exterior exit discharge, it is the intent to provide adequate area for transit and parking of wheeled carts or buggies used by customers. This area includes corral areas adjacent to exits that are constructed to restrict the movement of wheeled carts or buggies therefrom.

37.2.5.10 Exit access in Class A mercantile occupancies that are protected throughout by an approved, supervised automatic sprinkler system in accordance with Section 9.7 and exit access in all Class B and Class C mercantile occupancies shall be permitted to pass through storerooms, provided that the following conditions are met:

(1) Not more than 50 percent of exit access shall be provided through the storeroom.
(2) The storeroom shall not be subject to locking.
(3) The main aisle through the storeroom shall be not less than 44 in. (112 cm) wide.
(4) The path of travel through the storeroom, defined with fixed barriers, shall be direct and continuously maintained in an unobstructed condition.

in buildings where approved sprinkler systems are installed. The exception allows dead-end corridor pockets in new mercantile occupancies to be as long as 50 ft (15 m). Dead-end corridor pockets in existing mercantile occupancies are permitted to be 50 ft (15 m) long without any requirement for sprinklers.

Common path of travel limits are provided in 36/37.2.5.3. See the commentary following 7.5.1.6 for a detailed discussion on common path of travel. Also see the commentary on Exception No. 1 to 36/37.2.4, which allows the access to a single exit or a portion of the access to multiple exits to be common.

The provisions of 36/37.2.5.4 are intended to prevent constrictions in the means of egress system that would delay egress of building occupants. The aggregate width of aisles leading to an exit are required to provide egress width equal to that required of the exit to which they lead. Without this provision, occupants could be forced to squeeze through a relatively narrow aisle or similar constriction before reaching, for example, an expansive bank of doors to the outside. The exit capacity at the doors, rather than providing simultaneous egress for the large number of occupants assigned to that exit, would not be fully utilized. Occupants would move through the doors a few at a time as they passed slowly through the constriction. The requirement of 36/37.2.5.4 is illustrated in Exhibit 36/37.11 in the upper left and right corners of the floor plan of the mercantile occupancy.

The minimum 36-in. (91-cm) aisle width required for new mercantile occupancies by 36.2.5.5, and the minimum 28-in. (71-cm) aisle width required for existing mercantile occupancies by 37.2.5.5, are illustrated in Exhibit 36/37.11. These minimum widths are consistent with those of 7.3.4.1 and Exception No. 3 to 7.3.4.1.

The intent of 36/37.2.5.4 through 36/37.2.5.6 is to ensure that the interior arrangement of counters, racks, and displays of merchandise does not block or obscure access to an exit. Exhibit 36/37.11 illustrates an arrangement that meets the requirements for a Class A store. Essentially, the width of the exit determines the minimum width of the aisles, with the exception that one of the aisles must be at least 5 ft (152 cm) wide and lead directly to an exit.

In establishing the requirements of 36/37.2.5.7, the *Code* demonstrates its concern regarding the arrangement of many discount and variety stores that have one large main exit/entrance located in the front of the store and the other exits (which cannot be used as entrances) situated at points unfamiliar to the public. In these mercantile occupancy arrangements, the wall containing the main exit/entrance must be sized to handle two-thirds of the required egress ca-

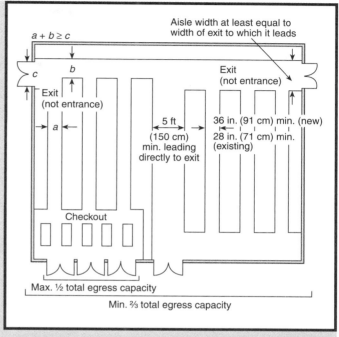

Exhibit 36/37.11 *Means of egress arrangement in a Class A mercantile occupancy.*

pacity of the store because the public is familiar with this entrance/exit and most customers will use it as an exit under emergency conditions. This requirement is illustrated in the lower portion of Exhibit 36/37.11.

Paragraph 36/37.2.5.8 contains one of the most frequently violated provisions of Chapter 36/37. In many supermarkets and discount and variety stores, it is necessary to pass through checkout counters, around shopping carts, and through turnstiles to exit the facility. This process causes congestion or blockage during an emergency. The *Code* requires at least one-half of all exits to be located so that occupants can avoid passing through or around these impediments to egress. See Exhibit 36/37.11.

Paragraph 36/37.2.5.9 addresses the potential encroachment on egress width by shopping carts. In jurisdicitons where returnable beverage bottle legislation has been enacted, stores and markets have had to create space for collecting empty bottles and refunding deposit charges. The area most commonly used is located near the entrance/exit where wheeled shopping carts were formerly stored to be clear of the path of egress travel. The displaced carts are now often stored so that they obstruct the means of egress.

CHAPTER 36 • New	CHAPTER 37 • Existing

This illustrates a situation where a properly designed, installed, and complying means of egress might be compromised abruptly by unexpected changes.

Paragraph 36/37.2.5.10 addresses egress paths through storerooms in the following occupancies:

(1) All Class C mercantile occupancies
(2) Existing Class B mercantile occupancies
(3) New Class B mercantile occupancies protected throughout by an approved, supervised automatic sprinkler system
(4) All Class A mercantile occupancies protected throughout by an approved, supervised automatic sprinkler system

Paragraph 36/37.2.5.10(1) limits the storeroom to

providing a maximum of 50 percent of the store's exit access in number of exits and exit capacity. Therefore, because two exits are required, neither of the following limits can be exceeded:

(1) Only one of the two required exits can be reached by exit access travel through the storeroom.
(2) A maximum of one-half of the store's occupant load is permitted to egress through the storeroom.

Exhibits 36/37.12 and 36/37.13 illustrate the application of the provisions of 36/37.2.5.10. The aisle within the storeroom must be defined by fixed barriers, such as those formed by the ends of shelving. The aisle must be kept unobstructed.

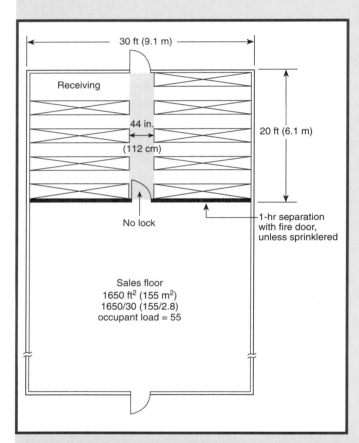

Exhibit 36/37.12 Exit access through a storeroom as permitted by 36/37.2.5.10.

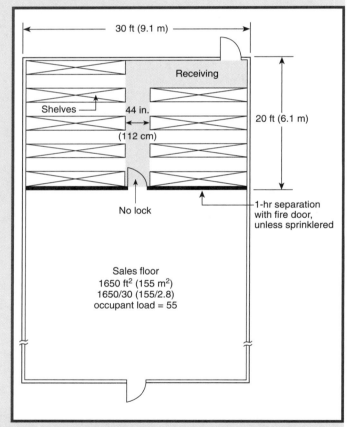

Exhibit 36/37.13 Exit access through a storeroom that is problematic because it passes through receiving area.

CHAPTER 36 • New

CHAPTER 37 • Existing

36.2.6 Travel Distance to Exits.

Travel distance to exits, measured in accordance with Section 7.6, shall not exceed 100 ft (30 m).

Exception: Travel distance shall not exceed 200 ft (60 m) in buildings protected throughout by an approved, supervised automatic sprinkler system in accordance with Section 9.7.

In accordance with Section 7.6, travel distance requirements apply to only the first (or nearest) exit from a given point in the building. In other words, the 100-ft (30-m) travel distance limit for new mercantile occupancies [150 ft (45 m) for existing occupancies] requires that at least one exit must be located within

37.2.6 Travel Distance to Exits.

Travel distance to exits, measured in accordance with Section 7.6, shall not exceed 150 ft (45 m).

Exception: Travel distance shall not exceed 200 ft (60 m) in buildings protected throughout by an approved automatic sprinkler system in accordance with Section 9.7.

100 ft (30 m) of a point in the building; it does not require that all exits must be within 100 ft (30 m) of that same point in the building. In sprinklered buildings this distance is permitted to be increased to 200 ft (60 m).

36.2.7 Discharge from Exits.

36.2.7.1 Exit discharge shall comply with Section 7.7 and 36.2.7.2.

36.2.7.2* Fifty percent of the exits shall be permitted to discharge through the level of exit discharge in accordance with 7.7.2 only where the building is protected throughout by an approved, supervised automatic sprinkler system in accordance with Section 9.7, and the distance of travel from the termination of the exit enclosure to an outside street door shall not exceed 50 ft (15 m).

A.36.2.7.2 The basis for the exception to the general rule on complete enclosure of exits up to their point of discharge to the outside of the building is that, with the specified safeguards, reasonable safety is maintained.

A stairway is not considered to discharge through the street floor area if it leads to the street through a fire resistance–rated enclosure (exit passageway) separating it from the main area, even though there are doors between the first floor stairway landing and the main area.

The provisions of 36.2.7.2 should not be confused with those for open stairways as permitted by 36.3.1, Exception No. 1.

37.2.7 Discharge from Exits.

37.2.7.1 Exit discharge shall comply with Section 7.7 and 37.2.7.2.

37.2.7.2* Fifty percent of the exits shall be permitted to discharge through the level of exit discharge in accordance with 7.7.2 only where the building is protected throughout by an approved automatic sprinkler system in accordance with Section 9.7, and the distance of travel from the termination of the exit enclosure to an outside street door shall not exceed 50 ft (15 m).

A.37.2.7.2 The basis for the exception to the general rule on complete enclosure of exits up to their point of discharge to the outside of the building is that, with the specified safeguards, reasonable safety is maintained.

A stairway is not considered to discharge through the street floor area if it leads to the street through a fire resistance– rated enclosure (exit passageway) separating it from the main area, even though there are doors between the first floor stairway landing and the main area.

The provisions of 37.2.7.2 should not be confused with those for open stairways as permitted by 37.3.1, Exception No. 1 and Exception No. 4.

The restriction imposed by 36/37.2.7.2 is intended to prevent more than 50 percent of the exits from any floor from discharging through the street floor. Furthermore, such exit discharge is permitted only where the building is sprinklered throughout. Note that the path of travel on the first floor from the stair enclosure to the outside door cannot exceed 50 ft (15 m). The

remaining 50 percent of the exits must discharge directly to the exterior.

The requirements of 36/37.2.7.2 are more stringent than those of 7.7.2, because they mandate automatic sprinkler protection throughout the building, set a 50-ft (15-m) interior exit discharge travel limit on the street floor, and require the street floor to have

CHAPTER 36 • New	**CHAPTER 37 • Existing**

an exit capacity that accommodates the occupant load of the street floor and the stairs discharging through the street floor. These requirements are not mandated by 7.7.2. The added requirements are imposed

in recognition of the high combustible load of merchandise that might be on display, which is characteristic of mercantile occupancies.

36.2.8 Illumination of Means of Egress.

Means of egress shall be illuminated in accordance with Section 7.8.

37.2.8 Illumination of Means of Egress.

Means of egress shall be illuminated in accordance with Section 7.8.

36.2.9 Emergency Lighting.

Class A and Class B mercantile occupancies and covered mall buildings shall have emergency lighting facilities in accordance with Section 7.9.

37.2.9 Emergency Lighting.

Class A and Class B mercantile occupancies and covered mall buildings shall have emergency lighting facilities in accordance with Section 7.9.

36.2.10 Marking of Means of Egress.

Means of egress shall have signs in accordance with Section 7.10.

Exception: Where an exit is immediately apparent from all portions of the sales area, the exit marking shall not be required.

37.2.10 Marking of Means of Egress.

Means of egress shall have signs in accordance with Section 7.10.

Exception: Where an exit is immediately apparent from all portions of the sales area, the exit marking shall not be required.

36.2.11 Special Means of Egress Features.

(Reserved.)

37.2.11 Special Means of Egress Features.

(Reserved.)

Note that illumination for the means of egress, addressed in 36/37.2.8, is not the same as emergency lighting. Failure of the building power supply might cause failure of the means of egress illumination system, which is not required to have a backup, auxiliary, or secondary power supply unless required by 36/37.2.9.

Emergency lighting is addressed in 36/37.2.9. Due to their small size and small occupant load, Class C mercantile occupancies are not required by the *Code* to have emergency lighting facilities.

The intent of the exception to 36/37.2.10 is to avoid requiring exit signs in small areas where the exit is readily apparent. For example, exit signs would not be required in the office of a service station, the purchase and eating areas of a small fast food restaurant, or in a Class C store where size and arrangement comply with the single-exit requirements of Exception No. 2 to 36/37.2.4.

Section 36.3 Protection

36.3.1 Protection of Vertical Openings.

Any vertical opening shall be enclosed or protected in accordance with 8.2.5.

Exception No. 1:   In Class A or Class B mercantile occupancies protected throughout by an approved, supervised

Section 37.3 Protection

37.3.1 Protection of Vertical Openings.

Any vertical opening shall be enclosed or protected in accordance with 8.2.5.

Exception No. 1:   In Class A or Class B mercantile occupancies protected throughout by an approved automatic

|

automatic sprinkler system in accordance with Section 9.7, unprotected vertical openings shall be permitted at one of the following locations:

(a) Between any two floors

(b) Among the street floor, the first adjacent floor below, and the first adjacent floor (or mezzanines) above

Exception No. 2: In Class C mercantile occupancies, unprotected openings shall be permitted between the street floor and the mezzanine.

Exception No. 3: In Class A or Class B mercantile occupancies protected throughout by an approved, supervised automatic sprinkler system in accordance with Section 9.7, unenclosed openings in accordance with 8.2.5.5 shall be permitted.

36.3.2 Protection from Hazards.

36.3.2.1* Hazardous areas including, but not limited to, areas used for general storage, boiler or furnace rooms, and maintenance shops that include woodworking and painting areas shall be protected in accordance with Section 8.4.

Exception: In general storage and stock areas protected by an automatic extinguishing system in accordance with Section 9.7, an enclosure, if provided, shall be exempt from the provisions of 8.4.1.2.

A.36.3.2.1 It is the intent to permit a suspended natural gas–fired unit heater that complies with the requirements of

---

sprinkler system in accordance with Section 9.7, unprotected vertical openings shall be permitted at one of the following locations:

(a) Among the street floor, the floor below, and the floor above

(b) Among the street floor, the floor below, and the street floor mezzanines

(c) Among the street floor, the street floor mezzanines, and the second floor, but not among more than three floor levels

(d) Among all floors permitted in Class B mercantile occupancies

(e) Among the floors permitted by (a), (b), (c), or (d) plus the floor immediately above if that floor is not used for sales purposes

Exception No. 2: In Class C mercantile occupancies, unenclosed vertical openings shall be permitted at one of the following locations:

(a) Between the street floor and the mezzanine

(b) Between the street floor and the floor below if the floor below is not used for sales purposes

(c) Between the street floor and the second floor if the second floor is not used for sales purposes

Exception No. 3: In Class A or Class B mercantile occupancies protected throughout by an approved, supervised automatic sprinkler system in accordance with Section 9.7, unenclosed openings in accordance with 8.2.5.5 shall be permitted.

Exception No. 4: In Class A or Class B mercantile occupancies, unenclosed openings shall be permitted between any two floors, such as between the street floor and the floor below, between the street floor and the mezzanine, or between the street floor and the second floor.

37.3.2 Protection from Hazards.

37.3.2.1* Hazardous areas including, but not limited to, areas used for general storage, boiler or furnace rooms, and maintenance shops that include woodworking and painting areas shall be protected in accordance with Section 8.4.

Exception: In general storage and stock areas protected by an automatic extinguishing system in accordance with Section 9.7, an enclosure, if provided, shall be exempt from the provisions of 8.4.1.2.

A.37.3.2.1 It is the intent to permit a suspended natural gas–fired unit heater that complies with the requirements of

CHAPTER 36 • New	CHAPTER 37 • Existing

Section 9.2 to be installed and used in a mercantile occupancy without classifying the area in which it is located as hazardous.

36.3.2.2* High hazard contents areas, as classified in Section 6.2, shall meet the following criteria:

(1) The area shall be separated from other parts of the building by fire barriers having a fire resistance rating of not less than 1 hour, with all openings therein protected by ¾-hour fire protection–rated self-closing fire doors.
(2) The area shall be protected by an automatic extinguishing system in accordance with Section 9.7.

A.36.3.2.2 The requirement for separating high hazard contents areas from other parts of the building is intended to isolate the hazard, and Exception No. 1 to 8.2.3.1.1 is applicable.

36.3.3 Interior Finish.

36.3.3.1 Interior finish shall be in accordance with Section 10.2.

36.3.3.2 Interior Wall and Ceiling Finish. Interior wall and ceiling finish complying with 10.2.3 shall be Class A or Class B.

36.3.3.3 Interior Floor Finish. (No requirements.)

Section 9.2 to be installed and used in a mercantile occupancy without classifying the area in which it is located as hazardous.

37.3.2.2* High hazard contents areas, as classified in Section 6.2, shall meet the following criteria:

(1) The area shall be separated from other parts of the building by fire barriers having a fire resistance rating of not less than 1 hour, with all openings therein protected by ¾-hour fire protection–rated self-closing fire doors.
(2) The area shall be protected by an automatic extinguishing system in accordance with Section 9.7.

A.37.3.2.2 The requirement for separating high hazard contents areas from other parts of the building is intended to isolate the hazard, and Exception No. 1 to 8.2.3.1.1 is applicable.

37.3.3 Interior Finish.

37.3.3.1 Interior finish shall be in accordance with Section 10.2.

37.3.3.2 Interior Wall and Ceiling Finish. Interior wall and ceiling finish complying with 10.2.3 shall be Class A or Class B.

Exception: Existing Class C interior wall and ceiling finish complying with 10.2.3 shall be permitted as follows:

> *(a) On walls*
>
> *(b) Throughout Class C stores*

37.3.3.3 Interior Floor Finish. (No requirements.)

Subsection 36/37.3.1 addresses vertical openings. Follow the provisions of 36/37.1.7 to properly assess that the occupant load provides sufficient egress capacity for a store in which floors or mezzanines are open to the street floor. Exception No. 1 to 36/37.3.1 specifies conditions under which such openings are permitted in sprinklered Class A and Class B mercantile occupancies.

Subsection 36/37.3.2 addresses the protection of hazardous areas. Paragraph 8.4.1.2 normally requires that a hazardous area protected by automatic sprinklers, rather than by enclosure with fire barriers with a 1-hour fire resistance rating and doors with a 45-minute fire protection rating, is to be enclosed by walls and doors that are at least smoke resisting. The exception to 36/37.3.2.1 allows hazardous areas comprised of general storage and stock areas in a mercan-

tile occupancy to be protected by automatic sprinklers without the need for a smoke-resisting enclosure. In a shoe store, for example, where the shoe storage area is sprinklered, no door would be required on the opening between the sales floor and the storage area.

Paragraphs 36/37.3.2.1 and 36/37.3.2.2 reflect the intent of Section 8.4, which requires one of the following:

(1) Separation of a hazardous contents area from the remainder of the occupancy by means of suitable construction
(2) Installation of an automatic sprinkler system in a hazardous area
(3) Both items (1) and (2) where the hazard is severe

Subsection 36/37.3.3 addresses interior finish. The exception to 37.3.3.2 states that, in existing Class

C stores only, all interior finish (walls and ceilings) is permitted to be rated as Class C (flame spread as high as 200). All existing Class A and B stores are

36.3.4 Detection, Alarm, and Communications Systems.

36.3.4.1 General. Class A mercantile occupancies shall be provided with a fire alarm system in accordance with Section 9.6.

36.3.4.2 Initiation. Initiation of the required fire alarm system shall be by manual means per 9.6.2.1(1).

Exception No. 1: Initiation shall be permitted to be by means of an approved automatic fire detection system in accordance with 9.6.2.1(2) that provides protection throughout the building.

Exception No. 2: Initiation shall be permitted to be by means of an approved automatic sprinkler system in accordance with 9.6.2.1(3) that provides protection throughout the building.

36.3.4.3 Notification.

36.3.4.3.1 Occupant Notification. During all times that the mercantile occupancy is occupied (see 7.2.1.1.3), the required fire alarm system, once initiated, shall perform one of the following functions.

(a) It shall activate a general alarm in accordance with 9.6.3 throughout the mercantile occupancy.

Exception: Positive alarm sequence in accordance with 9.6.3.4 shall be permitted.

(b) It shall activate an alarm signal in a continuously attended location for the purpose of initiating emergency action by personnel trained to respond to emergencies. Emergency action shall be initiated by means of live voice public address system announcements originating from the attended location where the alarm signal is received. The system shall be permitted to be used for other announcements, provided that the fire alarm use takes precedence over any other use.

Exception: Any other occupant notification means permitted by 9.6.3 shall be permitted in lieu of live voice public address system announcements.

permitted to use Class C interior finish on the walls, but such finish is prohibited on the ceiling.

37.3.4 Detection, Alarm, and Communications Systems.

37.3.4.1 General. Class A mercantile occupancies shall be provided with a fire alarm system in accordance with Section 9.6.

37.3.4.2 Initiation. Initiation of the required fire alarm system shall be by manual means per 9.6.2.1(1).

Exception No. 1: Initiation shall be permitted to be by means of an approved automatic fire detection system in accordance with 9.6.2.1(2) that provides protection throughout the building.

Exception No. 2: Initiation shall be permitted to be by means of an approved automatic sprinkler system in accordance with 9.6.2.1(3) that provides protection throughout the building.

37.3.4.3 Notification.

37.3.4.3.1 Occupant Notification. During all times that the mercantile occupancy is occupied (see 7.2.1.1.3), the required fire alarm system, once initiated, shall perform one of the following functions.

(a) It shall activate a general alarm in accordance with 9.6.3 throughout the mercantile occupancy.

Exception No. 1: Positive alarm sequence in accordance with 9.6.3.4 shall be permitted.

Exception No. 2: A presignal system in accordance with 9.6.3.3 shall be permitted.

(b) It shall activate an alarm signal in a continuously attended location for the purpose of initiating emergency action by personnel trained to respond to emergencies. Emergency action shall be initiated by means of live voice public address system announcements originating from the attended location where the alarm signal is received. The system shall be permitted to be used for other announcements, provided that the fire alarm use takes precedence over any other use.

Exception: Any other occupant notification means permitted by 9.6.3 shall be permitted in lieu of live voice public address system announcements.

CHAPTER 36 • New

CHAPTER 37 • Existing

36.3.4.3.2 Emergency Forces Notification. Emergency forces notification shall be provided and shall include notifying the following:

(1) The fire department in accordance with 9.6.4
(2) The local emergency organization, if provided

Class B and Class C mercantile occupancies are not required to have a fire alarm system.

Because all new Class A stores and most existing Class A stores must be sprinklered based on gross floor area (see 36/37.3.5.1), it is logical that the sprinkler system waterflow method described in Exception No. 2 to 36/37.3.4.2 will be used most commonly to activate the fire alarm system. The requirement for manual fire alarm boxes is waived if the sprinkler waterflow activates the fire alarm system. Nuisance alarms might be reduced by eliminating the manual fire alarm boxes and satisfying the initiation requirements by means of waterflow through the sprinkler system. However, in accordance with the provisions of 9.6.2.5, at least one manual fire alarm box must be provided at a location determined by the authority having jurisdiction.

36.3.5 Extinguishment Requirements.

36.3.5.1 Mercantile occupancies shall be protected by an approved automatic sprinkler system in accordance with Section 9.7 as follows:

(1) Throughout all mercantile occupancies three or more stories in height
(2) Throughout all mercantile occupancies exceeding 12,000 ft² (1115 m²) in gross area
(3) Throughout stories below the level of exit discharge where such stories have an area exceeding 2500 ft² (230 m²) used for the sale, storage, or handling of combustible goods and merchandise
(4) Throughout mixed occupancies in accordance with 6.1.14 where the conditions of 36.3.5.1(1), (2), or (3) apply to the mercantile occupancy

36.3.5.2 Automatic sprinkler systems in Class A mercantile occupancies shall be supervised in accordance with 9.7.2.

36.3.5.3 Portable fire extinguishers shall be provided in all mercantile occupancies in accordance with 9.7.4.1.

37.3.4.3.2 Emergency Forces Notification. Emergency forces notification shall be provided and shall include notifying the following:

(1) The fire department in accordance with 9.6.4
(2) The local emergency organization, if provided

The exception to 36.3.4.3.1(a) and Exception No. 1 to 37.3.4.3.1(a) recognize positive alarm sequence, which is an updated form of a presignal system for which numerous safeguards must be provided. Exception No. 2 to 37.3.4.3.1(a), which applies only to existing mercantile occupancies, continues to recognize presignal systems.

Note that 36/37.3.4.3.1 provides a choice between two methods of notification. Many Class A stores do have a continuously attended location, and, therefore, 36/37.3.4.3.1(b) can be used; if such a location is not provided or not considered reliable by the authority having jurisdiction, 36/37.3.4.3.1(a) must be applied to provide an automatic general alarm in accordance with 9.6.3.

Paragraph 9.6.4 allows for several different methods of automatically notifying the fire department.

37.3.5 Extinguishment Requirements.

37.3.5.1 Mercantile occupancies shall be protected by an approved automatic sprinkler system in accordance with Section 9.7 as follows:

(1) Throughout all mercantile occupancies with a story over 15,000 ft² (1400 m²) in area
(2) Throughout all mercantile occupancies exceeding 30,000 ft² (2800 m²) in gross area
(3) Throughout stories below the level of exit discharge where such stories have an area exceeding 2500 ft² (230 m²) used for the sale, storage, or handling of combustible goods and merchandise
(4) Throughout mixed occupancies in accordance with 6.1.14 where the conditions of 37.3.5.1(1), (2), or (3) apply to the mercantile occupancy

Exception: Single-story buildings that meet the requirements of a street floor as defined in 3.3.196.

37.3.5.2 (Reserved.)

37.3.5.3 Portable fire extinguishers shall be provided in all mercantile occupancies in accordance with 9.7.4.1.

CHAPTER 36 • New	CHAPTER 37 • Existing

For information on the proper criteria for an approved automatic sprinkler system, refer to the following:

(1) NFPA 13, *Standard for the Installation of Sprinkler Systems*[2]
(2) NFPA 25, *Standard for the Inspection, Testing, and Maintenance of Water-Based Fire Protection Systems*[3]
(3) *Automatic Sprinkler and Standpipe Systems*[4]

Paragraph 36/37.3.5.1(3) requires that all basement areas larger than 2500 ft² (230 m²) and used for sales, storage, or the handling of combustible merchandise are to be sprinklered to avoid the potential threat to occupants of the floors above. Studies have shown that there is a higher rate of fire incidence in basements than in other areas of stores. Because smoke and heat rise, a fire in a basement can quickly render exits and exit discharges located on the street

floor unusable. This danger is especially acute in mercantile occupancies, where allowances for various vertical openings in accordance with the provisions of 36/37.3.1 and its exceptions are more lenient than those for other occupancies.

The exception to 37.3.5.1 applies to existing buildings only. It is believed that, in existing, one-story, street-floor buildings that comply with all other provisions of the *Code*, including travel distance, adequate life safety is provided. Therefore, requiring a building to be sprinklered retroactively is unnecessary. The term *street floor* is defined in 3.3.196 and includes a maximum of three risers of ascent or descent to reach the ground level.

The portable fire extinguishers required by 36/37.3.5.3 are to be used by properly trained employees of the mercantile occupancy as required by 36/37.7.2.

36.3.6 Corridors.

36.3.6.1* Where access to exits is provided by corridors, such corridors shall be separated from use areas by walls having a fire resistance rating of not less than 1 hour in accordance with 8.2.3.

Exception No. 1:   Where exits are available from an open floor area.

Exception No. 2:   Within a space occupied by a single tenant.

Exception No. 3:   Within buildings protected throughout by an approved, supervised automatic sprinkler system in accordance with Section 9.7.

A.36.3.6.1 The intent of Exception No. 2 and Exception No. 3 to 36.3.6.1 is to permit spaces within single tenant spaces, or within buildings protected throughout by an approved, supervised automatic sprinkler system, to be open to the exit access corridor without separation.

36.3.6.2 Openings in corridor walls required by 36.3.6.1 to have a fire resistance rating shall be protected in accordance with 8.2.3.

37.3.6 Corridors.

(No requirements.)

36.3.7 Subdivision of Building Spaces.

(No special requirements.)

37.3.7 Subdivision of Building Spaces.

(No special requirements.)

| CHAPTER 36 • New | CHAPTER 37 • Existing |

36.3.8 Special Protection Features.

Nonrated glazing and nonrated opening protectives per the exception to 36.1.2.2 shall be permitted between mercantile occupancies and parking structures.

37.3.8 Special Protection Features.

Nonrated glazing and nonrated opening protectives per the exception to 37.1.2.2 shall be permitted between mercantile occupancies and parking structures.

Section 36.4 Special Provisions

36.4.1 Windowless or Underground Buildings.

(See Section 11.7.)

36.4.2 High-Rise Buildings.

High-rise buildings shall comply with the automatic sprinkler requirements of 11.8.2.1.

36.4.3 Open-Air Mercantile Operations.

36.4.3.1 Open-air mercantile operations, such as open-air markets, gasoline filling stations, roadside stands for the sale of farm produce, and other outdoor mercantile operations shall be arranged and conducted to maintain free and unobstructed ways of travel at all times. Such ways of travel shall allow prompt escape from any point of danger in case of fire or other emergency, with no dead ends in which persons might be trapped due to display stands, adjoining buildings, fences, vehicles, or other obstructions.

36.4.3.2 If mercantile operations are conducted in roofed-over areas, they shall be treated as mercantile buildings, provided that canopies over individual small stands to protect merchandise from the weather are not construed as constituting buildings for the purpose of this *Code*.

Section 37.4 Special Provisions

37.4.1 Windowless or Underground Buildings.

(See Section 11.7.)

37.4.2 High-Rise Buildings.

(No additional requirements.)

37.4.3 Open-Air Mercantile Operations.

37.4.3.1 Open-air mercantile operations, such as open-air markets, gasoline filling stations, roadside stands for the sale of farm produce, and other outdoor mercantile operations shall be arranged and conducted to maintain free and unobstructed ways of travel at all times. Such ways of travel shall allow prompt escape from any point of danger in case of fire or other emergency, with no dead ends in which persons might be trapped due to display stands, adjoining buildings, fences, vehicles, or other obstructions.

37.4.3.2 If mercantile operations are conducted in roofed-over areas, they shall be treated as mercantile buildings, provided that canopies over individual small stands to protect merchandise from the weather are not construed as constituting buildings for the purpose of this *Code*.

The provisions of Section 11.8, whether applied singly, in various combinations, or in total, must be mandated by specific occupancy chapter requirements. In new high-rise mercantile occupancies, 36.4.2 requires only the provisions of 11.8.2.1—an approved, supervised, automatic sprinkler system with an additional sprinkler control valve and waterflow device on each floor. The new high-rise mercantile occupancy must have a sprinkler system in accordance with 36.3.5.1 and the associated system supervision requirement of 36.3.5.2 for Class A stores, regardless of the reference to 11.8.2.1.

Paragraph 36/37.4.3.1 is virtually an open-ended provision that provides guidance for the arrangement, use, and display of merchandise for sale in open-air mercantile operations. The phrase "ways of travel" is purposely used to avoid confusion with means of egress. The term *means of egress* (see definition in 3.3.121) is strictly defined, and its use implies the application of the minimum requirements of Chapter 7. The phrase "ways of travel" is not defined and implies no specific minimum *Code* provisions. Most open-air mercantile operations have unlimited means of entering and evacuating the areas used to display goods. For this reason, it is not necessary to provide specific *Code* requirements beyond the precautionary measures expressed in this paragraph.

The intent of 36/37.4.3.2 is to exempt small merchandise stands with canopies from classification as mercantile buildings. All other roofed-over areas should be treated as buildings, classified by area and height as Class A, Class B, or Class C mercantile occupancies and subject to the appropriate provisions of Chapter 36/37.

36.4.4 Covered Mall Buildings.

The purpose of 36.4.4 is to establish minimum standards of life safety for covered mall buildings having not more than three levels. *(See 3.3.25.3.)*

36.4.4.1 The covered mall building shall be treated as a single building for the purpose of calculation of means of egress and shall be subject to the requirements for appropriate occupancies, except as modified by the provisions of 36.4.4. The covered mall shall be of a clear width not less than that needed to accommodate egress requirements as set forth in other sections of this *Code*.

Exception: The covered mall shall be permitted to be considered a pedestrian way, in which case the travel distance within a tenant space to an exit or to the covered mall shall not exceed 200 ft (60 m) (see 36.2.6, exception) or shall not exceed the maximum for the appropriate occupancy. An additional 200 ft (60 m) shall be permitted for travel through the covered mall space if all the following requirements are met.

(a) The covered mall shall be of a clear width not less than that needed to accommodate egress requirements as set forth in other sections of this chapter but shall be not less than 20 ft (6.1 m) wide in its narrowest dimension.

(b)* On each side of the mall floor area, the covered mall shall be provided with an unobstructed exit access of not less than 10 ft (3 m) in clear width parallel to and adjacent to the mall tenant front. Such exit access shall lead to an exit having a width of not less than 66 in. (168 cm). (See 36.4.4.2.)

A.36.4.4.1 Exception (b) The minimum requirement for terminating mall exit access in not less than 66 in. (168 cm) of egress width relates to the minimum requirement for not less than one aisle in Class A mercantile occupancies (30,000 ft² (2800 m²) or greater sales area) to be 5 ft (152 cm) in width.

(c) The covered mall and all buildings connected thereto shall be protected throughout by an approved, supervised automatic sprinkler system in accordance with Section 9.7. The system shall be installed in such a manner that any portion of the system serving tenant spaces can be taken out of service without affecting the operation of the portion of the system serving the covered mall.

(d) Walls dividing tenant spaces from each other shall extend from the floor to the underside of the roof deck, floor deck above, or ceiling where the ceiling is constructed to limit the transfer of smoke. Where the tenant areas are provided with an engineered smoke control system, walls

37.4.4 Covered Mall Buildings.

The purpose of 37.4.4 is to establish minimum standards of life safety for covered mall buildings. *(See 3.3.25.3.)*

37.4.4.1 The covered mall building shall be treated as a single building for the purpose of calculation of means of egress and shall be subject to the requirements for appropriate occupancies, except as modified by the provisions of 37.4.4. The covered mall shall be of a clear width not less than that needed to accommodate egress requirements as set forth in other sections of this *Code*.

Exception: The covered mall shall be permitted to be considered a pedestrian way, in which case the travel distance within a tenant space to an exit or to the covered mall shall not exceed 200 ft (60 m) (see 37.2.6, exception) or shall not exceed the maximum for the appropriate occupancy. An additional 200 ft (60 m) shall be permitted for travel through the covered mall space if all the following requirements are met.

(a) The covered mall shall be of a clear width not less than that needed to accommodate egress requirements as set forth in other sections of this chapter but shall be not less than 20 ft (6.1 m) wide in its narrowest dimension.

(b)* On each side of the mall floor area, the covered mall shall be provided with an unobstructed exit access of not less than 10 ft (3 m) in clear width parallel to and adjacent to the mall tenant front. Such exit access shall lead to an exit having a width of not less than 66 in. (168 cm). (See 37.4.4.2.)

A.37.4.4.1 Exception (b) The minimum requirement for terminating mall exit access in not less than 66 in. (168 cm) of egress width relates to the minimum requirement for not less than one aisle in Class A mercantile occupancies (30,000 ft² (2800 m²) or greater sales area) to be 5 ft (152 cm) in width.

(c) The covered mall and all buildings connected thereto shall be protected throughout by an approved, supervised automatic sprinkler system in accordance with Section 9.7.

(d) Walls dividing tenant spaces from each other shall extend from the floor to the underside of the roof deck, floor deck above, or ceiling where the ceiling is constructed to limit the transfer of smoke. Where the tenant areas are provided with an engineered smoke control system, walls

shall not be required to divide tenant spaces from each other. No separation shall be required between a tenant space and the covered mall.

(e)* The covered mall shall be provided with a smoke control system.

A.36.4.4.1 Exception (e) Fire experience in covered mall shopping centers indicates that the most likely place of fire origin is in the tenant space where the combustible fire load is far greater than in the covered mall proper.

Furthermore, any fires resulting from the comparatively low fire load in the covered mall proper are more likely to be detected and extinguished in their incipient stages. Early detection is likely due to the nature of the covered mall proper as a high traffic pedestrian way. Such fires produce less smoke development in a greater volume of space than fires in the more confined adjacent tenant space.

Smoke control systems that address fire experience in covered malls are necessary in order to achieve the following:

(1) Ensure the integrity of the covered mall as a pedestrian way by maintaining it reasonably free of the products of combustion for a duration not less than that required to evacuate the building
(2) Confine the products of combustion to the area of origin
(3) Remove the products of combustion with a minimum of migration of such products of combustion from one tenant to another

Systems, or combinations of systems, that can be engineered to address fires in covered malls include the following:

(1) Separate mechanical exhaust or control systems
(2) Mechanical exhaust or control systems in conjunction with heating, ventilating, and air conditioning systems
(3) Automatically or manually released gravity roof vent devices, such as skylights, relief dampers, or smoke vents
(4) Combinations of items (1), (2), and (3) in this list, or any other engineered system designed to accomplish the purpose of this section

36.4.4.2 Means of Egress Details.

36.4.4.2.1 Every floor of a covered mall shall be provided with the number of means of egress specified by Section 7.4, with not less than two means of egress remotely located from each other.

36.4.4.2.2 Class A and Class B mercantile occupancies connected to a covered mall shall be provided with the number

shall not be required to divide tenant spaces from each other. No separation shall be required between a tenant space and the covered mall.

(e)* The covered mall shall be provided with a smoke control system.

A.37.4.4.1 Exception (e) Fire experience in covered mall shopping centers indicates that the most likely place of fire origin is in the tenant space where the combustible fire load is far greater than in the covered mall proper.

Furthermore, any fires resulting from the comparatively low fire load in the covered mall proper are more likely to be detected and extinguished in their incipient stages. Early detection is likely due to the nature of the covered mall proper as a high traffic pedestrian way. Such fires produce less smoke development in a greater volume of space than in the more confined adjacent tenant space.

Smoke control systems that address fire experience in covered malls are necessary in order to achieve the following:

(1) Ensure the integrity of the covered mall as a pedestrian way by maintaining it reasonably free of the products of combustion for a duration not less than that required to evacuate the building
(2) Confine the products of combustion to the area of fire origin
(3) Remove the products of combustion with a minimum of migration of such products of combustion from one tenant to another

Systems, or combinations of systems, that can be engineered to address fires in covered malls include the following:

(1) Separate or mechanical exhaust or control systems
(2) Mechanical exhaust or control systems in conjunction with heating, ventilating, and air conditioning systems
(3) Automatically or manually released gravity roof vent devices, such as skylights, relief dampers, or smoke vents
(4) Combinations of items (1), (2), and (3) in this list, or any other engineered system designed to accomplish the purpose of this section

37.4.4.2 Means of Egress Details.

37.4.4.2.1 Every floor of a covered mall shall be provided with the number of means of egress specified by Section 7.4, with not less than two means of egress remotely located from each other.

37.4.4.2.2 Class A and Class B mercantile occupancies connected to a covered mall shall be provided with the number of means of egress required by Section 7.4, with not less than two means of egress remotely located from one another.

36.4.4.2.3* Each individual anchor store shall have means of egress independent of the covered mall.

A.36.4.4.2.3 It is not the intent of 36.4.4.2.3 to require that large tenant spaces be considered anchor stores. A tenant space not considered in determining the occupant load of the mall is required to be arranged so that all of its means of egress will be independent of the covered mall.

36.4.4.2.4 Every covered mall shall be provided with unobstructed exit access parallel to and adjacent to the mall tenant fronts. This exit access shall extend to each mall exit.

36.4.4.2.5* Rooms housing building service equipment, janitor closets, and service elevators shall be permitted to open directly onto exit passageways, provided that the following criteria are met:

(1) The required fire resistance rating between such rooms or areas and the exit passageway is maintained in accordance with 7.1.3.2.
(2) Such rooms or areas are protected by an approved, supervised automatic sprinkler system in accordance with Section 9.7; however, the exceptions in NFPA 13, *Standard for the Installation of Sprinkler Systems,* that permit the omission of sprinklers from such rooms are not permitted.
(3) Service elevators opening into the exit passageway shall not open into areas other than exit passageways.
(4) Where exit stair enclosures discharge into the exit passageway, the provisions of 7.2.1.5.2 shall apply regardless of the number of stories served.

A.36.4.4.2.5 Rooms opening onto the exit passageway are intended to include building service elevators, elevator machine rooms, electrical rooms, telephone rooms, janitor closets, restrooms, and similar normally unoccupied spaces not requiring hazardous area protection in accordance with Section 8.4.

36.4.4.2.6 Emergency Lighting. *(See 36.2.9.)*

36.4.4.3 Detection, Alarm, and Communications Systems.

36.4.4.3.1 General. Covered malls shall be provided with a fire alarm system in accordance with Section 9.6.

36.4.4.3.2 Initiation. Initiation of the required fire alarm system shall be by means of the required automatic sprinkler system in accordance with 9.6.2.1(3).

of means of egress required by Section 7.4, with not less than two means of egress remotely located from one another.

37.4.4.2.3* Each individual anchor store shall have means of egress independent of the covered mall.

A.37.4.4.2.3 It is not the intent of 37.4.4.2.3 to require that large tenant spaces be considered anchor stores. A tenant space not considered in determining the occupant load of the mall is required to be arranged so that all of its means of egress will be independent of the covered mall.

37.4.4.2.4 Every covered mall shall be provided with unobstructed exit access parallel to and adjacent to the mall tenant fronts. This exit access shall extend to each mall exit.

37.4.4.2.5* Rooms housing building service equipment, janitor closets, and service elevators shall be permitted to open directly onto exit passageways, provided that the following criteria are met:

(1) The required fire resistance rating between such rooms or areas and the exit passageway is maintained in accordance with 7.1.3.2.
(2) Such rooms or areas are protected by an approved automatic sprinkler system in accordance with Section 9.7; however, the exceptions in NFPA 13, *Standard for the Installation of Sprinkler Systems,* that permit the omission of sprinklers from such rooms are not permitted.
(3) Service elevators opening into the exit passageway shall not open into areas other than exit passageways.
(4) Where exit stair enclosures discharge into the exit passageway, the provisions of 7.2.1.5.2 shall apply regardless of the number of stories served.

A.37.4.4.2.5 Rooms opening onto the exit passageway are intended to include building service elevators, elevator machine rooms, electrical rooms, telephone rooms, janitor closets, restrooms, and similar normally unoccupied spaces not requiring hazardous area protection in accordance with Section 8.4.

37.4.4.2.6 Emergency Lighting. *(See 37.2.9.)*

37.4.4.3 Detection, Alarm, and Communications Systems.

37.4.4.3.1 General. Covered malls shall be provided with a fire alarm system in accordance with Section 9.6.

37.4.4.3.2 Initiation. Initiation of the required fire alarm system shall be by means of the required automatic sprinkler system in accordance with 9.6.2.1(3).

CHAPTER 36 • New

CHAPTER 37 • Existing

36.4.4.3.3 Notification.

36.4.4.3.3.1 Occupant Notification. During all times that the covered mall is occupied (see 7.2.1.1.3), the required fire alarm system, once initiated, shall perform one of the following functions.

(a) It shall activate a general alarm in accordance with 9.6.3 throughout the covered mall.

Exception: Positive alarm sequence in accordance with 9.6.3.4 shall be permitted.

(b) It shall activate an alarm signal in a continuously attended location for the purpose of initiating emergency action by personnel trained to respond to emergencies. Emergency action shall be initiated by means of live voice public address system announcements originating from the attended location where the alarm signal is received. The system shall be permitted to be used for other announcements, provided that the fire alarm use takes precedence over any other use.

Exception: Any other occupant notification means permitted by 9.6.3 shall be permitted in lieu of live voice public address system announcements.

36.4.4.3.3.2 Emergency Forces Notification. Emergency forces notification shall be provided and shall include notifying the following:

(1) The fire department in accordance with 9.6.4
(2) The local emergency organization, if provided

36.4.4.3.4 Emergency Control. The fire alarm system shall be arranged to automatically actuate smoke management or smoke control systems in accordance with 9.6.5.2(3).

37.4.4.3.3 Notification.

37.4.4.3.3.1 Occupant Notification. During all times that the covered mall is occupied (see 7.2.1.1.3), the required fire alarm system, once initiated, shall perform one of the following functions:

(a) It shall activate a general alarm in accordance with 9.6.3 throughout the covered mall.

Exception No. 1: Positive alarm sequence in accordance with 9.6.3.4 shall be permitted.

Exception No. 2: A presignal system in accordance with 9.6.3.3 shall be permitted.

(b) It shall activate an alarm signal in a continuously attended location for the purpose of initiating emergency action by personnel trained to respond to emergencies. Emergency action shall be initiated by means of live voice public address system announcements originating from the attended location where the alarm signal is received. The system shall be permitted to be used for other announcements, provided that the fire alarm use takes precedence over any other use.

Exception: Any other occupant notification means permitted by 9.6.3 shall be permitted in lieu of live voice public address system announcements.

37.4.4.3.3.2 Emergency Forces Notification. Emergency forces notification shall be provided and shall include notifying the following:

(1) The fire department in accordance with 9.6.4
(2) The local emergency organization, if provided

37.4.4.3.4 Emergency Control. The fire alarm system shall be arranged to automatically actuate smoke management or smoke control systems in accordance with 9.6.5.2(3).

The provisions for new covered mall buildings in 36.4.4 apply only to buildings up to three stories in height. For new covered mall buildings with more than three stories, the equivalency concept of Section 1.5 should be used to engineer a unique life safety system that meets the intent of the *Code*. For existing covered mall buildings, the provisions of 37.4.4 apply, regardless of number of stories.

It is common for covered mall buildings to have food courts and areas for live performances. Such spaces with occupant loads of 50 or more are consid-

ered assembly occupancies. Paragraph 36/37.4.4.1 clarifies that the provisions for the applicable occupancies need to be followed, except as modified by 36/37.4.4. One of the modifications relates to sizing the means of egress from the covered mall using a calculation based on gross leasable area. The use of the gross leasable area (GLA) concept for sizing the means of egress for the covered mall typically will result in adequate capacity, even where large assembly occupancies are located in part of the covered mall building.

Consider the following examples.

Example 1

A 5000-seat cinema complex (that is, a large assembly occupancy) is to be housed within a new covered mall building. The cinema seating area, lobby, and circulation space will occupy 100,000 ft² (9290 m²). The covered mall building will have 550,000 ft² (51,100 m²) of GLA [450,000 ft² (41,800 m²) for mercantile use and 100,000 ft² (9290 m²) for the cinema complex].

Using Figure 7.3.1.2, the GLA of the cinema will require that the covered mall have sufficient egress capacity to accommodate 2000 persons from the 5000-seat cinema. This is based on a calculation in which 100,000 ft² (9290 m²) is divided by 55 ft² (5.1 m²) per person, because the covered mall building's GLA exceeds 400,000 ft² (37,160 m²). Also, the covered mall must have adequate egress capacity for another 8180 persons due to the GLA associated with the mercantile areas. This additional capacity is based on a calculation in which 450,000 ft² (41,800 m²) is divided by 55 ft² (5.1 m²) per person. Given the main entrance/exit requirement of Chapter 12/13, egress for half the cinema occupant load (that is, 2500 persons) will be provided through doors leading directly to the outside or through exit passageways. If the cinema was occupied to 100 percent capacity, the other 2500 persons would be expected to use the covered mall as exit access. Although there might appear to be a capacity deficiency of 500 persons, the system provides safeguards as follows:

(a) Cinemas do not operate at 100 percent capacity. Management typically stops selling tickets at 80 percent capacity, because the larger crowds make for inefficient access to the highly profitable concession stands, thus reducing revenue. Yet the occupant load is established by counting all seats.

(b) The covered mall, not the covered mall building, is required to have a fire alarm system. This requirement considers that it is very unusual to evacuate the entire covered mall building due to a fire in either the covered mall or one of the tenant spaces. Thus, the covered mall egress capacity is not fully used simultaneously, although the covered mall has excess capacity that easily absorbs the cinema occupants not otherwise considered.

(c) If the number of persons entering the covered mall from the tenant space—for emergency egress—is greater than that for which the covered mall's egress system was sized, it doesn't mean that the additional persons are unable to leave the building. Rather, it means that it takes longer to discharge all occupants to the outside. The requirements for sprinkler protection throughout the covered mall building, and for smoke control within the covered mall, help to maintain tenable conditions to permit a longer egress time. The covered mall provides for safe exit access similar to that provided within an atrium.

Example 2

A restaurant with an occupant load of 300 persons is to be located within a new covered mall building that has GLA of 200,000 ft² (18,580 m²). The restaurant's 300-person occupant load is derived by dividing the 4500 ft² (418 m²) of net area usable for patron standing and seating by the 15 ft² (1.4 m²) per person occupant load factor characteristic of the assembly use. However, the restaurant occupies a total GLA of 6000 ft² (557 m²).

Using Figure 7.3.1.2, the GLA of the restaurant requires the covered mall to provide sufficient egress capacity to accommodate 150 persons from the 300-person restaurant. This egress capacity is based on a calculation in which 6000 ft² (557 m²) is divided by 40 ft² (3.7 m²) per person because the covered mall building's GLA is 200,000 ft² (18,580 m²). Also, the covered mall must have adequate egress capacity for another 4850 persons due to the GLA associated with the mercantile areas. This additional capacity is based on a calculation in which 194,000 ft² (18,020 m²) is divided by 40 ft² (3.7 m²) per person. Given the main entrance/exit requirement of Chapter 12/13, egress for one-half the restaurant occupant load (that is, 150 persons) will be provided through doors leading directly to the outside or through exit passageways. The other 150 persons would be expected to use the covered mall as exit access. This results in a perfect match between the 150-persons who egress from the restaurant into the covered mall and the 150-person egress capacity imposed on the covered mall based on the GLA of the restaurant.

In recent years, covered mall shopping areas have increased in both number and size. Two approaches in addressing the life safety aspects of these complexes were developed. The first approach (described in the base paragraph of 36/37.4.4.1) treats the mall and the attached stores essentially as one large Class A store subject to all the provisions of Chapter

36/37. If viewed in this way, the covered mall would be treated as an aisle of a store.

The second approach permits the mall to be considered as a pedestrian way through which occupants of the attached stores are permitted to egress during a fire. The phrase "pedestrian way" is intended to convey the meaning of the term *exit access*. See definition in 3.3.62.

The exception to 36/37.4.4.1 recognizes that, if the mall and all the buildings attached to the mall are protected by automatic sprinklers, occupants fleeing into the mall from a fire in a store are then moving into a space whose volume, size, and arrangement affords most of the benefits provided by an enclosed stair or a horizontal exit, as well as providing many of the benefits of an outdoor area. The exception considers the mall to be a safe area for the occupants of the tenant spaces attached to it, despite the fact that the mall is not separated from these attached spaces by the type of construction normally provided for an exit as required by 7.1.3.2.

Where a covered mall is considered as a pedestrian way, the maximum travel distance to an exit or to the covered mall from any point within a store attached to the covered mall is 200 ft (60 m). The reasoning behind this provision is that use of the covered mall for egress is as acceptable as the use of an exit. A travel distance of up to 200 ft (60 m), in addition to the 200 ft (60 m) allowed within the store, is permitted within the covered mall if all of the following conditions are met.

(a) The covered mall building (the covered mall and all attached buildings) must be sprinklered. The sprinkler system must be electrically supervised. Note that, if the shopping complex is considered as one building rather than as a covered mall building with a complying pedestrian way, sprinkler protection most likely is also required under the 12,000-ft² (1115-m²) gross area criterion of 36.3.5.1(2).

(b) The clear width of the mall must be at least 20 ft (6.1 m) or wider if mandated by the egress capacity. Note that, where the covered mall of a shopping center is considered as a pedestrian way, an occupant load is not calculated for the covered mall based on its area. The required capacity of the means of egress for the covered mall is calculated on the basis of aggregate gross leasable area of the attached stores (excluding anchor stores), including mid-mall kiosks and similar sales areas.

(c) At least 10 ft (3 m) of clear, unobstructed space must be available for exit access in front of all store fronts. This requirement is designed to prohibit displays of merchandise, kiosks, or small sales stands from being located within 10 ft (3 m) of the store fronts and ensures that the mall will have a minimum clear width of 20 ft (6.1 m).

(d) Each exit access must terminate at an exit with a minimum width of 66 in. (168 cm).

(e) Walls separating stores must run continuously from the floor slab to the roof slab or floor slab above, but not necessarily through the roof or floor. The vertical continuity of such walls is exempted if the tenant spaces are provided with an engineered smoke control system. Walls are not required to be fire resistance rated. The intent of such separation is to resist the passage of smoke. The store front need not be separated from the mall by construction.

(f) The covered mall, but not the stores, must have a smoke control system. Since the individual stores are open to the mall, this requirement is essential if the mall is to be used as a safe means of egress. For detailed guidance on the design, installation, and maintenance of smoke control systems, see NFPA 92B, *Guide for Smoke Management Systems in Malls, Atria, and Large Areas.*[5]

If the conditions of (a) through (f) are not met, the covered mall is still permitted to be used as part of the exit access from the covered mall building, but the additional travel distance to an exit would not be allowed. Therefore, from any point within the overall covered mall building, which includes the stores and the covered mall, travel distance would be limited to 100 ft (30 m) for new construction or 150 ft (45 m) for existing mercantile occupancies [200 ft (60 m) in both new and existing mercantile occupancies if the stores and covered mall are sprinklered]. In the majority of configurations, this restriction would preclude the use of the mall as an exit access.

Exhibit 36/37.14 illustrates many of the requirements necessary to qualify a mall as a pedestrian way.

The NFPA *Fire Protection Handbook* contains a discussion of the hazards to life safety associated with covered mall buildings.[6]

Paragraph 36/37.4.4.2.1 reaffirms the fundamental *Code* requirement for providing at least two independent means of egress—more if the occupant load exceeds 500 persons, in accordance with 7.4.1.2.

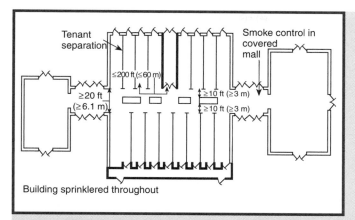

Exhibit 36/37.14 *Covered mall meeting the requirements of a pedestrian way.*

Note that in larger stores (Class A and B mercantile occupancies) the second exit must be remote from the first exit. This requirement is usually met by evacuating occupants directly from the store to the outside or directly into an exit passageway without entering the covered mall.

Subparagraph 36/37.4.4.2.4 repeats the provisions of subpart (b) of the exception to 36/37.4.4.1 without stating that the exit access mall at the front of the stores within the covered mall must have a clear width of at least 10 ft (3 m).

Although the requirements of Chapter 7 prohibit normally unoccupied rooms from having doors open directly onto an exit enclosure, 36/37.4.4.2.5 specifically allows rooms housing building service equipment, janitor closets, and service elevators to open directly onto exit passageways in covered mall buildings, provided that the additional criteria specified in 36/37.4.4.2.5(1) through (4) are met. The *Code* permits this allowance in recognition of operational needs and the incorporation of current design criteria in covered mall buildings. The conditions that are unique to this type of facility include the following:

(1) A limitation on the number of floors (not more than three for new construction)
(2) A main concourse for occupant movement, with specific requirements for size and smoke control, that leads to multiple points of egress
(3) Facilities that are required to be fully protected by an automatic sprinkler system

Paragraph 36/37.4.4.2.5(1) states that the exit passageway with door openings from support spaces is

not to be treated as a corridor but as an exit passageway meeting the fire-rated separation requirements of 7.1.3.2.

Paragraph 36/37.4.4.2.5(2) requires that all areas that open onto the exit passageway be protected by an automatic sprinkler system. This requirement is restated to prevent use of the provisions in NFPA 13, *Standard for the Installation of Sprinkler Systems,* which permit the omission of sprinkler protection if certain conditions are met.

Paragraph 36/37.4.4.2.5(3) addresses the issue of communication among floors by an elevator shaft and its associated openings. This requirement permits only those openings associated with an elevator that opens onto an exit passageway. This limitation would prohibit an elevator from opening to another use area, such as a storage or loading area, thereby limiting the exposure from the effects of fire from areas other than exit passageways.

Paragraph 36/37.4.4.2.5(4) requires that stairwell re-entry is maintained in a continuous occupant control, in accordance with 7.2.1.5.2. It prohibits the use of Exception No. 1 to 7.2.1.5.2, which permits doors to be locked from the stairwell side if the building does not exceed four stories.

The annex text to 36/37.4.4.2.5 clarifies the types of spaces that are permitted to have doors that open directly onto the exit passageway. Such spaces include rooms with contents that are no more hazardous than those typically found in a covered mall building. These spaces are usually small and are associated with limited amounts of combustibles.

In a covered mall building, it is necessary to provide for services to the tenant spaces that are maintained by the mall management (for example, water, electricity, telephone, fire protection). These services must be located in a common space controlled by the mall management and, therefore, cannot be located within the tenant spaces. Frequently, these services are logically located with direct access to service corridors or exit passageways/corridors at the rear of the tenant spaces.

This common design practice has prompted many designers to seek specific approval of such designs from local authorities to allow numerous buildings to be built in this manner. There is a long history of covered mall buildings built in this manner with no adverse experience.

Although the provisions of 36/37.4.4 address the overall covered mall building, the provisions of

CHAPTER 36 • New   **CHAPTER 37 • Existing**

36/37.4.4.3.1, which apply to alarm systems, require only that the alarm system be provided for the covered mall (the covered pedestrian way). In addition, the provisions of 36/37.3.4.1 require that any Class A mercantile occupancy within the covered mall building also be provided with an alarm system. Therefore, Class B and Class C mercantile occupancies within the covered mall building are not required to have alarm systems.

Note that, per 36/37.4.4.3.2, manual pull boxes are not required, but the sprinkler system must have a waterflow alarm that initiates the fire alarm system. However, in accordance with the provisions of 9.6.2.5, at least one manual fire alarm box must be provided at a location determined by the authority having jurisdiction.

Subsection 9.6.4 allows for several different methods of automatically notifying the fire department.

Note that 36/37.4.4.3.3.1 provides a choice between two methods of notification. Many large shopping malls do have a continuously attended location, and 36/37.4.4.3.3.1(b) can be used. If such a location is not provided or not considered reliable by the authority having jurisdiction, 36/37.4.4.3.3.1(a) must be applied. In either case, the notification must be provided to the occupants of the covered mall but is not required to be provided within the individual stores.

A system that applies 36/37.4.4.3.3.1(b) is permitted to use an automatic voice alarm or regular alarm-sounding device in lieu of the live voice alarm.

36.4.5 Bulk Merchandising Retail Buildings.

New bulk merchandising retail buildings exceeding 12,000 ft² (1100 m²) in area shall comply with the requirements of this chapter as modified by 36.4.5.1 through 36.4.5.6.

36.4.5.1 Minimum Construction Requirements. Bulk merchandising retail buildings shall have a distance of not less than 16 ft (4.9 m) from the floor to the ceiling, from the floor to the floor above, or from the floor to the roof of any story.

36.4.5.2 Means of Egress Requirements. All means of egress shall be in accordance with Chapter 7 and this chapter. Not less than 50 percent of the required egress capacity shall be located independent of the main entrance/exit doors.

36.4.5.3 Storage, Arrangement, Protection, and Quantities of Hazardous Commodities.

36.4.5.3.1 The storage, arrangement, protection, and quantities of hazardous commodities shall be in accordance with the applicable portions of the following:

(1) NFPA 13, *Standard for the Installation of Sprinkler Systems*
(2) NFPA 30, *Flammable and Combustible Liquids Code*
(3) NFPA 30B, *Code for the Manufacture and Storage of Aerosol Products*
(4) NFPA 230, *Standard for the Fire Protection of Storage*
(5) NFPA 231D, *Standard for Storage of Rubber Tires*
(6) NFPA 430, *Code for the Storage of Liquid and Solid Oxidizers*

37.4.5 Bulk Merchandising Retail Buildings.

Existing bulk merchandising retail buildings exceeding 15,000 ft² (1400 m²) in area shall comply with the requirements of this chapter as modified by 37.4.5.1 through 37.4.5.6.

37.4.5.1 Minimum Construction Requirements. (No requirement.)

37.4.5.2 Means of Egress Requirements. All means of egress shall be in accordance with Chapter 7 and this chapter. Not less than 50 percent of the required egress capacity shall be located independent of the main entrance/exit doors.

37.4.5.3 Storage, Arrangement, Protection, and Quantities of Hazardous Commodities.

37.4.5.3.1 The storage, arrangement, protection, and quantities of hazardous commodities shall be in accordance with the applicable portions of the following:

(1) NFPA 13, *Standard for the Installation of Sprinkler Systems*
(2) NFPA 30, *Flammable and Combustible Liquids Code*
(3) NFPA 30B, *Code for the Manufacture and Storage of Aerosol Products*
(4) NFPA 230, *Standard for the Fire Protection of Storage*
(5) NFPA 231D, *Standard for Storage of Rubber Tires*
(6) NFPA 430, *Code for the Storage of Liquid and Solid Oxidizers*

(7) NFPA 432, *Code for the Storage of Organic Peroxide Formulations*

(8) NFPA 434, *Code for the Storage of Pesticides*

36.4.5.3.2* High hazard commodities without protective containers shall not be stored or displayed within 100 ft (30 m) of the main entrance/exit doors.

A.36.4.5.3.2 An example of a high hazard commodity without protective containers is mineral spirits (flammable liquids) in plastic containers.

36.4.5.4 Detection, Alarm, and Communications Systems.

36.4.5.4.1 General. Bulk merchandising retail buildings shall be provided with a fire alarm system in accordance with Section 9.6.

36.4.5.4.2 Initiation. Initiation of the required fire alarm system shall be by means of the required approved automatic sprinkler system *(see 36.4.5.5)* in accordance with 9.6.2.1(3).

36.4.5.4.3 Occupant Notification. During all times that the building is occupied *(see 7.2.1.1.3)*, the required fire alarm system, once initiated, shall perform one of the following functions.

(a) It shall activate a general alarm in accordance with 9.6.3 throughout the building.

Exception: Positive alarm sequence in accordance with 9.6.3.4 shall be permitted.

(b) It shall activate an alarm signal in a continuously attended location for the purpose of initiating emergency action by personnel trained to respond to emergencies. Emergency action shall be initiated by means of live voice public address system announcements originating from the attended location where the alarm signal is received. The system shall be permitted to be used for other announcements, provided that the fire alarm use takes precedence over any other use.

Exception: Any other occupant notification means permitted by 9.6.3 shall be permitted in lieu of live voice public address system announcements.

36.4.5.4.4 Emergency Forces Notification. Emergency forces notification shall be provided and shall include notifying the following:

(1) The fire department in accordance with 9.6.4
(2) The local emergency organization, if provided

(7) NFPA 432, *Code for the Storage of Organic Peroxide Formulations*

(8) NFPA 434, *Code for the Storage of Pesticides*

37.4.5.3.2* High hazard commodities without protective containers shall not be stored or displayed within 100 ft (30 m) of the main entrance/exit doors.

A.37.4.5.3.2 An example of a high hazard commodity without protective containers is mineral spirits (flammable liquids) in plastic containers.

37.4.5.4 Detection, Alarm, and Communications Systems.

37.4.5.4.1 General. Bulk merchandising retail buildings shall be provided with a fire alarm system in accordance with Section 9.6.

37.4.5.4.2 Initiation. Initiation of the required fire alarm system shall be by means of the required approved automatic sprinkler system *(see 37.4.5.5)* in accordance with 9.6.2.1(3).

37.4.5.4.3 Occupant Notification. During all times that the building is occupied *(see 7.2.1.1.3)*, the required fire alarm system, once initiated, shall perform one of the following functions.

(a) It shall activate a general alarm in accordance with 9.6.3 throughout the building.

Exception No. 1: Positive alarm sequence in accordance with 9.6.3.4 shall be permitted.

Exception No. 2: A presignal system in accordance with 9.6.3.3 shall be permitted.

(b) It shall activate an alarm signal in a continuously attended location for the purpose of initiating emergency action by personnel trained to respond to emergencies. Emergency action shall be initiated by means of live voice public address system announcements originating from the attended location where the alarm signal is received. The system shall be permitted to be used for other announcements, provided that the fire alarm use takes precedence over any other use.

Exception: Any other occupant notification means permitted by 9.6.3 shall be permitted in lieu of live voice public address system announcements.

37.4.5.4.4 Emergency Forces Notification. Emergency forces notification shall be provided and shall include notifying the following:

(1) The fire department in accordance with 9.6.4
(2) The local emergency organization, if provided

36.4.5.5 Extinguishing Requirements. Bulk merchandising retail buildings shall be protected throughout by an approved, supervised automatic sprinkler system in accordance with Section 9.7 and the applicable provisions of the following:

(1) NFPA 13, *Standard for the Installation of Sprinkler Systems*
(2) NFPA 30, *Flammable and Combustible Liquids Code*
(3) NFPA 30B, *Code for the Manufacture and Storage of Aerosol Products*
(4) NFPA 230, *Standard for the Fire Protection of Storage*
(5) NFPA 231D, *Standard for Storage of Rubber Tires*

36.4.5.6 Emergency Plan and Employee Training. There shall be in effect an approved written plan for the emergency egress and relocation of occupants. All employees shall be instructed and periodically drilled with respect to their duties under the plan.

37.4.5.5 Extinguishing Requirements. Bulk merchandising retail buildings shall be protected throughout by an approved, supervised automatic sprinkler system in accordance with Section 9.7 and the applicable provisions of the following:

(1) NFPA 13, *Standard for the Installation of Sprinkler Systems*
(2) NFPA 30, *Flammable and Combustible Liquids Code*
(3) NFPA 30B, *Code for the Manufacture and Storage of Aerosol Products*
(4) NFPA 230, *Standard for the Fire Protection of Storage*
(5) NFPA 231D, *Standard for Storage of Rubber Tires*

37.4.5.6 Emergency Plan and Employee Training. There shall be in effect an approved written plan for the emergency egress and relocation of occupants. All employees shall be instructed and periodically drilled with respect to their duties under the plan.

Bulk merchandising retail buildings provide life safety challenges that differ from typical mercantile occupancies. Fires in bulk merchandising retail buildings demonstrate the need for specific requirements to help ensure adequate life safety of building occupants. Subsection 36/37.4.5 codifies a package of requirements that, in conjunction with those of the remainder of Chapter 36/37, help fill a void in previous *Code* requirements. The provisions of 36/37.4.5 apply to new bulk merchandising retail buildings exceeding 12,000 ft² (1100 m²) and existing facilities exceeding 15,000 ft² (1400 m²).

The term *bulk merchandising retail building* (see definition in 3.3.26) specifies that the storage height is in excess of 12 ft (3.7 m), which differentiates it from a typical mercantile occupancy. Where the storage and display of combustible materials exceed 12 ft (3.7 m) in height, the requirements are to be applied.

The minimum 16-ft (4.9-m) ceiling height requirement for new construction (see 36.4.5.1) is intended to provide a full 10 ft (3 m) of clearance above the heads of building occupants to allow for smoke accumulation early in the fire while building evacuation takes place.

The requirement that not less than 50 percent of the required egress capacity be located independent of the main entrance/exit doors (see 36/37.4.5.2) will help to provide for a better distribution of egress capacity around the perimeter of the building, thus providing occupants with multiple, independent routes for egress.

Bulk merchandising retail buildings are characterized by the storage and display of significant quantities of hazardous commodities. Thus, reference is made to numerous NFPA documents that address hazardous materials (see 36/37.4.5.3.1). Some of the documents include specific requirements that address the display of such materials.

The prohibition on high hazard commodities without protective containers stored or displayed within 100 ft (30 m) of the main entrance/exit doors (see 36/37.4.5.3.2) is intended to keep access to those doors available for safe egress, because occupants tend to return to the doors through which they entered a facility. By restricting the presence of the high hazard commodities without protective containers to other parts of the facility, it should be possible to move away from, rather than toward, such hazards, while egressing the building.

The extinguishing requirements refer to Section 9.7 (see 36/37.4.5.5) and, therefore, adopt the requirements of NFPA 13, *Standard for the Installation of Sprinkler Systems*. In addition, the companion specialized storage standards are mandatorily referenced.

As the history of fires in bulk merchandising retail buildings has shown, it is important to have an approved, written emergency evacuation plan with employees instructed and periodically drilled in their duties (see 36/37.4.5.6, 36/37.7.1, and 36/37.7.2).

Section 36.5 Building Services

36.5.1 Utilities.

Utilities shall comply with the provisions of Section 9.1.

36.5.2 Heating, Ventilating, and Air Conditioning.

Heating, ventilating, and air conditioning equipment shall comply with the provisions of Section 9.2.

36.5.3 Elevators, Escalators, and Conveyors.

Elevators, escalators, and conveyors shall comply with the provisions of Section 9.4.

36.5.4 Rubbish Chutes, Incinerators, and Laundry Chutes.

Rubbish chutes, incinerators, and laundry chutes shall comply with the provisions of Section 9.5.

Section 36.6 Reserved

Section 36.7 Operating Features

36.7.1 Drills.

In every Class A or Class B mercantile occupancy, employees shall be periodically trained in accordance with Section 4.7.

36.7.2 Extinguisher Training.

Employees of mercantile occupancies shall be periodically instructed in the use of portable fire extinguishers.

The extent of the extinguisher training required by 36/37.7.2 (for example, instruction only or instruction and hands-on use) is determined by the authority having jurisdiction.

References Cited in Commentary

1. NFPA 30, *Flammable and Combustible Liquids Code*, 1996 edition, National Fire Protection Association, Quincy, MA.
2. NFPA 13, *Standard for the Installation of Sprinkler Systems*, 1999 edition, National Fire Protection Association, Quincy, MA.

Section 37.5 Building Services

37.5.1 Utilities.

Utilities shall comply with the provisions of Section 9.1.

37.5.2 Heating, Ventilating, and Air Conditioning.

Heating, ventilating, and air conditioning equipment shall comply with the provisions of Section 9.2.

37.5.3 Elevators, Escalators, and Conveyors.

Elevators, escalators, and conveyors shall comply with the provisions of Section 9.4.

37.5.4 Rubbish Chutes, Incinerators, and Laundry Chutes.

Rubbish chutes, incinerators, and laundry chutes shall comply with the provisions of Section 9.5.

Section 37.6 Reserved

Section 37.7 Operating Features

37.7.1 Drills.

In every Class A or Class B mercantile occupancy, employees shall be periodically trained in accordance with Section 4.7.

37.7.2 Extinguisher Training.

Employees of mercantile occupancies shall be periodically instructed in the use of portable fire extinguishers.

3. NFPA 25, *Standard for the Inspection, Testing, and Maintenance of Water-Based Fire Protection Systems*, 1998 edition, National Fire Protection Association, Quincy, MA.
4. John L. Bryan, *Automatic Sprinkler and Standpipe Systems*, 3d edition, National Fire Protection Association, Quincy, MA, 1997.
5. NFPA 92B, *Guide for Smoke Management Systems in Malls, Atria, and Large Areas*, 1995 edition, National Fire Protection Association, Quincy, MA.
6. NFPA *Fire Protection Handbook*, 18th edition, National Fire Protection Association, Quincy, MA, 1997.

CHAPTERS 38 and 39

New and Existing Business Occupancies

Business occupancies are typically occupied by persons who are awake and ready to begin emergency egress or relocation, with little or no staff assistance, as soon as the occupants become aware of a fire. Historical evidence validates that the package of life safety features imposed on business occupancies by the *Code* doesn't need to be very extensive. At the time that this commentary was written early in 2000, 1989 was the last year in which a multiple-death business occupancy fire occurred in the United States. That fire took place in an Atlanta, Georgia, high-rise office building and resulted in five deaths. One of the fire victims was intimate with the fire source in an electrical vault; the other four victims were occupying their areas on the same floor when the fire began. This was the first office building fire in 17 years to cause three or more fatalities.

The bombing of the Alfred Murrah Federal Office Building in Oklahoma City, Oklahoma, in 1995 killed 168 people and injured 475. The bomb caused about one-third of the floor area of the 9-story building to collapse. The *Code* cannot protect against the effects of catastrophic occurrences such as the bombing of a building.

It is common for business occupancies to occupy high-rise buildings. Where business occupancies are located in new high-rise buildings, the complete protection package detailed in Section 11.8 is mandated; for existing business occupancies in high-rise buildings, either sprinkler protection or an engineered life safety system that provides protection equivalent to that of sprinklers is required.

The life safety features in Chapter 38/39 center on arrangement of the means of egress as well as alarm and occupant notification provisions. The travel distance and common path of travel allowances are generous. Fire resistance–rated corridor walls or other mitigating features, such as sprinkler protection, are required in an effort to keep the means of egress system usable.

Section 38.1 General Requirements

38.1.1 Application.

38.1.1.1 The requirements of this chapter apply to the following:

(1) New buildings or portions thereof used as business occupancies *(see 1.4.1)*
(2) Additions made to, or used as, a business occupancy *(see 4.6.6 and 38.1.1.3)*
(3) Alterations, modernizations, or renovations of existing business occupancies *(see 1.11.7)*
(4) Existing buildings or portions thereof upon change of occupancy to a business occupancy *(see 4.6.11)*

Section 39.1 General Requirements

39.1.1 Application.

39.1.1.1 The requirements of this chapter apply to existing buildings or portions thereof currently occupied as business occupancies. *(See also 38.1.1.1.)*

Exception: * *Facilities where the authority having jurisdiction has determined equivalent safety is provided in accordance with Section 1.5.*

A.38.1.1.1 Exception In determining equivalency for conversions, modernizations, renovations, or unusual design concepts of business occupancies, the authority having jurisdiction might permit evaluations based on NFPA 101A, *Guide on Alternative Approaches to Life Safety,* Chapter 7, utilizing the parameters for new construction.

38.1.1.2 This chapter establishes life safety requirements for all new business buildings. Specific requirements for high-rise buildings *(see definition in 3.3.101)* are contained in paragraphs pertaining thereto.

38.1.1.3 Additions to existing buildings shall conform to the requirements for new construction. Existing portions of the structure shall not be required to be modified, provided that the new construction has not diminished the fire safety features of the facility.

Exception: * *Facilities where the authority having jurisdiction has determined equivalent safety is provided in accordance with Section 1.5.*

A.39.1.1.1 Exception In determining equivalency for business occupancies, the authority having jurisdiction might permit evaluations based on NFPA 101A, *Guide on Alternative Approaches to Life Safety,* Chapter 7, utilizing the parameters for existing buildings.

39.1.1.2 This chapter establishes life safety requirements for existing business buildings. Specific requirements for high-rise buildings *(see definition in 3.3.101)* are contained in paragraphs pertaining thereto.

To understand the full intent and scope of 39.1.1.1 for existing buildings, it is necessary to review it concurrently with Sections 1.3, 1.4, and 1.5. Although a building code might exclude existing buildings from coverage under some form of a grandfather clause, the *Life Safety Code,* by virtue of its interest in safety to life, does not condone existing building arrangements that do not comply with the *Code* requirements that apply to existing buildings. The requirements that apply to existing business occupancies are contained in Chapter 39.

If a building complies with an earlier edition of the *Code,* it is not grandfathered and, thereby, exempted from compliance with a more current edition of the *Code* that has been adopted as law in the building's jurisdiction. The committees on safety to life are especially careful to avoid adopting requirements for existing buildings that become more stringent from one edition of the *Code* to the next, unless the change is absolutely necessary to enhance the overall package of safety to life intended by the *Code.* Thus, the old adage of "once in compliance, always in compliance" does not hold.

The provisions of Chapter 39 are to be applied retroactively. Due consideration has been given to the practical difficulties of making alterations in existing, functioning facilities. The specified provisions, viewed as a whole, establish minimum, acceptable criteria for safety to life that reasonably minimize the likelihood of a life-threatening fire.

The requirements of Chapter 39 are permitted to be modified in instances where compliance is impractical or where alternate but equal provisions are proposed. The modifications must provide a level of protection equivalent to that achieved by compliance with the corresponding *Code* provisions.

The exception to 38/39.1.1.1 emphasizes that Section 1.5 permits alternatives to literal *Code* compliance that maintains a building design as *Code*-conforming. However, the authority having jurisdiction ultimately determines whether equivalent safety has been provided.

Paragraph 38/39.1.1.1 and its accompanying exception do not limit the methods that an authority having jurisdiction might use to determine equivalency. However, as noted in A.38/A.39.1.1.1, NFPA 101A, *Guide on Alternative Approaches to Life Safety,* provides an equivalency system that uses numerical values to analyze the fire safety effectiveness of a building design.[1] This system is known as the Fire Safety Evaluation System (FSES). The system provides a method by which alternative designs can be evaluated as options to literal *Code* compliance.

The 2001 edition of NFPA 101A, although published one year after this 2000 edition of the *Life Safety Code,* is the proper edition of NFPA 101A to consult for one potential equivalency system for business occupancies. Its measurement system has been calibrated against the requirements of the 2000 edition of the *Code,* whereas the fire safety evaluation systems contained in the 1998 edition of NFPA 101A were calibrated against the requirements of the 1997 edition of the *Code*.

In providing the equivalency concept, the *Code* does not limit equivalency evaluations to those based solely on the system presented for business occupancies in NFPA 101A. The authority having jurisdiction retains the power to evaluate and approve alternative designs on the basis of appropriate supporting data. The FSES is permitted to be used to aid in this evaluation. This exception in no way mandates the use of the FSES, nor does it require the authority having jurisdiction to accept the results of an evaluation using the NFPA 101A equivalency system.

Although the FSES was primarily developed to evaluate alternative designs in existing buildings, it is particularly useful for determining equivalency for conversions, modernizations, renovations, or unusual design concepts—all of which are considered new construction. However, the FSES is only a tool to help determine equivalency, and it should not be used to circumvent *Code* requirements. *Code* requirements must be met, or equivalent safety must be provided by alternative means approved by the authority having jurisdiction.

Paragraph 38.1.1.3 addresses additions to existing buildings. Although construction of an addition generally does not require existing portions of the building to be modified, Exhibit 38/39.1 illustrates a case where the planned new construction would diminish the fire safety features of the existing building and thus necessitate corrective action within the existing portion of the building. The location of new room A creates an excessively long, dead-end corridor, B, which must be corrected.

In Exhibit 38/39.1, in addition to creating an unacceptable dead-end corridor, the construction of room A diminishes the fire safety features in two other ways; however, both are negligible and do not warrant correction. The door from corridor B into room A was formerly an exit door to the outside. Thus, with the new addition, the number of exits has been decreased from three to two; also, the travel distance for occupants in some of the rooms off corridor B has been increased, because the nearest exit for those occupants becomes the pair of doors at the front of the building (that is, at the bottom of the figure). If the occupant load of the floor doesn't exceed 500 persons, only two exits are required (see 7.4.1.2), and the loss of one of the three exits is permitted without

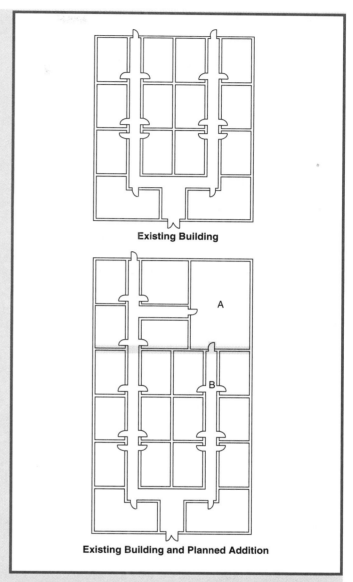

Existing Building

Existing Building and Planned Addition

Exhibit 38/39.1 An addition that diminishes existing life safety features.

further correction. Also, if the maximum allowable travel distance [200 ft (60 m) where the building is not sprinklered and 300 ft (90 m) where the building is sprinklered in accordance with 38/39.2.6] is not exceeded, the travel distance increase caused by the addition of room A is permitted without further correction. Thus, as explained in the preceding paragraph of this commentary, only the newly created, excessively long, dead-end corridor needs to be corrected.

38.1.2 Mixed Occupancies.

38.1.2.1 Mixed occupancies shall comply with 6.1.14.

38.1.2.2 Combined Business Occupancies and Parking Structures. Walls separating parking structures from business occupancies shall have a fire resistance rating of not less than 2 hours.

Exception: In enclosed parking structures that are protected throughout by an approved, supervised automatic sprinkler system in accordance with Section 9.7, or in open-air parking structures, nonrated glazing and nonrated opening protectives shall be permitted if all of the following conditions are met:

(a) The openings do not exceed 25 percent of the area of the wall in which they are located.

(b) The openings are used as the main entrance and for associated sidelight functions.

(c) The enclosed connecting business building is protected throughout by an approved, supervised automatic sprinkler system in accordance with Section 9.7.

(d) The floor elevation of the business occupancy is not less than 4 in. (10.2 cm) above the floor level of the parking structure.

(e) No vehicle is able to park or drive within 10 ft (3 m) of the openings.

(f) The openings are protected by not less than a glass membrane.

(g) Any doors in the glass membrane are self-closing.

39.1.2 Mixed Occupancies.

39.1.2.1 Mixed occupancies shall comply with 6.1.14.

39.1.2.2 Combined Business Occupancies and Parking Structures. Walls separating parking structures from business occupancies shall have a fire resistance rating of not less than 2 hours.

Exception: In enclosed parking structures that are protected throughout by an approved automatic sprinkler system in accordance with Section 9.7, or in open-air parking structures, nonrated glazing and nonrated opening protectives shall be permitted if all of the following conditions are met:

(a) The openings do not exceed 25 percent of the area of the wall in which they are located.

(b) The openings are used as the main entrance and for associated sidelight functions.

(c) The enclosed connecting business building is protected throughout by an approved automatic sprinkler system in accordance with Section 9.7.

(d) The floor elevation of the business occupancy is not less than 4 in. (10.2 cm) above the floor level of the parking structure.

(e) No vehicle is able to park or drive within 10 ft (3 m) of the openings.

(f) The openings are protected by not less than a glass membrane.

(g) Any doors in the glass membrane are self-closing.

Minor office occupancies that are incidental to operations in another occupancy are considered part of the predominate occupancy, rather than part of a mixed occupancy, and are subject to the *Code* provisions that apply to the predominate occupancy. The commentary associated with 38/39.1.4 discusses classification of business occupancies in more detail.

The determination of those criteria that constitute a minor or incidental office area cannot be based solely on percentage of business area in comparison to overall building area. For example, a 200-ft² (19-m²) office area in a 4000-ft² (370-m²) warehouse can reasonably be judged as incidental to the storage operations and result in the building being classified as a storage occupancy. A 20,000-ft² (1860-m²) office area in a 400,000-ft² (37,200-m²) distribution warehouse represents the same proportion of business use area as the 200-ft² (19-m²) office in the 4000-ft²

(370-m²) example but cannot be judged as incidental (see Exhibit 38/39.2). The 20,000-ft² (1860-m²) office area probably has an occupant load of approximately 200 persons. The *Code* requirements that apply to business occupancies, which are more stringent than those that apply to storage occupancies, are needed to protect the occupants of the office area adequately. The distribution warehouse is classified as a mixed occupancy that is part storage occupancy and part business occupancy. If packaging operations take place in the warehouse, it might also be classified as part industrial occupancy. Consequently, the requirements of 6.1.14 for mixed occupancies apply.

The provisions of 38/39.1.2.2 address combined business occupancies and parking structures and are very similar to the requirements of 36/37.1.2.2, which address combined mercantile occupancies and parking structures. It is very common for multistory busi-

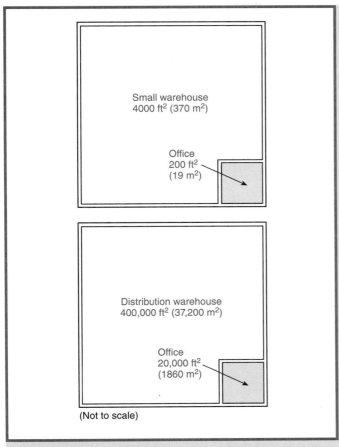

Small warehouse
4000 ft² (370 m²)

Office
200 ft²
(19 m²)

Distribution warehouse
400,000 ft² (37,200 m²)

Office
20,000 ft²
(1860 m²)

(Not to scale)

Exhibit 38/39.2 *Incidental and nonincidental office use.*

ness occupancies, such as office buildings, and multistory mercantile occupancies, such as department stores and shopping mall buildings, to be attached to multistory parking garages. These garages provide access to the business or mercantile occupancy at multiple levels. The exception to 38/39.1.2.2 outlines a set of provisions that, where applied in total, will safely allow a reduction in the 2-hour fire resistance–rated separation requirement of 38/39.1.2.2. This reduction allows flexibility in the number and type of openings and considers the stringent requirements for opening protectives such as fire doors and windows. The reduction also permits the use of nonrated glazing and opening protectives, which allows the use of glass doors and sidelights in the barrier between the business occupancy and the garage. Security in the garage is thereby increased, because occupants can view the area through the glass doors or sidelights. This feature, in turn, helps to meet the security concerns of office building managers and tenants.

Note that all eight requirements mandated by the exception to 38/39.1.2.2—the sprinkler requirement for enclosed garages per the base paragraph of the exception and the seven requirements of subparts (a) through (g) of the exception—must be met as a whole to apply the exception to the rule. Otherwise a 2-hour fire resistance–rated separation between the business occupancy and the parking structure is required.

38.1.3 Special Definitions.

(None.)

38.1.4 Classification of Occupancy.

Business occupancies shall include all buildings and structures or parts thereof with occupancy as defined in 6.1.11.

38.1.5 Classification of Hazard of Contents.

38.1.5.1 The contents of business occupancies shall be classified as ordinary hazard in accordance with Section 6.2.

38.1.5.2 For purposes of the design of an automatic sprinkler system, a business occupancy shall be classified as a light hazard occupancy in accordance with NFPA 13, *Standard for the Installation of Sprinkler Systems.*

39.1.3 Special Definitions.

(None.)

39.1.4 Classification of Occupancy.

Business occupancies shall include all buildings and structures or parts thereof with occupancy as defined in 6.1.11.

39.1.5 Classification of Hazard of Contents.

39.1.5.1 The contents of business occupancies shall be classified as ordinary hazard in accordance with Section 6.2.

39.1.5.2 For purposes of the design of an automatic sprinkler system, a business occupancy shall be classified as a light hazard occupancy in accordance with NFPA 13, *Standard for the Installation of Sprinkler Systems.*

38.1.6 Minimum Construction Requirements.

(No requirements.)

38.1.7 Occupant Load.

The occupant load, in number of persons for whom means of egress and other provisions are required, shall be determined on the basis of the occupant load factors of Table 7.3.1.2 that are characteristic of the use of the space or shall be determined as the maximum probable population of the space under consideration, whichever is greater.

39.1.6 Minimum Construction Requirements.

(No requirements.)

39.1.7 Occupant Load.

The occupant load, in number of persons for whom means of egress and other provisions are required, shall be determined on the basis of the occupant load factors of Table 7.3.1.2 that are characteristic of the use of the space or shall be determined as the maximum probable population of the space under consideration, whichever is greater.

Classification of occupancy is addressed in 38/39.1.4. Note that the *Code's* definition of a business occupancy (see 6.1.11.1) does not include types of stores that, although considered businesses, are covered under the provisions of Chapter 36/37. These stores include, for example, supermarkets, department stores, and other occupancies that display and sell merchandise. Also not included are the assembly portions of city halls, town halls, and courthouses, which are covered by Chapter 12/13.

The following constitute business occupancies and are covered by the provisions of Chapter 38/39:

(1) Occupancies used for the transaction of business (other than those classified as mercantile occupancies)
(2) Occupancies used for keeping accounts and records and for similar purposes

Items (1) and (2) include doctors' offices, dentists' offices (see Chapter 20/21 for ambulatory health care centers), and general offices, as well as city halls, town halls, and courthouses, all of which have areas for keeping books and records and transacting public business. Other occupancies included under the definition of business occupancies are service facilities common to office buildings, such as newsstands, lunch counters (serving fewer than 50 people), barber shops, and beauty parlors.

Birth centers occupied by fewer than four patients, not including infants, at any one time should be classified as business occupancies in accordance with the guidelines of A.6.1.11.1 and the definition of the term *birth center* in 3.3.22 and its corresponding annex text in A.3.3.22.

Classification of hazard of contents is addressed in 38/39.1.5. Most occupancy chapters refer to Section 6.2 for classification of hazard of contents. However, the requirement of 38/39.1.5.1 emphasizes that, un-

less an extraordinarily hazardous situation exists, the contents of business occupancies are to be classified as ordinary hazard. This requirement is intended to prevent the user from classifying the hazard of contents as high hazard, except where a combustible load far in excess of the usual, yet considerable, quantity of boxed records and paper files exists. Isolated hazardous contents areas within the overall ordinary hazard business occupancy, such as storage rooms, must be protected or separated in accordance with the requirements of 38/39.3.2.

The classification of hazard of contents listed and defined in Section 6.2 is to be applied independently from the hazard classifications specified in NFPA 13, *Standard for the Installation of Sprinkler Systems*.[2] Therefore, an ordinary hazard business occupancy might be protected by a light hazard sprinkler system.

The intent of 38/39.1.5.2 is to clarify that contents classified by the *Code* as ordinary for the purpose of life safety are not always classified as ordinary under NFPA 13. Paragraph 38/39.1.5.2 states that, for purposes of sprinkler design, the anticipated fuel load of business occupancies in Chapter 38/39 is classified as light hazard.

Subsection 38/39.1.6 is a placeholder for which there is no requirement. Some occupancy chapters, such as Chapter 18/19, which addresses the life safety needs of nonambulatory health care occupants, require a minimum building construction type to help ensure the structural integrity required for a lengthy evacuation or for safe refuge within the building. Because business occupancies are normally occupied by those who are ambulatory, and because they do not provide sleeping accommodations, there are no minimum construction requirements imposed.

Subsection 38/39.1.7 references Table 7.3.1.2 for determining the occupant load factors that apply to the use areas of a business occupancy. Because the number of people expected to occupy certain types of office buildings can be determined with a great degree of accuracy (such as by means of a company's detailed account of its office space), it might be beneficial to compare that occupant load with one calculated on the basis of one person per 100 ft² (9.3 m²) of gross floor area (see Table 7.3.1.2). In office occupancies where people work in highly concentrated groups (such as a bullpen or secretarial pool area), the actual number of people occupying a space might exceed the figure calculated by gross area. As emphasized in Section 7.3, where this is the case, the egress capacity must be designed to accommodate the actual (larger) occupant load. Note that the converse is not true; that is, if the actual occupant load is less than the gross area calculation, the *Code* still requires that the gross area calculation (that is, the larger occupant load) be used to determine the occupant load for which the egress capacity must be provided.

Section 38.2 Means of Egress Requirements

38.2.1 General.

38.2.1.1 All means of egress shall be in accordance with Chapter 7 and this chapter.

38.2.1.2 If, owing to differences in grade, any street floor exits are at points above or below the street or ground level, such exits shall comply with the provisions for exits from upper floors or floors below the street floor.

38.2.1.3 Where two or more floors below the street floor are occupied for business use, the same stairs or ramps shall be permitted to serve each.

Exception: No inside open stairway or inside open ramp shall be permitted to serve as a required egress facility from more than one floor level.

38.2.1.4 Floor levels below the street floor used only for storage, heating, and other service equipment and not subject to business occupancy shall have means of egress in accordance with Chapter 42.

Section 39.2 Means of Egress Requirements

39.2.1 General.

39.2.1.1 All means of egress shall be in accordance with Chapter 7 and this chapter.

39.2.1.2 If, owing to differences in grade, any street floor exits are at points above or below the street or ground level, such exits shall comply with the provisions for exits from upper floors or floors below the street floor.

39.2.1.3 Where two or more floors below the street floor are occupied for business use, the same stairs, escalators, or ramps shall be permitted to serve each.

Exception: No inside open stairway, inside open escalator, or inside open ramp shall be permitted to serve as a required egress facility from more than one floor level.

39.2.1.4 Floor levels below the street floor used only for storage, heating, and other service equipment and not subject to business occupancy shall have means of egress in accordance with Chapter 42.

Exhibit 38/39.3 illustrates a case where two floors qualify as street floors in accordance with 38/39.2.1.2, because each floor has one side located at a ground level. Note, however, that each of the two floors has its other sides located either above or below the building's other ground level. As a result, floors 1 and 2 must have their exits arranged to allow horizontal travel to the exterior at one end of the floor and vertical travel (either up or down to ground level) at the other end of the floor. The egress capacity of the doors to the exterior on floor 1 must accommodate that portion of the occupant load from an upper floor that is expected to travel down to and through the exits to the exterior from floor 1. This portion of the occupant load is to be added to the portion of the floor 1 occupant load assigned to a given exit. The reverse is true for floor 2, which must increase the size of its exterior exit capacity to accommodate occupants traveling up from floor 1, as well as those traveling down to and through the exterior exits on floor 2. Paragraphs 7.3.1.5, 7.3.1.6, and 38/39.2.3.3 explain how to add egress capacity based on the number of occupants expected to discharge from floors above and below the street floor. Exhibit 38/39.7 provides an example of how to calculate exit capacity for a street floor such as that illustrated by floor 2 in Exhibit 38/39.3.

The exception to 38/39.2.1.3 prohibits the use of unenclosed interior stairs or unenclosed interior ramps as exit access for more than one floor; it does not establish permission for the use of an open stairway or open ramp. See 38/39.3.1, which addresses the protection of business occupancy vertical openings, to determine if the stair or ramp is permitted to be unenclosed. The required width of the stair or ramp serving multiple floors is determined by the floor with the largest occupant load. This requirement ensures that a stair or other component of a means of egress will accommodate its assigned portion of the population of any floor it serves.

The implementation of 38/39.2.1.4 results in a significant reduction in the number and size of exits for floors located below the street floor that are used only for storage or for heating and service equipment and that are not subject to business occupancy use. These reductions are permitted because the expected population of such floors will be well below that of a floor used as a typical business occupancy. Also see Section 7.12, which specifically governs boiler rooms and similar spaces.

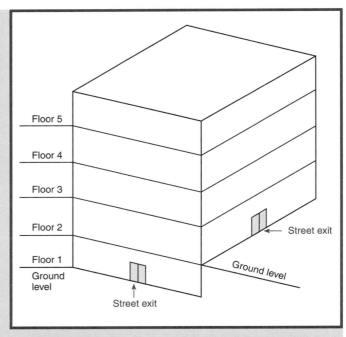

Exhibit 38/39.3 *Business occupancy with two street floors.*

38.2.2 Means of Egress Components.

38.2.2.1 Means of egress components shall be limited to the types described in 38.2.2.2 through 38.2.2.12.

38.2.2.2 Doors.

38.2.2.2.1 Doors complying with 7.2.1 shall be permitted.

38.2.2.2.2* Locks complying with Exception No. 2 to 7.2.1.5.1 shall be permitted only on principal entrance/exit doors.

A.38.2.2.2.2 The words "principal entrance/exit doors" describe doors that the authority having jurisdiction can reasonably expect to be unlocked in order for the facility to do business.

38.2.2.2.3 (Reserved.)

38.2.2.2.4 Delayed-egress locks complying with 7.2.1.6.1 shall be permitted.

39.2.2 Means of Egress Components.

39.2.2.1 Means of egress components shall be limited to the types described in 39.2.2.2 through 39.2.2.12.

39.2.2.2 Doors.

39.2.2.2.1 Doors complying with 7.2.1 shall be permitted.

39.2.2.2.2* Locks complying with Exception No. 2 to 7.2.1.5.1 shall be permitted only on principal entrance/exit doors.

A.39.2.2.2.2 The words "principal entrance/exit doors" describe doors that the authority having jurisdiction can reasonably expect to be unlocked in order for the facility to do business.

39.2.2.2.3 The re-entry provisions of 7.2.1.5.2 shall not apply. *(See 7.2.1.5.2, Exception No. 2(a).)*

39.2.2.2.4 Delayed-egress locks complying with 7.2.1.6.1 shall be permitted.

CHAPTER 38 • New

38.2.2.2.5 Access-controlled egress doors complying with 7.2.1.6.2 shall be permitted.

38.2.2.2.6 Where horizontal or vertical security grilles or doors are used as part of the required means of egress from a tenant space, such grilles or doors shall comply with Exception No. 2 to 7.2.1.4.1.

38.2.2.2.7 (Reserved.)

38.2.2.2.8 Revolving doors complying with 7.2.1.10 shall be permitted.

CHAPTER 39 • Existing

39.2.2.2.5 Access-controlled egress doors complying with 7.2.1.6.2 shall be permitted.

39.2.2.2.6 Where horizontal or vertical security grilles or doors are used as part of the required means of egress from a tenant space, such grilles or doors shall comply with Exception No. 2 to 7.2.1.4.1.

39.2.2.2.7 Existing horizontal-sliding or vertical-rolling fire doors shall be permitted in existing means of egress under the following conditions:

(1) They are held open by fusible links.
(2) The links are rated at not less than 165°F (74°C).
(3) The fusible links are located not more than 10 ft (3 m) above the floor.
(4) The fusible link is in immediate proximity to the door opening.
(5) The fusible link is not located above a ceiling.
(6) The door is not credited with providing any protection under this *Code*.

39.2.2.2.8 Revolving doors complying with 7.2.1.10 shall be permitted.

Subparagraph 38/39.2.2.2.2 permits only the principal entrance/exit doors of a business occupancy to be equipped with the special key-operated dead bolt lock described by the provisions of Exception No. 2 to 7.2.1.5.1. It must be easy to determine that the device is locked by using means such as a flag indicator that can be seen at a distance from the door. Other doors along the perimeter of the building are prohibited from being equipped with a key-operated dead bolt lock, because it cannot be guaranteed that these locks will be disengaged simultaneously when the principal entrance/exit door is unlocked each day at the opening of business. See Exhibit 38/39.4.

Note that, per 39.2.2.2.3, existing business occupancies are exempt from the re-entry provisions of 7.2.1.5.2, which apply to exit stair enclosure doors.

Subparagraph 38/39.2.2.2.4 permits the use of the delayed-egress lock covered by 7.2.1.6.1 on any door in recognition of the security needs of a business occupancy. The building must be protected throughout by an approved, supervised automatic sprinkler system or an approved, supervised automatic fire detection system to apply the delayed-release locking provisions. In effect, the allowable 15-second - or 30-second delay will be experienced only under nonfire conditions or very early in a fire's growth, because

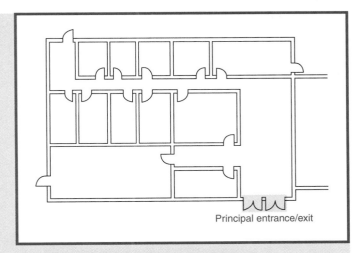

Exhibit 38/39.4 *Principal entrance/exit.*

the door must be usable immediately upon sprinkler operation, smoke or heat detection, or loss of power that controls the locking mechanism.

Subparagraph 38/39.2.2.2.5 recognizes access-controlled egress doors in business occupancies as security measures that do not compromise the use of the means of egress system.

Although Exception No. 2 to 7.2.1.4.1 establishes

provisions for the arrangement and use of horizontal or vertical security grilles or doors, it requires that an occupancy chapter specifically recognize the use of such security grilles or doors. Subparagraph 38/39.2.2.2.6 provides this recognition for business occupancies.

Horizontal-sliding or vertical-rolling fire doors exist in many business occupancies for purposes of property protection. Although the *Code* normally does not recognize these doors within the required means of egress, 39.2.2.2.7 provides a special exemption for existing horizontal-sliding or vertical-rolling fire doors. By requiring the fusible link to be positioned in immediate proximity to the door opening, to be rated 165°F (74°C) or higher, and to be located not more than 10 ft (3 m) above the floor, the *Code* helps to ensure that the door will remain open until rising temperatures make it unsafe to pass through the door opening. The door will not close early in the fire development; therefore, it cannot be credited as a fire door for life safety purposes. However, the door might serve for property protection. See Exhibit 38/39.5.

Subparagraph 38/39.2.2.2.8 addresses revolving doors. The provisions of 7.2.1.10 specify that the use of a revolving door, regardless of whether it is permitted as part of the required means of egress, requires a conforming side-hinged swinging door to be positioned and usable within the same wall as, and to be

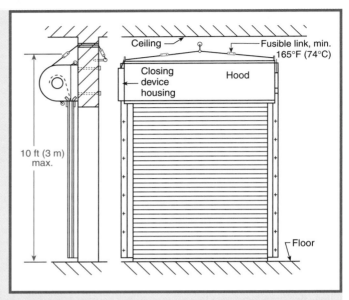

Exhibit 38/39.5 *Existing vertical-rolling fire door in accordance with 39.2.2.2.7.*

located within 10 ft (3 m) of, the revolving door. This requirement helps to ensure that, once people move toward the door, if the collapsibility and other safety features of the door fail and render it unusable, egress from the vicinity would still be possible without retracing steps and requiring travel toward the fire.

38.2.2.3 Stairs.

38.2.2.3.1 Stairs complying with 7.2.2 shall be permitted.

38.2.2.3.2 Spiral stairs complying with 7.2.2.2.3 shall be permitted.

38.2.2.4 Smokeproof Enclosures. Smokeproof enclosures complying with 7.2.3 shall be permitted.

38.2.2.5 Horizontal Exits. Horizontal exits complying with 7.2.4 shall be permitted.

38.2.2.6 Ramps. Ramps complying with 7.2.5 shall be permitted.

38.2.2.7 Exit Passageways. Exit passageways complying with 7.2.6 shall be permitted.

39.2.2.3 Stairs.

39.2.2.3.1 Stairs complying with 7.2.2 shall be permitted.

39.2.2.3.2 Spiral stairs complying with 7.2.2.2.3 shall be permitted.

39.2.2.3.3 Winders complying with 7.2.2.2.4 shall be permitted.

39.2.2.4 Smokeproof Enclosures. Smokeproof enclosures complying with 7.2.3 shall be permitted.

39.2.2.5 Horizontal Exits. Horizontal exits complying with 7.2.4 shall be permitted.

39.2.2.6 Ramps. Ramps complying with 7.2.5 shall be permitted.

39.2.2.7 Exit Passageways. Exit passageways complying with 7.2.6 shall be permitted.

38.2.2.8 (Reserved.)

38.2.2.9 (Reserved.)

38.2.2.10 Fire Escape Ladders. Fire escape ladders complying with 7.2.9 shall be permitted.

38.2.2.11 Alternating Tread Devices. Alternating tread devices complying with 7.2.11 shall be permitted.

38.2.2.12 Areas of Refuge. Areas of refuge complying with 7.2.12 shall be permitted.

Exception: In buildings protected throughout by an approved, supervised automatic sprinkler system in accordance with Section 9.7, two rooms or spaces separated from each other by smoke-resistant partitions in accordance with the definition of area of refuge in 3.3.14 shall not be required.

39.2.2.8 Escalators and Moving Walks. Escalators and moving walks complying with 7.2.7 shall be permitted.

39.2.2.9 Fire Escape Stairs. Fire escape stairs complying with 7.2.8 shall be permitted.

39.2.2.10 Fire Escape Ladders. Fire escape ladders complying with 7.2.9 shall be permitted.

39.2.2.11 Alternating Tread Devices. Alternating tread devices complying with 7.2.11 shall be permitted.

39.2.2.12 Areas of Refuge. Areas of refuge complying with 7.2.12 shall be permitted.

Exception: In buildings protected throughout by an approved, supervised automatic sprinkler system in accordance with Section 9.7, two rooms or spaces separated from each other by smoke-resistant partitions in accordance with the definition of area of refuge in 3.3.14 shall not be required.

Paragraph 38/39.2.2.4 does not mandate the use of smokeproof enclosures. However, it does recognize a smokeproof enclosure as part of the means of egress system in a business occupancy only if the smokeproof enclosure meets the requirements of 7.2.3. For an example of an occupancy requiring a smokeproof enclosure, see 31.2.11, which specifies that existing nonsprinklered, high-rise apartment buildings are required to be provided with smokeproof enclosures in accordance with 7.2.3. See 38/39.2.2.1.

Paragraph 39.2.2.8 permits existing escalators and moving walks to serve within the means of egress of existing business occupancies. Note that 7.2.7 allows escalators and moving walks to continue to be permitted within the required means of egress if permitted by an occupancy chapter. In earlier editions of the *Code*, such escalators and moving walks might have been permitted and credited with providing egress capacity for 75 persons. To qualify as exits, escalators and moving walks must also meet the requirements of 7.1.3.2, which addresses exit enclosures. Escalators protected using the sprinkler-vent, spray nozzle, rolling shutter, or partial enclosure method do not constitute acceptable exits but could continue to serve as exit access if previously approved as such.

Paragraph 39.2.2.9 permits existing fire escape stairs to serve within the means of egress of existing business occupancies. Note that Exception No. 1 to

7.2.8.1.2 permits existing buildings to continue to use fire escape stairs for no more than 50 percent of their required egress capacity.

Alternating tread devices are addressed in 38/39.2.2.11. The provisions of 7.2.11, in effect, restrict the use of alternating tread devices to locations where the *Code* recognizes the use of fire escape ladders. See 38/39.2.2.10, 7.2.9, and 7.2.11.

Areas of refuge are addressed in 38/39.2.2.12. Paragraph 7.5.4.1 requires that areas accessible to persons with severe mobility impairment in new buildings are to be provided with accessible means of egress. Existing business occupancies are exempt from the provisions of 7.5.4.1. For the stories above the level of exit discharge, where providing ramps is usually not feasible, areas of refuge (see 7.2.12) will typically be used to meet the requirements for accessible means of egress in new construction. The exception to 38/39.2.2.12 allows a sprinklered story of a business occupancy to be considered an area of refuge, even if an occupant does not have access to any of the tenant spaces. The effectiveness of sprinkler systems should allow an occupant with mobility impairment to remain on the floor without experiencing untenable conditions. Doors to tenant spaces that are locked create inaccessibility to spaces other than the corridor, so the corridor effectively serves as the area of refuge.

38.2.3 Capacity of Means of Egress.

38.2.3.1 The capacity of means of egress shall be in accordance with Section 7.3.

38.2.3.2* The clear width of any corridor or passageway serving an occupant load of 50 or more shall be not less than 44 in. (112 cm).

A.38.2.3.2 It is not the intent that this provision apply to noncorridor or nonpassageway areas of exit access, such as the spaces between rows of desks created by office layout or low-height partitions.

38.2.3.3 Street floor exits shall be sufficient for the occupant load of the street floor plus the required capacity of stairs and ramps discharging through the street floor.

39.2.3 Capacity of Means of Egress.

39.2.3.1 The capacity of means of egress shall be in accordance with Section 7.3.

39.2.3.2 The clear width of any corridor or passageway serving an occupant load of 50 or more shall be not less than 44 in. (112 cm).

39.2.3.3 Street floor exits shall be sufficient for the occupant load of the street floor plus the required capacity of stairs, ramps, escalators, and moving walks discharging through the street floor.

Chapter 7 mandates that any required egress capacity from a mezzanine that passes through the room below must be added to the required egress capacity of the room through which the egress passes.

Exhibit 38/39.6 illustrates a case in which a mezzanine is open to the street floor. The exits from the street floor must accommodate the following:

(1) Occupant load of the street floor
(2) Occupant load of the mezzanine in accordance with 7.3.1.6
(3) Required capacity provided by the stairs from other floors discharging through the street floor in accordance with 38/39.2.3.3

To determine the exit capacity for the street floor, the occupant load of the mezzanine (1000 persons) is added to the occupant load of the street floor (2000 persons). In addition, because one-half of the exits from the upper floors discharge through the street floor, the egress capacity of the street floor must accommodate the capacity of the exit stair enclosure that discharges through that floor. The maximum occupant load of any upper floor is 2000 (second floor); and 38/39.2.7, in accordance with its reference to Section 7.7, permits a maximum of one-half of the exits or one-half of the exit capacity to discharge through the street floor, provided that the requirements of 7.7.2 are met. Those requirements most typically involve the sprinklering of the level of exit discharge. Therefore, the street floor must be provided with egress capacity for 4000 persons or 800 in. (2030 cm) of exit width using the factor of 0.2 in. (0.5 cm) per

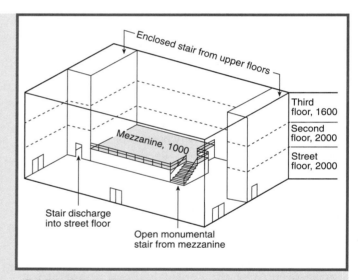

Exhibit 38/39.6 Business occupancy with a mezzanine open to the street floor.

person for level exit components found in Table 7.3.3.1 (2000 for street floor + 1000 for mezzanine + 1000 for upper floors = 4000).

Paragraph 38/39.2.3.2 requires a minimum 44-in. (112-cm) wide corridor only if the corridor serves an occupant load of 50 or more persons. If a corridor serves fewer than 50 persons, the minimum 36-in. (91-cm) width—mandated by 7.3.4.1 for egress components in general—would apply.

A corridor with the minimum 44-in. (112-cm) width required by 38/39.2.3.2 has sufficient egress capacity, where calculated using the 0.2 in. (0.5 cm) per person capacity factor of Table 7.3.3.1 for level components, for 220 persons; that is, 44 in. / 0.2 in. per person (approximately 112 cm / 0.5 cm per person). For example, in a corridor that runs from one end of a building to the other end with an exit stair located at each end, 220 persons can travel from the midpoint of that corridor to the exit enclosure at one end. Another 220 persons can travel to the exit enclosure at the other end. Therefore, in this example, the occupant load of the floor would have to exceed 440 persons before the minimum 44-in. (112-cm) corridor width must be increased.

Paragraph 38/39.2.3.3 requires that the exits for the street floor of a business occupancy have sufficient capacity to handle the occupant load of the street floor and the capacity of the exits discharging through the street floor. An example is an enclosed exit stair that accommodates occupants who, when exiting the building during an emergency, must travel up from the basement area or down from the upper floors and mix with the occupants already occupying the street floor.

Because people move more quickly in the horizontal direction than in the vertical direction, it is permissible to provide less door width than stair width within any given egress path. For example, in business occupancies, in accordance with the egress capacity factors of Table 7.3.3.1, level components and ramps require only 0.2 in. (0.5 cm) of width per person, whereas stairs require 0.3 in. (0.8 cm) of width per person. As a rough approximation, for every 44 in. (112 cm) of stair discharging through the street floor, an additional 30 in. (76 cm) of door width opening to the outside must be added for the street floor. Exhibit 38/39.7 provides an example of the calculation method for determining the required exit capacity for the street floor.

Street floor occupant load	1000
Maximum upper floor occupant load discharging back through street floor (500 / 2)	+ 250
Basement occupant load discharging back through street floor (400 / 2)	+ 200
	1450 Total occupant load

1450 persons × 0.2 in. (0.5 cm) per person for level exit components per 7.3.3.1 = 290 in. (737 cm) of exit width required from the street floor egress system

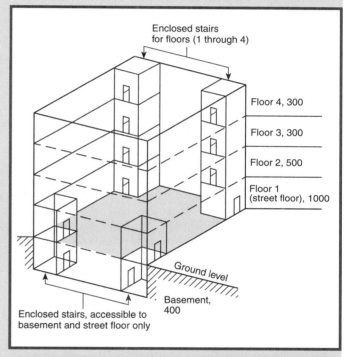

Exhibit 38/39.7 Calculation of exit capacity required for a street floor in accordance with 38/39.2.3.3.

38.2.4 Number of Exits.

38.2.4.1 (Reserved.)

38.2.4.2 Not less than two separate exits shall meet the following criteria:

(1) They shall be provided on every story.
(2) They shall be accessible from every part of every story and mezzanine.

39.2.4 Number of Exits.

39.2.4.1 The number of exits shall be in accordance with 39.2.4.2. The requirements of 7.4.1.2 shall not apply.

39.2.4.2 Not less than two separate exits shall meet the following criteria:

(1) They shall be provided on every story.
(2) They shall be accessible from every part of every story and mezzanine.

CHAPTER 38 • New	CHAPTER 39 • Existing

Exception No. 1: Exit access travel shall be permitted to be common for the distances permitted as common paths of travel by 38.2.5.3.

Exception No. 2: A single exit shall be permitted for a room or area with a total occupant load of fewer than 100 persons, provided that the following criteria are met:

(a) The exit shall discharge directly to the outside at the level of exit discharge for the building.

(b) The total distance of travel from any point, including travel within the exit, shall not exceed 100 ft (30 m).

(c) Such travel shall be on the same floor level or, if traversing of stairs is necessary, such stairs shall not exceed 15 ft (4.5 m) in height, and the stairs shall be provided with complete enclosures to separate them from any other part of the building, with no door openings therein.

(d) A single outside stair in accordance with 7.2.2 shall be permitted to serve all floors permitted within the 15-ft (4.5-m) vertical travel limitation.

Exception No. 3: Any business occupancy not exceeding three stories, and not exceeding an occupant load of 30 people per floor, shall be permitted a single separate exit to each floor. This exception shall be permitted only where the total travel distance to the outside of the building does not exceed 100 ft (30 m) and where the exit is enclosed in accordance with 7.1.3.2, serves no other levels, and discharges directly to the outside. A single outside stair in accordance with 7.2.2 shall be permitted to serve all floors.

Exception No. 4: A single means of egress shall be permitted from a mezzanine within a business occupancy, provided that the common path of travel does not exceed 75 ft (23 m), or 100 ft (30 m) if protected throughout by an approved, supervised automatic sprinkler system in accordance with Section 9.7.

Exception No. 5: A single exit shall be permitted for a maximum two-story, single-tenant space/building protected throughout by an approved, supervised automatic sprinkler system in accordance with Section 9.7 where the total travel to the outside does not exceed 100 ft (30 m).

Paragraph 38/39.2.4.2 requires a minimum of two exits. For new business occupancies, see 7.4.1.2, which requires a minimum of three means of egress or a minimum of four means of egress where the occupant load exceeds 500 and 1000, respectively.

The provisions of 38/39.2.4, which apply to the required number of exits for business occupancies,

---

Exception No. 1: Exit access travel shall be permitted to be common for the distances permitted as common paths of travel by 39.2.5.3.

Exception No. 2: A single exit shall be permitted for a room or area with a total occupant load of fewer than 100 persons, provided that the following criteria are met:

(a) The exit shall discharge directly to the outside at the level of exit discharge for the building.

(b) The total distance of travel from any point, including travel within the exit, shall not exceed 100 ft (30 m).

(c) Such travel shall be on the same floor level or, if traversing of stairs is necessary, such stairs shall not exceed 15 ft (4.5 m) in height, and the stairs shall be provided with complete enclosures to separate them from any other part of the building, with no door openings therein.

(d) A single outside stair in accordance with 7.2.2 shall be permitted to serve all floors permitted within the 15-ft (4.5-m) vertical travel limitation.

Exception No. 3: Any business occupancy not exceeding three stories, and not exceeding an occupant load of 30 people per floor, shall be permitted a single separate exit to each floor. This exception is permitted only where the total travel distance to the outside of the building does not exceed 100 ft (30 m) and where the exit is enclosed in accordance with 5.1.3.2, serves no other levels, and discharges directly to the outside. A single outside stair in accordance with 7.2.2 shall be permitted to serve all floors.

Exception No. 4: A single means of egress shall be permitted from a mezzanine within a business occupancy, provided that the common path of travel does not exceed 75 ft (23 m), or 100 ft (30 m) if protected throughout by an approved automatic sprinkler system in accordance with Section 9.7.

Exception No. 5: A single exit shall be permitted for a maximum two-story, single-tenant space/building protected throughout by an approved automatic sprinkler system in accordance with Section 9.7 where the total travel to the outside does not exceed 100 ft (30 m).

---

clarify that any level that constitutes a story must have at least two exits located on that story. This subsection requires that the occupants of the story must be able to enter an exit (such as an enclosed exit stair on an upper floor of a multistory building) without having to travel to another story to reach the entrance to the exit. Because a mezzanine that meets

CHAPTER 38 • New

CHAPTER 39 • Existing

the maximum one-third area rule of 8.2.6 does not constitute a story (see 8.2.6.1), two exits are not required on the mezzanine. However, the criteria of 38/39.2.4.2(2) must be met with respect to providing access to two separate exits, or the provisions of Exception No. 1 or Exception No. 4 to 38/39.2.4.2 must be met.

Exception No. 1 to 38/39.2.4.2 applies only to 38/39.2.4.2(2), which requires access to two separate exits from every part of every level (story or mezzanine). Exception No. 1 indicates that 38/39.2.5.3 allows the occupant to travel in one direction for a maximum distance (the common path allowance) before requiring access in two separate directions. Therefore, although the story or mezzanine must eventually provide access to two exits in accordance with 38/39.2.4.2(2), that access is required to be available only at the point where the allowable common path is expended.

Exhibits 38/39.8 and 38/39.9 illustrate two cases where a single exit from a room or area in a business occupancy is allowed in accordance with Exception No. 2 to 38/39.2.4.2. In the first case, the travel distance from the area is located on the same floor level as the exit. In the second case, stairs must be traversed.

The criteria for allowing the single exit in accordance with Exception No. 2 to 38/39.2.4.2 follow:

(1) Occupant load fewer than 100 persons
(2) Direct exit to a street or to an open exterior area at ground level

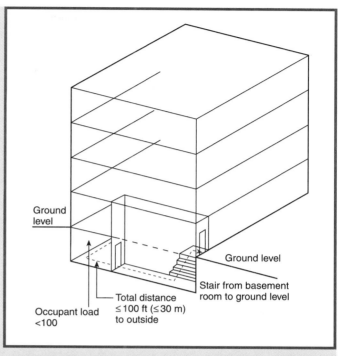

Exhibit 38/39.9 Single exit from area or room in business occupancy in accordance with Exception No. 2 to 38/39.2.4.2—stairs traversed in traveling from the area to the exit.

(3) Total distance of not more than 100 ft (30 m) from any point in the room to the exterior [note that this is total distance from any point to the exterior, not travel distance as measured in Section 7.6; therefore, total distance includes the distance traveled on enclosed stairs (exit)]
(4) Stairs not more than 15 ft (4.5 m) in height
(5) Stairs completely enclosed with no door openings between the stair enclosure and the rest of the building, or stairs meet requirements applicable to outside stairs (see 7.2.2.6.3)

To use the exception, all five criteria must be met.

Exhibit 38/39.10 illustrates a single exit from the third floor of a business occupancy in accordance with Exception No. 3 to 38/39.2.4.2. The stair is totally enclosed, has an opening onto a building floor only at third floor, and discharges directly to street with no communication at second and first floors. A similar, but separate, arrangement could be provided for the second floor of the same building.

The criteria for allowing a single exit in accordance with Exception No. 3 to 38/39.2.4.2 follow:

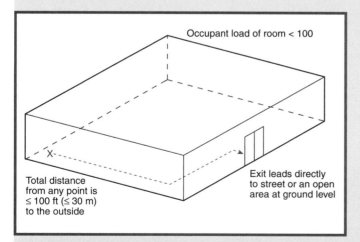

Exhibit 38/39.8 Single exit from area or room in business occupancy in accordance with Exception No. 2 to 38/39.2.4.2—travel from area to exit without stairs.

CHAPTER 38 • New   **CHAPTER 39 • Existing**

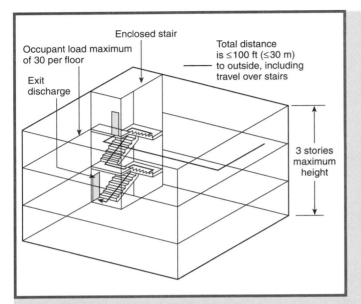

Exhibit 38/39.10 Single exit from third floor of a business occupancy in accordance with Exception No. 3 to 38/39.2.4.2.

(1) Building height not more than 3 stories
(2) Occupant load of each floor not more than 30
(3) Total distance from any point on any floor to exterior at ground level not more than 100 ft (30 m), including travel over stairs [note that this is total distance from any point to the exterior, not travel distance as measured in Section 7.6; therefore,

total distance includes the distance traveled on enclosed stairs (exit)]
(4) Stair is not used by, nor has an opening to, any other floor
(5) Stair is totally enclosed or meets the requirements applicable to outside stairs (see 7.2.2.6.3)

To use the exception, all five criteria must be met.

Although Exception No. 1 to 38/39.2.4.2 allows common access to the two required means of egress for limited distances, Exception No. 4 to 38/38.2.4.2 exempts a mezzanine in a business occupancy from providing a point where access to two exits is available if the single means of egress leads to an exit within the same limited distances as those allowed for common path of travel.

Exception No. 5 to 38/39.2.4.2 provides some relief from the requirement that mandates two separate exits on every story, which affects town house–type, sprinklered business occupancies. These town house–type business occupancies typically have two stories with an open interior stair and are of such limited size that, if a second stair were added, little usable space would remain, and the two stairs would, in effect, be located side by side. The exception offers any single-tenant space in a fully sprinklered building with a maximum of two stories, or any sprinklered single-tenant building with a maximum of two stories, the option of providing only one exit if the total travel distance to the outside does not exceed 100 ft (30 m).

38.2.5 Arrangement of Means of Egress.

38.2.5.1 Means of egress shall be arranged in accordance with Section 7.5.

38.2.5.2 Dead-end corridors shall not exceed 20 ft (6.1 m).

Exception: In buildings protected throughout by an approved, supervised automatic sprinkler system in accordance with Section 9.7, dead-end corridors shall not exceed 50 ft (15 m).

38.2.5.3 Common paths of travel shall not exceed 75 ft (23 m).

39.2.5 Arrangement of Means of Egress.

39.2.5.1 Means of egress shall be arranged in accordance with Section 7.5.

39.2.5.2* Dead-end corridors shall not exceed 50 ft (15 m).

A.39.2.5.2 It is recognized that dead ends exceeding the permitted limits exist and, in some cases, are impractical to eliminate. The authority having jurisdiction might permit such dead ends to continue to exist, taking into consideration any or all of the following:

(1) Tenant arrangement
(2) Automatic sprinkler protection
(3) Smoke detection
(4) Exit remoteness

39.2.5.3* Common paths of travel shall not exceed 75 ft (23 m).

CHAPTER 38 • New   **CHAPTER 39 • Existing**

Exception No. 1: *A common path of travel shall be permitted for the first 100 ft (30 m) in a building protected throughout by an approved, supervised automatic sprinkler system in accordance with Section 9.7.*

Exception No. 2: *A common path of travel shall be permitted for the first 100 ft (30 m) within a single tenant space having an occupant load not exceeding 30 persons.*

Exception No. 1: *A common path of travel shall be permitted for the first 100 ft (30 m) on a story protected throughout by an approved automatic sprinkler system in accordance with Section 9.7.*

Exception No. 2: *A single tenant space with an occupant load not exceeding 30 people shall be permitted to have a single exit access, provided that the corridor to which that exit access leads does not have a dead end exceeding 50 ft (15 m).*

A.39.2.5.3 It is recognized that common paths of travel exceeding the permitted limits exist and, in some cases, are impractical to eliminate. The authority having jurisdiction might permit such common paths of travel to continue to exist, taking into consideration any or all of the following:

(1) Tenant arrangement
(2) Automatic sprinkler protection
(3) Smoke detection
(4) Exit remoteness

Because they have separate and distinct requirements, the *Code* separates dead-end corridors and common path of travel into two distinct and separate paragraphs. Dead-end corridors are limited to 20 ft (6.1 m) in new business occupancy buildings that are not protected throughout by an approved, supervised automatic sprinkler system. Existing business occupancies are permitted a 50-ft (15-m) dead-end corridor, regardless of the presence of sprinklers. The exception to 38.2.5.2 recognizes the additional level of safety to life that a complete automatic sprinkler system provides. This exception also allows added flexibility when designing the location of corridors and exits in buildings where approved sprinkler systems are installed by permitting the dead-end corridor pocket to be as long as 50 ft (15 m).

Three typical dead-end corridors are illustrated in Exhibit 38/39.11. Dead-end pockets are located in the corridor between points B and C, F and G, and H and I. They are limited to a maximum length of 20 ft (6.1 m) [50 ft (15 m) for existing business occupancies or sprinklered new business occupancies].

See the commentary associated with 7.5.1.6 for a detailed discussion on common path of travel. Also see the commentary associated with Exception No. 1 to 38/39.2.4.2, which allows a portion of the access to a single exit or multiple exits to be common.

The restriction on common path of travel is separate and distinct from the restriction on dead-end corridors. A common path of travel might sometimes involve a dead-end corridor, and dead ends might involve common path of travel, but not in every case.

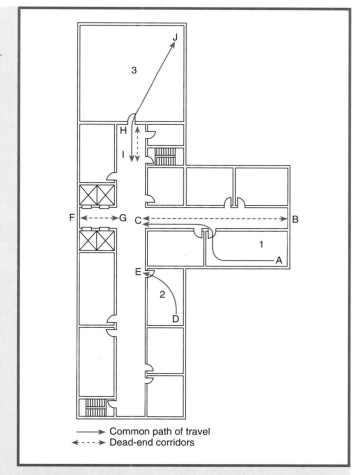

$\longrightarrow$ Common path of travel
$\leftarrow\text{- - -}\rightarrow$ Dead-end corridors

Exhibit 38/39.11 *Dead-end corridor pockets and common path of travel.*

For an example, the elevator lobby shown in Exhibit 38/39.11 is a dead-end corridor but not a common path of travel.

Common path of travel is measured similarly to travel distance (see Section 7.6). The difference is that, instead of terminating at the entrance to an exit, common path of travel measurement often ends before the exit entrance, because it terminates at the point where the occupant has a choice of two distinct and separate paths to an exit (see the definition of the term *common path of travel* in 3.3.32). The starting point for measurement of common path of travel is the same as the starting point for travel distance measurement. Specifically, the starting point is the most remote point. See rooms 1, 2, and 3 in Exhibit 38/39.11 where common paths of travel occur between points A and C, D and E, and J and I.

Exception No. 1 to 38/39.2.5.3 allows the common path of travel to be extended from 75 ft (23 m) to 100 ft (30 m) if sprinklers are provided. For new business occupancies, the building must be protected throughout by an approved, supervised automatic sprinkler system; for existing business occupancies, the sprinkler system is not required to be supervised and is not required to protect the entire building but only at least the floor on which the increased common path is located. The exception recognizes the additional level of safety to life that automatic sprinkler protection provides and allows added flexibility when designing the location of corridors and exits in buildings where approved sprinkler systems are installed.

Exception No. 2 to 38.2.5.3 permits common path of travel in a new business occupancy to be extended from 75 ft (23 m) to 100 ft (30 m), without requiring the sprinkler protection addressed in Exception No. 1 to 38.2.5.3, if the common path of travel occurs wholly within a maximum 30-person [normally, approximately 3000 ft² (270 m²), based on the business occupant load factor of 100 ft² (9.3 m²) per person] single-tenant space, with no additional common path encountered once the common space, such as the corridor, is reached. In Exhibit 38/39.11, Exception No. 2 could be applied to room 2 but not to room 1 or room 3 because, upon leaving those rooms, additional common path of travel is encountered within the corridor.

The criteria addressed by Exception No. 2 to 38.2.5.3 are not included in Chapter 39, because an existing business occupancy is offered the 25-ft (7.6-m) extension in allowable common path of

travel—to 100 ft (30 m) as specified in Exception No. 2 to 39.2.5.3—which is easier to meet. Exception No. 2 to 39.2.5.3 exempts a single-tenant space with a maximum occupant load of not more than 30 people from the common path of travel requirement. The tenant space would normally have an area of approximately 3000 ft² (270 m²), based on the business occupant load factor of 100 ft² (9.3 m²) per person. This exception can be used only if the single door from that tenant space leads to a corridor that does not have a dead end in excess of 50 ft (15 m). For an existing business occupancy, Exception No. 2 to 39.2.5.3 might permit the common path of travel indicated between points J and I in Exhibit 38/39.11.

Exhibit 38/39.12 is an additional example of common path of travel in a business occupancy. Also see the commentary associated with Section 7.5 on arrangement of means of egress.

In Suite A of Exhibit 38/39.12, the travel from

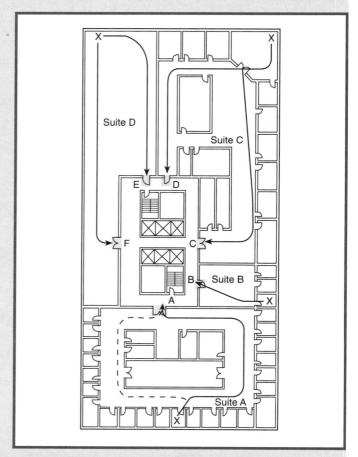

Exhibit 38/39.12 *Common path of travel.*

point X to point A is a common path of travel; although there are two routes to reach the corridor, they both merge at common point A. In Suite B, the travel from point X to point B is common path of travel, and does not appear to exceed the 75-ft (23-m) maximum; if it were in excess of 75 ft (23 m) but no more than 100 ft (30 m), it would be permitted by either Exception No. 1 to 38/39.2.5.3 (involving sprinkler protection) or Exception No. 2 to 38/39.2.5.3 (involving single tenant space). Although Suites C and D do not have common paths of travel, the remoteness of the two exit access doors from each suite is questionable. See 7.5.1.3 and 7.5.1.4.

The common path of travel restriction regulates where an office space requires two exit access doors. If the common path of travel is exceeded, a second door from the office space is required. The door must be positioned so that any resulting common path of travel complies with the allowable distances. In addition, the second door must be remotely located from the first door (see 7.5.1.3 and 7.5.1.4), and each door must lead to remote exits by means of remote paths. Therefore, in a single requirement, the *Code* not only regulates the number of exit access doors required from an office area but also regulates the arrangement of these doors.

38.2.6 Travel Distance to Exits.

Travel distance to exits, measured in accordance with Section 7.6, shall not exceed 200 ft (60 m).

Exception: Travel distance shall not exceed 300 ft (91 m) in buildings protected throughout by an approved, supervised automatic sprinkler system in accordance with Section 9.7.

38.2.7 Discharge from Exits.

Exit discharge shall comply with Section 7.7.

38.2.8 Illumination of Means of Egress.

Means of egress shall be illuminated in accordance with Section 7.8.

38.2.9 Emergency Lighting.

38.2.9.1 Emergency lighting shall be provided in accordance with Section 7.9 in any building where any one of the following conditions exists:

(1) The building is two or more stories in height above the level of exit discharge.
(2) The occupancy is subject to 50 or more occupants above or below the level of exit discharge.
(3) The occupancy is subject to 300 or more total occupants.

38.2.9.2 Emergency lighting in accordance with Section 7.9 shall be provided for all underground and windowless structures as defined in 3.3.205 and 3.3.212.

38.2.10 Marking of Means of Egress.

Means of egress shall have signs in accordance with Section 7.10.

39.2.6 Travel Distance to Exits.

Travel distance to exits, measured in accordance with Section 7.6, shall not exceed 200 ft (60 m).

Exception: Travel distance shall not exceed 300 ft (91 m) in buildings protected throughout by an approved automatic sprinkler system in accordance with Section 9.7.

39.2.7 Discharge from Exits.

Exit discharge shall comply with Section 7.7.

39.2.8 Illumination of Means of Egress.

Means of egress shall be illuminated in accordance with Section 7.8.

39.2.9 Emergency Lighting.

39.2.9.1 Emergency lighting shall be provided in accordance with Section 7.9 in any building where any one of the following conditions exists:

(1) The building is two or more stories in height above the level of exit discharge.
(2) The occupancy is subject to 100 or more occupants above or below the level of exit discharge.
(3) The occupancy is subject to 1000 or more total occupants.

39.2.9.2 Emergency lighting in accordance with Section 7.9 shall be provided for all underground and windowless structures as defined in 3.3.205 and 3.3.212.

39.2.10 Marking of Means of Egress.

Means of egress shall have signs in accordance with Section 7.10.

CHAPTER 38 • New

CHAPTER 39 • Existing

38.2.11 Special Means of Egress Features.

(Reserved.)

39.2.11 Special Means of Egress Features.

(Reserved.)

Travel distance is addressed in 38/39.2.6. In accordance with Section 7.6, travel distance requirements apply to only the first (or nearest) exit from a given point in a building. In other words, the 200-ft (60-m) travel distance limit requires that at least one exit is to be located within 200 ft (60 m) of any point in the building; it does not require that all exits are to be within 200 ft (60 m) of any point in the building.

The exception to 38/39.2.6 allows the travel distance to be increased to 300 ft (91 m) if the building is protected throughout by an approved automatic sprinkler system. To use the exception to 38.2.6 for

new business occupancies, the sprinkler system must be supervised. The exception recognizes the additional level of safety to life that a complete automatic sprinkler system provides and allows added flexibility in the design and arrangement of the means of egress.

If any of the three conditions of 38/39.2.9.1 exist, emergency lighting as specified in Section 7.9 is required for the building. Note that 38/39.2.9.1(1) specifically mentions buildings that have two stories or more located above the level of exit discharge, or a minimum of three stories.

Section 38.3 Protection

38.3.1 Protection of Vertical Openings.

38.3.1.1 Any vertical opening shall be enclosed or protected in accordance with 8.2.5.

Exception No. 1:   Unenclosed vertical openings in accordance with 8.2.5.8 shall be permitted.

Exception No. 2:   Exit access stairs shall be permitted to be unenclosed in two-story single-tenant spaces that are provided with a single exit in accordance with Exception No. 4 to 38.2.4.2.

Section 39.3 Protection

39.3.1 Protection of Vertical Openings.

39.3.1.1 Any vertical opening shall be enclosed or protected in accordance with 8.2.5.

Exception No. 1:   Unenclosed vertical openings in accordance with 8.2.5.8 shall be permitted.

Exception No. 2:   Exit access stairs shall be permitted to be unenclosed in two-story single-tenant spaces that are provided with a single exit in accordance with Exception No. 4 to 39.2.4.2.

Exception No. 3:   In buildings protected throughout by an approved automatic sprinkler system in accordance with Section 9.7, unprotected vertical openings shall be permitted. This exception shall be permitted only where no unprotected vertical opening serves as any part of any required means of egress and all required exits consist of outside stairs in accordance with 7.2.2, smokeproof enclosures in accordance with 7.2.3, or horizontal exits in accordance with 7.2.4.

38.3.1.2 Floors below the street floor used for storage or other than business occupancy shall have no unprotected openings to business occupancy floors.

39.3.1.2 Floors below the street floor used for storage or other than business occupancy shall have no unprotected openings to business occupancy floors.

Paragraph 38/39.3.1.1 references 8.2.5. Paragraph 8.2.5.5 permits the three-story vertical opening unless there is a prohibition on such use in the applicable occupancy chapter. Chapter 38/39 doesn't prohibit the use of 8.2.5.5. Note that 8.2.5.5 requires that, if

the communicating space (the vertical opening and all areas open to it) contains ordinary hazard contents, it must be protected by automatic sprinklers. In accordance with 38/39.1.5, business occupancies are classified as ordinary hazard.

Exception No. 1 to 38/39.3.1.1—via its reference to 8.2.5.8—permits, for example, a two-level office or a reference library in an office building to have an unenclosed convenience stair.

Exception No. 2 to 38/39.3.1.1 completes the single-exit package for townhouse-type and similarly arranged business occupancies by allowing the single means of egress to include an unenclosed stair. See the commentary associated with Exception No. 5 to 38/39.2.4.2.

Application of Exception No. 3 to 39.3.1.1 requires not only that the building housing the existing business occupancy be protected with complete automatic sprinkler protection, but it also requires that all building exits are to be either smokeproof enclosures,

38.3.2 Protection from Hazards.

38.3.2.1* Hazardous areas including, but not limited to, areas used for general storage, boiler or furnace rooms, and maintenance shops that include woodworking and painting areas shall be protected in accordance with Section 8.4.

A.38.3.2.1 It is not the intent of this provision that rooms inside individual tenant spaces, used to store routine office supplies for that tenant, be required to be either separated or sprinklered.

38.3.2.2* High hazard contents areas, as classified in Section 6.2, shall meet the following criteria:

(1) The area shall be separated from other parts of the building by fire barriers having a fire resistance rating of not less than 1 hour, with all openings therein protected by ¾-hour fire protection–rated self-closing fire doors.
(2) The area shall be protected by an automatic extinguishing system in accordance with Section 9.7.

A.38.3.2.2 The requirement for separating high hazard contents areas from other parts of the building is intended to isolate the hazard, and Exception No. 1 to 8.2.3.1.1 is applicable.

Paragraphs 38/39.3.2.1 and 38/39.3.2.2 reflect the intent of Section 8.4, which requires one of the following:

(1) Separation of a hazardous area from the remainder of the occupancy by means of suitable construction
(2) Installation of an automatic extinguishing system in the hazardous area

outside stairs, horizontal exits, or doors leading directly to the outside at ground level. Otherwise, the unprotected vertical openings must be suitably enclosed.

The separation requirement of 38/39.3.1.2 prevents the possibility that a fire in a basement housing a hazardous area with a high fuel load (such as areas used for workshops, repairs, or storage of maintenance supplies, files, and records) might directly expose the floor of exit discharge through an unprotected vertical opening. A fire in a basement can quickly cause exits and exit discharges located on the street floor to become unusable when smoke and heat rise.

39.3.2 Protection from Hazards.

39.3.2.1* Hazardous areas including, but not limited to, areas used for general storage, boiler or furnace rooms, and maintenance shops that include woodworking and painting areas shall be protected in accordance with Section 8.4.

A.39.3.2.1 It is not the intent of this provision that rooms inside individual tenant spaces, used to store routine office supplies for that tenant, be required to be separated or sprinklered.

39.3.2.2* High hazard contents areas, as classified in Section 6.2, shall meet the following criteria:

(1) The area shall be separated from other parts of the building by fire barriers having a fire resistance rating of not less than 1 hour, with all openings therein protected by ¾-hour fire protection–rated self-closing fire doors.
(2) The area shall be protected by an automatic extinguishing system in accordance with Section 9.7.

A.39.3.2.2 The requirement for separating high hazard contents areas from other parts of the building is intended to isolate the hazard, and Exception No. 1 to 8.2.3.1.1 is applicable.

(3) Protection by both items (1) and (2) where the hazard is severe

Subsection 8.4.1 requires that, where a hazardous area is protected by automatic sprinklers, the hazardous area is required to be enclosed by walls and doors that are at least smoke resisting. See 8.4.1.

Section 8.4 contains two additional mandatory

provisions. One is a reference to NFPA 30, *Flammable and Combustible Liquids Code*.[3] The other refers to

NFPA 45, *Standard on Fire Protection for Laboratories Using Chemicals*.[4] See 8.4.3 and 8.4.4.

38.3.3 Interior Finish.

38.3.3.1 Interior finish shall be in accordance with Section 10.2.

38.3.3.2 Interior Wall and Ceiling Finish. Interior wall and ceiling finish complying with 10.2.3 shall be Class A or Class B in exits and in enclosed corridors furnishing access to exits; and Class A, Class B, or Class C in office areas.

38.3.3.3 Interior Floor Finish. Interior floor finish complying with 10.2.7 shall be Class I or Class II in corridors and exits.

39.3.3 Interior Finish.

39.3.3.1 Interior finish shall be in accordance with Section 10.2.

39.3.3.2 Interior Wall and Ceiling Finish. Interior wall and ceiling finish complying with 10.2.3 shall be Class A or Class B in exits and in enclosed corridors furnishing access to exits; and Class A, Class B, or Class C in office areas.

39.3.3.3 Interior Floor Finish. (No requirements.)

Chapter 38, applicable to new business occupancies and the installation of new materials (that is, interior floor finish in this case) in existing business occupancies, is among the few occupancy chapters that regulate interior floor finish. The requirement that such finish be Class I or Class II (see Section 10.2) applies only to exits, such as enclosed stairs, and to corridors. The intent is that the interior floor finish materials used in corridors and exits are to resist the spread of

fire if the interior floor finish in these areas is exposed to the radiant energy from a fully developed room fire by means of an open door. Subsection 10.2.8 contains a provision that allows a reduction for one class of interior floor finish (that is, from Class I to Class II, or from Class II to no rating required) in sprinklered buildings. No rating is required for floor finish in sprinklered business occupancy buildings, because Chapter 38 specifies Class II interior floor finish.

38.3.4 Detection, Alarm, and Communications Systems.

38.3.4.1 General. A fire alarm system in accordance with Section 9.6 shall be provided in any business occupancy where any one of the following conditions exists:

(1) The building is two or more stories in height above the level of exit discharge.
(2) The occupancy is subject to 50 or more occupants above or below the level of exit discharge.
(3) The occupancy is subject to 300 or more total occupants.

38.3.4.2 Initiation. Initiation of the required fire alarm system shall be by manual means in accordance with 9.6.2.1(1).

Exception No. 1: Initiation shall be permitted by means of an approved automatic fire detection system in accordance with 9.6.2.1(2) that provides protection throughout the building.

39.3.4 Detection, Alarm, and Communications Systems.

39.3.4.1 General. A fire alarm system in accordance with Section 9.6 shall be provided in any business occupancy where any one of the following conditions exists:

(1) The building is two or more stories in height above the level of exit discharge.
(2) The occupancy is subject to 100 or more occupants above or below the level of exit discharge.
(3) The occupancy is subject to 1000 or more total occupants.

39.3.4.2 Initiation. Initiation of the required fire alarm system shall be by manual means in accordance with 9.6.2.1(1).

Exception No. 1: Initiation shall be permitted by means of an approved automatic fire detection system in accordance with 9.6.2.1(2) that provides protection throughout the building.

Exception No. 2: Initiation shall be permitted by means of an approved automatic sprinkler system in accordance with 9.6.2.1(3) that provides protection throughout the building.

38.3.4.3 Occupant Notification. During all times that the building is occupied (see 7.2.1.1.3), the required fire alarm system, once initiated, shall perform one of the following functions.

(a) It shall activate a general alarm in accordance with 9.6.3 throughout the building.

Exception: Positive alarm sequence in accordance with 9.6.3.4 shall be permitted.

(b) It shall activate an alarm signal in a continuously attended location for the purpose of initiating emergency action by personnel trained to respond to emergencies. Emergency action shall be initiated by means of live voice public address system announcements originating from the attended location where the alarm signal is received. The system shall be permitted to be used for other announcements, provided that the fire alarm use takes precedence over any other use.

Exception: Any other occupant notification means permitted by 9.6.3 shall be permitted in lieu of live voice public address system announcements.

Exception No. 2: Initiation shall be permitted by means of an approved automatic sprinkler system in accordance with 9.6.2.1(3) that provides protection throughout the building.

39.3.4.3 Occupant Notification. During all times that the building is occupied *(see 7.2.1.1.3)*, the required fire alarm system, once initiated, shall perform one of the following functions.

(a) It shall activate a general alarm in accordance with 9.6.3 throughout the building.

Exception No. 1: Positive alarm sequence in accordance with 9.6.3.4 shall be permitted.

Exception No. 2: A presignal system in accordance with 9.6.3.3 shall be permitted.

(b) It shall activate an alarm signal in a continuously attended location for the purpose of initiating emergency action by personnel trained to respond to emergencies. Emergency action shall be initiated by means of live voice public address system announcements originating from the attended location where the alarm signal is received. The system shall be permitted to be used for other announcements, provided that the fire alarm use takes precedence over any other use.

Exception: Any other occupant notification means permitted by 9.6.3 shall be permitted in lieu of live voice public address system announcements.

A fire alarm system is required in a business occupancy under the same conditions as those under which emergency lighting is required (see 38/39.2.9.1). If any one of the three conditions of 38/39.3.4.1 exists, a fire alarm system must be provided. Note that, in 38/39.3.4.1(1), "two or more stories in height above the level of exit discharge" usually describes a building with three or more stories.

Paragraph 38/39.3.4.2 states that a required fire alarm system must have initiation means but waives the requirement for manual fire alarm boxes if the system is initiated by either an automatic fire detection system providing protection throughout the building or an automatic sprinkler system providing protection throughout the building. This waiver does not exempt the fire alarm system but only the manual fire alarm boxes. However, 9.6.2.5 requires at least one manual fire alarm box to be provided at the location designated by the authority having jurisdiction.

Paragraph 38/39.3.4.3 requires that, when the required fire alarm system is initiated (see 38/39.3.4.2), either the system must automatically sound a general alarm throughout the building; or, if a continuously attended location is provided (as is often the case in high-rise or other large office buildings), the alarm is permitted to sound at that location only, with the appropriate emergency action initiated at that location.

It is preferable for a voice alarm system to be controlled from the continuously attended location referred to in 38/39.3.4.3. The exception would be used primarily in buildings where a continuously attended location is not provided and would allow either a recorded voice system or a general audible alarm.

Note that the exceptions to 38/39.3.4.3(a) permit presignal systems in existing business occupancies only; the better, fail-safe feature, positive alarm sequence, is permitted for both new and existing business occupancies. See 9.6.3.3 and 9.6.3.4.

CHAPTER 38 • New

CHAPTER 39 • Existing

38.3.5 Extinguishment Requirements.

Portable fire extinguishers shall be provided in every business occupancy in accordance with 9.7.4.1. *(See also Section 38.4.)*

Although no requirements for automatic sprinkler systems are provided in 38/39.3.5, 38.4.2 has the effect of requiring new high-rise office buildings to be protected by automatic sprinklers, because the referenced provisions of Section 11.8 require sprinklers. Also, if the atrium provisions of 8.2.5.6 are used, a sprinkler system is required throughout the building. Additional incentives with respect to the following features are provided to encourage sprinkler installation:

(1) Nonrated openings to attached parking structures (38/39.1.2.2)
(2) Delayed-egress locks (38/39.2.2.2.4)

39.3.5 Extinguishment Requirements.

Portable fire extinguishers shall be provided in every business occupancy in accordance with 9.7.4.1. *(See also Section 39.4.)*

(3) Floors constituting an area of refuge (38/39.2.2.12)
(4) Number of exits (38/39.2.4)
(5) Dead-end corridors (38/39.2.5.2)
(6) Common path of travel (38/39.2.5.3)
(7) Travel distance (38/39.2.6)
(8) Discharge of exits through the level of exit discharge (38/39.2.7 per Section 7.7)
(9) Protection from hazards (38/39.3.2)
(10) Interior finish (38/39.3.3 per Section 10.2)
(11) Elimination of manual fire alarm boxes (38/39.3.4.2)
(12) Corridors (38.3.6.1)

38.3.6 Corridors.

38.3.6.1* Where access to exits is provided by corridors, such corridors shall be separated from use areas by walls having a fire resistance rating of not less than 1 hour in accordance with 8.2.3.

A.38.3.6.1 The intent of Exception No. 2 and Exception No. 3 to 38.3.6.1 is to permit spaces within single-tenant spaces, or within buildings protected throughout by an approved, supervised automatic sprinkler system, to be open to the exit access corridor without separation.

Exception No. 1:* Where exits are available from an open floor area.

A.38.3.6.1 Exception No. 1 Where exits are available from an open floor area, such as open plan buildings, corridors are not required to be separated. An example of an open plan building is a building in which the work spaces and accesses to exits are delineated by the use of tables, desks, bookcases, or counters or by partitions that are less than floor-to-ceiling height.

Exception No. 2:* Within a space occupied by a single tenant.

A.38.3.6.1 Exception No. 2 It is the intent of this exception that a single tenant be limited to an area occupied under a single management and work the same hours. The concept is that people under the same employ working the same

39.3.6 Corridors.

(No requirements.)

hours would likely be familiar with their entire tenant space. It is not the intent to apply this provision simply because tenants are owned by the same organization. For example, in a government-owned office building, the offices of different federal agencies would be considered multiple tenants because an employee normally works for one agency. The agencies might work various hours. Another example of multiple tenancy would be a classroom building of a university, since some classrooms might be in use at times when other classrooms are not being used.

Exception No. 3:   Within buildings protected throughout by an approved, supervised automatic sprinkler system in accordance with Section 9.7.

38.3.6.2 Openings in corridor walls required by 38.3.6.1 to have a fire resistance rating shall be protected in accordance with 8.2.3.

Corridors in new business occupancies are addressed in 38.3.6; no corridor requirements are specified for existing business occupancies.

Exception No. 1 to 38.3.6.1 provides for the popular "office landscape" or "open office" arrangement. If there is direct access to exits from the open area, it is not necessary to provide corridors. This exception recognizes that a fire in an open space is subject to more rapid observation and response than a fire in an enclosed room or office.

Exception No. 2 to 38.3.6.1 recognizes that, in areas occupied by a single tenant, there is a high level of familiarity with the area, and the partitioned offices or spaces are occupied by the same people on a regular basis. Such spaces are exempt from corridor requirements.

Exception No. 3 to 38.3.6.1 recognizes the value of automatic sprinklers as a life safety feature that helps to control fire growth and, thus, maintains the exit access usable for a longer time. Such sprinklered buildings are exempt from any corridor requirement.

38.3.7 Subdivision of Building Spaces.

(No special requirements.)

38.3.8 Special Protection Features.

Nonrated glazing and nonrated opening protectives per the exception to 38.1.2.2 shall be permitted between business occupancies and parking structures.

39.3.7 Subdivision of Building Spaces.

(No special requirements.)

39.3.8 Special Protection Features.

Nonrated glazing and nonrated opening protectives per the exception to 39.1.2.2 shall be permitted between business occupancies and parking structures.

Section 38.4 Special Provisions

38.4.1 Windowless or Underground Buildings.

(See Section 11.7.)

38.4.2* High-Rise Buildings.

High-rise buildings shall comply with Section 11.8.

Section 39.4 Special Provisions

39.4.1 Windowless or Underground Buildings.

(See Section 11.7.)

39.4.2 High-Rise Buildings.

|

A.38.4.2 In the design of high-rise buildings, special consideration should also be given to a life safety system including, but not limited to, the following features:

(1) Movement of occupants to safety
(2) Control of fire and smoke
(3) Psychological features
(4) Communications systems
(5) Elevators
(6) Emergency planning
(7) Overall system reliability

39.4.2.1 All high-rise business occupancy buildings shall be provided with a reasonable degree of safety from fire. Such degree of safety shall be accomplished by the installation of a complete, approved, supervised automatic sprinkler system in accordance with Section 9.7 or an engineered life safety system. An engineered life safety system shall be developed by a registered professional engineer who is experienced in fire and life safety systems design. The system shall be approved by the authority having jurisdiction and might include any or all of the following systems:

(1) Partial automatic sprinkler protection
(2) Smoke detection alarms
(3) Smoke control
(4) Compartmentation
(5) Other approved systems

39.4.2.2* A limited but reasonable time shall be permitted for compliance with any part of 39.4.2.1, commensurate with the magnitude of expenditure and the disruption of services.

A.39.4.2.2 In some cases, appreciable cost might be involved in bringing an existing occupancy into compliance. Where this is true, it would be appropriate for the authority having jurisdiction to prescribe a schedule determined jointly with the facility, allowing suitable periods of time for the correction of the various deficiencies and giving due weight to the ability of the owner to secure the necessary funds.

39.4.2.3 In addition to the requirements of 39.4.2, all buildings, regardless of height, shall comply with all other applicable provisions of this chapter.

Section 38.5 Building Services

38.5.1 Utilities.

Utilities shall comply with the provisions of Section 9.1.

38.5.2 Heating, Ventilating, and Air Conditioning.

Heating, ventilating, and air conditioning equipment shall comply with the provisions of Section 9.2.

38.5.3 Elevators, Escalators, and Conveyors.

Elevators, escalators, and conveyors shall comply with the provisions of Section 9.4.

Section 39.5 Building Services

39.5.1 Utilities.

Utilities shall comply with the provisions of Section 9.1.

39.5.2 Heating, Ventilating, and Air Conditioning.

Heating, ventilating, and air conditioning equipment shall comply with the provisions of Section 9.2.

39.5.3 Elevators, Escalators, and Conveyors.

Elevators, escalators, and conveyors shall comply with the provisions of Section 9.4.

38.5.4 Rubbish Chutes, Incinerators, and Laundry Chutes.

Rubbish chutes, incinerators, and laundry chutes shall comply with the provisions of Section 9.5.

Section 38.6 Reserved

Section 38.7 Operating Features

38.7.1 Drills.

In any business occupancy building occupied by more than 500 persons or more than 100 persons above or below the street level, employees and supervisory personnel shall be periodically instructed in accordance with Section 4.7 and shall hold drills periodically where practicable.

38.7.2 Extinguisher Training.

Designated employees of business occupancies shall be periodically instructed in the use of portable fire extinguishers.

The extent of the portable fire extinguisher training required by 38/39.7.2 (for example, instruction only, or instruction and hands-on use) is determined by the authority having jurisdiction.

References Cited in Commentary

1. NFPA 101A, *Guide on Alternative Approaches to Life Safety,* 1998 edition, National Fire Protection Association, Quincy, MA. (The edition of NFPA 101A

39.5.4 Rubbish Chutes, Incinerators, and Laundry Chutes.

Rubbish chutes, incinerators, and laundry chutes shall comply with the provisions of Section 9.5.

Section 39.6 Reserved

Section 39.7 Operating Features

39.7.1 Drills.

In any business occupancy building occupied by more than 500 persons or more than 100 persons above or below the street level, employees and supervisory personnel shall be periodically instructed in accordance with Section 4.7 and shall hold drills periodically where practicable.

39.7.2 Extinguisher Training.

Designated employees of business occupancies shall be periodically instructed in the use of portable fire extinguishers.

that corresponds with the 2000 edition of NFPA 101®, *Life Safety Code®,* will be published in 2001.)
2. NFPA 13, *Standard for the Installation of Sprinkler Systems,* 1999 edition, National Fire Protection Association, Quincy, MA.
3. NFPA 30, *Flammable and Combustible Liquids Code,* 1996 edition, National Fire Protection Association, Quincy, MA.
4. NFPA 45, *Standard on Fire Protection for Laboratories Using Chemicals,* 1996 edition, National Fire Protection Association, Quincy, MA.

CHAPTER 40

Industrial Occupancies

Industrial occupancy is a broad classification. The following are examples of industrial occupancies:

(1) Factories of all kinds
(2) Pumping stations
(3) Telephone exchanges
(4) Gas plants
(5) Laundries
(6) Laboratories
(7) Recycling plants
(8) Refineries
(9) Food processing plants
(10) Dry cleaning plants
(11) Autobody and repair shops
(12) Sawmills
(13) Hangars (for servicing aircraft)
(14) Power plants
(15) Post office central sorting, maintenance facilities

The range of facilities that are classified as industrial occupancies is diverse. Industrial occupancies comprise a wide variety of building configurations, uses, and equipment types. Some industrial occupancies might be considered innocuous with respect to the threat of fire hazard, such as a factory that manufactures concrete blocks. An industrial hazard subject to the threat of serious fire hazard might be a petroleum processing and refining plant where the threat of explosion is always present. The subclassification system used in 40.1.4.1 is intended to assist the user in establishing the level of hazard to the occupants of an industrial occupancy.

The requirements of Chapter 40 were written to provide adequate life safety without unduly restricting the functional operations for which a facility exists. For example, 40.2.2.10 and 40.2.2.11 permit fire escape ladders and slide escapes as part of an occupant protection package that balances the need for rapid escape from platforms and other industrial structures with the ability of the occupants to use such egress devices. By permitting the use of fire escape ladders and slide escapes, Chapter 40 recognizes that functional requirements necessitate occupant access to unusual spaces within the industrial facility and that efficient egress from these spaces is important.

A unique life safety consideration addressed in Chapter 40 involves egress for occupants of ancillary facilities. Paragraph 40.2.5.5 recognizes that some types of industrial processes and equipment cannot be immediately abandoned if the building fire alarm sounds. If workers do not remain in the building long enough to effect orderly shutdown during a fire emergency, dangers greater than fire might result. The protection measures required by 40.2.5.5 provide for the safety of occupants who must remain while others leave the building.

Another unique feature that the *Code* addresses for industrial occupancies is the equipment access dimensional criteria of Table 40.2.5.6. These dimensional criteria, although more lenient than those of Chapter 7, provide adequate egress paths for the small number of occupants using any of those routes to reach major aisles that lead to exits.

The statistics provided by the national fire incident databases demonstrate that the potential loss of life from fire in an industrial occupancy is directly related to the hazard of the industrial operation or process. Most multiple-death industrial fires are the result of flash fires caused by highly combustible material or explosions involving combustible dusts, flammable liquids, or gases.

Although industrial fire losses constitute a high percentage of the annual property loss from fire, such fires have not, as a general rule, resulted in extensive loss of life. A number of operating features common to industrial occupancies have contributed to this favorable record. Continued emphasis on proper egress design and maintenance and day-to-day attention to industrial safety and training programs can help to perpetuate this trend.

One of the major features to be considered in the design of an industrial building's life safety system is the widespread use of automatic sprinkler protection. Originally developed for industrial property protection, the automatic sprinkler has also been largely responsible for an excellent life safety record in industrial occupancies. This record has been recognized by the fire protection community, as evidenced by the widespread use of automatic sprinkler systems for life safety protection in buildings with significant hazards to life. Automatic sprinkler protection in industrial occupancies has been a principal factor in ensuring safety to life through the control of fire spread. Limiting the size of a fire by means of sprinklers provides sufficient time for the safe evacuation of occupants exposed to fire. The contribution of the automatic sprinkler to safety to life can be fully appreciated only when the wide range of fire risks associated with the many processes used in an industrial facility are recognized.

Employees and other occupants of industrial buildings are generally ambulatory and capable of quick response to fires. They are also able to exit rapidly once properly alerted. To capitalize on this employee capability, many industrial facilities include life safety measures in their emergency preplanning. A well-conceived plan provides a valuable tool in preventing loss of life. Provisions that should be part of the emergency preplan include the following:

(1) Measures for alerting employees
(2) Identification and posting of exit access routes
(3) Establishment of group assembly areas for occupants once they have evacuated the building
(4) Procedures for determining that all employees have safely evacuated

Responsibilities are usually established and assigned in the preplan to ensure that the tasks necessary to facilitate safe evacuation of the building are performed. The preplan should routinely be evaluated through simulated fire exercises and drills. Only through the execution of such drills can flaws in the preplan be recognized and modified.

Although the life safety record in industry has been good, the trend toward constructing large industrial plants that house hazardous operations might prove problematic. The introduction of new materials, such as extensive quantities of plastics, has increased the need for additional measures to help protect employees from fire. Compared with the industrial buildings of the early twentieth century, the modern industrial complex has placed a larger number of employees in a more complex and increasingly hazardous environment. This trend has increased the need for industrial management to concentrate on life safety principles not only during the design stage but also during day-to-day plant operations.

As part of their employee training programs, most industrial firms include education in the use of first aid fire-fighting equipment, such as in-plant standpipes, hose, and portable fire extinguishers. Industrial training of this type, where fully utilized, has resulted in a major reduction in property loss and life loss. Although first aid fire-fighting measures are primarily a property protection measure, they also provide a significant life safety benefit. In situations where the spread of a fire is checked through effective employee action, employee life safety is also provided. If fire spread is restricted to the incipient stages, no significant threat to life safety develops.

Section 40.1 General Requirements

40.1.1 Application.

The requirements of this chapter shall apply to both new and existing industrial occupancies. Industrial occupancies shall include factories making products of all kinds and properties used for operations such as processing, assembling, mixing, packaging, finishing or decorating, repairing, and similar operations. Incidental high hazard operations protected in accordance with Section 8.4 and 40.3.2 in occupancies containing low or ordinary hazard contents shall not be the basis for high hazard industrial occupancy classification.

Unlike most occupancies covered in the *Code*, both new and existing industrial occupancies are covered in one chapter. Where requirements vary, exceptions that apply to existing industrial occupancies are often provided, or additional requirements that are limited to new industrial occupancies are specified.

40.1.2 Mixed Occupancies.

In any building occupied for both industrial and other purposes, means of egress shall comply with 6.1.14.

In addition to requiring that the means of egress is to comply with 6.1.14, which covers mixed occupancies, the intent of 40.1.2 is that the other life safety features addressed by the *Code* also comply with 6.1.14.

40.1.3 Special Definitions.

(None.)

Although no special definitions are listed in 40.1.3, industrial occupancies are subclassified and defined in 40.1.4.1(a), (b), and (c) under the labels general industrial occupancy, special purpose industrial occupancy, and high hazard industrial occupancy. See also 3.3.134.8.1, 3.3.134.8.2, and 3.3.134.8.3.

40.1.4 Classification of Occupancy. *(See 6.1.12.)*

The method for determining the degree of hazard to life safety posed by an industrial occupancy is, at best, a matter of personal judgment and not science. The authority having jurisdiction must use judgment based on past experience, a review of reference materials, and full discussion with third parties to evaluate the life safety measures in an industrial occupancy. The *Code* establishes broad categories of occupancy classification so that the relative risks to life safety posed by various types of buildings can be assessed.

A common error made when classifying industrial occupancies is the use of hazard categories for automatic sprinklers contained in NFPA 13, *Standard for the Installation of Sprinkler Systems,* to determine the hazard to life safety.[1] While the guidelines in NFPA 13 might not differ greatly from those of the *Life Safety Code* where classifying occupancies with high hazards, the remaining categories specified in NFPA 13 are usually not suitable for the general industrial occupancy classification of the *Code.* The use of NFPA 13 is particularly inappropriate where classifying low hazard occupancies, which are classified differently by NFPA 13 (light hazard) than by the *Life Safety Code.* The distinction is that the life safety industrial occupancy classification is concerned with determining the overall hazard to occupants in a manufacturing building for purposes of implementing an adequate means of egress system, while the NFPA 13 classification system is concerned with defining the hazard so that a sprinkler system can be designed to meet the challenge of the hazard.

To examine the conflicts between life safety occupancy classification and classifications in other fire codes, consider a metalworking plant using a flammable solvent in a dip tank coating operation. From a life safety standpoint, the normally ordinary hazard classification of the metalworking plant should not be changed to high hazard solely because of the presence of a dip tank coater. An adequate means of safe egress leading away from the coater is required to ensure the safety of the occupants. However, additional exits and a reduction in travel distance to an exit, as specified for a high hazard contents area, are not required. Nevertheless, if the coater is the principal piece of equipment in a separately enclosed area, that area might be considered as a high hazard industrial occupancy.

When determining the life safety hazard classification for an industrial occupancy, the authority having jurisdiction should carefully analyze the nature of that industrial operation to ensure an accurate evaluation of the hazard to occupants. A number of resources are available for properly determining the degree of risk to life safety. One resource that should not be overlooked is the expertise of the industrial plant operator, who can provide a wealth of hazard information. However, such information might be treated as confidential material to prevent competitors from learning the details of an industrial process. An enforcing authority should earn the trust of the operator by handling such information with discretion. It is vital that industrial process data be kept confidential, because, once an enforcing authority is known to be an outside source of data on industrial secrets, further cooperation will be difficult to obtain.

Another resource is the engineering department of the company responsible for a facility's insurance coverage. In addition, discussions with officials who oversee jurisdictions where similar facilities exist and a review of NFPA literature will provide further information on a particular process and its associated hazards.

To assess the risk to life safety in an industrial occupancy, a number of factors should be considered. It should be determined if the manufacturing process includes the handling of flammable, reactive, or explosive materials in quantities that could directly expose occupants to a fire or explosion. If so, the occupancy is a strong candidate for a high hazard classification.

It should also be determined whether the manufacturing process requires a large number of people or whether it is basically a large collection of machines or equipment occasionally attended by operators. In some instances, operators might be clustered in one location, such as a control room. If a building is predominantly occupied by machinery or equipment and is used by few employees, the building can be classified as a special purpose industrial occupancy. See 40.1.4.1(b).

If an industrial building is used mostly for storage of materials (such as preparatory stock for assembly or finished goods), it might meet the requirements for classification as a storage occupancy. See Chapter 42.

Occupancy classification is based on the burning and explosive characteristics of the materials contained in a building, not on the quantity of combustibles. For example, there is no reason to classify a building as high hazard simply because it is associated with a manufacturing process that requires extensive quantities of ordinary combustible materials to be distributed in such a manner that the process involves a high combustible load.

The classification of an industrial occupancy, for life safety purposes, is not based on the type of structure housing the industrial process. The basic purpose of the hazard classification in Section 6.2 is to evaluate the risk of contents. The classification is determined by an evaluation of the contents and other factors in a fire's development that affect the time available for safe evacuation of the occupants. Once employees are evacuated to a safe location, the extent of fire spread in the structure becomes a threat to property. As long as life safety measures are met, the threat of heavy fire damage to a building is beyond the scope of the *Life Safety Code*. Also see the commentary following 40.1.4.1(b) and 40.1.4.1(c).

ployee population, with much of the area occupied by machinery or equipment.

It can be difficult to determine if a building qualifies as a special purpose industrial occupancy. For example, a structure is often erected to protect a large machine or equipment from weather. Once constructed, authorities might try to impose exit requirements applicable to a general industrial occupancy, despite the fact that only a handful of personnel are to occupy the building. Steel mills, paper plants, power-generating plants, and other operations with large machines are examples of the types of industrial occupancies requiring massive structures for process control and weather protection. These structures often represent minimum hazards to life safety and should be classified as special purpose industrial occupancies. In many of the more modern operations, all process control is conducted from a control room by remote means, which further reduces the number of occupants likely to be exposed to a fire in the equipment areas.

The special purpose industrial occupancy classification must not be applied to a building simply to reduce egress requirements. Economic considerations, or staffing limitations that result in occupancy by fewer employees than usual, cannot be used as justification for reducing life safety features; the full number and arrangement of exits required for a general industrial occupancy should be maintained. A reduction in aisles, doors, stairways, and other components of the means of egress cannot be justified by the temporary classification of a building as a special purpose industrial occupancy.

40.1.4.1 Subclassification of Industrial Occupancies. Each industrial occupancy shall be subclassified according to its use as follows.

(a) *General Industrial Occupancy.* A general industrial occupancy conducts ordinary and low hazard industrial operations in buildings of conventional design suitable for various types of industrial processes. Also included are multistory buildings where floors are occupied by different tenants or buildings suitable for such occupancy and, therefore, subject to possible use for types of industrial processes with a high density of employee population.

(b) *Special Purpose Industrial Occupancy.* A special purpose industrial occupancy conducts ordinary and low hazard industrial operations in buildings designed for, and suitable only for, particular types of operations. Such occupancy is characterized by a relatively low density of em-

(c)* *High Hazard Industrial Occupancy.* A high hazard industrial occupancy conducts industrial operations that use high hazard materials or processes or houses high hazard contents. Incidental high hazard operations in low or ordinary occupancies that are protected in accordance with Section 6.2 and 40.3.2 shall not be the basis for overall occupancy classification.

A.40.1.4.1(c) Additional information can be found in the annex for the definition of *Occupancy, Industrial, High Hazard* in A.3.3.134.8.2.

A high hazard occupancy classification is limited to those industrial buildings housing extremely hazardous operations. Incidental use of restricted quantities of flammable liquids in a building does not constitute a high hazard, although some additional life safety precautions might be required during the limited period of use. Refer to NFPA 30, *Flammable and Combustible Liquids Code,* for guidance.[2] Storage of flammable liquids, such as paint, in sealed containers does not require a high hazard occupancy classification, unless the operation includes mixing or blending operations that require the containers to be opened. Mixing and blending of flammable liquids is permitted to be conducted in a separate room with a fire barrier between the storage and mixing areas. The mixing and blending room would be considered a high hazard industrial occupancy, while the adjacent, fire-separated storage area would be considered a general purpose industrial occupancy or possibly a storage occupancy subject to the requirements of Chapter 42.

Combustible dusts released from an industrial or manufacturing process constitute a significant threat to life safety and might justify a high hazard classification. Major loss of life has occurred in industrial occupancies that release extensive quantities of combustible dusts. Opportunity for the rapid escape of employees who work in operations that release combustible dust should be provided to prevent injury or loss of life if a dust explosion occurs. In high hazard occupancies that are subject to explosions, the provisions of 40.3.2 require special consideration of the techniques for explosion suppression or venting to ensure the life safety of occupants. Full use of fire protection engineering techniques should be employed in these occupancies to minimize the risk to life safety.

The industrial occupancies that clearly require classification as high hazard are those associated with the production of explosives or highly reactive chemicals. In some especially hazardous operations, additional exits will be necessary to ensure rapid egress to prevent loss of life in the event of an explosion or fire. Where the installation of the preventive or protective measures specified in 40.3.2 is not possible due to the nature of the industrial operation, consideration should be given to operating procedures that restrict access to a limited number of people during the hazardous portion of the operation. The operating procedures would limit the potential threat to those trained personnel who are fully aware of the extent of the hazard. Procedures should also include a record of personnel who have signed in or out. This procedure ensures prompt determination of the number of personnel exposed to a hazardous operation and, thus, the number who might require rescue.

40.1.4.2 Changing from one subclassification of industrial occupancy to another shall be permitted only if the structure, building, or portion thereof conforms with the requirements of this chapter applying to new construction for the new use.

Paragraph 4.6.11 requires that upon change of occupancy (for example, an industrial occupancy factory building that is renovated to become a residential occupancy apartment building), the building is to meet the requirements that apply to new construction for the new occupancy classification. Paragraph 40.1.4.2 expands the concept to include changes in industrial occupancy subclassification. In each of the following examples, the industrial occupancy that results from a change in subclassification must meet the requirements of Chapter 40 that apply to new industrial occupancies:

(1) A general industrial occupancy is reclassified as a high hazard industrial occupancy based on the introduction of flammable liquids throughout the various processes used to manufacture the product.

(2) A high hazard industrial occupancy is reclassified as a general industrial occupancy based on replacing flammable solvents, which had been used throughout the various manufacturing processes, with noncombustible materials.

(3) A special purpose industrial occupancy with an automated, metal-casting line is reclassified as a general industrial occupancy following the removal of the line equipment and the introduction of metal-machining lathes and skilled operators.

40.1.5 Classification of Hazard of Contents.

Classification of hazard of contents shall be in accordance with Section 6.2.

40.1.6 Minimum Construction Requirements.

(No requirements.)

Some occupancy chapters, such as Chapter 18/19, which address the life safety needs of nonambulatory health care occupants, specify minimum building construction type requirements to ensure structural integrity for the time needed for a lengthy evacuation or for safe refuge within the building. No minimum construction requirements are imposed in Chapter 40, because industrial occupancies characteristically have ambulatory occupants and do not provide sleeping accommodations. Occupants should be able to egress the building quickly before the fire-resisting qualities of the building construction become an issue.

40.1.7* Occupant Load.

The occupant load, in number of persons for whom means of egress and other provisions are required, shall be determined on the basis of the occupant load factors of Table 7.3.1.2 that are characteristic of the use of the space or shall be determined as the maximum probable population of the space under consideration, whichever is greater.

A.40.1.7 In most cases, the requirements for maximum travel distance to exits will be the determining factor rather than numbers of occupants, as exits provided to satisfy travel distance requirements will be sufficient to provide egress capacity for all occupants, except in cases of unusual arrangement of buildings or high occupant load of a general manufacturing occupancy.

The occupant load of an industrial building is based on an average of 100 ft² (9.3 m²) of gross floor area per occupant in accordance with Table 7.3.1.2. Many industrial users of the *Code* confuse this concept with the actual number of employees who use the facility. The usual complaint is that the number of potential employees calculated for egress purposes in accordance with the 100-ft² (9.3-m²) criterion far exceeds the anticipated or actual number of employees. Many industrial managers argue that using the larger number as a basis for egress design requires more exits, wider doors, and more passageways than are needed for emergency egress purposes, reducing productive work space and resulting in increased cost.

The concept of determining occupant load by using an occupant load factor is useful, although it does not necessarily relate directly to the actual number of building occupants. The occupant load factor is used as a means of calculating the minimum egress requirements, based on the needs of an average industrial occupancy. Although actual conditions might vary in an individual location, the egress width determined by the occupant load calculation will normally provide the necessary, adequate, and required means of egress for a typical industrial building with little or no penalty to the building's owner/operator.

See Exhibit 40.1 for examples of occupant load determination using the occupant load factor for a general industrial occupancy and using the probable number of occupants for a special purpose industrial occupancy.

In Exhibit 40.1, illustration (a), the general indus-

trial occupancy must provide a means of egress for at least 2000 persons based on use of an occupant load factor of 1 person per 100 ft² (9.3 m²).

In Exhibit 40.1, illustration (b), a special purpose industrial occupancy can size its means of egress for the maximum 20 persons (actual anticipated employee population) who are expected to occupy the facility under any probable condition.

In Exhibit 40.1, illustration (c), the 200-person tour groups that visit this special purpose industrial occupancy on the first Monday of each month must be added to the 45 employees (actual employee population) who are normally present, for a total occupant load of 245 persons.

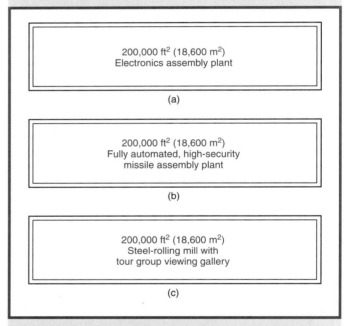

Exhibit 40.1 *Determination of occupant load of industrial occupancies.*

Section 40.2 Means of Egress Requirements

40.2.1 General.

Each required means of egress shall be in accordance with the applicable portions of Chapter 7.

40.2.2 Means of Egress Components.

40.2.2.1 Components of means of egress shall be limited to the types described in 40.2.2.2 through 40.2.2.13.

40.2.2.2 Doors.

40.2.2.2.1 Doors complying with 7.2.1 shall be permitted.

40.2.2.2.2 Delayed-egress locks complying with 7.2.1.6.1 shall be permitted.

Use of the delayed-egress locking device covered by 7.2.1.6.1 is allowed on any door in recognition of the security needs of some industrial occupancies. In effect, the allowable 15-second or 30-second delay will be experienced only under nonfire conditions or very early in a fire's growth, because the door must be usable immediately upon sprinkler operation, smoke or heat detection, or loss of power that controls the locking mechanism. The building must be protected throughout by an approved, supervised automatic sprinkler system or an approved, supervised automatic fire detection system.

40.2.2.2.3 Access-controlled egress doors complying with 7.2.1.6.2 shall be permitted.

Paragraph 40.2.2.2.3 recognizes access-controlled egress doors in industrial occupancies as security measures that do not compromise the use of the means of egress system.

40.2.2.2.4 Existing horizontal-sliding fire doors shall be permitted in the means of egress under the following conditions:

(1) They are held open by fusible links.
(2) The links are rated at not less than 165°F (74°C).
(3) The fusible links are located not more than 10 ft (3 m) above the floor.
(4) The fusible link is in immediate proximity to the door opening.
(5) The fusible link is not located above a ceiling.
(6) The door is not credited with providing any protection under this *Code*.

Horizontal-sliding fire doors exist in many industrial occupancies for property protection purposes. Although the *Code* normally does not recognize these doors within the required means of egress, 40.2.2.2.4 makes a special exemption for existing horizontal-sliding fire doors. By requiring the fusible link to be positioned in immediate proximity to the door opening, to be rated 165°F (74°C) or higher, and to be located not more than 10 ft (3 m) above the floor,

the *Code* helps to ensure that the door will remain open until rising temperatures make it unsafe to pass through the door opening. Because the door will not close early in the fire development, the door cannot be credited as a fire door for life safety purposes. However, the door might serve as a means of property protection. See Exhibit 40.2.

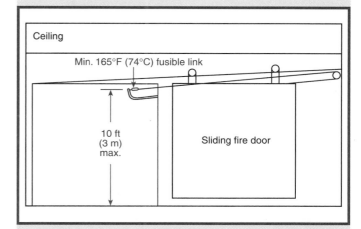

Exhibit 40.2 *Existing horizontal-sliding fire door in accordance with 40.2.2.2.4.*

40.2.2.3 Stairs.

40.2.2.3.1 Stairs complying with 7.2.2 shall be permitted.

Exception No. 1:   Noncombustible, grated stair treads and noncombustible, grated landing floors.

Exception No. 2:   Industrial equipment access in accordance with 40.2.5.6.

40.2.2.3.2 Spiral stairs complying with 7.2.2.2.3 shall be permitted.

40.2.2.3.3 Existing winders complying with 7.2.2.2.4 shall be permitted.

Exception No. 1 to 40.2.2.3.1 exempts stair treads and landings in industrial occupancies from the provisions of 7.2.2.3.3, which would otherwise require that all stair treads and stair landing floors be solid. Although the requirement for solid treads and landing floors is intended to prevent occupants from avoiding the use of the stairs because they become afraid when they are able to see through the openings to the floor or ground below, occupants of industrial occupancies are usually more familiar, and thus more comfortable, with grated or expanded metal treads and landings.

The grated walking surfaces provide slip resistance in what can sometimes be greasy and slippery surroundings. For consistency, Exception No. 1 to 7.2.2.3.3 alerts the user that industrial occupancies, in accordance with Chapter 40, are exempt from the solid tread and landing provisions.

Exception No. 2 to 40.2.2.3.1 serves to remind the user that 40.2.5.6 has special provisions for industrial equipment access stairs that differ from the requirements of Chapter 7. See the commentary following 40.2.5.6.

40.2.2.4 Smokeproof Enclosures. Smokeproof enclosures complying with 7.2.3 shall be permitted.

Paragraph 40.2.2.4 does not mandate the use of smokeproof enclosures. However, it does recognize a smokeproof enclosure as part of the means of egress system in an industrial occupancy only if the smokeproof enclosure meets the requirements of 7.2.3. For an example of an occupancy requiring a smokeproof enclosure, see 31.2.11, which specifies that existing, nonsprinklered high-rise apartment buildings are required to be provided with smokeproof enclosures in accordance with 7.2.3. See 40.2.2.1.

40.2.2.5 Horizontal Exits.

40.2.2.5.1 Horizontal exits complying with 7.2.4 shall be permitted.

40.2.2.5.2* In horizontal exits where the doorway is protected by a fire door on each side of the wall in which it is located, one fire door shall be of the swinging type as provided in 7.2.4.3.6, and the other shall be permitted to be an automatic-sliding fire door that shall be kept open whenever the building is occupied.

A.40.2.2.5.2 The customary building code requirement for fire doors on both sides of an opening in a fire wall is permitted to be met by having an automatic-sliding fire door on one side, and a self-closing fire door swinging out from the other side of the wall. This arrangement qualifies only as a horizontal exit from the side of the sliding door. For further information, see A.7.2.4.3.8.

Subparagraph 40.2.2.5.1 does not mandate the use of horizontal exits. However, it does recognize a horizontal exit as part of the means of egress system in an industrial occupancy only if the horizontal exit meets the requirements of 7.2.4, as modified by 40.2.2.5.2.

Subparagraph 40.2.2.5.2 and A.40.2.2.5.2 recognize the common practice of combining a horizontal exit that is used for life safety with a fire barrier having a significant fire resistance rating that is used for property protection. Opening protectives for such a fire barrier can require the use of a set of doors to achieve the required fire protection rating. It is impractical for both doors to swing in the same direction without interfering with each other; yet, operation of two doors that swing in opposite directions is cumbersome for daily or frequent use. One swinging and one sliding door, as shown in Exhibit 40.3, provide an acceptable arrangement for day-to-day functioning of the building. The open sliding door does not compromise life safety, because by the time its fusible link mechanism releases the door and allows it to close, temperatures in the vicinity of the door opening render use of the door impractical. See also the commentary following 40.2.2.2.4(6). The provisions of 40.2.2.2.4 also permit an existing horizontal-sliding door (as depicted in Exhibit 40.2) to serve within the means of egress.

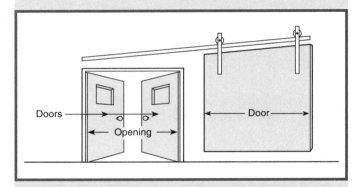

Exhibit 40.3 *Combination swinging and sliding doors permitted by 40.2.2.5.2.*

40.2.2.6 Ramps. Ramps complying with 7.2.5 shall be permitted.

Exception: Industrial equipment access in accordance with 40.2.5.6.

Paragraph 40.2.2.6 does not mandate the use of ramps in industrial occupancies. However, it does recognize a ramp as part of the means of egress system only if the ramp meets the requirements of 7.2.5. See 40.2.2.1.

The exception to 40.2.2.6 serves to remind the user that 40.2.5.6 has special provisions for industrial equipment access ramps that differ from the requirements of Chapter 7. See the commentary following 40.2.5.6.

40.2.2.7 Exit Passageways. Exit passageways complying with 7.2.6 shall be permitted.

Paragraph 40.2.2.7 does not mandate the use of exit passageways in industrial occupancies. However, it does recognize an exit passageway as part of the means of egress system only if the exit passageway meets the requirements of 7.2.6. See 40.2.2.1.

40.2.2.8 Escalators and Moving Walks. Existing, previously approved escalators and moving walks complying with 7.2.7 and located within the required means of egress shall be permitted.

Note that 7.2.7 permits existing escalators and moving walks to continue to be recognized within the required means of egress if specified by an occupancy chapter. In earlier editions of the *Code*, such escalators and moving walks were recognized as providing egress capacity for 75 persons. To qualify as exits, escalators and moving walks must also meet the requirements of 7.1.3.2, which addresses exit enclosures.

Note that escalators protected in accordance with the sprinkler-vent, spray nozzle, rolling shutter, or partial enclosure method do not constitute acceptable exits but can continue to serve as exit access if previously approved as such.

40.2.2.9 Fire Escape Stairs. Existing fire escape stairs complying with 7.2.8 shall be permitted.

40.2.2.10 Fire Escape Ladders. Fire escape ladders complying with 7.2.9 shall be permitted.

Exception: Fixed industrial stairs in accordance with the minimum requirements for fixed stairs in ANSI A1264.1, Safety Requirements for Workplace Floor and Wall Openings, Stairs and Railings Systems, shall be permitted where fire escape ladders are permitted in accordance with 7.2.9.1.

The geometry associated with the incline angle and the size and shape of surfaces intended for foot placement on fire escape ladders falls within the range permitted for fixed industrial stairs. However, most fixed industrial stairs meet criteria that result in a safer arrangement than that provided by the fire escape ladder detailed in 7.2.9. Therefore, the exception

to 40.2.2.10 recognizes fixed industrial stairs as a substitute for fire escape ladders.

40.2.2.11 Slide Escapes. Approved slide escapes complying with 7.2.10 shall be permitted as components in 100 percent of the required means of egress for both new and existing high hazard industrial occupancies. Slide escapes shall be counted as means of egress only where regularly used in emergency egress drills so that occupants are familiar with their use through practice.

The intent of 40.2.2.11 is to allow the use of slide escapes, which are a common means of egress from areas that house explosives or other highly hazardous materials in chemical industry buildings. This provision allows consideration of slide escapes as part of the required means of egress from both new and existing high hazard industrial occupancies. In many high hazard industrial occupancies, slide escapes are the only practical means of ensuring safe egress prior to an explosion or flash fire.

40.2.2.12 Alternating Tread Devices. Alternating tread devices complying with 7.2.11 shall be permitted.

The provisions of 7.2.11, in effect, limit the use of alternating tread devices to those locations where the *Code* recognizes the use of fire escape ladders (and fixed industrial stairs). See 40.2.2.10, the exception to 40.2.2.10, 7.2.9, and 7.2.11.

40.2.2.13 Areas of Refuge. Areas of refuge complying with 7.2.12 shall be permitted.

40.2.3 Capacity of Means of Egress.

The capacity of means of egress shall be in accordance with Section 7.3.

Exception: In special purpose industrial occupancies, means of egress shall be sized to accommodate the occupant load as determined in accordance with Table 7.3.1.2; spaces not subject to human occupancy because of the presence of machinery or equipment shall not be included.

Prior to 1991, the *Code* required a minimum 44-in. (112-cm) width for corridors and passageways within the required means of egress of industrial occupancies. A corridor or passageway of that minimum width would have provided egress capacity for 220 persons [that is, 44 in. / 0.2 in. per person (approximately 112 cm / 0.5 cm per person) in accordance with Table 7.3.3.1 for level travel components]. The prior requirement produced artificially large egress systems, relative to the occupant load, in many industrial occupancies. The requirement was eliminated, and the minimum 36-in. (91-cm) width requirement of 7.3.4.1, which addresses the minimum width of any exit access, was made applicable to industrial occupancies. Exit access is required to be wider than 36 in. (91 cm) only if a corridor or passageway in an industrial occupancy is to provide capacity for more than 180 persons [that is, 36 in. / 0.2 in. per person (approximately 91 cm / 0.5 cm per person)]. See the commentary following A.40.1.7.

The exception to 40.2.3 imposes practical limits on the number of required means of egress and on the arrangement of the means of egress in a special purpose industrial occupancy. No life safety purpose is served by providing exits from the center of a large machine or equipment installation that is unoccupied under normal operating conditions. A number of industries provide weather shelter for large processes and equipment. Typical examples include steel-rolling mills, paper extruders, and metalworking machines, all of which occupy a majority of the floor space in the sheltered building. In many of the more sophisticated operations, full process control is conducted from a remotely located control room. Personnel normally occupy the building only for maintenance and adjustment purposes, and then only on a limited basis. The provision of exits from these special purpose industrial occupancies serves no useful purpose and could unjustly impose an economic penalty in the name of safety.

The large areas normally enclosed by special purpose structures would require excessive egress width if the occupant load were calculated on the basis of 100 ft² (9.3 m²) per person. Provisions for the capacity of the means of egress in a special purpose industrial occupancy based on the requirements specified for general industrial occupancies would result in extensive egress facilities for nonexistent occupants. Such arrangements might actually require exits from the interior of machinery and equipment installations, which would be incompatible with the equipment's design. In many cases, these exits would originate from locations that, even under normal operating conditions, would be considered dangerous for humans. Poorly conceived exit facilities serve no life safety purpose and detract from an otherwise well-designed exit system.

40.2.4 Number of Means of Egress.

(See also Section 7.4.)

40.2.4.1 Not less than two means of egress shall be provided from every story or section, and not less than one exit shall be reached without traversing another story.

Exception: In low and ordinary hazard industrial occupancies, a single means of egress shall be permitted from any story or section, provided that the exit can be reached within the distance permitted as common path of travel. (See 40.2.5.3.)

40.2.4.2 Floors or portions thereof with an occupant load of more than 500 shall have the minimum number of separate and remote means of egress specified by 7.4.1.2.

Exception: Existing buildings.

40.2.4.3 Areas with high hazard contents shall comply with Section 7.11.

The provisions of 40.2.4.1, which apply to the minimum required number of means of egress for industrial occupancies, clarify that, in addition to providing every story or section with access to at least two means of egress, one of the exits must be located on each floor so that the entrance to that exit (for example, a door that opens into an enclosed exit stair) can be reached without traveling to another floor.

The exception to 40.2.4.1 recognizes that there are small floors or areas in low and ordinary hazard industrial occupancies that, if provided with access to only a single exit, are no less safe than larger areas of a building that have access to two exits where an occupant must first travel through the maximum allowable common path. Where a single exit is provided, the occupant travels the 50 ft (15 m) [or 100 ft (30 m) in sprinklered buildings] of common path allowed by 40.2.5.3, enters the exit (see Exhibit 40.4), and is judged to have reached a point of safety. In larger buildings and larger building areas that do not meet the limited travel distance for a single exit, a minimum of two exits must be provided. By traveling to the nearer of the two exits, the occupant is permitted to travel the same 50 ft (15 m) [or 100 ft (30 m) in sprinklered buildings] of common path that the occupant of the single-exit building traveled to reach the one exit before reaching the point where travel to the two exits in different directions is possible. Although the occupant of the single-exit building has reached an exit by this point, the occupant of the multiple-exit building is then allowed an additional

150 ft (45 m) [200 ft (60 m) if building is sprinklered] of exit access travel before the safety of an exit must be reached. Therefore, the exception for the single exit provides a level of life safety that is at least equivalent to that of the multiple-exit building. See Exhibit 40.4.

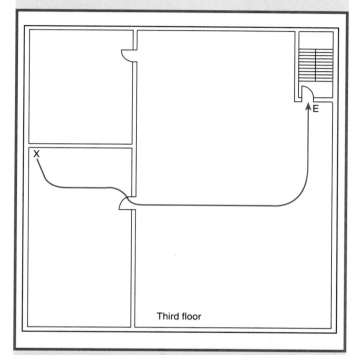

Exhibit 40.4 *Single means of egress from story of low or ordinary hazard industrial occupancy.*

Historically, the *Code* has required more than two exits based on occupant load for assembly occupancies only. Third, fourth, and subsequent exits were provided in industrial occupancies to meet travel distance requirements or as a convenience for day-to-day use. Paragraph 7.4.1.2 expands the concept of requiring three or four exits based on occupant load to apply to all occupancies. The exception to 40.2.4.2, in compliance with the option offered by the exception to 7.4.1.2, exempts existing buildings from the requirement for third and fourth exits to avoid forcing existing, previously complying means of egress systems into noncompliance.

Section 7.11 includes an adequate set of provisions for high hazard areas and is referenced by this chapter to provide commensurate protection to industrial occupancies that contain high hazard areas. The provisions of Section 7.11 are vital to life safety in high hazard occupancies. The requirement for two means of egress for all high hazard occupancies recognizes the possibility that a fire or explosion might block or destroy one of the two exits. Two separate and equal means of egress from high hazard areas provide a necessary redundancy to ensure the evacuation of occupants under fire or explosion conditions and to minimize the potential for injury or loss of life. Subsection 7.11.3 recognizes that it is not necessary to require two means of egress from very small high hazard areas [maximum 200 ft² (18.6 m²)] with limited occupant load (maximum three persons) if the room door can be reached within 25 ft (7.6 m) of travel.

40.2.5 Arrangement of Means of Egress.

40.2.5.1 Means of egress shall be arranged in accordance with Section 7.5.

40.2.5.2 Dead-end corridors in general industrial and special purpose industrial occupancies shall not exceed 50 ft (15 m).

40.2.5.3 Common paths of travel in general industrial and special purpose industrial occupancies shall not exceed 50 ft (15 m).

Exception: In buildings protected throughout by an approved, supervised automatic sprinkler system in accordance with Section 9.7, common path of travel shall not exceed 100 ft (30 m).

40.2.5.4 Common paths of travel shall be prohibited in high hazard industrial occupancies.

Exception: As permitted by 7.11.3.

See the discussion of dead-end corridor pockets and common path of travel in A.7.5.1.6 and its associated commentary.

40.2.5.5 Ancillary Facilities.

40.2.5.5.1* Ancillary facilities shall be arranged to allow travel in independent directions after leaving the ancillary facility so that both means of egress paths do not become compromised by the same fire or similar emergency.

Exception: Existing facilities.

A.40.2.5.5.1 Ancillary facilities located within industrial occupancies might include administrative office, laboratory, control, and employee service facilities that are incidental to the predominant industrial function and are of such size that separate occupancy classification is not warranted.

40.2.5.5.2* Ancillary facilities in special purpose industrial occupancies where delayed evacuation is anticipated shall have not less than a 2-hour fire resistance–rated separation from the predominant industrial occupancy and shall have one means of egress that is separated from the predominant industrial occupancy by 2-hour fire resistance–rated construction.

Exception: Existing facilities.

A.40.2.5.5.2 Occupants of ancillary facilities located within special purpose industrial occupancies might be required by administrative controls to remain in the facility when a fire occurs in the predominant industrial area so that they can perform an orderly shutdown of process equipment to control the spread of the fire and minimize damage to important equipment.

The presence of ancillary facilities within an industrial occupancy can create unusual challenges to life safety. For example, the means of egress for factory office workers, who might have little knowledge of the industrial processes and operations and their respective hazards, might require leaving the safety of an office area and traveling across the factory production floor. In other cases, safe egress is not assured to employees assigned to a control room who might have to perform orderly shutdown of certain processes in order to control the spread of fire before evacuating a building. The requirements of 40.2.5.5.1 and 40.2.5.5.2 are illustrated in Exhibit 40.5.

In Exhibit 40.5, an occupant of control room 1, which is elevated and has a single means of egress via a stair leading down to the main production floor, is forced to travel in one direction only into the open manufacturing area. This arrangement does not meet the requirement of 40.2.5.5.1, which mandates that egress be arranged to allow travel in independent directions after leaving the ancillary facility so that both means of egress paths are not compromised by the same fire or similar emergency. Control room 1 requires a second exit access door and stair remotely located from the first.

Control room 2 in Exhibit 40.5 meets the requirements of both 40.2.5.5.1 and 40.2.5.5.2. Control room 2 permits egress travel in independent directions, so that both means of egress paths are not compromised by the same fire or similar emergency. Further, it provides one of the two means of egress via an exit passageway-like arrangement separated from the predominant industrial occupancy by 2-hour fire resistance–rated construction. Also, control room 2 itself is surrounded by 2-hour fire resistance–rated

construction. This protection permits occupants charged with special emergency duties to delay their egress and still be afforded adequate life safety.

The requirements of 40.2.5.5 for ancillary facilities were added to the *Code* in 1997 and are not retroactively applied to existing facilities.

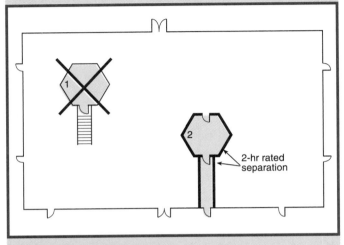

Exhibit 40.5 *Ancillary facilities.*

40.2.5.6 Industrial equipment access walkways, platforms, ramps, and stairs that serve as a component of the means of egress from the involved equipment shall be permitted in accordance with the applicable provisions of Chapter 7 as modified by Table 40.2.5.6. Any such means of egress component shall serve not more than 20 people.

Table 40.2.5.6 Equipment Access Dimensional Criteria

Minimum horizontal dimension of any walkway, landing, or platform	22 in. (55.9 cm) clear
Minimum stair or ramp width	22 in. (55.9 cm) clear between rails
Minimum tread width	22 in. (55.9 cm) clear
Minimum tread depth	10 in. (25.4 cm)
Maximum riser height	9 in. (22.9 cm)
Maximum height between landings	12 ft (3.7 m)
Minimum headroom	6 ft 8 in. (203 cm)

Paragraph 40.2.5.6 permits industrial equipment access walkways, platforms, ramps, and stairs serving not more than 20 persons to deviate from some of the usual dimensional criteria specified by Chapter 7. The dimensional criteria detailed in Table 40.2.5.6 are illustrated in Exhibit 40.6.

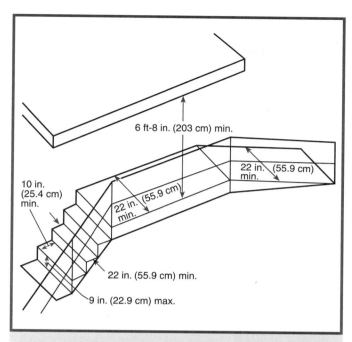

Exhibit 40.6 Industrial equipment access dimensional criteria.

40.2.6 Travel Distance to Exits.

40.2.6.1 Travel distance, measured in accordance with Section 7.6, shall not exceed 200 ft (60 m).

Exception No. 1: Travel distance shall not exceed 250 ft (76 m) in buildings protected throughout by an approved, supervised automatic sprinkler system in accordance with Section 9.7.

Exception No. 2: As permitted by 40.2.6.2.

Exception No. 3: As permitted by 40.2.6.3.

Exception No. 4: Travel distance to exits in high hazard industrial occupancies shall not exceed 75 ft (23 m).

40.2.6.2 In low or ordinary hazard general industrial occupancies, travel distance shall not exceed 400 ft (122 m) if the following additional provisions are met in full:

(1) Application shall be limited to one-story buildings.
(2)* Smoke venting and heat venting shall be provided by engineered means or by building configuration to ensure that occupants are not overtaken by spread of fire or smoke within 6 ft (1.8 m) of floor level before they have time to reach exits.

A.40.2.6.2(2) Smoke venting and heating venting should be in accordance with NFPA 204, *Guide for Smoke and Heat Venting.*

(3) Approved, supervised automatic sprinkler systems or other approved, supervised automatic fire extinguishing

systems in accordance with Section 9.7 shall be provided.

40.2.6.3 In low or ordinary hazard special purpose industrial occupancies, travel distance shall not exceed 300 ft (91 m), or, if the building is protected throughout by a supervised automatic sprinkler system in accordance with Section 9.7, travel distance shall not exceed 400 ft (122 m).

The travel distance provisions of 40.2.6.2 are meant to provide flexibility in determining the layout of the means of egress system in a single-story industrial building with a large floor area that houses a low or ordinary hazard general industrial occupancy.

The construction of tunnels and elevated means of egress that originate from the center of an industrial building with an extensive floor area is rarely attempted. Only a handful of buildings have ever been provided with such egress facilities, and most were World War II airframe manufacturing buildings of massive size. In most industrial buildings, it is not practicable or economical to construct exit tunnels or overhead passageways. These special types of means of egress are not easily altered if modifications are necessary to adjust to changes in the layout of the facility. In addition, the construction costs for tunnels and elevated passageways are high due to the special design features required to ensure their safety, including fire resistance–rated supports for the elevated passageways, waterproofing, and other features necessary to maintain the integrity of underground tunnels. Another negative factor in such construction is the confining nature of a tunnel or elevated passage, which tends to discourage the use of these means of egress.

The use of horizontal exits that pass through fire walls is common in many industrial occupancies. The provisions in Chapter 7 are required to be fully considered to ensure the safe use of horizontal exits. A common violation of the provisions of Chapter 7 is the failure to provide the proper type of fire door in a fire wall. A horizontal-sliding fire door cannot be considered as an acceptable life safety feature. Such a door is permitted in existing installations in accordance with 40.2.2.2.4, but, even then, the door is not credited with protecting the opening. Because a horizontal exit might be used from both sides of a fire wall, careful consideration of the direction of door swing is necessary to ensure that the *Code* will recognize this use. In many instances, two doors swinging in opposite directions will be required so that the exit is permitted to be used as a means of egress from both sides of the fire wall. See 7.2.1.4, 7.2.4.3.6, and 40.2.2.5.

The increase in allowable travel distance to 400 ft (122 m) permitted by 40.2.6.2(1) through (3) is often applied to exits in a general purpose industrial occupancy that is classified as a low or ordinary hazard.

Paragraph 40.2.6.2(1) limits the use of the increased travel distance provisions to one-story buildings. Any stairs or other impediments to the rapid movement of occupants would result in slower evacuation of the building and increase the possibility of exposure to smoke or fire.

To satisfy the intent of 40.2.6.2(2), judgment must be exercised in the design of systems for smoke venting and heat venting. The provisions of Annex A of the *Code* that recommend use of the guidelines of NFPA 204, *Guide for Smoke and Heat Venting,* should be sufficient in most instances.[3] In addition, in accordance with the recommendations of A.9.3.1, NFPA 92B, *Guide for Smoke Management Systems in Malls, Atria, and Large Areas,* can be consulted when designing buildings with ceilings of heights that approximate those of covered mall buildings and atria.[4]

The limitation on smoke accumulation in 40.2.6.2(2) is a key factor in the design of the smoke removal system. The average evacuation speed of a person who is walking is approximately 250 ft (76 m) per minute, or a little over 4 ft (1.2 m) per second. Where this evacuation speed is applied to the 400-ft (122-m) travel distance allowed by the *Code,* the maximum time required to reach an exit should not exceed 2 minutes. It is an extremely rare situation in which the smoke that accumulates in an industrial building is so extensive that it fills the structure and descends to less than 6 ft (1.8 m) above the floor level in 2 minutes. The added benefit of a properly designed system for smoke and heat venting ensures that there will be little possibility that the means of egress will be blocked by smoke.

The use of available, computerized, smoke-filling and evacuation time models can provide documentation that permits a designer to meet the smoke and heat venting requirements in some buildings by providing only a high ceiling and no mechanical smoke-removal equipment.

The installation of a complete automatic extinguishing system as required by 40.2.6.2(3) is intended to ensure control and extinguishment of incipient fires and ultimately minimize exposure of the occupants to fire. It is not the intent of 40.2.6.2(3) to allow only an automatic sprinkler system to provide the required protection, because a number of equally effective extinguishing agents and systems are permitted to be used for specific industrial fire hazards. The importance of this provision is the requirement

for automatic initiation of the fire control and extinguishing system to minimize the extent of the occupants' exposure to fire. The installed system is required to be fully supervised to ensure that it will operate when a fire occurs. Adequate procedures must be provided by the building's owner or tenant to ensure the prompt correction of any impairments to the extinguishing systems. In some facilities, the degree of fire risk during the impairment period might require limitations on hazardous operations and the number of occupants, so that the level of safety to life will be equivalent to that provided when the extinguishing system is operational.

Low and ordinary hazard special purpose industrial occupancies, which are characterized by large, specialized equipment and low occupant load, are permitted an increase in travel distance beyond that allowed for low and ordinary general industrial occupancies. Paragraph 40.2.6.3 permits an increase to 300 ft (91 m) if the building is not sprinklered, and an increase to 400 ft (122 m) if the building is protected throughout by a supervised sprinkler system, without mandating the additional requirements of 40.2.6.2.

For a summary of the various travel distance allowances for industrial occupancies, see Exhibit 40.7.

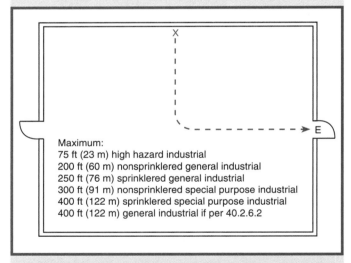

Exhibit 40.7 *Summary of industrial occupancy travel distance options permitted by 40.2.6.*

40.2.7 Discharge from Exits.

Discharge from exits shall be in accordance with Section 7.7.

The purpose of the requirement of 7.7.2 is to control the arrangement of exits from upper stories that discharge to the outside through the level of exit discharge. Subsection 7.7.2 modifies the general rule for complete enclosure of exits up to their point of discharge to the outside of the building, because the safeguards specified in 7.7.2—especially those for automatic sprinkler protection of the level of exit discharge—maintain reasonable safety. When the arrangement of exits is evaluated, a stairway is not considered as discharging through the level of discharge if it leads to the outside through an exit passageway in accordance with 7.2.6. This evaluation is valid, despite the fact that doors are located in the exit passageway walls between the base of the enclosed stairway and the door to the outside on the level of exit discharge.

40.2.8 Illumination of Means of Egress.

Means of egress shall be illuminated in accordance with Section 7.8.

Exception: Structures occupied only during daylight hours, with skylights or windows arranged to provide the required level of illumination on all portions of the means of egress during such hours.

40.2.9* Emergency Lighting.

Emergency lighting shall be provided in accordance with Section 7.9.

Exception No. 1: Special purpose industrial occupancies without routine human habitation.

Exception No. 2: Structures occupied only during daylight hours, with skylights or windows arranged to provide the required level of illumination on all portions of the means of egress during such hours.

A.40.2.9 The authority having jurisdiction should review the facility and designate the stairs, aisles, corridors, ramps, and passageways that should be required to be provided with emergency lighting. In large locker rooms or laboratories using hazardous chemicals, for example, the authority having jurisdiction should determine that emergency lighting is needed in the major aisles leading through those spaces.

40.2.10 Marking of Means of Egress.

Means of egress shall have signs in accordance with Section 7.10.

The intent of 40.2.8 is not to require the installation of extensive and unneeded illumination systems in

industrial occupancies. Illumination is required for the exit access, which is limited to designated aisles, corridors, and passageways that lead to an exit. No requirement is specified for the provision of illumination throughout the building, which in many industrial occupancies would involve lighting an extensive floor area. The purpose of the lighting system is to ensure that occupants are able to see the means of egress and not to illuminate the operation of production facilities.

In addition, the *Code* does not require illumination of the means of egress if the building is occupied during the daylight hours only. To meet the requirements of the exception to 40.2.8, the building, including stairways, must have sufficient windows and skylights to ensure natural illumination. The authority having jurisdiction should make certain that the building is not occupied after daylight hours.

Exception No. 1 and Exception No. 2 to 40.2.9 for emergency lighting are included for the same reasons that illumination of the means of egress is not required (see the exception to 40.2.8). Exception No. 1 addresses special-purpose industrial occupancies that are not routinely occupied. There is no need to install an extensive and costly emergency lighting system in an unoccupied building.

40.2.11 Special Means of Egress Features.

(Reserved.)

Section 40.3 Protection

40.3.1 Protection of Vertical Openings.

Any vertical opening shall be enclosed or protected in accordance with 8.2.5.

Exception No. 1: In special purpose industrial and high hazard industrial occupancies where unprotected vertical openings exist and are necessary to manufacturing operations, such openings shall be permitted beyond the specified limits. This exception shall be permitted only where every floor level has direct access to one or more enclosed stairs or other exits protected against obstruction by any fire or smoke in the open areas connected by the unprotected vertical openings.

Exception No. 2: Existing open stairs, existing open ramps, and existing escalators shall be permitted where connecting only two floor levels.

Exception No. 3: Existing unprotected vertical openings in buildings with low or ordinary hazard contents that are protected throughout by an approved automatic sprinkler system in accordance with Section 9.7 shall be permitted, provided that the vertical opening does not serve as a required exit. Under the conditions of this exception, all required exits shall consist of outside stairs in accordance with 7.2.2, smokeproof enclosures in accordance with 7.2.3, or horizontal exits in accordance with 7.2.4.

Exception No. 4: Openings in accordance with 8.2.5.8 shall be permitted.

Exception No. 1 to 40.3.1 strictly limits the use of unprotected vertical openings in high hazard and special purpose industrial occupancies. Direct access to one or more enclosed stairways or to other exits is required from any areas connected by unprotected vertical openings. This provision recognizes that many high hazard and special purpose industrial occupancies require openings between floor levels to accommodate piping, conveyors, and other devices and equipment essential to the orderly operation of the facility. In most of these situations, full enclosure is not practical or feasible. In high hazard occupancies, the provision of two means of egress will, in most situations, be sufficient to comply with this exception. In special-purpose industrial occupancies, additional exits or other special arrangements will normally be required for compliance with the provision that stairways and exits be protected against obstruction from fire and smoke in open areas connected by unprotected vertical openings.

Exception No. 2 to 40.3.1 limits the use of existing open stairways, existing open ramps, and existing escalators that are unenclosed or unprotected by permitting them to connect only two floors. An existing open stairway connecting three floors would have to be enclosed, protected, or permitted by another of the exceptions to 40.3.1.

Exception No. 3 to 40.3.1 recognizes that an existing industrial occupancy might contain unprotected vertical openings and still provide a reasonable level of safety to life if the building houses only low or ordinary hazard contents and is protected by a complete automatic sprinkler system. Smokeproof enclosures and outside stairways (the only types of vertical exits permitted by this exception) must be fully enclosed or protected against vertical fire spread and must meet the requirements of Chapter 7. The unenclosed vertical openings are not permitted to serve as part of the means of egress, although they can remain as convenience openings and stairways to be used for normal operations.

Although the major reason for allowing this pro-

vision is economic (enclosing all vertical openings in existing buildings is expensive), there is actually little effect on the life safety of occupants where a building houses low or ordinary hazard contents. However, some difficulties in fire control are created, because unprotected vertical openings can contribute to fire spread in buildings and result in extensive property damage and potential impact on occupants prior to evacuation; therefore, a complete automatic sprinkler system is required.

40.3.2* Protection from Hazards.

Every high hazard industrial occupancy, operation, or process shall have approved, supervised automatic extinguishing systems in accordance with Section 9.7 or other protection appropriate to the particular hazard, such as explosion venting or suppression. Protection shall be provided for any area subject to an explosion hazard to minimize danger to occupants in case of fire or other emergency before they have time to use exits to escape. Activation of the fire extinguishing or suppression system shall initiate the required building fire alarm system in accordance with 40.3.4.3.4. Hazardous areas in industrial occupancies protected by approved automatic extinguishing systems in accordance with Section 9.7 shall be exempt from the smoke-resisting enclosure requirement of 8.4.1.2.

A.40.3.2 Emergency lighting should be considered where operations require lighting to perform orderly manual emergency operation or shutdown, maintain critical services, or provide safe start-up after a power failure.

The intent of 40.3.2 is to provide for the life safety of the occupants of industrial buildings by controlling the risk associated with hazardous operations. The alternatives offered in 40.3.2 are not all-inclusive, and a proper fire protection engineering solution might not incorporate the listed provisions. The *Code* intends to allow for engineering judgment in a wide range of potentially hazardous situations, including some where protection might be limited. The intent of the paragraph is also broad in application, because, in many highly hazardous operations, an explosion might be immediately preceded by a fire or other emergency, such as an overheated reactor vessel, an exothermic reaction, or increased pressure. Because such conditions might initiate an explosion, depending on the process and arrangement of the equipment, immediate egress from the facility might be necessary. If fire or other emergencies are likely to develop rapidly into an explosion, adequate precautions are necessary for life safety. Where a sprinkler system is used to provide the protection required by 40.3.2, it must be supervised.

In many modern facilities, provisions that prove adequate for the life safety of occupants might already be included for process control and property protection, and any additional measures will not increase the life safety of operators to an appreciable degree.

Chapters 13 and 14 of Section 4 of the NFPA *Fire Protection Handbook* discuss the basic principles of explosion prevention, venting, and suppression.[5] These chapters also contain an extensive bibliography on the subject. Recommendations for the design and use of vents to limit pressures developed by explosions are specified in NFPA 68, *Guide for Venting of Deflagrations*.[6] Standards for explosion prevention systems are found in NFPA 69, *Standard on Explosion Prevention Systems*.[7]

Paragraph 8.4.1.2 requires that, where a hazardous area is protected by automatic sprinklers, the hazardous area must be enclosed by smoke partitions rather than with fire barriers with a 1-hour fire resistance rating and doors with a 45-minute fire protection rating. The last sentence of 40.3.2 exempts hazardous areas in industrial occupancies from the requirement for smoke partitions if those areas are protected by automatic sprinklers. For consistency, similar wording appears in Exception No. 2 to 8.4.1.2.

40.3.3 Interior Finish.

40.3.3.1 Interior finish shall be in accordance with Section 10.2.

40.3.3.2 Interior Wall and Ceiling Finish. Interior wall and ceiling finish complying with 10.2.3 shall be Class A, Class B, or Class C in operating areas and shall be as required by 7.1.4 in exit enclosures.

40.3.3.3 Interior Floor Finish. (No requirements.)

40.3.4 Detection, Alarm, and Communications Systems.

40.3.4.1 General. Industrial occupancies shall be provided with a fire alarm system in accordance with Section 9.6.

Exception: If the total capacity of the building is under 100 persons and fewer than 25 persons are above or below the level of exit discharge.

40.3.4.2 Initiation. Initiation of the required fire alarm system shall be by manual means in accordance with 9.6.2.1(1).

Exception No. 1: Initiation shall be permitted by means of an approved automatic fire detection system in accordance

with 9.6.2.1(2) that provides protection throughout the building.

Exception No. 2: Initiation shall be permitted by means of an approved, supervised automatic sprinkler system in accordance with 9.6.2.1(3) that provides protection throughout the building.

40.3.4.3 Notification.

40.3.4.3.1 The required fire alarm system shall meet one of the following criteria:

(1) It shall provide occupant notification in accordance with 9.6.3.
(2) It shall sound an audible and visible signal in a constantly attended location for the purposes of initiating emergency action.

40.3.4.3.2 Positive alarm sequence in accordance with 9.6.3.4 shall be permitted.

40.3.4.3.3 Existing presignal systems in accordance with 9.6.3.3 shall be permitted.

40.3.4.3.4 In high hazard industrial occupancies as described in 40.1.4.1(c), the required fire alarm system shall automatically initiate an occupant evacuation alarm signal in accordance with 9.6.3.

The requirements of 40.3.4.3.1 and 40.3.4.3.4 specify two separate and distinct provisions for audible alarms activated by the fire alarm system required by 40.3.4.1. In low and ordinary hazard industrial occupancies (see 40.3.4.3.1), the system is permitted to activate an evacuation alarm or it is permitted to sound an alarm in a constantly attended location for the purpose of initiating emergency action. This provision allows an interface between the alarm system and the plant's emergency organization. The alarm system is permitted to be controlled from a central security console or a similar location. The key feature is that the location from which the alarm sounds must be constantly staffed. This requirement is not intended to mandate the installation of supervisory service, such as that connected to a central station, but the location must be fully attended at all times when the building is occupied.

In high hazard occupancies (see 40.3.4.3.4), the alarm must be arranged to provide evacuation signals, because the safety of the occupants of these areas depends on their immediate notification of a fire.

Note that 40.3.4.3.3 recognizes existing presignal systems but not new presignal systems. If an automatic form of delay is desired for an existing alarm system that doesn't already have a presignal feature, or for a new alarm system, the more reliable system feature known as *positive alarm sequence* is permitted. The positive alarm sequence option might be applied to the high hazard industrial occupancies addressed in 40.3.4.3.4 for which an automatic form of occupant notification is needed. Also, positive alarm sequence might be used in industrial occupancies, other than those that are high hazard, where the provisions of 40.3.4.3.1(1) are used instead of those of 40.3.4.3.1(2).

40.3.5 Extinguishment Requirements.

(None.)

40.3.6 Corridors.

The provisions of 7.1.3.1 shall not apply.

Without the exemption to the requirements of 7.1.3.1 provided by 40.3.6, all new industrial occupancy corridors serving more than 30 persons would be required to have a 1-hour fire resistance rating, with openings protected by 20-minute fire protection–rated door assemblies. The exemption to 7.1.3.1 was adopted because of the ambulatory nature of occupants of industrial occupancies and the operational need for openings, even where corridors are provided.

Section 40.4 Special Provisions

40.4.1 High-Rise Buildings.

High-rise industrial occupancies shall comply with the automatic sprinkler requirements of 11.8.2.1.

Exception No. 1:   Low hazard industrial occupancies.

Exception No. 2:   Special purpose industrial occupancies.

Exception No. 3:   Existing industrial occupancies.

Subsection 40.4.1 references a portion of the high-rise building provisions of Section 11.8 that were written to allow an occupancy chapter to mandate their use. New, high-rise, general-purpose industrial occupancy buildings that are classified as ordinary hazard and new high-rise industrial occupancy buildings that are classified as high hazard are required to be protected throughout by an approved, supervised au-

tomatic sprinkler system in accordance with 11.8.2.1. The remainder of Section 11.8 is not mandated for high-rise industrial occupancy buildings.

Section 40.5 Building Services

40.5.1 Utilities.

Utilities shall comply with the provisions of Section 9.1.

40.5.2 Heating, Ventilating, and Air Conditioning.

Heating, ventilating, and air conditioning equipment shall comply with the provisions of Section 9.2.

40.5.3 Elevators, Escalators, and Conveyors.

Elevators, escalators, and conveyors shall comply with the provisions of Section 9.4.

40.5.4 Rubbish Chutes, Incinerators, and Laundry Chutes.

Rubbish chutes, incinerators, and laundry chutes shall comply with the provisions of Section 9.5.

Section 40.6* Special Provisions for Aircraft Servicing Hangars

A.40.6 For further information on aircraft hangars, see NFPA 409, *Standard on Aircraft Hangars.*

40.6.1 The requirements of Sections 40.1 through 40.5 shall be met, except as modified by 40.6.2 through 40.6.4.

40.6.2 Exits from aircraft servicing areas shall be provided at intervals not exceeding 150 ft (45 m) on all exterior walls. There shall be not less than two means of egress from each aircraft servicing area. Horizontal exits through interior fire walls shall be provided at intervals not exceeding 100 ft (30 m) along the wall.

Exception: Dwarf, or "smash," doors used in doors that accommodate aircraft shall be permitted for compliance with these requirements.

40.6.3 Means of egress from mezzanine floors in aircraft servicing areas shall be arranged so that the travel distance to the nearest exit from any point on the mezzanine does not exceed 75 ft (23 m). Such means of egress shall lead directly to a properly enclosed stair discharging directly to the exterior, to a suitable cutoff area, or to outside stairs.

40.6.4 Dead ends shall not exceed 50 ft (15 m).

Exception: No dead end shall be permitted for high hazard contents areas.

Section 40.6, which addresses aircraft servicing hangars, is nearly identical to Section 42.6, which addresses aircraft storage hangars. Because aircraft hangars are used for both storage and repair, corresponding requirements can be found in both Chapters 40 and 42.

References Cited in Commentary

1. NFPA 13, *Standard for the Installation of Sprinkler Systems,* 1999 edition, National Fire Protection Association, Quincy, MA.
2. NFPA 30, *Flammable and Combustible Liquids Code,* 1996 edition, National Fire Protection Association, Quincy, MA.
3. NFPA 204, *Guide for Smoke and Heat Venting,* 1998 edition, National Fire Protection Association, Quincy, MA.
4. NFPA 92B, *Guide for Smoke Management Systems in Malls, Atria, and Large Areas,* 1995 edition, National Fire Protection Association, Quincy, MA.
5. NFPA *Fire Protection Handbook,* 18th edition, National Fire Protection Association, Quincy, MA, 1997.
6. NFPA 68, *Guide for Venting of Deflagrations,* 1998 edition, National Fire Protection Association, Quincy, MA.
7. NFPA 69, *Standard on Explosion Prevention Systems,* 1997 edition, National Fire Protection Association, Quincy, MA.

CHAPTER 41

Reserved

Typically, the occupancy chapters are paired so that the even-numbered chapter in the pair addresses new facilities of the occupancy type and the odd-numbered chapter addresses existing facilities of the occupancy type. Chapter 40, which precedes this chapter, addresses both new and existing industrial occupancies in a single chapter. Chapter 41 has been reserved to permit the chapter on storage occupancies to be assigned an even number (that is, Chapter 42). The reserved chapter number might be used at a future date if the requirements for industrial occupancies are split into a pair of chapters—one for new construction and one for existing buildings.

CHAPTER 42

Storage Occupancies

Storage occupancies include all buildings or structures used primarily for the storage or sheltering of goods, merchandise, products, vehicles, or animals. The following are examples of storage occupancies:

(1) Barns
(2) Stables
(3) Hangars (for aircraft storage only)
(4) Freight terminal
(5) Bulk oil storage
(6) Truck and marine terminals
(7) Parking garages
(8) Cold storage
(9) Grain elevators
(10) Warehouses

This final chapter of the *Code* covers a range of facilities used for storage of a wide variety of commodities. While the same life safety philosophy that prevails in the other occupancy chapters applies to storage occupancies, the protection scheme is less complicated, given the relatively small number of people who characteristically occupy a storage occupancy. Although some warehouse facilities are substantially larger than buildings housing other occupancies, they are typically occupied by few people.

Once the basic characteristics of a given storage occupancy are determined, the general protection measures of Section 42.2 and Section 42.3 can be applied. In addition to these measures, the supplementary provisions that are specific to a particular type of storage occupancy can be applied. These provisions include those for aircraft storage hangars (Section 42.6), grain and bulk storage elevators (Section 42.7), and parking garages (Section 42.8).

Section 42.1 General Requirements

42.1.1 Application.

The requirements of this chapter shall apply to both new and existing storage occupancies. Storage occupancies shall include all buildings or structures used primarily for the storage or sheltering of goods, merchandise, products, vehicles, or animals.

Note that this chapter applies to both new and existing storage occupancies. Where the requirements vary, exceptions that apply to existing storage occupancies are often provided, or additional requirements that are limited to new storage occupancies are specified.

Minor storage that is incidental to another occupancy is treated as part of the other occupancy. See the exception to 6.1.14.2.

42.1.2 Mixed Occupancies.

(See 6.1.14 and 42.1.4.)

42.1.3 Special Definitions.

(None.)

42.1.4 Classification of Occupancy.

42.1.4.1 Storage occupancies shall include all buildings and structures or parts thereof with occupancy as defined in 6.1.13. Incidental storage in another occupancy shall not be the basis for overall occupancy classification.

42.1.4.2 Storage occupancies or areas of storage occupancies that are used for the purpose of packaging, labeling, sorting, special handling, or other operations requiring an occupant load greater than that normally contemplated for storage shall be classified as industrial occupancies. *(See Chapter 40.)*

Life safety provisions for storage locations are not extensive, because the number of occupants is generally low and many of those who occupy such a structure are present for only short periods of time. Furthermore, employees of storage occupancies normally do not remain in one location; instead, their assignments require that they move about and perform activities of a short-term nature.

Due to the special characteristics of storage occupancies, a number of provisions are included in the *Code* to modify, as required, those provisions that normally apply to occupancies with larger populations.

The purpose of the 42.1.4.2 is to provide suitable egress facilities for storage occupancies, or portions of storage occupancies, where a storage building has a population greater than normally expected. It is common practice to employ large numbers of people in a storage building for industrial types of operations, such as labeling, sorting, or packaging. Such operations require additional egress in accordance with the provisions of Chapter 40 for industrial occupancies.

42.1.5 Classification of Hazard of Contents.

Contents of storage occupancies shall be classified as low hazard, ordinary hazard, or high hazard, in accordance with Section 6.2, depending on the character of the materials stored, their packaging, and other factors.

No basis for comparison exists between the hazard categories for storage facilities in NFPA 13, *Standard for the Installation of Sprinkler Systems* and those of the *Life Safety Code.*[1] The hazard categories for storage facilities contained in NFPA 13 are established for the design of automatic sprinkler systems. When determining hazards to life safety, all storage commodity classifications in NFPA 13 should be treated as low or ordinary hazard contents, as defined in Section 6.2 of the *Life Safety Code.*

There is a strong inclination to use the potential for rapid fire growth associated with high-piled or racked storage as justification for establishing strict life safety provisions. However, the arrangement of buildings typical for this type of storage is adequate

to allow safe and rapid egress at the first notification or discovery of fire. If a building is not protected by automatic sprinklers, the *Code* provides adequate provisions—such as those for travel distance to an exit—to help ensure the survival of the occupants.

42.1.6 Minimum Construction Requirements.

(No requirements.)

Some occupancy chapters, such as Chapter 18/19, which address the life safety needs of nonambulatory health care occupants, specify minimum building construction type requirements to ensure structural integrity for the time needed for a lengthy evacuation or for safe refuge within the building. No minimum construction requirements are imposed in Chapter 42, because storage occupancies characteristically have few occupants and those few occupants are ambulatory.

42.1.7* Occupant Load.

The occupant load, in number of persons for whom means of egress and other provisions are required, shall be determined on the basis of the maximum probable population of the space under consideration.

A.42.1.7 There is no occupant load factor specified for storage occupancies. Rather, the actual probable maximum number of persons present needs to be considered in determining the occupant load.

Although 42.1.7 and Table 7.3.1.2 do not provide a required occupant load factor for calculating a minimum occupant load to size a means of egress system in a storage occupancy, it is necessary to establish an occupant load. The occupant load is determined based on the maximum number of persons expected to occupy the storage occupancy under any anticipated facility operation. Due to the low occupant load characteristic of storage occupancies, compliance with other *Code* provisions, such as the following, generally provides a means of egress system capable of handling the actual occupant load, without specifically considering the occupant load when the means of egress is designed:

(1) Minimum widths for doors, corridors, or passageways
(2) Minimum number of exits
(3) Travel distance allowances

Section 42.2 Means of Egress Requirements

42.2.1 General.

Each required means of egress shall be in accordance with the applicable portions of Chapter 7.

42.2.2 Means of Egress Components.

42.2.2.1 Components of means of egress shall be limited to the types described in 42.2.2.2 through 42.2.2.12.

42.2.2.2 Doors.

42.2.2.2.1 Doors complying with 7.2.1 shall be permitted.

42.2.2.2.2 Delayed-egress locks complying with 7.2.1.6.1 shall be permitted.

42.2.2.2.3 Access-controlled egress doors complying with 7.2.1.6.2 shall be permitted.

42.2.2.2.4 Existing horizontal-sliding fire doors shall be permitted in the means of egress under the following conditions:

(1) They are held open by fusible links.
(2) The links are rated at not less than 165°F (74°C).
(3) The fusible links are located not more than 10 ft (3 m) above the floor.
(4) The fusible link is in immediate proximity to the door opening.
(5) The fusible link is not located above a ceiling.
(6) The door is not credited with providing any protection under this *Code*.

> Use of the delayed-egress locking device covered by 7.2.1.6.1 is allowed on any door in recognition of the security needs of some storage occupancies. In effect, the allowable 15-second or 30-second delay will be experienced only under nonfire conditions or very early in a fire's growth, because the door must be usable immediately upon sprinkler operation, smoke or heat detection, and upon loss of power that controls the locking mechanism. The building must be protected throughout by an approved, supervised automatic sprinkler system or an approved, supervised automatic fire detection system.
>
> Paragraph 42.2.2.2.3 recognizes access-controlled egress doors in storage occupancies as security measures that do not compromise the use of the means of egress.
>
> Horizontal-sliding doors exist in many storage occupancies for property protection purposes. Al-

though the *Code* normally does not recognize these doors within the required means of egress, 42.2.2.2.4 makes a special exemption for existing horizontal-sliding fire doors. By requiring the fusible link to be positioned in immediate proximity to the door opening, to be rated 165°F (74°C) or higher, and to be located not more than 10 ft (3 m) above the floor, the *Code* helps to ensure that the door will remain open until rising temperatures make it unsafe to pass through the door opening. Because the door will not close early in the fire development, the door cannot be credited as a fire door for life safety purposes. However, the door might serve as a means of property protection. See Exhibit 42.1.

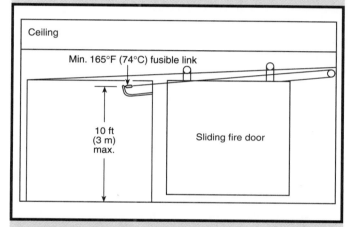

Exhibit 42.1 *Existing horizontal sliding fire door in accordance with 42.2.2.2.4.*

42.2.2.3 Stairs.

42.2.2.3.1 Stairs complying with 7.2.2 shall be permitted.

42.2.2.3.2 Spiral stairs complying with 7.2.2.2.3 shall be permitted.

42.2.2.3.3 Existing winders complying with 7.2.2.2.4 shall be permitted.

42.2.2.4 Smokeproof Enclosures. Smokeproof enclosures complying with 7.2.3 shall be permitted.

> Paragraph 42.2.2.4 does not mandate the use of smokeproof enclosures. However, it does recognize a smokeproof enclosure as part of the means of egress system in a storage occupancy only if the smokeproof enclosure meets the requirements of 7.2.3. For an example of an occupancy requiring a smokeproof enclosure, see 31.2.11, which specifies that existing non-sprinklered, high-rise apartment buildings are

required to be provided with smokeproof enclosures in accordance with 7.2.3. See 42.2.2.1.

42.2.2.5 Horizontal Exits.

42.2.2.5.1 Horizontal exits complying with 7.2.4 shall be permitted.

42.2.2.5.2* In horizontal exits where the doorway is protected by a fire door on each side of the wall in which it is located, one fire door shall be of the swinging type as provided in 7.2.4.3.6, and the other shall be permitted to be an automatic-sliding fire door that shall be kept open whenever the building is occupied.

A.42.2.2.5.2 The customary building code requirement for fire doors on both sides of an opening in a fire wall is permitted to be met by having an automatic-sliding fire door on one side and a self-closing fire door swinging out from the other side of the wall. This arrangement qualifies only as a horizontal exit from the side of the sliding door. For further information, see A.7.2.4.3.8.

Subparagraph 42.2.2.5.1 does not mandate the use of horizontal exits. However, it does recognize a horizontal exit as part of the means of egress system in a storage occupancy only if the horizontal exit meets the requirements of 7.2.4, as modified by 42.2.2.5.2.

Subparagraph 42.2.2.5.2 and A.42.2.2.5.2 recognize the common practice of combining a horizontal exit that is used for life safety with a fire barrier of a significant fire resistance rating that is used for property protection. Opening protectives for such a fire barrier can require the use of a set of two doors to achieve the required fire protection rating. It is impractical for both doors to swing in the same direction without interfering with each other; yet, operation of two doors that swing in opposite directions is cumbersome for daily or frequent use. One swinging and one sliding door, as shown in Exhibit 42.2, provide an acceptable arrangement for day-to-day functioning of the building. The open sliding door does not compromise life safety, because by the time its fusible link mechanism releases the door and allows it to close, temperatures in the vicinity of the door opening render use of the door impractical.

42.2.2.6 Ramps. Ramps complying with 7.2.5 shall be permitted.

Paragraph 42.2.2.6 does not mandate the use of ramps in storage occupancies. However, it does recognize a

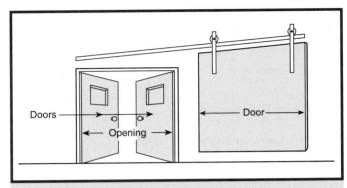

Exhibit 42.2 *Combination swinging and sliding doors permitted by 42.2.2.5.2.*

ramp as part of the means of egress system only if the ramp meets the requirements of 7.2.5. See 42.2.2.1.

42.2.2.7 Exit Passageways. Exit passageways complying with 7.2.6 shall be permitted.

Paragraph 42.2.2.7 does not mandate the use of exit passageways in storage occupancies. However, it does recognize an exit passageway as part of the means of egress system only if the exit passageway meets the requirements of 7.2.6. See 42.2.2.1.

42.2.2.8 Fire Escape Stairs. Existing fire escape stairs complying with 7.2.8 shall be permitted.

42.2.2.9 Fire Escape Ladders. Fire escape ladders complying with 7.2.9 shall be permitted.

42.2.2.10 Slide Escapes. Existing slide escapes complying with 7.2.10 shall be permitted.

The intent of 42.2.2.10 is to allow the continued use of existing slide escapes, which are a common means of egress from areas that house explosives or other highly hazardous materials in warehouses associated with the chemical industry. The provision allows slide escapes to be considered as part of the required means of egress from existing storage occupancies only if the slide escape meets the requirements of 7.2.10.

42.2.2.11 Alternating Tread Devices. Alternating tread devices complying with 7.2.11 shall be permitted.

The provisions of 7.2.11, in effect, limit the use of alternating tread devices to those locations where the *Code* recognizes the use of fire escape ladders. See 42.2.2.9, 7.2.9, and 7.2.11.

42.2.2.12 Areas of Refuge. Areas of refuge complying with 7.2.12 shall be permitted.

42.2.3 Capacity of Means of Egress.

The capacity of means of egress shall be in accordance with Section 7.3.

Prior to 1991, the *Code* required a minimum 44-in. (112-cm) width for corridors and passageways within the required means of egress of storage occupancies. A corridor or passageway of that minimum width would have provided egress capacity for 220 persons [that is, 44 in. / 0.2 in. per person (approximately 112 cm / 0.5 cm per person) in accordance with Table 7.3.3.1 for level travel components]. The prior requirement produced artificially large egress systems, relative to the occupant load, in many storage occupancies. The requirement was eliminated, and the minimum 36-in. (91-cm) width requirement of 7.3.4.1, which addresses the minimum width of any exit access, was made applicable to storage occupancies. Exit access is required to be wider than 36 in. 91 cm) only if a corridor or passageway in a storage occupancy is to provide capacity for more than 180 persons [that is, 36 in. / 0.2 in. per person (approximately 91 cm / 0.5 cm per person)].

See the commentary following A.42.1.7.

42.2.4 Number of Means of Egress.

(See also Section 7.4.)

42.2.4.1 Every building or structure used for storage and every section thereof considered separately shall have not less than two separate means of egress as remotely located from each other as practicable.

Exception No. 1:   In low hazard storage occupancies, a single means of egress shall be permitted from any story or section.

Exception No. 2:   In ordinary hazard storage occupancies, a single means of egress shall be permitted from any story or section, provided that the exit can be reached within the distance permitted as common path of travel. (See 42.2.5.4.)

42.2.4.2 Floors or portions thereof with an occupant load of more than 500 persons shall have the minimum number of separate and remote means of egress specified by 7.4.1.2.

Exception: Existing buildings.

Exception No. 1 and Exception No. 2 to 42.2.4.1 modify the requirement for two, separate, remotely located means of egress due in part to the small number of employees typically found in a storage occupancy and the exemplary life safety fire record of such facilities. Exception No. 1 recognizes that a low hazard storage occupancy is not subject to a self-propagating fire, and, therefore, considers a single means of egress to be safe. Exception No. 2 allows a single means of egress in an ordinary hazard storage occupancy if the total travel distance to the single exit does not exceed the 50-ft (15-m) or 100-ft (30-m) common path of travel allowance for nonsprinklered and sprinklered buildings, respectively (see 42.2.5.4 and its exception). This allowance is made because such a single-exit arrangement is equivalent or superior to a two-exit arrangement that applies the maximum common path of travel allowance and subsequently requires additional travel distance to reach an exit. See Exhibit 42.3.

In Exhibit 42.3, a single exit is depicted in illustration (a). It is located within the distance permitted for common path of travel (see 42.2.5.4 and its excep-

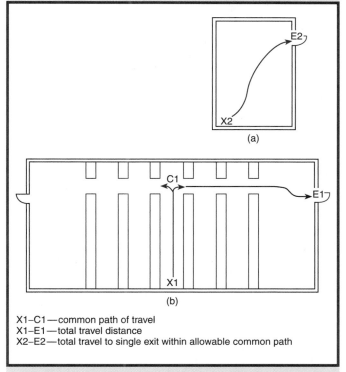

X1–C1—common path of travel
X1–E1—total travel distance
X2–E2—total travel to single exit within allowable common path

Exhibit 42.3 *Common path of travel in single-exit building compared to that in two-exit building.*

tion), as addressed byException No. 2 to 42.2.4.1 for ordinary hazard storage occupancies, and creates a situation no more dangerous than the common path of travel shown as X1–C1 in the two-exit building depicted in illustration (b).

42.2.5 Arrangement of Means of Egress.

42.2.5.1 Means of egress shall be arranged in accordance with Section 7.5.

42.2.5.2 In storage occupancies with low hazard contents, dead-end corridors and common paths of travel shall be permitted without limitation.

By definition, no self-propagating fire can occur in low hazard contents. If a fire will not spread or continue to burn, building occupants will not be subject to an emergent need to egress the building by means of paths that avoid the fire. Therefore, the *Code* establishes no maximum dead-end corridor and no maximum common path of travel for storage occupancies with low hazard contents. See Section 6.2.

42.2.5.3 In storage occupancies with ordinary hazard contents, dead-end corridors shall not exceed 50 ft (15 m).

Exception: Dead-end corridors shall not exceed 100 ft (30 m) in buildings protected throughout by an approved, supervised automatic sprinkler system in accordance with Section 9.7.

42.2.5.4 In storage occupancies with ordinary hazard contents, common paths of travel shall not exceed 50 ft (15 m).

Exception: Common paths of travel shall not exceed 100 ft (30 m) in buildings protected throughout by an approved, supervised automatic sprinkler system in accordance with Section 9.7.

An ordinary hazard storage occupancy, despite its characteristically low occupant load, is not permitted to provide a common path of travel that forces an occupant to travel in one direction only for more than 50 ft (15 m) [100 ft (30 m) in a sprinklered building] without providing a route to a second remotely located exit.

42.2.5.5 Dead-end corridors and common paths of travel shall be prohibited in high hazard storage occupancies.

Exception: As permitted by 7.11.3.

By definition, an extremely rapid–developing fire or the potential for explosion are characteristics of high hazard contents. If a fire spreads with extreme rapidity, building occupants will have an emergent need to egress the building by means of paths that avoid the fire. Therefore, the *Code* permits no dead-end corridors and no common path of travel for storage occupancies with high hazard contents. See Section 6.2.

42.2.6* Travel Distance to Exits.

(See also Section 7.6.)

A.42.2.6 The travel distance to exits specified recognizes a low population density. Consideration should be given to locating areas that have a relatively high population, such as lunchrooms, meeting rooms, packaging areas, and offices, near the outside wall of the building to keep the travel distance to a minimum.

42.2.6.1 In low hazard storage occupancies, limitations on travel distance to exits shall not be required.

42.2.6.2 In ordinary hazard storage occupancies, travel distance shall not exceed 200 ft (60 m).

Exception: In buildings protected throughout by an approved, supervised automatic sprinkler system in accordance with Section 9.7, travel distance shall not exceed 400 ft (122 m).

42.2.6.3 Every area used for the storage of high hazard commodities shall have an exit within 75 ft (23 m) of any point in the area where persons might be present.

Exception No. 1: In areas used for the storage of high hazard commodities that are protected throughout by an approved, supervised automatic sprinkler system in accordance with Section 9.7, travel distance to an exit shall be within 100 ft (30 m) of any point in the area where persons might be present.

Exception No. 2: In storage occupancies where flammable and combustible liquid products are stored and protected in accordance with NFPA 30, Flammable and Combustible Liquids Code, travel distance to an exit shall be permitted to be not more than 150 ft (45 m).

A.42.2.6.3 Exception No. 2 The exception for extended travel distance in protected flammable and combustible liquids warehouses is addressed within the storage occupancy provisions rather than in the generalized high hazard contents provisions of Section 7.11. The 1996 edition of NFPA 30, *Flammable and Combustible Liquids Code*, represents an enhancement over earlier editions and is based on research. Where the protection is provided in accordance with the 1996 edition of NFPA 30, the increase in travel distance to 150 feet (45 m) is justified.

Subsection 42.2.6 establishes limitations on travel distance for storage occupancies. Note that the provisions create a direct relationship between the level of hazard of contents housed within a building and its life safety requirements. Therefore, in low hazard storage occupancies, no limitation is imposed on travel distance. As the level of hazard of contents increases, travel distance limitations are imposed. Storage buildings housing ordinary hazards and lacking sprinkler protection are limited to 200 ft (60 m) of travel distance to an exit. A distance of 400 ft (122 m) is permitted if complete automatic sprinkler protection is provided. In high hazard storage occupancies, travel distance is restricted to a maximum of 75 ft (23 m) in nonsprinklered buildings and 100 ft (30 m) if the building is equipped with a complete automatic sprinkler system.

The absence of travel distance restrictions for low hazard storage occupancies is reasonable, because the small fire risk posed by low hazard materials, coupled with the low number of occupants, provides a minimal risk to life safety. The imposition of restrictive provisions would not be consistent with good fire protection and reasonable life safety requirements, because the possibility of fire is very low, and occupants are not expected to experience difficulty in evacuating the building. See Section 6.2 for guidelines on low hazard contents.

Exception No. 2 to 42.2.6.3 and A.42.2.6.3, Exception No. 2, address an increase in travel distance for storage occupancies where flammable and combustible liquid products are stored and protected in accordance with NFPA 30, *Flammable and Combustible Liquids Code*.[2] Note that A.42.2.6.3, Exception No. 2, specifies that if the protection is in accordance with an earlier edition of NFPA 30, but not the 1996 edition, it cannot be assured that adequate safeguards have been provided. Without the protection afforded by compliance with the 1996 edition of NFPA 30, the 75-ft (23-m) increase in travel distance is not permitted.

42.2.7 Discharge from Exits.

Discharge from exits shall be in accordance with Section 7.7.

42.2.8 Illumination of Means of Egress.

Means of egress shall be illuminated in accordance with Section 7.8.

Exception: In structures occupied only during daylight hours, with windows arranged to provide the required level of illumination on all portions of the means of egress during such hours, illumination requirements shall be permitted to be waived by the authority having jurisdiction.

The intent of 42.2.8 is not to require the installation of extensive and unneeded exit illumination systems in storage occupancies. Illumination is required for the exit and for the exit access, which is limited to designated aisles, corridors, and passageways that lead to an exit. Limiting the extent of the lighting system to egress areas eliminates the necessity for installing specialized lighting systems throughout storage areas, a practice that might be extremely costly while providing little or no return in safety to life.

The exception to 42.2.8 waives the requirement for illumination systems if a building, including the stairways, is sufficiently lit during periods of occupancy by means of natural lighting. The term *windows*, as used in the text of the exception, should not be interpreted literally. The term is meant to include skylights, open wall sections, and similar means of illumination by natural sources. The provisions are based on the fact that there is no need for a lighting system if the building is unoccupied during nondaylight hours.

42.2.9 Emergency Lighting.

Emergency lighting shall be provided in accordance with Section 7.9.

Exception No. 1: Storage occupancies shall not require emergency lighting where not normally occupied.

Exception No. 2: In structures occupied only during daylight hours, with skylights or windows arranged to provide the required level of illumination on all portions of the means of egress during such hours, emergency lighting shall not be required.

Exception No. 1 and Exception No. 2 to 42.2.9 for emergency lighting are included for the reasons stated in the commentary following 42.2.8. Exception No. 1 to 42.2.9 allows circuit arrangements that disconnect power from emergency lighting systems when the building is unoccupied. In many warehouses, power is turned off during periods when the building is unoccupied. This power disconnection serves fire prevention, energy conservation, and security purposes.

42.2.10 Marking of Means of Egress.

Means of egress shall have signs in accordance with Section 7.10.

42.2.11 Special Means of Egress Features.

(Reserved.)

Section 42.3 Protection

42.3.1 Protection of Vertical Openings.

Any vertical opening shall be enclosed or protected in accordance with 8.2.5.

Exception No. 1: Existing, unprotected vertical openings in buildings with low or ordinary hazard contents that are protected throughout by an approved automatic sprinkler system in accordance with Section 9.7 shall be permitted where they do not serve as required exits. Under the conditions of this exception, all required exits shall consist of outside stairs in accordance with 7.2.2, smokeproof enclosures in accordance with 7.2.3, or horizontal exits in accordance with 7.2.4.

Exception No. 2: Vertical openings in accordance with 8.2.5.8 shall be permitted.

Exception No. 1 to 42.3.1 recognizes that an existing storage occupancy might contain unprotected vertical openings and still provide a reasonable level of safety to life if the building houses only low or ordinary hazard contents and is protected by a complete automatic sprinkler system. Smokeproof enclosures and outside stairways (the only types of vertical exits permitted by this exception) must be fully enclosed or protected against vertical fire spread and must meet the requirements of Chapter 7. The unenclosed vertical openings are not permitted to serve as part of the means of egress, although they can remain as convenience openings and stairways to be used for normal operations.

Although the major reason for allowing this provision is economic (enclosing all vertical openings in existing buildings is expensive) there is actually little

effect on the life safety of occupants where a building houses low or ordinary hazard contents. However, some difficulties in fire control are created, because unprotected vertical openings can contribute to fire spread in buildings and result in extensive property damage and potential impact on occupants prior to evacuation; therefore, a complete automatic sprinkler system is required.

42.3.2 Protection from Hazards.

(No requirements.) *(See also Section 8.4.)*

42.3.3 Interior Finish.

42.3.3.1 Interior finish shall be in accordance with Section 10.2.

42.3.3.2 Interior Wall and Ceiling Finish. Interior wall and ceiling finish complying with 10.2.3 shall be Class A, Class B, or Class C in storage areas and shall be as required by 7.1.4 in exit enclosures.

42.3.3.3 Interior Floor Finish. (No requirements.)

42.3.4 Detection, Alarm, and Communications Systems.

42.3.4.1 General. Storage occupancies shall be provided with a fire alarm system in accordance with Section 9.6.

Exception No. 1: Storage occupancies limited to low hazard contents.

Exception No. 2: Storage occupancies with ordinary or high hazard contents not exceeding an aggregate floor area of 100,000 ft² (9300 m²).

Exception No. 3: Storage occupancies protected throughout by approved automatic extinguishment protection.

42.3.4.2 Initiation. Initiation of the required fire alarm system shall be by manual means in accordance with 9.6.2.1(1).

Exception: Initiation shall be permitted by means of an approved automatic fire detection system in accordance with 9.6.2.1(2) that provides protection throughout the building.

42.3.4.3 Notification.

42.3.4.3.1 The required fire alarm system shall meet one of the following criteria:

(1) It shall provide occupant notification in accordance with 9.6.3.
(2) It shall sound an audible and visible signal in a constantly attended location for the purposes of initiating emergency action.

42.3.4.3.2 Positive alarm sequence in accordance with 9.6.3.4 shall be permitted.

42.3.4.3.3 Existing presignal systems in accordance with 9.6.3.3 shall be permitted.

42.3.4.3.4 In high hazard storage occupancies, the required fire alarm system shall automatically initiate an occupant evacuation alarm signal in accordance with 9.6.3.

Subsection 42.3.4 requires the installation of a fire alarm system in nonsprinklered storage occupancies with an aggregate floor area of over 100,000 ft² (9300 m²). An alarm system is not required in a storage occupancy limited to housing low hazard contents, regardless of its size, nor is one required in a sprinklered storage occupancy, regardless of size. Storage placement limits visibility in buildings with large floor areas. As a result, personnel who work in storage areas might be unaware of the occurrence of fire for a long period. If fire spreads, which is highly possible in an unprotected storage building, means of exit access could be blocked. An alarm system provides a means of alerting all occupants to the presence of fire and allows for timely egress.

The requirements of 42.3.4.3.1 and 42.3.4.3.4 specify two separate and distinct provisions for audible alarms activated by the fire alarm system required by 42.3.4.1. In low and ordinary hazard storage occupancies (see 42.3.4.3.1), the system is permitted to activate an evacuation alarm or it is permitted to sound an alarm in a constantly attended location for the purpose of initiating emergency action. This provision allows an interface between the alarm system and the building's emergency organization. The alarm system is permitted to be controlled from a central security console or a similar location. The key feature is that the location from which the alarm sounds must be constantly staffed. This requirement is not intended to mandate the installation of supervisory service, such as that connected to a central station, but the location must be fully attended at all times when the building is occupied.

In high hazard storage occupancies (see 42.3.4.3.4), the alarm must be arranged to provide evacuation signals, because the safety of the occupants of these areas depends on their immediate notification of a fire.

Note that 42.3.4.3.3 recognizes existing presignal systems but not new presignal systems. If an automatic form of delay is desired for an existing alarm system that doesn't already have a presignal feature, or for a new alarm system, the more reliable system

feature known as *positive alarm sequence* is permitted. The positive alarm sequence option might be applied to the high hazard storage occupancies addressed in 42.3.4.3.4 for which an automatic form of occupant notification is needed. Also, positive alarm sequence might be used in storage occupancies, other than those that are high hazard, where the provisions of 42.3.4.3.1(1) are used instead of those of 42.3.4.3.1(2).

The *Code* does not specify an alarm system as a property protection requirement, although the probability of property loss is reduced in any occupancy where an alarm system is installed.

42.3.5 Extinguishment Requirements.

(None.)

42.3.6 Corridors.

The provisions of 7.1.3.1 shall not apply.

Without the exemption to the requirements of 7.1.3.1 provided by 42.3.6, all new storage occupancy corridors serving more than 30 persons would be required to have a 1-hour fire resistance rating, with openings protected by 20-minute fire protection–rated door assemblies. The exemption to 7.1.3.1 was adopted because of the ambulatory nature of occupants of storage occupancies; the operational need for openings, even where corridors are provided; and the functional need served by open floor areas.

Section 42.4 Special Provisions

42.4.1 High-Rise Buildings.

High-rise storage occupancies shall comply with the automatic sprinkler requirements of 11.8.2.1.

Exception No. 1:   Low hazard storage occupancies.

Exception No. 2:   Existing storage occupancies.

The provisions of 42.4.1, which apply to high-rise storage occupancy buildings, reference a portion of the high-rise building provisions of Section 11.8 that were written to allow an occupancy chapter to mandate their use. New high-rise storage occupancy buildings that are classified as ordinary hazard or high hazard are required to be protected throughout by an approved, supervised automatic sprinkler system in accordance with 11.8.2.1. The remainder of Section 11.8 is not mandated for high-rise storage occupancy buildings.

Section 42.5 Building Services

42.5.1 Utilities.

Utilities shall comply with the provisions of Section 9.1.

42.5.2 Heating, Ventilating, and Air Conditioning.

Heating, ventilating, and air conditioning equipment shall comply with the provisions of Section 9.2.

42.5.3 Elevators, Escalators, and Conveyors.

Elevators, escalators, and conveyors shall comply with the provisions of Section 9.4.

42.5.4 Rubbish Chutes, Incinerators, and Laundry Chutes.

Rubbish chutes, incinerators, and laundry chutes shall comply with the provisions of Section 9.5.

Section 42.6* Special Provisions for Aircraft Storage Hangars

A.42.6 For further information on aircraft hangars, see NFPA 409, *Standard on Aircraft Hangars.*

42.6.1 The requirements of Sections 42.1 through 42.5 shall be met, except as modified by 42.6.2 through 42.6.4.

42.6.2 Exits from aircraft storage areas shall be provided at intervals not exceeding 150 ft (45 m) on all exterior walls. There shall be not less than two means of egress serving each aircraft storage area. Horizontal exits through interior fire walls shall be provided at intervals not exceeding 100 ft (30 m) along the wall.

Exception: Dwarf, or "smash," doors used in doors that accommodate aircraft shall be permitted for compliance with these requirements.

42.6.3 Means of egress from mezzanine floors in aircraft storage areas shall be arranged so that the travel distance to

the nearest exit from any point on the mezzanine does not exceed 75 ft (23 m). Such means of egress shall lead directly to a properly enclosed stair discharging directly to the exterior, to a suitable cutoff area, or to outside stairs.

42.6.4 Dead ends shall not exceed 50 ft (15 m).

Exception: No dead end shall be permitted for high hazard contents areas.

For those provisions that apply to aircraft servicing hangars, see Section 40.6.

Paragraph 42.6.2 specifies two alternate methods of providing egress from aircraft storage hangars. Where egress is possible through the outside wall, a distance of 150 ft (45 m) between exit doors is adequate. In larger hangars, the servicing bay might have offices and shops located along one or more sides, with the walls constructed of fire resistance–rated materials. In those cases where the wall has a fire resistance rating, exit spacing of up to 100 ft (30 m) is specified. If the wall is nonrated, access to the outside is required. During inclement weather, large hangar doors are typically closed, so it is common procedure to provide small access doors for personnel in the larger aircraft hangar door. The small door can be considered a normal means of egress from an aircraft hangar. If possible, the door should swing in the direction of egress; however, this might not be possible due to the design of the aircraft door. For further information on aircraft hangars, see NFPA 409, *Standard on Aircraft Hangars.*[3]

42-7* Special Provisions for Grain or Other Bulk Storage Elevators

A.42.7 For further information, see NFPA 61, *Standard for the Prevention of Fires and Dust Explosions in Agricultural and Food Products Facilities.* The egress requirements for storage elevators are based on the possibility of fire and are not based on the possibility of grain dust explosions.

42.7.1 The requirements of Sections 42.1 through 42.5 shall be met, except as modified by 42.7.2 through 42.7.4.

42.7.2 There shall be not less than two means of egress from all working levels of the head house. One of these means of egress shall be a stair to the level of exit discharge that is enclosed by a dust-resistant 1-hour fire resistance–rated enclosure in accordance with 7.1.3.2. The second means of egress shall be one of the following:

(1) An exterior stair or basket ladder–type fire escape accessible from all working levels of the head house that provides a passage to ground level

(2) An exterior stair or basket ladder–type fire escape accessible from all working levels of the head house that provides access to the top of adjoining structures and that provides a continuous path to the means of egress described in 42.7.3

Exception: Stair enclosures in existing structures shall be permitted to have non-fire-rated dust-resistant enclosures.

42.7.3 An exterior stair or basket ladder–type fire escape shall provide passage to ground level from the top of the end of an adjoining structure, such as a silo, conveyor, gallery, or gantry.

42.7.4 Underground Spaces.

42.7.4.1 Underground spaces shall have not less than two means of egress, one of which shall be permitted to be a means of escape. The means of escape shall be arranged to eliminate dead ends.

42.7.4.2 Travel distance to means of escape or exit shall not exceed 200 ft (60 m).

Exception No. 1: Existing facilities.

Exception No. 2: In a building protected throughout by an approved, supervised automatic sprinkler system in accordance with Section 9.7, travel distance shall not exceed 400 ft (122 m).

Section 42.7 establishes the following three basic requirements:

(1) Two means of egress from all working levels of the head house
(2) A means of egress at the end of all galleries and similar spaces, thereby eliminating dead ends
(3) A means of escape provided to eliminate dead ends in underground areas

Subsection 42.7.2 requires that one means of egress from the head house must be an enclosed stair. The alternate means of egress can be either an outside stair or a basket ladder–type fire escape connecting all working levels and leading to either the ground or the top of an adjoining structure that complies with 42.7.3.

The principal hazard of elevator storage structures that handle combustible materials is dust explosion. A dust explosion can be violent enough to damage or destroy the primary means of egress required in 42.7.2.

It is not the intent of 42.7.2 to require a fully dusttight shaft, because the door will allow passage of limited amounts of dust during the normal course of daily operations. However, the shaft should be separated from the operating areas by fire resistance–rated construction and should be as free of dust as possible.

Section 42.8 Special Provisions for Parking Structures

42.8.1 General Requirements.

42.8.1.1* Application. The following provisions shall apply to parking structures of the closed or open type, above or below ground, but shall not apply to mechanical or exclusively attendant-type parking facilities that are not occupied by customers. The requirements of Sections 42.1 through 42.7 shall not apply.

A.42.8.1.1 For further information on garages, including a definition of open garage, see NFPA 88A, *Standard for Parking Structures.*

The intent of the special provisions for garages is to provide adequate life safety for the patrons of parking facilities, who probably will be unfamiliar with the garage and its arrangement. Where parking attendants are the only occupants that enter the parking area, the *Code*'s intent is to provide exits in accordance with the previous sections of Chapter 42. In such instances, the provisions for ordinary hazard contents storage occupancies apply.

Section 42.8 is self-contained and, therefore, independent of Sections 42.1 through 42.7, which apply to other storage occupancies. However, Section 42.8 does reference other portions of the *Code*, mainly Chapters 1 through 7.

For further information on garages, see NFPA 88A, *Standard for Parking Structures.*[4]

42.8.1.2 Mixed Occupancies.

42.8.1.2.1 Where both parking and repair operations are conducted in the same building, the entire building shall comply with Chapter 40.

Exception: If the parking and repair sections are separated by not less than 1-hour fire-rated construction, the parking and repair sections shall be permitted to be treated separately.

The exception to 42.8.1.2.1 allows a building to house parking and repair operations simultaneously and permits such operations to be treated independently if they are separated by 1-hour fire resistance–rated construction. The repair operation would be governed by the provisions of Chapter 40 and the parking facilities by those of Section 42.8. Guidelines for the rating of construction assemblies can be found in NFPA 220, *Standard on Types of Building Construction.*[5] Special requirements for repair garages can be found in NFPA 88B, *Standard for Repair Garages.*[6]

42.8.1.2.2 In areas where repair operations are conducted, the means of egress shall comply with Chapter 40.

42.8.1.3 Special Definition.

   Open-Air Parking Structure. See 3.3.139.

The definition of the term *open-air parking structure* (see 3.3.139) specifies uniform distribution of openings with respect to the minimum number of exterior walls, the minimum percentage of overall building lineal perimeter, and the minimum percentage of total wall area per level. Parking structures that meet the definition of open-air parking structure provide sufficient area in exterior walls to vent the products of combustion to a greater degree than an enclosed parking structure. Open-air parking structures—as contrasted with enclosed parking structures—are permitted to use vehicle ramps as a second means of egress, have longer travel distance allowances, and are exempt from the alarm system requirement. See Exception No. 1 to 42.8.2.2.6.1, Exception No. 1 to 42.8.2.6, and Exception No. 1 to 42.8.3.4.1.

42.8.1.4 Classification of Occupancy. Incidental vehicle parking in another occupancy shall not be the basis for overall occupancy classification.

42.8.1.5 Classification of Hazard of Contents. Parking structures used only for the storage of vehicles shall be classified as ordinary hazard in accordance with Section 6.2.

Paragraph 42.8.1.5 appropriately classifies the hazard of contents as ordinary hazard for garages used only for the storage of vehicles. With the increased use of plastic materials in vehicle bodies and interiors, a garage presents a hazard greater than that of low

hazard contents as defined by the hazard of contents classifications specified in Section 6.2.

42.8.1.6 Minimum Construction Requirements. (No requirements.)

42.8.1.7 Occupant Load. (No requirements.)

42.8.2 Means of Egress Requirements.

42.8.2.1 General. Means of egress shall be in accordance with Chapter 7 and this section.

42.8.2.2 Means of Egress Components.

42.8.2.2.1 Components of means of egress shall be limited to the types described in 42.8.2.2.2 through 42.8.2.2.9.

42.8.2.2.2 Doors.

42.8.2.2.2.1 Doors complying with 7.2.1 shall be permitted.

42.8.2.2.2.2 Special locking arrangements complying with 7.2.1.6 shall be permitted.

The requirement of 42.8.2.2.2.2 permits the delayed-egress release lock described in 7.2.1.6.1, which requires that the building be protected throughout by automatic sprinklers or a complete fire detection system.

42.8.2.2.2.3 An opening for the passage of automobiles shall be permitted to serve as an exit from a street floor, provided that no door or shutter is installed therein.

42.8.2.2.3 Stairs.

42.8.2.2.3.1 Stairs complying with 7.2.2 shall be permitted.

42.8.2.2.3.2 Existing winders complying with 7.2.2.2.4 shall be permitted.

42.8.2.2.3.3 Exception No. 2 to 7.2.2.4.6(3) shall not apply to guards for parking garages that are accessible to the general public.

42.8.2.2.4 Smokeproof Enclosures. Smokeproof enclosures complying with 7.2.3 shall be permitted.

42.8.2.2.5 Horizontal Exits. Horizontal exits complying with 7.2.4 shall be permitted.

42.8.2.2.6 Ramps.

42.8.2.2.6.1 Ramps complying with 7.2.5 shall be permitted and shall not be subject to normal vehicular traffic where used as an exit.

Exception No. 1: In a ramp-type open-air parking structure with open vehicle ramps not subject to closure, the ramp shall be permitted to serve in lieu of the second means of egress from floors above the level of exit discharge, provided that the ramp discharges directly outside at the street level.

Exception No. 2: For parking structures extending only one floor level below the level of exit discharge, a vehicle ramp leading directly to the outside shall be permitted to serve in lieu of the second means of egress, provided that no door or shutter is installed therein.

42.8.2.2.6.2 Exception No. 2 to 7.2.2.4.6(3) shall not apply to guards for parking garages that are accessible to the general public.

Exception No. 1 and Exception No. 2 to 42.8.2.2.6.1 permit the use of vehicle ramps as part of the means of egress. Properly arranged ramps can facilitate safe egress to a degree well in excess of that required for the given number of occupants.

Exception No. 1 allows consideration of ramps in open-air parking structures as an alternate secondary means of egress from floors located above the street level where they are arranged to provide clear and unobstructed discharge to the street level. Ramps from floors located above the street level are required to be open and must not be enclosed by walls or other means that will confine smoke and heat in the ramp structure. Ramps located in closed garages—except those addressed by Exception No. 2 to 42.8.2.2.6.1—cannot be considered as part of the egress system, and normal means of egress (specified in 42.8.2.2) needs to be provided.

Exception No. 2 allows a ramp to be used as an alternate secondary means of egress in a garage that extends not more than one floor level below the level of exit discharge. The ramp must not have a door or a shutter and must lead directly outside.

42.8.2.2.7 Exit Passageways. Exit passageways complying with 7.2.6 shall be permitted.

42.8.2.2.8 Fire Escape Stairs. Fire escape stairs complying with 7.2.8 shall be permitted for existing parking structures only.

42.8.2.2.9 Areas of Refuge. Areas of refuge complying with 7.2.12 shall be permitted.

42.8.2.3 Capacity of Means of Egress. *(See also 42.8.2.4 and 42.8.2.5.)*

42.8.2.4 Number of Means of Egress. *(See also Section 7.4.)*

42.8.2.4.1 Not less than two means of egress shall be provided from every floor or section of every parking structure.

Note that there is no single-exit exception to the two-exit rule for parking garages.

42.8.2.4.2 Floors or portions thereof with an occupant load of more than 500 persons shall have the minimum number of separate and remote means of egress specified by 7.4.1.2.

Exception: Existing buildings.

42.8.2.5 Arrangement of Means of Egress. *(See also Section 7.5.)*

42.8.2.5.1 Means of egress shall be arranged so that, from any point in the parking structure, the paths of travel to the two exits are in different directions.

Exception: A common path of travel shall be permitted for the first 50 ft (15 m) from any point in the parking structure.

42.8.2.5.2 Dead ends shall not exceed 50 ft (15 m).

42.8.2.5.3 If fuel-dispensing devices are located within a parking structure, travel away from the fuel-dispensing device in any direction shall lead to an exit with no dead end in which occupants might be trapped by fire. Within closed parking structures, exits shall be arranged and located to meet the following additional requirements:

(1) Exits shall lead to the outside of the building on the same level or to stairs; no upward travel shall be permitted unless direct outside exits are available from that floor.
(2) Any story below that story at which fuel is being dispensed shall have exits leading directly to the outside via outside stairs or doors at ground level.

Subparagraph 42.8.2.5.3 specifies the conditions required for protection of the occupants of parking garages from fires that might be caused by gasoline-dispensing operations located inside the building. Additional provisions apply where gasoline-dispensing takes place in enclosed parking structures. Subpart (2) requires that direct access to the outside be provided from floors located below those on which gasoline is dispensed. This requirement prevents gasoline vapors, which are heavier than air, from accumulating in enclosed portions of a means of egress, such as inside exit stairways.

The hazards associated with dispensing gasoline inside buildings are avoided by dispensing fuel outdoors, as in the case of ordinary gasoline filling stations. See NFPA 30A, *Automotive and Marine Service Station Code,* for requirements on dispensing gasoline indoors.[7]

42.8.2.6 Travel Distance to Exits. Means of egress in parking structures shall be arranged so that no point is more than 150 ft (45 m), measured in accordance with Section 7.6, from the nearest exit.

Exception No. 1: Travel distance shall not exceed 300 ft (91 m) for open floors of nonsprinklered, open-air parking structures or 400 ft (120 m) in open-air parking structures protected throughout by an approved, supervised automatic sprinkler system.

Exception No. 2: Travel distance shall not exceed 200 ft (60 m) for enclosed parking structures protected throughout by an approved automatic sprinkler system in accordance with Section 9.7.

Exception No. 3: Travel distance in parking structures open not less than 50 percent on all sides shall not exceed 400 ft (120 m).

42.8.2.7 Discharge from Exits. Exit discharge shall comply with Section 7.7.

42.8.2.8 Illumination of Means of Egress. Parking structures shall be provided with illumination of means of egress in accordance with Section 7.8.

Exception: Structures occupied only during daylight hours, arranged to provide the required level of illumination of all portions of the means of egress by natural means, shall not require artificial illumination where permitted by the authority having jurisdiction.

42.8.2.9 Emergency Lighting. Parking structures shall be provided with emergency lighting in accordance with Section 7.9.

Exception: In structures occupied only during daylight hours, arranged to provide the required level of illumination of all portions of the means of egress by natural means, emergency lighting shall not be required.

42.8.2.10 Marking of Means of Egress. Means of egress shall have signs in accordance with Section 7.10.

42.8.2.11 Special Means of Egress Features. (Reserved.)

42.8.3 Protection.

42.8.3.1 Protection of Vertical Openings. (No requirements.)

42.8.3.2 Protection from Hazards. (No requirements.)

42.8.3.3 Interior Finish.

42.8.3.3.1 Interior finish shall be in accordance with Section 10.2.

42.8.3.3.2 Interior Wall and Ceiling Finish. Interior wall and ceiling finish complying with 10.2.3 shall be Class A, Class B, or Class C in parking structures and shall be as required by 7.1.4 in exit enclosures.

42.8.3.3.3 Interior Floor Finish. (No requirements.)

42.8.3.4 Detection, Alarm, and Communications Systems.

42.8.3.4.1 General. Parking structures exceeding an aggregate floor area of 100,000 ft² (9300 m²) shall be provided with a fire alarm system in accordance with Section 9.6.

Exception No. 1: Open-air parking structures.

Exception No. 2: Parking structures protected throughout by an approved automatic sprinkler system in accordance with Section 9.7.

42.8.3.4.2 Initiation. Initiation of the required fire alarm system shall be by manual means in accordance with 9.6.2.1(1).

Exception: Initiation shall be permitted by means of an approved automatic fire detection system in accordance with 9.6.2.1(2) that provides protection throughout the building.

42.8.3.4.3 Notification.

42.8.3.4.3.1 The required fire alarm system shall sound an audible alarm in a continuously attended location for purposes of initiating emergency action.

42.8.3.4.3.2 Positive alarm sequence in accordance with 9.6.3.4 shall be permitted.

42.8.3.4.3.3 Existing presignal systems in accordance with 9.6.3.3 shall be permitted.

42.8.3.5 Extinguishing Requirements. (None.)

42.8.3.6 Corridors. The provisions of 7.1.3.1 shall not apply.

42.8.4 Special Provisions.

42.8.4.1 High-Rise Buildings. (No requirements.)

42.8.5 Building Services.

42.8.5.1 Utilities. Utilities shall comply with the provisions of Section 9.1.

42.8.5.2 Heating, Ventilating, and Air Conditioning. Heating, ventilating, and air conditioning equipment shall comply with the provisions of Section 9.2, except as otherwise required in Section 42.8.

42.8.5.3 Elevators, Escalators, and Conveyors. Elevators, escalators, and conveyors shall comply with the provisions of Section 9.4.

42.8.5.4 Rubbish Chutes, Incinerators, and Laundry Chutes. Rubbish chutes, incinerators, and laundry chutes shall comply with the provisions of Section 9.5.

References Cited in Commentary

1. NFPA 13, *Standard for the Installation of Sprinkler Systems,* 1999 edition, National Fire Protection Association, Quincy, MA.
2. NFPA 30, *Flammable and Combustible Liquids Code,* 1996 edition, National Fire Protection Association, Quincy, MA.
3. NFPA 409, *Standard on Aircraft Hangars,* 1995 edition, National Fire Protection Association, Quincy, MA.
4. NFPA 88A, *Standard for Parking Structures,* 1998 edition, National Fire Protection Association, Quincy, MA.
5. NFPA 220, *Standard on Types of Building Construction,* 1999 edition, National Fire Protection Association, Quincy, MA.
6. NFPA 88B, *Standard for Repair Garages,* 1997 edition, National Fire Protection Association, Quincy, MA.
7. NFPA 30A, *Automotive and Marine Service Station Code,* 1996 edition, National Fire Protection Association, Quincy, MA.

ANNEX A

Explanatory Material

The material contained in Annex A of the 2000 edition of the *Life Safety Code* is not a part of the requirements of the *Code* but is included with the *Code* for informational purposes only. For the convenience of readers, in this handbook the Annex A material is interspersed among the verbiage of Chapters 1 through 42 and, therefore, is not repeated here.

ANNEX B

Nonmandatory Referenced Publications

Note that the mandatory referenced publications appear in Chapter 2. Many of the documents shown in Annex B also appear in Chapter 2, and although shown here for advisory purposes, they remain mandatory in the body of the *Code* (Chapters 1 through 42).

B-1

The following documents or portions thereof are referenced within this *Code* for informational purposes only and are thus not considered part of the requirements of this *Code* unless also listed in Chapter 2. The edition indicated here for each reference is the current edition as of the date of the NFPA issuance of this *Code*.

B-1.1 NFPA Publications.

National Fire Protection Association, 1 Batterymarch Park, P.O. Box 9101, Quincy, MA 02269-9101.

NFPA 10, *Standard for Portable Fire Extinguishers,* 1998 edition.

NFPA 11, *Standard for Low-Expansion Foam,* 1998 edition.

NFPA 12, *Standard on Carbon Dioxide Extinguishing Systems,* 2000 edition.

NFPA 12A, *Standard on Halon 1301 Fire Extinguishing Systems,* 1997 edition.

NFPA 13, *Standard for the Installation of Sprinkler Systems,* 1999 edition.

NFPA 13D, *Standard for the Installation of Sprinkler Systems in One- and Two-Family Dwellings and Manufactured Homes,* 1999 edition.

NFPA 13R, *Standard for the Installation of Sprinkler Systems in Residential Occupancies up to and Including Four Stories in Height,* 1999 edition.

NFPA 14, *Standard for the Installation of Standpipe, Private Hydrant, and Hose Systems,* 2000 edition.

NFPA 15, *Standard for Water Spray Fixed Systems for Fire Protection,* 1996 edition.

NFPA 17, *Standard for Dry Chemical Extinguishing Systems,* 1998 edition.

NFPA 22, *Standard for Water Tanks for Private Fire Protection,* 1998 edition.

NFPA 30, *Flammable and Combustible Liquids Code,* 1996 edition.

NFPA 58, *Liquefied Petroleum Gas Code,* 1998 edition.

NFPA 61, *Standard for the Prevention of Fires and Dust Explosions in Agricultural and Food Products Facilities,* 1999 edition.

NFPA 68, *Guide for Venting of Deflagrations,* 1998 edition.

NFPA 70, *National Electrical Code®,* 1999 edition.

NFPA 72, *National Fire Alarm Code®,* 1999 edition.

NFPA 80, *Standard for Fire Doors and Fire Windows,* 1999 edition.

NFPA 88A, *Standard for Parking Structures,* 1998 edition.

NFPA 90A, *Standard for the Installation of Air-Conditioning and Ventilating Systems,* 1999 edition.

NFPA 92A, *Recommended Practice for Smoke-Control Systems,* 1996 edition.

NFPA 92B, *Guide for Smoke Management Systems in Malls, Atria, and Large Areas,* 1995 edition.

NFPA 99, *Standard for Health Care Facilities,* 1999 edition.

NFPA 101A, *Guide on Alternative Approaches to Life Safety,* 1998 edition.

NFPA 105, *Recommended Practice for the Installation of Smoke-Control Door Assemblies,* 1999 edition.

NFPA 110, *Standard for Emergency and Standby Power Systems,* 1999 edition.

NFPA 170, *Standard for Fire Safety Symbols,* 1999 edition.

NFPA 204, *Guide for Smoke and Heat Venting,* 1998 edition.

NFPA 211, *Standard for Chimneys, Fireplaces, Vents, and Solid Fuel-Burning Appliances,* 2000 edition.

NFPA 220, *Standard on Types of Building Construction,* 1999 edition.

NFPA 241, *Standard for Safeguarding Construction, Alteration, and Demolition Operations,* 1996 edition.

NFPA 251, *Standard Methods of Tests of Fire Endurance of Building Construction and Materials,* 1999 edition.

NFPA 253, *Standard Method of Test for Critical Radiant Flux of Floor Covering Systems Using a Radiant Heat Energy Source,* 2000 edition.

NFPA 255, *Standard Method of Test of Surface Burning Characteristics of Building Materials,* 2000 edition.

NFPA 259, *Standard Test Method for Potential Heat of Building Materials,* 1998 edition.

NFPA 260, *Standard Methods of Tests and Classification System for Cigarette Ignition Resistance of Components of Upholstered Furniture,* 1998 edition.

NFPA 261, *Standard Method of Test for Determining Resistance of Mock-Up Upholstered Furniture Material Assemblies to Ignition by Smoldering Cigarettes,* 1998 edition.

NFPA 265, *Standard Methods of Fire Tests for Evaluating Room Fire Growth Contribution of Textile Wall Coverings,* 1998 edition.

NFPA 266, *Standard Method of Test for Fire Characteristics of Upholstered Furniture Exposed to Flaming Ignition Source,* 1998 edition.

NFPA 267, *Standard Method of Test for Fire Characteristics of Mattresses and Bedding Assemblies Exposed to Flaming Ignition Source,* 1998 edition.

NFPA 269, *Standard Test Method for Developing Toxic Potency Data for Use in Fire Hazard Modeling,* 2000 edition.

NFPA 286, *Standard Methods of Fire Tests for Evaluating Contribution of Wall and Ceiling Interior Finish to Room Fire Growth,* 2000 edition.

NFPA 307, *Standard for the Construction and Fire Protection of Marine Terminals, Piers, and Wharves,* 1995 edition.

NFPA 409, *Standard on Aircraft Hangars,* 1995 edition.

NFPA 501A, *Standard for Fire Safety Criteria for Manufactured Home Installations, Sites, and Communities,* 1999 edition.

NFPA 601, *Standard for Security Services in Fire Loss Prevention,* 2000 edition.

NFPA 701, *Standard Methods of Fire Tests for Flame Propagation Textiles and Films,* 1999 edition.

NFPA 705, *Recommended Practice for a Field Flame Test for Textiles and Films,* 1997 edition.

NFPA 914, *Recommended Practice for Fire Protection in Historic Structures,* 1994 edition.

NFPA 1221, *Standard for the Installation, Maintenance, and Use of Emergency Services Communications Systems,* 1999 edition.

NFPA 2001, *Standard on Clean Agent Fire Extinguishing Systems,* 2000 edition.

NFPA, *Fire Protection Handbook,* 18th edition, 1997.

NFPA SPP-53, *Smoke Control in Fire Safety Design,* Butcher and Parnell.

B-1.2 Other Publications.

ACI 2/6R, *Guide for Determining the Fire Endurance of Concrete Elements,* American Concrete Institute, P.O. Box 9094, Farmington Hills, MI 48333.

ADAAG Americans with Disabilities Act Accessibility Guidelines.

AISI, *Designing Fire Protection for Steel Beams,* American Iron and Steel Institute, 1011 17th Street, NW, 13th floor, Washington, DC 20036.

AISI, *Designing Fire Protection for Steel Columns,* American Iron and Steel Institute, 1011 17th Street, NW, 13th floor, Washington, DC 20036.

AISI, *Designing Fire Protection for Steel Trusses,* American Iron and Steel Institute, 1011 17th Street, NW, 13th floor, Washington, DC 20036.

American Forest & Paper Association, *Design of Fire-Resistive Exposed Wood Members,* American Forest & Paper Association, 1111 19th Street, NW, Suite 800, Washington, DC 20036.

ANSI/BHMA A156.10, *American National Standard for Power Operated Pedestrian Doors,* American National Standards Institute, Inc., 11 West 42nd Street, 13th floor, New York, NY 10036.

ANSI/BHMA A156.19, *American National Standard for Power Assist & Low Energy Power Operated Doors,*

American National Standards Institute, Inc., 11 West 42nd Street, 13th floor, New York, NY 10036.

ASHRAE *Guideline 5: Guideline for Commissioning Smoke Management Systems,* American Society of Heating, Refrigerating and Air Conditioning Engineers, Inc., 1791 Tullie Circle, NE, Atlanta, GA 30329-2305.

ASHRAE Handbook and Product Directory— Fundamentals, American Society of Heating, Refrigerating and Air Conditioning Engineers, Inc., 1791 Tullie Circle, NE, Atlanta, GA 30329-2305.

ASME/ANSI A17.1-1993, *Safety Code for Elevators and Escalators,* American National Standards Institute, Inc., 11 West 42nd Street, 13th floor, New York, NY 10036.

ASME A17.3-1993, *Safety Code for Existing Elevators and Escalators,* American National Standards Institute, Inc., 11 West 42nd Street, 13th floor, New York, NY 10036.

ASTM E 814-83, *Methods for Fire Tests of Through-Penetration Fire Stops,* American Society for Testing and Materials, 100 Barr Harbor Drive, West Conshohocken, PA 19428-2959.

ASTM E 1355, *Standard Guide for Evaluating the Predictive Capability of Fire Models,* American Society for Testing and Materials, 100 Barr Harbor Drive, West Conshohocken, PA 19428-2959.

ASTM E 1537, *Standard Method of Fire Testing of Real Scale Upholstered Furniture Items,* American Society of Testing and Materials, 100 Barr Harbor Drive, West Conshohocken, PA 19428-2959.

ASTM E 1590, *Standard Method for Fire Testing of Real Scale Mattresses,* American Society of Testing and Materials, 100 Barr Harbor Drive, West Conshohocken, PA 19428-2959.

ASTM F 1637, *Standard Practice for Safe Walking Surfaces,* American Society for Testing and Materials, 100 Barr Harbor Drive, West Conshohocken, PA 19428-2959.

ASTM 1472, *Standard Guide for Documenting Computer Software,* American Society for Testing and Materials, 100 Barr Harbor Drive, West Conshohocken, PA 19428-2959.

Australian Fire Engineering Guidelines, Fire Code Reform Centre, Limited, Sydney, Australia, 1996.

British Standard Firesafety Engineering in Buildings, DD240: Part 1, British Standards Institution, London, England, 1997.

CABO/ANSI A117.1-1992, *American National Standard for Accessible and Usable Buildings and Facilities,* American National Standards Institute, Inc., 11 West 42nd Street, 13th floor, New York, NY 10036.

16 *CFR* 1632.

16 *CFR* 1630, *Standard for the Surface Flammability of Carpets and Rugs,* FF 1-70.

28 *CFR* 31, Appendix A, Section 4.28, Alarms.

28 *CFR* 36, Appendix A, Sections 9.1.3, 9.1.5 and 9.2.2(8).

CMIFC, *Analytical Methods of Determining Fire Endurance of Concrete and Masonry Members—Model Code Approved Procedures,* Concrete and Masonry Industry Firesafety Committee, 5420 Old Orchard Road, Skokie, IL 60077-4321.

CRSI, *Reinforced Concrete Fire Resistance,* Concrete Reinforcing Steel Institute, 933 N. Plum Grove Road, Schaumburg, IL 60173-4753.

FF4-72, *Standard for the Flammability of Mattresses.*

Gann et al., *Fire and Materials,* 18 193 (1994).

Groner, N. E., and Levin, M. L. "Human Factors Considerations in the Potential for Using Elevators in Building Emergency Evacuation Plans," National Institute of Standards and Technology, NIST-GCR-92-615, 1992.

Kaplan et al., *Journal of Fire Science,* 2, 286–305 (1984).

Klote, J. H., and Milke, J. A., *Design of Smoke Management Systems,* American Society of Heating, Refrigerating and Air Conditioning Engineers, Inc., 1791 Tullie Circle, NE, Atlanta, GA 30329-2305.

Levin, B. M., and Groner, N. E., "Human Behavior Aspects of Staging Areas for Fire Safety in GSA Buildings," National Institute of Standards and Technology, NIST-GCR-92-606, 1992.

Levin, B. M., and Groner, N. E., "Human Factors Considerations for the Potential Use of Elevators for Fire Evacuation of FAA Air Traffic Control Towers," National Institute of Standards and Technology, NIST-GCR-94-656, 1994.

National Building Code, Building Officials and *Code* Administrators International, Inc., 4051 West Flossmoor Road, Country Club Hills, IL 60478-5795.

OSHA *Regulations for Emergency Procedures and Fire Brigades,* 29 *CFR* 1910, Subparts E and L, Occupational Safety & Health Administration, Office of Administrative Services, 200 Constitution Ave., NW, Rm 5452, Washington, DC 20210.

PCI, *Design for Fire Resistance of Precast Prestressed Concrete,* Precast Prestressed Concrete Institute, 175 West Jackson Blvd., Chicago, IL 60604.

SFPE Engineering Guide to Performance-Based Fire Protection Analysis and Design of Buildings, Society of Fire Protection Engineers, Bethesda, MD, 1998.

SFPE Handbook of Fire Protection Engineering, National Fire Protection Association, 1 Batterymarch Park, P. O. Box 9101, Quincy, MA 02269-9101, 2nd edition.

Standard Building Code, Southern Building Code Congress International, Inc., 900 Montclair Road, Birmingham, AL 35213-1206.

Templer, J. A., *The Staircase: Studies of Hazards, Falls, and Safer Design,* Cambridge, MA: MIT Press, 1992.

Uniform Building Code, 5360 South Workman Mill Road, Whittier, CA 90601.

UBC, *Methods for Calculating Fire Resistance of Wood-Framed Walls, Floors and Roofs,* Uniform Building Code, 5360 South Workman Mill Road, Whittier, CA 90601.

UL *Fire Resistance Directory,* Underwriters Laboratories Inc., 333 Pfingsten Road, Northbrook, IL 60062.

UL 1975, *Standard for Fire Tests for Foamed Plastics Used for Decorative Purposes,* Underwriters Laboratories Inc., 333 Pfingsten Road, Northbrook, IL 60062.

UL 2079, *Test for Fire Resistance of Building Joint Systems,* 1st edition, 1994, Underwriters Laboratories Inc., 333 Pfingsten Road, Northbrook, IL 60062.

PART TWO

Supplements

The seven supplements collected in Part Two of this handbook were written by recognized experts in the fields they cover. Printed in black within a green box, these supplements are not part of the *Code* or the commentary. They present additional, useful information about specialized subjects in more depth than is allowed by the *Code*-and-commentary format of this handbook. The supplements give case histories of fires that influenced the *Life Safety Code*; provide an overview of how fire alarm, sprinkler, elevator, and fire test requirements interact with the requirements found in NFPA *101*; guide the user in adopting the *Life Safety Code* into law; and bring the reader up to date on the issue of building security versus life safety. Much like the commentary, the supplements are intended to provide useful guidance for *Code* users.

SUPPLEMENT 1

Case Histories: Fires Influencing the *Life Safety Code*

Paul E. Teague, M.A.

Codes and standards are living documents. Born of the efforts of men and women to make their environment safer, codes and standards grow into maturity based on fire experience and the observations and research of those responsible for them. The best codes and standards, such as those produced by NFPA, never age, as they are continually updated with new information that allows them to adapt to an ever-changing world.

Such is the case with NFPA *101, Life Safety Code*. Originally known as the *Building Exits Code*, it had its origins in the effort to make factories safer for workers in the early days of this century. Its first focus was on the hazards of stairways and fire escapes, the need for fire drills in various occupancies, and the construction and arrangement of exits.

However, as American society changed, technology blossomed, and fire experience accumulated, the *Code* grew in scope. It began to include provisions for sprinklers, alarm and detection systems, protection of interior finish, and other important features. Of the thousands of fires whose lessons are reflected in this latest edition of the *Code*, probably none has had a bigger impact than the Triangle Shirtwaist fire of March 25, 1911. It was that fire that prompted creation of NFPA's Committee on Safety to Life and, ultimately, development of the *Code* itself.

TRIANGLE SHIRTWAIST FIRE

Since its founding in 1896, the NFPA has always placed special importance on its life safety work. NFPA's original objectives, "establishing proper safeguards against loss of life and property by fire," placed life safety ahead of property protection. Yet, until the Triangle Shirtwaist fire there was not one technical committee devoted exclusively to life safety concerns.

The Triangle Shirtwaist Company was located on the eighth, ninth, and tenth floors of the Asch Building at the intersection of Washington Place and Green Street in New York City's Washington Square. The building was a "loft," typical of many in its day. The Triangle Company, with more than 500 employees, was reportedly the largest business of its kind in the city. Most of the employees were young women, many of them recent immigrants, who worked six days a week in cramped and dirty quarters.

Numerous Fire Hazards

New York City law at the time required buildings 11 stories and higher to have stone floors and metal window frames. The Asch Building was only ten stories high and was constructed with wood floors, wood trim, and wood window frames. Unsafe as they were, these features of the building's construction were only part of the fire danger that workers unwittingly faced every day.

Buildings with 10,000 ft² of floor space per floor were required to have three staircases per floor. The Asch Building had two. The building's architect had pleaded for approval of two staircases, because there was also an outside fire escape that could be reached by windows on each floor. The fire escape terminated at the second floor, not at the ground.

Labor laws in effect at the time required that factory doors open outward, *if practical*. The architect claimed it was not practical in the Asch Building, because each landing was only one stair width from the door. All doors had to open inward.

Those same labor laws required that factory doors be kept unlocked during the workday. Doors at the Triangle Company reportedly were usually locked during the workday to keep track of the workers and prevent them from stealing material.

Rags consisting of cutaway cloth materials regularly accumulated on the floors at the Triangle Company. At the time of the fire, the rags had not been removed for about two months. When last collected, an accumulation of 2252 pounds of rags had been removed.

The Triangle workers were crowded together on the top three floors of the Asch Building. Aisles leading to exits were narrow and obstructed. Partitions were placed in front of doors and elevators. A fire insurance inspector had recommended in 1909 that the company keep the doors unlocked during the workday and conduct fire drills. The Triangle owners took no action on those recommendations.

Fire Begins in the Rags. No NFPA investigative report was written on the Triangle Shirtwaist fire, but two books describe the horror that took place: *The Triangle Shirtwaist Fire* (Franklin Watts, Inc., 1971), by Corinne Naden, and *The Triangle Fire*, by Leon Stein (J. B. Lippincott, 1962). The descriptions of the building and the fire reported here are summarized from these two books.

It was near quitting time on March 25, 1911, when one of the workers on the eighth floor noticed smoke coming from one of the rag bins. A fire in a rag bin was reportedly not unusual, but this fire spread with astonishing speed, despite the attempts of supervisors to extinguish it using pails of water. The fire spread from the rags to cutting tables and then to cloth patterns hanging on wire above the tables. In no time, flames consumed the wood floor trim, the sewing tables, and partitions and then spread to the ceiling.

Workers on the eighth floor rushed for the doors. One door was locked. When workers finally got it unlocked, it opened inward. The panicked workers piled up against the door, making it difficult for those who arrived first to open it. Eventually, they were able to open the door, and workers rushed into the stairway. However, some fell at the seventh floor level, and those behind piled up until there was no more room in the stairway. A policeman, who had seen the fire from the street, saw the pile-up as he ran up the stairs to help. He untangled the pile-up, and about 125 workers escaped down that stairway.

Other workers frantically rang for the elevators.

However, the elevators had been summoned to the tenth floor, where the executive offices were located, so, at first, they didn't stop on the eighth floor. When they did stop, workers crowded into them, one on top of another. The elevators made so many trips to save workers on the eighth and tenth floors that the operators were overcome by smoke and exhaustion.

Some workers on the eighth floor climbed out the windows to the narrow fire escape. At least one worker fell down the fire escape to the courtyard below. Others climbed down to the sixth floor, went back into the building through a window, and walked down the inside staircase.

On the eighth floor, a telephone was connected to the executive offices on the tenth floor. One of the workers called the tenth floor to report the fire. Someone on the tenth floor rang for the elevators, which at first bypassed the eighth and ninth floors to rescue people on the tenth floor. Many of the workers on the tenth floor escaped to the roof of the building, where they were rescued by law students from an adjacent building. Of the approximately 70 workers on that floor, only one died. That death occurred because the victim jumped from a window.

The only telephone communication to the ninth floor was through the tenth-floor switchboard. No one on the tenth floor notified the ninth-floor workers of the fire.

Ninth-Floor Workers Were the Last to Be Informed. There were about 260 workers on the ninth floor. There were also eight double rows of sewing machines on 75-ft-long tables that took up nearly the entire floor. The only way to leave the tables was to walk to the north end of the building. Workers sitting at the south end had to walk the entire length of the rows of tables to reach the area where the exits were located. Along the way, they had to negotiate around chairs, wicker baskets, and other items that obstructed the passageways.

When the quitting bell rang, one worker walked down one of the stairways to go home. When he reached the eighth floor, he saw it was in flames. He was the first ninth-floor worker to learn of the fire. Confused, he simply continued moving. By the time he thought of running back up the stairs to warn his coworkers, it was too late. He was unable to get back up the stairway.

The rest of the workers on the ninth floor learned of the fire when flames leaped through the windows. About 150 workers raced for the Green Street exit, and more than 100 of them made it down to the sidewalk. Other workers ran to the Washington Place exit, but it was locked. Some rushed for the fire escape. Jammed with people and hot from the fire, the fire escape pulled away from the building and partially collapsed, sending bodies flying to the courtyard below.

Many workers, including those who found the Washington Place exit locked, congregated at the elevators and summoned them. However, the elevators were already packed with people from the eighth and tenth floors. Some of the workers jumped or were pushed into the elevator shafts. A few slid down the cables, some landing on the roofs of the elevators.

To escape the searing heat and suffocating smoke, many of the workers climbed out to the window ledge and jumped to their death. The impact of their bodies was so great that it not only broke the fire department nets, but also smashed holes in the concrete and glass pavement.

The fire department arrived at the scene early but could do little except cool the exterior of the building. Its equipment was good for fighting fires only up to seven stories. In total, about 147 people died in the Triangle Shirtwaist fire.

Move for Reform

The Asch Building was a fire trap, but it was not the worst one in the city. In 1910, a public agency investigated conditions in 1243 coat and suit shops. Nine days before the Triangle Shirtwaist fire, a local New York City newspaper published excerpts from the agency's report. The report stated that 99 percent of the shops were deficient in safety. Many had only one exit, many others had locked doors during the workday, and 94 percent had doors that opened inward rather than outward.

Whether that report by itself would have generated remedial action is open to question. The dismal record of previous attempts by unions and others to mobilize action indicates that improvements would not likely have been made. The Triangle Shirtwaist fire, however, illustrated more than a report ever could the dangers lurking in lofts and other types of buildings.

In fact, the Triangle Shirtwaist fire aroused the nation and eventually revolutionized an industry. Unions, particularly the garment workers' union, intensified their activities to bring about improvements in working conditions for their members. Citizens of all economic classes in New York City banded together to work for safer factories, and politicians passed new laws to protect workers.

Almost immediately after the fire, New York City residents formed the Committee on Safety. Among its members was Frances Perkins, who later became

U.S. Secretary of Labor. The chairman was Henry Stimson, who soon left that position to become Secretary of War. He was succeeded as chairman by Henry Morgenthau. The committee became a focus for efforts to pass laws mandating improvements in factories and other buildings.

In June 1911, New York Governor John Alden Dix created the New York State Factory Investigating Commission to look into conditions in all factories and allocated the commission a $10,000 budget. Chairman of the commission was Robert Wagner, Sr., then a state senator. Samuel Gompers was also on the commission.

In October of the same year, the Sullivan–Hoey Law was passed, which established the New York City Fire Prevention Bureau, the first in the country, and expanded the powers of the fire commissioner.

NFPA Broadens Its Focus to Include Life Safety. NFPA members were shocked but not surprised by the fire. For years, they had warned of many of the dangers present in buildings like the Asch Building. In particular, they had warned about the problems of fire escapes. The April 1911 *NFPA Quarterly* stated that it had long been recognized that fire escapes were a "delusion." For a quarter of a century, fire escapes have "contributed the principal element of tragedy to all fires where panic resulted. Iron is quickly heated and expansion of the bolts, stays, and fastenings soon pulls the frame loose so that the weight of a single body may precipitate it into a street or alley."

At the NFPA Annual Meeting in May 1911, R. H. Newbern presented a paper on private fire departments and fire drills and referred to the value of drills in educating factory workers in procedures that help avoid panic and promote survival. A year later, Mr. Newbern's recommendations were published in a pamphlet titled "Exit Drills in Factories, Schools, Department Stores, and Theatres." This was the first safety-to-life publication produced by NFPA. However, there was still no specific NFPA committee devoted exclusively to life safety.

Formation of the Safety to Life Committee. At the 1913 NFPA Annual Meeting, President H. L. Phillips suggested to members that they could include "a section or committee having for its object the consideration of safety of life against accidents of every description." Later during that meeting, members listened to a speech titled "The Social and Human Cost of Fire" by Frances Perkins of the New York Committee on Safety. She urged them to study hazardous industries, publish the results, and publish rules that would make people in factories safe.

Perkins had witnessed the Triangle Shirtwaist fire. She saw workers leap from the ninth floor to the street below, and she was horrified. She told NFPA members that when she counted the social, human, and economic cost of that fire, she found it was enormous. "We lost not only those workers in the Triangle Shirtwaist fire," she said, "we lost their valuable services to society as economic factors. . . . It is because that social and human loss is to the entire community that this problem of fire deserves the closest attention of all people who are interested in the general progress and welfare of humanity. . . . Nothing is so important as human health and happiness . . . and if it costs dollars and cents to procure . . . then we must pay . . . and if it reduces profits we must reduce those profits. . . . You who are more or less technical . . . must help us by giving . . . the correct information . . . which we will be only too glad to use."

On June 23, 1913, NFPA's Executive Committee formed the Committee on Safety to Life and left it to this new committee to suggest the scope of its work. The July 1913 *Quarterly* stated that the formation of the committee was "the crystalization of a latent feeling which has for some time existed in the membership" for focusing attention on life safety.

The new committee, headed by H. W. Forster, spent the first few years studying fires involving loss of life and attempting to analyze the cause of that loss of life. At the 1914 Annual Meeting, the committee delivered its first report, which included a special section on egress, a statement that sprinklers can save lives, and preliminary specifications for outside fire escapes.

The committee said its studies showed that existing laws "are exceedingly deficient in this very important matter of egress. A number of states report frankly that they have no real legislation upon the subject."

The preliminary specifications for outside fire escapes were controversial and received a great deal of attention from the membership. The committee members did not like outside fire escapes, and many felt they were a delusion, as stated in the 1911 *Quarterly*. Nevertheless, the committee felt they had to face the fact that fire escapes existed and would be used.

"Admitting . . . that a fire escape on a building is usually an admission that life is not safe in it, the fact remains that the outside fire escape is the commonest special provision for escape . . . [and] this Association should determine upon proper precautions for such escapes, and use its influence to have them adopted and enforced," the committee wrote.

At the 1915 Annual Meeting, the NFPA adopted revised specifications for fire escapes. In 1916, the committee's work was published in a pamphlet, "Outside Stairs for Fire Exits." In 1918, another committee report was published in a pamphlet titled "Safeguarding Factory Workers from Fire." The pamphlets were widely circulated, put into general use, and, with other documents, form the basis of the present *Life Safety Code*.

In 1921, the Committee on Safety to Life was enlarged to include representation from interested groups not previously participating in its work. Work was started on the further development and integration of previous committee publications to provide a comprehensive guide to exits and related features of life safety from fires in all classes of occupancy. This work resulted in the publication in 1927 of the first edition of NFPA's *Building Exits Code*.

COCOANUT GROVE FIRE

As anyone involved in any safety endeavor will attest, it often takes a tragedy to alert society to dangers that must be addressed. The Triangle Shirtwaist fire moved the nation toward the prevention of many fire hazards. However, as time passes, the public forgets the lessons it learned and is forced to learn them once again through another tragedy. Thirty-one years after the Triangle Shirtwaist fire, in which locked exits trapped and doomed many workers, the United States witnessed another major fire in a building with locked exits.

The fire occurred in 1942 at the Cocoanut Grove, one of the most popular night clubs in Boston. It was a one-story-and-basement structure originally built in 1916. The original property was of reinforced concrete construction. Several additions had been made to the building, and a rolling roof had been installed over the dance floor.

State of Fire Protection: 1911 to 1942

There are many differences between the fires at the Triangle Shirtwaist Company and the Cocoanut Grove. One building was a high-rise factory, and the other was a single-story nightclub. The biggest difference lies in the state of the art of fire protection at the time. In 1911, when the Triangle Shirtwaist fire erupted, there were no universally recognized standards for exits. In 1942, when the Cocoanut Grove burned, those standards existed and were part of NFPA's *Building Exits Code*. Evidently, they were ignored.

Virtually all the hazards at the Cocoanut Grove were covered by the 1942 edition of the *Building Exits Code*. The main problems appear to have been the chaotic condition of Boston's building regulations and lax enforcement.

Four hundred and ninety-two people died in the fire. As the *Christian Science Monitor* said in an editorial after the fire, "action will be taken to prevent another Cocoanut Grove, and somebody could have taken action to prevent this one."

The late Robert S. Moulton, long-time NFPA Technical Secretary and Secretary to the Committee on Safety to Life, wrote a report on the fire that was widely circulated. Much of the information that follows comes from that report.

Fire Hazards in the Popular Night Spot

In 1942, the Broadway Cocktail Lounge was added to the Cocoanut Grove night club. The lounge was installed in a group of old brick-joisted buildings varying in height from two stories to three and one-half stories and was connected to the main property by a passageway and doorways leading to dressing rooms for entertainers.

The basement of the original structure contained the Melody Lounge, another cocktail area. The Melody Lounge had false walls made of light wooden frame covered with light wallboard. Decorations in the lounge included colorful fabrics, artificial leather on the walls, and cloth on the ceiling. In addition, there were imitation coconut palm trees in the lounge and in the main dining/dancing hall. Light fixtures were made from coconut shells, with the wiring concealed in the "foliage." These decorations had reportedly been flame-proofed.

No Easy Way Out. There was only one obvious exit from the Melody Lounge. It was a door at the top of the stairway that led to a narrow hallway on the first floor, then to a foyer and the main entrance. Another door, leading to an outside alley, was concealed behind the false walls of the lounge. It was locked. A door leading to the street from the narrow hallway at the head of the stairs to the Melody Lounge was equipped with panic hardware. This door was locked, however.

According to writer Paul Benzaquin in his book, *Holocaust* (Henry Holt and Company, 1959), there was also a passageway from the Melody Lounge to the kitchen, but it seems that only employees knew of this passageway. That door was painted and draped and unlikely to be seen by those who didn't know it was there. Nevertheless, it was counted as an exit by the city's fire commissioner in his post-fire report.

Many other doors were locked as well, and some opened inward. Many of the windows were obscured by the false walls, and the main doorway of the Cocoanut Grove was blocked by a revolving door.

A Capacity Crowd That Kept Getting Bigger. The official seating capacity of the nightclub was about 600 persons. No one knows exactly how many patrons were there the night of November 28, but unofficial estimates indicate that there were about 1000 people. Benzaquin reports that waiters were setting up more tables to accommodate additional patrons.

Overcrowding was not (and probably is still not) unusual in nightclubs. They are businesses established to make a profit, and the more patrons served, the greater the profit. Moulton said he was told the club was often congested, particularly on Saturday evenings.

According to Benzaquin, the club's application for a new license requested permission to install an additional 30 fixed stools for the new cocktail lounge. He writes that the stools were installed *before* permission was granted, on the assumption that there would be no objection.

That was probably a reasonable assumption. A member of the city's licensing board testified at the fire commissioner's hearing that the Cocoanut Grove got its original license and several renewals without any hearings to determine whether it complied with regulations.

The 12-Minute Fire. Benzaquin states in his book that the fire lasted about 12 minutes. It started in the Melody Lounge and was possibly ignited accidentally by a match held by a bus boy who was replacing a light bulb in one of the fake palm trees. As Moulton reported, however, the exact source of ignition was of less importance than the inadequacy of the exits and the extensive use of combustible decorations.

According to the fire commissioner's report, the fire immediately spread throughout the Melody Lounge along the underside of the false ceiling. Feeding on the combustible decorations, the fire reached and ascended the stairway and passed through the connecting passageway into the foyer, past the main entrance, and into the dining room and other areas of the club.

When the fire began to spread rapidly, panic ensued. Most of the patrons in the Melody Lounge raced for the stairway, their only obvious exit. Many died on those stairs. Those who escaped the basement lounge through the stairway piled up in the corridor while attempting to reach the main entrance. If the door from that corridor to the outside had been unlocked, many might have been saved.

Led by a few quick-thinking employees, a few patrons made their escape from the lounge by going through the concealed door to the kitchen area, and some of them escaped through a door to an alley outside. Others tried to get to the main floor but could not because of the heat. A few escaped through a basement window into a courtyard, and a few others survived the fire by seeking refuge in a large refrigerator.

Moulton wrote that about 100 people died at the Broadway entrance to the club, more than 190 ft from the stairway leading from the Melody Lounge, where the fire started. He reported that about 200 were trapped behind the revolving door at the main entrance. That revolving door, which under the best of conditions would slow exit travel, jammed and blocked the exit.

Lessons Learned

There were few "new" lessons to be learned from the Cocoanut Grove fire. Even before the Triangle Shirtwaist fire in 1911, the danger of locked, blocked, and concealed exits was known. The NFPA had publicized its views on exits and means of egress in pamphlet form after the Triangle Shirtwaist fire.

The 1942 *Building Exits Code* prohibited revolving doors as exits in places of assembly and required that other occupancies that used revolving doors must have swinging doors immediately adjacent or within 20 ft.

That same edition of the *Code* required that "decorations of theatres and assembly halls shall be of fire resistive or nonflammable materials. Fabrics and papers used for such purposes shall be treated with an effective flame-proofing material." A cautionary note warned, "Paper and cloth decorative materials should be kept to a minimum in places of assembly since such flimsy materials increase the hazard of the kindling and spread of fire."

The decorative materials in the Cocoanut Grove were supposedly flameproofed, but, if this were true, the flameproofing was ineffective. The fire did demonstrate, once again, that "fireproof" buildings, which was the status of the Cocoanut Grove when first erected, can still be death traps due to their contents. It also proved that fire inspections should be conducted when facilities are in operation. According to Moulton, the Boston building inspector reported that he had inspected the building and found the exits adequate. This might have been true

when the building was not crowded with 1000 people and the doors were unlocked.

"There is a real danger in attempting to remedy conditions such as were responsible for the Cocoanut Grove tragedy by the enactment of more laws," wrote Moulton. "In our opinion, building and fire officials can now do practically everything that is necessary to assure public safety from fire without any more laws."

Six months after the fire, at the 1943 NFPA Annual Meeting, Moulton reported to the membership that, due to the war, the Safety to Life Committee had been unable to meet. The committee members did exchange correspondence, however, and Moulton said they believed "our existing recommendations, that date back to 1913, are adequate."

Code Changes. There was one change involving the *Building Exits Code* that did come about immediately after and as a direct result of the Cocoanut Grove fire: The *Code* was adopted by many more jurisdictions across the country, due in large part to the efforts of the fire service. The Committee on Safety to Life reported on that increased usage at the 1945 NFPA Annual Meeting.

During the 1945 NFPA Annual Meeting, the Committee recommended a change in the method of exit measurement, clarification of the need for stairway enclosure, provisions covering loose chairs in nightclubs, and changes in lighting and signs. Those changes were incorporated into the 1946 edition of the *Code*, as was a special note on interior finish.

Interior Finish. While combustible decorations were a factor in the Cocoanut Grove fire, interior finish was becoming more and more of a fire problem in the 1940s. In 1946, the nation witnessed the LaSalle and Winecoff hotel fires. The latter, with 119 fatalities, was the largest multiple-death hotel fire up to that time during the twentieth century.

The Committee on Safety to Life was concerned about the dangers of combustible interior finish. Therefore, it recommended, and the full membership approved, a caution in the 1946 *Code*, which stated that "where interior finish materials are used having a higher combustibility, greater rate of fire spread, or potentialities of greater generation of smoke or fumes than wood, the exits specified in the *Code* may not be sufficient to provide adequate life safety from fire."

The lack of a standard way to measure the combustibility of interior finish hampered the committee. In the July 1943 *Quarterly*, A. J. Steiner of Underwriters

Laboratories described a new method he was developing to test the combustibility of interior finish. The Steiner Tunnel Test was recommended for adoption at the 1953 NFPA Annual Meeting by the NFPA Building Construction Committee. It was eventually incorporated into the *Building Exits Code*.

OUR LADY OF ANGELS SCHOOL FIRE

Combustible interior finish was one of the factors that led to fire spread at the Our Lady of Angels School in Chicago in December 1958. Wood trim in one corridor and combustible ceiling tile in classrooms in one wing (and perhaps in other areas of the building) provided fuel for this fire.

Avoidable Problem

The primary cause of loss of life, according to the NFPA investigative report of the fire, was *the inadequacy of the exit facilities*. As a result of this completely avoidable problem, 90 pupils and 3 nuns died.

Adequacy of exits, as determined by proper enclosure; provision of at least two exits remote from each other; and sufficient exit capacity were well-established fundamentals of fire protection by 1958. The Triangle Shirtwaist fire, the Cocoanut Grove fire, and hundreds of other fires had demonstrated the consequences of exits that were neglected. The 1958 edition of the *Building Exits Code* specified exact requirements for adequate exits and for other elements of school fire safety.

Chester I. Babcock, then manager of the NFPA fire records department, and Rex Wilson, then an NFPA engineer and currently a consultant, investigated the fire for the NFPA. A year later, Babcock wrote, "We know now and have known since before most of today's schools were built how to design and protect a school so that the lives of the pupils and teachers will be safe from fire. Refinements and improvements are needed and undoubtedly will come, but this does not mean that fire protection engineering has been groping for an answer. Practical methods of assuring life safety from fire that have stood the test of time and are based on sound fire protection engineering principles have been available for years."

One Fire Area. In 1953, the two-story school building was connected to another old, two-story, brick, wood-joisted building by a two-story, brick-joisted annex. The NFPA report of the fire stated that the building constituted one fire area, due to open stairways and the fact that the masonry division wall between the north wing and the annex had substandard doorway protection.

The stairways in the school were open except for two located in the front of the north wing. Those stairs were enclosed at the second-story level by substandard doors that were held open at the time of the fire. Because the three stairways from the second floor corridor of the north wing were connected through a common corridor, pupils in second-story classrooms, in effect, had no way out.

Origin of the Fire. About 2:25 p.m., one half-hour before school was normally dismissed, fire broke out in combustible materials at the bottom of the rear stairway of the north wing. Pupils from one of the second-floor classrooms had taken trash to the boiler room incinerator, as was their routine, returned to the classroom at 2:30 p.m., and reported that they had smelled smoke. Their teacher informed a teacher in a nearby room, who went to find the principal. When the principal could not be found, both teachers led their classes out of the building to the parish church. Smoke was already at head level in the second-floor corridor. Only after they had their classes settled in the church did one of the teachers run back to the school and operate the fire alarm signal.

The school's janitor noticed smoke and ran to the parish house to tell the housekeeper to call the fire department. Apparently, the housekeeper waited a few minutes before placing the call. The fire department reported that at about 2:42 p.m. it received the first of some 15 calls reporting the fire.

Hot fire gases and smoke billowed up the chimney-like stairwell and mushroomed through the second-story corridor. Eventually the hot gases and combustible interior finish in the corridor ignited. The heat broke the large glass transoms over the classroom doors, and the hot gases and flames entered the rooms.

Those Who Escaped and Those Who Did Not. As soon as the fire alarm rang, occupants of the first floor left the building by means of the five available stairways, according to the NFPA report. The evacuation of pupils in the second-floor annex and south wing was hampered by smoke that came through an open door in the division wall at that level. Either the janitor or a fire fighter closed the door.

Pupils in the second-floor north wing did not escape as easily. Their travel through the corridor to the stairways was blocked by heavy smoke and heat. Some jumped from their classroom windows. Others were taken down fire department ladders. Many died in their classrooms, some at their desks.

Aftermath of the Fire

One immediate effect of the Our Lady of Angels fire was a public awakening to the hazards in the nation's schools. According to Babcock's follow-up report a year after the fire, hazardous conditions had been eliminated in thousands of schools across the country.

Throughout this country's history, major improvements in safety have been made after terrible fires. The Iroquois Theater fire brought about improvements in theater safety; the Triangle Shirtwaist fire brought about improvements in factories; the Cocoanut Grove fire resulted in improvements in nightclubs; and the LaSalle, Winecoff, MGM Grand, Stouffer's, and DuPont Plaza fires resulted in improvements in hotels.

In 1959, the NFPA sampled more than 2000 fire departments to analyze the level of improvement made in school safety. Many had been made. Nearly every community had acted on such issues as frequent and improved exit drills, tighter control of waste disposal, inspections, and proper storage of combustible supplies. However, that same survey revealed that needed improvements had not been made in about 30,000 schools.

The NFPA conducted another informal telephone survey in 1978, twenty years after the fire. The consensus from that informal survey was that schools were safer. (Indeed, one respondent said they couldn't help but be safer than they were in 1958, when they were the "lousiest-constructed buildings in existence!") Unfortunately, they were not as safe as fire professionals had hoped. The passage of time and the growing concern with vandalism and security had blocked out the memories of the Our Lady of Angels tragedy.

LA School Fire Tests. The most publicized result of the fire was the fire test program conducted by the Los Angeles Fire Department. The tests, conducted under the direction of then Los Angeles Fire Marshal Raymond M. Hill, were designed to investigate methods of protecting multistory, open-stairway school buildings.

The tests were conducted in 1959 and 1960. One of the conclusions drawn from the tests was the fact that complete automatic sprinkler protection offered the best chance for escape.

The 1958 edition of the *Building Exits Code* provided for sprinklers in schools. The 1960 edition retained those provisions and totally reorganized the section of the *Code* covering educational occupancies. That edition classified schools as follows:

Group A: One-story buildings with exterior or interior access, or multistory buildings with access only by exterior balconies and outside stairs

Group B: Buildings of two stories or more with egress through corridors and interior stairways

Group C: Sprinklered buildings

Group D: Open-plan schools

Group E: Existing buildings

There were somewhat different requirements for each group.

A great deal of discussion took place among members of the Committee on Safety to Life in 1960 regarding whether they should recommend permitting open stairways in two-story sprinklered schools. The committee decided not to make this recommendation that year. The 1961 edition of the *Code*, however, did permit open stairs in sprinklered two-story schools. One reason for this decision was that committee members noted that, in two-story buildings, pupils constantly pass through the doors anyway.

In 1966, the year the *Building Exits Code* was reorganized and renamed the *Life Safety Code*, a provision was added that required all parts of school buildings below grade to be sprinklered. In addition, the allowable travel distance to the nearest exit was increased from 100 ft to 150 ft, under normal conditions, and up to 200 ft in sprinklered school buildings.

BEVERLY HILLS SUPPER CLUB FIRE

Those who study fires can't help but have a feeling of *déja vu.* It seems that the same fire problems return to haunt us time and again. Inadequate means of egress, lack of employee preparedness and training, and a general noncompliance with proven provisions of the *Life Safety Code* were all factors in the Triangle, Cocoanut Grove, and Our Lady of Angels fires, as well as in countless others.

These problems were critical factors again on May 28, 1977, at the Beverly Hills Supper Club. In a fire at the club, a public assembly occupancy that billed itself as "The Showplace of the Nation," 164 people died. The NFPA conducted an in-depth investigation of the fire, and much of what follows was taken from the investigative report prepared by Richard L. Best.

Fire Conditions in the Showplace of the Nation

The Beverly Hills was a glamorous nightclub in Southgate, Kentucky, just outside Cincinnati, Ohio. Banquets, dinner dances, balls, floor shows, fashion shows, weddings, wedding receptions, and business meetings were all held in the club's "18" function rooms.

The quotation marks around the number 18 represent the advertised number of function rooms. There were actually five main dining rooms, the large "Cabaret Room," a small function room called the "Zebra Room," and the main bar. Three of the large dining rooms could be subdivided into smaller rooms by the use of folding partitions.

There had been a wedding reception in the Zebra Room on the day of the fire. The wedding party had left at approximately 8:00 p.m. Performers were scheduled to entertain guests in the Cabaret Room around 8:30 p.m. There were an estimated 1200 to 1300 guests in the Cabaret Room, about triple the number that could be accommodated safely. Numerous patrons later said that tables were squeezed together, and the narrow aisles were obstructed with chairs. There were about 2400 to 2800 patrons in the club altogether.

Delayed Notification. The fire was discovered by employees between 8:45 p.m. and 8:50 p.m. in the empty Zebra Room. It had begun in a concealed space, and the origin was presumed by investigators to have been electrical in nature.

Employees alerted the club's hostess, while other employees ran around looking for the management. Two managers tried to fight the fire with portable fire extinguishers. Busboys and waiters helped them, but their efforts were to no avail. One of the managers eventually ran to the hostess and told her to evacuate the patrons. By that time, it was about 9:00 p.m. Someone notified the fire department about a minute later.

As this general description of events indicates, about 15 minutes might have elapsed between discovery of the fire and notification of employees. That delay was a critical factor in evacuation efforts. Also, it seems that there was some degree of staff confusion regarding evacuation procedures, since employees had not been trained.

Once notification of patrons was begun, an interesting phenomenon took place. According to interviews conducted by the Kentucky State Police after the fire, waiters and waitresses instinctively took responsibility for the safety of the patrons they were serving. They went directly to those guests and to other guests in those rooms and told them to leave. They did not, however, necessarily take responsibility for guests they were not serving who were in different parts of the building.

The Cabaret Room was isolated from the rest of the club once the show was in progress. There were no waiters, waitresses, busboys, or hostesses travel-

ing to and from the kitchen or standing in the service halls between dining room seatings. This indicates that employees serving the Cabaret Room did not see other employees rushing around notifying patrons and the management of the fire, so they were totally unaware of the danger. However, one busboy, who had just left the Cabaret Room to work in another room, learned of the fire and decided to take action.

Quick Thinking. In a display of courage, calmness, and good sense, the busboy took upon himself the responsibility of evacuating patrons in the Cabaret Room. He was walking down one of the main corridors from the Cabaret Room to the Viennese Room when he learned of the fire. He looked toward the Zebra Room and saw smoke coming through the top edge of the closed doors. He quickly told a bartender to leave, then spun around and ran back to the Cabaret Room.

When he arrived there, he told the host to open the doors of the room. The host also moved the rope divider and reservations stand from the corridor and instructed people waiting in line to walk toward the Garden Room area in another part of the building.

The busboy then walked into the Cabaret Room, calmly climbed up onto the stage where a performance was taking place, took the microphone, and spoke to the guests in the room. This is what he told the post-fire investigators:

> The first thing I did was . . . ask them to look at the exit sign . . . "I want you to all notice that exit sign and I want you to look at the other corner of the room and there will be another exit sign . . . I want the left side of my room to go out of the exit sign behind that I'm pointing to now . . . I want my right half of the room to go out of the other exit sign . . . There is a fire in the small room on the other side of the building . . . I don't think there is any reason to panic or rush . . . you should leave.

Although he later said that some people looked at him as if he were crazy, people did begin to leave. Of the 164 fatalities in the fire, most occurred in the Cabaret Room. There is no way of knowing how many more would have died if the busboy had not taken charge.

Once he was back in the hallway, the busboy saw smoke billowing toward him, so he went to an exit. "There were just three doors, and one was locked," he said. "I tried to bang it open with my shoulder [but] I couldn't."

The Human Factor. Post-fire interviews showed, not surprisingly, that people, in general, did not take the fire threat too seriously at first. Much of the evacuation in the early stages of the fire was without difficulty, partly because people proceeded calmly and deliberately, some perhaps not even believing there was a serious fire in the making.

When heavy smoke and intense heat descended on patrons trying to leave the Cabaret Room, those people suddenly did realize the seriousness of the situation. Some began to rush and push, and some stumbled and fell, blocking exits with their bodies. One fire fighter reported seeing people stacked two and three high.

One bartender told of a young woman who had fallen near an exit. Other people fell on top of her. The bartender and one of his coworkers tried to pull her out, but they were unable to move her. "And there was a man that was on top," the bartender said. "He was a heavy guy and he was reaching up his arms and so I thought he was all right . . . the first thought was to get him off the top so you can do something with the bottom ones . . . I had him wrap his arms around my neck and I pushed up against this door as hard as I could . . . and I didn't have enough strength to lift him and he just looked at me and shook his head . . . there was nothing I could do."

Familiar Factors Contributed to Deaths

The rapid fire spread along the main corridor of the club, delay in notifying patrons in the Cabaret Room, insufficient exit capacity, and an excessive number of people in the Cabaret Room were all major factors that resulted in employees and guests having insufficient time to escape this fire. Virtually all of these factors were covered in the *Life Safety Code* in existence at that time. Some specific factors are examined below.

Construction. Class A places of assembly have a capacity of 1000 people or more. The Beverly Hills Supper Club's total occupant load was 2375. Unprotected, noncombustible construction such as that of the Beverly Hills Supper Club was not permitted for Class A. That construction was permitted for Class C occupancies, which have capacity for 300 people or less. (It is now permitted, but only if the building is fully sprinklered.)

Number of Exits. The number of exits, based on 100 persons per unit of exit width and on square footage, should have been 27.5 exit units. The actual number was 16.5. The second floor had no exits with components permitted by the *Code*. (The Melody Lounge at the Cocoanut Grove was also overcrowded.) The

Cabaret Room should have had four exits, since it was itself a Class A place of assembly. It had only three. (The Cocoanut Grove's Melody Lounge had only one obvious exit.) There was evidence of locked doors and chains and locks on panic hardware. (The same was true at the Cocoanut Grove.) Exits were not well marked. A door to the corridor, for example, appeared to be part of the wall paneling, and it was not marked as an exit. (The Cocoanut Grove's Melody Lounge had a door that was painted and draped and not likely to be seen by patrons. In addition, some windows were concealed by false walls.)

Obstructions. There was seating in the aisles in the Cabaret Room. Tables were placed too close together, and there were too many chairs and other items restricting the aisles. There also were chairs and tables stored on the platform outside the Viennese Room that led to steps to double doors. (Chairs and tables also blocked aisles at the Cocoanut Grove.)

Enclosures. Vertical openings should be enclosed. The curved stairway in the club's "Hallway of Mirrors" was neither enclosed nor protected.

Interior Finish. The 1976 *Code* required interior finish in all means of egress in all places of assembly to be Class A, that is, with a flame spread rating of 0–25. The interior finish in the Hallway of Mirrors and the main north–south corridor had a flame spread rating greater than 25. It is interesting to note how many of these factors were present in the Cocoanut Grove fire 35 years before.

Alarm Systems. One of the factors that made it difficult for patrons to escape was a delay in notification of the fire. An alarm system would have avoided that delay. The *Code* required alarm systems in all occupancies except storage facilities and places of assembly. Committee members had discussed the importance of alarm systems for a long time, but many felt an alarm system could cause panic. The Beverly Hills fire demonstrated the need for an alarm system, however, and so the requirement was added for public assembly occupancies in the next edition of the *Code*, which was published in 1981. Still concerned with the potential for panic and aware of tests showing the value of voice alarms, the committee added an interesting note to its alarm requirements.

Manual pull stations were required to alert occupants. The pull stations send an alarm to a central office or other location on the property that is continuously staffed while the occupancy is in use. The central office must have a way of then notifying occupants, either through a voice alarm over a public address system or a vocal fire alarm system. The alarm notification requirement was made retroactive to apply to new and existing buildings.

Sprinklers. Historically, the *Code* had required sprinklers in assembly occupancies used as exhibit halls. Cost was a perceived prohibitive factor in efforts to spread that requirement to other public assembly occupancies. After the Beverly Hills fire, however, the committee said, in effect, that cost is important, but lives are more important.

The committee approached sprinkler requirements in the following two ways. Members reassessed construction requirements for all classes of assembly occupancies, consolidated them, and required sprinklers based on construction type and location of assembly occupancy within the building. It was decided that even fire-resistive buildings having four or more stories above the exit discharge should be sprinklered. These provisions applied to new buildings, and some were made retroactive for existing buildings.

In addition, every Class A and Class B occupancy was required to be sprinklered throughout. This requirement applied only to new construction. There were some exceptions, but none applied to facilities such as the Beverly Hills Supper Club.

Discussion of the value of sprinklering all places of assembly was ongoing after the Beverly Hills Supper Club. Numerous fires, including the Gulliver's Discotheque fire in New York and the Upstairs Lounge fire in New Orleans, both of which took place during the 1970s, highlighted similar problems and emphasized the need for sprinklers. (In the incidents at the Upstairs Lounge and Gulliver's Discotheque, fire blocked a means of egress.)

ONGOING CHALLENGE

The story of fire protection is one that continues. Fire protection professionals study history and conduct research to determine code requirements that are needed to protect lives. They continuously use their influence to ensure that those requirements are adopted and enforced. Unfortunately, it often takes

a tragedy to bolster their efforts, and, even then, if action isn't taken immediately, people forget.

In Nevada, momentum toward tighter codes had slowed down a year after the 1980 MGM Grand fire. Subsequent fires brought back memories of that tragedy. Today, the Bally Las Vegas (formerly the MGM) has installed about 30,000 sprinklers, 8000 loud speakers, and other fire protection equipment. In addition, the American Automobile Association now includes fire protection among the factors they consider when rating hotels in their travel guides.

Sometimes fires demonstrate the wisdom of committee members. For example, the 1987 DuPont Plaza Hotel fire illustrated that the Committee on Life Safety was correct in requiring corridors and lobbies to be separated from assembly areas by 1-hour walls, unless the building is sprinklered or unless 50 percent of the egress is independent of the lobby.

The Las Vegas Hilton fire illustrated that committee members were correct in restricting carpeting on walls. That fire saw flames leap-frogging up the side of the building, entering windows, and spreading along carpeting on the walls and ceilings. The committee had been convinced of the dangers of carpeting on walls by fire tests sponsored by the carpeting industry, which had pushed for regulation of its own products.

It is always tempting to concentrate on the tragedies, because they are so obvious. However, there are positive results to consider even if they are not as well documented.

It is impossible to know the number of lives saved because vertical openings were enclosed, exits were adequate and unlocked, and alarm, detection, and sprinkler systems were in place, since fires in such buildings don't get out of hand.

The key, once requirements are put into codes and the codes are adopted, is enforcement. The challenge for everyone who reads this handbook is to make certain that the codes, which contain the accumulated fire protection knowledge of generations, are enforced. To paraphrase Frances Perkins' speech to the 1913 NFPA Annual Meeting: People are not always their own masters. "It is necessary for organizations like yours . . . to insist on safety for them." That is our job.

SUPPLEMENT 2

Fire Alarm Systems for *Life Safety Code* Users

Robert P. Schifiliti, P.E.

INTRODUCTION

This supplement is an introduction to fire alarm systems. It explains the various types of systems addressed by the *Life Safety Code* and describes their components in detail. In this supplement the term *fire alarm* is intended to include detection systems and systems that provide control functions, such as elevator recall, and alarm information or notification to occupants and emergency forces.

The review of fire detection devices emphasizes proper selection in order to meet fire safety goals and to reduce the likelihood of false and nuisance alarms. The discussion of circuit types and allowable wiring methods includes references to other NFPA codes and standards. A review of testing and maintenance needs for fire detection and signaling systems provides the reader with an understanding of how to extend a system's life, reduce nuisance alarms, and ensure system operation during a fire emergency. Finally, new to the 2000 edition of this supplement are comments on modeling the performance of fire detection and occupant notification.

Specific requirements and designs for various occupancies are not discussed in this supplement. The occupancy chapters of the *Life Safety Code* should be consulted for specific requirements. The additional commentary contained in other chapters of this handbook provides a good explanation of the requirements and the philosophy behind their intent. This supplement provides an introduction to the operation of required devices and systems. Designers, owners, installers, and inspectors will find useful information to assist them in choosing among options not specifically addressed within the *Code*. For exam-

ple, a choice might need to be made between using photoelectric or ionization smoke detectors, or information might be required on how to reduce the likelihood of false and nuisance alarms.

OVERVIEW OF FIRE ALARM SYSTEMS

Four principal types of fire alarm systems are required or recommended by various chapters of the *Life Safety Code*:

(1) Household fire warning equipment
(2) Manual fire alarm systems
(3) Automatic fire alarm systems
(4) Supervisory systems for extinguishing systems or other fire or building systems

Each of these categories can be viewed as consisting of three components, as shown in Exhibit S2.1. Detection and initiating devices are either manual or automatic, as shown in the figure, and are referred to as input devices. Manual initiating devices, such as manual fire alarm boxes, are operated by people and, in turn, signal the control system. Automatic detection devices sense a change in the environment or equipment that is monitored and signal the control portion of the system. The control or processing section receives the incoming signals and initiates output signals. The control system can also supply power and supervise the system's various components and circuits and provide output signals when a fault occurs or maintenance is needed. The control or processor interfaces with people and other systems through output signals.

The simplest form of system described in Exhibit

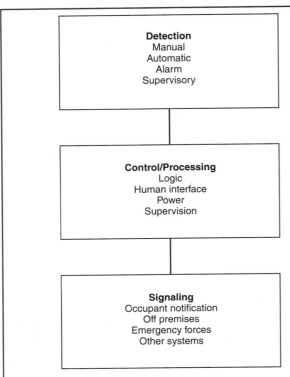

Exhibit S2.1 *Overview of components of fire alarm systems.*

S2.1 is a self-contained smoke alarm. It contains a smoke sensor and a control system that includes a power source and a notification system, usually a horn, used for occupant notification. In more complex systems, initiating devices and notification appliances are separate, self-contained units connected to a control panel by electrical circuits or radio waves. In these component systems, power is usually provided to the input and output devices through the control unit. However, it is also possible for power to be provided directly to those units that require it. Each of these three principal components is discussed in more detail in later sections of this supplement.

Each occupancy chapter of the *Life Safety Code* specifies fire alarm requirements where appropriate. Those that do contain requirements include subsections that provide the requirements for initiation and notification. Where initiation is addressed, the occupancy chapter refers to either a complete system or a partial system. In addition, the system will be described as manual, automatic, or both. Chapter 9, Building Service and Fire Protection Equipment, defines complete, partial, manual, and automatic systems. Where automatic detection is required, most chapters of the *Code* specify smoke detection, either partial or complete. If an automatic fire detection system is required but the type of detection is not specified, any automatic units that comply with NFPA 72, *National Fire Alarm Code*, are permitted to be used interchangeably. An occupancy chapter might also require separate smoke detection within dwelling units in addition to any required partial or complete system.

Household fire warning equipment is intended for use within dwelling units such as apartments, hotel rooms, dormitory rooms, and one- or two-family dwellings. These devices or systems are intended to detect smoke conditions and alert the occupants of the dwelling units. In occupancies such as hotels, apartment buildings, and dormitories, these devices are not intended to be connected to the overall building fire alarm system.

Within the dwelling unit, household fire warning equipment might be self-contained smoke alarms, or it might be a small system with detectors, a control panel, and notification appliances such as bells, horns, or strobe lights. The building system can consist of manual and automatic initiating devices, extinguishing system supervisory devices, and notification appliances that are all connected to a control unit. Therefore, there are two categories of fire alarm: one that is located within the family dwelling unit and one that is intended to protect the entire building.

In some cases, an occupancy chapter of the *Code* might require a partial automatic detection system that covers all common spaces. In addition, household fire warning equipment might be required in dwelling units. For purposes of occupant notification, the building system would cover all occupiable spaces, including the dwelling units. The household equipment is required to signal only within the dwelling unit. Some building fire alarm systems are capable of having system-connected smoke detectors in the dwelling units programmed to operate like smoke alarms. In this configuration, they receive power, including backup power, from the building system and are monitored for faults and sensitivity. When they alarm, these systems provide an alarm signal (audible, visible, or both) only in the dwelling unit. They can also send a supervisory signal to an attended location.

In other cases, a complete automatic detection system might be required in addition to the requirements for the dwelling unit. The building system must then provide detection within all spaces, including the dwelling units. This detection for the dwelling units is not redundant. The intent is for the household fire warning equipment to provide an alarm of smoke conditions to the occupants of the dwelling unit. The additional detectors connected to the building system would be heat detectors, which would notify the other occupants before a fire in the dwelling unit became a threat to those outside the dwelling unit. This design concept is described thoroughly in the commentary of the occupancy chapters in which it is required.

NFPA 72 deals with the application, installation, performance, and maintenance of fire alarm systems and their components. NFPA 72 is a combination of the following:

NFPA 72, *Standard for the Installation, Maintenance, and Use of Protective Signaling Systems,* 1990

NFPA 72E, *Standard on Automatic Fire Detectors,* 1990

NFPA 74, *Standard for the Installation, Maintenance, and Use of Household Fire Warning Equipment,* 1990

NFPA 71, *Standard for the Installation, Maintenance, and Use of Signaling Systems for Central Station Service,* 1990

NFPA 72G, *Guide for the Installation, Maintenance, and Use of Notification Appliances for Protective Signaling Systems,* 1989

NFPA 72H, *Testing Procedures for Local, Auxiliary, Remote Station, and Proprietors Protective Signaling Systems,* 1988

NFPA 1221, *Public Fire Service Communication Systems,* 1991

The organization of the *National Fire Alarm Code* is as follows:

Chapter 1, Fundamentals of Fire Alarm Systems

Chapter 2, Initiating Devices

Chapter 3, Protected Premises Fire Alarm Systems

Chapter 4, Notification Appliances for Fire Alarm Systems

Chapter 5, Supervising Station Fire Alarm Systems

Chapter 6, Public Fire Alarm Reporting Systems

Chapter 7, Inspection, Testing, and Maintenance

Chapter 8, Fire Warning Equipment for Dwelling Units

When the standards and guides previously listed were combined into the 1993 edition of NFPA 72, they were rewritten to eliminate conflicts and redundancy. Further revisions have been incorporated into the 1996 and 1999 editions of NFPA 72. Chapter 1, Fundamentals of Fire Alarm Systems, contains requirements that apply to all the other chapters except Chapter 8. Chapter 8, Fire Warning Equipment for Dwelling Units, was written to stand alone and possi-

bly to be adopted and applied independently of the rest of NFPA 72.

Similar to this handbook, the *National Fire Alarm Code Handbook* contains the text of NFPA 72 along with explanatory information. The *National Fire Alarm Code Handbook,* by Merton Bunker, Jr., P.E., and Wayne D. Moore, P.E., is a good source of background information on the *National Fire Alarm Code.*

FIRE SIGNATURES

Fire signatures are changes in the normal environment caused by a fire. Understanding fire signatures is important because it affects the choice of fire detector for a given area. The objective is to choose a fire detector that will respond to an expected fire signature without responding to similar signatures normally present in the area. At the same time, the response time of the detector in reaction to the range of expected fires must meet the fire safety goals and objectives of the system.

Fire signatures can be placed in two categories, as shown in Exhibit S2.2. The first group is categorized by the energy produced by the fire, which is transferred in three ways—conduction, convection, and radiation. The second signature group is categorized by the physical/chemical changes that take place. This group is comprised of solids, liquids, and gases produced by the fire. The solid and liquid particles are grouped together and called smoke or aerosols.

Conduction occurs when, during the combustion process, some of the energy released is conducted through the fuel to further the combustion process. Any time the temperature of one part of a material

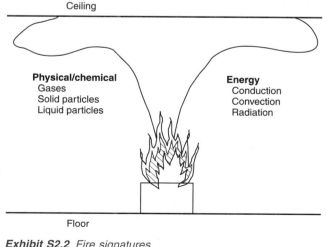

Exhibit S2.2 Fire signatures.

differs from another part, heat energy is conducted from the hotter portion to the cooler portion.

Convection occurs when heat is transferred by fluid motion. During combustion, hot fire gases rise, entraining fresh air, which then heats and also rises until the mixture either collects at the ceiling or cools to approximately room temperature. The energy carried away by the hot gases is referred to as convected energy.

Electromagnetic radiation is the third mode of energy transfer that occurs during the combustion process. Thermal radiation is one form of electromagnetic radiation and is proportional to an object's temperature. Light is another form of electromagnetic radiation produced during the combustion process. Unlike conduction and convection, a solid, liquid, or gaseous material is not needed to transfer energy by radiation. Electromagnetic radiation can travel through a vacuum such as space. Radiation travels in all directions and in straight lines. Thermal radiation behaves in the same way as visible light radiation; if you turn your back to it, you can't "see" it. Therefore, when you stand in front of a fire, your face is warmed by thermal radiation, but your back is not heated. You might, however, see or feel the effects of reflected radiation.

Smoke and gases are produced by all fires in varying quantities. Perfect combustion of most fuels (hydrocarbon based) produces only carbon dioxide and water, in addition to the energy released. Other materials are produced when combustion is not 100 percent efficient. These materials include gases such as carbon monoxide and liquids and solids such as tar, carbon soot, and more complex hydrocarbon particles.

The solid and liquid particles, which together are called smoke, are produced in a wide range of sizes. Some are small and invisible to the human eye, and others are large and obscure our vision. Some particle sizes are produced in larger quantities than others. The color of the smoke also varies. Many of these factors depend on the fuel and also on the efficiency of the combustion process. For instance, well-ventilated, hot, efficient fires produce mostly small, invisible, grayish particles in large quantities. Compared to flaming fires, inefficient, smoldering combustion produces mainly a smaller number of large black particles.

INITIATING DEVICES

Manual Fire Alarm Boxes

Manual fire alarm boxes are either coded or noncoded. Noncoded manual fire alarm boxes are the most common in use on new systems. When a noncoded fire alarm box is operated, a switch closes. All noncoded devices produce the same single bit of information—a switch closure. Therefore, if more than one switch is on a circuit, the circuit does not know which switch operated. The exception is addressable, microprocessor-based systems that can "talk" to and recognize each device.

Coded manual fire alarm boxes house a mechanical code wheel that, when operated, turns and, through its teeth, taps out a coded signal on a circuit. These coded wheels are essentially automatic telegraph keys, and each box has a different code through which information is transmitted. This code might be transferred to a bell circuit in order to notify the occupants of a building as to which box has been operated.

Today's addressable systems act like the older manually coded systems. Because the control unit knows exactly which device has originated an alarm, it can generate unique alarm signals. The control unit can also activate or actuate a unique set of output functions, such as starting or stopping certain fans and closing some doors but not others.

Manual fire alarm boxes, coded or noncoded, can be single action or double action. When operating a single-action box, the hand is used to pull the station. When operating a double-action station, two actions are required—either the door is opened and the station is pulled or the glass is broken and a button is pushed. Double-action manual fire alarm boxes tend to reduce false alarms caused by accidental operation. They also reduce nuisance alarms to some degree.

Pull station protectors are clear plastic covers that are mounted over manual boxes to provide protection from weather, dust, dirt, and mechanical damage. They also serve to convert a single-action station into a double-action station. When these covers are placed over a double-action station, three actions are required to initiate an alarm signal—the protector must be lifted, the cover must be opened, and the box must be pulled.

Some versions of pull station protectors are available with an internal battery-operated buzzer. This feature has been shown to greatly reduce nuisance alarms in schools, shopping centers, and other public areas. When the cover is lifted, the local buzzer sounds, which tends to scare away vandals before they can operate the station. In locations such as schools or other crowded public areas, someone is likely to see or catch a vandal before the station is operated. However, when the cover is removed and the local buzzer sounds, a person might think the building's fire alarm system has been initiated. For this reason, it is important that pull station protectors be labeled properly and that the usual occupants of the area be instructed in their use.

Where an occupancy chapter of the *Life Safety Code* requires manual fire alarm boxes, Chapter 9 describes the quantity and location. NFPA 72 also contains requirements concerning the location and operation of manual fire alarm boxes. Essentially, manual fire alarm boxes are located at each required exit in the natural path of egress.

Therefore, in a corridor with exits at each end, a manual fire alarm box is located at the door to each exit. Each box should be located on the same side as the door handle so that it is easily seen by someone exiting from the space. In most cases, it is best to locate the box within the corridor, not on the other side of the door, so that the pull station is located within the space it serves. If a manual box were located on the other side of the door—for instance, in the stair tower—an occupant from the fifth floor might pull the box on the second floor, possibly slowing discovery of the fire's location.

In addition to locations at required exits, additional manual fire alarm boxes are required to ensure that there is less than a 200-ft (60-m) travel distance to a station. Manual fire alarm boxes also should be provided near the telephone operator's area of a hotel or hospital and near portable extinguishers placed adjacent to hazardous operations in a factory. NFPA 72 requires the mounting height of boxes to be between $3^1/_2$ ft (1.1 m) and $4^1/_2$ ft (1.4 m), although some locally adopted codes for the disabled might limit the height to no more than 4 ft (1.2 m).

Automatic Fire Detectors—General

Chapter 2 of NFPA 72 classifies automatic fire detectors as either spot-type, line-type, or air-sampling detectors. Spot-type detectors include conventional smoke and heat detectors. A spot-type detector's response to a given fire varies with the radial distance from the detector, with the farther a fire from the detector, the slower its response time. To illustrate, if a circle were drawn and the detector placed in the center, a given fire anywhere along the perimeter of the circle would result in the same response time.

Projected beam smoke detectors and heat-sensitive cable are examples of line-type detectors. The response time is about the same when a particular fire is burning anywhere directly under the line, except where close to the ends. As that same fire moves farther away to a position perpendicular to the line-type detector, response time increases. Similarly, response time anywhere along a line parallel to the

line-type detector, except at the ends, would be about the same for a given fire.

Air-sampling detectors draw air from the protected area back to a remotely located detector. The tube or pipe might have several holes or sampling ports or it may have only one. In any case, NFPA 72 treats the sampling port like a spot-type detector with respect to its location and spacing.

Spot- and line-type detectors can be restorable or nonrestorable. Restorable detectors reset themselves after the fire signature is no longer present, provided they are not severely exposed to a fire. For instance, some heat detectors heat until they respond, cool off, and then return to their original state. Self-contained household smoke alarms automatically reset after the smoke has cleared from their chamber (a slight time delay might be built into the detector). Nonrestorable detectors are destroyed with use and must be replaced after exposure to the fire signature for which they were designed.

There are advantages and disadvantages to both restorable and nonrestorable detectors. Nonrestorable detectors generally provide a positive visual indication of operation, whereas a restorable detector might not have any visual cue that it is, or has been, in the alarm state. This is true of most heat detectors, but not smoke detectors, which have visual alarm indicators. Restorable heat detectors can also be provided with visual indicators, although this feature greatly increases the cost of a relatively inexpensive detector. One key advantage to restorable detectors is their ability to test the units with the same signature for which they are designed to respond. Most addressable heat detectors are restorable and include an indicator light on the unit.

Heat Detection

Three basic types of heat detectors are available commercially—fixed-temperature, rate-of-rise, and rate compensation detectors. The *Life Safety Code* allows any of these units to be used interchangeably wherever heat detection is required.

Heat detectors respond to hot smoke and fire gases—that is, to convected energy. Because it takes time for a heat detector to absorb heat, the air and fire gases surrounding a detector might be much hotter than the detector element. This response is called thermal lag. Thermal lag can be illustrated by imagining a fixed-temperature heat detector, such as a 165°F (74°C) sprinkler, that is dropped into a pan of boiling water. Although the water is 212°F (100°C), there is a time delay before the sprinkler link melts. The longer the delay, the greater the thermal lag. The smaller the mass of the link or detector element, the shorter the thermal lag. Thermal lag is a measure of detector sensitivity. The shorter the thermal lag, the greater the sensitivity of the unit.

Thermal lag enables a detector with a fixed temperature of 200°F (93°C) to respond to a fire more quickly than would a sprinkler with a fixed temperature of 165°F (74°C). It is only necessary to use a detector with a more sensitive element (shorter thermal lag) than the sprinkler. It is detector sensitivity that determines the number of detectors needed for a particular application.

There are several ways to measure detector sensitivity. The term *response time index* (RTI) is used to measure sprinkler sensitivity. The smaller the RTI, the more sensitive the unit. The RTI of a unit can be used in calculations to determine when that unit will respond to a given fire scenario. For heat detectors, the current measurement of sensitivity is the Underwriters Laboratories listed spacing or Factory Mutual approved spacing. The higher the spacing rating, the more sensitive the detector. For instance, a detector with a listed spacing of 50 ft (15 m) is more sensitive than one with a listed spacing of 30 ft (9 m). The listed spacing of a detector is determined by fire testing and cannot be used directly as part of any engineering calculations.

Where heat detectors are used, NFPA 72, Chapter 2, requires that they be spaced on smooth ceilings less than 10 ft (3 m) high, in accordance with their listed spacing. The installed spacing is equal to the listed or approved spacing. For ceilings higher than 10 ft (3 m), NFPA 72 contains reduction factors to be applied to the listed spacing. Therefore, as ceiling height increases, the installed spacing becomes less than the listed spacing. Reduction factors for joisted, beamed, and sloped ceilings are also contained in NFPA 72. The beams or joists must be at least 4 in. (10.1 cm) deep before reductions are required for heat detectors. Each of these factors (high ceilings, ceilings that are not smooth, and so on) affects detector response. The reduction and correction factors contained in NFPA 72 are intended to provide some adjustments for these effects. NFPA 72 should be referenced for a list of all the various correction factors.

Spacing reductions are often missed by designers, installers, and inspectors; yet they can have a dramatic effect on detector response time during a fire. The NFPA three-day seminar on fire detection and alarm systems covers these requirements in detail.

Fixed-Temperature Detectors. Fixed-temperature heat detectors respond when the temperature of their element reaches a preset level. To reduce the likelihood of false alarms, the temperature rating selected for an application should be at least 20°F (11°C) above the maximum expected ambient temperature. These detectors are available in a wide range of temperature ratings, the most common being 135°F to 140°F (57°C to 60°C) and 190°F to 200°F (88°C to 93°C). Fixed-temperature detectors are available as spot type and as line type.

Fixed-temperature heat detectors use several methods of operation. The two most common use a fusible or bi-metal element. Fusible elements melt at a preset temperature and are spring-loaded to close or open a set of electrical contacts. Bi-metal units use two or more metals that expand at different rates, causing the element to change shape and initiate operation of a set of electrical contacts. Line-type, fixed-temperature heat detectors generally operate either when insulation melts, allowing two conductors to short circuit, or when heat causes a decrease in electrical resistance and an increase in conductivity between two conductors.

NFPA 72, Chapter 2, contains basic, operational descriptions of these and other detection principals. For a more detailed discussion of the many different types of heat detectors available, consult the NFPA *Fire Protection Handbook* or the *Fire Alarm Signaling Systems Handbook*.

Rate-of-Rise Detectors. Rate-of-rise heat detectors respond when their temperature or the temperature of the air surrounding them rises faster than some preset rate—regardless of their actual fixed temperature. Units are available with various alarm rates, a common one being 15°F/min (8°C/min). The speed with which a detector responds depends on how hot the fire gases are compared to the detector's starting temperature and also on the detector's sensitivity. Therefore, if a rate-of-rise detector is initially monitoring a room temperature of 65°F (18°C) and a fire causes the temperature around the detector to rise quickly, it will respond in a given time, *t*. If the detector is in a freezer at -20°F (-29°C) and the temperature rises at the same rate, the response time would be about the same.

Depending on environmental conditions, detector sensitivity, and the fire growth rate, rate-of-rise detectors can respond much faster than fixed-temperature units. In many situations, however, a rate-of-rise detector will not respond to a real fire, for example, to a slowly igniting fire. For this reason, testing laboratories, codes, and standards require these detectors to be backed up with fixed-temperature elements.

As with fixed-temperature detectors, rate-of-rise heat detectors are available in many different configurations. The most common spot-type unit works on a pneumatic principle. As the detector is heated, air inside a chamber is heated and expands. The air escapes through a vent hole when heated slowly. However, when heated faster than its preset rate, the air cannot escape quickly enough, and pressure builds up in the detector. As the pressure increases, a diaphragm moves and activates a set of electrical contacts. Line-type, rate-of-rise detectors are also available using this pneumatic principle. Other rate-of-rise detectors use bi-metal elements or electrical conductivity to detect rapid temperature changes.

When using rate-of-rise heat detectors, it is important to ensure that they will not be subjected to changes in ambient conditions that might cause false alarms. For instance, they should not be located too close to air supply vents or directly over heat sources such as ovens, radiators, or large sinks, where hot steam might set them off. They can be used in high-temperature areas, but caution should be used in situations where the temperature might cool rapidly, then rise again quickly enough to set off the rate-of-rise units. In a large boiler house, for example, the temperature at the ceiling might be 100°F to 150°F (38°C to 66°C) under normal circumstances. As long as the fixed-temperature backup to the rate-of-rise detector is at least 170°F (77°C), there should be no false actuation. However, if a large door is opened in the winter, the temperature could drop quickly. When the door is closed, the temperature at the ceiling could rise fast enough to set off the rate-of-rise portion of the detector.

Rate Compensation Detectors. Rate compensation heat detectors are more complex in operation than either fixed-temperature or rate-of-rise devices. In short, they combine the principles of both in order to compensate for thermal lag. When the air temperature is rising at a rate of about 40°F/min or less, the unit is designed to respond almost exactly at the point when the air temperature reaches the unit's rated temperature; it does not lag while it absorbs the heat and rises to that temperature. At faster rates of temperature rise, the unit responds more quickly than most fixed-temperature detectors, even though some thermal lag still occurs. In addition, with these very fast temperature rises, rate-of-rise detectors generally respond more quickly than either fixed-temperature or rate compensation detectors.

Because of the precision associated with their operation, rate compensation heat detectors are well suited for use in areas where thermal lag must be minimized to provide fast response when temperatures exceed a certain level. At the same time, they are stable even in areas where temperatures fluctuate but do not exceed the preset alarm level. Therefore, rate compensation detectors respond more quickly to most fires than do fixed-temperature detectors without producing false alarms due to moderate temperature fluctuations, which can occur with the use of rate-of-rise units. They are also suitable where precise temperature actuation is needed.

Smoke Detection

General. Four principal types of smoke detection equipment are currently on the market:

(1) Spot-type ionization detectors
(2) Spot-type, light-scattering, photoelectric detectors
(3) Line-type, projected beam, light obscuration detectors
(4) Air-sampling detectors

The *Life Safety Code* allows each of these types to be used interchangeably wherever smoke detection is required.

By definition and by design, smoke detectors respond to the solid and liquid aerosols produced by a fire. Each type responds differently to different types of smoke. Because they respond to aerosols from non-fire sources, an understanding of their operating characteristics is helpful in their correct selection and placement to reduce the chances of false and nuisance alarms. Therefore, selection of a smoke detection principle should be based on the type of fire and fuel expected, as well as on environmental characteristics.

At some point, the smoke detector transmits an alarm signal either by sounding an internal alarm or by signaling a control panel. With newer digital and analog/digital systems, the detector can send information on the amount of smoke in the chamber back to the control panel, where a decision is made to perform some function, such as sounding an alarm. Such units are often called "smart" or "intelligent" devices. Because they send all information back to a control panel or processor and do not make alarm decisions, these units are often referred to as "sensors" rather than detectors. In the case of conventional detectors, a decision to alarm is made internally. The conventional detector then signals an alarm with either an internal audible or visual device or by signaling the control panel. Additional information on how conventional and digital smoke detectors signal a control panel is contained later in the subsection Wiring Methods.

Where required by an occupancy chapter, household smoke detectors, often called single- or multiple-station smoke detectors, must be located and installed in accordance with NFPA 72, Chapter 8. The location and placement of required smoke detectors for protected premises systems is governed by NFPA 72, Chapter 2. Unless otherwise noted, all requirements and recommendations for smoke detector spacing contained in Chapter 2 apply equally to ionization or photoelectric spot-type smoke detectors, to projected beam detectors, and to the sampling ports or heads of a sampling-type system.

For general area coverage with smoke detectors, Chapter 2 of NFPA 72 requires that spacing be based on manufacturer's recommendations. Chapter 2 also recommends an installed spacing of 30 ft (9 m) between detectors. This recommendation applies to smooth, flat ceilings and is also in agreement with the recommendation of most manufacturers. Therefore, in many cases, the installed spacing is the manufacturer's recommended spacing, which is usually 30 ft (9 m), center to center. There is no listed or approved spacing of smoke detectors as is provided for heat detectors. Also, there is no specific requirement for changing detector spacing, depending on the sensitivity of the unit.

Chapter 2 of NFPA 72 requires detector spacing to be reduced for ceilings with beams or joists. Where using smoke detectors, the beams or joists must be at least 4 in. (10 cm) deep before reductions are required. Spacing adjustment is also required when airflow in the space is greater than about 8 minutes per air change.

Unlike its provisions for heat detectors, Chapter 2 does not contain specific spacing reductions for smoke detectors where ceiling height exceeds 10 ft (3 m). Instead, it advises on the use of the manufacturers' recommendations and good engineering judgment. Other factors that must be considered are discussed later in the section Selection and Placement.

Spot-type smoke detector sensitivity is generally based on the percentage of light obscuration per foot required for the unit to signal an alarm. The alarm threshold can also be expressed in optical density per foot or per meter, which can be directly converted to obscuration per foot.

The *Life Safety Code* does not require that detectors have any minimum or maximum sensitivity, only that they comply with the *National Fire Alarm Code*. These documents also do not contain any explicit requirements regarding detector sensitivity. NFPA 72, Chapter 2, only requires the detector to be tested and

listed for its intended use. It is the listing company, acceptable to the authority having jurisdiction, that determines the range of acceptable smoke detector sensitivity for a given application.

The *National Fire Alarm Code* requires detectors to be tested and listed. ANSI/UL 217, *Standard for Single and Multiple Station Smoke Detectors*, and ANSI/UL 268, *Standard for Smoke Detectors for Fire Protective Signaling Systems*, contain requirements for minimum and maximum detector sensitivity to gray smoke.

The range of possible sensitivities for spot-type detectors is generally between 1.0 and 4.0 percent per foot (0.3 m) of obscuration due to gray smoke. This range provides the designer of a smoke detection system some choice with regard to sensitivity. The importance of this is covered more under the heading Selection and Placement later in this supplement.

Ionization Detectors. Exhibit S2.3 shows an ionization smoke detector. Ionization smoke detectors have two parallel electrically charged plates separated by an air gap. A small, low-strength radioactive source causes the air between the plates to be ionized. Because of the voltage between the plates, the positive ions travel to the negative plate and the negative ions travel to the positive plate. This creates a small electrical current. As smoke particles enter the detector, they slow down the movement of the ionized air between the plates. The corresponding change in electrical current is measurable by the detector and is proportional to the number and size of the smoke particles between the plates. In the case of ionization smoke detectors, the strongest signal is obtained when there are a large number of small particles in the chamber.

Photoelectric Detectors. Exhibit S2.4 shows a photoelectric smoke detector. Spot-type photoelectric

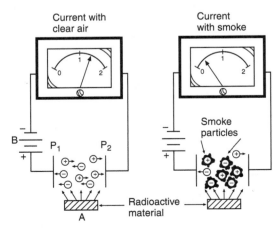

Exhibit S2.3 *Ionization smoke detector.*

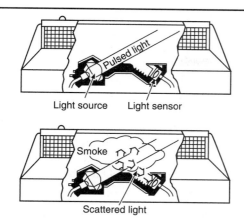

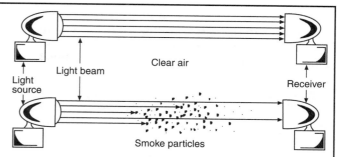

Exhibit S2.5 Projected beam smoke detector.

Exhibit S2.4 Photoelectric smoke detector.

smoke detectors operate on the light-scattering principle. A small light source, usually an infrared LED, shines a beam into the detector chamber. A light-sensitive receiver is located so that it normally sees only a very small amount of light from the source reflected from the detector chamber. When smoke enters the detector chamber, additional light is scattered within the chamber, some of which reaches the photosensitive receiver and changes the detector signal. As with ionization detectors, the magnitude of the signal is related to the number and size of the smoke particles.

Many other factors also affect the signal from a light-scattering smoke detector. The color of the smoke affects the amount of light that is scattered. Dark smoke, such as that from some plastics and hydrocarbon fuels, absorbs more light than it reflects, so more light is required before the signal reaches the alarm threshold. Light-colored particles reflect a lot of light, so smaller quantities can produce strong signals. Particle shape also affects the amount of light reflected, as does the wavelength of the light source and the angle between the source and receiver. However, in general, in the case of a particular scattering-type photoelectric detector design, the strongest signal is obtained when large, light-colored smoke particles are in the chamber.

Projected Beam Detectors. Projected beam smoke detectors, as illustrated in Exhibit S2.5, operate on the light obscuration principle. These detectors consist of a source that projects a light beam across a space to a receiver. As smoke enters the beam path, some of the light is absorbed and some is scattered, reducing the total amount reaching the receiver. The color and shape of the smoke particles are not as important as for spot-type photoelectric detectors. In the case of

projected beam smoke detectors, it is the size and quantity of smoke particles in the path that has the greatest effect on the detector's signal.

Projected beam smoke detectors respond to the total amount of light obscuration in their paths. When the percentage of light obscured reaches a given threshold, the unit sounds an alarm. Typically, the units are available with adjustable sensitivities between 20 and 70 percent total obscuration. If the light beam is suddenly and totally obscured, the unit should not alarm but should give a trouble signal after a short time period. In general, fires do not suddenly and totally obscure a light beam. Similarly, a very slow, gradual loss of light is also probably not indicative of a fire but is more likely an accumulation of dust or a misalignment of the beam. This situation should also produce a trouble signal, not an alarm signal.

Very large, fast developing fires, such as a large spill of flammable liquid, can cause a rapid decrease in the signal received by a projected beam smoke detector. For this reason, the detector might have a setting that results in fast blockage, causing an alarm signal rather than a trouble or supervisory signal. This setting should be used only where there is a real possibility of these types of fires.

Air-Sampling Detectors. Sampling-type smoke detection devices are designed to draw air samples from the protected space to a separate detection chamber. The sampling portion might consist of a combination of air pumps, filters, and tubing or piping fitted with sampling heads or perforated to draw room air samples. The detection device might be self-contained or might be part of, or served by, a control panel.

Air-sampling detectors should not be confused with duct smoke detectors. Sampling-type detectors use positive ventilation methods to draw an air sample. Duct smoke detectors are usually only spot-type photoelectric or ionization detectors in special housings. Duct smoke detectors might use a sampling tube that penetrates the duct to allow natural pressure differences to draw air into the detector housing.

There are two principal types of air-sampling smoke detection systems. One type uses a cloud chamber to detect very small particles in the air from the protected space. In a cloud chamber, humidity is added to the air sample, and the pressure is reduced to lower its temperature. This causes water to condense on small particles present in the sample. The resulting cloud is measured by an LED light source and a phototransistor light receiver. These units are very sensitive to very small (submicron) particles.

The second principal type of air-sampling smoke detection system uses a very sensitive photoelectric light-scattering detector. Unlike a spot-type, light-scattering smoke detector, this system uses a high-power strobe light or a laser beam rather than an infrared LED. Where combined with a sensitive light receiver, the unit can detect submicron-sized particles in very small concentrations. Other sampling-type smoke detectors might use other detection principles such as an ionization chamber.

Other Detection Principles

Radiant Energy Detectors. Radiant energy detectors are often called flame detectors. However, the broader name, radiant energy detectors, includes units designed to sense smoldering and glowing ember combustion.

The radiant energy emitted during combustion of a fuel falls predominantly into three categories, distinguished by the wavelength of the radiation:

(1) *Ultraviolet:* wavelength smaller than visible radiation (smaller than about 0.35 microns)
(2) *Visible:* wavelength larger than ultraviolet radiation but smaller than infrared radiation (between about 0.35 microns and 0.75 microns)
(3) *Infrared:* wavelength larger than visible radiation (more than about 0.75 microns)

The two most common wavelengths used by radiant energy detectors are the ultraviolet and infrared band widths. Except in very special applications, visible light comes from so many normal sources that it cannot be used effectively as a fire signature.

The application of radiant energy sensing detectors is beyond the scope of this supplement. The selection and use of flame and spark detectors is complex and requires thorough knowledge of fuel behavior, environmental conditions, and specific detector characteristics. Generally, these detectors are used in special applications such as in aircraft hangars and areas where flammable and combustible solids, liquids, and gases are handled, used, or conveyed. Subject to the approval of the authority having jurisdiction, these detectors can be used as part of an automatic fire detection system required by the *Life Safety Code* where specific detection, such as smoke, is not mentioned in the occupancy chapter.

Chapter 2 of NFPA 72 contains descriptions of these radiant energy detection principles. For more detailed information on these detectors and their applications, consult the *Fire Protection Handbook*, the *Fire Alarm Signaling Systems Handbook*, and the manufacturers' literature.

Other Fire Detectors. Chapter 2 of NFPA 72 recognizes that there are, or might someday be, detectors suitable for use as automatic fire detectors other than those already discussed. As with any detector, their selection, application, and use are governed by their principle of operation, their testing and/or listing, if any, and their manufacturers' recommendations.

Any fire detector listed or approved for its specific intended purpose is permitted to be used where the *Life Safety Code* requires automatic fire detection but does not specify the type. The selection must be approved by the authority having jurisdiction.

Monitoring Other Fire Protection Systems

Fire detection and alarm systems can be interconnected to receive signals from other fire prevention and protection systems. These systems might be required by parts of the *Life Safety Code* and include the following:

(1) Sprinkler systems
(2) Fire pumps
(3) Other extinguishing systems
(4) Heating, ventilating, and air-conditioning systems (CO_2, halon, dry chemical, wet chemical, foam, and so on)
(5) Smoke control systems

The signals received from systems or devices such as those already listed might be a fire alarm or a supervisory signal indicating the status of the system or device. Detailed descriptions of these systems are not possible in this brief introduction to detection and alarm signaling. However, some information on sprinklers, the most common of these systems, is warranted.

Where an occupancy chapter of the *Life Safety Code* requires an automatic sprinkler system, the requirement indicates whether the system must be supervised. Section 9-7 defines a supervised sprinkler system. Under Extinguishment Requirements, the occupancy chapter might also state that the system is required to be connected to the fire alarm system. Under Detection, Alarm, and Communications Systems of the same occupancy chapter, the section titled Initiation indicates whether alarm signals must be activated by the sprinkler system.

Where a supervised automatic sprinkler system is required, it must produce a distinct signal to indicate conditions that might impair the satisfactory operation of the sprinkler system. This requires monitoring of such features as the opening and closing of control valves and fire pump operation and water tank level. The chapter also requires supervisory signals to terminate within the protected premises at a constantly attended location or in an approved remote receiving facility.

Chapter 7 of the *Life Safety Code* also requires waterflow alarm signals from required, supervised sprinkler systems to be transmitted to an approved auxiliary, remote station, proprietary, or central station facility. These systems are introduced later in this supplement in the section entitled Signaling. Where the occupancy chapter requires a sprinkler system to be monitored by and to produce an alarm on the protected premise system, NFPA 72 contains requirements for its connection.

At the local protected premise, NFPA 72 has specific definitions of *alarm, trouble,* and *supervisory signals.* Alarm signals indicate an emergency requiring immediate action. A supervisory signal indicates the need to initiate a specific action regarding some type of protective service or equipment, such as guard tour or extinguishing systems. For example, a closed-valve signal on a sprinkler system is a supervisory signal indicating the need to investigate the signal and take corrective action (that is, open the valve) when appropriate. A trouble signal, on the other hand, indicates a fault or problem with a protective signaling system. Trouble signals occur because of faults in the protective signaling system, and supervisory signals are signals initiated in conjunction with other systems or services.

The three different signals must be distinct from one another. In the case of trouble and supervisory signals at the protected premise, they are permitted to have the same audible signal as long as they have separate and distinct visual signals. Therefore, it is clear that the common practice of wiring a valve tamper switch to open the waterflow alarm circuit and cause a trouble signal is not acceptable. The valve tamper switch would break the circuit just as a broken wire would. Both would result in a trouble condition at the control panel. Correct and incorrect methods for monitoring supervisory devices are addressed in the section on wiring.

Selection and Placement

Within the context of the *Life Safety Code*, some degree of decision making is necessary concerning the type of detector to be used in a given situation. For instance, where the *Code* requires a supervised fire alarm system with initiation by smoke detection, it does not specify what type of smoke detection is permitted to be used. In such a case, the *Code* intends that life safety fire detection goals for this particular occupancy be met by smoke detection designed, installed, maintained, and tested in accordance with NFPA 72. The same is true for a required household fire warning smoke detector in a dwelling unit. The opportunity to choose a smoke detection method allows design flexibility for performance and economy.

The majority of detectors used to meet the intent of this *Code* are spot-type ionization, spot-type photoelectric, or projected beam. Air-sampling smoke detectors are very sensitive and cost more than systems using spot- and beam-type detectors. Their use is generally limited to clean, high-value areas such as computer rooms and industrial clean rooms for manufacturing semiconductors. They have also found use in telecommunications facilities and power plant control rooms. Because of their cost and sensitivity, these detectors are not a common choice for meeting requirements of the *Life Safety Code*, despite the fact that they are allowed. Design considerations for these systems are complex and beyond the scope of this supplement.

The first step in selecting a smoke detector is to consider the type of fire likely to occur in the area. Photoelectric or projected beam detectors would provide a faster response if the fire is likely to smolder for some time because of the large particles produced during smoldering combustion. If the fire is most likely to be fast and hot with open flames, the larger quantity of small smoke particles will set off an ionization smoke detector more quickly than will either a photoelectric or projected beam detector.

The expected color of smoke should also be considered. Color is important to photoelectric light-scattering detectors but not to projected beam and ionization detectors. If black smoke is expected, projected beam or ionization detectors will give the best response. If the smoke is expected to be mostly large black particles, the ionization detector falls further down the list of choices. The projected beam detector would probably respond first, followed by either photoelectric or ionization.

Ambient environmental conditions must also be considered when selecting a smoke detection method. Smoke detectors cannot be used where the temperature is above or below the manufacturer's stated range. This range is usually 32°F to 120°F (0°C to 49°C), although lower and higher temperature units might be found.

Cooking odors are blamed for a large number of nuisance alarms. The odors that are produced by cooking contain a large number of small invisible particles. A smoke detector's response to cooking odors is not a false alarm; it is a response to a valid fire signature. An ionization smoke detector would probably trigger a nuisance alarm in response to cooking odors, whereas a photoelectric smoke detector would probably not activate the alarm unless the food was well burnt and producing visible smoke. Therefore, unless the detector can be located far enough from the kitchen to avoid odors, the better choice is a photoelectric detector.

Steam from showers and large sinks contains lots of small water drops and has much the same effect as cooking odors in causing nuisance alarms from smoke detectors. The heavier the steam, the more likely it is to also cause photoelectric smoke detectors to alarm. However, the highly reflective nature of small water droplets in steam causes even photoelectric detectors to alarm. Detectors can often be located to avoid these sources of false fire signatures.

Insects can set off either type of spot smoke detector. They are not likely to cause an alarm from a projected beam smoke detector because of the small amount of light they obscure. Detectors with good bug screens stop most insects, but some still manage to get into the detector chamber. Ionization smoke detectors are less prone to nuisance alarms from insects than spot-type photoelectric smoke detectors. Another solution that has been reported to be successful is to place an insecticide strip on or near the detector. The detector manufacturer should be consulted before taking this action. Some insecticides might produce enough fumes to set off ionization detectors or harm electronic components. An insecticide should never be sprayed in or near a functioning detector. It would probably set off the alarm, as would any aerosol spray, and it could harm the detector.

Cigarette smoke causes nuisance alarms from ionization and photoelectric smoke detectors. When the smoke dissipates to a light cloud, the ionization detector is likely to alarm first. When the smoke is heavy and thick, either type will alarm. Often, detectors can be placed to avoid such conditions. For instance, in elevator lobbies, smoke detectors should not be placed directly in front of the doors where people stand and where drafts from the shaft might bring dust into contact with the detector. In office areas, smoke detectors should not be placed directly over a smoker's desk or too close to a break room or cafeteria room, where smokers might congregate or where cooking might take place. Incidental cigarette smoke is not likely to set off projected beam smoke detectors. As a smoker passes near the beam, a cloud of smoke 3 ft to 10 ft (1 m to 3 m) wide might be produced, but it would not be thick enough to alarm the detector.

Detectors of the ionization or photoelectric type can be purchased with different sensitivities. Detector sensitivity is usually labeled on the detector and on its specification sheet. The sensitivity is typically between 1 percent and 4 percent per foot (0.3 m) obscuration. This is the amount of light obscuration measured immediately outside the detector when it alarms during tests with gray smoke. Comparing labels on a photoelectric and an ionization smoke detector usually indicates the ionization unit to be more sensitive. Typically, ionization smoke detectors have labeled sensitivities on the order of 1 percent to 2 percent per foot (0.3 m). Photoelectric detectors range from 1 percent to 4 percent per foot (0.3 m). This does not mean that ionization detectors are always more sensitive than photoelectric detectors, only that they might be more sensitive to fires that produce smoke similar to the gray smoke used in the test. A true comparison of detector sensitivity must include consideration of the type of smoke expected, as discussed in the previous paragraphs and in the section on fire signatures.

Sensitivity comparison is made more difficult by the fact that light obscuration is not comparable to those factors that set off either spot detector type. For photoelectric detectors, it is the light scattered, not the light obscured, that is important. For ionization units, it is the quantity and size of the particle. The amount of light obscured across a given distance is only partly related to these factors. The published numbers are useful only as a relative comparison between detectors of a given type as they react to a given type of smoke. A photoelectric detector having an alarm threshold of 2 percent per foot (0.3 m) obscuration is more sensitive than one with a threshold of 3 percent per foot (0.3 m). Similarly, an ionization detector with an alarm threshold of 1 percent per foot (0.3 m) is more sensitive than one with a threshold of 2 percent per foot (0.3 m). However, one cannot say that a photoelectric detector with a 2 percent per foot (0.3 m) threshold is as sensitive as an ionization detector with a 2 percent per foot (0.3 m) threshold. It might possibly be equally sensitive to the same gray smoke used by the testing laboratories to evaluate the units. In a real fire, many factors, including smoke color and size, cause one detector to respond before the other.

By nature of their design, projected beam smoke detectors are a good choice for large, open spaces. The source and the receiver of commercially available units might be placed as far as 300 ft (91 m) apart, with 30 ft (9 m) or more between adjacent beams. Therefore, there might be considerably fewer units to install, although each unit will be more expensive. The sensitivity of projected beam smoke detectors is stated in total percent obscuration required to alarm the unit, not percent per foot, as is the case with spot-type detectors. The sensitivity is usually adjustable, between about 20 percent and 70 percent total obscuration, allowing adjustment for different distances between the source and the receiver.

Because projected beam detectors respond to the accumulated smoke in their path, they are sensitive to real fires while remaining insensitive to many environmental factors that would alarm a spot-type detector. For instance, insects in the light path are not likely to block 20 percent of the beam. Similarly, a cigarette smoker might create a cloud of 1 percent to 2 percent per foot (0.3 m) smoke, which would be 5 ft or 10 ft (1.5 m or 3 m) in diameter. If this cloud were under a spot-type smoke detector, it would probably alarm unless a less sensitive unit were installed. However, the same cloud produces between 5 percent and 20 percent total obscuration of a beam projected through the cloud, which projected beam detectors can be set to disregard. Nevertheless, in a real fire scenario, a 20- to 30-ft (6- to 9-m) cloud of smoke, which is 1 percent to 2 percent per foot (0.3 m) on average, is likely to be produced by the time a spot-type detector is activated and goes into alarm. A beam projected through this cloud would be obscured about 20 percent to 60 percent, which would set off a beam detector that had been calibrated in that range. The projected beam detector could be set for 30 percent total obscuration to respond sooner to a real fire while still disregarding small sources of activation such as tobacco smokers, sinks, and kitchenettes.

Many other factors should be considered when selecting smoke detectors. For instance, in a room with moderate to high air movement, smoke from a fire that would normally set off a spot-type detector might be dissipated to form a thin haze. The fire must grow larger before there is enough smoke present to set off a spot-type detector. Use of either projected-beam or air-sampling detectors would overcome this delayed response. For more discussion of this and other factors affecting detector selection, consult NFPA 72, Chapter 2, as well as the *National Fire Alarm Code Handbook*, the *Fire Protection Handbook*, or the *Fire Alarm Signaling Systems Handbook*. A review of manufacturers' specification sheets and the standards used by testing laboratories for listing or approval can also provide some insight on detector selection.

The *Code* contains other choices concerning detector selection. In some cases heat detectors might be required or smoke detection simply cannot be used due to normal ambient conditions. In some locations, the authority having jurisdiction might require the area to be made suitable for smoke detectors. In other cases, it might be judged that heat detectors could be used and the life safety intent of the *Code* would still be met. These situations demand that a choice be made between the various types of heat detectors.

If the area has no friendly sources that produce rapid temperature changes, rate compensation or combination rate-of-rise/fixed-temperature heat detectors provide good results. If a fast-growing fire occurs, these detectors respond before a fixed-temperature heat detector. If a fire is slow-growing, they respond in about the same time as a fixed-temperature heat detector. Where rapid temperature changes are expected during normal conditions, fixed-temperature detectors should be chosen.

Detectors installed as household fire warning equipment must be installed in accordance with NFPA 72, Chapter 8. This category includes single- and multiple-station self-contained smoke alarms and small systems installed to meet the requirements within the dwelling unit. (The distinction among single, multiple, and system detectors is explained in the section on wiring.) Application of the *Life Safety Code*, combined with Chapter 8 of NFPA 72, usually results in the installation of smoke detectors on each level of a dwelling unit, outside of the bedrooms, and at the base of any stairs leading to upper levels. In new construction, detectors would also be placed in each bedroom.

However, where the smoke detectors also contain the alarm sounder to alert occupants, additional units might be needed to achieve audibility in all spaces of the dwelling unit. Additional detectors might also be warranted to provide longer escape times for some occupants or to provide faster response when complex floor plans are involved and smoke must travel a good distance to reach a required detector.

Where the *Code* requires an automatic fire alarm system initiated by smoke detection or heat detection, the spacing and placement of the chosen detectors is governed by NFPA 72, Chapter 2. The first step is to place detectors as close as possible to known hazards and as far away as possible from nuisance alarm sources. Any remaining space is then covered with evenly spaced detectors. This approach might result in a few more detectors than are required but will provide better fire detection and reduced chances of false and nuisance alarms. For example, in a hall of a college dormitory, conditions might allow smoke detectors to be spaced 35 ft (10.7 m) on center. However, if such spacing results in a detector immediately outside a shower room, it might be best to use a different increment of spacing, such as 28 ft (8.5 m), and to put detectors no closer to the shower room door than 14 ft (4.3 m).

The maximum spacing between detectors and the maximum distance from any point on the ceiling to a detector is determined by the many factors previously discussed for each detector type. For heat detectors, begin with the listed or approved spacing, then make corrections for ceiling height, beams, joists, and slopes. Where using smoke detectors, start with the manufacturer's recommended spacing, usually 30 ft (9 m), and make adjustments for ceiling height, beams, joists, slopes, and high airflow. Note that the actual correction factors in NFPA 72 for smoke detectors are different from the factors for heat detectors. Consult NFPA 72 for the exact correction factors to be used.

Once a detector spacing has been determined, detectors must be located in accordance with other requirements of NFPA 72. Exhibit S2.6, reproduced from Chapter 2 of NFPA 72, shows that ceiling-mounted detectors must be installed at least 4 in. (10 cm) from walls. If the detector is to be wall-mounted, it should be installed at least 4 in. (10 cm), but no more than 12 in. (30 cm), from the top of the wall. The 4 in. × 4 in. (10 cm × 10 cm) space is called the dead air space. Detectors in that space will respond more slowly because smoke and heat from a small fire tend to circumvent the wall–ceiling intersection.

When all correction factors have been applied to determine a required spacing for detectors, area coverage begins by locating the first detectors at one-half that distance from a wall. Exhibit S2.7, reproduced from NFPA 72, demonstrates this concept. One part of the exhibit illustrates how spot-type detectors would be spaced, and the other half indicates how line-type detectors would be evenly located. In the diagram, S is the corrected, or installed, spacing. These examples assume that the corrected spacing results in a square, such as 30 ft × 30 ft (9 m × 9 m) or 25 ft × 25 ft (7.6 m × 7.6 m). In the case of beams or joists, the corrected spacing would create a rectangle such as 15 ft × 30 ft (4.6 m × 9 m), the shorter distance being measured perpendicular to the joists or beams. Note in Exhibit S2.7 that no point on the ceiling can

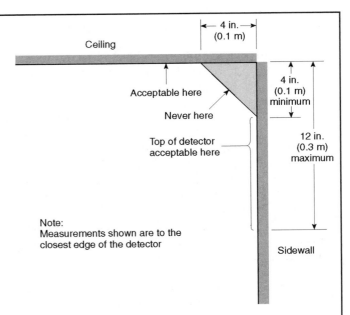

Exhibit S2.6 *Dead air space.*

be farther from a detector than 0.7 times the installed spacing. This maximum distance applies to all points on a ceiling and is useful in laying out systems in irregularly shaped spaces. This concept is discussed in detail in NFPA 72.

If a ceiling has solid beams or joists, it must be decided whether the detector should be located on the bottom of the beams or joists or in the ceiling pocket. In the case of joists, NFPA 72 always requires the detector, whether smoke or heat, to be located on the bottom of the joists. Joists are described as more than 4 in. (20 cm) deep and no more than 3 ft (1 m) apart. Beams are more than 4 in. (10 cm) deep and more than 3 ft (1 m) apart. In the case of beamed ceilings, the detector could be located on the bottom of the beams or on the ceiling in the pocket, depending on the beam depth, beam spacing, and ceiling height. The reader should refer to NFPA 72 for specific requirements. Note that bar joists and trusses might not significantly impede the movement of smoke and heat. Unless the top cord of the bar joist or truss that is in direct contact with the ceiling is more than 4 in. (10 cm) deep, the ceiling is considered smooth. In that case, the detectors must be mounted on the ceiling. Required detectors are not permitted to be mounted on the bottom of bar joists or trusses.

Detectors must also be located for ease of testing and maintenance. A smoke detector located over the open part of a stair tower probably cannot be reached very easily once scaffolding is removed. As a result, smoke detectors are often not tested or cleaned and

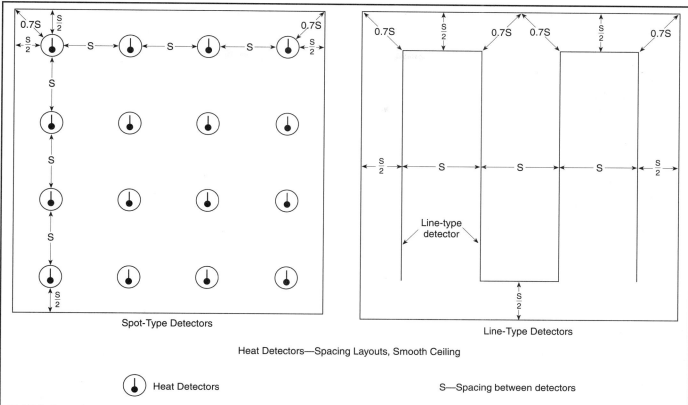

Spot-Type Detectors

Line-Type Detectors

Heat Detectors—Spacing Layouts, Smooth Ceiling

Heat Detectors

S—Spacing between detectors

Exhibit S2.7 Spot- and line-type detector spacing.

might fail in a fire or cause false or nuisance alarms. They should be located over a landing or where a ladder can be placed to reach them. There is no need to place the detector in the middle of the space. The space is considered to be adequately covered as long as all points on the ceiling are within the detector's protection radius (0.7 times the installed spacing).

Construction dust is one of the largest causes of false and nuisance alarms from smoke detectors. When smoke detectors are installed before all construction work is complete, they collect dust in their chambers. The dust can cause immediate alarms, or it can bring the detector close to alarming. As a result, the slightest physical disturbance, such as air movement or people walking, might set it off. If dust has caused a detector to become more sensitive, even small amounts of cigarette smoke or other aerosols will set it off. Plaster and gypsum board dust are very difficult to clear from a detector without disassembly and recalibration after cleaning by factory-trained service personnel.

Early installation of detectors must be resisted despite demands for a certificate of occupancy. This will only lead to future problems. NFPA 72 specifically states that smoke detectors are not permitted to be installed prior to the completion and cleanup of all other trade work. If acceptable to the authority having jurisdiction, however, the detectors might be installed while covered with bags or part of their original packaging. However, covering will render the smoke detectors unable to respond to smoke during a fire. The remainder of the system will be operational. Nevertheless, the life safety aspects of the system will have been compromised until the smoke detectors are uncovered.

In an open office area with a 20-ft (6-m) ceiling height, spot-type detectors might be used. However, once the area is occupied, maneuvering a high ladder for the purpose of testing is nearly impossible. This constitutes the perfect application for a projected beam smoke detector. The sender and receiver can be located on opposite walls where a ladder can be leaned to reach the units for cleaning and testing.

Many factors other than those discussed here affect the selection and placement of fire detectors. Temperature stratifications might prevent smoke from reaching the ceiling; airflow might speed the response of properly located detectors and slow the response of poorly located detectors; the height and width of fire and smoke doors might require additional smoke detectors for door release; machinery vibrations or radio frequency interference might result in the relocation of detectors to avoid false alarms. Complete familiarity with NFPA 72 is the source of a reliable system. The reference list following this supplement contains other valuable references to assist designers, installers, inspectors, and owners in achieving reliable fire detection while minimizing the chance of false or nuisance alarms.

POWER SOURCES AND SYSTEM WIRING METHODS

Household Fire Warning Equipment

Dwelling units are most often equipped with either single-station or multiple-station smoke detectors. In some cases, small systems designed as household fire warning equipment, with detectors, a control panel, and some notification appliances, are used. Often, the control panel also serves as part of a security system.

Single-station smoke detectors are stand-alone units that detect smoke and provide occupant notification. Multiple-station units are actually single-station detectors that can be interconnected so that, if one is activated, all units sound an alarm. Most single- and multiple-station smoke detectors contain only an internal horn, although some contain flashing lights as well. Units are also available with internal relays that can be used to control other functions, such as door release, a nurse call signaling system, activation of a bed vibrator to alert a hearing-impaired person, or operation of a light outside the dwelling unit.

For existing construction, the detectors are permitted to be powered by battery or by commercial light and power (usually 120 V AC). NFPA 72, Chapter 8, requires detectors used in new construction to have both primary AC power and secondary power by a battery. In existing households, AC power is preferred. However, where not practical, NFPA 72 allows the use of a monitored battery as the power source. Within the *Life Safety Code*, some occupancy chapters require AC power, even in existing facilities, where NFPA 72 would allow battery-operated units.

One reason AC-powered detectors are preferred is that the detector is less likely to be subject to tampering. Battery-powered units are often disabled when the battery is "borrowed" for a toy or other device. When batteries die, moreover, they are often not replaced for some time, leaving part or all of the dwelling unit without smoke detection.

Some argue that battery power is superior because, during a power outage, people resort to can-

dles for light and to fireplaces, stoves, or portable heaters for heat, all of which increase the possibility of fire. However, the increased chance of fire does not offset the fact that, over time, loss of commercial power is less likely and shorter in duration than loss of battery power. NFPA 72 reflects the belief that the chance of fire during a power outage is smaller than the chance of fire occurring when a detector is rendered useless because it has no battery.

Single-station smoke detectors are now available with integral battery backup. These units are allowed, but not required, by both the *Life Safety Code* and NFPA 72 for existing construction, but they are required for new construction. Local codes, ordinances, or authorities can, however, require their use.

NFPA 72, Chapter 8, requires that AC power not be controlled by a switch and that the circuit not have a ground fault interrupter. Direct wiring to a power circuit is preferred. However, if a plug-in electrical cord is used, the standard requires some restraining method to make certain the unit is not accidentally unplugged. It is preferred that AC-powered detectors be connected to an often-used light circuit, such as one feeding kitchen or hallway lights. Therefore, if a fault occurs, such as a blown fuse or circuit breaker, it is likely to receive immediate attention. If the detectors were connected to their own circuit or to one infrequently used, loss of power might go unnoticed until the units were tested. AC-powered units must also have a visual "power on" indicator.

Chapter 8 of NFPA 72 contains requirements for units that use batteries for primary power. Basically, they must be designed so the battery will last for at least one year of normal use, including weekly testing. Also, they must provide an audible trouble signal when the battery is low, well before the unit fails to operate. The unit must be capable of sounding a trouble condition at least once a minute for seven days and still have enough battery power to operate the alarm sounder for 4 minutes. Because of this requirement, it is very important that only battery types recommended by the manufacturer be used. Additionally, the smoke detectors must visually indicate when the battery has been removed.

Mechanically powered devices are allowed by NFPA 72, Chapter 8, and by the *Life Safety Code* unless otherwise stated in the occupancy chapter. Although not commonly used, these devices might be powered by compressed gas, a windup spring, or some other means. As with any equipment, they must be tested and listed or approved for the intended purpose. One reason mechanical devices are not common is that electrical power is required by commercially available smoke detection devices. The sound portion of the self-contained unit is permitted to be mechanical, as long as it meets the requirement for 4 minutes of alarm power and visually indicates when sufficient power is not available.

Where multiple-station units are used, they most often are connected to the same power circuit and also have a trip wire that interconnects them. When using multiple-station detectors, the manufacturer's wiring diagrams and instructions should be followed closely. There is a limit on how many units should be interconnected. Some models allow only five or six to be interconnected, while others allow up to thirty in a chain. However, Chapter 8 does not allow more than 12 multiple-station smoke detectors to be interconnected. Detectors from different manufacturers cannot be interconnected. Different models from the same manufacturer might not be compatible for interconnection. Compatibility between different models allows both ionization and photoelectric detectors to be used on the same circuit where each is advantageous and also allows various sensitivities to be used in different areas of the dwelling unit.

The *Life Safety Code* and NFPA 72, Chapter 8, both allow the use of component systems, rather than single- or multiple-station units, within a dwelling unit. The system must be listed or approved for use as household fire warning equipment. NFPA 72 contains requirements, including supervision of detector circuits, for the performance of component systems used within the dwelling unit. Supervision is not required when occurrence of fault still allows the detectors to perform as single-station units. Another exception allows the use of wireless radio as the signal transmission medium, provided each detector has its own transmitter and the unit automatically sends a test signal at least once every 24 hours. The installation of hard wiring for component systems is required to meet Article 760 of NFPA 70, *National Electrical Code.*®

The use of combination systems is allowed by NFPA 72, provided the fire detection and alarm portion takes precedence over all other functions. Alarm signals for fire and any other function, such as burglary, must be distinctive.

NFPA 72 Protected Premises and Supervising Station Systems

Power. Systems intended to meet the requirements of NFPA 72 are required to have two power sources— primary power and secondary power. Primary power must come from a reliable source and is usually taken from a commercial light and power source, although NFPA 72 allows other sources such as engine-driven

generators. Primary power must come from a dedicated branch circuit. Access to the circuit disconnecting means must be restricted and clearly marked "FIRE ALARM CIRCUIT CONTROL."

Secondary power is intended to operate all functions of the system in the event that primary power is lost. Most often, secondary power is provided by standby batteries. Engine-driven generators are also permitted to be used. The capacity of secondary power sources depends on the type of signaling system. Local, central station, and proprietary systems must be provided with secondary power capable of operating the system for 24 hours under normal loading conditions. Auxiliary and remote station systems must have 60 hours of supervisory power. At the end of the normal supervisory period, each system must have 5 minutes of alarm power available. An emergency voice/alarm communication system is required for 24 hours of supervisory power plus enough capacity to operate the system for 2 hours.

NFPA 72 Circuit Classifications. In addition to power supply circuits, three principal types of circuits are used in fire protective signaling systems:

(1) Initiating device circuits (IDCs)
(2) Signaling line circuits (SLCs)
(3) Notification appliance circuits (NACs)

An initiating device circuit (IDC) connects manual and automatic devices to a control panel or system. The main characteristic of an initiating device circuit is that the signal received at the control panel does not identify the device that operated. These circuits are also called initiating zones of the fire detection panel. Because the devices are not readily identified at the panel, the quantity of devices on a circuit and the area served by the circuit should be limited to make identification of the source a bit easier.

In addition, because the control panel cannot recognize the individual devices on the circuit, alarm devices cannot be mixed with supervisory devices, such as valve tamper switches, on the same circuit. Exhibit S2.8 shows one version of incorrect and correct methods for monitoring waterflow and valve tamper switches where using initiating device circuits.

A signaling line circuit (SLC) might connect initiating devices to a control panel or system or might interconnect various pieces of control equipment. An SLC is characterized by its ability to carry multiple signals, often in two directions, and to identify the source of the signal. For instance, multiplex systems, often called smart systems, communicate with initiat-

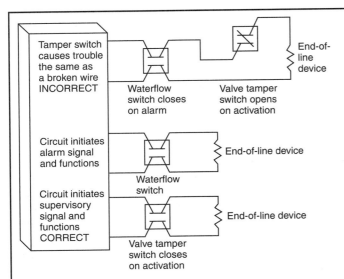

Exhibit S2.8   Incorrect and correct wiring of valve tamper switch.

ing and control devices. Each device or group of devices might have a unique address. The panel signals to a specific address and asks for the status of that "point." The device responds by repeating its address and its current status, such as "alarm" or "trouble." Therefore, the circuit is carrying multiple pieces of information and there is two-way communication.

Where signaling line circuits are used, it is possible to combine alarm and supervisory devices on the same circuit or data pathway. Because each device or group of devices is recognized at the control equipment, different output signals can be programmed for each.

The third type of circuit, the notification appliance circuit (NAC), serves appliances such as horns, bells, lights, and other notification appliances. NACs are often called signal circuits because they connect to devices intended to signal the occupants of a fire emergency. Even though occupant notification appliances generate a signal, care must be exercised not to confuse the circuit designations within the scope of NFPA 72. There are requirements for signaling line circuits that differ from those for notification appliance circuits.

Circuit Supervision. NFPA 72 requires all means for interconnecting equipment and devices to be monitored for integrity. This is commonly referred to as circuit supervision. The *Code* also contains requirements for monitoring power supplies as well as the circuits to detectors and notification appliances. Monitoring power sources is primarily a function of the control equipment. Compliance with NFPA 72

requirements is checked during testing and listing or approval of the system. See NFPA 72, Chapters 1 and 3, for performance and installation requirements.

The performance of IDCs, SLCs, and NACs is a function of the equipment and the installation of the circuits. Tables in NFPA 72 describe the performance of each type of circuit, including open circuits, ground faults, and short circuits, during various faults. Circuits are categorized by class and by style. IDCs, SLCs, and NACs are either Class A or Class B, depending on their ability to operate during a single open circuit or ground fault condition. Circuit style designations are based on their ability to operate during different combinations of faults, including grounds, opens, and short circuits. Neither the *Life Safety Code* nor NFPA 72 specify the class or style of circuits that must be used for a given application. Unless the authority having jurisdiction specifies a certain style, it is up to the designer to make a selection.

Some systems use selective signaling systems for occupant notification during a fire. These systems would sound evacuation signals or relocation signals only to certain areas of a building, such as the fire floor, floor above, and floor below. These are often part of a protected premises system, forming what is called a "combination system." The circuits connected to speakers and lights are still referred to as notification appliance circuits. Because these systems are most often used in high-rise buildings or in areas subject to levels of hazard that are higher than normal, NFPA 72 contains requirements for survivability of the notification functions when the circuits are attacked by fire. By requiring the system to survive an attack by fire in certain locations, the standard narrows the choice of circuit styles and the methods of installation. For more information on these requirements, consult NFPA 72, Chapter 3.

The discussion of circuits for controlling auxiliary functions, such as door release, fan control, and elevator recall, is beyond the scope of this supplement. Note, however, that the *Life Safety Code* and NFPA 72 require these circuits to be supervised to within 3 ft of the device being controlled. See Chapter 9 of the *Life Safety Code* and Chapter 3 of NFPA 72 for more information on these circuits.

Device Compatibility. Initiating devices and notification appliances must be compatible with the control equipment to which they are connected. Where addressable, multiplex-type equipment is used, there is no doubt that the equipment must be compatible and must be designed specifically to work together. With notification appliances and conventional initiating devices, however, there is more flexibility in choice.

In the case of notification appliances, compatibility is primarily a function of voltage and power consumption. Therefore, it is easy for designers, suppliers, and installers to match devices from one source with control equipment from another source. For initiating devices, compatibility depends on whether the device requires operating power. Mechanical devices such as manual fire alarm boxes, most heat detectors, and waterflow switches do not require power to operate. When they go into alarm, they close a set of contacts, as a light switch does, to signal the control panel. There is no compatibility issue; these devices can be mixed and matched among various manufacturers.

If a device does require operating power, as a smoke detector does, compatibility depends on whether its source of operating power comes from the initiating device circuit (often called the detection zone) or from a separate, external power circuit. Where power comes from a circuit other than the one used to signal the control panel, there is no compatibility issue. As in the case of notification appliances, compatibility is then only a function of voltage and power consumption from the external power circuit. When the detector alarms, it closes a set of contacts to signal the control panel via the initiating device circuit in the same way a mechanical pull station does.

However, where a device such as a smoke detector obtains its operating power from the same circuit it uses to signal an alarm, compatibility is very important. These devices are often referred to as two-wire, zone-powered, or circuit-powered detectors. The electrical characteristics of the control panel and the detectors, including supervisory currents and alarm currents, must be matched carefully to ensure proper operation. Detector compatibility is a very complex issue. For more information on this subject, consult manufacturers' data sheets, NFPA 72, the *Fire Alarm Signaling Systems Handbook*, and the approval or test agency's performance standards.

To check system compatibility, it is necessary to know the specific model of control panel as well as the model and quantity of the initiating device in question. Compatibility should be checked by consulting each manufacturer and the testing or approval agency acceptable to the authority having jurisdiction.

Wiring Methods. Article 760 of NFPA 70, *National Electrical Code*, covers the installation of wiring for fire alarm systems operating at 600 V or less. Two types of wiring methods are allowed by Article 760—

power-limited and non–power-limited. For a circuit to be designated as power-limited, it must meet certain voltage and power limitations. These are checked by the listing or approval agency. Where a circuit is designated as power-limited, the requirements for the wiring type and installation are less restrictive than if the circuit is non–power-limited.

In addition to defining power-limited and non–power-limited circuits, Article 760 provides detailed requirements for wiring methods. Included are requirements for wire gauges, insulation requirements, minimum requirements for stranded wires, overcurrent protection, circuit identification, and wiring raceways. Also included are restrictions on combining the use of power-limited and non–power-limited circuits and other nonfire circuits in the same raceway or enclosure.

The *National Electrical Code* should be consulted for details on wiring requirements. Additional discussion of Article 760 is contained in the *National Electrical Code Handbook*, which provides an explanation of the reasoning and intent behind specific code paragraphs.

SIGNALING

The subject of this section is output signaling, as opposed to the type of signaling that occurs between detectors and control equipment discussed in the section on wiring. The principal signaling functions of a system are off-premises signaling to emergency forces and occupant notification.

Off-premises signaling may be transmitted to a remote supervising station that is part of a central station system, an auxiliary system, a remote station system, or a proprietary signaling system in accordance with NFPA 72. Where off-premises signaling is required or desirable, NFPA 72, Chapter 5, should be consulted concerning installation and performance requirements for the system. This chapter contains requirements for the transmitter at the protected premises, the transmission method, and the receiving system. The standards allow only certain signaling methods that have shown themselves to be reliable. Telephone tape dialers, for example, and digital communicators with only one phone line are not recognized by NFPA 72.

Each occupancy chapter of the *Life Safety Code* clearly states where occupant notification and/or emergency forces signaling is required. The chapter might also require specific occupant notification systems such as emergency voice/alarm communication systems in high-rise hotels and dormitories. Each occupancy chapter should be carefully reviewed to determine which initiating devices are required to activate occupant notification signals and off-premises signaling. In most cases, all initiating devices operate as general alarm devices and activate all output functions. However, there are cases where detectors in specific areas of a building might not be required to sound evacuation signals.

Where occupant notification is required, it must be distinct and clearly audible in all occupiable spaces. NFPA 72, Chapter 4, contains criteria for the definition of audible. The recommended noise level from an alarm system is at least 15 dBA above the 24-hour average ambient level or at least 5 dBA above any peak background noise that lasts one minute or more; dBA stands for decibels, A-weighted. This is a way of measuring sound pressure levels and adjusting for the way the human ear hears.

The use of inexpensive meters (under $40) allows background levels in existing areas to be checked and systems to be installed appropriately. Ambient and fire alarm noise levels should be measured with all intervening doors closed and with common equipment such as air conditioners operating. For new construction, NFPA 72, Appendix A, provides examples of ambient noise levels in a variety of occupancies.

Once background levels have been determined, design methods can be used to determine where audible notification appliances should be located. One such procedure is presented and discussed in *The SFPE Handbook of Fire Protection Engineering*, published by NFPA. Calculations are not needed for existing construction. Portable appliances can be tried in a variety of locations before final mounting.

In most new construction, due to minimum insulation requirements and privacy laws, it is not possible to place alarm devices in common hallways and expect them to meet audibility requirements in adjacent spaces. Tests show that, in most cases, an audible device may be loud enough in only one or two immediately adjacent spaces. Therefore, a large number of units would be required in the common halls of occupancies such as apartments or dormitories. Cost estimates often indicate that it is less expensive to put smaller devices in each space, rather than to provide the required number of larger devices in common spaces.

In addition to audible appliances, the *Life Safety Code* might require visual appliances for occupant notification. NFPA 72, Chapter 4, would then be consulted for the proper selection and placement of visual appliances to meet specific needs. For instance, unlike the Americans with Disabilities Act Accessibility Guidelines (ADAAG), NFPA 72 treats visible signaling differently in nonsleeping versus sleeping

areas. The requirements for visible signaling are based on actual research on threshold alerting levels for hearing impaired persons conducted by Underwriters Laboratories. The 1996 and 1999 editions of NFPA 72 have been determined to be "equivalent facilitation," and in some cases superior, to the ADAAG.

The signal produced by notification appliances must also convey the following information: FIRE EMERGENCY. This is where the requirement for distinct signals is applied. For instance, in a school, bells should not be used on a fire alarm system if bells are also used to signal class changes and recess. Similarly, in buildings equipped with earthquake warning systems, the fire signal needs to be distinct and recognizable by the occupants. NFPA 72 permits more than one signal to be used in a building, such as chimes in patient care areas of a hospital and horns elsewhere. However, both must be distinct and not used for any other purpose.

NFPA 72 has a requirement for a standard audible evacuation signal. The signal, referred to as a temporal coded three signal, can be produced on a variety of appliances such as bells, horns, speakers, and chimes. A coded three signal is recognized internationally as a distress signal. Thus, it would be the pattern of the signal, not the particular sound, that would convey the information that there is a fire emergency.

Improvements and cost reductions in voice signaling equipment have made it economical to provide prerecorded and manual voice announcement systems in many applications. Most codes, including the *Life Safety Code*, require the use of voice signaling only in high-rise buildings, in large assembly occupancies, and in difficult to evacuate situations. Nevertheless, these system can be used effectively in a variety of applications. Because the NAC circuits are connected to speakers, driven by amplifiers, it is easier and less restrictive to add additional appliances when audibility is an issue than with conventional direct current devices. Also, speakers generally have adjustable power taps permitting minor adjustment in audibility that is not possible with most conventional sounders. Finally, it is well known that a properly implemented voice announcement will result in faster and more complete evacuation of occupants.

Other types of signaling that might be required include the following:

(1) Fan and damper control
(2) Heating, ventilating, and air-conditioning systems
(3) Smoke control systems

(4) Elevator control systems

(5) Emergency lighting systems

(6) Process control systems

The design, installation, testing, and maintenance of these systems should be performed by qualified fire protection engineers, technicians, and inspection professionals. Where activation of these or other emergency control systems is required by a chapter of the *Life Safety Code*, specific requirements are found in Chapter 7.

SYSTEM TESTING AND MAINTENANCE

Surveys and general field experience continue to demonstrate the importance of continued testing and maintenance of fire detection and signaling systems. Testing identifies problems before they impair a system's ability to perform during an emergency. Maintenance reduces false and nuisance alarms and keeps systems in service.

The *Life Safety Code* requires all fire detection and signaling equipment to be maintained and tested in accordance with the appropriate signaling standard. In the case of household fire warning equipment, NFPA 72, Chapter 8, is the governing standard. For other systems, NFPA 72, Chapter 7, contains requirements for acceptance and periodic tests, visual inspections, and maintenance.

NFPA 72, Chapter 7, contains three important tables. The first lists the methods for testing specific components, devices, and appliances. The second table lists the required frequency for visual inspections. The third table lists the required frequency for actual testing of the specific components, devices, and appliances.

Whenever a system or device is to be tested, it is important to notify those who might hear or receive a signal from the system. Usually, this means several days of advance notice to authorities and regular occupants of the area. In addition, when testing or working on systems, the authority having jurisdiction must be notified, even for periodic tests that they might not witness. Other trades or specialists might require notice to participate in the tests. For instance, testing of smoke detectors used for elevator recall might require elevator technicians to be present. Similarly, HVAC mechanics or electricians may be required to reset air-moving equipment or dampers after the system is tested. In addition, posting notices at entrances to the premises to alert people as they arrive is usually advisable. Notices should include phone numbers or brief procedures for reporting emergencies while the system is being tested or serviced.

When testing occupant notification systems, it is important to keep to a posted schedule and minimize the time of testing to prevent occupants from becoming desensitized to the signaling. This requires having sufficient personnel and equipment to do a thorough and fast test. Consider recruiting key occupants to assist in qualitative examination of the notification system. Try to minimize the frequency and duration of the tests. For example, test only at 10:00 a.m. and again at 2:00 p.m. and for only 30 to 60 seconds.

Household Fire Warning Equipment

The requirements for testing and maintenance of household fire warning equipment are kept simple so that, in most cases, the work can be done by the homeowner. NFPA 72 requires that battery-operated units get new batteries in accordance with the manufacturers' recommendations. In most cases, manufacturers recommend replacement of batteries at least once a year. Recent educational and awareness programs have promoted battery changing at the same time that clocks are changed from daylight savings time to standard time in the fall of each year. Scheduled replacement tends to increase confidence that the detector will work when needed, rather than waiting for the signal that indicates the need for replacement. Facilities with large numbers of battery-operated detectors save time and labor by replacing all batteries at the same time, whether or not it is necessary.

NFPA 72 requires monthly testing of household fire warning equipment. Where small systems with detectors and control panels are used in lieu of single- or multiple-station smoke detectors, NFPA 72 requires the owner to have the system tested by qualified technicians at least every 3 years. An Internet site (http://www.testyoursmokealarms.com) is available where homeowners can sign up for a monthly e-mail with fire safety tips and a reminder to test their smoke alarms.

All tests, inspections, and maintenance recommended by the manufacturer must be performed in accordance with its instructions. This emphasizes the importance of providing the owner, member of the household, or occupant with the manufacturer's instruction booklet(s). Without the proper documentation, the individuals performing the test may not be aware of their responsibilities or the correct methods for testing and maintenance. NFPA 72 requires the installer or supplier to provide this and other information to the owner. In addition to the instructions, the owner must receive information on how to establish an evacuation plan and information on parts that require regular replacement, such as batteries. The owner must also receive written information on where to obtain repair and replacement service.

Each smoke detector for use in an NFPA 72, Chapter 8, application is required to have an integral test method to permit testing of the system and sensitivity. This is usually a test button or switch. Unless otherwise recommended by the manufacturer, this test button is the best way for the occupant to test the detector. By using the test button, the detector is checked for operation at the limit of sensitivity allowed by the ANSI/UL test standards for the detector. Using unmeasured aerosols such as cigarette smoke or canned smoke does not measure sensitivity. This might prove that a detector is operational, but the sensitivity may be so low that the amount of smoke required to alarm it is enough to have already caused harm or a delay in detector response to a real fire. An aerosol should be used to verify that the smoke detector is not blocked by excessive dust accumulation or by intential blocking of the screen or ports. It is often not possible to tell by visual inspection alone if a detector has been blocked.

Cleaning of smoke detectors is necessary to prevent false and nuisance alarms and to ensure detector operation during a fire. NFPA 72 leaves the methods and frequency of cleaning up to each manufacturer. Most manufacturers recommend cleaning once or twice a year by vacuuming around the outside of the detector. Some detectors are now available that can be washed in a soap/water solution. Most manufacturers do not recommend disassembly of detectors for cleaning except by qualified technicians. If the detector is cleaned and properly maintained from the time it is new, the need for factory cleaning and calibration is almost eliminated.

Acceptance Testing

NFPA 72 requires 100 percent testing of the entire system upon completion of any installation or alteration. The test must include all devices and equipment and must test the system in all modes, including alarm, trouble, and supervisory. Satisfactory tests must be made in the presence of the authority having jurisdiction or a designated representative. NFPA 72 recognizes reacceptance tests on parts of systems affected by alterations or repairs.

A preliminary certificate of completion is required to be issued to the owner and, if requested, to the authority having jurisdiction prior to the final acceptance test. The preliminary certificate is issued after installation and wiring tests have been completed. A final version is to be issued and distributed after all operational acceptance tests have been completed. A sample copy of a certificate of completion is included in NFPA 72.

Following final acceptance of the system, the installer or supplier must provide the owner with an owner's manual or manufacturer's installation instruction as well as final "as-built" drawings. During acceptance or reacceptance testing, the certificate of completion and as-built drawings must be verified for accuracy and completeness. If necessary, corrections should be made to the master documents, and any old copies should be replaced or updated.

Installation testing includes checking the entire system for stray voltages, ground faults, short circuits, and open circuits. Ground fault testing includes testing all conductors not intentionally connected to ground.

The loop resistance of initiating and notification appliance circuits must be measured and recorded. The measured value should be checked against the maximum allowable loop resistance indicated by the manufacturer of the control equipment. Signaling line circuits should also be tested in accordance with the manufacturer's recommendations. This will usually include measurement of circuit capacitance in addition to resistance.

System testing is done after all installation tests have been performed. After replacing any equipment removed during testing of the circuits, the control unit and all devices should be verified as being in the normal supervisory mode. Each circuit should be checked for proper supervision and integrity. This includes testing open circuit trouble indication as well as ground fault and short circuit fault indicators where provided. Where the style of circuit allows alarm receipt during specific faults, correct operation should be checked by testing devices electrically before and after the location of the test fault. It is useful during the testing to use a copy of the wiring style tables from NFPA 72 as a checklist.

Every initiating device and indicating appliance must be checked for correct alarm operation. This verifies correct operation of the device, the circuit, and the control equipment. For systems that respond differently and result in different outputs depending on the device or devices in alarm, a programming matrix should be prepared and checked. The matrix, or system description, should explain what occurs when each particular device or group of devices is operated. For instance, an alarm from any first floor detector might cause bells to ring, doors to release, and a connection to the fire department to be activated. On the other hand, perhaps only certain smoke detectors will activate a smoke management system. The use of a table or matrix describing these options speeds testing and future work on the system.

Power supplies must also be tested during acceptance and reacceptance tests, including testing the switchover from primary to secondary power by disconnecting the primary supply. While the system is powered by the secondary supply, the standby current should be measured in accordance with the manufacturer's recommendations. The required standby capacity can then be calculated and compared to that which was provided. While on secondary power, the system should be tested for full alarm performance for at least 5 minutes. This test should be repeated with the system on primary power and with any secondary supply disconnected. Supervision of power supplies should also be tested.

Smoke detectors must be tested in accordance with Chapter 7 of NFPA 72. During an acceptance test, it is not necessary to measure the detector's sensitivity. A pass/fail or go/no-go test using smoke or another unmeasured aerosol is acceptable. All smoke detectors, including duct and air-sampling types, must be checked to ensure that smoke is entering the detector's chamber. In all cases, the manufacturer's directions should be followed.

The NFPA 72 requirement for retention of test records is 2 years. All equipment should be tested in accordance with the requirements of the standards and the manufacturers' recommendations.

Periodic Testing

In addition to provisions for acceptance testing, NFPA 72 contains requirements for periodic tests and maintenance. Essentially, NFPA 72 requires all testing to be performed by qualified persons who understand the equipment. Ultimately, the owner of the system is responsible for ensuring that all required tests are done on time. Owners are permitted to rely on a written maintenance agreement with others rather than develop and use their own specialists. Delegation of responsibility for testing and maintenance must be in writing.

The required frequency for testing a device varies. Chapter 7 of NFPA 72 contains the required frequencies for all devices.

NFPA 72 requires the sensitivity of all smoke detectors to be checked within 1 year of the acceptance test, and every other year thereafter. During the years when sensitivity tests are not required, a pass/fail test using smoke or another unmeasured aerosol is still required. The intent of the sensitivity test is to

ensure that the detector is within its listed and marked sensitivity range. Detectors that are more than 0.25 percent per foot (0.3 m) obscuration out of range must be recalibrated or replaced.

The most common methods for testing detector sensitivity use either control panels that can check detector sensitivity remotely or meters that plug into the detector for testing. In some cases, the meters are common volt–amp meters and in other cases they are factory-supplied devices. There are also test instruments that generate measured smoke clouds that can be used to test any brand of detector. Using unmeasured aerosols such as cigarette smoke or canned smoke does not measure sensitivity. It might prove that a detector is operational, but the sensitivity might be so low that the amount of smoke required to cause an alarm is enough to have already caused harm or a delay in detector response to a real fire. On the other side of the issue, a detector might alarm when tested with cigarette smoke but be so sensitive that it would also nuisance alarm due to small amounts of friendly smoke.

In terms of smoke detector cleaning, NFPA 72 simply states that the frequency of service should be based on the ambient conditions. If the area is very clean, 1 to 2 years between cleanings might be possible. In very dusty or dirty areas, or areas with high airflow, cleaning might be required every 3 to 6 months. In most residential, business, and institutional-type occupancies, yearly cleaning is usually sufficient. A sensitivity test must be performed on any detector that has been washed or disassembled for any reason, including cleaning.

Once a year, air duct smoke detectors must be checked to verify that they are properly sampling the air stream. The manufacturer's recommendations for testing should be followed. This may involve measuring the pressure difference between the air sampling and air return tubes.

CONCLUSION

Fire alarm systems range from very simple units to large complex systems. This supplement has only briefly introduced the reader to the many requirements and good practices associated with their design, installation, testing, and use.

The *Life Safety Code* and the *National Fire Alarm Code* contain a wealth of information for persons involved with any phase of a fire alarm system's life. By drawing on the expertise of hundreds of professionals and specialists, users of these NFPA documents benefit from years of combined experience, which no one person or company could hope to attain.

REFERENCES

For additional information concerning the design, installation, testing, maintenance, and use of fire alarm systems, consult these references:

1. Richard W. Bukowski, Robert J. O'Laughlin, and Charles E. Zimmerman, ed., *Fire Alarm Signaling Systems Handbook*, National Fire Protection Association, Quincy, MA, 1994.
2. *Fire Protection Handbook*, 18th edition, National Fire Protection Association, Quincy, MA, 1997.
3. *The SFPE Handbook of Fire Protection Engineering*, 2nd ed., National Fire Protection Association, Quincy, MA, 1995.
4. *Training Manual on Fire Alarm Systems*, National Electrical Manufacturers Association, 2101 L Street, Washington, D.C. 20037, 1997.
5. *Guide for Proper Use of System Smoke Detectors*, National Electrical Manufacturers Association, 2101 L Street, Washington, D.C. 20037, 1997.
6. *Guide for Proper Use of Smoke Detectors in Duct Applications*, National Electrical Manufacturers Association, 2101 L Street, Washington, D.C. 20037, 1997.
7. NFPA 72, *National Fire Alarm Code®*, 1999 edition, National Fire Protection Association, Quincy, MA.
8. NFPA 90A, *Standard for the Installation of Air-Conditioning and Ventilating Systems*, 1999 edition, National Fire Protection Association, Quincy, MA.

In addition to the preceding publications listed and state and local authorities, the following organizations are sources for information on fire detection and signaling systems:

Automatic Fire Alarm Association, P.O. Box 1652, Barrington, IL 60011

Factory Mutual System, P.O. Box 9102, Norwood, MA 02062

National Fire Protection Association, 1 Batterymarch Park, Quincy, MA 02269-9101

National Institute for Certification in Engineering Technologies, 1420 King Street, Alexandria, VA 22314-2715

Underwriters Laboratories Inc., 333 Pfingsten Road, Northbrook, IL 60062-2096

SUPPLEMENT 3

A Brief Introduction to Sprinkler Systems for *Life Safety Code* Users

Revised by Milosh Puchovsky, P.E.

The very first edition of the *Life Safety Code,* published in 1927, included provisions for the use of sprinkler systems. Back in 1927, however, sprinkler systems were associated more with property protection than with life safety. This is not surprising, since in 1896, it was largely property insurance interests that developed the first set of rules for sprinkler system installations in North America. Since that time, however, the effectiveness of sprinkler systems as life safety devices has been widely demonstrated.

Sprinkler system effectiveness in terms of life safety is best summarized by the following statement, which is based on fire incident data. "NFPA has no record of a fire killing more than two people in a completely sprinklered building where the system was properly operating, except in an explosion or flash fire or where industrial or fire brigade members or employees were killed during fire suppression operations." This statement is particularly impressive because it pertains to statistics concerning system performance since the turn of the twentieth century, when sprinkler system effectiveness was uncertain.

Over the years, technological advancements and experience have increased sprinkler system effectiveness and reliability, improved design and installation practices, and produced more cost-effective systems. Where properly designed, installed, and maintained, no other stand-alone fire protection system, active or passive, provides a higher level of protection to building occupants. The use of a sprinkler system in combination with other life safety systems such as fire alarms and compartmentation results in a

much more complete and comprehensive life safety package.

NFPA SPRINKLER SYSTEM STANDARDS

The National Fire Protection Association publishes three standards that address the design and installation of sprinkler systems. NFPA *101* references each of these standards. NFPA 13, *Standard for the Installation of Sprinkler Systems,* has the broadest scope and is the oldest and most comprehensive of the sprinkler system standards. NFPA 13 addresses both property protection and life safety for a wide range of facilities, including those used for public assembly, education, detention, health care, residential, business, mercantile, manufacturing, and storage.

Interestingly, it was concerns about a lack of a uniform set of rules for sprinkler system installations that prompted the creation of the National Fire Protection Association and NFPA 13 in 1896. Once established, NFPA expanded its scope to address many safety-related concerns, including those associated with electricity, which was a new technology back at the turn of the twentieth century.

NFPA also publishes NFPA 13R, *Standard for the Installation of Sprinkler Systems in Residential Occupancies Up to and Including Four Stories in Height,* and NFPA 13D, *Standard for the Installation of Sprinkler Systems in One- and Two-Family Dwellings and Manufactured Homes.* These standards are relatively new compared to NFPA 13, having been developed within the past 25 years primarily to address life safety concerns in certain types of residential occupancies. Property protection is not the primary objective for NFPA 13D and NFPA 13R.

Other NFPA codes and standards also include information about sprinkler system design and installation for specialized hazards. In all, over 40 such documents exist. For example, NFPA 30, *Flammable and Combustible Liquids Code,* addresses sprinkler systems for the protection of flammable liquids, and NFPA 130, *Standard for Fixed Guideway Transit and Passenger Rail Systems,* includes requirements for sprinkler systems specific to transit systems.

NFPA *101* does not reference standards specific to specialized hazards, because the sprinkler system information in these standards usually extends beyond that needed for life safety. Fire safety objectives concerning property protection are usually more difficult to achieve than those for life safety. NFPA 13, NFPA 13D, and NFPA 13R are adequate for the life safety concerns addressed by NFPA *101.* It is worth noting that the 1999 edition of NFPA 13 has been expanded to include or reference sprinkler system information from all other NFPA codes and standards.

Some Basic Principles of NFPA 13

Certain underlying principles about sprinkler systems have existed since the first edition of NFPA 13. To begin, sprinkler systems are designed to protect against the occurrence of a single fire in a building at one given time. Designing for more than one fire is usually considered unnecessary, given the rarity of multiple ignition sources. Designing for more than one ignition source would greatly increase sprinkler system costs while providing minimal benefit.

Sprinkler systems are limited in size, depending on the associated fire hazards in the building. This restriction serves to control the impact of a sprinkler system impairment on the overall fire protection of large facilities. Additionally, each sprinkler system is required to be equipped with a waterflow indicating device, as well as a local alarm that indicates when waterflow is occurring.

Sprinkler systems are characterized as being automatic and must include an automatic water supply. Sprinkler systems are designed to discharge a specified amount of water from a predetermined number of sprinklers during a fire. An automatic sprinkler system will automatically flow water when one or more sprinklers on the system activate. A sprinkler system that relies on human intervention to initiate waterflow is not considered automatic, is not permitted by NFPA 13, and would be ineffective for most life safety concerns.

A sprinkler system's water supply must be adequate and reliable. This statement means the available water supply must meet or exceed the sprinkler system's water demand 24 hours a day, seven days a week, 365 days a year. A sprinkler system's water demand is most commonly determined though hydraulic calculations and is expressed in units of flow, pressure, and time. The requirement for reliability exists because it is often impossible to predict with a sufficient degree of confidence when a fire will occur. As a means of further addressing the reliability of water supplies consisting of a water works system, NFPA 13 requires a certain allowance for fire hose demand. In addition, most systems require a connection for the fire department to supplement the automatic water supply.

With the exception of certain types of systems used for industrial and commercial property protection concerns, most automatic sprinkler systems utilize automatic sprinklers. Automatic sprinklers are heat-sensitive devices that operate only when exposed to a certain quantity of heat. Therefore, only those sprinklers in close proximity to a fire will operate. Unlike incorrect portrayals often depicted in movies and television, automatic sprinklers do not operate when exposed to smoke or when someone initiates the building fire alarm. Additionally, when one automatic sprinkler activates, all the sprinklers in the building or the compartment do not activate unless the entire space protected by the sprinklers is burning.

For a sprinkler system to be effective, sprinklers must be located where a fire is anticipated. The success of a sprinkler system in controlling or suppressing a fire depends on the sprinkler discharge reaching the fire area when the fire is in its early stages of development and relatively small. Where a fire is severely shielded from sprinkler system discharge or the fire starts in an unsprinklered area, the chances for successful sprinkler system performance greatly decrease. With few exceptions, NFPA 13 requires that sprinklers be located in all areas throughout the building, that each sprinkler cover a certain size floor area, and that sprinklers be positioned to allow for timely activation and an undisrupted spray pattern.

Piping, sprinklers, valves, and other components that make up a sprinkler system are regulated to ensure an adequate degree of overall system reliability. Like other fire protection systems, sprinkler systems are emergency systems and, as such, are not intended to operate routinely as are other building systems. When the sprinkler system does operate, it is during a fire, and therefore the system and all its components must perform as intended under adverse conditions. One means of ensuring proper system reliability is to require the use of only listed system components. Listed components are thoroughly evaluated by a testing laboratory and have a higher degree of reliability than nonlisted components. Another additional means necessary to achieve adequate system reliability is to conduct routine inspection, testing, and maintenance activities on the system. These activities are discussed later in this supplement.

Modifications to the Basic Principles of NFPA 13

Because NFPA 13 addresses both property protection and life safety, its requirements are the most restrictive of the three sprinkler system standards. Other NFPA codes and standards, including NFPA *101*, supplement or modify the requirements of NFPA 13 in order to achieve other objectives related to protection against certain types of fire hazards. The most obvious of the modifications to NFPA 13 concerns the location of sprinklers.

As already indicated, NFPA 13 requires that sprinklers be located throughout the premises with very few exceptions. Although NFPA 13 acknowledges the concept of a partial sprinkler system, it provides no provisions for such a system. NFPA *101*, on the other hand, permits partial systems for certain types of facilities. For example, Chapter 31, dealing with existing apartment buildings, allows an option for providing sprinkler coverage in selected areas of the building only. More specifically 31.3.5.2 requires that sprinklers be provided only in corridors, provided the doors to the dwelling units have at least a 20-minute fire protection rating and are self-closing. This partial sprinkler system is intended to protect building occupants against a fire that would impede the occupants' ability to exit the building. Sprinkler protection against fires in other areas that could cause severe property damage is not required because it is expected that building occupants can safely egress the building with the aid of other fire protection systems and features. However, it is important to note that partial sprinkler protection is permitted by NFPA *101* only for specific facilities and under limited conditions.

Another of the differences between NFPA *101* and NFPA 13 concerns the sounding of the sprinkler's waterflow alarm. NFPA 13 requires that initiation of

the waterflow device only sound a local alarm at some point on the premises. NFPA *101* requires that the waterflow device be part of the building's fire alarm system and that initiation of the waterflow device sound a building-wide evacuation alarm.

The differences between NFPA 13 and NFPA *101* with respect to sprinkler system requirements can best be explained by the purpose of NFPA 13: to protect property as well as human life. In most cases, where sprinklers are used to protect property, protection of life will also be accomplished. Property protection is usually a more difficult goal to achieve with sprinklers than is life safety. Areas exempted from requiring sprinklers in NFPA *101* are those in which sprinklers would not be expected to have an impact on the number of injuries or fatalities from a fire. That same fire, however, might result in significant property damage; therefore, NFPA 13 contains no similar exemptions.

NFPA 13D

NFPA 13D, *Standard for the Installation of Sprinkler Systems in One- and Two-Family Dwellings and Manufactured Homes*, was first published in 1975 in response to *America Burning: The Report of the Commission on Fire Prevention and Control*, which was released in 1973. The America Burning Report revealed that, of the estimated 12,000 fire deaths occurring in the United States each year, a disproportionate number occurred in the home. The commission recommended that a low-cost fire protection system for the home be developed.

The first edition of NFPA 13D included the use of existing technology addressed by NFPA 13 for the protection of commercial properties, with broader exceptions for omitting sprinkler coverage and reducing water supply duration. NFPA 13D mandates a minimum water supply duration of 10 minutes, whereas NFPA 13's minimum is 30 minutes under certain conditions. Shortly after the first edition of NFPA 13D was published, the United States Fire Administration (USFA) announced a research program to develop residential sprinkler system technology specifically for life safety.

Automatic sprinkler systems using standard spray sprinklers have been effective in reducing loss of life due to fire, primarily by providing protection to occupants in areas adjacent to or outside the room of fire origin. The aim of the USFA residential sprinkler research program was to develop a sprinkler that would control a fire in an occupied room for the period of time necessary for occupants to escape.

Response time, discharge pattern, duration of water supply, and fire loading in residential occupancies were among other factors investigated during the research program. The outcome of the program was the development of the residential sprinkler. The residential sprinkler differs from existing standard spray sprinklers in that it has a fast response operating element—that is, the sprinkler responds sooner during a fire because it requires less heat to activate. It also possesses a discharge pattern that sprays water higher on a wall. The higher wall wetting characteristics of the sprinkler impede radiative feedback from the wall onto other combustibles in the room and significantly slow fire growth and spread. The second edition of NFPA 13D, published in 1980, incorporated the new technology of residential sprinklers.

NFPA 13R

NFPA 13R, *Standard for the Installation of Sprinkler Systems in Residential Occupancies Up to Four Stories in Height*, was first published in 1989 and is also geared toward life safety. The scope of NFPA 13R is limited to apartments, hotels, motels, select board and care facilities, and rooming houses four stories or less in height. NFPA 13R provides a high but not absolute level of life safety to building occupants and a lesser degree of property protection than NFPA 13.

NFPA 13R was developed in response to the success of the residential sprinkler and the growing need to apply this technology to larger residential occupancies. Certain communities were requiring sprinkler systems in multifamily residential occupancies and were developing their own installation rules. Although NFPA 13 would have been acceptable for use in such properties, these communities desired a more cost-effective option that would provide a sufficient level of life safety and some degree of property protection.

NFPA 13R considers the economics of sprinkler protection by allowing the omission of sprinklers from more areas than that permitted by NFPA 13. However, the omissions are not as extensive as those in NFPA 13D. Such omissions result in the need for less hardware and therefore less labor to install the systems, thus reducing overall costs. NFPA 13R permits the omission of sprinklers in certain bathrooms, closets, porches, balconies, and concealed spaces that contain combustible construction materials. A significant area from which sprinklers are exempted is the attic. This exemption is based on the attic's not being used for living purposes or for storage. In most parts of the United States, an attic would require the use

of a dry pipe system or an antifreeze system. These systems can significantly increase overall costs.

As with NFPA 101, the primary distinction between NFPA 13 and NFPA 13R is the designation of areas that do and do not require sprinklers. Rules concerning component installation, allowable materials, and design between NFPA 13R and NFPA 13 are identical.

NFPA 13R is specified for use in numerous occupancies by NFPA 101, including those addressed in Chapters 24 through 33. One difference in scope between NFPA 13R and NFPA 101 centers on the application of NFPA 13R in certain residential board and care occupancies. In 32.3.3.5.1 and 33.3.3.5.1, NFPA 101 permits the use of NFPA 13R systems, regardless of the evacuation capability of residents, in facilities defined as "large." Conversely, NFPA 13R has intended to limit its scope to board and care facilities having 16 or fewer occupants in the slow evacuation category or any number of occupants who might fit into the prompt evacuation category. Since NFPA 13R permits the omission of sprinklers in a number of spaces, fires that occur in these unsprinklered areas are likely to have a greater impact on residents who require additional evacuation time.

DETERMINING THE FIRE HAZARD

Proper determination of the fire hazards present is crucial to the overall success of a sprinkler system. Sprinkler systems are not generic, where "one size fits all." Each system must be individually designed so that it can adequately control or suppress the fire hazards anticipated in a given facility.

With few exceptions, such as where certain sprinklers will be used for storage facilities or dwelling units, fire hazards are to be categorized according to one of five *occupancy hazards* presented in NFPA 13. The occupancy hazards range from the least severe (light hazard) to the most severe (extra hazard, group 2).

The occupancy hazards provide a convenient means for categorizing the fuel loads and fire severity associated with certain building operations, and they present a relationship between the burning characteristics of these fuels and the ability of a sprinkler system to control the associated types of fires. The likelihood of ignition is not considered in the occupancy hazard classifications.

To a large degree, determination of the proper occupancy hazard classification in accordance with NFPA 13 is the most critical decision. This determination impacts all sprinkler system design and installation factors such as sprinkler discharge criteria, sprinkler spacing, and water supply requirements. Fundamentally, the less severe the fire hazard, the smaller the water demand for the sprinkler system. Additionally, each sprinkler will be permitted to cover a larger floor area, thus resulting in a fewer number of sprinklers for the building. Likewise, the more severe the fire hazard, the larger the total water demand and the smaller the floor area that can be protected by a single sprinkler.

It is important to note that an entire building does not necessarily have to fall within a single occupancy hazard classification. Rather, each space needs to be considered individually when determining the occupancy hazard. For example, NFPA 13 would typically treat an educational facility as a light hazard occupancy, a classification that holds true for spaces such as classrooms, offices, and cafeteria seating areas. However, the light hazard classification is not valid for such areas as a wood shop, laboratory, and food preparation area. Spaces such as the wood shop contain more hazardous materials with a higher heat release rate, and therefore that portion of the sprinkler system that is effective for classrooms cannot be expected to be effective for a fire in a wood shop.

The occupancy hazards presented in NFPA 13 should not be interpreted as a generic description or quantification of fire hazards, and they are not intended to parallel the occupancy classifications used in the *Life Safety Code*. Although these two concepts are similar in some ways, they have different meanings. *Occupancy classification* refers to the relative fire threat to building occupants from the contents and operations of that building. *Occupancy hazard* is associated with the description of the relative fire challenge present in a building and the ability of the sprinkler system to control it.

NFPA 13 provides a comprehensive list of *occupancy hazards* to determine the design parameters for a sprinkler system. In a similar way that Chapter 6 of the *Life Safety Code* provides descriptions of the classification of occupancies. Table S3.1 illustrates some of the differences between the occupancy hazards defined in NFPA 13 and the hazard of contents classifications used by the *Life Safety Code*. Table S3.1 represents a partial listing of the occupancies addressed by NFPA 13 and NFPA *101* and is representative of the 1999 and 2000 editions of these documents respectively.

SYSTEM COMPONENTS AND HARDWARE

Regardless of which sprinkler standard is used, similar components and concepts are employed for the design and installation of a sprinkler system. For example, all systems consist of a pipe network for delivering water to the sprinklers. Hangers attached to the building structure support the pipe network. Control valves serve to isolate the water supply and other portions of the system. A waterflow device and an alarm mechanism notify building occupants or others that water is flowing through the system. NFPA's sprinkler standards ensure that all system components are properly coordinated to ensure reliable and effective system performance.

Sprinklers

Sprinklers vary in shape and form and differ in use or purpose. When the first "conventional" sprinkler was developed in the 1870s, it was primarily intended for use in industrial environments. In the 1950s the spray sprinkler was introduced and became the dominant sprinkler. The standard spray sprinkler continues to be effective in controlling fires for a broad range of occupancies. However, other types of sprinklers have since been introduced.

The standard spray sprinkler is available as an upright, pendent, or sidewall model. Exhibit S3.1 illustrates a standard spray pendent sprinkler manufactured by Grinnell Sprinkler. As will be discussed, this sprinkler uses a standard response operating element. Depending on the occupancy being protected

Table S3.1 NFPA 13/NFPA 101 Occupancies

Occupancy	NFPA 13 Occupancy Hazard	NFPA *101* Hazard of Contents
Assembly	Light hazard	Ordinary hazard
Health care	Light hazard	Ordinary hazard
Mercantile	Ordinary hazard (group 2)	Ordinary hazard
Storage up to 12 ft (3.7 m) in height	Ordinary hazard (group 2)	Ordinary hazard
Industrial (using flammable and combustible liquids)	Extra hazard (group 2)	High hazard

Exhibit S3.1 Grinnell standard spray pendent sprinkler.

and the construction features of the space, the sprinkler's discharge could adequately cover a floor area of up to 225 ft² (20.8 m²).

Since the introduction of the standard spray sprinkler, numerous other varieties of sprinklers have been introduced. Technology associated with sprinklers has advanced further than the technology for any other sprinkler system component. These advances have been spurred by past successes with sprinkler systems, the desire for more cost-effective systems, and the need for systems to specifically achieve life safety and fire suppression.

Residential Sprinklers. Since 1896, sprinklers have been designed to control fire growth rather than to suppress or extinguish fire. This concept was especially apparent during the residential sprinkler program undertaken in the mid-1970s that focused on and resulted in the production of listed residential sprinklers. Residential sprinklers are designed to provide a tenable environment for occupants in the room of fire origin, not necessarily to protect an occupant in the room of fire origin who is intimate with the ignition source.

Although residential sprinklers were specifically developed for use in NFPA 13D systems, they are acceptable for use in any of the residential occupancies addressed by NFPA 13R and NFPA 13. Residential sprinklers are currently listed using UL 1626, *Standard for Residential Sprinklers,* and FM Class 2030, *Approval*

Standard for Residential Automatic Sprinklers. Residential sprinklers are evaluated for their ability to control air temperatures at a level 5 ft (1.5 m) above the floor and to minimize the production of carbon monoxide. In addition, residential sprinklers are thermally sensitive and are designed to activate during a fire's early stages of development. Residential sprinklers fall under the category of fast-response sprinklers. The fast-response characteristic, along with the sprinkler's unique discharge pattern, makes it possible to maintain tenable conditions in the room of fire origin.

Residential sprinklers are available in either pendent or sidewall models. Exhibit S3.2 shows a horizontal sidewall residential sprinkler manufactured by Viking Corporation, and Exhibit S3.3 shows the installation of a sidewall sprinkler in a hotel room. The criteria for installing residential sprinklers differ from those required for standard spray sprinklers and are addressed by NFPA 13, NFPA 13R, and NFPA 13D. In general, the minimum required flow rate from each residential sprinkler is determined when the sprinkler is listed. However, at the time this supplement was being prepared, this minimum flow rates for residential sprinklers installed in accordance with NFPA 13 and NFPA 13R are being re-evaluated.

Over the course of approximately 14 years, the use of the residential sprinkler has been responsible for several "saves," as documented by Operation Life Safety, a program conducted by the International Association of Fire Chiefs. Residential sprinklers per-

Exhibit S3.2 Viking horizontal sidewall residential sprinkler.

Exhibit S3.3 Installation of sidewall sprinkler in a hotel room.

Exhibit S3.4 Viking upright-mounted quick-response sprinkler.

formed as intended in fires characterized by a wide range of residential fire scenarios.

Quick-Response Sprinklers. A direct result of the residential sprinkler program was the development of other fast-response sprinklers such as the quick-response (QR) sprinkler. Listed QR sprinklers are similar to standard spray sprinklers except that they possess a fast-response operating element. Other characteristics, such as discharge pattern, remain the same. QR sprinklers are available as upright, pendent, or sidewall sprinklers. An upright quick-response sprinkler manufactured by Viking Corporation is illustrated in Figure S3.4.

Although differences between QR sprinklers and residential sprinklers exist, QR sprinklers are permitted for use in both residential and nonresidential occupancies, with certain limitations. The QR sprin-

kler is evaluated according to UL 199, *Standard for Automatic Sprinklers for Fire Protection Service*, or FM class 2000, *Approval Standard for Automatic Sprinklers for Fire Protection*. These product standards are used to evaluate the effectiveness of QR sprinklers as well as other types of standard response sprinklers.

QR sprinklers discharge their spray pattern in a manner that differs from that of residential sprinklers. Therefore, QR sprinklers are not specifically designed for the same purpose as residential sprinklers, although they provide a higher level of protection to occupants than standard response sprinklers. In recognition of this fact, NFPA *101* allows the use of QR sprinklers in certain occupancies in the same manner as the residential sprinkler.

Recognizing the associated life safety benefits, NFPA 13 mandates the use of quick-response sprinklers in all light hazard occupancies as defined by NFPA 13. The exception is that residential sprinklers can be used in residential occupancies. Additionally, NFPA 13 includes incentives for using QR sprinklers in ordinary hazard occupancies. Because of the types of fires expected and the overall fire safety objectives, the use of QR sprinklers in extra hazard occupancies is not currently advocated.

There is a tendency to use the terms *residential sprinkler* and *quick-response sprinkler* interchangeably. Although similar in some respects, these two sprinklers differ in terms of their intended use, discharge characteristics, and positioning requirements. Exhibit S3.5 provides an overview of the various types of fast-response sprinklers.

The most common measure for determining a

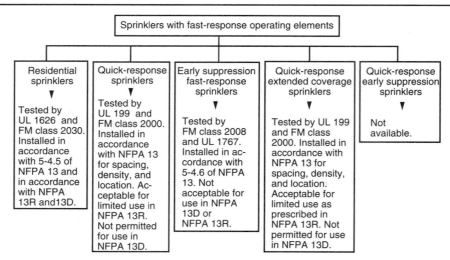

Exhibit S3.5 *Types of fast-response sprinklers.*

sprinkler's responsiveness to heat from a fire is the response time index (RTI). RTI values are used to gauge the thermal sensitivity of a sprinkler to determine whether it meets the criteria for a fast-response sprinkler. In general, this measurement is determined by the rapidity at which the thermal element will operate under a standardized test condition.

Other Sprinkler Types and Styles. In addition to the creation of the residential sprinkler, the USFA residential program initiated further sprinkler research. Today, numerous types and styles of sprinklers exist. Sprinklers have literally become a specialty item, considering the form and function of sprinklers in today's market. For example, sprinklers are now available with custom color finishes that blend with certain wall and ceiling finishes. Other devices are low profile and streamlined to the point that they are not easily noticed. Certain sprinklers can be installed behind special concealed plates coated by the sprinkler manufacturer to match the ceiling background. Exhibits S3.6, S3.7, and S3.8 illustrate the use of concealed sprinklers in residential dwelling units. It is important to note that coatings applied to a sprinkler to enhance its appearance or corrosion protection are permitted to be applied only by the sprinkler manufacturer.

Extended coverage (EC) sprinklers are available for use in today's sprinkler systems. As its name implies, this device is tested and listed to cover relatively large areas. For example, some EC sprinklers are capable of covering a 20 ft × 20 ft (6.1 m × 6.1 m) area, whereas a standard spray sprinkler is limited to maximum of 15 ft × 15 ft (4.6 m × 4.6 m) under ideal conditions.

Exhibit S3.6 *Concealed sprinkler application in a bathroom.*

Exhibit S3.7 *Concealed sprinkler application in a living room.*

Exhibit S3.9 illustrates a Model M pendent-mounted extended-coverage sprinkler manufactured by Viking Sprinkler. This sprinkler can protect larger floor areas than those protected by a single standard spray sprinkler. Another advantage of using the extended coverage sprinkler is that fewer sprinklers are needed to protect a building. However, the downside is that EC sprinklers require a higher operating pressure and a greater rate of waterflow.

EC sprinklers are available as upright, pendent, or sidewall models. In addition, EC sprinklers can possess more thermally sensitive operating elements, since the sprinklers can be located at a distance farther from a potential fire. However, just because an EC sprinkler contains a more thermally sensitive operating element, it should not necessarily be considered a fast-response sprinkler unless specifically listed as such. On the other hand, some EC sprinklers are listed as such and are referred to as quick-response, extended-coverage (QREC) sprinklers.

Identification of Sprinklers. One of the changes to the 1999 edition of NFPA 13 includes the establishment of a sprinkler identification marking to become effective in January 2001. The marking aims to provide a degree of order among the large number of sprinkler types and styles available on the worldwide market and will better facilitate the interchangeabil-

ity of sprinklers. The marking will be stamped on the sprinkler and entered into a database to be maintained by the listing laboratories and the International Fire Sprinkler Association. The database will be available through the Internet.

The sprinkler marking will identify the manufacturer and the model number so that the sprinkler's function and application can be more easily identified. Sprinkler characteristics such as orifice size and shape, deflector characteristic, and thermal sensitivity will also be more easily referenced. It is intended that the marking be checked against the database to ensure that the sprinklers are used properly and within the limitations of their listings.

In addition to the model number, other markings might also be imprinted on the device. These additional items can include the temperature rating, orifice diameter, identification of the listing organization, and a designation indicating the orientation or type of sprinkler. Although not specifically mandated, the coding given in Table S3.2 is often used to identify certain sprinkler types.

Sprinklers for High-Challenge Fires. In the case of high-challenge fires, such as those found in warehouses, standard spray sprinklers with large orifices, large-drop sprinklers, and early-suppression, fast-response (ESFR) sprinklers are commonly used. These

Exhibit S3.8 *Concealed sprinkler application in a residential kitchen.*

Table S3.2 Identification Codes for Sprinkler Types

Sprinkler	Coding
Standard spray pendent	SSP
Standard spray upright	SSU
Extended coverage	EC
Quick-response	QR
Quick-response, extended-coverage	QRES
Residential	RES

sprinklers have undergone a significant amount of full-scale fire testing in conjunction with the application of fire engineering principles to verify their performance and installation criteria.

The large-drop sprinkler program managed by the Factory Mutual Research Corporation in the mid-1980s developed a sprinkler capable of producing water droplets of size and mass sufficient to penetrate the fire plumes typical of storage-type fires. The result of this effort was the large-drop sprinkler as shown in Exhibit S3.10. Formerly, a standard response sprinkler was used to control warehouse fires. This research program continued to pursue the development of a sprinkler that could suppress rather than just control a warehouse fire.

In 1988, Factory Mutual granted approval for the ESFR sprinkler. This device combines fast-response technology, a very high rate of waterflow, and the production of large water droplets to penetrate the

Exhibit S3.9 *Viking Model M Pendent-Mounted Extended-Coverage Sprinkler.*

Exhibit S3.10 *Viking Model A large-drop sprinkler.*

upward momentum of the fire plume and deliver water to the surface of the burning materials. Several varieties of ESFR sprinklers are now available, as shown in Exhibits S3.11 and S3.12. The largest of these has an orifice of about 1 in. and is required to flow approximately 178 gpm (674 L/min). The ESFR sprinkler is the only suppression-mode sprinkler currently available.

High-challenge sprinklers are not intended for use in most of the occupancies addressed by NFPA *101*. These sprinklers are intended for use in large

Exhibit S3.11 *Pendent-type ESFR sprinklers.*

Exhibit S3.12

storage facilities and are not specified for use by NFPA *101*.

Pipe Materials

Some pipe materials have been permitted for use by NFPA 13 for more than 100 years. For example, schedule 40 steel pipe has been the prominent material used for sprinkler systems for many years. In the 1950s, copper tubing was introduced as an acceptable material, but its use was not fully recognized by NFPA 13 until 1965. The standard currently allows three different types of copper tubing to be used. Both steel pipe and copper tube fabricated to one of the manufacturing standards identified by NFPA 13, 13R, and 13D do not need to be specifically listed for fire protection service.

NFPA 13 also permits the use of steel pipe that is not fabricated to one of the manufacturing standards specified, provided such steel pipe is specifically listed for fire protection service. Thin-wall steel pipe has been made available for use in sprinkler systems. This material results in somewhat better hydraulic characteristics and is easier to handle due to its lighter weight.

In 1984, the Shell Oil Company made a significant breakthrough in sprinkler system component technology when it introduced the first nonmetallic pipe for sprinkler systems. This material, polybutylene (PB) pipe, is specifically listed for fire protection service and was initially permitted for use only in systems designed under the requirements of NFPA 13D. In 1986, permission for its use was extended to all light hazard occupancies as defined by NFPA 13. This material continues to be acceptable for use in light hazard occupancies as well as in those facilities addressed by NFPA 13R and NFPA 13D. However, the resin used in the manufacture of various grades of PB pipe is no longer produced because of problems with other types of PB products.

Another nonmetallic product entered the market in 1986. The BF Goodrich Tire and Rubber Company developed a resin and licensed several manufacturers to produce chlorinated polyvinyl chloride (CPVC) pipe. This pipe is also specifically listed for fire protection service and is fully recognized as an acceptable component in sprinkler system design. As with PB pipe, its use is limited to light hazard occupancies as defined by NFPA 13 and to systems designed according to NFPA 13D and NFPA 13R.

Both PB and CPVC pipe come with unique installation restrictions and rules as set by the manufacturer and the listing laboratory. These rules include but are not limited to (1) use only in wet pipe systems;

(2) mandatory installation behind a protective barrier, such as a ceiling (note that the CPVC product is permitted to be installed exposed under special conditions); and (3) support of the pipe in accordance with the manufacturer's instructions.

Selection of those pipe materials permitted by NFPA's sprinkler system standards for a specific project could be based on a number of factors that need to be considered in unison. Each pipe material possesses its own advantages and disadvantages. For example, the advantage of using a lighter material, such as nonmetallic pipe, needs to be weighed against the need to follow specific manufacturer's technical data sheets to ensure correct installation. Another example includes schedule 40 steel pipe, which has a thicker wall and is more forgiving when threading or cut grooving the ends. In this instance, the tradeoff involves greater weight per length of pipe, which might translate to higher labor costs and perhaps less effective hydraulic characteristics when compared to thinner walled pipe.

Some sprinkler contractors prefer the use of copper tube or nonmetallic pipe for the installation of new systems in existing buildings. The advantage of lighter materials plus the flexibility associated with these materials is a key consideration. This can result in reduced labor costs. In many cases, the pipe material used is based on the capabilities, resources, and comfort level of the installing contractor.

Fittings

NFPA 13 has similar rules for fittings as it does for pipe materials. NFPA 13 permits the use of nonlisted cast iron, malleable iron, steel and copper fittings to be used provided they are manufactured to certain standards. A number of special fittings that are specifically listed for fire protection service are also available. Specially listed fittings usually reduce the effort needed to join pipe materials, but they can possess less desirable hydraulic characteristics. Additionally, special fittings possess unique installation instructions as set by the manufacturers and the listing laboratory.

Specially listed fittings are evaluated for their compatibility with specific types of pipe and their ease of installation. Grooved end fittings, for example, are listed for use only with specific types of listed couplings and listed rubber gaskets. In most cases, the fitting, coupling, and gasket are made by the same manufacturer. The availability of such fittings can decrease installation time and effort, but it requires that the authority having jurisdiction verify the compatibility of the assemblies.

INSPECTION, TESTING, AND MAINTENANCE OF SPRINKLER SYSTEMS

Inspection, testing, and maintenance activities are crucial for effective sprinkler system performance. This is especially true because of the inactive nature of a sprinkler system. Unlike other types of building systems intended for use on a routine basis, the sprinkler system will only be used during emergency situations. The system's proper operating condition is not verifiable through day-to-day operations as are the heating, air-conditioning, and plumbing systems. Therefore, NFPA 13 requires that the building owner or designated representative employ and follow an inspection, testing, and maintenance program specified in NFPA 25, *Standard for the Inspection, Testing, and Maintenance of Water-Based Fire Protection Systems*. Additionally, 9.7.5 of NFPA *101* also requires compliance with NFPA 25.

NFPA 25 provides a detailed program for conducting visual examinations (inspections), physical checks (tests), and work (maintenance) on various system components to keep water-based fire protection systems in proper working condition. Chapter 2 of NFPA 25 pertains specifically to sprinkler systems. However, certain portions of Chapter 9 from NFPA 25 are also applicable, since it addresses all valves associated with water-based fire protection systems, including sprinkler systems. Table S3.3, from NFPA 25, summarizes the requirements specific to sprinkler systems.

Some of the inspection items are relatively straightforward and require only a visible observation of the specified component. For example, when inspecting sprinklers it must verified that the sprinklers have not been damaged or painted and that their discharge pattern will remain unobstructed. Inspection of pipe and pipe hangers should determine that the pipe is undamaged and that the hangers remain securely attached to the building structure and the pipe it is supporting.

Testing of certain system components requires a more hands-on approach and a more through understanding of sprinkler systems. Testing normally requires that water be flowed through portions of the system and that certain measurements such as elapsed time and pressure change be recorded. Testing activities serve to ensure proper operation of the component being operated during the test as well as to verify overall operation of the system.

Maintenance activities typically require more effort. Even the more basic activities such as replacing a painted sprinkler require that the entire sprinkler system or a portion of it be shut down and drained

Table S3.3 Summary of Sprinkler System Inspection, Testing, and Maintenance

Item	Activity	Frequency	Reference
Gauges (dry, preaction deluge systems)	Inspection	Weekly/monthly	2-2.4.2
Control valves	Inspection	Weekly/monthly	Table 9-1
Alarm devices	Inspection	Quarterly	2-2.6
Gauges (wet pipe systems)	Inspection	Monthly	2-2.4.1
Hydraulic nameplate	Inspection	Quarterly	2-2.7
Buildings	Inspection	Annually (prior to freezing weather)	2-2.5
Hanger/seismic bracing	Inspection	Annually	2-2.3
Pipe and fittings	Inspection	Annually	2-2.2
Sprinklers	Inspection	Annually	2-2.1.1
Spare sprinklers	Inspection	Annually	2-2.1.3
Fire department connections	Inspection		Table 9-1
Valves (all types)	Inspection		Table 9-1
Alarm devices	Test	Quarterly	2-3.3
Main drain	Test	Annually	Table 9-1
Antifreeze solution	Test	Annually	2-3.4
Gauges	Test	5 years	2-3.2
Sprinklers—extra-high temp.	Test	5 years	2-3.1.1 Exception No. 3
Sprinklers—fast response	Test	At 20 years and every 10 years thereafter	2-3.1.1 Exception No. 2
Sprinklers	Test	At 50 years and every 10 years thereafter	2-3.1.1
Valves (all types)	Maintenance	Annually or as needed	Table 9-1
Obstruction investigation	Maintenance	5 years or as needed	Chapter 10

before the sprinkler can be replaced. Other maintenance activities can become more involved, such as investigating the interior of system piping to determine whether obstructions are present and then removing the obstructions.

Although inspection, testing, and maintenance activities are usually associated with specific components of the sprinkler system, the scope of NFPA 25 extends beyond these activities. The purpose of NFPA 25 is to provide a means to ensure that the sprinkler system will perform as intended in accordance with NFPA 13 or NFPA 13R. Therefore, NFPA 25 addresses any occurrence that can impair a sprinkler system's ability to control or suppress a fire. Changes in building use or construction fall into this category. The operations of a given facility can vary significantly over time and change the overall fire hazard or the fire hazard in certain spaces. More common is the relocation of walls and other building features that can delay sprinkler activation times and obstruct spray patterns. These potential building modifications must be properly accounted for when conducting inspection, testing, and maintenance activities, and when evaluating the adequacy of an existing sprinkler system.

A sprinkler system not in compliance with the requirements of NFPA 25 is not in compliance with NFPA 13. An improperly maintained system is likely to be impaired in some way and cannot be expected to meet its fire protection objectives. In terms of life safety, an impaired system can have a more detrimental effect on overall building fire safety than if no sprinkler protection was provided at all. For example, the *Life Safety Code* provides certain provisions for increasing travel distances and reducing construction ratings where sprinkler systems are installed. Therefore, if a sprinkler system is impaired, the building occupant would be at a greater disadvantage.

CLOSING REMARKS

Sprinkler systems have established an enviable record for achieving life safety and property protection for well over 100 years. However, it is imperative that the appropriate NFPA sprinkler system standard be followed for designing, installing, and maintaining these systems. While NFPA's sprinkler system standards provide many options for achieving effective system performance, these documents are not textbooks providing basic instruction about sprinkler systems. Proper sprinkler system performance requires that only knowledgeable, qualified people design, install, maintain, inspect, and review plans for these systems.

Through the Fire Protection Research Foundation and other associated organizations, as well as the research and development activities undertaken by sprinkler system component manufacturers and insurance interests, new sprinkler system breakthroughs occur each year. These efforts continue to build on the impressive record of sprinkler systems and will lead to even more options for effective and economical systems.

Additional Readings

For those interested in further information on sprinkler system design and theory, the following texts are recommended.

John L. Bryan, *Automatic Sprinkler and Standpipe Systems*, 3rd ed., National Fire Protection Association, Quincy, MA, 1997.

Automatic Sprinkler Systems Handbook, 8th ed., National Fire Protection Association, Quincy, MA, 1999.

The SFPE Handbook of Fire Protection Engineering, 2nd ed., Society of Fire Protection Engineers, National Fire Protection Association, Quincy, MA, 1995.

NFPA, *Fire Protection Handbook*, 18th edition, National Fire Protection Association, Quincy, MA.

The following report from NFPA discusses the effectiveness of automatic sprinklers:

John Hall, Jr., *U.S. Experience with Sprinklers: Who Has Them? How Well Do They Work?* National Fire Protection Association, Quincy, MA, 1997.

Extracts from ASME *Elevator Code and Handbook*

Extracts from ASME A17.1, Section 211, Emergency Operation and Signaling Devices†

Rule 211.1 Car Emergency Signaling Devices

Elevators shall be provided with the following signaling devices.

(a) In all buildings, the elevator shall be provided with the following:

(1) An audible signaling device, operable from the emergency stop switch, where required by Rule 210.2(e), and from a switch marked "ALARM," which is located in or adjacent to each car operating panel. The switch marked "ALARM" shall illuminate when actuated. The signaling device shall be located inside the building and audible inside the car and outside the hoistway. One signaling device may be used for a group of elevators.

The audible signaling device shall

(a) Have a rated sound pressure rating of not less than 80 dBA nor greater than 90 dBA at 10 ft (3.05 m);

(b) Respond without delay after the switch has been activated;

(c) Be located inside the building and audible inside the car and outside the hoistway;

(d) For elevators with a travel greater than 100 ft (30.48 m), be duplicated as follows:

†Reprinted with permission from ASME A17.1, *Safety Code for Elevators and Escalators*, American Society of Mechanical Engineers, Three Park Avenue, New York, New York 10016-5990.

(1) One device shall be mounted on the car; and

(2) A second device shall be placed at the designated level.

(e) One signaling device may be used for a group of elevators.

(2) Means of two-way conversation between the car and a readily accessible point outside the hoistway, which is available to emergency personnel (telephone, intercom, etc.). The means to activate the two-way conversation system does not have to be provided in the car.

(3) If the audible signaling device(s), or the means of two-way conversation, or both, are normally connected to the building power supply, they shall automatically transfer to a source of standby or emergency power as required by the applicable building code or, where applicable, *Standard for Health Care Facilities* (ANSI/NFPA 99) after the normal power supply fails. The power source shall be capable of providing for the operation of the audible signaling device and of the alarm switch for at least 1 h, and the means of two-way conversation for at least 4 h.

(b) In buildings in which a building attendant (building employee, watchman, etc.) is not continuously available to take action when the required emergency signal is operated, the elevators shall be provided with a means within the car for communicating with or signaling to a service which is capable of taking appropriate action when a building attendant is not available. A standby or emergency power system shall be provided conforming to the requirements of Rule 211.1(a)(3).

(c) A means of two-way conversation between the car and the machine room (telephone, intercom, etc.) as required by Rule 210.14(i)(3).

Rule 211.2 Standby Power

An elevator may be powered by a standby power system, subject to the following requirements:

(a) When operating on such standby power there shall be conformance with the requirements of Rules 207.8 and 210.10, except that where the standby power system is designed to operate only one elevator at a time, the energy absorption means, if required, may be located on the power side of the elevator power disconnecting means, provided all other requirements of Rule 210.10 are conformed to when operating any of the elevators the system serves.

(b) Other building loads such as power and light that may be supplied by the standby power system shall not be considered as a means of absorbing the regenerated energy for the purpose of conforming to Rule 210.10 unless such loads are using their normal power from the standby power system when it is activated.

(c) A manual elevator standby power selection switch shall be provided at the designated level to override any automatic sequence operation. Operation of this standby power selection switch shall cause power to be removed from an elevator only when that elevator is stopped.

(d) Operation of the standby power selection switch shall be of the key-operated type or be under a locked cover. Keys, including locked cover keys, shall conform to the requirements of Rule 211.8.

Rule 211.3 Firefighters' Service—Automatic Elevators

All automatic (nondesignated attendant) elevators shall conform to the requirements of this rule. The requirements of this rule do not apply when the hoistway, or portion thereof, is not required to be fire-resistive construction (Rule 100.1a), the travel does not exceed 6 ft 8 in. (2.03 m) and the hoistway does not penetrate a floor.

211.3a Phase I Emergency Recall Operation. A three-position key-operated switch shall be provided only at the designated level for each single elevator or for each group of elevators. The three-position switch shall be marked "BYPASS," "OFF," and "ON" (in that order) with the "OFF" position as the center

position. The three-position switch shall be located in the lobby within sight of the elevator or all elevators in that group and shall not be located behind a locked door or cover. An additional two-position ("OFF" and "ON," in that order) key-operated switch shall be permitted at a central control station for fire department operations. The switch(es) shall be rotated clockwise to go from the "OFF" to "ON" position. All keys shall be removable only in the "OFF" and "ON" positions.

No device, other than the Phase I switch(es) or the smoke detectors in the elevator lobbies, machine room, or hoistway (Rule 211.3b), shall initiate Phase I operation.

Normal elevator service shall be provided and the operation from the smoke detectors required by Rule 211.3b shall be functional when all Phase I switches are in the "OFF" position, except as specified in Rule 211.3a(10).

When the designated-level three-position switch is in the "BYPASS" position, normal elevator service shall be restored regardless of the status of the smoke detectors required by Rule 211.3b.

When the three-position switch or two-position switch, when provided, is in the "ON" position:

(1) All cars controlled by this switch which are on automatic service shall return nonstop to the designated level and power-operated doors shall open and remain open. On cars with two entrances, if both entrances can be opened at the designated level, doors serving the lobby where the three-position Phase I switch is located shall open and remain open.

(2) A car traveling away from the designated level shall reverse at or before the next available landing without opening its doors.

(3) A car stopped at a landing shall have the in-car emergency stop switch or in-car stop switch rendered inoperative as soon as the car moves away from the landing. A moving car shall have the in-car emergency stop switch or in-car stop switch rendered inoperative without delay. Once the in-car emergency stop switch or in-car stop switch has been rendered inoperative, it shall remain inoperative while the car is on Phase I operation. All other stop switches required by Rule 210.2 shall remain operative.

(4) A car standing at a landing other than the designated level, with the doors open and the in-car emergency stop switch or in-car stop switch in the run position, shall conform to the following:

(a) Elevators having automatic power-operated horizontally sliding doors shall close the doors without delay and proceed to the designated level.

(b) Elevators having power-operated vertically sliding doors provided with automatic or momentary pressure closing operation per Rule 112.3d shall have the closing sequence initiated without delay in accordance with Rules 112.3d(1), (2), (3), and (5), and the car shall proceed to the designated level.

(c) Elevators having power-operated doors provided with continuous pressure closing operation per Rule 112.3b or elevators having manual doors, shall be provided with a visual and audible signal system to alert an operator to close the doors and shall, when the doors are closed, conform to the requirements of Rule 211.3a. Sequence operation, if provided, shall remain effective.

(5) Door reopening devices, for power-operated doors, which are sensitive to smoke or flame shall be rendered inoperative without delay. Door reopening devices not sensitive to smoke or flame (e.g., mechanically actuated devices) are permitted to remain operative. Door closing for power-operated doors shall conform to the requirements of Rule 112.5.

(6) All car and corridor call buttons shall be rendered inoperative. All call registered lights and directional lanterns shall be extinguished and remain inoperative. Car position indicators, where provided, shall remain in service. Hall position indicators, where provided, shall be extinguished and remain inoperative except at the designated level and the central control station, where they shall remain in service for fire department operations.

(7) Where provided on installations with vertical slide doors, corridor door open and corridor door close buttons shall remain operative.

(8) All cars shall be provided with an illuminated visual and audible signal system which shall be activated to alert the passengers that the car is returning nonstop to the designated level. The visual graphic shall be as shown in [Exhibit S4.1]. The signals shall remain activated until the car has returned to the designated level.

(9) A car stopped at a landing shall have the in-car door open button rendered inoperative as soon as the car moves away from the landing. A moving car shall have the in-car door open button rendered inoperative without delay. Once the in-car door open button has been rendered inoperative, it shall remain inoperative until the car has returned to the designated level.

(10) If an additional two-position Phase I switch is provided, it shall not affect Phase I operation if the designated-level smoke detector [Rule 211.3b(2)] has been activated.

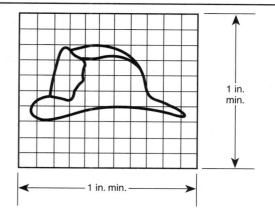

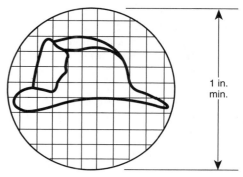

Exhibit S4.1 *Visual signal. (From ASME A17.1, Section 211, Figure 211.3a)*

(11) The "BYPASS" position on the three-position Phase I switch shall not restore the elevator to normal service if the two-position Phase I switch is in the "ON" position.

211.3b Smoke Detectors. System-type smoke detectors conforming to the requirements of UL 268 shall be installed in each elevator lobby and associated machine room in accordance with NFPA 72, Chapter 3. Smoke detectors are not required in elevator lobbies at unenclosed landings. System-type smoke detectors shall be permitted to be installed in any hoistway and shall be installed in hoistways which are sprinklered (see Rule 102.2).

(1) The activation of a smoke detector in any elevator lobby, other than at the designated level, shall cause all cars that serve that lobby to return nonstop to the designated level. The activation of a smoke detector in any elevator hoistway shall cause all elevators having any equipment located in the hoistway, and any associated elevators of a group automatic operation, to return nonstop to the designated level, except that smoke detectors in hoistways installed at

or below the lowest landing of recall, when activated, shall cause the car to be sent to the upper level of recall. The operation shall conform to the requirements of Rule 211.3a.

(2) When the smoke detector at the designated level is activated, the operation shall conform to the requirements of Rule 211.3a, except that the cars shall return to an alternate level approved by the enforcing authority, unless the designated-level three-position Phase I switch (Rule 211.3a) is in the "ON" position.

(3) The activation of a smoke detector in any elevator machine room, except a machine room at the designated level, shall cause all elevators having any equipment located in that machine room, and any associated elevators of a group automatic operation, to return nonstop to the designated level. The activation of a smoke detector in any elevator machine room at the designated level shall cause all elevators having any equipment located in that machine room, and any associated elevators of a group automatic operation, to return nonstop to the alternate level, or the appointed level when approved by the authority having jurisdiction.

(4) Elevators shall only react to the first smoke detector zone which is activated for that group.

(5) Phase I operation, when initiated by a smoke detector, shall be maintained until canceled by moving the Phase I switch to the "BYPASS" position [see also Rule 211.3a(10)]. Smoke detectors and/or smoke detector systems shall not be self-resetting.

NOTE (Rule 211.3b): In buildings with fire alarm systems, see NFPA 72A for additional information.

211.3c Phase II Emergency In-Car Operation. A three-position ("OFF," "HOLD," and "ON," in that order) key-operated switch shall be provided in an operating panel in each car. The switch shall be rotated clockwise to go from the "OFF" to "HOLD" to "ON" position. It shall become effective only when the designated level Phase I switch (Rule 211.3a) is in the "ON" position or a smoke detector (Rule 211.3b) has been activated, and the car has returned to the designated or alternate level by Phase I operation.

The key shall be removable in each position. The "OFF," "HOLD," and "ON" positions shall not change the operation until the car is at a landing with the doors in the normal open position.

(1) When the Phase II switch is in the "ON" position, the elevator shall be on Phase II operation, for use by trained emergency service personnel only, and the elevator shall operate as follows:

(a) The elevator shall be operable only by a person in the car.

(b) All corridor call buttons and directional lanterns shall remain inoperative. Car position indicators, where provided, shall remain in service. Hall position indicators, where provided, shall remain inoperative except at the designated level and the central control station, where they shall remain in service for fire department operations.

(c) The opening of power-operated doors shall be controlled only by a continuous pressure door open button. If the button is released prior to the doors reaching the normal open position, the doors shall automatically reclose. Rules 112.4a, 112.3c, and 112.3d do not apply. On cars with two entrances, if both entrances can be opened at the same landing, separate door-open buttons shall be provided for each entrance.

(d) Open power-operated doors shall be closed only by continuous pressure on the door close button. If the button is released prior to the doors reaching the fully closed position, horizontally sliding doors shall automatically reopen and vertically sliding doors shall automatically stop or stop and reopen. On cars with two entrances, if both entrances can be opened at the same landing, a separate door-close button shall be provided for each entrance.

(e) Opening and closing of power operated car doors or gates which are opposite manual swing or manual slide hoistway doors shall conform to the requirements of Rules 211.3c(1)(c) and (d). Door opening and closing buttons shall be provided in the car operating panel.

(f) All door reopening devices shall be rendered inoperative. Full speed closing is permitted. Corridor door opening and closing buttons, if provided, shall be rendered inoperative.

(g) Every car shall be provided with a button marked "CALL CANCEL," located in the same car operating panel as the Phase II switch, which shall be effective during Phase II operation. When activated, all registered calls shall be canceled and a traveling car shall stop at or before the next available landing.

(h) Floor selection buttons shall be provided in the car to permit travel to all landings served by the car and they shall be operative at all times. Means to prevent the operation of the floor selection buttons or door operating buttons shall be rendered inoperative.

(i) A traveling car shall stop at the next available landing for which a car call was registered. When a car stops at a landing, all registered car calls shall be canceled.

(2) When the Phase II switch is in the "HOLD" position, the elevator shall be on Phase II operation. The car shall remain at the landing with its doors open. The door close buttons shall be inoperative.

(3) When the Phase II switch is in the "OFF" position, the elevator is not at the designated level, and Phase I is in effect, the elevator shall operate as follows:

(a) Automatic power-operated horizontally sliding doors shall close automatically and the car shall revert to Phase I operation (Rule 211.3a) upon completion of door closing. All door reopening devices shall remain inoperative. Door open buttons shall remain operative. Full speed closing is permitted. If the Phase II switch is turned to the "ON" or "HOLD" position prior to the completion of door closing, the doors shall reopen.

(b) Elevators having power-operated vertically sliding doors shall have corridor door open and close buttons rendered operative. All door reopening devices shall remain inoperative. Door closing shall be in accordance with the requirements of Rule 211.3c(1)(d). Full speed closing is permitted. If the Phase II switch is turned to the "ON" or "HOLD" position prior to the completion of door closing, the doors shall reopen. The car shall revert to Phase I operation (Rule 211.3a) upon completion of door closing.

(c) Elevators having manual doors shall revert to Phase I operation (Rule 211.3a) upon completion of door closing.

(4) When the Phase II switch is in the "OFF" position and the car is not at the designated level, and Phase I is not in effect, the car shall remain at the landing with the doors open and door-close buttons inoperative.

(5) Elevators shall only be removed from Phase II operation when:

(a) The Phase II switch is in the "OFF" position and the car is at the designated level with the doors in the normal open position; or

(b) The Phase II switch is in the "OFF" position when Phase I is in effect [Rule 211.3c(3)].

211.3d Interruption of Power. Upon the resumption of power (normal, emergency, or standby), the car may move to reestablish absolute car position. Restoration of electrical power following a power interruption shall not cause any elevator to be removed from Phase I or Phase II operation.

211.3e Multideck Elevators. Multideck elevators shall also conform to the following requirements.

(1) The Phase I switch (Rule 211.3a) shall be located at the designated level served by the upper deck.

(2) The Phase II switch (Rule 211.3c) shall be located in the upper compartment. The elevator shall be provided with a means for placing the lower deck out of service, located in that deck or adjacent to the entrance at the lower lobby landing.

Rule 211.4 Firefighters' Service—Nonautomatic Elevators

All nonautomatic elevators shall conform to the requirements of this rule. The requirements of this rule do not apply when

(a) The hoistway, or portion thereof, is not required to be fire-resistive construction (Rule 100.1a);

(b) The travel does not exceed 6 ft 8 in. (2.03 m); and

(c) The hoistway does not penetrate a floor.

211.4a Phase I Emergency Recall Operation. A three-position key-operated switch shall be provided only at the designated level for each single elevator or for each group of elevators. The three-position switch shall be marked "BYPASS," "OFF," and "ON" (in that order). An additional two-position key-operated switch marked "OFF" and "ON" (in that order) may be provided at any location, however, it shall not affect Phase I operation if the designated-level smoke detector (Rule 211.4b) has been activated. The switch(es) shall be rotated clockwise to go from the "OFF" to "ON" position. All keys shall be removable only in the "OFF" and "ON" positions.

No device, other than the Phase I switch(es) or the smoke detectors in the elevator lobbies, machine room, or hoistway shall initiate Phase I operation.

When all switches are in the "OFF" position, normal elevator service shall be retained and operation from the smoke detectors required by Rule 211.4b shall be functional.

When the designated-level three-position switch is in the "BYPASS" position, normal elevator service shall be restored independent of the smoke detectors required by Rule 211.4b.

When a Phase I switch is in the "ON" position, a visual and audible signal shall be provided to alert the attendant to return nonstop to the designated or alternate level. The visual signal shall read "FIRE RECALL—RETURN TO [insert level to which the car should be returned (the designated or alternate level)]." The signal system shall be activated when Phase I is in effect.

If an additional two-position Phase I switch is provided, it shall not affect the visual signal if the designated-level smoke detector [Rule 211.3b(2)] has been activated.

The "BYPASS" position on the three-position Phase I switch shall not restore the elevator to normal service if the two-position Phase I switch is in the "ON" position.

211.4b Smoke Detectors. System-type smoke detectors conforming to the requirements of UL 268 shall be installed in each elevator lobby and associated machine room in accordance with NFPA 72, Chapter 3. Smoke detectors are not required in elevator lobbies at unenclosed landings. System-type smoke detectors may be installed in any hoistway and shall be installed in hoistways which are sprinklered (see Rule 102.2).

Phase I operation, conforming to Rule 211.4a, shall be initiated when any smoke detector in the elevator lobbies, machine room, or hoistway is activated.

Phase I operation, when initiated by a smoke detector, shall be maintained until canceled by moving the Phase I switch to the "BYPASS" position. Smoke detectors and/or smoke detector systems shall not be self-resetting.

Rule 211.5 Firefighters' Service—Automatic Elevators with Designated-Attendant Operation

(a) When on without-designated-attendant operation, elevators shall conform to the requirements of Rule 211.3.

(b) When operated by a designated attendant in the car (except hospital service):

(1) Elevators parked at a floor shall conform to the requirements of Rule 211.3a(8). At the completion of a time delay of not less than 15 seconds nor more than 60 seconds, elevators shall conform to the requirements of Rule 211.3.

(2) A moving car shall conform to the requirements of Rule 211.3.

(c) When operated by a designated attendant in the car on hospital service, the visual and audible signal shall activate while Phase I is in effect.

Rule 211.6 Firefighters' Service—Inspection Operation

When an elevator which is provided with firefighters' service is on inspection operation, a continuous audi-

ble signal which is audible on top of the car shall sound when the Phase I switch(es) (Rule 211.3a) is in the "ON" position or when the smoke detector (Rule 211.3b) is activated to alert the operator of an emergency. Car shall remain under the control of the operator until removed from inspection operation or hoistway access operation. The top of car operating device (Rule 210.1d) shall take precedence over Phase I and Phase II operations.

Rule 211.7 Firefighters' Service Operating Procedures

(a) Instructions for operation of elevators under Phase I shall be incorporated with or adjacent to the Phase I switch at the designated level. They shall include the wording shown in [Exhibit S4.2(a)].

(b) Instructions for operation of elevators under Phase II shall be incorporated with or adjacent to the switch, in or adjacent to the operating panel in each car. They shall include the wording shown in [Exhibit S4.2(b)].

Firefighters' Operation
To recall elevators
Insert fire key and turn to "ON"

Exhibit S4.2(a) *Phase I instructions. [From ASME A17.1, Section 211, Figure 211.7(a)]*

Firefighters' Operation

To operate car	Insert fire key and turn to "ON"
	Press desired floor button
To cancel floor selection	Press "CALL CANCEL" button
To close door	Press and hold "DOOR CLOSE" button
To open door	Press and hold "DOOR OPEN" button
To hold car at floor	With doors open, turn key to "HOLD"
To return car to recall floor	With doors open, turn key to "OFF"

Exhibit S4.2(b) *Phase II instructions. [From ASME A17.1, Section 211, Figure 211.7(b)]*

(c) Instructions shall be in letters not less than 1/8 in. (3.2 mm) in height and shall be permanently installed and protected against removal or defacement.

Rule 211.8 Switch Keys

The switches required by Rules 211.2 through 211.5, for all elevators in a building, shall be operable by the same key. This key shall only be made available to authorized personnel. This key shall not operate any other switch and shall not be part of the building master key system. There shall be a key for the designated level switch and for each elevator in the group. These keys shall be kept on the premises in a location readily accessible to authorized personnel, but not where they are available to the public.

NOTE (Rule 211.8): Local authorities may specify a uniform keyed lock box to contain the necessary keys.

Rule 211.9 Emergency Identification Numbering

When the machinery of more than one elevator is in a hoistway or machine room, each elevator shall be assigned a different number. The number shall be painted on, engraved, or securely attached to

(a) The driving machine;

(b) Main line disconnect switch;

(c) The crosshead, or where there is no crosshead, the car frame, such that it is visible from the top of the car; and

(d) The car operating panel.

The identification number required by Rules 211.9(a), (b), and (c) shall be a minimum of 1½ in. (38 mm) in height. The identification number required by Rule 211.9(d) shall be a minimum of ½ in. (13 mm) in height.

EXTRACTS FROM ASME A17.1 HANDBOOK, SECTION 211, EMERGENCY OPERATION AND SIGNAL DEVICES†

Rule 211.1 Car Emergency Signaling Devices

All elevators must be provided with an audible signaling device and a means of two-way conversation to an accessible point outside the hoistway. See [Exhibit

---

†Reprinted with permission from *Handbook on ASME A17.1, Safety Code for Elevators and Escalators*, American Society of Mechanical Engineers, Three Park Avenue, New York, New York 10016-5990. Handbook authored by Edward A. Donoghue.

S4.3] for a diagrammatic description of these requirements. The two-way communications system does not have to be provided with a means of activating from within the car. Most communications systems, excluding telephones, are activated in the main lobby or building emergency control center. The alarm bell is a means that is provided to signal that there is a problem. The means of two-way conversation is provided to assure occupants that their signal has been received and measures are being instituted to get them out of the stalled car.

One telephone could be used to meet both the requirements of Rule 211.1(a)(2) and 211.1(b) provided that it is capable of reaching someone outside of the hoistway who can take appropriate action.

The intent of the requirement in Rule 211.1(a)(2) is that the telephone or intercom is to be connected to a point where two-way conversation can be established by emergency personnel with the occupants of the car, assuring them that help is on the way. A "readily accessible point" is a location which is accessible to emergency personnel. The intent of this requirement is that emergency personnel have the ability to establish a communications link from within the building to the car. The exact location is determined on a local basis. The emergency signaling system is used to signal a problem and the communication system is then used to communicate with the occupants of the car, to alleviate fears, prevent panic, and prevent dangerous attempts to exit the car without assistance.

Rule 211.1(b) requires a means of signaling or communicating with a service which can take appropriate action in an emergency. It should be noted that only a means of signaling and not communicating is acceptable.

Requirements for emergency communications can also be found in the Americans with Disabilities Act Accessibility Guidelines (ADAAG) CABO A117.1 and Uniform Federal Accessibility Standards. All three standards state "the emergency intercommunication system shall not require voice communication." These requirements address the needs of those with hearing and speech impairments.

The use of a light indicating the call has been received and responded to, will provide a system that meets the intent for the hearing impaired. The light on the handsfree phone panel should only be illuminated or blink when activated by the recipient of the call. Those who are blind will be able to use the phone to hear that help is on the way. The instructions on the use of light(s), need not be raised or in Braille as this feature is not being provided for those with a vision impairment. Finally, although an illuminated

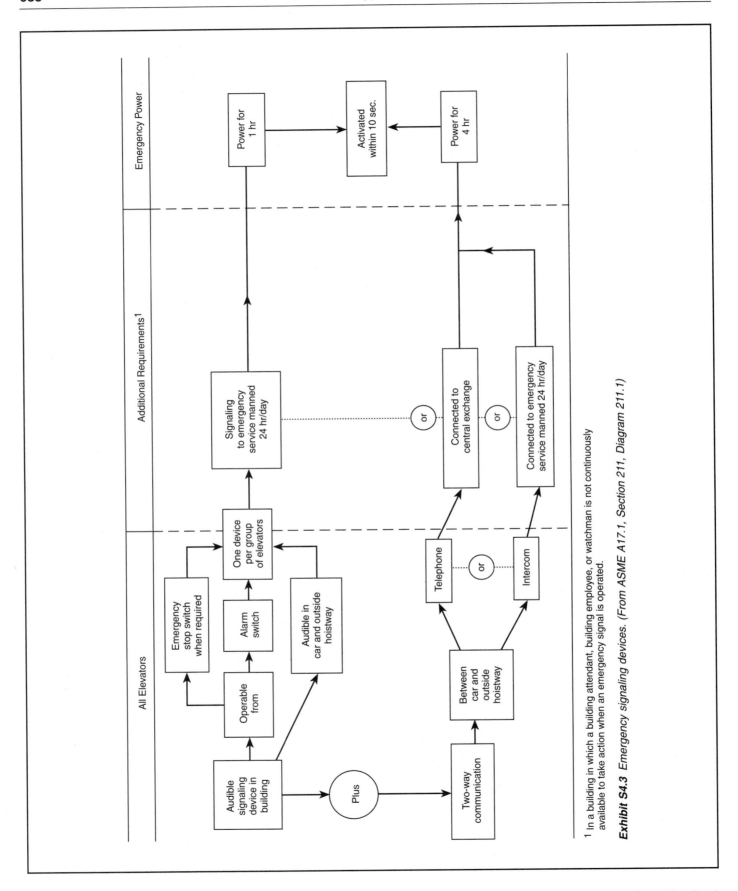

Exhibit S4.3 *Emergency signaling devices. (From ASME A17.1, Section 211, Diagram 211.1)*

[1] In a building in which a building attendant, building employee, or watchman is not continuously available to take action when an emergency signal is operated.

alarm button is now required by ASME A17.1, it does not by itself meet the full intent of ADAAG.

In addition to these requirements, the model building codes (*National Building Code, Uniform Building Code, Standard Building Code*) require that all elevators in high-rise buildings (see building code for definition) have a communication system from the elevator lobby, car, and machine rooms to the building's central control station. . . See also commentary on car lighting in Rule 204.7a.

Rule 211.2 Standby Power

Standby power for an elevator is not required by this Code. If standby power is provided, then it must comply with this Rule. The model building codes (*National Building Code, Uniform Building Code, Standard Building Code*) require standby power for at least one elevator that can travel to each floor in a high-rise building. . . One elevator does not have to stop at every floor, but every floor must be served by at least one elevator that is supplied with standby power. As an example, in a 20-story building, elevator group A serves floors 1 through 10 and elevator group B serves floors 1 and 11 through 20. Standby power would have to be supplied to one elevator in group A and one elevator in group B. If the same 20-story building had an elevator that served all floors 1 through 20, then standby power could be supplied to that elevator only.

The model building codes with their 1993 editions have addressed the need to provide accessible means of egress during a fire. Accessible means of egress typically include elevators, operating on Phase II emergency operation. When accessible means of egress include elevators, they shall be provided with standby power.

The *National Electrical Code®* (NEC) has requirements for both legally required standby power systems (Article 701) and optional standby power systems (Article 702). Legally required standby power systems provide electric power when normal power is interrupted to aid fire fighting, rescue operations, control of health hazards, and similar operations. Optional standby power systems provide electric power when normal power is interrupted to eliminate physical discomfort, interruption of an industrial process, damage to equipment, or disruption of business.

Emergency power systems are those power systems which are essential for safety to human life and must conform to the requirements of the *NEC*, Article 700. For additional information see NFPA 110, *Standard for Emergency and Standby Power Systems*.

Legally required standby power systems have re-

quirements which are very similar to emergency power systems. At the loss of normal power, the legally required standby power system must be able to supply power within 60 seconds and the emergency power system within 10 seconds. Wiring for legally required standby power systems can be installed in the same raceway, cables, and boxes as other general wiring. Emergency power system wiring must be kept entirely independent of all other wiring.

Elevators are normally hooked into legally required standby power systems and not emergency power systems.

Rule 211.2(c) permits but does not require automatic sequence operation. If automatic sequencing is provided, it must be so arranged that it can be overridden by the manual selection switch. This switch must not stop the elevator when in motion; power will be transferred only after the elevator is stopped.

See also the commentary on Rule 210.10 and Section 620-101 of the *National Electrical Code* in Chart 210.4.

Rule 211.3 Firefighters' Service—Automatic Elevators

In 1969, the National Fire Protection Association reported 12,100 fire fatalities in the United States. Not a single fire loss occurred in a high-rise building. The next year, however, five fire deaths occurred in high-rise office buildings in New York City. Although this number was relatively small, it did trigger serious concern about safety in high-rise buildings. A firefighter's nightmare is an out-of-control fire in a high-rise building during office hours. A major catastrophe, resulting in hundreds of deaths, could become a reality rather than a nightmare. The potential for this catastrophe does exist. Skyscrapers of 40 or 50 years ago contained steel desks, steel files, steel partitions, and masonry enclosed stock rooms. In contrast, today they contain an unbelievable amount of paper that is generated and stored in, and on, desks, cardboard boxes, open racks, computer printouts and libraries, as well as non-fire-resistive furnishings. Thus, the modern high-rise is a veritable container of a tremendous fire load, and this fire load is increasing yearly. In the past decade, it is estimated that over 400 buildings seven stories and higher have been built in this country. High-rise buildings are usually defined as buildings which are more than 75 ft (22.9 m) high, which is generally as high as fire department equipment can reach from the street.

High-rise buildings present new and different problems to fire suppression forces, yet the cause of fires in high-rise buildings and the materials used, including furniture and fixtures, are not any different from that used in conventional low-rise buildings. However, if a fire breaks out in the top story of a megastructure, firefighters have to lug their equipment up the stairs or risk riding the elevator. Evacuation of this type of building also presents a special problem. It is estimated that it would take over an hour to evacuate a 50-story building even if all went well.

Let's review some of the reasons why elevators are unsafe in a fire and what led to the Code requirements for firefighters' operation of elevators. Elevators are unsafe in a fire because

(a) Persons may push a corridor button and have to wait for an elevator that may never respond; valuable time in which to escape is lost.

(b) Elevators respond to car and corridor calls; one of these calls may be at the fire floor.

(c) Elevators cannot start until the car and hoistway doors are closed. A panic could lead to overcrowding of an elevator and the blockage of the doors, thus preventing closing.

(d) Power failure during a fire can happen at any time and thus lead to entrapment.

Fatal delivery of the elevator to the fire floor can be caused by any of the following:

(a) An elevator passenger pressing the car button for the fire floor;

(b) One or both of the corridor call buttons may be pushed on the fire floor;

(c) Heat may melt or deform the corridor push button or its wiring at the fire floor; or

(d) Normal functioning of the elevators, such as high or low call reversal, may occur at the fire floor.

The A17.1 Code recognized all of this and reacted by mandating elevator recall, more commonly referred to as Phase I Firefighters' Service.

The features described in Rule 211.3 are known as firefighters' service or special emergency service (SES) features. The Code committee is striving to standardize the operation to assure that there are no variations to confuse firefighters or other operators of the elevator during an emergency. The automatic or manual return of elevators to the designated level (see Section 3 for definition) is what is referred to as Phase I operation. The provision to allow emergency personnel to operate the elevator from within the car on emergency in-car operation is commonly referred to as Phase II. See [Exhibit S4.4].

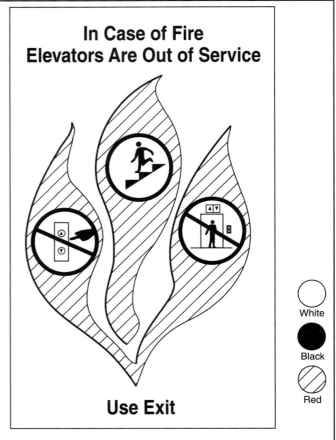

**In Case of Fire
Elevators Are Out of Service**

Use Exit

○ White

● Black

⊘ Red

Exhibit S4.4 Elevator corridor call station pictograph. (From ASME A17.1, Section 211, Diagram 211.3)

211.3a Phase I Emergency Call Operation. As of A17.1b–1992 all elevators must be equipped with Phase I so that they are recalled in the event of a fire. Also, if sprinklers are provided in the hoistway or machine room, a means of automatically recalling the elevator should be provided when smoke is present. This requirement will reduce the possibility of trapping passengers due to sprinkler activation.

A17.1b–1989 through A17.1b–1992 required Phase I for an elevator with a travel of 25 ft or more. Under earlier editions of the Code, an elevator could have nearly 50 ft of travel (24 ft 11 in. above the designated landing, and 24 ft 11 in. below the designated landing), and still not be required to have Phase I and Phase II operations.

The term "designated level" refers to the main floor or other level that best serves the needs of emergency personnel for fire fighting or rescue purposes. A three-position key-operated switch must be provided in the designated level lobby for each single elevator or for a group of elevators. The location of the three-position Phase I switch has been specified for standardization and to make sure that it is located where all of the elevators will be within sight. The key should be removable only in the "ON" and "OFF" positions. The "BYPASS" position allows the restoration of normal elevator service when a lobby smoke detector is malfunctioning. The requirement that the key not be removable in the "BYPASS" position encourages building owners to repair a malfunctioning smoke detector. An unattended key left in the lobby key switch could soon be in the possession of unauthorized personnel. An additional Phase I key switch is permitted and often is used at fire control centers. This second key switch is not allowed to have the "BYPASS" position. It was felt that a key switch with a "BYPASS" position in a locked room would encourage elevator operation without repairing smoke detectors.

Phase I operation assures that the elevator is not available to the general public when its continued use may be hazardous during a fire emergency. When an elevator is out of service during a fire, the public is unable to use it as a means of exit from the building. Earlier versions of the Code addressed only automatic door operation. The 1981 and later editions of the Code cover the operation of vertically sliding doors, doors controlled by push buttons, and manual doors. The only time an automatic elevator will not return upon activation of Phase I is when that car is at a landing with its door(s) open and the in-car stop switch, emergency stop switch or some other electrical protective device, is activated, or if on inspection or designated-attendant operation. The Rule recognizes that an elevator at a landing with the in-car stop switch or emergency stop switch in the "STOP" position should not be captured, as this is not a normal condition. The stop switch may have been activated to facilitate an inspection or maintenance and capturing the elevator could be a hazard to the inspection or maintenance personnel. The in-car stop switch should be disabled, just like the emergency stop button, so that the car cannot be inadvertently taken off of recall operation. A person with access to the key for the in-car stop switch, such as a building cleaning person, might be inclined to activate the switch while the elevator is being recalled. This would be unsafe.

For passenger safety, Rule 211.3a(5) requires elevators to close their doors at a slower speed when a door reopening device is rendered inoperative. This Rule also recognizes that mechanically actuated door reopening devices are not sensitive to smoke or flame, and can remain operative. Flame is the glowing gaseous part of a fire. Smoke or flame can register a signal whereas a fire will destroy. The reference to

Rule 112.5 recognized "nudging" and, therefore, it is not unsafe to disconnect mechanically actuated door reopening devices.

Rules 211.3a(6) and (7) allow full control of those doors that may have to be closed from the corridor. Also, the automatic closing of vertical slide doors requires an active open or stop button on the corridor. The corridor door-open button must be operative to cover the case where a manual gate is open with the hoistway door closed. A firefighter may need the door-open button to open the door to see if anyone is inside the car.

The requirement for position indicators to remain operative is intended to assist emergency personnel in locating the elevator if it does not return to the designated level.

Unless the car is at the fire floor, it is safer to keep the doors open for inspection by fire fighting personnel. The open hoistway door at the main floor or other designated level will admit air to the hoistway. If the fire is on a floor below the neutral pressure plane, the additional air will reduce the amount of smoke that can enter the hoistway from the fire floor, a beneficial side effect. If the fire is above the neutral pressure plane, there will be an increased flow of air from the hoistway to the floor, which is also beneficial.

Visual and audible signals alert passengers in an automatically operated elevator of the emergency and can minimize any apprehension that the passengers have when the elevator is returning to the main floor. In an attendant operated elevator, this signal alerts the attendant of the emergency and warns him to return immediately to the designated level. When on inspection operation, the inspector or maintenance personnel are also alerted to the emergency by this signal.

Rule 211.3a(10) recognized that if the smoke detector at the designated level is activated, turning the additional Phase I switch to the "ON" position will not override the smoke detector sending the car to the designated level, since this switch may be at a location where the condition of the designated level lobby cannot be determined.

211.3b Smoke Detectors. Some systems are improperly designed by initiating recall from smoke detectors that are a considerable distance from the elevator lobby. The action of the distant smoke detector does not warrant elevator recall. For instance, a wastepaper basket fire some distance from the elevator may trigger a smoke detector in the immediate area. This in itself is not cause for elevator recall. Accordingly, only the activation of the smoke detector in the elevator lobby, hoistway, or machine room is permitted to initiate elevator recall. There is no problem in isolating the elevator lobby, hoistway, or machine room detectors from the balance of smoke detectors on the floor. Smoke detectors are not required at unenclosed landings, exposed to the outside environment, though all the other requirements for firefighters' service must still be provided. If sprinklers are placed in the hoistway, a smoke detector must be provided in the vicinity of the sprinkler head. It is anticipated that this smoke detector will activate Phase I recall before the sprinkler is activated. If a hoistway smoke detector in the pit area is activated, the car is required to be recalled to the higher of the two levels (designated or alternate level) as it most likely indicates there is a pit fire. See commentary on Rule 102.2.

A17.1 does not define elevator lobby. The term lobby is also used in the model building codes and NFPA standards but is not defined. The intent of the term as used in Rule 211.3b is the space in front of the hoistway where one awaits the arrival of a car.

A requirement added in the 1981 edition of the Code requires a smoke detector to be installed at the designated level elevator lobby which will cause the elevators to return to an alternate level in the event of a fire at the main floor. A requirement was also added in the 1981 edition for a smoke detector in the associated machine room which would also activate Phase I, as a fire in the machine room could seriously affect the safe operation of the elevator. These changes put the A17.1 Code in harmony with the requirements of the model building codes.

211.3b(3). This requirement specifically states that the elevator only responds to the first detector which was activated. The likelihood of two simultaneous fires is infinitesimal. It is assumed that the smoke detector at the fire floor will be the first one that is activated. Subsequent alarms would most likely be due to smoke migration and should not affect the choice of the recall floor.

211.3b(4). This requirement establishes a standard means of canceling Phase I once activated by a smoke detector and prohibits the cancellation of Phase I operation by automatic means, a short in the smoke detector circuit, or by loss of power. When Phase I is activated by a smoke detector and you want to restore normal elevator operation, you would either

(1) Reset smoke detector and/or smoke detector system, then turn Phase I lobby switch to "BYPASS" and then to "OFF" position; or

(2) If smoke detector and/or smoke detector system cannot be reset, normal elevator service can be restored by placing Phase I lobby switch in "BYPASS" position.

The Note to Rule 211.3b makes reference to NFPA 72A, which gives guidance on the installation of smoke detectors for elevator recall in buildings with fire alarm systems. This standard coordinates the requirements for smoke detectors used for elevator recall with other devices utilized in fire alarm systems (i.e., building smoke detectors, heat detectors, sprinkler flow valves, pull stations, etc.).

The following is the basis for alternate floor recall. It is not preordained that the designated level has the lowest fuel load of any other floor in the buildings. This may be the case in some major, high-rise office buildings, but it certainly is not applicable to many other buildings, such as apartments, hotels, showrooms or buildings with elaborate reception areas. But, even if it were a fact, a fire bomb can suddenly provide an enormous fuel load on an otherwise sterile floor.

The preponderance of buildings have elevators without an express zone. In the event that there are express zones, it is safer to park away from any potential fire floor. It is feared that if the mandatory alternate floor requirement is repealed and made permissive, then many buildings would ultimately revert to the early Code requirements that only require return to the designated level.

What is often overlooked is the fact that if the elevators are returned to an alternate level, the firefighters have not lost control of the elevators. If conditions dictate that the designated level can provide safe egress, there is no reason why the firefighters cannot exercise the option of calling the elevators to the designated level by turning the required three position keyed switch to the "ON" position. The key switch overrides the alternate floor and will return all elevators to the designated level, even though the elevators may be parked at a floor above an express zone.

Typically the designated level is also the location of the central command station. It would be difficult to effectively utilize a designated level central command station if the designated level is engulfed in a rapidly spreading fire such as the one that destroyed the main floor of the MGM Hotel. Elevators that are returned to, or parked at, the main floor are of no value if the result is loss of life.

It may also be assumed that sprinklers will reduce the probability of a large fire, but one cannot rule out the possibility that smoke in dangerous quantities may be produced. Although sprinkler manufacturers say that sprinklers have been proven effective in stopping fire in a large number of buildings, smoke control advocates note that smoke, not the flames themselves cause the majority of fire deaths and say that sprinklers allow too much smoke to develop before the sprinklers are activated.

The effectiveness of smoke detectors for the recall function has also been questioned because of the possibility that smoke may be present on floors above and/or below the fire floor. The Code has addressed this by indicating that the fire smoke detector activation determines what floor the elevators are returned to. This is based on the fact that it is highly improbable that the smoke detectors on floors other than the fire floor would be activated beforehand.

As a corollary to smoke detectors that are now required to initiate elevator recall, it has been cited that the water flow switch associated with the on-floor sprinkler system is more positive. Smoke detectors were chosen in order to initiate elevator recall, as soon as possible in order to prevent the elevators from being used by building occupants during a fire when their use may be hazardous.

211.3c Phase II Emergency In-Car Operation. Phase II firefighters' operation is for the benefit of firefighters. Some of the input received from firefighters are as follows.

(1) Hoistway doors of elevators at the recall floor should remain open. Upon arrival, firefighters cannot afford the luxury of the time required to ascertain if all elevators are present and accounted for, or if an elevator is somewhere else in the building. A glance will reveal what elevators have been recalled and what elevators have to be located to assure that there are no trapped passengers.

(2) Firefighters want the elevator for their use. They take command during a fire, and they will determine whether the elevators are to be used. They are willing to accept the risks that are associated with running elevators during a fire. It is standard operating procedure for the firefighters to use the elevator not only to carry equipment or for fire fighting or evacuation purposes, but to also dispense fire personnel to non-fire floors. The presence of a firefighter reduces occupant panic, and firefighters can direct occupant movement strategy since they are in constant communication with the fire command post.

Many firefighters stated that there are times when they cannot afford the luxury of using personnel to operate an elevator on a return trip to the main floor. They requested that placing the Phase II switch in the elevator to the "OFF" position would automatically cause the elevator to return to the main floor for use by later arriving firefighters.

There also is a requirement that when the car is on Phase II operation, turning the switch in the car to the "HOLD" position at a floor will permit the firefighter to remove the key, and leave the car without the danger of someone taking the car to another floor.

The Phase II key must be removable in all positions because the storage of available emergency service keys could prevent the required number of cars from being put into Phase II service if the key were not removable in the "ON" position as well as other positions. Also, the door open button is active in the "ON" and "OFF" positions of the in-car key switch. If the switch is turned to "OFF" and the door starts to close automatically, the door open button can be pushed to fully reopen the doors and then the switch setting can be changed to "HOLD" or "ON."

Requirements for Phase II operation [Rule 211.3a(2)] were made more stringent in the 1981 edition. The previous edition of the Code required Phase II operation at 70 ft (21.3 m) above or below the main floor. The 1981 edition calls for Phase II operation whenever Phase I operation is required. The old requirement was predicated on the needs of emergency personnel only. The rule considers the need for evacuating the disabled during an emergency by emergency personnel. Disabled persons are always a concern, but the term "handicapped" in the normal context is no longer applicable; under fire conditions, even a firefighter can be considered disabled, especially when he is near exhaustion or if his oxygen supply is gone. Further, able-bodied occupants can become disabled from smoke, from walking up or down steps, or from hysteria. Therefore, when you hear that provisions must be made for the disabled during a fire, expand your overall picture, because even normal ambulatory persons can suddenly become non-ambulatory.

The A17 Code Committee was aware of the need to evacuate the disabled during a fire. A17.1a–1992 requires firefighters' service on all elevators. The model building code and the American with Disabilities Act Accessibility Guidelines (ADAAG) envision the use of elevators operating on Phase II as a principal means of evacuating the disabled during a fire.

Rules 211.3c(1)(c) and (d) recognize that compliance with Rule 112.4 is not necessary since constant pressure door controls are required. These rules also establish appropriate requirements for cars with more than one entrance.

Rule 211.3c(1)(d) recognizes that on large vertically sliding doors with continuous pressure closing, reopening is impractical and could introduce a delay factor that may impair safety.

Rule 211.3c(1)(f) recognizes that door reopening devices are not necessary since constant pressure operation is required.

For standardization, Rule 211.3c(4) defines Phase II operation in the "OFF" position when Phase I is not in effect and the car is not at the designated level.

211.3d Interruption of Power. This Rule clarifies that even in the case of power interruption upon restoration of power, Phase I or II would continue to remain in effect.

Rule 211.4 Firefighters' Service—Nonautomatic Elevators

This rule establishes the operation requirement of elevators which are not covered by Rule 211.3. A standard sign is required to alert the operator as to which floor the elevator should be returned to. See commentary on Rule 211.3.

Rule 211.5 Firefighters' Service—Automatic Elevators with Designated-Attendant Operation

A car could be left at the fire door, exposing the hoistway to fire, when it could be recalled. The delay is to give ample warning prior to recall. Hospital service has been excluded, since there may be valid reasons for not returning the car.

Rule 211.7 Firefighters' Service Operating Procedures

Operating procedures must be incorporated with or be adjacent to the Phase I and Phase II key-operated switches to assure that during an emergency, emergency personnel have quick access to available instructions for their use.

Since firefighters' service is now standardized, the Code specifies signs with simple and clear wording which explain the operation of the elevators.

An explanation of the "BYPASS" position is not necessary on the Phase I sign because this is a building function, not a firefighters' operation.

Rule 211.8 Switch Keys

A Note is included to suggest that local jurisdictions may legislate uniform keyed lock box requirements to assure the availability of emergency keys when building personnel are not available. It is not within the jurisdiction of A17 to make such a requirement so it is only suggested through the use of the Note. The use of lock boxes is preferred over the use of uniform keys as the lock box method provides more assurance that the keys are controlled. The uniform key method has resulted in disruption of normal elevator service as there are no means of controlling the distribution of elevator keys.

The required switch keys for Phase I and Phase II operation must be the same to assure a speedy response to the emergency situation.

Rule 211.9 Emergency Identification Numbering

This requirement will allow emergency personnel to pinpoint the elevator on which they want to disconnect the power for safe evacuation of passengers. This will also assist inspectors in identifying elevator equipment.

SUPPLEMENT 5

Fire Tests for *Life Safety Code* Users

Walter P. Sterling

This supplement can assist the reader on the application and applicability of the fire test standards found in the *Life Safety Code*. These documents include those test standards related to fire barriers, opening protectives, interior finishes, interior furnishings, and performance-based provisions in fire modeling.

Evaluating the level of performance or prescribed function offered by tested materials or assemblies requires an understanding of the mechanics of a particular test and its limitations. In its scope, a test standard establishes the parameters of the test procedures and the application or limitations of the test results. One example of using test results incorrectly involves a material that has been tested in accordance with NFPA 255, *Standard Method of Test of Surface Burning Characteristics of Building Materials,* and a given flame spread index but then is used in an application that requires the material to be noncombustible or limited combustible, which is determined by testing in accordance with ASTM E 139, *Standard Test Methods for Conducting Creep, Creep-Rupture, and Stress Rupture Tests of Metallic Materials,* or NFPA 259, *Standard Test Method for Potential Heat of Building Materials,* for potential heat amounts, respectively. This demonstrates that one test represents the material's ability to promulgate flame across its surface and the other is related to the particular properties of a material as it relates to its overall combustibility.

Many of the tests referred to in this *Code* have equivalent counterparts administered by other organizations such as the American Society for Testing and Materials (ASTM) and Underwriters Laboratories (UL). See Table S5.1. Section 1.5 of the *Code* permits the application or use of equivalent alterna-

tives. Alternatives could include fire test documents different from those specified, or they could include different test protocols if the proper technical documentation is provided to demonstrate the equivalency and that it fulfills the intended purpose of the applicable code requirement.

FIRE BARRIERS

Fire barriers are intended to be used as separation barriers or to provide protection of building elements from the effects of fire for a given time as required by Chapter 8, Features of Fire Protection. A fire resistance rating can be obtained by testing an assembly in accordance with the testing protocol of a recognized test standard. The appropriate test standard for determining the fire resistance properties of building elements and assemblies is NFPA 251, *Standard Methods of Tests of Fire Endurance of Building Construction and Materials.* Other documents, developed by other organizations, include ASTM E 119, *Standard Test Methods for Fire Tests of Building Construction and Materials,* and UL 263, *Standard for Safety Fire Tests of Building Construction and Materials.* Additional information on fire ratings associated with archaic materials can be found in Appendix D of NFPA 914, *Recommended Practice for Fire Protection in Historic Structures,* and in Appendix L of NFPA 909, *Standard for the Protection of Cultural Resources Including Museums, Libraries, Place of Worship, and Historical Properties.*

NFPA 251 provides testing requirements for fire barrier assemblies that are dependent on the intended end use of the barrier, such as those used in rated fire barrier walls, floors, or ceilings. The follow-

Table S5.1 Documents That Are Common to NFPA Fire Test Standards

NFPA	ASTM	UL
251, Standard Methods of Tests of Fire Endurance of Building Construction and Materials	E 119, Standard Test Methods for Fire Tests of Building Construction and Materials	263, Standard for Safety Fire Tests of Building Construction and Materials
252, Standard Methods of Fire Tests of Door Assemblies	E 152, Standard Methods of Fire Tests of Door Assemblies	10B, Standard for Safety Fire Tests of Door Assemblies
253, Standard Method of Test for Critical Radiant Flux of Floor Covering Systems Using a Radiant Heat Energy Source	E 648, Standard Test Method for Critical Radiant Flux of Floor-Covering Systems Using a Radiant Heat Energy Source	
255, Standard Method of Test of Surface Burning Characteristics of Building Materials	E 84, Standard Test Method for Surface Burning Characteristics of Building Materials	723, Standard for Safety Test for Surface Burning Characteristics of Building Materials
256, Standard Methods of Fire Tests of Roof Coverings	E 108, Standard Test Methods for Fire Tests of Roof Coverings	790, Tests for Fire Resistance of Roof Covering Materials
257, Standard on Fire Test of Window and Glass Block Assemblies	E 163, Standard Method for Fire Tests of Window Assemblies	9, Standard for Safety Fire Tests of Window Assemblies
258, Standard Research Test Method for Determining Smoke Generation of Solid Materials	E 662, Standard Test Method for Specific Optical Density of Smoke Generated by Solid Materials	
259, Standard Test Method for Potential Heat of Building Materials		
260, Standard Methods of Tests and Classification System for Cigarette Ignition Resistance of Components of Upholstered Furniture	E 1353, Standard Test Methods for Cigarette Ignition Resistance of Components of Upholstered Furniture	
261, Standard Method of Test for Determining Resistance of Mock-Up Upholstered Furniture Material Assemblies to Ignition by Smoldering Cigarettes	E 1352, Standard Test Method for Cigarette Ignition Resistance of Mock-Up Upholstered Furniture Assemblies	
262, Standard Method of Test for Flame Travel and Smoke of Wires and Cables for Use in Air-Handling Spaces		910, Standard for Safety Test for Flame-Propagation and Smoke-Density Values for Electrical and Optical-Fiber Cables Used in Spaces Transporting Environmental Air
263 (no longer in print)	E 906, Standard Test Method for Heat and Visible Smoke Release Rates for Materials and Products	
265, Standard Methods of Fire Tests for Evaluating Room Fire Growth Contribution of Textile Wall Coverings		1715, Standard for Safety Fire Test of Interior Finish Material
266, Standard Method of Test for Fire Characteristics of Upholstered Furniture Exposed to Flaming Ignition Source	E 1537, Standard Test Method for Fire Testing of Upholstered Furniture	1056, Standard for Safety Fire Test of Upholstered Furniture
267, Standard Method of Test for Fire Characteristics of Mattresses and Bedding Assemblies Exposed to Flaming Ignition Source	E 1590, Standard Test Method for Fire Testing of Mattresses	1895, Standard for Safety Fire Test of Mattresses
269, Standard Test Method for Developing Toxic Potency Data for Use in Fire Hazard Modeling	E 1678, Standard Test Method for Measuring Smoke Toxicity for Use in Fire Hazard Analysis	
271, Standard Method of Test for Heat and Visible Smoke Release Rates for Materials and Products Using an Oxygen Consumption Calorimeter	E 1354, Standard Test Method for Heat and Visible Smoke Release Rates for Materials and Products Using an Oxygen Consumption Calorimeter	

Table S5.1 Continued

NFPA	ASTM	UL
272, Standard Method of Test for Heat and Visible Smoke Release Rates for Upholstered Furniture Components or Composites and Mattresses Using an Oxygen Consumption Calorimeter	E 1354, Standard Test Method for Heat and Visible Smoke Release Rates for Materials and Products Using an Oxygen Consumption Calorimeter	
	E 1474, Test Method for Determining the Heat Release Rate of Upholstered Furniture and Mattress Components or Composites Using a Bench Scale Oxygen Consumption Calorimeter	
701, Standard Methods of Fire Tests for Flame Propagation of Textiles and Films	E 568 (withdrawn)	214, Standard for Safety Tests for Flame-Propagation of Fabrics and Films

ing information highlights testing criteria for those assemblies used as enclosures or separation fire barriers. The testing criteria in NFPA 251 is used to evaluate the duration of an assembly sample, when exposed to a standard fire exposure, in containing a fire or retaining the structural integrity of the assembly. The test standard provides criteria for measuring the transmission of heat through the assembly, measuring the transmission of gases hot enough to ignite cotton waste, and evaluating the ability to sustain the load-bearing capacity of the assembly if required to support a load.

Testing of Fire Barriers

The test assembly (fire barrier) is constructed, then placed in a furnace or is part of the furnace enclosure. The furnace is capable of providing the prescribed temperatures over a given period of time, as shown in Exhibit S5.1. In establishing the temperatures of the furnace, the averages of nine thermocouple readings are taken throughout the test chamber. These readings must average to within 10 percent of the temperature–time curve. Temperature readings on the unexposed assembly surface are also taken in at least nine locations in order to monitor the temperature on the unexposed side. In addition, test specimens are subjected to a hose stream test if tested for at least 60 minutes. If the condition of acceptance requires a hose stream test, then a duplicate assembly is tested in the furnace for half of the time period desired but for not more than 1 hour. The assembly is removed from the furnace and immediately subjected to a hose stream test. The hose stream is delivered by a 2½-in. (64-mm) hose with an 1⅛-in. (285-mm) standard play pipe nozzle at a distance of 20 ft (6.1 m) from the test specimen. The nozzle pressure

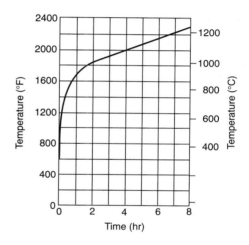

Exhibit S5.1 *Standard temperature–time curve.*

ranges from 30 psi to 45 psi (207 kPa to 310 kPa) for a duration not exceeding 6 minutes for each 100 ft² (9.3 m²) of area, depending on the hourly rating for which the assembly is tested. The hose stream application is applied in a specific pattern to fully develop the effects of impact, cooling, and erosion on the entire test specimen.

The acceptance conditions for these test specimens are based on the assembly's having withstood the fire and hose stream endurance tests. The fire endurance test stipulates that, while under the applied load, the assembly must not develop any passage of flame or gases hot enough to ignite cotton waste on the unexposed side for the time period to which it is tested. The specimen must withstand the hose stream test such that no openings are created that would permit projection of water from the hose stream to the unexposed side. Another test acceptance criterion is that the transmission of heat through the assembly must not have raised the temperature of the unexposed surface more than 250°F (139°C) above the test specimen's initial temperature.

Testing Limitations

Although test assemblies have been rated for a specific period, it is recognized that, under actual field conditions, some assemblies fail prematurely and others remain in place longer than expected. The simulated test exposure used in the test protocol was established in 1920. It represents one level of fire severity considered a "typical office building" scenario of that era. The varying types of fuel loads found in today's occupancies bear some discussion if a more challenging temperature–time curve should evolve to represent these conditions than what the current test threshold represents.

Another area of concern for the test assembly is its integrity, or the protection of through-penetrations. The test criteria in NFPA 251 do not address conventional openings found in assemblies, such as electrical receptacles, plumbing pipes, utility services, and construction joints, unless they have been specifically tested as part of the assembly. All penetrations require special review and consideration. A source for evaluating certain penetrations permitted in rated assemblies can be found in the introduction of the UL *Fire Resistance Directory*. This document addresses the hourly ratings for beams, floors, roofs, columns, walls, and partitions. Its design information section provides information pertaining to the different penetrations found in rated assemblies and the required protection or limitations.

Penetrations of a rated assembly that require special consideration are usually tested to a recognized test procedures. One test that establishes the testing protocols for through-penetrations is ASTM E 814, *Standard Method for Fire Tests of Through-Penetration* Fire Stops. Additional information can be found in A.8.2.5.2 of NFPA *101* and in the documents published by the individual listing agencies for assemblies that have been tested for specific fire ratings.

Using Fire Barriers In Building Construction

Fire rated building construction, as noted in NFPA 220, *Standard on Types of Building Construction*, or in Table A.8.6.2.1, uses fire barriers to provide minimum hourly ratings for structural elements. These elements include exterior-bearing walls, interior-bearing walls, columns, beams, girders, trusses, floor construction, and roof construction. The ratings are derived from testing done in accordance with the

applicable provisions for that construction element as found in NFPA 251.

Interior- and exterior-bearing walls that consist of a wall assembly are evaluated as described previously for fire barriers. The elements that address columns, beams, and floor and roof assemblies each have their own particular testing criteria, which are detailed in NFPA 251. Unlike the function served by walls and partitions to limit temperature transmission and flaming on the unexposed surface, beams and columns must also sustain an applied load for a period of time equal to the desired classification. An alternative test for columns, designed not to carry a load, measures the ability of the protection to control the transmission of heat through the specimen during the specified period of fire exposure. The average temperature of the steel must not rise above 1000°F (538°C), and the temperature in any one of the measured points cannot exceed 1200°F (649°C).

Beams that are required to have a fire resistance rating must sustain the applied load and prevent certain levels of temperature from being reached on the building construction element. The maximum temperature levels shall not exceed 1300°F (704°C) at any one location or an average over 1100°F (593°C) during the testing period. For additional information on acceptable temperature levels for specific construction materials and designs used in beams, see NFPA 251.

Floor and roof assemblies are also required to have a sustained applied load during the testing for the duration of the classification period. During the test, the assembly must not develop conditions that ignite cotton waste on its unexposed side. The transmission of heat through the test assembly during the classification period must not raise the average temperature on the unexposed surface to more than 250°F (139°C) above its initial temperature. Depending on the structural design of the assembly, certain levels of temperature must not be exceeded at any one point, or an average temperature should not be exceeded with temperature limitations ranging from 800°F to 1300°F (427°C to 704°C).

Further information on specific testing criteria and testing limitations can be found in NFPA 251. Currently, there is discussion on the application of the testing procedures, how they can be applied to particular fire modeling programs, and what the pass/fail criteria should be. The current testing protocol is related only to one specific criterion and should be evaluated on how it can be applied to a particular application. A good example is the recent studies on high-strength concrete that indicate explosive spalling occurs at relatively low temperatures This finding could have an adverse effect on the fire protection properties assumed.

Fire Barrier Opening Protectives

Where the *Code* permits openings in fire barriers, the appropriate protection of these openings is of extreme importance so that the integrity of the fire barrier assembly can be maintained. The degree of fire resistance rating required for the opening protectives depends on the assembly rating and the intended use of the fire barrier. Minimum requirements associated with the openings in a fire barrier can be found in 8.2.3.2.3.

Fire Doors. Door assemblies in fire barriers must be tested according to NFPA 252, *Standard Methods of Fire Tests of Door Assemblies*. This standard is similar to UL 10B, *Standard for Safety Fire Tests of Door Assemblies.* NFPA 252 provides methods for measuring the relative performance of fire door assemblies where exposed to a prescribed fire test exposure followed by a prescribed hose stream application. The effectiveness of the opening protective is dependent on a satisfactory performance of the entire door assembly, which consists of the door, door frame, and associated hardware. Accordingly, fire door assemblies are required to be tested as a complete assembly, including all the applicable door components.

The procedures of NFPA 252 are similar to those of NFPA 251. The fire door assembly specimen is mounted in a furnace wall and exposed to the standard temperature–time curve. Fire door performance is evaluated based on its effectiveness in withstanding the effects of the fire endurance test and hose stream test without developing any gaps or openings through the assembly. No flaming should occur on the unexposed surface of a door assembly during the first 30 minutes of the classification period. Some intermittent light flames for periods not exceeding 5-minute intervals are permitted along the edges of doors. Light flaming on the unexposed surface area of the door is also permitted during the last 15 minutes of the classification period, provided such flaming is contained within a distance of 1½ in. (38 mm) from the vertical edge and 3 in. (76 mm) from the top edge of the door or frame of the vision panel. Where the door hardware is also evaluated for use on fire doors, it must keep the door in a closed position for an exposure period of 3 hours. The latch bolt must remain projected and be intact after the fire exposure test.

A hose stream test, which subjects the test assembly to the impact, erosion, and cooling effects of the hose stream, is applied immediately following the fire endurance test. The hose stream is directed at the middle and then at all parts of the exposed surface, slowly making changes in direction. As in NFPA 251, the stream is applied through a 1⅛-in. (285-mm) standard play pipe nozzle at a 20-ft (6-m) distance from the door assembly, with nozzle pressure ranging from 30 psi to 45 psi (207 kPa to 310 kPa).

Certain provisions within the *Life Safety Code* provide for the installation of door assemblies without the hose stream test. One must carefully evaluate the particular requirements associated with the opening protective so that it satisfies the minimum acceptable criteria.

A recent trend within code-writing organizations is to require certain applications of fire door assemblies to be tested under a positive pressure scenario. This provision requires that the door assemblies be tested with a neutral pressure plane located 40 in. (1016 mm) above the finished floor. NFPA 252 has been revised so that it no longer stipulates the height of the neutral plane but records the height in the test results. This revision permits the test standard to accommodate the many gradients of pressure planes at which a furnace can be operated. The test report document issued following a classification test records the location of the neutral pressure plane to which the door assembly has been tested. Currently, 8.2.3.2.1(a) of the *Life Safety Code* does not stipulate the minimum required height of the neutral pressure plane for testing the door. If a neutral plane is not established, then it is assumed that the door will be tested under normal testing procedures, which is running the furnace at near atmospheric pressure. This would establish the neutral pressure plane at the top of the door assembly. It is generally recognized that, if a lower neutral pressure plane is established on the door assembly within the furnace, then the test could be considered to be more severe. A door tested under a positive pressure should be accepted as equivalent to the current requirements under Section 1.9. Listing agencies are now discussing how to list and label doors currently being tested with a positive pressure. Additional information associated with these criteria can be found in NFPA 80, *Standard for Fire Doors and Fire Windows.* NFPA 80 should be consulted for the installation requirements associated with all types of fire doors.

Fire Window Assemblies. Fire window assemblies permitted in 8.2.3.2.2 can be used in fire barriers that have a fire resistance rating of 1 hour or less and up to 25 percent of the fire barrier. Fire windows must be tested in accordance with NFPA 257, *Standard on Fire Test for Window and Glass Block Assemblies.* This test standard is similar to either ASTM E 163, *Standard Method of Fire Tests of Window Assemblies,* or UL 9, *Standard for Safety Fire Tests of Window Assemblies.* The NFPA 257 test method is intended to evaluate the ability of a window or other light-transmitting assembly to remain in an opening during a predetermined test exposure period. See Exhibit S5.2. In the revisions to the 1996 edition of NFPA 257, all references to a particular time limit for testing were deleted. The earlier editions limited testing to 45 minutes, but now the test is permitted to be run for the length of time a test sponsor requests. The period of time is then recorded on the appropriate test records. A time limit is no longer specified because new materials and technology can now be used in window assemblies that will permit increased exposure times and maintain the integrity of the fire barriers in which they are installed. The limitations associated with fire window assemblies are found in 8.2.3.2.2.

Discussions are continuing on the amount of radiant heat permitted to transfer through the window assembly to the unexposed side of the window. Currently, the radiant heat transferred is not required to be recorded. A test procedure is available to measure this radiant heat flux and is detailed in Appendix B of NFPA 257. Additional information on radiant heat transmissions can be found in the 2000 edition of NFPA 257. The conditions associated with radiant energy could be considered as a factor in the application of a fire modeling program that might have an occupant passing by such opening protectives. All consid-

erations and applications for a material's particular use should be reviewed with the limitations of the test results in mind.

The test specimen is exposed to a standard fire exposure (temperature–time) such as those found in NFPA 251 and NFPA 252 testing scenarios. A window assembly is considered to have met the requirements for acceptable performance if it remains in the opening during the fire endurance and hose stream tests, within the following limitations:

(1) Separation of glass edges from the glazing frame must not create any openings during the fire exposure.
(2) The window assembly must not loosen from its fastenings.
(3) A separation of glass edges during the hose stream test must not create an opening that exceeds 30 percent of each individual glass light perimeter.

Exhibits S5.3(a) and S5.3(b) represent two views of an assembly that has been exposed to both the fire endurance and the hose stream tests. As with fire doors, fire windows are installed in accordance with the provisions of NFPA 80, *Standard for Fire Doors and Fire Windows.* The glazing material installed in fire window assemblies is limited to the size and total area as detailed in NFPA 80. Fire window assemblies having a rating of one-half or one-third hour are limited to the size that has been tested. One should review the appropriate listing associated with the protection rating given to a fire window assembly. A three-quarter-hour window protection is limited to the maximum area tested and must have no exposed area of individual glazing material exceeding 1296 in.² (8361 cm²) and no dimension exceeding 54 in. (137 cm), unless it has been specifically tested with dimensions in excess of these values. Glazing is currently available that has been tested with dimensions that exceed the 54-in. (137-cm) limitation as found in NFPA 80. NFPA 80 requires that each individual glazing unit have a label that is visible after installation.

Many types of glazing materials are being introduced in the market. Wire glass has been an acceptable glazing component for many years, but now other types of fire-rated glazing products satisfy the acceptance criteria of NFPA 257. It is important that the installation and testing limitations be reviewed for the particular installation.

Technological advances within the glazing industry have provided a system using fire-resistant glazing materials that are actually fire barrier walls. These glazing walls would have been tested in accordance

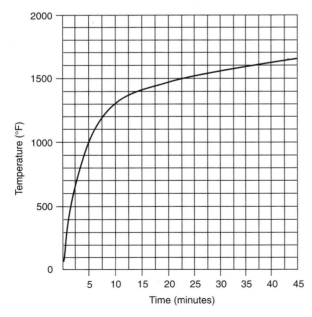

Exhibit S5.2 *Window assembly temperature–time curve.*

Exhibit S5.3(a) *Unexposed side of window assembly after fire exposure and hose stream application.*

Exhibit S5.3(b) *Exposed side of window assembly after fire exposure and hose stream application.*

with NFPA 251 and satisfy the particular pass/fail criteria for fire barriers. These criteria include the limitation of temperature rise on the unexposed side of the test specimen and a hose stream application. The installation requirements and limitations for these glazing wall assemblies would be highlighted in the applicable listing requirements and the manufacturers' specifications. This type of glazing would not be required to comply with the provisions of NFPA 80 for installation requirements, because it is not considered an opening protective device.

Penetrations of Fire Barriers

Generally, when fire barriers are tested for a particular hourly rating, these wall assemblies are tested without any penetrations. It is recognized that within a building these fire barriers will have various penetrations for building services, utilities, and other applications. Penetrations of fire barriers require the appropriate protection by devices or materials that have been tested and listed for that particular application to maintain the fire barrier's integrity.

Through-Penetrations. Through-penetration systems for fire barriers are required to be tested as part

of the fire barrier assembly when tested in accordance with NFPA 251 or with ASTM E 814, *Standard Test Method for Fire Tests of Through-Penetration Fire Stops*. The ASTM E 814 test protocol establishes F and T ratings as one part of the acceptance criteria for through-penetration systems. The F rating signifies the ability of the penetrating firestop system to withstand a prescribed fire test for a period of time without permitting the passage of flame through the opening or the occurrence of flaming on any element of the unexposed side of the penetrating firestop system. The T rating relates to the transmission of heat through the penetrating firestop system for a given period of time. An acceptable T rating is one that limits the rise of the temperature on the unexposed surface of the penetrating firestop system or penetrating item to no more than 325°F (181°C) above the initial temperature and for which there is no flame occurrence.

The penetrating firestop is exposed to the same fire test conditions created by the temperature–time curve as detailed in accordance with NFPA 251. NFPA 221, *Standard for Fire Walls and Fire Barrier Walls*, and the building codes require that the penetrating firestop be under a minimum positive pressure differential of 0.01 in. (2.5 Pa) of water at the location of the penetrating item. This positive pressure must be maintained for the duration for which it is being tested. The penetrating firestop system must have the same time period as that of the fire barrier in which it is installed. The penetrating firestop system must also be subjected to the effects of an applied hose stream test.

Joints. Joints used in the construction of fire barriers can include expansion, seismic, and control joints. These joints are tested at their maximum joint width in accordance with NFPA 251. The test includes joints to their full height or length of the test assembly. The fire-resistive joint system tested must include a splice or a method of connecting two or more lengths of the joint system. The test must be conducted so that the joint system is tested under a minimum positive pressure differential of 0.01 in. (2.5 Pa) of water for the total time of the test. Fire-resistive joint systems that are designed to accommodate movement must be preconditioned by cycling under the conditions of ASTM E 1399, *Standard Test Method for Cyclic Movement and Measuring the Minimum and Maximum Joint Widths of Architectural Joint Systems.*

Fire Dampers. Fire dampers used to protect penetrations of fire barriers are required to be listed for the particular application. Fire dampers are tested either for static systems, where the HVAC system is automatically shut down in the event of a fire, or for dynamic systems, where the HVAC system does not shut down. Fire dampers used in dynamic systems are investigated for closure under their maximum recommended airflow. Fire dampers are tested in accordance with UL 555, *Standard for Safety Fire Dampers.* Fire dampers used in rated fire-resistive floor–ceiling and roof–ceiling assemblies are tested in accordance with UL 555C, *Standard for Safety Ceiling Dampers.* The fire dampers are tested in assemblies under the conditions of the fire exposure of the temperature–time curve in accordance with NFPA 251. The UL documents provide the acceptance criteria in regard to the flaming on the unexposed side, closing time of the damper, air leakage if applicable, and hose stream application. It should be noted that fire dampers are not tested for the limitation of heat transmission through the fire damper assembly. This particular condition is recognized in the requirements of NFPA 90A, *Standard for the Installation of Air Conditioning and Ventilating Systems,* associated with the limitation on the number of fire dampers permitted to be installed in a vertical duct that has multiple floor penetrations.

INTERIOR FINISH

Interior finish as it relates to the *Code* refers to the exposed interior wall surfaces, exposed interior ceiling finishes, and exposed interior floor finishes. These provisions should not be associated or confused with fire resistance ratings. The concepts of an interior finish rating (resistance to flame promulgation) and a fire resistance rating of an assembly are quite different. Fire resistance is the ability of an assembly to withstand a prescribed exposure to a fire test for a given time, where interior finish ratings refer to the ability of a material to contribute to overall fire growth and spread. An interior finish classification should also not be compared or confused with a material's combustibility or the degrees of combustibility.

Testing of Interior Finish

A couple of different tests are now being used to evaluate interior finishes. Each use of a material for a particular application of interior finish needs to be coordinated with the appropriate testing procedure, and each interior finish testing method has a specific scope and application. There is a possibility that a single product could be used in many different applications. The end use application must be identified, because that knowledge stipulates the appropriate test method and applicable results. For example, textile materials that are used as wall coverings can be tested in accordance with any of the following:

(1) NFPA 255, *Standard Method of Test of Surface Burning Characteristics of Building Materials,* as permitted by the *Code*
(2) NFPA 265, *Standard Methods of Fire Tests for Evaluating Room Fire Growth Contribution of Textile Wall Coverings*
(3) NFPA 286, *Standard Methods of Fire Tests for Evaluating Contribution of Wall and Ceiling Interior Finish to Room Fire Growth.*

If used as a flooring material, the same material could also be tested in accordance with the requirements of NFPA 253, *Standard Method of Test for Critical Radiant Flux of Floor Covering Systems Using a Radiant Heat Energy Source.* If this textile material is used as a loosely hanging drapery or similar furnishing, then the appropriate test would be NFPA 701, *Standard Methods of Fire Tests for Flame Propagation of Textiles and Films.* If the material is also used as an element in upholstered furniture, then NFPA 260, *Standard Methods of Tests and Classification System for Cigarette Ignition Resistance of Components of Upholstered Furniture,* and NFPA 261, *Standard Method of Test for De-*

termining Resistance of Mock-Up Upholstered Furniture Material Assemblies to Ignition by Smoldering Cigarettes, could be the appropriate test standards that are required to be satisfied.

Interior Wall and Ceiling Finish

Depending on occupancy use, the *Life Safety Code* attempts to limit the relative rate of flame propagation and smoke development on the exposed wall and ceiling surfaces. The *Code* provides three classifications based on a flame spread index (FSI) and a smoke development index (SDI), as detailed in 10.2.3.2 and shown here.

	FSI	SDI
Class A	0–25	0–450
Class B	26–75	0–450
Class C	76–200	0–450

The FSI reflects the comparative burning characteristic of a material being tested to two established benchmarks. These values are the results of testing done in accordance with NFPA 255. This test is similar to ASTM E 84, *Standard Test Method for Surface Burning Characteristics of Building Materials,* and UL 723, *Standard for Safety Test for Surface Burning Characteristics of Building Materials.* This characteristic consists of evaluating the flame spread over the material's surface when exposed to a prescribed gas-fed fire. The FSI is derived from the comparison of the test results

of two known products over a given period of time. Inorganic, reinforced cement board has an FSI of 0, and red oak has an FSI of 100. The FSI is a nondimensional figure and does not directly represent a flame speed or velocity. The results of the test specimen material are then compared to these two known values. The FSI is not an indication of the material's fire resistance or its combustibility but only of the ability of the material to resist propagation of flame spread across its surface. It is possible that a material with a low ability to spread flame (for example, bare sheet metal) could also exhibit little or no fire resistance when exposed to the testing criteria of NFPA 251. Although the *Life Safety Code* and the model building codes specify limits for a smoke development index, the terminology used in NFPA 255 is for a "smoke density index." Although the terminology differs, both the *Code*-specified value and the test standard measurement value are one in the same.

The SDI is also derived from the testing of materials in accordance with NFPA 255. The SDI is also a nondimensional value. Within the *Life Safety Code,* the SDI values range from 0 to 450. The smoke density is a degree of obscuration and is measured by a photoelectric cell mounted in the test chamber's exhaust outlet, opposite a light source. A reduction in the light due to the smoke particulates that pass by the photoelectric cell is recorded and used to calculate the SDI. It should be noted that there is no direct relationship between the flame spread and smoke development values. It is possible that a material hav-

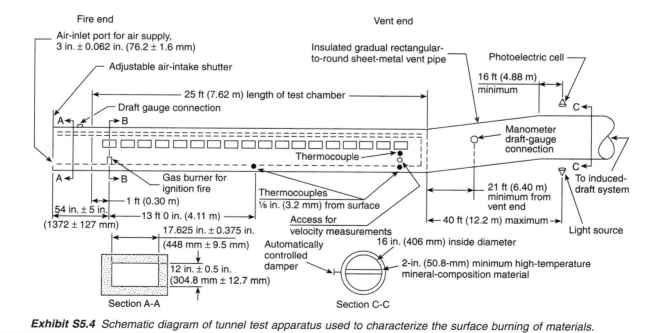

Exhibit S5.4 *Schematic diagram of tunnel test apparatus used to characterize the surface burning of materials.*

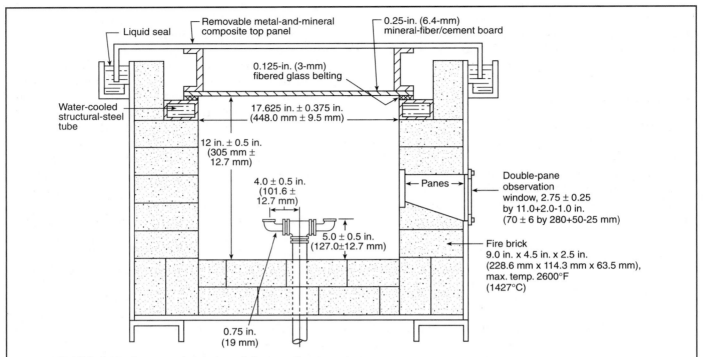

Exhibit S5.5 *Cross-sectional view of the tunnel test apparatus.*

ing a low flame spread index could have a very high smoke development index.

NFPA 255 is often referred to as the "tunnel test" or the "Steiner tunnel test." The testing apparatus used in NFPA 255 is shown in Exhibits S5.4 and S5.5. The specimens are required to be at least 20 in. (508 mm) wide by 24 ft (7.3 m) long and are placed within the test apparatus. A gas flame is applied at one end of the tunnel, and a regulated constant draft is applied through the tunnel from the flame end. Flame-front progress is observed through side windows for a 10-minute period.

Specimens must be representative of the material for which test results are desired. When specific materials and products are considered for use or are reviewed for compliance with a provision of this *Code*, it is critical that the intended end use correspond with the tested configuration. If the material or product differs in composition or is mounted or applied in a manner that deviates from the tested specimen, it could have an adverse effect. The actual FSI and SDI could be different from those established from the original test results. It is very important to follow the manufacturer or listing instructions when installing or applying the interior finish for material. Appendix B of NFPA 255 provides guidance on the different mounting configurations for some types of building materials when tested in the tunnel. This appendix

is provided as a guide, and caution should be used when applying it to particular materials. It has been demonstrated that some materials that cannot support themselves in the tunnel and that are artificially supported by a wire mesh can have FSI characteristics that are significantly different from those found in actual field installations. Consideration should be given when using these materials as interior finishes that a different test protocol might be required. An appropriate test for these types of materials would be NFPA 286, *Standard Methods of Fire Tests for Evaluating Contribution of Wall and Ceiling Interior Finish to Room Fire Growth.*

Another Test For Interior Finishes

This edition of the *Code* recognizes a new test procedure for interior finishes—NFPA 286. NFPA 286 is a test standard that was developed to address recent activities associated with the Life Safety Technical Committee on Furnishings and Contents. The technical committee attempted to modify the testing procedures of NFPA 265, *Standard Methods of Fire Tests for Evaluating Room Fire Growth Contribution of Textile Wall Coverings*, to address those interior finishes that do not remain in place during the testing when done in accordance with NFPA 255. The proposed modification would have established a test protocol for NFPA

265 that was outside the scope of this test procedure. NFPA 286 is a test standard that can evaluate the contribution of the wall or ceiling finishes to a room fire growth during a specified fire exposure. This standard addressed those concerns of the technical committee and is now referenced in Section 10.2, Interior Finishes.

The NFPA 286 test procedure is appropriate for the testing of interior finish materials that are installed on walls and ceilings except for textile materials. The reason for this exclusion is that NFPA 265 was specifically developed to address the testing of textile materials on walls only. These two test procedures use the same fire room configuration, canopy hood, and exhaust duct for the collection of the combustion products leaving the fire room. The significant difference is in the placement of the ignition source (gas burner) and the amount of exposure. The initial exposure rate for the test specimens, at 40 kW for 5 minutes, is the same for these two standards. The difference is in the next level of exposure for the next 10 minutes. NFPA 265 requires a 150-kW exposure, whereas NFPA 286 requires a 160-kW exposure for this time period. This particular increase in the level of exposure creates a condition of direct flame impingement on the ceiling during the NFPA 286 test procedure.

The other difference is in the placement of the gas feed burner. NFPA 265 positions the burner 12 in. (30.5 cm) above the floor and 2 in. (5.1 cm) from the side walls. NFPA 286 positions the burner at the same height but places it so that it is in direct contact with the walls. It has been shown that, due to this difference in configuration, there are differences in the severity of the test. There are ongoing discussions on the effects of the burner location on the overall severity of the exposure on the test specimens.

Due to these differences and the fact that NFPA 265 was original developed for the testing of textile materials on walls, it was determined that two separate test procedures would be maintained at this time, one for textile materials on walls (NFPA 265) and one for all other wall and ceiling interior finishes (NFPA 286). Testing to evaluate the application of the testing protocol of NFPA 286 on textile materials is ongoing. Once the data have been generated and analyzed, it will be then reviewed to determined whether NFPA 265 should be incorporated into NFPA 286.

A provision associated with NFPA 286, but not with NFPA 265, is the *Code*'s requirement that new interior finish installations tested to NFPA 286 must have a maximum total smoke release as defined in 10.2.3.5.3. The value of the total smoke release is expressed as a smoke optical density in square meters.

This was also expressed as a concern associated with textile materials required to be tested to NFPA 265, that they would have to have a total smoke release criterion. Currently, textile materials are not required to maintain a particular level of total smoke release when tested to NFPA 265. Additional data are being developed for evaluating the available textile materials and their relationship to the established threshold for total smoke released.

Textile Wall Coverings

Interior finishes that are classified as textile materials require special consideration and appropriate testing. Textile wall covering materials can include napped, tufted, looped, woven, and nonwoven or similar materials. The current edition of the *Code* recognizes two test methods for the testing of textile wall and ceiling coverings. One method, as noted earlier, was for textile materials having a Class A FSI as developed by testing to NFPA 255 and installed in accordance with the *Code* provisions of 10.2.4.1. The other method is NFPA 265, *Standard Methods of Fire Tests for Evaluating Room Fire Growth Contribution of Textile Wall Coverings*, which is specific for textile wall coverings. The NFPA 265 text procedure was established because fire research has shown that textile material having a Class A flame spread index does not accurately predict the overall burning characteristic behavior of this material in this particular end use. Fire research involving the full-scale room corner fire test scenarios has documented that Class A textile materials have a burning behavior that is not similar to the conclusions made from the results of testing done in accordance with NFPA 255.

Because of this activity, the *Code* now requires textile materials to be tested in accordance with NFPA 265. This standard is similar to UL 1715, *Standard for Safety Fire Test of Interior Finish Material*. The NFPA 265 standard provides a method for determining the contribution of textile wall coverings to the overall room fire growth during specified fire exposure conditions. This method is used to evaluate the flammability characteristics of textile wall coverings where these materials constitute the exposed interior surfaces of buildings. The limitations of the application of NFPA 265, as noted in its scope, relate to textile coverings used on a wall. If the textile material is used on the ceiling as an interior finish, NFPA 286, *Standard Methods of Fire Tests for Evaluating Room Fire Growth Contribution of Wall and Ceiling Interior Finish*, should be used for evaluation purposes.

Testing of Textile Wall Coverings. Two test protocols, Method A and Method B, are approved for testing a textile material. Method A uses a corner test exposure and mounts the test specimen on two walls of the test compartment. Method B uses the same test compartment configuration but covers three walls with the test specimen. The test room or compartment consists of an 8 ft × 12 ft × 8 ft (2.44 m × 3.66 m × 2.44 m) room with a 30 × 80 in. (0.76 × 2.03 m) doorway in the center of the 8 ft × 8 ft (2.44 m × 2.44 m) wall. Each of these test protocols uses a gas burner to produce a diffusion flame that will expose the walls in the corner of the room where the specimens are mounted to a predetermined energy source. The energy source, which has the burner positioned 2 in. (51 mm) from the walls, produces a heat output of 40 kW for 5 minutes followed by a 150-kW output for 10 minutes, for a total exposure period of 15 minutes. For Method A, the test specimens are mounted on the rear wall and left side wall and extend 2 ft (0.6 m) down from the ceiling. Method B requires the

specimens to be mounted so that they fully cover both the 8 ft × 12 ft (2.44 m × 3.66 m) walls and the rear 8 ft × 8 ft (2.44 m × 2.44 m) wall not having the door. See Exhibit S5.6. The combustion products from the test room are collected in a hood that is fed into a 3 ft × 3 ft (0.91 m × 0.91 m) plenum that is connected to an exhaust duct. Within this exhaust duct, measurements of gas velocity, temperature, and concentrations of selected gases are made. The hood is designed to develop a minimum flow rate of 7000 cfm (204 m³/m) at the standard temperature with 16,100 cfm (456 m³/m) at 750°F (399°C). This provides the necessary capture velocity to accumulate the products of combustion being expelled from the fire test room.

For textile material to be considered acceptable, flames must not spread to the ceiling during the 40-kW exposure and during the 150-kW exposure flames must not spread to the outer extremity of the test

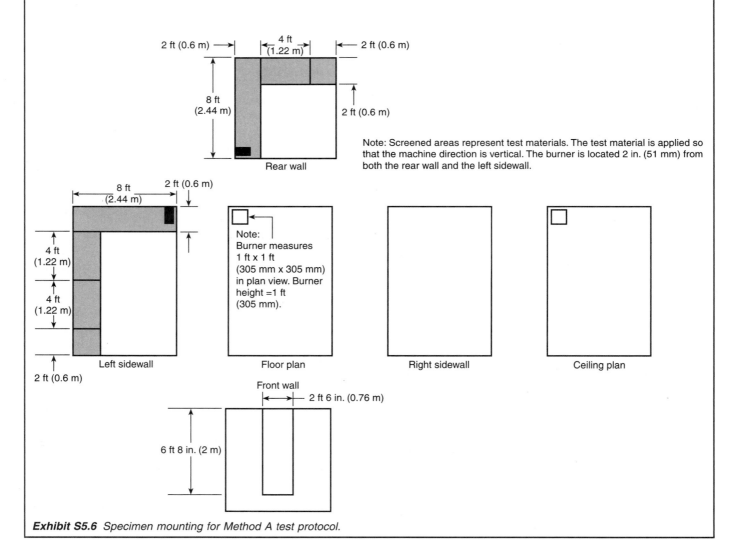

Exhibit S5.6 *Specimen mounting for Method A test protocol.*

specimen. Additionally, the test specimen in the room must not develop a flashover characteristic. Flashover is determined to have occurred in the test chamber when any two of the following conditions have been attained:

(1) A heat flux at the floor reaches 25 kW/m².
(2) The average upper air temperature exceeds 1200°F (649°C).
(3) Flames exit the doorway.
(4) A paper target on the floor ignites spontaneously.

Additional Considerations. Addition considerations should be given to the end use of textile materials as required by 10.2.3.1. Textile materials used as floor coverings, such as carpeting, that have a Class I or a Class II rating cannot be installed on walls or ceilings. This classification is from the testing results from NFPA 253, *Standard Method of Test for Critical Radiant Flux of Floor Covering Systems Using a Radiant Heat Energy Source,* and is applicable only when the material is installed as a floor covering. It is important that the materials be tested to the tests appropriate to the end use application.

Interior Floor Finish

Interior floor finishes are required to have a rating when specified by the *Code* or where the authority having jurisdiction determines that an unusual floor covering is being used and must be regulated due to its particular burning characteristics. These unusual floor coverings can include the rubber matting that covers a gym floor or the paper protection placed over newly finished floors. These materials provide a covering to protect the finished floor, but they are also used as a floor covering that could contribute to overall fire growth. The appropriate test for floor coverings is NFPA 253, *Standard Method of Test for Critical Radiant Flux of Floor Covering Systems Using a Radiant Heat Energy Source.* This test is similar to ASTM E 648, *Standard Test Method for Critical Radiant Flux of Floor-Covering Systems Using a Radiant Heat Energy Source.* This testing scenario was developed specifically to address the floor finish concerns. It evaluates the tendency of a floor covering material to propagate flame across its surface in relationship to a defined and measured energy source over a period of time.

The test method measures the critical radiant flux (CRF) behavior of a horizontally mounted floor covering system exposed to a flaming ignition source in a test chamber. The test method measures the CRF at the point of flame-out, which is when the material does not continue to support flaming. It provides a

basis for estimating one aspect of fire exposure behavior for floor covering systems. It should be noted that this test is intended for evaluating floor coverings installed in building corridors having little or no combustible wall or ceiling finish. A corridor with combustible finishes could be expected to produce a greater fire hazard.

A gas-fired panel serving as a radiant heat energy source is installed at one end of the chamber on an incline so that it extends over the test specimen. A pilot burner is located at the edge of the test specimen to provide ignition. The test specimens are required, insofar as possible, to simulate actual field installation practices. Exhibits S5.7(a), S5.7(b), and S5.8 show

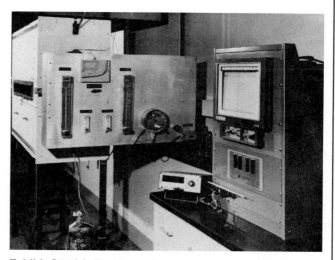

Exhibit S5.7(a) Flooring radiant panel tester apparatus.

Exhibit S5.7(b) Flooring radiant panel test showing carpet specimen and gas-fueled panel.

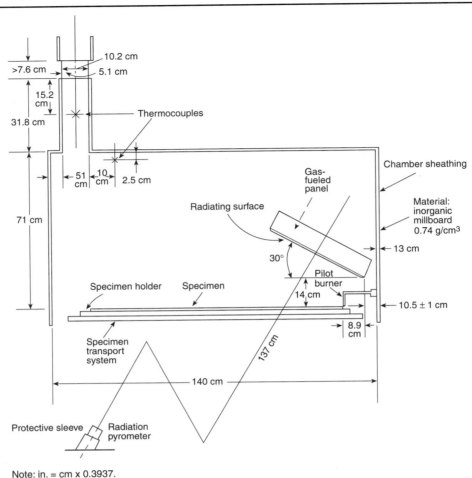

Note: in. = cm x 0.3937.

Exhibit S5.8 *Flooring radiant panel schematic side elevation.*

the apparatus used to test the floor covering specimens.

The CRF is determined by measuring the distance that has burned. The test specimen is tested for 10 minutes following the exposure to a radiant energy source to a maximum of 1 W/cm². The distance burned is converted to a CRF value by plotting the distance on the standard radiant heat energy flux profile. See Exhibit S5.9. The CRF is the level of incident radiant heat energy at the time the test specimen ceases flaming or glowing activities. The higher the CRF, the more resistant to the radiant exposure the material is and, subsequently, flame propagation across the surface, than materials with a lower CRF. The *Code* recognizes two classes of interior floor finishes: Class I, with a minimum CRF of 0.45 watt/cm², and Class II, with a minimum CRF of 0.22 watt/cm². With the test protocol's defined radiant energy source, the largest CRF value that can be obtained when testing in accordance with NFPA 253 is 1.0 watt/cm². Additional information pertaining to the federal flammability standards for carpets and rugs can be found in A.10.2.7.1.

TEST METHODS FOR SMOKE MEASUREMENTS

It is important to recognize that the values being developed for smoke density or obscuration might not have application or correlation to the particular base performance fire scenarios or other end use applications. Activities are ongoing to address some of these concerns.

The NFPA Fire Tests Committee has recently undertaken the activity to revise NFPA 258, *Standard Research Test Method for Determining Smoke Generation of Solid Materials*. The scope of this standard indicates that the measurement of smoke obscuration using a conical radiant source in a single closed chamber must be used only for research and as a development tool. The Fire Tests Committee felt that the test results

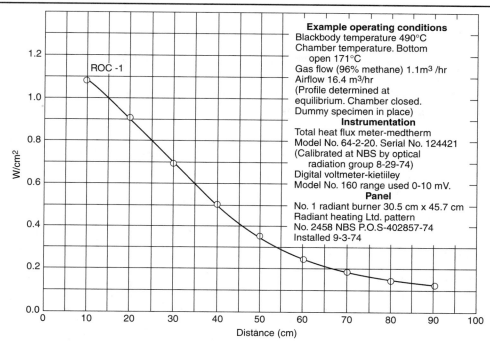

Note: in. = cm x 0.3937; Btu/ft² • sec = W/cm² x 1.135.

Exhibit S5.9 *Standard radiant heat energy flux profile.*

of this procedure were being used as a regulatory tool and were finding their way into fire modeling applications. Because of this activity, NFPA 258 was revised to become a guide and a new standard—NFPA 270, *Standard Test Method for Measurement of Smoke Obscuration Using a Conical Radiant Source in a Single Closed Chamber*—was developed that could be used for regulatory purposes. Even though this document has been revised for this purpose, the values associated with a material's optical density should be used with caution when being applied for regulatory purposes.

In 1.1.7, NFPA 270 is very specific in that this test method does not provide information on the fire performance of the test specimens under fire conditions other than those specified in the method. There are some observations that the measurement of smoke optical density is not well related to the open burning of the same combustible material. Appendix C of NFPA 270 provides additional information related to smoke obscuration measurements between different test methods. It notes that there exists little information on the correlation between the different test methods that measure smoke obscuration. This is important when evaluating a material's behavior on various its performance criteria associated with a particular fire modeling scenario or code requirement. The nondimensional values generated for a

level of smoke obscuration of NFPA 271—specific optical density, D_s—can resemble the same values as those derived for the smoke density index from NFPA 255. They might be the same numerical value, but they are not comparable. Each value was derived from different calculation methods and forms of measurement. Experience and sound judgment, with additional large-scale testing, should be considered when using the smoke optical densities developed from NFPA 270 testing for particular applications.

INTERIOR FURNISHINGS AND DECORATIONS

Another element to be considered for fire involvement includes furnishings such as upholstered furniture, mattresses, and decorations, including curtains, draperies, and other similar loosely hanging materials. Certain occupancies of the *Life Safety Code* require that these particular elements possess a certain degree of flame resistance and do not propagate or assist in flame spread. The overall fire growth in certain fires has been related directly to the types of furnishings and decorations found within the facility.

Testing of Curtains and Draperies

NFPA 701, *Standard Methods of Fire Tests for Flame Propagation of Textiles and Films*, is mandated for testing of curtains, drapes, or similar loosely hanging furnishings or decorations. NFPA 701 provides the means to evaluate the propagation of flame beyond the area exposed to the source of ignition. There are two methods of assessing flame propagation resistance as described in NFPA 701—Test Method 1 and Test Method 2. The test method to be used depends on the weight and the end use of the fabric. Test Method 1 is used on fabrics that weigh 21 oz/yd^2 (700 g/m^2) or less. Test Method 2 is used for fabrics greater than 21 oz/yd^2 (700 g/m^2) and for fabrics used in awnings and tents. These test methods were introduced in the revisions between the 1989 edition and 1996 edition of NFPA 701. Test Method 1 replaced the previous small-scale test.

The difference between Test Method 1 and the previous small-scale test is that the test specimen is larger and the overall time exposure to the flame is increased. This test employs ten 2.9 in. × 15.75 in. (150 mm × 400 mm) specimens of material that are exposed to a bunsen gas burner for 45 seconds. The other test, Test Method 2, has the same specimen size and test protocol as the previous large-scale test. The test specimens for the large-scale test involve specimens that are tested as folded or flat having sizes 24 in. × 46.25 in. (610 mm × 1.2 m) or 5 in. × 46.25 in. (125 mm × 1.2 m), respectively. Each test specimen is then exposed to a bunsen gas burner for 2 minutes. The acceptance criterion for NFPA 701 testing is a pass/fail criterion. Test Method 1 requires that there be no flaming for more than 2 seconds after the test flame is removed and that the average weight loss of the test specimen is not greater than 40 percent. The acceptance criteria for Test Method 2 also includes no flaming for more than 2 seconds after the test flame is removed. The length of char on an individual folded test specimen must not exceed 41.34 in. (1050 mm), and the length of char on any flat test specimen that is tested must not exceed 40.76 in. (1035 mm). Both test methods require that, if any portions or residues of the test specimen drip or fall to the test chamber floor during or after application of the test flame, flaming will not continue.

The results of the different tests stipulated in NFPA 701 should not be compared to each other. Test Method 1 uses a weight loss calculation for determining the pass/fail criteria. Test Method 2 uses the char length to calculate the acceptance criteria. One may assume that, because Test Method 2 uses a 2-minute exposure, it would represent a more severe condition than Test Method 1, which uses a 45-second exposure. Because they each use different calculation methods, it is impossible to compare the results to determine

whether one test method could be considered more challenging than another.

NFPA 701 stipulates that each fabric is to be subjected to exposures applicable to its intended use, such as laundering, dry cleaning, weathering, and other exposure to water. It is believed that the accelerated exposure tests that are detailed in NFPA 701 provide sufficient conditioning to permit a reasonable appraisal of the durability of the fire retardant treatment for the useful life of the fabric. Procedures on how to provide accelerated dry cleaning, laundering, weathering, and water leaching for the fabrics are provided in NFPA 701.

NFPA 705, *Recommended Practice for a Field Flame Test for Textiles and Films*, was originally Chapter 10 of NFPA 701, 1989 edition. During the revision to the 1996 edition of NFPA 701, Chapter 10 was developed as a stand-alone document. NFPA 705 provides guidance to enforcement officials for the field application of an open-flame ignition source to textiles and films that have been in use in the field or for which reliable laboratory data are not available. This recommended practice provides the authority having jurisdiction with a field procedure for determining the tendency of textiles and films to sustain burning subsequent to the application of a relatively small open flame. There is no correlation between the testing provisions found in NFPA 705 and the testing methods of NFPA 701. Field application of the NFPA 705 testing procedures is useful but must be used with good judgment and within limitations. Field tests should not be relied on as a sole means for ensuring adequate flame resistance of decorative materials. However, they are useful in augmenting a comprehensive regulatory program.

Testing of Interior Furnishings

The applicable provisions of the *Life Safety Code* that require when upholstered furniture is to resist cigarette ignition can be found in the occupancy chapters and in 10.3.1. Two test standards are applicable. One is NFPA 260, *Standard Methods of Tests and Classification System for Cigarette Ignition Resistance of Components of Upholstered Furniture*, which is similar to ASTM E 1353, *Standard Test Methods for Cigarette Ignition Resistance of Components of Upholstered Furniture*. The other is NFPA 261, *Standard Method of Test for Determining Resistance of Mock-Up Upholstered Furniture Material Assemblies to Ignition by Smoldering Cigarettes*, which is similar to ASTM E 1352, *Standard Test Method for Cigarette Ignition Resistance of Mock-Up Upholstered Furniture Assemblies*. NFPA 260 provides tests to determine whether upholstered furniture components such as cover fabrics, welt cords, decking materials, interior fabrics, and filling and padding materials are relatively resistant to ignition by smoldering cigarettes. This standard establishes a classification system for determining the resistance of upholstered furniture components to ignition. The *Code* requires, in certain occupancies, that the components of upholstered furniture have a Class 1 designation. A Class 1 designation under NFPA 260 designates materials that are considered resistant to cigarette ignition. To be designated as a Class 1, the material should not show evidence of ignition on any part of the test assembly and as a general rule does not have a char length exceeding 1.5 in. (38 mm).

NFPA 261 provides test methods to evaluate the ignition resistance of upholstered furniture assemblies when exposed to smoldering cigarettes under specific conditions. This test incorporates the use of upholstered furniture mock-ups for testing purposes. The mock-up testing is useful in assessing the relative resistance of continuing combustion of individual materials used in furniture such as cover fabrics, filling materials, and welt tape in realistic combinations and in an ideal, geometric arrangement of the seat cushions, backs, and arms. The reporting of the test results under NFPA 261 measures the maximum char length distance to the nearest 0.2 in. (5 mm) from the center of the original location of the test cigarettes. The *Life Safety Code* requires that char lengths not exceed 1.5 in. (38 mm) where tested in accordance with NFPA 261.

Two California documents are referenced by some state agencies for the flame and smoldering resistance testing of furniture components: California Technical Bulletin 116, *Cigarette Test of Upholstered Furniture*, and California Technical Bulletin 117, *Flame and Smoldering Resistance of Furniture Components*. There are some similarities in the testing procedures between the California Technical Bulletins 116 and 117, and NFPA 260 and 261, respectively. There are some differences in the pass/fail criteria; if a comparison will be made between them, it should be done with caution.

Other provisions that are related to upholstered furniture include the heat release rates. For determining the rates of heat release, the *Life Safety Code* recognizes NFPA 266, *Standard Method of Test for Fire Characteristics of Upholstered Furniture Exposed to Flaming Ignition Source*. A similar test standard is ASTM E 1537, *Standard Test Method for Fire Testing of Upholstered Furniture*. This test standard uses a full-scale furniture calorimeter to measure heat release, smoke density,

weight loss, and generation of carbon monoxide. These elements are important when developing certain fire performance criteria for fire modeling. The standard uses an open flame ignition source on an actual upholstered furniture or full size mock-up.

Another test procedure used to evaluate the properties of upholstered furniture is NFPA 272, *Standard Method of Test for Heat and Visible Smoke Release Rates for Upholstered Furniture Components or Composites and Mattresses Using an Oxygen Consumption Calorimeter* (renumbered from NFPA 264A). This test uses an oxygen consumption calorimeter that can be used to determine heat release, smoke density, weight loss, and generation of carbon monoxide from an upholstered furniture component. This test procedure exposes a component of the upholstered furniture to controlled levels of radiant energy from an electric heater. Performance data from these tests have been useful in assessing the fire hazards of upholstered furniture for product development and design. California Technical Bulletin 133, *Flammability Test Procedures for Seating Furniture and Use in Public Occupancies*, has also been demonstrated to provide comparable results for test specimens having heat release rates of 600 kW or less.

Mattresses

The *Life Safety Code* does address the heat release rates for mattresses for certain occupancies. The test standard recognized by the *Code* is NFPA 267, *Standard Method of Test for Fire Characteristics of Mattresses and Bedding Assemblies Exposed to Flaming Ignition Source*. Similar standards are ASTM E 1590, *Fire Testing of Mattresses*, and California Technical Bulletin 129. The NFPA 267 test method uses an open calorimeter environment to determine heat release, smoke density, weight loss, and generation of carbon monoxide of the test specimen. The limitation on the rate of heat release of mattresses as noted in the *Code* is a peak of 250 kW and a total energy release during the first 5 minutes of the test to 40 MJ.

CONE CALORIMETER TESTING

NFPA 271, *Standard Method of Test for Heat and Visible Smoke Release Rates for Materials and Products Using an Oxygen Consumption Calorimeter*, is a test procedure for determining the ignitibility, heat release rate, mass loss rates, effective heat of combustion, and visible smoke development of materials and products. The test procedure uses a cone calorimeter apparatus that exposes a test specimen to a controlled level of radiant heating. The test results are useful in the evaluation of materials, mathematical modeling, and product research and development. It is important that the results of this test procedure and many of the others that use a small sample for testing are used with caution in their final application. These tests use only a small test specimen exposed to a controlled energy source that might not truly reflect the end use and the open burning characteristics exhibited by the product.

TESTING LABORATORIES

It is not the intent of the *Code* to require the use of any specific testing laboratory. The *Code* leaves the evaluation of laboratories to the authorities having jurisdiction. The *Code* provides the minimum standards that dictate the testing methods and leaves the option as to how and who will perform this testing procedure to the appropriate responsible individuals. NFPA does not approve, inspect, or certify installations, procedures, materials, or equipment, nor does it approve or evaluate testing laboratories. Obtaining information on testing labs is not a simple task. There are a few directories that provide categories or listings of testing labs by their characteristics of what they do. There are the larger known testing laboratories such as Underwriters Laboratories, Factory Mutual Research Corporation, Warnock Hersey, Southwest Research Institute, Omega Point Laboratories, and United States Testing Company. But there are also many independent testing labs that perform tests that meet the criteria of the referenced standards in the *Life Safety Code*. More information on labs available to do a particular test can be found in the following reference sources:

(1) ASTM Directory of Testing Labs, American Society of Testing and Materials, 100 Barr Harbor Drive, West Conshocken, PA 19428
(2) American Council of Independent Laboratories Directory, American Council of Independent Laboratories Inc., 1725 Case Street NW, Washington, DC 20006
(3) U.S. Department of Commerce, *Directory of Accredited Laboratories*, National Voluntary Laboratory Accreditation Program, National Institute of Standards and Technology, Gaithersburg, MD 20899. NIST Special Publication 810

SUPPLEMENT 6

How to Adopt the *Life Safety Code* into Law

Dennis J. Berry, Esq.

INTRODUCTION

This supplement to the handbook addresses the recommended and most popular methods by which the *Life Safety Code*, or any model code, can be adopted into the law of a state, city, or town. The purpose is to assist those who are considering the adoption of the *Code* for their jurisdiction.

There are, generally speaking, two methods by which this adoption can be accomplished: either adoption by transcription or adoption by reference. The former method requires that the adopting ordinance reproduce, in full, the code or standard being adopted. The latter method requires only that the adopted code or standard be referenced in the laws of the jurisdiction by means of a full and adequate description.

Adoption by reference of a technical standard or code is a widely accepted (see Table S6.1) and often preferable procedure for a legislative or regulatory body to follow in establishing fire and building regulations. There are three reasons why this particular procedure can be advantageous for governing authorities. First, adoption by reference avoids the necessity of printing in full a highly technical code that will often be several hundred pages in length. Thus, a reference statute or ordinance minimizes the ever-increasing bulk of official statute books and avoids the often prohibitive cost of reprinting and successive publication. Second, technical codes and standards are constantly improved and updated by the issuing organization. Such updated standards are easily adopted by the appropriate authority simply by adopting a new provision with an updated reference. Third, there is less opportunity for a lobbying influence to weaken the provisions of a code when the principal thrust is to adopt the entire work by reference.

The fundamental constitutionality of adoption by reference is not in doubt, nor, generally speaking, is its legality as long as the adoption is properly executed. Legal authorities appear to be in agreement that, "in the absence of statutory or charter provisions to the *contrary*, adoption of documents in municipal ordinance by incorporation by reference is valid where the document adopted is sufficiently identified and is made a part of the public record."* Numerous cases that have addressed and enforced regulations adopted by reference have been reported.** Furthermore, the federal government, almost every state, and the District of Columbia have, to some extent, used this method of legislation (see Table S6.1). On the local level, adoption by reference is even more widely used in recognition of the advantages mentioned above. In more than thirty states, statutes specifically

---

*See C. J. Antieu, *Municipal Corporation Law*, Vol. 1, §4.17, pp. 4–34 [emphasis added]; see also 73 C.J.S., *Public Administrative Law and Procedure* §107 & n. 63.

**See, e.g., *Associated Builders and Contractors, Inc. v. Brock*, 862 F.2d 63 (3rd Cir. 1988); *Noblecraft Industries, Inc. v. Secretary of Labor*, 614 F.2d 199 (9th Cir. 1980); *City of Syracuse v. Penny*, 59 Misc. 2d 818, 300 NYS2d 679 (1969); *Friedman v. Goodman*, 219 Ga. 152, 132 S.E.2d 60 (1963); *Banks v. Civil Service Commissioner*, 10 Cal. 2d 435, 74 P.2d 741 (1937).

Table S6.1 Survey of Adoption by Reference Method in the United States

Examples of State-Level References

To Privately Developed Codes and Standards	To State Statutes Enabling Local Governments to Adopt by Reference
Alabama	
Ala. Code §9-17-120 et seq.	Ala. Code §11-45-8(c)
Alaska	Alaska Stat. §29.25.040
Arizona	Ariz. Rev. Stat. Ann. §9-802
California	Cal. Government Code §50022.2
Colorado	
Colo. Rev. Stat. §12-23-104 (2)(a)	Colo. Rev. Stat. §31-16-201-208 et seq.
Connecticut	
Conn. Gen. Stat. §29-252	
Delaware	
Del. Code Ann. tit. 16, §6603	
District of Columbia	
D.C. Code Ann. Tit. 5, §1302	
Florida	
Fla. Stat. Ann. tit. 23, §320.822	
Hawaii	
Haw. Rev. Stat. tit. 10, §132-3	Haw. Rev. Stat. tit. 46-1.5 (14)
Idaho	
Idaho Code tit. 41, Ch. 2, §41-253	Idaho Code tit. 31, Ch. 7, §31-715
Illinois	65 ILCS 5/1-3-1, et seq.
Indiana	
Ind. Code Ann. §22-8-1.1-15	Ind. Code Ann. §36-1-5-4
Iowa	
Iowa Code Ann. §101A.5	Iowa Code Ann. §380.10
Kansas	
Kan. Stat. Ann. §75-1220	Kan. Stat. Ann. Art. 33 §12-301 et seq.
Kentucky	
Kentucky Rev. Stat. Ann. §227.570	
Louisiana	
La. Rev. Stat. Ann. Ch. 51, §911.23	La. Rev. Stat. Ann. Ch. 33, §1363
Maine	Me. Rev. Stat. Ann. tit. 30, §3003
Maryland	Md. Code Ann. art. 23A, §6
Michigan	
Mich. Stat. Ann. §5.2949(4)	
Minnesota	
Minn. Stat. Ann. §§327.31, 327.32	Minn. Stat. Ann. §471.62
Missouri	
Mo. Ann. Stat. §700.010	
Mississippi	
Miss. Code Ann. §75-57-35	Miss. Code Ann. §21-19-25
Montana	
Mon. Code Ann. §50-60-401	Mon. Code Ann. §§7-5-4202
Nebraska	
Neb. Rev. Stat. §81-502	Neb. Rev. Stat. §18-132
Nevada	
Nev. Rev. Stat. §278.583	Nev. Rev. Stat. §266.115
New Hampshire	
N.H. Rev. Stat. Ann. §153:5	
New Jersey	N.J. Stat. Ann. §40:49-5.1

Table S6.1 Continued

Examples of State-Level References

To Privately Developed Codes and Standards	To State Statutes Enabling Local Governments to Adopt by Reference
New Mexico N.M. Stat. Ann. §60-14-4	N.M. Stat. Ann. §3-17-6
New York N.Y. State Uniform Fire Prevention and Building Code Part 610	
North Carolina N.C. Gen. Stat. §143-138(c)	N.C. Gen. Stat. §160A-76(b)
North Dakota N.D. Century Code Ann. 54-21.3-03	N.D. Cent. Code §40-05-01
Ohio	Ohio Rev. Code Ann. §731.231
Oklahoma	Okla. Stat. Ann. tit. 75, §251 (D)
Oregon	Or. Rev. Stat. §§215.605, 221.330
Pennsylvania	Pa. Stat. Ann. tit. 53, §36014
Rhode Island R.I. Gen. Laws §§23-28.31-3,23-28.31-9	
South Carolina	S.C. Code Ann. §6-9-60
South Dakota S.D. Codified Laws Ann. §34-38-35	S.D. Codified Laws Ann. §6-54-502
Tennessee Tenn. Code Ann. §68-120-101	Tenn. Code Ann. §9-19-7
Virginia Va. Code Ann. §27-97	
Washington Wa. Rev. Code §§19. 27.031, 19.27A.010	
West Virginia W.Va. Code §21-3-3a	W.Va. Code §8-11-4
Wisconsin Wis. Stat. Ann. §101.94	
Wyoming Wyo. Stat. §35-9-106	Wyo. Stat. §15-1-119

enable local governmental bodies to adopt technical codes and standards by reference.

In those states that have specific statutory procedures for adopting an ordinance, those procedures must generally be followed closely. However, the legal position stated previously makes clear that even in those states that have no specific statute enabling municipal governments to adopt standards by reference, that procedure is nonetheless available unless specifically prohibited.

There have been cases in which adopted standards or regulations have been denied enforcement. In some cases, they have been struck down com-

pletely, while, in others, they have simply not been enforced in the case before the court. However, such cases are usually due to failure to follow all procedural requirements in the adoption and filing processes, rather than due to a basic flaw in the concept of adoption by reference.

Courts have, in some instances, drawn a distinction between requirements for adoption that are mandatory and those that are directory. Failure to meet those requirements that are mandatory can be fatal to adoption, while failure to meet a requirement that is directory may not cause the entire ordinance to be unenforceable. Careful attention to state requirements should prevent any flaws, mandatory or directory, from preventing full enforcement.

It should be noted that enforcement of adopted codes and standards is usually sought by a municipal official in a proceeding in which a court is being asked to assess fines or impose other penalties against individuals who allegedly failed to meet the standards. In such a case, particularly if it is deemed by state law to be a criminal proceeding, the court is likely to resolve all doubts concerning both the facts and the law in favor of the defendant. Thus, counsel for the defendant will thoroughly review the entire record of the adoption, as well as the statutory conditions under which the adoption took place, in order to uncover any possible flaws. If able to find procedural flaws that have arguable validity, the defendant may well prevail and thereby cause doubt regarding the enforceability of the whole statute. In such situations, the basic concept behind adoption of the code is not in question as much as the procedural steps by which it was accomplished. Adherence to the statutory procedure of the jurisdiction is thus of vital importance.

Therefore, it falls on counsel for a municipality, rule-making body, or legislature seeking to adopt a particular standard by reference to ensure that the adoption process is properly followed in every respect.

METHODS OF ADOPTING AND USING PRIVATELY DEVELOPED STANDARDS

This section presents a description of adoption by reference and a description of the two other common methods of adopting or using fire and building codes or standards. It also presents model state and local legislation designed to implement each of these methods. (See Table S6.1 for a survey of the status of the adoption by reference method in the United States.) The basic intent of this section is to present and explain the means by which jurisdictions may adopt the *Life Safety Code* and other privately developed standards into local laws, ordinances, or regulations without incurring the often prohibitive costs of development and separate publication.

The model drafts included herein are typical methods and offer only broad guidelines. The constitution or charter of the subject jurisdiction and the enabling legislation and any applicable court decisions should be reviewed in preparation for the adoption process. The focus is on the adoption of the *Life Safety Code* and other privately developed standards. It has become increasingly popular to adopt by refer-

ence standards promulgated by the state or federal government or agencies thereof. Standards promulgated by another level of government may appear to have an inherent credibility not shared by privately developed standards. In fact, there is little difference in the adoption or ultimate credibility of privately developed standards as opposed to those promulgated by another unit of government. The principles involved in such adoption will not change.

Like all forms, these present only a basis from which counsel for the group seeking adoption or municipal counsel can work to propose the actual legislation.

Adoption by Reference

This is the most economical procedure for adopting privately developed codes and standards. An act or ordinance simply references the applicable standard by title, edition, and date. The date of the standard is important. To adopt the standard without reference to a particular edition or date may cause the adoption to be struck down. It may seem logical to simply adopt the *Life Safety Code* and allow it to be changed as the NFPA adopts each new edition. The flaw in this logic is that to do so would, in effect, give the NFPA the right to change the law of a jurisdiction. This could be considered an improper delegation of legislative authority.

If a standard is adopted by reference, usually only the referencing legislation, not the entire standard, need be published. The legislation must generally indicate where the standard is available for public inspection, where copies of the standard may be purchased, and what penalties are provided for violation of the standards. In most cases, it is mandatory that all penalty provisions be published.

Different jurisdictions have different filing and availability requirements. These should be addressed during the adoption process or be contained in the adoption legislation itself. Adherence to these requirements is important. A popular method of attack consists of arguing that a defendant did not have reasonable opportunity to know the law that has been broken.

The adopting authority may want to amend or delete certain provisions of the referenced standard. All such changes must also be published in the legislation, and they must be identified as changes.

Adoption by Transcription

This procedure involves transcribing the privately developed code or standard into a statute or ordinance.

Permission for the reproduction should be obtained from the organization that developed and holds copyright in the document. Once that is secured, one section of the published act must acknowledge the originating group as the copyright owner of the provision transcribed. Adoption by transcription obviously lacks some of the simplicity of adoption by reference, since the entire code must be published in full. This method may discourage desired updating of the standard, because this would involve complete republication. In addition to the code or standard, penalty provisions should be specifically set out.

Prima Facie* Evidence Method

This is not a procedure for adopting a standard into law. Instead, it is a rule of law regarding the admissability of a standard. It is mentioned here only because it may prove helpful to those in authority who may be attempting to enforce the provisions of the *Life Safety Code*. The applicable legislation simply defines the legal standard to be a "reasonable standard of safety," and provides that a particular edition of the *Life Safety Code* or another standard shall be prima facie evidence of what is "reasonable." Thus, any condition that meets the requirements of the cited standard will be considered legally "reasonable" within the meaning of the act. The published legislation must indicate where a copy of the standard can be obtained. It is possible that other standards or even an ad hoc activity also could be found to be reasonable.

This method may appear to be the simplest of all, but its inherent lack of certainty with regard to the requirements of the law makes prospective regulatory enforcement difficult. The rule of law actually comes into play only after the fact. It would be difficult to enforce regulations against an individual who chose to ignore the appropriate standard and take the chance that injury would not occur.

Model Legislation: State

Model State Act to Incorporate a Privately Developed Code or Standard by Reference. The state of . . . does ordain as follows:

Section 1. In the interest of public safety, the standards as set forth in . . . *[identify the standard]* . . . are hereby adopted, as if set forth herein, as safety standards for . . . *[subject matter]*.

*Prima facie: Presumed to be true unless disproved by evidence to the contrary.

Section 2. The following sections of the said . . . *[identify the standard]* . . . are amended to read as indicated: (a) Section . . . is amended to read: *[insert new language]*. (b) Section . . . is deleted. (c) Section . . . (etc).

Section 3. Any person who shall violate any provisions of this Act, or who shall fail to comply with any of the requirements thereof, shall be guilty of a misdemeanor punishable by a fine of not more than . . . dollars or by imprisonment not exceeding . . . year(s), or by both.

Section 4. The Office of the . . . *[appropriate state official]* . . . shall keep *[required number]* copies of the said . . . *[identify the standard]* . . . Additional copies are available from the . . . *[name and address of the originating group]*.

Model State Statute to Adopt a Privately Developed Standard by Transcription. The state of . . . does ordain as follows:

Section 1. In the interest of public safety, the following standards shall govern . . . *[subject matter]* . . ..

Section 2. The . . . *[promulgating authority]* . . . recognizes the copyright owner to be the . . . *[name and address of originating group]*.

Section 3. The following sections of the . . . *[identify the standard]* . . ., herein called . . . *[official name of state code]* . . ., have been added, amended, or deleted: *[List section numbers of all changes.]*

Section 4. . . .*[the standard transcribed with indicated changes]*.

Section 5. . . .*[indicate penalties for violations]* . . .

Model State Statute Using a Privately Developed Standard as Prima Facie Evidence. The state of . . . does hereby ordain as follows:

Section 1. In the interest of public safety, the . . . *[name of state code or act]* . . . is created to read and provide as follows:

Section 2. All . . . *[equipment named]* . . . hereafter installed, sold, or offered for sale shall be reasonably safe to persons and property.

(a) Installation, etc., of . . . *[equipment]* . . . that complies with the standards recommended by the . . . *[name of originating group]* . . . in the . . . *[identify the standard]* . . . shall be considered prima facie evidence of providing reasonable safety to persons and property in compliance with the intent of this Act.

Section 3. Copies of the . . . *[identify the standard]* . . . may be obtained from the . . . *[name and address of originating group]* . . . .

Section 4. . . . *[indicate penalties for violations]* . . . .

Model State Statute Enabling Municipal Governments to Adopt Privately Developed Standards by Reference. The state of . . . does ordain as follows:

Section 1. As used in this Act, unless the context otherwise requires:

(a) Municipality means . . . *[applicable state subdivisions]* . . .

(b) Code means a published "Code" or "Standard" as prepared and published by the . . . *[originating group]* . . .

(c) Related Document means those provisions of a published document that are adopted by reference in a code directly or indirectly by successive adoptions by reference through other printed documents.

(d) Adoption by Reference includes references making provisions of another document applicable.

(e) Published, as used in this Act, means printed, lithographed, multigraphed, mimeographed, or issued in other similar form.

Section 2. An ordinance of any municipality may adopt by reference a code, or any parts thereof, without setting forth the provisions of the code, or parts thereof, provided that copies of the code, or the pertinent parts thereof, and any related documents are filed in accordance with Section 3 of this Act. The title and date of publication shall be set forth in the ordinance. The requirements of law regarding the publication and posting of ordinances shall apply to the ordinance but not to the provisions that it adopts by reference, or any parts thereof, without setting forth the provisions of the related documents.

Section 3. Not less than three (3) copies of the code, or the pertinent parts thereof, and the related document shall be filed with the . . . *[appropriate official]* . . . and shall be available for public examination during regular business hours.

Section 4. The procedure authorized by this act for the enactment of ordinances shall apply to the amendment of ordinances enacted hereunder and to the amendment of all other ordinances prescribing

standards or regulations with respect to the matters referred to in subsection (b) of Section 1 of this Act.

Section 5. This Act may be cited as the Adoption by Reference Act.

Model Legislation: Local

Note: Local legislation follows the same basic pattern as the state legislation above; therefore, only one example of a local ordinance is included herein.

Model Municipal Ordinance to Adopt a Privately Developed Standard by Reference. Section 1. An ordinance to provide for the city of . . . rules and regulations to improve safety of the public by promoting the control of fire hazards; regulating the installation, use, and maintenance of equipment; regulating the use of structures, premises, and open areas; providing for the abatement of fire hazards; and setting forth standards for compliance to achieve these objectives. (See NOTE below.)

[NOTE: A preamble of this type may be altered or amended as appropriate to include the hazard meant to be regulated. It is permissible to be comprehensive and nonspecific and to include hazards other than those that are to be addressed specifically by the adopted standard, but at least the general nature of the hazard should be included in the preamble list.]

Section 2. It shall be unlawful for any person to violate this ordinance, to permit or maintain such violation, to refuse to obey any provision thereof, or to fail or refuse to comply with any such provision or regulation except as variation may be allowed by action of the . . . *[title of enforcing official]* . . . in writing. Proof of such unlawful act or failure to act shall be deemed prima facie evidence that such act is that of the owner. Prosecution or lack thereof of either the owner or the occupant shall not be deemed to relieve the other.

Section 3. The provision shall apply equally to both public and private property. It shall apply to all new structures and their occupancies, including buildings, structures, equipment, etc., and, except as otherwise specified within its own terms, to existing structures and their occupancies, including buildings, structures, equipment, etc., that constitute a clear and present hazard to life or to property.

Section 4. The standard for . . . *[subject matter]* . . . shall be the standard set forth in . . . *[identify the standard]* . . . , and said code shall be part of this ordinance as though set out herein.

Section 5. The following sections of . . . *[identify the standard]* . . . are amended to read as indicated:

[List any sections changed along with the changes made.]

Section 6. . . . *[indicate penalties for violations]* . . .

Section 7. The Office of the . . . *[appropriate official]* . . . shall keep three (3) copies of the . . . *[identify the standard]* . . . on file and accessible to the public during regular business hours.

Section 8. Copies of the . . . *[identify the standard]* . . . are available from the . . . *[name and address of originating group]*.

Retroactivity and Variances

Among the most popular additions to adopted codes are provisions regarding retroactivity and variances. Certain of the "model drafts" included herein may, if desired, be modified to include further language on "retroactivity" and on "variances." The decision to do so will depend on local needs, the legal terms of the enforcing authority, and whether the particular standard being incorporated into law contains such provisions. It should be noted that the *Life Safety Code* contains a provision on retroactivity. Therefore, in the adoption of the *Code*, there is no reason to provide a special section addressing the subject.

The following are suggested sections that may be included in any adopted statute or ordinance to provide language to cover these situations when they are determined to be necessary. These should be considered in light of the practices and intent of the authority having jurisdiction.

Section. . . *[number of section]* Retroactivity: Existing structures, facilities, and installations, as may be covered by regulations promulgated under the authority of this Act in service or under construction as of the effective date of this Act and which are not in strict compliance with the terms of this Act, may be continued or placed in use provided these do not constitute a distinct hazard to life or adjoining property. Where . . . *[name appropriate board or committee]* deems that the continued use will constitute a distinct hazard to life or adjoining property, it shall notify the owner or operator and specify reason in writing.

Section . . . *[number of section]* Variances: The . . . *[name appropriate board or committee]* shall have the power to grant exemption of application from specific requirements of regulations promulgated pursuant to this Act upon request in writing to do so when such request shows that the enforcement of the specific requirement will cause unnecessary hardship to the petitioner or in order to take advantage of new methods or equipment of recognized adequacy, provided that such request shall not be granted unless the requested equipment or use will, in the opinion of the . . . *[name appropriate board or committee]*, conform with all the fundamental requirements for safety. The particulars of such exemptions, when granted, shall be entered upon the approval granted. A copy thereof shall be retained by the . . . *[name appropriate board, committee, or official]*.

SUPPLEMENT 7

Home Security and Fire Safety

Sharon Gamache
and
Michelle Perrault

In recent years, deaths by fire have declined, as have most measures of loss due to crime. However, the public's perception of crime hasn't always kept pace with reality. One result is that more and more people seek and adapt further built-in security measures to protect themselves, such as installing security bars and grilles. Some of these security measures to block intruders pose a significant risk of trapping occupants seeking to flee a fire. And, in fact, since 1980 there has been a dramatic increase in the number and percentage of fire deaths that can be attributed to blocked exits. This supplement to the *Life Safety Code Handbook* describes the threat that window and door security bars pose to life safety. It reports on the current problem, details the efforts of the National Fire Protection Association to address the problem, and recommends future action.

PROBLEM DEFINITION

The threat to life safety from security bars is hard to measure but appears to be on the rise. There are three main aspects to the problem: increased use of security measures in homes, difficulty in collecting hard data to quantify the problem, and the essentially unregulated state of the security bar industry.

Home Security Trends

While solid statistics on practices and usage are elusive, most observers and the home security industry believe that fear of crime has led more and more citizens to blockade themselves inside their homes. Some of these measures are ill-conceived, some are

makeshift (e.g., nailing windows shut), and some are even illegal. In their attempts to protect their families and properties by locking out intruders, these people seem unaware they might be locking themselves into a potentially life-threatening situation. At the same time, they might also be preventing fire fighters from ready access into their homes.

Despite a downward trend in overall fire deaths in the United States, the number of fire deaths related to the use of security bars has risen. An average of less that one fire death per year was attributed to "illegal gates or locks" for 1980 through 1985. This figure increased dramatically to an average of nearly 16 deaths a year for the 1986 through 1991 period. In 1993, seven children died in a Detroit house fire and in Mississippi eight family members perished in a dwelling fire. During 1996, 12 people died in three incidents in California. Four children perished in a fire in 1997 in Tampa, a family of five died in a Bessemer, Alabama, fire, and in East Palo Alto, California, nine people were killed. In all of these fatal fires, security bars on windows and locked doors prevented escape from the fire and prevented fire fighters from successfully completing any rescue attempts.

Socioeconomic circumstances make the problem worse. Most of these fatal fires occur in low-income, high-crime neighborhoods. Due to a heightened fear of crime in these neighborhoods, people take measures to secure their homes and discourage intruders from entering, thereby, either consciously or unconsciously, placing security over fire safety. This is particularly dangerous because people living in high-crime and/or low-income areas usually face increased fire risk as well. Increased fire risk, combined with blocked exits, is most dangerous for young children, the elderly, and the disabled, for whom escape might be more difficult, even under ordinary circumstances.

Data Collection Difficulties

Although fire deaths related to security measures have increased dramatically, the number is still small enough to pose problems for the sample-based estimation procedures used to track U.S. fire problems. This problem is made more severe by the dominance of multiple-death fires among the known incidents. And there are additional problems unique to the issue. Fire death and injury reports might omit information related to security bars, because the question that captures security measure involvement also addresses other issues. There are a number of options, but only one option can be selected. A further complication is that the option on many forms reads "illegal bars or gates." Because the legal status of the security bars or gates is often unclear, the likelihood of the presence of the gates or bars being identified as impediments to escape is reduced. The data classification defined in NFPA 901, *Standard Classification for Incident Reporting and Fire Protection Data,* has been changed to delete the term *illegal.* In addition, new systems collecting data are adding the capability of listing multiple contributing factors. However, it will take time before these changes are used by everyone in the field.

The Security Bar Industry

Fragmentation. The nature of the security bar industry presents some substantial obstacles to solving the life safety problem these bars pose. Research reveals that the security bar and gate industry is highly fragmented, with considerable regional differences in professional standards and little understanding of the possible consequences of permanently installed bars or inadequate release mechanisms. Until recently, there have been no standard of design and no consistent use of quick-release mechanisms on security bars or gates. Differences and variations among installation companies are even greater. Some are one- or two-person welding shops that focus on security and only install permanent window bars. Other companies offer several options, including easy-release components.

Market Forces. Working against standardization are the market forces behind the industry's product development. Figure S7.1 depicts the various market

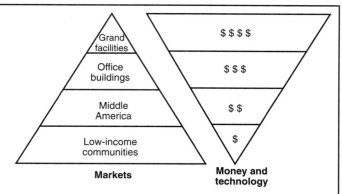

Exhibit S7.1 *Security bar industry market segments versus investment.*

segments of the security and fire safety industries and how they relate to the amount of money and technology invested in them.

The market segments are displayed in pyramid form, with the top, smallest section representing large facilities, such as convention centers and courthouses, which have the most sophisticated types of alarms, locking devices, and fire safety systems. The next section includes large office buildings and shopping centers, which also have relatively sophisticated security and fire safety systems with automatic releases or delayed egress locking devices and which represent a somewhat larger segment of the market. The next section of the triangle represents a still larger segment of the market that includes "middle America." This market segment is the major customer base for NOMMA (National Ornamental & Miscellaneous Metals Association), a trade group representing manufacturers and suppliers of gates, bars, and other security devices, as well as ornamental iron work. The last and largest segment represents the many low-income communities in both urban and rural areas.

Next to this triangle is an inverted triangle with the same four divisions made. This second triangle represents the amounts of money and technology invested in the corresponding market segments. The smallest market segment represents a few grand facilities, like convention centers, but has the greatest investment of resources. The largest market segment represents numerous low-income communities and has the fewest available resources.

This information about resource distribution shows the economic incentives and possible disincentives for the companies in this business. Clearly, there is more incentive for security bar manufacturers to invest in systems for large, public facilities, which would yield higher profits, than there is to invest in safety measures for low-tech devices in low-income communities.

Range of Products. Security devices that can assure life safety do exist in the low-income market, though. Security locks with inside release and quick-release bars are readily available. Some manufacturers even customize security systems with life safety features such as fluorescent labels that increase visibility at night. The link between the manufacturers, installers, and end users of these systems is often weak, however. Manufacturers often don't install their product, and installers and end users aren't necessarily aware of the life-safety advantages of some products over others.

Groups Affected by the Problem

The final key to understanding the security bar–life safety issue is the identification of the various groups that would necessarily have to become part of the solution.

Users. Those who have security bars on windows or doors in their homes, particularly those in low-income communities

Security Bar Industry. Those companies that design and manufacture security bars and those companies that install them

Code Groups. Those groups responsible for creating and revising national codes, such as NFPA 101, and regional building codes

Local Fire and Building Officials. Those groups or individuals responsible for local modification and enforcement of fire and building codes

Fire Service. Those in fire suppression, fire data analysis, and fire safety education

Law Enforcement. Police groups and associations and, especially, local police officers dealing with citizens' security concerns

Governing Bodies. State legislatures, agencies, and local officials writing bills, regulations, and ordinances

Social Service Agencies. Public and private groups working in low-income communities

Housing Authorities. Local, state, and federal groups dealing with housing issues

Public Health Officials. Those responsible for public health and safety

Insurance Industry. Companies dealing with both property loss and liability issues

PROGRESS TO DATE

The NFPA Center for High-Risk Outreach Home Security and Fire Safety Task Force was established in 1993 to find engineering, enforcement, and educational solutions to the problem of people being trapped in fires because of bars on windows or doors. Members of the task force come from diverse backgrounds and include fire marshals, public educators, police officers, and industry representatives. They help track legislation, progress of community outreach programs, and improvements in technology. Some of the accomplishments of the task force include the following:

- Underwriters Laboratories Inc.® *Subject 2326 Research Bulletin Releasing Systems for Window Bars in Residential Occupancies* has been published. It provides requirements for the evaluation, construction and performance of window bar releasing systems and can be used as a basis for state and local laws and regulations.

- Changes have been made in NFPA 901, *Standard Classifications for Incident Reporting and Fire Protection Data,* to eliminate the word *illegal* pertaining to security bars, in an effort to improve data collection.

- Incidents and statistics, codes and standards changes, proposed legislation, and updates from the security bar industry are constantly monitored.

- An information packet describing the dangers of security bars, fire safety messages, and the typical types of release devices has been produced and distributed to thousands of community and church groups, fire safety educators, law enforcement groups, and many others.

- Security bar messages have been incorporated in the NFPA educational brochures and Fire Prevention Week materials.

- The NFPA Center continues to cooperate with model programs in communities such as Ft. Lauderdale, Florida, and Oakland, California, where coalitions have been formed to provide retrofitting of security bars with quick-release devices and community educational programs on fire safety and security and escape planning.

- A partnership with State Farm Insurance has resulted in the gathering of sample release mechanisms, which helped in the development of the Underwriters Laboratories Inc.® bulletin for releasing systems and the development of a State Farm educational video and brochures on the importance of release devices.

- Partnerships with organizations such as the National Association of Hispanic Firefighters (NAHF), the International Association of Black Professional Fire Fighters (IABPFF), and the New York City Police Department have resulted in the dissemination of information and education to their constituents for outreach in urban communities.

- Regulation at the state government level has been encouraged. For example, California passed two bills related to security bars in 1996. One requires emergency escape warning labels on all bars sold through retail outlets, and the other gives local cities and towns the authority to regulate installation of security bars, including those on existing buildings. Bills have also been passed in Mississippi and Texas.

FUTURE ACTION

Recommendations for future action and potential solutions can be placed in one of three categories: engineering, enforcement, and education.

Engineering

Code Development. The NFPA Technical Committee on Means of Egress, which is responsible for Chapter 7 of NFPA *101, Life Safety Code*, should consider several issues related to means of escape in the next code cycle.

First, the differences between operability requirements for means of escape and means of egress should be clarified and emphasized. Means of egress must be operable without the use of a key, tool, special knowledge, or excessive force, while means of escape must simply be operable. This *Code* language seems to be suggesting that some special level of knowledge or special effort is acceptable in the operation of emergency escape openings.

Second, requirements specifying the operability of impediments to the means of escape should be incorporated in the *Code* (e.g., if a window is only required to be operable but might require special knowledge to open, any security feature installed in addition to it should be operable without the use of a key, tool, special knowledge, or excessive force).

Third, the minimum number and type of means of escape should be examined. If security measures are employed or if operation of an emergency escape mechanism is somewhat complicated, the time required to operate all of the features of the means of escape might prevent successful escape.

Fourth, if some, but not all, of the openings provided from a given room or space are used as a means of escape (as is currently the case), some consideration should be given to how these openings should be identified so that occupants can readily identify them in the event of an emergency, or at the very least when preparing their escape plans. At present there are significant differences among manufacturers.

Fifth, consideration should be given to requirements for mechanical or electrical releasing means for emergency escape openings where those mechanisms are employed. How should they operate? What fail-safe modes or interlocks should be required?

In addition to changes to NFPA *101*, efforts to correlate the provisions of NFPA *1, Fire Prevention Code,* of the *Model Building Codes,* and of other nationally recognized fire prevention codes should be undertaken concerning security measures and means of escape. Although widespread concurrence on means of escape requirements, especially opening dimensions, already exists, the regulatory vacuum on security measures has been filled rapidly, and conflicts between the competing objectives of security and fire safety might exist.

In this same vein, security issues should be integrated directly into discussions of code requirements, rather than resolving security/life safety conflicts after they emerge. The emphasis on life safety from fire often produces perceived conflicts with security. While both of these concepts are related to the larger subject of loss prevention, their relationship to each other is often complicated and confusing. In practice, though, both objectives can be satisfied.

Standards Development. Several types of standards might need to be developed to ensure that security-related products and designs meet the intent of code requirements for operability, reliability, and durability. Product standards should be developed to describe the requirements for proper design, installation, and operation of products and their main components. These standards should recognize that window bars are not the only design that can be employed. Grates, shutters, impact-resistant glazing, and locks may also be used. Testing standards to evaluate how well products perform their intended functions (security and life safety), as well as how reliably they perform over time, should be developed. Inspection and maintenance standards, written to be understood by homeowners and describing how to verify and ensure the continued proper operation of products, should also be developed.

Any standards that are developed should be performance-oriented rather than prescriptive or proprietary and should be the product of an open consensus process. Given the absence of technical standards in this area at present, the degree of industry inconsistency in design and installation, and the relative lack of recognition of the problems in this area, it should be assumed that the process of developing new code and standards requirements will be lengthy.

Enforcement

New installations of security devices clearly should be regulated via legislation. A generic model could be developed for use by all states. This model should include the following:

- Identification of problem
- Reference to code requirements that only approved (i.e., releasing) equipment be used
- Reference to product standard or required listed equipment
- Establishment of penalties (civil and/or criminal)

To address issues surrounding existing security bars and gates, an educational rather than regulatory approach should be taken.

Existing regulatory processes could be used to enforce legislation. To ensure that they are addressed in inspections, security bars could be added to the jurisdiction of fire and building departments. The question of licensing installers remains debatable. On the one hand, licensing ensures higher-quality, regulated work and provides a channel for fire safety information. On the other hand, licensing is not as effective as a permit process, which requires inspection and involves additional paperwork that could place unnecessary restraints on installers. Additional enforcement steps that should be taken include requiring existing noncomplying security devices to be replaced/fixed upon sale of a building, promoting financial incentives for replacing noncomplying existing devices, and involving the insurance industry in future discussions.

Education

The education component should take a two-tiered approach by separating the message and outreach into two groups: the experts (those who are somehow involved specifically in the issue) and the general public.

Experts. Experts consist of industry, law enforcement, and code officials. Efforts to educate the security bar industry should focus on the hazards of security devices if improperly designed, installed, or manufactured. In addition, an industry standard for security devices should be developed and monitored to ensure compliance. Finally, industry should become a partner in educating consumers by developing educational materials for dissemination in conjunction with promotional pieces to potential customers.

The law enforcement community, including the fire service and social service agencies, should recognize that people who install burglar bars are motivated by security concerns and consult the police—not the fire department—for advice about what security measures to take. The police should work with fire departments to ensure that fire and life safety issues are addressed. To facilitate this cooperation, the definition of *security* should be broadened to include fire safety concerns in addition to crime prevention. There are measures one can take to ensure the ability to escape without sacrificing the ability to keep intruders out. To bring all of law enforcement into the loop, a brochure or fact sheet with safety advice, industry standards, and recommended devices should be disseminated to public entities having any exposure to regulations, inspections, or enforcement of codes or ordinances.

Code officials, including permitting, enforcement, and plan review officials, should be educated about standards, requirements, potential hazards, and operations of security devices. These groups could then distribute information on various devices, their use and installation, and design features.

General Public. Schools and community organizations should be actively involved in educating the public about the types of devices available as well as their proper use and application. Insurance companies and other groups should be encouraged to require that minimum standards be met if security devices are installed on premises that are rented, leased, or insured on behalf of others. Most importantly, widespread printing and disseminating of educational materials is vital. Individuals need to be made aware of alternatives to "target hardening" measures.

Life Safety Code Cross-Reference Table 2000–1997 Editions

This table was developed to assist readers familiar with the 1997 Life Safety Code *to locate provisions within the 2000* Life Safety Code. *To use this table, find the desired paragraph number(s) under the 1997 column. The corresponding paragraph in the 2000* Code *will appear in the opposite column. The table also indicates which paragraphs from the 1997 edition might have been renumbered for, deleted in, or added to the 1997 edition. Users who are new to the* Code *or have used editions prior to 1997 should refer to the expanded index, which follows this cross-reference table. The index will lead the reader to the desired provisions.*

2000 Edition	1997 Edition	2000 Edition	1997 Edition	2000 Edition	1997 Edition
Chapter 1	Chapter 1	3.2	3-2	4.6.3	1-3.4
1.1	1-1	3.3	3-2	4.6.4	1-3.2
1.1.1	1-1.1	Chapter 4	Chapter 1 and	4.6.5	1-3.5
1.2	1-2		Chapter 2	4.6.6	1-3.6
1.3.1	1-2.1	4.1	New in 2000	4.6.7	1-3.7
1.2.1	1-2.2	4.1.1	1-4.1	4.6.8	1-3.9
1.2.2	1-2.3	4.1.2	New in 2000	4.6.9	1-3.10
1.2.3	1-2.4	4.2	1-4.2	4.6.9.1	1-3.10
1.2.4	1-2.6, 1-2.7	4.2.1	1-4.2, 2-2	4.6.9.2	New in 2000
1.3	1-4	4.2.2	New in 2000	4.6.10	1-3.11
1.3.1	1-4.1	4.2.3	New in 2000	4.6.10.1	1-3.11.1
4.1.1	1-4.2	4.3	1-5	4.6.10.2	1-3.11.2
A.1.3.1	1-4.3	4.3.1	1-5.1	4.6.10.3	1-3.11.3
A.1.3	1-4.4	4.4	New in 2000	4.6.11	1-3.12
1.4	1-3	4.4.1	New in 2000	4.6.12	1-3.13
1.4.1	1-3.1	4.4.2	New in 2000	4.6.12.1	1-3.13.1
1.4.2	1-2.5	4.4.2.1	New in 2000	4.6.12.2	1-3.13.2
1.5	1-6	4.4.2.2	1-3.8	4.6.12.3	1-3.13.3
1.5.1	1-6.1	4.4.3	New in 2000	4.6.12.4	1-3.13.4
1.5.2	1-6.2	4.5	Chapter 2	4.7	1-7
1.6	1-8	4.5.1	2-1	4.7.1	1-7.1
1.6.1	1-8.1	4.5.2	2-3	4.7.2	1-7.2
1.6.2	1-8.2	4.5.3	New in 2000	4.7.3	1-7.3
1.6.3	1-8.3	4.5.3.1	2-8	4.7.4	1-7.4
1.7	New in 2000	4.5.3.2	2-4	4.7.5	1-7.5
1.7.1	1-3.3	4.5.3.3	2-5	4.7.6	New in 2000
Chapter 2	Chapter 33	4.5.3.4	2-6	Chapter 5	New in 2000
2.1	33-1	4.5.4	2-7	Chapter 6	Chapter 4
2.1.1	33-1.1	4.5.5	2-9	6.1	4-1
2.1.2	33-1.2	4.5.6	New in 2000	6.1.1	New in 2000
Chapter 3	Chapter 3	4.5.7	1-3.13.1	6.1.1.1	4-1.1
3.1	3-1	4.6	New in 2000	6.1.1.2	4-1.1
3.1.1	3-1.1	4.6.1	1-3.3	6.1.2	4-1.2
3.1.2	3-1.2	4.6.1.1	1-3.3	6.1.2.1	4-1.2
3.1.3	3-1.3	4.6.1.2	New in 2000	6.1.2.2	4-1.2
		4.6.1.3	2-10	6.1.3	4-1.3
		4.6.2	New in 2000	6.1.3.1	4-1.3

2000 Edition	1997 Edition	2000 Edition	1997 Edition	2000 Edition	1997 Edition
6.1.3.2	4-1.3	7.1.10.1	5-1.9.1	7.2.2.2.3	5-2.2.2.4
6.1.3.3	4-1.3	7.1.10.2	5-1.9.2	7.2.2.2.3.1	5-2.2.2.4
6.1.4	4-1.11	7.1.10.2.1	5-1.9.2.1	7.2.2.2.3.2	New in 2000
6.1.4.1	4-1.11	7.1.10.2.2	5-1.9.2.2	7.2.2.2.3.3	5-2.2.2.4
6.1.5	4-1.4	7.1.10.2.3	5-1.9.2.3	7.2.2.2.3.4	5-2.2.2.4
6.1.5.1	4-1.4	7.2	5-2	7.2.2.2.4	5-2.2.2.5
6.1.6	4-1.4	7.2.1	5-2.1	7.2.2.3	5-2.2.3
6.1.6.1	12-1.3, 13-1.3	7.2.1.1	5-2.1.1	7.2.2.3.1	5-2.2.3.1
6.1.7	4-1.5	7.2.1.1.1	5-2.1.1.1	7.2.2.3.1.1	5-2.2.3.1.1
6.1.7.1	4-1.5	7.2.1.1.2	5-2.1.1.2	7.2.2.3.1.2	5-2.2.3.1.2
6.1.7.2	4-1.5	7.2.1.1.3	5-2.1.1.3	7.2.2.3.2	5-2.2.3.2
6.1.8	4-1.6	7.2.1.2	New in 2000	7.2.2.3.3	5-2.2.3.3
6.1.8.1	4-1.6	7.2.1.2.1	New in 2000	7.2.2.3.4	5-2.2.3.4
6.1.9	4-1.6(e)	7.2.1.2.2	New in 2000	7.2.2.3.5	5-2.2.3.5
6.1.9.1	22-1.3, 23-1.3	7.2.1.2.3	5-2.1.2.2	7.2.2.3.6	5-2.2.3.6
6.1.10	4-1.7	7.2.1.3	5-2.1.3	7.2.2.4	5-2.2.4
6.1.10.1	4-1.7	7.2.1.4	5-2.1.4	7.2.2.4.1	5-2.2.4.1
6.1.11	4-1.8	7.2.1.4.1	5-2.1.4.1	7.2.2.4.2	5-2.2.4.2
6.1.11.1	4-1.8	7.2.1.4.2	5-2.1.4.2	7.2.2.4.3	5-2.2.4.3
6.1.12	4-1.9	7.2.1.4.3	5-2.1.4.3	7.2.2.4.4	5-2.2.4.4
6.1.12.1	4-1.9	7.2.1.4.4	5-2.1.4.4	7.2.2.4.5	5-2.2.4.5
6.1.13	4-1.10	7.2.1.4.5	5-2.1.4.5	7.2.2.4.6	5-2.2.4.6
6.1.13.1	4-1.10	7.2.1.4.6	5-2.1.4.6	7.2.2.5	5-2.2.5
6.1.14	4-1.12	7.2.1.5	5-2.1.5	7.2.2.5.1	5-2.2.5.1
6.1.14.1	4-1.12	7.2.1.5.1	5-2.1.5.1	7.2.2.5.2	5-2.2.5.2
6.1.14.2	4-1.12	7.2.1.5.2	5-2.1.5.2	7.2.2.5.3	5-2.2.5.3
6.2	4-2	7.2.1.5.3	New in 2000	7.2.2.5.4	5-2.2.5.4
6.2.1	4-2.1	7.2.1.5.4	5-2.1.5.3	7.2.2.5.5	5-2.2.5.5
6.2.1.1	4-2.1.1	7.2.1.5.5	5-2.1.5.4	7.2.2.6	5-2.2.6
6.2.1.2	4-2.1.2	7.2.1.5.6	5-2.1.5.5	7.2.2.6.1	5-2.2.6.1
6.2.1.3	4-2.1.3	7.2.1.6	5-2.1.6	7.2.1.3	5-2.2.6.2
6.2.2	4-2.2	7.2.1.6.1	5-2.1.6.1	7.2.2.6.2	5-2.2.6.3
6.2.2.1	4-2.2.1	7.2.1.6.2	5-2.1.6.2	7.2.2.6.3	5-2.2.6.4
6.2.2.2	4-2.2.2	7.2.1.7	5-2.1.7	7.2.2.6.4	5-2.2.6.5
6.2.2.3	4-2.2.3	3.3.72, 3.3.142	5-2.1.7.1	7.2.2.6.5	5-2.2.6.6
6.2.2.4	4-2.2.4	7.2.1.7.1	5-2.1.7.2	7.2.2.6.6	5-2.2.6.7
Chapter 7	Chapter 5	7.2.1.7.2	5-2.1.7.3	7.2.3	5-2.3
7.1	5-1	7.2.1.7.3	5-2.1.7.4	7.2.3.1	5-2.3.1
7.1.1	5-1.1	7.2.1.8	5-2.1.8	7.2.3.2	5-2.3.2
7.1.2	5-1.2	7.2.1.8.1	5-2.1.8	7.2.3.3	5-2.3.3
7.1.3	5-1.3	7.2.1.8.2	5-2.1.8 exception	7.2.3.4	5-2.3.4
7.1.3.1	5-1.3.1	7.2.1.9	5-2.1.9	7.2.3.5	5-2.3.5
7.1.3.2	5-1.3.2	7.2.1.9.1	5-2.1.9	7.2.3.6	5-2.3.6
7.1.3.2.1	5-1.3.2.1	7.2.1.9.2	New in 2000	7.2.3.7	5-2.3.7
7.1.3.2.2	5-1.3.2.2	7.2.1.10	5-2.1.10	7.2.3.8	5-2.3.8
7.1.3.2.3	5-1.3.2.3	7.2.1.10.1	5-2.1.10.1	7.2.3.9	5-2.3.9
7.2.6.2	5-1.3.3	7.2.1.10.2	5-2.1.10.2	7.2.3.9.1	5-2.3.9.1
7.1.4	5-1.4	7.2.1.10.3	5-2.1.10.3	7.2.3.9.2	5-2.3.9.2
7.1.5	5-1.5	7.2.1.11	5-2.1.11	7.2.3.10	5-2.3.10
7.1.6	New in 2000	7.2.1.11.1	5-2.1.11.1	7.2.3.10.1	5-2.3.10.1
7.1.6.1	New in 2000	7.2.1.11.2	5-2.1.11.2	7.2.3.10.2	5-2.3.10.2
7.1.6.2	New in 2000	7.2.1.11.3	5-2.1.11.3	7.2.3.11	5-2.3.11
7.1.6.3	New in 2000	7.2.1.12	5-2.1.12	7.2.3.12	5-2.3.12
7.1.6.4	New in 2000	7.2.1.13	5-2.1.13	7.2.3.13	5-2.3.13
7.1.7	5-1.6	7.2.1.14	5-2.1.14	7.2.4	5-2.4
7.1.7.1	5-1.6.1	7.2.2	5-2.2	7.2.4.1	5-2.4.1
7.1.7.2	5-1.6.2	7.2.2.1	5-2.2.1	7.2.4.1.1	New in 2000
7.1.8	5-1.7	7.2.2.2	5-2.2.2	7.2.4.1.2	5-2.4.1
7.1.9	5-1.8, 5-1.8.2	7.2.2.2.1	5-2.2.2.1	7.2.4.2	5-2.4.2
Deleted	5-1.8.1	Deleted	5-2.2.2.2	7.2.4.2.1	5-2.4.2.1
7.1.10	5-1.9	7.2.2.2.2	5-2.2.2.3	7.2.4.2.2	5-2.4.2.2

2000 Edition	1997 Edition	2000 Edition	1997 Edition	2000 Edition	1997 Edition
7.2.4.2.3	5-2.4.2.3	7.2.8.7.2	5-2.8.7.2	7.3.1.1	5-3.1.1
7.2.4.2.4	5-2.4.2.4	7.2.8.7.3	5-2.8.7.3	7.3.1.2	5-3.1.2
7.2.4.3	5-2.4.3	7.2.8.7.4	5-2.8.7.4	Table 7.3.1.2	___-1.7 of occu-
7.2.4.3.1	5-2.4.3.1	7.2.8.7.5	5-2.8.7.5		pancy chapters
7.2.4.3.2	5-2.4.3.2	7.2.8.7.6	5-2.8.7.6	7.3.1.3	5-3.1.3
7.2.4.3.3	5-2.4.3.3	7.2.8.7.7	5-2.8.7.7	7.3.1.3.1	5-3.1.3
7.2.4.3.4	5-2.4.3.4	7.2.8.7.8	5-2.8.7.8	7.3.1.3.2	5-3.1.3
7.2.4.3.5	5-2.4.3.5	7.2.8.7.9	5-2.8.7.9	7.3.1.4	5-3.1.
7.2.4.3.6	5-2.4.3.6	7.2.8.8	5-2.8.8	7.3.1.5	5-3.1.5
7.2.4.3.7	5-2.4.3.7	7.2.8.8.1	5-2.8.8.1	7.3.1.6	5-3.1.6
7.2.4.3.8	5-2.4.3.8	7.2.8.8.2	5-2.8.8.2	7.3.2	5-3.2
7.2.4.4	5-2.4.4	7.2.9	5-2.9	7.3.3	5-3.3
7.2.4.4.1	5-2.4.4.1	7.2.9.1	5-2.9.1	7.3.3.1	5-3.3.1
7.2.4.4.2	5-2.4.4.2	7.2.9.2	5-2.9.2	7.3.3.2	5-3.3.2
7.2.4.4.3	5-2.4.4.3	7.2.9.2.1	5-2.9.2.1	7.3.4	5-3.4
7.2.4.4.4	5-2.4.4.4	7.2.9.2.2	5-2.9.2.2	7.3.4.1	5-3.4.1
7.2.4.4.5	5-2.4.4.5	Deleted	5-2.9.2.3	7.3.4.2	5-3.4.2
7.2.4.4.6	5-2.4.4.6	7.2.9.3	5-2.9.3	7.4	5-4
7.2.5	5-2.5	7.2.10	5-2.10	7.4.1	5-4.1
7.2.5.1	5-2.5.1	7.2.10.1	5-2.10.1	7.4.1.1	5-4.1.1
7.2.5.2	5-2.5.2	7.2.10.1.1	5-2.10.1.1	7.4.1.2	5-4.1.2
7.2.5.3	5-2.5.3	7.2.10.1.2	5-2.10.1.2	7.4.1.3	5-4.1.3
7.2.5.3.1	5-2.5.3.1	7.2.10.2	5-2.10.2	7.4.1.4	5-4.1.4
7.2.5.3.2	5-2.5.3.2	7.2.10.2.1	5-2.10.2.1	7.4.1.5	5-4.1.5
7.1.6.4	5-2.5.3.3	7.2.10.2.2	5-2.10.2.2	7.4.1.6	5-4.1.6
7.2.5.3.3	5-2.5.3.4	7.2.11	5-2.11	7.5	5-5
7.2.5.4	5-2.5.4	7.2.11.1	5-2.11.1	7.5.1	5-5.1
7.2.5.5	5-2.5.5	7.2.11.2	5-2.11.2	7.5.1.1	5-5.1.1
7.2.5.6	5-2.5.6	7.2.12	5-2.12	7.5.1.2	5-5.1.2
7.2.1.3	5-2.5.6.1	7.2.12.1	5-2.12.1	7.5.1.3	5-5.1.3
7.2.5.6.1	5-2.5.6.2	7.2.12.2	5-2.12.2	7.5.1.4	5-5.1.4
7.2.5.6.2	5-2.5.6.3	7.2.12.2.1	5-2.12.2.1	7.5.1.5	5-5.1.5
7.2.6	5-2.6	7.2.12.2.2	5-2.12.2.2	7.5.1.6	5-5.1.6
7.2.6.1	5-2.6.1	7.2.12.2.3	5-2.12.2.3	7.5.1.7	5-5.1.7
7.2.6.2	5-1.3.3	7.2.12.2.4	5-2.12.2.4	7.5.2	5-5.2
7.2.6.3	5-1.3.3	7.2.12.2.5	5-2.12.2.5	7.5.2.1	5-5.2.1
7.2.6.4	5-2.6.2	7.2.12.2.6	5-2.12.2.6	7.5.2.2	5-5.2.2
7.2.6.5	5-2.6.3	7.2.12.3	5-2.12.3	7.5.3	5-5.3
7.2.7	5-2.7	7.2.12.3.1	5-2.12.3.1	7.5.3.1	5-5.3.1
7.2.8	5-2.8	7.2.12.3.2	5-2.12.3.2	7.5.3.2	5-5.3.2
7.2.8.1	5-2.8.1	7.2.12.3.3	5-2.12.3.3	7.5.3.3	5-5.3.3
7.2.8.1.1	5-2.8.1.1	7.2.12.3.4	5-2.12.3.4	Deleted	5-5.3.4
7.2.8.1.2	5-2.8.1.2	7.2.12.3.5	5-2.12.3.5	Deleted	5-5.3.5
7.2.8.1.3	5-2.8.1.3	7.2.12.3.6	5-2.12.3.6	Deleted	5-5.3.7
7.2.8.2	5-2.8.2	7.2.13	5-2.13	Deleted	5-5.3.8
7.2.8.3	5-2.8.3	7.2.13.1	5-2.13.1	Deleted	5-5.3.9
7.2.8.3.1	5-2.8.3.1	7.2.13.2	5-2.13.2	Deleted	5-5.3.10
7.2.8.3.2	5-2.8.3.1 exception	7.2.13.2.1	5-2.13.2.1	7.5.3.4	5-5.3.6
7.2.8.3.3	5-2.8.3.2	7.2.13.2.2	5-2.13.2.2	7.5.4	5-5.4
7.2.8.3.4	5-2.8.3.3	7.2.13.3	5-2.13.3	7.5.4.1	5-5.4.1
7.2.8.4	5-2.8.4	7.2.13.4	5-2.13.4	7.5.4.2	5-5.4.2
7.2.8.4.1	5-2.8.4	7.2.13.5	5-2.13.5	7.5.4.3	5-5.4.3
7.2.8.4.2	New in 2000	7.2.13.6	5-2.13.6	7.5.4.4	5-5.4.4
7.2.8.5	5-2.8.5	7.2.13.7	5-2.13.7	7.5.4.5	5-5.4.5
7.2.8.5.1	5-2.8.5.1	7.2.13.8	5-2.13.8	7.5.4.6	5-5.4.6
7.2.8.5.2	5-2.8.5.2	7.2.13.9	5-2.13.9	7.5.4.7	5-5.4.7
7.2.8.6	5-2.8.6	7.2.13.10	5-2.13.10	7.6	5-6
7.2.8.6.1	5-2.8.6.1	7.2.13.11	5-2.13.11	7.6.1	5-6.1
7.2.8.6.2	5-2.8.6.2	7.2.13.12	5-2.13.12	7.6.2	5-6.2
7.2.8.7	5-2.8.7	7.3	5.3	7.6.3	5-6.3
7.2.8.7.1	5-2.8.7.1	7.3.1	5-3.1	7.6.4	5-6.4

2000 Edition	1997 Edition	2000 Edition	1997 Edition	2000 Edition	1997 Edition
7.6.5	5-6.5	7.11.2	5-11.2	8.2.6.2.3	6-2.5.2.3
7.7	5-7	7.11.3	5-11.3	8.2.6.3	6-2.5.3
7.7.1	5-7.1	7.11.4	5-11.4	8.2.7	6-2.6
7.7.2	5-7.2	7.11.5	5-11.5	8.2.7.1	6-2.6.1
7.7.3	5-7.3	7.12	5-12	8.2.7.2	6-2.6.2
7.7.4	5-7.4	7.12.1	5-12.1	8.3	6-3
7.7.5	5-7.5	7.12.2	5-12.2	8.3.1	6-3.1
7.7.6	5-7.6	Chapter 8	Chapter 6	8.3.2	6-3.2
7.8	5-8	8.1	6-1	8.3.3	6-3.3
7.8.1	5-8.1	8.1.1	6-1.1	8.3.4	6-3.4
7.8.1.1	5-8.1.1	8.2	6-2	8.3.4.1	6-3.4.1
7.8.1.2	5-8.1.2	8.2.1	6-2.1	8.3.4.2	6-3.4.2
7.8.1.3	5-8.1.3	8.2.2	6-2.2	8.3.4.3	6-3.4.3
7.8.1.4	5-8.1.4	8.2.2.1	6-2.2.1	8.3.5	6-3.5
7.8.1.5	5-8.1.5	8.2.2.2	6-2.2.2	8.3.5.1	6-3.5.1
7.8.2	5-8.2	8.2.3	6-2.3	8.3.5.2	6-3.5.2
7.8.2.1	5-8.2.1	8.2.3.1	6-2.3.1	8.3.5.3	6-3.5.3
7.8.2.2	5-8.2.2	8.2.3.1.1	6-2.3.1.1	8.3.6	6-3.6
7.9	5-9	8.2.3.1.2	6-2.3.1.2	8.3.6.1	6-3.6.1
7.9.1	5-9.1	8.2.3.2	6-2.3.2	8.3.6.2	6-3.6.2
7.9.1.1	5-9.1.1	8.2.3.2.1	6-2.3.2.1	8.4	6-4
7.9.1.2	5-9.1.2	8.2.3.2.2	6-2.3.2.2	8.4.1	6-4.1
7.9.2	5-9.2	8.2.3.2.3	6-2.3.2.3	8.4.1.1	6-4.1.1
7.9.2.1	5-9.2.1	8.2.3.2.3.1	6-2.3.2.3.1	8.4.1.2	6-4.1.2
7.9.2.2	5-9.2.2	8.2.3.2.3.2	6-2.3.2.3.2	8.4.1.3	6-4.1.3
7.9.2.3	5-9.2.3	8.2.3.2.4	6-2.3.2.4	8.4.2	6-4.2
7.9.2.4	5-9.2.4	8.2.3.2.4.1	6-2.3.2.4.1	8.4.3	6-4.3
7.9.2.5	5-9.2.5	8.2.3.2.4.2	6-2.3.2.4.2	8.4.3.1	6-4.3.1
7.9.3	5-9.3	8.2.4	New in 2000	8.4.3.2	6-4.3.2
7.10	5-10	8.2.4.1	New in 2000	8.4.4	6-4.4
7.10.1	5-10.1	8.2.4.2	New in 2000	8.4.5	New in 2000
7.10.1.1	5-10.1.1	8.2.4.3	New in 2000	Chapter 9	Chapter 7
7.10.1.2	5-10.1.2	8.2.4.3.1	New in 2000	9.1	7-1
7.10.1.3	5-10.1.3	8.2.4.3.2	New in 2000	9.1.1	7-1.1
7.10.1.4	5-10.1.4	8.2.4.3.3	New in 2000	9.1.2	7-1.2
7.10.1.5	5-10.1.5	8.2.4.3.4	New in 2000	9.1.3	7-1.3
7.10.1.6	5-10.1.7	8.2.4.3.5	New in 2000	9.1.4	7-1.4
7.10.1.7	5-10.1.6	8.2.4.4	New in 2000	9.2	7-2
7.10.2	5-10.4.1, 5-10.4.1.1	8.2.4.4.1	New in 2000	9.2.1	7-2.1
7.10.3	5-10.2.1	8.2.4.4.2	New in 2000	9.2.2	7-2.2
7.10.4	5-10.3.5	8.2.4.4.3	New in 2000	9.2.3	7-2.3
Deleted	5-10.4	8.2.5	6-2.4	9.2.4	7-2.4
7.10.5	5-10.3	8.2.5.1	6-2.4.1	9.3	7-3
7.10.5.1	5-10.3.1	8.2.5.2	6-2.4.2	9.3.1	7-3.1
7.10.5.2	5-10.3.4	8.2.5.3	6-2.4.3	9.4	7-4
7.10.6	New in 2000	8.2.5.4	6-2.4.4	9.4.1	7-4.1
7.10.6.1	5-10.2, 5-10.2.1	8.2.5.5	6-2.4.5	9.4.2	New in 2000
7.10.6.2	5-10.4.1.2	8.2.5.6	6-2.4.6	9.4.2.1	7-4.2
7.10.6.3	5-10.3.2	8.2.5.7	6-2.4.7	9.4.2.2	7-4.3
Deleted	5-10.3.3	8.2.5.8	6-2.4.8	9.4.3	New in 2000
7.10.7	New in 2000	8.2.5.9	6-2.4.9	9.4.3.1	7-4.4
7.10.7.1	5-10.2.2	8.2.5.10	6-2.4.10	9.4.3.2	7-4.5
7.10.7.2	New in 2000	8.2.5.11	6-2.4.11	9.4.4	7-4.6
7.10.8	5-10.4.2	8.2.5.12	6-2.4.12	9.4.5	7-4.7
7.10.8.1	5-10.4.2	8.2.5.13	6-2.4.12 Exception No. 3	9.4.6	7-4.8
7.10.8.2	5-10.4.3			9.4.7	7-4.9
7.10.9	5-10.5	8.2.6	6-2.5	9.5	7-5
7.10.9.1	5-10.5.1	8.2.6.1	6-2.5.1	9.5.1	7-5.1
7.10.9.2	5-10.5.2	8.2.6.2	6-2.5.2	9.5.2	7-5.2
7.11	5-11	8.2.6.2.1	6-2.5.2.1	9.6	7-6
7.11.1	5-11.1	8.2.6.2.2	6-2.5.2.2	9.6.1	7-6.1

2000 Edition	1997 Edition	2000 Edition	1997 Edition	2000 Edition	1997 Edition
9.6.1.1	7-6.1.1	9.7.2	7-7.2	10.3.4	6-6.4
9.6.1.2	7-6.1.2	9.7.2.1	7-7.2.1	10.3.5	6-6.5
9.6.1.3	7-6.1.3	9.7.2.2	7-7.2.2	10.3.6	6-6.6
9.6.1.4	7-6.1.4	9.7.3	7-7.3	10.3.7	6-6.7
9.6.1.5	7-6.1.5	9.7.3.1	7-7.3.1	Chapter 11	Chapter 32
9.6.1.6	7-6.1.6	9.7.3.2	7-7.3.2	11.1	32-1
9.6.1.7	7-6.1.7	9.7.4	7-7.4	11.1.1	32-1.1
9.6.1.8	7-6.1.8	9.7.4.1	7-7.4.1	11.1.2	32-1.2
9.6.1.9	7-6.1.9	9.7.4.2	7-7.4.2	11.1.3	32-1.3
9.6.2	7-6.2	9.7.5	7-7.5	11.1.4	32-1.4
9.6.2.1	7-6.2.1	9.7.6	New in 2000	11.1.5	32-1.5
9.6.2.2	7-6.2.2	9.7.6.1	7-7.6	11.1.6	32-1.6
9.6.2.3	7-6.2.3	9.7.6.2	7-7.6	11.1.7	32-1.7
9.6.2.4	7-6.2.4	Chapter 10	6-5	11.2	32-2
9.6.2.5	7-6.2.5	10.1	6-5.1	11.2.1	32-2.1
9.6.2.6	7-6.2.6	10.1.1	New in 2000	11.2.1.1	32-2.1.1
9.6.2.7	7-6.2.7	10.1.2	6-5.1.1, 6-5.1.2,	11.2.1.2	32-2.1.2
9.6.2.8	7-6.2.8		6-5.1.3	11.2.2	32-2.2
9.6.2.9	7-6.2.9	10.2	6-5	11.2.2.1	32-2.2.1
9.6.2.10	7-6.2.10	10.2.1	6-5.1, 6-5.1.4	11.2.2.2	32-2.2.2
9.6.2.10.1	7-6.2.10	10.2.2	6-5.2	11.2.2.2.1	32-2.2.2.1
9.6.2.10.2	7-6.2.10.1	10.2.2.1	6-5.2.1	11.2.2.3	32-2.2.3
9.6.2.10.3	7-6.2.10.2	10.2.2.2	6-5.2.2	11.2.2.4	32-2.2.4
9.6.2.10.4	7-6.2.10.2.1	10.2.3	6-5.4	11.2.2.4.1	32-2.2.4.1
9.6.2.11	7-6.2.11	10.2.3	6-5.5	11.2.2.4.2	32-2.2.4.2
9.6.3	7-6.3	10.2.3.1	6-5.4.1	11.2.2.5	32-2.2.5
9.6.3.1	7-6.3.1	10.2.3.2	6-5.5.1	11.2.2.6	32-2.2.6
9.6.3.2	7-6.3.2	10.2.3.3	6-5.5.3	11.2.2.7	32-2.2.7
9.6.3.3	7-6.3.2, Exception No. 1	10.2.3.4	6-5.5.2	11.2.2.8	32-2.2.8
		10.2.3.5	6-5.3.1.5	11.2.2.9	32-2.2.9
9.6.3.4	7-6.3.2, Exception No. 2	10.2.3.5.1	6-5.3.1.5.1	11.2.2.10	32-2.2.10
		10.2.3.5.2	6-5.3.1.5.2	11.2.3	32-2.3
9.6.3.5	7-6.3.3	10.2.3.5.3	New in 2000	11.2.3.1	32-2.3.1
9.6.3.6	7-6.3.4	10.2.4	6-5.3	11.2.3.2	32-2.3.2
9.6.3.7	7-6.3.5	10.2.4.1	6-5.3.1	11.2.3.3	32-2.3.3
9.6.3.8	7-6.3.6	10.2.4.1.1	6-5.3.1.1	11.2.3.4	32-2.3.4
9.6.3.9	7-6.3.7	10.2.4.1.2	6-5.3.1.2	11.2.3.5	32-2.3.5
9.6.3.10	7-6.3.8	10.2.4.1.3	6-5.3.1.3	11.3	32-3
9.6.3.11	7-6.3.9	10.2.4.1.4	6-5.3.1.4	11.3.1	32-3.1
9.6.3.12	7-6.3.10	10.2.4.1.5	6-5.3.1.5	11.3.1.1	32-3.1.1
9.6.4	7-6.4	10.2.4.2	6-5.3.5, 6-5.3.5.1,	11.3.1.2	32-3.1.2
9.6.5	7-6.5		6-5.3.5.2	11.3.2	32-3.2
9.6.5.1	7-6.5.1	10.2.4.3	6-5.3.2	11.3.2.1	32-3.2.1
9.6.5.2	7-6.5.2	10.2.4.4	6-5.3.3	11.3.2.2	32-3.2.2
9.6.5.3	7-6.5.3	10.2.4.5	6-5.3.4	11.3.2.2.1	32-3.2.2.1
9.6.5.4	7-6.5.4	10.2.4.6	6-5.3.6	11.3.2.2.2	32-3.2.2.2
9.6.6	7-6.6	10.2.5	6-5.7	11.3.2.3	32-3.2.3
9.6.7	7-6.7	10.2.6	6-5.8	11.3.2.3.1	32-3.2.3.1
9.6.7.1	7-6.7.1	10.2.6.1	6-5.8.1	11.3.2.3.2	32-3.2.3.2
9.6.7.2	7-6.7.2	10.2.6.2	6-5.8.2	11.3.2.4	32-3.2.4
9.6.7.3	7-6.7.3	10.2.7	6-5.6	11.3.2.4.1	32-3.2.4.1
9.6.7.4	7-6.7.4	10.2.7.1	6-5.6.1	11.3.2.4.2	32-3.2.4.2
9.6.7.5	7-6.7.5	10.2.7.2	6-5.6.2	11.3.2.5	32-3.2.5
9.6.7.6	7-6.7.6	10.2.7.3	6-5.6.3	11.3.2.6	32-3.2.6
9.6.7.7	7-6.7.7	10.2.8	6-5.9	11.3.2.7	32-3.2.7
9.7	7-7	10.2.8.1	6-5.9.1	11.3.2.8	32-3.2.8
9.7.1	7-7.1	10.2.8.2	6-5.9.2	11.3.2.9	32-3.2.9
9.7.1.1	7-7.1.1	10.3	6-6	11.3.2.9.1	32-3.2.9.1
9.7.1.2	7-7.1.2	10.3.1	6-6.1	11.3.2.9.2	32-3.2.9.2
9.7.1.3	7-7.1.3	10.3.2	6-6.2	11.3.2.9.3	32-3.2.9.3
9.7.1.4	7-7.1.4	10.3.3	6-6.3	11.3.2.10	32-3.2.10

2000 Edition	1997 Edition	2000 Edition	1997 Edition	2000 Edition	1997 Edition
11.3.2.10.1	32-3.2.10.1	11.7.4.4	32-7.4.3	12.2.2.3.2.2	8-2.2.3.2.2
11.3.2.10.2	32-3.2.10.2	11.7.4.5	32-7.4.4	12.2.2.4	8-2.2.4
11.3.3	32-3.3	11.8	32-8	12.2.2.5	8-2.2.5
11.3.3.1	32-3.3.1	11.8.1	32-8.1	12.2.2.6	8-2.2.6
11.3.3.1.1	32-3.3.1.1	11.8.1.1	32-8.1.1	12.2.2.7	8-2.2.7
11.3.3.1.2	32-3.3.1.2	11.8.1.2	32-8.1.2	12.2.2.8	New in 2000 —
11.3.3.2	32-3.3.2	11.8.2	32-8.2		Reserved
11.3.3.3	32-3.3.3	11.8.2.1	32-8.2.1	12.2.2.9	New in 2000 —
11.3.3.4	32-3.3.4	11.8.2.2	32-8.2.2		Reserved
11.3.3.5	32-3.3.5	11.8.3	32-8.3	12.2.2.10	8-2.2.8
11.3.3.6	32-3.3.6	11.8.3.1	32-8.3.1	12.2.2.11	8-2.2.9
11.4	32-4	11.8.3.2	32-8.3.2	12.2.2.12	8-2.2.10
11.4.1	32-4.1	11.8.4	32-8.4	12.2.3	8-2.3
11.4.1.1	32-4.1.1	11.8.4.1	32-8.4.1	12.2.3.1	8-2.3.1
11.4.1.2	32-4.1.2	11.8.4.2	32-8.4.2	12.2.3.2	8-2.3.2
11.4.2	32-4.2	11.8.5	32-8.5	12.2.3.3	8-2.3.3
11.4.2.1	32-4.2.1	11.9 (entire section)	New in 2000	12.2.3.4	8-2.3.4
11.4.2.2	32-4.2.2	11.10 (entire sec-	New in 2000	12.2.3.5	8-2.3.5
11.4.2.3	32-4.2.3	tion)		12.2.4	8-2.4
11.4.2.4	32-4.2.4	11.11 (entire sec-	New in 2000	12.2.4.1	8-2.4.1
11.4.2.5	32-4.2.5	tion)		12.2.4.2	8-2.4.2
11.4.2.6	32-4.2.6	Chapter 12	Chapter 8	12.2.4.3	8-2.4.3
11.4.2.7	32-4.2.7	12.1	8-1	12.2.4.4	8-2.4.4
11.4.2.8	32-4.2.8	12.1.1	8-1.1	12.2.4.5	8-2.4.5
11.4.2.9	32-4.2.9	12.1.2	8.1.2	12.2.4.6	8-2.4.6
11.4.2.9.1	32-4.2.9.1	12.1.2.1	8-1.2.1	12.2.5	8-2.5
11.4.2.9.2	32-4.2.9.2	12.1.2.2	8-1.2.2	12.2.5.1	8-2.5.1
11.4.2.10	32-4.2.10	12.1.2.3	8-1.2.3	12.2.5.2	8-2.5.2
11.4.3	32-4.3	12.1.2.4	8-1.2.4	12.2.5.3	8-2.5.3
11.4.3.1	32-4.3.1	12.1.2.5	New in 2000	12.2.5.4	8-2.5.4
11.4.3.2	32-4.3.2	Deleted	8-1.2.5	12.2.5.4.1	8-2.5.4.1
11.4.3.3	32-4.3.3	24/26/28/30/	8-1.2.5.1	12.2.5.4.2	8-2.5.4.2
11.4.3.4	32-4.3.4	32.1.2.2		12.2.5.4.3	8-2.5.4.3
11.4.3.5	32-4.3.5	24/26/28/30/	8-1.2.5.2	12.2.5.4.4	8-2.5.4.4
11.4.3.6	32-4.3.6	32.1.2.3		12.2.5.4.5	8-2.5.4.5
11.5	32-5	12.1.3	8-1.3	12.2.5.4.6	8-2.5.4.6
11.5.1	32-5.1	12.1.4	8-1.4	12.2.5.5	8-2.5.5
11.5.2	32-5.2	12.1.5	8-1.5	12.2.5.5.1	8-2.5.5.1
11.5.3	32-5.3	12.1.6	8-1.6	12.2.5.5.2	8-2.5.5.2
11.6	32-6	12.1.7	8-1.7	12.2.5.5.3	8-2.5.5.3
11.6.1	32-6.1	12.1.7.1	8-1.7.1	12.2.5.5.4	8-2.5.5.4
11.6.2	32-6.2	Deleted	8-1.7.2	12.2.5.5.5	8-2.5.5.5
11.7	32-7	12.1.7.1, 7.3.1.3	8-1.7.3	12.2.5.5.6	8-2.5.5.6
11.7.1	32-7.1	12.1.7.2	8-1.7.4	12.2.5.6	8-2.5.6
11.7.2	32-7.2	12.1.7.3	8-1.7.5	12.2.5.6.1	8-2.5.6.1
11.7.3	32-7.3	12.2	8-2	12.2.5.6.2	8-2.5.6.2
11.7.3.1	32-7.2 Windowless	12.2.1	8-2.1	12.2.5.6.3	8-2.5.6.3
	Structure	12.2.2	8-2.2	12.2.5.6.4	8-2.5.6.4
11.7.3.2	32-7.2	12.2.2.1	8-2.2.1	12.2.5.6.5	8-2.5.6.5
	Underground Struc-	12.2.2.2	8-2.2.2	12.2.5.6.6	8-2.5.6.6
	ture exception	12.2.2.2.1	8-2.2.2.1	12.2.5.6.7	8-2.5.6.7
11.7.3.3	32-7.3.1	12.2.2.2.2	8-2.2.2.2	12.2.5.6.8	8-2.5.6.8
11.7.3.4	32-7.3.2	12.2.2.2.3	8-2.2.2.3	12.2.5.7	8-2.5.7
11.7.4	32-7.4	12.2.2.2.4	8-2.2.2.4	12.2.5.7.1	8-2.5.7.1
11.7.4.1	32-7.2	12.2.2.2.5	8-2.2.2.5	12.2.5.7.2	8-2.5.7.2
	Underground Struc-	12.2.2.2.6	8-2.2.2.6	12.2.5.7.3	8-2.5.7.3
	ture exception	12.2.2.2.7	8-2.2.2.7	12.2.5.7.4	8-2.5.7.4
11.7.4.2	32-7.4.1	12.2.2.3	8-2.2.3	12.2.5.8	8-2.5.8
11.7.4.3	32-7.4.2	12.2.2.3.1	8-2.2.3.1	12.2.5.8.1	8-2.5.8.1
		12.2.2.3.2	8-2.2.3.2	12.2.5.8.2	8-2.5.8.2
		12.2.2.3.2.1	8-2.2.3.2.1	12.2.5.8.3	8-2.5.8.3

2000 Edition	1997 Edition
12.2.5.9	8-2.5.9
12.2.6	8-2.6, 8-2.6.1
12.2.7	8-2.7
12.2.7.1	8-2.7.1
12.2.7.2	8-2.7.2
12.2.7.3	8-2.7.3
12.2.8	8-2.8
12.2.9	8-2.9
12.2.10	8-2.10
12.2.11	8-2.11
12.2.11.1	8-2.11.1
12.2.11.1.1	8-2.11.1.1
12.2.11.1.2	8-2.11.1.2
12.2.11.1.3	8-2.11.1.3
12.2.11.1.4	8-2.11.1.4
12.2.11.1.5	8-2.11.1.5
12.2.11.1.6	8-2.11.1.6
12.3	8-3
12.3.1	8-3.1
12.3.2	8-3.2
12.3.2.1	8-3.2.1
12.3.2.1.1	8-3.2.1.1
12.3.2.1.2	8-3.2.1.2
12.3.2.1.3	8-3.2.1.3
12.3.3	8-3.3
12.3.3.1	8-3.3.1
12.3.3.2	8-3.3.2
12.3.3.3	8-3.3.3
12.3.3.4	8-3.3.4
12.3.3.5	8-3.3.5
12.3.4	8-3.4
12.3.4.1	8-3.4.1
12.3.4.2	8-3.4.2
12.3.4.2.1	8-3.4.2.1
12.3.4.2.2	8-3.4.2.2
12.3.4.3	8-3.4.3
12.3.4.3.1	8-3.4.3.1
12.3.4.3.2	8-3.4.3.2
12.3.4.3.3	8-3.4.3.3
12.3.4.3.4	8-3.4.3.4
12.3.5	8-3.5, 8-3.5.1
12.3.6	8-3.6
12.4	8-4
12.4.1	8-4.1
12.4.1.1	8-4.1.1
12.4.1.2	8-4.1.2
12.4.1.3	8-4.1.3
12.4.2	8-4.2
12.4.2.1	8-4.2.1
12.4.2.2	8-4.2.2
12.4.2.3	8-4.2.3
12.4.2.4	8-4.2.4
12.4.2.5	8-4.2.5
12.4.2.6	8-4.2.6
12.4.2.7	8-4.2.7
12.4.2.8	8-4.2.8
12.4.3	8-4.3
12.4.3.1	8-4.3.1
12.4.3.2	8-4.3.2
12.4.3.3	8-4.3.3
12.4.3.3.1	8-4.3.3.1
12.4.3.3.2	8-4.3.3.2
12.4.3.3.3	8-4.3.3.3
12.4.3.3.4	8-4.3.3.4
12.4.3.4	8-4.3.4
12.4.3.5	8-4.3.5
12.4.4	8-4.4
12.4.5	8-4.5
12.4.5.1	8-4.5.1
12.4.5.2	8-4.5.2
12.4.5.3	8-4.5.3
12.4.5.3.1	8-4.5.3.1
12.4.5.3.2	8-4.5.3.2
12.4.5.3.3	8-4.5.3.3
12.4.5.4	8-4.5.4
12.4.5.5	8-4.5.5
12.4.5.6	8-4.5.6
12.4.5.7	8-4.5.7
12.4.5.8	8-4.5.8
12.4.5.9	8-4.5.9
12.4.5.10	8-4.5.10
12.4.5.11	8-4.5.11
12.4.5.12	8-4.5.12
12.4.6	8-4.6
12.4.6.1	8-4.6.1
12.4.6.2	8-4.6.2
12.4.6.2.1	8-4.6.2.1
12.4.6.2.2	8-4.6.2.2
12.4.6.2.3	8-4.6.2.3
12.4.6.2.4	8-4.6.2.4
12.4.6.2.5	8-4.6.2.5
12.4.6.2.6	8-4.6.2.6
12.4.6.3	8-4.6.3
12.4.7	8-4.7
12.4.7.1	8-4.7.1
12.4.7.2	8-4.7.2
12.4.7.3	8-4.7.3
12.4.7.4	8-4.7.4
12.4.7.4.1	8-4.7.4.1
Deleted	8-4.7.4.2
12.4.7.4.2	8-4.7.4.3
12.4.7.4.3	8-4.7.4.4
12.4.7.5	8-4.7.5
12.4.8	8-4.8
12.4.8.1	New in 2000
12.4.8.2	8-4.8
12.4.8.2.1	8-4.8.1
12.4.8.2.2	New in 2000
12.4.8.2.3	New in 2000
12.4.8.2.4	New in 2000
12.4.8.3	New in 2000
12.4.8.3.1	New in 2000
12.4.8.3.2	New in 2000
12.4.8.3.3	New in 2000
12.4.8.4	New in 2000
12.4.8.4.1	New in 2000
12.4.8.4.2	New in 2000
12.4.8.4.3	New in 2000
12.4.8.5	New in 2000
12.4.8.6	8-4.8.2
12.4.8.6.1	8-4.8.2.1
12.4.8.6.2	8-4.8.2.2
12.4.8.6.3	8-4.8.2.3
12.4.8.6.4	8-4.8.2.4
12.4.8.6.5	8-4.8.2.5
12.4.9	New in 2000
12.4.9.1	New in 2000
12.4.9.2	New in 2000
12.4.9.2.1	New in 2000
12.4.9.2.2	New in 2000
12.4.9.2.3	New in 2000
12.4.9.3	New in 2000
12.4.9.3.1	New in 2000
12.4.9.3.2	New in 2000
12.4.9.3.3	New in 2000
12.4.9.3.4	New in 2000
12.4.9.3.5	New in 2000
12.5	8-5
12.5.1	8-5.1
12.5.2	8-5.2
12.5.3	8-5.3
12.5.4	8-5.4
12.6	8-6
12.7	8-7
12.7.1	8-7.1
12.7.1.1	8-7.1.1
12.7.1.2	8-7.1.2
12.7.1.3	8-7.1.3
12.7.1.4	8-7.1.4
12.7.2	8-7.2
12.7.2 Exception No. 1	8-7.3
12.7.3	8-7.4
12.7.3.1	8-7.4.1
12.7.3.2	8-7.4.2
12.7.3.3	8-7.4.3
12.7.4	8-7.5
12.7.4.1	8-7.5.1
12.7.4.2	8-7.5.2
12.7.4.3	8-7.5.3
12.7.4.3.1	8-7.5.3.1
12.7.4.3.2	8-7.5.3.2
12.7.4.3.3	8-7.5.3.3
12.7.4.3.4	8-7.5.3.4
12.7.4.3.5	8-7.5.3.5
12.7.4.3.6	8-7.5.3.6
12.7.4.3.7	8-7.5.3.7
12.7.4.3.8	8-7.5.3.8
12.7.4.3.9	8-7.5.3.9
12.7.4.3.10	8-7.5.3.10
12.7.4.3.11	8-7.5.3.11
12.7.4.4	8-7.5.4
12.7.4.4.1	8-7.5.4.1
12.7.4.4.2	8-7.5.4.2
12.7.4.4.3	8-7.5.4.3
12.7.4.4.4	8-7.5.4.4
12.7.4.4.5	8-7.5.4.5
12.7.4.5	8-7.5.5
12.7.4.6	8-7.5.6
12.7.5	8-7.6
12.7.6	8-7.7
12.7.6.1	8-7.7.1
12.7.6.2	8-7.7.2

2000 Edition	1997 Edition
12.7.6.3	8-7.7.3
12.7.7	8-7.8
12.7.7.1	8-7.8.1
12.7.7.2	8-7.8.2
12.7.7.3	8-7.8.3
12.7.7.4	8-7.8.4
12.7.8	8-7.9
12.7.8.1	8-7.9.1
12.7.8.2	8-7.9.2
12.7.8.3	8-7.9.3
12.7.9	New in 2000
12.7.10	New in 2000
12.7.10.1	New in 2000
12.7.10.2	New in 2000
12.7.11	8-7.10
Chapter 13	Chapter 9
13.1	9-1
13.1.1	9-1.1
13.1.1.1	9-1.1.1
13.1.1.2	9-1.1.2
13.1.1.3	9-1.1.3
13.1.2	9-1.2
13.1.2.1	9-1.2.1
13.1.2.2	9-1.2.2
13.1.2.3	9-1.2.3
13.1.2.4	9-1.2.4
Deleted	9-1.2.5
24/26/29/31/ 33.1.2.2	9-1.2.5.1
24/26/29/31/ 33.1.2.3	9-1.2.5.2
24/26/29/31.1.2.3	9-1.2.5.3
13.1.2.5	New in 2000
13.1.3	9-1.3
13.1.4	9-1.4
13.1.5	9-1.5
13.1.6	9-1.6
13.1.7	9-1.7
13.1.7.1	9-1.7.1
Deleted	9-1.7.2
13.1.7.1, 7.3.1.3	9-1.7.3
13.1.7.2	9-1.7.4
13.1.7.3	9-1.7.5
13.2	9-2
13.2.1	9-2.1
13.2.2	9-2.2
13.2.2.1	9-2.2.1
13.2.2.2	9-2.2.2
13.2.2.2.1	9-2.2.2.1
13.2.2.2.2	9-2.2.2.2
13.2.2.2.3	9-2.2.2.3
13.2.2.2.4	9-2.2.2.4
13.2.2.2.5	9-2.2.2.5
13.2.2.2.6	9-2.2.2.6
13.2.2.2.7	9-2.2.2.7
13.2.2.3	9-2.2.3
13.2.2.3.1	9-2.2.3.1
13.2.2.3.2	9-2.2.3.2
13.2.2.3.2.1	9-2.2.3.2.1
13.2.2.3.2.2	9-2.2.3.2.2
13.2.2.4	9-2.2.4

2000 Edition	1997 Edition
13.2.2.5	9-2.2.5
13.2.2.6	9-2.2.6
13.2.2.7	9-2.2.7
13.2.2.8	9-2.2.8
13.2.2.9	9-2.2.9
13.2.2.10	9-2.2.10
13.2.2.11	9-2.2.11
13.2.2.12	9-2.2.12
13.2.3	9-2.3
13.2.3.1	9-2.3.1
13.2.3.2	9-2.3.2
13.2.3.3	9-2.3.3
13.2.3.4	9-2.3.4
13.2.4	9-2.4
13.2.4.1	9-2.4.1
13.2.4.2	9-2.4.2
13.2.4.3	9-2.4.3
13.2.4.4	9-2.4.4
13.2.4.5	9-2.4.5
13.2.4.6	9-2.4.6
13.2.5	9-2.5
13.2.5.1	9-2.5.1
13.2.5.2	9-2.5.2
13.2.5.3	9-2.5.3
13.2.5.4	9-2.5.4
13.2.5.4.1	9-2.5.4.1
13.2.5.4.2	9-2.5.4.2
13.2.5.4.3	9-2.5.4.3
13.2.5.4.4	9-2.5.4.4
13.2.5.4.5	9-2.5.4.5
13.2.5.4.6	9-2.5.4.6
13.2.5.5	9-2.5.5
13.2.5.5.1	9-2.5.5.1
13.2.5.5.2	9-2.5.5.2
13.2.5.5.3	9-2.5.5.3
13.2.5.5.4	9-2.5.5.4
13.2.5.5.5	9-2.5.5.5
13.2.5.5.6	9-2.5.5.6
13.2.5.6	9-2.5.6
13.2.5.6.1	9-2.5.6.1
13.2.5.6.2	9-2.5.6.2
13.2.5.6.3	9-2.5.6.3
13.2.5.6.4	9-2.5.6.4
13.2.5.6.5	9-2.5.6.5
13.2.5.6.6	9-2.5.6.6
13.2.5.6.7	9-2.5.6.7
13.2.5.6.8	9-2.5.6.8
13.2.5.7	9-2.5.7
13.2.5.7.1	9-2.5.7.1
13.2.5.7.2	9-2.5.7.2
13.2.5.7.3	9-2.5.7.3
13.2.5.7.4	9-2.5.7.4
13.2.5.8	9-2.5.8
13.2.5.8.1	9-2.5.8.1
13.2.5.8.2	9-2.5.8.2
13.2.5.8.3	9-2.5.8.3
13.2.5.9	9-2.5.9
13.2.6	9-2.6, 9-2.6.1
13.2.7	9-2.7
13.2.7.1	9-2.7.1
13.2.7.2	9-2.7.2

2000 Edition	1997 Edition
13.2.7.3	9-2.7.3
13.2.8	9-2.8
13.2.9	9-2.9
13.2.10	9-2.10
13.2.11	9-2.11
13.2.11.1	9-2.11.1
13.2.11.1.1	9-2.11.1.1
13.3	9-3
13.3.1	9-3.1
13.3.2	9-3.2
13.3.2.1	9-3.2.1
13.3.2.1.1	9-3.2.1.1
13.3.2.1.2	9-3.2.1.2
13.3.2.1.3	9-3.2.1.3
13.3.3	9-3.3
13.3.3.1	9-3.3.1
13.3.3.2	9-3.3.2
13.3.3.3	9-3.3.3
13.3.3.4	9-3.3.4
13.3.3.5	9-3.3.5
13.3.4	9-3.4
13.3.4.1	9-3.4.1
13.3.4.2	9-3.4.2
13.3.4.2.1	9-3.4.2.1
13.3.4.2.2	9-3.4.2.2
13.3.4.3	9-3.4.3
13.3.4.3.1	9-3.4.3.1
13.3.4.3.2	9-3.4.3.2
13.3.4.3.3	9-3.4.3.3
13.3.4.3.4	9-3.4.3.4
13.3.5	9-3.5
13.3.5.1	9-3.5.1
13.3.5.2	9-4.4
13.3.6	9-3.6
13.4	9-4
13.4.1	9-4.1
13.4.1.1	9-4.1.1
13.4.1.2	9-4.1.2
13.4.1.3	9-4.1.3
13.4.2	9-4.2
13.4.2.1	9-4.2.1
13.4.2.2	9-4.2.2
13.4.2.3	9-4.2.3
13.4.2.4	9-4.2.4
13.4.2.5	9-4.2.5
13.4.2.6	9-4.2.6
13.4.2.7	9-4.2.7
13.4.2.8	9-4.2.8
13.4.3	9-4.3
13.4.4	9-4.4
13.4.5	9-4.5
13.4.5.1	9-4.5.1
13.4.5.2	9-4.5.2
13.4.5.3	9-4.5.3
13.4.5.4	9-4.5.4
13.4.5.5	9-4.5.5
13.4.5.6	9-4.5.6
13.4.5.7	9-4.5.7
13.4.5.8	9-4.5.8
13.4.5.9	9-4.5.9
13.4.5.10	9-4.5.10

2000 Edition	1997 Edition	2000 Edition	1997 Edition	2000 Edition	1997 Edition
13.4.5.11	9-4.5.11	13.6	9-6	14.1.2	10-1.2
13.4.5.12	9-4.5.12	13.7	9-7	14.1.2.1	10-1.2.1
13.4.6	9-4.6	13.7.1	9-7.1	14.1.2.2	10-1.2.2
13.4.6.1	9-4.6.1	13.7.1.1	9-7.1.1	14.1.2.3	10-1.2.3
13.4.6.2	9-4.6.2	13.7.1.2	9-7.1.2	14.1.3	10-1.3
13.4.6.2.1	9-4.6.2.1	13.7.1.3	9-7.1.3	14.1.4	10-1.4
13.4.6.2.2	9-4.6.2.2	13.7.1.4	9-7.1.4	14.1.4.1	10-1.4.1
13.4.6.2.3	9-4.6.2.3	13.7.2	9-7.2	14.1.4.2	10-1.4.2
13.4.6.2.4	9-4.6.2.4	13.7.2 Exception	9-7.3	14.1.4.3	10-1.4.3
13.4.6.2.5	9-4.6.2.5	No. 1		14.1.4.4	10-1.4.4
13.4.6.2.6	9-4.6.2.6	13.7.3	9-7.4	14.1.5	10-1.5
13.4.6.3	9-4.6.3	13.7.3.1	9-7.4.1	14.1.6	10-1.6
13.4.7	9-4.7	13.7.3.2	9-7.4.2	14.1.7	10-1.7
13.4.7.1	9-4.7.1	13.7.3.3	9-7.4.3	14.1.7.1	10-1.7.1
13.4.7.2	9-4.7.2	13.7.4	9-7.5	Deleted	10-1.7.2
13.4.7.3	9-4.7.3	13.7.4.1	9-7.5.1	14.1.7.2	10-1.7.3
13.4.7.4	9-4.7.4	13.7.4.2	9-7.5.2	Deleted	10-1.7.4
13.4.7.4.1	9-4.7.4.1	13.7.4.3	9-7.5.3	14.2	10-2
Deleted	9-4.7.4.2	13.7.4.3.1	9-7.5.3.1	14.2.1	10-2.1
13.4.7.4.2	9-4.7.4.3	13.7.4.3.2	9-7.5.3.2	14.2.1.1	10-2.1.1
13.4.7.4.3	9-4.7.4.4	13.7.4.3.3	9-7.5.3.3	14.2.1.2	10-2.1.2
13.4.7.5	9-4.7.5	13.7.4.3.4	9-7.5.3.4	14.2.2	10-2.2
13.4.8	9-4.8	13.7.4.3.5	9-7.5.3.5	14.2.2.1	10-2.2.1
13.4.8.1	9-4.8.1	13.7.4.3.6	9-7.5.3.6	14.2.2.2	10-2.2.2
13.4.8.2	9-4.8	13.7.4.3.7	9-7.5.3.7	14.2.2.2.1	10-2.2.2.1
13.4.8.2.1	New in 2000	13.7.4.3.8	9-7.5.3.8	14.2.2.2.2	10-2.2.2.2
13.4.8.2.2	New in 2000	13.7.4.3.9	9-7.5.3.9	14.2.2.2.3	10-2.2.2.3
13.4.8.2.3	New in 2000	13.7.4.3.10	9-7.5.3.10	Deleted	10-2.2.2.4
13.4.8.2.4	New in 2000	13.7.4.3.11	9-7.5.3.11	Deleted	10-2.2.2.5
13.4.8.3	New in 2000	13.7.4.4	9-7.5.4	14.2.2.3	10-2.2.3
13.4.8.3.1	New in 2000	13.7.4.4.1	9-7.5.4.1	14.2.2.4	10-2.2.4
13.4.8.3.2	New in 2000	13.7.4.4.2	9-7.5.4.2	14.2.2.5	10-2.2.5
13.4.8.3.3	New in 2000	13.7.4.4.3	9-7.5.4.3	14.2.2.6	10-2.2.6
13.4.8.4	New in 2000	13.7.4.4.4	9-7.5.4.4	14.2.2.7	10-2.2.7
13.4.8.4.1	New in 2000	13.7.4.4.5	9-7.5.4.5	14.2.2.8	10-2.2.8
13.4.8.4.2	New in 2000	13.7.4.5	9-7.5.5	14.2.2.9	10-2.2.9
13.4.8.4.3	New in 2000	13.7.4.6	9-7.5.6	14.2.2.10	10-2.2.10
13.4.8.5	New in 2000	13.7.5	9-7.6	14.2.3	10-2.3
13.4.8.6	9-4.8.2	13.7.6	9-7.7	14.2.3.1	10-2.3.1
13.4.8.6.1	9-4.8.2.1	13.7.6.1	9-7.7.1	14.2.3.2	10-2.3.2, 10-2.3.2.1
13.4.8.6.2	9-4.8.2.2	13.7.6.2	9-7.7.2	Deleted	10-2.3.2.2
13.4.8.6.3	9-4.8.2.3	13.7.6.3	9-7.7.3	14.2.4	10-2.4
13.4.8.6.4	New in 2000	13.7.7	9-7.8	14.2.5	10-2.5
13.4.8.6.5	New in 2000	13.7.7.1	9-7.8.1	14.2.5.1	10-2.5.1
13.4.9	New in 2000	13.7.7.2	9-7.8.2	14.2.5.2	10-2.5.1
13.4.9.1	New in 2000	13.7.7.3	9-7.8.3	14.2.5.3	10-2.5.1
13.4.9.2	New in 2000	13.7.7.4	9-7.8.4	14.2.5.4	10-2.5.2
13.4.9.2.1	New in 2000	13.7.8	9-7.9	Deleted	10-2.5.3
13.4.9.2.2	New in 2000	13.7.8.1	9-7.9.1	14.2.5.5	10-2.5.4
13.4.9.2.3	New in 2000	13.7.8.2	9-7.9.2	14.2.5.6	10-2.5.5
13.4.9.3	9-4.8.2	13.7.8.3	9-7.9.3	14.2.5.7	10-2.5.6, 10-2.5.6.1
13.4.9.3.1	9-4.8.2.1	13.7.9	New in 2000	Deleted	10-2.5.6.2
13.4.9.3.2	9-4.9.2.2	13.7.10	New in 2000	Deleted	10-2.5.6.3
13.4.9.3.3	9-4.8.2.3	13.7.10.1	New in 2000	14.2.6	10-2.6
13.4.9.3.4	New in 2000	13.7.10.2	New in 2000	14.2.7	10-2.7
13.4.9.3.5	New in 2000	13.7.11	9-7.10	14.2.8	10-2.8
13.5	9-5	Chapter 14	Chapter 10	14.2.9	10-2.9
13.5.1	9-5.1	14.1	10-1	14.2.10	10-2.10
13.5.2	9-5.2	14.1.1	10-1.1	14.2.11	10-2.11
13.5.3	9-5.3	14.1.1.1	10-1.1.1	14.2.11.1	10-2.11.1
13.5.4	9-5.4	14.1.1.2	10-1.1.2	14.3	10-3

2000 Edition	1997 Edition	2000 Edition	1997 Edition	2000 Edition	1997 Edition
14.3.1	10-3.1	Deleted	10-7.1.3	15.2.3.1	11-2.3.1
14.3.2	10-3.2	Deleted	10-7.1.4	15.2.3.2	11-2.3.2, 11-2.3.2.1
14.3.2.1	10-3.2.1	Deleted	10-7.1.5	Deleted	11-2.3.2.2
14.3.2.2	10-3.2.2	Deleted	10-7.1.6	15.2.4	11-2.4
Deleted	10-3.2.3	Deleted	10-7.1.7	15.2.5	11-2.5
14.3.2.3	10-3.2.4	Deleted	10-7.1.8	15.2.5.1	11-2.5.1
14.3.3	10-3.3	Deleted	10-7.1.9	15.2.5.2	11-2.5.1
14.3.3.1	10-3.3.1	14.7.1.3	10-3.4.3.4	15.2.5.3	11-2.5.1
14.3.3.2	10-3.3.2	14.7.2	10-7.2	15.2.5.4	11-2.5.2
14.3.3.3	10-3.3.3	14.7.2.1	10-7.2.1	Deleted	11-2.5.3
14.3.4	10-3.4	14.7.2.2	10-7.2.2	15.2.5.5	11-2.5.4
14.3.4.1	10-3.4.1	14.7.3	10-7.3	15.2.5.6	11-2.5.5
14.3.4.2	10-3.4.2	14.7.3.1	10-7.3.1	15.2.5.7	11-2.5.6, 11-2.5.6.1
14.3.4.2.1	10-3.4.2.1	14.7.3.2	10-7.3.2	Deleted	11-2.5.6.2
14.3.4.2.2	10-3.4.2.2	14.7.3.3	10-7.4	Deleted	11-2.5.6.3
14.3.4.2.3	10-3.4.2.3	Chapter 15	Chapter 11	15.2.6	11-2.6
14.3.4.3	10-3.4.3	15.1.1	11-1.1	15.2.7	11-2.7
14.3.4.3.1	New in 2000	15.1.1.1	11-1.1.1	15.2.8	11-2.8
14.3.4.3.1.1	10-3.4.3.1	15.1.1.2	11-1.1.2	15.2.9	11-2.9
14.3.4.3.1.2	10-3.4.3.2	15.1.2	11-1.2	15.2.10	11-2.10
14.3.4.3.1.3	10-3.4.3.5	15.1.2.1	11-1.2.1	15.2.11	11-2.11
14.3.4.3.2	10-3.4.3.3	15.1.2.2	11-1.2.2	15.2.11.1	11-2.11.1
14.3.5	10-3.5	15.1.2.3	11-1.2.3	15.3	11-3
14.3.5.1	10-3.5	15.1.3	11-1.3	15.3.1	11-3.1
14.3.5.2	10-3.1 Exception No. 1	15.1.4	11-1.4	15.3.2	11-3.2
14.3.6	10-3.6	15.1.4.1	11-1.4.1	15.3.2.1	11-3.2.1
14.3.7	10-3.7	15.1.4.2	11-1.4.2	15.3.2.2	11-3.2.2
14.3.7.1	10-3.7.1	15.1.4.3	11-1.4.3	Deleted	11-3.2.3
14.3.7.2	10-3.7.2	15.1.4.4	11-1.4.4	15.3.2.3	11-3.2.4
14.4	10-4	15.1.5	11-1.5	15.3.3	11-3.3
14.4.1	10-4.1, 10-4.1.1	15.1.6	11-1.6	15.3.3.1	11-3.3.1
Deleted	10-4.1.2	15.1.7	11-1.7	15.3.3.2	11-3.3.2
Deleted	10-4.1.3	15.1.7.1	11-1.7.1	15.3.3.3	11-3.3.3
Deleted	10-4.1.3.1	Deleted	11-1.7.2	15.3.4	11-3.4
Deleted	10-4.1.3.2	15.1.7.2	11-1.7.3	15.3.4.1	11-3.4.1
Deleted	10-4.1.3.3	Deleted	11-1.7.4	15.3.4.2	11-3.4.2
Deleted	10-4.1.3.4	15.2	11-2	15.3.4.2.1	11-3.4.2.1
Deleted	10-4.1.4	15.2.1	11-2.1	15.3.4.2.2	11-3.4.2.2
Deleted	10-4.1.5	15.2.1.1	11-2.1.1	15.3.4.2.3	11-3.4.2.3
Deleted	10-4.1.6	15.2.1.2	11-2.1.2	15.3.4.3	11-3.4.3
14.4.2	10-4.2	15.2.2	11-2.2	15.3.4.3.1	11-3.4.3.1
14.4.3	10-4.3	15.2.2.1	11-2.2.1	15.3.4.3.1.1	11-3.4.3.1
14.4.3.1	10-4.3.1	15.2.2.2	11-2.2.2	15.3.4.3.1.2	11-3.4.3.2
14.4.3.2	10-4.3.2	15.2.2.2.1	11-2.2.2.1	15.3.4.3.1.3	11-3.4.3.5
14.4.3.3	10-4.3.3	15.2.2.2.2	11-2.2.2.2	15.3.4.3.2	11-3.4.3.3
14.4.3.4	10-4.3.4	15.2.2.2.3	11-2.2.2.3	15.7.1.3	11-3.4.3.4
14.5	10-5	Deleted	11-2.2.2.4	15.3.5	11-3.5
14.5.1	10-5.1	Deleted	11-2.2.2.5	15.3.5.1	11-3.5
14.5.2	10-5.2	15.2.2.3	11-2.2.3	15.3.5.2	New in 2000
14.5.2.1	10-5.2.1	15.2.2.3.1	11-2.2.3.1	15.3.6	11-3.6
14.5.2.2	10-5.2.2, 10-7.5	15.2.2.3.2	11-2.2.3.2	15.3.7	11-3.7
14.5.3	10-5.3	15.2.2.3.3	11-2.2.3.2 exception	15.3.7.1	11-3.7.1
14.5.4	10-5.4	15.2.2.4	11-2.2.4	15.3.7.2	11-3.7.2
14.6	10-6	15.2.2.5	11-2.2.5	15.3.7.3	11-3.7.3
14.7	10-7	15.2.2.6	11-2.2.6	15.4	11-4
14.7.1	10-7.1	15.2.2.7	11-2.2.7	15.4.1	11-4.1
14.7.1.1	10-7.1.1	15.2.2.8	11-2.2.8	15.4.2	11-4.2
14.7.1.2	10-7.1.2, 10-7.1.2.1, 10-7.1.2.2	15.2.2.9	11-2.2.9	15.4.3	11-4.3
		15.2.2.10	11-2.2.10	15.4.3.2	11-4.3.2
		15.2.3	11-2.3	15.4.3.3	11-4.3.3
				15.4.3.4	11-4.3.4

2000 Edition	1997 Edition	2000 Edition	1997 Edition	2000 Edition	1997 Edition
15.5	11-5	16.2.2.10	30-2.2.8	16.6.1.1.5	30-6.1.1.4
15.5.1	11-5.1	16.2.3	30-2.3	16.6.1.2	30-6.1.2
15.5.2	11-5.2	16.2.4	30-2.4	16.6.1.3	30-6.1.3
15.5.2.1	11-5.2.1	16.2.5	30-2.5	16.6.1.4	30-6.1.4
15.5.2.2	11-5.2.2, 11-7.5	16.2.5.1	30-2.5.1	Deleted	30-6.1.4.1
15.5.3	11-5.2.3	16.2.5.2	30-2.5.1	16.6.1.4.1	30-6.1.4.2
15.5.4	11-5.4	16.2.5.3	New in 2000	16.6.1.4.2	New in 2000
15.6	11-6	16.2.6	30-2.6	16.6.1.5	30-6.1.5
15.7	11-7	16.2.6.1	30-2.6.1	16.6.1.6	30-6.1.6
15.7.1	11-7.1	16.2.6.2	30-2.6.2	16.6.1.7	30-6.1.7
15.7.1.1	11-7.1.1	16.2.7	30-2.7	16.6.2	30-6.2
15.7.1.2	11-7.1.2	16.2.8	30-2.8	16.6.2.1	30-6.2.1
15.7.1.3	11-3.4.3.4	16.2.9	30-2.9	16.6.2.2	30-6.2.2
15.7.2	11-7.2	16.2.10	30-2.10	16.6.2.3	30-6.2.3
15.7.2.1	11-7.2.1	16.2.11	30-2.11	16.6.2.4	30-6.2.4.1
15.7.2.2	11-7.2.2	16.2.11.1	30-2.11.1	16.6.2.4.1	30-6.2.4.1.1
15.7.3	11-7.3	16.3	30-3	16.6.2.4.2	30-6.2.4.1.2
15.7.3.1	11-7.3.1	16.3.1	30-3.1	16.6.2.4.3	30-6.2.4.1.3
15.7.3.2	11-7.3.2	16.3.2	30-3.2	16.6.2.4.4	30-6.2.4.1.4
15.7.3.3	11-7.4	16.3.2.1	30-3.2.1	16.6.2.5	30-6.2.5
15.5.2.2	11.7.5	16.3.2.2	30-3.2.1 exception	16.6.2.5.1	30-6.2.5.1
Chapter 16	Chapter 30	16.3.3	30-3.3	16.6.2.5.2	30-6.2.5.2
16.1	30-1	16.3.3.1	30-3.3.1	16.6.2.5.3	30-6.2.5.2
16.1.1	30-1.1	16.3.3.2	30-3.3.2	16.6.2.6	30-6.2.6
16.1.1.1	30-1.1.1	16.3.3.3	30-3.3.3	16.6.2.7	30-6.2.7
16.1.1.2	30-1.1.2	16.3.4	30-3.4	16.6.2.8	30-6.2.8
16.1.1.3	30-1.1.3	16.3.4.1	30-3.4.1 exception	16.6.2.9	30-6.2.9
16.1.1.4	30-1.1.4	16.3.4.2	30-3.4.2 exception	16.6.2.10	30-6.2.10
16.1.1.5	30-1.1.5	16.3.4.3	30-3.4.3	16.6.3	30-6.3
16.1.2	30-1.2	16.3.4.3.1	30-3.4.3	16.6.3.1	30-6.3.1
16.1.3	30-1.3	16.3.4.3.2	New in 2000	16.6.3.2	30-6.3.2
16.1.4	30-1.4	16.3.4.4	30-3.4.4	16.6.3.3	30-6.3.3
16.1.4.1	30-1.4.1	16.3.4.5	30-3.4.5	16.6.3.3.1	30-6.3.3.1
16.1.4.2	30-1.4.2	16.3.5	30-3.5	16.6.3.3.2	30-6.3.3.2
16.1.4.3	30-1.5.4.3	16.3.6	30-3.6	16.6.3.3.3	30-6.3.3.3
16.1.5	30-1.6	16.4	30-4	16.6.3.3.4	30-6.3.3.4
16.1.6	30-1.6	16.4.1	30-4.1	16.6.3.4	30-6.3.4
16.1.6.1	30-1.6.1	16.4.2	30-4.2	16.6.3.4.1	30-6.3.4.1
Table 16.1.6.1	30-1.6.1	16.4.3	30-4.3	16.6.3.4.2	30-6.3.4.2
16.1.6.2	30-1.6.2	16.4.3.1	30-4.3.1	16.6.3.4.3	30-6.3.4.3
16.1.7	30-1.7	16.4.3.2	30-4.3.3	16.4	30-6.4
16.1.7.1	30-1.7.1	16.4.3.3	30-4.3.4	16.4.1	30-6.4.1
16.1.7.2	30-1.7.2	16.4.3.4	30-4.3.2	16.4.2	30-6.4.2
16.2	30-2	16.5	30-5	16.5	30-6.5
16.2.1	30-2.1	16.5.1	30-5.1	16.5.1	30-6.5.1
16.2.1.1	30-2.1.1	16.5.1.1	30-5.1.1	16.5.1.1	30-6.5.1.1
16.2.2	30-2.2	16.5.1.2	30-5.1.2	16.5.1.2	30-6.5.1.2
16.2.2.1	30-2.2.1	16.5.2	30-5.2	16.5.2	30-6.5.2
16.2.2.2	30-2.2.2	16.5.2.1	30-5.2.1	16.5.2.1	30-6.5.2.1
16.2.2.2.1	30-2.2.2.1	16.5.2.2	30-5.2.2, 30-7.6	16.5.2.2	30-6.5.2.2
16.2.2.2.2	30-2.2.2.2	16.5.2.3	30-5.2.3	16.5.2.3	30-6.5.2.3
16.2.2.2.3	30-2.2.2.5	16.5.3	30-5.3	16.7	30-7
16.2.2.2.4	30-2.2.2.6	16.5.4	30-5.4	16.7.1	New in 2000
16.2.2.2.5	30-2.2.2.7	16.6	30-6	16.7.2	New in 2000
16.2.2.3	30-2.2.3	16.6.1	30-6.1	16.7.2.1	New in 2000
16.2.2.4	30-2.2.6	16.6.1.1	30-6.1.1	16.7.2.2	New in 2000
16.2.2.5	30-2.2.5	16.6.1.1.1	30-6.1.1.1	16.7.3	30-7.2
16.2.2.6	30-2.2.6	16.6.1.1.2	30-6.1.1.2	16.7.3.1	30-7.2.1
16.2.2.7	30-2.2.7	16.6.1.1.3	30-6.1.1.3	16.7.3.2	30-7.2.2
16.2.2.8	30-2.5.1	16.6.1.1.4	30-6.1.1.2 exception	16.7.3.3	30-7.2.3
16.2.2.9	New in 2000			16.7.4	30-7.3

2000 Edition	1997 Edition	2000 Edition	1997 Edition	2000 Edition	1997 Edition
16.7.4.1	30-7.3.1	17.2.5	31-2.5	17.6.1.4	31-6.1.4
16.7.4.2	30-7.3.2	17.2.5.1	31-2.5.2	17.6.1.4.1	31-6.1.4.2
16.7.4.3	30-7.3.3	17.2.5.2	31-2.5.2	17.6.1.4.2	New in 2000
Deleted	30-7.3.4	17.2.5.3	New in 2000	17.6.1.5	31-6.1.5
16.7.5	30-7.4	17.2.5.4	New in 2000	17.6.1.6	31-6.2.4.1.4
Deleted	30-7.5	17.2.6	31-2.6	17.6.1.7	31-6.1.7
16.5.2.2	30-7.6	17.2.6.1	31-2.6.1	17.6.2	31-6.2
Chapter 17	Chapter 31	17.2.6.2	31-2.6.2	17.6.2.1	31-6.2.1
17.1	31-1	17.2.7	31-2.7	17.6.2.2	31-6.2.2
17.1.1	31-1.1	17.2.8	31-2.8	17.6.2.3	31-6.2.3
17.1.1.1	31-1.1.1	17.2.9	31-2.9	17.6.2.4	31-6.2.4
Table A.17.1.1	31-1.1.2	17.2.10	31-2.10	17.6.2.4.1	31-6.2.4.1.1
17.1.1.2	31-1.1.3	17.2.11	31-2.11	17.6.2.4.2	31-6.2.4.1.2
Deleted	31-1.1.4	17.2.11.1	31-2.11.1	17.6.2.4.3	31-6.2.4.1.3
17.1.1.3	31-1.1.5	17.3	31-3	17.6.2.4.4	31-6.2.4.1.4
17.1.1.4	31-1.1.6	17.3.1	31-3.1	17.6.2.5	31-6.2.5
17.1.1.5	31-1.1.7	17.3.2	31-3.2	17.6.2.5.1	31-6.2.5.1
17.1.2	31-1.2	17.3.2.1	31-3.2.1	17.6.2.5.2	31-6.2.5.2
17.1.3	31-1.3	Deleted	31-3.2.2	17.6.2.5.3	31-6.2.5.2
17.1.4	31-1.4	17.3.2.2	31-3.2.1 exception	17.6.2.6	31-6.2.6
17.1.4.1	New in 2000	17.3.3	31-3.3	17.6.2.7	31-6.2.7
17.1.4.2	31-1.4.3	17.3.3.1	31-3.3.1	17.6.2.8	31-6.2.8
17.1.4.3	New in 2000	17.3.3.2	31-3.3.2	17.6.2.9	31-6.2.9
17.1.5	31-1.5	17.3.3.3	31-3.3.3	17.6.2.10	31-6.2.10
17.1.6	31-1.6	17.3.4	31-3.4	17.6.3	31-6.3
17.1.6	31-1.6.1	17.3.4.1	31-3.4.1	17.6.3.1	31-6.3.1
Deleted	31-1.6.2	17.3.4.2	31-3.4.2	17.6.3.2	31-6.3.2
17.1.7	31-1.7	17.3.4.3	31-3.4.3	17.6.3.3	31-6.3.3
17.1.7.1	31-1.7.1	17.3.4.3.1	31-3.4.3	17.6.3.3.1	31-6.3.3.1
17.1.7.2	31-1.7.2	17.3.4.3.2	New in 2000	17.6.3.3.2	31-6.3.3.2
17.2	31-2	17.3.4.4	31-3.4.4	17.6.3.3.3	31-6.3.3.3
17.2.1	31-2.1	17.3.4.5	31-3.4.5	17.6.3.3.4	31-6.3.3.4
17.2.2	31-2.2	17.3.5	New in 2000	17.6.3.4	31-6.3.4
17.2.2.1	31-2.2.1	17.3.6	31-3.6	17.6.3.4.1	31-6.3.4.1
17.2.2.2	31-2.2.2	17.4	31-4	17.6.3.4.2	31-6.3.4.2
17.2.2.2.1	31-2.2.2.1	17.4.1	31-4.1	17.6.3.4.3	31-6.3.4.3
17.2.2.2.2	31-2.2.2.2	17.4.2	31-4.2	17.4	31-6.4
Deleted	31-2.2.2.3	17.4.3	31-4.3	17.4.1	31-6.4.1
17.2.2.2.3	31-2.2.2.5	17.4.3.1	New in 2000	17.4.2	31-6.4.2
17.2.2.2.4	31-2.2.2.6	17.4.3.2	New in 2000	17.5	31-6.5
17.2.2.2.5	31-2.2.2.7	17.4.3.3	New in 2000	17.5.1	31-6.5.1
17.2.2.3	31-2.2.3	17.5	31-5	17.5.1.1	31-6.5.1.1
17.2.2.3.1	31-2.2.3.1	17.5.1	31-5.1	17.5.1.2	31-6.5.1.2
17.2.2.3.2	31-2.2.3.2	17.5.1.1	31-5.1.1	17.5.2	31-6.5.2
17.2.2.3.3	31-2.2.3.2 exception	17.5.1.2	31-5.1.2	17.5.2.1	31-6.5.2.1
17.2.2.4	31-2.2.4	17.5.2	31-5.2	17.5.2.2	31-6.5.2.2
17.2.2.5	31-2.2.5	17.5.2.1	31-5.2.1	17.5.2.3	31-6.5.2.3
17.2.2.5.1	31-2.2.5.1	17.5.2.2	31-5.2.2, 31-7.6	17.7	31-7
17.2.2.5.2	31-2.2.5.2	17.5.2.3	31-5.2.3	17.7.1	New in 2000
17.2.2.6	31-2.2.6	17.5.3	31-5.3	Deleted	31-7.1
17.2.2.7	31-2.2.7	17.5.4	31-5.4	17.7.2	New in 2000
17.2.2.8	New in 2000	17.6	31-6	Deleted	31-7.1.2
17.2.2.9	New in 2000	17.6.1	31-6.1	17.7.2.1	New in 2000
17.2.2.10	31-2.2.8	17.6.1.1	31-6.1.1	Deleted	31-7.1.3
17.2.3	31-2.3	17.6.1.1.1	New in 2000	17.7.2.2	New in 2000
17.2.4	31-2.4	17.6.1.1.2	31-6.1.1.1	Deleted	31-7.1.4
17.2.4.1	31-2.4.1	17.6.1.1.3	31-6.1.1.2	Deleted	31-7.1.5
17.2.4.2	31-2.4.2	17.6.1.1.4	New in 2000	Deleted	31-7.1.6
17.2.4.2.1	31-2.4.2.1	17.6.1.1.5	31-6.1.1.3	Deleted	31-7.1.7
17.2.4.2.2	31-2.4.2.2	17.6.1.2	31-6.1.2	Deleted	31-7.1.8
		17.6.1.3	31-6.1.3	Deleted	31-7.1.9

2000 Edition	1997 Edition	2000 Edition	1997 Edition	2000 Edition	1997 Edition
17.7.3	31-7.2	18.2.2.2	12-2.2.2	18.2.10.2	12-2.10.2
17.7.3.1	31-7.2.1	18.2.2.2.1	12-2.2.2.1	18.2.11	12-2.11
17.7.3.2	31-7.2.2	18.2.2.2.2	12-2.2.2.2	18.3	12-3
17.7.3.3	31-7.2.3	18.2.2.2.3	12-2.2.2.3	18.3.1	12-3.1
17.7.4	31-7.3	18.2.2.2.4	12-2.2.2.4	18.3.1.1	12-3.1.1
17.7.4.1	31-7.3.1	18.2.2.2.5	12-2.2.2.5	18.3.1.2	12-3.1.2
17.7.4.2	31-7.3.2	18.2.2.2.6	12-2.2.2.6	18.3.2	12-3.2
17.7.4.3	31-7.3.3	18.2.2.2.7	12-2.2.2.7	18.3.2.1	12-3.2.1
Deleted	31-7.3.4	18.2.2.2.8	12-2.2.2.8	18.3.2.2	12-3.2.2
17.7.5	31-7.4	18.2.2.2.9	12-2.2.2.9	18.3.2.3	12-3.2.3
Deleted	31-7.5	18.2.2.3	12-2.2.3	18.3.2.4	12-3.2.4
17.5.2.2	31-7.6	18.2.2.4	12-2.2.4	18.3.2.5	12-3.2.5
Chapter 18	Chapter 12	18.2.2.5	12-2.2.5	18.3.2.6	12-3.2.6
18.1	12-1	18.2.2.5.1	12-2.2.5.1	18.3.2.7	12-3.2.7
18.1.1	12-1.1	18.2.2.5.2	12-2.2.5.6	18.3.3	12-3.3
18.1.1.1	12-1.1.1	18.2.2.5.3	12-2.2.5.2	18.3.3.1	12-3.3.1
18.1.1.1.1	12-1.1.1.1	18.2.2.5.4	12-2.2.5.3	18.3.3.2	12-3.3.2
18.1.1.1.2	12-1.1.1.2	18.2.2.5.5	12-2.2.5.4	18.3.3.3	12-3.3.3
18.1.1.1.3	12-1.1.1.3	18.2.2.5.6	12-2.2.5.5	18.3.4	12-3.4
18.1.1.1.4	12-1.1.1.6	18.2.2.6	12-2.2.6	18.3.4.1	12-3.4.1
3.3.134.7	12-1.1.1.4	18.2.2.6.1	12-2.2.6.1	18.3.4.1	12-3.4.1.1
18.1.1.1.5	12-1.1.1.7	18.2.2.6.2	12-2.2.6.2	Deleted	12-3.4.1.2
Deleted	12-1.1.1.5	18.2.2.7	12-2.2.7	18.3.4.2	12-3.4.2
18.1.1.1.6	12-1.1.1.8	18.2.2.8	12-2.2.8	18.3.4.3	12-3.4.3
18.1.1.1.7	12-1.1.1.10	18.2.2.9	12-2.2.9	18.3.4.3.1	12-3.4.3.1
18.1.1.1.8	12-1.1.1.11	18.2.2.10	12-2.2.10	18.3.4.3.2	12-3.4.3.2
Deleted	12-1.1.1.9	18.2.3	12-2.3	18.3.4.3.3	12-3.4.3.3
18.1.1.2	12-1.1.2	18.2.3.1	12-2.3.1	18.3.4.4	12-3.4.4
18.1.1.3	12-1.1.3	18.2.3.2	12-2.3.2	18.3.4.5	12-3.4.5
18.1.1.4	12-1.1.4	18.2.3.3	12-2.3.3	18.3.4.5.1	12-3.4.5.1
18.1.1.4.1	12-1.1.4.1	18.2.3.4	12-2.3.4	18.3.4.5.2	12-3.4.5.2
18.1.1.4.2	12-1.1.4.2	18.2.3.5	12-2.3.5	18.3.4.5.3	12-3.4.5.3
18.1.1.4.3	12-1.1.4.3	18.2.4	12-2.4	18.3.5	12-3.5
18.1.1.4.4	12-1.1.4.4	18.2.4.1	12-2.4.1	18.3.5.1	12-3.5.1
18.1.1.4.5	12-1.1.4.5	18.2.4.2	12-2.4.2	18.3.5.2	12-3.5.2
18.1.1.4.6	12-1.1.4.6	18.2.4.3	12-2.4.3	18.3.5.3	New in 2000 — Reserved
18.1.2	12-1.2	18.2.5	12-2.5		
18.1.2.1	12-1.2.1	18.2.5.1	12-2.5.1	18.3.5.4	New in 2000 — Reserved
18.1.2.2	12-1.2.2	18.2.5.2	12-2.5.2		
18.1.2.3	12-1.2.3	18.2.5.3	12-2.5.3	18.3.5.5	12-3.5.3
18.1.2.4	12-1.2.4	18.2.5.4	12-2.5.4	18.3.5.6	12-3.5.4
18.1.2.5	12-1.2.5	18.2.5.5	12-2.5.5	18.3.6	12-3.6
18.1.2.6	12-1.2.6	18.2.5.6	12-2.5.6	18.3.6.1	12-3.6.1
18.1.2.7	12-1.2.7	18.2.5.7	12-2.5.7	18.3.6.2	12-3.6.2
18.1.2.8	12-1.2.8	18.2.5.8	12-2.5.8	18.3.6.3	12-3.6.3
18.1.3	12-1.3	18.2.5.9	12-2.5.9	18.3.6.3.1	12-3.6.3.1
18.1.4	12-1.4	18.2.5.10	12-2.5.10	18.3.6.3.2	12-3.6.3.2
18.1.5	12-1.5	18.2.6	12-2.6	18.3.6.3.3	New in 2000
18.1.6	12-1.6	18.2.6.1	12-2.6.1	18.3.6.3.4	12-3.6.3.3
18.1.6.1	12-1.6.1	18.2.6.2	12-2.6.2	18.3.6.3.5	12-3.6.3.4
18.1.6.2	12-1.6.2	18.2.6.2.1	12-2.6.2.1	18.3.6.3.6	12-3.6.3.5
Table 18.1.6.2	Table 12-1.6.2	18.2.6.2.2	12-2.6.2.2	18.3.6.4	12-3.6.4
18.1.6.3	12-1.6.3	18.2.6.2.3	12-2.6.2.3	18.3.6.5	12-3.6.5
Deleted	12-1.6.4	18.2.6.2.4	12-2.6.2.4	18.3.7	12-3.7
Deleted	12-1.6.5	18.2.7	12-2.7	18.3.7.1	12-3.7.1
18.1.6.4	12-1.6.6	18.2.8	12-2.8	18.3.7.2	12-3.7.2
18.1.7	12-1.7	18.2.9	12-2.9	18.3.7.3	12-3.7.3
18.2	12-2	18.2.9.1	12-2.9.1	18.3.7.4	12-3.7.4
18.2.1	12-2.1	18.2.9.2	12-2.9.2	18.3.7.5	12-3.7.5
18.2.2	12-2.2	18.2.10	12-2.10	18.3.7.6	12-3.7.6
18.2.2.1	12-2.2.1	18.2.10.1	12-2.10.1	18.3.7.7	12-3.7.7

2000 Edition	1997 Edition	2000 Edition	1997 Edition	2000 Edition	1997 Edition
18.3.7.8	12-3.7.8	19.1.1.4.1	13-1.1.4.1	19.2.4	13-2.4
18.3.8	12-3.8	19.1.1.4.2	13-1.1.4.2	19.2.4.1	13-2.4.1
18.4	12-4	19.1.1.4.3	13-1.1.4.3	19.2.4.2	13-2.4.2
18.4.1	12-4.1	19.1.1.4.4	13-1.1.4.4	19.2.4.3	13-2.4.3
18.4.2	12-4.2	19.1.1.4.5	13-1.1.4.5	19.2.5	13-2.5
18.5	12-5	19.1.1.4.6	13-1.1.4.6	19.2.5.1	13-2.5.1
18.5.1	12-5.1	Deleted	13-1.1.5	19.2.5.2	13-2.5.2
18.5.1.1	12-5.1.1	19.1.2	13-1.2	19.2.5.3	13-2.5.3
18.5.1.2	12-5.1.2	19.1.2.1	13-1.2.1	19.2.5.4	13-2.5.4
18.5.1.3	12-5.1.3	19.1.2.2	13-1.2.2	19.2.5.5	13-2.5.5
18.5.2	12-5.2	19.1.2.3	13-1.2.3	19.2.5.6	13-2.5.6
18.5.2.1	12-5.2.1	19.1.2.4	13-1.2.4	19.2.5.7	13-2.5.7
18.5.2.2	12-5.2.2	19.1.2.5	13-1.2.5	19.2.5.8	13-2.5.8
18.5.3	12-5.3	19.1.2.6	13-1.2.6	19.2.5.9	13-2.5.9
18.5.4	12-5.4	19.1.2.7	13-1.2.7	19.2.5.10	13-2.5.9 exception
18.5.4.1	12-5.4.1	19.1.2.8	13-1.2.8	19.2.6	13-2.6
18.5.4.2	12-5.4.2	19.1.3	13-1.3	19.2.6.1	13-2.6.1
18.5.4.3	12-5.4.3	19.1.4	13-1.4	19.2.6.2	13-2.6.2
18.5.4.4	12-5.4.4	19.1.5	13-1.5	19.2.6.2.1	13-2.6.3
Chapter 20	12-6	19.1.6	13-1.6	19.2.6.2.2	13-2.6.4
18.6	New in 2000 — Reserved	19.1.6.1	13-1.6.1	19.2.6.2.3	13-2.6.2.3
		19.1.6.2	13-1.6.2	19.2.6.2.4	13-2.6.2.4
18.7	12-7	19.1.6.3	13-1.6.3	19.2.7	13-2.7
18.7.1	12-7.1	Deleted	13-1.6.4	19.2.8	13-2.8
18.7.1.1	12-7.1.1	19.1.6.4	13-1.6.5	19.2.9	13-2.9
18.7.1.2	12-7.1.2	19.1.7	13-1.7	19.2.9.1	13-2.9
18.7.1.3	18-7.1.3	19.2	13-2	19.2.10	13-2.10
18.7.2	12-7.2	19.2.1	13-2.1	19.2.10.1	13-2.10
18.7.2.1	12-7.2.1	19.2.2	13-2.2	19.2.11	13-2.11
18.7.2.2	12-7.2.2	19.2.2.1	13-2.2.1	19.3	13-3
18.7.2.3	12-7.2.3	19.2.2.2	13-2.2.2	19.3.1	13-3.1
18.7.3	12-7.3	19.2.2.2.1	13-2.2.2.1	19.3.1.1	13-1.1
18.7.4	12-7.4	19.2.2.2.2	13-2.2.2.2	19.3.1.2	13-3.1.2
18.7.5	12-7.5	19.2.2.2.3	13-2.2.2.3	19.3.2	13-3.2
18.7.5.1	12-7.5.1	19.2.2.2.4	13-2.2.2.4	19.3.2.1	13-3.2.1
18.7.5.2	12-7.5.2	19.2.2.2.5	13-2.2.2.5	19.3.2.2	13-3.2.2.
18.7.5.3	12-7.5.3	19.2.2.2.6	13-2.2.2.6	19.3.2.3	13-3.2.3
18.7.5.4	12-7.5.4	19.2.2.2.7	13-2.2.2.7	19.3.2.4	13-3.2.4
18.7.5.5	12-7.5.5	19.2.2.2.8	13-2.2.2.8	19.3.2.5	13-3.2.5
18.7.6	New in 2000	19.2.2.2.9	13-2.2.2.9	19.3.2.6	13-3.2.6
18.7.7	12-7.6	19.2.2.3	13-2.2.3	19.3.3	13-3.3
18.7.8	12-7.7	19.2.2.4	13-2.2.4	19.3.3.1	13-3.3.1
18.7.9	12-7.8	19.2.2.5	13-2.2.5	19.3.3.2	13-3.3.2
18.7.9.1	12-7.8.1	19.2.2.5.1	13-2.2.5.1	19.3.3.3	13-3.3.3
18.7.9.2	12-7.8.2	19.2.2.5.2	13-2.2.5.2	19.3.4	13-3.4
Chapter 19	Chapter 13	19.2.2.5.3	13-2.2.5.3	19.3.4.1	13-3.4.1
19.1	13-1	19.2.2.5.4	13-2.2.5.4	19.3.4.2	13-3.4.2
19.1.1	13-1.1	19.2.2.6	13-2.2.6	19.3.4.3	13-3.4.3
19.1.1.1.1	13-1.1.1.1	19.2.2.6.1	13-2.2.6.1	19.3.4.3.1	13-3.4.3.1
19.1.1.1.2	13-1.1.1.2	19.2.2.6.2	13-2.2.6.2	19.3.4.3.2	13-3.4.3.2
19.1.1.1.3	13-1.1.1.3	19.2.2.7	13-2.2.7	19.3.4.4	13-3.4.4
19.1.1.1.4	13-1.1.1.4	19.2.2.8	13-2.2.8	19.3.4.5	13-3.4.5
Deleted	13-1.1.1.5	19.2.2.9	13-2.2.9	19.3.4.5.1	13-3.4.5.1
19.1.1.1.5	13-1.1.1.7	19.2.2.10	13-2.2.10	19.3.4.5.2	13-3.4.5.2
19.1.1.1.6	13-1.1.1.8	19.2.3	13-2.3	19.3.5	13-3.5
19.1.1.1.7	13-1.1.1.10	19.2.3.1	13-2.3.1	19.3.5.1	13-3.5.1
19.1.1.1.8	13-1.1.1.11	19.2.3.2	13-2.3.2	19.3.5.2	13-3.5.2
Deleted	13-1.1.1.9	19.2.3.3	13-2.3.3		
19.1.1.2	13-1.1.2	19.2.3.4	New in 2000 — Reserved		
19.1.1.3	13-1.1.3				
19.1.1.4	13-1.1.4	19.2.3.5	13-2.3.4		

2000 Edition	1997 Edition	2000 Edition	1997 Edition	2000 Edition	1997 Edition
19.3.5.3	13-3.5.3	19.7.1.2	13-7.1.2	20.1.6.3	12-6.1.6.3
19.3.5.4	13-3.5.4	19.7.1.3	13-7.1.3	20.1.6.4	12-6.1.6.4
19.3.5.5	13-3.5.5	19.7.2	13-7.2	20.1.6.5	12-6.1.6.5
19.3.5.6	13-3.5.6	19.7.2.1	13-7.2.1	20.1.6.6	12-1.6.3
19.3.6	13-3.6	19.7.2.2	13-7.2.2	20.1.6.7	12.1.6.6
19.3.6.1	13-3.6.1	19.7.2.3	13-7.2.3	20.1.7	12-6.1.7
19.3.6.2	13-3.6.2	19.7.3	13-7.3	20.2	12-6.2
19.3.6.2.1	13-3.6.2.1	19.7.4	13-7.4	20.2.1	12-6.2.1
19.3.6.2.2	13-3.6.2.2	19.7.5	13-7.5	20.2.2	12-6.2.2
19.3.6.2.3	13-3.6.2.3	19.7.5.1	13-7.5.1	20.2.2.1	12-6.2.2.1
19.3.6.3	13-3.6.3	19.7.5.2	13-7.5.2	20.2.2.2	12-6.2.2.2
19.3.6.3.1	13-3.6.3.1	19.7.5.3	13-7.5.3	20.2.2.3	12-6.2.2.3
19.3.6.3.2	13-3.6.3.2	19.7.5.4	13-7.5.4	20.2.2.4	12-6.2.2.4
19.3.6.3.3	New in 2000	19.7.5.5	13-7.5.5	20.2.3	12-6.2.3
19.3.6.3.4	13-3.6.3.3	19.7.6	New in 2000	20.2.3.1	12-6.2.3.1
19.3.6.3.5	13-3.6.3.4	19.7.7	13-7.6	20.2.3.2	12-6.2.3.2
19.3.6.3.6	13-3.6.3.7	19.7.8	13-7.7	20.2.3.3	12-6.2.3.3
19.3.6.3.7	13-3.6.3.5	19.7.9	13-7.8	20.2.4	12-6.2.4
19.3.6.3.8	13-3.6.3.6	19.7.9.1	13-7.8.1	20.2.4.1	12-6.2.4.1
19.3.6.4	13-3.6.4	19.7.9.2	13-7.8.2	20.2.4.2	12-6.2.4.2
19.3.6.5	13-3.6.5	Chapter 20	12-6	20.2.4.3	12-6.2.4.3
19.3.7	13-3.7	20.1	12-6.1	20.2.5	12-6.2.5
19.3.7.1	13-3.7.1	20.1.1	12-6.1.1	20.2.6	12-6.2.6
19.3.7.2	13-3.7.2	20.1.1.1	New in 2000	20.2.6.1	12-6.2.6.1
19.3.7.3	13-3.7.3	20.1.1.1.1	New in 2000	20.2.6.2	12-6.2.6.2
19.3.7.4	13-3.7.4	20.1.1.1.2	12-6.1.1.1	20.2.7	12-6.2.7
19.3.7.5	13-3.7.5	20.1.1.1.3	12-6.1.1.2	20.2.8	12-6.2.8
19.3.7.6	13-3.7.6	20.1.1.1.4	12-1.1.1.6	20.2.9	12-6.2.9
19.3.7.7	13-3.7.7	20.1.1.1.5	12-1.1.1.7	20.2.9.1	12.6.2.9.1
19.3.8	13-3.8	20.1.1.1.6	12-1.1.1.11	20.2.9.2	12-6.2.9.2
19.3.8	13-3.8.1	20.1.1.2	12-1.1.2	20.2.10	12-6.2.10
19.4	13-4	20.1.1.3	12-1.1.3	20.2.11	12-2.11
19.4.1	13-4.1	20.1.1.4	12-1.1.4	20.3	12-6.3
19.4.2	13-4.2	20.1.1.4.1	12-1.1.4.1	20.3.1	12-6.3.1
19.5	13-5	20.1.1.4.2	12-1.1.4.2	20.3.2	12-6.3.2
19.5.1	13-5.1	20.1.1.4.3	12-1.1.4.3	20.3.2.1	12-6.3.2.2
19.5.2	13-5.2	20.1.1.4.4	New in 2000	20.3.2.2	12-6.3.2.3
19.5.2.1	13-5.2.1	20.1.1.4.5	12-1.1.4.5	20.3.3	12-6.3.3
19.5.2.2	13-5.2.2	20.1.1.4.6	12-1.1.4.6	20.3.4	12-6.3.4
19.5.3	13-5.3	20.1.2	12-1.2	20.3.4.1	12-6.3.4.1
19.5.4	13-5.4	20.1.2.1	12-1.2.1	20.3.4.2	12-6.3.4.2
19.5.4.1	13-5.4.1	20.1.2.2	12-1.2.5	20.3.4.3	12-6.3.4.3.1
19.5.4.2	13-5.4.1.2	20.1.2.3	12-1.2.5	20.3.4.4	12-6.3.4.3.2
19.5.4.3	13-5.4.3	20.1.2.4	12-1.2.7	20.3.4.5	12-6.3.4.4
19.5.4.4	13-5.4.4	20.1.2.5	12-1.2.8	20.3.5	12-6.3.5
19.6	New in 2000 — Reserved	20.1.3	12-6.1.3	20.3.5.1	12-6.3.5.1
		20.1.4	12-6.1.4	20.3.5.2	12-6.3.5.2
Chapter 21	13-6	20.1.5	12-6.1.5	20.3.6	12-6.3.6
19.7	13-7	20.1.6	12-6.1.6	20.3.6.1	12-6.3.6.1
19.7.1	13-7.1	20.1.6.1	12-6.1.6.1	20.3.6.2	12-6.3.6.2
19.7.1.1	13-7.1.1	20.1.6.2	12-6.1.6.2	20.3.7	12-6.3.7

2000 Edition	1997 Edition	2000 Edition	1997 Edition	2000 Edition	1997 Edition
20.3.7.1	12-6.3.7.1	21.1.1.3	13-1.1.3	21.2.11	13-2.11
20.3.7.2	12-6.3.7.2	21.1.1.4	13-1.1.4	21.3	13-6.3
20.3.7.3	12-6.3.7.3	21.1.1.4.1	13-1.1.4.1	21.3.1	13-6.3.1
20.3.7.4	12-6.3.7.4	21.1.1.4.2	13-1.1.4.2	21.3.2	13-6.3.2
20.3.7.5	12-6.3.7.5	21.1.1.4.3	13-1.1.4.3	21.3.2.1	13-6.3.2.2
20.3.7.6	12-6.3.7.6	21.1.1.4.4	New in 2000	21.3.2.2	13-6.3.2.3
20.3.7.7	12-6.3.7.7	21.1.1.4.5	13-1.1.4.5	21.3.3	13-6.3.3
20.4	12-6.4	21.1.1.4.6	13-1.1.4.6	21.3.4	13-6.3.4
20.5	12-6.5	21.1.2	13-1.2	21.3.4.1	13-6.3.4.1
20.5.1	12-6.5.1	21.1.2.1	13-1.2.1	21.3.4.2	13-6.3.4.2
20.5.2	12-6.5.2	21.1.2.2	13-1.2.5	21.3.4.3	13-6.3.4.3.1
20.5.2.1	12-6.5.2.1	21.1.2.3	13-1.2.5	21.3.4.4	13-6.3.4.3.2
20.5.2.2	12-6.5.2.2	21.1.2.4	13-1.2.7	21.3.4.5	13-6.3.4.4
20.5.3	12-6.5.3	21.1.2.5	13-1.2.8	21.3.5	13-6.3.5
20.5.4	12-6.5.4	21.1.3	13-6.1.3	21.3.5.1	13-6.3.5.1
20.6	New in 2000 —	21.1.4	13-6.1.4	21.3.5.2	13-6.3.5.2
	Reserved	21.1.5	13-6.1.5	21.3.6	13-6.3.6
20.7	12-7	21.1.6	13-6.1.6	21.3.6.1	13-6.3.6.1
20.7.1	12-7.1	21.1.6.1	13-6.1.6.1	21.3.6.2	13-6.3.6.2
20.7.1.1	12-7.1.1	21.1.6.2	13-6.1.6.2	21.3.7	13-6.3.7
20.7.1.2	12-7.1.2	21.1.6.3	13-6.1.6.3	21.3.7.1	13-6.3.7.1
20.7.1.3	12-7.1.3	21.1.6.4	13-6.1.6.4	21.3.7.2	13-6.3.7.2
20.7.2	12-7.2	21.1.6.5	13-6.1.6.5	21.3.7.3	13-6.3.7.3
20.7.2.1	12-7.2.1	21.1.6.6	13-1.6.3	21.3.7.4	13-6.3.7.4
20.7.2.2	12-7.2.2	21.1.6.7	12.1.6.6	21.3.7.5	13-6.3.7.5
20.7.2.3	12-7.2.3	21.1.7	13-6.1.7	21.3.7.6	13-6.3.7.6
20.7.3	12-7.3	21.2	13-6.2	21.3.7.7	13-6.3.7.7
20.7.4	12-7.4	21.2.1	13-6.2.1	21.4	13-6.4
20.7.5	12-7.5	21.2.2	13-6.2.2	21.5	13-6.5
20.7.5.1	12-7.5.1	21.2.2.1	13-6.2.2.1	21.5.1	13-6.5.1
20.7.5.2	12-7.5.2	21.2.2.2	13-6.2.2.2	21.5.2	13-6.5.2
20.7.5.3	12-7.5.3	21.2.2.3	13-6.2.2.3	21.5.2.1	13-6.5.2.1
20.7.5.4	12-7.5.4	21.2.2.4	13-6.2.2.4	21.5.2.2	13-6.5.2.2
20.7.5.5	12-7.5.5	21.2.3	13-6.2.3	21.5.3	13-6.5.3
20.7.6	New in 2000	21.2.3.1	13-6.2.3.1	21.5.4	13-6.5.4
20.7.7	12-7.6	21.2.3.2	13-6.2.3.2	21.6	New in 2000 —
20.7.8	12-7.7	21.2.3.3	13-6.2.3.3		Reserved
20.7.9	12-7.8	21.2.4	13-6.2.4	21.7	13-7
20.7.9.1	12-7.8.1	21.2.4.1	13-6.2.4.1	21.7.1	13-7.1
20-7.9.2	12-7.8.2	21.2.4.2	13-6.2.4.2	21.7.1.1	13-7.1.1
Chapter 21	13-6	21.2.4.3	13-6.2.4.3	21.7.1.2	13-7.1.2
21.1	13-6.1	21.2.5	13-6.2.5	21.7.1.3	13-7.1.3
21.1.1	13-6.1.1	21.2.6	13-6.2.6	21.7.2	13-7.2
21.1.1.1	New in 2000	21.2.6.1	13-6.2.6.1	21.7.2.1	13-7.2.1
21.1.1.1.1	New in 2000	21.2.6.2	13-6.2.6.2	21.7.2.2	13-7.2.2
21.1.1.1.2	13-6.1.1.1	21.2.7	13-6.2.7	21.7.2.3	13-7.2.3
21.1.1.1.3	13-6.1.1.2	21.2.8	13-6.2.8	21.7.3	13-7.3
21.1.1.1.4	13-1.1.1.6	21.2.9	13-6.2.9	21.7.4	13-7.4
21.1.1.1.5	13-1.1.1.7	21.2.9.1	12.6.2.9.1	21.7.5	13-7.5
21.1.1.1.6	13-1.1.1.11	21.2.9.2	13-6.2.9.2	21.7.5.1	13-7.5.1
21.1.1.2	13-1.1.2	21.2.10	13-6.2.10	21.7.5.2	13-7.5.2

2000 Edition	1997 Edition	2000 Edition	1997 Edition	2000 Edition	1997 Edition
21.7.5.3	13-7.5.3	22.2.2.6	14-2.2.6	22.3.3	14-3.3
21.7.5.4	13-7.5.4	22.2.2.7	14-2.2.7	22.3.3.1	14-3.3.1
21.7.5.5	13-7.5.5	22.2.2.8	New in 2000 —	22.3.3.2	14-3.3.2
21.7.6	New in 2000		Reserved	22.3.3.3	14-3.3.3
21.7.7	13-7.6	22.2.2.9	14-2.2.8	22.3.4	14-3.4
21.7.8	13-7.7	22.2.2.10	14-2.2.9	22.3.4.1	14-3.4.1
21.7.9	13-7.8	22.2.2.11	14-2.2.10	22.3.4.1.1	14-3.4.1.1
21.7.9.1	13-7.8.1	22.2.3	14-2.3	22.3.4.1.2	14-4.4.1.2
21.7.9.2	13-7.8.2	22.2.3.1	14-2.3.1	Deleted	14-3.4.1.3
Chapter 22	Chapter 14	22.2.3.2	14-2.3.2	22.3.4.2	14-3.4.2
22.1	14-1	22.2.3.3	14-2.3.3	22.3.4.3	14-3.4.3
22.1.1	14-1.1	22.2.4	14-2.4	22.3.4.3.1	14-3.4.3.1
22.1.1.2	14-1.1.2	22.2.4.1	14-2.4.1	22.3.4.3.2	14-3.4.3.2
22.1.1.3	14-1.1.3	22.2.4.2	14-2.4.2	22.3.4.4	14-3.4.4
22.1.1.4	14-1.1.4	22.2.5	14-2.5	22.3.4.4.1	14-3.4.4 Exception
22.1.1.5	14-1.1.5	22.2.5.1	14-2.5.1		No. 1
22.1.1.6	14-1.1.6	22.2.5.2	14-2.5.2	22.3.4.4.2	14-3.4.4 Exception
22.1.1.7	14-1.1.7	22.2.5.3	14-2.5.3		No. 3
22.1.2	14-1.2	22.2.5.4	14-2.5.4	22.3.4.4.3	New in 2000
22.1.2.1	14-1.2.1	22.2.6	14-2.6	22.3.5	14-3.5
22.1.2.2	14-1.2.2	22.2.6.1	14-2.6.1	22.3.5.1	14-3.5.1
22.1.2.3	14-1.2.3	22.2.6.2	14-2.6.2	22.3.5.2	14-3.5.2
22.1.2.4	14-1.2.4	22.2.6.3	14-2.6.3	22.3.5.3	14-3.5.3
22.1.2.5	14-1.2.5	22.2.7	14-2.7	22.3.5.4	14-3.5.4
22.1.2.6	14-1.2.6	22.2.7.1	14-2.7.1	22.3.5.5	14-3.5.5
22.1.3	14-1.3	22.2.7.2	14-2.7.2	22.3.6	14-3.6
22.1.4	14-1.4	22.2.8	14-2.8	22.3.7	14-3.7
22.1.4.1	14-1.4.1	22.2.9	14-2.9	22.3.7.1	14-3.7.1
22.1.4.2	14-1.4.2	22.2.10	14-2.10	22.3.7.2	14-3.7.2
22.1.4.3	14-1.4.3	22.2.11	14-2.11	22.3.7.3	14-3.7.3
22.1.5	14-1.5	22.2.11.1	14-2.11.1	22.3.7.4	14-3.7.4
22.1.6	14-1.6	22.2.11.2	14-2.11.2	22.3.7.5	14-3.7.5
22.1.6.1	14-1.6.1	22.2.11.3	14-2.11.3	22.3.7.6	14-3.7.6
22.1.6.2	New in 2000 —	22.2.11.4	14-2.11.4	22.3.7.7	14-3.7.7
	Reserved	22.2.11.5	14-2.11.5	22.3.7.8	14-3.7.8
22.1.6.3	14-1.6.3	22.2.11.6	14-2.11.6	22.3.7.9	14-3.7.9
22.1.6.4	14-1.6.4	22.2.11.7	14-2.11.7	22.3.8	14-3.8.1
22.1.7	14-1.7	22.2.11.8	14-2.11.10	22.4	14-4
22.2	14-2	22.2.11.9	14-2.11.8	22.4.1	14-4.1
22.2.1	14-2.1	22-2.11.10	14-2.11.9	22.4.4.12.1	14-4.1.1
22.2.2	14-2.2	22.3	14-3	22.4.4.12.2	14-4.1.2
22.2.2.1	14-2.2.1	22.3.1	14-3.1	22.4.2	14-4.2
22.2.2.2	14-2.2.2	22.3.1.1	14-3.1.1	22.4.3	14-4.3
22.2.2.3	14-2.2.3	22.4.4.6.1	14-3.1.2	22.4.4	New in 2000
22.2.2.3.1	14-2.2.3.1	22.4.4.6.2	14-3.1.2.1	22.4.4.1	14-1.1.7 exception
22.2.2.3.2	14-2.2.3.2	22.4.4.6.3	14-3.1.2.2	22.4.4.2	New in 2000
22.2.2.4	14-2.2.4	22.4.4.6.4	14-3.1.2.3	22.4.4.2.1	14-1.6.3
22.2.2.5	14-2.2.5	22.3.2	14-3.2	22.4.4.2.2	14-1.6.2
22.2.2.5.1	14-2.2.5.1	22.3.2.1	14-3.2.1	22.4.4.3	14-2.2.5.3
22.2.2.5.2	14-2.2.5.2	22.3.2.2	14-3.2.2	22.4.4.4	14-2.5.3
22.4.4.3	14-2.2.5.3	22.3.2.3	14-3.2.3	22.4.4.5	New in 2000

2000 Edition	1997 Edition	2000 Edition	1997 Edition	2000 Edition	1997 Edition
22.4.4.5.1	14-2.6.1	22.7.4.2	New in 2000 —	23.2.2.5.4	15-2.2.5.4
22.4.4.5.2	14-2.6.2		Reserved	23.2.2.6	15-2.2.6
22.4.4.6	14-3.1	22.7.4.3	New in 2000 —	23.2.2.7	15-2.2.7
22.4.4.6.1	14-3.1.2		Reserved	23.2.2.8	15-2.2.8
22.4.4.6.2	14-3.1.2.1	22.4.4.13.2	14-7.4.2	23.2.2.9	15-2.2.9
22.4.4.6.3	14-3.1.2.2	22.4.4.13.2	14-7.4.3	23.2.2.10	15-2.2.10
22.4.4.6.4	14-3.1.2.3	22.7.4.4	14-7.4.4	23.2.2.11	15-2.2.11
22.4.4.7	14-3.2.1	22.7.4.5	14-7.4.5	23.2.3	15-2.3
22.4.4.8	New in 2000	22.7.5	14-7.5	23.2.3.1	15-2.3.1
22.4.4.8.1	14-3.3.2	22.7.6	14-7.6	23.2.3.2	15-2.3.2
22.4.4.8.2	14-3.3.3	Chapter 23	Chapter 15	23.2.3.3	15-2.3.3
22.4.4.9	New in 2000	23.1	15-1	23.2.4	15-2.4
22.4.4.9.1	14-3.4.2	23.1.1	15-1.1	23.2.4.1	15-2.4.1
22.4.4.9.2	14-3.4.4	23.1.1.1	15-1.1.1	23.2.4.2	15-2.4.2
22.4.4.9.2.1	14-3.4.4 Exception	23.1.1.2	15-1.1.2	23.2.5	15-2.5
	No. 1	23.1.1.3	15-1.1.3	23.2.5.1	15-2.5.1
22.4.4.9.2.2	14-3.4.4 Exception	23.1.1.4	15-1.1.4	23.2.5.2	15-2.5.2
	No. 3	23.1.1.5	15-1.1.5	23.2.5.3	15-2.5.3
22.4.4.10	14-3.7.2	23.1.1.6	15-1.1.6	23.2.5.4	15-2.5.4
22.4.4.11	14-3.8.1	23.1.1.7	15-1.1.7	23.2.6	15-2.6
22.4.4.12	14-4.1	23.1.2	15-1.2	23.2.6.1	15-2.6.1
22.4.4.12.1	14-4.1.1	23.1.2.1	15-1.2.1	23.2.6.2	15-2.6.2
22.4.4.12.2	14-4.1.2	23.1.2.2	15-1.2.2	23.2.6.3	15-2.6.3
22.4.4.13	14-7.4	23.1.2.3	15-1.2.3	23.2.7	15-2.7
22.4.4.13.1	14-7.4.2	23.1.2.4	15-1.2.4	23.2.7.1	15-2.7.1
22.4.4.13.2	14-7.4.3	23.1.2.5	15-1.2.5	23.2.7.2	15-2.7.2
22.5	14-5	23.1.2.6	15-1.2.6	23.2.8	15-2.8
22.5.1	14-5.1	23.1.3	15-1.3	23.2.9	15-2.9
22.5.1.1	14-5.1.1	23.1.4	15-1.4	23.2.10	15-2.10
22.5.1.2	14-5.1.2	23.1.4.1	15-1.4.1	23.2.11	15-2.11
22.5.2	14-5.2	23.1.4.2	15-1.4.2	23.2.11.1	15-2.11.1
22.5.2.1	14-5.2.1	23.1.4.3	15-1.4.3	23.2.11.2	15-2.11.2
22.5.2.2	14-5.2.2	23.1.5	15-1.5	23.2.11.3	15-2.11.3
22.5.2.3	14-5.2.3	23.1.6	15-1.6	23.2.11.4	15-2.11.4
22.5.3	14-5.3	23.1.6.1	15-1.6.1	23.2.11.5	15-2.11.5
22.5.4	14-5.4	23.1.6.2	15-1.6.2	23.2.11.6	15-2.11.6
22.5.4.1	14-5.4.1	23.1.6.3	15-1.6.3	23.2.11.7	15-2.11.7
22.5.4.2	14-5.4.2	23.1.7	15-1.7	23.2.11.8	15-2.11.8
22.5.4.3	14-5.4.3	23.2	15-2	23.3	15-3
22.5.4.4	14-5.4.4	23.2.1	15-2.1	23.3.1	15-3.1
22.6	14-6	23.2.2	15-2.2	23.3.1.1	15-3.1.1
22.7	14-7	23.2.2.1	15-2.2.1	23.3.1.2	15-3.1.2
22.7.1	14-7.1	23.2.2.2	15-2.2.2	23.3.1.2.1	15-3.1.2.1
22.7.1.1	14-7.1.1	23.2.2.3	15-2.2.3	23.3.1.2.2	15-3.1.2.2
22.7.1.2	14-7.1.2	23.2.2.3.1	15-2.2.3.1	23.3.1.2.3	15-3.1.2.3
22.7.1.3	14-7.1.3	23.2.2.3.2	15-2.2.3.2	23.3.1.3	15-3.1.3
22.7.1.4	14-7.1.4	23.2.2.4	15-2.2.4	23.3.2	15-3.2
22.7.2	14-7.2	23.2.2.5	15-2.2.5	23.3.2.1	15-3.2.1
22.7.3	14-7.3	23.2.2.5.1	15-2.2.5.1	23.3.2.2	15-3.2.2
22.7.4	14-7.4	23.2.2.5.2	15-2.2.5.2	23.3.2.3	15-3.2.3
22.7.4.1	14-7.4.1	23.2.2.5.3	15-2.2.5.3	23.3.3	15-3.3

2000 Edition	1997 Edition	2000 Edition	1997 Edition	2000 Edition	1997 Edition
23.3.3.1	15-3.3.1	23.5.2.3	15-5.2.3	24.2.4.5	21-2.4.5
23.3.3.2	15-3.3.2	23.5.3	15-5.3	24.2.4.6	21-2.4.6
23.3.3.3	15-3.3.3	23.5.4	15-5.4	24.2.5	21-2.5
23.3.4	15-3.4	23.5.4.1	15-5.4.1	24.2.5.1	21-2.5.1
23.3.4.1	15-3.4.1	23.5.4.2	15-5.4.2	24.2.5.2	21-2.5.2
23.3.4.1.1	15-3.4.1.1	23.5.4.3	15-5.4.3	24.2.5.3	21-2.5.3
Deleted	15-3.4.1.2	23.5.4.4	15-5.4.4	24.2.5.4	21-2.5.4
23.3.4.1.2	15-3.4.1.3	23.6	15-6	24.2.6	21-2.6
23.3.4.2	15-3.4.2	23.7	15-7	24.3	21-3
23.3.4.3	15-3.4.3	23.7.1	15-7.1	24.3.1	21-3.1
23.3.4.3.1	15-3.4.3.1	23.7.1.1	15-7.1.1	24.3.2	New in 2000 —
23.3.4.3.2	15-3.4.3.2	23.7.1.2	15-7.1.2		Reserved
23.3.4.4	15-3.4.4	23.7.1.3	15-7.1.3	24.3.3	21-3.2
23.3.4.4.1	15-3.4.4 Exception	23.7.1.4	15-7.1.4	24.3.3.1	21-3.3.1
	No. 1	23.7.2	15-7.2	24.3.3.2	21-3.2.2
23.3.4.4.2	15-3.4.4 Exception	23.7.3	15-7.3	24.3.4	21-3.3
	No. 3	23.7.4	15-7.4	24.3.5	New in 2000
23.3.4.4.3	New in 2000	23.7.4.1	15-7.4.1	24.4	21-4
23.3.4.4.4	15-3.4.4 Exception	23.7.4.2	15-7.4.2	24.5	21-5
	No. 2	23.7.4.3	15-7.4.3	24.5.1	21-5.1
23.3.5	15-3.5	23.7.4.4	15-7.4.4	24.5.1.1	21-5.1.1
23.3.5.1	15-4.3	23.7.4.5	15-7.4.5	24.5.1.2	21-5.1.2
23.3.5.2	15-3.5.2	23.7.5	15-7.5	Chapter 25	New in 2000 —
23.3.5.3	15-3.5.3	23.7.6	15-7.6		Reserved
23.3.5.4	15-3.5.4	Chapter 24	Chapter 21	Chapter 26	Chapter 20
23.3.5.5	15-3.5.5	24.1	21-1	26.1	20-1
23.3.6	15-3.6	24.1.1	21-1.1	26.1.1	20-1.1
23.3.7	15-3.7	24.1.1.1	21-1.1.1	26.1.1.1	20-1.1.1
23.3.7.1	15-3.7.1	24.1.1.2	21-1.1.2	26.1.1.2	20-1.1.2
23.3.7.2	15-3.7.2	24.1.2	21-1.2	26.1.2	20-1.2
23.3.7.3	15-3.7.3	24.1.2.1	21-1.2.1	26.1.2.1	20-1.2.1
23.3.7.4	15-3.7.4	24.1.2.2	21-1.2.2	26.1.2.2	20-1.2.2
23.3.7.5	15-3.7.5	24.1.2.3	21-1.2.2	26.1.2.3	20-1.2.2
23.3.7.6	15-3.7.6	24.1.3	21-1.3	26.1.3	20-1.3
23.3.7.7	15-3.7.7	24.1.4	21-1.4	26.1.4	20-1.4
23.3.7.8	15-3.7.8	24.1.5	21-1.5	26.1.5	20-1.5
23.3.7.9	15-3.7.9	24.1.6	21-1.6	26.1.6	20-1.6
23.3.8	15-3.8	24.1.7	21-1.7	26.1.7	20-1.7
23.4	15-4	24.2	21-2	26.2	20-2
23.4.1	15-4.1	24.2.1	21-2.1	26.2.1	20-2.1
23.4.1.1	15-4.1.1	24.2.2	21-2.2	26.2.1.1	20-2.1.1
23.4.1.2	15-4.1.2	24.2.2.1	21-2.2.1	26.2.1.2	20-2.1.2
23.4.2	15-4.2	24.2.2.2	21-2.2.2	26.2.1.3	20-2.1.3
23.4.3	15-4.3	24.2.2.3	21-2.2.3	26.2.2	20-2.2
23.5	15-5	24.2.2.4	21-2.2.4	26.2.3	20-2.3
23.5.1	15-5.1	24.2.3	21-2.3	26.2.4	20-2.4
23.5.1.1	15-5.1.1	24.2.4	21-2.4	26.2.5	20-2.5
23.5.1.2	15-5.1.2	24.2.4.1	21-2.4.1	26.2.6	20-2.6
23.5.2	15-5.2	24.2.4.2	21-2.4.2	26.2.7	20-2.7
23.5.2.1	15-5.2.1	24.2.4.3	21-2.4.3	26.2.8	20-2.8
23.5.2.2	15-5.2.2	24.2.4.4	21-2.4.4	26.3	20-3

2000 Edition	1997 Edition	2000 Edition	1997 Edition	2000 Edition	1997 Edition
26.3.1	20-3.1	28.2.2.2.4	16-2.2.2.4	28.3.4.3.2	16-3.4.3.2
26.3.1.1	20-3.1.1	28.2.2.3	16-2.2.3	28.3.4.3.3	16-3.4.3.3
26.3.1.2	20-3.1.2	28.2.2.4	16-2.2.4	28.3.4.3.4	16-3.4.3.4
26.3.2	20-3.2	28.2.2.5	16-2.2.5	28.3.4.3.5	16-3.4.3.5
26.3.2.1	20-3.2.1	28.2.2.6	16-2.2.6	28.3.4.4	16-3.4.4
26.3.2.2	20-3.2.2	28.2.2.7	16-2.2.7	28.3.4.5	16-3.4.4.2
26.3.2.3	20-3.2.3	28.2.2.8	New in 2000 —	28.3.5	16-3.5
26.3.3	20-3.3		Reserved	28.3.5.1	16-3.5.1
26.3.3.1	20-3.3.1	28.2.2.9	New in 2000 —	28.3.5.2	16-3.5.2
26.3.3.2	20-3.3.2		Reserved	28.3.5.3	16-3.5.3
26.3.3.3	20-3.3.3	28.2.2.10	16-2.2.8	28.3.5.4	16-3.5.4
26.3.3.4	New in 2000 —	28.2.2.11	16-2.2.9	28.3.5.5	16-3.5.5
	Reserved	28.2.2.12	16-2.2.10	28.3.6	16-3.6
26.3.3.5	20-3.3.4	28.2.3	16-2.3	28.3.6.1	16-3.6.1
26.3.4	20-3.4	28.2.3.1	16-2.3.1	28.3.6.2	16-3.6.2
26.3.5	20-3.5	28.2.3.2	16-2.3.2	28.3.6.3	16-3.6.3
26.3.5.1	20-3.5.1	28.2.3.3	16-2.3.3	28.3.6.4	16-3.6.4
26.3.5.2	20-3.5.2	28.2.4	16-2.4	28.3.6.5	16-3.6.5
26.4	20-4	28.2.5	16-2.5	28.3.7	16-3.7
26.5	20-5	28.2.5.1	16-2.5.1	28.3.8	16-3.8
26.5.1	20-5.1	28.2.5.2	16-2.5.2	28.4	16-4
26.5.2	20-5.2	28.2.5.3	16-2.5.3	28.4.1	16-4.1
26.5.2.1	20-5.2.1	28.2.5.4	16-2.5.4	28.5	16-5
26.5.2.2	20-5.2.2	28.2.6	16-2.6	28.5.1	16-5.1
26.5.3	20-5.3	28.2.6.1	16-2.6.1	28.5.2	16-5.2
Chapter 27	New in 2000 —	28.2.6.2	16-2.6.2	28.5.2.1	16-5.2.1
	Reserved	28.2.7	16-2.7	28.5.2.2	16-5.2.2
Chapter 28	Chapter 16	28.2.7.1	16-2.7.1	28.5.3	16-5.3
28.1	16-1	28.2.7.2	16-2.7.2	28.5.4	16-5.4
28.1.1	16-1.1	28.2.7.3	16-2.7.3	28.6	16-6
28.1.1.1	16-1.1	28.2.8	16-2.8	28.7	16-7
28.1.1.2	16-1.3 Hotels	28.2.9	16-2.9	28.7.1	16-7.1
28.1.2	16-1.2	28.2.10	16-2.10	28.7.1.1	16-7.1.1
28.1.2.1	16-1.2.1	28.2.11	16-2.11	28.7.1.2	16-7.1.2
28.1.2.2	16-1.2.2	28.3	16-3	28.7.2	16-7.2
28.1.2.3	16-1.2.2	28.3.1	16-3.1	28.7.3	16-7.3
28.1.3	16-1.3	28.3.1.1	16-3.1.1	28.7.4	16-7.4
28.1.4	16-1.4	28.3.1.2	16-3.1.2	28.7.4.1	16-7.4.1
28.1.5	16-1.5	28.3.2	16-3.2	28.7.4.2	16-7.4.2
28.1.6	16-1.6	28.3.2.1	16-3.2.1	Chapter 29	Chapter 17
28.1.7	16-1.7	28.3.2.2	16-3.2.2	29.1	17-1
28.2	16-2	28.3.3	16-3.3	29.1.1	17-1.1
28.2.1	16-2.1	28.3.3.1	16-3.3.1	29.1.1.1	17-1.1.1
28.2.2	16-2.2	28.3.3.2	16-3.3.2	29.1.1.2	17-1.3 Hotels
28.2.2.1	16-2.2.1	28.3.3.3	16-3.3.3	29.1.2	17-1.2
28.2.2.1.1	16-2.2.1.1	28.3.3.4	16-3.3.4	29.1.2.1	17-1.2.1
28.2.2.1.2	16-2.2.1.2	28.3.4	16-3.4	29.1.2.2	17-1.2.2
28.2.2.2	16-2.2.2	28.3.4.1	16-3.4.1	29.1.2.3	17-1.2.2
28.2.2.2.1	16-2.2.2.1	28.3.4.2	16-3.4.2	29.1.3	17-1.3
28.2.2.2.2	16-2.2.2.2	28.3.4.3	16-3.4.3	29.1.4	17-1.4
28.2.2.2.3	16-2.2.2.3	28.3.4.3.1	16-3.4.3.1	29.1.5	17-1.5

2000 Edition	1997 Edition	2000 Edition	1997 Edition	2000 Edition	1997 Edition
29.1.6	17-1.6	29.3.3.3	17-3.3.3	30.1.2	18-1.2
29.1.7	17-1.7	29.3.3.4	17-3.3.4	30.1.2.1	18-1.2.1
29.2	17-2	29.3.4	17-3.4	30.1.2.2	18-1.2.2
29.2.1	17-2.1	29.3.4.1	17-3.4.1	30.1.2.3	18-1.2.2
29.2.2	17-2.2	29.3.4.2	17-3.4.2	30.1.3	18-1.3
29.2.2.1.1	17-2.2.1.1	29.3.4.3	17-3.4.3	30.1.4	18-1.4
29.2.2.1.2	17-2.2.1.2	29.3.4.3.1	17-3.4.3.1	30.1.5	18-1.5
29.2.2.2	17-2.2.2	29.3.4.3.2	17-3.4.3.2	30.1.6	18-1.6
29.2.2.2.1	17-2.2.2.1	29.3.4.4	17-3.4.4	30.1.7	18-1.7
29.2.2.2.2	17-2.2.2.2	29.3.4.5	17-3.4.4.2	30.2	18-2
29.2.2.2.3	17-2.2.2.3	29.3.5	17-3.5	30.2.1	18.2.1
29.2.2.2.4	17-2.2.2.4	29.3.5.1	17-3.5.1	30.2.2	18-2.2
29.2.2.3	17-2.2.3	29.3.5.2	17-3.5.2	30.2.2.1	18-2.2.1
29.2.2.4	17-2.2.4	29.3.5.3	New in 2000 —	30.2.2.1.1	18-2.2.1.1
29.2.2.5	17-2.2.5		Reserved	30.2.2.1.2	18-2.2.1.2
29.2.2.6	17-2.2.6	29.3.5.4	New in 2000 —	30.2.2.2	18-2.2.2
29.2.2.7	17-2.2.7		Reserved	30.2.2.2.1	18-2.2.2.1
29.2.2.8	17-2.2.8	29.3.5.5	17-3.5.3	30.2.2.2.2	18-2.2.2.2
29.2.2.9	17-2.2.9	29.3.6	17-3.6	30.2.2.2.3	18-2.2.2.3
29.2.2.2.10	17-2.2.10	29.3.6.1	17-3.6.1	30.2.2.2.4	18-2.2.2.4
29.2.2.11	17-2.2.11	29.3.6.2	17-3.6.2	30.2.2.3	18-2.2.3
29.2.2.12	17-2.2.12	29.3.6.3	17-3.6.3	30.2.2.3.1	18-2.2.3.1
29.2.3	17-2.3	29.3.6.4	17-3.6.4	30.2.2.3.2	18-2.2.3.2
29.2.3.1	17-2.3.1	29.3.6.5	17-3.6.5	30.2.2.3.3	18-2.2.3.3
29.2.3.2	17-2.3.2	29.3.7	17-3.7	30.2.2.3.4	18-2.2.3.4
29.2.4	17-2.4	29.3.8	17-3.8	30.2.2.4	18-2.2.4
29.2.5	17-2.5	29.4	17-4	30.2.2.5	18-2.2.5
29.2.5.1	17-2.5.1	29.4.1	17-4.1	30.2.2.6	18-2.2.6
29.2.5.2	17-2.5.2	29.5	17-5	30.2.2.7	18-2.2.7
29.2.5.3	17-2.5.3	29.5.1	17-5.1	30.2.2.8	New in 2000 —
29.2.6	17-2.6	29.5.2	17-5.2		Reserved
29.2.6.1	17-2.6.1	29.5.2.1	17-5.2.1	30.2.2.9	New in 2000 —
29.2.6.2	17-2.6.2	29.5.2.2	17-5.2.2		Reserved
29.2.7	17-2.7	29.5.3	17-5.3	30.2.2.10	18-2.2.8
29.2.7.1	17-2.7.1	29.5.4	17-5.4	30.2.2.11	18-2.2.9
29.2.7.2	17-2.7.2	29.6	17-6	30.2.2.12	18-2.2.10
29.2.7.3	17-2.7.3	29.7	17-7	30.2.3	18-2.3
29.2.8	17-2.8	29.7.1	17-7.1	30.2.3.1	18-2.3.1
29.2.9	17-2.9	29.7.1.1	17-7.1.1	30.2.3.2	18-2.3.2
29.2.10	17-2.10	29.7.1.2	17-7.1.2	30.2.3.3	18-2.3.3
29.2.11	17-2.11	29.7.2	17-7.2	30.2.4	18-2.4
29.3	17-3	29.7.3	17-7.3	30.2.5	18-2.5
29.3.1	17-3.1	29.7.4	17-7.4	30.2.5.1	18-2.5.1
29.3.1.1	17-3.1.1	29.7.4.1	17-7.4.1	30.2.5.2	18-2.5.2
29.3.1.2	17-3.1.2	29.7.4.2	17-7.4.2	30.2.5.3	18-2.5.3
29.3.2	17-3.2	Chapter 30	Chapter 18	30.2.6	18-2.6
29.3.2.1	17-3.2.1	30.1	18-1	30.2.6.1	18-2.6.1
29.3.2.2	17-3.2.2	30.1.1	18-1.1	30.2.6.2	18-2.6.2
29.3.3	17-3.3	30.1.1.1	18-1.1	30.2.6.3	18-2.6.3
29.3.3.1	17-3.3.1	30.1.1.2	18-1.3 Apartment	30.2.7	18-2.7
29.3.3.2	17-3.3.2		Buildings	30.2.8	18-2.8

2000 Edition	1997 Edition	2000 Edition	1997 Edition	2000 Edition	1997 Edition
30.2.9	18-2.9	30.5.2.2	18-5.2.2	31.2.5	19-2.5
30.2.10	18-2.10	30.5.3	18-5.3	31.2.5.1	19-2.5.1
30.2.11	18-2.11	30.5.4	18-5.4	31.2.5.2	19-2.5.2
30.3	18-3	30.6	18-6	31.2.5.3	19-2.5.3
30.3.1	18-3.1	30.7	18-7	31.2.6	19-2.6
30.3.1.1	18-3.1.1	30.7.1	18-7.1	31.2.6.1	19-2.6.1
30.3.1.2	18-3.1.2	Chapter 31	Chapter 19	31.2.6.2	19-2.6.2
30.3.1.3	18-3.1.1 Exception	31.1	19-1	31.2.7	19-2.7
	No. 4	31.1.1	19-1	31.2.7.1	19-2.7.1
30.3.2	18-3.2	31.1.1.1	19-1.1	31.2.7.2	19-2.7.2
30.3.2.1	18-3.2.1	31.1.1.2	19-1.3 Apartment	31.2.7.3	19-2.7.3
30.3.3	18-3.3		Buildings	31.2.8	19-2.8
30.3.3.1	18-3.3.1	31.1.2	19-1.2	31.2.9	19-2.9
30.3.3.2	18-3.3.2	31.1.2.1	19-1.2.1	31.2.10	19-2.10
30.3.3.3	18-3.3.3	31.1.2.2	19-1.2.2	31.2.11	19-2.11
30.3.4	18-3.4	31.1.2.3	19-1.2.2	31.3	19-3
30.3.4.1	18-3.4.1	31.1.3	19-1.3	31.3.1	19-3.1
30.3.4.2	18-3.4.2	31.1.4	19-1.4	31.3.1.1	19-3.1.1
30.3.4.2.1	18-3.4.2.1	31.1.5	19-1.5	31.3.1.2	19-3.1.2
30.3.4.2.2	18-3.4.2.2	31.1.6	19-1.6	31.3.2	19-3.2
30.3.4.3	18-3.4.3	31.1.7	19-1.7	31.3.2.1	19-3.2.1
30.3.4.3.1	18-3.4.3.1	31.2	19-2	31.3.3	19-3.3
30.4.3.3.2	18-3.4.3.2	31.2.1	19-2.1	31.3.3.1	19-3.3.1
30.4.4	18-3.4.4	31.2.2	19-2.2	31.3.3.2	19-3.3.2
30.3.4.5	18-3.4.4	31.2.2.1	19-2.2.1	31.3.3.3	19-3.3.3
30.3.4.5.1	18-3.4.4.1	31.2.2.1.1	19-2.2.1.1	31.3.4	19-3.4
30.3.4.5.2	18-3.4.4.2	31.2.2.1.2	19-2.2.1.2	31.3.4.1	19-3.4.1
30.3.5	18-3.5	31.2.2.1.3	19-2.2.1.3	31.3.4.2	19-3.4.2
30.3.5.1	18-3.5.1	31.2.2.2	19-2.2.2	31.3.4.2.1	19-3.4.2.1
30.3.5.2	18-3.5.2	31.2.2.2.1	19-2.2.2.1	31.3.4.2.2	19-3.4.2.2
30.3.5.3	18-3.5.3	31.2.2.2.2	19-2.2.2.2	31.3.4.2.3	19-3.4.2.3
30.3.5.4	18-3.5.5	31.2.2.2.3	19-2.2.2.3	31.3.4.2.4	19-3.4.2.4
30.3.5.5	18-3.1.1 Exception	31.2.2.2.4	19-2.2.2.4	31.3.4.3	19-3.4.3
	No. 5	31.2.2.3	19-2.2.3	31.3.4.3.1	19-3.4.3.1
30.3.5.6	New in 2000 —	31.2.2.3.1	19-2.2.3.1	31.3.4.3.2	19-3.4.3.2
	Reserved	31.2.2.3.2	19-2.2.3.2	31.3.4.4	19-3.4.4.2
30.3.5.7	18-3.5.4	31.2.2.3.3	19-2.2.3.3	31.3.4.5	19-3.4.4
30.3.6	18-3.6	31.2.2.3.4	19-2.2.3.4	31.3.4.5.1	19-3.4.4.1
30.3.6.1	18-3.6.1	31.2.2.4	19-2.2.4	31.3.5	19-3.5
30.3.6.2	18-3.6.2	31.2.2.5	19-2.2.5	31.3.5.1	19-3.5.1
30.3.6.3	18-3.6.3	31.2.2.6	19-2.2.6	31.3.5.2	19-3.5.2
30.3.6.4	18-3.6.4	31.2.2.7	19-2.2.7	31.3.5.3	19-3.5.3
30.3.6.5	18-3.6.5	31.2.2.8	19-2.2.8	31.3.5.4	19-3.5.4
30.3.7	18-3.7	31.2.2.9	19-2.2.9	31.3.5.5	19-3.5.5
30.3.8	18-3.8	31.2.2.10	19-2.2.10	31.3.5.6	19-3.5.6
30.4	18-4	31.2.2.11	19-2.2.11	31.3.5.7	19-3.5.7
30.4.1	18-4.1	31.2.2.12	19-2.2.12	31.3.6	19-3.6
30.5	18-5	31.2.3	19-2.3	31.3.6.1	19-3.6.1
30.5.1	18-5.1	31.2.3.1	19-2.3.1	31.3.6.2	19-3.6.2
30.5.2	18-5.2	31.2.3.2	19-2.3.2	31.3.6.3	19-3.6.3
30.5.2.1	18-5.2.1	31.2.4	19-2.4	31.3.6.4	19-3.6.4

2000 Edition	1997 Edition	2000 Edition	1997 Edition	2000 Edition	1997 Edition
31.3.6.5	19-3.6.5	32.2.2.6	22-2.2.6	32.3.2	22-3.2
31.3.7	19-3.7	32.2.2.6.1	22-2.2.6.1	32.3.2.1	22-3.2.1
31.3.8	19-3.8	32.2.2.6.2	22-2.2.6.2	32.3.2.2	22-3.2.2
31.4	19-4	32.2.3	22-2.3	32.2.2.2.1	22-3.2.2.1
31.4.1	19-4.1	32.2.3.1	22-2.3.1	32.3.2.2.2	22-3.2.2.2
31.5	19-5	32.2.3.1.1	22-2.3.1.1	32.3.2.2.3	22-3.2.2.3
31.5.1	19-5.1	32.2.3.1.2	22-2.3.1.2	32.3.2.2.4	23-3.2.2.4
31.5.2	19-5.2	32.2.3.2	22-2.3.2	32.3.2.2.5	22-3.2.2.5
31.5.2.1	19-5.2.1	32.2.3.2.1	New in 2000	32.3.2.2.6	22-3.2.2.6
31.5.3	19-5.3	32.2.3.2.2	22-2.3.2.1	32.3.2.2.7	22-3.2.2.7
31.5.4	19-5.4	32.2.3.2.3	22-2.3.2.2	32.3.2.2.8	22-3.2.2.8
31.6	19-6	32.2.3.3	22-2.3.3	32.3.2.2.9	22-3.2.2.9
31.7	19-7	32.2.3.3.1	22-2.3.3.1	32.3.2.2.10	22-3.2.2.10
31.7.1	19-7.1	32.2.3.3.2	22-2.3.3.2	32.3.2.3	22-3.2.3
Chapter 32	Chapter 22	32.2.3.3.3	22-2.3.3.3	32.3.2.3.1	22-3.2.3.1
32.1	22-1	32.2.3.4	22-2.3.4	32.3.2.3.2	22-3.2.3.2
32.1.1	22-1.1	32.2.3.4.1	22-2.3.4.1	32.3.2.3.3	22-3.2.3.3
32.1.1.1	22-1.1.1	32.2.3.4.2	22-2.3.4.2	32.3.2.4	22-3.2.4
32.1.1.2	22-1.1.2	32.2.3.4.3	22-2.3.4.3	32.3.2.5	22-3.2.5
32.1.1.3	22-1.3 Conversion	32.2.3.4.3.1	22-2.3.4.3.1	32.3.2.5.1	22-3.2.5.1
32.1.2	22-1.2	32.2.3.4.3.2	22-2.3.4.3.2	32.3.2.5.2	22-3.2.5.2
32.1.2.1	22-1.2	32.2.3.5	22-2.3.5	32.3.2.5.3	22-3.2.5.3
32.1.2.2	New in 2000	32.2.3.5.1	22-2.3.5.1	32.3.2.5.4	22-3.2.5.4
32.1.2.3	New in 2000	32.2.3.5.2	22-2.3.5.2	32.3.2.6	22-3.2.6
32.1.3	22-1.3	32.2.3.5.3	New in 2000	32.3.2.6.1	22-3.2.6.1
32.1.4	22-1.4	32.2.3.5.4	22-2.3.5.3	32.3.2.6.2	22-3.2.6.2
32.1.5	22-1.5	32.2.3.5.5	22-2.3.5.4	32.3.2.7	22-3.2.7
32.1.6	New in 2000 — Reserved	32.2.3.6	22-2.3.6	32.3.2.8	22-3.2.8
		32.2.3.6.1	22-2.3.6.1	32.3.2.9	22-3.2.9
32.1.7	New in 2000 — Reserved	32.2.3.6.2	22-2.3.6.2	32.3.2.10	22-3.2.10
		32.2.3.6.3	22-2.3.6.3	32.3.2.11	22-3.2.11
32.2	22-2	32.2.3.6.4	22-2.3.6.4	32.3.3	22-3.3
32.2.1	22-2.1	32.2.4	22-2.4	32.3.3.1	22-3.3.1
32.2.1.1	22-2.1.1	32.2.5	22-2.5	32.3.3.1.1	22-3.3.1.1
32.2.1.2	22-2.1.2	32.2.5.1	22-2.5.1	32.3.3.1.2	22-3.3.1.2
32.2.1.2.1	22-2.1.2	32.2.5.2	22-2.5.2	32.3.3.2	22-3.3.2
32.2.1.2.2	New in 2000	32.2.5.2.1	22-2.5.2.1	32.3.3.2.1	22-3.3.2.1
32.2.1.3	22-2.1.3	32.2.5.2.2	22-2.5.2.2	32.3.3.2.2	22-3.3.2.2
32.2.2	22-2.2	32.2.5.2.3	22-2.5.2.3	32.3.3.3	22-3.3.3
32.2.2.1	22-2.2.1	32.2.5.3	22-2.5.3	32.3.3.3.1	22-3.3.3.1
32.2.2.2	22-2.2.2	32.3	22-3	32.3.3.3.2	22-3.3.3.2
32.2.2.3	22-2.2.3	32.3.1.1	22-3.1.1	32.3.3.3.3	22-3.3.3.3
32.2.2.4	22-2.2.4	32.3.1.2	22-3.1.2	32.3.3.4	22-3.3.4
32.2.2.5	22-2.2.5	32.3.1.2.1	22-3.1.2.1	32.3.3.4.1	22-3.3.4.1
32.2.2.5.1	22-2.2.5.1	32.3.1.2.2	22-3.1.2.2	32.3.3.4.2	22-3.3.4.2
32.2.2.5.2	22-2.2.5.2	32.3.1.2.3	23-3.1.2.3	32.3.3.4.3	22-3.3.4.3
32.2.2.5.3	22-2.2.5.3	32.3.1.3	22-3.1.3	32.3.3.4.4	22-3.3.4.4
32.2.2.5.4	22-2.2.5.4	32.3.1.3.1	22-3.1.3.1	32.3.3.4.5	22-3.3.4.5
32.2.2.5.5	22-2.2.5.5	32.3.1.3.2	22-3.1.3.2	32.3.3.4.6	22-3.3.4.6
32.2.2.5.6	22-2.2.5.6	32.3.1.3.3	22-3.1.3.3	32.3.3.4.7	22-3.3.4.7
32.2.2.5.7	22-2.2.5.7	32.3.1.4	22-3.1.4	32.3.3.4.8	22-3.3.4.8

2000 Edition	1997 Edition	2000 Edition	1997 Edition	2000 Edition	1997 Edition
32.3.3.5	22.3.3.5	32.7.5.1	22-7.5.1	33.2.3.2.1	New in 2000
32.3.3.5.1	22-3.3.5.1	32.7.5.2	22-7.5.2	33.2.3.2.2	23-2.3.2.1
32.3.3.5.2	New in 2000 — Reserved	32.7.5.3	22-7.5.3	33.2.3.2.3	23-2.3.2.2
		Chapter 33	Chapter 23	33.2.3.3	23-2.3.3
32.3.3.5.3	22-3.3.5.2	33.1	23-1	33.2.3.4	23-2.3.4
32.3.3.5.4	New in 2000 — Reserved	33.1.1	23-1.1	33.2.3.4.1	23-2.3.4.1
		33.1.1.1	23-1.1.1	33.2.3.4.2	23-2.3.4.2
32.3.3.5.5	22-3.3.5.3	33.1.1.2	23-1.1.2	33.2.3.4.3	23-2.3.4.3
32.3.3.6	22-3.3.6	33.1.1.3	23-1.3 Conversion	33.2.3.5	23-2.3.5
32.3.3.6.1	22-3.3.6.1	33.1.2	23-1.2	33.2.3.5.1	New in 2000 — Reserved
32.3.3.6.2	22-3.3.6.2	33.1.2.1	23-1.2		
32.3.3.6.3	22-3.3.6.3	33.1.2.2	New in 2000	33.2.3.5.2	23-2.3.5.1
32.3.3.6.4	22-3.3.6.4	33.1.2.3	New in 2000	33.2.3.5.3	23-2.3.5.2
32.3.3.6.5	22-3.3.6.5	33.1.3	23-1.3	33.2.3.5.4	New in 2000 — Reserved
32.3.3.6.6	22-3.3.6.6	33.1.4	23-1.4		
32.3.3.7	22-3.3.7	33.1.5	23-1.5	33.2.3.5.5	23-2.3.5.3
32.3.4	22-3.4	33.1.6	23-1.6	33.2.3.6	23-2.3.6
32.3.5	22-3.5	33.1.7	23-1.7	33.2.3.6.1	23-2.3.6.1
32.3.6	22-3.6	33.2	23-2	33.2.3.6.2	23-2.3.6.2
32.3.6.1	22-3.6.1	33.2.1	23-2.1	33.2.3.6.3	23-2.3.6.3
32.3.6.2	22-3.6.2	33.2.1.1	23-2.1.1	33.2.3.6.4	23-2.3.6.4
32.3.6.2.1	22-3.6.2.1	33.2.1.2	23-2.1.2	33.2.4	23-2.4
32.3.6.2.2	22-3.6.2.2	33.2.1.2.1	23-2.1.2	33.2.5	23-2.5
32.3.6.2.3	22-3.6.2.3	33.2.1.2.2	New in 2000	33.2.5.1	23-2.5.1
32.3.6.3	22-3.6.3	33.2.1.3	23-2.1.3	33.2.5.2	23-2.5.2
32.3.6.3.1	22-3.6.3.1	33.2.1.3.1	23-2.1.3.1	33.2.5.2.1	23-2.5.2.1
32.3.6.3.2	22-3.6.3.2	33.2.1.3.2	23-2.1.3.2	33.2.5.2.2	23-2.5.2.2
32.3.6.4	22-3.6.4	33.2.1.3.3	23-2.1.3.3	33.2.5.2.3	23-2.5.2.3
32.4	22-4	33.2.2	23-2.2	33.3	23-3
32.4.1	22-4.1	33.2.2.1	23-2.2.1	33.3.1	23-3.1
32.4.1.1	22-4.1.1	33.2.2.2	23-2.2.2	33.3.1.1	23-3.1.1
32.4.1.2	22-4.1.2	33.2.2.2.1	23-2.2.2.1	33.3.1.2	23-3.1.2
32.4.1.3	22-4.1.3	32.2.2.2.2	23-2.2.2.2	33.3.1.2.1	23-3.1.2.1
32.4.1.3.1	22-4.1.3.1	33.2.2.3	23-2.2.3	33.3.1.2.2	23-3.1.2.2
32.4.1.3.2	22-4.1.3.2	33.2.2.4	23-2.2.4	33.3.1.2.3	New in 2000
32.4.1.4	22-4.1.4	33.2.2.5	23-2.2.5	33.3.1.3	23-3.1.3
32.4.2	22-4.2	33.2.2.5.1	23-2.2.5.1	33.3.1.3.1	23-3.1.3.1
32.4.3	22-4.3	33.2.2.5.2	23-2.2.5.2	33.3.1.3.2	23-3.1.3.2
32.4.3.1	22-4.3.1	33.2.2.5.3	23-2.2.5.3	33.3.1.3.3	23-3.1.3.3
32.4.3.2	22-4.3.2	33.2.2.5.4	23-2.2.5.4	33.3.1.4	23-3.1.4
32.4.3.3	22-4.3.3	33.2.2.5.5	23-2.2.5.5	33.3.2	23-3.2
32.5	22-5	33.2.2.5.6	23-2.2.5.6	33.3.2.1	23-3.2.1
32.6	22-6	33.2.2.5.7	23-2.2.5.7	33.3.2.2	23-3.2.2
32.7	22-7	33.2.2.6	23-2.2.6	33.3.2.2.1	23-3.2.2.1
32.7.1	22-7.1	33.2.2.6.1	23-2.2.6.1	33.3.2.2.2	23-3.2.2.2
32.7.2	22-7.2	33.2.2.6.2	23-2.2.6.2	33.3.2.2.3	23-3.2.2.3
32.7.3	22-7.3	33.2.3	23-2.3	33.3.2.2.4	23-3.2.2.4
32.7.4	22-7.4	33.2.3.1	23-2.3.1	33.3.2.2.5	23-3.2.2.5
32.7.4.1	New in 2000	33.2.3.1.1	23-2.3.1.1	33.3.2.2.6	23-3.2.2.6
32.7.4.2	22-7.4	33.2.3.1.2	23-2.3.1.2	33.3.2.2.7	23-3.2.2.7
32.7.5	22-7.5	33.2.3.2	23-2.3.2	33.3.2.2.8	23-3.2.2.8

2000 Edition	1997 Edition	2000 Edition	1997 Edition	2000 Edition	1997 Edition
33.3.2.2.9	23-3.2.2.9	33.3.3.7	23-3.3.7	24/26/28/30/	24-1.2.2.1
33.3.2.2.10	23-3.2.2.10	33.3.4	23-3.4	32.1.2.2	
33.3.2.3	23-3.2.3	33.3.5	23-3.5	24/26/28/30/	24-1.2.2.2
33.3.2.3.1	23-3.2.3.1	33.3.6	23-3.6	32.1.2.3	
33.3.2.3.2	23-3.2.3.2	33.3.6.1	23-3.6.1	36.1.2.2	24-1.2.3
33.3.2.3.3	23-3.2.3.3	33.3.6.2	23-3.6.2	36.1.3	24-1.3
33.3.2.4	23-3.2.4	33.3.6.2.1	23-3.6.2.1	36.1.4	24-1.4
33.3.2.5	23-3.2.5	33.3.6.2.2	23-3.6.2.2	36.1.4.1	24-1.4.1
33.3.2.5.1	23-3.2.5.1	33.3.6.2.3	23-3.6.2.3	36.1.4.2	24-1.4.2
33.3.2.5.2	23-3.2.5.2	33.3.6.3	23-3.6.3	36.1.4.2.1	24-1.4.2.1
33.3.2.5.3	23-3.2.5.3	33.3.6.4	23-3.6.4	36.1.4.2.2	24-1.4.2.2
33.3.2.6	23-3.2.6	33.4	23-4	36.1.4.2.3	24-1.4.2.3
33.3.2.6.1	23-3.2.6.1	33.4.1	23-4.1	36.1.4.2.4	24-1.4.2.4
33.3.2.6.2	23-3.2.6.2	33.4.1.1	23-4.1.1	36.1.5	24-1.5
33.3.2.7	23-3.2.7	33.4.1.2	23-4.1.2	36.1.5.1	24-1.5
33.3.2.8	23-3.2.8	33.4.1.3	23-4.1.3	36.1.5.2	24-1.5
33.3.2.9	23-3.2.9	33.4.1.3.1	23-4.1.3.1	36.1.6	24-1.6
33.3.2.10	23-3.2.10	33.4.1.3.2	23-4.1.3.2	36.1.7	24-1.7
33.3.2.11	23-3.2.11	33.4.1.4	23-4.1.4	36.2	24-2
33.3.3	23-3.3	33.4.2	23-4.2	36.2.1	24-2.1
33.3.3.1	23-3.3.1	33.4.3	23-4.3	36.2.1.1	24-2.1.1
33.3.3.1.1	23-3.3.1.1	33.4.3.1	23-4.3.1	36.2.1.2	24-2.1.2
33.3.3.1.2	23-3.3.1.2	33.4.3.2	23-4.3.2	36.2.1.3	24-2.1.3
33.3.3.2	23-3.3.2	33.4.3.3	23-4.3.3	36.2.1.4	24-2.1.4
33.3.3.2.1	23-3.3.2.1	33.5	23-5	36.2.1.5	24-2.1.5
33.3.3.2.2	23-3.3.2.2	33.6	23-6	36.2.2	24-2.2
33.3.3.3	23-3.3	33.7	23-7	36.2.2.1	24-2.2.1
33.3.3.4	23-3.3.4	33.7.1	23-7.1	36.2.2.2	24-2.2.2
33.3.3.4.1	23-3.3.4.1	33.7.2	23-7.2	36.2.2.2.1	24-2.2.2.1
33.3.3.4.2	23-3.3.4.2	33.7.3	23-7.3	36.2.2.2.2	24-2.2.2.2
33.3.3.4.3	New in 2000 —	33.7.4	23-7.4	36.2.2.2.3	New in 2000 —
	Reserved	33.7.4.1	New in 2000		Reserved
33.3.3.4.4	23-3.3.4.3	33.7.4.2	23-7.4	36.2.2.2.4	24-2.2.2.3
33.3.3.4.5	New in 2000 —	33.7.5	23-7.5	36.2.2.2.5	24-2.2.2.4
	Reserved	33.7.5.1	23-7.5.1	36.2.2.2.6	24-2.2.2.5
33.3.3.4.6	23-3.3.4.4	33.7.5.2	23-7.5.2	36.2.2.2.7	24-2.2.2.6
33.3.3.4.7	23-3.3.4.5	33.7.5.3	23-7.5.3	36.2.2.2.8	24-2.2.2.7
33.3.3.4.8	23-3.3.4.6	Chapter 34	New in 2000 —	36.2.2.3	24-2.2.3
33.3.3.5	23-3.3.5		Reserved	36.2.2.3.1	24-2.2.3.1
33.3.3.5.1	23-23.3.5.1	Chapter 35	New in 2000 —	36.2.2.3.2	24-2.2.3.2
33.3.3.5.2	New in 2000		Reserved	36.2.2.4	24-2.2.4
33.3.3.5.3	New in 2000	Chapter 36	Chapter 24	36.2.2.5	24-2.2.5
33.3.3.5.4	23-3.3.5.2	36.1	24-1	36.2.2.6	24-2.2.6
33.3.3.5.5	23-3.3.5.3	36.1.1	24-1.1	36.2.2.7	24-2.2.7
33.3.3.6	23-3.3.6	36.1.1.1	24-1.1.1	36.2.2.8	New in 2000 —
33.3.3.6.1	23-3.3.6.1	36.1.1.2	24-1.1.2		Reserved
33.3.3.6.2	23-3.3.6.2	36.1.1.3	24-1.1.3	36.2.2.9	New in 2000 —
33.3.3.6.3	23-3.3.6.3	36.1.1.4	24-1.1.3		Reserved
33.3.3.6.4	23-3.3.6.4	36.1.2	24-1.2	36.2.2.10	24-2.2.8
33.3.3.6.5	23-3.3.6.5	36.1.2.1	24-1.2.1	36.2.2.11	24-2.2.9
33.3.3.6.6	23-3.3.6.6	Deleted	24-1.2.2	36.2.2.12	24-2.2.10

2000 Edition	1997 Edition
36.2.3	24-2.3
36.2.3.1	24-2.3.1
36.2.3.2	24-2.3.2
36.2.4	24-2.4
36.2.5	24-2.5
36.2.5.1	24-2.5.1
36.2.5.2	24-2.5.2
36.2.5.3	24-2.5.3
36.2.5.4	24-2.5.4
36.2.5.5	24-2.5.5
36.2.5.6	24-2.5.6
36.2.5.7	24-2.5.7
36.2.5.8	24-2.5.8
36.2.5.9	24-2.5.9
36.2.5.10	24-2.5.10
36.2.6	24-2.6
36.2.7	24-2.7
36.2.7.1	24-2.7.1
36.2.7.2	24-2.7.2
36.2.8	24-2.8
36.2.9	24-2.9
36.2.10	24-2.10
36.2.11	24-2.11
36.3	24-3
36.3.1	24-3.1
36.3.2	24-3.2
36.3.2.1	24-3.2.1
36.3.2.2	24-3.2.2
36.3.3	24-3.3
36.3.3.1	24-3.3.1
36.3.3.2	24-3.3.2
36.3.3.3	24-3.3.3
36.3.4	24-3.4
36.3.4.1	24-3.4.1
36.3.4.2	24-3.4.2
36.3.4.3	24-3.4.3
36.3.4.3.1	24-3.4.3.1
36.3.4.3.2	24-3.4.3.2
36.3.5	24-3.5
36.3.5.1	24-3.5.1
36.3.5.2	24-3.5.2
36.3.5.3	24-3.5.3
36.3.6	24-3.6
36.3.6.1	24-3.6.1
36.3.6.2	24-3.6.1.2
36.3.7	24-3.7
36.3.8	24-3.8
36.4	24-4
36.4.1	24-4.1
36.4.2	24-4.2
36.4.3	24-4.3

2000 Edition	1997 Edition
36.4.3.1	24-4.3.1
36.4.3.2	24-4.3.2
36.4.4	24-4.4
36.4.4.1	24-4.4.1
36.4.4.2	24-4.4.2
36.4.4.2.1	24-4.4.2.1
36.4.4.2.2	24-4.4.2.2
36.4.4.2.3	24-4.4.2.3
36.4.4.2.4	24-4.4.2.4
36.4.4.2.5	24-4.4.2.5
36.4.4.2.5	24-4.4.2.6
36.4.4.2.6	24-4.4.2.7
36.4.4.3	24-4.4.3
36.4.4.3.1	24-4.4.3.1
36.4.4.3.2	24-4.4.3.2
36.4.4.3.3	24-4.4.3.3
36.4.4.3.3.1	24-4.4.3.3.1
36.4.4.3.3.2	24-4.4.3.3.2
36.4.4.3.4	24-4.4.3.4
36.4.5	24-4.5
36.4.5.1	24-4.5.1
36.4.5.2	24-4.5.2
36.4.5.3	24-4.5.3
36.4.5.3.1	24-4.5.3.1
36.4.5.3.2	24-4.5.3.2
36.4.5.4	24-4.5.4
36.4.5.4.1	24-4.5.4.1
36.4.5.4.2	24-4.5.4.2
36.4.5.4.3	24-4.5.4.3
36.4.5.4.4	24-4.5.4.4
36.4.5.5	24-4.5.5
36.4.5.6	24-4.5.6
36.5	24-5
36.5.1	24-5.1
36.5.2	24-5.2
36.5.3	24-5.3
36.5.4	24-5.4
36.6	24-6
36.7	24-7
36.7.1	24-7.1
36.7.2	24-7.2
Chapter 37	Chapter 25
37.1	25-1
37.1.1	25-1.1
37.1.1.1	25-1.1.1
37.1.1.2	25-1.1.2
37.1.1.3	25-1.1.3
37.1.1.4	25-1.1.3
37.1.2	25-1.2
37.1.2.1	25-1.2.1
37.1.2.2	25-1.2.3

2000 Edition	1997 Edition
Deleted	25-1.2.2
24/26/29/31/33.1.2.2	25-1.2.2.1
24/26/29/31/33.1.2.3	25-1.2.2.2
24/26/29/31.1.2.3	25-1.2.2.3
37.1.3	25-1.3
37.1.4	25-1.4
37.1.4.1	25-1.4.1
37.1.4.2	25-1.4.2
37.1.4.2.1	25-1.4.2.1
37.1.4.2.2	25-1.4.2.2
37.1.4.2.3	25-1.4.2.3
37.1.4.2.4	25-1.4.2.4
37.1.5	25-1.5
37.1.5.1	25-1.5
37.1.5.2	25-1.5
37.1.6	25-1.6
37.1.7	25-1.7
37.2	25-2
37.2.1	25-2.1
37.2.1.1	25-2.1.1
37.2.1.2	25-2.1.2
37.2.1.3	25-2.1.3
37.2.1.4	25-2.1.4
37.2.1.5	25-2.1.5
37.2.2	25-2.2
37.2.2.1	25-2.2.1
37.2.2.2	25-2.2.2
37.2.2.2.1	25-2.2.2.1
37.2.2.2.2	25-2.2.2.2
37.2.2.2.3	25-2.2.2.3
37.2.2.2.4	25-2.2.2.4
37.2.2.2.5	25-2.2.2.5
37.2.2.2.6	25-2.2.2.6
37.2.2.2.7	25-2.2.2.7
37.2.2.2.8	25-2.2.2.8
37.2.2.2.9	25-2.2.2.9
37.2.2.3	25-2.2.3
37.2.2.3.1	25-2.2.3.1
37.2.2.3.2	25-2.2.3.2
37.2.2.3.3	25-2.2.3.3
37.2.2.4	25-2.2.4
37.2.2.5	25-2.2.5
37.2.2.6	25-2.2.6
37.2.2.7	25-2.2.7
37.2.2.8	25-2.2.8
37.2.2.9	25-2.2.9
37.2.2.10	25-2.2.10
37.2.2.11	25-2.2.11
37.2.2.12	25-2.2.12

2000 Edition	1997 Edition
37.2.3	25-2.3
37.2.3.1	25-2.3.1
37.2.3.2	25-2.3.2
37.2.4	25-2.4
37.2.5	25-2.5
37.2.5.1	25-2.5.1
37.2.5.2	25-2.5.2
37.2.5.3	25-2.5.3
37.2.5.4	25-2.5.4
37.2.5.5	25-2.5.5
37.2.5.6	25-2.5.6
37.2.5.7	25-2.5.7
37.2.5.8	25-2.5.8
37.2.5.9	25-2.5.9
37.2.5.10	25-2.5.10
37.2.6	25-2.6
37.2.7	25-2.7
37.2.7.1	25-2.7.1
37.2.7.2	25-2.7.2
37.2.8	25-2.8
37.2.9	25-2.9
37.2.10	25-2.10
37.2.11	25-2.11
37.3	25-3
37.3.1	25-3.1
37.3.2	25-3.2
37.3.2.1	25-3.2.1
37.3.2.2	25-3.2.2
37.3.3	25-3.3
37.3.3.1	25-3.3.1
37.3.3.2	25-3.3.2
37.3.3.3	25-3.3.3
37.3.4	25-3.4
37.3.4.1	25-3.4.1
37.3.4.3	25-3.4.3
37.3.4.3.1	25-3.4.3.1
37.3.4.3.2	25-3.4.3.2
37.3.5	25-3.5
37.3.5.1	25-3.5.1
37.3.5.2	New in 2000 — Reserved
37.3.5.3	25-3.5.2
37.3.6	25-3.6
37.3.7	25-3.7
37.3.8	25-3.8
37.4	25-4
37.4.1	25-4.1
37.4.2	25-4.2
37.4.3	25-4.3
37.4.3.1	25-4.3.1
37.4.3.2	25-4.3.2

2000 Edition	1997 Edition
37.4.4	25-4.4
37.4.4.1	25-4.4.1
37.4.4.2	25-4.4.2
37.4.4.2.1	25-4.4.2.1
37.4.4.2.2	25-4.4.2.2
37.4.4.2.3	25-4.4.2.3
37.4.4.2.4	25-4.4.2.4
37.4.4.2.5	25-4.4.2.5
37.4.4.2.5	25-4.4.2.6
37.4.4.2.6	25-4.4.2.7
37.4.4.3	25-4.4.3
37.4.4.3.1	25-4.4.3.1
37.4.4.3.2	25-4.4.3.2
37.4.4.3.3	25-4.4.3.3
37.4.4.3.3.1	25-4.4.3.3.1
37.4.4.3.3.2	25-4.4.3.3.2
37.4.4.3.4	25-4.4.3.4
37.4.5	25-4.5
37.4.5.1	25-4.5.1
37.4.5.2	25-4.5.2
37.4.5.3	25-4.5.3
37.4.5.3.1	25-4.5.3.1
37.4.5.3.2	25-4.5.3.2
37.4.5.4	25-4.5.4
37.4.5.4.1	25-4.5.4.1
37.4.5.4.2	25-4.5.4.2
37.4.5.4.3	25-4.5.4.3
37.4.5.4.4	25-4.5.4.4
37.4.5.5	25-4.5.5
37.4.5.6	25-4.5.6
37.5	25-5
37.5.1	25-5.1
37.5.2	25-5.2
37.5.3	25-5.3
37.5.4	25-5.4
37.6	25-6
37.7	25-7
37.7.1	25-7.1
37.7.2	25-7.2
Chapter 38	Chapter 26
38.1	26-1
38.1.1	26-1.1
38.1.1.1	26-1.1.1
38.1.1.2	26-1.1.2
38.1.1.3	26-1.1.3
38.1.2	26-1.2
38.1.2.1	26-1.2.1
Deleted	26-1.2.2
24/26/28/30/ 32.1.2.2	26-1.2.2.1

2000 Edition	1997 Edition
24/26/28/30/ 32.1.2.3	26-1.2.2.2
38.1.2.2	26-1.2.3
38.1.3	26-1.3
38.1.4	26-1.4
38.1.5	26-1.5
38.1.5.1	26-1.5.1
38.1.5.2	26-1.5.2
38.1.6	26-1.6
38.1.7	26-1.7
38.2	26-2
38.2.1	26-2.1
38.2.1.1	26-2.1.1
38.2.1.2	26-2.1.2
38.2.1.3	26-2.1.3
38.2.1.4	26-2.1.4
38.2.2	26-2.2
38.2.2.1	26-2.2.1
38.2.2.2	26-2.2.2
38.2.2.2.1	26-2.2.2.1
38.2.2.2.2	26-2.2.2.2
38.2.2.2.3	New in 2000 — Reserved
38.2.2.2.4	26-2.2.2.3
38.2.2.2.5	26-2.2.2.4
38.2.2.2.6	26-2.2.2.5
38.2.2.2.7	New in 2000 — Reserved
38.2.2.2.8	26-2.2.2.6
38.2.2.3	26-2.2.3
38.2.2.3.1	26-2.2.3.1
38.2.2.3.2	26-2.2.3.2
38.2.2.4	26-2.2.4
38.2.2.5	26-2.2.5
38.2.2.6	26-2.2.6
38.2.2.7	26-2.2.7
38.2.2.8	New in 2000 — Reserved
38.2.2.9	New in 2000 — Reserved
38.2.2.10	26-2.2.8
38.2.2.11	26-2.2.9
38.2.2.12	26-2.2.10
38.2.3	26-2.3
38.2.3.1	26-2.3.1
38.2.3.2	26-2.3.2
38.2.3.3	26-2.3.3
38.2.4	26-2.4
38.2.4.1	New in 2000 — Reserved
38.2.4.2	26-2.4
38.2.5	26-2.5

2000 Edition	1997 Edition	2000 Edition	1997 Edition	2000 Edition	1997 Edition
38.2.5.1	26-2.5.1	39.1.2	27-1.2	39.2.6	27-2.6
38.2.5.2	26-2.5.2	39.1.2.1	27-1.2.1	39.2.7	27-2.7
38.2.5.3	26-2.5.3	39.1.2.2	27-1.2.3	39.2.8	27-2.8
38.2.6	26-2.6	39.1.3	27-1.3	39.2.9	27-2.9
38.2.7	26-2.7	39.1.4	27-1.4	39.2.9.1	27-2.9.1
38.2.8	26-2.8	39.1.5	27-1.5	39.2.9.2	27-2.9.2
38.2.9	26-2.9	39.1.5.1	27-1.5.1	39.2.10	27-2.10
38.2.9.1	26-2.9.1	39.1.5.2	27-1.5.2	39.2.11	27-2.11
38.2.9.2	26-2.9.2	39.1.6	27-1.6	39.3	27-3
38.2.10	26-2.10	39.1.7	27-1.7	39.3.1	27-3.1
38.2.11	26-2.11	39.2	27-2	39.3.1.1	27-3.1.1
38.3	26-3	39.2.1	27-2.1	39.3.1.2	27-3.1.2
38.3.1	26-3.1	39.2.1.1	27-2.1.1	39.3.2	27-3.2
38.3.1.1	26-3.1.1	39.2.1.2	27-2.1.2	39.3.2.1	27-3.2.1
38.3.1.2	26-3.1.2	39.2.1.3	27-2.1.3	39.3.2.2	27-3.2.2
38.3.2	26-3.2	39.2.1.4	27-2.1.4	39.3.3	27-3.3
38.3.2.1	26-3.2.1	39.2.2	27-2.2	39.3.3.1	27-3.3.1
38.3.2.2	26-3.2.2	39.2.2.1	27-2.2.1	39.3.3.2	27-3.3.2
8.4.4	26-3.2.3	39.2.2.2	27-2.2.2	39.3.3.3	27-3.3.3
38.3.3	26-3.3	39.2.2.2.1	27-2.2.2.1	39.3.4	27-3.4
38.3.3.1	26-3.3.1	39.2.2.2.2	27-2.2.2.2	39.3.4.1	27-3.4.1
38.3.3.2	26-3.3.2	39.2.2.2.3	27-2.2.2.3	39.3.4.2	27-3.4.2
38.3.3.3	26-3.3.3	39.2.2.2.4	27-2.2.2.4	39.3.4.3	27-3.4.3
38.3.4	26-3.4	39.2.2.2.5	27-2.2.2.5	39.3.4.3	27-3.4.3.1
38.3.4.1	26-3.4.1	39.2.2.2.6	27-2.2.2.6	39.3.5	27-3.5
38.3.4.2	26-3.4.2	39.2.2.2.7	27-2.2.2.7	39.3.6	27-3.6
38.3.4.3	26-3.4.3	39.2.2.2.8	27-2.2.2.8	39.3.7	27-3.7
38.3.4.3	26-3.4.3.1	39.2.2.3	27-2.2.3	39.3.8	27-3.8
38.3.5	26-3.5	39.2.2.3.1	27-2.2.3.1	39.4	27-4
38.3.6	26-3.6	39.2.2.3.2	27-2.2.3.2	39.4.1	27-4.1
38.3.6.1	26-3.6.1	39.2.2.3.3	27-2.2.3.3	39.4.2	27-4.2
38.3.6.2	26-3.6.2	39.2.2.4	27-2.2.4	39.4.2.1	27-4.2.1
38.3.7	26-3.7	39.2.2.5	27-2.2.5	39.4.2.2	27-4.2.2
38.3.8	26-3.8	39.2.2.6	27-2.2.6	39.4.2.3	27-4.2.3
38.4	26-4	39.2.2.7	27-2.2.7	39.5	27-5
38.4.1	26-4.1	39.2.2.8	27-2.2.8	39.5.1	27-5.1
38.4.2	26-4.2	39.2.2.9	27-2.2.9	39.5.2	27-5.2
38.5	26-5	39.2.2.10	27-2.2.10	39.5.3	27-5.3
38.5.1	26-5.1	39.2.2.11	27-2.2.11	39.5.4	27-5.4
38.5.2	26-5.2	39.2.2.12	27-2.2.12	39.6	27-6
38.5.3	26-5.3	39.2.3	27-2.3	39.7	27-7
38.5.4	26-5.4	39.2.3.1	27-2.3.1	39.7.1	27-7.1
38.6	26-6	39.2.3.2	27.2.3.2	39.7.2	27-7.2
38.7	26-7	39.2.3.3	27-2.3.3	Chapter 40	Chapter 28
38.7.1	26-7.1	39.2.4	27-2.4	40.1	28-1
38.7.2	26-7.2	39.2.4.1	27-2.4.1	40.1.1	28-1.1
Chapter 39	Chapter 27	39.2.4.2	27-2.4.2	40.1.2	28-1.2
39.1	27-1	39.2.5	27-2.5	40.1.3	28-1.3
39.1.1	27-1.1	39.2.5.1	27-2.5.1	40.1.4	28-1.4
39.1.1.1	27-1.1.1	39.2.5.2	27-2.5.2	40.1.4.1	28-1.4.1
39.1.1.2	27-1.1.2	39.2.5.3	27-2.5.3	40.1.4.2	New in 2000

2000 Edition	1997 Edition	2000 Edition	1997 Edition	2000 Edition	1997 Edition
40.1.5	28-1.5	40.3	28-3	42.2.2.3	29-2.2.3
40.1.6	28-1.6	40.3.1	28-3.1	42.2.2.3.1	29-2.2.3.1
40.1.7	28-1.7	40.3.2	28-3.2	42.2.2.3.2	29-2.2.3.2
40.2	28-2	40.3.3	28-3.3	42.2.2.3.3	29-2.2.3.3
40.2.1	28-2.1	40.3.3.1	28-3.3.1	42.2.2.4	29-2.2.4
40.2.2	28-2.2	40.3.3.2	28-3.3.2	42.2.2.5	29-2.2.5
40.2.2.1	28-2.2.1	40.3.3.3	28-3.3.3	42.2.2.5.1	29-2.2.5.1
40.2.2.2	28-2.2.2	40.3.4	28-3.4	42.2.2.5.2	29-2.2.5.2
40.2.2.2.1	28-2.2.2.1	40.3.4.1	28-3.4.1	42.2.2.6	29-2.2.6
40.2.2.2.2	28-2.2.2.2	40.3.4.2	28-3.4.2	42.2.2.7	29-2.2.7
40.2.2.2.3	28-2.2.2.3	40.3.4.3	28-3.4.3	42.2.2.8	29-2.2.8
40.2.2.2.4	28-2.2.2.4	40.3.4.3.1	28-3.4.3.1	42.2.2.9	29-2.2.9
40.2.2.3	28-2.2.3	40.3.4.3.2	28-3.4.3.2	42.2.2.10	29-2.2.10
40.2.2.3.1	28-2.2.3.1	40.3.4.3.3	28-3.4.3.3	42.2.2.11	29-2.2.11
40.2.2.3.2	28-2.2.3.2	40.3.4.3.4	28-3.4.3.4	42.2.2.12	29-2.2.12
40.2.2.3.3	28-2.2.3.3	40.3.5	28-3.5	42.2.3	29-2.3
40.2.2.4	28-2.2.4	40.3.6	28-3.6	42.2.4	29-2.4
40.2.2.5	28-2.2.5	40.4	28-4	42.2.4.1	29-2.4.1
40.2.2.5.1	28-2.2.5.1	40.4.1	28-4.1	42.2.4.2	29-2.4.2
40.2.2.5.2	28-2.2.5.2	40.5	28-5	42.2.5	29-2.5
40.2.2.6	28-2.2.6	40.5.1	28-5.1	42.2.5.1	29-2.5.1
40.2.2.7	28-2.2.7	40.5.2	28-5.2	42.2.5.2	29-2.5.2
40.2.2.8	28-2.2.8	40.5.3	28-5.3	42.2.5.3	29-2.5.3
40.2.2.9	28-2.2.9	40.5.4	28-5.4	42.2.5.4	29-2.5.4
40.2.2.10	28-2.2.10	40.6	28-6	42.2.5.5	29-2.5.5
40.2.2.11	28-2.2.11	40.6.1	28-6.1	42.2.6	29-2.6
40.2.2.12	28-2.2.12	40.6.2	28-6.2	42.2.6.1	29-2.6 Exception No. 2
40.2.2.13	28-2.2.13	40.6.3	28-6.3	42.2.6.2	29-2.6
40.2.3	28-2.3	40.6.4	28-6.4	42.2.6.3	29-2.6 Exception No. 3
40.2.4	28-2.4	Chapter 41	New in 2000 — Reserved	42.2.7	29-2.7
40.2.4.1	28-2.4.1	Chapter 42	Chapter 29	42.2.8	29-2.8
40.2.4.2	28-2.4.2	42.1	29-1	42.2.9	29-2.9
40.2.4.3	28-2.4.3	42.1.1	29-1.1	42.2.10	29-2.10
40.2.5	28-2.5	42.1.2	29-1.2	42.2.11	29-2.11
40.2.5.1	28-2.5.1	42.1.3	29-1.3	42.3	29-3
40.2.5.2	28-2.5.2	42.1.4	29-1.4	42.3.1	29-3.1
40.2.5.3	28-2.5.3	42.1.4.1	29-1.4	42.3.2	29-3.2
40.2.5.4	28-2.5.4	42.1.4.2	29-1.4	42.3.3	29-3.3
40.2.5.5	28-2.5.5	42.1.5	29-1.5	42.3.3.1	29-3.3.1
40.2.5.5.1	28-2.5.5.1	42.1.6	29-1.6	42.3.3.2	29-3.3.2
40.2.5.5.2	28-2.5.5.2	42.1.7	29-1.7	42.3.3.3	29-3.3.3
40.2.5.6	28-2.5.6	42.2	29-2	42.3.4	29-3.4
40.2.6	28-2.6	42.2.1	29-2.1	42.3.4.1	29-3.4.1
40.2.6.1	28-2.6.1	42.2.2	29-2.2	42.3.4.2	29-3.4.2
40.2.6.2	28-2.6.2	42.2.2.1	29-2.2.1	42.3.4.3	29-3.4.3
40.2.6.3	28-2.6.3	42.2.2.2	29-2.2.2	42.3.4.3.1	29-3.4.3.1
40.2.7	28-2.7	42.2.2.2.1	29-2.2.2.1	42.3.4.3.2	29-3.4.3.3
40.2.8	28-2.8	42.2.2.2.2	29-2.2.2.2	42.3.4.3.3	29-3.4.3.2
40.2.9	28-2.9	42.2.2.2.3	29-2.2.2.3	42.3.4.3.4	29-3.4.3.4
40.2.10	28-2.10	42.2.2.2.4	29-2.2.2.4		
40.2.11	28-2.11				

2000 Edition	1997 Edition
42.3.5	29-3.5
42.3.6	29-3.6
42.4	29-4
42.4.1	29-4.1
42.5	29-5
42.5.1	29-5.1
42.5.2	29-5.2
42.5.3	29-5.3
42.5.4	29-5.4
42.6	29-6
42.6.1	29-6.1
42.6.2	29-6.2
42.6.3	29-6.3
42.6.4	29-6.4
42.7	29-7
42.7.1	29-7.1
42.7.2	29-7.2
42.7.3	29-7.3
42.7.4	29-7.4
42.7.4.1	29-7.4.1
42.7.4.2	29-7.4.2
42.8	29-8
42.8.1	29-8.1
42.8.1.1	29-8.1.1
42.8.1.2	29-8.1.2
42.8.1.2.1	29-8.1.2.1
42.8.1.2.2	29-8.1.2.2
42.8.1.3	29-8.1.3
42.8.1.4	29-8.1.4

2000 Edition	1997 Edition
42.8.1.5	29-8.1.5
42.8.1.6	29-8.1.6
42.8.1.7	29-8.1.7
42.8.2	29-8.2
42.8.2.1	29-8.2.1
42.8.2.2	29-8.2.2
42.8.2.2.1	29-8.2.2.1
42.8.2.2.2	29-8.2.2.2
42.8.2.2.2.1	29-8.2.2.2.1
42.8.2.2.2.2	29-8.2.2.2.2
42.8.2.2.2.3	29-8.2.2.2.3
42.8.2.2.3	29-8.2.2.3
42.8.2.2.3.1	29-8.2.2.3.1
42.8.2.2.3.2	29-8.2.2.3.2
42.8.2.2.3.3	29-8.2.2.3.3
42.8.2.2.4	29-8.2.2.4
42.8.2.2.5	29-8.2.2.5
42.8.2.2.6	29-8.2.2.6
42.8.2.2.6.1	29-8.2.2.6
42.8.2.2.6.2	29-8.2.2.6.1
42.8.2.2.7	29-8.2.2.7
42.8.2.2.8	29-8.2.2.8
42.8.2.2.9	29-8.2.2.9
42.8.2.3	29-8.2.3
42.8.2.4	29-8.2.4
42.8.2.4.1	29-8.2.4.1
42.8.2.4.2	29-8.2.4.2
42.8.2.5	29-8.2.5
42.8.2.5.1	29-8.2.5.1
42.8.2.5.2	29-8.2.5.2

2000 Edition	1997 Edition
42.8.2.5.3	29-8.2.5.3
42.8.2.6	29-8.2.6
42.8.2.7	29-8.2.7
42.8.2.8	29-8.2.8
42.8.2.9	29-8.2.9
42.8.2.10	29-8.2.10
42.8.2.11	29-8.2.11
42.8.3	29-8.3
42.8.3.1	29-8.3.1
42.8.3.2	29-8.3.2
42.8.3.3	29-8.3.3
42.8.3.3.1	29-8.3.3.1
42.8.3.3.2	29-8.3.3.2
42.8.3.3.3	29-8.3.3.3
42.8.3.4	29-8.3.4
42.8.3.4.1	29-8.3.4.1
42.8.3.4.2	29-8.3.4.2
42.8.3.4.3	29-8.3.4.3
42.8.3.4.3.1	29-8.3.4.3.1
42.8.3.4.3.2	29-8.3.4.3.3
42.8.3.4.3.3	29-8.3.4.3.2
42.8.3.5	29-8.3.5
42.8.3.6	29-8.3.6
42.8.4	29-8.4
42.8.4.1	29-8.4.1
42.8.5	29-8.5
42.8.5.1	29-8.5.1
42.8.5.2	29-8.5.2
42.8.5.3	29-8.5.3
42.8.5.4	29-8.5.4

Code Index

Common path of travel, A.7.5.1.6, Table
  A.7.6.1
  Definition, 3.3.32, A.3.3.32
Communicating spaces, 8.2.5.5,
  A.8.2.5.5(7)
Communication systems, 9.6, A.9.6
  Areas of refuge, 7.2.12.2.5
  Bulk merchandising retail buildings,
    36.4.5.4, 37.4.5.4
  Covered mall buildings, 36.4.4.3, 37.4.4.3
  Elevators, 7.2.13.8, A.7.2.13.8
  Emergency control, A.9.6.5.4
  Existing ambulatory health care occupancies, 21.3.4
  Existing apartment buildings, 31.3.4
  Existing assembly occupancies, 13.3.4,
    A.13.3.4.2.2
  Existing business occupancies, 39.3.4
  Existing day-care homes, 17.6.3.4
  Existing day-care occupancies, 17.3.4
  Existing detention and correctional occupancies, 23.3.4, A.23.3.4
  Existing educational occupancies, 15.3.4
  Existing health care occupancies, 19.3.4
  Existing hotels and dormitories, 29.3.4,
    A.29.3.4
  Existing mercantile occupancies, 37.3.4,
    37.4.4.3, 37.4.5.4
  Existing residential board and care occupancies, 33.2.3.4, 33.3.3.4
  High-rise buildings, 11.8.3, A.11.8.3.1
  Industrial occupancies, 40.3.4
  Lodging houses, 26.3.3, A.26.3.3.3
  New ambulatory health care occupancies,
    20.3.4
  New apartment buildings, 30.3.4,
    A.30.4.5.1
  New assembly occupancies, 12.3.4,
    A.12.3.4.2.2
  New business occupancies, 38.3.4
  New day-care homes, 16.6.3.4
  New day-care occupancies, 16.3.4
  New detention and correctional occupancies, 22.3.4, 22.4.4.9, A.22.3.4
  New educational occupancies, 14.3.4
  New health care occupancies, 18.3.4,
    A.18.3.4
  New hotels and dormitories, 28.3.4
  New mercantile occupancies, 36.3.4,
    36.4.4.3, 36.4.5.4
  New residential board and care occupancies, 32.2.3.4, 32.3.3.4
  One- and two-family dwellings, 24.3.4
  Parking structures, 42.8.3.4
  Rooming houses, 26.3.3, A.26.3.3.3
  Special structures, 11.2.3.4, 11.3.3.4,
    11.4.3.4
  Storage occupancies, 42.3.4
Compartmentation, 8.2.2, 8.2.5.1, A.8.2.2
Concealed spaces, 8.2.7, A.8.2.7.1

Construction; *see also* Corridor wall construction
  Apartment buildings as board and care occupancies, 32.4.1.4, 33.4.1.4
  Existing ambulatory health care occupancies, 21.1.6, 21.7.9
  Existing assembly occupancies, 13.1.6
  Existing day-care homes, 17.6.1.6
  Existing day-care occupancies, 17.1.6
  Existing detention and correctional occupancies, 23.1.6
  Existing health care occupancies,
    19.1.1.4.6, 19.1.6, 19.7.9, A.19.1.6.2,
    A.19.1.6.3
  Existing residential board and care occupancies, 33.2.1.3, 33.3.1.3, 33.4.1.4
  Fire escape ladders, 7.2.9.2
  Fire protection features, 8.2.1, A.8.2.1
  New ambulatory health care occupancies,
    20.1.1.4.6, 20.1.6, 20.7.9
  New assembly occupancies, 12.1.6
  New day-care homes, 16.6.1.6
  New day-care occupancies, 16.1.6
  New detention and correctional occupancies, 22.1.6, 22.4.4.2
  New educational occupancies, 14.1.6
  New health care occupancies, 18.1.1.4.6,
    18.1.6, 18.7.9
  New mercantile occupancies, 36.4.5.1
  New residential board and care occupancies, 32.3.1.3, 32.4.1.4
  Operations, 4.6.10, A.4.6.10
  Platforms, 12.4.5.2
  Ramps, 7.2.5.3.1
  Stages, 12.4.5.3
  Stairs, 7.2.2.3.1
Contained, Use Condition V
  Existing detention and correctional occupancies, 23.1.4.1(e), A.23.1.4.1
  New detention and correctional occupancies, 22.1.4.1(e), A.22.1.4.1
Contents, 10.3, A.10.3; *see also* Furnishings;
  Hazard of contents
  Definition, 3.3.33
Control systems; *see* Emergency control
Conversions
  Existing ambulatory health care occupancies, 21.1.1.4.4
  Existing day-care occupancies, 17.1.4.3,
    17.6.1.4.2, A.17.1.4.3, A.17.6.1.4.2
  Existing health care occupancies,
    19.1.1.4.4
  Existing residential board and care occupancies, 33.1.1.3
  New ambulatory health care occupancies,
    20.1.1.4.4
  New day-care occupancies, 16.1.4.3,
    16.6.1.4.2, A.16.1.4.3, A.16.6.1.4.2
  New health care occupancies, 18.1.1.4.4
  New residential board and care occupancies, 32.1.1.3

Conveyors, 9.4.7
  Ambulatory health care occupancies,
    20.5.3, 21.5.3
  Apartment buildings, 30.5.3, 31.5.3
  Assembly occupancies, 12.5.3, 13.5.3
  Business occupancies, 38.5.3, 39.5.3
  Day-care occupancies, 16.5.3, 17.5.3
  Detention and correctional occupancies,
    22.5.3, 23.5.3
  Educational occupancies, 14.5.3, 15.5.3
  Health care occupancies, 18.5.3, 19.5.3
  Hotels and dormitories, 28.5.3, 29.5.3,
    A.28.5.3
  Industrial occupancies, 40.5.3
  Lodging houses, 26.5.3
  Mercantile occupancies, 36.5.3, 37.5.3
  Parking structures, 42.8.5.3
  Residential board and care occupancies,
    32.2.5.3, 32.3.6.3, 33.3.6.3
  Rooming houses, 26.5.3
  Storage occupancies, 42.5.3
Cooking equipment/facilities, 9.2.3
  Exhibits, 12.7.4.3.9, 13.7.4.3.9
  Existing assembly occupancies, 13.7.1,
    13.7.4.3.9, A.13.7.1.4(5)
  Existing health care occupancies, 19.3.2.6,
    A.19.3.2.6
  New assembly occupancies, 12.7.1.4,
    12.7.4.3.9, A.12.7.1.4(5)
  New health care occupancies, 18.3.2.6,
    A.18.3.2.6
  Portable, 12.7.1.4, 12.7.4.3.9, 13.7.1.4,
    13.7.4.3.9, A.12.7.1.4(5),
    A.13.7.1.4(5)
Correctional occupancies; *see* Detention
  and correctional occupancies
Corridor doors
  Existing apartment buildings, 31.3.6.2 to
    31.3.6.5
  Existing health care occupancies, 19.3.6.3,
    A.19.3.6.3
  Existing hotels and dormitories, 29.3.6.2
    to 29.3.6.5
  New apartment buildings, 30.3.6.2 to
    30.3.6.5
  New health care occupancies, 18.3.6.3,
    A.18.3.6.3
  New hotels and dormitories, 28.3.6.2 to
    28.3.6.5
Corridor wall construction
  Apartment buildings as board and care occupancies, 32.4.3.2, 33.4.3.2
  Existing health care occupancies, 19.3.6.2,
    A.19.3.6.2
  Existing residential board and care occupancies, 33.2.3.6, 33.4.3.2
  New health care occupancies, 18.3.6.2,
    A.18.3.6.2
  New residential board and care occupancies, 32.2.3.6, 32.4.3.2

Parking structures, 42.8.3.4

Rooming houses, 26.3.3, A.26.3.3.3

Special structures, 11.2.3.4, 11.3.3.4, 11.4.3.4

Storage occupancies, 42.3.4

Detention and correctional occupancies;
see also Existing detention and correctional occupancies; New detention and correctional occupancies

Classification of occupancy, 6.1.7, 22.1.4, 23.1.4, A.6.1.7.1 to A.6.1.7.2

Crowd control, A.4.1.2

Definition, 3.3.134.5, 6.1.7.1, A.3.3.134.5, A.6.1.7.1

Nonresidential uses, 6.1.7.2, A.6.1.7.2

Directional signs and indicators, 7.10.2, 7.10.6.2, A.7.10.2, A.10.7.10.6.2

Discharge from exits; *see* Exit discharge

Doors; *see also* Corridor doors; Smoke barriers

Alarm devices, 7.2.1.5, A.7.2.1.5

Balanced, 7.2.1.13

Egress width, 7.2.1.2, A.7.2.1.2 to A.7.2.1.2.2

Elevator lobby; *see* Elevator lobby door

Elevators, 7.4.1.5

Existing ambulatory health care occupancies, 21.2.2.2 to 21.2.2.4, 21.2.3.3, 21.3.7.1, 21.3.7.6 to 21.3.7.7, A.21.3.7.6

Existing apartment buildings, 31.2.2.2, 31.3.6.2 to 31.3.6.5

Existing assembly occupancies, 13.2.2.2

Existing business occupancies, 39.2.2.2, A.39.2.2.2.2

Existing day-care occupancies, 17.2.2.2, A.17.2.2.2.4

Existing detention and correctional occupancies, 23.2.2.2, 23.2.11.1 to 23.2.11.7, 23.3.7.1 Ex. 2, 23.3.7.6 to 23.3.7.7, A.23.2.11.3, A.23.2.11.6, A.23.3.7.1 Ex. 2

Existing educational occupancies, 15.2.2.2, 15.2.5.4 to 15.2.5.5, 15.3.7.3

Existing health care occupancies, 19.2.2.2, 19.2.2.5.3 to 19.2.2.5.4, 19.3.6.3, 19.3.7.5 to 19.3.7.7, 19.3.8, A.19.2.2.2.4, A.19.2.2.2.6, A.19.2.2.2.8, A.19.3.6.3, A.19.3.7.6

Existing hotels and dormitories, 29.2.2.2, 29.3.6.2

Existing mercantile occupancies, 37.2.2.2, A.37.2.2.2.2

Existing residential board and care occupancies, 33.2.2.5, 33.2.3.6, 33.3.2.2.2, 33.3.3.6.4 to 33.3.3.6.6

Exit discharge, 7.7.4

In fire barriers, 8.2.3.2.1, 8.2.3.2.3.1(3) Ex., A.8.2.3.2.1(a), A.8.2.3.2.3

Floor/threshold level, 7.2.1.3

Folding partitions, 7.2.1.12

General, 7.2.1.1, A.7.2.1.1.3

Horizontal exits, 7.2.4.3.5 to 7.2.4.3.8, A.7.2.4.3.7 to A.7.2.4.3.8

Industrial occupancies, 40.2.2.2

Locks/latches, 7.2.1.5 to 7.2.1.6, A.7.1.2.5 to A.7.2.1.6

Lodging or rooming houses, 26.2.3 to 26.2.8

Mirrors on exit doors, 7.1.10.2.3, 7.5.2.2

New ambulatory health care facilities, 20.3.7.1, 20.3.7.6 to 20.3.7.7, A.20.3.7.6

New ambulatory health care occupancies, 20.2.2.2 to 20.2.2.4, 20.2.3.3, 20.3.7.1

New apartment buildings, 30.2.2.2, 30.3.6.2 to 30.3.6.5, A.30.2.2.2.2

New assembly occupancies, 12.2.2.2

New business occupancies, 38.2.2.2, A.38.2.2.2.2

New day-care occupancies, 16.2.2.2, A.16.2.2.2.4

New detention and correctional occupancies, 22.2.2.2, 22.2.11.1 to 22.2.11.10, 22.3.7.1 Ex. 2, 22.3.7.6 to 22.3.7.7, A.22.2.11.3, A.22.2.11.6, A.22.3.7.1 Ex. 2

New educational occupancies, 14.2.2.2, 14.2.5.4 to 14.2.5.5

New health care occupancies, 18.2.2.2, 18.2.2.5.3, 18.3.6.3, 18.3.8, A.18.2.2.2.4, A.18.2.2.2.6, A.18.3.6.3, A.18.3.8

New hotels and dormitories, 28.2.2.2

New mercantile occupancies, 36.2.2.2, A.36.2.2.2.2

New residential board and care occupancies, 32.2.2.5, 32.3.2.2.2, 32.3.3.6.4 to 32.3.3.6.6

One- and two-family dwellings, 24.2.2.3, 24.2.4, A.24.2.4.6

Panic hardware/fire exit hardware, 7.2.1.7

Parking structures, 42.8.2.2.2

Performance-based design option, 5.3.2(3)

Powered, 7.2.1.9, A.7.2.1.9

Revolving, 7.2.1.10, 12.2.2.2.6, 13.2.2.2.6

Screen/storm, 7.2.1.4.6

Self-closing devices, 7.2.1.8, 7.2.1.9.2, 8.2.3.2.1(b), A.7.2.1.8.1

Sliding horizontal, 7.2.1.14

Smoke partitions, 8.2.4.3, A.8.2.4.3.4

Smokeproof enclosures, door closure, 7.2.3.11

Storage occupancies, 42.2.2.2

Swing/force to open, 7.2.1.4, 7.2.4.3.6, A.7.2.1.4

Turnstiles, 7.2.1.11

Dormitories; *see* Hotels and dormitories

Draft stop, 8.2.7.2

Definition, 3.3.47

Drills; *see* Fire exit drills

Ducts, smoke dampers in, 8.3.5.2

Dumbwaiters, 9.4.2 to 9.4.3, 9.4.7, 32.3.6.3, 33.3.6.3

Dwelling unit (definition), 3.3.48

-E-

Earthquake protection, elevators, 7.2.13.11

Educational occupancies; *see also* Existing educational occupancies; New educational occupancies

Classification of occupancy, 6.1.3, 14.1.4, 15.1.4, A.6.1.3.1

Definition, 3.3.134.6, 6.1.3.1, A.3.3.134.6, A.6.1.3.1

Incidental instruction, 6-1.3.3

Egress; *see* Means of egress

Electrical energy systems, stored, 9.1.4

Electrical systems, essential, 20.2.9, 21.2.9

Electrical wiring and equipment, 9.1.2

Electroluminescent (definition), 3.3.50, A.3.3.50

Elevated platforms, 7.2.11.1(3)

Elevator lobby, 7.2.13.3, 7.4.1.6

Definition, 3.3.52

Elevator lobby doors, 7.2.13.4 to 7.2.13.5

Definition, 3.3.53

Elevator machine rooms, 9.4.5, A.9.4.5

Elevators, 9.4; *see also* Bulk storage elevators; Grain storage elevators; Vertical openings

Accessible means of egress, 7.5.4.5, 7.5.4.7

Ambulatory health care occupancies, 20.5.3, 21.5.3

Apartment buildings, 30.5.3, 31.5.3

Areas of refuge, 7.2.12.2, 7.2.12.2.2, 7.2.12.2.4, A.7.2.12.2

Assembly occupancies, 12.5.3, 13.5.3

Business occupancies, 38.5.3, 39.5.3

Capacity, evacuation system, 7.2.13.2

Communication systems, 7.2.13.8, A.7.2.13.8

Day-care occupancies, 16.5.3, 17.5.3

Detention and correctional occupancies, 22.5.3, 23.5.3

Doors, 7.4.1.5

Earthquake protection, 7.2.13.11

Educational occupancies, 14.5.3, 15.5.3

Evacuation system (definition), 3.3.51

Health care occupancies, 18.5.3, 19.5.3

Hoistway enclosures

Fire barrier walls, 8.2.5.2, A.8.2.5.2

Number of hoistways, 8.2.5.9

Hotels and dormitories, 28.5.3, 29.5.3, A.28.5.3

Industrial occupancies, 40.5.3

Lodging houses, 26.5.3

Maintenance, 7.2.13.10

Means of egress, use as, 7.2.13, 9.4.1, A.7.2.13, A.9.4.1

Mercantile occupancies, 36.5.3, 37.5.3

Operation, 7.2.13.9, A.7.2.13.9
Parking structures, 42.8.5.3
Power and control wiring, 7.2.13.7,
A.7.2.13.7
Residential board and care occupancies,
32.2.5.3, 32.3.6.3, 33.3.6.3,
A.32.3.6.3.2
Rooming houses, 26.5.3
Service openings, closing devices for,
8.2.5.10
Signs, 7.10.8.2, A.7.10.8.2
Special structures, 11.3.2.2.2
Storage occupancies, 42.5.3
Water protection, 7.2.13.6, A.7.2.13.6
Emergency access openings (definition),
3.3.54
Emergency control, 9.6.1.9(c), 9.6.5,
A.9.6.5.4
Ambulatory health care occupancies,
20.3.4.5
Covered mall buildings, 37.4.4.3.4
Existing ambulatory health care occupan-
cies, 21.3.4.5
Health care occupancies, 18.3.4.4, 19.3.4.4
Location of controls, 9.6.6
Mercantile occupancies, 36.4.4.3.4,
37.4.4.3.4
Emergency forces notification, 9.6.4
Covered mall buildings, 36.4.4.3.3.2,
37.4.4.3.3.2
Existing ambulatory health care occupan-
cies, 21.3.4.4
Existing day-care occupancies, 17.3.4.4
Existing detention and correctional occu-
pancies, 23.3.4.3.2
Existing educational occupancies,
15.3.4.3.2
Existing health care occupancies,
19.3.4.3.2
Existing mercantile occupancies,
37.3.4.3.2, 37.4.5.4.4
Existing residential board and care occu-
pancies, 33.3.3.4.6, A.33.3.3.4.6
New ambulatory health care occupancies,
20.3.4.4
New day-care occupancies, 16.3.4.4
New detention and correctional occupan-
cies, 22.3.4.3.2
New educational occupancies, 14.3.4.3.2
New health care occupancies, 18.3.4.3.2
New hotels and dormitories, 28.3.4.3.5,
A.28.3.4.3.5
New mercantile occupancies, 36.3.4.3.2,
36.4.4.3.3.2, 36.4.5.4.4
New residential board and care occupan-
cies, 32.3.3.4.6, A.32.3.3.4.6
Emergency generators, 9.1.3
**Emergency instructions for guests/resi-
dents**
Existing apartment buildings, 31.7.1

Existing hotels and dormitories, 29.7.4,
A.29.7.4
New apartment buildings, 30.7.1
New hotels and dormitories, 28.7.4,
A.28.7.4
Emergency lighting, 7.9, A.7.9
Covered mall buildings, 36.2.9, 37.4.4.2.6
Existing ambulatory health care occupan-
cies, 21.2.9
Existing apartment buildings, 31.2.9
Existing assembly occupancies, 13.2.9
Existing business occupancies, 39.2.9
Existing day-care occupancies, 17.2.9
Existing detention and correctional occu-
pancies, 23.2.9
Existing educational occupancies, 15.2.9
Existing health care occupancies, 19.2.9
Existing hotels and dormitories, 29.2.9
Existing mercantile occupancies, 37.2.9,
37.4.4.2.6
Existing residential board and care occu-
pancies, 33.3.2.9
Exit signs, 7.10.4, 7.10.9.2, A.7.10.4
High-rise buildings, 11.8.4, A.11.8.4.2
Industrial occupancies, 40.2.9, A.40.2.9
New ambulatory health care occupancies,
20.2.9
New apartment buildings, 30.2.9
New business occupancies, 38.2.9
New day-care occupancies, 16.2.9
New detention and correctional occupan-
cies, 22.2.9
New educational occupancies, 14.2.9
New health care occupancies, 18.2.9
New hotels and dormitories, 28.2.9
New mercantile occupancies, 36.2.9
New residential board and care occupan-
cies, 32.3.2.9
Parking structures, 42.8.2.9
Performance, 7.9.2, A.7.9.2
Performance-based design option,
5.3.2(11)
Special structures, 11.2.2.9, 11.3.2.9,
11.4.2.9
Storage occupancies, 42.2.9
Testing, periodic, 7.9.3, 7.10.9.2
**Emergency organization, hotels and dor-
mitories,** 28.7.1, 29.7.1, A.28.7.1,
A.29.7.1
Emergency plans
Bulk merchandising retail buildings,
36.4.5.6, 37.4.5.6
Existing ambulatory health care occupan-
cies, 21.7.1.1, 21.7.2.1 to 21.7.2.2,
A.21.7.2.1
Existing day-care occupancies, 17.7.1
Existing detention and correctional occu-
pancies, 23.7.1.3
Existing health care occupancies, 19.7.1.1,
19.7.2.1 to 19.7.2.2

Existing residential board and care occu-
pancies, 33.7.1
New ambulatory health care occupancies,
20.7.1.1, 20.7.2.1 to 20.7.2.2,
A.20.7.2.1
New day-care occupancies, 16.7.1
New detention and correctional occupan-
cies, 22.7.1.3
New health care occupancies, 18.7.1.1,
18.7.2.1 to 18.7.2.2
New residential board and care occupan-
cies, 32.7.1
Emergency response personnel, 5.4.6
Enclosed courts; *see* Courts
Enclosures; *see also* Smokeproof enclosures
Elevator hoistway
Fire barrier walls, 8.2.5.2, A.8.2.5.2
Number of hoistways, 8.2.5.9
Exit, 7.1.3.2, A.7.1.3.2.1, A.7.1.3.2.3
Exit passageways, 7.2.6.2
Floor opening, 8.2.5.4, A.8.2.5.4
Ramps, 7.2.5.5
Stairs, 7.1.3.2, 7.2.2.5, 7.2.6.3, A.7.1.3.2.1,
A.7.1.3.2.3, A.7.2.2.5.2 to A.7.2.2.5.4
Visual enclosures, fire escape stairs,
7.2.8.5
Enforcement of code, 1.7
Engineer; *see* Professional engineer
Entrances; *see* Main entrances
Equipment; *see* Fire protection equipment;
Service equipment
Equivalency to code, 1.5, A.1.5
Escalators, 7.2.7, 8.2.5.11 to 8.2.5.13, 9.4.2
to 9.4.3, A.8.2.5.12
Existing ambulatory health care occupan-
cies, 21.5.3
Existing apartment buildings, 31.2.2.8,
31.5.3, A.31.2.2.8
Existing assembly occupancies, 13.2.2.8,
13.5.3
Existing business occupancies, 39.2.2.8,
39.5.3
Existing day-care occupancies, 17.5.3
Existing detention and correctional occu-
pancies, 23.5.3
Existing educational occupancies, 15.5.3
Existing health care occupancies, 19.5.3
Existing hotels and dormitories, 29.2.2.8,
29.5.3, A.29.2.2.8
Existing mercantile occupancies, 37.2.2.8,
37.5.3
Exit discharge, 7.7.4
Industrial occupancies, 40.2.2.8, 40.5.3
Lodging houses, 26.5.3
New ambulatory health care occupancies,
20.5.3
New apartment buildings, 30.5.3
New assembly occupancies, 12.5.3
New business occupancies, 38.5.3
New day-care occupancies, 16.5.3

2000 Life Safety Code Handbook

-F-

New mercantile occupancies, 36.2.5, A.36.2.5.9
New residential board and care occupancies, 32.3.2.5
Parking structures, 42.8.2.5
Special structures, 11.2.2.5, 11.3.2.5, 11.4.2.5
Storage occupancies, 42.2.5
Means of egress capacity, 7.3, A.7.3
Existing ambulatory health care occupancies, 21.2.3
Existing apartment buildings, 31.2.3
Existing assembly occupancies, 13.2.3, A.13.2.3.3
Existing business occupancies, 39.2.3
Existing day-care occupancies, 17.2.3
Existing detention and correctional occupancies, 23.2.3
Existing educational occupancies, 15.2.3
Existing health care occupancies, 19.2.3, A.19.2.3.3
Existing hotels and dormitories, 29.2.3
Existing mercantile occupancies, 37.2.3
Existing residential board and care occupancies, 33.3.2.3
Industrial occupancies, 40.2.3
New ambulatory health care occupancies, 20.2.3
New apartment buildings, 30.2.3
New assembly occupancies, 12.2.3, A.12.2.3.3
New business occupancies, 38.2.3, A.38.2.3.2
New day-care occupancies, 16.2.3
New detention and correctional occupancies, 22.2.3
New educational occupancies, 14.2.3
New health care occupancies, 18.2.3, A.18.2.3.3, A.18.2.3.4
New hotels and dormitories, 28.2.3, A.28.2.3.3
New mercantile occupancies, 36.2.3
New residential board and care occupancies, 32.3.2.3
Occupant load, 7.3.1, A.7.3.1.2, Table A.7.3.1.2
Parking structures, 42.8.2.3
Performance-based design option, 5.3.2(8)
Special structures, 11.2.2.3, 11.3.2.3, 11.4.2.3
Storage occupancies, 42.2.3
Width
Measurement of, 7.3.2, A.7.3.2
Minimum, 7.3.4, A.7.3.4.1
Means of egress components, 7.2, A.7.2; *see also* specific components, e.g. Alternating tread devices
Existing ambulatory health care occupancies, 21.2.2
Existing apartment buildings, 31.2.2, A.31.2.2

Existing assembly occupancies, 13.2.2
Existing business occupancies, 39.2.2
Existing day-care occupancies, 17.2.2, A.17.2.2.2.4, A.17.2.2.3
Existing detention and correctional occupancies, 23.2.2, A.23.2.2
Existing educational occupancies, 15.2.2
Existing health care occupancies, 19.2.2, A.19.2.2
Existing hotels and dormitories, 29.2.2, A.29.2.2.12
Existing mercantile occupancies, 37.2.2
Existing residential board and care occupancies, 33.3.2.2
Industrial occupancies, 40.2.2
New ambulatory health care occupancies, 20.2.2
New apartment buildings, 30.2.2, A.30.2.2
New assembly occupancies, 12.2.2
New business occupancies, 38.2.2
New day-care occupancies, 16.2.2, A.16.2.2
New detention and correctional occupancies, 22.2.2
New educational occupancies, 14.2.2
New health care occupancies, 18.2.2, A.18.2.2
New hotels and dormitories, 28.2.2, A.28.2.2.12
New mercantile occupancies, 36.2.2
New residential board and care occupancies, 32.3.2.2
Parking structures, 42.8.2.2
Special structures, 11.2.2.2, 11.3.2.2, 11.4.2.2
Storage occupancies, 42.2.2
Means of egress illumination, 4.5.3.4, 7.8, A.7.8; *see also* Emergency lighting
Existing ambulatory health care occupancies, 21.2.8
Existing apartment buildings, 31.2.8
Existing assembly occupancies, 13.2.8
Existing business occupancies, 39.2.8
Existing day-care homes, 17.6.2.8
Existing day-care occupancies, 17.2.8
Existing detention and correctional occupancies, 23.2.8
Existing educational occupancies, 15.2.8
Existing health care occupancies, 19.2.8
Existing hotels and dormitories, 29.2.8
Existing mercantile occupancies, 37.2.8
Existing residential board and care occupancies, 33.3.2.8
Industrial occupancies, 40.2.8
New ambulatory health care occupancies, 20.2.8
New apartment buildings, 30.2.8
New business occupancies, 38.2.8
New day-care occupancies, 16.2.8, 16.6.2.8

New detention and correctional occupancies, 22.2.8
New educational occupancies, 14.2.8
New health care occupancies, 18.2.8
New hotels and dormitories, 28.2.8
New mercantile occupancies, 36.2.8
New residential board and care occupancies, 32.3.2.8
Parking structures, 42.8.2.8
Performance-based design option, 5.3.2(10)
Photoluminescent signs, 7.10.7.2, A.7.10.7.2
Power source, 7.10.3, A.7.10.3
Signs, 7.10.1.4 to 7.10.1.7, 7.10.4 to 7.10.7, 7.10.9, A.7.10.1.4 to A.7.10.1.7, A.7.10.4 to A.7.10.7
Sources, 7.8.2, A.7.8.2.1
Special structures, 11.2.2.8, 11.3.2.8, 11.4.2.8
Storage occupancies, 42.2.8
Means of egress marking, 7.10, A.7.10
Aisles, 12.2.5.6.8, A.12.2.5.6.8
Directional signs and indicators, 7.10.2, 7.10.6.2, A.7.10.2, A.10.7.10.6.2
Elevator signs, 7.10.8.2, A.7.10.8.2
Existing ambulatory health care occupancies, 21.2.10
Existing apartment buildings, 31.2.10
Existing assembly occupancies, 13.2.10
Existing business occupancies, 39.2.10
Existing day-care occupancies, 17.2.10
Existing detention and correctional occupancies, 23.2.10
Existing educational occupancies, 15.2.10
Existing health care occupancies, 19.2.10
Existing hotels and dormitories, 29.2.10
Existing mercantile occupancies, 37.2.10
Existing residential board and care occupancies, 33.3.2.10
Exit access, marking of, 7.10.1.4, A.7.10.1.4
Exit discharge, 7.7.3
Floor proximity egress path marking, 7.10.1.6, A.7.10.1.6
Floor proximity exit signs, 7.10.1.5, A.7.10.1.5
Illumination of signs, 7.10.1.4 to 7.10.1.7, 7.10.4 to 7.10.7, 7.10.9, A.7.10.1.4 to A.7.10.1.7, A.7.10.4 to A.7.10.7
Industrial occupancies, 40.2.10
New ambulatory health care occupancies, 20.2.10
New apartment buildings, 30.2.10
New assembly occupancies, 12.2.10
New business occupancies, 38.2.10
New day-care occupancies, 16.2.10
New detention and correctional occupancies, 22.2.10
New educational occupancies, 14.2.10
New health care occupancies, 18.2.10

Commentary Index

Note: Entries can be found in the commentary following the section numbers given.

8

The commentary text contains hands-on examples that show how *Code* provisions can be applied in real-world situations. These examples walk the user, step by step, through potentially complicated scenarios.

Exhibit 12/13.22 Minimum 12-in. (30.5-cm) aisle accessway at tables.

12 ft (3.7 m) from the center of the seat farthest from an aisle. In accordance with 12/13.2.5.7.2, the presence of chairs at one side of the aisle accessway increases the table-to-table spacing by 19 in. (48.3 cm) above that attributable to the required aisle accessway clear

(30.5 cm) plus 0.5 in. (1.3 cm) for each additional 12 in. (30.5 cm) of aisle accessway beyond the initial 12 in. (3.7 m) from the center seat farthest from an aisle. The aisle accessway clear width is calculated as follows:

$$X = 12 \text{ in.} + [0.5 \text{ in./ft} (36 \text{ ft} - 12 \text{ ft})]$$
$$= 12 \text{ in.} + 12 \text{ in.}$$
$$= 24 \text{ in.}$$

For SI (metric) units,

$$X = 30.5 \text{ cm} + [4.25 \text{ cm/m} (10.9 \text{ m} - 3.7 \text{ m})]$$
$$= 30.5 + 30.5$$
$$= 61 \text{ cm}$$

With the 19-in. (48.3-cm) space required for the chairs, the table-to-table spacing must be ≥43 in. (109 cm).

9

The following illustrates the use of calculating fire resistance as allowed by Exception No. 2 to 8.2.3.1.1.

A designer who wants to provide a 2-hour fire resistance rating for a W14 × 233 steel column by boxing the column with gypsum wallboard cannot find such an assembly in the *Underwriters Laboratories Fire Resistance Directory*. Design No. X520 and design No. X521 come very close to providing the needed information but deal with W14 × 228 steel columns; they show that, with one layer of ½-in. (1.3-cm) thick

The total weight (W') of both the column and its gypsum wallboard protection is calculated using the following formula:

$$W' = W + \frac{50(h)(D)}{144}$$

where W = weight of steel column (lb/ft).

Performing the calculations yields the following:

$$D = 2(a + b)$$
$$= 2(15.89 + 16.04)$$
$$= 63.86 \text{ in.}$$

Calculations interspersed within the commentary show how *Code* requirements are applied. These are intended to simplify the design process for even the most seasoned professional.

10

The seven supplements that appear at the end of the handbook are not part of the *Code* or the commentary. They provide additional, useful information for *Code* users and include drawings, photographs, tables, and extended text. The supplements are set in black type inside a green box.

996   Supplement 5 • Fire Tests for *Life Safety Code* Users

Table S5.1 Documents That Are Common to NFPA Fire Test Standards

NFPA	ASTM	UL
251, Standard Methods of Tests of Fire Endurance of Building Construction and Materials	E 119, Standard Test Methods for Fire Tests of Building Construction and Materials	263, Standard for Safety Fire Tests of Building Construction and Materials
252, Standard Methods of Fire Tests of Door Assemblies	E 152, Standard Methods of Fire Tests of Door Assemblies	10B, Standard for Safety Fire Tests of Door Assemblies
253, Standard Method of Test for Critical Radiant Flux of Floor Covering Systems Using a Radiant Heat Energy Source	E 648, Standard Test Method for Critical Radiant Flux of Floor-Covering Systems Using a Radiant Heat Energy Source	
255, Standard Method of Test of Surface Burning Characteristics of Building Materials	E 84, Standard Test Method for Surface Burning Characteristics of Building Materials	723, Standard for Safety Test for Surface Burning Characteristics of Building Materials
256, Standard Methods of Fire Tests of Roof Coverings	E 108, Standard Test Methods for Fire Tests of Roof Coverings	790, Tests for Fire Resistance of Roof Covering Materials
257, Standard on Fire Test of Window and Glass Block Assemblies	E 163, Standard Method for Fire Tests of Window Assemblies	9, Standard for Safety Fire Tests of Window Assemblies
258, Standard Research Test Method for Determining Smoke Generation of Solid	E 662, Standard Test Method for Specific Optical Density of Smoke Generated by	